Just for California!

California Algebra 1
Concepts, Skills, and Problem Solving

Features of the California Student and Teacher Wraparound Editions

Additional California Resources

❧ **Mastering the California Mathematics Standards, Algebra 1**   Multiple formats to practice and assess the California Mathematics standards.

❧ **California Noteables™ Interactive Study Notebook with FOLDABLES™**   Research-based note-taking guide for every lesson builds key skills for taking and organizing notes.

❧ **5-Minute Check Transparencies with California Standards Practice**   Assess student progress after each lesson. Each transparency includes references to standards assessed on that transparency.

❧ **California Interactive Classroom**   A Microsoft® PowerPoint® presentation for each lesson that shows the Additional Examples from the California Teacher Wraparound Edition fully-worked out with additional Your Turn exercises. This DVD also includes the 5-Minute Check Transparencies and Concepts in Motion.

❧ **California TeacherWorks™ Plus**   An all-in-one lesson planner and resource center that helps you customize lesson plans and reproduce classroom resources quickly and easily.

❧ **California StudentWorks™ Plus**   This backpack solution allows students instant access to the Student Edition, lesson worksheet pages, and web resources.

❧ **California ExamView Assessment Suite CD-ROM**   A customizable testmaker with built-in California curriculum correlations.

For More Information visit ca.algebra1.com

Teacher Wraparound Edition

Glencoe McGraw-Hill

California
Algebra 1

Concepts, Skills, and Problem Solving

Authors
Holliday • Luchin • Cuevas • Carter
Marks • Day • Casey • Hayek

Glencoe

New York, New York   Columbus, Ohio   Chicago, Illinois   Woodland Hills, California

About the Cover

The cable car railway system was invented specifically to operate on San Francisco's famous hills. Every cable car is pulled along its track by an underground cable. The cable is gripped with a vise-like mechanism that is operated by the driver using a grip lever in the front of the car. In Chapter 4, you will learn about slopes like the slope of a hill.

About the Graphics

Twisted torus. Created with *Mathematica*.
A torus with rose-shaped cross section is constructed. Then the cross section is rotated around its center as it moves along a circle to form a twisted torus. For more information, and for programs to construct such graphics, see: www.wolfram.com/r/textbook.

Dinah Zike's Foldables™ photos provided by StudiOhio.
Image Credits: T2 Masterfile; **T9** Garry Black/Masterfile; **R96** George Lee White/CORBIS; **R99** LWA-Dann Tardif/CORBIS STOCK MARKET; **R101** Gabe Palmer/CORBIS

Glencoe

The *McGraw·Hill* Companies

Send all inquiries to:
Glencoe/McGraw-Hill
8787 Orion Place
Columbus, OH 43240-4027

ISBN: 978-0-07-877853-7 *(Teacher Wraparound Edition)*
MHID: 0-07-877853-0 *(Teacher Wraparound Edition)*
ISBN: 978-0-07-877852-0 *(Student Edition)*
MHID: 0-07-877852-2 *(Student Edition)*

Printed in the United States of America.

3 4 5 6 7 8 9 10 043/079 15 14 13 12 11 10 09 08

Contents in Brief

Authors

Berchie Holliday, Ed.D.
National Mathematics
  Consultant
Silver Spring, MD

Gilbert J. Cuevas, Ph.D.
Professor of Mathematics
  Education
University of Miami
Miami, FL

Beatrice Luchin
Mathematics Consultant
League City, TX

John A. Carter, Ph.D.
Director of Mathematics
Adlai E. Stevenson High
  School
Lincolnshire, IL

Daniel Marks, Ed.D.
Professor Emeritus of
  Mathematics
Auburn University at
  Montgomery
Montgomery, AL

Roger Day, Ph.D.
Mathematics Department
  Chairperson
Pontiac Township High
  School
Pontiac, IL

Math Online Meet the Authors at ca.algebra1.com

Ruth M. Casey
Mathematics Teacher
  Department Chair
Anderson County High
  School
Lawrenceburg, KY

Linda M. Hayek
Mathematics Teacher
Ralston Public Schools
Omaha, NE

Contributing Authors

Carol E. Malloy, Ph.D.
Associate Professor
University of North Carolina
  at Chapel Hill
Chapel Hill, NC

Viken Hovsepian
Professor of Mathematics
Rio Hondo College
Whittier, CA

FOLDABLES **Dinah Zike**
Educational Consultant,
  Dinah-Might Activities, Inc.
San Antonio, TX

v

California Mathematics Advisory Board

Glencoe wishes to thank the following professionals for their invaluable feedback during the development of the program. They reviewed the table of contents, the prototype of the Teacher Wraparound Edition, and the Get Ready for the California Test chapter.

Cheryl L. Avalos
Mathematics Consultant
  Retired Teacher
  Hacienda Heights, California

William M. Bokesch
Rancho Bernardo
  High School
  San Diego, California

Patty Brown
Teacher
  John Muir Elementary
  Fresno, California

David J. Chamberlain
Secondary Mathematics
  Resource Teacher
  Capistrano Unified School
    District
  San Juan Capistrano, California

Eppie Chung
K-6 Teacher
  Modesto City Schools
  Modesto, California

Lisa Marie Cirrincione
Middle School Teacher
  Lincoln Middle School
  Oceanside, California

Carol Cronk
Mathematics Program Specialist
  San Bernardino City Unified
    School District
  San Bernardino, California

Ilene Foster
Teacher Specialist – Mathematics
  Pomona Unified School District
  Pomona, California

Grant A. Fraser, Ph.D.
Professor of Mathematics
  California State University,
    Los Angeles
  Los Angeles, California

Suzanne Bocskai Freire
Teacher
  Kingswood Elementary
  Citrus Heights, California

Beth Holguin
Teacher
  Graystone Elementary
  San Jose, California

Donna M. Kopenski, Ed.D.
Mathematics Coordinator K-5
  City Heights Educational
    Collaborative
  San Diego, California

Kelly Mack
6th Grade Teacher
   Captain Jason Dahl Elementary
   San Jose, California

Juvenal Martinez
Dual Immersion/ESL Instructor
   Aeolian Elementary
   Whittier, California

John McGuire
Associate Principal
   Pacific Union School
   Arcata, California

Dr. Donald R. Price
Teacher, Adjunct Professor,
   Motivational Speaker
   Rowland Unified School
   District
   Rowland Heights, California

Kasey St. James
Mathematics Teacher
   Sunny Hills High School
   Fullerton, California

Arthur K. Wayman, Ph.D.
Professor of Mathematics
   Emeritus
   California State University,
   Long Beach
   Long Beach, California

Beverly Wells
First Grade Teacher
   Mineral King Elementary
   School
   Visalia, California

Frances Basich Whitney
Project Director,
   Mathematics K-12
   Santa Cruz County Office
   of Education
   Capitola, California

Glencoe/McGraw-Hill wishes to thank the following professionals for their feedback. They were instrumental in providing valuable input toward the development of this program in these specific areas.

Mathematical Content

Viken Hovsepian
Professor of Mathematics
Rio Hondo College
Whittier, California

Grant A. Fraser, Ph.D.
Professor of Mathematics
California State University, Los Angeles
Los Angeles, California

Bob McCollum
Associate Principal
Curriculum and Instruction
Glenbrook South High School
Glenview, Illinois

Arthur K. Wayman, Ph.D.
Professor of Mathematics Emeritus
California State University, Long Beach
Long Beach, California

Differentiated Instruction

Nancy Frey, Ph.D.
Associate Professor of Literacy
San Diego State University
San Diego, California

English Language Learners

Mary Avalos, Ph.D.
Assistant Chair, Teaching and Learning
Assistant Research Professor
University of Miami, School of Education
Coral Gables, Florida

Jana Echevarria, Ph.D.
Professor, College of Education
California State University, Long Beach
Long Beach, California

Josefina V. Tinajero, Ph.D.
Dean, College of Educatifon
The University of Texas at El Paso
El Paso, Texas

Gifted and Talented

Ed Zaccaro
Author
Mathematics and science books for gifted children
Bellevue, Iowa

Graphing Calculator

Ruth M. Casey
Mathematics Teacher
Department Chair
Anderson County High School
Lawrenceburg, Kentucky

Jerry Cummins
Past President
National Council of Supervisors of Mathematics
Western Springs, Illinois

Learning Disabilities

Kate Garnett, Ph.D.
Chairperson, Coordinator Learning Disabilities
School of Education
Department of Special Education
Hunter College, CUNY
New York, New York

Mathematical Fluency

Jason Mutford
Mathematics Instructor
Coxsackie-Athens Central School District
Coxsackie, New York

Pre-AP

Dixie Ross
AP Calculus Teacher
Pflugerville High School
Pflugerville, Texas

Reading and Vocabulary

Douglas Fisher, Ph.D.
Director of Professional Development and Professor
City Heights Educational Collaborative
San Diego State University
San Diego, California

Lynn T. Havens
Director of Project CRISS
Kalispell School District
Kalispell, Montana

 **Meet the Authors at** ca.algebra1.com

California Reviewers

 Each California Reviewer reviewed at least two chapters of the Student Edition, giving feedback and suggestions for improving the effectiveness of the mathematics instruction.

Tammera Boehme
Mathematics Chairperson
Las Plumas High School
Oroville, California

Don Castle
Geometry Teacher
Carter High School
Rialto, California

Karen D. Cliffe
Mathematics Department Chair
Bonita Vista High School
Chula Vista, California

Barbara R. Donner
Teacher
Chadwick School
Palos Verdes Peninsula, California

Michael R. Erickson
Teacher
Niguel Hills
Laguna Niguel, California

Shayne B. Fleming
Mathematics Teacher
Alameda Unified School District
Alameda, California

Kris Fondaw
Mathematics Dept. Chair/Teacher
Christian High School
El Cajon, California

Anna L. Garfinkel
Mathematics Teacher
Diegueño Middle School
Encinitas, California

Marlene Greco
Mathematics Teacher
Rancho Santa Margarita Intermediate School
Rancho Santa Margarita, California

John T. Guseman
Mathematics Teacher
Mission Hills High School
San Marcos, California

Susan A. Holtzapple
Mathematics Teacher
Cupertino Middle School
Sunnyvale, California

Alice M. Keeler
Mathematics Teacher
Clovis High School
Clovis, California

Eric Kimmel
Department Chair of Mathematics
Frontier High School
Bakersfield, California

Jennifer Marple
Mathematics Teacher
Monroe High School
North Hills, California

Jeff Matthew
Mathematics & Science Department Chairman
Hughson High School
Hughson, California

Jennifer Moening
Mathematics Teacher
Santiago High School
Garden Grove, California

Terry Murray
Teacher
Crystal Middle School
Suisun City, California

Glenn Quan
Mathematics Teacher
Richard Henry Dana Middle School
San Pedro, California

Ryan Rienstra
Mathematics Teacher
Northview High School
Covina, California

Laurie Riggs
Associate Professor
California State Polytechnic University
Pomona, California

David Robathan
Teacher
Shasta High School
Redding, California

Brian Shay
Mathematics Chairperson and Teacher
Canyon Crest Academy
San Diego, California

Kathryn E. Sinclear
Mathematics Department Chair
Los Banos High School
Los Banos, California

Douglas S. Taylor
Mathematics Teacher
Taft Union High School
Taft, California

Martha Tikalsky
Mathematics Teacher
Sam Lawson Middle School
Cupertino, California

Beatrice Tyk
Mathematics Teacher
Sylvan Middle School
Citrus Heights, California

Joanne Wainscott
Mathematics Department Chairperson
La Jolla High School
La Jolla, California

Greg Wood
Mathematics Teacher
Los Banos Junior High School
Los Banos, California

David Zylstra
Mathematics Teacher
Hughson High School
Hughson, California

State Flower:
California poppy

California Teacher Handbook

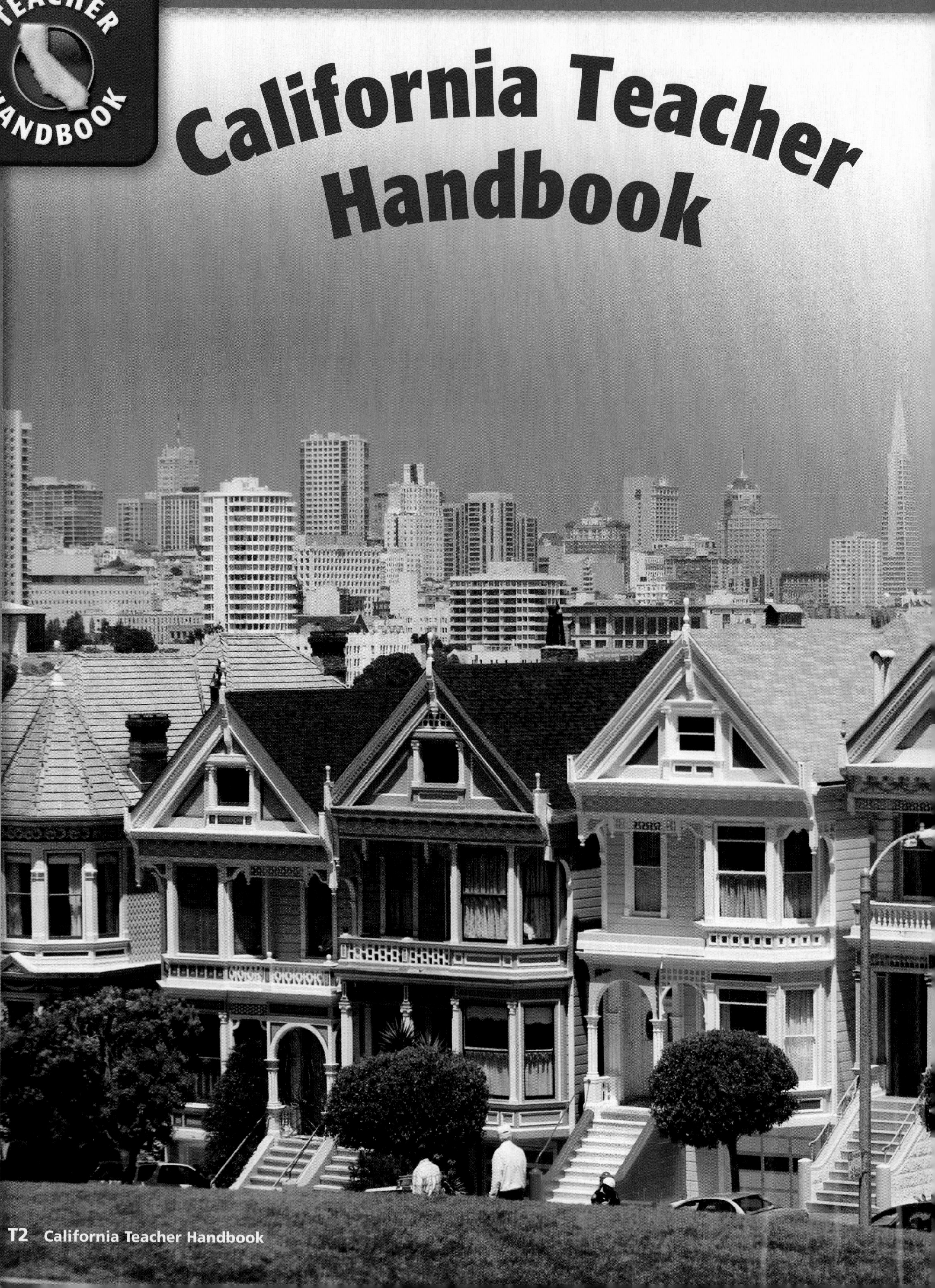

Table of Contents

Welcome to California Mathematics

Concepts • Skills • Problem Solving

The only true vertically aligned K–12
Mathematics Curriculum

What is Vertical Alignment?

Vertical alignment is a process that provides learners with an articulated, coherent sequence of content. It ensures that content standards and units of study are introduced, reinforced, and assessed and that instruction is targeted on student needs and California Standards.

Why is Vertical Alignment Important?

Strong vertical alignment accommodates a wide variety of developmental levels. It allows teachers increased precision in their teaching because they are not teaching content that is covered elsewhere or that students have previously mastered.

5 Keys to Success

❶ Back-Mapping

According to The College Board, about 80% of students who successfully complete Algebra I and Geometry by 10th grade attend and succeed in college. That 80% is nearly constant regardless of race. (*Changing the Odds: Factors Increasing Access to College,* 1990) *California Mathematics: Concepts, Skills, and Problem Solving* was conceived and developed with the final result in mind—student success in Algebra I and beyond. The authors, using the California Mathematics Standards as their guide, developed this brand-new series by "back-mapping" from the desired result of student success in Algebra I, Geometry, and beyond.

California Mathematics: Concepts, Skills, and Problem Solving

California Math Triumphs is designed for students who need intensive intervention to meet grade-level standards.

Kindergarten	Grade 1	Grade 2	Grade 3	Grade 4	Grade 5

The K–8 mathematics program prepares students for success in Algebra I by using consistent vocabulary and concept presentation throughout the program.

② Balanced, In-Depth Content

California Mathematics: Concepts, Skills, and Problem Solving was developed to specifically target the skills and topics that give students the most difficulty.

Grades K–2	Grades 3–5
1. Problem Solving 2. Money 3. Time 4. Measurement 5. Fractions 6. Computation	1. Problem Solving 2. Fractions 3. Measurement 4. Decimals 5. Time 6. Algebra
Grades 6–8	**Grades 9–12**
1. Fractions 2. Problem Solving 3. Measurement 4. Algebra 5. Computation	1. Problem Solving 2. Fractions 3. Algebra 4. Geometry 5. Computation 6. Probability

– *K–12 Math Market Analysis Survey,*
Open Book Publishing, 2005

③ Ongoing Assessment

California Mathematics: Concepts, Skills, and Problem Solving includes diagnostic, formative, and summative assessment; data-driven instruction; intervention options; and performance tracking, as well as remediation, acceleration, and enrichment tools throughout the program.

④ Intervention and Differentiated Instruction

In order for students to overcome difficulties with mathematics learning, attention is paid to their backgrounds, the nature of their previous instruction, and underlying learning differences. *California Mathematics: Concepts, Skills, and Problem Solving* includes a two-pronged approach to intervention.

Strategic Teachers can use the myriad of intervention tips and ancillary materials to address the needs of students who need strategic intervention.

Intensive For students who are two or more years below grade level, *California Math Triumphs* provides step-by-step instruction, vocabulary support, and data-driven decision making to help students succeed.

For students not ready for Algebra I in Grade 8, *California Algebra Readiness* provides highly focused instructional materials to help students rebuild foundational skills and concepts and prepare for algebra success.

⑤ Professional Development

California Mathematics: Concepts, Skills, and Problem Solving includes many opportunities for teacher professional development. Additional learning opportunities in various formats–video, online, and on-site instruction–are fully aligned and articulated from grade K through Algebra II.

| Grade 6 | Grade 7 | Algebra Readiness/Algebra I | Geometry | Algebra II |

California Algebra Readiness is for students who are not ready for Algebra I in 8th grade.

Program Development

Checklist

Articulation Macmillan/McGraw-Hill and Glencoe/McGraw-Hill's suite of fully articulated programs include:

- *Mathematics: Concepts, Skills, and Problem Solving,* PreKindergarten
- *California Mathematics: Concepts, Skills, and Problem Solving,* Grades K–7
- *California Math Triumphs: Intervention for Intensive Students,* Grades 4–7
- *California Algebra Readiness: Concepts, Skills, and Problem Solving*
- *California Algebra 1: Concepts, Skills, and Problem Solving*
- *California Geometry: Concepts, Skills, and Problem Solving*
- *California Algebra 2: Concepts, Skills, and Problem Solving*

These brand new programs form a comprehensive, standards-based K–12 program that follows the specific requirements of the Mathematics Framework for California Public Schools to ensure success in your classroom.

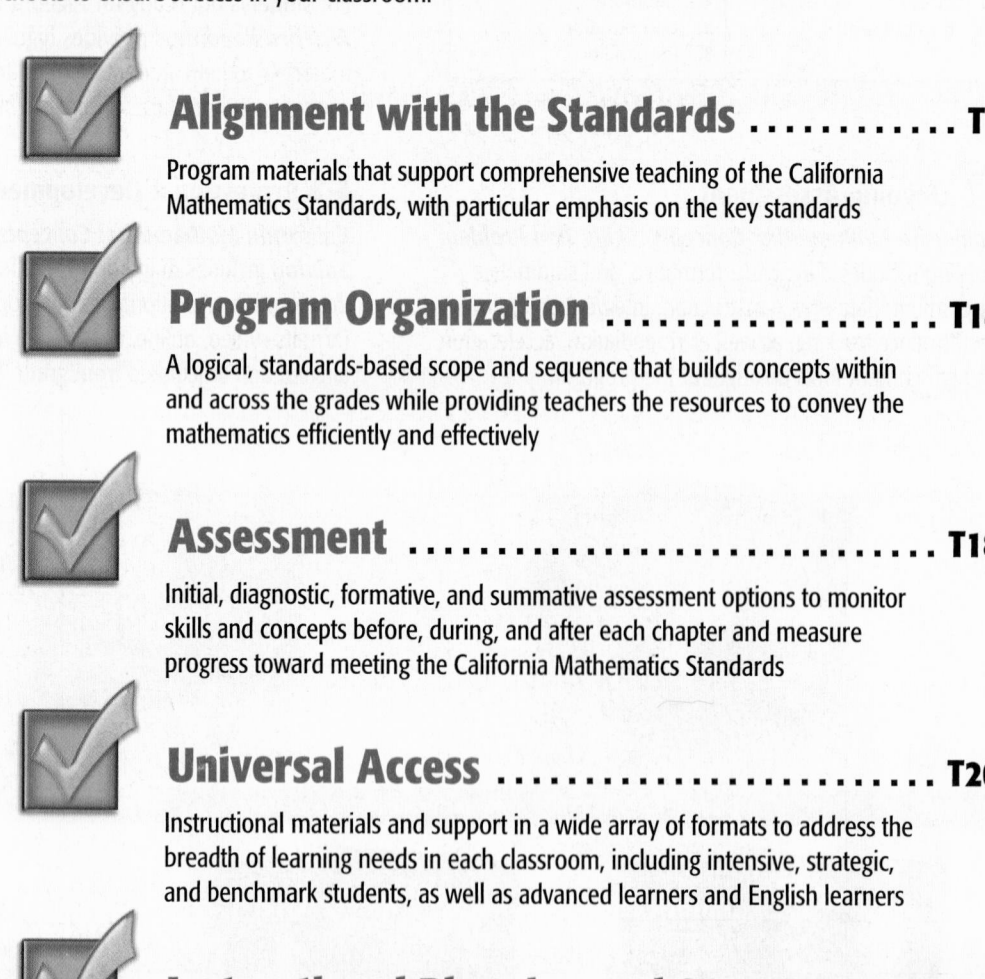

Alignment with the Standards T7

Program materials that support comprehensive teaching of the California Mathematics Standards, with particular emphasis on the key standards

Program Organization T14

A logical, standards-based scope and sequence that builds concepts within and across the grades while providing teachers the resources to convey the mathematics efficiently and effectively

Assessment T18

Initial, diagnostic, formative, and summative assessment options to monitor skills and concepts before, during, and after each chapter and measure progress toward meeting the California Mathematics Standards

Universal Access T20

Instructional materials and support in a wide array of formats to address the breadth of learning needs in each classroom, including intensive, strategic, and benchmark students, as well as advanced learners and English learners

Instructional Planning and Support T22

A clear, easy-to-use Teacher Edition that provides efficient planning and pacing suggestions with ample instructional support for presenting skills and concepts

 # Alignment with the Standards

California Algebra I Content Standards
Correlated to *California Algebra 1*

🔑 denotes Key standards
 * denotes standards assessed on the California High School Exit Examination (CAHSEE)

Standard Number	Standard	Primary Citation(s)	Supporting Citation(s)
1.0	Students identify and use the arithmetic properties of subsets of integers and rational, irrational, and real numbers, including closure properties for the four basic arithmetic operations where applicable.	21–31, 46–52, 536–540, CA4	33–37, 78–90, 92–97, 694–708
1.1	Students use properties of numbers to demonstrate whether assertions are true or false.	21–25, 45, 314, CA5	423
🔑 2.0*	Students understand and use such operations as taking the opposite, finding the reciprocal, taking a root, and raising to a fractional power. They understand and use the rules of exponents.	46–52, 358–364, 366–373, 528–540, 696–699, 701, CA6–CA7	21–25, 541–546
3.0*	Students solve equations and inequalities involving absolute values.	322–327, 329–333, CA8	716
🔑 4.0*	Students simplify expressions before solving linear equations and inequalities in one variable, such as $3(2x - 5) + 4(x - 2) = 12$.	92–103, 308–320, CA9–CA10	15–20, 26–37, 78–90, 122–128, 294–299, 301–307, 700–701
🔑 5.0*	Students solve multistep problems, including word problems, involving linear equations and linear inequalities in one variable and provide justification for each step.	92–103, 111–121, 294–299, 308–313, 315–320, CA11–CA12	77–91, 105–110, 122–128, 300–307
🔑 6.0*	Students graph a linear equation and compute the x- and y-intercepts (e.g., graph $2x + 6y = 4$). They are also able to sketch the region defined by linear inequality (e.g., they sketch the region defined by $2x + 6y < 4$).	155–163, 204–211, 334–340, CA13–CA14	253–258, 341–345
🔑 7.0*	Students verify that a point lies on a line, given an equation of the line. Students are able to derive linear equations by using the point-slope formula.	155–161, 219–225, CA15–CA16	226, 253–258
8.0*	Students understand the concepts of parallel lines and perpendicular lines and how those slopes are related. Students are able to find the equation of a line perpendicular to a given line that passes through a given point.	236–241, CA17	253–258
🔑 9.0*	Students solve a system of two linear equations in two variables algebraically and are able to interpret the answer graphically. Students are able to solve a system of two linear inequalities in two variables and to sketch the solution sets.	253–270, 272–278, 280–284, 341–345, CA18–CA19	252, 279
🔑 10.0*	Students add, subtract, multiply, and divide monomials and polynomials. Students solve multistep problems, including word problems, by using these techniques.	358–364, 366–373, 382–388, 390–409, 601–606, CA20–CA21	26–31, 33–37, 374–381, 583–588, 590–599, 608–619
11.0	Students apply basic factoring techniques to second- and simple third-degree polynomials. These techniques include finding a common factor for all terms in a polynomial, recognizing the difference of two squares, and recognizing perfect squares of binomials.	425–439, 441–452, 454–460, CA22	420–424, 583–588, 590–599, 601–606, 608–619

Standard Number	Standard	Primary Citation(s)	Supporting Citation(s)
🔑 12.0	Students simplify fractions with polynomials in the numerator and denominator by factoring both and reducing them to the lowest terms.	583–589, 600, 620–625, CA23–CA24	626–632
🔑 13.0	Students add, subtract, multiply, and divide rational expressions and functions. Students solve both computationally and conceptually challenging problems by using these techniques.	590–599, 608–632, CA25–CA26	366–373, 583–588
🔑 14.0	Students solve a quadratic equation by factoring or completing the square.	434–439, 441–452, 454–460, 486–491, CA27–CA28	426–431
🔑 15.0*	Students apply algebraic techniques to solve rate problems, work problems, and percent mixture problems.	105–110, 122–129, 626–632, CA29–CA30	260–265, 272–278
16.0	Students understand the concepts of a relation and a function, determine whether a given relation defines a function, and give pertinent information about given relations and functions.	53–59, 143–154, 172–176, CA31	142, 155–161
17.0	Students determine the domain of independent variables and the range of dependent variables defined by a graph, a set of ordered pairs, or a symbolic expression.	53–58, 143–148, 328, 547, CA32	59, 149–161, 471–477
18.0	Students determine whether a relation defined by a graph, a set of ordered pairs, or a symbolic expression is a function and justify the conclusion.	149–154, 176, CA33	176, 471–479
🔑 19.0	Students know the quadratic formula and are familiar with its proof by completing the square.	493–499, 530 , 533, CA34	486–491, 528–529, 531–532
🔑 20.0	Students use the quadratic formula to find the roots of a second-degree polynomial and to solve quadratic equations.	493–499, CA35–CA36	471–477, 480–491, 500–501
🔑 21.0	Students graph quadratic functions and know that their roots are the x-intercepts.	471–485, CA37–CA38	493–499
22.0	Students use the quadratic formula or factoring techniques or both to determine whether the graph of a quadratic function will intersect the x-axis in zero, one, or two points.	480–485, 493–499, CA39	471–477
🔑 23.0	Students apply quadratic equations to physical problems, such as the motion of an object under the force of gravity.	500–501, CA40–CA41	426–431, 441–452, 454–460, 470–477, 480–491, 493–498
24.0	Students use and know simple aspects of a logical argument.	39–44, CA42	45, 171
24.1	Students explain the difference between inductive and deductive reasoning and identify and provide examples of each.	171	39–44, 172–176
24.2	Students identify the hypothesis and conclusion in logical deduction.	39–44	
24.3	Students use counterexamples to show that an assertion is false and recognize that a single counterexample is sufficient to refute an assertion.	39–44	102, 114, 148, 154, 306, 363, 380, 423, 484, 539, 618, 631, 669
25.0	Students use properties of the number system to judge the validity of results, to justify each step of a procedure, and to prove or disprove statements.	33–37, CA43	21–31, 39–44

Standard Number	Standard	Primary Citation(s)	Supporting Citation(s)
25.1	Students use properties of numbers to construct simple, valid arguments (direct and indirect) for, or formulate counterexamples to, claimed assertions.	21–31, 45	33–37, 39–44, 102, 114, 148, 154, 306, 363, 372, 380, 423, 453, 484, 539, 618, 631, 669
25.2	Students judge the validity of an argument according to whether the properties of the real number system and the order of operations have been applied correctly at each step.	38	13, 28, 30, 90, 260–265, 277, 307, 363, 372, 387, 439, 446, 451, 452, 498, 545, 593, 613
25.3	Given a specific algebraic statement involving linear, quadratic, or absolute value expressions or equations or inequalities, students determine whether the statement is true sometimes, always, or never.	45	24, 83, 96, 114, 258, 298, 326, 402, 459

Natural Arch, Sierra Nevada Mountains, Lone Pine, California

 # Alignment with the Standards

California Algebra 1: Concepts, Skills, and Problem Solving
Correlated to California Algebra I Mathematics Content Standards

Lesson	Page(s)	Standard(s)
1-1 Variables and Expressions	6–9	Reinforcement of 7AF1.1
1-2 Order of Operations	10–14	Reinforcement of 7AF1.2, 25.2
1-3 Open Sentences	15–20	Preparation for 4.0, 25.2
1-4 Identity and Equality Properties	21–25	1.0, 1.1, 2.0, 25.0, 25.1, 25.3
1-5 The Distributive Property	26–31	1.0, 4.0, 10.0, 25.0, 25.1, 25.2
1-6 Commutative and Associative Properties	33–37	1.0, 4.0, 10.0, 25.0, 25.1
Reading Math Arguments with Properties of Numbers	38	25.2
1-7 Logical Reasoning and Counterexamples	39–44	24.0, 24.1, 24.2, 24.3, 25.0, 25.1
Extend 1-7 Logic and Properties of Numbers	45	1.1, 24.0, 25.1, 25.3
1-8 Number Systems	46–52	1.0 2.0
1-9 Functions and Graphs	53–58	16.0, 17.0
Extend 1-9 Algebra Lab: Investigating Real-World Functions	59	16.0
2-1 Writing Equations	70–76	Reinforcement of 7AF1.1
Explore 2-2 Algebra Lab: Solving Addition and Subtraction Equations	77	Preparation for 5.0
2-2 Solving Equations by Using Addition and Subtraction	78–84	4.0, Preparation for 5.0, 25.3
2-3 Solving Equations by Using Multiplication and Division	85–90	4.0, Preparation for 5.0, 25.2
Explore 2-4 Algebra Lab: Solving Multi-Step Equations	91	Preparation for 4.0, 5.0
2-4 Solving Multi-Step Equations	92–97	Preparation for 4.0, Preparation for 5.0, 25.3
2-5 Solving Equations with the Variable on Each Side	98–103	4.0, 5.0, 24.3, 25.1
2-6 Ratios and Proportions	105–110	5.0, 15.0
2-7 Percent of Change	111–115	5.0, 24.3, 25.1, 25.3
Reading Math Sentence Method & Proportion Method	116	5.0
2-8 Solving for a Specific Variable	117–121	5.0
2-9 Weighted Averages	122–128	4.0, 5.0, 15.0
Extend 2-9 Spreadsheet Lab: Weighted Averages	129	15.0
Explore 3-1 Algebra Lab: Modeling Relations	142	Preparation for 16.0
3-1 Representing Relations	143–148	Preparation for 16.0, 17.0, 24.3, 25.1
3-2 Representing Functions	149–154	16.0, 18.0, 24.3, 25.1
3-3 Linear Functions	155–161	6.0, 7.0, 16.0, 17.0
Extend 3-3 Graphing Calculator Lab: Graphing Linear Functions	162–163	6.0
3-4 Arithmetic Sequences	165–170	Reinforcement of 7AF3.4

Lesson	Page(s)	Standard(s)
Reading Math Inductive & Deductive Reasoning	171	24.1
3-5 Describing Number Patterns	172–176	16.0, 24.1
Explore 4-1 Algebra Lab: Steepness of a line	186	Reinforcement of 7AF3.4, 8.0
4-1 Rate of Change and Slope	187–195	Reinforcement of 7AF3.3
4-2 Slope and Direct Variation	196–202	Reinforcement of 7AF4.2
Explore 4-3 Graphing Calculator Lab: Investigating Slope-Intercept Form	203	Reinforcement of 7AF1.5
4-3 Graphing Equations in Slope-Intercept Form	204–209	6.0
Extend 4-3 Graphing Calculator Lab: The Family of Linear Graphs	210–211	6.0
4-4 Writing Equations in Slope-Intercept Form	213–218	Reinforcement of 7AF1.1
4-5 Writing Equations in Point-Slope Form	219–225	7.0
Reading Math Understanding the Questions	226	7.0
4-6 Statistics: Scatter Plots and Lines of Fit	227–233	PS 8.0
Extend 4-6 Graphing Calculator Lab: Regression and Median-Fit Lines	234–235	Preparation for APPS12.0, Preparation for APPS13.0
4-7 Geometry: Parallel and Perpendicular Lines	236–241	8.0
Explore 5-1 Spreadsheet Lab: Systems of Equations	252	9.0
5-1 Graphing Systems of Equations	253–258	6.0, 7.0, 8.0, 9.0, 25.3
Extend 5-1 Graphing Calculator Lab: Systems of Equations	259	9.0
5-2 Substitution	260–265	9.0, 15.0, 25.2
5-3 Elimination Using Addition and Subtraction	266–270	9.0
5-4 Elimination Using Multiplication	272–278	9.0, 15.0, 25.2
Reading Math Making Concept Maps	279	9.0
5-5 Applying Systems of Linear Equations	280–284	9.0
6-1 Solving Inequalities by Addition and Subtraction	294–299	4.0, 5.0, 25.3
Explore 6-2 Algebra Lab: Solving Inequalities	300	Preparation for 5.0
6-2 Solving Inequalities by Multiplication and Division	301–307	4.0, Preparation for 5.0, 24.3, 25.1, 25.2
6-3 Solving Multi-Step Inequalities	308–313	4.0, 5.0
Reading Math Compound Statements	314	1.1
6-4 Solving Compound Inequalities	315–320	4.0, 5.0
6-5 Solving Open Sentences Involving Absolute Value	322–327	3.0, 25.3
Extend 6-5 Graphing Calculator Lab: Graphing Absolute Value Functions	328	17.0
6-6 Solving Inequalities Involving Absolute Value	329–333	3.0, 25.3
6-7 Graphing Inequalities in Two Variables	334–339	6.0, 9.0
Extend 6-7 Graphing Calculator Lab: Graphing Inequalities	340	6.0
6-8 Graphing Systems of Inequalities	341–345	6.0, 9.0
7-1 Multiplying Monomials	358–364	2.0, 10.0, 24.3, 25.1, 25.2
Extend 7-1 Algebra Lab: Investigating Surface Areas and Volumes	365	Preparation for G11.0
7-2 Dividing Monomials	366–373	2.0, 10.0, 25.1, 25.2

Program Organization

Alignment McGraw-Hill's ***California Algebra 1: Concepts, Skills, and Problem Solving*** differs from other mathematics programs because it:

- is fully aligned to the California Mathematics Standards for Grade 8.
- is paced to ensure in-depth coverage of all assessed standards by the test date.
- provides for comprehensive review of the California Standards before the test date.

Standards

Students and parents know exactly which **California Standards** are addressed by the lesson. The portion of the standard in bold is the specific part being addressed in the lesson.

Vocabulary

Both **New Vocabulary** and **Review Vocabulary** help students identify terms being presented.

Key Concepts

Key Concepts use multiple representations to demonstrate the skills being presented.

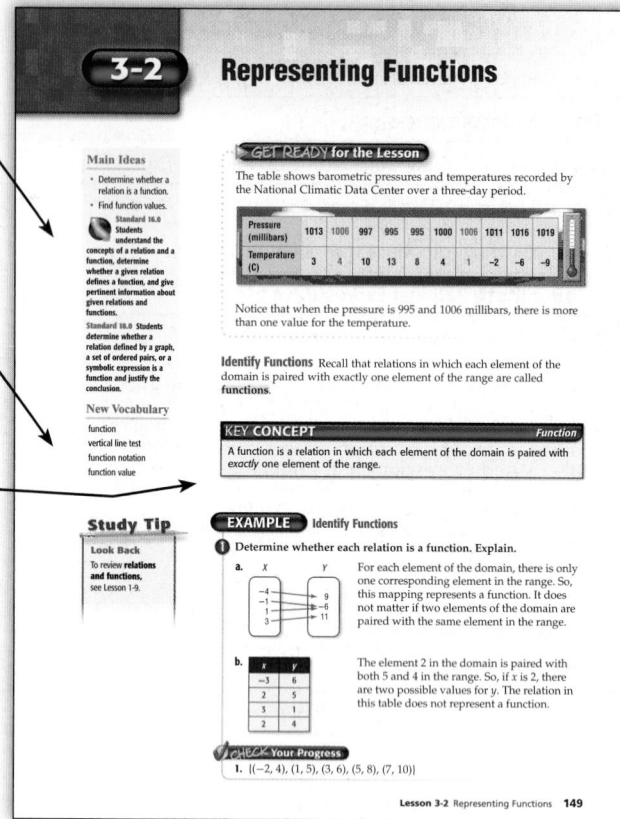

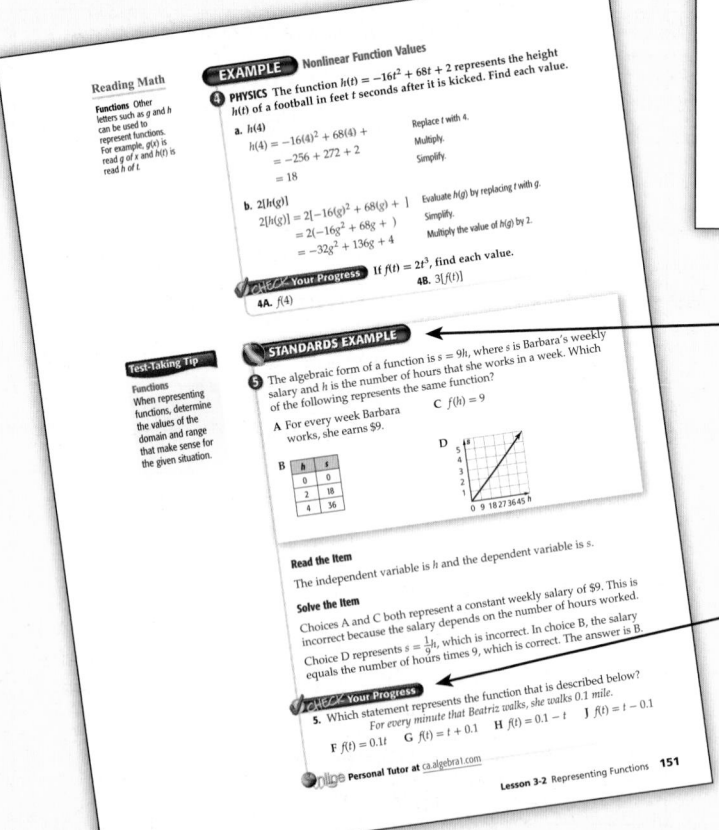

Examples

Fully worked-out **Examples** enable students and parents to see how to solve problems step by step. **California Standards Examples** help students practice the Standards using multiple-choice questions.

Check Your Progress

Check Your Progress exercises act as *diagnostic assessment* by showing you whether students understand the concepts presented.

Check Your Understanding

Check Your Understanding exercises can be used as *formative assessment* to monitor student progress and guide your instruction toward helping students achieve the standards.

Multi-Step Word Problems

Multi-step word problems are not simple computation problems using the numbers given. Students must analyze exactly what the problem is asking and how to use the information given. These problems are starred in the Teacher Wraparound Edition.

Homework Help

Homework Help guides students and parents to an example that is similar to the problems they are trying to solve.

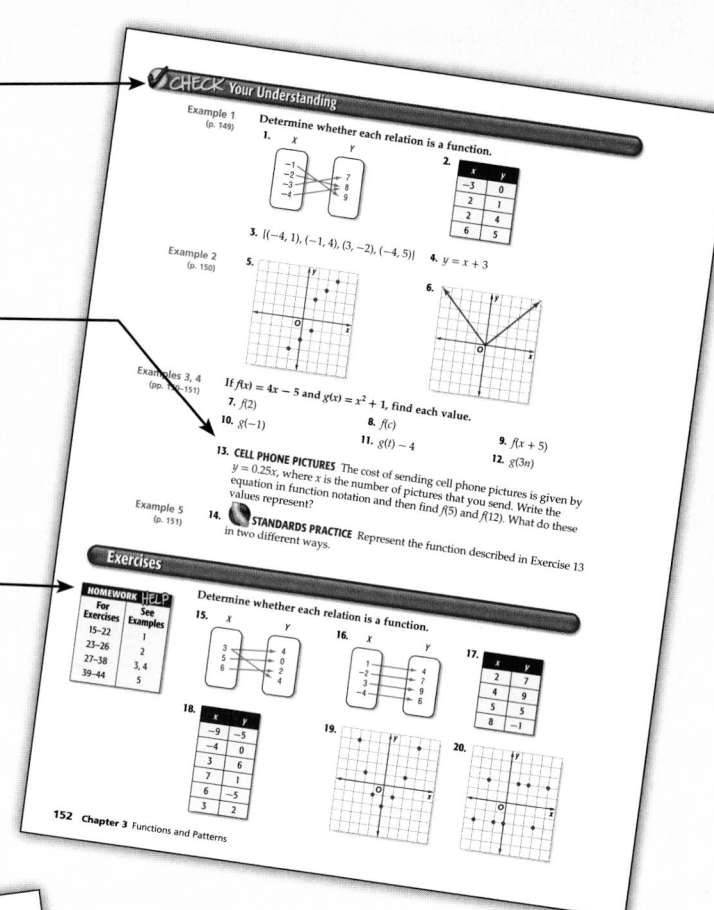

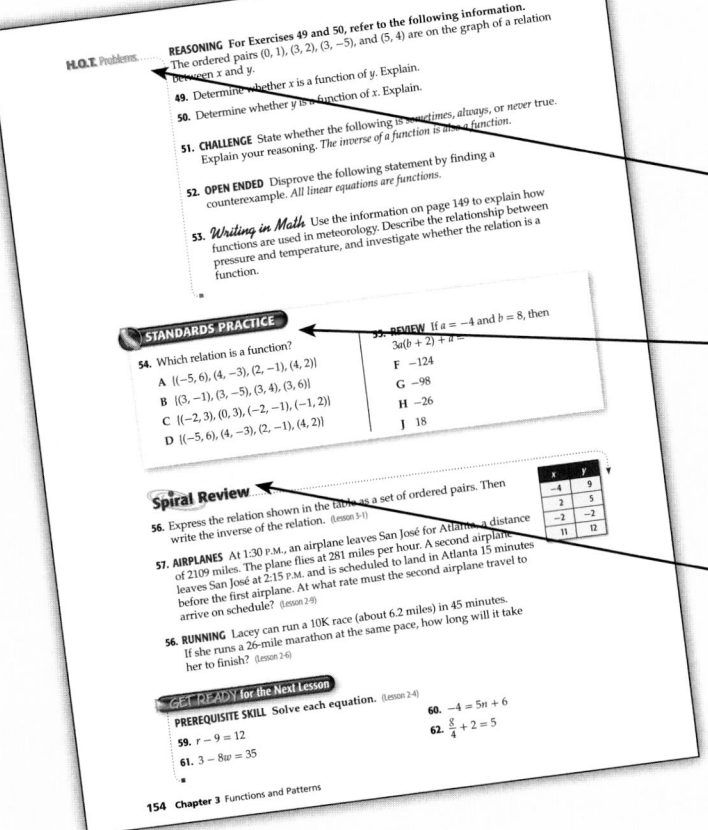

H.O.T. Problems

H.O.T. Problems require students to use **Higher Order Thinking** skills to solve problems.

 ## Standards Practice

Every lesson includes **California Standards Practice** questions that are similar to those found on state assessments. The assessed California Standards are noted in the Teacher Wraparound Edition.

Spiral Review

Spiral Review provides constant reinforcement of skills from previous lessons. The last few exercises let you assess whether students have the **prerequisite skills** for the next lesson.

Program Organization

Balance McGraw-Hill's *California Algebra 1: Concepts, Skills, and Problem Solving* is designed to provide students a balanced approach to mathematics learning by offering them the opportunity to:

- investigate concepts and build their conceptual understanding,
- review, learn, and practice basic computational and procedural skills, and
- apply mathematics to problem solving in real-world situations.

 Standards Review

This special chapter gives students additional review of the California Standards and additional practice in how to become better test takers.

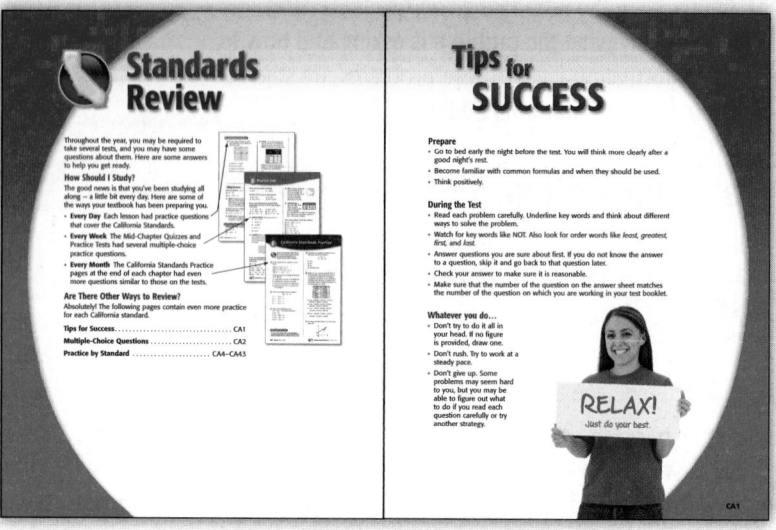

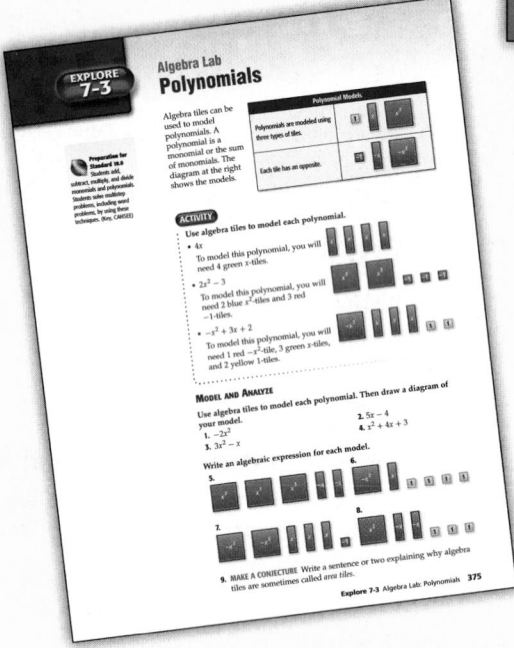

Labs

Some labs act as an introduction to a mathematical topic, while others extend the topic just presented. **Algebra Labs** use models to bridge the gap between concrete understanding and mathematical symbolism.

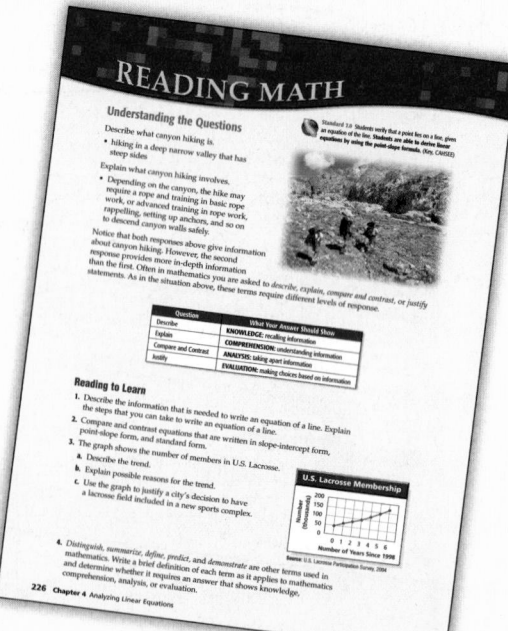

Reading Math

Helps students understand and interpret mathematical language.

Concepts in Motion

Concepts in Motion are online illustrations of key concepts through animations, Interactive Labs, and BrainPOPs®.

Reading Mathematics Tips

These tips provide hints on vocabulary and understanding mathematical terminology.

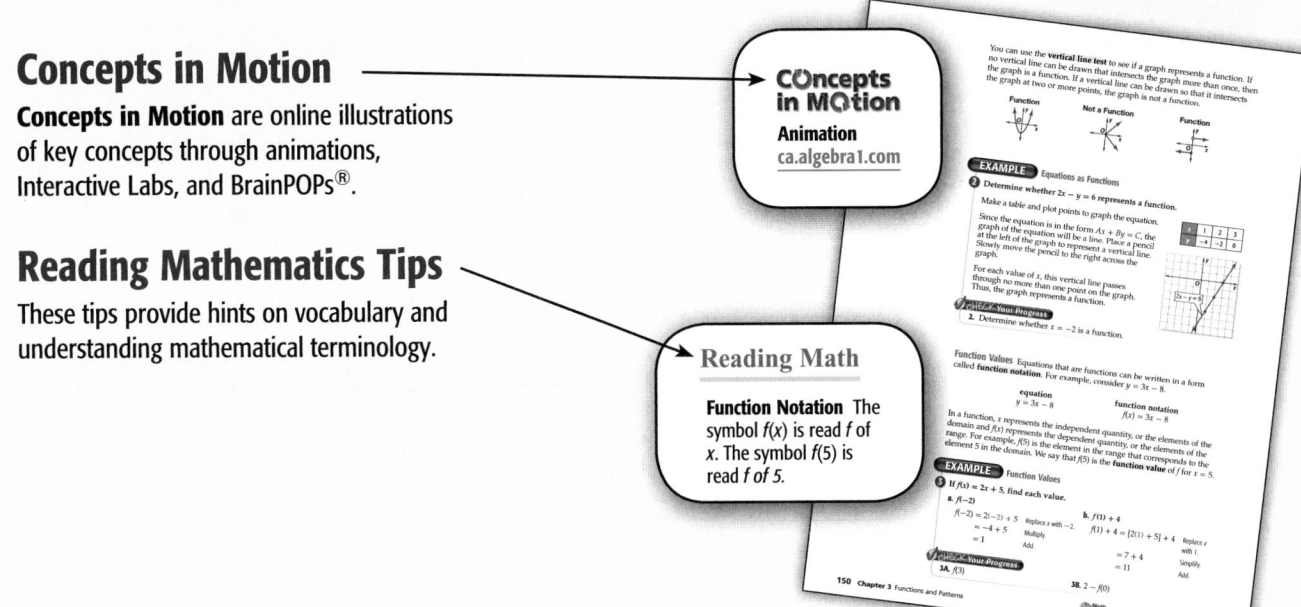

Three Built-In Workbooks in the Student Edition

① Prerequisite Skills

Use the **Prerequisite Skills** with students who need a review of previously taught concepts.

② Extra Practice

For additional exercises that are modeled after the exercises in each lesson, refer to the **Extra Practice** section.

③ Mixed Problem Solving

Additional word problems for each chapter are provided in **Mixed Problem Solving**.

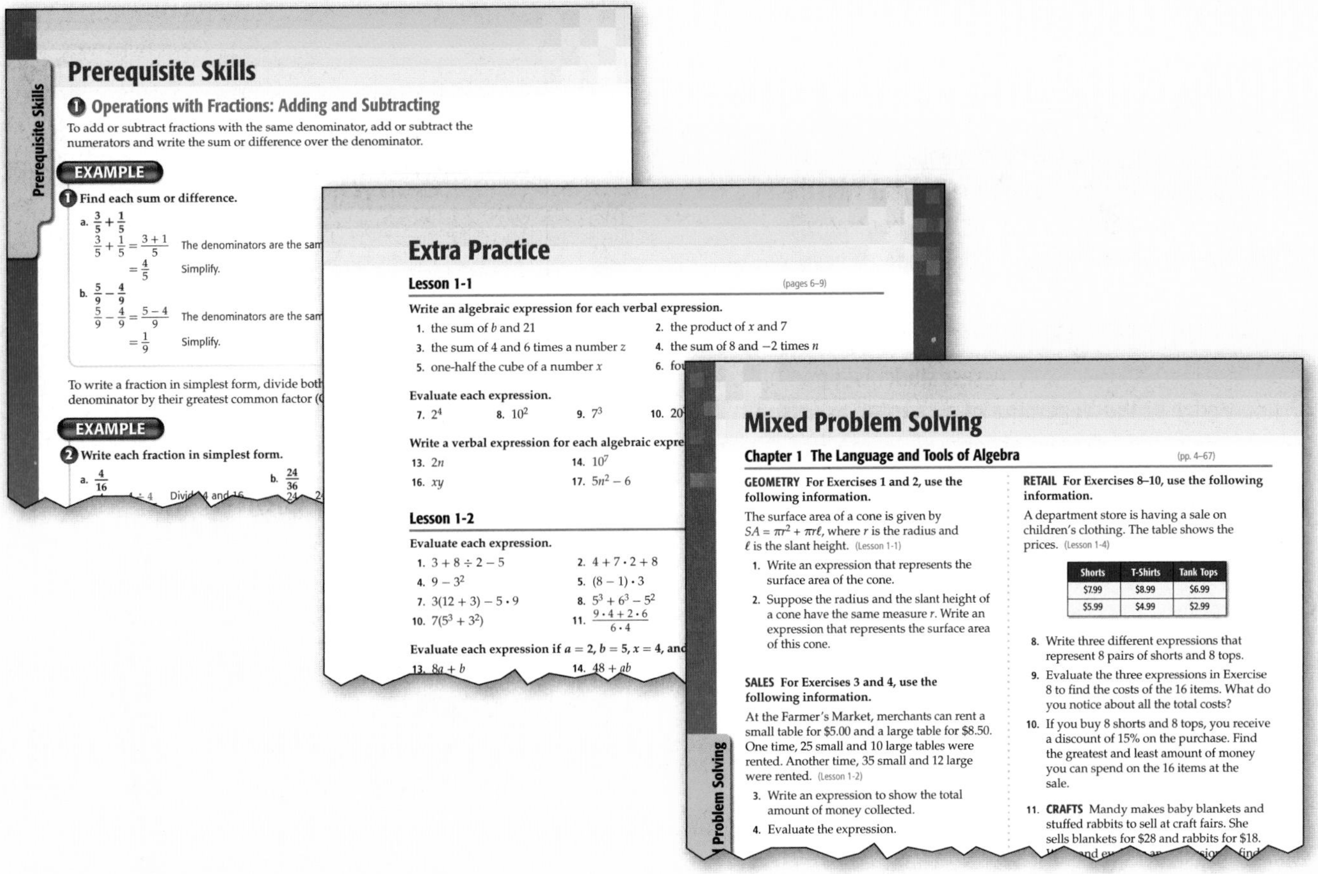

Assessment

Data-Driven Decision Making

McGraw-Hill's *California Algebra 1: Concepts, Skills, and Problem Solving* offers frequent and meaningful assessment of student progress within the curriculum structure and teacher support materials.

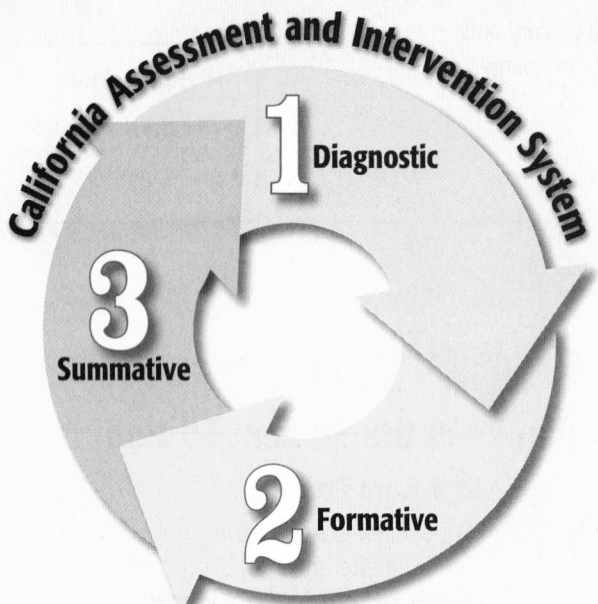

California Assessment and Intervention System

1 Diagnostic

2 Formative

3 Summative

1 Diagnostic

Initial Assessment Assess students' prior knowledge **at the beginning of the year** with the *Diagnostic and Placement Tests*. This booklet will help you determine whether your students need additional materials and resources to meet the grade-level or intensive intervention standards.

Entry Level Assessment Assess students' prior knowledge **at the beginning of a chapter or lesson** with one of the following options.

Student Edition

- Get Ready for the Chapter
- Get Ready for the Next Lesson

Teacher Wraparound Edition

- Chapter Assessment Planner

Other Resources

- Chapter Resource Masters
- ExamView Assessment Suite
- Chapter Readiness at <u>ca.algebra1.com</u>

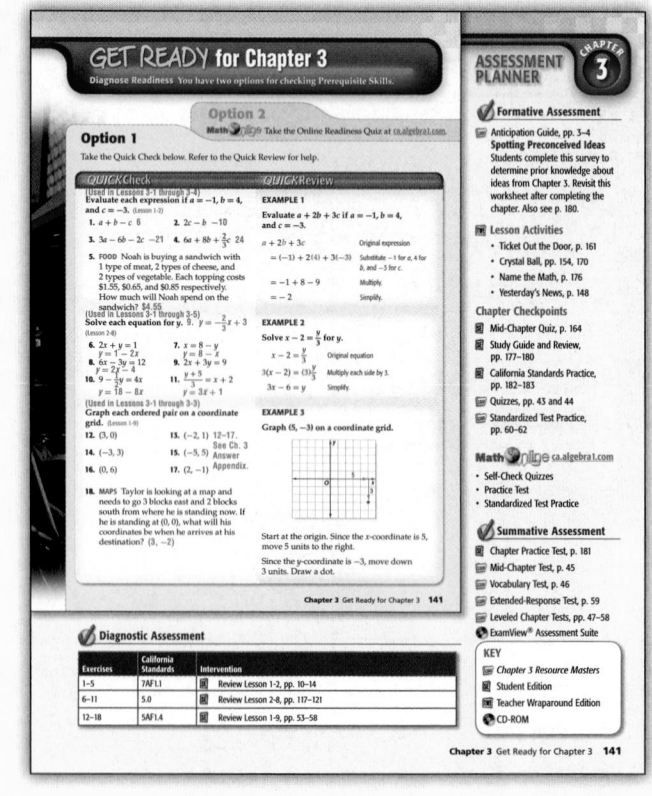

Formative

Progress Monitoring Determine if students are progressing adequately as you teach each lesson, and use the assessments to differentiate lesson instruction and practice.

Student Edition
- Check Your Progress
- Check Your Understanding
- Mid-Chapter Quiz
- Study Guide and Review

Teacher Wraparound Edition
- Chapter Assessment Planner
- Step 4 (Assess) of the Teaching Plan
- Data-Driven Decision Making

Other Resources
- Chapter Resource Masters
- ExamView Assessment Suite
- Self-Check Quizzes at ca.algebra1.com

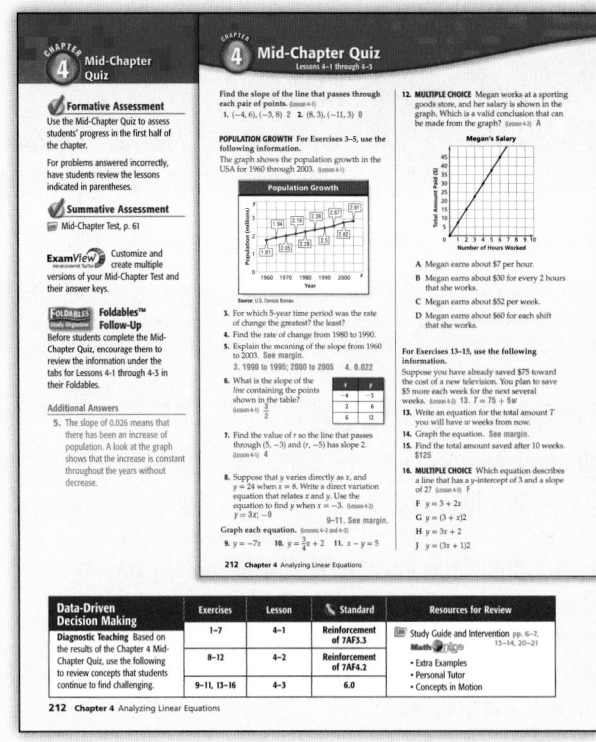

Summative

Summative Evaluation Assess student success in learning the concepts in each chapter.

Student Edition
- Chapter Practice Test
- California Standards Practice

Teacher Wraparound Edition
- Chapter Assessment Planner
- Data-Driven Decision Making

Other Resources
- Chapter Resource Masters
  - 6 forms of Chapter Tests
  - 4 Quizzes
  - Vocabulary Test
  - Extended-Response Test
  - Standardized Test Practice
- ExamView Assessment Suite
- Chapter Tests at ca.algebra1.com

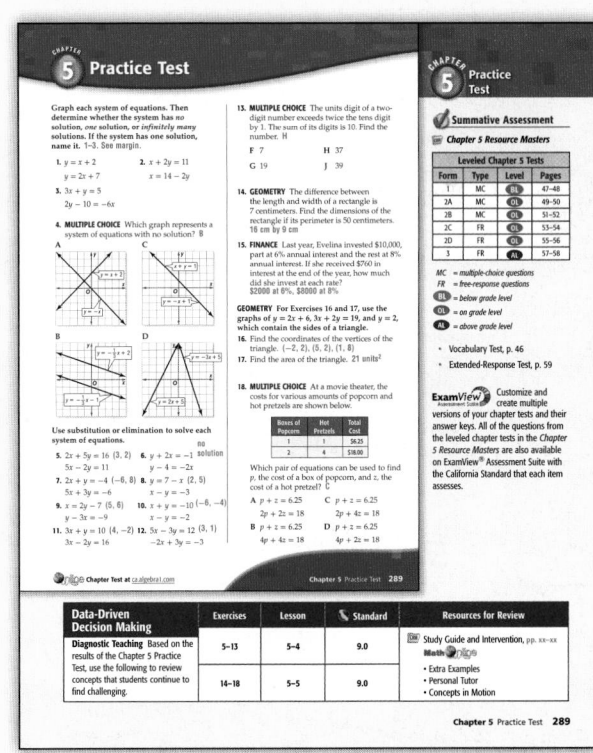

Universal Access

Options McGraw-Hill's *California Algebra 1: Concepts, Skills, and Problem Solving* provides extensive support for universal access.

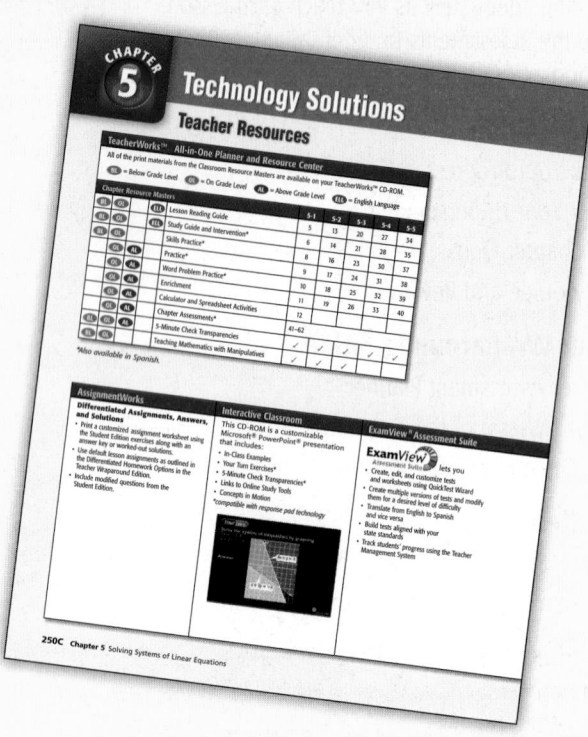

Leveled Resources

All of the blackline masters and transparencies that accompany the program, as well as all of the Teacher Wraparound Edition pages, are available on the TeacherWorks Plus™ CD-ROM. Resources and assignments are leveled for students who are **below grade level** **BL**, **on grade level** **OL**, and **above grade level** **AL**, and for students who are **English learners** **ELL**.

Technology

In addition to the Student Edition and Teacher Wraparound Edition, *California Algebra 1: Concepts, Skills, and Problem Solving* includes extensive resources online, on CD-ROM, and on DVD.

Online Resources for teachers, students, and parents can be found at ca.algebra1.com. These resources include a variety of activities to teach, reinforce, review, and assess mathematical concepts.

CD-ROM/DVD In addition to all of the Student Edition pages, all of the student workbooks that accompany the program are available on the StudentWorks Plus™ CD-ROM. This resource offers full audio of the text to support students with hearing challenges or language difficulty.

Additional tools for class presentations and assessment are available on a variety of CD-ROMs and DVDs.

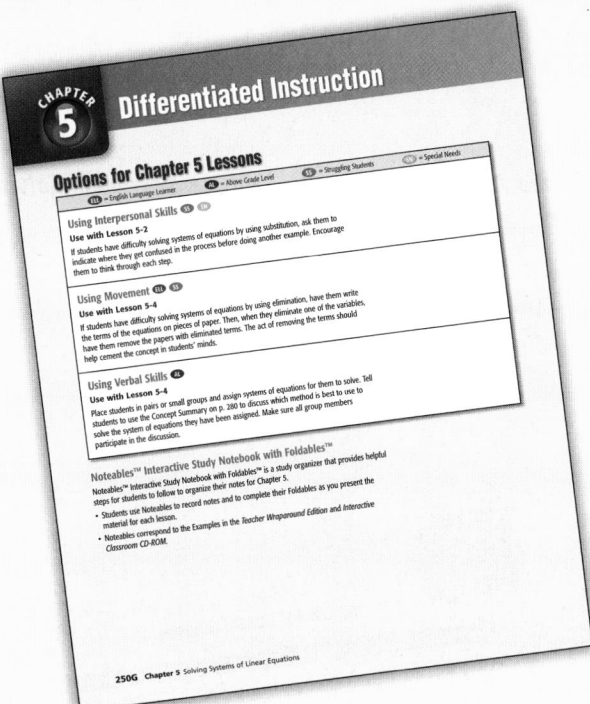

Differentiated Instruction

Diagnostic Teaching Every chapter and lesson includes suggestions for identifying and meeting your students' needs. Strategies include differentiation in pacing and student grouping, alternate approaches, ways to enhance instruction with manipulatives, questions to promote higher order thinking, and language hints.

Personalize instruction for:

- Struggling students
- English language learners
- Students with special needs
- Students who are above grade level in their comprehension of mathematics

Intervention

Strategic Resources and assignments that are coded for students who are below level may be used to provide strategic intervention in your classroom. **Teaching Tips** and other margin resources in the Teacher Wraparound Edition can also be used to target your instruction.

The data-driven decision-making tools in the Teacher Wraparound Edition help teachers identify intensive students, implement targeted intervention, and accelerate students' learning.

In addition, you may want to suggest that students use the *Quick Review Math Handbook* to review mathematical concepts.

Advanced Learners

Acceleration and Enrichment Resources and assignments that are coded for students who are above level may be used with advanced learners. In particular, the **Enrichment Masters** may provide students with valuable opportunities for extending your lessons. **Pre-AP Activities** provide additional opportunities for extension.

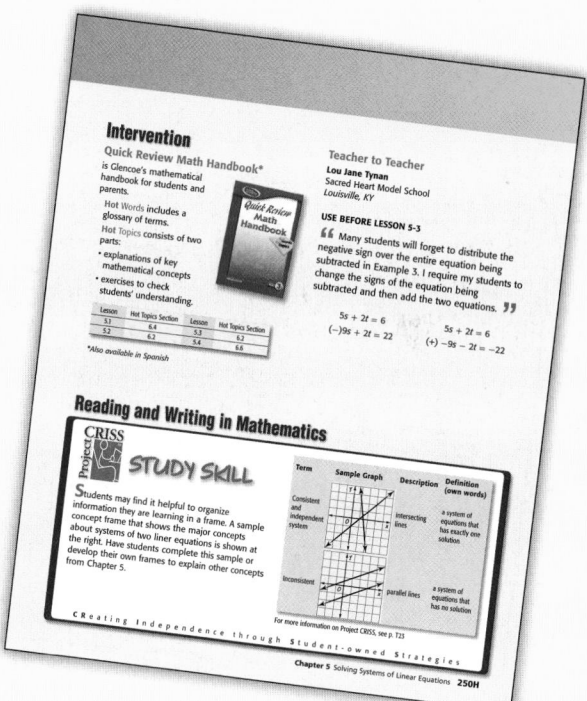

Instructional Planning and Support

Strong Pedagogy McGraw-Hill's *California Algebra 1: Concepts, Skills, and Problem Solving* has a strong instructional model that includes:

- differentiated instructional options,
- reteaching, reinforcement, and extension options,
- Teacher Tips to help address various learners,
- Pre-AP/Advanced items, and
- assessment linked with instruction.

Planning for Success

The **Chapter Overview** helps you plan your instruction by showing the objectives to be covered, the California Standards to be mastered, and the suggested pacing.

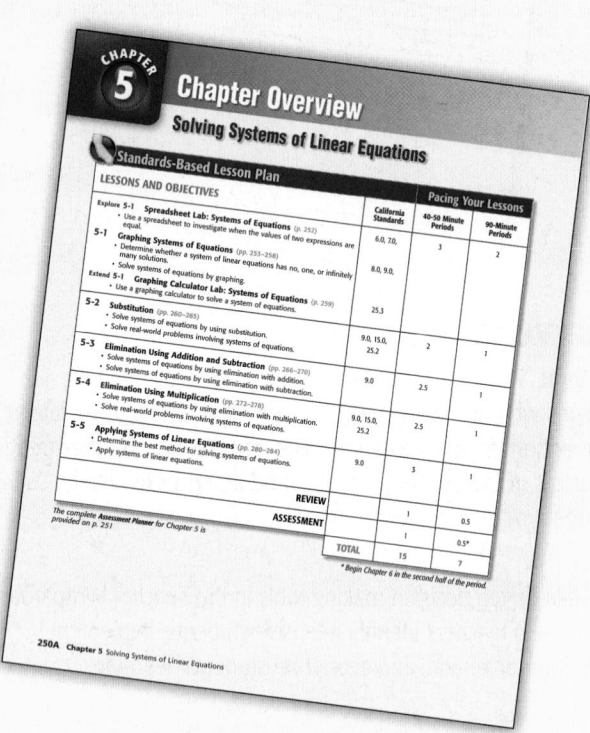

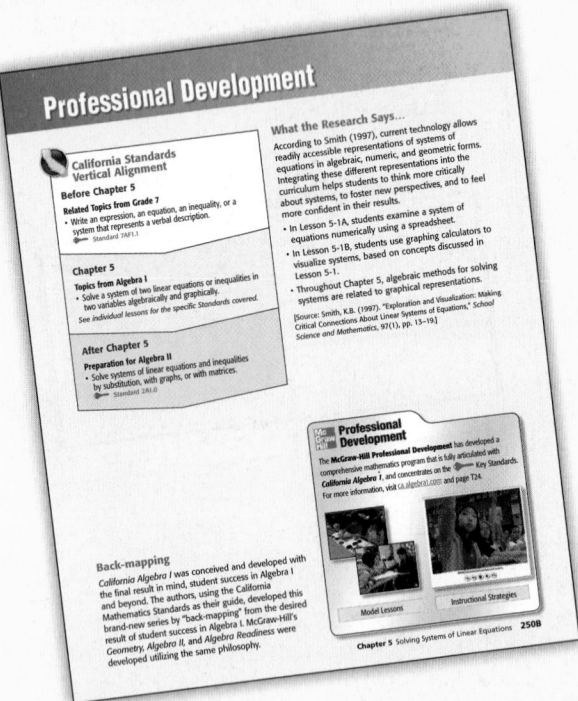

Vertical Alignment

Topics are presented to build upon prior skills and concepts and to serve as a foundation for future topics.

What the Research Says

Citations from **research** help to validate McGraw-Hill's *California Mathematics* program.

Focus on Mathematical Content

Highlights the **Big Ideas** in each chapter and the basic understanding that students should have upon completing the chapter. Lesson summaries describe the key mathematical content in each lesson.

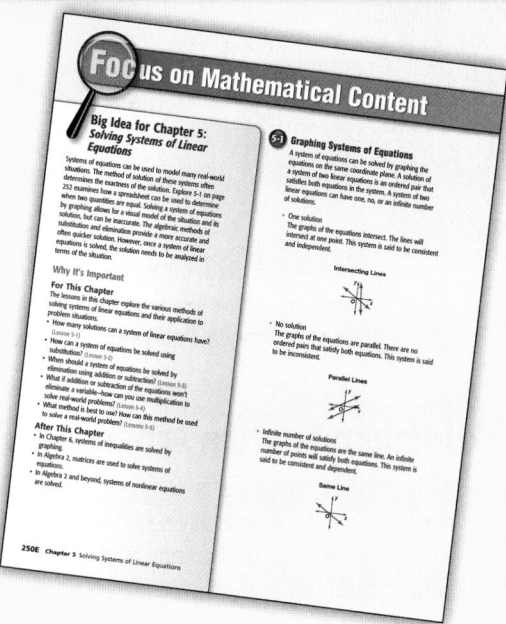

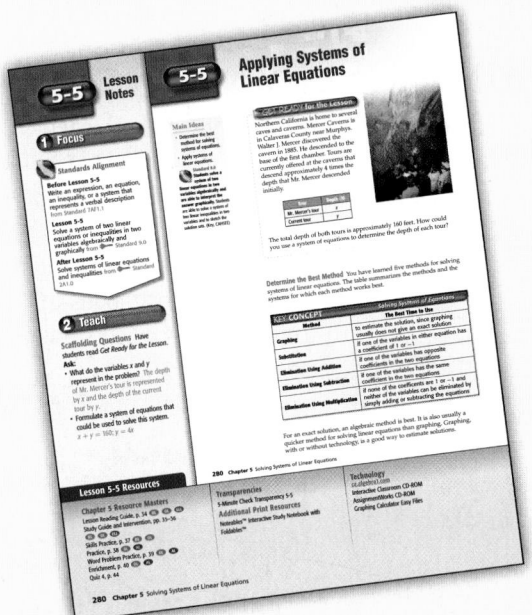

Four-Step Teaching Plan

Organizes your instruction as you **Focus** and **Teach** and help your students **Practice** and **Assess** what they've learned.

Standards Alignment

California Standards Alignment shows the Standards that lead into and follow the current lesson's content for a coherent K–12 scope and sequence.

Scaffolding Questions

Each lesson contains **Scaffolding Questions** for you to use to help students investigate and understand the main ideas of the lesson.

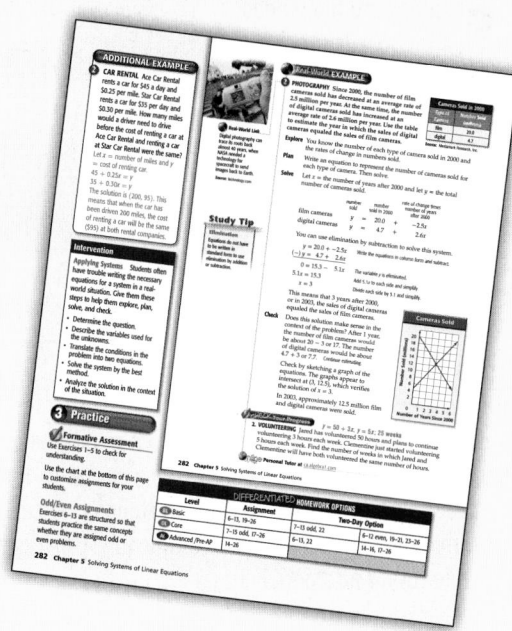

Additional Examples

Each **Additional Example** mirrors the Example in the Student Edition. The Additional Examples are also available as a PowerPoint® presentation on the **California Interactive Classroom** CD-ROM. Students also have access to these examples in their **California Noteables: Interactive Study Notebook**.

Differentiated Homework Options

Because most classrooms include students at a wide range of ability levels, **Differentiated Homework Options** allow you to customize your assignments.

Instructional Planning and Support

Professional Development McGraw-Hill Professional Development provides a comprehensive professional development plan for mathematics that is fully aligned and articulated with *California Mathematics: Concepts, Skills, and Problem Solving.*

Textbook Implementation Modules

These are video-enhanced CD programs in which users see an experienced teacher showing a new teacher how to use McGraw-Hill Teacher Editions, Student Editions, and program ancillaries to enhance classroom instruction.

Video Workshops

- **Self-Study** Users watch video clips of classroom lessons and guest educators who discuss issues and best practices. Then they complete short, self-paced lessons and activities in which they analyze the demonstrated teaching strategies and consider how to apply them in their classrooms.

- **Mentor-Led** Groups watch video clips of classroom lessons and guest educators. Then school coaches or facilitators use the videos as springboards for discussion and group professional development activities.

Accredited Online Courses

(Available for purchase)

Each 3- to 5-hour online module emphasizes the strategies and techniques used to teach mathematics. Users watch video clips of classroom lessons, complete interactive exercises, and develop electronic portfolios that can be printed and submitted to verify course completion. University credit is available for an additional charge.

Customized On-Site Training Materials

These workshop materials allow coaches to create a customized sequence of mathematics professional development sessions that directly address the specific needs of a school or district.

Mini-Clip Video Library

The video library includes several hundred short video clips that are referenced at point of use in the *California Mathematics: Concepts, Skills, and Problem Solving* Teacher Editions. These clips illustrate math content or instructional strategies and may include demonstrations or commentaries by curriculum specialists.

McGraw Hill Professional Development

Targeted professional development has been articulated throughout the *California Mathematics: Concepts, Skills, and Problem Solving* series. The **McGraw-Hill Professional Development Video Library** provides short videos that support the Key Standards. For more information, visit ca.algebra1.com.

Professional Development Web Sites

- **MHPD Online** (mhpdonline.com) is a Web site for K-12 educators where they can view video clips of instructional strategies, link to Web sites for relevant educational information, download grade-level student activities and worksheets, review monthly book suggestions, and read about the latest news and issues in education.

- **Teaching Today** (glencoe.com/sec/teachingtoday/index. phtml) is a Web site for secondary teachers of all disciplines that makes use of the extensive resources and expertise available from all of Glencoe/McGraw-Hill's secondary subject areas.

Glencoe McGraw-Hill

California

Algebra 1

Concepts, Skills, and Problem Solving

McGraw Hill Glencoe

New York, New York   Columbus, Ohio   Chicago, Illinois   Woodland Hills, California

Unit 1

Foundations for Functions

* For formative and summative assessment options,
see page 5.

Prerequisite Skills

- Get Ready for Chapter 1 **5**
- Get Ready for the Next Lesson
  9, 14, 20, 25, 31, 37, 44, 52

Reading and Writing Mathematics

- Reading Math **38**
- Vocabulary Link **26, 33**
- Writing in Math **9, 14, 19, 25, 31, 37, 44, 52, 58**

California Standards Practice

- Multiple Choice **9, 14, 20, 25, 31, 37, 42, 44, 52, 58**
- Worked Out Example **41**

H.O.T. Problems
Higher Order Thinking

- Challenge **9, 14, 19, 24, 31, 37, 44, 52, 58**
- Find the Error **13, 30**
- Open Ended **9, 14, 19, 25, 30, 37, 44, 52, 58**
- Reasoning **9, 19, 25, 30, 44, 58**
- Which One Doesn't Belong? **37**

x

CHAPTER 2 Solving Linear Equations

* For formative and summative assessment options,
see page 69.

Prerequisite Skills
- Get Ready for Chapter 2   69
- Get Ready for the Next Lesson
  76, 84, 90, 97, 103, 110, 115, 121

Reading and Writing Mathematics
- Reading Math   116
- Vocabulary Link   104
- Writing in Math   76, 83, 90, 96, 102,
  110, 115, 121, 128

 California Standards Practice
- Multiple Choice   76, 84, 90, 97, 103,
  110, 115, 121, 128
- Worked Out Example   100

H.O.T. Problems
Higher Order Thinking
- Challenge   75, 83, 89, 96, 102, 110,
  114, 121, 128
- Find the Error   90, 115
- Open Ended   75, 83, 89, 96, 102,
  110, 114, 121, 128
- Reasoning   89, 96, 102, 110, 121
- Which One Doesn't Belong?   83

Unit 2
Linear Functions

Functions and Patterns

* For formative and summative assessment options,
see page 140.

Prerequisite Skills
- Get Ready for Chapter 3 **141**
- Get Ready for the Next Lesson
  148, 154, 161, 170

Reading and Writing Mathematics
- Reading Math **171**
- Writing in Math **148, 154, 160, 170, 176**

 **California Standards Practice**
- Multiple Choice **148, 154, 161, 170, 176**
- Worked Out Example **151**

H.O.T. Problems
Higher Order Thinking
- Challenge **148, 154, 160, 169, 176**
- Find the Error **170**
- Open Ended **148, 154, 160, 169, 176**
- Reasoning **154, 160**

CHAPTER 4 Analyzing Linear Equations

* For formative and summative assessment options,
see page 185.

Prerequisite Skills
- Get Ready for Chapter 4   **185**
- Get Ready for the Next Lesson
  195, 202, 209, 218, 225, 233, 241

Reading and Writing Mathematics
- Reading Math   **226**
- Vocabulary Link   **189, 216**
- Writing in Math   **195, 202, 209, 218,
  225, 233, 241**

California Standards Practice
- Multiple Choice   **195, 202, 209, 216,
  218, 225, 233, 241**
- Worked Out Example   **214**

H.O.T. Problems
Higher Order Thinking
- Challenge   **194, 195, 202, 208, 218,
  225, 233, 241**
- Find the Error   **195, 224**
- Open Ended   **194, 202, 208, 218,
  225, 233, 241**
- Reasoning   **218, 233**
- Which One Doesn't Belong?   **202**

CHAPTER 5 — Solving Systems of Linear Equations

* For formative and summative assessment options,
see page 251.

Prerequisite Skills

Reading and Writing Mathematics

California Standards Practice

H.O.T. Problems
Higher Order Thinking

CHAPTER 6 Solving Linear Inequalities

* For formative and summative assessment options,
see page 294.

xv

Unit 3

Polynomials and Nonlinear Functions

CHAPTER 7 Polynomials

* For formative and summative assessment options,
see page 358.

Prerequisite Skills

Reading and Writing Mathematics

California Standards Practice

H.O.T. Problems
Higher Order Thinking

CHAPTER 8 Factoring

* For formative and summative assessment options,
see page 420.

Prerequisite Skills
- Get Ready for Chapter 8　**419**
- Get Ready for the Next Lesson
　423, 430, 439, 446, 452

Reading and Writing Mathematics
- Reading Math　**453**
- Writing in Math　**423, 430, 439, 446,
　452, 460**

California Standards Practice
- Multiple Choice　**423, 430, 439, 446,
　452, 460**
- Worked Out Example　**449**

H.O.T. Problems
Higher Order Thinking
- Challenge　**423, 430, 439, 445,
　451, 460**
- Find the Error　**439, 446, 451**
- Open Ended　**423, 430, 438, 445,
　451, 460**
- Reasoning　**423, 430, 438, 452, 459**
- Which One Doesn't Belong?　**460**

CHAPTER

9 **Quadratic and Exponential Functions**

* For formative and summative assessment options,
see page 470.

Prerequisite Skills
- Get Ready for Chapter 9   **469**
- Get Ready for the Next Lesson
  477, 485, 491, 499, 508

Reading and Writing Mathematics
- Writing in Math   **477, 485, 491, 498, 508, 514**

California Standards Practice
- Multiple Choice   **475, 477, 485, 491, 499, 508, 514**
- Worked Out Example   **474**

H.O.T. Problems
Higher Order Thinking
- Challenge   **477, 484, 490, 498, 507**
- Find the Error   **498, 507**
- Open Ended   **476, 484, 490, 498, 507, 514**
- Reasoning   **476, 477, 485, 490, 498, 507, 514**
- Which One Doesn't Belong?   **490**

Unit 4

Advanced Expressions and Data Analysis

 **CHAPTER 10** Radical Expressions and Triangles

* For formative and summative assessment options, see page 528.

CHAPTER 11 Rational Expressions and Equations

* **For formative and summative assessment options,**
  see page 565.

Prerequisite Skills

Reading and Writing Mathematics

 California Standards Practice

H.O.T. Problems
Higher Order Thinking

CHAPTER 12 Statistics and Probability

*For formative and summative assessment options, see page 642.

Student Handbook

Built-In Workbooks

Reference

Prerequisite Skills

Reading and Writing Mathematics

 California Standards Practice

H.O.T. Problems
Higher Order Thinking

Correlation

California Algebra I Content Standards
Correlated to *California Algebra 1*

 denotes Key standards

* denotes standards assessed on the California High School Exit Examination (CAHSEE)

Standard Number	Standard	Primary Citation(s)	Supporting Citation(s)
1.0	Students identify and use the arithmetic properties of subsets of integers and rational, irrational, and real numbers, including closure properties for the four basic arithmetic operations where applicable.	21–31, 46–52, 536–540, CA4	33–37, 78–90, 92–97, 694–708
1.1	Students use properties of numbers to demonstrate whether assertions are true or false.	21–25, 45, 314, CA5	423
2.0*	Students understand and use such operations as taking the opposite, finding the reciprocal, taking a root, and raising to a fractional power. They understand and use the rules of exponents.	46–52, 358–364, 366–373, 528–540, 696–701, CA6–CA7	21–25, 541–546
3.0*	Students solve equations and inequalities involving absolute values.	322–327, 329–333, CA8	716
4.0*	Students simplify expressions before solving linear equations and inequalities in one variable, such as $3(2x - 5) + 4(x - 2) = 12$.	92–103, 308–320, CA9–CA10	15–20, 26-37, 78–90, 122–128, 294–299, 301–307, 700–701
5.0*	Students solve multistep problems, including word problems, involving linear equations and linear inequalities in one variable and provide justification for each step.	92–103, 111–121, 294–299, 308–313, 315–320, CA11–CA12	77–91, 105–110, 122–128, 300–307
6.0*	Students graph a linear equation and compute the x- and y-intercepts (e.g., graph $2x + 6y = 4$). They are also able to sketch the region defined by linear inequality (e.g., they sketch the region defined by $2x + 6y < 4$).	155–163, 204–211, 334–340, CA13–CA14	253–258, 341–345
7.0*	Students verify that a point lies on a line, given an equation of the line. Students are able to derive linear equations by using the point-slope formula.	155–161, 219–225, CA15–CA16	226, 253–258
8.0*	Students understand the concepts of parallel lines and perpendicular lines and how those slopes are related. Students are able to find the equation of a line perpendicular to a given line that passes through a given point.	236–241, CA17	253–258
9.0*	Students solve a system of two linear equations in two variables algebraically and are able to interpret the answer graphically. Students are able to solve a system of two linear inequalities in two variables and to sketch the solution sets.	253–270, 272–278, 280–284, 341–345, CA18–CA19	252, 279
10.0*	Students add, subtract, multiply, and divide monomials and polynomials. Students solve multistep problems, including word problems, by using these techniques.	358–364, 366–373, 382–388, 390–409, 601–606, CA20–CA21	26–31, 33–37, 374–381, 583–588, 590–599, 608–619
11.0	Students apply basic factoring techniques to second- and simple third-degree polynomials. These techniques include finding a common factor for all terms in a polynomial, recognizing the difference of two squares, and recognizing perfect squares of binomials.	425–439, 441–452, 454–460, CA22	420–424, 583–588, 590–599, 601–606, 608–619

Standard Number	Standard	Primary Citation(s)	Supporting Citation(s)
🗝 12.0	Students simplify fractions with polynomials in the numerator and denominator by factoring both and reducing them to the lowest terms.	583–589, 600, 620–625, CA23–CA24	626–632
🗝 13.0	Students add, subtract, multiply, and divide rational expressions and functions. Students solve both computationally and conceptually challenging problems by using these techniques.	590–599, 608–632, CA25–CA26	366–373, 583–588
🗝 14.0	Students solve a quadratic equation by factoring or completing the square.	434–439, 441–452, 454–460, 486–491, CA27–CA28	426–431
🗝 15.0*	Students apply algebraic techniques to solve rate problems, work problems, and percent mixture problems.	105–110, 122–129, 626–632, CA29–CA30	260–265, 272–278
16.0	Students understand the concepts of a relation and a function, determine whether a given relation defines a function, and give pertinent information about given relations and functions.	53–59, 143–154, 172–176, CA31	142, 155–161
17.0	Students determine the domain of independent variables and the range of dependent variables defined by a graph, a set of ordered pairs, or a symbolic expression.	53–58, 143–148, 328, 547, CA32	59, 149–161, 471–477
18.0	Students determine whether a relation defined by a graph, a set of ordered pairs, or a symbolic expression is a function and justify the conclusion.	149–154, 176, CA33	176, 471–479
🗝 19.0	Students know the quadratic formula and are familiar with its proof by completing the square.	493–499, 530, 533, CA34	486–491, 528–529, 531–532
🗝 20.0	Students use the quadratic formula to find the roots of a second-degree polynomial and to solve quadratic equations.	493–499, CA35–CA36	471–477, 480–491, 500–501
🗝 21.0	Students graph quadratic functions and know that their roots are the x-intercepts.	471–485, CA37–CA38	493–499
22.0	Students use the quadratic formula or factoring techniques or both to determine whether the graph of a quadratic function will intersect the x-axis in zero, one, or two points.	480–485, 493–499, CA39	471–477
🗝 23.0	Students apply quadratic equations to physical problems, such as the motion of an object under the force of gravity.	500–501, CA40–CA41	426–431, 441–452, 454–460, 470–477, 480–491, 493–498
24.0	Students use and know simple aspects of a logical argument.	39–44, CA42	45, 171
24.1	Students explain the difference between inductive and deductive reasoning and identify and provide examples of each.	171	39–44, 172–176
24.2	Students identify the hypothesis and conclusion in logical deduction.	39–44	
24.3	Students use counterexamples to show that an assertion is false and recognize that a single counterexample is sufficient to refute an assertion.	39–44	102, 114, 148, 154, 306, 363, 380, 423, 484, 539, 618, 631, 669
25.0	Students use properties of the number system to judge the validity of results, to justify each step of a procedure, and to prove or disprove statements.	33–37, CA43	21–31, 39–44

Standard Number	Standard	Primary Citation(s)	Supporting Citation(s)
25.1	Students use properties of numbers to construct simple, valid arguments (direct and indirect) for, or formulate counterexamples to, claimed assertions.	21–31, 45	33–37, 39–44, 102, 114, 148, 154, 306, 363, 372, 380, 423, 453, 484, 539, 618, 631, 669
25.2	Students judge the validity of an argument according to whether the properties of the real number system and the order of operations have been applied correctly at each step.	38	13, 28, 30, 90, 260–265, 277, 307, 363, 372, 387, 439, 446, 451, 452, 498, 545, 593, 613
25.3	Given a specific algebraic statement involving linear, quadratic, or absolute value expressions or equations or inequalities, students determine whether the statement is true sometimes, always, or never.	45	24, 83, 96, 114, 258, 298, 326, 402, 459

Introduction

In this unit, students explore using variables to represent numbers and values. They learn to use variables to write expressions, which they evaluate and simplify. This knowledge, along with the properties of real numbers, lays the groundwork for writing and solving linear equations.

This unit concludes with using equations to solve problems that involve ratio and proportion, percent of change, and weighted averages. Students are also asked to solve equations for a specific variable.

Assessment Options

Unit 1 Test Page 93 of the *Chapter 2 Resource Masters* may be used as a test or review for Unit 1. This assessment contains both multiple-choice and short answer items.

ExamView®
Assessment Suite

Create additional customized Unit Tests and review worksheets for differentiated instruction.

UNIT 1
Foundations for Functions

Focus
Use symbols to express relationships and solve real-world problems.

CHAPTER 1
The Language and Tools of Algebra

BIG Idea Identify and use the arithmetic properties of subsets of integers and rational, irrational, and real numbers.

BIG Idea Use properties of numbers to demonstrate whether assertions are true or false and to construct simple, valid arguments (direct or indirect) for, or formulate counterexamples to claimed assertions.

CHAPTER 2
Solving Linear Equations

BIG Idea Simplify expressions before solving linear equations and inequalities in one variable.

BIG Idea Solve multistep problems, including word problems, involving linear equations and linear inequalities in one variable.

BIG Idea Apply algebraic techniques to solve rate problems, work problems, and percent mixture problems.

2 Unit 1

Real-Life Math Videos *Real-Life Math Videos* engage students by showing them how math is used in everyday situations. Use Video 1 with this unit.

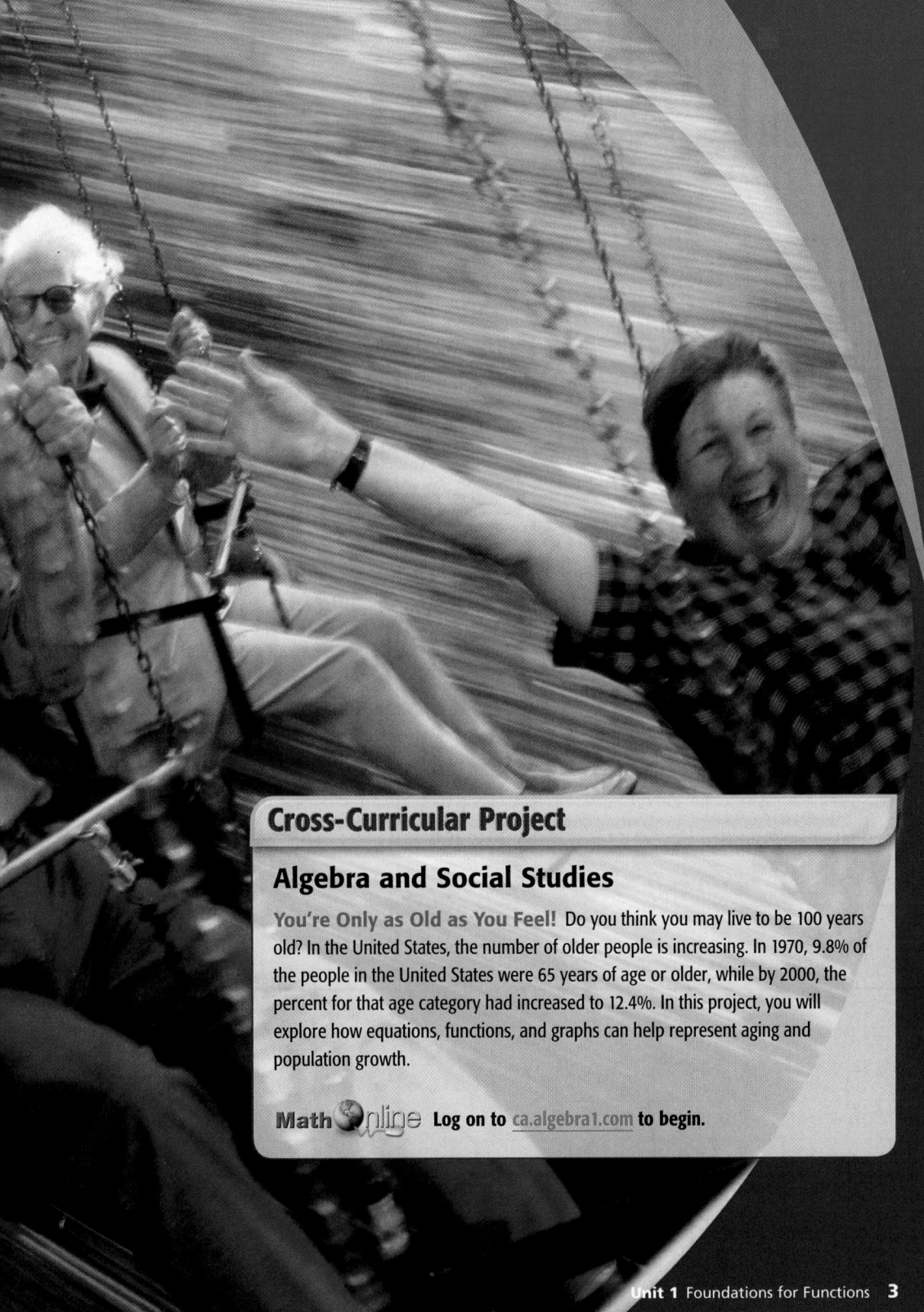

Cross-Curricular Project

Algebra and Social Studies

You're Only as Old as You Feel! Do you think you may live to be 100 years old? In the United States, the number of older people is increasing. In 1970, 9.8% of the people in the United States were 65 years of age or older, while by 2000, the percent for that age category had increased to 12.4%. In this project, you will explore how equations, functions, and graphs can help represent aging and population growth.

Math Online Log on to ca.algebra1.com to begin.

Algebra and Social Studies

You're Only as Old as You Feel! This Cross-Curricular Project is an online project in which students do research on the Internet, gather data, and make presentations using word processing, graphing, page-making, or presentation software. In each chapter, students advance to the next step in their project. At the end of Chapter 2, the project culminates with a presentation of their findings.

Math Online
ca.algebra1.com Log on for teaching suggestions and sample answers for this project.

Team Teaching You can use this Cross-Curricular Project with your students' health or social studies teacher to make the connection from mathematics to the topics of aging and population growth your students are studying.

The **Cross-Curricular Projects** send students to the Web to work on ongoing interdisciplinary projects.

Chapter Overview

The Language and Tools of Algebra

Standards-Based Lesson Plan		Pacing Your Lessons	
LESSONS AND OBJECTIVES	California Standards	40–50 Minute Periods	90-Minute Periods
1-1 Variables and Expressions (pp. 6–9) • Write mathematical expressions for verbal expressions. • Write verbal expressions for mathematical expressions.	7AF1.1	1	1
1-2 Order of Operations (pp. 10–14) • Evaluate numerical expressions by using the order of operations. • Evaluate algebraic expressions by using the order of operations.	7AF1.2, 25.2	1	1
1-3 Open Sentences (pp. 15–20) • Solve open sentence equations. • Solve open sentence inequalities.	4.0, 25.2	2	0.5
1-4 Identity and Equality Properties (pp. 21–25) • Recognize the properties of identity and equality. • Use the properties of identity and equality.	1.0, 1.1, 2.0, 25.0, 25.1, 25.3	1	0.5
1-5 The Distributive Property (pp. 26–31) • Use the Distributive Property to evaluate expressions. • Use the Distributive Property to simplify algebraic expressions.	1.0, 4.0, 10.0, 25.0, 25.1, 25.2	1	0.5
1-6 Commutative and Associative Properties (pp. 33–37) • Recognize the Commutative and Associative Properties. • Use the Commutative and Associative Properties to simplify algebraic expressions.	1.0, 4.0, 10.0, 25.0, 25.1	1	0.5
1-7 Logical Reasoning and Counterexamples (pp. 39–44) • Identify the hypothesis and conclusion in a conditional statement. • Use a counterexample to show that an assertion is false. Extend 1-7 **Algebra Lab: Logic and Properties of Numbers** (p. 45)	24.0, 24.1 24.2, 24.3, 25.0, 25.1 1.1, 25.3	1.5	0.5
1-8 Number Systems (pp. 46–52) • Classify and graph real numbers. • Find square roots and order real numbers.	1.0. 2.0	1.5	0.5
1-9 Functions and Graphs (pp. 53–58) • Interpret graphs of functions. • Draw graphs of functions. Extend 1-9 **Algebra Lab: Investigating Real-World Functions** (p. 59)	16.0, 17.0	2	1.5
REVIEW		1	0.5
ASSESSMENT		1	0.5*
*The complete **Assessment Planner** for Chapter 1 is provided on p. 5.*	**TOTAL**	14	7.5

* *Begin Chapter 2 in the second half of the period.*

Professional Development

California Standards Vertical Alignment

Before Chapter 1

Related Topics from Grade 7

- Use variables and operations to write an expression that represents a verbal description ⟜ Standard 7AF1.1

- Simplify numerical expressions by applying properties of rational numbers ⟜ Standard 7AF1.3

- Differentiate between rational and irrational numbers ⟜ Standard 7NS1.4

- Graph functions of the form $y = nx^2$ and $y = nx^3$ and use in solving ⟜ Standard 7AF3.1

Chapter 1

Topics from Algebra I

- Students identify and use the arithmetic properties of real numbers

- Students use properties of numbers to demonstrate whether assertions are true or false

- Students use properties to construct valid arguments for, or formulate counterexamples to claimed assertions

See individual lessons for the specific Standards covered.

After Chapter 1

Preparation for Algebra II

- Solve equations and inequalities involving absolute value ⟜ Standard 2A1.0

- Simplify complicated rational expressions ⟜ Standard 2A7.0

- Operations on polynomials, including long division ⟜ Standard 2A3.0

- Use mathematical induction to prove general statements about the positive integers ⟜ Standard 2A21.0

- Justify steps in combining and simplifying functions ⟜ Standard 2A25.0

- Solve and graph quadratic equations, including the complex number system ⟜ Standard 2A8.0

Back-Mapping

California Algebra 1 was conceived and developed with the final result in mind, student success in Algebra I and beyond. The authors, using the California Mathematics Standards as their guide, developed this brand-new series by "back-mapping" from the desired result of student success in Algebra I and beyond. McGraw-Hill's *California Geometry, California Algebra 2,* and *California Algebra Readiness* were developed utilizing the same philosophy.

What the Research Says...

According to the Rand Mathematics Study Panel (2002), connecting algebra with arithmetic, geometry, and statistics helps build student understanding.

- Throughout Chapter 1, algebraic expressions are used to describe areas and volumes of geometric figures.

- In Lesson 1-4, identity and equality properties are used to compare statistical data.

- In Lesson 1-8, values of variables are described in terms of properties of real numbers.

Professional Development

Targeted professional development has been articulated throughout the *California Mathematics: Concepts, Skills, and Problem Solving* series. The **McGraw-Hill Professional Development Video Library** provides short videos that support the ⟜ Key Standards. For more information, visit ca.algebra1.com.

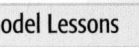

| Model Lessons | Instructional Strategies |

Technology Solutions

Teacher Resources

TeacherWorks™ All-in-One Planner and Resource Center

All of the print materials from the Classroom Resource Masters are available on your TeacherWorks™ CD-ROM.

BL = Below Grade Level   **OL** = On Grade Level   **AL** = Above Grade Level   **ELL** = English Language Learner

Chapter Resource Masters				1-1	1-2	1-3	1-4	1-5	1-6	1-7	1-8	1-9
BL OL **ELL**	Lesson Reading Guide			5	12	20	28	35	42	49	56	64
BL OL **ELL**	Study Guide and Intervention*			6	13	21	29	36	43	50	57	65
BL OL	Skills Practice*			8	15	23	31	38	45	52	59	67
OL AL	Practice*			9	16	24	32	39	46	53	60	68
OL AL	Word Problem Practice*			10	17	25	33	40	47	54	61	69
OL AL	Enrichment			11	18	26	34	41	48	55	62	70
OL AL	Calculator and Spreadsheet Activities				19	27					63	
OL AL	Chapter Assessments*			71–93								
BL OL AL	5-Minute Check Transparencies			✓	✓	✓	✓	✓	✓	✓	✓	✓
BL OL	Teaching Mathematics with Manipulatives				✓			✓		✓		✓

Also available in Spanish.

AssignmentWorks

Differentiated Assignments, Answers, and Solutions

- Print a customized assignment worksheet using the Student Edition exercises along with an answer key or worked out solutions.
- Use default lesson assignments as outlined in the Differentiated Homework Options in the Teacher Wraparound Edition.
- Includes modified questions from the Student Edition.

Interactive Classroom

This CD-ROM is a customizable Microsoft® PowerPoint® presentation that includes:

- In-Class Examples
- Your Turn Exercises*
- 5-Minute Check Transparencies
- Links to Online Study Tools
- Concepts in Motion

compatible with response pad technology

> **Example 1**
> Sports Medicine Name the ordered pair at point E and explain what it represents.
>
> **Blood Flow After Concussion**
>
> Answer: Point E is at 6 along the x-axis and 100 along the y-axis. So, its ordered pair is (6, 100). This represents 100% normal blood flow 6 days after the injury.
>
> Source: *Scientific American*
>
> End of slide

ExamView®Assessment Suite

ExamView® Assessment Suite lets you

- Create, edit, and customize tests and worksheets using QuickTest Wizard
- Create multiple versions of tests and modify them for a desired level of difficulty
- Translate from English to Spanish and vice versa
- Build tests aligned with your state standards
- Track students' progress using the Teacher Management System

This program is supported by a wealth of **technology options** on CD-ROM, on DVD, and online.

Student Resources

StudentWorks™ Plus

Textbook, Audio, Workbooks, and more

This CD-ROM is a valuable resource for students to access content online and use online resources to continue learning Chapter 1 concepts. Includes:

• Complete Student Editions in both English and Spanish
• English audio integrated throughout the text
• Links to Concepts in Motion, Personal Tutor, and other online resources
• Access to all student worksheets
• Daily Assignments and Grade Log

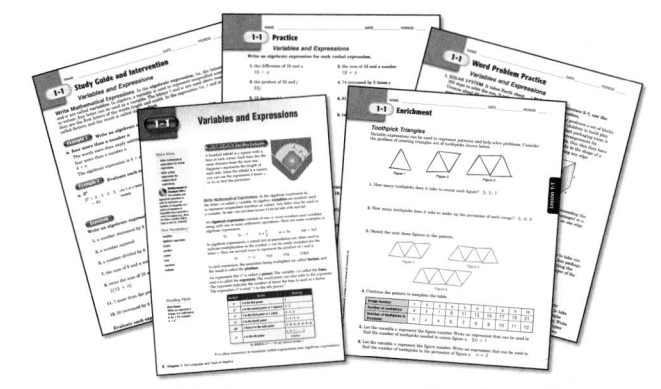

Super DVD

The Super DVD contains two Glencoe multimedia products.

MindJogger Plus An alternative review of concepts in which students work as teams in a game show format to gain points for correct answers.

What's Math Got to Do With It? Real Life Math Videos Engaging video that shows students how math is used in everyday situations

Unit 1 Theme: Foundations for Functions

Internet Resources

Math Online ca.algebra1.com

TEACHER	PARENT	STUDENT	Online Study Tools
	•	•	Online Student Edition
•	•	•	Multilingual Glossary
			Lesson Resources
	•	•	BrainPOP®
•	•	•	Concepts in Motion
•	•	•	Extra Examples
	•	•	Other Calculator Keystrokes
•			Problem of the Week Cards
	•	•	Real-World Careers
	•	•	Self-Check Quizzes
			Chapter Resources
	•	•	Chapter Readiness
	•	•	Chapter Test
	•	•	Standardized Test Practice
	•	•	Vocabulary Review/Chapter Review Activities
			Unit Resources
•		•	Cross-Curricular Internet Project
			Other Resources
•			Dinah Zike's Foldables
	•	•	Hotmath Homework Help
•			Key Concepts
•	•	•	Meet the Authors
	•	•	Personal Tutor
•			Project CRISS℠
	•	•	Scavenger Hunts and Answer Sheets
•			Vocabulary PuzzleMakers

Focus on Mathematical Content

Big Idea for Chapter 1:
The Language and Tools of Algebra

Learning how to use the tools and symbols of algebra enables students to express generalizations that can be used to represent mathematical and real-world relationships. The key to all problem solving lies in understanding the basic concepts of algebra, from expressions to equations and inequalities, to variables and inequality symbols, to number systems and how they are related, to functions and how they are graphed, and to processes of reasoning.

Why It's Important

For This Chapter
The lessons in this chapter provide a foundation of the skills required to manipulate symbols and simplify algebraic expressions.
- How are variables, numbers, and operations used to express mathematical or real-life relationships? (Lesson 1-1)
- What is the order of operations rule and why is it necessary to use it when evaluating expressions? (Lesson 1-2)
- What does it mean to solve open sentences? (Lesson 1-3)
- How are the Identity and Equality Properties and the Distributive Property used to evaluate expressions and solve equations? (Lessons 1-4 and 1-5)
- How can the Commutative and Associative Properties help you evaluate and simplify expressions? (Lesson 1-6)
- How is logical reasoning helpful in solving real-world problems? (Lesson 1-7)
- What are the distinctions between different number systems and how are they related? (Lesson 1-8)
- What is the difference between a discrete and a continuous function? (Lesson 1-9)

After This Chapter
- In Chapter 2, you will use the language and tools of algebra to solve equations.
- In Chapter 3, you will use the language of functions to represent and graph linear functions.
- In Chapter 6, you will apply the concept of solving open sentences to solving inequalities.

1-1 Variables and Expressions

Algebraic expressions contain one or more variables, numbers, and arithmetic operations. They can be written as mathematical expressions or verbal expressions. They do not contain an equals sign.

- A variable is a symbol used to represent an unknown number or value. Though any letter can be used as a variable, many letters used as variables are chosen because they are the first letter of what they represent, such as p for page.
- Algebraic expressions may contain powers. When evaluating a power, the exponent tells you how many times the base is used as a factor.

1-2 Order of Operations

The order of operations is a rule that specifies which operation to perform first when evaluating an expression.

- Perform the operation inside grouping symbols first. Grouping symbols include parentheses, brackets, braces, and fraction bars. If more than one grouping symbol is used, perform the operation inside the innermost grouping symbol first.
- Then, evaluate all powers.
- Next, perform all multiplications and/or divisions from left to right, and then all additions and/or subtractions from left to right.

1-3 Open Sentences

An open sentence is an algebraic statement that contains at least one variable and either an equals sign or an inequality symbol.

- An open sentence that contains an equals sign is called an equation.
- An open sentence that contains the symbol $<$, $\leq$, $>$, or $\geq$ is called an *inequality*.
- An open sentence is neither true nor false until the variables have been replaced with specific values.
- The process of finding a value of the variable that makes an open sentence true is called *solving the open sentence*. A solution set is a set of numbers that makes an open sentence true.

Identity and Equality Properties

Identity and Equality Properties can be used to justify each step when evaluating expressions and solving equations.

- The two properties of identity are the Additive Identity Property and the Multiplicative Identity Property. The Additive Identity Property states that adding zero to any number or expression does not change its value. The Multiplicative Identity Property states that multiplying any number or expression by 1 does not change its value.
- The Properties of Equality are often used to solve equations. These properties include the Reflexive, Symmetric, Transitive, and Substitution Properties.

 ## The Distributive Property

The Distributive Property can be used to evaluate numerical expressions and simplify algebraic expressions.

- In the Distributive Property, a term outside the parentheses is distributed to each of the terms inside the parentheses. So, $25(8 + 4)$ can be rewritten as $25(8) + 25(4)$, making it easier to evaluate the expression.
- By applying the Distributive Property to algebraic expressions, like terms can be combined and the expression can be simplified. For example, the expression $13a + 29a$ can be rewritten as $(13 + 29)a$, which can be simplified as $42a$.

 ## Commutative and Associative Properties

The Commutative and Associative Properties can be applied to expressions containing addition and multiplication. They do not apply to subtraction and division because order and grouping affect their difference or quotient.

- The Commutative Property states that the order in which numbers are added or multiplied does not change their sum or product.
- The Associative Property states that the way three or more numbers are grouped when adding or multiplying does not affect their sum or product.

Using these properties can often help make mental calculations easier.

 ## Logical Reasoning and Counterexamples

Logical reasoning encompasses conditional statements, deductive reasoning, and counterexamples.

- A conditional statement has a hypothesis and a conclusion, and is often written in if-then form, with the "if" part of the statement the hypothesis, and the "then" part of the statement the conclusion.
- Deductive reasoning is a process that uses facts and rules to reach a valid conclusion.
- A counterexample is a specific example that can be used to show that a statement is false.

 ## Number Systems

All real numbers are either rational or irrational. Square roots of perfect squares are rational, but the square roots of numbers that are not perfect squares are irrational.

- Rational numbers can be written as a ratio of two integers $\frac{a}{b}$, where $b \neq 0$. Rational numbers can be expressed as either terminating or repeating decimals. The set of rational numbers includes integers, whole numbers, and natural numbers.
- Irrational numbers cannot be expressed as terminating or repeating decimals. The square root of 7 and π are two examples of irrational numbers.

 ## Functions and Graphs

A function can be graphed on a coordinate system or coordinate plane.

- A coordinate plane consists of a horizontal axis, the x-axis, and a vertical axis, the y-axis. Each point in the plane is named by an ordered pair (x, y). The x-coordinate is the independent variable and the y-coordinate is the dependent variable.
- A function is a relationship between input and output in which there is exactly one output for each input value. The set of input values is the domain of the function, and the set of output values is the range.

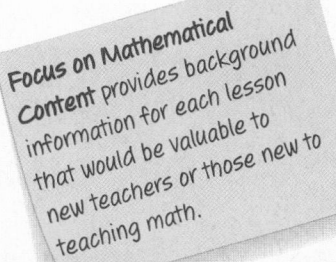

Focus on Mathematical Content provides background information for each lesson that would be valuable to new teachers or those new to teaching math.

CHAPTER 1

Differentiated Instruction

Options for Chapter 1 Lessons

ELL = English Language Learner   **AL** = Above Grade Level   **SS** = Struggling Students   **SN** = Special Needs

Connecting Mathematics to Nature **SS** **AL**

Use with Lesson 1-3

Challenge students to write open sentences about a plant or animal they are interested in. For example, the gestation period of armadillos can be described using the sentence 60 days $\leq$ gestation period $\leq$ 120 days.

Using Visual Learning **ELL** **SS**

Use with Lesson 1-6

If students have difficulty with the concepts of the Commutative and Associative Properties, consider using manipulatives to reinforce the concepts. Express each property using objects that visually verify the property. For example, a big bucket of water and a small bucket of water is the same as a small bucket of water and a big bucket of water.

Connecting Mathematics to Music **SS** **SN**

Use with Lesson 1-8

Play a song with a fast tempo for 10 seconds. Then play a slow song for 10 seconds. Help students understand that the amount of time the song was played is not affected by the tempo, so time is the independent variable. The number of beats played, which is affected by the tempo, is dependent on the amount of time the music played, so it is the dependent variable.

Noteables™ Interactive Study Notebook with Foldables™

Noteables™ Interactive Study Notebook with Foldables™ is a study organizer that provides helpful steps for students to follow to organize their notes for Chapter 1.

- Students use Noteables to record notes and to complete their Foldables as you present the material for each lesson.
- Noteables correspond to the Examples in the *Teacher Wraparound Edition* and *Interactive Classroom CD-ROM*.

Each chapter includes ideas for differentiating instruction in your classroom. These hints are keyed for English learners, students above grade level, struggling students, and students with special needs.

Intervention

Quick Review Math Handbook*

is Glencoe's mathematical handbook for students and parents.

Hot Words includes a glossary of terms.

Hot Topics consists of two parts:

- explanations of key mathematical concepts
- exercises to check students' understanding.

Lesson	Hot Topics Section	Lesson	Hot Topics Section
1-1	6.1, 6.3	1-6	1.2, 6.3
1-2	1.3, 6.2	1-7	2.8, 5.1, 5.2
1-3	2.4, 6.4, 6.6	1-8	3.2
1-4	1.2, 6.3	1-9	4.2, 6.7
1-5	1.2, 7.5		

*Also available in Spanish

Teacher to Teacher

Larry Hummel
Central City High School
Central City, NE

USE BEFORE LESSON 1-9

❝ I like to introduce the CBL or CBR with a graphing calculator with Example 3. I give students a graph and see if they can duplicate it by moving back and forth in front of the range finder. It really makes them think about what the graph represents. ❞

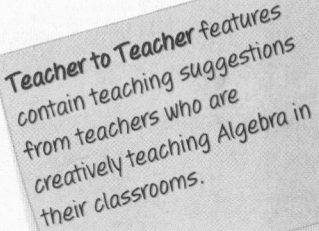

Teacher to Teacher features contain teaching suggestions from teachers who are creatively teaching Algebra in their classrooms.

Reading and Writing in Mathematics

Project CRISS℠ STUDY SKILL

Encourage students to write process notes as they study new concepts and algorithms.

Process notes help students work through the steps of problem solving by writing the steps in the left column and the sample steps for an example in the right column.

These process notes describe how to use the order of operations to evaluate an expression, which student study in Lesson 1-2.

	Topic: Notes
Step 1 Evaluate expressions inside grouping symbols.	$14 - 30 \div 5 + (6 - 2)^2$
Step 2 Evaluate all powers.	$= 14 - 30 \div 5 + (4)^2$
Step 3 Do all multiplications and/or divisions from left to right.	$= 14 - 30 \div 5 + 16$
Step 4 Do all additions and subtractions from left to right.	$= 14 - 6 + 16$ $= 8 + 16$ $= 24$

CReating **I**ndependence through **S**tudent-owned **S**trategies

Dinah Zike's Foldables™

Focus Students write notes about algebraic properties and skills as they are presented in each lesson of this chapter.

Teach Have students make and label their Foldables as illustrated.

Have students write a word or concept on the front of each tab and its definition on the back. Under the tabs, ask students to include an example of each concept.

When to Use It Encourage students to add to their Foldables as they work through the chapter and to use them to review for the chapter test.

A version of a completed Foldable is shown on p. 60.

Differentiated Instruction

📄 Student-Built Glossary, pp. 1–2

Students complete the chart by providing a definition and example for each term as they progress through Chapter 1. This study tool can be used to review for the chapter test.

CHAPTER 1

The Language and Tools of Algebra

🔘 BIG Ideas

- **Standard 1.0** Students identify and use the arithmetic properties of subsets of integers and rational, irrational, and real numbers, including closure properties for the four basic arithmetic operations where applicable.
- **Standard 1.1** Students use properties of numbers to demonstrate whether assertions are true or false.
- **Standard 25.1** Students use properties to construct simple, valid arguments (direct and indirect) for, or formulate counterexamples to claimed assertions.

Key Vocabulary

algebraic expression (p. 6)

coefficient (p. 29)

equation (p. 15)

function (p. 53)

🌐 Real-World Link

Architecture Architects can use algebraic expressions to describe the shapes of the structures they design. The buildings in San Francisco have shapes that resemble a rectangle, a triangle, or even a pyramid.

FOLDABLES™ Study Organizer

The Language and Tools of Algebra Make this Foldable to help you organize information about algebraic properties. Begin with a sheet of notebook paper.

 1 **Fold** lengthwise to the holes.

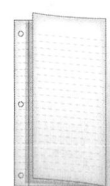 **2** **Cut** along the top line and then cut 10 tabs.

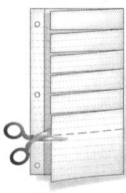 **3** **Label** the tabs using the lesson numbers and concepts.

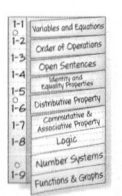

1-1	Variables and Equations
1-2	Order of Operations
1-3	Open Sentences
1-4	Identity and Equality Properties
1-5	Distributive Property
1-6	Commutative & Associative Property
1-7	Logic
1-8	Number Systems
1-9	Functions & Graphs

Materials Needed for Chapter 1

- algebra tiles (Lesson 1-5)
- product mat (Lesson 1-5)
- Internet (Reading Math, Lesson 1-7)

Foldables™ are a unique way to enhance students' study skills. Encourage students to add to their Foldable as they work through the chapter and to use it for review.

GET READY for Chapter 1

Diagnose Readiness You have two options for checking Prerequisite Skills.

Option 1

Take the Quick Check below. Refer to the Quick Review for help.

Option 2

Math Online Take the Online Readiness Quiz at ca.algebra1.com.

QUICK Check

(Used in Lesson 1-1)
Write each fraction in simplest form. If the fraction is already in simplest form, write *simplest form.* (Prerequisite Skill)

1. $\frac{52}{13}$ **4**
2. $\frac{6}{18}$ **$\frac{1}{3}$**
3. $\frac{9}{15}$ **$\frac{3}{5}$**
4. $\frac{13}{25}$ **simplest form**
5. $\frac{26}{100}$ **$\frac{13}{50}$**
6. $\frac{3}{81}$ **$\frac{1}{27}$**
7. $\frac{17}{1}$ **17**
8. $\frac{15}{75}$ **$\frac{1}{5}$**

9. **SURVEY** Thirty-three out of 198 students surveyed said that they preferred hockey to all other sports. What fraction of students surveyed is this? **$\frac{1}{6}$**

(Used in Lessons 1-1 through 1-6)
Find the perimeter of each figure.
(Prerequisite Skill)

10. 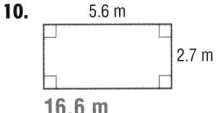 5.6 m, 2.7 m **16.6 m**
11. 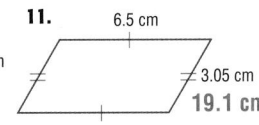 6.5 cm, 3.05 cm **19.1 cm**
12. 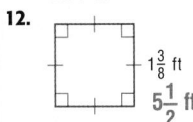 $1\frac{3}{8}$ ft **$5\frac{1}{2}$ ft**
13. 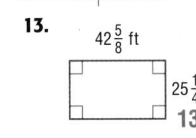 $42\frac{5}{8}$ ft, $25\frac{1}{4}$ ft **$135\frac{3}{4}$ ft**

14. **HOMES** The dimensions of a rectangular backyard are 45 feet by 84 feet. What is its perimeter? **258 ft**

(Used in Lessons 1-1 through 1-5)
Find each product or quotient.
(Prerequisite Skill)

15. $6 \cdot 1.12$ **6.72**
16. $0.5 \cdot 3.9$ **1.95**
17. $3.24 \div 1.8$ **1.8**
18. $10.64 \div 1.4$ **7.6**
19. $\frac{3}{4} \cdot 12$ **9**
20. $1\frac{2}{3} \cdot \frac{3}{4}$ **$1\frac{1}{4}$**
21. $\frac{5}{16} \div \frac{9}{12}$ **$\frac{5}{12}$**
22. $\frac{5}{6} \div \frac{2}{3}$ **$\frac{5}{4}$ or $1\frac{1}{4}$**

QUICK Review

EXAMPLE 1

Write $\frac{30}{36}$ in simplest form.

Find the greatest common factor (GCF) of 30 and 36.

factors of 30: 1, 2, 3, 5, ⑥, 10, 15, 30

factors of 36: 1, 2, 3, 4, ⑥, 9, 12, 18, 36

The GCF of 30 and 36 is 6.

$\frac{30 \div 6}{36 \div 6} = \frac{5}{6}$ Divide the numerator and denominator by their GCF, 6.

EXAMPLE 2

Find the perimeter of the figure.

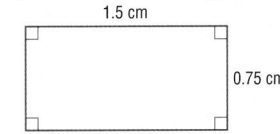 1.5 cm, 0.75 cm

$P = 2\ell + 2w$
$P = 2(1.5) + 2(0.75)$ $\ell = 1.5$ and $w = 0.75$
$P = 3 + 1.5$ or 4.5 Simplify.

The perimeter is 4.5 centimeters.

EXAMPLE 3

Find $\frac{4}{5} \div \frac{12}{15}$.

$\frac{4}{5} \div \frac{12}{15} = \frac{4}{5}\left(\frac{15}{12}\right)$ Multiply $\frac{4}{5}$ by $\frac{15}{12}$, the reciprocal of $\frac{12}{15}$.

$= \frac{4(15)}{5(12)}$ Multiply the numerators and the denominators.

$= \frac{60}{60}$ or 1 Simplify.

Chapter 1 Get Ready For Chapter 1 **5**

✓ Diagnostic Assessment

Exercises	California Standards	Intervention
1–9	7NS1.1	*Prerequisite Skills Workbook*, pp. 39–40
10–14	7MG2.1	**[SE]** Prerequisite Skill, pp. 704–705
15–22	7NS1.2	**[SE]** Prerequisite Skill, pp. 698–699, 700–701 *Prerequisite Skills Workbook*, pp. 25–32, 47–52

1-1

Variables and Expressions

1 Focus

Standards Alignment

Before Lesson 1-1
Write and evaluate an algebraic expression from ⚊ Standard 6AF1.2

Lesson 1-1
Write an expression, an equation, an inequality, or a system that represents a verbal description from ⚊ Standard 7AF1.1

After Lesson 1-1
Solve equations and inequalities involving absolute value from ⚊ Standard 2A1.0

2 Teach

Scaffolding Questions Have students look at the diagram, read *Get Ready for the Lesson,* and look at the table on powers.
Ask:
• How do you find the perimeter of a square? Add the lengths of each side.
• What does the expression 4*s* stand for? four times *s,* the length of a side
• How do you find the area of the baseball infield? Multiply one side length by the other.
• What expression could represent the area of the baseball infield? Since it is a square, *s* × *s,* or *s²*.

Lesson 1-1 Resources

Chapter 1 Resource Masters
Lesson Reading Guide, p. 5 **BL OL ELL**
Study Guide and Intervention, pp. 6–7 **BL OL ELL**
Skills Practice, p. 8 **BL OL**
Practice, p. 9 **OL AL**
Word Problem Practice, p. 10 **OL AL**
Enrichment, p. 11 **OL AL**

Transparencies
5-Minute Check Transparency 1-1
Additional Print Resources
Noteables™ Interactive Study Notebook with Foldables™

Technology
ca.algebra1.com
Interactive Classroom CD-ROM
AssignmentWorks CD-ROM
Graphing Calculator Easy Files

 All of the Lesson Resources are leveled for students who are below grade level, on grade level, and above grade level, and for students who are English language learners.

Main Ideas

• Write mathematical expressions for verbal expressions.
• Write verbal expressions for mathematical expressions.

 Reinforcement of Standard 7AF1.1 Use variables and appropriate operations to write an expression, an equation, an inequality, or a system of equations or inequalities that represents a verbal description (e.g., three less than a number, half as large as area A). (CAHSEE)

New Vocabulary

variables
algebraic expression
factors
product
power
base
exponent
evaluate

Reading Math

First Power
When no exponent is shown, it is understood to be 1. For example, $a = a^1$.

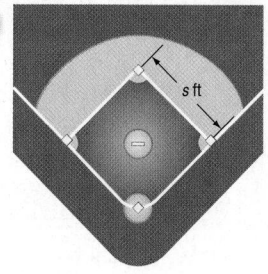

> ## GET READY for the Lesson
>
> A baseball infield is a square with a base at each corner. Each base lies the same distance from the next one. Suppose *s* represents the length of each side. Since the infield is a square, you can use the expression 4 times *s,* or 4*s,* to find the perimeter.

s ft

Write Mathematical Expressions In the algebraic expression 4*s,* the letter *s* is called a variable. In algebra, **variables** are symbols used to represent unspecified numbers or values. Any letter may be used as a variable. *The letter s was used above because it is the first letter of the word side.*

An **algebraic expression** consists of one or more numbers and variables along with one or more arithmetic operations. Here are some examples of algebraic expressions.

$$5x \qquad 3x - 7 \qquad 4 + \frac{p}{q} \qquad m \times 5n \qquad 3ab \div 5cd$$

In algebraic expressions, a raised dot or parentheses are often used to indicate multiplication as the symbol × can be easily mistaken for the letter *x.* Here are several ways to represent the product of *x* and *y.*

$$xy \qquad x \cdot y \qquad x(y) \qquad (x)y \qquad (x)(y)$$

In each expression, the quantities being multiplied are called **factors,** and the result is called the **product.**

An expression like x^n is called a **power.** The variable *x* is called the **base,** and *n* is called the **exponent.** The word *power* can also refer to the exponent. The exponent indicates the number of times the base is used as a factor. The expression x^n is read "*x* to the *n*th power."

Symbols	Words	Meaning
3^1	3 to the first power	3
3^2	3 to the second power or 3 squared	$3 \cdot 3$
3^3	3 to the third power or 3 cubed	$3 \cdot 3 \cdot 3$
3^4	3 to the fourth power	$3 \cdot 3 \cdot 3 \cdot 3$
$2b^6$	2 times *b* to the sixth power	$2 \cdot b \cdot b \cdot b \cdot b \cdot b \cdot b$
x^n	*x* to the *n*th power	$\underbrace{x \cdot x \cdot x \cdot \ldots \cdot x}_{n \text{ factors}}$

By definition, $x^0 = 1$ for any nonzero number *x.*

It is often necessary to translate verbal expressions into algebraic expressions

EXAMPLE Write Algebraic Expressions

1 Write an algebraic expression for each verbal expression.

  a. eight more than a number

  The words *more than* suggest addition. Let n represent the number. Thus, the algebraic expression is $n + 8$.

  b. 7 less the product of 4 and a number x

  Less implies subtract, and *product* implies multiply. So the expression can be written as $7 - 4x$.

  c. one third of the original area a

  The word *of* implies multiply. The expression can be written as $\frac{1}{3}a$ or $\frac{a}{3}$.

  d. the product of 7 and m to the fifth power

  $7m^5$

 **Your Progress**

1A. 13 less than a number $n - 13$

1B. 9 more than the quotient of b and 5 $\frac{b}{5} + 9$

1C. three-fourths of the perimeter p $\frac{3}{4}p$

1D. n cubed divided by 2 $\frac{n^3}{2}$

Personal Tutor at ca.algebra1.com

Reading Math

Subtraction
5 less x is $5 - x$.
5 less than x is $x - 5$.

To **evaluate** an expression means to find its value.

 EXAMPLE Evaluate Powers

2 Evaluate 2^6.

  $2^6 = 2 \cdot 2 \cdot 2 \cdot 2 \cdot 2 \cdot 2$ Use 2 as a factor 6 times.
  $= 64$ Multiply.

Your Progress

2. Evaluate 4^3. **64**

Study Tip

Multiple Translations

There may be more than one way to translate an algebraic expression into a verbal expression.

$4m^3 \rightarrow$
  4 times m cubed

$c^2 + 21d \rightarrow$
  c squared plus the product of 21 and d

Write Verbal Expressions Another important skill is translating algebraic expressions into verbal expressions.

EXAMPLE Write Verbal Expressions

3 Write a verbal expression for each algebraic expression.

  a. $4m^3$
    4 times m to the third power

  b. $c^2 + 21d$
    the sum of c squared and 21 times d

Your Progress

3. Write a verbal expression for $x^4 - \frac{y}{9}$. **See margin.**

 Math Online **Extra Examples at** ca.algebra1.com

Lesson 1-1 Variables and Expressions **7**

Write Mathematical Expressions

Example 1 shows how to translate a verbal expression into an algebraic expression. **Example 2** shows how to evaluate a power.

 Formative Assessment

Use the Check Your Progress exercises after each example to determine students' understanding of concepts.

ADDITIONAL EXAMPLES

 Write an algebraic expression for each verbal expression.

  a. 5 less than a number c $c - 5$

  b. 9 plus the product of 2 and the number d $9 + 2d$

  c. two thirds of the original volume v $\frac{2}{3}v$

  d. the product of $\frac{3}{4}$ and a to the seventh power $\frac{3}{4}a^7$

2 Evaluate 3^4. **81**

Additional Examples are also in:

• Noteables™ Interactive Study Notebook with Foldables™

• Interactive Classroom PowerPoint® Presentations

Write Verbal Expressions

Example 3 shows how to translate an algebraic expression into a verbal expression.

ADDITIONAL EXAMPLE

 Write a verbal expression for each algebraic expression.

  a. $\frac{8x^2}{5}$ the quotient of 8 times x squared and 5

  b. $y^5 - 16y$ the difference of y to the fifth power and 16 times y

Additional Answer

3. Sample answer: x to the fourth power minus the quotient of y and 9.

Differentiated Instruction

Verbal/Linguistic The transition from verbal expressions to algebraic expressions and vice versa is easier for some students than others. When you identify students who have trouble writing mathematical or verbal expressions, pair them with other students as mentors for practicing these skills.

Focus on Mathematical Content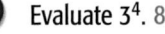

Evaluating Powers An expression such as 8^3 is a power, where 8 is the base and 3 is the exponent. When evaluating a power, the exponent indicates the number of times the base is used as a factor.

Lesson 1-1 Variables and Expressions **7**

Formative Assessment

Use Exercises 1–12 to check for understanding.

Use the chart at the bottom of this page to customize assignments for your students.

Odd/Even Assignments

Exercises 13–37 are structured so that students practice the same concepts whether they are assigned odd or even problems.

Real-World Connections

After students finish Exercise 41, suggest that they write an expression that represents an item they would like to buy with their savings. Ask them to write a verbal expression to represent their savings plans and then an algebraic expression. Have them use their expressions to explain the difference between the verbal expression and the algebraic expression in Exercise 41.

4 Assess

Ticket Out the Door Give each student a slip of paper with an algebraic expression. As they leave the room, ask each student to translate the algebraic expression into a verbal expression.

 **Foldables™ Follow-Up**

Remind students to use the first tab of their Foldables to record notes on what they have learned about variables and expressions. Students should also include information like that in the chart on p. 6.

Additional Answer

39. Sample answer: 12 times z squared divided by 5

Example 1
(p. 7)

Write an algebraic expression for each verbal expression.

1. the sum of a number and 14 $n + 14$
2. 6 less a number t $6 - t$
3. 24 less than 3 times a number $3n - 24$
4. 1 minus the quotient of r and 7 $1 - \frac{r}{7}$
5. two-fifths of a number j squared $\frac{2}{5}j^2$
6. n cubed increased by 5 $n^3 + 5$

7. **MONEY** Lorenzo bought a bag of peanuts that cost p dollars, and he gave the cashier a $20 bill. Write an expression for the amount of change that he will receive. $20 - p$

Example 2
(p. 7)

Evaluate each expression.

8. 9^2 81
9. 4^4 256

Example 3
(p. 7)

Write a verbal expression for each algebraic expression.

10. $2m$ Sample answer: the product of 2 and m
11. $\frac{1}{2}n^3$ Sample answer: one half of n cubed
12. $a^2 - 18b$ Sample answer: a squared minus 18 times b

Exercises

HOMEWORK HELP	
For Exercises	See Examples
13–25	1
26–29	2
30–37	3

Exercise Levels
A: 13–37
B: 38–41
C: 42–45

30–37. See Ch. 1 Answer Appendix.

EXTRA PRACTICE
See pages 714, 744.

 Self-Check Quiz at ca.algebra1.com

Write an algebraic expression for each verbal expression.

13. x more than 7 $7 + x$
14. a number less 35 $n - 35$
15. 5 times a number $5n$
16. one third of a number $\frac{1}{3}n$
17. f divided by 10 $\frac{f}{10}$
18. the quotient of 45 and r $\frac{45}{r}$
19. 49 increased by twice a number $49 + 2x$
20. 18 decreased by 3 times d $18 - 3d$
21. k squared minus 11 $k^2 - 11$
22. 20 divided by t to the fifth power $\frac{20}{t^5}$

23. **GEOMETRY** The area of a circle is the number π times the square of the radius. Write an expression that represents the area of a circle with a radius r. πr^2

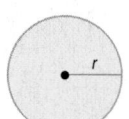

RECYCLING For Exercises 24 and 25, use the following information.
Each person in the United States produces about 3.5 pounds of trash a day.

24. Write an expression to describe the pounds of trash produced per day by a family with m members. $3.5m$
25. Use the expression you wrote to predict the amount of trash produced by a family of four each day. 14 lb

Evaluate each expression.

26. 8^2 64
27. 10^6 1,000,000
28. 3^5 243
29. 15^3 3375

Write a verbal expression for each algebraic expression.

30. $7p$
31. $\frac{1}{8}y$
32. $15 + r$
33. $w - 24$
34. $3x^2$
35. $\frac{r^4}{9}$
36. $2a + 6$
37. $n^3 \cdot p^5$

Write a verbal expression for each algebraic expression.

38. $17 - 4m^5$ 17 minus 4 times m to the fifth power
39. $\frac{12z^2}{5}$ See margin.
40. $3x^2 - 2x$ 3 times x squared minus 2 times x

 **DIFFERENTIATED HOMEWORK OPTIONS**

Level	Assignment	Two-Day Option	
BL Basic	13–37, 42–43, 45–54	13–37 odd, 46–48	14–36 even, 42–43, 45, 49–54
OL Core	13–41 odd, 42, 43, 45–54	13–37, 46–48	38–43, 45, 49–54
AL Advanced /Pre-AP	38–48 (optional: 49–54)		

41. SAVINGS Kendra is saving to buy a new computer. Write an expression to represent the total amount of money she will have if she has s dollars saved and she adds d dollars per week for the next 12 weeks. $s + 12d$

H.O.T. Problems

42. MUSIC Mario has 55 CDs. Write an expression to represent the total number of CDs he will have after 18 months if he buys x CDs per month. $55 + 18x$

43. Sometimes; the product is negative when a is a positive number, the product is positive when a is a negative value. The product is zero when a is zero.

43. REASONING Determine whether the product given by the expression $-3a$ is *always*, *sometimes*, or *never* a negative number. Explain.

44. CHALLENGE In the square, x represents a positive whole number. Find the value of x such that the area and the perimeter of the square have the same value. $x = 4$

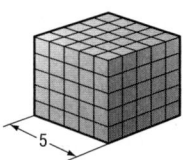

x

45. *Writing in Math* Use the data about baseball found on page 6 to explain how expressions can be used to find the perimeter of a baseball diamond. Include two different verbal expressions and an algebraic expression other than $4s$ to represent the perimeter of a square.
See Ch. 1 Answer Appendix.

STANDARDS PRACTICE 10.0, 7MG2.1

46. Which expression best represents the perimeter of the rectangle? **C**

ℓ
w

A $2\ell w$ C $2\ell + 2w$

B $\ell + w$ D $4(\ell + w)$

47. The yards of fabric needed to make curtains is 3 times the width of a window in inches, divided by 36. Which expression best represents the yards of fabric needed in terms of the width of the window w? **G**

F $\dfrac{3 + w}{36}$ H $\dfrac{3}{36w}$

G $\dfrac{3w}{36}$ J $3w(36)$

48. REVIEW Which expression best represents the volume of the cube? **D**

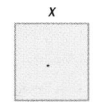

5

A the product of five and three

B three to the fifth power

C five squared

D five cubed

GET READY for the Next Lesson

PREREQUISITE SKILL Evaluate each expression. (Pages 696–697)

49. $10 - 3.24$ 6.76   **50.** 1.04×4.3 4.472   **51.** $15.36 \div 4.8$ 3.2

52. $\dfrac{1}{3} + \dfrac{2}{5}$ $\dfrac{11}{15}$ **53.** $\dfrac{3}{8} \times \dfrac{4}{9}$ $\dfrac{1}{6}$ **54.** $\dfrac{7}{10} \div \dfrac{3}{5}$ $\dfrac{7}{6}$ or $1\dfrac{1}{6}$

Enrichment
CRM p. 11 **OL AL**

1-1 **Enrichment**

Toothpick Triangles

Variable expressions can be used to represent patterns and help solve problems. Consider the problem of creating triangles out of toothpicks shown below.

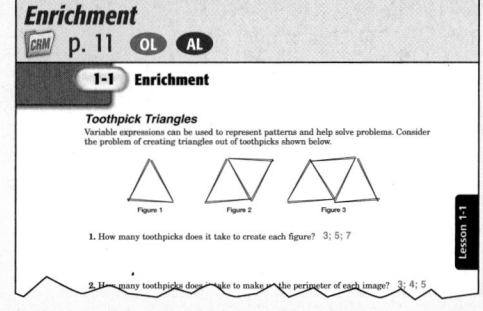

Figure 1   Figure 2   Figure 3

1. How many toothpicks does it take to create each figure? 3; 5; 7

2. How many toothpicks does it take to make the perimeter of each image? 3; 4; 5

1-1 **Study Guide and Intervention**

Variables and Expressions

Write Mathematical Expressions In the algebraic expression, ℓw, the letters ℓ and w are called **variables**. In algebra, a variable is used to represent unspecified numbers or values. Any letter can be used as a variable. The letters ℓ and w are used above because they are the first letters of the words *length* and *width*. In the expression ℓw, ℓ and w are called **factors**, and the result is called the **product**.

Example 1 Write an algebraic expression for each verbal expression.

a. four more than a number n
The words *more than* imply addition.
four more than a number n
$4 + n$
The algebraic expression is $4 + n$.

b. the difference of a number squared and 8
The expression *difference of* implies subtraction.
the difference of a number squared and 8
$n^2 - 8$
The algebraic expression is $n^2 - 8$.

Example 2 Evaluate each expression.

a. 3^4
$3^4 = 3 \cdot 3 \cdot 3 \cdot 3$ Use 3 as a factor 4 times.
$= 81$ Multiply

b. five cubed
Cubed means raised to the third power.
$5^3 = 5 \cdot 5 \cdot 5$ Use 5 as a factor 3 times.
$= 125$ Multiply

Exercises

Write an algebraic expression for each verbal expression.

1. a number decreased by 8 $b - 8$
2. a number divided by 8 $\dfrac{n}{8}$
3. a number squared n^2
4. four times a number $4n$
5. a number divided by 6 $\dfrac{n}{6}$
6. a number multiplied by 37 $37n$
7. the sum of 9 and a number $9 + n$
8. 3 less than 5 times a number $5n - 3$
9. twice the sum of 15 and a number $2(15 + n)$
10. one-half the square of b $\dfrac{1}{2}b^2$
11. 7 more than the product of 6 and a number $6n + 7$
12. 30 increased by 3 times the square of a number $30 + 3n^2$

Evaluate each expression.

13. 5^2 25
14. 3^3 27
15. 10^4 10,000
16. 12^2 144
17. 8^3 512
18. 2^8 256

Chapter 1   6   Glencoe Algebra 1

Practice
CRM p. 9 **OL AL**

1-1 **Practice**

Variables and Expressions

Write an algebraic expression for each verbal expression.

1. the difference of 10 and u $10 - u$
2. the sum of 18 and a number $18 + x$
3. the product of 33 and j $33j$
4. 74 increased by 3 times y $74 + 3y$
5. 15 decreased by twice a number $15 - 2x$
6. 91 more than the square of a number $x^2 + 91$
7. three fourths the square of b $\dfrac{3}{4}b^2$
8. two fifths the cube of a number $\dfrac{2}{5}x^3$

Evaluate each expression.

9. 11^2 121
10. 8^3 512
11. 5^4 625
12. 4^5 1024
13. 9^3 729
14. 6^4 1296
15. 10^5 100,000
16. 12^3 1728
17. 100^4 100,000,000

Write a verbal expression for each algebraic expression. 18–25. Sample answers are given.
18. $23f$
the product of 23 and f
19. 7^3
seven cubed
20. $5m^2 + 2$
2 more than 5 times m squared
21. $4d^3 - 10$
4 times d cubed minus 10
22. $x^3 \cdot y^4$ x cubed times y to the fourth power
23. $b^3 - 3c$ b squared minus 3 times c cubed
24. $\dfrac{k^5}{6}$ one sixth of the fifth power of k
25. $\dfrac{4n^2}{7}$ one seventh of 4 times n squared

26. **BOOKS** A used bookstore sells paperback fiction books in excellent condition for $2.50 and in fair condition for $0.50. Write an expression for the cost of buying e excellent-condition paperbacks and f fair-condition paperbacks. $2.50e + 0.50f$

27. **GEOMETRY** The surface area of the side of a right cylinder can be found by multiplying twice the number π by the radius times the height. If a circular cylinder has radius r and height h, write an expression that represents the surface area of its side. $2\pi rh$

Chapter 1   9   Glencoe Algebra 1

Word Problem Practice
CRM p. 10 **OL AL**

1-1 **Word Problem Practice**

Variables and Expressions

1. **SOLAR SYSTEM** It takes Earth about 365 days to orbit the sun. It takes Uranus about 85 times as long. Write a numerical expression to describe the number of days it takes Uranus to orbit the sun. 365×85

BLOCKS For Exercises 5–7, use the following information.
A toy manufacturer produces a set of blocks that can be used by children to build play structures. The product packaging team is analyzing different arrangements for packaging their blocks. One idea they have is to arrange the blocks in the shape of a cube, with b blocks along one edge.

2. **TECHNOLOGY** There are 1024 bytes in a kilobyte. Write an expression that describes the number of bytes in a computer chip with n kilobytes. $1024 \times n$ or $1024n$

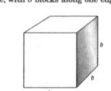

3. **THEATER** Howard Hughes, Professor Emeritus of Texas Wesleyan College, reportedly attended a record 6136 theatrical shows. Write an expression to represent the average number of theater shows attended if he accumulated the record over y years. Use the expression to find the average number of shows Mr. Hughes attended in a theater for 31 years. $\dfrac{6136}{y}$ or about 198 shows per year

5. Write an expression representing the total number of blocks packaged in a cube measuring b blocks on one side. b^3

6. The packaging team decides to take one layer of blocks off the top of this package. Write an expression representing the number of blocks in the top layer of the package. b^2

4. **TIDES** The difference between high and low tides along the Maine coast in November is 19 feet on Monday and x feet on Tuesday. Write an expression to show the average rise and fall of the tide for Monday and Tuesday. $\dfrac{19 + x}{2}$

7. The team finally decides that their favorite package arrangement is to take 2 layers of blocks off the top of the cube measuring b blocks along one edge. Write an expression representing the number of blocks left behind after the top two layers are removed. $b^3 - 2b^2$ or $(b - 2) \times b^2$

Chapter 1   10   Glencoe Algebra 1

1-2 Order of Operations

1 Focus

 Standards Alignment

Before Lesson 1-2
Evaluate expressions and justify each step in the process from — Standard 6AF1.3

Lesson 1-2
Use order of operations to evaluate algebraic expressions from — Standard 7AF1.2

After Lesson 1-2
Evaluate and simplify complicated rational expressions from — Standard 2A7.0

2 Teach

Scaffolding Questions Have students read *Get Ready for the Lesson.* **Ask:**

• How would you translate
4.95 + 0.99(117 − 100)? 4.95 plus 0.99 times the quantity 117 minus 100

• What are the three operations in the expression? addition, multiplication, and subtraction

• What does 117 − 100 represent? the number of hours above 100 hours

Evaluate Numerical Expressions

Examples 1 and 2 show how to evaluate numerical expressions using the order of operations.

Main Ideas

• Evaluate numerical expressions by using the order of operations.

• Evaluate algebraic expressions by using the order of operations.

 Reinforcement of Standard 7AF1.2 Use the correct order of operations to evaluate algebraic expressions such as 3(2x + 5)². (CAHSEE)

New Vocabulary

order of operations

Students and parents know exactly which California Standards are addressed by the lesson. The portion of the standard in bold is the specific part of the lesson being addressed.

> **GET READY for the Lesson**

Nicole's Internet service provider charges $4.95 a month, which includes 100 hours of access. If she is online more than 100 hours, she pays an additional $0.99 per hour. Suppose Nicole is online 117 hours this month. The expression below represents what she must pay for the month.

@home.net
$4.95 per month
- includes 100 free hours
- accessible anywhere
$0.99 per hour after 100 hours

$$4.95 + 0.99(117 − 100)$$

Evaluate Numerical Expressions Numerical expressions often contain more than one operation. A rule is needed to let you know which operation to perform first. This rule is called the **order of operations**.

KEY **CONCEPT**	*Order of Operations*

Step 1 Evaluate the expressions inside grouping symbols.

Step 2 Evaluate all powers.

Step 3 Multiply and/or divide in order from left to right.

Step 4 Add and/or subtract in order from left to right.

> **EXAMPLE** Evaluate Expressions

1 Evaluate $15 \div 3 \cdot 6 - 4^2$.

$15 \div 3 \cdot 6 - 4^2 = 15 \div 3 \cdot 6 - 16$	Evaluate power.
$= 5 \cdot 6 - 16$	Divide 15 by 3.
$= 30 - 16$	Multiply 5 by 6.
$= 14$	Subtract 16 from 30.

 CHECK Your Progress

Evaluate each expression.

1A. $8 - 6 \cdot 4 \div 3$ 0   **1B.** $32 + 7^2 - 5 \cdot 2$ 71

10 Chapter 1 The Language and Tools of Algebra

Chapter 1 Resource Masters

Lesson Reading Guide, p. 12 BL OL ELL
Study Guide and Intervention, pp. 13–14
BL OL ELL
Skills Practice, p. 15 BL OL
Practice, p. 16 OL AL
Word Problem Practice, p. 17 OL AL
Enrichment, p. 26 OL AL
Spreadsheet, p. 27

Transparencies

5-Minute Check Transparency 1-2

Additional Print Resources

Noteables™ Interactive Study Notebook with Foldables™
Teaching Algebra with Manipulatives

Technology

ca.algebra1.com
Interactive Classroom CD-ROM
AssignmentWorks CD-ROM
Graphing Calculator Easy Files

Grouping symbols such as parentheses ( ), brackets [ ], and braces { } are used to clarify or change the order of operations. They indicate that the expression within the grouping symbol is to be evaluated first. A fraction bar also acts as a grouping symbol. It indicates that the numerator and denominator should each be treated as a single value.

 EXAMPLE Grouping Symbols

2 Evaluate each expression.

a. $2(5) + 3(4 + 3)$

$$2(5) + 3(4 + 3) = 2(5) + 3(7) \quad \text{Evaluate inside parentheses.}$$
$$= 10 + 21 \quad \text{Multiply expressions left to right.}$$
$$= 31 \quad \text{Add 10 and 21.}$$

b. $2[5 + (30 \div 6)^2]$

$$2[5 + (30 \div 6)^2] = 2[5 + (5)^2] \quad \text{Evaluate innermost expression first.}$$
$$= 2[5 + 25] \quad \text{Evaluate power.}$$
$$= 2[30] \quad \text{Evaluate expression inside grouping symbols.}$$
$$= 60 \quad \text{Multiply.}$$

c. $\dfrac{6 + 4}{3^2 \cdot 4}$

$$\frac{6 + 4}{3^2 \cdot 4} = \frac{10}{3^2 \cdot 4} \quad \text{Add 6 and 4 in the numerator.}$$
$$= \frac{10}{9 \cdot 4} \quad \text{Evaluate the power in the denominator.}$$
$$= \frac{10}{36} \text{ or } \frac{5}{18} \quad \text{Multiply 9 and 4 in the denominator. Then simplify.}$$

 Your Progress

2A. $(15 - 9) + 3 \cdot 6$ **24**   **2B.** $45 + [(1 + 1)^3 \div 4]$ **47**   **2C.** $\dfrac{6^2 - 8}{4(3 + 7)}$ $\dfrac{7}{10}$

Grouping Symbols

When more than one grouping symbol is used, start evaluating within the innermost grouping symbols.

Evaluate Algebraic Expressions To evaluate an algebraic expression, replace the variables with their values. Then, find the value of the numerical expression using the order of operations.

EXAMPLE Evaluate an Algebraic Expression

3 Evaluate $a^2 - (b^3 - 4c)$ if $a = 7$, $b = 3$, and $c = 5$.

$$a^2 - (b^3 - 4c) = 7^2 - (3^3 - 4 \cdot 5) \quad \text{Replace } a \text{ with 7, } b \text{ with 3, and } c \text{ with 5.}$$
$$= 49 - (27 - 4 \cdot 5) \quad \text{Evaluate } 7^2 \text{ and } 3^3.$$
$$= 49 - (27 - 20) \quad \text{Multiply 4 and 5.}$$
$$= 49 - 7 \quad \text{Subtract 20 from 27.}$$
$$= 42 \quad \text{Subtract.}$$

 Your Progress

3. Evaluate $x(y^3 + 8) \div 12$ if $x = 3$ and $y = 4$.   **18**

 Extra Examples at ca.algebra1.com

Lesson 1-2 Order of Operations   **11**

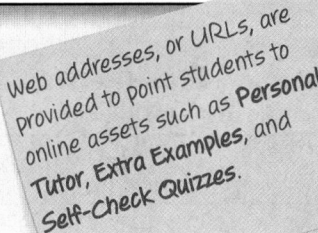
Web addresses, or URLs, are provided to point students to online assets such as Personal Tutor, Extra Examples, and Self-Check Quizzes.

 Formative Assessment

Use the Check Your Progress exercises after each example to determine students' understanding of concepts.

ADDITIONAL EXAMPLES

1 Evaluate $48 \div 2^3 \cdot 3 + 5$. **23**

2 Evaluate each expression.

a. $(8 - 3) \cdot 3(3 + 2)$ **75**

b. $4[12 \div (6 - 2)]^2$ **36**

c. $\dfrac{2^5 - 6 \cdot 2}{3^3 - 5 \cdot 3 - 2}$ **2**

Additional Examples are also in:

- Noteables™ Interactive Study Notebook with Foldables™
- Interactive Classroom PowerPoint® Presentations

Evaluate Algebraic Expressions

Example 3 shows how to evaluate an algebraic expression by replacing a variable with a number and applying the order of operations. **Example 4** shows how to find the value of a variable in a formula when the values of all the other variables are known.

ADDITIONAL EXAMPLE

3 Evaluate $2(x^2 - y) + z^2$ if $x = 4$, $y = 3$, and $z = 2$. **30**

 Focus on Mathematical Content

Grouping Symbols Grouping symbols include parentheses, ( ), brackets, [ ], braces, { }, and fraction bars, as in $\dfrac{5 + 7}{2}$. Evaluate expressions inside grouping symbols first when using the order of operations.

Lesson 1-2 Order of Operations   **11**

ADDITIONAL EXAMPLE

4 **ARCHITECTURE** Each side of the Great Pyramid of Giza, Egypt, is a triangle. The base of each triangle once measured 230 meters. The height of each triangle once measured 187 meters. The area of a triangle is one-half the product of the base b and its height h.

a. Write an expression that represents the area of one side of the Great Pyramid. $\frac{1}{2}(bh)$

b. Find the area of one side of the Great Pyramid. $21{,}505\ m^2$

3 Practice

Formative Assessment

Use Exercises 1–13 to check for understanding.

Use the chart at the bottom of this page to customize assignments for your students.

Odd/Even Assignments

Exercises 14–33 are structured so that students practice the same concepts whether they are assigned odd or even problems.

Student Misconceptions

Caution that not all calculators follow the order of operations when evaluating expressions. Nonscientific calculators evaluate expressions in the order they are entered. All scientific calculators (including graphing calculators) follow the order of operations. However, for longer expressions, you may have to use grouping symbols or be creative when entering the expression in order to get the correct answer.

Real-World Career
Architect
Architects use math to find measures and calculate areas. They must consider the function, safety, and appearance when they design buildings.

Math Online
For more information, go to ca.algebra1.com.

EXAMPLE

4 **ARCHITECTURE** The Pyramid Arena in Memphis, Tennessee, is the third largest pyramid in the world. The area of its base is 360,000 square feet, and it is 321 feet high. The volume of a pyramid is one third of the product of the area of the base B and its height h.

a. Write an expression that represents the volume of a pyramid.

Words	one third	of	the product of area of base and height
Variables	B = area of base and h = height		
Expression	$\frac{1}{3}$	$\times$	$(B \cdot h)$ or $\frac{1}{3}Bh$

b. Find the volume of the Pyramid Arena.

$V = \frac{1}{3}(Bh)$ Volume of a pyramid

$= \frac{1}{3}(360{,}000 \cdot 321)$ Replace B with 360,000 and h with 321.

$= \frac{1}{3}(115{,}560{,}000)$ Multiply 360,000 by 321.

$= 38{,}520{,}000$ Multiply $\frac{1}{3}$ by 115,560,000.

The volume of the Pyramid Arena is 38,520,000 cubic feet.

✓CHECK Your Progress

According to market research, the average consumer spends $78 per trip to the mall on weekends and only $67 per trip during the week.

4A. Write an algebraic expression to represent how much the average $78x + 67y$ consumer spends at the mall in x weekend trips and y weekday trips.

4B. Evaluate the expression to find what the average consumer spends after going to the mall twice during the week and 5 times on the weekends. $524

Online **Personal Tutor at** ca.algebra1.com

★ indicates multi-step problem

✓CHECK Your Understanding

Examples 1, 2 (pp. 10–11)

Evaluate each expression.

1. $30 - 14 \div 2$ **23**   **2.** $5 \cdot 5 - 1 \cdot 3$ **22**   **3.** $6^2 + 8 \cdot 3 + 7$ **67**

4. $(4 + 6)7$ **70**   **5.** $50 - (15 + 9)$ **26**   **6.** $[8(2) - 4^2] + 7(4)$ **28**

7. $\frac{11 - 8}{1 + 7 \cdot 2}$ $\frac{3}{15}$ or $\frac{1}{5}$ **8.** $\frac{(4 \cdot 3)^2}{9 + 3}$ **12**   **9.** $\frac{3 + 2^3}{5^2(6)}$ $\frac{11}{150}$

Example 3 (p. 11)

Evaluate each expression if $a = 4$, $b = 6$, and $c = 8$.

10. $8b - a$ **44**   **11.** $2a + (b^2 \div 3)$ **20**   **12.** $\frac{b(9 - c)}{a^2}$ $\frac{6}{16}$ or $\frac{3}{8}$

Example 4 (p. 12)

★ **13.** **GEOMETRY** Write an algebraic expression to represent the area of the rectangle. Then evaluate it to find the area when $n = 4$ centimeters. $n(2n + 3)$; 44 cm^2

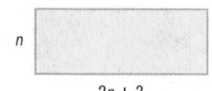

$2n + 3$

12 **Chapter 1** The Language and Tools of Algebra

DIFFERENTIATED HOMEWORK OPTIONS

Level	Assignment	Two-Day Option	
BL Basic	14–33, 43, 44, 46–62	15–33 odd, 47, 48	14–32 even, 43, 44, 46, 49–62
OL Core	15–39 odd, 41–44, 46–62	14–33, 47, 48	34–44, 46, 49–62
AL Advanced /Pre-AP	34–56 (optional: 57–62)		

12 **Chapter 1** The Language and Tools of Algebra

HOMEWORK HELP	
For Exercises	See Examples
14–17	1
18–25	2
26–31	3
32–33	4

Exercise Levels
A: 14–33
B: 34–42
C: 43–46

Evaluate each expression.

14. $22 + 3 \cdot 7$ 43

15. $18 \div 9 + 2 \cdot 6$ 14

16. $10 + 8^3 \div 16$ 42

17. $12 \div 3 \cdot 5 - 4^2$ 4

18. $(11 \cdot 7) - 9 \cdot 8$ 5

19. $29 - 3(9 - 4)$ 14

20. $(12 - 6) \cdot 5^2$ 150

21. $3^5 - (1 + 10^2)$ 142

22. $108 \div [3(9 + 3^2)]$ 2

23. $[(6^3 - 9) \div 23]4$ 36

24. $\dfrac{8 + 3^3}{12 - 7}$ 7

25. $\dfrac{(1 + 6)9}{5^2 - 4}$ 3

Evaluate each expression if $r = 2$, $s = 3$, and $t = 11$.

26. $r + 6t$ 68

27. $7 - rs$ 1

28. $(2t + 3r) \div 4$ 7

29. $s^2 + (r^3 - 8)5$ 9

30. $t^2 + 8st + r^2$ 389

31. $3r(r + s)^2 - 1$ 149

★ **32. BOOKS** At a bookstore, Luna bought one new book for $20 and three used books for $4.95 each. Write and evaluate an expression to find how much money the books cost, not including sales tax. $20 + 3 \times 4.95$; $34.85

★ **33. ENTERTAINMENT** Derrick sold tickets for the school musical. He sold 50 tickets for floor seats and 90 tickets for balcony seats. Write and evaluate an expression to find how much money Derrick collected. $50(7.5) + 90(5)$; $825

School Musical Tickets	
Type of Seat	Cost per Ticket ($)
floor	7.50
balcony	5.00

Evaluate each expression.

34. $\dfrac{2 \cdot 8^2 - 2^2 \cdot 8}{2 \cdot 8}$ 6

35. $6 - \left[\dfrac{2 + 7}{3} - (2 \cdot 3 - 5)\right]$ $\dfrac{4}{}$

36. $7^3 - \dfrac{2}{3}(13 \cdot 6 + 9)4$ 111

Evaluate each expression if $x = 12$, $y = 8$, and $z = 3$.

37. $\dfrac{2xy - z^3}{z}$ 55

38. $\left(\dfrac{x}{y}\right)^2 - \dfrac{z}{(x - y)^2}$ $2\dfrac{1}{16}$

39. $\dfrac{x - z^2}{xy} + \dfrac{2y - x}{y^2}$ $\dfrac{3}{32}$

★ **40. BIOLOGY** The cells of a certain type of bacteria double in number every 20 minutes. Suppose 100 of these cells are in one culture dish and 250 cells are in another culture dish. Write and evaluate an expression to find the total number of bacteria cells in both dishes after 20 minutes. $100 \cdot 2 + 250 \cdot 2$; 700 bacteria cells

BUSINESS For Exercises 41 and 42, use the following information.
A sales representative receives an annual salary s, an average commission each month c, and a bonus b for each sales goal that she reaches.

41. Write an algebraic expression to represent her total earnings in one year if she receives four equal bonuses. $s + 12c + 4b$

42. Suppose her annual salary is $52,000 and her average commission is $1225 per month. If each bonus is $1150, how much does she earn in a year? $71,300

EXTRA PRACTICE
See pages 717, 744.
Math Online
Self-Check Quiz at
ca.algebra1.com

H.O.T. Problems

43. FIND THE ERROR Leonora and Chase are evaluating $3[4 + (27 \div 3)]^2$. Who is correct? Explain your reasoning. Chase; Leonora squared the incorrect quantity.

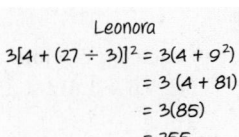

Leonora
$3[4 + (27 \div 3)]^2 = 3(4 + 9^2)$
$= 3(4 + 81)$
$= 3(85)$
$= 255$

Chase
$3[4 + (27 \div 3)]^2 = 3(4 + 9)^2$
$= 3(13)^2$
$= 3(169)$
$= 507$

BL = Below Grade Level
OL = On Grade Level
AL = Above Grade Level
ELL = English Language Learner

Additional pages not shown:
CRM **Lesson Reading Guide**, p. 12 BL OL ELL
CRM **Skills Practice**, p. 15 BL OL

Find the Error For Exercise 43, students should see that Leonora and Chase have done something different in the first step. Explain to students that once they have identified a difference, they do not need to look at subsequent steps.

 Preventing Errors

Students may be reluctant to take time to show all the steps they use when evaluating an expression. Help them to see that these steps enable them to diagnose errors and to prevent calculation errors that may keep them from getting correct values.

 **4 Assess**

Name the Math Write a numerical and an algebraic expression on the board. Have students work with a partner and take turns explaining how to evaluate one of the expressions using the order of operations.

FOLDABLES Study Organizer **Foldables™ Follow-Up**
Remind students to use the second tab on their Foldables to record the order of operations.

Additional Answers

44. Sample answer: $(2 + 4) \div 3$; Addition is the first step because the parentheses that surround $2 + 4$ indicate that these numbers are to be added first.

45. Sample answer: using 1, 2, 3:
$1 + 2 + 3 = 6; 1 + 2 \cdot 3 = 7;$
$1 \cdot 2 + 3 = 5; 3 - 2 \cdot 1 = 1;$
$(2 - 1) \cdot 3 = 3$

54. Sample answer: 5 plus n divided by 2

55. Sample answer: q squared minus 12

56. Sample answer: x cubed divided by 9

---

46. Use the order of operations to determine how many extra hours were used and then how much extra hours cost. Then find the total cost. Answers should include the expression $6(4.95 + 0.99n) - 25$.

44. OPEN ENDED Write a numerical expression involving division in which the first step in evaluating the expression is addition. Discuss why addition rather than division is the first step. **See margin.**

45. CHALLENGE Choose three numbers from 1 to 6. Using each of the numbers exactly once in each expression, write five expressions that have different results when they are evaluated. Justify your choices. **See margin.**

46. *Writing in Math* Use the information about the Internet on page 10 to explain how expressions can be used to determine the monthly cost of Internet service. Include an expression for the cost of service if Nicole has a coupon for $25 off her base rate for her first six months.

STANDARDS PRACTICE 7MG2.1, 25.2

47. REVIEW What is the perimeter of the triangle if $a = 9$ and $b = 10$? **B**

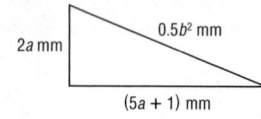
$0.5b^2$ mm
$2a$ mm
$(5a + 1)$ mm

A 164 mm

B 114 mm

C 28 mm

D 4 mm

48. Simplify: $[10 + 15(2^3)] \div [7(2^2) - 2]$

Step 1 $[10 + 15(8)] \div [7(4) - 2]$

Step 2 $[10 + 120] \div [28 - 2]$

Step 3 $130 \div 26$

Step 4 $\frac{1}{5}$

Which is the first *incorrect* step? **J**

F Step 1

G Step 2

H Step 3

J Step 4

Spiral Review

Write an algebraic expression for each verbal expression. (Lesson 1-1)

49. the product of 13 and p **$13p$**

50. one eighth of a number b **$\frac{1}{8}b$**

51. 20 increased by twice a number **$20 + 2n$**

52. 6 less than the square of y **$y^2 - 6$**

53. TRAVEL Sari's car has 23,500 miles on the odometer. She takes a trip and drives an average of m miles each day for two weeks. Write an expression that represents the mileage on Sari's odometer after her trip. (Lesson 1-1) **$23,500 + 14m$**

Write a verbal expression for each algebraic expression. (Lesson 1-1) **54–56. See margin.**

54. $5 + \frac{n}{2}$

55. $q^2 - 12$

56. $\frac{x^3}{9}$

GET READY for the Next Lesson

PREREQUISITE SKILL Find the value of each expression. (pages 696–697, 700–701)

57. $0.5 - 0.075$ **0.425**

58. $5.6 + 1.612$ **7.212**

59. $2.4(6.425)$ **15.42**

60. $4\frac{1}{8} - 1\frac{1}{2}$ **$2\frac{5}{8}$**

61. $\frac{3}{5} + 2\frac{5}{7}$ **$3\frac{11}{35}$**

62. $8 \div \frac{2}{9}$ **36**

14 Chapter 1 The Language and Tools of Algebra

Pre-AP Activity

Write the numbers 2, 3, 4, and 8 on the board. Tell students to make the number 8 by using each of the four numbers exactly once along with any operation and grouping symbol. Sample answers:
$(4 + 8) \div 3 \cdot 2; 8 \div 4 \cdot 3 + 2$

Main Ideas

- Solve open sentence equations.
- Solve open sentence inequalities.

 **Preparation for Standard 4.0** Students simplify expressions before solving linear equations and inequalities in one variable, such as $3(2x - 5) + 4(x - 2) = 12$. (Key, CAHSEE)

New Vocabulary

open sentence

solving the open sentence

solution

equation

replacement set

set

element

solution set

inequality

GET READY for the Lesson

The Daily News sells garage sale ads and kits. Spring Creek residents are planning a community garage sale, and their budget for advertising is \$135. The expression $15.50 + 5n$ represents the cost of an ad and n kits. The open sentence below can be used to ensure that the budget is met.

$$15.50 + 5n \leq 135$$

Garage
Sale Ad
\$15.50

Garage Sale Kit
\$5.00
- Signs
- Announcements
- Balloons
- Price stickers
- Sales sheet

Solve Equations A mathematical statement with one or more variables is called an **open sentence**. An open sentence is neither true nor false until the variables have been replaced by specific values. The process of finding a value for a variable that results in a true sentence is called **solving the open sentence**. This replacement value is called a **solution**. A sentence that contains an equals sign, =, is called an **equation**.

A set of numbers from which replacements for a variable may be chosen is called a **replacement set**. A **set** is a collection of objects or numbers. It is often shown using braces, { }. Each number in the set is called an **element**, or member. The **solution set** of an open sentence is the set of elements from the replacement set that make the open sentence true.

EXAMPLE   Use a Replacement Set to Solve an Equation

① Find the solution set for each equation if the replacement set is {3, 4, 5, 6, 7}.

a. $6n + 7 = 37$

Replace n in $6n + 7 = 37$ with each value in the replacement set.

n	$6n + 7 = 37$	True or False?
3	$6(3) + 7 \overset{?}{=} 37 \rightarrow 25 \neq 37$	false
4	$6(4) + 7 \overset{?}{=} 37 \rightarrow 31 \neq 37$	false
5	$6(5) + 7 \overset{?}{=} 37 \rightarrow 37 = 37$	true ✓
6	$6(6) + 7 \overset{?}{=} 37 \rightarrow 43 \neq 37$	false
7	$6(7) + 7 \overset{?}{=} 37 \rightarrow 49 \neq 37$	false

Since $n = 5$ makes the equation true, the solution of $6n + 7 = 37$ is 5. The solution set is {5}.

Lesson 1-3 Open Sentences   **15**

1 Focus

Standards Alignment

Before Lesson 1-3
Write an expression, an equation, an inequality, or a system that represents a verbal description from Standard 7AF1.1

Lesson 1-3
simplify expressions before solving linear equations and inequalities from Standard 4.0

After Lesson 1-3
Solve equations and inequalities involving absolute value from Standard 2A1.0

2 Teach

Scaffolding Questions Have students read *Get Ready for the Lesson.* **Ask:**

- What does the symbol $\leq$ mean? less than or equal to
- How would you translate the sentence $15.50 + 5n \leq 135$? 15.50 plus five times n is less than or equal to 135
- What does the variable n represent in the sentence? the number of garage sale kits purchased
- Why is n multiplied by 5? additional kits cost \$5 each

Lesson 1-3 Resources

Chapter 1 Resource Masters

Lesson Reading Guide, p. 20 BL OL ELL

Study Guide and Intervention, pp. 21–22 BL OL ELL

Skills Practice, p. 23 BL OL

Practice, p. 24 OL AL

Word Problem Practice, p. 25 OL AL

Enrichment, p. 26 OL AL

Spreadsheet, p. 27

Quiz 1, p. 73

Transparencies

5-Minute Check Transparency 1-3

Additional Print Resources

Noteables™ Interactive Study Notebook with Foldables™

Science and Mathematics Lab Manual, pp. 135–138

Technology

ca.algebra1.com

Interactive Classroom CD-ROM

AssignmentWorks CD-ROM

Graphing Calculator Easy Files

Solve Equations

Example 1 shows how to use a replacement set to solve equations.
Example 2 shows how to use the order of operations to solve an equation.

 Formative Assessment

Use the Check Your Progress exercises after each example to determine students' understanding of concepts.

ADDITIONAL EXAMPLES

1 Find the solution set for each equation if the replacement set is {2, 3, 4, 5, 6}.

a. $4a + 7 = 23$ {4}

b. $3(8 - b) = 6$ {6}

2 Solve $\dfrac{5(8 + 2)}{18 - (5 - 3)^3} = k.$ 5

Additional Examples are also in:

- Noteables™ Interactive Study Notebook with Foldables™

- Interactive Classroom PowerPoint® Presentations

Additional Examples exactly parallel the examples in the text. Step-by-step solutions for these examples are included in Interactive Classroom and Noteables: Interactive Study Notebook with Foldables .

Solve Inequalities

Example 3 shows how to use a replacement set to solve a real-world problem involving an inequality.
Example 4 shows how to solve an inequality involving a real-world situation.

---

b. $5(x + 2) = 40$

Replace x in $5(x + 2) = 40$ with each value in the replacement set.

x	$5(x + 2) = 40$	True or False?
3	$5(3 + 2) \overset{?}{=} 40 \rightarrow 25 \neq 40$	false
4	$5(4 + 2) \overset{?}{=} 40 \rightarrow 30 \neq 40$	false
5	$5(5 + 2) \overset{?}{=} 40 \rightarrow 35 \neq 40$	false
6	$5(6 + 2) \overset{?}{=} 40 \rightarrow 40 = 40$	true ✓
7	$5(7 + 2) \overset{?}{=} 40 \rightarrow 45 \neq 40$	false

The solution of $5(x + 2) = 40$ is 6. The solution set is {6}.

✓ CHECK Your Progress

Find the solution set for each equation if the replacement set is {0, 1, 2, 3}.

1A. $8m - 7 = 17$ {3}   **1B.** $28 = 4(1 + 3d)$ {2}

You can often solve an equation by applying the order of operations.

EXAMPLE   Use Order of Operations to Solve an Equation

2 Solve $q = \dfrac{13 + 2(4)}{3(5 - 4)}$.

$q = \dfrac{13 + 2(4)}{3(5 - 4)}$ Original equation

$q = \dfrac{13 + 8}{3(1)}$ Multiply 2 and 4 in the numerator.
Subtract 4 from the 5 in the denominator.

$q = \dfrac{21}{3}$ Simplify.

$q = 7$ Divide.   The solution is 7.

✓ CHECK Your Progress

Solve each equation.

2A. $t = 9^2 \div (2 + 1)$ 27   **2B.** $x = \dfrac{3^2 - (7 - 5)}{3(4) + (2 + 1)}$ $\dfrac{7}{15}$

Reading Math

Symbols Inequality symbols are read as follows.

$<$ *is less than*
$\leq$ *is less than or equal to*
$>$ *is greater than*
$\geq$ *is greater than or equal to*

Solve Inequalities An open sentence that contains the symbol $<$, $\leq$, $>$, or $\geq$ is called an **inequality**. Inequalities can be solved in the same way as equations.

Real-World EXAMPLE

3 **SHOPPING** Meagan had $18. After she went to the used book store, she had less than $10 left. Could she have spent $8, $9, $10, or $11? Find the solution set for $18 - y < 10$ if the replacement set is {8, 9, 10, 11}.

Replace y in $18 - y < 10$ with each value in the replacement set.

16   **Chapter 1** The Language and Tools of Algebra   Math**nline** **Extra Examples** at ca.algebra1.com

---

Focus on Mathematical Content

Open Sentences An open sentence is a mathematical statement that contains one or more variables. An open sentence with an equal sign, $=$, is an equation. An open sentence with the symbol $<$, $\leq$, $>$, or $\geq$ is an inequality.

y	$18 - y < 10$	True or False?
8	$18 - 8 \overset{?}{<} 10 \rightarrow 10 \not< 10$	false
9	$18 - 9 \overset{?}{<} 10 \rightarrow 9 < 10$	true ✓
10	$18 - 10 \overset{?}{<} 10 \rightarrow 8 < 10$	true ✓
11	$18 - 11 \overset{?}{<} 10 \rightarrow 7 < 10$	true ✓

The solution set is {9, 10, 11}. So, Meagan could have spent $9, $10, or $11.

✓CHECK Your Progress

Find the solution set for each inequality if the replacement set is {5, 6, 7, 8}.

3A. $30 + n \geq 37$ {7, 8}

3B. $19 > 2y - 5$ {5, 6, 7, 8}

COncepts in MOtion
Interactive Lab
ca.algebra1.com

🌐 Real-World EXAMPLE

④ FUND-RAISING Refer to the application at the beginning of the lesson. If the residents buy an ad, what is the maximum number of garage sale kits they can buy and stay within their budget?

Explore The residents can spend no more than $135. Let n = the number of kits. The situation can be represented by the inequality $15.50 + 5n \leq 135$.

Plan Estimate to find reasonable values for the replacement set.

Solve Start by letting $n = 10$ and then adjust values as needed.

$15.50 + 5n \leq 135$ Original inequality

$15.50 + 5(10) \overset{?}{\leq} 135$ Replace n with 10.

$15.50 + 50 \overset{?}{\leq} 135$ Multiply 5 and 10.

$65.50 \leq 135$ Add 15.50 and 50.

The inequality is true, but the estimate is too low. Increase the value of n.

n	$15.50 + 5n \leq 135$	Reasonable?
20	$15.50 + 5(20) \overset{?}{\leq} 135 \rightarrow 115.50 \leq 135$	too low
25	$15.50 + 5(25) \overset{?}{\leq} 135 \rightarrow 140.50 \leq 135$	too high
23	$15.50 + 5(23) \overset{?}{\leq} 135 \rightarrow 130.50 \leq 135$	almost
24	$15.50 + 5(24) \overset{?}{\leq} 135 \rightarrow 135.50 \leq 135$	too high

Check The solution set is {0, 1, 2, 3, …, 21, 22, 23}. In addition to the ad, the residents can buy as many as 23 garage sale kits.

Study Tip

Ellipsis
In {1, 2, 3, 4, …}, the three dots are an *ellipsis*. In math, an ellipsis is used to indicate that numbers continue in the same pattern.

✓CHECK Your Progress

4. ENTERTAINMENT Trevor and his brother have a total of $15. They plan to buy 2 movie tickets at $6.50 each and then play video games in the arcade for $0.50 each. Write and solve an inequality to find the greatest number of video games v that they can play. $2(6.50) + 0.50v \leq 15$; 4 games

 Personal Tutor at ca.algebra1.com

ADDITIONAL EXAMPLE

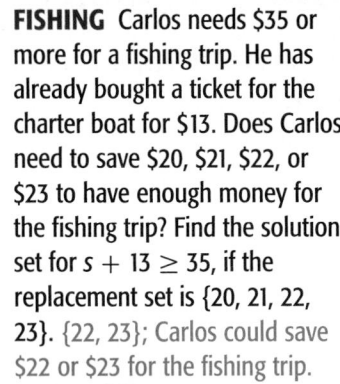

③ FISHING Carlos needs $35 or more for a fishing trip. He has already bought a ticket for the charter boat for $13. Does Carlos need to save $20, $21, $22, or $23 to have enough money for the fishing trip? Find the solution set for $s + 13 \geq 35$, if the replacement set is {20, 21, 22, 23}. {22, 23}; Carlos could save $22 or $23 for the fishing trip.

④ OUTDOORS A four-wheel drive tour of Canyon de Chelly National Monument in Arizona costs $45 for the first vehicle and $15 for each additional vehicle. How many vehicles can the Velo family take on the tour if they want to spend no more than $100? They can take up to 4 vehicles.

Tips for New Teachers

Reading Tip

Remind students to pay close attention to the inequality sign when finding solutions for inequalities. Point out that if students mistake a less than or equal sign ($\leq$) for a less than sign ($<$) in Example 3, they may mistakenly include 8 in the solution set.

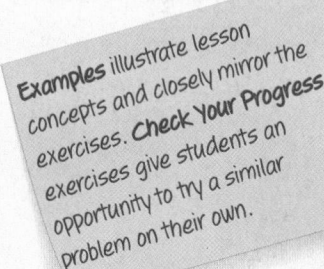

Examples illustrate lesson concepts and closely mirror the exercises. **Check Your Progress** *exercises give students an opportunity to try a similar problem on their own.*

3 Practice

✓ Formative Assessment

Use Exercises 1–13 to check for understanding.

Use the chart at the bottom of this page to customize assignments for your students.

Odd/Even Assignments

Exercises 14–39 are structured so that students practice the same concepts whether they are assigned odd or even problems.

Additional Answers

38. $2a + 3c \leq 200$, where a is the cost for an adult and c is the cost for a child; yes, it would cost $164.95 for everyone to go to the park.

39. $3(41.99) + 26.99c \leq 300$, where c is the number of the children. 6 children could go to the park with 3 adults

46. Sample answer: $c =$ number of Calories; $c = \dfrac{3500 \cdot 4}{14}$

50. Sample answer: An open sentence has at least one variable because it is neither true nor false until specific values are used for the variable.

✓ CHECK Your Understanding

Example 1 (p. 15)

Find the solution of each equation if the replacement set is {11, 12, 13, 14, 15}.

1. $n + 10 = 23$ **13**

2. $7 = \dfrac{c}{2}$ **14**

3. $29 = 3x - 7$ **12**

4. $(k - 8)12 = 84$ **15**

Find the solution of each equation using the given replacement set.

5. $36 = 18 + a$; {14, 16, 18, 20} **18**

6. $\dfrac{d + 5}{11} = 2$; {4, 17, 23, 30, 45} **17**

Example 2 (p. 16)

Solve each equation.

7. $x = 4(6) + 3$ **27**

8. $\dfrac{14 - 8}{2} = w$ **3**

9. $\dfrac{3(9) - 2}{1 + 4} = d$ **5**

10. $j = 15 \div 3 \cdot 5 - 4^2$ **9**

Example 3 (pp. 16–17)

Find the solution set of each inequality using the given replacement set.

11. $\dfrac{a}{5} \geq 2$; {5, 10, 15, 20, 25}

12. $24 - 2x \geq 13$; {0, 1, 2, 3, 4, 5, 6}

Example 4 (p. 17)

11. {10, 15, 20, 25}

12. {0, 1, 2, 3, 4, 5}

★ **13. ANALYZE TABLES** Suppose you have $102.50 to buy sweaters from an online catalog. Using the information in the table, write and solve an inequality to find the maximum number of sweaters that you can purchase.
$39n + 10.95 \leq 102.50$; **2 sweaters**

Online Catalog Prices	
Item	Cost ($)
sweaters	39.00 each
shipping	10.95 per order

Exercises

HOMEWORK HELP	
For Exercises	See Examples
14–25	1
26–33	2
34–37	3
38–39	4

Exercise Levels
A: 14–39
B: 40–47
C: 48–52

Find the solution of each equation if the replacement sets are $a = \{0, 3, 5, 8, 10\}$ and $b = \{12, 17, 18, 21, 25\}$.

14. $b - 12 = 9$ **21**

15. $22 = 34 - b$ **12**

16. $\dfrac{15}{a} = 3$ **5**

17. $68 = 4b$ **17**

18. $31 = 3a + 7$ **8**

19. $5(a - 1) = 10$ **3**

20. $\dfrac{40}{a} - 4 = 0$ **10**

21. $27 = a^2 + 2$ **5**

Find the solution of each equation using the given replacement set.

22. $t - 13 = 7$; {10, 13, 17, 20} **20**

23. $14(x + 5) = 126$; {3, 4, 5, 6, 7} **4**

24. $22 = \dfrac{n}{3}$; {62, 64, 66, 68, 70} **66**

25. $35 = \dfrac{g - 8}{2}$; {78, 79, 80, 81} **78**

Solve each equation.

26. $a = 32 - 9(2)$ **14**

27. $w = 56 \div (2^2 + 3)$ **8**

28. $\dfrac{27 + 5}{16} = g$ **2**

29. $\dfrac{12 \cdot 5}{15 - 3} = y$ **5**

30. $r = \dfrac{9(6)}{(8 + 1)3}$ **2**

31. $a = \dfrac{4(14 - 1)}{3(6) - 5} + 7$ **11**

★ **32. FOOD** During a lifetime, the average American drinks 15,579 glasses of milk, 6220 glasses of juice, and 18,995 glasses of soda. Write and solve an equation to find g, the total number of glasses of milk, juice, and soda that the average American drinks in a lifetime. $g = 15{,}579 + 6220 + 18{,}995$; **40,794 glasses**

★ **33. ENERGY** A small electric generator can power 3550 watts of electricity. Write and solve an equation to find the most 75-watt light bulbs one small generator could power. $3550 = 75x$; **about 47 light bulbs**

18 Chapter 1 The Language and Tools of Algebra

DIFFERENTIATED HOMEWORK OPTIONS

Level	Assignment	Two-Day Option	
BL Basic	14–39, 48–50, 52–73	15–39 odd, 53–56	14–38 even, 48–50, 52, 57–73
OL Core	15–45 odd, 46–50, 52–73	14–39, 53–56	40–50, 52, 57–73
AL Advanced /Pre-AP	40–67 (optional: 68–73)		

Find the solution set for each inequality using the given replacement set.

34. $s - 2 < 6$; $\{6, 7, 8, 9, 10, 11\}$ $\{6, 7\}$ **35.** $5a + 7 > 22$; $\{3, 4, 5, 6, 7\}$ $\{4, 5, 6, 7\}$

36. $3 \geq \dfrac{25}{m}$; $\{1, 3, 5, 7, 9, 11\}$ $\{9, 11\}$ **37.** $\dfrac{2a}{4} \leq 8$; $\{12, 14, 16, 18, 20, 22\}$ $\{12, 14, 16\}$

ENTERTAINMENT For Exercises 38 and 39, use the table. 38–39. See margin.

★ **38.** Mr. and Mrs. Conkle are taking their three children to an amusement park. Write and solve an inequality to determine whether they can all go to the park for under $200. Describe what the variables in your inequality represent and explain your answer.

★ **39.** Write and solve an inequality to find how many children can go with three adults if the budget is $300. Determine whether your answer is reasonable.

Amusement Park Admission Prices	
Person	**Cost ($)**
Adult	41.99
Child	26.99

Find the solution of each equation or inequality using the given replacement set.

40. $x + \dfrac{2}{5} = 1\dfrac{3}{20}$; $\left\{\dfrac{1}{4}, \dfrac{1}{2}, \dfrac{3}{4}, 1, 11, 4\right\}$ $\dfrac{3}{4}$

41. $\dfrac{2}{5}(x + 1) = \dfrac{8}{15}$; $\left\{\dfrac{1}{6}, \dfrac{1}{3}, \dfrac{1}{2}, \dfrac{2}{3}\right\}$ $\dfrac{1}{3}$

42. $2.7(x + 5) = 17.28$; $\{1.2, 1.3, 1.4, 1.5\}$ 1.4

43. $16(x + 2) = 70.4$; $\{2.2, 2.4, 2.6, 2.8\}$ 2.4

44. $4a - 3 \geq 10.6$; $\{3.2, 3.4, 3.6, 3.8, 4\}$ $\{3.4, 3.6, 3.8, 4\}$

45. $3(12 - x) + 2 \leq 28$ $\{2.5, 3, 3.5, 4\}$ $\{3.5, 4\}$

EXTRA PRACTICE
See pages 717, 744.

Math Online
Self-Check Quiz at
ca.algebra1.com

NUTRITION For Exercises 46 and 47, use the following information. 46. See margin
A person must burn 3500 Calories to lose one pound of weight.

46. Define a variable and write an equation for the number of Calories that a person would have to burn each day to lose four pounds in two weeks.

47. How many Calories would the person have to burn each day? 1000 Calories

H.O.T. Problems ....

48. REASONING Describe the difference between an expression and an open sentence. **Sample answer: An open sentence contains an equals sign or inequality sign.**

49. OPEN ENDED Write an inequality that has a solution set of $\{8, 9, 10, 11, ...\}$. Explain your reasoning. **Sample answer: $x \geq 8$ represents the inequality because it includes the set of all whole numbers greater than or equal to 8.**

50. REASONING Explain why an open sentence always has at least one variable. **See margin.**

51. CHALLENGE Describe the solution set for x if $3x \leq 1$. **The solution set includes all numbers less than or equal to $\dfrac{1}{3}$.**

52. *Writing in Math* Use the information about budgets on page 15 to explain how you can use open sentences when you have to stay within a budget. Also explain and give examples of real-world situations in which you would use inequalities and equations. **See Ch. 1 Answer Appendix.**

Lesson 1-3 Open Sentences **19**

BL = Below Grade Level
OL = On Grade Level
AL = Above Grade Level
ELL = English Language Learner

Additional pages not shown:
CRM *Lesson Reading Guide,* p. 20 BL OL ELL
CRM *Skills Practice,* p. 23 BL OL

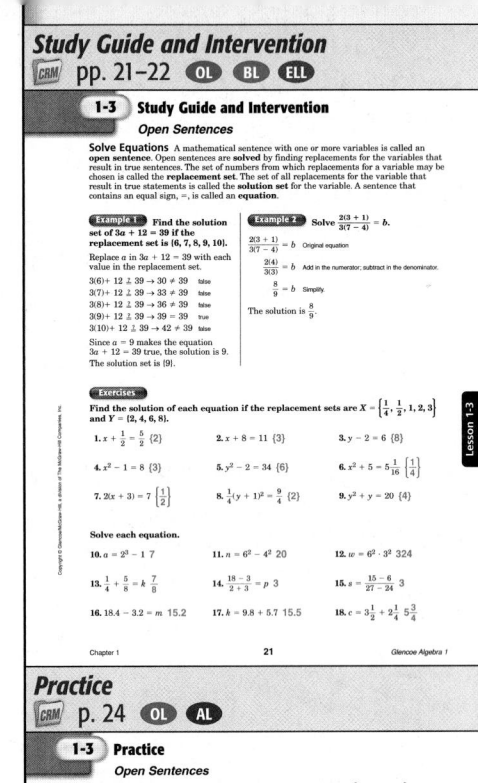

Study Guide and Intervention
CRM pp. 21–22 OL BL ELL

1-3 Study Guide and Intervention
Open Sentences

Solve Equations A mathematical sentence with one or more variables is called an **open sentence**. Open sentences are **solved** by finding replacements for the variable that result in true sentences. The set of numbers from which replacements for the variable may be chosen is called the **replacement set**. The set of all replacements for the variable that result in true statements is called the **solution set** for the variable. A sentence that contains an equal sign, =, is called an **equation**.

Example 1 Find the solution set of $3a + 12 = 39$ if the replacement set is $\{6, 7, 8, 9, 10\}$.

Replace a in $3a + 12 = 39$ with each value in the replacement set.

$3(6) + 12 = 39 \rightarrow 30 \neq 39$ false
$3(7) + 12 = 39 \rightarrow 33 \neq 39$ false
$3(8) + 12 = 39 \rightarrow 36 \neq 39$ false
$3(9) + 12 = 39 \rightarrow 39 = 39$ true
$3(10) + 12 = 39 \rightarrow 42 \neq 39$ false

Since $a = 9$ makes the equation $3a + 12 = 39$ true, the solution is 9. The solution set is $\{9\}$.

Example 2 Solve $\dfrac{2(3 + 1)}{3(7 - 4)} = b$.

$\dfrac{2(3 + 1)}{3(7 - 4)} = b$ Original equation

$\dfrac{2(4)}{3(3)} = b$ Add in the numerator; subtract in the denominator.

$\dfrac{8}{9} = b$ Simplify

The solution is $\dfrac{8}{9}$.

Exercises

Find the solution of each equation if the replacement sets are $X = \left\{\dfrac{1}{4}, \dfrac{1}{2}, 1, 2, 3\right\}$ and $Y = \{2, 4, 6, 8\}$.

1. $x + \dfrac{1}{2} = \dfrac{5}{2}$ $\{2\}$ 2. $x + 8 = 11$ $\{3\}$ 3. $y - 2 = 6$ $\{8\}$

4. $x^2 - 1 = 8$ $\{3\}$ 5. $y^2 - 2 = 34$ $\{6\}$ 6. $x^2 + 5 = 5\dfrac{1}{16}$ $\left\{\dfrac{1}{4}\right\}$

7. $2(x + 3) = 7$ $\left\{\dfrac{1}{2}\right\}$ 8. $\dfrac{1}{4}(y + 1)^2 = \dfrac{9}{4}$ $\{2\}$ 9. $y^2 + y = 20$ $\{4\}$

Solve each equation.

10. $a = 2^3 - 1$ 7 11. $n = 6^2 - 4^2$ 20 12. $w = 6^2 \cdot 3^2$ 324

13. $\dfrac{1}{4} + \dfrac{5}{8} = k$ $\dfrac{7}{8}$ 14. $\dfrac{18 - 3}{2 + 3} = p$ 3 15. $s = \dfrac{15 - 6}{27 - 24}$ 3

16. $18.4 - 3.2 = m$ 15.2 17. $k = 9.8 + 5.7$ 15.5 18. $c = 3\dfrac{1}{2} + 2\dfrac{1}{4}$ $5\dfrac{3}{4}$

Chapter 1   21   Glencoe Algebra 1

Practice
CRM p. 24 OL AL

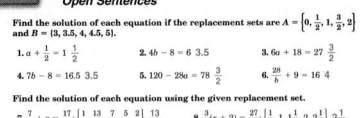

1-3 Practice
Open Sentences

Find the solution of each equation if the replacement sets are $A = \left\{0, \dfrac{1}{2}, 1, \dfrac{3}{2}, 2\right\}$ and $B = \{3, 3.5, 4, 4.5, 5\}$.

1. $a + \dfrac{1}{2} = 1$ $\dfrac{1}{2}$ 2. $4b - 8 = 6$ 3.5 3. $6a + 18 = 27$ $\dfrac{3}{2}$

4. $7b = 16.5$ 3.5 5. $120 - 28a = 78$ $\dfrac{3}{2}$ 6. $\dfrac{28}{b} + 9 = 16$ 4

Find the solution of each equation using the given replacement set.

7. $\dfrac{7}{8} + x = \dfrac{17}{12}$; $\left\{\dfrac{1}{3}, \dfrac{13}{24}, \dfrac{7}{12}, \dfrac{5}{8}, \dfrac{2}{3}\right\}$ $\dfrac{13}{24}$ 8. $\dfrac{3}{4}(x + 2) = \dfrac{27}{8}$; $\left\{1, 1\dfrac{1}{4}, 1\dfrac{1}{2}, 2, 2\dfrac{1}{2}\right\}$ $2\dfrac{1}{2}$

9. $1.4(x + 3) = 5.32$; $\{0.4, 0.6, 0.8, 1.0, 1.2\}$ 0.8 10. $12(x + 4) = 76.8$; $\{2, 2.4, 2.8, 3.2, 3.6\}$ 2.4

Solve each equation.

11. $x = 18.3 - 4.8$ 13.5 12. $w = 20.2 - 8.95$ 11.25 13. $\dfrac{37 - 9}{18 - 11} = d$ 4

14. $\dfrac{97 - 25}{41 - 23} = h$ 4 15. $y = \dfrac{4(22 - 4)}{3(6) + 6}$ 3 16. $\dfrac{5(2^2) + 4(3)}{4(2^2 - 4)} = p$ 2

Find the solution set for each inequality using the given replacement set.

17. $a + 7 < 10$; $\{2, 3, 4, 5, 6, 7\}$ $\{2\}$ 18. $3y \geq 42$; $\{10, 12, 14, 16, 18\}$ $\{14, 16, 18\}$

19. $4x - 2 < 5$; $\{0.5, 1, 1.5, 2, 2.5\}$ $\{0.5, 1, 1.5\}$ 20. $4b - 4 > 3$; $\{1.2, 1.4, 1.6, 1.8, 2.0\}$ $\{1.8, 2.0\}$

21. $\dfrac{3y}{2} \leq 2$; $\{0, 2, 4, 6, 8, 10\}$ $\{0, 2\}$ 22. $4a \geq 3$; $\left\{\dfrac{1}{8}, \dfrac{1}{4}, \dfrac{3}{8}, \dfrac{1}{2}, \dfrac{5}{8}, \dfrac{3}{4}\right\}$ $\left\{\dfrac{3}{4}\right\}$

23. TEACHING A teacher has 15 weeks in which to teach six chapters. Write and then solve an equation that represents the number of lessons the teacher must teach per week if there is an average of 8.5 lessons per chapter. $n = \dfrac{6(8.5)}{15}$; 3.4

LONG DISTANCE For Exercises 24 and 25, use the following information.
Gabriel talks an average of 20 minutes per long-distance call. During one month, he makes eight in-state long-distance calls averaging $2.00 each. A 20-minute state-to-state call costs Gabriel $1.50. His long-distance budget for the month is $20.

24. Write an inequality that represents the number of 20 minute state-to-state calls Gabriel can make this month. $8(2) + 1.5s \leq 20$

25. What is the maximum number of 20-minute state-to-state calls that Gabriel can make this month? 2

Chapter 1   24   Glencoe Algebra 1

Word Problem Practice
CRM p. 25 OL AL

1-3 Word Problem Practice
Open Sentences

1. **TIME** There are 6 time zones in the United States. The eastern part of the U.S., including New York City, is in the Eastern Time Zone. The central part of the U.S., including Dallas, is in the Central Time Zone, which is one hour behind Eastern Time. San Diego is in the Pacific Time Zone, which is 3 hours behind Eastern Time. Write and solve an equation to determine what time it is in California if it is noon in New York.
$12 - c = 3$; 9:00 AM

2. **FOOD** Part of the Nutrition Facts label from a box of macaroni and cheese is shown below.

Nutrition Facts
Serving Size 1 cup (228g)
Servings Per Container 2

Write and solve an inequality to determine how many servings of this item that Alisa can have for lunch if she is restricted to no more than 45 grams of cholesterol.
$c \leq \dfrac{45}{30}$; 1.5 servings or less

3. **CRAFTS** You need at least 30 yards of yarn to crochet a small scarf. Cheryl bought a 100-yard ball of yarn and has already used 10 yards. Write and solve an inequality to find how many scarves she can crochet. $100 - 10 \geq 30s$; no more than 3 scarves

4. **POOLS** There are approximately 202 gallons per cubic yard of water. Write and solve an equation for the number of gallons of water that fill a pool with a volume of 1161 cubic feet. (*Hint:* There are 27 cubic feet per cubic yard.)
$g = $ gal in pool
$g = \dfrac{1161}{27} \times 202$; 8686 gal

VEHICLES For Exercises 5 and 6, use the following information.
Recently developed hybrid cars contain both an electric and a gasoline engine. Hybrid car batteries store extra energy, such as the energy produced by braking. Since the car can use this stored energy to power the car, the hybrid uses less gasoline per mile than cars powered only by gasoline. Suppose a new hybrid car is rated to drive 45 miles per gallon of gasoline.

5. It costs $40 to fill the gasoline tank with gas that costs $2.50 per gallon. Write and solve an equation to find the distance the hybrid car can go using one tank of gas.
$\dfrac{40}{2.50}(45) = m$; 720 mi

6. Write and solve an equation to find the cost of gasoline per mile for this hybrid car. Round to the nearest cent.
$\dfrac{2.50}{45} = c$; ≈ 6¢ per mi

Chapter 1   25   Glencoe Algebra 1

4 Assess

Yesterday's News Ask students to write a brief statement on how yesterday's lesson on evaluating expressions helped them with today's lesson on finding solutions for open sentences.

The Four-step Teaching Plan shows you how to Focus, Teach, Practice, and Assess each lesson. Each lesson ends with a creative strategy for closing the lesson.

Formative Assessment

Check for student understanding of concepts in Lessons 1-1, 1-2, and 1-3.
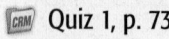 Quiz 1, p. 73

 **Foldables™ Follow-Up**

Remind students to use the third tab of their Foldables to record notes on what they have learned about open sentences. Students should include information on reading inequality symbols.

STANDARDS PRACTICE 5.0, 4.0, 7MG2.3, 6AF1.2

53. What is the solution set of the inequality $(5 + n^2) - n < 50$ if the replacement set is {5, 7, 9}? **B**

A {5} C {7}
B {5, 7} D {7, 9}

54. $27 \div 3 + (12 - 8) =$ **H**

F $-\dfrac{11}{5}$ H 17

G $\dfrac{27}{11}$ J 25

55. REVIEW A box in the shape of a rectangular prism has a volume of 56 cubic inches. If the length of each side is multiplied by 2, what will be the approximate volume of the resulting box? **D**

A 112 in³ C 336 in³
B 224 in³ D 448 in³

56. REVIEW Ms. Beal had 1 bran muffin, 16 ounces of orange juice, 3 ounces of sunflower seeds, 2 slices of turkey, and a half cup of spinach. According to the table, which equation best represents the total grams of protein that she consumed? **J**

Protein Content	
Food	**Protein (g)**
bran muffin (1)	3
orange juice (8 oz)	2
sunflower seeds (1 oz)	6
turkey (1 slice)	12
spinach (1 c)	5

F $P = 3 + 2 + 6 + 12 + 5$

G $P = 3 + \frac{1}{2}(2) + \frac{1}{3}(6) + \frac{1}{2}(12) + 2(5)$

H $P = 3 + 16(2) + 3(6) + 2(12) + 2(5)$

J $P = 3 + 2(2) + 3(6) + 2(12) + \frac{1}{2}(5)$

Spiral Review

Evaluate each expression. (Lesson 1-2)

57. $5 + 3(4^2)$ **53**

58. $\dfrac{38 - 12}{2 \cdot 13}$ **1**

59. $[5(1 + 1)]^3 + 4$ **1004**

★ **60. RING TONES** Andre downloaded three standard ringtones for $1.99 each and two premium ringtones at $3.49 each. Write and evaluate an expression to find how much the ringtones cost. (Lesson 1-2) **3(1.99) + 2(3.49); $12.95**

62. Sample answer: *r* squared increased by 3 times *s*
Write a verbal expression for each algebraic expression. (Lesson 1-1)

61. $n^5 - 8$
Sample answer: *n* to the fifth power minus 8

62. $r^2 + 3s$

63. $b \div 5a$. Sample answer: *b* divided by the product of 5 and *a*

Write an algebraic expression for each verbal expression.

64. two-thirds the square of a number $\frac{2}{3}n^2$
65. 6 increased by one half of a number *n* $6 + \frac{1}{2}n$
66. one-half the cube of *x* $\frac{1}{2}x^3$
67. one fourth of the cube of a number $\frac{1}{4}n^3$

GET READY for the Next Lesson

PREREQUISITE SKILL Find each product. Express answers in simplest form. (pages 700–701)

68. $\frac{1}{6} \cdot \frac{2}{5}$ $\frac{1}{15}$ **69.** $\frac{4}{9} \cdot \frac{3}{7}$ $\frac{4}{21}$ **70.** $\frac{5}{6} \cdot \frac{15}{16}$ $\frac{25}{32}$

71. $\frac{6}{14} \cdot \frac{12}{18}$ $\frac{2}{7}$ **72.** $\frac{2}{5} \cdot \frac{3}{4}$ $\frac{3}{10}$ **73.** $\frac{11}{12} \cdot \frac{4}{5}$ $\frac{11}{15}$

20 Chapter 1 The Language and Tools of Algebra

Pre-AP Activity Use after Exercises

Write the solution set {15} on the board. Have students write two open sentences, based on real-world situations, that match the solution set. One open sentence should be an equation and the other an inequality. For example, students could write "Bryce scored $p + 71 = 86$ on a science test, where *p* represents points for extra credit."

Identity and Equality Properties

Main Ideas

- Recognize the properties of identity and equality.
- Use the properties of identity and equality.

Standard 1.0 **Students identify and use the** arithmetic properties of subsets of integers and rational, irrational, and real numbers, including closure properties for the four basic arithmetic operations where applicable.

Standard 1.1 Students use properties of numbers to demonstrate whether assertions are true or false.

Standard 25.1 Students use properties to construct simple, valid arguments (direct and indirect) for, or formulate counterexamples to claimed assertions.

New Vocabulary

additive identity
additive inverse
multiplicative identity
multiplicative inverse
reciprocal

Key Concept boxes highlight definitions, formulas, and other important ideas. Multiple representations—words, symbols, examples, models—aid students' understanding.

▶ **GET READY for the Lesson**

The table shows the last three rankings of the top five teams for the 2005 college football season. The open sentence below represents the change in rank of USC from Week 6 to Week 7.

College Football Team	Week 6	Week 7	Final Rank
Texas	2	2	1
Southern California	1	1	2
Penn State	16	5	3
Ohio State	6	15	4
West Virginia	34	26	5

Rank in Week 6	plus	change in rank	equals	rank for Week 7.
1	+	r	=	1

The solution of this equation is 0. USC's rank changed by 0 from Week 6 to Week 7. In other words, $1 + 0 = 1$.

Identity and Equality Properties The sum of any number and 0 is equal to the number. Thus, 0 is called the **additive identity**.

KEY CONCEPT   *Additive Identity*

Words	For any number a, the sum of a and 0 is a.
Symbols	$a + 0 = a, 0 + a = a$
Examples	$5 + 0 = 5, 0 + 5 = 5$

Two numbers with a sum of zero are called **additive inverses**. For example $a + (-a) = 0$.

There are also special properties associated with multiplication. Consider the following equations.

$7 \cdot n = 7$ The solution of the equation is 1. Since the product of any number and 1 is equal to the number, 1 is called the **multiplicative identity**.

$9 \cdot m = 0$ The solution of the equation is 0. The product of any number and 0 is equal to 0. This is called the **Multiplicative Property of Zero**.

$\frac{1}{p} \cdot p = 1$ Two numbers whose product is 1 are called **multiplicative inverses** or **reciprocals**. Zero has no reciprocal because any number times 0 is 0.

Lesson 1-4 Identity and Equality Properties   **21**

1 Focus

Standards Alignment

Before Lesson 1-4
Simplify numerical expressions and justify the process used from ⊶ Standard 7AF1.3

Lesson 1-4
Identify and use properties of numbers to demonstrate whether assertions are true or false from ⊶ Standards 1.0 and 1.1

After Lesson 1-4
Are adept at operations on polynomials, including long division from ⊶ Standard 2A3.0

2 Teach

Scaffolding Questions Have students read *Get Ready for the Lesson*.
Ask:
- Did any of the teams change in rank from Week 6 to Week 7? yes
- By how many positions did Texas change between Week 7 and the final ranking? They did not change position.
- In an equation, how would you represent Ohio State's change from Week 6 to Week 7? $6 + r = 15$

Lesson 1-4 Resources

Chapter 1 Resource Masters
Lesson Reading Guide, p. 28 **BL** **OL** **ELL**
Study Guide and Intervention, pp. 29–30 **BL** **OL** **ELL**
Skills Practice, p. 31 **BL** **OL**
Practice, p. 32 **OL** **AL**
Word Problem Practice, p. 33 **OL** **AL**
Enrichment, p. 34 **OL** **AL**

Transparencies
5-Minute Check Transparency 1-4
Additional Print Resources
Noteables™ Interactive Study Notebook with Foldables™

Technology
ca.algebra1.com
Interactive Classroom CD-ROM
AssignmentWorks CD-ROM
Graphing Calculator Easy Files

Identity and Equality Properties

Example 1 shows how to use multiplication properties to solve equations.

 Formative Assessment

Use the Check Your Progress exercises after each example to determine students' understanding of concepts.

ADDITIONAL EXAMPLE

1. Find the value of n in each equation. Then name the property that is used.

   a. $n \cdot 12 = 0$ Multiplicative Property of Zero; $n = 0$

   b. $n \cdot \dfrac{1}{5} = 1$ Multiplicative Inverse Property; $n = 5$

Additional Examples are also in:

- Noteables™ Interactive Study Notebook with Foldables™
- Interactive Classroom PowerPoint® Presentations

Focus on Mathematical Content

Properties of Multiplication Some of the properties of multiplication include the Multiplicative Identity Property, the Multiplicative Property of Zero, and the Multiplicative Inverse Property. The Multiplicative Identity Property states that the product of any number and 1 is that number; the Multiplicative Property of Zero states that the product of any number and zero is 0; and the Multiplicative Inverse Property states that the product of a number and its reciprocal is 1.

Study Tip

Properties

These properties are true for all *real numbers*. You will learn more about real numbers in Lesson 1-8.

The multiplicative properties are summarized in the following table.

KEY CONCEPT			Multiplication Properties
Property	**Words**	**Symbols**	**Examples**
Multiplicative Identity	For any number a, the product of a and 1 is a.	$a \cdot 1 = a$, $1 \cdot a = a$	$12 \cdot 1 = 12$, $1 \cdot 12 = 12$
Multiplicative Property of Zero	For any number a, the product of a and 0 is 0.	$a \cdot 0 = 0$, $0 \cdot a = 0$	$8 \cdot 0 = 0$, $0 \cdot 8 = 0$
Multiplicative Inverse	For every number $\dfrac{a}{b}$, where $a, b \neq 0$, there is exactly one number $\dfrac{b}{a}$ such that the product of $\dfrac{a}{b}$ and $\dfrac{b}{a}$ is 1.	$\dfrac{a}{b} \cdot \dfrac{b}{a} = 1$, $\dfrac{b}{a} \cdot \dfrac{a}{b} = 1$	$\dfrac{2}{3} \cdot \dfrac{3}{2} = \dfrac{6}{6} = 1$, $\dfrac{3}{2} \cdot \dfrac{2}{3} = \dfrac{6}{6} = 1$

EXAMPLE Identify Properties

1. **Find the value of n in each equation. Then name the property that is used.**

   a. $42 \cdot n = 42$

   $n = 1$, since $42 \cdot 1 = 42$. This is the Multiplicative Identity Property.

   b. $n \cdot 9 = 1$

   $n = \dfrac{1}{9}$, since $\dfrac{1}{9} \cdot 9 = 1$. This is the Multiplicative Inverse Property.

✓ CHECK **Your Progress**

1. Find the value of n in the equation $28n = 0$. Then name the property that is used. **0; Multiplicative Property of Zero**

Several properties of equality are summarized below.

KEY CONCEPT			Properties of Equality
Property	**Words**	**Symbols**	**Examples**
Reflexive	Any quantity is equal to itself.	For any number a, $a = a$.	$7 = 7, 2 + 3 = 2 + 3$
Symmetric	If one quantity equals a second quantity, then the second quantity equals the first.	For any numbers a and b, if $a = b$, then $b = a$.	If $9 = 6 + 3$, then $6 + 3 = 9$.
Transitive	If one quantity equals a second quantity and the second quantity equals a third quantity, then the first quantity equals the third quantity.	For any numbers a, b, and c, if $a = b$, and $b = c$, then $a = c$.	If $5 + 7 = 8 + 4$, and $8 + 4 = 12$, then $5 + 7 = 12$.
Substitution	A quantity may be substituted for its equal in any expression.	If $a = b$, then a may be replaced by b in any expression.	If $n = 15$, then $3n = 3(15)$.

 Extra Examples at ca.algebra1.com

Tips for New Teachers **Study Tip**

Some students may have difficulty remembering the names of the properties in this lesson. Remind these students that they already know how to use the properties. Encourage them to think of word associations that will help them relate what they know to the correct names of the properties.

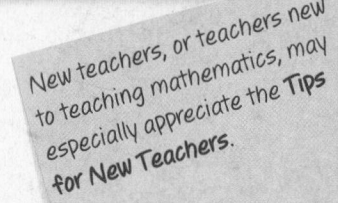

New teachers, or teachers new to teaching mathematics, may especially appreciate the **Tips for New Teachers**.

Use Identity and Equality Properties The properties of identity and equality can be used to justify each step when evaluating an expression.

 **EXAMPLE** Evaluate Using Properties

② Evaluate $2(3 \cdot 2 - 5) + 3 \cdot \frac{1}{3}$. Name the property used in each step.

$$2(3 \cdot 2 - 5) + 3 \cdot \frac{1}{3} = 2(6 - 5) + 3 \cdot \frac{1}{3} \quad \text{Substitution; } 3 \cdot 2 = 6$$

$$= 2(1) + 3 \cdot \frac{1}{3} \quad \text{Substitution; } 6 - 5 = 1$$

$$= 2 + 3 \cdot \frac{1}{3} \quad \text{Multiplicative Identity; } 2 \cdot 1 = 2$$

$$= 2 + 1 \quad \text{Multiplicative Inverse; } 3 \cdot \frac{1}{3} = 1$$

$$= 3 \quad \text{Substitution; } 2 + 1 = 3$$

2. $8 + (15 - 3 \cdot 5)$
$= 8 + (15 - 15)$
Substitution
$= 8 + 0$ Substitution
$= 8$ Additive
Identity

✓**CHECK Your Progress**

2. Evaluate $8 + (15 - 3 \cdot 5)$. Name the property used in each step.

Personal Tutor at ca.algebra1.com

★ indicates multi-step problem

✓**CHECK Your Understanding**

Example 1
(p. 22)

Find the value of n in each equation. Then name the property that is used.

1. $13n = 0$ **2.** $17 + 0 = n$ **3.** $1 = \frac{1}{6}n$
1–3. See Ch. 1 Answer Appendix.

Example 2
(p. 23)

Evaluate each expression. Name the property used in each step.

4. $11 + 2(8 - 7)$ **5.** $6(12 - 48 \div 4)$ **6.** $\left(15 \cdot \frac{1}{15} + 8 \cdot 0\right) \cdot 12$
4–6. See Ch. 1 Answer Appendix.

7. $4(20) + 7$
$= 80 + 7$
Substitution
$= 87$ Substitution
87 yr

7. HISTORY Abraham Lincoln's Gettysburg Address began "Four score and seven years ago…." Since a score is equal to 20, the expression $4(20) + 7$ represents this quote. Evaluate the expression to find how many years Lincoln was referring to. Name the property used in each step.

Exercises

HOMEWORK HELP	
For Exercises	See Examples
8–17	1
18–25	2

Exercise Levels
A: 8–25
B: 26–34
C: 35–39

Find the value of n in each equation. Then name the property that is used.

8. $12n = 12$ **9.** $n \cdot 1 = 5$ 8–17. See Ch. 1 Answer Appendix.

10. $8n = 1$ **11.** $1.5 = n + 1.5$

12. $6 = 6 + n$ **13.** $1 = 2n$

14. $n + 0 = \frac{1}{3}$ **15.** $4 \cdot \frac{1}{4} = n$

16. $4 - n = 0$ **17.** $n - \frac{1}{2} = 0$

Evaluate each expression. Name the property used in each step.   18–23. See Ch. 1 Answer Appendix.

18. $(1 \div 5)5 \cdot 14$ **19.** $7 + (9 - 3^2)$ **20.** $\frac{3}{4}[4 \div (7 - 4)]$

21. $[3 \div (2 \cdot 1)]\frac{2}{3}$ **22.** $2(3 \cdot 2 - 5) + 3 \cdot \frac{1}{3}$ **23.** $6 \cdot \frac{1}{6} + 5(12 \div 4 - 3)$

Lesson 1-4 Identity and Equality Properties   **23**

Use Identity and Equality Properties

Example 2 shows how to use the properties of identity and equality to justify each step when evaluating expressions.

ADDITIONAL EXAMPLE

② Evaluate
$\frac{1}{4}(12 - 8) + 3(15 \div 5 - 2)$.
Name the property used in each step.

$$\frac{1}{4}(12 - 8) + 3(15 \div 5 - 2)$$
$$= \frac{1}{4}(4) + 3(15 \div 5 - 2)$$
Substitution; $12 - 8 = 4$
$$= \frac{1}{4}(4) + 3(3 - 2)$$
Substitution; $15 \div 5 = 3$
$$= \frac{1}{4}(4) + 3(1)$$
Substitution; $3 - 2 = 1$
$$= \frac{1}{4}(4) + 3$$
Multiplicative Identity;
$3 \cdot 1 = 3$
$$= 1 + 3 = 4$$
Multiplicative Inverse;
$\frac{1}{4}(4) = 1$
$$= 4$$
Substitution; $1 + 3 = 4$

**3 Practice**

✓**Formative Assessment**

Use Exercises 1–7 to check for understanding.

Use the chart at the bottom of this page to customize assignments for your students.

Odd/Even Assignments

Exercises 8–25 are structured so that students practice the same concepts whether they are assigned odd or even problems.

DIFFERENTIATED HOMEWORK OPTIONS

Level	Assignment	Two-Day Option	
BL Basic	8–25, 37–50	9–25 odd, 40, 41	8–24 even, 37–39, 42–50
OL Core	9–31 odd, 32–34, 37–50	8–25, 40, 41	26–34, 37–39, 42–50
AL Advanced /Pre-AP	26–46 (optional: 47–50)		

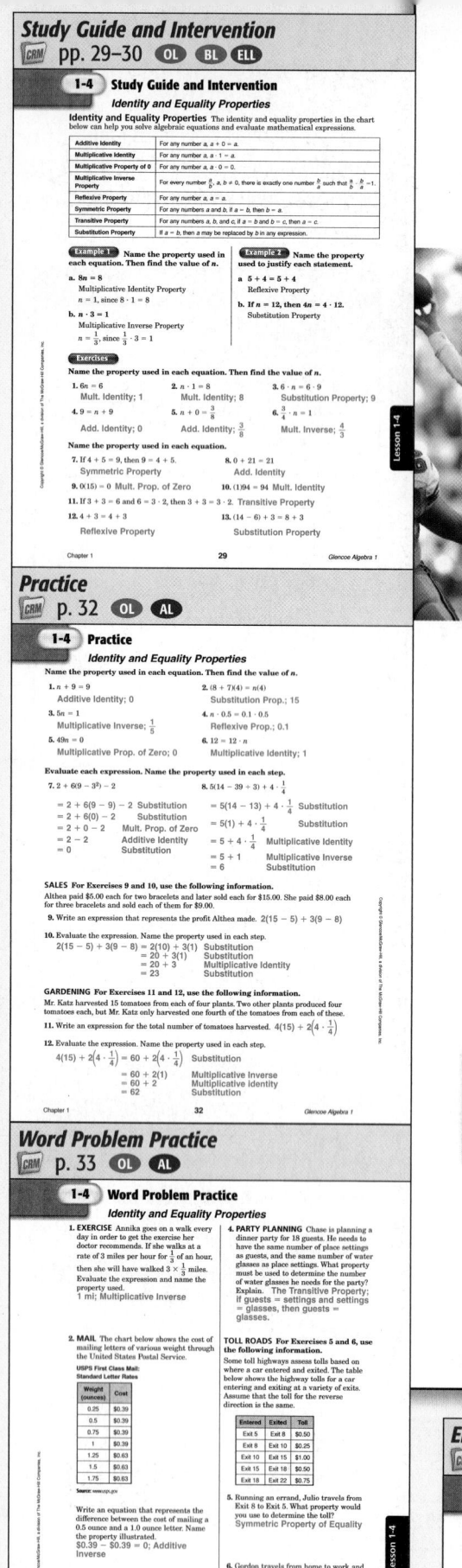

Study Guide and Intervention
📕 pp. 29–30 OL BL ELL

1-4 Study Guide and Intervention

Identity and Equality Properties

Identity and Equality Properties The identity and equality properties in the chart below can help you solve algebraic equations and evaluate mathematical expressions.

Additive Identity	For any number a, $a + 0 = a$.
Multiplicative Identity	For any number a, $a \cdot 1 = a$.
Multiplicative Property of 0	For any number a, $a \cdot 0 = 0$.
Multiplicative Inverse Property	For every number $\frac{a}{b}$, $a, b \ne 0$, there is exactly one number $\frac{b}{a}$ such that $\frac{a}{b} \cdot \frac{b}{a} = 1$.
Reflexive Property	For any number a, $a = a$.
Symmetric Property	For any numbers a and b, if $a = b$, then $b = a$.
Transitive Property	For any numbers a, b, and c, if $a = b$ and $b = c$, then $a = c$.
Substitution Property	If $a = b$, then a may be replaced by b in any expression.

Example 1 Name the property used in each equation. Then find the value of n.

a. $8n = 8$
Multiplicative Identity Property
$n = 1$, since $8 \cdot 1 = 8$

b. $n \cdot 3 = 1$
Multiplicative Inverse Property
$n = \frac{1}{3}$, since $\frac{1}{3} \cdot 3 = 1$

Example 2 Name the property used to justify each statement.

a. $5 + 4 = 5 + 4$
Reflexive Property

b. If $n = 12$, then $4n = 4 \cdot 12$.
Substitution Property

Exercises

Name the property used in each equation. Then find the value of n.

1. $6n = 6$ — Mult. Identity; 1
2. $n \cdot 1 = 8$ — Mult. Identity; 8
3. $6 \cdot n = 6 \cdot 9$ — Substitution Property; 9
4. $9 = n + 9$ — Add. Identity; 0
5. $n + 0 = \frac{3}{8}$ — Add. Identity; $\frac{3}{8}$
6. $\frac{3}{4} \cdot n = 1$ — Mult. Inverse; $\frac{4}{3}$

Name the property used in each equation.

7. If $4 + 5 = 9$, then $9 = 4 + 5$. — Symmetric Property
8. $0 + 21 = 21$ — Add. Identity
9. $0(15) = 0$ — Mult. Prop. of Zero
10. $(1.94 = 94$ Mult. Identity
11. If $3 + 3 = 6$ and $6 = 3 \cdot 2$, then $3 + 3 = 3 \cdot 2$. — Transitive Property
12. $4 + 3 = 4 + 3$ — Reflexive Property
13. $(14 - 6) + 3 = 8 + 3$ — Substitution Property

Chapter 1   29   Glencoe Algebra 1

Practice
📕 p. 32 OL AL

1-4 Practice

Identity and Equality Properties

Name the property used in each equation. Then find the value of n.

1. $n + 9 = 9$ — Additive Identity; 0
2. $(8 + 7 \times 4) = n(4)$ — Substitution Prop.; 15
3. $5n = 1$ — Multiplicative Inverse; $\frac{1}{5}$
4. $n \cdot 0.5 = 0.1 \cdot 0.5$ — Reflexive Prop.; 0.1
5. $49n = 0$ — Multiplicative Prop. of Zero; 0
6. $12 = 12 \cdot n$ — Multiplicative Identity; 1

Evaluate each expression. Name the property used in each step.

7. $2 + 6(9 - 3^2) - 2$
= $2 + 6(9 - 9) - 2$ Substitution
= $2 + 6(0) - 2$ Substitution
= $2 + 0 - 2$ Mult. Prop. of Zero
= $2 - 2$ Additive Identity
= 0 Substitution

8. $5(14 - 39 \div 3) + 4 \cdot \frac{1}{4}$
= $5(14 - 13) + 4 \cdot \frac{1}{4}$ Substitution
= $5(1) + 4 \cdot \frac{1}{4}$ Substitution
= $5 + 4 \cdot \frac{1}{4}$ Multiplicative Identity
= $5 + 1$ Multiplicative Inverse
= 6 Substitution

SALES For Exercises 9 and 10, use the following information.
Althea paid $5.00 each for two bracelets and later sold each for $15.00. She paid $8.00 each for three bracelets and sold each of them for $9.00.

9. Write an expression that represents the profit Althea made. $2(15 - 5) + 3(9 - 8)$

10. Evaluate the expression. Name the property used in each step.
$2(15 - 5) + 3(9 - 8)$ = $2(10) + 3(1)$ Substitution
= $20 + 3(1)$ Substitution
= $20 + 3$ Multiplicative Identity
= 23 Substitution

GARDENING For Exercises 11 and 12, use the following information.
Mr. Katz harvested 15 tomatoes from each of four plants. Two other plants produced four tomatoes each, but Mr. Katz only harvested one fourth of the tomatoes from each of these.

11. Write an expression for the total number of tomatoes harvested. $4(15) + 2\left(4 \cdot \frac{1}{4}\right)$

12. Evaluate the expression. Name the property used in each step.
$4(15) + 2\left(4 \cdot \frac{1}{4}\right) = 60 + 2\left(4 \cdot \frac{1}{4}\right)$ Substitution
= $60 + 2(1)$ Multiplicative Inverse
= $60 + 2$ Multiplicative Identity
= 62 Substitution

Chapter 1   32   Glencoe Algebra 1

Word Problem Practice
📕 p. 33 OL AL

1-4 Word Problem Practice

Identity and Equality Properties

1. **EXERCISE** Annika goes on a walk every day in order to get the exercise her doctor recommends. If she walks at a rate of 3 miles per hour for $\frac{1}{3}$ of an hour, then she will have walked $3 \times \frac{1}{3}$ miles. Evaluate the expression and name the property used. 1 mi; Multiplicative Inverse

2. **MAIL** The chart below shows the cost of mailing letters of various weight through the United States Postal Service.

USPS First Class Mail: Standard Letter Rates

Weight (ounces)	Cost
0.25	$0.39
0.5	$0.39
0.75	$0.39
1	$0.39
1.25	$0.63
1.5	$0.63
1.75	$0.63

Source: www.usps.gov

Write an equation that represents the difference between the cost of mailing a 0.5 ounce and a 1.0 ounce letter. Name the property illustrated.
$0.39 - $0.39 = 0$; Additive Inverse

3. **CAPACITY** Use the substitution and transitive properties to find how many 1-cup servings there are in 1 gallon of sports drink. 16 c

4. **PARTY PLANNING** Chase is planning a dinner party for 18 guests. He needs to have the same number of place settings as guests, and the same number of water glasses as place settings. What property must be used to determine the number of water glasses he needs for the party? Explain. The Transitive Property; if guests = settings and settings = glasses, then guests = glasses.

TOLL ROADS For Exercises 5 and 6, use the following information.
Some toll highways assess tolls based on where a car entered and exited. The table below shows the highway tolls for a car entering and exiting at a variety of exits. Assume that the toll for the reverse direction is the same.

Entered	Exited	Toll
Exit 5	Exit 8	$0.50
Exit 8	Exit 10	$0.25
Exit 10	Exit 15	$1.00
Exit 15	Exit 18	$0.50
Exit 18	Exit 22	$0.75

5. Running an errand, Julio travels from Exit 8 to Exit 5. What property would you use to determine the toll? Symmetric Property of Equality

6. Gordon travels from home to work and back each day. He lives at Exit 15 on the toll road and works at Exit 22. Write and evaluate an expression to find his daily toll cost. What property or properties did you use? $t = 2 \times (\$0.50 + \$0.75)$; $t = \$2.50$; Substitution

Chapter 1   33   Glencoe Algebra 1

★ **24. MILITARY PAY** An enlisted member of the military at grade E-2 earns $1427.40 per month in the first year of service. After 5 years of service, a person at grade E-2 earns $1427.40 per month. Write and solve an equation using addition that shows the change in pay from 1 year of service to 5 years. Name the property or identity used.
$1427.40 + y = $1427.40; y = 0$; Additive Identity

25. GEOMETRY The expression $2 \cdot \frac{22}{7} \cdot 14^2 + 2 \cdot \frac{22}{7} \cdot 14 \cdot 7$ approximates the surface area of the cylinder at the right. Evaluate this expression to find the surface area. Name the property used in each step. **See Ch. 1 Answer Appendix.**

7 in.

14 in.

Find the value of n in each equation. Then name the property that is illustrated.

26. $\frac{9}{4}$; Multiplicative Inverse

26. $1 = \frac{(9 - 5)}{3^2}\, n$

27. $n\left(5^2 \cdot \frac{1}{25}\right) = 3$

28. $6\left(\frac{1}{2} \cdot n\right) = 6$

27. 3; Multiplicative Identity   28. 2; Multiplicative Identity

Evaluate each expression. Name the property used in each step.
29–32. **See Ch. 1 Answer Appendix.**

29. $3 + 5(4 - 2^2) - 1$

30. $7 - 8(9 - 3^2)$

31. $\left[\frac{5}{8}\left(1 + \frac{3}{8}\right)\right] \cdot 17$

32. FOOTBALL The table shows various bonus plans for the NFL in a recent year. Write an expression that could be used to determine what a team owner would pay in bonuses for the following:
- eight players who keep their weight below 240 pounds and have averaged 4.5 yards per carry, and
- three players who score 12 touchdowns and score 76 points.

Name the property used in each step.

NFL Bonuses	
Goal	Bonuses($)
Average 4.5 yards per carry	50,000
12 touchdowns	50,000
76 points scored	50,000
Keep weight below 240 pounds	100,000

Source: ESPN Sports Almanac

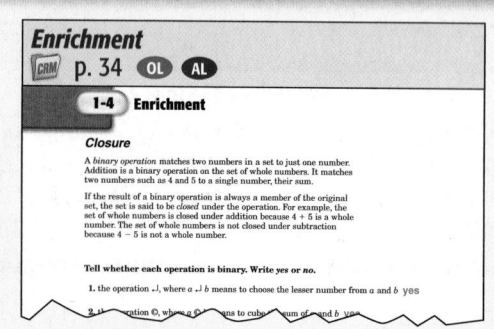

🌐 **Real-World Link**

Nationally organized football began in 1920 and originally included five teams. In 2005, there were 32 professional teams.

Source: www.infoplease.com

ANALYZE TABLES For Exercises 33 and 34, use the following information.
The spirit club at Marshall High School is selling school bumper stickers, buttons, and caps. The profit for each item is the difference between the selling price and the cost.

School Spirit items		
Item	Cost ($)	Selling Price ($)
Bumper Sticker	0.30	2.00
Button	1.00	2.50
Cap	6.00	10.00

33. Write an expression that represents the profit for selling 25 bumper stickers, 80 buttons, and 40 caps. $25(2 - 0.3) + 80(2.5 - 1) + 40(10 - 6)$

34. Evaluate the expression, indicating the property used in each step. **See Ch. 1 Answer Appendix.**

EXTRA PRACTICE
See pages, 718, 744.

Math Online
Self-Check Quiz at ca.algebra1.com

H.O.T. Problems

35. CHALLENGE The **Transitive Property of Inequality** states that if $a < b$ and $b < c$, then $a < c$. Use this property to determine whether the following statement is *sometimes*, *always*, or *never* true. Give examples to support your answer. **See Ch. 1 Answer Appendix.**

If $x > y$ and $z > w$, then $xz > yw$.

24 Chapter 1 The Language and Tools of Algebra

Enrichment
📕 p. 34 OL AL

1-4 Enrichment

Closure

A *binary operation* matches two numbers in a set to just one number. Addition is a binary operation on the set of whole numbers. It matches two numbers such as 4 and 5 to a single number, their sum.

If the result of a binary operation is always a member of the original set, the set is said to be *closed* under the operation. For example, the set of whole numbers is closed under addition because $4 + 5$ is a whole number. The set of whole numbers is not closed under subtraction because $4 - 5$ is not a whole number.

Tell whether each operation is binary. Write *yes* or *no*.

1. the operation ⌐, where $a ⌐ b$ means to choose the lesser number from a and b yes

---

BL = Below Grade Level
OL = On Grade Level
AL = Above Grade Level
ELL = English Language Learner

Additional pages not shown:
📕 *Lesson Reading Guide*, p. 28 BL OL ELL
📕 *Skills Practice*, p. 31 BL OL

36. REASONING Explain whether 1 can be an additive identity. Give an example to justify your answer. **No; $3 + 1 \neq 3$.**

37. OPEN ENDED Write two equations showing the Transitive Property of Equality. Justify your reasoning. **See margin.**

38. REASONING Explain why 0 has no multiplicative inverse.
Sample answer: You cannot divide by zero.

39. *Writing in Math* Use the data about football on page 21 to explain how properties can be used to compare data. Include an example of the Transitive Property using three teams' rankings as an example. **See margin.**

STANDARDS PRACTICE 25.0

40. Which illustrates the Symmetric Property of Equality? **A**

  A If $a = b$, then $b = a$.

  B If $a = b$ and $b = c$, then $a = c$.

  C If $a = b$, then $b = c$.

  D If $a = a$, then $a + 0 = a$.

41. Which property is used below?

  If $4xy^2 = 8y^2$ and $8y^2 = 72$,

  then $4xy^2 = 72$. **J**

  F Reflexive Property

  G Substitution Property

  H Symmetric Property

  J Transitive Property

Spiral Review

Find the solution set for each inequality using the given replacement set. (Lesson 1-3)

42. $10 - x > 6$; $\{3, 5, 6, 8\}$ **{3}**

43. $4x + 2 < 58$; $\{11, 12, 13, 14, 15\}$ **{11, 12, 13}**

44. EXERCISE It takes about 2000 steps to walk one mile. Use the table to determine how many miles of walking it would take to burn all the Calories contained in a cheeseburger and two 12-ounce sodas. (Lesson 1-3)
7.245 mi

Steps Needed to Burn Calories	
Food	**Number of Steps**
cheeseburger	7590
12 oz. soda	3450

45. SHOPPING In a recent year, the average U.S. household spent $213 on toys and games. In San Jose, California, the average spending was $59 less than twice this amount. Write and evaluate an expression to find the average spending on toys and games in San Jose during that year. (Lesson 1-2) **$2(213) - 59$; $367**

46. Write an algebraic expression for *the sum of twice a number squared and 7.*
(Lesson 1-1) **$2x^2 + 7$**

GET READY for the Next Lesson

PREREQUISITE SKILL Evaluate each expression. (Lesson 1-2)

47. $10(6) + 10(2)$ **80**   **48.** $(15 - 6) \cdot 8$ **72**   **49.** $12(4) - 5(4)$ **28**   **50.** $3(4 + 2)$ **18**

Pre-AP Activity   **Use after Exercise 34**

Have students use a real-world situation to explain and demonstrate one of the properties of equality. For example, Lee Ann pays $8 + $3 for a notebook and paper and Rick pays $9 + $2 for a notebook and paper. If Lee Ann's total is equal to Rick's total and Rick paid $11, then Lee Ann paid $11 too. This illustrates the Transitive Property of Equality, which states that if $a = b$ and $b = c$, then $a = c$. In this case, $a = 8 + 3$, $b = 9 + 2$, and $c = 11$.

---

4 Assess

Crystal Ball Ask students to write a brief statement on how they think the properties of identity and equality connect to the next lesson on the Distributive Property.

FOLDABLES Study Organizer
Foldables™ Follow-Up
Remind students to use the fourth flap in their Foldables to list the properties of identity and equality they learned in this lesson. Students should include an example of each property.

Additional Answers

37. Sample answer: $5 = 3 + 2$ and $3 + 2 = 4 + 1$, so $5 = 4 + 1$; $5 + 7 = 8 + 4$, and $8 + 4 = 12$, so $5 + 7 = 12$.

39. You can use the Identity and Equality properties to see if data is the same. Answers should include the following: Reflexive: $r = r$, or Symetric: $a = b$, so $b = a$; Southern California, week $1 = a$, week $2 = b$ week $3 = c$. $a = b$ and $b = c$, so $a = c$.

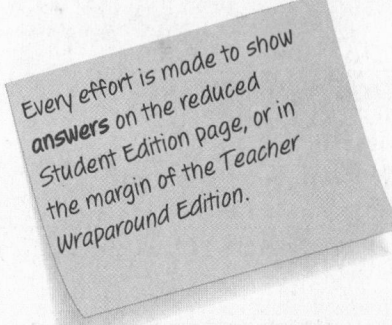
Every effort is made to show answers on the reduced Student Edition page, or in the margin of the Teacher Wraparound Edition.

97830018

1-5 # The Distributive Property

1 Focus

Standards Alignment

Before Lesson 1-5
Simplify numerical expressions and justify the process used from ⚷ Standard 7AF1.3

Lesson 1-5
Students use properties to construct arguments for, or formulate counter-examples to claimed assertions from ⚷ Standards 1.0 and 25.1

After Lesson 1-5
Are adept at operations on polynomials, including long division from ⚷ Standard 2A3.0

2 Teach

Scaffolding Questions Have students read *Get Ready for the Lesson.*
Ask:
- How can you represent the price of a bargain game and a new release as one quantity? $14.95 + 34.95$

Scaffolding Questions give direction and momentum to the lesson, clarify its purpose, and keep students on task.

Main Ideas
- Use the Distributive Property to evaluate expressions.
- Use the Distributive Property to simplify algebraic expressions.

Standard 1.0 Students identify and use the arithmetic properties of subsets of integers and rational, irrational, and real numbers, including closure properties for the four basic arithmetic operations where applicable.

Standard 25.1 Students use properties to construct simple, valid arguments (direct and indirect) for, or formulate counterexamples to claimed assertions.

New Vocabulary

term
like terms
equivalent expressions
simplest form
coefficient

Vocabulary Link
Distribute
Everyday Use
to divide among several or many

Distributive
Math Use
property that allows you to multiply each number in a sum or difference by a number outside the parentheses

▶ GET READY for the Lesson

Instant Replay Video Games sells new and used games. During a sale, the first 8 customers each bought a bargain game and a new release. To calculate the total sales for these customers, you can use the Distributive Property.

Sale Prices	
Used Games	$9.95
Bargain Games	$14.95
Regular Games	$24.95
New Releases	$34.95

Evaluate Expressions There are two methods you could use to calculate the video game sales.

Method 1			**Method 2**		
sales of bargain games	plus	sales of new releases	number of customers	times	each customer's purchase price
$8(14.95)$	$+$	$8(34.95)$	8	$\times$	$(14.95 + 34.95)$
$= 119.60 + 279.60$			$= 8(49.90)$		
$= 399.20$			$= 399.20$		

Either method gives total sales of $399.20 because the following is true.

$$8(14.95) + 8(34.95) = 8(14.95 + 34.95)$$

This is an example of the **Distributive Property.**

KEY CONCEPT		*Distributive Property*
Symbols	For any numbers a, b, and c, $a(b + c) = ab + ac$ and $(b + c)a = ba + ca$ and $a(b - c) = ab - ac$ and $(b - c)a = ba - ca$.	
Examples	$3(2 + 5) = 3 \cdot 2 + 3 \cdot 5$ $3(7) = 6 + 15$ $21 = 21 \checkmark$	$4(9 - 7) = 4 \cdot 9 - 4 \cdot 7$ $4(2) = 36 - 28$ $8 = 8 \checkmark$

Notice that it does not matter whether a is placed on the right or the left of the expression in the parentheses. The Symmetric Property of Equality allows the Distributive Property to be written as follows.

If $a(b + c) = ab + ac$, then $ab + ac = a(b + c)$.

Lesson 1-5 Resources

Real-World Link

Ramona is America's oldest continuing outdoor drama. It has been performed since 1923 for more than 2 million people. Its location, called the *Ramona Bowl*, has been designated a California State Historical Landmark.

Source: ramonabowl.com

EXAMPLE Distribute Over Addition or Subtraction

① Tickets for a play are $8. A group of 10 adults and 4 children are planning to go. Rewrite 8(10 + 4) using the Distributive Property. Then evaluate to find the total cost for the group.

$$8(10 + 4) = 8(10) + 8(4) \quad \text{Distributive Property}$$
$$= 80 + 32 \quad \text{Multiply.}$$
$$= 112 \quad \text{Add.}$$

✓CHECK Your Progress

Rewrite each expression using the Distributive Property. Then evaluate.

1A. $(5 + 1)9$ $5(9) + 1(9); 54$ **1B.** $3(11 - 8)$ $3(11) - 3(8); 9$

🌐 **Personal Tutor at** ca.algebra1.com

The Distributive Property can be used to simplify mental calculations involving multiplication. To use this method, rewrite one factor as a sum or difference. Then use the Distributive Property to multiply. Finally, find the sum or difference.

EXAMPLE The Distributive Property and Mental Math

② Use the Distributive Property to rewrite 15 · 99. Then evaluate.

$$15 \cdot 99 = 15(100 - 1) \quad \text{Think: } 99 = 100 - 1$$
$$= 15(100) - 15(1) \quad \text{Distributive Property}$$
$$= 1500 - 15 \quad \text{Multiply}$$
$$= 1485 \quad \text{Subtract.}$$

✓CHECK Your Progress

Use the Distributive Property to rewrite each expression. Then evaluate.

2A. $402(12)$ $(400 + 2)(12); 4824$ **2B.** $60 \cdot 7\frac{2}{3}$ $60\left(7 + \frac{2}{3}\right); 460$

Simplify Expressions You can use algebra tiles to investigate how the Distributive Property relates to algebraic expressions.

ALGEBRA LAB

The Distributive Property

Use a product mat and algebra tiles to model $3(x + 2)$ as the area of a rectangle with dimensions of 3 and $(x + 2)$.

Make a rectangle with algebra tiles that is 3 units wide and $x + 2$ units long. The rectangle has 3 x-tiles and 6 1-tiles. The area of the rectangle is $x + 1 + 1 + x + 1 + 1 + x + 1 + 1$ or $3x + 6$. Therefore, $3(x + 2) = 3x + 6$.

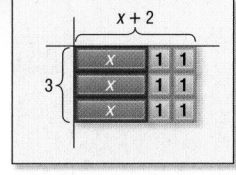

(continued on the next page)

Algebra Lab

To save time and algebra tile sets, consider having students work in groups. Give each group a set of algebra tiles and a product mat. Remind students that one of the quantities being multiplied goes on the left side of the mat and the other quantity goes on the top.

Algebra Labs use manipulatives and models to help students learn key concepts. There are teacher notes for every Algebra Lab in the Student Edition.

- Since 8 customers bought a bargain game and a new release, by what would you multiply the quantity to find the total amount paid in? by 8
- How can you represent the price of 8 bargain games and new releases, as one quantity? $8(14.95 + 34.95)$

Evaluate Expressions

Examples 1 and 2 show how to use the Distributive Property to rewrite and evaluate expressions.

✓ Formative Assessment

Use the Check Your Progress exercises after each example to determine students' understanding of concepts.

ADDITIONAL EXAMPLES

① Julia walks 5 days a week. She walks at a fast rate for 7 minutes and cools down for 2 minutes. Rewrite $5(7 + 2)$ using the Distributive Property. Evaluate to find the total number of minutes Julia walks.

$$5(7 + 2) = 5(7) + 5(2)$$
$$\text{Distributive Property}$$
$$= 35 + 10 \text{ Multiply.}$$
$$= 45 \text{ Add.}$$

② Use the Distributive Property to rewrite 12 · 82. Then evaluate. 984

Additional Examples are also in:

- Noteables™ Interactive Study Notebook with Foldables™
- Interactive Classroom PowerPoint® Presentations

🔍 Focus on Mathematical Content

Distributive Property

Multiplication can be distributed over addition or subtraction. If a, b, and c are any numbers, then $a(b \pm c) = a(b) \pm a(c)$. The number a on the left side of the equation is distributed over the addition or subtraction of b and c.

Simplify Expressions

Example 3 shows how to use the Distributive Property to rewrite products and then simplify the expressions.
Example 4 shows how to use the Distributive Property to combine like terms and then simplify the expressions.

MODEL AND ANALYZE
Find each product by using algebra tiles.

1. $2(x + 1)$ $2x + 2$ **2.** $5(x + 2)$ $5x + 10$ **3.** $2(2x + 1)$ $4x + 2$

Tell whether each statement is *true* or *false*. Justify your answer with algebra tiles and a drawing. 4–6. See margin for drawings.

4. $3(x + 3) = 3x + 3$ false **5.** $x(3 + 2) = 3x + 2x$ **6.** $2(2x + 1) = 2x + 2$ false
                                              true

You can apply the Distributive Property to algebraic expressions.

EXAMPLE Algebraic Expressions

3 **Rewrite each product using the Distributive Property. Then simplify.**

a. $5(g - 9)$

$5(g - 9) = 5 \cdot g - 5 \cdot 9$ Distributive Property
$= 5g - 45$ Multiply.

b. $3(x^2 + x - 1)$

$3(x^2 + x - 1) = 3(x^2) + 3(x) - 3(1)$ Distributive Property
$= 3x^2 + 3x - 3$ Simplify.

 Your Progress

3A. $2(8 + n)$ $2(8) + 2(n); 16 + 2n$ **3B.** $-6(r - 3s - t)$ $-6(r) + (-6)(-3s) + (-6)(-t)$
                                                                 $-6r + 18s + 6t$

Reading Math

Algebraic Expressions
The expression $5(g - 9)$ is read *5 times the quantity g minus 9* or *5 times the difference of g and 9.*

COncepts in MOtion
BrainPOP®
ca.algebra1.com

A **term** is a number, a variable, or a product or quotient of numbers and variables. For example, y, p^3, $4a$, and $5g^2h$ are all terms. **Like terms** contain the same variables, with corresponding variables having the same power.

$$\underbrace{2x^2 + 6x + 5}_{\text{three terms}}$$ $$3a^2 + \underbrace{5a^2}_{\text{like terms}} + \underbrace{2a}_{\text{unlike terms}}$$

The Distributive Property and the properties of equality can be used to show that $5n + 7n = 12n$. In this expression, $5n$ and $7n$ are like terms.

$$5n + 7n = (5 + 7)n \quad \text{Distributive Property}$$
$$= 12n \quad \text{Substitution}$$

The expressions $5n + 7n$ and $12n$ are called **equivalent expressions** because they denote the same number. An expression is in **simplest form** when it is replaced by an equivalent expression having no like terms or parentheses.

EXAMPLE Combine Like Terms

4 a. Simplify $15x + 18x$.

$15x + 18x = (15 + 18)x$ Distributive Property
$= 33x$ Substitution

 Extra Examples at ca.algebra1.com

Additional Answers

4.

	$x + 3$		
x	1	1	1
x	1	1	1
x	1	1	1

$= 3x + 9$

5.

	3 + 2				
x	x	x	x	x

$= 5x$

6.

	2x + 1		
x	x	1
x	x	1

$= 4x + 2$

b. Simplify $10n + 3n^2 + 9n^2$.

$$10n + 3n^2 + 9n^2 = 10n + (3 + 9)n^2 \quad \text{Distributive Property}$$
$$= 10n + 12n^2 \quad \text{Substitution}$$

✓**CHECK Your Progress**

Simplify each expression. If not possible, write *simplified*.

4A. $6t - 4t$ **2t**   **4B.** $b^2 + 13b + 13$ **simplified**

Reading Math

Like terms may be defined as terms that are the same or vary only by the coefficient.

The **coefficient** of a term is the numerical factor. For example, in $17xy$, the coefficient is 17, and in $\frac{3y^2}{4}$, the coefficient is $\frac{3}{4}$. In the term m, the coefficient is 1 since $1 \cdot m = m$ by the Multiplicative Identity Property.

★ indicates multi-step problem

✓**CHECK Your Understanding**

Example 1
(p. 27)

Rewrite each expression using the Distributive Property. Then evaluate.

1. $6(12 - 3)$ **2.** $8(1 + 5)$ **3.** $(19 + 3)10$
$6(12) - 6(3)$; 54 $8(1) + 8(5)$; 48 $19(10) + 3(10)$; 220

★ **4. COSMETOLOGY** A hair stylist cut 12 customers' hair. She earned $29.95 for each haircut and received an average tip of $4 for each. Write and evaluate an expression to determine the total amount that she earned.
$12(29.95 + 4)$ or $12(29.95) + 12(4)$; $407.40

Example 2
(p. 27)

Use the Distributive Property to rewrite each expression. Then find the product.

5. $16(103)$ $16(100 + 3)$; 1648   **6.** $\left(3\frac{1}{17}\right)(34)$ $\left(3 + \frac{1}{17}\right)34$; 104

Example 3
(p. 28)

Rewrite each expression using the Distributive Property. Then simplify.

7. $2(4 + t)$ $8 + 2t$ **8.** $5(g - 9)$ $5g - 45$

Example 4
(pp. 28–29)

Simplify each expression. If not possible, write *simplified*.

9. $13m + m$ **14m**   **10.** $14a^2 + 13b^2 + 27$ **simplified**   **11.** $3(x + 2x)$ **9x**

Exercises

HOMEWORK HELP	
For Exercises	See Examples
12–19	1
20–23	2
24–27	3
28–33	4

Exercise Levels
A: 12–33
B: 34–42
C: 43–47

Rewrite each expression using the Distributive Property. Then evaluate.

12. $(5 + 7)8$ **13.** $7(13 + 12)$ **14.** $6(6 - 1)$
15. $(3 + 8)15$ **16.** $12(9 - 5)$ **17.** $(10 - 7)13$
12–17. See margin.

★ **18. COMMUNICATION** A consultant keeps a log of all contacts she makes. In a typical week, she averages 5 hours using e-mail, 18 hours on the telephone, and 12 hours of meetings in person. Write and evaluate an expression to predict how many hours she will spend on these activities over the next 12 weeks. $12(5 + 12 + 18)$; 420 h

★ **19. OLYMPICS** The table shows the average daily attendance for two venues at the 2004 Summer Olympics. Write and evaluate an expression to estimate the total number of people at these venues over a 4-day period. $4(110,000 + 17,500)$; 510,000

Average Olympic Attendance	
Venue	Number of People
Olympic Stadium	110,000
Aquatic Center	17,500

Source: www.olympic.org

Lesson 1-5 The Distributive Property **29**

Preventing Errors

 Tips for New Teachers

To make it easier for students to identify the coefficient of expressions such as $\frac{3y^2}{4}$, remind them that since y^2 is in the numerator, they can rewrite the expression as $\frac{3}{4}y^2$. Write the following on the board for clarification.

$$\frac{3}{4} \cdot y^2 = \frac{3}{4} \cdot \frac{y^2}{1} = \frac{3y^2}{4}$$

3 Practice

✓ **Formative Assessment**

Use Exercises 1–11 to check for understanding.

Use the chart at the bottom of this page to customize assignments for your students.

Odd/Even Assignments

Exercises 12–33 are structured so that students practice the same concepts whether they are assigned odd or even problems.

⚠ **Exercise Alert!**

Find the Error Remind students that when they simplify expressions using the Distributive Property, they must distribute the term outside the parentheses over both terms inside the parentheses. Tell students to look at the first step in Courtney's and Che's simplifications.

Additional Answers

12. $5(8) + 7(8)$; 96
13. $7(13) + 7(12)$; 175
14. $6(6) - 6(1)$; 30
15. $3(15) + 8(15)$; 165
16. $12(9) - 12(5)$; 48
17. $10(13) - 7(13)$; 39

DIFFERENTIATED HOMEWORK OPTIONS			
Level	**Assignment**	**Two-Day Option**	
BL Basic	12–33, 43–45, 47–60	13–33 odd, 48, 49	12–32 even, 43–45, 47, 50–60
OL Core	13–33 odd, 34–35, 37–41 odd, 43–45, 47–60	12–33, 48, 49	34–45, 47, 50–60
AL Advanced /Pre-AP	34–57 (optional: 58–60)		

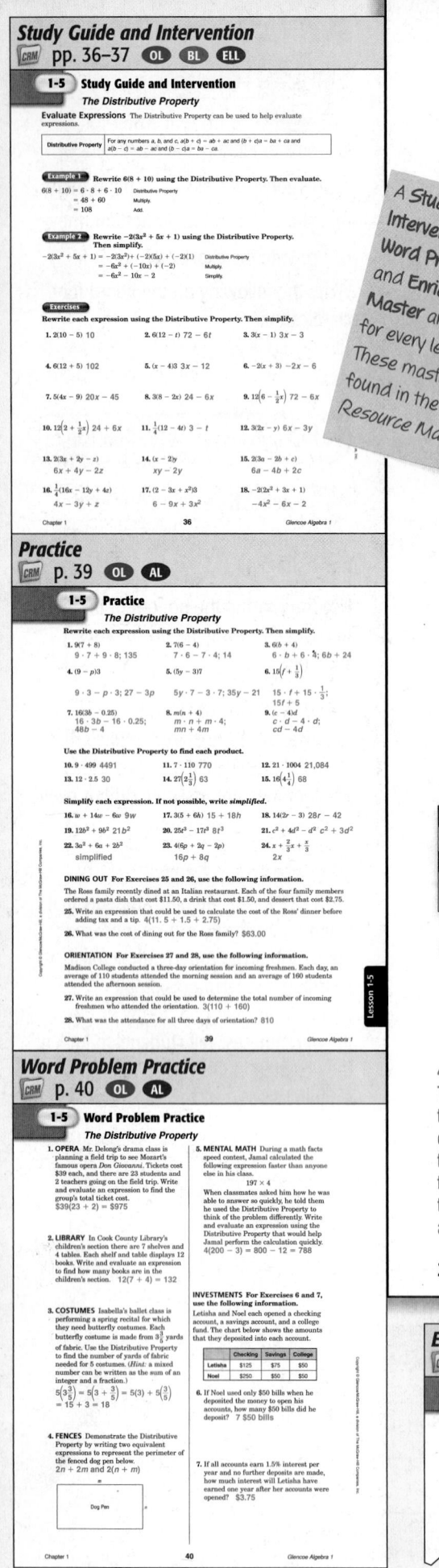

Use the Distributive Property to rewrite each expression. Then find the product.

20. $5 \cdot 97$ $5(90 + 7)$; 485

21. $8(990)$ $8(900 + 90)$; 7920

22. $18 \cdot 2\frac{1}{9}$ $18\left(2 + \frac{1}{9}\right)$; 38

23. $\left(3\frac{1}{6}\right)48$ $\left(3 + \frac{1}{6}\right)48$; 152

Rewrite each expression using the Distributive Property. Then simplify.

24. $2(x + 4)$ $2x + 8$

25. $3(5 + n)$ $15 + 3n$

26. $8(4 - 3m)$ $32 - 24m$

27. $-3(x - 6)$ $-3x + 18$

Simplify each expression. If not possible, write *simplified*.

28. $2x + 9x$ $11x$

29. $4b - 1 + 5b$ $9b - 1$

30. $5n^2 - 7n$ simplified

31. $3a^2 + a + 14a^2$ $17a^2 + a$

32. $12(4 + 3c)$ $48 + 36c$

33. $(3x - 5)15$ $45x - 75$

ANALYZE TABLES For Exercises 34 and 35, use the table that shows the monthly cost of a company health plan.

Available Insurance Plans – Monthly Charges			
Coverage	Medical	Dental	Vision
Employee	$78	$20	$12
Family (additional charge)	$50	$15	$7

★ **34.** Write and evaluate an expression to calculate the total cost of medical, dental, and vision insurance for an employee for 6 months.
$6(78 + 20 + 12)$; $660

35. How much would an employee expect to pay for family medical and dental coverage per year? **$1956**

Rewrite each expression using the Distributive Property. Then simplify.

36. $27\left(\frac{1}{3} - 2b\right)$ $9 - 54b$

37. $4(p + q - r)$ $4p + 4q - 4r$

38. $-6(2 - d^2 + d)$
$-12 + 6d^2 - 6d$

39. $5(6m^3 + 4n - 3n)$ $30m^3 + 5n$

Simplify each expression. If not possible, write *simplified*.

40. $6x^2 + 14x - 9x$
$6x^2 + 5x$

41. $4y^3 + 3y^3 + y^4$
$7y^3 + y^4$

42. $a + \frac{a}{5} + \frac{2}{5}a$ $\frac{8}{5}a$

H.O.T. Problems

43. REASONING Explain why the Distributive Property is sometimes called the Distributive Property of Multiplication Over Addition.

43. Sample answer: The numbers inside the parentheses are each multiplied by the number outside the parentheses, then the products are added.

44. OPEN ENDED Write an expression that has five terms, three of which are like terms and one that has a coefficient of 1. Describe how to simplify the expression. **See Ch. 1 Answer Appendix.**

45. FIND THE ERROR Courtney and Che are simplifying $3(x + 4)$. Who is correct? Explain your reasoning. **See Ch. 1 Answer Appendix.**

Courtney
$3(x + 4) = 3(x) + 3(4)$
$= 3x + 12$

Che
$3(x + 4) = 3(x) + 4$
$= 3x + 4$

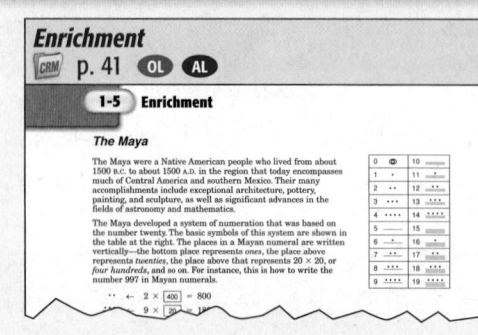

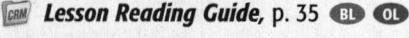

BL = Below Grade Level

OL = On Grade Level

AL = Above Grade Level

ELL = English Language Learner

Additional pages not shown:

Lesson Reading Guide, p. 35 **BL** **OL** **ELL**

Skills Practice, p. 38 **BL** **OL**

EXTRA PRACTICE
See pages 718, 744.
Math Online
Self-Check Quiz at
ca.algebra1.com

46. CHALLENGE The expression $2(\ell + w)$ can be used to find the perimeter of a rectangle with a length ℓ and width w. What are the length and width of a rectangle if the area is $13\frac{1}{2}$ square units and the length of one side is $\frac{1}{5}$ the measure of the perimeter? Explain your reasoning. **See margin.**

47. *Writing in Math* Use the data about video game prices on page 26 to explain how the Distributive Property can be used to calculate quickly. Also, compare and contrast the two methods of finding the total video game sales. **See margin.**

STANDARDS PRACTICE 5.0, 7MG2.3

48. In three months, Mayuko had 108 minutes of incoming calls on her voice mail. What was the total cost of voice mail for those three months? **C**

Voice Mail	
Item	**Cost**
service fee	$4.95 per month
incoming calls	$0.07 per minute

A $7.61

B $12.51

C $22.41

D $37.80

49. REVIEW If each dimension of the prism is tripled, which expression represents the new volume? **J**

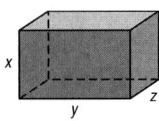

F $x^3y^3z^3$

G $3xyz$

H $3(x + y + z)$

J $27xyz$

Spiral Review

Name the property illustrated by each statement or equation. (Lesson 1-4) **50. Symmetric**

50. If $7 \cdot 2 = 14$, then $14 = 7 \cdot 2$.

51. $mnp = 1mnp$ **Multiplicative Identity**

52. $\frac{3}{4} \cdot \frac{4}{3} = 1$ **Multiplicative Inverse**

53. $32 + 21 = 32 + 21$ **Reflexive**

★ **54. PHYSICAL SCIENCE** Sound travels through air at an approximate speed of 344 meters per second. Write and solve an equation to find how far sound travels through air in 2 seconds. (Lesson 1-3) $d = 344(2)$; **688 m**

Evaluate each expression if $a = 4$, $b = 6$, and $c = 3$. (Lesson 1-2)

55. $3b - c$ **15**

56. $8(a - c)^2 + 3$ **11**

57. $\frac{6ab}{2(c + 5)}$ **9**

GET READY for the Next Lesson

PREREQUISITE SKILL Find the area of each figure. (Pages 704–705)

58. **45 in²**

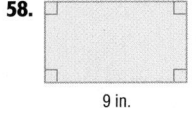

5 in.

9 in.

59. **168 cm²**

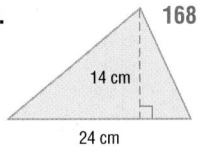

14 cm

24 cm

60. **72.25 m²**

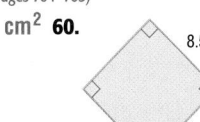

8.5 m

Lesson 1-5 The Distributive Property **31**

4 Assess

Name the Math Write $6(m + 8)$ on the board. Have students tell what procedure(s) they would use to simplify the expression.

Check for student understanding of concepts in Lessons 1–4 and 1–5.
[CRM] Quiz 2, p. 73

FOLDABLES Study Organizer **Foldables™ Follow-Up**

Remind students to use the fifth flap of their Foldables to record notes on what they have learned about the Distributive Property. Students should include examples.

Study Tip

Tips for New Teachers Some students are confused when an expression is presented with the parentheses first, such as $(4 - 3)6$. Suggest that students rewrite the expression as $6(4 - 3)$ to avoid confusion.

Additional Answers

46. $\ell = 4\frac{1}{2}$ units, $w = 3$; $w = \frac{1}{5} \cdot 2(\ell + w)$, so $\ell = \frac{3}{2}w$. Substituting $\frac{3}{2}w$ for ℓ into the Area formula gives $w = 3$. So, $\ell = 4\frac{1}{2}$.

47. You can use the Distributive Property to calculate quickly by expressing any number as a sum or difference of a more convenient number. Answers should include the following: Both methods result in the correct answer. In one method you multiply then add, and in the other you add then multiply.

Pre-AP Activity

Ask students to demonstrate whether they can distribute division over addition in the same way that they distribute multiplication over addition. Sample answer: It depends on how the division is written.

$24 \div (2 + 6) \overset{?}{=} 24 \div 2 + 24 \div 6$

$24 \div 8 \overset{?}{=} 12 + 4$

$3 \neq 16$

$(2 + 6) \div 24 = \frac{2}{24} + \frac{6}{24}$

$8 \div 24 = \frac{1}{12} + \frac{3}{12}$

$\frac{1}{3} = \frac{4}{12}$

CHAPTER 1 Mid-Chapter Quiz

Formative Assessment

Use the Mid-Chapter Quiz to assess student progress in the first half of the chapter.

For the problems answered incorrectly, have students review the lessons indicated in parentheses.

Summative Assessment

CRM Mid-Chapter Test, p. 75

 Customize and create multiple versions of your Mid-Chapter Test and their answer keys.

 Foldables™ Follow-Up

Before students complete the Mid-Chapter Quiz, encourage them to review the information on the tabs of their Foldables.

Additional Answers

4. Sample answer: five times n plus two

5. Sample answer: a cubed

The Mid-Chapter Quiz reviews skills and concepts presented in previous lessons. Students' results on the quiz can be used for Data-Driven Decision Making.

Write an algebraic expression for each verbal expression. (Lesson 1-1)

1. the quotient of y and 3 $\frac{y}{3}$
2. 5 minus the product of 7 and t $5 - 7t$
3. x squared increased by 2 $x^2 + 2$

Write a verbal expression for each algebraic expression. (Lesson 1-1) **4–5. See margin.**

4. $5n + 2$ 5. a^3

6. **GOLF** At a driving range, a small bucket of golf balls costs $6 and a large bucket costs $8. Write an expression for the total cost of buying s small and t large buckets. (Lesson 1-1) $6s + 8t$

7. **MULTIPLE CHOICE** Jasmine bought a satellite radio receiver and a subscription to satellite radio. What was her total cost after 7 months? (Lesson 1-2) **B**

Satellite Radio	
Item	**Cost**
receiver	$78
subscription	$12.95 per month

A $90.95   C $558.95

B $168.65   D $636.65

Evaluate each expression. (Lesson 1-2)

8. $2 + 18 \div 9$ **4**   9. $6 \cdot 9 - 2(8 + 5)$ **28**

10. $9(3) - 4^2$ **11**   11. $\dfrac{(5-2)^2}{4 \times 2 - 7}$ **9**

12. Evaluate $\dfrac{5a^2 + c - 2}{6 + b}$ if $a = 4$, $b = 5$, and $c = 10$. (Lesson 1-2) **8**

Find the solution of each equation if the replacement set is {10, 11, 12, 13}. (Lesson 1-3)

13. $x - 3 = 10$ **13**   14. $25 = 2r + 1$ **12**

15. $\dfrac{t}{5} = 2$ **10**   16. $4y - 9 = 35$ **11**

17. Find the solution set for $2n^2 + 3 \le 75$ if the replacement set is {4, 5, 6, 7, 8, 9}. (Lesson 1-3)
{4, 5, 6}

---

18. **MULTIPLE CHOICE** Dion bought 1 pound of dried greens, 3 pounds of sesame seeds, and 2 pounds of flax seed to feed his birds. According to the table, which expression best represents the total cost? (Lesson 1-3) **H**

Bird Food	Cost ($)
dried greens (0.5 lb)	4.95
sesame seeds (1 lb)	5.75
flax seed (2 lb)	2.75

F $4.95 + 5.75 + 2.75$

G $4.95 + 3(5.75) + 2(2.75)$

H $2(4.95) + 3(5.75) + 2.75$

J $0.5(4.95) + 5.75 + 2(2.75)$

Find the value of n in each equation. Then name the property that is used. (Lesson 1-4)

19. $n = 11 + 0$ 20. $\frac{1}{3} \cdot 3 = n$
11; Additive Identity   **1; Multiplicative Inverse**

21. **GEOMETRY** The expression $\frac{1}{2}(7)(a + b)$ represents the area of the trapezoid. What is the area if $a = 22.4$ centimeters and $b = 10.8$ centimeters? (Lesson 1-5) **116.2 cm²**

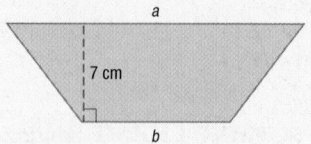

22. **MULTIPLE CHOICE** Which expression represents the second step of simplifying the algebraic expression? (Lesson 1-5) **B**

Step 1 $9(x + 4y) + 5 + 2(x + 7)$
Step 2   _____
Step 3 $11x + 36y + 19$

A $9x + 36y + 7(x + 7)$

B $9x + 36y + 5 + 2x + 14$

C $9(x + 4y + 5) + 2x + 14$

D $9(x + 5) + 4y + 2x + 14$

Data-Driven Decision Making	Exercises	Lesson	🌐 Standard	Resources for Review
Diagnostic Teaching Based on the results of the Chapter 1 Mid-Chapter Quiz, use the following to review concepts that students continue to find challenging.	1–6	1–1	**Reinforcement of 7AF1.1**	CRM Study Guide and Intervention, pp. 6–7, 13–14, 21–22, 29–30, 36–37
	7–12	1–2	**Reinforcement of 7AF1.2**	Math Online
	13–18	1–3	**Preparation for 4.0**	• Extra Examples
	19–20	1–4	**1.0**	• Personal Tutor
	21–22	1–5	**1.0**	• Concepts in Motion

Commutative and Associative Properties

Main Ideas

- Recognize the Commutative and Associative Properties.
- Use the Commutative and Associative Properties to simplify algebraic expressions.

 Standard 25.0 Students use properties of the number system to judge the validity of results, **to justify each step of a procedure,** and to prove or disprove statements.

▶ GET READY for the Lesson

The South Line of the Atlanta subway leaves Five Points and heads for Garnett and then West End. The distance from Five Points to West End can be found by evaluating $0.4 + 1.5$. Likewise, the distance from West End to Five Points can be found by evaluating $1.5 + 0.4$.

Atlanta Subway

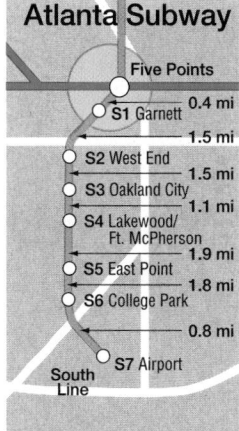

Five Points
S1 Garnett — 0.4 mi
— 1.5 mi
S2 West End
— 1.5 mi
S3 Oakland City
— 1.1 mi
S4 Lakewood/ Ft. McPherson
— 1.9 mi
S5 East Point
— 1.8 mi
S6 College Park
— 0.8 mi
S7 Airport
South Line

Commutative and Associative Properties In the situation above, the distance from Five Points to West End is the same as the distance from West End to Five Points.

The distance from Five Points to West End	equals	the distance from West End to Five Points.
$0.4 + 1.5$	$=$	$1.5 + 0.4$

 **Vocabulary Link**

Commute

Everyday Use to travel back and forth, as in commute to work

Commutative

Math Use property that allows you to change the order in which numbers are added or multiplied

This is an example of the **Commutative Property** for addition.

KEY CONCEPT — *Commutative Property*

Words	The order in which you add or multiply numbers does not change their sum or product.
Symbols	For any numbers a and b, $a + b = b + a$ and $a \cdot b = b \cdot a$.
Examples	$5 + 6 = 6 + 5$, $3 \cdot 2 = 2 \cdot 3$

Vocabulary Link

Associate

Everyday Use to come together as in associate with friends

Associative

Math Use property that allows you to group three or more numbers when adding or multiplying

An easy way to find the sum or product of numbers is to group, or associate, the numbers using the **Associative Property**.

KEY CONCEPT — *Associative Property*

Words	The way you group three or more numbers when adding or multiplying does not change their sum or product.
Symbols	For any numbers a, b, and c, $(a + b) + c = a + (b + c)$ and $(ab)c = a(bc)$.
Examples	$(2 + 4) + 6 = 2 + (4 + 6)$, $(3 \cdot 5) \cdot 4 = 3 \cdot (5 \cdot 4)$

Lesson 1-6 Commutative and Associative Properties **33**

① Focus

Standards Alignment

Before Lesson 1-6
Simplify numerical expressions and justify the process used from ▶ Standard 7AF1.3

Lesson 1-6
Judge the validity of results. Justify each step of a procedure. Prove or disprove statements from ▶ Standard 25.0

After Lesson 1-6
Are adept at operations on polynomials, including long division from ▶ Standard 2A3.0

② Teach

Scaffolding Questions Have students read *Get Ready for the Lesson.* **Ask:**

- Evaluate $0.4 + 1.5$. 1.9
- Evaluate $1.5 + 0.4$. 1.9
- Because $0.4 + 1.5$ and $1.5 + 0.4$ have the same sum, what can you say about the order in which you add two numbers? The order does not matter. The result is the same.
- Does the order in which numbers are subtracted matter? Explain.
  Sample answer: Yes; for example, $0.4 - 1.5 = -1.1$, but $1.5 - 0.4 = 1.1$.

Lesson 1-6 Resources

Chapter 1 Resource Masters

Lesson Reading Guide, p. 42 (BL) (OL) (ELL)
Study Guide and Intervention, pp. 43–44 (BL) (OL) (ELL)
Skills Practice, p. 45 (BL) (OL)
Practice, p. 46 (OL) (AL)
Word Problem Practice, p. 47 (OL) (AL)
Enrichment, p. 48 (OL) (AL)

Transparencies

5-Minute Check Transparency 1-6

Additional Print Resources

Noteables™ Interactive Study Notebook with Foldables™

Technology

ca.algebra1.com
Interactive Classroom CD-ROM
AssignmentWorks CD-ROM
Graphing Calculator Easy Files

Commutative and Associative Properties

Example 1 shows how to use the Commutative and Associative Properties for Addition to solve a real-world problem. **Example 2** shows how to use the Commutative and Associative Properties for Multiplication to evaluate a numeric expression.

 Formative Assessment

Use the Check Your Progress exercises after each example to determine students' understanding of concepts.

Focus on Mathematical Content

Commutative and Associative Properties The Commutative Property states that the order in which you add or multiply numbers does not change their sum or product. The Associative Property states that the way you group 3 or more numbers when you add or multiply them does not change their sum or product.

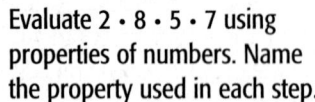

Real-World Link

New York City has the most extensive subway system, covering 842 miles of track and serving about 4.3 million passengers per day.

Source: *The Guinness Book of Records*

COncepts in MOtion

BrainPOP®
ca.algebra1.com

Concepts in Motion are online illustrations of key concepts through animations, Interactive Labs, and BrainPOPs®.

 **Real-World EXAMPLE** Use Addition Properties

1 **TRANSPORTATION** Refer to the beginning of the lesson. Find the distance between Five Points and Lakewood/Ft. McPherson.

Five Points to Garnett		Garnett to West End		West End to Oakland City		Oakland City to Lakewood/Ft. McPherson
0.4	+	1.5	+	1.5	+	1.1

$0.4 + 1.5 + 1.5 + 1.1 = 0.4 + 1.1 + 1.5 + 1.5$ Commutative (+)

$= (0.4 + 1.1) + (1.5 + 1.5)$ Associative (+)

$= 1.5 + 3.0$ or 4.5   Add mentally.

Lakewood/Ft. McPherson is 4.5 miles from Five Points.

✓CHECK Your Progress

Evaluate each expression using properties of numbers. Name the property used in each step. See Ch. 1 Answer Appendix.

1A. $35 + 17 + 5 + 3$ **1B.** $8\frac{3}{4} + 12 + 5\frac{1}{4}$

EXAMPLE Use Multiplication Properties

2 Evaluate $8 \cdot 2 \cdot 3 \cdot 5$ using properties of numbers. Name the property used in each step.

$8 \cdot 2 \cdot 3 \cdot 5 = 8 \cdot 3 \cdot 2 \cdot 5$ Commutative ($\times$)

$= (8 \cdot 3) \cdot (2 \cdot 5)$ Associative ($\times$)

$= 24 \cdot 10$ or 240   Multiply mentally.

✓CHECK Your Progress

Evaluate each expression using properties of numbers. Name the property used in each step. See Ch. 1 Answer Appendix.

2A. $2.9 \cdot 4 \cdot 10$ **2B.** $\frac{5}{3} \cdot 25 \cdot 3 \cdot 2$

Simplify Expressions The Commutative and Associative Properties can be used with other properties when evaluating and simplifying expressions.

CONCEPT SUMMARY   *Properties of Numbers*

The following properties are true for any numbers a, b, and c.

Properties	Addition	Multiplication
Commutative	$a + b = b + a$	$ab = ba$
Associative	$(a + b) + c = a + (b + c)$	$(ab)c = a(bc)$
Identity	0 is the identity. $a + 0 = 0 + a = a$	1 is the identity. $a \cdot 1 = 1 \cdot a = a$
Zero	—	$a \cdot 0 = 0 \cdot a = 0$
Distributive	$a(b + c) = ab + ac$ and $(b + c)\,a = ba + ca$	
Substitution	If $a = b$, then a may be substituted for b.	

 Math Online Extra Examples at ca.algebra1.com

EXAMPLE Write and Simplify an Expression

3 Use the expression *four times the sum of a and b increased by twice the sum of a and 2b.*

a. Write an algebraic expression for the verbal expression.

Words	four times the sum of *a* and *b* increased by twice the sum of *a* and 2*b*
Variables	Let *a* and *b* represent the numbers.
Expression	$4(a + b) + 2(a + 2b)$

b. Simplify the expression and indicate the properties used.

$4(a + b) + 2(a + 2b) = 4(a) + 4(b) + 2(a) + 2(2b)$	Distributive Property
$= 4a + 4b + 2a + 4b$	Multiply. Assoc. ($\times$)
$= 4a + 2a + 4b + 4b$	Commutative ($+$)
$= (4a + 2a) + (4b + 4b)$	Associative ($+$)
$= (4 + 2)a + (4 + 4)b$	Distributive Property
$= 6a + 8b$	Substitution

CHECK Your Progress

3A. Write an algebraic expression for *5 times the difference of q squared and r plus 8 times the sum of 3q and 2r.* Then simplify the expression and indicate the properties used.

3B. Simplify $6(x - 2y) + 4(-3x + y)$ and indicate the properties used.

3A–3B. See Ch. 1 Answer Appendix.

Personal Tutor at ca.algebra1.com

Concepts in Motion
BrainPOP®
ca.algebra1.com

★ indicates multi-step problem

CHECK Your Understanding

Examples 1, 2
(p. 34)

Evaluate each expression using properties of numbers. Name the property used in each step. **1–4. See Ch. 1 Answer Appendix.**

1. $14 + 18 + 26$

2. $3\frac{1}{2} + 4 + 2\frac{1}{2}$

3. $5 \cdot 3 \cdot 6 \cdot 4$

4. $\frac{5}{6} \cdot 16 \cdot \frac{3}{4}$

Example 3
(p. 35)

Simplify each expression.

5. $4x + 5y + 6x$ **$10x + 5y$**

6. $5a + 3b + 2a + 7b$ **$7a + 10b$**

7. $3(4x + 2) + 2x$ **$14x + 6$**

8. $7(ac + 2b) + 2ac$ **$9ac + 14b$**

9. GEOMETRY Find the perimeter of the triangle. **$xy + 10 + 2x$**

★ **10.** Write an algebraic expression for *half the sum of p and 2q increased by three-fourths q.* Then simplify, indicating the properties used. **See Ch. 1 Answer Appendix.**

Lesson 1-6 Commutative and Associative Properties **35**

Simplify Expressions

Example 3 shows how to write an algebraic expression and then use properties of numbers to simplify the expression. This develops the foundation of algebraic proof.

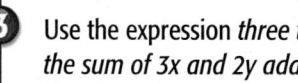
ADDITIONAL EXAMPLE

3 Use the expression *three times the sum of 3x and 2y added to five times the sum of x and 4y.*

a. Write an algebraic expression for the verbal expression.

$3(3x + 2y) + 5(x + 4y)$

b. Simplify the expression and indicate the properties used.

$3(3x + 2y) + 5(x + 4y)$
$= 3(3x) + 3(2y) +$
$\quad 5(x) + 5(4y)$
$\qquad$ Distributive Property
$= 9x + 6y + 5x + 20y$
$\qquad$ Multiply.
$= 9x + 5x + 6y + 20y$
$\qquad$ Commutative ($+$)
$= (9x + 5x) + (6y + 20y)$
$\qquad$ Associative ($+$)
$= (9 + 5)x + (6 + 20)y$
$\qquad$ Distributive Property
$= 14x + 26y$ $\quad$ Substitution

Additional Examples are also in:

• Noteables™ Interactive Study Notebook with Foldables™

• Interactive Classroom PowerPoint® Presentations

3 Practice

Formative Assessment

Use Exercises 1–10 to check for understanding.

Use the chart at the bottom of this page to customize assignments for your students.

Odd/Even Assignments

Exercises 11–34 are structured so that students practice the same concepts whether they are assigned odd or

DIFFERENTIATED HOMEWORK OPTIONS

Level	Assignment	Two-Day Option	
BL Basic	11–34, 45–61	11–33 odd, 48, 49	12–34 even, 45–47, 50–61
OL Core	11–39 odd, 41–43, 45–61	11–34, 48, 49	35–43, 45–47, 50–61
AL Advanced /Pre-AP	35–57 (optional: 58–61)		

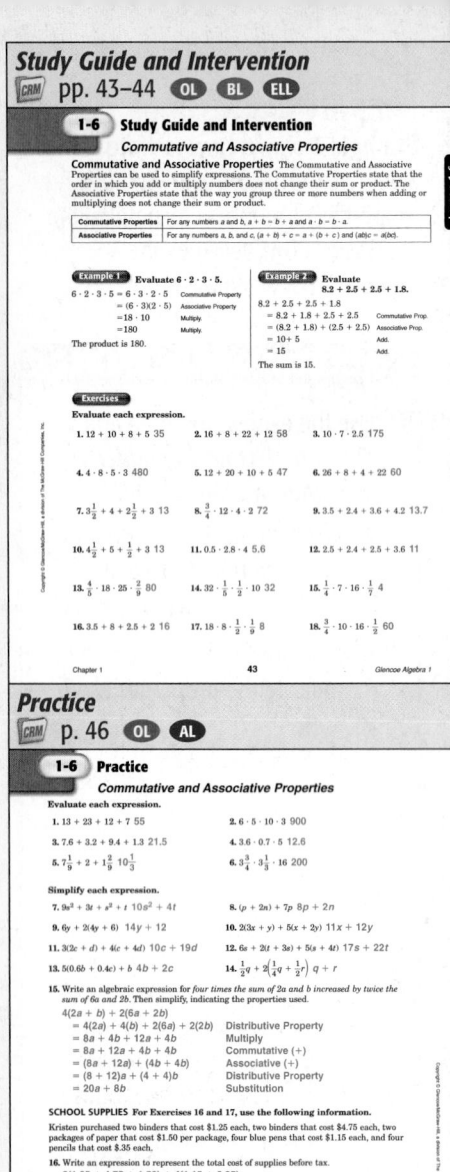
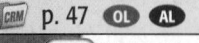
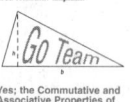
Exercises

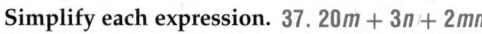

HOMEWORK HELP	
For Exercises	See Examples
11–16	1
17–22	2
23–34	3

Exercise Levels
A: 11–34
B: 35–43
C: 44–47

Evaluate each expression using properties of numbers. Name the property used in each step.

11. $17 + 6 + 13 + 24$ **60**

12. $8 + 14 + 22 + 9$ **53**

13. $4.25 + 3.50 + 8.25$ **16**

14. $6.2 + 4.2 + 4.3 + 5.8$ **20.5**

15. $6\frac{1}{2} + 3 + \frac{1}{2} + 2$ **12**

16. $2\frac{3}{8} + 4 + 3\frac{3}{8}$ **9$\frac{3}{4}$**

17. $5 \cdot 11 \cdot 4 \cdot 2$ **440**

18. $3 \cdot 10 \cdot 6 \cdot 3$ **540**

19. $0.5 \cdot 2.4 \cdot 4$ **4.8**

20. $8 \cdot 1.6 \cdot 2.5$ **32**

21. $3\frac{3}{7} \cdot 14 \cdot 1\frac{1}{4}$ **60**

22. $2\frac{5}{8} \cdot 24 \cdot 6\frac{2}{3}$ **420**

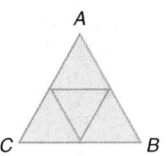

★ **23. GEOMETRY** Find the area of $\triangle ABC$ if each small triangle has a base of 5.2 inches and a height of 4.5 inches. **46.8 in²**

24. GEOMETRY A regular hexagon measures $(3x + 5)$ units on each side. What is the perimeter? **$(18x + 30)$ units**

Simplify each expression. **27. $6x^2 + 5x$**

25. $4a + 2b + a$ **5a + 2b**

26. $2y + 2x + 8y$ **2x + 10y**

27. $x^2 + 3x + 2x + 5x^2$

28. $4a^3 + 6a + 3a^3 + 8a$
7a³ + 14a

29. $6x + 2(2x + 7)$
10x + 14

30. $4(3n + 9) + 5n$
17n + 36

Write an algebraic expression for each verbal expression. Then simplify, indicating the properties used. 31–34. See Ch. 1 Answer Appendix.

★ **31.** twice the sum of s and t decreased by s

★ **32.** 5 times the product of x and y increased by $3xy$

★ **33.** the product of 6 and the square of z, increased by the sum of 7, z^2, and 6

★ **34.** 6 times the sum of x and y squared minus 3 times the sum of x and y squared

Simplify each expression. **37. $20m + 3n + 2mn$**

35. $\frac{1}{4}q + 2q + 2\frac{3}{4}q$ **5q**

36. $3.2(x + y) + 2.3(x + y) + 4x$ **9.5x + 5.5y**

37. $3(4m + n) + 2m(4 + n)$

38. $6(0.4f + 0.2g) + 0.5f$ **2.9f + 1.2g**

39. $\frac{3}{4} + \frac{2}{3}(s + 2t) + s$ **$\frac{3}{4} + \frac{5}{3}s + \frac{4}{3}t$**

40. $2p + \frac{3}{5}\left(\frac{1}{2}p + 2q\right) + \frac{2}{3}$ **$\frac{2}{3} + \frac{23}{10}p + \frac{6}{5}q$**

41. ANALYZE TABLES A traveler checks into a hotel on Friday and checks out the following Tuesday morning. Use the table to find the total cost including tax. **$291**

Hotel Rates Per Day		
Day	Room Charge	Sales Tax
Monday–Friday	$72	$5.40
Saturday–Sunday	$63	$5.10

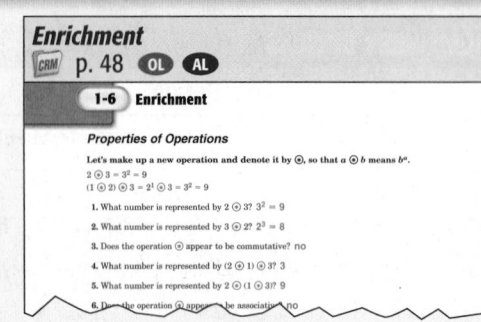

Real-World Link

In 1943, Jacques Cousteau and Emile Gagnan invented the *aqualung*, or SCUBA (Self-Contained Underwater Breathing Apparatus).

Source: howstuffworks.com

SCUBA DIVING For Exercises 42 and 43, use the following information.
A scuba diving store rents air tanks for $7.50, dive flags for $5.00, and wet suits for $10.95. The store also sells disposable underwater cameras for $18.99.

★ **42.** Write two expressions to represent the total sales after renting 2 wet suits, 3 air tanks, 2 dive flags, and selling 5 underwater cameras. **See Ch. 1 Answer Appendix.**

43. What are the total sales? **$149.35**

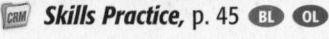
BL = Below Grade Level
OL = On Grade Level
AL = Above Grade Level
ELL = English Language Learner

Additional pages not shown:

CRM **Lesson Reading Guide**, p. 42 BL OL ELL

CRM **Skills Practice**, p. 45 BL OL

44. CHALLENGE Does the Commutative Property *sometimes*, *always*, or *never* hold for subtraction? Explain your reasoning.
Sometimes; sample answer: $4 - 3 \neq 3 - 4$, but $4 - (3 + 1) = (3 + 1) - 4$

45. Which One Doesn't Belong? Identify the sentence that does not belong with the other three. Explain your reasoning. See margin.

| $x + 12 = 12 + x$ | $7h = h \cdot 7$ | $1 + a = a + 1$ | $n \div 2 = 2 \div n$ |

46. OPEN ENDED Write examples of the Commutative Property of Addition and the Associative Property of Multiplication using the numbers 1, 5, and 8 in each. Justify your examples.
Sample answer: $1 + 5 + 8 = 8 + 1 + 5$ $(1 \cdot 5)8 = 1(5 \cdot 8)$

47. *Writing in Math* Use the information about subways on page 33 to explain how the Commutative and Associative Properties are useful in performing calculations. Include an expression using the properties that could help you find the distance from the airport to Five Points Station. See margin.

 **STANDARDS PRACTICE** 4.0, 7NS1.3

48. Which expression is equivalent to $4 + 6(ac + 2b) + 2ac$? **A**

A $4 + 8ac + 12b$

B $4 + 10ab + 2ac$

C $4 + 12abc + 2ac$

D $12ac + 20b$

49. REVIEW Daniel is buying a jacket that is regularly $59.99 and is on sale for $\frac{1}{3}$ off. Which expression can he use to estimate the discount on the jacket? **J**

F 0.0003×60

G 0.003×60

H 0.03×60

J 0.33×60

 Spiral Review

Simplify each expression. If not possible, write *simplified*. (Lesson 1-5)

50. $5x - 8 + 7x$ $12x - 8$ **51.** $7m + 6n + 8$ simplified   **52.** $t^2 + 2t + 4t$ $t^2 + 6t$

53. $3(5 + 2p)$ $15 + 6p$ **54.** $(a + 2b)3 - 3a$ $6b$ **55.** $(d + 5)8 + 2f$ $8d + 40 + 2f$

56. Evaluate $3(5 - 5 \cdot 1^2) + 21 \div 7$. Name the property used in each step. (Lesson 1-4) See Ch. 1 Answer Appendix.

57. LAUNDRY Jonathan is meeting friends for dinner in 3 hours and he wants to do laundry beforehand. If it takes 50 minutes to do each load of laundry, write and use an inequality to find the maximum number of loads that he can finish. (Lesson 1-3) Sample answer: $50x \leq 180$; 3 loads

GET READY for the Next Lesson

PREREQUISITE SKILL Evaluate each expression. (Lesson 1-2)

58. If $x = 4$, then $2x + 7 = \underline{?}$. 15   **59.** If $x = 8$, then $6x + 12 = \underline{?}$. 60

60. If $n = 6$, then $5n - 14 = \underline{?}$. 16   **61.** If $n = 7$, then $3n - 8 = \underline{?}$. 13

Pre-AP Activity   Use to Summarize the Lesson

Have students develop a lesson demonstration that uses manipulatives to show the Associative Property, the Commutative Property, or both. They can use coins, counters, or other types of manipulatives. The lesson demonstration should give step-by-step instructions on how to use the manipulatives and explain how each step demonstrates the property.

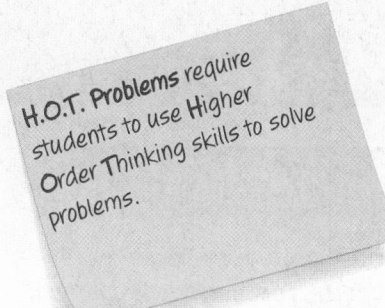
H.O.T. Problems require students to use Higher Order Thinking skills to solve problems.

4 **Assess**

Ticket Out the Door Give each student a slip of paper with either the Associative Property or the Commutative Property written on it. As the students leave the room, ask them to give either a numeric or algebraic example of the property.

FOLDABLES **Foldables™**
Study Organizer **Follow-Up**
Remind students to use the sixth flap in their Foldables to record notes on what they have learned about the Commutative and Associative Properties. Students should include examples.

Tips for New Teachers   **Study Tip**

Remind students to look for pairs of numbers that will make calculations easier when using the Commutative and Associative Properties.

Additional Answers

45. $n \div 2 = 2 \div n$; This equation is true for $n = 2$ or $n = -2$ only because division is not commutative. The other three sentences illustrate the Commutative Property of Addition or Multiplication and are therefore true for all values of the variables.

47. You can use the Commutative and Associative Properties to rearrange and group numbers for easier calculations. Answers should include: $d = (0.4 + 1.1) + (1.5 + 1.5) + (1.9 + 1.8 + 0.8)$.

READING MATH

READING MATH

Standard 25.2 Students judge the validity of an argument according to whether the properties of the real number system and the order of operations have been applied correctly at each step.

1 Focus

Write the words *Distributive Property, Commutative Property of Addition,* and *Associative Property of Addition* on the board. Ask the students to give an example of each property.

Ask:

How can these properties be used in a mathematical argument?

Sample answer: These properties are used to justify mathematical statements.

What are the characteristics of a valid argument?

Sample answer: If each statement is presented in a logical sequence and there is a justification provided fore each, then the argument is valid.

2 Teach

Have students work through the example. Point out that the error may be in one of the steps or the justification.

Have students complete Exercises 1-2.

 English Language Learners may benefit from working in small groups. Have the students take turns reading the steps in their native language and in English. The skills used in this activity are needed for algebraic proof which is formally introduced in Chapter 8.

3 Assess

Ask students to summarize how to judge the validity of an argument.

Arguments with Properties of Real Numbers

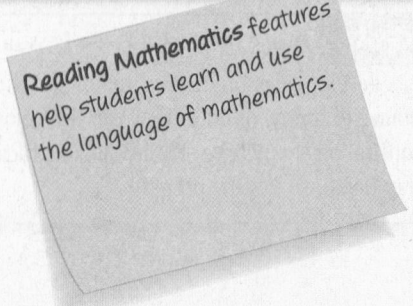

A lawyer who is presenting a case in court pays careful attention to make statements that are accurate, that follow a logical order, and that are justified.

In writing an argument that uses many steps, it is important to evaluate each step to check for errors. It is also important to provide the correct justification for each statement.

Example

Manuel has simplified the expression $3y + 5(x + y) - 3(y - x) + 2x$ and listed the properties used in each step. Evaluate each step. Determine whether the solution is accurate. If not, indicate the correct steps.

Step 1	$3y + 5(x + y) - 3(y - x) + 2x$	Original expression
Step 2	$3y + 5x + 5y - 3y + 3x + 2x$	Distributive Property
Step 3	$3y + 5y - 3y + 5x + 3x + 2x$	Commutative Property of Addition
Step 4	$(3y + 5y - 3y) + (5x + 3x + 2x)$	Commutative Property of Addition
Step 5	$(3 + 5 - 3)y + (5 + 3 + 2)x$	Distributive Property
Step 6	$5y + 10x$	Substitution

Manuel's solution is accurate until Step 4. The property used in this step is the Associative Property of Addition, not the Commutative Property of Addition. There are no other errors.

READING TO LEARN 1. The Distributive Property was not applied correctly in Step 6. Step 6 should be $(3 + 4 - 3)x + 6 - 32$. Then Step 7 is $4x - 26$.

Evaluate each step. Determine whether the solution is accurate. If not, indicate the correct steps.

1.
Step 1	$3(2 + x) + 4(x - 8) - 3x$	Original expression
Step 2	$3(2) + 3(x) + 4(x) + 4(-8) - 3x$	Distributive Property
Step 3	$6 + 3x + 4x - 32 - 3x$	Multiply.
Step 4	$3x + 4x - 3x + 6 - 32$	Commutative Property of Addition
Step 5	$(3x + 4x - 3x) + 6 - 32$	Associative Property of Addition
Step 6	$(1 + 4 - 3)x + 6 - 32$	Distributive Property
Step 7	$2x - 26$	Substitution

2.
Step 1	$4(3b - 2a) + 3(a + b) + b + 2(a - b)$	Original expression
Step 2	$12b - 2a + 3a + 3b + b + 2a - 2b$	Distributive Property
Step 3	$12b + 3b + b - 2b - 2a + 3a + 2a$	Commutative Property of Addition
Step 4	$(12b + 3b + b - 2b) + (-2a + 3a + 2a)$	Associative Property of Addition
Step 5	$(12 + 3 + 1 - 2)b + (-2 + 3 + 2)a$	Distributive Property
Step 6	$14b + 3a$	Substitution

The error is in Step 2. After using the Distributive Property, the second term should be $-8a$.

Reading Mathematics features help students learn and use the language of mathematics.

Logical Reasoning and Counterexamples

Main Ideas

- Identify the hypothesis and conclusion in a conditional statement.
- Use a counterexample to show that an assertion is false.

 Standard 24.0 Students use and know simple aspects of a logical argument.

Standard 24.2 Students identify the hypothesis and conclusion in logical deduction.

Standard 24.3 Students use counterexamples to show that an assertion is false and recognize that a single counterexample is sufficient to refute an assertion.

Standard 25.1 Students use properties to construct simple, valid arguments (direct and indirect) for, or formulate counterexamples to claimed assertions.

New Vocabulary

conditional statement
if-then statement
hypothesis
conclusion
deductive reasoning
counterexample

Reading Math

If-Then Statements
Note that "if" is not part of the hypothesis and "then" is not part of the conclusion.

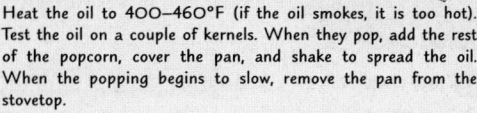 **GET READY for the Lesson**

The directions at the right can help you make perfect popcorn.

If the popcorn burns, then the heat was too high or the kernels heated unevenly.

> **Stovetop Popping**
> To pop popcorn on a stovetop, you need:
> - A 3- to 4-quart pan with a loose lid that allows steam to escape
> - Enough popcorn to cover the bottom of the pan, one kernel deep
> - 1/4 cup of oil for every cup of kernels
>
> Heat the oil to 400–460°F (if the oil smokes, it is too hot). Test the oil on a couple of kernels. When they pop, add the rest of the popcorn, cover the pan, and shake to spread the oil. When the popping begins to slow, remove the pan from the stovetop.
>
> **Source:** Popcorn Board

Conditional Statements The statement *If the popcorn burns, then the heat was too high or the kernels heated unevenly* is called a conditional statement. **Conditional statements** can be written in the form *If A, then B*. Statements in this form are called **if-then statements**.

If   *A,*   then   *B.*
If   the popcorn burns,   then   the heat was too high or the
                                          kernels heated unevenly.

The part of the statement immediately following *if* is called the **hypothesis**.

The part of the statement immediately following *then* is called the **conclusion**.

EXAMPLE Identify Hypothesis and Conclusion

1 Identify the hypothesis and conclusion of each statement.

a. ENTERTAINMENT If it is Friday, then Ofelia and Miguel are going to the movies.

The hypothesis follows the word *if* and the conclusion follows the word *then*.

Hypothesis: it is Friday

Conclusion: Ofelia and Miguel are going to the movies

b. If $4x + 3 > 27$, then $x > 6$.

Hypothesis: $4x + 3 > 27$ Conclusion: $x > 6$

✓ CHECK Your Progress 1A. See Ch. 1 Answer Appendix.

1A. If it is warm this afternoon, then we will have the party outside.

1B. If $8w - 5 = 11$, then $w = 2$. H: $8w - 5 = 11$; C: $w = 2$

Lesson 1-7 Logical Reasoning and Counterexamples **39**

---

1 Focus

Standards Alignment

Before Lesson 1-7
Formulate and justify mathematical conjectures from Standard 7MR1.2

Lesson 1-7
Use and know simple aspects of a logical argument from Standards 24.0 and 24.2

After Lesson 1-7
Apply the method of mathematical induction to prove general statements from Standard 2A21.0

2 Teach

Scaffolding Questions Have students read *Get Ready for the Lesson.*
Ask:
- What is the purpose of the following sentence? *If the popcorn burns, then the heat was too high or the kernels heated unevenly.* It gives two reasons why the popcorn might burn.
- Does this mean the popcorn will burn? Explain. No; the sentence begins with *if.*
- Suppose the heat is too high. What does the sentence tell you about this situation? The popcorn will likely burn.

Lesson 1-7 Resources

Conditional Statements

Conditional Statements

Example 1 shows how to identify the hypothesis and conclusion of conditional statements. **Example 2** shows how to write a statement in if-then form after identifying the hypothesis and conclusion of the statement.

 Formative Assessment

Use the Check Your Progress exercises after each example to determine students' understanding of concepts.

ADDITIONAL EXAMPLES

1 Identify the hypothesis and conclusion of each statement.

a. **SPORTS** If it is raining, then Jon and Chloe will not play softball.
Hypothesis: It is raining.
Conclusion: Jon and Chloe will not play softball.

b. If $7y + 5 \leq 26$, then $y \leq 3$.
Hypothesis: $7y + 5 \leq 26$
Conclusion: $y \leq 3$

2 Identify the hypothesis and conclusion of each statement. Then write each statement in if-then form.

a. I eat light meals.
Hypothesis: I eat a meal.
Conclusion: It is light.
If I eat a meal, then it is light.

b. For a number a such that $8 + 5a = 43$, $a = 7$.
Hypothesis: $8 + 5a = 43$
Conclusion: $a = 7$
If $8 + 5a = 43$, then $a = 7$.

Additional Examples are also in:
- Noteables™ Interactive Study Notebook with Foldables™
- Interactive Classroom PowerPoint® Presentations

Real-World Link
In 2005, more than 74 million people attended a Major League baseball game.
Source: ballparksofbaseball.com

Study Tip

Common Misconception

Suppose the conclusion of a conditional is true. This does not mean that the hypothesis is true. Consider the conditional "If it rains, Annie will stay home." If Annie stays home, it does not necessarily mean that it is raining.

Sometimes a conditional statement is written without using the words *if* and *then*. But a conditional statement can always be rewritten in if-then form.

EXAMPLE Write a Conditional in If-Then Form

 2 Identify the hypothesis and conclusion of each statement. Then write each statement in if-then form.

a. I will go to the ball game with you on Saturday.
Hypothesis: it is Saturday
Conclusion: I will go to the ball game with you
If it is Saturday, then I will go to the ball game with you.

b. For a number x such that $6x - 8 = 16$, $x = 4$.
Hypothesis: $6x - 8 = 16$
Conclusion: $x = 4$
If $6x - 8 = 16$, then $x = 4$.

✓ **CHECK Your Progress** 2A–2B. See margin.

2A. Brianna wears goggles when she is swimming.
2B. A rhombus with side lengths of $(x - y)$ units has a perimeter of $(4x - 4y)$ units.

Deductive Reasoning and Counterexamples **Deductive reasoning** is the process of using facts, rules, definitions, or properties to reach a valid conclusion. Suppose you have a true conditional and you know that the hypothesis is true for a given case. Deductive reasoning allows you to say that the conclusion is true for that case.

EXAMPLE Deductive Reasoning

3 Determine a valid conclusion that follows from the statement below for each condition. If a valid conclusion does not follow, write *no valid conclusion* and explain why.

"If two numbers are odd, then their sum is even."

a. The two numbers are 7 and 3.
7 and 3 are odd, so the hypothesis is true.
Conclusion: The sum of 7 and 3 is even.
CHECK $7 + 3 = 10$ ✓ The sum, 10, is even.

b. The sum of two numbers is 14.
The conclusion is true. If the numbers are 11 and 3, the hypothesis is true also. However, if the numbers are 8 and 6, the hypothesis is false. Therefore, there is no valid conclusion that can be drawn from the given conditional.

✓ **CHECK Your Progress**

Determine a valid conclusion that follows from the statement "There will be a quiz every Wednesday." 3A. There will be a quiz.

3A. It is Wednesday.   **3B.** It is Tuesday. See Ch. 1 Answer Appendix.

 Math Online Extra Examples at ca.algebra1.com

Tips for New Teachers **Classroom Management**

Logic is a branch of mathematics that is not familiar to most students. Have students work together discussing examples in this lesson. You may also want them to complete some exercises cooperatively.

Additional Answers

2A. H: Brianna is swimming; C: she wears goggles; If Brianna is swimming, then she is wearing goggles.

2B. H: A rhombus has side lengths of $(x - y)$ units; C: the perimeter is $(4x - 4y)$ units; If a rhombus has side lengths of $(x - y)$ units, then the perimeter is $(4x - 4y)$ units.

To show that a conditional is false, we can use a counterexample. A **counterexample** is a specific case in which the hypothesis is true and the conclusion is false. For example, consider the conditional *if a triangle has a perimeter of 3 centimeters, then each side measures 1 centimeter*. A counterexample is a triangle with perimeter 3 and sides 0.9, 0.9, and 1.2 centimeters long. It takes only one counterexample to show that a statement is false.

 STANDARDS EXAMPLE Find a Counterexample

4 Rachel believes that if $x \div y = 1$, then x and y are whole numbers. José states that this theory is not always true. Which pair of values for x and y could José use to disprove Rachel's theory?

A $x = 2, y = 2$ **C** $x = 0.25, y = 0.25$

B $x = 1.2, y = 0.6$ **D** $x = 6, y = 3$

Read the Item

The question is asking for a counterexample. Find the values of x and y that make the statement false.

Solve the Item

Replace x and y in the equation $x \div y = 1$ with the given values.

A $x = 2, y = 2$
$$2 \div 2 \stackrel{?}{=} 1$$
$$1 = 1 \checkmark$$

The hypothesis is true, and both values are whole numbers. The statement is true.

C $x = 0.25, y = 0.25$
$$0.25 \div 0.25 \stackrel{?}{=} 1$$
$$1 = 1 \checkmark$$

The hypothesis is true, but 0.25 is not a whole number. Thus, the statement is false.

B $x = 1.2, y = 0.6$
$$1.2 \div 0.6 \stackrel{?}{=} 1$$
$$2 \neq 1$$

The hypothesis is false, and the conclusion is false. This is not a counterexample.

D $x = 6, y = 3$
$$6 \div 3 \stackrel{?}{=} 1$$
$$2 \neq 1$$

The hypothesis is false. Therefore, this is not a counterexample even though the conclusions are true.

The only values that prove the statement false are $x = 0.25$ and $y = 0.25$. So these numbers are counterexamples. The answer is C.

Test-Taking Tip

Checking Results
Since choice C is the correct answer, you can check your results by testing the other values.

✓CHECK **Your Progress**

4. Which numbers disprove the statement below? **F**
$$\text{If } x + y > xy, \text{ then } x > y.$$
F $x = 1, y = 2$ **G** $x = 2, y = 3$ **H** $x = 4, y = 1$ **J** $x = 4, y = 2$

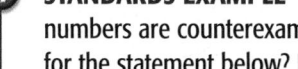 **Personal Tutor at** ca.algebra1.com

Every chapter includes a worked-out **California Standards Example** that is similar to problems found on state assessments. The appropriate California Standard is noted with each example.

Deductive Reasoning and Counterexamples

Example 3 shows how to use deductive reasons to determine whether a conclusion is valid. **Example 4** shows how to answer a multiple-choice question using a counterexample.

ADDITIONAL EXAMPLES

3 Determine a valid conclusion that follows from the statement below for each condition. If a valid conclusion does not follow, write *no valid conclusion* and explain why.

> *If one number is odd and another number is even, then their sum is odd.*

a. The two numbers are 5 and 12. 5 is odd and 12 is even, and $5 + 12 = 17$. Conclusion: The sum of 5 and 12 is odd.

b. The two numbers are 8 and 26. 8 and 26 are even so the hypothesis is false. No valid conclusion.

4 **STANDARDS EXAMPLE** Which numbers are counterexamples for the statement below? B
$$x - y \neq y - x$$
A $x = 2, y = 3$ **C** $x = 0, y = 1$
B $x = 4, y = 4$ **D** $x = 7, y = -7$

Focus on Mathematical Content

Deductive Reasoning and Counterexamples You can use deductive reasoning to determine whether a valid conclusion follows from a conditional statement. You can show that a conditional statement is false by using a counterexample. Deductive reasoning uses facts, rules, definitions, or properties to show whether a conditional statement is valid. A counterexample is a specific case that shows a conditional statement is false. You need only one counterexample to show that a statement is false.

3 Practice

✓ Formative Assessment

Use Exercises 1–14 to check for understanding.

Use the chart at the bottom of this page to customize assignments for your students.

Odd/Even Assignments

Exercises 15–38 are structured so that students practice the same concepts whether they are assigned odd or even problems.

 **Common Error**

Caution students to read Exercise 13 carefully. Some students may fail to notice that one inequality symbol represents *greater than or equal to* and the other represents *greater than.* Such an oversight may result in the inability to find a counterexample.

⚠ Exercise Alert!

Internet Exercise 39 requires the use of the Internet or other reference materials.

Additional Answers

4. H: Colin does not have homework; C: he watches television; If Colin does not have homework, then he watches television.

5. H: a number divisible by 10; C: it is divisible by 5; If a number is divisible by 10, then it is divisible by 5.

6. H: a quadrilateral with four right angles; C: rectangle; If a quadrilateral has four right angles, then it is a rectangle.

19. H: it is Monday; C: the trash is picked up; If it is Monday, then the trash is picked up.

20. H: it is after school; C: Vito will call; If it is after school, then Vito will call.

★ indicates multi-step problem

✓ CHECK Your Understanding

Example 1
(p. 39)

Identify the hypothesis and conclusion of each statement.

1. If it is April, then it might rain. H: it is April; C: it might rain

2. If you play tennis, then you run fast. H: you play tennis; C: you run fast

3. If $34 - 3x = 16$, then $x = 6$. H: $34 - 3x = 16$; C: $x = 6$

Example 2
(p. 40)

Identify the hypothesis and conclusion of each statement. Then write each statement in if-then form. **4–6. See margin.**

★ **4.** Colin watches television when he does not have homework.

★ **5.** A number that is divisible by 10 is also divisible by 5.

★ **6.** A rectangle is a quadrilateral with four right angles.

Example 3
(p. 40)

Determine a valid conclusion that follows from the statement below for each given condition. If a valid conclusion does not follow, write *no valid conclusion* and explain why.

If the last digit of a number is 2, then the number is divisible by 2.

7. The number is 10,452. The number is divisible by 2.

8. The number is divisible by 2. No valid conclusion; the last digit could be any even number.

9. The number is 946. No valid conclusion; the last digit is 6.

Example 4
(p. 41)

Find a counterexample for each conditional statement.

10. If Anna is in school, then she has a science class. Anna has a schedule without science class

11. If you can read 8 pages in 30 minutes, then you can read a book in a day. **11. A book can have more than 384 pages.**

12. If a number x is squared, then $x^2 > x$. $x = 1$

13. If $3x + 7 \geq 52$, then $x > 15$. $x = 15$

24.3 ★ **14.** **STANDARDS PRACTICE** Which number disproves the statement $x < 2x$? A

    A 0   **B** 1   **C** 2   **D** 4

15. H: both parents have red hair; C: their children have red hair

16. H: you are in Hawaii; C: you are in the tropics

Exercises

HOMEWORK HELP

For Exercises	See Examples
15–18	1
19–24	2
25–28	3
29–38	4

Exercise Levels
A: 15–38
B: 39–42
C: 43–46

Identify the hypothesis and conclusion of each statement.

15. If both parents have red hair, then their children have red hair.

16. If you are in Hawaii, then you are in the tropics.

17. If $2n - 7 > 25$, then $n > 16$. H: $2n - 7 > 25$; C: $n > 16$

18. If $a = b$ and $b = c$, then $a = c$. H: $a = b$ and $b = c$; C: $a = c$

19–20. See margin.
Identify the hypothesis and conclusion of each statement. Then write each statement in if-then form. **21–24. See Ch. 1 Answer Appendix.**

★ **19.** The trash is picked up on Monday. ★ **20.** Vito will call after school.

★ **21.** For $x = 8$, $x^2 - 3x = 40$. ★ **22.** $4s + 6 > 42$ when $s > 9$.

★ **23.** A triangle with all sides congruent is an equilateral triangle.

★ **24.** The sum of the digits of a number is a multiple of 9 when the number is divisible by 9.

42 Chapter 1 The Language and Tools of Algebra

DIFFERENTIATED HOMEWORK OPTIONS

Level	Assignment	Two-Day Option	
BL Basic	15–38, 44–63	15–37 odd, 47–49	16–38 even, 44–46, 50–63
OL Core	15–37 odd, 39–42, 44–63	15–38, 47–49	39–42, 44–46, 50–63
AL Advanced /Pre-AP	39–59 (optional: 60–63)		

Determine whether a valid conclusion follows from the statement below for each given condition. If a valid conclusion does not follow, write *no valid conclusion* and explain why. **25–28. See Ch. 1 Answer Appendix.**

If a DVD box set costs less than $70, then Ian will buy one.

25. A DVD box set costs $59. **26.** A DVD box set costs $89.

27. Ian will not buy a DVD box set. **28.** Ian bought 2 DVD box sets.
29–30. See Ch. 1 Answer Appendix.

Find a counterexample for each conditional statement. **31.** $2 \cdot 3 = 6$

29. If you were born in North Carolina, then you live in North Carolina.

30. If you are a professional basketball player, then you play in the United States.

31. If the product of two numbers is even, then both numbers must be even.

32. If two times a number is greater than 16, then the number must be greater than 7. $2(8) = 16$

33. If $4n - 8 \geq 52$, then $n > 15$. $4(15) - 8 = 52$

34. If $x \cdot y = 1$, then x or y must equal 1. $2 \cdot \frac{1}{2} = 1$

GEOMETRY For Exercises 35 and 36, use the following information. If points P, Q, and R lie on the same line, then Q is between P and R.

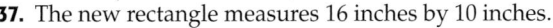

35–36. See Ch. 1 Answer Appendix.
35. Copy the diagram. Label the points so that the conditional is true.
36. Copy the diagram. Provide a counterexample for the conditional.
37. See Ch. 1 Answer Appendix.
Determine whether a valid conclusion follows from the statement below for each given condition. If a valid conclusion does not follow, write *no valid conclusion* and explain why.

If the dimensions of rectangle ABCD are doubled, then the perimeter is doubled.

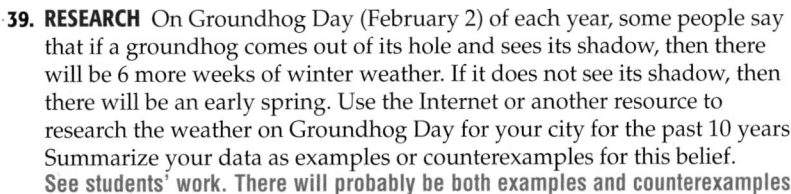

37. The new rectangle measures 16 inches by 10 inches.

38. The perimeter of the new rectangle is 52 inches.
No valid conclusion; the new rectangle could be 20 inches by 6 inches.

39. RESEARCH On Groundhog Day (February 2) of each year, some people say that if a groundhog comes out of its hole and sees its shadow, then there will be 6 more weeks of winter weather. If it does not see its shadow, then there will be an early spring. Use the Internet or another resource to research the weather on Groundhog Day for your city for the past 10 years. Summarize your data as examples or counterexamples for this belief.
See students' work. There will probably be both examples and counterexamples.

NUMBER THEORY For Exercises 40–42, use the following information. Copy the Venn diagram and place the numbers 1 to 25 in the appropriate places on the diagram.

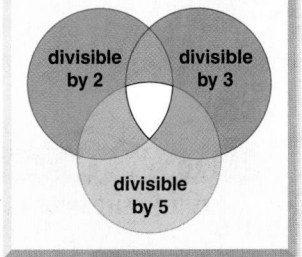

40. What conclusions can you make about the numbers and where they appear on the diagram? **40–41. See Ch. 1 Answer Appendix.**

41. What conclusions can you form about numbers that are divisible by both 2 and 3?

42. Provide a counterexample for the data you have collected if possible.
no counterexamples

Lesson 1-7 Logical Reasoning and Counterexamples **43**

Real-World Connections For Exercise 44, have students write conditional statements that apply to their daily lives and describe how they can use the statements to solve problems.

 Assess

Name the Math Have students work with partners. Ask them to explain to their partners when they would use deductive reasoning or a counterexample to show that a conditional statement is true or false.

Check for student understanding of concepts in Lessons 1-6 and 1-7.

 Quiz 3, p. 74

 **Foldables™ Follow-Up**
Remind students to use the seventh flap in their Foldables to record notes on what they have learned about the logical reasoning and counterexamples. Students should include examples.

 **Student Misconceptions**
Some students may question the value of learning the concepts in this lesson. Remind students that reasoning questions appear on tests and that the ability to reason from facts, rules, definitions, and properties provides a foundation for drawing valid conclusions in their daily lives.

Additional Answers

45. Sample answer: You can use deductive reasoning to determine whether a hypothesis and its conclusion are both true and whether one or both are false.

46. Sample answer: You can use if-then statements to help determine when food is finished cooking. Hypothesis: You have small, underpopped kernels; conclusion: you have not used enough oil in your pan.

44 Chapter 1 The Language and Tools of Algebra

H.O.T. Problems

43. No; sample answer: Let $a = 1$ and $b = 2$; then $1 * 2 = 1 + 2(2)$ or 5 and $2 * 1 = 2 + 2(1)$ or 4.

44. Sample answer: If you go swimming, then you get wet; H: you go swimming; C: you get wet.

43. CHALLENGE Determine whether the following statement is always true. If it is not, provide a counterexample.

> If the mathematical operation * is defined for all numbers a and b as $a * b = a + 2b$, then the operation * is commutative.

44. OPEN ENDED Write a conditional statement and label the hypothesis and conclusion. Describe how conditional statements are used to solve problems.

45. REASONING Explain how deductive reasoning is used to show that a conditional is true or false. **See margin.**

46. *Writing in Math* Use the information about popcorn found on page 39 to explain how logical reasoning is helpful in cooking. Include in your answer the hypothesis and conclusion of the statement *If you have small, underpopped kernels, then you have not used enough oil in your pan.* **See margin.**

STANDARDS PRACTICE 24.3, MR1.2, 5.0

47. Which number serves as a counterexample to the statement below? **A**

$$2x < 3x$$

A -2 **B** $\frac{1}{4}$ **C** $\frac{1}{2}$ **D** 2

48. REVIEW If $4a = a$, which of the following is true? **J**

F $a > 4$ **H** $a = 1$

G $a = 4$ **J** $a = 0$

49. What value of n makes the following statement true? **A**

> If $14n - 12 \geq 100$, then $n \geq$ _____.

A 8

B 10

C 12

D 24

Spiral Review

Simplify each expression. (Lesson 1-6)

50. $2x + 5y + 9x$ $11x + 5y$

51. $4(5mn + 6) + 3mn$ $23mn + 24$

52. $2(3a + b) + 3b + 4$ $6a + 5b + 4$

53. ENVIRONMENT A typical family of four uses the water shown in the table. Write two expressions that represent the amount of water a typical family of four uses for these activities in d days. (Lesson 1-5)
$100d + 80d + 8d$; $(100 + 80 + 8)d$

Average Water Usage Per Day	
Activity	**Gallons Used**
flushing toilet	100
showering/bathing	80
using bathroom sink	8

Source: U.S. Environmental Protection Agency

Find the value of n in each expression. Then name the property used. (Lesson 1-4)

54. $1(n) = 64$ 64; Multiplicative identity

55. $12 + 7 = 12 + n$ 7; Reflexive

56. $-6 + n = 0$ 6; Additive Inverse

57. $4n = 1$ $\frac{1}{4}$; Multiplicative Inverse

58. $n + 18 = 18$ 0; Additive Identity

59. $36n = 0$ 0; Multiplicative Property of Zero

GET READY for the Next Lesson

PREREQUISITE SKILL Evaluate each expression. (Lesson 1-2)

60. 6^2 36

61. $(-8)^2$ 64

62. 1.6^2 2.56

63. $(-11.5)^2$ 132.25

Pre-AP Activity   Use as an Extension

A *paradox* is a statement that seems contrary to common sense; that is, it contradicts itself. The statement below is a paradox.

> *I am not telling the truth.*

Have students write paradoxical statements and share their statements with the class.

Algebra Lab
Logic and Properties of Numbers

Standard 1.1 Students use properties of numbers to demonstrate whether assertions are true or false.
Standard 25.3 Given a specific algebraic statement involving linear, quadratic, or absolute value expressions or equations or inequalities, **students determine whether the statement is true sometimes, always, or never.**

You can apply what you have learned about the properties of numbers to determine whether a mathematical statement is *always*, *sometimes*, or *never* true.

ACTIVITY 1

Determine whether $2y \leq 6$ is *always*, *sometimes*, or *never* true.

First determine the greatest value of y that satisfies the inequality.
$2(3) \leq 6$ Substitute 3 for y.
$6 \leq 6$ Simplify.

Next, substitute a value less than 3 for y and a value greater than 3.
$2(2) \leq 6$ Substitute 2 for y. $2(4) \leq 6$ Substitute 4 for y.
$4 \leq 6$ Simplify. $8 \nleq 6$ Simplify.

Substituting 2 for y yields a true inequality. The inequality is true when $y \leq 3$. When $y > 3$, the inequality is not true. Therefore the inequality is sometimes true.

ACTIVITY 2

Determine whether the following statement is *true* or *false*.
Use the properties of numbers to justify your answer.
The equation $y = 2(x + 4) - 3$ is negative when $x < 0$.

Substitute a negative value for x in the equation.
$y = 2(x + 4) - 3$ Original equation
$y = 2(-1 + 4) - 3$ Substitute -1 for x.
$y = -2 + 8 - 3$ Distributive Property
$y = 3$ Add.

Since substituting -1 for x into the equation yields a positive value for y, the statement is false.

EXERCISES

Determine whether each statement or inequality is *always*, *sometimes*, or *never* true.

1. $3t > -6$
sometimes; when $t > -2$

2. $-2v < 4$
sometimes; when $v > -2$

3. $3w + 4 > 0$
sometimes; when $w > -\frac{4}{3}$

Determine whether each statement is *true* or *false*. Use the properties of numbers to justify your answer.

4. In the equation $y = 3(x + 2)$, y is positive when $x > 0$.

4. True; $y = 3(1 + 2)$ by substitution. $y = 3 + 6$ by the Distributive Property. So, $y = 9$, which is positive.

5. In the linear equation $y = -2x$, y is always positive.
False; substitute 1 for x to get $y = -2(1)$. By the Multiplicative Identity, $y = -2$.

1 Focus

Hand Graphic Materials for Each Group
• Pencil and paper

Teaching Tip
Caution students to read the questions carefully in order to avoid overlooking the difference between the symbols for *greater than or equal to* and *greater than*.

2 Teach

Working in Cooperative Groups
Put students in pairs, mixing abilities. Have groups complete Exercises 1-5.

Ask:
• Why is it important to determine the greatest value of y that satisfies the inequality? The statement may be false for that value or y even if the statement is true everywhere else.

Practice Have students complete Exercises 1-5.

3 Assess

✓ Formative Assessment

Use Exercise 3 to assess whether students can determine whether a specific algebraic statement is true sometimes, always, or never. Use Exercise 4 to assess whether students can use the properties of numbers to determine the truth or falsity of an algebraic statement.

From Concrete to Abstract
Ask students to think of real world situations that are true sometimes, always, and never.

Extending the Concept

Ask:
• Ask students how determining when a statement is true or false helps in graphing the inequality. The graph is shaded where values produce a true statement.
• Ask students to write conditional statements using their answers to exercises 1-5.

1 Focus

Standards Alignment

Before Lesson 1-8
Differentiate between rational and irrational numbers from ⚷ Standard 7NS1.4

Lesson 1-8
Understand and use the rules of exponents from ⚷ Standard 1.0 and 2.0

After Lesson 1-8
Use properties to justify steps in combining and simplifying functions from ⚷ Standard 2A25.0

2 Teach

Scaffolding Questions Have students read *Get Ready for the Lesson*.
Ask:

• What operations do you need to perform to find the surface area?
Multiply, divide, and find the square root.

• What operation is the opposite of multiplication? division

• What operation is the opposite of division? multiplication

• How might the name of the operation *square root* help you to determine its opposite operation? Sample answer: The term *square* might indicate that finding the square root is the opposite of finding the square.

Lesson 1-8 Resources

Chapter 1 Resource Masters
Lesson Reading Guide, p. 56 **BL** **OL** **ELL**
Study Guide and Intervention, pp. 57–58 **BL** **OL** **ELL**
Skills Practice, p. 59 **BL** **OL**
Practice, p. 60 **OL** **AL**
Word Problem Practice, p. 61 **OL** **AL**
Enrichment, p. 62 **OL** **AL**
Graphing Calculator, p. 63

Transparencies
5-Minute Check Transparency 1-8
Additional Print Resources
Noteables™ Interactive Study Notebook with Foldables™

Technology
ca.algebra1.com
Interactive Classroom CD-ROM
AssignmentWorks CD-ROM
Graphing Calculator Easy Files

Main Ideas

• Classify and graph real numbers.

• Find square roots and order real numbers.

Standard 1.0 Students identify and use the arithmetic properties of subsets of integers and rational, irrational, and real numbers, including closure properties for the four basic arithmetic operations where applicable.

Standard 2.0 Students understand and use such operations as taking the opposite, finding the reciprocal, **taking a root**, and raising to a fractional power. They understand and use the rules of exponents. (Key, CAHSEE)

New Vocabulary

positive number
negative number
natural number
whole number
integers
rational number
square root
perfect square
irrational numbers
real numbers
Closure Property
graph
coordinate
radical sign
principal square root
rational approximation

COncepts in MOtion
Animation at ca.algebra1.com

▶ GET READY for the Lesson

In the 2000 Summer Olympics, Australian sprinter Cathy Freeman wore a special running suit that covered most of her body. The surface area of the human body may be approximated using the expression
$\sqrt{\dfrac{height \times weight}{3600}}$, where height is in centimeters, weight is in kilograms, and surface area is in square meters. The symbol $\sqrt{}$ designates a nonnegative square root of a nonnegative number.

Classify and Graph Real Numbers A number line can be used to show the sets of natural numbers, whole numbers, and integers. Values greater than 0, or **positive numbers**, are listed to the right of 0, and values less than 0, or **negative numbers**, are listed to the left of 0.

natural numbers: 1, 2, 3, …

whole numbers: 0, 1, 2, 3, …

integers: …, −3, −2, −1, 0, 1, 2, 3, …

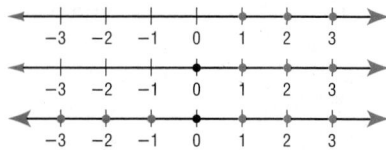

rational numbers: numbers that can be expressed in the form $\frac{a}{b}$, where a and b are integers and $b \neq 0$.

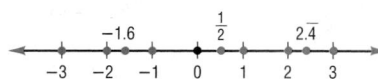

A rational number can also be expressed as a decimal that terminates, or as a decimal that repeats indefinitely.

We call a the **square root** of a number b if $a^2 = b$. For example, one square root of 64, written as $\sqrt{64}$, is 8 since 8 · 8 or 8^2 is 64. Another square root of 64 is −8 since (−8) · (−8) or $(-8)^2$ is also 64. A number like 64, with a square root that is a rational number, is called a **perfect square**. The square roots of a perfect square are rational numbers.

A number such as $\sqrt{3}$ is the square root of a number that is *not* a perfect square. It cannot be expressed as a terminating or repeating decimal.

$\sqrt{3} = 1.73205080\ldots$

Numbers that cannot be expressed as terminating or repeating decimals, or in the form $\frac{a}{b}$, where a and b are integers and $b \neq 0$, are called **irrational numbers**. Irrational numbers and rational numbers together form the set of **real numbers**.

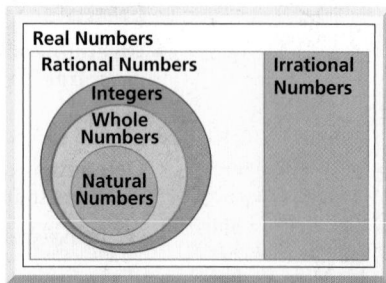

Study Tip

Common Misconception

Pay close attention to the placement of a negative sign when working with square roots. $\sqrt{-81}$ is undefined for real numbers since no real number multiplied by itself can result in a negative product.

Study Tips offer students helpful information about the topics they are studying.

EXAMPLE Classify Real Numbers

1 Name the set or sets of numbers to which each real number belongs.

a. $\frac{5}{22}$

Because 5 and 22 are integers and $5 \div 22 = 0.2272727\ldots$ or $0.2\overline{27}$, which is a repeating decimal, this number is a rational number.

b. $\sqrt{81}$

Because $\sqrt{81} = 9$, this number is a natural number, a whole number, an integer, and a rational number.

c. $\sqrt{56}$

Because $\sqrt{56} = 7.48331477\ldots$, which is not a repeating or terminating decimal, this number is irrational.

✓ CHECK Your Progress

1A. $\frac{6}{11}$ rationals   **1B.** $-\sqrt{9.16}$ irrationals

---

In Lesson 1-4, you learned about properties of real numbers. Another property of real numbers is the **Closure Property**. For example, the sum of any two whole numbers is a whole number. So, the set of whole numbers is said to be *closed* under addition.

EXAMPLE Closure Property

2 Determine whether each set of numbers is closed under the indicated operation.

a. whole numbers, multiplication

Select two different whole numbers and then determine whether the product is a whole number.

$0 \times 4 = 0$ $5 \times 2 = 10$ $1 \times 6 = 6$

Since the products of each pair of whole numbers are whole numbers, the set of whole numbers is closed under multiplication.

b. whole numbers, subtraction

We need to determine whether the difference of any two whole numbers is a whole number.

$3 - 4 = -1$

This is not a whole number, so the set of whole numbers is not closed under subtraction.

✓ CHECK Your Progress

2A. integers, division   **2B.** integers, addition

2A. No; sample answer: $2 \div 3 = \frac{2}{3}$, which is not an integer.

2B. Yes; sample answer: $-2 + 4 = 2$, which is an integer.

To **graph** a set of numbers means to draw, or plot, the points named by those numbers on a number line. The number that corresponds to a point on a number line is called the **coordinate** of that point. The rational numbers alone do not complete the number line. By including irrational numbers, the number line is complete.

Classify and Graph Real Numbers

Example 1 shows how to classify real numbers. **Example 2** shows how to graph real numbers.

 Formative Assessment

Use the Check Your Progress exercises after each example to determine students' understanding of concepts.

ADDITIONAL EXAMPLES

1 Name the set or sets of numbers to which each real number belongs.

a. $\sqrt{17}$ Because $\sqrt{17} = 4.1231056\ldots$, which is not a repeating or terminating decimal, this number is irrational.

b. $\frac{1}{6}$

Because 1 and 6 are integers and $1 \div 6 = 0.1666\ldots$ is a repeating decimal, this number is a rational number.

c. $\sqrt{169}$ Because $\sqrt{169} = 13$, this number is a natural number, a whole number, an integer, and a rational number.

2 Determine whether each set of numbers is closed under the indicated operation.

a. whole numbers, multiplication
The set of whole numbers is closed under multiplication.

b. whole numbers, subtraction
The set of whole numbers is not closed under subtraction.

Additional Examples are also in:

• Noteables™ Interactive Study Notebook with Foldables™

• Interactive Classroom PowerPoint® Presentations

Intervention

Repeating and Nonrepeating Decimals   At first glance, some decimals that repeat may appear not to repeat, and some decimals that do not repeat may appear to repeat. For example, if you represent $\frac{1}{7}$ as $0.142857\ldots$, it appears not to repeat. But an examination of 12 digits shows these 6 digits repeat and $\frac{1}{7}$ should be represented as $0.142857142857\ldots$. Conversely, if you represent $\sqrt{24}$ as $4.8989\ldots$, it appears that 2 digits repeat. An examination of 6 digits shows that $\sqrt{24}$ is $4.898979\ldots$ and does not repeat.

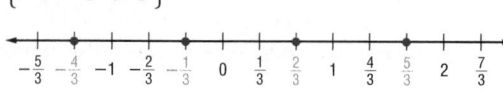
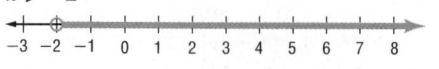

Focus on Mathematical Content

Real Numbers The set of real numbers contains rational and irrational numbers. Rational numbers include natural numbers, whole numbers, and integers. They can be written as a ratio of two integers, assuming the denominator is not zero. They can be expressed as terminating or repeating decimals. Irrational numbers cannot be written as a ratio of two integers nor can they be expressed as terminating or repeating decimals.

Square Roots A square root is indicated by the symbol $\sqrt{\ }$, which is called a radical sign. It indicates the nonnegative principal square root of the number under the radical sign. A number a is the square root of a number b if $a^2 = b$. A square root can be positive or negative. For example, 121 has two square roots: 11 since $11 \cdot 11 = 121$, and -11 since $-11 \cdot -11 = 121$.

Square Roots and Ordering Real Numbers

Example 3 shows how to find positive and negative square roots. **Example 4** shows how to approximate a square root to find the surface area of an athlete. **Example 5** shows how to compare two real numbers. **Example 6** shows how to order a set of real numbers from least to greatest.

ADDITIONAL EXAMPLES

3 Graph each set of numbers.

a. $\left\{-\dfrac{3}{2}, -\dfrac{1}{2}, 1, \dfrac{3}{2}\right\}$

b. $y \leq 8$

c. $z > -5$

EXAMPLE — Graph Real Numbers

3 Graph each set of numbers.

a. $\left\{-\dfrac{4}{3}, -\dfrac{1}{3}, \dfrac{2}{3}, \dfrac{5}{3}\right\}$

b. $x > -2$

The heavy arrow indicates that all numbers to the right of -2 are included in the graph. Not only does this set include integers like 3 and -1, but it also includes rational numbers like $\dfrac{3}{8}$ and $-\dfrac{12}{13}$ and irrational numbers like $\sqrt{40}$ and π. The circle at -2 indicates -2 is *not* included in the graph.

c. $a \leq 4.5$

The heavy arrow indicates that all points to the left of 4.5 are included in the graph. The dot at 4.5 indicates that 4.5 *is* included in the graph.

CHECK Your Progress

3A. $\{-5, -4, -3, -2, \ldots\}$ **3B.** $x \leq 8$ **3A–3B.** See Ch. 1 Answer Appendix.

Reading Math

Square Roots
$\pm\sqrt{64}$ is read *plus or minus the square root of 64*.
Exponents can also be used to indicate the square root. $9^{\frac{1}{2}}$ means the same thing as $\sqrt{9}$.
$9^{\frac{1}{2}}$ is read *nine to the one-half power*.
$9^{\frac{1}{2}} = 3$.

Square Roots and Ordering Real Numbers The symbol $\sqrt{\ }$, called a **radical sign**, is used to indicate a nonnegative or **principal square root** of the expression under the radical sign.

$$\sqrt{64} = 8 \quad\longleftarrow\quad \boxed{\sqrt{64} \text{ indicates the } \textit{principal} \text{ square root of 64.}}$$

$$-\sqrt{64} = -8 \quad\longleftarrow\quad \boxed{-\sqrt{64} \text{ indicates the } \textit{negative} \text{ square root of 64.}}$$

$$\pm\sqrt{64} = \pm8 \quad\longleftarrow\quad \boxed{\pm\sqrt{64} \text{ indicates } \textit{both} \text{ square roots of 64.}}$$

EXAMPLE — Find Square Roots

4 Find $-\sqrt{\dfrac{49}{256}}$.

$-\sqrt{\dfrac{49}{256}}$ represents the negative square root of $\dfrac{49}{256}$.

$\sqrt{\dfrac{49}{256}} = \left(\dfrac{7}{16}\right)^2 \rightarrow -\sqrt{\dfrac{49}{256}} = -\dfrac{7}{16}$

CHECK Your Progress

Find each square root.

4A. $\sqrt{\dfrac{4}{121}} \quad \dfrac{2}{11}$ **4B.** $\pm\sqrt{1.69} \quad \pm1.3$

48 Chapter 1 The Language and Tools of Algebra

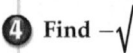
Preventing Errors

Emphasize that real numbers in the graphs of Examples 3b and 3c include numbers other than those shown on the number line. Ask students whether numbers such as $-\dfrac{2}{5}$, 3.01, $\sqrt{5}$, and so on are included in the sets of numbers shown on the graphs.

Real-World EXAMPLE

5 **SPORTS SCIENCE** Refer to the application at the beginning of the lesson. Find the surface area of an athlete whose height is 192 centimeters and whose weight is 48 kilograms.

$$\text{surface area} = \sqrt{\frac{\text{height} \times \text{weight}}{3600}} \quad \text{Write the formula.}$$

$$= \sqrt{\frac{192 \times 48}{3600}} \quad \text{Replace height with 192 and weight with 48.}$$

$$= \sqrt{\frac{9216}{3600}} \quad \text{Simplify.}$$

$$= \sqrt{\left(\frac{96}{60}\right)^2} \quad \frac{9216}{3600} = \left(\frac{96}{60}\right)^2$$

$$= \frac{96}{60} \text{ or } 1.6 \quad \text{Simplify.}$$

The surface area of the athlete is 1.6 square meters.

✓ CHECK Your Progress

5. Find the surface area of the athlete whose height is 200 centimeters and whose weight is 50 kilograms. $\frac{5}{3}$ or 1.67

 **Personal Tutor at** ca.algebra1.com

We often find it more practical to approximate irrational numbers with a close rational number, which we call a **rational approximation**. For example, a rational approximation of $\sqrt{2}$ is 1.414.

EXAMPLE Compare Real Numbers

6 Replace each ● with <, >, or = to make each sentence true.

a. $\sqrt{19} \ ● \ 3.\overline{8}$

Find two perfect squares closest to $\sqrt{19}$, and write an inequality.

$16 < \ 19 \ < 25 \qquad$ 19 is between 16 and 25.

$\sqrt{16} < \sqrt{19} < \sqrt{25} \qquad$ Find the square root of each number.

$4 < \sqrt{19} < 5 \qquad \sqrt{19}$ is between 4 and 5.

Since $\sqrt{19}$ is between 4 and 5, it must be greater than $3.\overline{8}$. So, $\sqrt{19} > 3.\overline{8}$.

b. $7.\overline{2} \ ● \ \sqrt{52}$

You can use a calculator to find an approximation for $\sqrt{52}$.

$\sqrt{52} = 7.211102551...$

$7.\overline{2} = 7.222... \qquad$ Therefore, $7.\overline{2} > \sqrt{52}$.

✓ CHECK Your Progress

6A. $2\frac{2}{3} \ ● \ \sqrt{5}$ >

6B. $0.\overline{8} \ ● \ \frac{8}{9}$ =

Real-World Career

Scientist

Sports scientists use math to conduct experiments and interpret data. One of their jobs is to help athletes enhance their performance.

Math Online

For more information, go to ca.algebra1.com.

ADDITIONAL EXAMPLES

4 Find $-\sqrt{\frac{16}{9}}$. $-\frac{4}{3}$

5 **SPORTS SCIENCE** Find the surface area of an athlete whose height is 147 centimeters and whose weight is 48 kilograms. The surface area is 1.4 square meters.

6 Replace each ● with <, >, or = to make each sentence true.

a. $\sqrt{72} \ ● \ 7.8$

$\sqrt{72}$ is between $\sqrt{64}$ and $\sqrt{81}$, so $\sqrt{72} < 7.8$.

b. $\sqrt{48} \ ● \ 6.\overline{9}$

$\sqrt{48} = 6.9282032...$, so $\sqrt{48} < 6.\overline{9}$.

Differentiated Instruction

Modeling Some students who have difficulty understanding square roots might benefit from using manipulatives. Arrange 16 square tiles into a 4-by-4 grid and show how the side length models $\sqrt{16}$. Give students other square numbers, such as 9 and 25, and have them model the square roots.

3 Practice

Formative Assessment

Use Exercises 1–21 to check for understanding.

Use the chart at the bottom of this page to customize assignments for your students.

Odd/Even Assignments

Exercises 22–55 are structured so that students practice the same concepts whether they are assigned odd or even problems.

Additional Answers

5. No; sample answer: $3 \div 4 = \frac{3}{4}$

6. Yes; sample answer: $\frac{3}{4} + \frac{1}{2} = \frac{5}{4}$

7. Yes; sample answer: $3.2 \div 1.5 = 2.1\overline{3}$

8. No; sample answer: $2 - 6 = -4$

60.

-2.4 -1.6 -0.8   0   0.8

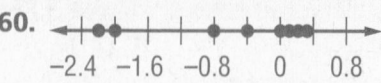
Check Your Understanding exercises are intended to be completed in class. Example references show students where to look back for review. In the Exercises, Homework Help boxes function in the same way.

To order a set of real numbers from greatest to least or from least to greatest, find a decimal approximation for each number in the set and compare.

EXAMPLE Order Real Numbers

7 Order $2.\overline{63}$, $-\sqrt{7}$, $\frac{8}{3}$, and $\frac{53}{-20}$ from least to greatest.

$2.\overline{63} = 2.6363636\ldots$ or about 2.636

$-\sqrt{7} = -2.64575131\ldots$ or about -2.646

$\frac{8}{3} = 2.66666666\ldots$ or about 2.667

$\frac{53}{-20} = -2.65$

$-2.65 < -2.646 < 2.636 < 2.667$

The numbers arranged in order from least to greatest are $\frac{53}{-20}$, $-\sqrt{7}$, $2.\overline{63}$, $\frac{8}{3}$.

CHECK Your Progress

Order each set of numbers from greatest to least.

7A. $\sqrt{0.42}$, $0.\overline{63}$, $\sqrt{\frac{4}{9}}$

7B. $-1.\overline{46}$, 0.2, $\sqrt{2}$, $-\frac{1}{6}$

7A. $\sqrt{\frac{4}{9}}$, $\sqrt{0.42}$, $0.\overline{63}$

7B. $\sqrt{2}$, 0.2, $-\frac{1}{6}$, $-1.\overline{46}$

★ indicates multi-step problem

CHECK Your Understanding

Example 1
(p. 47)

Name the set or sets of numbers to which each real number belongs.

1. $-\sqrt{64}$ integers, rationals
2. $\frac{8}{3}$ rationals
3. $\sqrt{28}$ irrationals
4. $\frac{56}{7}$ naturals, whole, integers, rationals

Example 2
(p. 47)

Determine whether each set of numbers is closed under the indicated operation. 5–8. See margin.

5. whole, division
6. rational, addition
7. rational, division
8. natural, subtraction

Example 3
(p. 48)

Graph each set of numbers. 9–11. See Ch. 1 Answer Appendix.

9. $\{-4, -2, 1, 5, 7\}$
10. $x < -3.5$
11. $x \geq -7$

Example 4
(p. 48)

Find each square root.

12. $-\sqrt{25}$ -5
13. $\sqrt{1.44}$ 1.2
14. $\pm\sqrt{\frac{16}{49}}$ $\pm\frac{4}{7}$
15. $\sqrt{361}$ 19

Example 5
(p. 49)

16. **PHYSICAL SCIENCE** The time it takes a falling object to travel a distance d is given by $t = \sqrt{\frac{d}{16}}$, where t is in seconds and d is in feet. If Isabel drops a ball from 29.16 feet, how long will it take for it to reach the ground? 1.35 s

Example 6
(p. 49)

Replace each ● with <, >, or = to make each sentence true.

17. $\sqrt{17}$ ● $4\frac{1}{10}$ >
18. $\frac{2}{9}$ ● $0.\overline{2}$ =
19. $\frac{1}{6}$ ● $\sqrt{6}$ <

Example 7
(p. 50)

Order each set of numbers from least to greatest.

20. $\frac{1}{8}$, $\sqrt{\frac{1}{4}}$, $0.\overline{15}$, -15 -15, $\sqrt{\frac{1}{4}}$, $\frac{1}{8}$, $0.\overline{15}$

21. $\sqrt{30}$, $5\frac{4}{9}$, 13, $\sqrt{\frac{1}{30}}$ $\sqrt{\frac{1}{30}}$, $5\frac{4}{9}$, $\sqrt{30}$, 13

DIFFERENTIATED HOMEWORK OPTIONS

Level	Assignment	Two-Day Option	
BL Basic	22–55, 67–78	23–55 odd, 69, 70	22–54 even, 67, 68, 71–78
OL Core	23–59 odd, 60–63, 67–78	22–55, 69, 70	56–63, 67, 68, 71–78
AL Advanced /Pre-AP	56–77 (optional: 78)		

HOMEWORK HELP

For Exercises	See Examples
22–27	1
28–37	2
38–41	3
42–47	4, 5
48–51	6
52–55	7

Exercise Levels
A: 22–55
B: 56–63
C: 64–68

Name the set or sets of numbers to which each real number belongs.

22. $-\sqrt{22}$ irrationals

23. $\frac{36}{6}$ naturals, wholes, integers, rationals

24. $-\frac{5}{12}$ rationals

25. $\sqrt{10.24}$ rationals

26. $\frac{-54}{19}$ rationals

27. $\sqrt{\frac{82}{20}}$ irrationals

Determine whether each set of numbers is closed under the indicated operation. 28–37. See Ch. 1 Answer Appendix for sample answers.

28. irrational, addition no

29. irrational, subtraction no

30. natural, addition yes

31. natural, multiplication yes

32. irrational, multiplication no

33. irrational, division no

34. integers, subtraction yes

35. rational, subtraction yes

36. rational, multiplication yes

37. integers, multiplication yes

Graph each set of numbers. 38–41. See Ch. 1 Answer Appendix.

38. $\{-4, -2, -1, 1, 3\}$

39. $\{\ldots -2, 0, 2, 4, 6\}$

40. $x > -12$

41. $x \geq -10.2$

Find each square root.

42. $\sqrt{49}$ 7

43. $\pm\sqrt{0.64}$ ± 0.8

44. $\pm\sqrt{5.29}$ ± 2.3

45. $-\sqrt{6.25}$ -2.5

46. $\sqrt{\frac{169}{196}}$ $\frac{13}{14}$

47. $\sqrt{\frac{25}{324}}$ $\frac{5}{18}$

Replace each ● with <, >, or = to make each sentence true.

48. $5.\overline{72} ● \sqrt{5}$ >

49. $\sqrt{22} ● 4.7$ <

50. $\sqrt{\frac{2}{3}} ● \frac{2}{3}$ >

51. $8 ● \sqrt{67}$ <

Order each set of numbers from least to greatest.

52. $0.\overline{24}, \sqrt{0.06},$ $\sqrt{\frac{9}{144}}$

52. $\sqrt{0.06}, 0.\overline{24}, \sqrt{\frac{9}{144}}$

53. $0.6, \sqrt{\frac{16}{49}}, \frac{5}{9}$ $\frac{5}{9}, \sqrt{\frac{16}{49}}, 0.6$

54. $-4.\overline{83}, 0.4, \sqrt{8}, -\frac{3}{8}$ $-4.\overline{83}, -\frac{3}{8}, 0.4, \sqrt{8}$

55. $-0.25, 0.\overline{14}, -\sqrt{\frac{5}{8}}, \sqrt{0.5}$ $-\sqrt{\frac{5}{8}}, -0.25, 0.\overline{14}, \sqrt{0.5}$

Evaluate each expression if $a = 4$, $b = 9$, and $c = 100$.

56. $2 \cdot \sqrt{a}$ 4

57. $\sqrt{a} \cdot \sqrt{b}$ 6

58. $\sqrt{a \cdot b}$ 6

59. $\sqrt{a} + \sqrt{c}$ 12

61. side lengths: 1 unit, 2 units, 3 units, 4 units, 5 units; perimeters: 4 units, 8 units, 12 units, 16 units, 20 units

62. The length of the side is the square root of the area.

★ 60. **RIVERS** The table shows the change in river depths for various rivers over a 24-hour period. Use a number line to graph these values and compare the changes in each river. See margin.

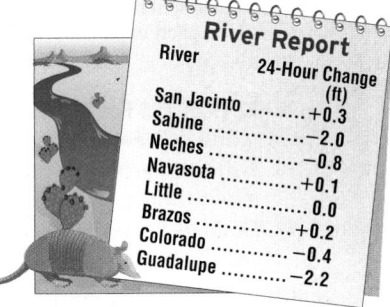

River Report

River	24-Hour Change (ft)
San Jacinto	+0.3
Sabine	−2.0
Neches	−0.8
Navasota	+0.1
Little	0.0
Brazos	+0.2
Colorado	−0.4
Guadalupe	−2.2

GEOMETRY For Exercises 61–63, consider squares with the following areas: 1 unit², 4 units², 9 units², 16 units², and 25 units².

61. Find the side length and perimeter of each square.

★ 62. Describe the relationship between the lengths of the sides and the areas.

63. Write an expression to find the perimeter of a square with a area of a units². $4\sqrt{a}$

EXTRA PRACTICE
See pages 719, 744.

Math Online
Self-Check Quiz at
ca.algebra1.com

BL = Below Grade Level
OL = On Grade Level
AL = Above Grade Level
ELL = English Language Learner

Additional pages not shown:

CRM **Lesson Reading Guide**, p. 56 **BL OL ELL**

CRM **Skills Practice**, p. 59 **BL OL**

Enrichment
CRM p. 62 **OL AL**

1-8 Enrichment

Scale Drawings
The map at the left below shows building lots for sale. The scale ratio is 1:2400. At the right below is the floor plan for a two-bedroom apartment. The length of the living room is 6 m. On the plan the living room is 6 cm long.

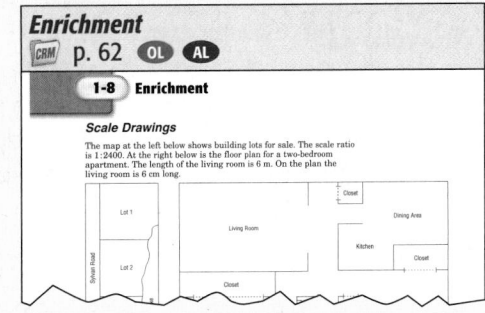

Study Guide and Intervention
CRM pp. 57–58 **OL BL ELL**

1-8 Study Guide and Intervention
Number Systems

Square Roots A **square root** is one of two equal factors of a number. For example, the square roots of 36 are 6 and −6, since 6 · 6 or 6² is 36 and (−6)(−6) or (−6)² is also 36. A rational number like 36, whose square root is a rational number, is called a **perfect square**.
The symbol $\sqrt{}$ is a **radical sign**. It indicates the nonnegative, or **principal**, square root of the number under the radical sign. So $\sqrt{36} = 6$ and $-\sqrt{36} = -6$. The symbol $\pm\sqrt{36}$ represents both square roots.

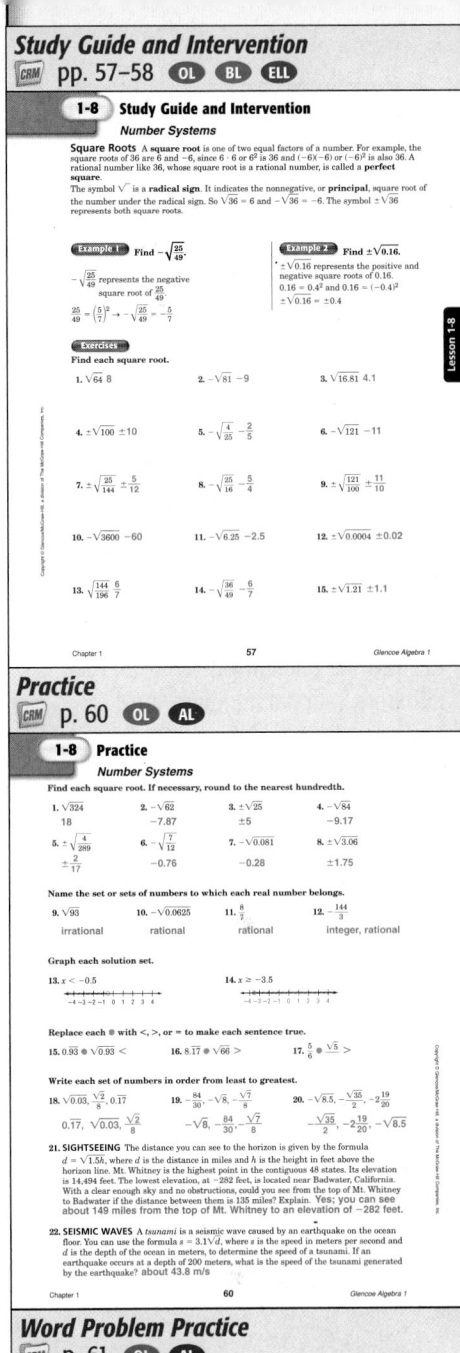

Practice
CRM p. 60 **OL AL**

1-8 Practice
Number Systems

Word Problem Practice
CRM p. 61 **OL AL**

1-8 Word Problem Practice
Number Systems

Ticket Out the Door Write various real numbers on slips of paper and hand one to each student. As students leave the classroom, have them name the set or sets of numbers to which the number on the paper belongs.

 **Foldables™**
Follow-Up

Remind students to use the eighth tab of the Foldables to record definitions and examples of rational and irrational numbers. They should include the diagram on p. 45 or a similar diagram to show the relationship between real numbers, rational numbers, and irrational numbers.

California Standards Practice exercises help students solidify their knowledge of the standards using exercises in a multiple-choice format. The appropriate California Standard is noted with each exercise.

Additional Answer

68. Sample answer: by using the formula

$$\text{surface area} = \sqrt{\dfrac{\text{height} \times \text{weight}}{3600}},$$

you need to use square roots to calculate the quantity. You must multiply height by weight first. Divide that product by 3600. Then determine the square root of that result. Sample answers: determining height, distance

---

H.O.T. Problems

64. REASONING Determine whether the following statement is *true* or *false*. Justify your answer. *Since the natural numbers are a subset of the whole numbers then for each operation that the whole numbers are closed, the natural numbers are closed also.* **True; see Ch. 1 Answer Appendix for justification.**

65. CHALLENGE Determine whether the following statement is *true* or *false*. Include an example or a counterexample in your answer. *The average of two irrational numbers is an irrational number.*
True; see Ch. 1 Answer Appendix for explanation.

66. CHALLENGE Determine when the following statements are all true for real numbers q and r. They are true if q and r are positive and $q > r$.

a. $q^2 > r^2$ **b.** $\dfrac{1}{q} < \dfrac{1}{r}$ **c.** $\sqrt{q} > \sqrt{r}$ **d.** $\dfrac{1}{\sqrt{q}} < \dfrac{1}{\sqrt{r}}$

67. OPEN-ENDED Give a real-life example in which numbers are ordered.
See students' work.

68. *Writing in Math* Use the information on page 46 to explain how square roots can be used to find the surface area of the human body.
See margin.

STANDARDS PRACTICE 7NS1.4, 4.0

69. REVIEW Which is an irrational number? **C**

 A -6

 B $\dfrac{3}{2}$

 C $-\sqrt{8}$

 D $-\sqrt{4}$

70. For what value of a is $-\sqrt{a} < -\dfrac{1}{\sqrt{a}}$ true? **F**

 F 2

 G $\dfrac{1}{3}$

 H 1

 J -4

Spiral Review

Find a counterexample for each statement. (Lesson 1-7)

71. If the sum of two numbers is even, then both numbers must be even. **3 + 3 = 6**

72. If $x^2 < 1$, then $x = 0$. $x = \dfrac{1}{2}$

Simplify each expression. (Lesson 1-6)

73. $8x + 2y + x$ **9x + 2y**   **74.** $7(5a + 3b) - 4a$ **75.** $4[1 + 4(5x + 2y)]$ **4 + 80x + 32y**
                                    31a + 21b

MOVIE THEATERS For Exercises 76 and 77, use the following information. (Lesson 1-2)
One adult ticket at a movie theater costs $8.50. One small popcorn costs $3.50.

76. Write an algebraic expression to represent how much could be spent at the movie theater. **8.50t + 3.50p**

77. Evaluate the expression to find the total cost if Julio and his three friends each bought a ticket and popcorn. **$48**

GET READY for the Next Lesson

PREREQUISITE SKILL

78. Refer to the table. If the pattern continues, what are the values for y if $x = 6$ and $x = 7$?
20; 23

x	0	1	2	3	4	5
y	2	5	8	11	14	17

Pre-AP Activity Use after Exercise 63

Officer Fitzpatrick can use the formula $s = \sqrt{24d}$ to estimate the speed, s, of a car in miles per hour by measuring the distance, d, in feet that a car skids on a dry road. On his way to work, Chiavo skidded and was involved in a minor accident. He told Officer Fitzpatrick that he was driving within the speed limit of 35 miles per hour. What is the greatest length the skid marks could be if Chiavo was driving within the speed limit? Round to the nearest whole number. **51 ft**

Main Ideas

- Interpret graphs of functions.
- Draw graphs of functions.

Standard 16.0 Students understand the concepts of a relation and a function, determine whether a given relation defines a function, **and give pertinent information about given relations and functions.**

Standard 17.0 Students determine the domain of independent variables and the range of dependent variables defined by a graph, a set of ordered pairs, or a symbolic expression.

New Vocabulary

function
coordinate system
y-axis
origin
x-axis
ordered pair
x-coordinate
y-coordinate
independent variable
dependent variable
relation
domain
range
discrete function
continuous function

GET READY for the Lesson

The graph shows that as the number of days after a concussion increases, the percent of blood flow increases.

The return of normal blood flow is said to be a function of the number of days since the concussion.

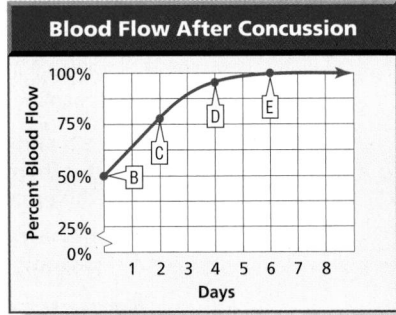

Source: *Scientific American*

Interpret Graphs A **function** is a relationship between input and output. In a function, the output depends on the input. There is exactly one output for each input. A function is graphed using a **coordinate system**, or *coordinate plane*. It is formed by the intersection of two number lines, the *horizontal axis* and the *vertical axis*.

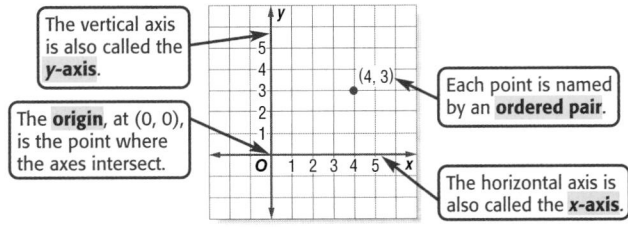

The vertical axis is also called the **y-axis**.

The **origin**, at (0, 0), is the point where the axes intersect.

Each point is named by an **ordered pair**.

The horizontal axis is also called the **x-axis**.

Each input *x* and its corresponding output *y* is graphed using an ordered pair in the form (x, y). The *x*-value, called the **x-coordinate** corresponds to the *x*-axis and the *y*-value, or **y-coordinate**, corresponds to the *y*-axis.

Real-World EXAMPLE Identify Coordinates

1 **MEDICINE** Refer to the application above. Name the ordered pair at point *C* and explain what it represents.

Point *C* is at 2 along the *x*-axis and about 80 along the *y*-axis. So, its ordered pair is (2, 80). This represents 80% normal blood flow 2 days after the injury.

CHECK Your Progress

1. Name the ordered pair at point *E* and explain what it represents.

1. (6, 100); 100% normal blood flow 6 days after the injury.

Lesson 1-9 Functions and Graphs **53**

1 Focus

Standards Alignment

Before Lesson 1-9
Graph functions of the form $y = nx^2$ and $y = nx^3$ and use in solving problems from Standard 7AF3.1

Lesson 1-9
Understand the concepts of a relation, a function, domain and range from Standards 16.0 and 17.0

After Lesson 1-9
Solve and graph quadratic equations and utilize the complex number system from Standard 2A8.0

2 Teach

Scaffolding Questions Have students read *Get Ready for the Lesson.*
Ask:
- What does point B on the graph represent? The blood flow to the brain at the time of the injury.
- About what percent of normal blood flow occurs two days after the injury? about 80%
- On what does the percent of blood flow depend? the number of days from the injury

Lesson 1-9 Resources

Chapter 1 Resource Masters
Lesson Reading Guide, p. 64 BL OL ELL
Study Guide and Intervention, pp. 65–66 BL OL ELL
Skills Practice, p. 67 BL OL
Practice, p. 68 OL AL
Word Problem Practice, p. 69 OL AL
Enrichment, p. 70 OL AL
Quiz 4, p. 74

Transparencies
5-Minute Check Transparency 1-9
Additional Print Resources
Noteables™ Interactive Study Notebook with Foldables™
Teaching Algebra with Manipulatives

Technology
ca.algebra1.com
Interactive Classroom CD-ROM
AssignmentWorks CD-ROM
Graphing Calculator Easy Files

Interpret Graphs

Example 1 shows how to identify the coordinates of a point on a coordinate plane and write its ordered pair. **Example 2** shows how to identify the independent and dependent variables for functions. **Example 3** shows how to analyze and interpret graphs.

 Formative Assessment

Use the Check Your Progress exercises after each example to determine students' understanding of concepts.

ADDITIONAL EXAMPLES

1 Refer to the graph on p. 51. Name the ordered pair at point E and explain what it represents. (6, 100); the point represents about 100% normal blood flow 6 days after the injury.

2 Identify the independent and the dependent variables for each function.

a. In warm climates, the average amount of electricity used rises as the daily average temperature increases and falls as the daily average temperature decreases. independent variable: temperature; dependent variable: amount of electricity used.

b. The number of calories you burn increases as the number of minutes that you walk increases. independent variable: time; dependent variable: number of calories burned

Additional Examples are also in:

• Noteables™ Interactive Study Notebook with Foldables™

• Interactive Classroom PowerPoint® Presentations

2A. independent: time; dependent: distance

2B. independent: dimensions of the square; dependent: area

In Example 1, the blood flow depends on the number of days from the injury. Therefore, the number of days from the injury is called the **independent variable** and the percent of normal blood flow is called the **dependent variable**.

EXAMPLE Independent and Dependent Variables

2 Identify the independent and dependent variables for each function.

a. In general, the average price of gasoline slowly and steadily increases throughout the year.

Time is the independent variable as it is unaffected by the price of gasoline, and the price is the dependent quantity as it is affected by time.

b. Art club members are drawing caricatures of students to raise money for their trip to New York City. The profit that they make increases as the price of their drawings increases.

In this case, price is the independent quantity. Profit is the dependent quantity as it is affected by the price.

CHECK Your Progress

2A. The distance a person runs increases with time.

2B. As the dimensions of a square decrease, so does the area.

Functions can be graphed without using a scale on either axis to show the general shape of the graph.

EXAMPLE Analyze Graphs

3 The graph at the right represents the speed of a school bus traveling along its morning route. Describe what is happening in the graph.

At the origin, the bus is stopped. It accelerates and maintains a constant speed. Then it begins to slow down, eventually stopping. After being stopped for a short time, the bus accelerates again. The process repeats continually.

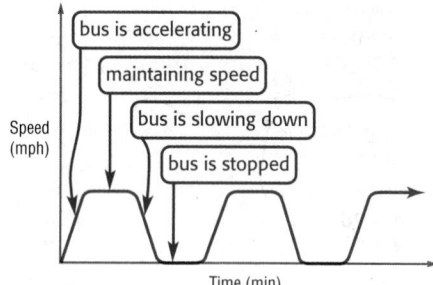

CHECK Your Progress

3. Identify the graph that represents the altitude of a space shuttle above Earth, from the moment it is launched until the moment it lands. Graph A

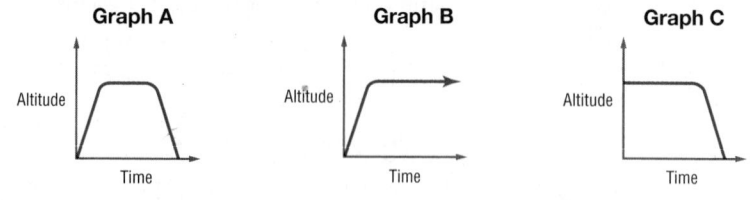

Graph A   Altitude   Time

Graph B   Altitude   Time

Graph C   Altitude   Time

Intervention

Independent and Dependent Variables   You may want to spend extra time on independent and dependent variables, since an understanding of these concepts provides the foundation for later work with functions. Some students may find it helpful if you relate independent and dependent variables to the input and output of a function. For example, the input (price of an object) affects the output (profit made on the object).

Draw Graphs Graphs can be used to represent many real-world situations.

Real-World EXAMPLE Draw Graphs

④ **SHOPPING** For every two pairs of earrings you buy at the regular price of $29 each, you get a third pair free.

a. **Make a table showing the cost of buying 1 to 5 pairs of earrings.**

Pairs of Earrings	1	2	3	4	5
Total Cost ($)	29	58	58	87	116

b. **Write the data as a set of ordered pairs. Then graph the data.**

Use the table. The number of pairs of earrings is the independent variable, and the cost is the dependent variable. So, the ordered pairs are (1, 29), (2, 58), (3, 58), (4, 87), and (5, 116).

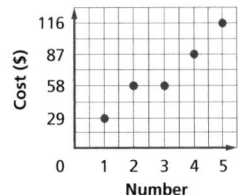

CHECK Your Progress

4A. Suppose you earn $0.25 for each book that you sell. Make a table showing how much you earn when you sell 1 to 5 books.

4B. Write the data as a set of ordered pairs. Then graph the data.

A set of ordered pairs, like those in Example 4, is called a **relation**. The set of the first numbers of the ordered pairs is the **domain**. The set of second numbers of the ordered pairs is the **range**. The function in Example 4 is a **discrete function** because its graph consists of points that are not connected. A function graphed with a line or smooth curve is a **continuous function**.

Real-World EXAMPLE Domain and Range

⑤ **EXERCISE** Rasha rides her bike an average of 0.25 mile per minute up to 36 miles each week. The distance that she travels each week is a function of the number of minutes that she rides.

a. **Identify a reasonable domain and range for this situation.**

The domain is the number of minutes that Rasha rides her bike. Since she rides up to 36 miles each week, she rides up to 36 ÷ 0.25 or 144 minutes a week. A reasonable domain would be values from 0 to 144 minutes. The range is the weekly distance traveled. A reasonable range is 0 to 36 miles.

b. **Draw a graph that shows the relationship.**

Graph the ordered pairs (0, 0) and (144, 36). Since she rides any number of miles up to 36 miles, connect the two points with a line to include those points.

Rasha's Bike Riding

c. **State whether the function is discrete or continuous. Explain.**

Since the points are connected with a line, this function is continuous.

Math Online Extra Examples at ca.algebra1.com

Lesson 1-9 Functions and Graphs **55**

Study Tip

Different Representations

Example 4 illustrates some of the ways data can be represented—tables, ordered pairs, and graphs.

Study Tip

Domain and Range

The domain contains all values of the independent variable. The range contains all values of the dependent variable.

Additional Answers

4A.

Number of Books Sold	Total Amount Earned ($)
1	0.25
2	0.50
3	0.75
4	1.00
5	1.25

Answer for Additional Example 4b.

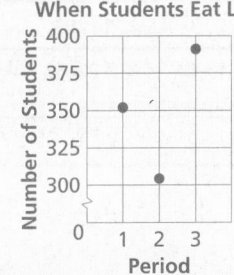

When Students Eat Lunch

ADDITIONAL EXAMPLE

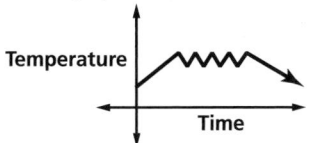

③ The graph represents the temperature in Ms. Ling's classroom on a winter school day. Describe what is happening in the graph.

Sample answer: The temperature is low until the heat is turned on. Then the temperature fluctuates up and down because of the thermostat. Finally, the temperature drops when the heat is turned off.

Draw Graphs

Example 4 shows how to create and use a table to write ordered pairs and then use the ordered pairs to draw a graph. **Example 5** shows how to find and use the domain and range to draw a graph, and how to determine whether a function is discrete or continuous.

ADDITIONAL EXAMPLE

④ **SCHOOL CAFETERIA** There are three lunch periods at a school. During the first period, 352 students eat. During the second period, 304 students eat. During the third period, 391 students eat.

a. Make a table showing the number of students for each of the three lunch periods.

Period	1	2	3
Number of Students	352	304	391

b. Write the data as a set of ordered pairs. Then graph the data. (1, 352), (2, 304), (3, 391) See bottom margin for graph.

5 TUTORING Mr. Ohms tutors students. He works at most 120 hours for $4 per hour.

a. Identify a domain and range for this situation. Domain: 0–120; Range: $0–$480

b. Draw a graph that shows the relationship.

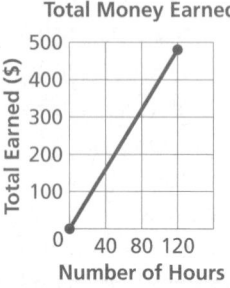

Total Money Earned

c. State whether the function is discrete or continuous. Explain. Since the points are connected with a line, this function is continuous.

---

3 Practice

Use Exercises 1–9 to check for understanding.

Use the chart at the bottom of this page to customize assignments for your students.

Odd/Even Assignments

Exercises 10–21 and 24–25 are structured so that students practice the same concepts whether they are assigned odd or even problems.

Additional Answers

5B.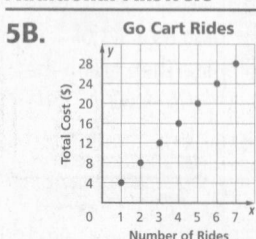
Go Cart Rides

5C. Discrete; the graph consists of individual points that are not connected.

✓ CHECK Your Progress

5A. At Go-Cart World, each go-cart ride costs $4. For a birthday party, a group of 7 friends are each allowed to take 1 go-cart ride. The total cost is a function of the number of rides. Identify a reasonable domain and range for this situation. **Sample answer: domain: 0 to 7 rides; range: $0 to $28**

5B. Draw a graph that shows the relationship between the number of rides and the total cost. **5B, 5C. See margin.**

5C. State whether the function is discrete or continuous. Explain.

nline **Personal Tutor at** ca.algebra1.com

✓ CHECK Your Understanding

For Exercises 1–3, use the graph at the right.

Example 1 (p. 53)
1. Name the ordered pair at point *A* and explain what it represents.

2. Name the ordered pair at point *B* and explain what it represents.

Example 2 (p. 54)
3. Identify the independent and dependent variables for the function.
1–3. See Ch. 1 Answer Appendix.

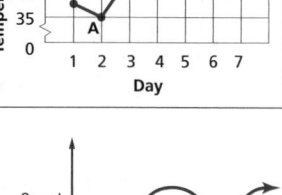
Average Temperatures

Example 3 (p. 54)
4. The graph at the right represents Alexi's speed as he rides his bike. Describe what is happening in the graph.
Sample answer: Alexi's speed decreases as he rides uphill, then increases as he rides downhill.

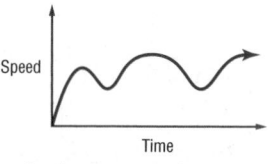

5. Identify the graph that represents the altitude of a skydiver just before she jumps from a plane until she lands. **Graph B**

Graph A | Graph B | Graph C

PHYSICAL SCIENCE For Exercises 6–9, use the table and the information.
Ms. Blackwell's students recorded the height of an object above the ground at several intervals after it was dropped from a height of 5 meters.

Time (s)	0	0.2	0.4	0.6	0.8	1
Height (cm)	500	480	422	324	186	10

6–9. See Ch. 1 Answer Appendix.

Example 4 (p. 55)
6. Write a set of ordered pairs representing the data in the table.

7. Draw a graph showing the relationship between the height of the falling object and time.

Example 5 (p. 55)
8. Identify the domain and range for this situation.

9. State whether the function is discrete or continuous. Explain.

DIFFERENTIATED HOMEWORK OPTIONS

Level	Assignment	Two-Day Option	
BL Basic	10–21, 24–27, 29–37	11–21 odd, 25, 30, 31	10–20 even, 24, 26, 27, 29, 32–37
OL Core	11–21 odd, 25–27, 29–37	10–21, 24, 25, 30, 31	22, 23, 26, 27, 29, 32–37
AL Advanced /Pre-AP	22, 23, 26–37		

For Exercises 10–12, use the graph at the right.

10. Name the ordered pair at point *A* and explain what it represents.

11. Name the ordered pair at point *B* and explain what it represents.

12. Identify the independent and dependent variables for the function.
10–12. See Ch. 1 Answer Appendix.

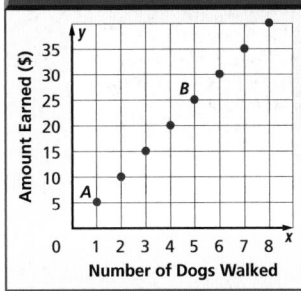

Dog-Walking

13–14. See Ch. 1 Answer Appendix.

For Exercises 13–15, use the graph at the right.

13. Name the ordered pair at point *C* and explain what it represents.

14. Name the ordered pair at point *D* and explain what it represents.

15. Identify the independent and dependent variables. **independent: year; dependent: sales**

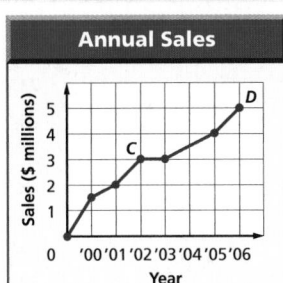

Annual Sales

16–17. See Ch. 1 Answer Appendix.

16. The graph below represents Teresa's temperature when she was sick. Describe what is happening in the graph.

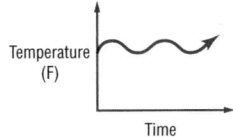

17. The graph below represents the altitude of a group of hikers. Describe what is happening in the graph.

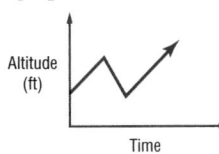

18. TOYS Identify the graph that displays the speed of a radio-controlled car as it moves along and then hits a wall. **Graph C**

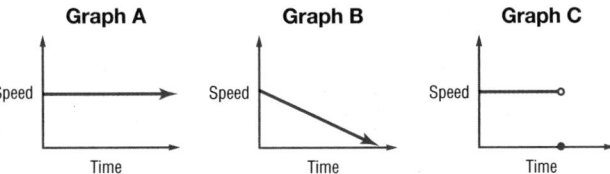

Graph A   Graph B   Graph C

19. INCOME In general, as people get older, their incomes increase steadily until they retire. Which of the graphs below represents this? **Graph B**

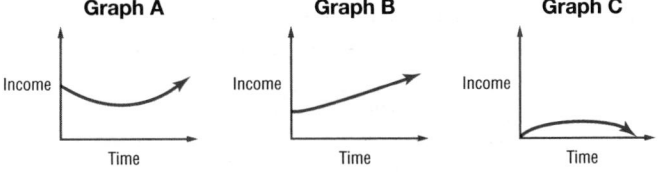

Graph A   Graph B   Graph C

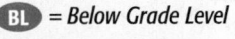
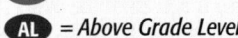

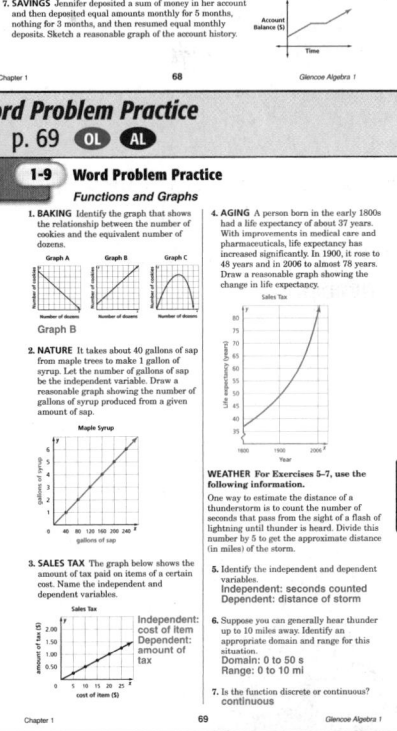
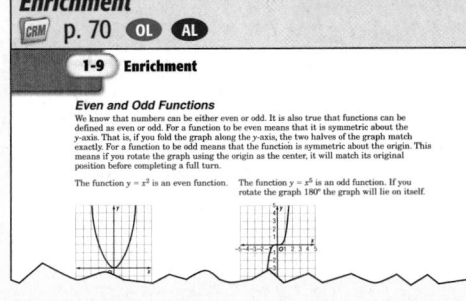

Name the Math Tell students that temperatures, in Fahrenheit, were 81°, 84°, 85°, 86°, and 88° on days 1–5. Ask students to identify the independent and dependent variables, the axes on which they would graph the variables, and whether the relation between variables is discrete or continuous and why.

Check for student understanding of concepts in Lessons 1-8 and 1-9.

 Quiz 4, p. 74

Foldables™ Follow-Up

Since this is the last lesson of the chapter, have students check that their Foldables contain notes from all nine lessons in the chapter. If they are missing notes for any of the lessons, suggest that they take time to update the appropriate tab. Remind students that they can use their Foldables to study for the chapter review test.

Additional Answers

20.

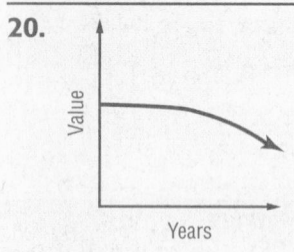

21.

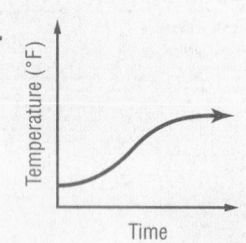

Pre-AP Activities help you cultivate skills that students will need to have success in higher mathematics.

Real-World Link

Most new cars lose 15 to 30 percent of their value in the first year. After about 12 years, more popular cars tend to increase in value.

Source: *Consumer Guide*

20. CARS Refer to the information at the left. A car was purchased new in 1990. The owner has taken excellent care of the car, and it has relatively low mileage. Draw a reasonable graph to show the value of the car from the time it was purchased to the present. **See margin.**

21. CHEMISTRY When ice is exposed to temperatures above 32°F, it begins to melt. Draw a reasonable graph showing the relationship between the temperature of a block of ice and the time after it is removed from a freezer. **See margin.**

GEOMETRY For Exercises 22–25, use the table below. 22–25. See Ch. 1 Answer Appe...

Polygon	triangle	quadrilateral	pentagon	hexagon	heptagon
Number of Sides	3	4	5	6	7
Interior Angle Sum	180	360	540	720	900

22. Identify the independent and dependent variables. Then graph the data.

23. Identify the domain and range for this situation.

24. State whether the function is discrete or continuous. Explain.

25. Predict the sum of the interior angles for an octagon, nonagon, and decagon.

H.O.T. Problems

26. REASONING Compare and contrast dependent and independent variables. See Ch. 1 Answer Appendix.

27. OPEN ENDED Give an example of a relation. Identify the domain and range. See students' work.

28. CHALLENGE Eva is 23 years older than Lisa. Draw a graph showing Eva's age as a function of Lisa's age for the first 40 years of Lisa's life. Then find the point on the graph when Eva is twice as old as Lisa. See Ch. 1 Answer Appendix.

29. *Writing in Math* Use the data about concussions on page 53 to explain how real-world situations can be modeled using graphs and functions. ■ See Ch. 1 Answer Appendix.

STANDARDS PRACTICE 17.0, 6AF1.1

30. What is the range for the function {(1, 3), (5, 7), (9, 11)}? **B**

  A {1, 5, 9}   C {3}

  B {3, 7, 11}   D ∅

31. REVIEW If $3x - 2y = 5$ and $x = 2$, what value of y makes the equation true? **F**

  F 0.5   H 2

  G 1   J 5

Spiral Review

32. What is $\pm\sqrt{121}$? (Lesson 1-8)   **−11, 11**

Identify the hypothesis and conclusion of each statement. (Lesson 1-7)

33. You can send e-mail with a computer. **H: you use a computer; C: you can send email**

34. The express lane is for shoppers with 9 or fewer items. 34–35. See Ch. 1 Answer Appendix.

35. Evaluate $ab(a + b)$ and name the property used in each step. (Lesson 1-6)

Write an algebraic expression for each verbal expression. (Lesson 1-1)

36. the product of 8 and a number x all raised to the fourth power $(8x)^4$

37. three times a number decreased by 10 $3x - 10$

Pre-AP Activity   Use after the Exercises

Have students draw a graph that shows the height of water in a tub as it is filling, when the water is turned off, when a person gets into the water, then out, and as it is draining. Remind students to label the axes of their graphs. See students' graphs. Students can also exchange and discuss their graphs.

Algebra Lab
Investigating Real-World Functions

Standard 16.0 **Students understand the concepts of a relation and a function,** determine whether a given relation defines a function, **and give pertinent information about given relations and functions.**

ACTIVITY

The table shows the number of students enrolled in elementary and secondary schools for the given years.

Year	1900	1920	1940	1960	1970	1980	1990	2000
Enrollment (thousands)	15,503	21,578	25,434	36,807	45,550	41,651	40,543	46,857

Source: *The World Almanac*

- On **grid paper**, draw a vertical and horizontal axis as shown. Make your graph large enough to fill most of the sheet. Label the horizontal axis 0 to 120 and the vertical axis 1 to 50,000.

- To make graphing easier, let x represent the number of years since 1900. Write the eight ordered pairs using this method. The first will be (0, 15,503).

- Graph the ordered pairs on your grid paper.

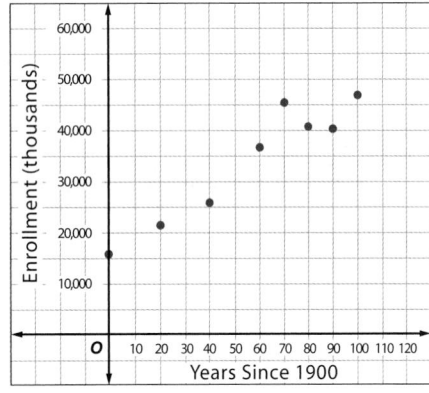

ANALYZE THE RESULTS 1–4. See margin.

1. Describe the graph you made.

2. Use your graph to estimate the number of students in elementary and secondary school in 1910, 1975, and 2020.

3. Describe the method you used to make estimates for Exercise 2.

4. Do you think your prediction for 2020 will be accurate? Explain your reasoning.

5. Graph this set of data, which shows the number of students per computer in U.S. schools. Predict the number of students per computer in 2010. Explain how you made your prediction.
See Ch. 1 Answer Appendix.

Year	Students per Computer	Year	Students per Computer	Year	Students per Computer
1984	125	1990	22	1996	10
1985	75	1991	20	1997	7.8
1986	50	1992	18	1998	6.1
1987	37	1993	16	1999	5.7
1988	32	1994	14		
1989	25	1995	10.5		

Source: *The World Almanac*

Extend 1–9 Algebra Lab: Investigating Real-World Functions **59**

1 Focus

Materials
- grid paper

Easy–to–Make Manipulatives
Teaching Algebra with Manipulatives

Template for grid paper, p. 1

Teaching Tip Point out that the enrollment numbers in the table represent the number of students in thousands. This means that each number is multiplied by 1000 to represent the actual number of enrolled students. For example, the number 15,503 represents 15,503,000 students.

2 Teach

Working in Cooperative Groups
Have students work in groups of 2 or 3 to complete the example and Analyze the Results 1 and 2. Suggest that they write the actual years on their graphs below the scale.

Practice Have students complete Analyze the Results 3 and 4.

3 Assess

✓ Formative Assessment
Use Analyze the Results 5 to assess whether students can represent data with graphs and use their graphs to make predictions.

From Concrete to Abstract
Ask the students the difference between estimating the enrollment in 1975 and predicting the number of students per computer in 2010. Sample answer: The estimate for 1975 is based on known values. The estimate for 2010 extends beyond known values.

Additional Answers

1. Sample answers: 19,000 in 1910; 44,000 in 1975

2. Sample answer: 52,000

3. Sample answer: Draw a line on the graph that is closest to most of the data points.

4. Sample answer: If the U.S. population does not increase as quickly as in the past, then the number of students may be too high.

Dinah Zike's Foldables™

Have students look through the chapter to make sure they have included notes and examples in their Foldables for each tab.

Suggest that students keep their Foldables handy while completing the Study Guide and Review pages. Point out that their Foldables can serve are a quick review tool for studying for the Chapter Test.

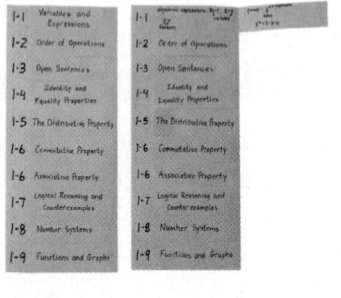

✓ Formative Assessment

Key Vocabulary The page reference after each word denotes where that term was first introduced. If students have difficulty answering questions 1–7, remind them that they can use these page references to refresh their memories about the vocabulary terms.

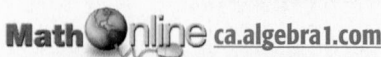

Vocabulary PuzzleMaker

improves students' mathematics vocabulary using four puzzle formats—crossword, scramble, word search using a word list, and word search using clues. Students can work online or from a printed worksheet.

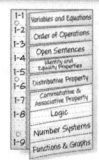

FOLDABLES Study Organizer — GET READY to Study

Be sure the following Key Concepts are noted in your Foldable.

Key Concepts

Order of Operations (Lesson 1-2)

Simplify the expression inside grouping symbols. Evaluate all powers. Multiply and divide then add and subtract in order from left to right.

Properties (Lessons 1-4, 1-5, and 1-6)

- Additive Identity: For any number a, the sum of a and 0 is a.
- Additive Inverse: For any number a, the sum of a and $-a$ is 0.

Multiplication Properties	
Identity	For any number a, $a \cdot 1 = a$
Property of Zero	For any number a, $a \cdot 0 = 0$
Inverse	For every number $\frac{a}{b}$, where a, $b \neq 0$, there is exactly one number $\frac{b}{a}$ such that $\frac{a}{b} \cdot \frac{b}{a} = 1$.

Properties of Equality	
Reflexive	For any numbers a, b, and c
Symmetric	$a = a$
Transitive	If $a = b$, then $b = a$.
Substitution	If $a = b$, then a may be replaced by b in any expression.
Distributive	$a(b + c) = ab + ac$ and $a(b - c) = ab - ac$
Commutative	$a + b = b + a$ and $ab = ba$
Associative	$(a + b) + c = a + (b + c)$ and $(ab)c = a(bc)$

Number Systems (Lesson 1-8)

- Real Numbers:
  - Natural Numbers: $\{1, 2, 3, ...\}$
  - Whole Numbers: $\{0, 1, 2, 3, ...\}$
  - Integers: $\{..., -2, -1, 0, 1, 2, ...\}$
  - Rational Numbers: $\frac{a}{b}$, where a and b are integers and $b \neq 0$

✓ Summative Assessment

CRM Vocabulary Test, p. 76

Key Vocabulary

algebraic expression (p. 6)	irrational numbers (p. 46)
coefficient (p. 29)	like terms (p. 28)
conditional statement (p. 39)	multiplicative inverses (p. 21)
continuous function (p. 55)	open sentence (p. 15)
coordinate system (p. 53)	order of operations (p. 10)
counterexample (p. 41)	perfect square (p. 46)
deductive reasoning (p. 40)	power (p. 6)
dependent variable (p. 54)	principal square root (p. 48)
discrete function (p. 55)	range (p. 55)
domain (p. 55)	rational approximation (p. 49)
exponent (p. 6)	rational number (p. 46)
factors (p. 6)	real numbers (p. 46)
function (p. 53)	reciprocal (p. 21)
independent variable (p. 54)	solution set (p. 15)
inequality (p. 16)	variable (p. 6)
integers (p. 46)	

Vocabulary Check

State whether each sentence is _true_ or _false_. If _false_, replace the underlined word or number to make a true sentence.

1. The vertical axis is also called the <u>y-axis</u>. **true**
2. Two numbers with a product of 1 are called <u>elements</u>. **false; multiplicative inverses**
3. A collection of objects or numbers is called a <u>function</u>. **false; set**
4. A nonnegative square root is called a <u>principal square root</u>. **true**
5. Irrational numbers and rational numbers together form the set of <u>negative</u> numbers. **false; real**
6. The <u>exponent</u> indicates the number of times the base is used as a factor. **true**
7. To <u>evaluate</u> an expression means to find its value. **true**

Students have multiple opportunities to review vocabulary: New and Review Vocabulary in the lessons, Vocabulary Check in the study Guide and Review, and using Vocabulary PuzzleMaker.

Lesson-by-Lesson Review

1–1 Variables and Expressions (pp. 6–9)

Write an algebraic expression for each verbal expression.

8. a number to the fifth power m^5

9. five times a number y squared $5y^2$

10. the sum of a number p and twenty-one $p + 21$

11. the difference of twice a number k and 8 $2k - 8$

Evaluate each expression.

12. 4^6 4,096

13. 2^5 32

Write a verbal expression for each algebraic expression.

14. $\frac{1}{2} + 7y$

15. $6p^2$

16. $3m^4 - 5$

17. **FROGS** A frog can jump twenty times the length of its body. If a frog's body length is b, write an algebraic expression to describe the length the frog could jump. $20b$

Example 1 Write an algebraic expression for *the sum of twice a number and five.*

Variable Let n represent the number.

Expression $2n + 5$

Example 2 Evaluate 7^5.

$7^5 = 7 \cdot 7 \cdot 7 \cdot 7 \cdot 7$ Use 7 as a factor 5 times.
$\quad\;\; = 16,807$ Multiply.

Example 3 Write a verbal expression for $4x^2 - 11$.

four times a number x squared minus eleven

14. the sum of one half and seven times a number y
15. six times the square of a number p
16. the difference of three times a number m to the fourth power and five

1–2 Order of Operations (pp. 10–14)

Evaluate each expression.

18. $3 + 16 \div 8 \cdot 5$ 13

19. $4^2 \cdot 3 - 5(6 + 3)$ 3

20. $288 \div [3(2^3 + 4)]$ 8

21. $\dfrac{6(4^3 + 2^2)}{9 + 3}$ 34

Evaluate each expression if $x = 3$, $t = 4$, and $y = 2$.

22. $t^2 + 3y$ 22

23. xty^3 96

24. $\dfrac{6ty}{x}$ 16

25. $8(x - y)^2 + 3t$ 20

26. **RUNNING** Alan ran twice as many miles on Tuesday as he did on Monday and five more miles on Wednesday than he did on Monday. Write and evaluate an expression to find the total number of miles he ran if he ran 5 miles on Monday.

Example 4 Evaluate $x^2 - (y + 2)$ if $x = 4$ and $y = 3$.

$x^2 - (y + 2) = 4^2 - (3 + 2)$ Replace x with 4 and y with 3.

$\qquad\qquad\quad = 4^2 - 5$ Add 3 and 2.

$\qquad\qquad\quad = 16 - 5$ Evaluate 4^2.

$\qquad\qquad\quad = 11$ Subtract 5 from 16.

26. $w + 2w + w + 5$; 25 mi

Lesson-by-Lesson Review
Intervention If the given examples are not sufficient to review the topics covered by the questions, remind students that the page references tell them where to review that topic in their textbooks.

Two-Day Option Have students complete the Lesson-by-Lesson Review on pp. 61–64. Then you can use ExamView® Assessment Suite to customize another review worksheet that practices all the objectives of this chapter or only the objectives on which your students need more help.

 For more information on ExamView® Assessment Suite, see p. 4C.

Differentiated Instruction
Super DVD: MindJogger Videoquizzes Use this DVD as an alternative format of review for the test. For more information on this game show format, see p. 4D.

 Students can complete the exercises in the **Lesson-by-Lesson Review** as they prepare for the chapter test. If they need extra help, examples are provided.

Additional Answers

28. $\{4, 5, 6, 7, 8\}$

36. 4; Additive Identity

37. $\frac{1}{5}$; Multiplicative Inverse

38. 0; Multiplicative Property of Zero

39. $3(4 \div 4)^2 - \frac{1}{4}(4)$

$\quad = 3(1)^2 - \frac{1}{4}(4)$ Substitution

$\quad = 3(1) - \frac{1}{4}(4)$ Substitution

$\quad = 3 - \frac{1}{4}(4)$ Substitution

$\quad = 3 - 1$ Multiplicative Inverse

$\quad = 2$ Substitution

40. $(7 - 7)(5) + 3 \cdot 1$

$\quad = (0)(5) + 3 \cdot 1$ Substitution

$\quad = 0 + 3 \cdot 1$ Multiplicative Property of Zero

$\quad = 0 + 3$ Multiplicative Identity

$\quad = 3$ Substitution

41. $\frac{1}{2} \cdot 2 + 2[2 \cdot 3 - 1]$

$\quad = \frac{1}{2} \cdot 2 + 2[6 - 1]$ Substitution

$\quad = \frac{1}{2} \cdot 2 + 2(5)$ Substitution

$\quad = \frac{1}{2} \cdot 2 + 10$ Substitution

$\quad = 1 + 10$ Multiplicative Inverse

$\quad = 11$ Substitution

1–3   **Open Sentences** (pp. 15–20)

Find the solution of each equation or the solution set of each inequality if the replacement set is $\{4, 5, 6, 7, 8\}$.

27. $g + 9 = 16$ $\{7\}$ **28.** $10 - p < 7$ See margin.

29. $\frac{x+1}{3} = 2$ $\{5\}$ **30.** $2a + 5 \geq 15$ $\{5, 6, 7, 8\}$

Solve each equation.

31. $w = 4 + 3^2$ 13   **32.** $d = \frac{7(4 \cdot 3)}{18 \div 3}$ 14

33. $k = 5[2(4) - 1^3]$ 35   **34.** $\frac{6(7) - 2(3)}{4^2 - 6(2)} = n$ 9

35. HOMECOMING Tickets to the homecoming dance are \$9 for one person and \$15 for two people. If a group of seven students wish to go to the dance, write and solve an equation that would represent the least expensive price p of their tickets. $p = 15(3) + 9(1);\ p = \$54$

Example 5 Find the solution set for $14 + 2h < 24$ if the replacement set is $\{1, 3, 5, 7\}$.

Replace h in $14 + 2h < 24$ with each value in the replacement set.

h	$14 + 2h < 24$	True or False?
1	$14 + 2(1) < 24$	True
3	$14 + 2(3) < 24$	True
5	$14 + 2(5) < 24$	False
7	$14 + 2(7) < 24$	False

The solution set is $\{1, 3\}$.

Example 6 Solve $5^2 - 3 = y$.

$5^2 - 3 = y$ Original equation

$25 - 3 = y$ Evaluate 5^2.

$22 = y$ Subtract 3 from 25.

The solution is 22.

1–4   **Identity and Equality Properties** (pp. 21–25)

Find the value of n in each equation. Name the property that is used.

36. $4 + 0 = n$ **37.** $5n = 1$ **38.** $0 = 17n$
36–38. See margin.

Evaluate each expression. Name the property used in each step. 39–41. See margin.

39. $3(4 \div 4)^2 - \frac{1}{4}(4)$

40. $(7 - 7)(5) + 3 \cdot 1$

41. $\frac{1}{2} \cdot 2 + 2[2 \cdot 3 - 1]$

42. COOKIES Emilia promised her brother one half of the cookies that she made. If she did not make any cookies, determine how many she owes her brother and identify the property represented. **Emilia does not owe Mark any cookies; Multiplicative Property of Zero.**

Example 7 Find the value of n in $n \cdot 9 = 9$. Name the property that is used.

$n = 1$, since $1 \cdot 9 = 9$. This is the Multiplicative Identity Property.

Example 8 Evaluate $7 \cdot 1 + 5(2 - 2)$. Name the property used in each step.

$7 \cdot 1 + 5(2 - 2) = 7 \cdot 1 + 5(0)$ Substitution

$\quad = 7 + 5(0)$ Multiplicative Identity

$\quad = 7 + 0$ Multiplicative Property of Zero

$\quad = 7$ Additive Identity

Mixed Problem Solving
For mixed problem-solving practice,
see page 744.

CHAPTER
1 **Study Guide and Review**

1-5 **The Distributive Property** (pp. 26–31)

43–44. See margin.
Rewrite each expression using the
Distributive Property. Then evaluate.

43. $8(15 - 6)$ **44.** $4(x + 1)$

Simplify each expression. If not possible,
write *simplified*.

45. $3w - w + 4v + 3v$ $2w + 7v$

46. $4np + 7mp$ simplified

47. EXPENSES Nikki's monthly expenses
are $550 for rent, $225 for groceries,
$110 for transportation, and $150 for
utilities. Use the Distributive Property
to write and evaluate an expression for
her total expenses for nine months.

Example 9 Rewrite $5(t + 3)$ using the
Distributive Property. Then evaluate.

$5(t + 3) = 5(t) + 5(3)$ Distributive Property

$\qquad = 5t + 15$ Multiply.

Example 10 Simplify $2x^2 + 4x^2 + 7x$.
If not possible, write *simplified*.

$2x^2 + 4x^2 + 7x = (2 + 4)x^2 + 7x$ Distributive
Property

$\qquad = 6x^2 + 7x$ Substitution

47. $9(550 + 225 + 110 + 150) = \$9,315$

1-6 **Commutative and Associative Properties** (pp. 33–37)

Simplify each expression.
48. $7w^2 + w + 2w^2$ $9w^2 + w$

49. $3(2 + 3x) + 21x$ $6 + 30x$

50. ZOO At a zoo, each adult admission
costs $9.75, and each child costs $7.25.
Find the cost of admission for two
adults and four children. **$48.50**

Example 11 Write an algebraic
expression for *five times the sum of x
and y increased by 2x.* Then simplify.

$5(x + y) + 2x = 5x + 5y + 2x$

$\qquad = 5x + 2x + 5y$

$\qquad = (5 + 2)x + 5y$

$\qquad = 7x + 5y$

1-7 **Logical Reasoning** (pp. 39–44)

51. Identify the hypothesis and conclusion
of the statement. Then write the
statement in if-then form.
School begins at 7:30 A.M. **See margin.**

52. Find a counterexample for *if you have
no umbrella, you will get wet.*
See margin.

53. LIGHTNING It is said that lightning never
strikes twice in the same place. Identify
the hypothesis and conclusion of this
statement and write it in if-then form.
See margin.

Example 12 Identify the hypothesis and
conclusion of the statement *The trumpet
player must audition to be in the band.*
Then write the statement in if-then form.

Hypothesis: a person is a trumpet player

Conclusion: the person must audition to be
in the band

If a person is a trumpet player, then the
person must audition to be in the band.

Additional Answers

43. $8(15) - 8(6) = 72$

44. $4(x) + 4(1) = 4x + 4$

51. H: it is a school day; C: the
day begins at 7:30 A.M.; If it is a
school day, then the day begins at
7:30 A.M.

52. Sample answers: It is not raining;
you were not outside; you wore a
poncho; you borrowed a friend's
umbrella.

53. H: lightning has struck twice; C: it
has not done so in the same place;
If lightning has struck twice, then it
has not done so in the same place.

Problem Solving Review

For additional practice in problem solving for Chapter 1, see the Mixed Problem Solving Appendix, p. 744 in the Student Handbook section.

Anticipation Guide

Have students complete the Chapter 1 Anticipation Guide and discuss how their responses have changed now that they have completed Chapter 1.

CRM Anticipation Guide, p. 3

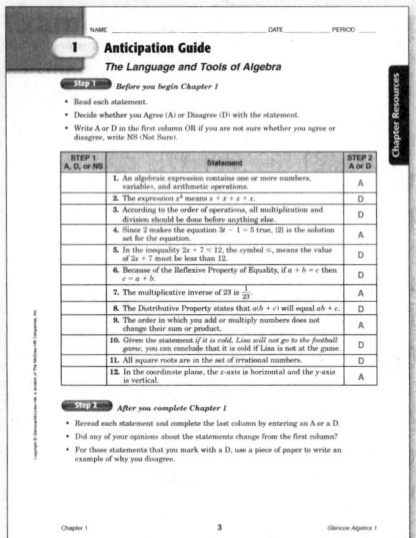

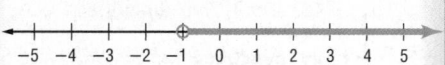

Six forms of chapter tests, and an Vocabulary Test, and an Extended-Response Test are provided for each chapter. These are available in the Chapter Resource Masters.

1–8 **Number Systems** (pp. 46–52)

Name the set or sets of numbers to which each real number belongs.

54. $\frac{7}{15}$ rationals **55.** $\sqrt{45}$ irrationals

Graph each set of numbers.

56. $\{-3, -1, 0, 2, 5\}$ **57.** $x \le 6.5$
See margin.   See margin.

Order each set of numbers from least to greatest. **58.** $-\sqrt{4}$, $\sqrt{11}$, 3.5 and $3\frac{11}{20}$

58. $-\sqrt{4}$, 3.5, $\sqrt{11}$, $3\frac{11}{20}$

59. $\sqrt{27}$, $5\frac{1}{5}$, $-\sqrt{34}$, $-\frac{47}{9}$
$-\sqrt{34}$, $-\frac{47}{9}$, $\sqrt{27}$ and $5\frac{1}{5}$

60. ROOMS Belinda's square bedroom is $10\frac{41}{50}$ feet long. The area of Jarrod's bedroom is 115 square feet. Whose bedroom is larger? Explain. **See margin.**

Example 13 Name the set or sets of numbers to which $\frac{48}{6}$ belongs.

$\frac{48}{6} = 8$, so $\frac{48}{6}$ is a natural number, a whole number, an integer, and a rational number.

Example 14 Graph $x > -1$.

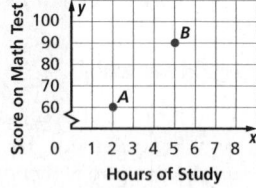

Example 15 Order $-\frac{29}{4}$, $\sqrt{7}$, and -7.85 from least to greatest.

$-\frac{29}{4} = -7.25$ Write each number as a decimal and compare.

$\sqrt{7} \approx 2.646$

So, the order is -7.85, $-\frac{29}{4}$, and $\sqrt{7}$.

1–9 **Functions and Graphs** (pp. 53–58)

For Exercises 61 and 62, use the graph in Example 16. **61–62. See margin.**

61. Name the ordered pair at point A and explain what it represents.

62. Identify the independent and dependent variables for the function. Explain.

63. ALTITUDE Identify the graph that represents the altitude of an airplane taking off, flying for a while, then landing. **Graph C**

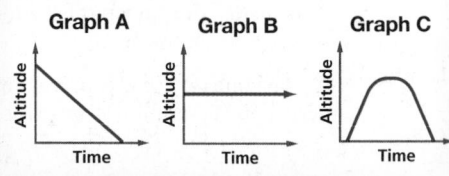

Graph A   Graph B   Graph C

Example 16 Name the ordered pair at point B and explain what it represents.

Point B is at 5 along the x-axis and 90 along the y-axis. So, its ordered pair is $(5, 90)$. This represents a score of 90 on the math test with 5 hours of study.

Additional Answers

56.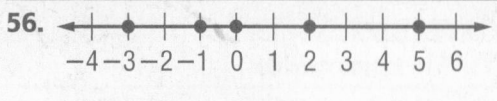

57.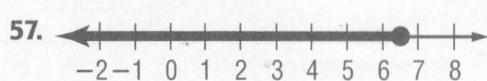

60. Belinda; her bedroom has an area of more than 117 square feet.

61. (2, 60); this represents a score of 60 on the math test with 2 hours of study.

62. Hours of study is the independent variable as it is unaffected by the score on the math test, and the score on the math test is the dependent variable as it is affected by hours of study.

Write an algebraic expression for each verbal expression.

1. the sum of a number x and 13 $x + 13$
2. 25 increased by the product of 2 and a number $25 + 2n$
3. 7 less a number y squared $7 - y^2$

Simplify each expression.

4. $5(9 + 3) - 3 \cdot 4$ **48**   5. $12 \cdot 6 \div 3 \cdot 2 \div 8$ **6**

Evaluate each expression if $a = 2$, $b = 5$, $c = 3$, and $d = 1$.

6. $a^2 b + c$ **23**   7. $(cd)^3$ **27**   8. $(a + d)c$ **9**

9. **MULTIPLE CHOICE** Tia owns a dog grooming business. How much did she earn in one week if she groomed 14 small dogs, 11 medium-size dogs, and 3 large dogs? **D**

Dog Grooming	
Size of Dog	Cost ($)
small	25.00
medium	27.50
large	36.50

A $117.00

B $636.65

C $700.00

D $762.00

Solve each equation.

10. $y = (4.5 + 0.8) - 3.2$ **2.1**
11. $4^2 - 3(4 - 2) = x$ **10**
12. Evaluate $3^2 - 2 + (2 - 2)$. Name the property used in each step. **See margin.**

Rewrite each expression in simplest form.

13. $4x + 2y - 2x + y$ $2x + 3y$
14. $3(2a + b) - 5a + 4b$ $a + 7b$

Find a counterexample for each conditional statement.

15. **EXERCISE** If you enjoy running, then you will run a marathon. **See margin.**
16. If $x \le 6$, then $2x - 3 < 9$. $x = 6$

Replace each ● with <, >, or = to make each sentence true.

17. $\sqrt{43}$ ● $6.\overline{5}$ **>**   18. $\frac{1}{10}$ ● $\sqrt{10}$ **<**

19. $-\sqrt{7}$ ● $-\frac{5}{2}$ **<**   20. $0.\overline{36}$ ● $\frac{4}{11}$ **=**

21. **MULTIPLE CHOICE** Which number serves as a counterexample to the statement below? **J**

   If n is a prime number, then n is odd.

   F 5

   G 4

   H 3

   J 2

22. **MULTIPLE CHOICE** Riders must be at least 52 inches tall to ride the newest ride at an amusement park. Which graph represents the heights of these riders? **A**

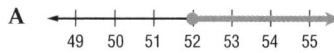

Sketch a reasonable graph for each situation.

23. A basketball is shot from the free throw line and falls through the net.
24. A nickel is dropped on a stack of pennies and bounces off.
23–24. See Ch. 1 Answer Appendix.

 **Summative Assessment**

CRM **Chapter 1 Resource Masters**

Leveled Chapter 1 Tests			
Form	Type	Level	Pages
1	MC	BL	77–78
2A	MC	OL	79–80
2B	MC	OL	81–82
2C	FR	OL	83–84
2D	FR	OL	85–86
3	FR	AL	87–88

MC = multiple-choice questions
FR = free-response questions
BL = below grade level
OL = on grade level
AL = above grade level

- Vocabulary Test, p. 76
- Extended-Response Test, p. 89

 **ExamView** Assessment Suite Customize and create multiple versions of your chapter tests and their answer keys. All of the questions from the leveled chapter tests in the *Chapter 1 Resource Masters* are also available on ExamView Assessment Suite with the California Standard that each item assesses.

Additional Answers

12. $3^2 - 2 + (2 - 2)$
   $= 3^2 - 2 + 0$ Substitution
   $= 9 - 2 + 0$ Substitution
   $= 7 + 0$ Substitution
   $= 7$ Additive Identity

15. You can enjoy running but never run a marathon.

Data-Driven Decision Making	Exercises	Lesson	Standard	Resources for Review
Diagnostic Teaching Based on the results of the Chapter 1 Practice Test, use the following to review concepts that students continue to find challenging.	13–14	1–6	25.0	CRM Study Guide and Intervention, pp. 43–44, 50–51, 57–58, 65–66 Math Online • Extra Examples • Personal Tutor • Concepts in Motion
	15–16, 21	1–7	24.3, 25.1	
	17–20	1–8	2.0	
	22–24	1–9	16.0, 17.0	

California Standards Practice
Chapter 1

 Read each question. Then fill in the correct answer on the answer document provided by your teacher or on a sheet of paper.

1 The radius of a circular flower garden is 4 meters. How many meters of edging will be needed to surround the garden? **C**

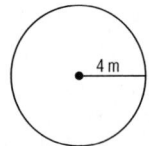

4 m

A 7.14 m

B 12.56 m

C 25.12

D 20.24 m

2 If $x = 6$ and $y = 2$, then $\left(\dfrac{x}{y}\right)^2 + (x)(y) =$ **21**

3 When is this statement true? **H**

> The opposite of a number is greater than the original number.

F This statement is never true.

G This statement is always true.

H This statement is true for negative numbers.

J This statement is true for positive numbers.

TEST-TAKING TIP

Question 3 If you are unsure of the correct answer to a multiple-choice question, eliminate the answers you know are incorrect. Then consider the remaining choices.

4 The graph below shows how many toy trains are assembled at a factory at the end of 10-minute intervals. What is the best prediction for the number of products assembled per hour? **H**

Toy Train Production

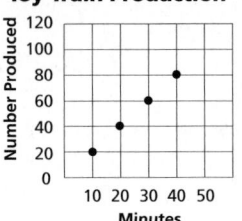

F 80

G 100

H 120

J 130

5

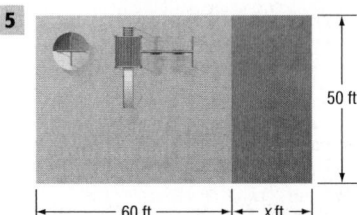

50 ft

60 ft — x ft

Karla has a backyard play area that has the dimensions shown above. She is expanding the play area by adding x feet to the 60-foot side. The area of the addition is $50x$. How can the area of the new play area be expressed in terms of x? **A**

A $3000 + 50x$

B $3000 - 50x$

C $60 + 50x$

D $60 - 50x$

66 Chapter 1 The Language and Tools of Algebra

 Math Online **California Standards Practice at** ca.algebra1.com

More California
Standards Practice
For practice by standard,
see pages CA1–CA43.

6 Which number serves as a counterexample to the statement below? **H**

> All positive integers are divisible by 3 and 5.

F 15
G 45
H 65
J 75

7 The square root of 8 is between **C**

A 0 and 1.
B 1 and 2.
C 2 and 3.
D 3 and 4.

8 Which expression represents the second step of simplifying the algebraic expression? **J**

Step 1: $3 + 2(6x + y) + 5(x + 4y)$

Step 2: [ ]

Step 3: $17x + 22y + 3$

F $25(6x + y)(x + 4y)$
G $5(6x + y) + 5x + 4y$
H $3 + 12x + y + 5x + 4y$
J $3 + 12x + 2y + 5x + 20y$

9 The chart below shows the number of books of different types checked out of the Middletown High School library each day one week.

	Books Checked Out		
	Science	**Philosophy**	**Literature**
Monday	912	412	902
Tuesday	314	234	397
Wednesday	298	337	487
Thursday	321	328	446
Friday	432	423	557

What is the mean number of Philosophy books checked out per day? **346.8**

Pre-AP/Anchor Problem

Record your answers on a sheet of paper. Show your work.

10 The Lee family is going to play miniature golf. The family is composed of two adults and four children. **10a. $2a + 4c \leq 30$**

	Greens Fees	
	Before 6 P.M.	**After 6 P.M.**
Adult (a)	$5.00	$6.50
Children (c)	$3.00	$4.50

a. Write an inequality to show the cost for the family to play miniature golf if they don't want to spend more than $30.

b. How much will it cost the family to play after 6 P.M.? **$31**

c. How much will it cost the family to play before 6 P.M.? **$22**

Item Analysis
Question 2 is a griddable question. In a griddable question, students arrive at an answer and then record it in a special grid by coloring the appropriate bubble under each digit of the answer.

Answer Sheet Practice
Have students simulate taking a standardized test by recording their answers on practice recording sheets.

[CRM] Student Recording Sheet, p. 71

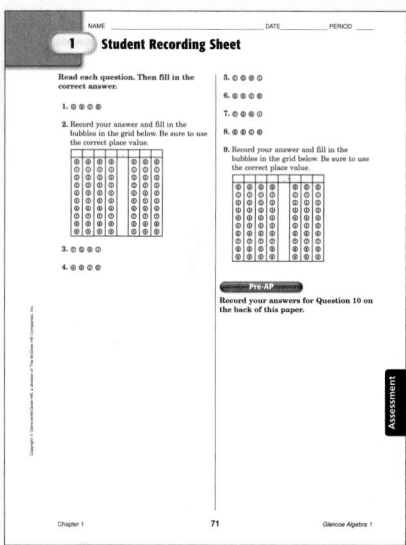

A *Student Recording Sheet* for the California Standards Practice is provided for each chapter in the Chapter Resource Masters.

NEED EXTRA HELP?										
If You Missed Question...	1	2	3	4	5	6	7	8	9	10
Go to Lesson or Page...	706	1-2	1-4	1-9	1-1	1-7	1-8	1-5	711	1-3
For Help with Standard...	7MG2.1	7AF1.2	25.3	7AF1.5	10.0	24.3	7NS2.4	5.0	6PS1.1	7AF1.2

Homework Option

Get Ready for Chapter 2 Assign students the exercises on p. 69 as homework to assess whether they possess the prerequisite skills needed for the next chapter.

Pages 8–9, Lesson 1-1

30. Sample answer: 7 times p

31. Sample answer: one eighth of y

32. Sample answer: fifteen plus r

33. Sample answer: w minus 24

34. Sample answer: 3 times x squared

35. Sample answer: r to the fourth power divided by 9

36. Sample answer: 6 more than the product 2 times a

37. Sample answer: n cubed times p to the fifth power

45. Sample answer: You can use the expression $4s$ to find the perimeter of a baseball diamond. The perimeter of a baseball diamond is four times the length of the sides and the sum of the four sides; $s + s + s + s$.

Page 19, Lesson 1-3

52. Sample answer: You can use equations to determine how much money you have to spend and how you can spend your money. Answers should include examples such as calculating gasoline required for a trip and cooking times.

Pages 23–24, Lesson 1-4

1. 0; Multiplicative Property of Zero

2. 17; Additive Identity

3. 6; Multiplicative Inverse

4. $11 + 2(8 - 7)$

$= 11 + 2(1)$ Substitution

$= 11 + 2$ Multiplicative Identity

$= 13$ Substitution

5. $6(12 - 48 \div 4)$

$= 6(12 - 12)$ Substitution

$= 6(0)$ Substitution

$= 0$ Multiplicative Property of Zero

6. $\left(15 \cdot \frac{1}{15} + 8 \cdot 0\right) \cdot 12$

$= (1 + 8 \cdot 0) \cdot 12$ Multiplicative Inverse Property

$= (1 + 0) \cdot 12$ Multiplicative Property of Zero

$= 1 \cdot 12$ Additive Identity

$= 12$ Multiplicative Identity

8. 1; Multiplicative Identity

9. 5; Multiplicative Identity

10. $\frac{1}{8}$; Multiplicative Inverse

11. 0; Additive Identity

12. 0; Additive Identity

13. $\frac{1}{2}$; Multiplicative Inverse

14. $\frac{1}{3}$; Additive Identity

15. 1; Multiplicative Inverse

16. 4; Additive Inverse

17. $\frac{1}{2}$; Additive Inverse

18. $(1 \div 5)5 \cdot 14$

$= \frac{1}{5}(5) \cdot 14$ Substitution

$= 1 \cdot 14$ Multiplicative Inverse

$= 14$ Multiplicative Identity

19. $7 + (9 - 3^2)$

$= 7 + (9 - 9)$ Substitution

$= 7 + 0$ Substitution

$= 7$ Additive Identity

20. $\frac{3}{4}[4 \div (7 - 4)]$

$= \frac{3}{4}[4 \div 3]$ Substitution

$= \frac{3}{4} \cdot \frac{4}{3}$ Substitution

$= 1$ Multiplicative Inverse

21. $[3 \div (2 \cdot 1)] \frac{2}{3}$

$= [3 \div 2] \frac{2}{3}$ Multiplicative Identity

$= \frac{3}{2} \cdot \frac{2}{3}$ Substitution

$= 1$ Multiplicative Inverse

22. $2(3 \cdot 2 - 5) + 3 \cdot \frac{1}{3}$

$= 2(6 - 5) + 3 \cdot \frac{1}{3}$ Substitution

$= 2(1) + 3 \cdot \frac{1}{3}$ Substitution

$= 2 + 3 \cdot \frac{1}{3}$ Multiplicative Identity

$= 2 + 1$ Multiplicative Inverse

$= 3$ Substitution

23. $6 \cdot \frac{1}{6} + 5(12 \div 4 - 3)$

$= 6 \cdot \frac{1}{6} + 5(3 - 3)$ Substitution

$= 6 \cdot \frac{1}{6} + 5(0)$ Substitution

$= 6 \cdot \frac{1}{6} + 0$ Multiplicative Property of Zero

$= 1 + 0$ Multiplicative Inverse

$= 1$ Additive Identity

Answers that don't fit on the student page or in the margin of the Teacher Wraparound Edition can be found in the Answer Appendix pages at the end of each chapter.

25. $2 \cdot \frac{22}{7} \cdot 14^2 + 2 \cdot \frac{22}{7} \cdot 14 \cdot 7$

$= 2 \cdot \frac{22}{7} \cdot 196 + 2 \cdot \frac{22}{7} \cdot 14 \cdot 7$ Substitution

$= \frac{44}{7} \cdot 196 + \frac{44}{7} \cdot 14 \cdot 7$ Substitution

$= 1232 + 616$ Substitution

$= 1848$ Substitution

1848 in^2

29. $3 + 5(4 - 2^2) - 1$

$= 3 + 5(4 - 4) - 1$ Substitution

$= 3 + 5(0) - 1$ Substitution

$= 3 + 0 - 1$ Multiplicative Property of Zero

$= 3 - 1$ Additive Identity

$= 2$ Substitution

30. $7 - 8(9 - 3^2)$

$= 7 - 8(9 - 9)$ Substitution

$= 7 - 8(0)$ Substitution

$= 7 - 0$ Multiplicative Property of Zero

$= 7$ Additive Identity

31. $\left[\frac{5}{8} \left(1 + \frac{3}{5} \right) \right] \cdot 17$

$= \frac{5}{8} \left(\frac{8}{5} \right) \cdot 17$ Substitution

$= 1 \cdot 17$ Multiplicative Inverse

$= 17$ Multiplicative Identity

32. $8(100{,}000 + 50{,}000) + 3(50{,}000 + 50{,}000)$

$= 8(150{,}000) + 3(100{,}000)$ Substitution

$= 1{,}200{,}000 + 300{,}000$ Substitution

$= 1{,}500{,}000$ Substitution

34. $25(2 - 0.3) + 80(2.5 - 1) + 40(10 - 6)$

$= 25(1.7) + 80(1.5) + 40(4)$ Substitution

$= 42.5 + 120 + 160$ Substitution

$= 322.50$ Substitution

35. Sometimes; sample answer: true: $x = 2, y = 1, z = 4, w = 3$; $2 \cdot 4 > 1 \cdot 3$; false: $x = 1, y = -1, z = -2, w = -3$; $1(-2) < (-1)(-3)$

Page 30, Lesson 1-5

44. Sample answer: $(4ab + 2ab + 7ab) + (3b + a)$. Use the Distributive Property to combine like terms $4ab$, $2ab$, and $7ab$.

45. Courtney; she correctly used the Distributive Property.

Pages 34–37, Lesson 1-6

1A. $35 + 17 + 5 + 3$

$= 35 + 5 + 17 + 3$ Commutative (+)

$= (35 + 5) + (17 + 3)$ Associative (+)

$= 40 + 20$ Add.

$= 60$ Add.

1B. $8\frac{3}{4} + 12 + 5\frac{1}{4}$

$= 8\frac{3}{4} + 5\frac{1}{4} + 12$ Commutative (+)

$= \left(8\frac{3}{4} + 5\frac{1}{4} \right) + 12$ Associative (+)

$= 14 + 12$ Add.

$= 26$ Add.

2A. $2.9 \cdot 4 \cdot 10$

$= 2.9 \cdot 10 \cdot 4$ Commutative (×)

$= (2.9 \cdot 10) \cdot 4$ Associative (×)

$= 29 \cdot 4$ Multiply.

$= 116$ Multiply.

2B. $\frac{5}{3} \cdot 25 \cdot 3 \cdot 2$

$= \frac{5}{3} \cdot 3 \cdot 25 \cdot 2$ Commutative (×)

$= \left(\frac{5}{3} \cdot 3 \right) \cdot (25 \cdot 2)$ Associative (×)

$= 5 \cdot 50$ Multiply.

$= 250$ Multiply.

3A. $5(q^2 - r) + 8(3q + 2r)$

$= 5(q^2) - 5(r) + 8(3q) + 8(2r)$ Distributive

$= 5q^2 - 5r + 24q + 16r$ Multiply and Associative (×)

$= 5q^2 + 24q + 16r - 5r$ Commutative (+)

$= 5q^2 + 24q + (16r - 5r)$ Associative (+)

$= 5q^2 + 24q + (16 - 5)r$ Distributive

$= 5q^2 + 24q + 11r$ Substitution (=)

3B. $6(x - 2y) + 4(-3x + y)$

$= 6(x) - 6(2y) + 4(-3x) + 4(y)$ Distributive

$= 6x - 12y - 12x + 16y$ Multiply and Associative (×)

$= (6x - 12x) + (-12y + 16y)$ Associative

$= (6 - 12)x + (-12 + 16)y$ Distributive

$= -12x + 4y$ Substitution

1. Sample answer:

$14 + 18 + 26$

$= 14 + 26 + 18$ Commutative (+)

$= (14 + 26) + 18$ Associative (+)

$= 40 + 18$ Add.

$= 58$ Add.

2. Sample answer:

$3\frac{1}{2} + 4 + 2\frac{1}{2}$

$= 3\frac{1}{2} + 2\frac{1}{2} + 4$ Commutative (+)

$= \left(3\frac{1}{2} + 2\frac{1}{2}\right) + 4$ Associative (+)

$= 6 + 4$ Add.

$= 10$ Add.

3. Sample answer:

$5 \cdot 3 \cdot 6 \cdot 4$

$= 5 \cdot 6 \cdot 3 \cdot 4$ Commutative ($\times$)

$= (5 \cdot 6) \cdot (3 \cdot 4)$ Associative ($\times$)

$= 30 \cdot 12$ Multiply.

$= 360$ Multiply.

4. Sample answer:

$\frac{5}{6} \cdot 16 \cdot \frac{3}{4}$

$= \frac{5}{6} \cdot \left(16 \cdot \frac{3}{4}\right)$ Associative ($\times$)

$= \frac{5}{6} \cdot 12$ Multiply.

$= 10$ Multiply.

10. Sample answer:

$\frac{1}{2}(p + 2q) + \frac{3}{4}q$

$= \frac{1}{2}(p) + \frac{1}{2}(2q) + \frac{3}{4}q$ Distributive

$= \frac{1}{2}p + q + \frac{3}{4}q$ Multiply.

$= \frac{1}{2}p + (q + \frac{3}{4}q)$ Associative (+)

$= \frac{1}{2}p + 1\frac{3}{4}q$ Add.

31. $2(s + t) - s$

$= 2(s) + 2(t) - s$ Distributive

$= 2s + 2t - s$ Multiply.

$= 2t + 2s - s$ Commutative (+)

$= 2t + s(2 - 1)$ Distributive

$= 2t + s(1)$ Subtract.

$= 2t + s$ Multiplicative Identity

32. $5(xy) + 3xy$

$= xy(5 + 3)$ Distributive

$= xy(8)$ Add.

$= 8xy$ Multiply.

33. $6z^2 + (7 + z^2 + 6)$

$= 6z^2 + (z^2 + 7 + 6)$ Commutative (+)

$= (6z^2 + z^2) + (7 + 6)$ Associative (+)

$= z^2(6 + 1) + (7 + 6)$ Distributive

$= z^2(7) + 13$ Add.

$= 7z^2 + 13$ Multiply.

34. $6(x + y^2) - 3(x + y^2)$

$= 6(x) + 6(y^2) - 3(x) - 3(y^2)$ Distributive

$= 6x + 6y^2 - 3x - 3y^2$ Multiply

$= 6x - 3x + 6y^2 - 3y^2$ Commutative (+)

$= x(6 - 3) + y^2(6 - 3)$ Distributive

$= x(3) + y^2(3)$ Subtract.

$= 3x + 3y^2$ Multiply.

42. Sample answer: $2(10.95) + 3(7.5) + 2(5) + 5(18.99)$; $2(10.95 + 5) + 3(7.5) + 5(18.99)$

56. $3(5 - 5 \cdot 1^2) + 21 \div 7$

$= 3(5 - 5 \cdot 1) + 21 \div 7$ Substitution

$= 3(5 - 5) + 21 \div 7$ Multiplicative Identity

$= 3(0) + 21 \div 7$ Substitution

$= 0 + 21 \div 7$ Multiplicative Property of Zero

$= 0 + 3$ Substitution.

$= 3$ Additive Identity.

Pages 39–43, Lesson 1-7

1A. H: It is warm this afternoon; C: We will have the party outside.

3B. No valid conclusion; the conditional statement does not say that there won't be quizzes on days other than Wednesday.

21. H: $x = 8$; C: $x^2 - 3x = 40$; If $x = 8$, then $x^2 - 3x = 40$

22. H: $s > 9$; C: $4s + 6 > 42$; If $s > 9$, then $4s + 6 > 42$

23. H: a triangle with all sides congruent; C: it is an equilateral triangle; If all the sides of a triangle are congruent, then it is an equilateral triangle.

24. H: a number divisible by 9; C: the sum of the digits of a number is a multiple of 9; If a number is divisible by 9, then the sum of its digits is a multiple of 9.

25. Ian will buy a DVD box set.

26. No valid conclusion; the hypothesis does not say that Ian won't buy a DVD box set if it costs more than $70.

27. The DVD box set cost $70 or more.

28. No valid conclusion; the conditional does not mention Ian buying 2 DVD box sets.

29. A person born in North Carolina moved to California.

30. There is a professional team in Canada.

35. Sample answer:

36. Sample answer:

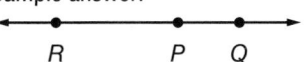

37. The perimeter is doubled.

40. If the number ends with an even number it is divisible by 2 and if a number ends with a five or zero it is divisible by 5.

41. Sample answer: If a number is divisible by 2 and 3 , the it must be a multiple of 6.

Pages 47–52, Lesson 1-8

3A.

3B.

9.

10.

11.

Page 51, Lesson 1-8

28. No; Sample answer: $-\sqrt{5} + \sqrt{5} = 0$

29. No; Sample answer: $\sqrt{5} - \sqrt{5} = 0$

30. Yes; Sample answer: $1 + 3 = 4$

31. Yes; Sample answer: $3 \times 2 = 6$

32. No; Sample answer: $\sqrt{6} \times \sqrt{6} = 6$

33. No; Sample answer: $2\sqrt{3} \div \sqrt{3} = 2$

34. Yes; Sample answer: $5 - 3 = 2$

35. Yes; Sample answer: $\frac{3}{5} - \frac{1}{5} = \frac{2}{5}$

36. Yes; Sample answer: $\frac{2}{5} \div \frac{5}{7} = \frac{14}{25}$

37. Yes; Sample answer: $-3 \times -8 = 24$

38.

39.

40.

41.

Page 52, Lesson 1-8

64. True; the whole numbers and the natural numbers are closed under addition and multiplication. Neither set of numbers are closed under subtraction or division.

65. True; the average of $\sqrt{2}$ and $\sqrt{3}$ is a decimal number that does not terminate or repeat, so it is irrational.

Pages 55–58, Lesson 1-9

4B. (1, 0.25), (2, 0.50), (3, 0.75), (4, 1.00), (5, 1.25)

Selling Books

1. (2, 35); On day 2, the average temperature is about 35°F.

2. (7, 49); On day 7, the average temperature is about 49°F.

3. independent: day; dependent: temperature

6. (0, 500), (0.2, 480), (0.4, 422), (0.6, 324), (0.8, 186), (1, 10)

7.

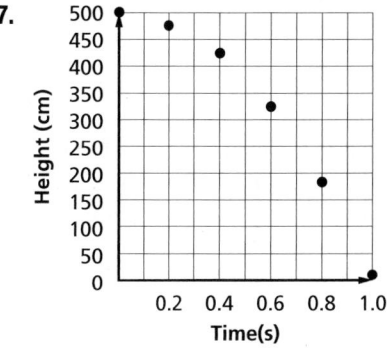

8. domain: {0, 0.2, 0.4, 0.6, 0.8, 1}; range: {10, 186, 324, 422, 480, 500}

9. The function is discrete because the points are not connected with a line or a curve.

10. (1,5); The dog walker earns $5 for walking 1 dog.

11. (5, 25); The dog walker earns $25 for walking 5 dogs.

12. independent: number of dogs walked; dependent: amount earned

13. (02, 3); In the year 2002, sales were about $3 million.

14. (06, 5); in the year 2006, sales were about $5 million.

16. Teresa gets a fever and takes some medicine. After a while her temperature comes down then slowly begins to go up again.

17. Their altitude is increasing as they ascend. Then they go down a steep incline. They then make a longer climb up another hill.

22. The independent variable is the number of sides and the dependent variable is the sum of the angle measures.

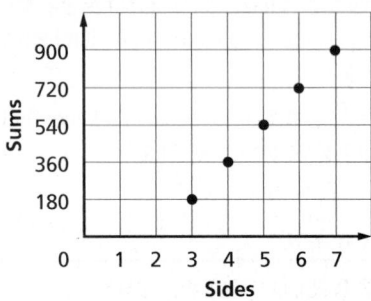

23. domain: {3, 4, 5, 6, 7} range: {180, 360, 540, 720, 900}

24. Discrete; the graph is a set of individual points.

25. 1080; 1260; 1440

26. Sample answer: A dependent variable is determined by the independent variable for a given function.

28.

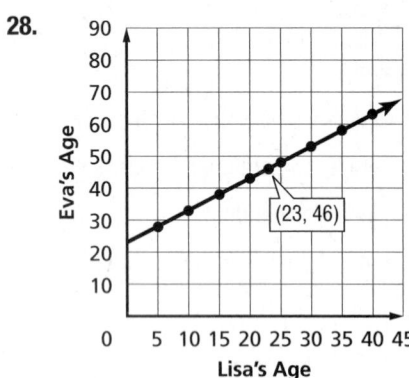

29. Sample answer: Real-world data can be recorded and visualized in a graph and by expressing an event as a function of another event. A graph gives you a visual representation of the situation which is easier to analyze and evaluate. During the first 24 hours, blood flow to the brain decreases to 50% at the moment of the injury and gradually increases to about 60%. Significant improvement occurs during the first two days.

34. H: a shopper has 9 or fewer items; C: the shopper can use the express lane

35. $ab(a + b) = (ab)a + (ab)b$ Distributive
$= a(ab) + (ab)b$ Commutative ($\times$)
$= (a \cdot a)b + a(b \cdot b)$ Associative ($\times$)
$= a^2b + ab^2$ Substitution

Page 59, Extend 1-9

5. Sample answer: The graph appears to be continuously decreasing, so a reasonable prediction is 1 or 2 computers per student. It does not seem likely that schools would have more computers than students.

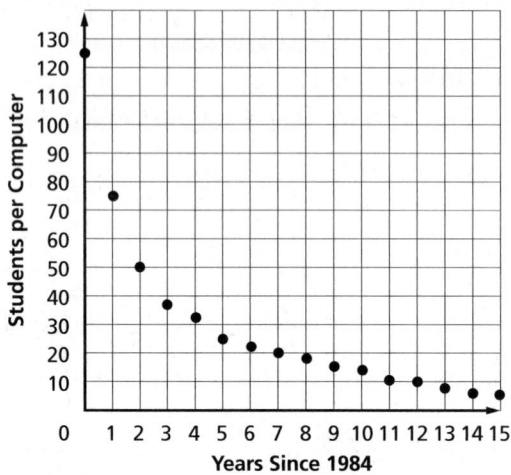

Page 65, Practice Test

23. Sample answer:

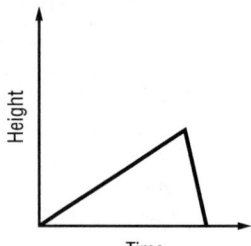

24. Sample answer:

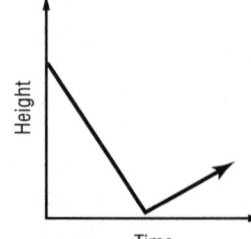

NOTES

Solving Linear Equations

Standards-Based Lesson Plan		Pacing Your Lessons	
LESSONS AND OBJECTIVES	California Standards	40–50 Minute Periods	90-Minute Periods
2-1 Writing Equations (pp. 70–76) • Translate verbal sentences into equations. • Translate equations into verbal sentences.	7AF1.1	1	0.5
Explore 2-2 Solving Addition and Subtraction Equations (p. 77) **2-2 Solving Equations by Using Addition and Subtraction** (pp. 78–84) • Solve equations by using addition. • Solve equations by using subtraction.	4.0, 5.0, 25.3	2	1
2-3 Solving Equations by Using Multiplication and Division (pp. 85–90) • Solve equations by using multiplication. • Solve equations by using division.	4.0, 5.0, 25.2	2	1
Explore 2-4 Solving Multi-Step Equations (p. 91) **2-4 Solving Multi-Step Equations** (pp. 92–97) • Solve equations involving more than one operation. • Solve consecutive integer problems.	4.0, 5.0, 25.3	2	1
2-5 Solving Equations with the Variable on Each Side (pp. 98–103) • Solve equations with the variable on each side. • Solve equations involving grouping symbols.	4.0, 5.0, 24.3, 25.1	2	1
2-6 Ratios and Proportions (pp. 105–110) • Determine whether two ratios form a proportion. • Solve proportions.	5.0, 15.0	2	1
2-7 Percent of Change (pp. 111–115) • Find percents of increase and decrease. • Solve problems involving percents of change.	5.0, 24.3, 25.1, 25.3	1	0.5
2-8 Solving for a Specific Variable (pp. 117–121) • Solve equations for given variables. • Use formulas to solve real-world problems.	5.0	2	0.5
2-9 Weighted Averages (pp. 122–128) • Solve uniform motion problems. • Solve mixture problems. **Extend 2-9 Weighted Averages** (p. 129)	4.0, 5.0, 15.0	2	1.5
REVIEW		1	0.5
ASSESSMENT		1	0.5*
*The complete **Assessment Planner** for Chapter 2 is provided on p. 69.*	**TOTAL**	**18**	**9**

* Begin Chapter 3 in the second half of the period.

Professional Development

California Standards Vertical Alignment

Before Chapter 2

Related Topics from Grade 7

- Write an expression, an equation, an inequality, or a system that represents a verbal description Standard 7AF1.1
- Convert fractions to decimals and percents and use these representations Standard 7NS1.3
- Solve multi-step problems involving rate, speed, distance and time ◄━━ Standard 7AF4.2

Chapter 2

Topics from Algebra I

- Simplify expressions before solving linear equations and inequalities ◄━━
- Solve multi-step problems involving linear equations and inequalities ◄━━
- Solve rate problems, work problems, and percent mixture problems ◄━━

See individual lessons for the specific Standards covered.

After Chapter 2

Preparation for Algebra II

- Solve equations and inequalities involving absolute value ◄━━ Standard 2A1.0
- Prove that triangles are congruent or similar Standard G5.0
- Can recognize and graph a circle, ellipse, parabola, or hyperbola. Standard 2A17.0

Back-Mapping

California Algebra 1 was conceived and developed with the final result in mind, student success in Algebra I and beyond. The authors, using the California Mathematics Standards as their guide, developed this brand-new series by "back-mapping" from the desired result of student success in Algebra I and beyond. McGraw-Hill's *California Geometry, California Algebra 2,* and *California Algebra Readiness* were developed utilizing the same philosophy.

What the Research Says...

According to Kaput and Sims-Knight (1983), representational activities of algebra interact with well-established natural language based habits. Students' underlying understanding of mathematical concepts can affect their ability to translate real-world relationships into algebraic expressions and equations.

- In Lesson 2-1, students use mathematical vocabulary and their knowledge of geometry and properties of equations to describe real-world situations with algebraic equations.
- In Lessons 2-2 through 2-5 and 2-9, students learn to solve equations that they have written to model real-world situations.
- Students write and solve equations involving ratio, proportion, and percent in Lessons 2-6 and 2-7.

Professional Development

Targeted professional development has been articulated throughout the *California Mathematics: Concepts, Skills, and Problem Solving* series. The **McGraw-Hill Professional Development Video Library** provides short videos that support the ◄━━ Key Standards. For more information, visit ca.algebra1.com.

| Model Lessons | Instructional Strategies |

CHAPTER 2

Technology Solutions

Teacher Resources

TeacherWorks™ All-in-One Planner and Resource Center

All of the print materials from the Classroom Resource Masters are available on your TeacherWorks™ CD-ROM.

BL = Below Grade Level **OL** = On Grade Level **AL** = Above Grade Level **ELL** = English Language Learner

Chapter Resource Masters				2-1	2-2	2-3	2-4	2-5	2-6	2-7	2-8	2-9
BL **OL**		**ELL**	Lesson Reading Guide	5	12	19	26	33	41	48	56	63
BL **OL**		**ELL**	Study Guide and Intervention*	6	13	20	27	34	42	49	57	64
BL **OL**			Skills Practice*	8	15	22	29	36	44	51	59	66
	OL **AL**		Practice*	9	16	23	30	37	45	52	60	67
	OL **AL**		Word Problem Practice*	10	17	24	31	38	46	53	61	68
	OL **AL**		Enrichment	11	18	25	32	39	47	54	62	69
	OL **AL**		Calculator and Spreadsheet Activities					40		55		
	OL **AL**		Chapter Assessments*	71–92								
BL **OL** **AL**			5-Minute Check Transparencies	✓	✓	✓	✓	✓	✓	✓	✓	✓
BL **OL**			Teaching Mathematics with Manipulatives	✓	✓	✓	✓	✓	✓	✓	✓	

Also available in Spanish.

AssignmentWorks

Differentiated Assignments, Answers, and Solutions

- Print a customized assignment worksheet using the Student Edition exercises along with an answer key or worked-out solutions.
- Use default lesson assignments as outlined in the Differentiated Homework Options in the Teacher Wraparound Edition.
- Includes modified questions from the Student Edition.

Interactive Classroom

This CD-ROM is a customizable Microsoft® PowerPoint® presentation that includes:

- In-Class Examples
- Your Turn Exercises*
- 5-Minute Check Transparencies*
- Links to Online Study Tools
- Concepts in Motion

compatible with response pad technology

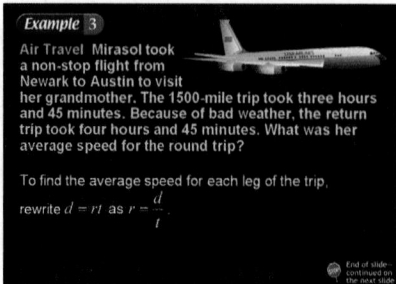

Example 3

Air Travel Mirasol took a non-stop flight from Newark to Austin to visit her grandmother. The 1500-mile trip took three hours and 45 minutes. Because of bad weather, the return trip took four hours and 45 minutes. What was her average speed for the round trip?

To find the average speed for each leg of the trip, rewrite $d = rt$ as $r = \dfrac{d}{t}$.

ExamView®Assessment Suite

 lets you

- Create, edit, and customize tests and worksheets using QuickTest Wizard
- Create multiple versions of tests and modify them for a desired level of difficulty
- Translate from English to Spanish and vice versa
- Build tests aligned with your state standards
- Track students' progress using the Teacher Management System

Student Resources

StudentWorks™ Plus

Textbook, Audio, Workbooks, and more

This CD-ROM is a valuable resource for students to access content online and use online resources to continue learning Chapter 2 concepts. Includes:

- Complete Student Editions in both English and Spanish
- English audio integrated throughout the text
- Links to Concepts in Motion, Personal Tutor, and other online resources
- Access to all student worksheets
- Daily Assignments and Grade Log

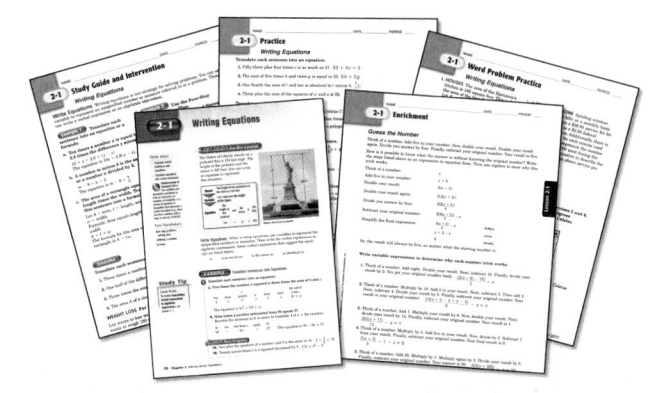

Super DVD

The Super DVD contains two Glencoe multimedia products.

MindJogger Plus An alternative review of concepts in which students work as teams in a game show format to gain points for correct answers.

What's Math Got to Do With It? Real Life Math Videos Engaging video that shows students how math is used in everyday situations

Unit 1 Theme: Foundations for Functions

Internet Resources

Math Online ca.algebra1.com

TEACHER	PARENT	STUDENT	Online Study Tools
	●	●	Online Student Edition
●	●	●	Multilingual Glossary
			Lesson Resources
	●	●	BrainPOP®
●	●	●	Concepts in Motion
●	●	●	Extra Examples
	●	●	Other Calculator Keystrokes
●			Problem of the Week Cards
	●	●	Real-World Careers
	●	●	Self-Check Quizzes
			Chapter Resources
	●	●	Chapter Readiness
	●	●	Chapter Test
		●	Standardized Test Practice
	●	●	Vocabulary Review/Chapter Review Activities
			Unit Resources
●		●	Cross-Curricular Internet Project
			Other Resources
●			Dinah Zike's Foldables
	●	●	Hotmath Homework Help
●			Key Concepts
●	●	●	Meet the Authors
	●	●	Personal Tutor
●			Project CRISS℠
	●	●	Scavenger Hunts and Answer Sheets
●			Vocabulary PuzzleMakers

Focus on Mathematical Content

Big Idea for Chapter 2:
Solving Linear Equations

Solving equations is more than finding the values of the variables that make an equation a true statement. The properties and steps used to maintain equivalent equations when isolating a variable in an equation are the same properties used in all math courses. Explores 2-2 and 2-4 on pages 75 and 81 examine solving equations. Equation mats and algebra tiles are used to model solving equations with one or more operations.

Why It's Important

For This Chapter
The lessons in this chapter help students obtain the crucial skills necessary for solving equations. These skills, such as those used in describing the effects of changes in parameters of linear functions, are applied to both real-world and mathematical situations.

- When writing an equation, what do you use to represent the unspecified numbers or measures referred to in the problem? (Lesson 2-1)
- What does it mean to *solve* an equation? How can you *undo* an operation? (Lessons 2-2 and 2-3)
- What strategies can you use to solve multi-step equations? (Lesson 2-4)
- What properties of equality can you use to get the variables all on one side of an equation? (Lesson 2-5)
- What is one way to determine whether two ratios form a proportion? (Lesson 2-6)
- How do you determine a percent of increase or decrease? (Lesson 2-7)
- What can you do to a formula that has more than one variable to help you solve a problem? (Lesson 2-8)
- What algebraic skills are necessary to solve mixture problems and uniform motion problems? (Lesson 2-9)

After This Chapter
- In Chapter 3, the algebraic skills required to solve equations can help you graph linear equations.
- Solving equations is a major concept that is used in all mathematics courses that students will study in the future.

2-1 Writing Equations

Just as when translating verbal expressions to algebraic expressions (Lesson 1-1), variables are used to represent unspecified amounts when writing equations from a verbal sentence. Key words such as *is, equals, times, and, sum, difference, less,* and *more* can be used to assist in writing equations. The ability to write an equation from a verbal sentence is needed when solving word problems.

The following four-step problem-solving plan can help you solve any word problem.

Step 1	Explore the problem.
Step 2	Plan the solution.
Step 3	Solve the problem.
Step 4	Examine the solution.

Sometimes a verbal sentence can be translated into a formula, an equation that states a rule for the relationships between certain quantities, and then used to solve problems about those quantities.

You can replace the variable and symbols with their key words in order to translate equations back into verbal sentences.

2-2 Solving Equations by Using Addition and Subtraction

Solving an equation means finding all the values of the variable in the equation that make the statement true. To solve an equation, isolate the variable so that it has a coefficient of 1 on one side of the equation. You can do this by using the Properties of Equality and undoing the operations that have been done to the variable.

- If a number is being added to the variable in the original equation, use the inverse operation, subtraction, to isolate the variable.
- If a number is being subtracted from the variable in the original equation, use the inverse operation, addition, to isolate the variable.
- When the same operation with the same number is performed to each side of an equation the result is an equivalent equation.

Solving Equations by Using Multiplication and Division

The Multiplication and Division Properties of Equality can be used to solve the equation in which the variable is multiplied or divided by a rational number.

- When multiplying a variable by a number in the equation, use the inverse operation, division, to find the value of the variable.
- If the variable is being divided by a number in the equation, use multiplication to find the value of the variable.
- When the same operation with the same number is performed to each side of an equation the result is an equivalent equation.

 ## Solving Multi-Step Equations

Multi-step equations are equations that involve more than one operation. The strategy of working backward can be used to help solve these types of equations.

To solve multi-step equations, first combine like terms. Then, the opposite of the order of operations is used: the Addition or Subtraction Property of Equality is performed before the Multiplication or Division Property of Equality.

 ## Solving Equations with the Variable on Each Side

To solve equations with variables on each side, the variable must first be isolated.

- If the equation contains grouping symbols, first use the Distributive Property to remove the grouping symbols.
- Combine like terms on each side of the equation.
- Then use the Addition and/or Subtraction Properties of Equality to isolate all variables on one side of the equation and all numeric terms on the other side.
- If the variable does not have a coefficient of 1, apply the Multiplication or Division Property of Equality. If during any of the above steps, all the variable terms are eliminated and the two sides of the equation are not equal numbers, there is no solution to the equation. If at any point in the solution process, both sides of the equation are identical, the equation is an identity. In this case, all numbers are solutions for the equation.

 ## Ratios and Proportions

A ratio is a comparison of two numbers by division. The ratio of x to y can be expressed as $x{:}y$, x to y, and $\frac{x}{y}$. A ratio is called a rate if the two numbers of a ratio represent measurements with different units, such as miles and hours. When making a model or drawing that is larger or smaller than the original, a ratio or rate called a scale is used.

A proportion is an equation stating that two ratios are equal. In a proportion, the product of the middle terms (means) equals the product of the first and last terms (extremes).

If a proportion contains a variable, the value of the variable can be determined by setting the product of the means equal to the product of the extremes. The resulting equation can be solved using the Division Property of Equality.

 ## Percent of Change

Percent is found by dividing a part by its corresponding whole amount. Percent of change is the percent amount a number increases or decreases. If the new number is greater than the original number, the percent of change is called a percent of increase. If the new number is less than the original number, it is called a percent of decrease. Percent of change can be found by solving a proportion. The ratio of the amount of change to the original number equals the ratio of the percent to 100.

 ## Solving for a Specific Variable

Some equations contain more than one variable. The processes for solving one-step or multi-step equations are used to solve these equations for one of the variables in terms of the other variables. Formulas are equations with multiple variables. Sometimes, solving a formula for a specific variable simplifies the computation.

 ## Weighted Averages

A weighted average is the sum of the product of the number of units in a set of data and the value per unit divided by the sum of the number of units. Mixture problems are problems in which two or more parts are combined into a whole. They can be solved using weighted averages. Uniform motion problems also use weighted averages. The distance formula, $d = rt$, is used to solve these problems. When solving mixture and uniform motion problems, tables are sometimes helpful.

Differentiated Instruction

Options for Chapter 2 Lessons

ELL = English Language Learner	**AL** = Above Grade Level	**SS** = Struggling Students	**SN** = Special Needs

Using Visualization **ELL** **SS**

Use with Lesson 2-2

Students will most easily grasp the concept of solving equations by addition and subtraction as they physically observe adding or removing objects from both sides of the equals sign. Use the procedures from the Algebra Lab on p. 77 to solve simple equations.

Connecting Mathematics to Music **AL**

Use with Lesson 2-3

Have students all clap twice per second for five seconds. Write on the chalkboard: 5 seconds = 10 claps. Have students clap twice per second for 10 seconds. Write × 2 under each side of the equation. Then write 10 seconds = 20 claps. Point out that each side of the equation doubled but the equation is still correct. In an equation, as long as you perform the same operation on each side, the equation remains correct.

Using Movement **ELL** **SS** **SN**

Use with Lesson 2-5

Students will benefit from manipulating or moving objects to help them solve equations with variables on both sides. Allow students to use equation mats and algebra tiles to model simple equations. Manipulating the tiles will give students a different way to learn the concepts in this lesson.

Noteables™ Interactive Study Notebook with Foldables™

Noteables™ Interactive Study Notebook with Foldables™ is a study organizer that provides helpful steps for students to follow to organize their notes for Chapter 2.

- Students use Noteables to record notes and to complete their Foldables as you present the material for each lesson.

- Noteables correspond to the Examples in the *Teacher Wraparound Edition* and *Interactive Classroom CD-ROM.*

Intervention

Quick Review Math Handbook*

is Glencoe's mathematical handbook for students and parents.

Hot Words includes a glossary of terms.

Hot Topics consists of two parts:

- explanations of key mathematical concepts
- exercises to check students' understanding.

Lesson	Hot Topics Section	Lesson	Hot Topics Section
2-1	2.3, 2.5, 6.1	2-6	2.8, 6.5
2-2	2.4, 2.6, 6.4	2-7	2.8, 6.4, 6.5
2-3	1.3, 6.4	2-8	6.2, 6.4
2-4	6.2, 6.4	2-9	6.4, 6.5
2-5	2.1, 6.4		

*Also available in Spanish

Teacher to Teacher

Barbara Szymczak
Bayonne High School
Bayonne, NJ

USE BEFORE LESSON 2-7

❝ When teaching percents, I have students cut out sales advertisements and make posters showing savings. They also cut out car ads to compute interest they would pay and compare companies for the best deals. ❞

Reading and Writing in Mathematics

STUDY SKILL

Venn diagrams are drawings that can be used to compare and contrast concepts. They may be helpful to students as they assimilate new knowledge.

Encourage students to look for the relationships between math concepts that are taught together. Often such relationships can be represented with Venn diagrams. Students can brainstorm ideas for Venn diagrams individually or as a cooperative learning activity.

The Venn diagram below represents the relationships among real numbers.

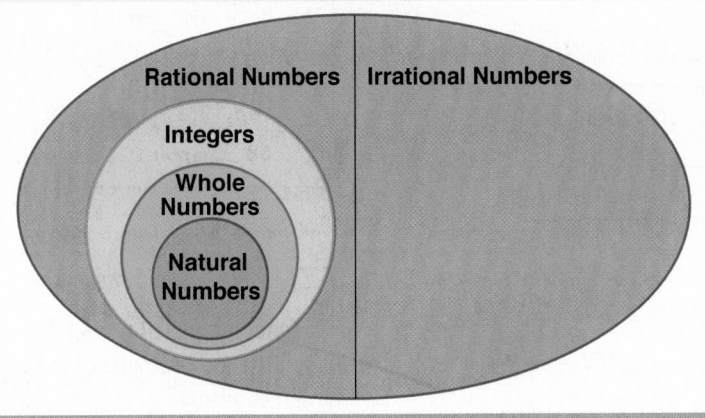

C R e a t i n g   **I** n d e p e n d e n c e   t h r o u g h   **S** t u d e n t - o w n e d   **S** t r a t e g i e s

Dinah Zike's Foldables™

Focus As students read and study this chapter, they should show examples and write notes about solving equations on their study cards.

Teach Have students make and label their Foldables as illustrated. Students use 3-inch by 5-inch index cards and sheets of folded notebook paper to create study cards for each lesson in this chapter.

Students should place the cards in the appropriate pockets as they cover each lesson in this chapter. As there are eight pockets, have them place Lessons 2–8 and 2–9 in the same pocket.

When to Use It At the end of each lesson, ask students to use the study cards to take notes, write and solve equations, solve real-world problems, or to record and define vocabulary words and concepts.

A version of a completed Foldable is shown on p. 130.

Materials Needed for Chapter 2

- scissors, rectangular box, calculator (Lesson 2–1)
- equation mats, algebra tiles (Explore 2–2 and Explore 2–4)
- ruler (Lesson 2–4)
- Internet (Lesson 2–7)
- computer, spreadsheet software (Extend 2–9)

CHAPTER 2 Solving Linear Equations

🔵 BIG Ideas

- **Standard 5.0** Students solve multistep problems, including word problems, involving linear equations and linear inequalities in one variable and provide justification for each step. (Key, CAHSEE)

- **Standard 15.0** Students apply algebraic techniques to solve rate problems, work problems, and percent mixture problems. (Key, CAHSEE)

Key Vocabulary

equivalent equations (p. 79)
identity (p. 99)
proportion (p. 105)
percent of change (p. 111)

🌐 Real-World Link

Baseball Linear equations can be used to solve problems in every facet of life. For example, a baseball player's slugging percentage is found by using an equation based on a mixture, or weighted average, of five factors, including at bats and hits.

FOLDABLES Study Organizer

Solving Linear Equations Make this Foldable to help you organize information about solving linear equations. Begin with 5 sheets of plain $8\frac{1}{2}$" by 11" paper.

1. **Fold** in half along the width.

2. **Fold** the bottom to form a pocket. Glue edges.

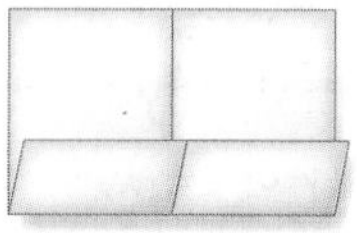

3. **Repeat** four times and glue all five pieces together.

4. **Label** each pocket. Place an index card in each pocket.

Differentiated Instruction

📄 Student-Made Glossary, pp. 1–2

Students complete the chart by providing a definition and example for each term as they progress through Chapter 2. This study tool can be used to review for the chapter test.

GET READY for Chapter 2

Diagnose Readiness You have two options for checking Prerequisite Skills.

Option 1

Take the Quick Check below. Refer to the Quick Review for help.

Option 2

Math Online Take the Online Readiness Quiz at ca.algebra1.com

QUICK Check

(Used in Lesson 2-1)

Write an algebraic expression for each verbal expression. (Lesson 1-1)

1. five greater than half a number t $\quad \frac{1}{2}t + 5$

2. the product of seven and s divided by the product of eight and y $\quad 7s \div 8y$

3. the sum of three times a and the square of b $\quad 3a + b^2$

4. w to the fifth power decreased by 37 $\quad w^5 - 37$

(Used in Lesson 2-4)

Evaluate each expression. (Lesson 1-2)

5. $3 \cdot 6 - \frac{12}{4}$ **15**

6. $5(13 - 7) - 22$ **8**

7. $5(7 - 2) - 3^2$ **16**

8. $\frac{2 \cdot 6 - 4}{2}$ **4**

9. $(25 - 4)(2^2 - 1)$ **63**

10. $36 \div 4 - 2 + 3$ **10**

11. $\frac{19 - 5}{7} + 3$ **5**

12. $\frac{1}{4}(24) - \frac{1}{2}(12)$ **0**

13. **MONEY** For his birthday, Brad received $25 from each of his four aunts. After putting 10% of this money in the bank, Brad bought 5 CDs at $10 each. How much money does he have left? **$40**

(Used in Lesson 2-7)

Find each percent. (Prerequisite Skill)

14. Five is what percent of 20? **25%**

15. What percent of 5 is 15? **300%**

16. What percent of 300 is 21? **7%**

17. **ELECTIONS** In an exit poll, 456 of 900 voters said that they voted for Dunlap. Approximately what percentage of voters polled voted for Dunlap? **51%**

QUICK Review

EXAMPLE 1

Write an algebraic expression for the phrase *two more than five times a number t.*

two	more than	five	times	a number t
2	+	5	×	t

The expression is $2 + 5t$.

EXAMPLE 2

Evaluate $7 - \frac{6}{3}[5(17 - 6) + 2] + 108$.

$= 7 - \frac{6}{3}[5(17 - 6) + 2] + 108$

$= 7 - \frac{6}{3}[5(11) + 2] + 108$ Evaluate inside the parentheses.

$= 7 - \frac{6}{3}[55 + 2] + 108$ Multiply.

$= 7 - \frac{6}{3}[57] + 108$ Add inside the brackets.

$= 7 - 2[57] + 108$ Simplify.

$= 7 - 114 + 108$ Multiply.

$= 1$ Simplify.

EXAMPLE 3

What percent of 64 is 6?

$\frac{a}{b} = \frac{p}{100}$ Use the percent proportion.

$\frac{6}{64} = \frac{p}{100}$ Replace a with 6 and b with 64.

$6(100) = 64p$ Find the cross products.

$600 = 64p$ Multiply.

$9.375 = p$ Divide each side by 64.

6 is 9.375% of 64.

Chapter 2 Get Ready for Chapter 2   **69**

✓ Diagnostic Assessment

Exercises	California Standards	Intervention
1–4	7AF1.1	SE Review Lesson 1-1, pp. 6–9
5–13	7AF1.2	SE Review Lesson 1-2, pp. 10–14
14–17	7NS1.6	SE Prerequisite Skill, pp. 702–703

ASSESSMENT PLANNER

CHAPTER 2

✓ Formative Assessment

CRM **Anticipation Guide, p. 3**
Spotting Preconceived Ideas
Students complete this survey to determine prior knowledge about ideas from Chapter 2. Revisit this worksheet after completing the chapter. Also see page 134.

TWE **Lesson Activities**
- Ticket Out the Door, pp. 76, 110, 121
- Crystal Ball, p. 84
- Name the Math, pp. 90, 103, 128
- Yesterday's News, pp. 97, 115

Chapter Checkpoints

SE Mid-Chapter Quiz, p. 104

SE Study Guide and Review, pp. 130–134

SE California Standards Practice, pp. 136–137

CRM Quizzes, pp. 73 and 74

CRM Standardized Test Practice, pp. 90–92

Math Online ca.algebra1.com
- Self-Check Quizzes
- Practice Test
- Standardized Test Practice

✓ Summative Assessment

SE Chapter Practice Test, p. 135

CRM Mid-Chapter Test, p. 75

CRM Vocabulary Test, p. 76

CRM Extended-Response Test, p. 89

CRM Leveled Chapter Tests, pp. 77–88

● ExamView® Assessment Suite

Key

CRM *Chapter 2 Resource Masters*

SE Student Edition

TWE Teacher Wraparound Edition

● CD-ROM

1 Focus

Standards Alignment

Before Lesson 2-1
Write and evaluate an algebraic expression for a given situation from Standard 6AF1.2

Lesson 2-1
Write an expression, an equation, an inequality, or a system that represents a verbal description. from Standard 7AF1

After Lesson 2-1
Solve equations and inequalities involving absolute value from  Standard 2A1.0

2 Teach

Scaffolding Questions Have students read *Get Ready for the Lesson*.
Ask:
- The total height of the statue, 305 feet, is equal to the sum of what two quantities? the height of the statue and the height of the pedestal
- Why is the height represented by a variable? The height is not given, so a variable is used.

- What is another equation that could be used to represent the situation?
$305 - s = 154$ or $305 - 154 = s$

Lesson 2-1 Resources

Main Ideas
- Translate verbal sentences into equations.
- Translate equations into verbal sentences.

 Reinforcement of Standard 7AF1.1
Use variables and appropriate operations to write an expression, an equation, an inequality, or a system of equations or inequalities that represents a verbal description (e.g., three less than a number, half as large as area A). (CAHSEE)

New Vocabulary
four-step problem-solving plan
defining a variable
formula

Study Tip

Look Back
To review **translating verbal expressions to algebraic expressions**, see Lesson 1-1.

GET READY for the Lesson

The Statue of Liberty stands on a pedestal that is 154 feet high. The height of the pedestal and the statue is 305 feet. You can write an equation to represent this situation.

Words	The height of the pedestal and the statue is 305 feet.
Variable	Let *s* represent the height of the statue.
Equation	The height of the pedestal and the statue is 305 feet.

$$154 + s = 305$$

Source: *World Book Encyclopedia*

Write Equations When writing equations, use variables to represent the unspecified numbers or measures. Then write the verbal expressions as algebraic expressions. Some verbal expressions that suggest the *equals sign* are listed below.

    is   is as much as   is the same as   is identical to

EXAMPLE Translate Sentences into Equations

1 Translate each sentence into an equation.

a. Five times the number *a* squared is three times the sum of *b* and *c*.

Five	times	*a* squared	is	three	times	the sum of *b* and *c*.
5	·	a^2	=	3	·	$(b + c)$

The equation is $5a^2 = 3(b + c)$.

b. Nine times a number subtracted from 95 equals 37.
Rewrite the sentence so it is easier to translate. Let n = the number.

95	less	nine times *n*	equals	37.
95	−	9n	=	37

The equation is $95 - 9n = 37$.

CHECK Your Progress

1A. Two plus the quotient of a number and 8 is the same as 16. $2 + \dfrac{n}{8} = 16$

1B. Twenty-seven times k is h squared decreased by 9. $27k = h^2 - 9$

Chapter 2 Resource Masters
Lesson Reading Guide, p. 5 **BL** **OL** **ELL**
Study Guide and Intervention, pp. 6–7 **BL** **OL** **ELL**
Skills Practice, p. 8 **BL** **OL**
Practice, p. 9 **OL** **AL**
Word Problem Practice, p. 10 **OL** **AL**
Enrichment, p. 11 **OL** **AL**

Transparencies
5-Minute Check Transparency 1-2
Additional Print Resources
Noteables™ Interactive Study Notebook with Foldables™
Teaching Algebra with Manipulatives

Technology
ca.algebra1.com
Interactive Classroom CD-ROM
AssignmentWorks CD-ROM
Graphing Calculator Easy Files

Using the **four-step problem-solving plan** can help you solve any word problem.

KEY CONCEPT	Four-Step Problem-Solving Plan

Step 1 Explore the problem.

Step 2 Plan the solution.

Step 3 Solve the problem.

Step 4 Check the solution.

Step 1 Explore the Problem
To solve a verbal problem, first read the problem carefully and explore what the problem is about.
- Identify what information is given.
- Identify what you are asked to find.

Step 2 Plan the Solution
One strategy you can use to solve a problem is to write an equation. Choose a variable to represent one of the unspecified numbers in the problem. This is called **defining a variable**. Then use the variable to write expressions for the other unspecified numbers.

Step 3 Solve the Problem
Use the strategy you chose in Step 2 to solve the problem.

Step 4 Check the Solution
Check your answer in the context of the original problem.
- Does your answer make sense?
- Does it fit the information in the problem?

Real-World EXAMPLE   Use the Four-Step Plan

2 ICE CREAM Use the information at the left. In how many days can 40,000,000 gallons of ice cream be produced in the United States?

Explore You know that 2,000,000 gallons of ice cream are produced in the United States each day. You want to know how many days it will take to produce 40,000,000 gallons of ice cream.

Plan Write an equation. Let *d* represent the number of days.

		the number		
2,000,000	times	of days	equals	40,000,000.
2,000,000	·	d	=	40,000,000

Solve $2{,}000{,}000d = 40{,}000{,}000$ Find *d* mentally by asking, "What number
            $d = 20$ times 2,000,000 equals 40,000,000?"

It will take 20 days to produce 40,000,000 gallons of ice cream.

Check If 2,000,000 gallons of ice cream are produced in one day, $2{,}000{,}000 \times 20$ or 40,000,000 gallons are produced in 20 days. The answer makes sense.

 Math Online Extra Examples at ca.algebra1.com

Write Equations

Example 1 shows how to translate sentences into equations. **Example 2** shows how the four-step problem-solving plan is used to solve a real-world problem. **Example 3** shows how to write a formula by making a model and translating a sentence.

 Formative Assessment

Use the Check Your Progress exercises after each example to determine students' understanding of concepts.

ADDITIONAL EXAMPLES

1 Translate each sentence into an equation.
   a. A number *b* divided by three is six less than *c*.
      $\frac{b}{3} = c - 6$
   b. Fifteen more than *z* times 6 is *y* times 2 minus eleven.
      $15 + 6z = 2y - 11$

2 **Jelly Beans** A jelly bean manufacturer produces 1,250,000 jelly beans per hour. How many hours does it take to produce 10,000,000 jelly beans? 8 hours

Additional Examples are also in:
- Noteables™ Interactive Study Notebook with Foldables™
- Interactive Classroom PowerPoint® Presentations

Pre-AP Activity   Use after Example 1

Even numbers that are in order and differ by 2, such as 2, 4, 6, are called *consecutive even numbers.*

a. Write an equation for three consecutive even numbers with a sum of 60 if *x* is the least of the three numbers. $x + x + 2 + x + 4 = 60$

b. Write an equation for three consecutive even numbers with a sum of 108 if *x* is the least of the three numbers. $x + x + 2 + x + 4 = 108$

Algebra Lab

For this algebra activity, each student or group of students needs scissors and a rectangular box. Suggest that in addition to marking the box sides with length, width, or height, students should also label the sides as front, back, side 1, side 2, top, and bottom. By cutting the sides of the box into individual rectangles, students can more easily see all six components that make up the surface area of the box.

ADDITIONAL EXAMPLE
---

③ Translate the sentence into a formula.

The perimeter of a square equals four times the length of the side.

$P = 4s$

Write Verbal Sentences

Example 4 shows how to translate equations into verbal sentences.
Example 5 shows how to make up a verbal problem from information given in equations.

Focus on Mathematical Content

Algebraic Expressions Algebraic expressions have one or more variables and usually contain some numbers and one or more operations. When writing an algebraic expression, variables are used to represent the unknown number or measure.

Tips for New Teachers

Preventing Errors

Some students may have memorized the formula for the perimeter of a rectangle from previous courses. Have these students work backward from the formula to confirm that it is a correct translation of the sentence.

2. GOVERNMENT There are 50 members in the North Carolina Senate. This is 70 fewer than the number in the North Carolina House of Representatives. How many members are in the North Carolina House of Representatives? **120**

A **formula** is an equation that states a rule for the relationship between certain quantities.

ALGEBRA LAB

Surface Area

- Mark each side of a rectangular box as the length ℓ, the width w, or the height h.
- Use scissors to cut the box so that each surface or face of the box is a separate piece.

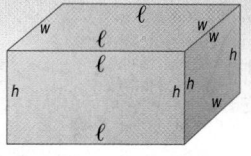

ANALYZE

Write an expression for the area of each side of the box.

1. front ℓh **2.** back ℓh **3.** left side wh

4. right side wh **5.** top ℓw **6.** bottom ℓw

7. The surface area S of a rectangular box is the sum of all the areas of the faces of the box. Write a formula for the surface area of a rectangular box.
$S = 2\ell h + 2wh + 2\ell w$

MAKE A CONJECTURE

8. If s represents the length of the side of a cube, write a formula for the surface area S of a cube. $S = 6s^2$

EXAMPLE   Write a Formula
---

③ Translate the sentence into a formula. *The perimeter of a rectangle equals two times the length plus two times the width.*

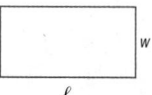

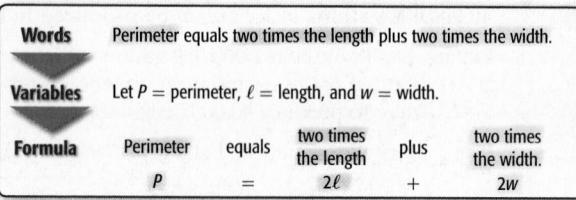

Words	Perimeter equals two times the length plus two times the width.			
Variables	Let P = perimeter, ℓ = length, and w = width.			
Formula	Perimeter	equals	two times the length	plus	two times the width.
	P	$=$	2ℓ	$+$	$2w$

The formula for the perimeter of a rectangle is $P = 2\ell + 2w$.

3. GEOMETRY Translate the sentence into a formula. *In a right triangle, the square of the measure of the hypotenuse c is equal to the sum of the squares of the measures of the legs, a and b.* $c^2 = a^2 + b^2$

Online Personal Tutor at ca.algebra1.com

Write Verbal Sentences You can also translate equations into verbal sentences or make up your own verbal problem if you are given an equation.

Differentiated Instruction

Verbal/Linguistic Learners Some students are able to translate sentences into equations easily. Pair those students with others who are having trouble translating sentences. Have the pairs work several example problems.

EXAMPLE — Translate Equations into Sentences

④ Translate each equation into a verbal sentence.

a. $3m + 5 = 14$

$$\underbrace{3m}_{\text{Three times } m} \;\; \underbrace{+}_{\text{plus}} \;\; \underbrace{5}_{\text{five}} \;\; \underbrace{=}_{\text{equals}} \;\; \underbrace{14}_{\text{fourteen.}}$$

b. $w + v = y^2$

$$\underbrace{w + v}_{\text{The sum of } w \text{ and } v} \;\; \underbrace{=}_{\text{equals}} \;\; \underbrace{y^2}_{\text{the square of } y.}$$

✓ CHECK Your Progress

4A. $13 = 2 + 6t$
Thirteen equals two plus the product of six and t.

4B. $\frac{1}{4}n + 5 = n - 7$ One fourth of a number plus five equals the number minus seven.

EXAMPLE — Write a Problem

⑤ Write a problem based on the given information.

$a =$ Rafael's age $a + 5 =$ Tierra's age $a + 2(a + 5) = 46$

The equation adds Rafael's age a plus twice Tierra's age $(a + 5)$ to get 46.

Sample problem:
Tierra is 5 years older than Rafael. The sum of Rafael's age and twice Tierra's age equals 46. How old is Rafael?

✓ CHECK Your Progress See margin.

5. $p =$ price of jeans $0.2p =$ discount $p - 0.2p = 31.20$

★ indicates multi-step problem

✓ CHECK Your Understanding

Example 1
(p. 70)

Translate each sentence into an equation.

1. Twice a number t decreased by eight equals seventy. $2t - 8 = 70$
2. Five times the sum of m and n is the same as seven times n. $5(m + n) = 7n$
3. Half of p is the same as p minus three. $\frac{1}{2}p = p - 3$
4. A number squared is as much as twelve more than the number. $n^2 = n + 12$

Example 2
(p. 71)

5. **SAVINGS** Misae has $1900 in the bank. She wishes to increase her account to a total of $2500 by depositing $30 per week from her paycheck. Write and use an equation to find how many weeks she needs to reach her goal.
$1900 + 30w = 2500$; 20 weeks

Example 3
(p. 72)

Translate each sentence into a formula. $A = \frac{1}{2}bh$

6. The area A of a triangle equals one half times the base b times the height h.
7. The circumference C of a circle equals the product of 2, π, and the radius r.
$C = 2\pi r$

Example 4
(p. 72)

Translate each equation into a verbal sentence. 8–10. See margin.

8. $1 = 7 + \frac{z}{5}$ 9. $14 + d = 6d$ 10. $\frac{1}{3}b - 4 = 2a$

Example 5
(p. 73)

Write a problem based on the given information. 11–12. See margin.

11. $c =$ cost of a suit
$c - 25 = 150$

12. $p =$ price of a new backpack
$0.055p =$ tax; $p + 0.055p = 31.65$

Lesson 2-1 Writing Equations   **73**

DIFFERENTIATED HOMEWORK OPTIONS

Level	Assignment	Two-Day Option	
BL Basic	13–34, 48–68	13–33 odd, 50, 51	14–34 even, 48, 49, 52–68
OL Core	13–33 odd, 35–68	13–34, 50, 51	35–47, 48, 49, 52–68
AL Advanced/Pre-AP	35–62 (optional: 63–67)		

Reading Tip

Remind students that there is often more than one way to translate an equation into a verbal sentence. For example, $3m + 5 = 14$ could also be translated as, "The sum of three times m and 5 is 14."

ADDITIONAL EXAMPLES

④ Translate each equation into a verbal sentence.

a. $12 - 2x = -5$ Twelve minus two times x equals negative five.

b. $a^2 + 3b = \frac{c}{6}$ a squared plus three times b equals c divided by 6.

⑤ Write a problem based on the given information.

$f =$ cost of fries
$f + 1.50 =$ cost of burger
$4(f + 1.50) - f = 8.25$
The cost of a burger is $1.50 more than the cost of fries. Four times the cost of a burger minus the cost of fries equals $8.25. How much do fries cost?

Additional Answer
(Check Your Progress)

5. Sample answer: The price of a pair of jeans is p dollars, and the discount is $0.2p$. If the total cost of the jeans minus the discount is $31.20, what is the price of the jeans before the discount?

③ Practice

✓ Formative Assessment

Use Exercises 1–12 to check for understanding.

Use the chart at the bottom of this page to customize assignments for your students.

For answers 8–12, see p. 74.

Lesson 2-1 Writing Equations   **73**

Additional Answers

8. Sample answer: 1 equals 7 plus the quotient of z and 5.

9. Sample answer: 14 plus d equals 6 times d.

10. Sample answer: $\frac{1}{3}$ of b minus 4 equals 2 times a.

11. Sample answer: The original cost of a suit is c. After a $25 discount, the suit costs $150. What is the original cost of the suit?

12. Sample answer: The price of a new backpack is p dollars and the tax on the backpack is $0.055p$. If the total cost of the backpack and the tax is $31.65, what is the price of the backpack?

13. Sample answer: $2r + 3s = 13$

14. Sample answer: $\frac{t}{40} = 12 - \frac{1}{2}s$

15. Sample answer: $200 - 3n = 9$

16. Sample answer: $\frac{1}{3}n + 25 = 2n$

30. Sample answer: 2 times a equals 7 times a minus b.

31. Sample answer: $\frac{3}{4}$ of p plus $\frac{1}{2}$ equals p.

32. Sample answer: $\frac{2}{5}$ times w equals $\frac{1}{2}$ times w plus 3.

33. Sample answer: Lindsey is 7 inches taller than Yolanda. If 2 times Yolanda's height plus Lindsey's height equals 193 inches, find Yolanda's height.

34. Sample answer: The price of a book is b dollars and the tax on the book is $0.065b$. If the total cost of two books including tax is $42.49, what is the price of each book?

Exercises

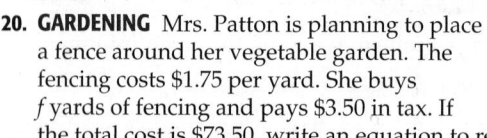

HOMEWORK HELP	
For Exercises	See Examples
13–20	1
21–22	2
23–26	3
27–32	4
33–34	5

Exercise Levels
A: 13–34
B: 35–46
C: 47–49

Real-World Link

More than 50 movies featuring Tarzan have been made. The first, *Tarzan of the Apes*, in 1918, was among the first movies to gross over $1 million.

Source: www.tarzan.org

Translate each sentence into an equation.   13–16. See margin.

13. The sum of twice r and three times s is identical to thirteen.
14. The quotient of t and forty is the same as twelve minus half of s.
15. Two hundred minus three times a number is equal to nine.
16. The sum of one-third a number and 25 is as much as twice the number.
17. The square of m minus the cube of n is sixteen. **Sample answer:** $m^2 - n^3 = 16$
18. Two times z is equal to two times the sum of v and w.
    Sample answer: $2z = 2(v + w)$

19. **GEOGRAPHY** The Pacific Ocean covers about 46% of Earth. If P represents the area of the Pacific Ocean and E represents the area of Earth, write an equation for this situation. $0.46E = P$

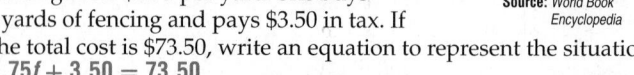

46% of Earth's Surface

Pacific Ocean

Source: *World Book Encyclopedia*

20. **GARDENING** Mrs. Patton is planning to place a fence around her vegetable garden. The fencing costs $1.75 per yard. She buys f yards of fencing and pays $3.50 in tax. If the total cost is $73.50, write an equation to represent the situation. $1.75f + 3.50 = 73.50$

21. **LITERATURE** Edgar Rice Burroughs published his first *Tarzan of the Apes* story in 1912. In 1928, the California town where he lived was named Tarzana. Let y represent the number of years after 1912 that the town was named. Write and use an equation to determine the number of years between the first Tarzan story and the naming of the town. $1912 + y = 1928$; 16 yr

22. **WRESTLING** Darius weighs 155 pounds. He wants to start the wrestling season weighing 160 pounds. If g represents the number of pounds he wants to gain, write an equation to represent this situation. Then use the equation to find the number of pounds Darius needs to gain.
$155 + g = 160$; 5 lb

Translate each sentence into a formula.

23. The area A of a parallelogram is the base b times the height h. $A = bh$

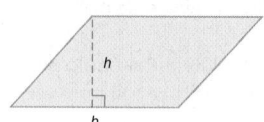

24. The volume V of a pyramid is one-third times the product of the area of the base B and its height h. $V = \frac{1}{3}Bh$

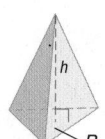

25. The perimeter P of a parallelogram is twice the sum of the lengths of the two adjacent sides, a and b. $P = 2(a + b)$

26. The volume V of a cylinder equals the product of π, the square of the radius r of the base, and the height. $V = \pi r^2 h$

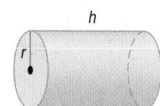

74   **Chapter 2** Solving Linear Equations

47. Sample answer: $S = 3ah + \dfrac{a^2\sqrt{3}}{2}$; the area of the two triangular bases is $2\left(\dfrac{1}{2}\right)(a)\left(\dfrac{a\sqrt{3}}{2}\right)$, which simplifies to $\dfrac{a^2\sqrt{3}}{2}$. The area of the three rectangular sides is $3ah$. So, the total surface area S is the sum $3ah + \dfrac{a^2\sqrt{3}}{2}$.

For answer 48, see p. 76.

27. Sample answer: d minus 14 equals 5.

28. Sample answer: 2 times f plus 6 equals 19.

29. Sample answer: k squared plus 17 equals 53 minus j.

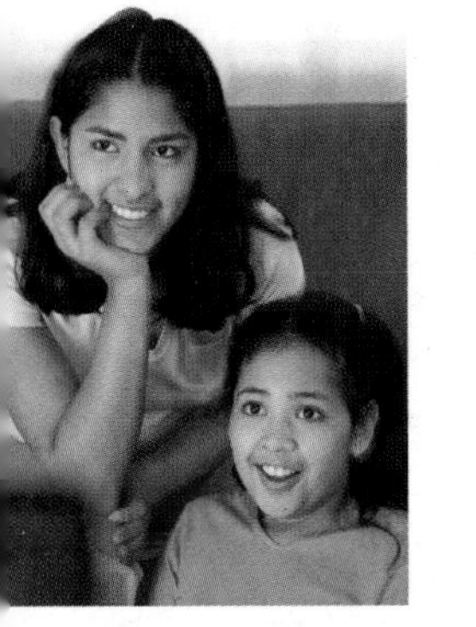

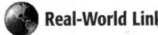

Real-World Link

A typical half-hour show runs for 22 minutes and has 8 minutes of commercials.

Source: gaebler.com

45. Sample answer: 4 times the quantity t minus s equals 5 times s plus 12.

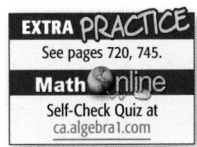

EXTRA PRACTICE See pages 720, 745.

Math Online Self-Check Quiz at ca.algebra1.com

H.O.T. Problems

Translate each equation into a verbal sentence. 30–32. See margin.

27. $d - 14 = 5$ **28.** $2f + 6 = 19$ **29.** $k^2 + 17 = 53 - j$

30. $2a = 7a - b$ **31.** $\frac{3}{4}p + \frac{1}{2} = p$ **32.** $\frac{2}{5}w = \frac{1}{2}w + 3$

Write a problem based on the given information. 33–34. See margin.

33. y = Yolanda's height in inches
$y + 7$ = Lindsey's height in inches
$2y + (y + 7) = 193$

34. b = price of a book
$0.065b$ = tax
$2(b + 0.065b) = 42.49$

Translate each sentence into an equation. 35. $\frac{1}{2}(9 + n) = n - 3$

35. Half the sum of nine and a number is the same as the number minus three.

36. The quotient of g and h is the same as seven more than twice the sum of g and h. $\frac{g}{h} = 2(g + h) + 7$

GEOMETRY For Exercises 37 and 38, use the following information.
The volume V of a cone equals one third times the product of π, the square of the radius r of the base, and the height h.

37. Write the formula for the volume of a cone. $V = \frac{1}{3}\pi r^2 h$

38. Find the volume of a cone if r is 10 centimeters and h is 30 centimeters. about 3142 cm^3

GEOMETRY For Exercises 39 and 40, use the following information.
The volume V of a sphere is four thirds times π times the radius r of the sphere cubed.

39. Write a formula for the volume of a sphere. $V = \frac{4}{3}\pi r^3$

40. Find the volume of a sphere if r is 4 inches. about 268 in^3

TELEVISION For Exercises 41–43, use the following information.
During a highly rated one-hour television show, the entertainment portion lasted 15 minutes longer than 4 times the advertising portion a.

41. Write an expression for the entertainment portion. $4a + 15$

42. Write an equation to represent the situation. $a + (4a + 15) = 60$

43. Use the guess-and-check strategy to determine the number of minutes spent on advertising. 9 min

44. The area A of a trapezoid equals one-half times the product of the height h and the sum of the bases, a and b.

44. GEOMETRY If a and b represent the lengths of the bases of a trapezoid and h represents its height, then the formula for the area A of the trapezoid is $A = \frac{1}{2}h(a + b)$. Write the formula in words.

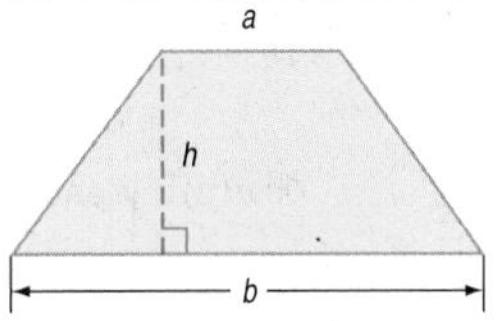

Translate each equation into a verbal sentence.

45. $4(t - s) = 5s + 12$ **46.** $7(x + y) = 35$

46. Sample answer: Seven times the sum of x and y equals 35.

47. CHALLENGE The surface area of a prism is the sum of the areas of the faces of the prism. Write a formula for the surface area of the triangular prism. Explain how you organized the parts into a simplified equation. 47–48. See margin.

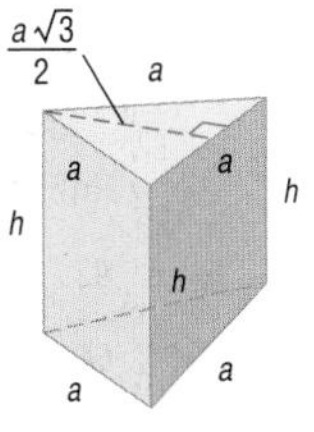

48. OPEN ENDED Apply what you know about writing equations to write a problem about a school activity that can be answered by solving $x + 16 = 30$.

Study Guide and Intervention

CRM pp. 6–7 OL AL ELL

2-1 Study Guide and Intervention
Writing Equations

Write Equations Writing equations is one strategy for solving problems. You can use a variable to represent an unspecified number or measure referred to in a problem. Then you can write a verbal expression as an algebraic expression.

Example 1 **Translate each sentence into an equation or a formula.**

a. Ten times a number x is equal to 2.8 times the difference y minus z.
$10 \times x = 2.8 \times (y - z)$
The equation is $10x = 2.8(y - z)$.

b. A number m minus 8 is the same as a number n divided by 2.
$m - 8 = n \div 2$
The equation is $m - 8 = \frac{n}{2}$.

c. The area of a rectangle equals the length times the width. Translate this sentence into a formula.
Let A = area, ℓ = length, and w = width.
Formula: *Area equals length times width.*
$A = \ell \times w$
The formula for the area of a rectangle is $A = \ell w$.

Example 2 **Use the Four-Step Problem-Solving Plan.**
The population of the United States in 2005 was about 297,000,000, and the land area of the United States is about 3,500,000 square miles. Find the average number of people per square mile in the United States.
Source: www.census.gov

Step 1 *Explore* You know that there are 297,000,000 people. You want to know the number of people per square mile.

Step 2 *Plan* Write an equation to represent the situation. Let p represent the number of people per square mile.
$3{,}500{,}000 \times p = 297{,}000{,}000$

Step 3 *Solve* $3{,}500{,}000 \times p = 297{,}000{,}000$.
$3{,}500{,}000p = 297{,}000{,}000$ Divide each side by 3,500,000.
$p \approx 84.86$
There about 85 people per square mile.

Step 4 *Check* If there are 85 people per square mile and there are 3,500,000 square miles, $85 \times 3{,}500{,}000 = 297{,}500{,}000$, or about 297,000,000 people. The answer makes sense.

Exercises

Translate each sentence into an equation or formula.

1. Three times a number t minus twelve equals forty. $3t - 12 = 40$
2. One-half of the difference of a and b is 54. $\frac{1}{2}(a - b) = 54$
3. Three times the sum of d and 4 is 32. $3(d + 4) = 32$
4. The area A of a circle is the product of π and the radius r squared. $A = \pi r^2$

WEIGHT LOSS For Exercises 5–6, use the following information.
Lou wants to lose weight to audition for a part in a play. He weighs 160 pounds now. He wants to weigh 150 pounds.

5. If p represents the number of pounds he wants to lose, write an equation to represent this situation. $160 - p = 150$
6. How many pounds does he need to lose to reach his goal? 10 lb

Chapter 2 6 Glencoe Algebra 1

Practice

CRM p. 9 OL AL

2-1 Practice
Writing Equations

Translate each sentence into an equation.

1. Fifty-three plus four times c is as much as 21. $53 + 4c = 21$
2. The sum of five times h and twice g is equal to 23. $5h + 2g = 23$
3. One fourth the sum of r and ten is identical to r minus 4. $\frac{1}{4}(r + 10) = r - 4$
4. Three plus the sum of the squares of w and x is 32. $3 + (w^2 + x^2) = 32$

Translate each sentence into a formula.

5. Degrees Kelvin K equals 273 plus degrees Celsius C. $K = 273 + C$
6. The total cost C of gas is the price p per gallon times the number of gallons g. $C = pg$
7. The sum S of the measures of the angles of a polygon is equal to 180 times the difference of the number of sides n and 2. $S = 180(n - 2)$

Translate each equation into a verbal sentence.

8. $q - (4 + p) = \frac{1}{3}q$ q minus the sum of 4 and p equals $\frac{1}{3}$ times q.
9. $\frac{3}{5}t + 2 = t$ Two more than $\frac{3}{5}$ of t equals t.
10. $9(y^2 + x) = 18$ 9 times the sum of y squared and x is 18.
11. $2(m - n) = v + 7$ Twice the quantity m minus n is v plus 7.

Write a problem based on the given information.

12. a = cost of one adult's ticket to zoo
$a - 4$ = cost of one children's ticket to zoo
$2a + 4(a - 4) = 38$
Sample answer: The cost of two adult's tickets and 4 children's tickets to the zoo is \$38. How much is an adult's ticket?

13. c = regular cost of one airline ticket
$0.20c$ = amount of 20% promotional discount
$3(c - 0.20c) = 330$
Sample answer: The cost of three airline tickets that are discounted 20% is \$330. What is the regular cost of a ticket?

14. **GEOGRAPHY** About 15% of all federally-owned land in the 48 contiguous states of the United States is in Nevada. If F represents the area of federally-owned land in these states, and N represents the portion in Nevada, write an equation for this situation. $0.15F = N$

FITNESS For Exercises 15–17, use the following information.
Deanna and Pietra each go for walks around a lake a few times per week. Last week, Deanna walked 7 miles more than Pietra.

15. If p represents the number of miles Pietra walked, write an equation that represents the total number of miles T the two girls walked. $T = p + (p + 7)$
16. If Pietra walked 9 miles during the week, how many miles did Deanna walk? 16 mi
17. If Pietra walked 11 miles during the week, how many miles did the two girls walk together? 29 mi

Chapter 2 9 Glencoe Algebra 1

Lesson 2-1

Word Problem Practice

CRM p. 10 OL AL

2-1 Word Problem Practice
Writing Equations

1. **HOUSES** The area of the Hartstein's kitchen is 182 square feet. This is 20% of the area of the first floor of their house. Let F represent the area of the first floor. Write an equation to represent the situation.
$182 = 0.2F$

2. **FAMILY** Katie is twice as old as her sister Mara. The sum of their ages is 24. Write a one-variable equation to represent the situation.
$m + 2m = 24$ or $3m = 24$

3. **GEOMETRY** The formula $F + V = E + 2$ shows the relationship between the number of faces F, edges E, and vertices V of a polyhedron, such as a pyramid. Write the formula in words.

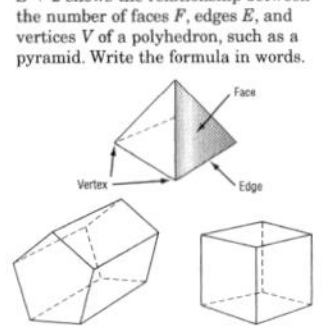

The sum of the number of faces and number of vertices is equal to the sum of two and the number of edges.

4. **WIRELESS PHONE** Spinfrog wireless phone company bills on a monthly basis. Each bill includes a \$29.95 service fee for 1000 minutes plus a \$2.95 federal communication tax. Additionally, there is a charge of \$0.05 for each minute used over 1000. Let m represent the number of minutes over 1000 used during the month. Write an equation to describe the cost c of the wireless phone service per month.
$c = 32.90 + 0.05m$

TEMPERATURE For Exercises 5 and 6, use the table showing degrees Fahrenheit and degrees Celsius temperatures.

Celsius	Fahrenheit
−20°	−4°
−10°	14°
0°	32°
10°	50°
20°	68°
30°	86°

5. Write a formula for converting Celsius temperatures to Fahrenheit temperatures.
$F = 1.8C + 32$

6. Find the Fahrenheit equivalents for 25°C and 35°C. 77° F and 95°F

Chapter 2 10 Glencoe Algebra 1

BL = Below Grade Level
OL = On Grade Level
AL = Above Grade Level
ELL = English Language Learner

Additional pages not shown:

CRM *Lesson Reading Guide,* p. 5 BL OL ELL

CRM *Skills Practice,* p. 8 BL OL

Enrichment

CRM p. 11 OL AL

2-1 Enrichment

Guess the Number

Think of a number. Add five to your number. Now, double your result. Double your result again. Divide you answer by four. Finally, subtract your original number. Your result is five.

How is it possible to know what the answer is without knowing the original number? Write the steps listed above as an expression in equation form. Then use algebra to show why this trick works.

Think of a number:	x
Add five to your number:	$x + 5$
Double your result:	$2(x + 5)$
Double your result again:	$2(2(x + 5))$
Divide you answer by four:	$\frac{2(2(x + 5))}{4}$

Lesson 2-1

Ticket Out the Door Make several copies of five different equations. Give one equation to each student. As students leave, ask them to give a verbal sentence for the equation.

 **Foldables™ Follow-Up**
Have students write several examples of equations and their verbal equivalents on index cards. Have them write the equation on one side and its verbal equivalent on the other side. Tell them to store these cards in the first pocket of the Foldable and label it "2-1: Writing Equations."

Additional Answers

48. Sample answer: After sixteen people joined the drama club, there were 30 members. How many members did the club have before the new members joined?

49. Sample answer: Equations can be used to describe the relationships of the heights of various parts of a structure. The equation representing the Sears Tower is $1454 + a = 1707$.

---

49. *Writing in Math* Use the information about the Statue of Liberty on page 70 to explain how equations are used to describe heights. Include an equation relating the heights of the Sears Tower, which is 1454 feet tall, the two antenna towers on top of the building, which are a feet tall, and the total height, which is 1707 feet. **See margin.**

STANDARDS PRACTICE 7AF1.1, 7AF4.2

50. Which equation *best* represents the relationship between the number of hours an electrician works h and the total charges c? **C**

Cost of Electrician	
emergency house call	$30 one-time fee
rate	$55/hour

A $c = 30 + 55$ C $c = 30 + 55h$

B $c = 30h + 55$ D $c = 30h + 55h$

51. REVIEW A car traveled at 55 miles per hour for 2.5 hours and then at 65 miles per hour for 3 hours. How far did the car travel in all? **J**

F 300.5 mi

G 305 mi

H 330 mi

J 332.5 mi

Spiral Review

52. ENTERTAINMENT Juanita has the volume on her stereo turned up. When her telephone rings, she turns the volume down. After she gets off the phone, she returns the volume to its previous level. Identify which graph shows the volume of Juanita's stereo during this time. (Lesson 1-9) **Graph C**

Graph A	Graph B	Graph C
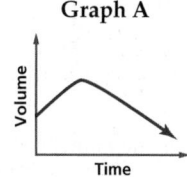	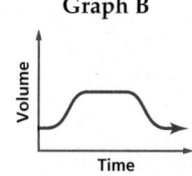	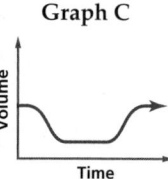

Find each square root. If necessary, round to the nearest hundredth. (Lesson 1-8)

53. $\sqrt{8100}$ **90**   **54.** $-\sqrt{\frac{25}{36}}$ $-\frac{5}{6}$ **55.** $\sqrt{90}$ **9.49**   **56.** $-\sqrt{55}$ **−7.42**

Simplify each expression. (Lesson 1-5)

57. $12d + 3 - 4d$ $8d + 3$ **58.** $7t^2 + t + 8t$ $7t^2 + 9t$ **59.** $3(a + 2b) + 5a$ $8a + 6b$

Evaluate each expression. (Lesson 1-2)

60. $5(8 - 3) + 7 \cdot 2$ **39**   **61.** $6(4^3 + 2)$ **396**   **62.** $7(0.2 + 0.5) - 0.6$ **4.3**

GET READY for the Next Lesson

PREREQUISITE SKILL Find each sum or difference. (Pages 694–697)

63. $0.57 + 2.8$ **3.37**   **64.** $5.28 - 3.4$ **1.88**   **65.** $9 - 7.35$ **1.65**

66. $\frac{2}{3} + \frac{1}{5}$ $\frac{13}{15}$ **67.** $\frac{1}{6} + \frac{2}{3}$ $\frac{5}{6}$ **68.** $\frac{7}{9} - \frac{2}{3}$ $\frac{1}{9}$

Algebra Lab
Solving Addition and Subtraction Equations

Preparation for Standard 5.0 Students solve multistep problems, including word problems, involving linear equations and linear inequalities in one variable and provide justification for each step. (Key, CAHSEE)

Reading Math

Variables You *isolate* the variable by getting it by itself on one side of the equation.

COncepts in MOtion

Animation ca.algebra1.com

You can use algebra tiles to solve equations. To solve an equation means to find the value of the variable that makes the equation true. After you model the equation, the goal is to get the *x*-tile by itself on one side of the mat using the rules stated below.

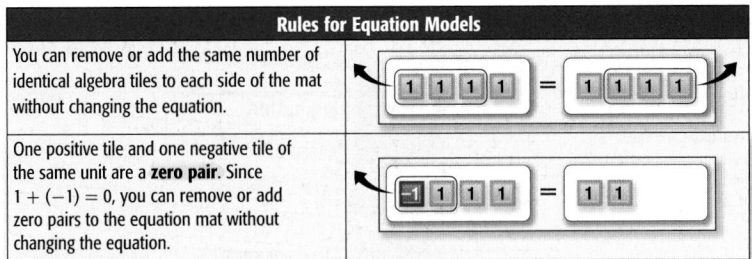

Rules for Equation Models

You can remove or add the same number of identical algebra tiles to each side of the mat without changing the equation.

One positive tile and one negative tile of the same unit are a **zero pair**. Since $1 + (-1) = 0$, you can remove or add zero pairs to the equation mat without changing the equation.

ACTIVITY

Use an equation model to solve $x - 3 = 2$.

Step 1 Model the equation.

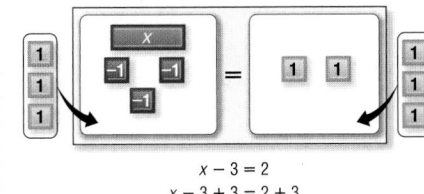

$$x - 3 = 2$$
$$x - 3 + 3 = 2 + 3$$

Place 1 *x*-tile and 3 negative 1-tiles on one side of the mat. Place 2 positive 1-tiles on the other side of the mat. Then add 3 positive 1-tiles to each side.

Step 2 Isolate the *x*-term.

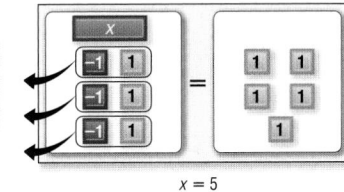

$$x = 5$$

Group the tiles to form zero pairs. Then remove all the zero pairs. The resulting equation is $x = 5$.

MODEL AND ANALYZE

Use algebra tiles to solve each equation.

1. $x + 5 = 7$ **2**
2. $x + (-2) = 8$ **10**
3. $x + 4 = 5$ **1**
4. $x + (-3) = 4$ **7**
5. $x + 3 = -4$ **−7**
6. $x + 7 = 2$ **−5**

MAKE A CONJECTURE

7. If $a = b$, what can you say about $a + c$ and $b + c$? $a + c = b + c$
8. If $a = b$, what can you say about $a - c$ and $b - c$? $a - c = b - c$

Explore 2-2 Algebra Lab: Solving Addition and Subtraction Equations **77**

From Concrete to Abstract Exercises 7–8 provide a symbolic representation for the activity.

Extending the Concept Ask students how to use algebra tiles to solve $2x - 4 = 2$. Sample answer: After isolating the two *x*-tiles, separate the 1-tiles into 2 equal groups to correspond with each *x*-tile. The number of 1-tiles corresponding to one *x*-tile gives the solution. In this case, there should be three 1-tiles for each *x*-tile.

1 Focus

Materials
- equation mats
- algebra tiles (*x*-tiles, 1-tiles)

Easy-to-Make Manipulatives

Teaching Algebra with Manipulatives

templates for:
- algebra tiles, pp. 10–11
- equation mat, p. 16

Teaching Tip Remind students that when modeling subtraction with algebra tiles, they must add negative tiles. Explain to students that they should get the *x*-tiles on one side of the mat.

2 Teach

Working in Cooperative Groups Put students in groups of 2 or 3, mixing abilities to complete the activity.

Explain the same number of identical algebra tiles can be removed or added to each side of the mat or a zero pair can be removed or added to one side of the mat.

Point out that there are not enough negative 1-tiles on the right side of the mat so that 3 negative 1-tiles can be removed from each side. Have students add 3 positive 1-tiles to both sides to create three zero-pairs on the left side.

Practice Have students complete Exercises 1–6.

3 Assess

 Formative Assessment

Use Exercise 6 to assess whether students comprehend how to form zero-pairs in order to isolate the *x*-tile.

 2-2 Solving Equations by Using Addition and Subtraction

1 Focus

 Standards Alignment

Before Lesson 2-2
Write an expression, an equation, an inequality, or a system that represents a verbal description from Standard 7AF1.1

Lesson 2-2
Solve multi-step problems involving linear equations and inequalities from Standard 5.0

After Lesson 2-2
Solve equations and inequalities involving absolute value from Standard 2A1.0

2 Teach

Scaffolding Questions
Have students read *Get Ready for the Lesson.*
Ask:
- Is the percent growth for medical assistants shown on the graph? no
- Why is the percent growth for medical assistants represented by a variable? The percent growth for medical assistants is unknown, so it is represented by the variable *m*.

(continued on the next page)

Lesson 2-2 Resources

Chapter 2 Resource Masters
Lesson Reading Guide, p. 12 **BL** **OL** **ELL**
Study Guide and Intervention, pp. 13–14
BL **OL** **ELL**
Skills Practice, p. 15 **BL** **OL**
Practice, p. 16 **OL** **AL**
Word Problem Practice, p. 17 **OL** **AL**
Enrichment, p. 18 **OL** **AL**

Main Ideas
- Solve equations by using addition.
- Solve equations by using subtraction.

Preparation for Standard 5.0 Students solve multistep problems, including word problems, involving linear equations and linear inequalities in one variable and provide justification for each step. (Key, CAHSEE)

New Vocabulary
equivalent equations
solve an equation

Study Tip

Look Back
To review **writing algebraic expressions,** see Lesson 1-1.

Transparencies
5-Minute Check Transparency 2-2
Additional Print Resources
Noteables™ Interactive Study Notebook with Foldables™
Teaching Algebra with Manipulatives

▶ **GET READY for the Lesson**

The graph shows some of the fastest-growing occupations from 1992 to 2005.

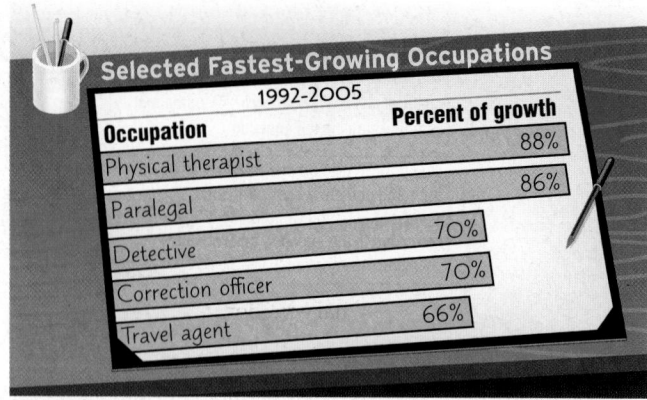

Selected Fastest-Growing Occupations
1992-2005

Occupation	Percent of growth
Physical therapist	88%
Paralegal	86%
Detective	70%
Correction officer	70%
Travel agent	66%

Source: Bureau of Labor Statistics

The percent of growth for travel agents is 5 less than the percent of growth for medical assistants. An equation can be used to find the percent of growth expected for medical assistants. If m is the percent of growth for medical assistants, then $66 = m - 5$. You can use a property of equality to find the value of m.

Solve Using Addition Suppose the boys' soccer team has 15 members and the girls' soccer team has 15 members. If each team adds 3 new players, the number of members on the boys' and girls' teams would still be equal.

$15 = 15$	Each team has 15 members before adding the new players.
$15 + 3 = 15 + 3$	Each team adds 3 new members.
$18 = 18$	Each team has 18 members after adding the new members.

This example illustrates the **Addition Property of Equality**.

KEY CONCEPT	*Addition Property of Equality*
Words	If an equation is true and the same number is added to each side, the resulting equation is true.
Symbols	For any numbers a, b, and c, if $a = b$, then $a + c = b + c$.
Examples	$7 = 7$ $\quad\quad\quad\quad$ $14 = 14$ $7 + 3 = 7 + 3$ $\quad$ $14 + (-6) = 14 + (-6)$ $10 = 10$ $\quad\quad\quad\quad$ $8 = 8$

78 Chapter 2 Solving Linear Equations

Technology
ca.algebra1.com
Interactive Classroom CD-ROM
AssignmentWorks CD-ROM
Graphing Calculator Easy Files

If the same number is added to each side of an equation, then the result is an equivalent equation. **Equivalent equations** have the same solution.

$$t + 3 = 5 \qquad \text{The solution of this equation is 2.}$$
$$t + 3 + 4 = 5 + 4 \qquad \text{Using the Addition Property of Equality, add 4 to each side.}$$
$$t + 7 = 9 \qquad \text{The solution of this equation is also 2.}$$

Study Tip

Coefficients
Remember that x means $1 \cdot x$. The coefficient of x is 1.

To **solve an equation** means to find all values of the variable that make the equation a true statement. One way to do this is to isolate the variable having a coefficient of 1 on one side of the equation. You can sometimes do this by using the Addition Property of Equality.

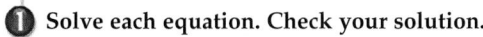 **Solve by Adding**

1 Solve each equation. Check your solution.

a. $m - 48 = 29$

$$m - 48 = 29 \qquad \text{Original equation}$$
$$m - 48 + 48 = 29 + 48 \qquad \text{Add 48 to each side.}$$
$$m = 77 \qquad -48 + 48 = 0 \text{ and } 29 + 48 = 77$$

To check that 77 is the solution, substitute 77 for m in the original equation.

$$\textbf{CHECK} \quad m - 48 = 29 \qquad \text{Original equation}$$
$$77 - 48 \overset{?}{=} 29 \qquad \text{Substitute 77 for } m.$$
$$29 = 29 \checkmark \qquad \text{Subtract.}$$

The solution 77 is correct.

b. $21 + q = -18$

$$21 + q = -18 \qquad \text{Original equation}$$
$$21 + q + (-21) = -18 + (-21) \qquad \text{Add } -21 \text{ to each side.}$$
$$q = -39 \qquad 21 + (-21) = 0 \text{ and } -18 + (-21) = -39$$

The solution is -39. To check, substitute -39 for q in the original equation.

 **Your Progress**

1A. $32 = r - 8$ **40** **1B.** $7 = 42 + t$ **−35**

Solve Using Subtraction Similar to the Addition Property of Equality, the **Subtraction Property of Equality** can also be used to solve equations.

KEY **CONCEPT**	*Subtraction Property of Equality*
Words	If an equation is true and the same number is subtracted from each side, the resulting equation is true.
Symbols	For any numbers a, b, and c, if $a = b$, then $a - c = b - c$.
Examples	$17 = 17 \qquad\qquad 3 = 3$ $17 - 9 = 17 - 9 \qquad 3 - 8 = 3 - 8$ $8 = 8 \qquad\qquad -5 = -5$

- Is the value of m greater than or less than 66? Explain your answer. The value of m is greater than 66 because the difference between m and 66 is a positive number, 5.

Solve Using Addition
Example 1 shows how to solve an equation by adding a positive or a negative number.

 Formative Assessment

Use the Check Your Progress exercises after each example to determine students' understanding of concepts.

ADDITIONAL EXAMPLE

1 Solve each equation. Check your solution.
a. $h - 12 = -27$ $h = -15$
b. $k + 63 = 92$ $k = 29$

Additional Examples are also in:
- Noteables™ Interactive Study Notebook with Foldables™
- Interactive Classroom PowerPoint® Presentations

Solve Using Subtraction
Example 2 shows how to solve an equation by subtracting a positive number. **Example 3** shows that subtracting a number is the same as adding its inverse. **Examples 4–5** show how to write and solve an equation for a problem.

Intervention

Isolating Variables Explain that when isolating a variable, it does not matter whether the variable ends up on the left or right side of an equation. For example, the solution of $8 = 15 + z$ is still -7, even though the final step may be $-7 = z$.

Focus on Mathematical Content

Solving Equations The Subtraction Property of Equality may be used to isolate the variable when solving an equation. When the same number is subtracted from each side of a true equation the resulting equation will also be true.

Tips for New Teachers — Preventing Errors

Before introducing the Subtraction Property of Equality, ask students whether the Addition Property of Equality could be revised to include subtraction. Students should note that adding a negative number is the same as subtracting that number. So if $a = b$, then $a + (-c) = b + (-c)$ is the same as $a - c = b - c$.

Students may also try to skip a step and solve the problem without first writing an equation. Tell students that they will make fewer mistakes in solving equations if they translate the sentence and write the equation before solving it.

ADDITIONAL EXAMPLES

2 Solve $c + 102 = 36$. Check your solution. $c = -66$

3 Solve $y + \dfrac{4}{5} = \dfrac{2}{3}$ in two ways. $y = -\dfrac{2}{15}$

4 Write an equation for the problem. Then solve the equation. *Fourteen more than a number is equal to twenty-seven. Find the number.* $14 + n = 27; n = 13$

EXAMPLE — Solve by Subtracting

2 Solve $142 + d = 97$. Check your solution.

$$142 + d = 97 \qquad \text{Original equation}$$
$$142 + d - 142 = 97 - 142 \qquad \text{Subtract 142 from each side.}$$
$$d = -45 \qquad 142 - 142 = 0 \text{ and } 97 - 142 = -45$$

The solution is -45. To check, substitute -45 for d in the original equation.

CHECK Your Progress Solve each equation. Check your solution.

2A. $27 + k = 30$ 3

2B. $-12 = p + 16$ -28

Remember that subtracting a number is the same as adding its inverse.

EXAMPLE — Solve by Adding or Subtracting

3 Solve $g + \dfrac{3}{4} = -\dfrac{1}{8}$ in two ways.

Method 1 Use the Subtraction Property of Equality.

$$g + \frac{3}{4} = -\frac{1}{8} \qquad \text{Original equation}$$
$$g + \frac{3}{4} - \frac{3}{4} = -\frac{1}{8} - \frac{3}{4} \qquad \text{Subtract } \tfrac{3}{4} \text{ from each side.}$$
$$g = -\frac{7}{8} \qquad \frac{3}{4} - \frac{3}{4} = 0 \text{ and } -\frac{1}{8} - \frac{3}{4} = -\frac{1}{8} - \frac{6}{8} \text{ or } -\frac{7}{8}$$

Method 2 Use the Addition Property of Equality.

$$g + \frac{3}{4} = -\frac{1}{8} \qquad \text{Original equation}$$
$$g + \frac{3}{4} + \left(-\frac{3}{4}\right) = -\frac{1}{8} + \left(-\frac{3}{4}\right) \qquad \text{Add } -\tfrac{3}{4} \text{ to each side.}$$
$$g = -\frac{7}{8} \qquad \frac{3}{4} + \left(-\frac{3}{4}\right) = 0 \text{ and } -\frac{1}{8} + \left(-\frac{3}{4}\right) = -\frac{1}{8} + \left(-\frac{6}{8}\right) \text{ or } -\frac{7}{8}$$

CHECK Your Progress

3. Solve $t + 10 = 55$ in two ways. 45

Study Tip

Checking Solutions

You should always check your solution in the context of the original problem. For instance, in Example 4, is 37 increased by 5 equal to 42? The solution checks.

EXAMPLE — Write and Solve an Equation

4 Write an equation for the problem. Then solve the equation.

A number increased by 5 is equal to 42. Find the number.

A number	increased by	5	is equal to	42.
n	$+$	5	$=$	42

$$n + 5 = 42 \qquad \text{Original equation}$$
$$n + 5 - 5 = 42 - 5 \qquad \text{Subtract 5 from each side.}$$
$$n = 37$$

The solution is 37.

CHECK Your Progress

4. Twenty-five is 3 less than a number. Find the number. $25 = n - 3; 28$

Tips for New Teachers — Student Misconception

After studying Example 3, some students may wonder which method they should use. Tell them they may use whichever method is most comfortable for them.

Real-World EXAMPLE

5 HISTORY In the fourteenth century, part of the Great Wall of China was repaired and the wall was extended. When the wall was completed, it was 2500 miles long. How much of the wall was added during the 1300s?

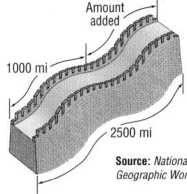

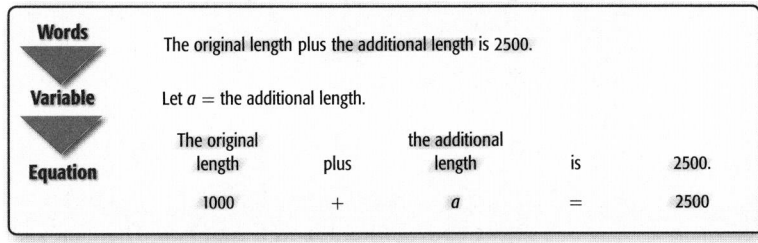

Words	The original length plus the additional length is 2500.
Variable	Let a = the additional length.
Equation	The original length — 1000 — plus — + — the additional length — a — is — = — 2500. — 2500

$$1000 + a = 2500 \qquad \text{Original equation}$$
$$1000 + a - 1000 = 2500 - 1000 \qquad \text{Subtract 1000 from each side.}$$
$$a = 1500 \qquad 1000 - 1000 = 0 \text{ and } 2500 - 1000 = 1500$$

The Great Wall of China was extended 1500 miles in the 1300s.

CHECK Your Progress

5. DEER In a recent year, 1286 female deer were born in Lewis County. That was 93 fewer than the number of male deer born. How many male deer were born that year? **1379**

Online Personal Tutor at ca.algebra1.com

Real-World Link

The first emperor of China, Qui Shi Huangdi, ordered the building of the Great Wall of China to protect his people from nomadic tribes that attacked and looted villages. By 204 B.C., this wall guarded 1000 miles of China's border.

Source: *National Geographic World*

★ indicates multi-step problem

✓ CHECK Your Understanding

Examples 1–3
(pp. 79–80)

Solve each equation. Check your solution. **6. −50**

1. $n - 20 = 5$ **25**
2. $104 = y - 67$ **171**
3. $-4 + t = -7$ **−3**
4. $g + 5 = 33$ **28**
5. $19 + p = 6$ **−13**
6. $15 = b - (-65)$
7. $h + \frac{2}{5} = \frac{7}{10}$ **$\frac{3}{10}$**
8. $-6 = \frac{1}{4} + m$ **$-6\frac{1}{4}$**
9. $\frac{2}{3} + w = 1\frac{1}{2}$ **$\frac{5}{6}$**

Example 4
(p. 80)

Write an equation for each problem. Then solve the equation and check your solution. **10. $n - 21 = -8$; 13**

10. Twenty-one subtracted from a number is −8. Find the number.
11. A number increased by 91 is 37. Find the number. $n + 91 = 37$; **−54**

Example 5
(p. 81)

★ **12. HISTORY** Over the years, the height of the Great Pyramid at Giza, Egypt, has decreased. Use the figure to write an equation to represent the situation. Then find the decrease in the height of the pyramid. $450 + d = 481$; **31 ft**

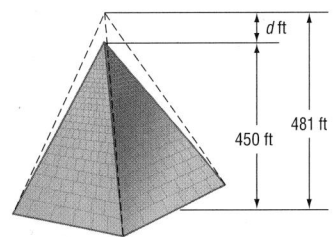

Source: *World Book Encyclopedia*

Lesson 2-2 Solving Equations by Using Addition and Subtraction **81**

ADDITIONAL EXAMPLE

5 HISTORY The Washington Monument in Washington, D.C., was built in two phases. During the first phase, the monument was built to a height of 152 feet. During the second phase, additional construction resulted in the monument's final height of 555 feet. How much of the monument was added during the second construction phase? Write an equation to solve the problem. $152 + a = 555$; $a = 403$ ft

3 Practice

✓ Formative Assessment

Use Exercises 1–12 to check for understanding.

Use the chart at the bottom of this page to customize assignments for your students.

DIFFERENTIATED HOMEWORK OPTIONS

Level	Assignment	Two-Day Option	
BL Basic	13–32, 48, 49, 52–66	13–31 odd, 53, 54	14–32 even, 48, 49, 52–66
OL Core	13–37 odd, 39–49, 52–66	13–32, 53, 54	33–49, 52, 53–66
AL Advanced/Pre-AP	33–62 (optional: 63–66)		

Odd/Even Assignments

Exercises 13–32 are structured so that students practice the same concepts whether they are assigned odd or even problems.

Real-World Connections

For Exercise 31, point out that most countries sell gasoline by the liter. Have students talk about places they have lived or visited and whether the gasoline there was sold by the gallon or by the liter.

Additional Answer

52. Sample answer: Equations can be used to describe the relationships of growth and decline in job opportunities. To solve the equation, add 5 to each side. The solution is $m = 71$. Sample problem: "The percent increase in growth for paralegals is 16 more than the percent increase in growth for detectives. If the growth rate for paralegals is 86%, what is the growth rate for detectives? $d + 16 = 86$; 70%."

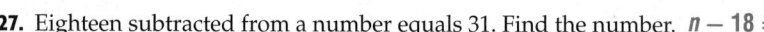

HOMEWORK HELP	
For Exercises	See Examples
13–26	1–3
27–30	4
31, 32	5

Exercise Levels
A: 13–32
B: 33–47

Solve each equation. Check your solution.

13. $v - 9 = 14$ **23**

14. $44 = t - 72$ **116**

15. $-61 = d + (-18)$ **−43**

16. $p + (-26) = 16$ **42**

17. $18 + z = 40$ **22**

18. $19 = c + 12$ **7**

19. $n + 23 = 4$ **−19**

20. $-67 = 11 + k$ **−78**

21. $18 - (-f) = 91$ **73**

22. $88 = 125 - (-u)$ **−37**

23. $\frac{2}{3} + r = -\frac{4}{9}$ **$-1\frac{1}{9}$**

24. $\frac{3}{4} = w + \frac{2}{5}$ **$\frac{7}{20}$**

25. $-\frac{1}{2} + a = \frac{5}{8}$ **$1\frac{1}{8}$**

26. $-\frac{7}{10} = y - \frac{3}{5}$ **$-\frac{1}{10}$**

Write an equation for each problem. Then solve the equation and check your solution.

27. Eighteen subtracted from a number equals 31. Find the number. $n - 18 = 31$; **49**

28. What number decreased by 77 equals −18? $n - 77 = -18$; **59**

29. A number increased by −16 is −21. Find the number. $n + (-16) = -21$; **−5**

30. The sum of a number and −43 is 102. What is the number? $n + (-43) = 102$; **145**

For Exercises 31 and 32, write an equation for each situation. Then solve the equation.

31. GAS MILEAGE A midsize car with a 4-cylinder engine goes 34 miles on a gallon of gasoline. This is 10 miles more than a luxury car with an 8-cylinder engine goes on a gallon of gasoline. How many miles does a luxury car travel on a gallon of gasoline? **Sample equation:** $\ell + 10 = 34$; 24 mi

32. IN THE MEDIA The world's biggest-ever passenger plane, the *Airbus A380*, was first used by Singapore Airlines in 2005. The following description appeared on a news Web site after the plane was introduced.

> "That airline will see the A380 transporting some 555 passengers, 139 more than a similarly set-up 747." **Source:** cnn.com

Real-World Link

The Airbus A380 is 239 feet 6 inches long, 79 feet 1 inch high, and has a wingspan of 261 feet 10 inches.

Source: nationalgeographic.com

How many passengers does a similarly set-up 747 transport? **Sample equation:** $555 = a + 139$; 416 passengers

Solve each equation. Then check your solution.

33. $k + 0.6 = -3.8$ **−4.4**

34. $8.5 + t = 7.1$ **−1.4**

35. $4.2 = q - 3.5$ **7.7**

36. $q - 2.78 = 4.2$ **6.98**

37. $6.2 = -4.83 + y$ **11.03**

38. $-6 = m + (-3.42)$ **−2.58**

Write an equation for each problem. Then solve the equation and check your solution. $n - \frac{1}{2} = -\frac{3}{4}$; $-\frac{1}{4}$

39. What number minus one half is equal to negative three fourths?

40. $19 + 42 + n = 87$; 26

40. The sum of 19 and 42 and a number is equal to 87. What is the number?

★ 41. CARS The average time t it takes to manufacture a car in the United States is 24.9 hours. This is 8.1 hours longer than the average time it takes to manufacture a car in Japan. Write and solve an addition equation to find the average time to manufacture a car in Japan. $\ell + 8.1 = 24.9; 16.8$ h

42. If $x - 7 = 14$, what is the value of $x - 2$? **19**

43. If $t + 8 = -12$, what is the value of $t + 1$? **−19**

44. $14.7 + x = 28.7; 14.0$ million volumes

45. $14.6 + x = 14.7; 0.1$ million volumes

46. $14.6 + x = 28.7; 14.1$ million volumes

ANALYZE GRAPHS For Exercises 44–47, use the graph at the right to write an equation for each situation. Then solve the equation.

44. How many more volumes does the Library of Congress have than the Harvard University Library?

45. How many more volumes does the Harvard University Library have than the Boston Public Library?

46. How many more volumes does the Library of Congress have than the Boston Public Library?

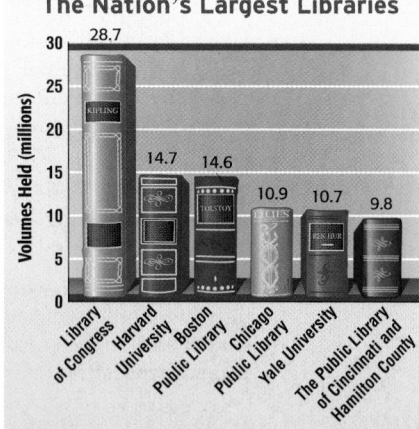

The Nation's Largest Libraries

Volumes Held (millions)

Library of Congress 28.7, Harvard University 14.7, Boston Public Library 14.6, Chicago Public Library 10.9, Yale University 10.7, The Public Library of Cincinnati and Hamilton County 9.8

Source: American Library Association

EXTRA PRACTICE
See pages 720, 745.

Math Online
Self-Check Quiz at
ca.algebra1.com

47. What is the total number of volumes in the three largest U.S. libraries?
$28.7 + 14.7 + 14.6 = x$; 58.0 million volumes

H.O.T. Problems

48. Which One Doesn't Belong? Identify the equation that does not belong with the other three. Explain your reasoning. $n - 16 = 29$; it is the only equation that does not have a solution of 13.

| $n + 14 = 27$ | $12 + n = 25$ | $n - 16 = 29$ | $n - 4 = 9$ |

49. OPEN ENDED Write an equation involving addition and demonstrate two ways to solve it. **See students' work.**

50. CHALLENGE If $a - b = x$, what values of a, b, and x would make the equation $a + x = b + x$ true? Explain your reasoning. $a = b, x = 0$; according to the Subtraction Property of Equality, if an equation is true and the same number or variable is subtracted from each side, the resulting equation is true.

51. CHALLENGE Determine whether each sentence is *sometimes*, *always*, or *never* true. Explain your reasoning.

a. $x + x = x$ Sometimes; if $x = 0$, $x + x = x$ is true.

b. $x + 0 = x$ Always; any number plus 0 always equals the number.

52. *Writing in Math* Use the data about occupations on page 78 to explain how equations can be used to compare data. Include a sample problem and related equation using the information in the graph and an explanation of how to solve the equation. **See margin.**

Lesson 2-2 Solving Equations by Using Addition and Subtraction **83**

BL = Below Grade Level
OL = On Grade Level
AL = Above Grade Level
ELL = English Language Learner

Additional pages not shown:

CRM Lesson Reading Guide, p. 12 **BL OL ELL**

CRM Skills Practice, p. 15 **BL OL**

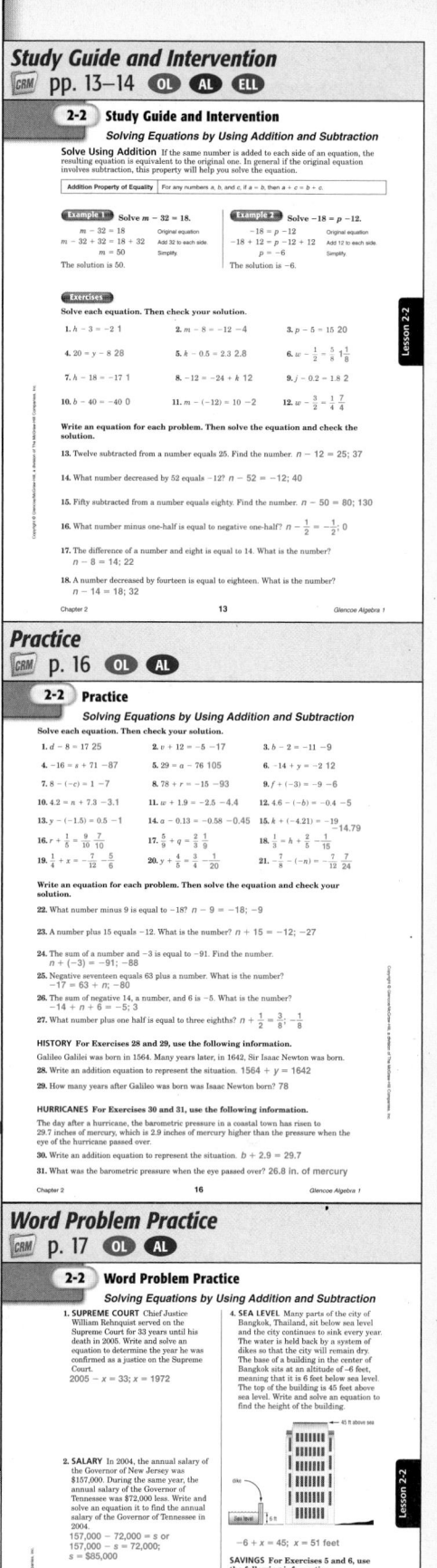

Study Guide and Intervention
CRM pp. 13–14 **OL AL ELL**

2-2 Study Guide and Intervention
Solving Equations by Using Addition and Subtraction

Solve Using Addition If the same number is added to each side of an equation, the resulting equation is equivalent to the original one. In general if the original equation involves subtraction, this property will help you solve the equation.

| **Addition Property of Equality** | For any numbers a, b, and c, if $a = b$, then $a + c = b + c$. |

Example 1 Solve $m - 32 = 18$.
$m - 32 = 18$ Original equation
$m - 32 + 32 = 18 + 32$ Add 32 to each side.
$m = 50$ Simplify.
The solution is 50.

Example 2 Solve $-18 = p - 12$.
$-18 = p - 12$ Original equation
$-18 + 12 = p - 12 + 12$ Add 12 to each side.
$p = -6$ Simplify.
The solution is −6.

Exercises

Solve each equation. Then check your solution.

1. $h - 3 = -2$ 1
2. $m - 8 = -12$ −4
3. $p - 5 = 15$ 20
4. $20 = y - 8$ 28
5. $k - 0.5 = 2.3$ 2.8
6. $w - \frac{1}{2} = \frac{5}{8}$ $1\frac{1}{8}$
7. $h - 18 = -17$ 1
8. $-12 = -24 + k$ 12
9. $j - 0.2 = 1.8$ 2
10. $b - 40 = -40$ 0
11. $n - (-12) = 10$ −2
12. $w - \frac{3}{2} = \frac{1}{4}$ $\frac{7}{4}$

Write an equation for each problem. Then solve the equation and check the solution.

13. Twelve subtracted from a number equals 25. Find the number. $n - 12 = 25$; 37
14. What number decreased by 52 equals −12? $n - 52 = -12$; 40
15. Fifty subtracted from a number equals eighty. Find the number. $n - 50 = 80$; 130
16. What number minus one-half is equal to negative one-half? $n - \frac{1}{2} = -\frac{1}{2}$; 0
17. The difference of a number and eight is equal to 14. What is the number? $n - 8 = 14$; 22
18. A number decreased by fourteen is equal to eighteen. What is the number? $n - 14 = 18$; 32

Chapter 2   13   Glencoe Algebra 1

Lesson 2-2

Practice
CRM p. 16 **OL AL**

2-2 Practice
Solving Equations by Using Addition and Subtraction

Solve each equation. Then check your solution.

1. $d - 8 = 17$ 25
2. $v + 12 = -5$ −17
3. $b - 2 = -11$ −9
4. $-16 = s + 71$ −87
5. $29 = a - 76$ 105
6. $-14 + y = -2$ 12
7. $8 - (-c) = 1$ −7
8. $78 + r = -15$ −93
9. $f + (-3) = -9$ −6
10. $4.2 = n + 7.3$ −3.1
11. $w + 1.9 = -2.5$ −4.4
12. $4.6 - (-b) = -0.4$ −5
13. $y - (-1.5) = 0.5$ −1
14. $a - 0.13 = -0.58$ −0.45
15. $k + (-4.21) = -19$ −14.79
16. $r + \frac{1}{5} = \frac{9}{10}$ $\frac{7}{10}$
17. $\frac{5}{9} + q = \frac{2}{3}$ $\frac{1}{9}$
18. $\frac{1}{3} = h + \frac{2}{15}$ $\frac{1}{5}$
19. $\frac{1}{4} + x = -\frac{7}{12}$ $-\frac{5}{6}$
20. $y + \frac{4}{5} = \frac{3}{4}$ $-\frac{1}{20}$
21. $-\frac{7}{8} - (-n) = -\frac{7}{12}$ $\frac{7}{24}$

Write an equation for each problem. Then solve the equation and check your solution.

22. What number minus 9 is equal to −18? $n - 9 = -18$; −9
23. A number plus 15 equals −12. What is the number? $n + 15 = -12$; −27
24. The sum of a number and −3 is equal to −91. Find the number. $n + (-3) = -91$; −88
25. Negative seventeen equals 63 plus a number. What is the number? $-17 = 63 + n$; −80
26. The sum of negative 14, a number, and 6 is −5. What is the number? $-14 + n + 6 = -5$; 3
27. What number plus one half is equal to three eighths? $n + \frac{1}{2} = \frac{3}{8}$; $-\frac{1}{8}$

HISTORY For Exercises 28 and 29, use the following information.
Galileo Galilei was born in 1564. Many years later, in 1642, Sir Isaac Newton was born.
28. Write an addition equation to represent the situation. $1564 + y = 1642$
29. How many years after Galileo was born was Isaac Newton born? 78

HURRICANES For Exercises 30 and 31, use the following information.
The day after a hurricane, the barometric pressure in a coastal town has risen to 29.7 inches of mercury, which is 2.9 inches of mercury higher than the pressure when the eye of the hurricane passed over.
30. Write an addition equation to represent the situation. $b + 2.9 = 29.7$
31. What was the barometric pressure when the eye passed over? 26.8 in. of mercury

Chapter 2   16   Glencoe Algebra 1

Word Problem Practice
CRM p. 17 **OL AL**

2-2 Word Problem Practice
Solving Equations by Using Addition and Subtraction

1. **SUPREME COURT** Chief Justice William Rehnquist served on the Supreme Court for 33 years until his death in 2005. Write and solve an equation to determine the year he was confirmed as a justice on the Supreme Court.
$2005 - x = 33$; $x = 1972$

2. **SALARY** In 2004, the annual salary of the Governor of New Jersey was $157,000. During the same year, the annual salary of the Governor of Tennessee was $72,000 less. Write and solve an equation it to find the annual salary of the Governor of Tennessee in 2004.
$157,000 - 72,000 = s$ or $157,000 - s = 72,000$; $s = \$85,000$

3. **WEATHER** On a cold January day, Mavis noticed that the temperature dropped 21 degrees over the course of the day to −9°C. Write and solve an equation to determine what the temperature was at the beginning of the day.
$x - 21 = -9$; $x = 12$°C

4. **SEA LEVEL** Many parts of the city of Bangkok, Thailand, sit below sea level and the city continues to sink every year. The water is held back by a system of dikes so that the city will remain dry. The base of a building in the center of Bangkok sits at an altitude of −6 feet, meaning that it is 6 feet below sea level. The top of the building is 45 feet above sea level. Write and solve an equation to find the height of the building.

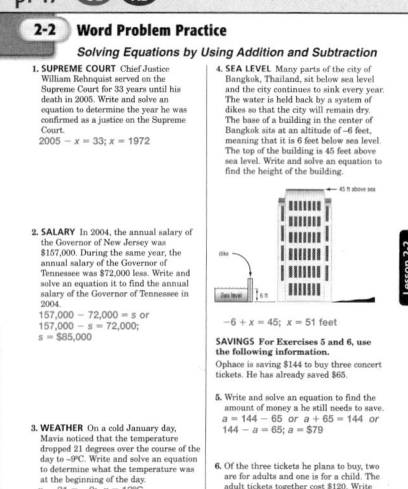

$-6 + x = 45$; $x = 51$ feet

SAVINGS For Exercises 5 and 6, use the following information.
Ophace is saving $144 to buy three concert tickets. He has already saved $65.

5. Write and solve an equation to find the amount of money a he still needs to save.
$a + 65 = 144$ or $a + 65 = 144$ or $144 - a = 65$; $a = \$79$

6. Of the three tickets he plans to buy, two are for adults and one is for a child. The adult tickets together cost $120. Write and solve an equation to find the cost of the child ticket.
$144 - 120 = c$; $c = \$24$

Chapter 2   17   Glencoe Algebra 1

Lesson 2-2

Enrichment
CRM p. 18 **OL AL**

2-2 Enrichment

Elevator Puzzle

Jose gets on the elevator and rides without pushing any buttons. First, the elevator goes up 4 floors where Bob gets on. Bob goes down 6 floors and gets off. At that same floor Florence gets on and goes up one floor before getting off. The elevator then moves down 8 floors to pick up the Hartt family who ride down 3 floors and get off. Then the elevator goes up one floor, picks up Kris, and goes down 6 floors to the street level where Jose exits the elevator.

1. Suppose x is your starting point. Write an equation that represents Jose's elevator ride.
$x + 4 - 6 + 1 - 8 - 3 + 1 - 6 = 0$

2. At what floor did Jose get on the elevator? **17th floor**

Now you know the starting point of Jose, the starting point of every other

Crystal Ball Tell students that the next lesson they will study is titled *Solving Equations by Using Multiplication and Division.* Ask them to write how they think what they have learned in this lesson will connect with the next lesson they study.

Additional Answers

60. H: it is Friday; C: there is a science quiz; If it is Friday, then there is a science quiz.

61. H: $y = 2$; C: $4y - 6 = 2$; If $y = 2$, then $4y - 6 = 2$.

STANDARDS PRACTICE 7AF1.1, 7PS1.2

53. Which problem is best represented by the equation $w - 15 = 33$? **C**

A Jake added w ounces of water to his water bottle, which originally contained 33 ounces of water. How much water did he add?

B Jake added 15 ounces of water to his water bottle, for a total of 33 ounces of water. How much water w was originally in the bottle?

C Jake drank 15 ounces of water from his water bottle and 33 ounces were left. How much water w was originally in the bottle?

D Jake drank 15 ounces of water from his water bottle, which originally contained 33 ounces. How much water w was left?

54. REVIEW The table shows the results of a survey given to 500 international travelers. Based on the data, which statement is true? **F**

Vacation Plans	
Destination	**Percent**
The Tropics	37
Europe	19
Asia	17
Other	17
No Vacation	10

F Fifty international travelers have no vacation plans.

G Fifteen international travelers are going to Asia.

H One third of international travelers are going to the tropics.

J One hundred international travelers are going to Europe.

Spiral Review

GEOMETRY For Exercises 55 and 56, use the following information. (Lesson 2-1)
The area of a circle is the product of π times the radius r squared.

55. Write the formula for the area of the circle. $A = \pi r^2$

56. If a circle has a radius of 16 inches, find its area. **about 804 in²**

Replace each ● with >, <, or = to make the sentence true. (Lesson 1-8)

57. $\frac{1}{2}$ ● $\sqrt{2}$ **<**   **58.** $\frac{3}{4}$ ● $\frac{2}{3}$ **>**   **59.** 0.375 ● $\frac{3}{8}$ **=**

Identify the hypothesis and conclusion of each statement. Then write the statement in if-then form. (Lesson 1-7) **60–61. See margin.**

60. There is a science quiz every Friday.   **61.** For $y = 2$, $4y - 6 = 2$.

★ **62. SHOPPING** Shawnel bought 8 bagels at $0.95 each, 8 doughnuts at $0.80 each and 8 small cartons of milk for $1.00 each. Write and solve an expression to determine the total cost. (Lesson 1-5) $8(0.95 + 0.8 + 1)$; $22.00

GET READY for the Next Lesson

PREREQUISITE SKILL Find each product or quotient. (Pages 698–701)

63. 6.5×2.8 **18.20**   **64.** $17.8 \div 2.5$ **7.12**   **65.** $\frac{2}{3} \times \frac{5}{8}$ $\frac{5}{12}$ **66.** $\frac{8}{9} \div \frac{4}{15}$ $3\frac{1}{3}$

84 Chapter 2 Solving Linear Equations

Pre-AP Activity **Use after the Exercises**

Write x and two numbers on the board. Give students the operation symbols $+$ and $-$. Tell them to use both of the numbers, x, and the operation symbols to write two equations for which the value of x is the same. Have students solve for x in both equations. For example, suppose the two numbers were 23 and 45. Students could write $x + 23 = 45$ and $x = 45 - 23$; $x = 22$.

Solving Equations by Using Multiplication and Division

Main Ideas

- Solve equations by using multiplication.
- Solve equations by using division.

Preparation for Standard 5.0 Students solve multistep problems, including word problems, involving linear equations and linear inequalities in one variable and provide justification for each step. (Key, CAHSEE)

GET READY for the Lesson

The diagram shows the distance between Earth and each star in the Big Dipper. Light travels at a rate of about 5,870 billion miles per year. The rate or speed at which something travels times the time equals the distance it travels. The following equation can be used to find the time it takes light from the closest star in the Big Dipper to reach Earth.

$$rt = d$$

$$5870t = 311{,}110$$

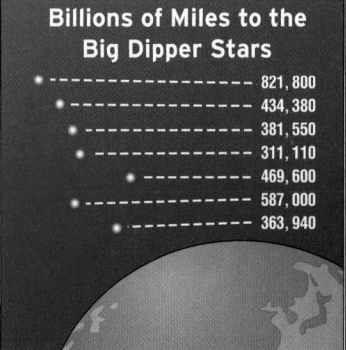

Billions of Miles to the Big Dipper Stars

- 821,800
- 434,380
- 381,550
- 311,110
- 469,600
- 587,000
- 363,940

Source: *National Geographic World*

Solve Using Multiplication To solve equations such as the one above, you can use the **Multiplication Property of Equality**.

KEY CONCEPT   *Multiplication Property of Equality*

Words   If an equation is true and each side is multiplied by the same number, the resulting equation is true.

Symbols   For any numbers a, b, and c, if $a = b$, then $ac = bc$.

Examples

$6 = 6$	$9 = 9$	$10 = 10$
$6 \times 2 = 6 \times 2$	$9 \times (-3) = 9 \times (-3)$	$10 \times \frac{1}{2} = 10 \times \frac{1}{2}$
$12 = 12$	$-27 = -27$	$5 = 5$

EXAMPLE   Solve Using Multiplication by a Positive Number

1 Solve $\frac{t}{3} = 7$. Check your solution.

$\frac{t}{3} = 7$ Original equation

$3\left(\frac{t}{3}\right) = 3(7)$ Multiply each side by 3.

$t = 21$ $\frac{t}{3}(3) = t$ and $7(3) = 21$

CHECK $\frac{t}{3} = 7$ Original equation

$\frac{21}{3} \stackrel{?}{=} 7$ Substitute 21 for t.

$7 = 7$ ✓   The solution is 21.

 CHECK Your Progress

Solve each equation. Check your solution.

1A. $18 = \frac{w}{2}$ 36

1B. $\frac{n}{3} = -\frac{2}{5}$ $-1\frac{1}{5}$

Lesson 2-3 Solving Equations by Using Multiplication and Division   **85**

1 Focus

Standards Alignment

Before Lesson 2-3
Write an expression, an equation, an inequality, or a system that represents a verbal description from Standard 7AF1.1

Lesson 2-3
Solve multi-step problems involving linear equations and inequalities from Standard 5.0

After Lesson 2-3
Solve equations and inequalities involving absolute value from Standard 2A1.0

2 Teach

Scaffolding Questions

Have students read *Get Ready for the Lesson*.

Ask:

- What is the unknown quantity in the equation given in the example? how much time it takes for light to reach Earth
- What variable represents the unknown quantity in the equation? t
- What do you need to accomplish to solve this equation? isolate the variable on one side of the equation

Lesson 2-3 Resources

Chapter 2 Resource Masters

Lesson Reading Guide, p. 19 BL OL ELL
Study Guide and Intervention, pp. 20–21 BL OL ELL
Skills Practice, p. 22 BL OL
Practice, p. 23 OL AL
Word Problem Practice, p. 24 OL AL
Enrichment, p. 25 OL AL
Quiz 1, p. 73

Transparencies

5-Minute Check Transparency 2-3

Additional Print Resources

Noteables™ Interactive Study Notebook with Foldables™
Teaching Algebra with Manipulatives

Technology

ca.algebra1.com
Interactive Classroom CD-ROM
AssignmentWorks CD-ROM
Graphing Calculator Easy Files

Solve Using Multiplication

Examples 1–2 show how to solve an equation by multiplying each side by the same number, whether the number is positive, negative, or a fraction.

Example 3 shows how to write and solve an equation for a real-world problem.

Formative Assessment

Use the Check Your Progress exercises after each example to determine students' understanding of concepts.

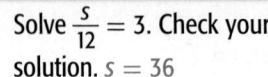

ADDITIONAL EXAMPLES

1 Solve $\frac{s}{12} = 3$. Check your solution. $s = 36$

2 Solve each equation.

a. $-1\frac{3}{8}k = \frac{2}{3}$ $\quad k = -\frac{16}{33}$

b. $-75 = -15b$ $\quad b = 5$

3 **SPACE TRAVEL** Using the information from Example 3, what is the weight of Neil Armstrong's suit and life-support backpacks on Mars if three times the Mars weight equals the Earth weight? 66 lb

Additional Examples are also in:

- Noteables™ Interactive Study Notebook with Foldables™
- Interactive Classroom PowerPoint® Presentations

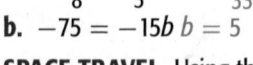

Focus on Mathematical Content

Properties of Equality The Multiplication Property may be used to isolate the variable when solving an equation. When each side of a true equation is multiplied by the same number the resulting equation will also be true.

---

2 Solve each equation.

a. $\left(2\frac{1}{4}\right)g = \frac{1}{2}$

$\left(2\frac{1}{4}\right)g = \frac{1}{2}$ Original equation

$\left(\frac{9}{4}\right)g = \frac{1}{2}$ Rewrite the mixed number as an improper fraction.

$\frac{4}{9}\left(\frac{9}{4}\right)g = \frac{4}{9}\left(\frac{1}{2}\right)$ Multiply each side by $\frac{4}{9}$, the reciprocal of $\frac{9}{4}$.

$g = \frac{2}{9}$ Check this result.

b. $42 = -6m$

$42 = -6m$ Original equation

$-\frac{1}{6}(42) = -\frac{1}{6}(-6m)$ Multiply each side by $-\frac{1}{6}$, the reciprocal of -6.

$-7 = m$ Check this result.

✓ CHECK **Your Progress**

2A. $\frac{3}{5}k = 6$ 10   **2B.** $-\frac{1}{4} = \frac{2}{3}b$ $-\frac{3}{8}$

Real-World EXAMPLE

3 **SPACE TRAVEL** Refer to the information at the left. An item's weight on the Moon is about one sixth its weight on Earth. What was the weight of Neil Armstrong's suit and life-support backpacks on Earth?

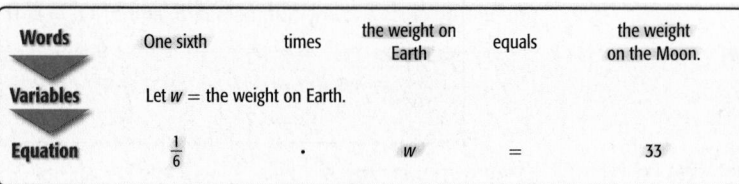

Words	One sixth	times	the weight on Earth	equals	the weight on the Moon.
Variables	Let w = the weight on Earth.				
Equation	$\frac{1}{6}$	·	w	=	33

$\frac{1}{6}w = 33$ Original equation

$6\left(\frac{1}{6}w\right) = 6(33)$ Multiply each side by 6.

$w = 198$ $\frac{1}{6}(6) = 1$ and $33(6) = 198$

Neil Armstrong's suit and backpacks were about 198 pounds on Earth.

✓ CHECK **Your Progress**

3. **SURVEYS** In a recent survey of 13- to 15-year-old girls, 225, or about $\frac{9}{20}$ of those surveyed, said they talk on the telephone while they watch television. About how many girls were surveyed? about 500

🌐 online **Personal Tutor** at ca.algebra1.com

Real-World Link

On July 20, 1969, Neil Armstrong stepped on the surface of the Moon. On the Moon, his suit and life-support backpacks weighed about 33 pounds.

Source: NASA

Making Connections

In Lesson 2-2, students learned that to solve an equation, the variable must be isolated on one side of the equation. Because the numbers were added to or subtracted from the variable, they added (or subtracted) the same quantity to each side of the equation to accomplish this. Ask students how the number is "connected" to the variable (multiplication). Then ask what is the opposite operation of multiplication.

Solve Using Division In Example 2b, the equation $42 = -6m$ was solved by multiplying each side by $-\frac{1}{6}$. The same result could have been obtained by dividing each side by -6. This method uses the **Division Property of Equality**.

Words	If an equation is true and each side is divided by the same non-zero number, the resulting equation is true.
Symbols	For any numbers a, b, and c with $c \neq 0$, if $a = b$, then $\frac{a}{c} = \frac{b}{c}$.
Examples	$15 = 15$ $\qquad$ $28 = 28$
	$\frac{15}{3} = \frac{15}{3}$ $\qquad$ $\frac{28}{-7} = \frac{28}{-7}$
	$5 = 5$ $\qquad$ $-4 = -4$

EXAMPLE Solve Using Division

4 **Solve each equation. Check your solution.**

a. $13s = 195$

$13s = 195$	Original equation	**CHECK** $\quad 13s = 195$	Original equation
$\frac{13s}{13} = \frac{195}{13}$	Divide each side by 13.	$13(15) \stackrel{?}{=} 195$	Substitute 15 for s.
$s = 15$ $\quad$ $\frac{13s}{13} = s$ and $\frac{195}{13} = 15$		$195 = 195$ ✓	Multiply.

b. $-3x = 12$

$-3x = 12$	Original equation	**CHECK** $\quad -3x = 12$	Original equation
$\frac{-3x}{-3} = \frac{12}{-3}$	Divide each side by -3.	$-3(-4) \stackrel{?}{=} 12$	Substitute -4 for x.
$x = -4$ $\quad$ $\frac{-3x}{-3} = x$ and $\frac{12}{-3} = -4$		$12 = 12$ ✓	Multiply.

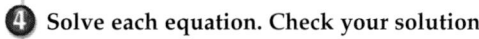 **Your Progress**

4A. $84 = 3b$ $\quad$ **28** $\qquad\qquad$ **4B.** $-42 = -3s$ $\quad$ **14**

EXAMPLE Write and Solve an Equation Using Division

5 **Write an equation for the problem below. Then solve the equation.**

Negative eighteen times a number equals -198.

Negative eighteen	times	a number	equals	-198.
-18	$\times$	n	$=$	-198

$-18n = -198$	Original equation
$\frac{-18n}{-18} = \frac{-198}{-18}$	Divide each side by -18.
$n = 11$	Check this result.

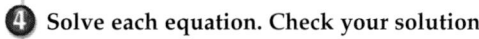 **Your Progress**

5. Write an equation for the following problem. Then solve the equation.
Negative forty-two equals the product of six and a number. $\quad -42 = 6n; -7$

Lesson 2-3 Solving Equations by Using Multiplication and Division **87**

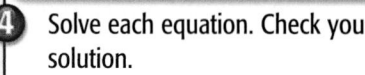 **Preventing Errors**

Remind students that the product of a fraction and its reciprocal is 1.

Solve Using Division

Example 4 shows how to solve an equation using division by positive and negative numbers. **Example 5** shows how to write and solve an equation using division.

ADDITIONAL EXAMPLES

4 Solve each equation. Check your solution.

a. $11w = 143$ $\quad w = 13$

b. $-8x = 96$ $\quad x = -12$

5 Write an equation for the problem below. Then solve the equation. *Negative fourteen times a number equals 224.*
$-14n = 224; n = -16$

Focus on Mathematical Content

Properties of Equality The Division Property may be used to isolate the variable when solving an equation. When each side of a true equation is divided by the same non-zero number the resulting equation will also be true.

Intervention

Coefficients Students are sometimes confused about what to do with a variable in an equation such as $-x = 27$. Point out that the variable actually has a coefficient of -1. Remembering that the product of two negative numbers is a positive, you can multiply each side of the equation by -1.
$(-1)(-x) = (-1)27; x = -27$

3 Practice

Formative Assessment

Use Exercises 1–13 to check for understanding.

Use the chart at the bottom of this page to customize assignments for your students.

Odd/Even Assignments

Exercises 14–37 are structured so that students practice the same concepts whether they are assigned odd or even problems.

Real-World Connection

For Exercise 26, explain that about one seventh of the world's population is left-handed. Ask students to calculate how many in their class are left-handed. Have students count the actual number of left-handed students.

For Exercise 27, have students measure the circumference of an actual doughnut and then find the diameter using the formula $C = \pi d$. Have students measure the diameter of the doughnut and compare the two values.

Additional Answer

52. Sample answer: $3x = -12$; On the last three downs of a football game, the offense lost a total of 12 yards. How many yards on average did they lose per down?

✓ CHECK Your Understanding

Examples 1 and 2
(pp. 85–86)

Solve each equation. Check your solution.

1. $\frac{t}{7} = -5$ -35

2. $\frac{a}{36} = \frac{4}{9}$ 16

3. $\frac{2}{3}n = 10$ 15

4. $\frac{8}{9} = \frac{4}{5}k$ $1\frac{1}{9}$

5. $12 = \frac{x}{-3}$ -36

6. $-\frac{r}{4} = \frac{1}{7}$ $-\frac{4}{7}$

Example 3
(p. 86)

7. GEOGRAPHY The *discharge* of a river equals the product of its width, its average depth, and its speed. At one location in St. Louis, the Mississippi River is 533 meters wide, its speed is 0.6 meter per second, and its discharge is 3198 cubic meters per second. How deep is the Mississippi River at this location? **10 m**

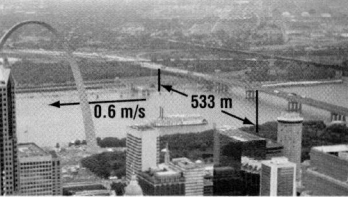
0.6 m/s   533 m

Example 4
(p. 87)

Solve each equation. Check your solution.

8. $8t = 72$ 9

9. $20 = 4w$ 5

10. $45 = -9a$ -5

11. $-2g = -84$ 42

13. $\frac{1}{3} = -7n$; $-\frac{1}{21}$

Example 5
(p. 87)

Write an equation for each problem. Then solve the equation.

12. Five times a number is 120. What is the number? $5n = 120$; **24**

13. One third equals negative seven times a number. What is the number?

Exercises

HOMEWORK HELP	
For Exercises	See Examples
14–25	1–2
26, 27	3
28–33	4
34–37	5

Exercise Levels
A: 14–37
B: 38–51
C: 52–56

Solve each equation. Check your solution.

14. $\frac{x}{9} = 10$ 90

15. $\frac{b}{7} = -11$ -77

16. $\frac{3}{4} = \frac{c}{24}$ 18

17. $\frac{2}{3} = \frac{1}{8}y$ $5\frac{1}{3}$

18. $\frac{2}{3}n = 14$ 21

19. $\frac{3}{5}g = -6$ -10

20. $4\frac{1}{5} = 3p$ $1\frac{2}{5}$

21. $-5 = 3\frac{1}{2}x$ $-1\frac{3}{7}$

22. $6 = -\frac{1}{2}n$ -12

23. $-\frac{2}{5} = -\frac{z}{45}$ 18

24. $-\frac{g}{24} = \frac{5}{12}$ -10

25. $-\frac{v}{5} = -45$ 225

26. GENETICS About two twenty-fifths of the male population in the world cannot distinguish red from green. If there are 14 boys in the ninth grade that cannot distinguish red from green, about how many ninth-grade boys are there in all? Write and solve an equation to find the answer. $14 = \frac{2}{25}b$; **175 boys**

27. WORLD RECORDS In 1998, Winchell's House of Donuts in Pasadena, California, created the world's largest doughnut. It weighed 2.5 tons and had a circumference of about 298.5 feet. What was its diameter? (*Hint:* $C = \pi d$) **about 95 ft**

Solve each equation. Check your solution.

28. $8d = 48$ 6

29. $-65 = 13t$ -5

30. $-5r = 55$ -11

31. $-252 = 36s$ -7

32. $-58 = -29h$ 2

33. $-26a = -364$ 14

DIFFERENTIATED HOMEWORK OPTIONS

Level	Assignment	Two-Day Option	
BL Basic	14–37, 52, 53, 55–67	15–37 odd, 57, 58	14–36 even, 52, 53, 55–56, 59–67
OL Core	15–43 odd, 44–53, 55–67	14–37, 57, 58	38–53, 55–56, 59–67
AL Advanced/Pre-AP	38–63 (optional: 64–67)		

Write an equation for each problem. Then solve the equation.

34. Seven times a number equals −84. What is the number? $7n = -84$; −12

35. Two fifths of a number equals −24. Find the number. $\frac{2}{5}n = -24$; −60

36. Negative 117 is nine times a number. Find the number. $-117 = 9n$; −13

37. Twelve is one fifth of a number. What is the number? $12 = \frac{1}{5}n$; 60

Solve each equation. Check your solution.

38. $\left(3\frac{1}{4}\right)p = 2\frac{1}{2}$ $\frac{10}{13}$ **39.** $-5h = -3\frac{2}{3}$ $\frac{11}{15}$ **40.** $\left(-2\frac{3}{5}\right)t = -22$ $8\frac{6}{13}$

41. $3.15 = 1.5y$ 2.1 **42.** $-11.78 = 1.9f$ −6.2 **43.** $-2.8m = 9.8$ −3.5

44. $-\frac{3}{8}n = 12$; −32 **45.** $2\frac{1}{2}n = 1\frac{1}{5}$; $\frac{12}{25}$

Write an equation for each problem. Then solve the equation.

44. Negative three eighths times a number equals 12. What is the number?

45. Two and one half times a number equals one and one fifth. Find the number.

46. One and one third times a number is −4.82. What is the number?
$\left(1\frac{1}{3}\right)n = -4.82$; −3.615

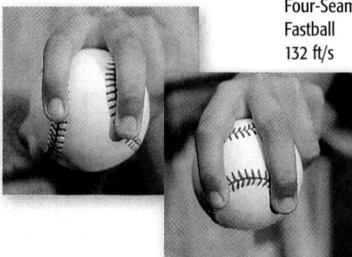

BASEBALL For Exercises 47 and 48, use the following information.

Two-Seam Fastball 126 ft/s

Four-Seam Fastball 132 ft/s

In baseball, if all other factors are the same, the speed of a four-seam fastball is faster than a two-seam fastball. The distance from the pitcher's mound to home plate is 60.5 feet.

47. How long does it take a two-seam fastball to go from the pitcher's mound to home plate? Round to the nearest hundredth. (*Hint*: $d = rt$) **0.48 s**

48. How much longer does it take for a two-seam fastball to reach home plate than a four-seam fastball? **about 0.02 s**

Source: *Baseball and Mathematics*

Real-World Link

Nolan Ryan pitched a fastball that was officially clocked by the *Guinness Book of World Records* at 100.9 miles per hour in a game played on August 20, 1974.

Source: www.baseball-almanac.com

PHYSICAL SCIENCE For Exercises 49–51, use the following information.

For every 8 grams of oxygen in water, there is 1 gram of hydrogen. In science lab, Ayame and her classmates are asked to determine how many grams of hydrogen and oxygen are in 477 grams of water.

49. If *x* represents the number of grams of hydrogen, write an expression to represent the number of grams of oxygen. **8x**

50. Write an equation to represent the situation. $x + 8x = 477$

51. How many grams of hydrogen and oxygen are in 477 grams of water?
53 g; 424 g

EXTRA PRACTICE
See pages 720, 745.

Math Online
Self-Check Quiz at
ca.algebra1.com

H.O.T. Problems

52. OPEN ENDED Write a multiplication equation that has a solution of −4. Then relate the equation and solution to a real-life problem. **See margin.**

53. REASONING Compare and contrast the Multiplication Property of Equality and the Division Property of Equality and explain why they can be considered the same property. **See Ch. 2 Answer Appendix.**

54. CHALLENGE Discuss how you can use $6y - 7 = 4$ to find the value of $18y - 21$. Then find the value of *y*. **See Ch. 2 Answer Appendix.**

Lesson 2-3 Solving Equations by Using Multiplication and Division **89**

BL = Below Grade Level
OL = On Grade Level
AL = Above Grade Level
ELL = English Language Learner

Additional pages not shown:

CRM **Skills Practice**, p. 22 BL OL

CRM **Lesson Reading Guide**, p. 19 BL OL

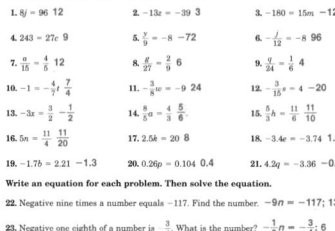

Study Guide and Intervention
CRM pp. 20–21 OL AL ELL

2-3 **Study Guide and Intervention**
Solving Equations by using Multiplication and Division

Solve Using Multiplication If each side of an equation is multiplied by the same number, the resulting equation is equivalent to the given one. You can use the property to solve equations involving multiplication and division.

Multiplication Property of Equality For any numbers *a*, *b*, and *c*, if $a = b$, then $ac = bc$.

Example 1 Solve $3\frac{1}{2}p = 1\frac{1}{2}$.

$3\frac{1}{2}p = 1\frac{1}{2}$ Original equation

$\frac{7}{2}p = \frac{3}{2}$ Rewrite each mixed number as an improper fraction.

$\frac{2}{7}\left(\frac{7}{2}p\right) = \frac{2}{7}\left(\frac{3}{2}\right)$ Multiply each side by $\frac{2}{7}$.

$p = \frac{3}{7}$ Simplify.

The solution is $\frac{3}{7}$.

Example 2 Solve $-\frac{1}{4}n = 16$.

$-\frac{1}{4}n = 16$ Original equation

$-4\left(-\frac{1}{4}n\right) = -4(16)$ Multiply each side by −4.

$n = -64$ Simplify.

The solution is −64.

Exercises
Solve each equation. Then check your solution.

1. $\frac{h}{3} = -2$ −6 2. $\frac{3}{8}m = 6$ 48 3. $\frac{1}{5}p = \frac{3}{5}$ 3

4. $5 = \frac{y}{12}$ 60 5. $-\frac{1}{4}k = -2.5$ 10 6. $-\frac{m}{8} = \frac{5}{8}$ −5

7. $-1\frac{1}{2}k = 4$ $-\frac{8}{3}$ 8. $-12 = -\frac{3}{4}k$ 8 9. $\frac{3}{2} = \frac{2}{5} + \frac{1}{5}$

10. $-3\frac{1}{3}k = 5$ $-1\frac{1}{2}$ 11. $\frac{7}{10}m = 10$ $14\frac{2}{7}$ 12. $\frac{2}{5} = -\frac{1}{4}$ $-1\frac{1}{4}$

Write an equation for each problem. Then solve the equation.

13. One-fifth of a number equals 25. Find the number. $\frac{1}{5}n = 25$; 125

14. What number divided by 2 equals −18? $\frac{n}{2} = -18$; −36

15. A number divided by eight equals 3. Find the number. $\frac{n}{8} = 3$; 24

16. One and a half times a number equals 6. Find the number. $1\frac{1}{2}n = 6$; 4

Chapter 2   20   Glencoe Algebra 1

Practice
CRM p. 23 OL AL

2-3 **Practice**
Solving Equations by Using Multiplication and Division
Solve each equation. Then check your solution.

1. $8j = 96$ 12 2. $-13z = -39$ 3 3. $-180 = 15m$ −12

4. $243 = 27c$ 9 5. $\frac{y}{9} = -8$ −72 6. $-\frac{f}{12} = -8$ 96

7. $\frac{a}{15} = \frac{4}{5}$ 12 8. $\frac{4}{27} = \frac{2}{9}$ 6 9. $\frac{9}{24} = \frac{1}{6}$ 4

10. $-1 = -\frac{4}{3}t$ $\frac{7}{4}$ 11. $-\frac{3}{8}w = -9$ 24 12. $-\frac{3}{15}t = 4$ −20

13. $-3x = \frac{3}{2} - \frac{1}{2}$ 14. $\frac{8}{5}a = \frac{4}{3}$ $\frac{5}{6}$ 15. $\frac{5}{4}h = \frac{11}{10}$ $\frac{11}{10}$

16. $5n = -\frac{11}{4}$ $\frac{11}{20}$ 17. $2.5k = 20$ 8 18. $-3.4e = -3.74$ 1.1

19. $-1.7b = 2.21$ −1.3 20. $0.26p = 0.104$ 0.4 21. $4.2q = -3.36$ −0.8

Write an equation for each problem. Then solve the equation.

22. Negative nine times a number equals −117. Find the number. $-9n = -117$; 13

23. Negative one eighth of a number is $-\frac{3}{4}$. What is the number? $-\frac{1}{8}n = -\frac{3}{4}$; 6

24. Five sixths of a number is $-\frac{5}{9}$. Find the number. $\frac{5}{6}n = -\frac{5}{9}$; $-\frac{2}{3}$

25. 2.7 times a number equals 8.37. What is the number? $2.7n = 8.37$; 3.1

26. One and one fourth times a number is one and one third. What is the number?
$1\frac{1}{4}n = 1\frac{1}{3}$; $1\frac{1}{15}$

27. **PUBLISHING** Two units of measure used in publishing are the *pica* and the *point*. A pica is one sixth of an inch. There are 12 points in a pica, so Points = 12 · Picas. How many picas are equivalent to 108 points? **9 picas**

ROLLER COASTERS For Exercises 28 and 29, use the following information.
Kingda Ka in New Jersey is the tallest and fastest roller coaster in the world. Riders travel at an average speed of 61 feet per second for 3118 feet. They reach a maximum speed of 187 feet per second.

28. If *x* represents the total time that the roller coaster is in motion for each ride, write an expression to represent the situation. (*Hint*: Use the distance formula $d = rt$.)
$61x = 3118$

29. How long is the roller coaster in motion? **51.1 seconds**

Chapter 2   23   Glencoe Algebra 1

Word Problem Practice
CRM p. 24 OL AL

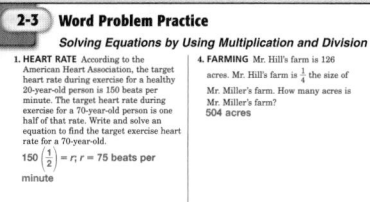

2-3 **Word Problem Practice**
Solving Equations by Using Multiplication and Division

1. **HEART RATE** According to the American Heart Association, the target heart rate during exercise for a healthy 20-year-old person is 150 beats per minute. The target heart rate during exercise for a 70-year-old person is one half of that rate. Write and solve an equation to find the target exercise heart rate for a 70-year-old.
$150\left(\frac{1}{2}\right) = r$; $r = 75$ beats per minute

4. **FARMING** Mr. Hill's farm is 126 acres. Mr. Hill's farm is $\frac{1}{4}$ the size of Mr. Miller's farm. How many acres is Mr. Miller's farm?
504 acres

NAUTICAL For Exercises 5 and 6, use the following information.
On the sea, distances are measured in nautical miles rather than miles.

| 1 nautical mile = 6080 feet |
| 1 knot = $\frac{1 \text{ nautical mile}}{\text{hour}}$ |

2. **TREES** A redwood tree can grow to be about six times as tall as a pine tree. Suppose a common pine tree measures about 56 feet tall. Write and solve an equation to find the approximate height of a redwood tree.
$r = 6 \times 56$; $r = 336$ ft

5. If a boat travels 16 knots in 1 hour, how far will it have traveled in feet? Write and solve an equation.
$6080 \times 16 = x$;
$x = 97,280$ ft

3. **SHOPPING** Raul bought fudge at the candy shop. After he gave his sister $\frac{1}{2}$ the fudge he bought, he still had $\frac{3}{4}$ of a pound. How much fudge did Raul originally buy?
$1\frac{1}{2}$ pounds or 1.5 pounds

6. About how fast was the boat traveling in miles per hour? Round your answer to the nearest hundredth.
$97,280 \div 5280 = 18.42$ mph

Chapter 2   24   Glencoe Algebra 1

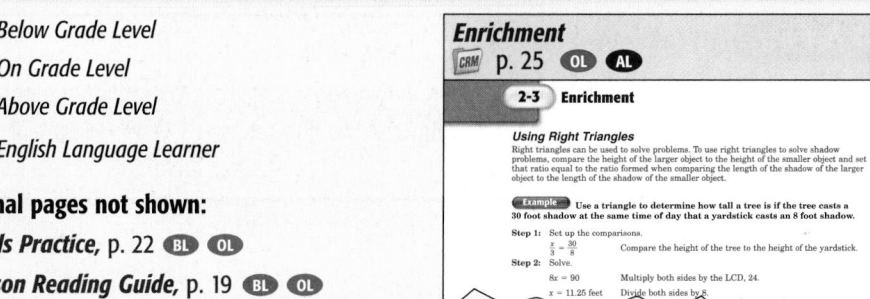

Enrichment
CRM p. 25 OL AL

2-3 **Enrichment**

Using Right Triangles
Right triangles can be used to solve problems. To use right triangles to solve shadow problems, compare the height of the larger object to the height of the smaller object and set that ratio equal to the ratio formed when comparing the length of the shadow of the larger object to the length of the shadow of the smaller object.

Example Use a triangle to determine how tall a tree is if the tree casts a 30 foot shadow at the same time of day that a yardstick casts an 8 foot shadow.

Step 1: Set up the comparisons.
$\frac{3}{3} = \frac{30}{8}$ Compare the height of the tree to the height of the yardstick.

Step 2: Solve.
$8x = 90$ Multiply both sides by the LCD, 24.
$x = 11.25$ feet Divide both sides by 8.

Exercise Alert!

Find the Error For Exercise 55, tell students to think of what operation must be performed to "undo" the operation in the equation. Emphasize that they should check their solution by substituting the value of the variable in the original equation.

4 Assess

Name the Math Write an equation involving multiplication or division on the board. Have students identify the operation in the equation. Based on the operation they identify, have students suggest the operation that might be used to solve the equation.

 Formative Assessment

Check for student understanding of concepts in Lessons 2-1, 2-2, and 2-3. [CRM] Quiz 1, p. 73.

 **Foldables™ Follow-Up**

Have students write one equation that uses multiplication and one that uses division on index cards and solve the equations on the other side of the cards. Tell them to store the cards in the third pocket of the Foldable™, label it "2-3: Solving Equations by Using Multiplication and Division."

Additional Answers

55. Camila; to find an equivalent equation with $1n$ on one side of the equation, you must divide each side by 8 or multiply each side by $\frac{1}{8}$. Casey incorrectly multiplied each side by 8.

56. Sample answer: You can use the Distance Formula and the speed of light to find the time it takes light from the stars to reach Earth. Solve the equation by dividing each side of the equation by 5870. The answer is 53 years. The equation $5870t = 821,800$ describes the situation for the star in the Big Dipper farthest from Earth.

90 Chapter 2 Solving Linear Equations

---

55. FIND THE ERROR Casey and Camila are solving $8n = -72$. Who is correct? Explain your reasoning. **See margin.**

> Casey
> $8n = -72$
> $8n(8) = -72(8)$
> $n = -576$

> Camila
> $8n = -72$
> $\frac{8n}{8} = \frac{-72}{8}$
> $n = -9$

56. *Writing in Math* Use the data about light speed on page 85 to explain how equations can be used to find how long it takes light to reach Earth. Include an explanation of how to find how long it takes light to reach Earth from the closest star in the Big Dipper and an equation describing the situation for the star in the Big Dipper farthest from Earth. **See margin.**

STANDARDS PRACTICE 7MR2.1, 7MG2.1

57. REVIEW Which is the *best* estimate for the number of minutes on the calling card advertised below? **D**

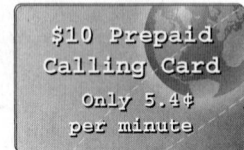

$10 Prepaid Calling Card
Only 5.4¢ per minute

A 10 min   **C** 50 min
B 20 min   **D** 200 min

58. REVIEW Mr. Morisson is draining his cylindrical, above ground pool. The pool has a radius of 10 feet and a standard height of 4.5 feet. If the pool water is pumped out at a constant rate of 5 gallons per minute, about how long will it take to drain the pool? $\left(1\ \text{ft}^3 = 7.5\ \text{gal}\right)$ **J**

F 0.63 h

G 7 h

H 25.4 h

J 35.3 h

Spiral Review

Solve each equation. Check your solution. (Lesson 2-2)

59. $m + 14 = 81$ **67**

60. $d - 27 = -14$ **13**

61. $17 - (-w) = -55$ **−72**

62. Translate the following sentence into an equation. (Lesson 2-1) $10a = 5(b + c)$
Ten times a number a is equal to 5 times the sum of b and c.

63. MUSIC Ryan practiced playing his violin 40 minutes on Monday and n minutes each on Tuesday, Wednesday, and Thursday. Write an expression for the total amount of time that he practiced during those four days. (Lesson 1-1) **40 + 3n**

GET READY for the Next Lesson

PREREQUISITE SKILL Use the order of operations to find each value. (Lesson 1-2)

64. $9 + 2 \times 8$ **25**

65. $24 \div 3 - 8$ **0**

66. $\frac{3}{8}(17 + 7)$ **9**

67. $\frac{15 - 9}{26 + 12}$ **$\frac{3}{19}$**

90 Chapter 2 Solving Linear Equations

Pre-AP Activity   Use after the Exercises

Write $\frac{30}{x} = 6$ on the board. Have students solve for x in two ways. Sample answers: Using mental math, think: 30 divided by what number is 6? Using cross multiplication, $\frac{30}{x} = \frac{6}{1}$, so $30 \times 1 = 6x$ or $30 = 6x$; $x = 5$.

Algebra Lab
Solving Multi-Step Equations

Preparation for Standard 4.0 Students simplify expressions before solving linear equations and inequalities in one variable, such as $3(2x - 5) + 4(x - 2) = 12$. (Key, CAHSEE) **Preparation for Standard 5.0** Students solve multistep problems, including word problems, involving linear equations and linear inequalities in one variable and provide justification for each step. (Key, CAHSEE)

You can use an equation model to solve multi-step equations.

ACTIVITY

C0ncepts in M0tion
Animation ca.algebra1.com

Solve $3x + 5 = -7$.

Step 1 Model the equation.

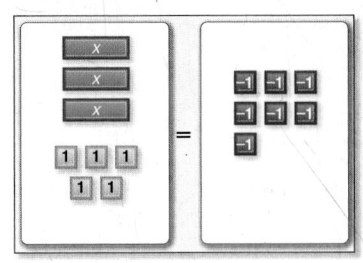

$3x + 5 = -7$

Place 3 x-tiles and 5 positive 1-tiles on one side of the mat. Place 7 negative 1-tiles on the other side of the mat.

Step 2 Isolate the x-term.

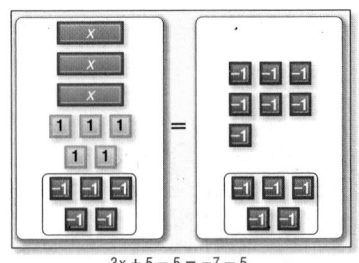

$3x + 5 - 5 = -7 - 5$

Since there are 5 positive 1-tiles with the x-tiles, add 5 negative 1-tiles to each side to form zero pairs.

Step 3 Remove zero pairs.

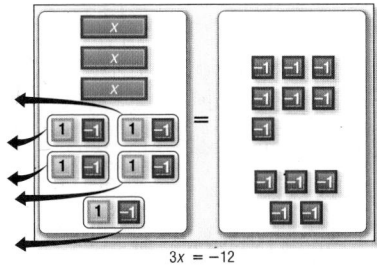

$3x = -12$

Group the tiles to form zero pairs and remove the zero pairs.

Step 4 Group the tiles.

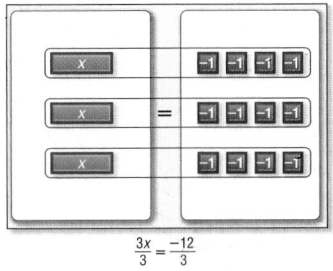

$\frac{3x}{3} = \frac{-12}{3}$

Separate the tiles into 3 equal groups to match the 3 x-tiles. Each x tile is paired with 4 negative 1 tiles. Thus, $x = -4$.

MODEL Use algebra tiles to solve each equation.

1. $2x - 3 = -9$ -3
2. $3x + 5 = 14$ 3
3. $3x - 2 = 10$ 4
4. $-8 = 2x + 4$ -6
5. $3 + 4x = 11$ 2
6. $2x + 7 = 1$ -3
7. $9 = 4x - 7$ 4
8. $7 + 3x = -8$ -5
9. $3x - 1 = -10$ -3

10. **MAKE A CONJECTURE** What steps would you use to solve $7x - 12 = -61$? See margin.

Explore 2-4 Algebra Lab: Solving Multi-Step Equations **91**

---

1 Focus

Materials
• equation mats
• algebra tiles (x-tiles, 1-tiles)

Easy-to-Make Manipulatives
Teaching Algebra with Manipulatives.

Templates for:
• algebra tiles, pp. 10–11
• equation mat, p. 16

Teaching Tip
You may need to review the method of forming zero pairs before beginning the activity.

2 Teach

Working in Cooperative Groups
Put students in groups of 2 or 3, mixing abilities. Have groups complete the activity and Exercises 1–3.

Point out that, in Step 4, separating the x-tiles and 1-tiles into 3 equivalent groups is a pictorial representation of dividing each side of the equation by 3.

Practice Have students complete Exercises 4–10.

From Concrete to Abstract Ask students to discuss how the steps for solving an equation are similar to or different from the order of operations. Sample answer: In solving an equation, addition and subtraction are done before multiplication and division. This is the reverse of the order of operations.

Additional Answer

10. First add 12 to each side, and then divide each side by 7.

3 Assess

Formative Assessment

Use Exercise 8 to assess whether students comprehend how to discover which side of the equation directs the method of solution.

Use Exercise 10 to assess whether students comprehend that addition and subtraction are done before multiplication and division when isolating the variable.

2-4 Solving Multi-Step Equations

1 Focus

Standards Alignment

Before Lesson 2-4
Write an expression, an equation, an inequality, or a system that represents a verbal description from Standard 7AF1.1

Lesson 2-4
Simplify expressions before solving multi-step linear equations and inequalities from Standards 4.0 and 5.0

After Lesson 2-4
Solve equations and inequalities involving absolute value from Standard 2A1.0

2 Teach

Scaffolding Questions

Have students read *Get Ready for the Lesson*.
Ask:
- What does the number 8 represent in the expression 8 + 12*a*? eight inches, the length of an alligator hatchling
- What does the 12*a* represent in the expression 8 + 12*a*? Twelve represents the number of inches the alligator grows per year, and *a* represents the number of years of growth.

(continued on the next page)

Main Ideas
- Solve equations involving more than one operation.
- Solve consecutive integer problems.

 Standard 4.0 Students simplify expressions before solving linear **equations** and inequalities **in one variable,** such as $3(2x - 5) + 4(x - 2) = 12$. (Key, CAHSEE)

Standard 5.0 Students solve multistep problems, including word problems, involving linear equations and linear inequalities **in one variable and provide justification for each step.** (Key, CAHSEE)

New Vocabulary
multi-step equations
consecutive integers
number theory

GET READY for the Lesson

An alligator hatchling 8 inches long grows about 12 inches per year. The expression $8 + 12a$ represents the length in inches of an alligator that is *a* years old.

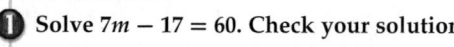

— 10 feet 4 inches —
$8 + 12a$

Since 10 feet 4 inches equals $10(12) + 4$ or 124 inches, the equation $8 + 12a = 124$ can be used to estimate the age of the alligator in the photograph. Notice that this equation involves more than one operation.

Solve Multi-Step Equations To solve equations with more than one operation, often called **multi-step equations**, undo operations by working backward.

EXAMPLE Solve Using Addition and Division

1 Solve $7m - 17 = 60$. Check your solution.

$7m - 17 = 60$	Original equation
$7m - 17 + 17 = 60 + 17$	Add 17 to each side.
$7m = 77$	Simplify.
$\dfrac{7m}{7} = \dfrac{77}{7}$	Divide each side by 7.
$m = 11$	Simplify.

CHECK	$7m - 17 = 60$	Original equation
	$7(11) - 17 \stackrel{?}{=} 60$	Substitute 11 for *m*.
	$77 - 17 \stackrel{?}{=} 60$	Multiply.
	$60 = 60$ ✓	

CHECK Your Progress

Solve each equation. Check your solution.

1A. $2a - 6 = 4$ 5
1B. $8 = 3r + 7$ $\frac{1}{3}$
1C. $\frac{t}{8} + 21 = 14$ -56

Chapter 2 Resource Masters
Lesson Reading Guide, p. 26 BL OL ELL
Study Guide and Intervention, pp. 27–28 BL OL ELL
Skills Practice, p. 29 BL OL
Practice, p. 30 OL AL
Word Problem Practice, p. 31 OL AL
Enrichment, p. 32 OL AL

Transparencies
5-Minute Check Transparency 2-4

Additional Print Resources
Noteables™ Interactive Study Notebook with Foldables™
Teaching Algebra with Manipulatives
Science and Mathematics Lab Manual, pp. 121–124

Technology
ca.algebra1.com
Interactive Classroom CD-ROM
AssignmentWorks CD-ROM
Graphing Calculator Easy Files

EXAMPLE Solve Using Multiplication and Addition

2 Solve $\frac{p-15}{9} = -6$.

$$\frac{p-15}{9} = -6 \qquad \text{Original equation}$$

$$9\left(\frac{p-15}{9}\right) = 9(-6) \qquad \text{Multiply each side by 9.}$$

$$p - 15 = -54 \qquad \text{Simplify.}$$

$$p - 15 + 15 = -54 + 15 \qquad \text{Add 15 to each side.}$$

$$p = -39 \qquad \text{Simplify.}$$

✓ CHECK Your Progress

Solve each equation. Check your solution.

2A. $\frac{k-12}{5} = 4$ **32**   **2B.** $\frac{n+1}{-2} = 15$ **−31**

Real-World EXAMPLE Write and Solve a Multi-Step Equation

3 **SKIING** Hugo is buying a pair of water skis that are on sale for $\frac{2}{3}$ of the original price. After he uses a $25 gift certificate, the total cost before taxes is $115. What was the original price of the skis? Write an equation for the problem. Then solve the equation.

Words	Two-thirds	of	the price	minus	25	is	115.
Variable	Let p = original price of the skis.						
Equation	$\frac{2}{3}$	$\cdot$	p	$-$	25	$=$	115

$$\frac{2}{3}p - 25 = 115 \qquad \text{Original equation}$$

$$\frac{2}{3}p - 25 + 25 = 115 + 25 \qquad \text{Add 25 to each side.}$$

$$\frac{2}{3}p = 140 \qquad \text{Simplify.}$$

$$\frac{3}{2}\left(\frac{2}{3}p\right) = \frac{3}{2}(140) \qquad \text{Multiply each side by } \frac{3}{2}.$$

$$p = 210 \qquad \text{Simplify.}$$

The original price of the skis was $210.

✓ CHECK Your Progress

3. Write an equation for the following problem. Then solve the equation. *Sixteen is equal to 7 increased by the product of 3 and a number.* $16 = 7 + 3n; 3$

Study Tip

Leading coefficients
Use the same steps to solve a multi-step equation if the leading coefficient is a fraction or an integer.

 Math Online Extra Examples at ca.algebra1.com

Lesson 2-4 Solving Multi-Step Equations   **93**

- What does this expression assume about the growth of an alligator over its lifetime? An alligator grows at a constant rate during its life.

Solve Multi-Step Equations

Example 1 shows how to undo operations to solve a multi-step problem using addition and division. **Example 2** shows how to undo operations to solve a multi-step problem using multiplication and addition. **Example 3** shows how to write and solve a multi-step equation.

✓ Formative Assessment

Use the Check Your Progress exercises after each example to determine students' understanding of concepts.

ADDITIONAL EXAMPLES

1 Solve $5q - 13 = 37$. Check your solution. $q = 10$.

2 Solve $\frac{s}{12} - 9 = -11$. $s = -24$

3 **SHOPPING** Susan had a $10 coupon for the purchase of any item. She bought a coat that was on sale for $\frac{1}{2}$ its original price. After using the coupon, Susan paid $125 for the coat before taxes. What was the original price of the coat? Write an equation for the problem. Then solve the equation. $\frac{1}{2}p - 10 = 125$; $p = 270$

Additional Examples are also in:

- Noteables™ Interactive Study Notebook with Foldables™
- Interactive Classroom PowerPoint® Presentations

Use the Pre-AP activity on the next page after Example 2.

Tips for New Teachers

Preventing Error

In Example 2, some students may not understand why both sides of the equation are multiplied by 9 before adding 15 to each side. Remind students that when solving a multi-step equation, they undo the operations in reverse of the order of operations. Use an example, such as $\frac{23-7}{8}$. Have a volunteer tell the steps used to simplify this expression. Explain that Example 2 is solved using the reverse of the steps used to simplify $\frac{23-7}{8}$.

Lesson 2-4 Solving Multi-Step Equations   **93**

94 **Chapter 2** Solving Linear Equations

Focus on Mathematical Content

Multi-Step Equations Multi-step equations include two or more operations. To solve a multi-step equation, "undo" the operations in reverse of the order of operations.

Solve Consecutive Integer Problems

Example 4 introduces students to number theory by showing how to solve a consecutive integer problem.

ADDITIONAL EXAMPLE

4 **NUMBER THEORY** Write an equation for the problem below. Then solve the equation and answer the problem.
Find three consecutive odd integers whose sum is 57.
$n + (n + 2) + (n + 4) = 57$, or $3n + 6 = 57$. The consecutive integers are 17, 19, and 21.

Preventing Errors

Ask students to explain why an equation to find consecutive odd integers looks like an equation to find consecutive even integers. Students should note that both odds and evens are calculated by adding 2 to the previous odd or even.

Solve Consecutive Integer Problems **Consecutive integers** are integers in counting order, such as 7, 8, and 9. Beginning with an even integer and counting by two will result in *consecutive even integers*. Beginning with an odd integer and counting by two will result in *consecutive odd integers*.

Consecutive Even Integers	Consecutive Odd Integers
$-4, -2, 0, 2, 4$	$-3, -1, 1, 3, 5$

The study of numbers and the relationships between them is called **number theory**.

EXAMPLE Solve a Consecutive Integer Problem

4 **NUMBER THEORY** Write an equation for the problem below. Then solve the equation and answer the problem.
Find three consecutive even integers whose sum is −42.

Let $n =$ the least even integer.

Then $n + 2 =$ the next greater even integer, and $n + 4 =$ the greatest of the three even integers.

Words	The sum of three consecutive even integers		is	−42.
Equation	$n + (n + 2) + (n + 4)$		=	−42

$n + (n + 2) + (n + 4) = -42$	Original equation
$3n + 6 = -42$	Simplify.
$3n + 6 - 6 = -42 - 6$	Subtract 6 from each side.
$3n = -48$	Simplify.
$\dfrac{3n}{3} = \dfrac{-48}{3}$	Divide each side by 3.
$n = -16$	Simplify.

$n + 2 = -16 + 2$ or -14 $n + 4 = -16 + 4$ or -12

The consecutive even integers are −16, −14, and −12.

CHECK −16, −14, and −12 are consecutive even integers.

$-16 + (-14) + (-12) = -42$ ✓

Study Tip

Representing Consecutive Integers
You can use the same expressions to represent either consecutive even integers or consecutive odd integers. It is the value of n (odd or even) that differs between the two expressions.

✓CHECK Your Progress

4. Write an equation for the following problem. Then solve the equation and answer the problem. $n + (n + 1) + (n + 2) = 21$; 6, 7, 8 *Find three consecutive integers whose sum is 21.*

 **Personal Tutor at** ca.algebra1.com

---

Pre-AP Activity Use after Exercise 2

Write $\dfrac{x}{10} + 3.2 = 4.7$ on the chalkboard. Ask students what would happen if each side of the equation were multiplied by 10. The result is an equivalent equation.

Ask a volunteer to explain why this might be a helpful first step in solving this type of equation.
Multiplying by 10 changes all of the numbers in the equation to integers, and it might be easier to work with integers than with decimals and fractions.

Ask students to solve the problem both ways and confirm which way was easier. $x = 15$

★ indicates multi-step problem

✓ CHECK Your Understanding

Examples 1–2
(pp. 92–93)

Solve each equation. Check your solution.

1. $4g - 2 = -6$ −1
2. $18 = 5p + 3$ 3
3. $9 = 1 + \frac{m}{7}$ 56
4. $\frac{3}{2}a - 8 = 11$ $12\frac{2}{3}$
5. $20 = \frac{n-3}{8}$ 163
6. $\frac{b+4}{-2} = -17$ 30

Example 3
(p. 93)

★ 7. **NUMBER THEORY** Twelve decreased by twice a number equals –34. Write an equation for this situation and then find the number. $12 - 2n = -34$; 23

8. **WORLD CULTURES** The English alphabet contains 2 more than twice as many letters as the Hawaiian alphabet. How many letters are there in the Hawaiian alphabet? **12 letters**

Example 4
(p. 94)

Write an equation and solve each problem.

9. Find three consecutive integers with a sum of 42. See margin.

10. Find three consecutive even integers with a sum of −12.
    $n + (n + 2) + (n + 4) = -12$; −6, −4, −2

Exercises

HOMEWORK HELP	
For Exercises	See Examples
11–22	1–2
23, 24	3
25–28	4

Exercise Levels
A: 11–28
B: 29–42
C: 43–46

Solve each equation. Check your solution.

11. $5n + 6 = -4$ −2
12. $-11 = 7 + 3c$ −6
13. $15 = 4a - 5$ 5
14. $7g - 14 = -63$ −7
15. $\frac{a}{7} - 3 = -2$ 7
16. $\frac{c}{-3} + 5 = 7$ −6
17. $9 + \frac{y}{5} = 6$ −15
18. $\frac{t}{8} - 6 = -12$ −48
19. $\frac{r+1}{3} = 8$ 23
20. $11 = \frac{5+m}{-2}$ −27
21. $14 = \frac{d-6}{2}$ 34
22. $\frac{17-s}{4} = -10$ 57

Write an equation and solve each problem. 23–28. See margin.

23. Six less than two thirds of a number is negative ten. Find the number.
24. Twenty-nine is thirteen added to four times a number. What is the number?
25. Find three consecutive odd integers with a sum of 51.
26. Find three consecutive even integers with a sum of −30.
27. Find four consecutive integers with a sum of 94.
28. Find four consecutive integers with a sum of 26.

29. **ANALYZE TABLES** Adele Jones is on a business trip and plans to rent a subcompact car from Speedy Rent-A-Car. Her company has given her a budget of $60 per day for car rental. What is the maximum distance Ms. Jones can drive in one day and still stay within her budget? **450.5 mi**

Speedy Rent-A-Car Price List

Subcompact
$14.95 per day plus $0.10 per mile

Compact
$19.95 per day plus $0.12 per mile

Full Size
$22.95 per day plus $0.15 per mile

Lesson 2-4 Solving Multi-Step Equations **95**

3 Practice

✓ Formative Assessment

Use Exercises 1–10 to check for understanding.

Use the chart at the bottom of this page to customize assignments for your students.

Odd/Even Assignments

Exercises 11–28 are structured so that students practice the same concepts whether they are assigned odd or even problems.

⚠ Exercise Alert!

Use a Ruler Exercise 41 requires students to measure their feet. Students will need to use a ruler or yardstick.

Additional Answers

9. $n + (n + 1) + (n + 2) = 42$; 13, 14, 15
23. $\frac{2}{3}n - 6 = -10$; −6
24. $29 = 13 + 4n$; 4
25. $n + (n + 2) + (n + 4) = 51$; 15, 17, 19
26. $n + (n + 2) + (n + 4) = -30$; −12, −10, −8
27. $n + (n + 1) + (n + 2) + (n + 3) = 94$; 22, 23, 24, 25
28. $n + (n + 1) + (n + 2) + (n + 3) = 26$; 5, 6, 7, 8

DIFFERENTIATED HOMEWORK OPTIONS

Level	Assignment	Two-Day Option	
BL Basic	11–28, 43, 44, 46–64	11–27 odd, 47–49	12–28 even, 43, 44, 46, 50–64
OL Core	11–27 odd, 29–31, 33–39 odd, 40–44, 46–64	11–28, 47–49	29–44, 46, 50–64
AL Advanced /Pre-AP	29–58 (optional: 59–64)		

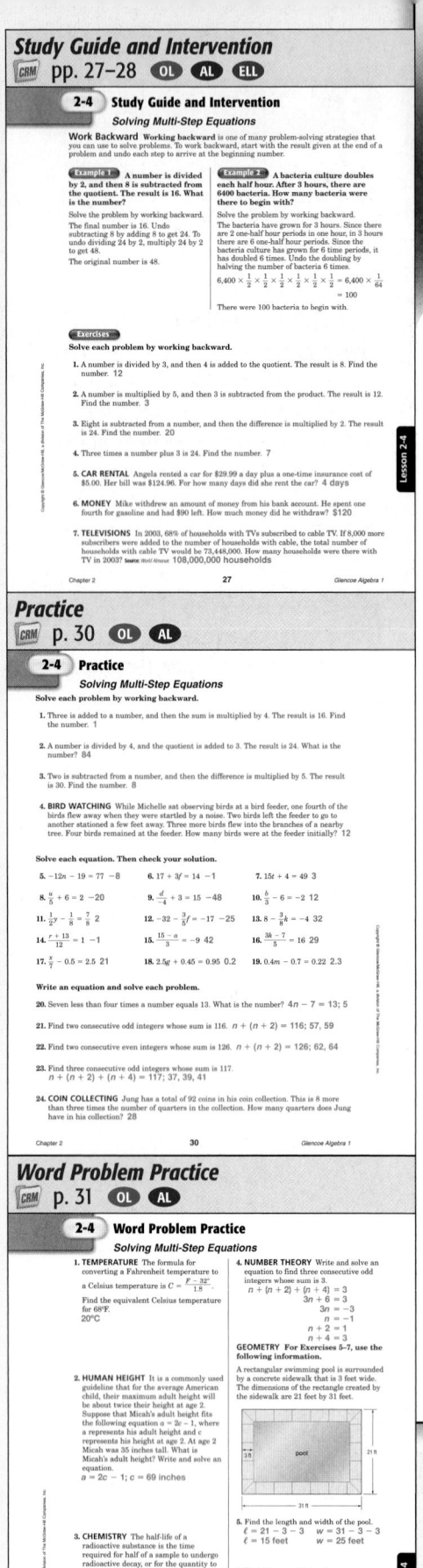

Study Guide and Intervention
CRM pp. 27–28 OL AL ELL

2-4 Study Guide and Intervention
Solving Multi-Step Equations

Practice
CRM p. 30 OL AL

2-4 Practice
Solving Multi-Step Equations

Word Problem Practice
CRM p. 31 OL AL

2-4 Word Problem Practice
Solving Multi-Step Equations

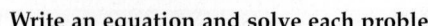

Real-World Link

Many mountain climbers experience altitude sickness caused by a decrease in oxygen. Climbers can acclimate themselves to these higher altitudes by camping for one or two weeks at various altitudes as they ascend the mountain.

Source: *Shape*

Write an equation and solve each problem.

30. NUMBER THEORY Maggie was thinking of a number. If she multiplied the number by 3, subtracted 8, added 2 times the original number, added −4, and then subtracted the original number, the result was 48. Write an equation that the number satisfies. Then solve the equation.
$3x - 8 + 2x - 4 - x = 48$; **15**

31. MOUNTAIN CLIMBING A general rule for those climbing more than 7000 feet above sea level is to allow a total of $\left(\dfrac{a - 7000}{2000} + 2\right)$ weeks of camping during the ascension. In this expression, a represents the altitude in feet. If a group of mountain climbers have allowed for 9 weeks of camping, how high can they climb without worrying about altitude sickness? **21,000 ft**

Solve each equation. Check your solution.

32. $-3d - 1.2 = 0.9$ **−0.7**

33. $-2.5r - 32.7 = 74.1$ **−42.72**

34. $0.2n + 3 = 8.6$ **28**

35. $-9 - \dfrac{p}{4} = 5$ **−56**

36. $\dfrac{-3j - (-4)}{-6} = 12$ **$25\frac{1}{3}$**

37. $3.5x + 5 - 1.5x = 8$ **1.5**

38. If $3a - 9 = 6$, what is the value of $5a + 2$? **27**

39. If $2x + 1 = 5$, what is the value of $3x - 4$? **2**

SHOE SIZE For Exercises 40 and 41, use the following information.
If ℓ represents the length of a person's foot in inches, the expression $2\ell - 12$ can be used to estimate his or her shoe size.

40. What is the approximate length of the foot of a person who wears size 8? **10 in.**

41. Measure your foot and use the expression to determine your shoe size. How does this number compare to the size of shoe you are wearing? **See students' work.**

42. GEOMETRY A rectangle is cut from the corner of a 10-inch by 10-inch piece of paper. The area of the remaining piece of paper is $\dfrac{4}{5}$ of the area of the original piece of paper. If the width of the rectangle removed from the paper is 4 inches, what is the length of the rectangle? **5 in.**

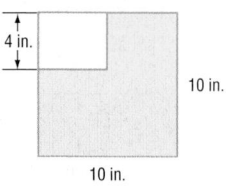

4 in.
10 in.
10 in.

EXTRA PRACTICE
See pages 721, 745.

Math Online
Self-Check Quiz at
ca.algebra1.com

H.O.T. Problems

43. OPEN ENDED Write a problem that can be modeled by the equation $2x + 40 = 60$. Then solve the equation and explain the solution in the context of the problem. **See students' work.**

44. REASONING Describe the steps used to solve $\dfrac{w + 3}{5} - 4 = 6$. **See margin.**

45. CHALLENGE Determine whether the following statement is *sometimes*, *always*, or *never* true. Explain your reasoning.
The sum of two consecutive even numbers equals the sum of two consecutive odd numbers. **See margin.**

46. *Writing in Math* Use the information about alligators on page 92 to explain how equations can be used to estimate the age of an animal. Include an explanation of how to solve the equation representing the alligator and an estimate of the age of the alligator. **See margin.**

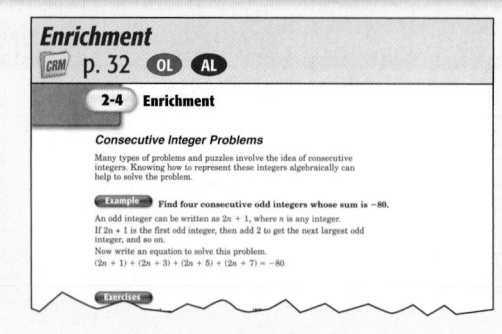

Enrichment
CRM p. 32 OL AL

2-4 Enrichment
Consecutive Integer Problems

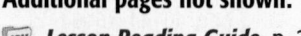
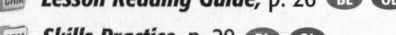

BL = Below Grade Level
OL = On Grade Level
AL = Above Grade Level
ELL = English Language Learner

Additional pages not shown:

CRM *Lesson Reading Guide*, p. 26 BL OL ELL
CRM *Skills Practice*, p. 29 BL OL

47. REVIEW A hang glider 25 meters above the ground started to descend at a constant rate of 2 meters per second. Which equation could be used to determine h, the hang glider's height after t seconds of descent? **D**

A $h = 25t + 2$

B $h = -25t + 2$

C $h = 2t + 25$

D $h = -2t + 25$

48. REVIEW Two rectangular walls each with a length of 12 feet and a width of 23 feet need to be painted. It costs $0.08 per square foot for paint. How much money will it cost to paint the two walls? **J**

F $22.08   H $34.50

G $23.04   J $44.16

49. Maddie works at Game Exchange. They are having a sale on video games and DVDs.

Item	Price	Special
Video Games	$20	Buy 2 Get 1 Free
DVDs	$15	Buy 1 Get 1 Free

She purchases four video games and uses her employee discount of 15%. If sales tax is 7.25%, how much does she spend on the games? **A**

A $54.70

B $55.35

C $60

D $64.35

Spiral Review

Solve each equation. Check your solution. (Lesson 2-3)

50. $-7t = 91$ **−13**

51. $\frac{r}{15} = -8$ **−120**

52. $26 = \frac{2}{3}b$ **39**

53. TRANSPORTATION In 2005, there were 9 more models of sport utility vehicles than there were in 2000. Write and solve an equation to find how many models of sport utility vehicles there were in 2000. (Lesson 2-2)
$m + 9 = 56$; **47 models**

Sport Utility Vehicles	
Year	Number of Models
2000	m
2005	56

Use the Distributive Property to rewrite each expression. Then find the product. (Lesson 1-5)

54. $17 \cdot 9$ **(10 + 7)9; 153**

55. $13(101)$ **13(100 + 1); 1313**

56. $18 \cdot 2\frac{1}{9}$
$18\left(2 + \frac{1}{9}\right)$; **38**

Write an algebraic expression for each verbal expression. (Lesson 1-1)

57. the product of 5 and m plus half of n $5m + \frac{n}{2}$

58. the sum of 3 times a and the square of b $3a + b^2$

GET READY for the Next Lesson

PREREQUISITE SKILL Simplify each expression. (Lesson 1-5)

59. $5d - 2d$ **3d**

60. $11m - 5m$ **6m**

61. $8t + 6t$ **14t**

62. $7g - 15g$ **−8g**

63. $-9f + 6f$ **−3f**

64. $-3m + (-7m)$
−10m

4 Assess

Yesterday's News Have students write how yesterday's lesson helped them with today's new material.

FOLDABLES Study Organizer
Foldables™ Follow-Up
Have students choose problems from Exercises 11–22 and write the problems and the steps needed to solve them on index cards. Tell them to store these cards in the fourth pocket of the Foldable and label it "2-4: Solving Multi-Step Equations."

Additional Answers

44. (1) Add 4 to each side.
(2) Multiply each side by 5.
(3) Subtract 3 from each side.

45. Never; let n and $n + 2$ be the even numbers and $m, m + 2$ be the odd numbers. Write and solve the equation $n + (n + 2) = m + (m + 2)$ gives the solution $n = m$. Thus, n must equal m, so n is not even or m is not odd.

46. Sample answer: By using the length at birth, the amount of growth each year, and the current length, you can write and solve an equation to find the age of the animal. To solve the equation, subtract 8 from each side and then divide each side by 12. The alligator is about 9 or 10 years old.

Solving Equations with the Variable on Each Side

 **Focus**

 Standards Alignment

Before Lesson 2-5
Write an expression, an equation, an inequality, or a system that represents a verbal description from Standard 7AF1.1

Lesson 2-5
Simplify expressions before solving multi-step linear equations and inequalities from Standards 4.0 and 5.0

After Lesson 2-5
Solve equations and inequalities involving absolute value from Standard 2A1.0

Teach

Scaffolding Questions
Have students read *Get Ready for the Lesson*.
Ask:
• In the example, the expression 46.9 – 3x represents Dial-up Internet users. In this expression, what do the 46.9 and the 3x represent? 46.9 (million) represents the number of dial-up users in 2003. 3x represents a loss of 3 million users per year for x years.

(continued on the next page)

Main Ideas
• Solve equations with the variable on each side.
• Solve equations involving grouping symbols.

 Standard 4.0 Students simplify expressions before solving linear equations and inequalities in one variable, such as $3(2x - 5) + 4(x - 2) = 12$. (Key, CAHSEE)

Standard 5.0 Students solve multistep problems, including word problems, involving linear equations and linear inequalities in one variable and provide justification for each step. (Key, CAHSEE)

New Vocabulary

identity

Study Tip

Solving Equations
The equation in Example 1 can also be solved by first subtracting 10p from each side.

COncepts in MOtion
BrainPOP® ca.algebra1.com

In 2003, about 46.9 million U.S. households had dial-up Internet service and about 26 million had broadband service. During the next five years, it was projected that the number of dial-up users would decrease an average of 3 million per year and the number of broadband users would increase an average of 8 million per year. The following expressions represent the number of dial-up and broadband Internet users x years after 2003.

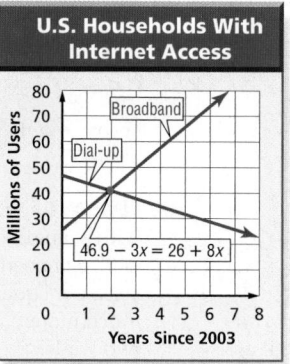

U.S. Households With Internet Access

Source: Strategy Analytics

Dial-Up Internet Users: $46.9 - 3x$
Broadband Internet Users: $26 + 8x$

The equation $46.9 - 3x = 26 + 8x$ represents the time at which the number of dial-up and broadband Internet users are equal. Notice that this equation has the variable x on each side.

Variables On Each Side To solve equations with variables on each side, first use the Addition or Subtraction Property of Equality to write an equivalent equation that has all of the variables on one side.

EXAMPLE Solve an Equation with Variables on Each Side

① Solve $-2 + 10p = 8p - 1$. Check your solution.

$-2 + 10p = 8p - 1$	Original equation
$-2 + 10p - 8p = 8p - 1 - 8p$	Subtract 8p from each side.
$-2 + 2p = -1$	Simplify.
$-2 + 2p + 2 = -1 + 2$	Add 2 to each side.
$2p = 1$	Simplify.
$\dfrac{2p}{2} = \dfrac{1}{2}$	Divide each side by 2.
$p = \dfrac{1}{2}$ or 0.5	Simplify.

The solution is $\frac{1}{2}$ or 0.5. Check by substituting into the original equation.

✓**CHECK Your Progress** Solve each equation. Check your solution.
1A. $3w + 2 = 7w$ $\frac{1}{2}$ **1B.** $\frac{s}{2} + 1 = \frac{1}{4}s - 6$ −28

98 Chapter 2 Solving Linear Equations

Transparencies
5-Minute Check Transparency 2-5

Additional Print Resources
Noteables™ Interactive Study Notebook with Foldables™
Teaching Algebra with Manipulatives

Technology
ca.algebra1.com
Interactive Classroom CD-ROM
AssignmentWorks CD-ROM
Graphing Calculator Easy Files

Grouping Symbols When solving equations that contain grouping symbols, first use the Distributive Property to remove the grouping symbols.

Review Vocabulary

Distributive Property:
For any numbers a, b, and c, $a(b + c) = ab + ac$ and $a(b - c) = ab - ac$.
(Lesson 1–5)

EXAMPLE Solve an Equation with Grouping Symbols

② Solve $4(2r - 8) = \frac{1}{7}(49r + 70)$. Check your solution.

$4(2r - 8) = \frac{1}{7}(49r + 70)$	Original equation
$8r - 32 = 7r + 10$	Distributive Property
$8r - 32 - 7r = 7r + 10 - 7r$	Subtract 7r from each side.
$r - 32 = 10$	Simplify.
$r - 32 + 32 = 10 + 32$	Add 32 to each side.
$r = 42$	Simplify.

CHECK

$4(2r - 8) = \frac{1}{7}(49r + 70)$	Original equation
$4[2(42) - 8] \stackrel{?}{=} \frac{1}{7}[49(42) + 70]$	Substitute 42 for r.
$4(84 - 8) \stackrel{?}{=} \frac{1}{7}(2058 + 70)$	Multiply.
$4(76) \stackrel{?}{=} \frac{1}{7}(2128)$	Add and subtract.
$304 = 304$ ✓	

 CHECK Your Progress Solve each equation. Check your solution.

2A. $8s - 10 = 3(6 - 2s)$ 2 **2B.** $7(n - 1) = -2(3 + n)$ $\frac{1}{9}$

Some equations may have no solution. That is, there is no value of the variable that will result in a true equation. Other equations are true for all values of the variables. An equation like this is called an **identity**.

EXAMPLE No Solutions or Identity

③ Solve each equation.

a. $2m + 5 = 5(m - 7) - 3m$

$2m + 5 = 5(m - 7) - 3m$	Original equation
$2m + 5 = 5m - 35 - 3m$	Distributive Property
$2m + 5 = 2m - 35$	Simplify.
$2m + 5 - 2m = 2m - 35 - 2m$	Subtract 2m from each side.
$5 = -35$	This statement is false.

Since $5 = -35$ is a false statement, this equation has no solution.

b. $3(r + 1) - 5 = 3r - 2$

$3(r + 1) - 5 = 3r - 2$	Original equation
$3r + 3 - 5 = 3r - 2$	Distributive Property
$3r - 2 = 3r - 2$	Reflexive Property of Equality

Since the expressions on each side of the equation are the same, this equation is an identity. It is true for all values of r.

Math Online Extra Examples at ca.algebra1.com

Lesson 2-5 Solving Equations with the Variable on Each Side **99**

- In the example, the expression $26 + 8x$ represents Broadband Internet users. In this expression, what do the 26 and the 8x represent? 26 million represents the number of broadband users in 2003. 8x represents 8 million more users per year for x years.
- In about how many years from 2003 will the number of broadband users equal the number of dial-up users? about 2 years
- How many dial-up and broadband users will there be in 2 years? about 41 million each

Variables On Each Side
Example 1 shows how to solve an equation with variables on each side using the Addition or Subtraction Property of Equality.

Formative Assessment
Use the Check Your Progress exercises after each example to determine students' understanding of concepts.

ADDITIONAL EXAMPLE

① Solve $8 + 5s = 7s - 2$. Check your solution. $s = 5$

Additional Examples are also in:
- Noteables™ Interactive Study Notebook with Foldables™
- Interactive Classroom PowerPoint® Presentations

Grouping Symbols
Example 2 shows how to use the Distributive Property to solve an equation containing grouping symbols. **Example 3** shows how to determine when an equation with the variable on each side has no solution and when it is an identity. **Example 4** shows how to write an equation to represent a situation and then use substitution to solve the equation.

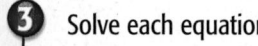

ADDITIONAL EXAMPLES

2 Solve $\frac{1}{3}(18 + 12q) = 6(2q - 7)$. Check your solution.
$q = 6$

3 Solve each equation.

a. $8(5c - 2) = 10(32 + 4c)$
no solution

b. $4(t + 20) = \frac{1}{5}(20t + 400)$
all numbers

4 **STANDARDS EXAMPLE** Find the value of H so that the figures have the same area. D

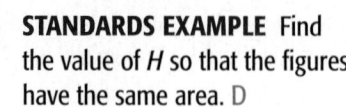

A 1   **C** 4

B 3   **D** 5

Intervention

Eliminating the Variable
Emphasize that there are only two possible outcomes under which the variable can be eliminated from an equation: either the equation has no solution (false statement) or the equation is an identity (true statement).

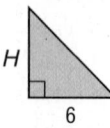 **Focus on Mathematical Content**

Grouping Symbols The Distributive Property may be used to simplify expressions with grouping symbols. When the expressions on each side of an equation are identical, the equation is true for every value of the variable. When the expressions simplify to a false statement, there are no solutions.

 **✓ CHECK Your Progress**

Solve each equation.

3A. $7x + 5(x - 1) = -5 + 12x$ **3B.** $6(y - 5) = 2(10 + 3y)$ no solution
all numbers

CONCEPT SUMMARY   *Steps for Solving Equations*

Step 1	Simplify the expressions on each side. Use the Distributive Property as needed.
Step 2	Use the Addition and/or Subtraction Properties of Equality to get the variables on one side and the numbers without variables on the other side. Simplify.
Step 3	Use the Multiplication or Division Property of Equality to solve.

STANDARDS EXAMPLE   5.0

4 Find the value of x so that the figures have the same area.

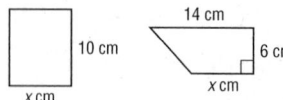

A 5
B 6
C 7
D 8

Test-Taking Tip

Substitution If you are asked to solve a complicated equation, it sometimes takes less time to check each possible answer rather than to actually solve the equation.

Read the Item

The equation $10x = \frac{1}{2}(14 + x)(6)$ represents this situation.

Solve the Item

You can solve the equation or substitute each value into the equation and see if it makes the equation true. We will solve by substitution.

A $10x = \frac{1}{2}(14 + x)(6)$

$10(5) \overset{?}{=} \frac{1}{2}(14 + 5)(6)$

$50 \overset{?}{=} \frac{1}{2}(19)(6)$

$50 \neq 57$

B $10x = \frac{1}{2}(14 + x)(6)$

$10(6) \overset{?}{=} \frac{1}{2}(14 + 6)(6)$

$60 \overset{?}{=} \frac{1}{2}(20)(6)$

$60 = 60$ ✓

Since the value 6 results in a true statement, you do not need to check 7 and 8. The answer is B.

✓ CHECK Your Progress

4. SHOPPING A purse is on sale for one fourth off the original price, or $12 off. What was the original price of the purse? H

   F $12   **G** $36   **H** $48   **J** $60

 **Personal Tutor at** ca.algebra1.com

---

Tips for New Teachers   **Preventing Errors**

Caution students to be careful when checking possible answers on multiple-choice test items. Often, some of the incorrect possible answers are similar to the correct answer. A substitution or arithmetic error when checking possible answers could lead them to inadvertently choose the incorrect answer.

★ indicates multi-step problem

✓CHECK Your Understanding

Examples 1 and 2
(pp. 98–99)

Solve each equation. Check your solution.

1. $20c + 5 = 5c + 65$ **4**

2. $\frac{3}{8} - \frac{1}{4}t = \frac{1}{2}t - \frac{3}{4}$ **$1\frac{1}{2}$**

3. $3(a - 5) = -6$ **3**

4. $6 = 3 + 5(d - 2)$ **2.6**

5. **NUMBER THEORY** Four times the greater of two consecutive integers is 1 more than five times the lesser number. Find the integers. **3, 4**

Example 3
(pp. 99–100)

Solve each equation. Check your solution.

6. $5 + 2(n + 1) = 2n$ **no solution**

7. $7 - 3r = r - 4(2 + r)$ **no solution**

8. $14v + 6 = 2(5 + 7v) - 4$ **all numbers**

9. $5h - 7 = 5(h - 2) + 3$ **all numbers**

Example 4
(p. 100)

5.0

10. **STANDARDS PRACTICE** Find the value of x so that the figures have the same perimeter. **A**

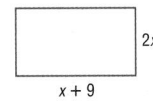

A 4
B 5
C 6
D 7

Exercises

HOMEWORK HELP	
For Exercises	See Examples
11–18, 25–28	1
19–24, 29, 30	2
31–34	3
43, 44	4

Exercise Levels
A: 11–32
B: 33–44
C: 45–48

Solve each equation. Check your solution.

11. $3k - 5 = 7k - 21$ **4**

12. $5t - 9 = -3t + 7$ **2**

13. $8s + 9 = 7s + 6$ **−3**

14. $3 - 4q = 10q + 10$ **−0.5**

15. $\frac{3}{4}n + 16 = 2 - \frac{1}{8}n$ **−16**

16. $\frac{1}{4} - \frac{2}{3}y = \frac{3}{4} - \frac{1}{3}y$ **$-1\frac{1}{2}$**

17. $\frac{c + 1}{8} = \frac{c}{4}$ **1**

18. $\frac{3m - 2}{5} = \frac{7}{10}$ **$1\frac{5}{6}$**

19. $8 = 4(3c + 5)$ **−1**

20. $7(m - 3) = 7$ **4**

21. $6(r + 2) - 4 = -10$ **−3**

22. $5 - \frac{1}{2}(x - 6) = 4$ **8**

23. $4(2a - 1) = -10(a - 5)$ **3**

24. $2(w - 3) + 5 = 3(w - 1)$ **2**

25. One half of a number increased by 16 is four less than two thirds of the number. Find the number. **120**

26. The sum of one half of a number and 6 equals one third of the number. What is the number? **−36**

27. Two less than one third of a number equals 3 more than one fourth of the number. Find the number. **60**

28. Two times a number plus 6 is three less than one fifth of the number. What is the number? **−5**

29. **NUMBER THEORY** Twice the greater of two consecutive odd integers is 13 less than three times the lesser number. Find the integers. **17, 19**

30. **NUMBER THEORY** Three times the greatest of three consecutive even integers exceeds twice the least by 38. What are the integers? **26, 28, 30**

EXTRA PRACTICE
See pages 721, 745.

Math Online
Self-Check Quiz at
ca.algebra1.com

Solve each equation. Check your solution. **34. all numbers**

31. $4(f - 2) = 4f$ **no solution**

32. $\frac{3}{2}y - y = 4 + \frac{1}{2}y$ **no solution**

33. $3(1 + d) - 5 = 3d - 2$ **all numbers** 34. $-3(2n - 5) = 0.5(-12n + 30)$

Lesson 2-5 Solving Equations with the Variable on Each Side **101**

3 Practice

✓ Formative Assessment

Use Exercises 1–10 to check for understanding.

Use the chart at the bottom of this page to customize assignments for your students.

Odd/Even Assignments

Exercises 11–34 and 43–44 are structured so that students practice the same concepts whether they are assigned odd or even problems.

DIFFERENTIATED HOMEWORK OPTIONS			
Level	**Assignment**	**Two-Day Option**	
BL Basic	11–34, 46–66	11–33 odd, 49, 50	12–34 even, 46–48, 51–66
OL Core	11–33 odd, 35, 36, 37–41 odd, 43, 44, 46–66	11–34, 49, 50	35–44, 46–48, 51–66
AL Advanced/Pre-AP	35–62 (optional: 63–66)		

Study Guide and Intervention
pp. 34–35 OL AL ELL

2-5 Study Guide and Intervention

Solving Equations with the Variable on Each Side

Variables on Each Side To solve an equation with the same variable on each side, first use the Addition or the Subtraction Property of Equality to write an equivalent equation that has the variable on just one side of the equation. Then solve the equation.

Example 1 Solve $5y - 8 = 3y + 12$.

$5y - 8 = 3y + 12$
$5y - 8 - 3y = 3y + 12 - 3y$
$2y - 8 = 12$
$2y - 8 + 8 = 12 + 8$
$2y = 20$
$\frac{2y}{2} = \frac{20}{2}$
$y = 10$

The solution is 10.

Example 2 Solve $-11 - 3y = 8y + 1$.

$-11 - 3y = 8y + 1$
$-11 - 3y + 3y = 8y + 1 + 3y$
$-11 = 11y + 1$
$-11 - 1 = 11y + 1 - 1$
$-12 = 11y$
$\frac{-12}{11} = \frac{11y}{11}$
$-1\frac{1}{11} = y$

The solution is $-1\frac{1}{11}$.

Exercises

Solve each equation. Then check your solution.

1. $6 - b = 5b + 30$
-4

2. $5y - 2y = 3y + 2$
no solution

3. $5x + 2 = 2x - 10$
-4

4. $4n - 8 = 3n + 2$
10

5. $1.2x + 4.3 = 2.1 - x$
-1

6. $4.4s + 6.2 = 8.8s - 1.8$
$\frac{20}{11}$

7. $\frac{1}{2}b + 4 = \frac{1}{8}b + 88$
224

8. $\frac{3}{4}k - 5 = \frac{1}{4}k - 1$
8

9. $8 - 5p = 4p - 1$
1

10. $4b - 8 = 10 - 2b$
3

11. $0.2x - 8 = -2 - x$
5

12. $3y - 1.8 = 3y - 1.8$
all numbers

13. $-4 - 3x = 7x - 6$
$\frac{1}{5}$

14. $8 + 4k = -10 + k$
-6

15. $20 - a = 10a - 2$
2

16. $\frac{2}{3}n + 8 = \frac{1}{2}n + 2$
-36

17. $\frac{2}{5}y - 8 = 9 - \frac{3}{5}y$
17

18. $-4r + 5 = 5 - 4r$
all numbers

19. $-4 - 3x = 6x - 6$
$\frac{2}{9}$

20. $18 - 4k = -10 - 4k$
no solution

21. $12 + 2y = 10y - 12$
3

Chapter 2   34   Glencoe Algebra 1

Practice
p. 37 OL AL

2-5 Practice

Solving Equations with the Variable on Each Side

Solve each equation. Then check your solution.

1. $5x - 3 = 13 - 3x$ 2

2. $-4c - 11 = 4c + 21$ -4

3. $1 - s = 6 - 6s$ 1

4. $14 + 5n = -4n + 17$ $\frac{1}{3}$

5. $\frac{1}{2}k - 3 = 2 - \frac{3}{4}k$ 4

6. $\frac{1}{2}(6 - z) = z$ 2

7. $3(c - 3x) = -9x - 4$ no solution

8. $4(4 - w) = 3(2w + 2)$ 1

9. $9(4b - 1) = 2(9b + 3)$ $\frac{5}{6}$

10. $3(6 + 5y) = 2(-5 + 4y)$ -4

11. $-5x - 10 = 2 - (x + 4)$ -2

12. $6 + 2(3j - 2) = 4(1 + j)$ 1

13. $\frac{5}{4}t - t = 8 + \frac{3}{4}t$ no solution

14. $1.4f + 1.1 = 8.3 - f$ 3

15. $\frac{2}{3}x - \frac{1}{6} = \frac{1}{2}x + \frac{5}{6}$ 6

16. $2 - \frac{3}{4}z = \frac{1}{8}z + 9$ -8

17. $\frac{3}{4}(3g - 2) = \frac{g}{6}$ $\frac{3}{4}$

18. $\frac{1}{5}(c + 1) = \frac{1}{6}(3c - 5)$ 7

19. $\frac{1}{4}(5 - 2h) = \frac{h}{2}$ $1\frac{1}{4}$

20. $\frac{1}{9}(2m - 16) = \frac{1}{3}(2m + 4)$ -7

21. $3(d - 8) - 5 = 9(d + 2) + 1$ -8

22. $2(a - 8) + 7 = 5(a + 2) - 3a - 19$ all numbers

23. Two thirds of a number reduced by 11 is equal to 4 more than the number. Find the number. -45

24. Five times the sum of a number and 3 is the same as 3 multiplied by 1 less than twice the number. What is the number? 18

25. **NUMBER THEORY** Tripling the greater of two consecutive even integers gives the same result as subtracting 10 from the lesser even integer. What are the integers? $-8, -6$

26. **GEOMETRY** The formula for the perimeter of a rectangle is $P = 2\ell + 2w$, where ℓ is the length and w is the width. A rectangle has a perimeter of 24 inches. Find its dimensions if its length is 3 inches greater than its width. 4.5 in. by 7.5 in.

Chapter 2   37   Glencoe Algebra 1

Word Problem Practice
p. 38 OL AL

2-5 Word Problem Practice

Solving Equations with the Variable on Each Side

1. **OLYMPICS** In the 2004 Summer Olympic Games in Athens, Greece, the United States athletes won 2 more than 3 times the number of gold metals won by the French athletes. The United States won 24 more gold metals than the French. Solve the equation $24 + F = 3F + 2$ to find the number of gold metals won by the French athletes. 11

2. **AGE** Diego's mother is twice as old as he is. She is also as old as the sum of the ages of Diego and both of his younger twin brothers. The twins are 11 years old. Solve the equation $2d = d + 11 + 11$ to find the age of Diego. 22 yr

3. **GEOMETRY** Supplementary angles are angles whose measures have a sum of 180°. Complementary angles are angles whose measures have a sum of 90°. Find the measure of an angle whose supplement is 10° more than twice its complement. Let $90 - x$ equal the degree measure of its complement and $180 - x$ equal the degree measure of its supplement. Write and solve an equation. $180 - x = 10 + 2(90 - x)$; 10

4. **NATURE** The table shows the current heights and average growth rates of two different species of trees. How long will it take for the two trees to be the same height?

Tree Species	Current Height	Annual growth
A	38 inches	4 inches
B	45.5 inches	2.5 inches

$38 + 4x = 45.5 + 2.5x$
$1.5x = 7.5$
$x = 5$ years

NUMBER THEORY For Exercises 5 and 6, use the following information.

Mrs. Simms told her class to find two consecutive even integers such that twice the lesser of two integers is 4 less than two times the greater integer.

5. Write and solve an equation to find the integers.
Let integers be n and $(n + 2)$
$2n = 2(n + 2) - 4$
$2n = 2n + 4 - 4$
$2n = 2n$
$1 = 1, n \neq 0$

6. Does the equation have one solution, no solutions, or is it an identity? Explain. It is an identity because it is true for every pair of consecutive even integers.

Chapter 2   38   Glencoe Algebra 1

★ 35. **HEALTH** When exercising, a person's pulse rate should not exceed a certain limit. This maximum rate is represented by the expression $0.8(220 - a)$, where a is age in years. Find the age of a person whose maximum pulse is 152. **30 yr**

★ 36. **HARDWARE** Traditionally, nails are given names such as 2-penny, 3-penny, and so on. These names describe the lengths of the nails. Use the diagram to find the name of a nail that is $2\frac{1}{2}$ inches long. **8-penny**

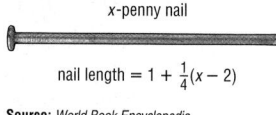

x-penny nail

nail length $= 1 + \frac{1}{4}(x - 2)$

Source: *World Book Encyclopedia*

Solve each equation. Check your solution.

37. $\frac{1}{4}(7 + 3g) = -\frac{g}{8}$ -2

38. $\frac{1}{6}(a - 4) = \frac{1}{3}(2a + 4)$ -4

39. $1.03p - 4 = -2.15p + 8.72$ 4

40. $18 - 3.8t = 7.36 - 1.9t$ **5.6**

41. $5.4w + 8.2 = 9.8w - 2.8$ **2.5**

42. $2[s + 3(s - 1)] = 18$ **3**

Real-World Link

The normal values for resting heart rates in beats per minute:

- infants: 100–160
- children 1–10 years: 70–120
- children over 10 and adults: 60–80
- well-trained athletes: 40–60

Source: MedlinePlus.com

★ 43. **ANALYZE TABLES** The table shows the households that had Brand A and Brand B of personal computers in a recent year and the average growth rates. How long will it take for the two brands to be in the same number of households? **about 5.6 yr**

Brand of Computer	Millions of Households with Computer	Growth Rate (million households per year)
A	4.9	0.275
B	2.5	0.7

★ 44. **GEOMETRY** The rectangle and square shown at right have the same perimeter. Find the dimensions of each figure. **2.5 by 0.5 and 1.5 by 1.5**

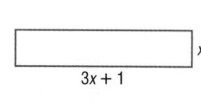
$3x + 1$ x

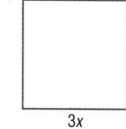
$3x$

H.O.T. Problems

45. **CHALLENGE** Write an equation that has one or more grouping symbols, the variable on each side of the equals sign, and a solution of -2. Discuss the steps you used to write the equation. **Sample answer: $3(x + 1) = x - 1$**

46. **OPEN ENDED** Find a counterexample to the statement *All equations have a solution*. Explain your reasoning. **Sample answer: $2x - 5 = 2x + 5$**

47. **REASONING** Determine whether each solution is correct. If the solution is not correct, describe the error and give the correct solution. **See margin.**

a.
$2(g + 5) = 22$
$2g + 5 = 22$
$2g + 5 - 5 = 22 - 5$
$2g = 17$
$g = 8.5$

b.
$5d = 2d - 18$
$5d - 2d = 2d - 18 - 2d$
$3d = -18$
$d = -6$

48. *Writing in Math* Use the information about Internet users on page 98 to explain how an equation can be used to determine when two populations are equal. Include the steps for solving the equation and the year when the number of dial-up Internet users will equal the number of broadband Internet users according to the model. Explain why this method can be used to predict events. **See margin.**

Enrichment
p. 39 OL AL

2-5 Enrichment

Identities

An equation that is true for every value of the variable is called an **identity**. When you try to solve an identity, you end up with a statement that is always true. Here is an example.

Example Solve $8 - (5 - 6x) = 3(1 + 2x)$.

$8 - (5 - 6x) = 3(1 + 2x)$
$8 - 5 - (-6x) = 3(1 + 2x)$
$8 - 5 + 6x = 3 + 6x$
$3 + 6x = 3 + 6x$

BL = Below Grade Level
OL = On Grade Level
AL = Above Grade Level
ELL = English Language Learner

Additional pages not shown:

Lesson Reading Guide, p. 33 BL OL ELL

Skills Practice, p. 36 BL OL

49. Which equation represents the second step of the solution process? **D**

Step 1 $4(2x + 7) - 6 = 3x$
Step 2 ☐
Step 3 $5x + 28 - 6 = 0$
Step 4 $5x = -22$
Step 5 $x = -4.4$

A $4(2x - 6) + 7 = 3x$

B $4(2x + 1) = 3x$

C $8x + 7 - 6 = 3x$

D $8x + 28 - 6 = 3x$

50. REVIEW Tanya sells cosmetics door-to-door. She makes $5 an hour and 15% commission on the total dollar value on whatever she sells. If Tanya's commission is increased to 17%, how much money will she make if she sells $300 dollars worth of product and works 30 hours? **F**

F $201

G $226

H $255

J $283

Spiral Review

Solve each equation. Check your solution. (Lesson 2-4)

51. $\frac{2}{9}v - 6 = 14$ **90**

52. $\frac{x-3}{7} = -2$ **−11**

53. $5 - 9w = 23$ **−2**

★ **54. HEALTH** A female burns 4.5 Calories per minute pushing a lawn mower. Write an equation to represent the number of Calories C burned if Ebony pushes a lawn mower for m minutes. How long will it take Ebony to burn 150 Calories mowing the lawn? (Lesson 2-3) $C = 4.5m$; $33\frac{1}{3}$ min

★ **55.** A teacher took a survey of his students to find out how many televisions they had in their homes. The results are shown in the table. Write a set of ordered pairs representing the data in the table and draw a graph showing the relationship between students and the number of televisions in their homes. (Lesson 1-9)
(1, 8), (2, 12), (3, 4), (4, 2); See Ch. 2 Answer Appendix for graph.

Televisions	Number of Students
1	8
2	12
3	4
4	2

Write an algebraic expression for each verbal expression. Then simplify, indicating the properties used. (Lesson 1-6)

56. twice the product of p and q increased by the product of p and q — $2pq + pq$; $3pq$; Distributive Property and Substitution

57. three times the square of x plus the sum of x squared and seven times x
$3x^2 + x^2 + 7x$; $4x^2 + 7x$; Distributive Property and Substitution

Find the solution set for each inequality, given the replacement set. (Lesson 1-3)

58. $3x + 2 > 2$; {0, 1, 2} {1, 2}

59. $2y^2 - 1 > 0$; {1, 3, 5} {1, 3, 5}

Evaluate each expression when $a = 5$, $b = 8$, and $c = 1$. (Lesson 1-2)

60. $5(b - a)$ **15**

61. $\frac{3a^2}{b+c}$ **$8\frac{1}{3}$**

62. $(a + 2b) - c$ **20**

GET READY for the Next Lesson

PREREQUISITE SKILL Simplify each fraction. (Pages 694–695)

63. $\frac{28}{49}$ **$\frac{4}{7}$**

64. $\frac{36}{60}$ **$\frac{3}{5}$**

65. $\frac{8}{120}$ **$\frac{1}{15}$**

66. $\frac{108}{9}$ **12**

Real-World Connection
For Exercise 35, have students calculate their own maximum heart rates using the expression given.

 Assess

Name the Math On index cards, have students solve $3(x + 2) = 5(x - 8)$. Beside each step, have students write one or two sentences explaining and justifying their methods.

 Formative Assessment

Check for student understanding of concepts in Lessons 2-4 and 2-5.
CRM Quiz 2, p. 73

Additional Answers

47a. Incorrect; the 2 must be distributed over both g and 5; 6.

47b. correct

48. Sample answer: Find the amount of change and express this change as a percent of the original number. To find the percent of increase, first find the amount of increase. Then find what percent the amount of increase is of the original number. The percent of increase from 1996 to 1999 is about 67%. An increase of 100 is a very large increase if the original number is 50, but a very small increase if the original number is 100,000. The percent of change will indicate whether the change is large or small relative to the original.

Pre-AP Activity Use after the Exercises

Remind students that they have learned that an equation can have 1, 0, or an endless number of solutions. Ask students to write an equation in which there are exactly two solutions for the variable. For example, in $|x| = 25$, $x = 25$ or -25 or $x^2 = 25$, $x = 5$ or -5.

CHAPTER
2 Mid-Chapter Quiz
Lessons 2–1 through 2–5

Formative Assessment

Use the Mid-Chapter Quiz to assess student progress in the first half of the chapter.

For problems answered incorrectly, have students review the lessons indicated in parentheses.

Summative Assessment

CRM Mid-Chapter Test, p. 75

Customize and create your own Mid-Chapter Tests and their answer keys.

Foldables™ Follow-Up

Before students complete the Mid-Chapter Quiz, encourage them to review the information on the index cards in their Foldables.

Additional Answers

1. Sample answer: 2 equals x minus 9.

2. Sample answer: 8 plus the product of 7 and t equals 22.

3. Sample answer: a equals 1 plus three fifths of b.

4. Sample answer: n squared minus 6 equals 5 times n.

11. $x + 4\frac{1}{2} = 12$

Translate each equation into a verbal sentence.
(Lesson 2-1) **1–4. See margin.**

1. $2 = x - 9$
2. $8 + 7t = 22$
3. $a = 1 + \frac{3}{5}b$
4. $n^2 - 6 = 5n$

GEOMETRY For Exercises 5 and 6, use the following information.

The surface area S of a sphere equals four times π times the square of the radius r. (Lesson 2-1)

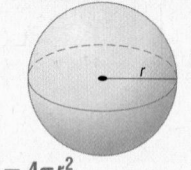

5. Write the formula for the surface area of a sphere. $S = 4\pi r^2$

6. What is the surface area of a sphere if the radius is 7 centimeters? **about 615 cm^2**

Solve each equation. Check your solution.
(Lesson 2-2)

7. $d + 18 = -27$ **−45**
8. $m - 77 = -61$ **16**
9. $-12 + a = -36$ **−24**
10. $t - (-16) = 9$ **−7**

PALEONTOLOGY For Exercises 11 and 12, use the following information. (Lesson 2-2)

The skeleton of a juvenile dinosaur was recently found in Illinois. If the dinosaur had been fully grown, it would have been $4\frac{1}{2}$ feet taller.

11. Write an equation to find the height x of the juvenile dinosaur if a fully grown dinosaur is 12 feet tall. **See margin.**

12. Solve the equation to find the height of the dinosaur. $7\frac{1}{2}$ **ft**

Solve each equation. Check your solution. (Lesson 2-3)

13. $\frac{2}{3}p = 18$ **27**
14. $-17y = 391$ **−23**
15. $5x = -45$ **−9**
16. $-\frac{2}{5}d = -10$ **25**

17. **TECHNOLOGY** In a phone survey of teens who have Internet access, three fourths, or 825 of those surveyed, said they use instant messaging. How many teens were surveyed? (Lesson 2-3) **1100 teens**

Solve each equation. Check your solution. (Lesson 2-4) 18. $-8\frac{1}{3}$

18. $-3x - 7 = 18$
19. $5 = \frac{m-5}{4}$ **25**
20. $4h + 5 = 11$ **1.5**
21. $5d - 6 = 3d + 9$ **7.5**

22. **MULTIPLE CHOICE** Coach Bronson recorded the heights of 130 freshmen and 95 seniors. Which expression could be used to find the average height of these freshmen and seniors? (Lesson 2-4) **A**

Students	Average Height
freshmen	5 feet 5 inches
seniors	5 feet 8 inches

A $\dfrac{65(130) + 68(95)}{225}$

B $[65(130) + 68(95)] \cdot 225$

C $65(130) + 68(95) \cdot \dfrac{1}{225}$

D $\dfrac{68(130) + 65(95)}{225}$

Solve each equation. Then check your solution. (Lesson 2-5)

23. $7 + 2(w + 1) = 2w + 9$ **all real numbers**
24. $-8(4 + 9r) = 7(-2 - 11r)$ **3.6**

25. **NUMBER THEORY** Two thirds of a number equals 3 increased by one half of the number. Find the number. (Lesson 2-5) **18**

26. **MULTIPLE CHOICE** The sides of the hexagon are the same length. If the perimeter of the hexagon is $18x + 9$ square centimeters, what is the length of each side? (Lesson 2-5) **H**

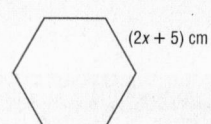
(2x + 5) cm

F 3.5 cm
G 7 cm
H 12 cm
J 33.5 cm

Data-Driven Decision Making	Exercises	Lesson	 Standard	Resources for Review
Diagnostic Teaching Based on the results of the Chapter 2 Mid-Chapter Quiz, use the following to review concepts that students continue to find challenging.	1–6	2–1	**Reinforcement of 7AF1.1**	CRM Study Guide and Intervention, pp. 6–7, 13–14, 20–21, 27–28, 34–35
	7–12	2–2	**Preparation for 5.0**	Math Online
	13–17	2–3	**Preparation for 5.0**	• Extra Examples
	18–22	2–4	**5.0**	• Personal Tutor
	23–26	2–5	**4.0**	• Concepts in Motion

104 Chapter 2 Solving Linear Equations

Main Ideas

- Determine whether two ratios form a proportion.
- Solve proportions.

 Standard 15.0 Students apply algebraic techniques to solve rate problems, work problems, and percent mixture problems. (Key, CAHSEE)

New Vocabulary

ratio
proportion
extremes
means
rate
scale

GET READY for the Lesson

The ingredients in the recipe will make 4 servings of honey frozen yogurt. Keri can use ratios and equations to find the amount of each ingredient needed to make enough yogurt for her club meeting.

Honey Frozen Yogurt	
2 cups 2% milk	2 eggs, beaten
$\frac{3}{4}$ cup honey	2 cups plain low-fat
1 dash salt	yogurt
	1 tablespoon vanilla

Ratios and Proportions A **ratio** is a comparison of two numbers by division. The ratio of x to y can be expressed in the following ways.

$$x \text{ to } y \qquad x{:}y \qquad \frac{x}{y}$$

The recipe above states that for 4 servings you need 2 cups of milk. The ratio of servings to milk may be written as 4 to 2, 4:2, or $\frac{4}{2}$. In simplest form, the ratio is written as 2 to 1, 2:1, or $\frac{2}{1}$.

Suppose you wanted to double the recipe to have 8 servings. The amount of milk required would be 4 cups. The ratio of servings to milk is $\frac{8}{4}$. When this ratio is simplified, the ratio is $\frac{2}{1}$. Notice that this ratio is equal to the original ratio. An equation stating that two ratios are equal is called a **proportion**. So, we can state that $\frac{4}{2} = \frac{8}{4}$ is a proportion.

$$\frac{4}{2} \overset{\div 2}{=} \frac{2}{1} \qquad \frac{8}{4} \overset{\div 4}{=} \frac{2}{1}$$

EXAMPLE — Determine Whether Ratios Form a Proportion

① Determine whether the ratios $\frac{4}{5}$ and $\frac{24}{30}$ form a proportion.

$$\frac{4}{5} \overset{\div 1}{=} \frac{4}{5} \qquad \frac{24}{30} \overset{\div 6}{=} \frac{4}{5}$$

The ratios are equal. Therefore, they form a proportion.

CHECK Your Progress

 Determine whether each pair of ratios forms a proportion. Write *yes* or *no*.

1A. $\frac{6}{10}, \frac{2}{5}$ no

1B. $\frac{1}{6}, \frac{5}{30}$ yes

1 Focus

Standards Alignment

Before Lesson 2-6
Use proportions to solve problems from ⬤ Standard 6NS1.3

Lesson 2-6
Solve rate, work and percent mixture problems from Standard 15.0

After Lesson 2-6
Prove that triangles are congruent or similar from Sandard G5.0

2 Teach

Scaffolding Questions Have students read *Get Ready for the Lesson*. **Ask:**

- The recipe is for 4 servings. If you want to double the recipe to make 8 servings, what would you do to the amounts for each ingredient? Double each amount.
- What would you do to the amount for each ingredient if you wanted to make enough frozen yogurt for two servings? Halve the amount of each ingredient.
- By what number would you multiply the amount of each ingredient to make six servings? You would multiply each amount by $1\frac{1}{2}$.

Lesson 2-6 Resources

Chapter 2 Resource Masters
Lesson Reading Guide, p. 41 BL OL ELL
Study Guide and Intervention, pp. 42–43 BL OL ELL
Skills Practice, p. 44 BL OL
Practice, p. 45 OL AL
Word Problem Practice, p. 46 OL AL
Enrichment, p. 47 OL AL

Transparencies
5-Minute Check Transparency 2-6

Additional Print Resources
Noteables™ Interactive Study Notebook with Foldables™
Teaching Algebra with Manipulatives

Technology
ca.algebra1.com
Interactive Classroom CD-ROM
AssignmentWorks CD-ROM
Graphing Calculator Easy Files

Ratios and Proportions

Example 1 shows how to determine whether ratios form a proportion using division. **Example 2** shows how to determine whether ratios form a proportion using cross products.

 Formative Assessment

Use the Check Your Progress exercises after each example to determine students' understanding of concepts.

ADDITIONAL EXAMPLES

1 Determine whether the ratios $\frac{7}{8}$ and $\frac{49}{56}$ form a proportion. The ratios are equal when expressed in simplest form. Therefore, they form a proportion.

2 Use cross products to determine whether each pair of ratios forms a proportion.
a. $\frac{0.25}{0.6}, \frac{1.25}{2}$ not a proportion
b. $\frac{4}{5}, \frac{16}{20}$ a proportion

Additional Examples are also in:
- Noteables™ Interactive Study Notebook with Foldables™
- Interactive Classroom PowerPoint® Presentations

There are special names for the terms in a proportion.

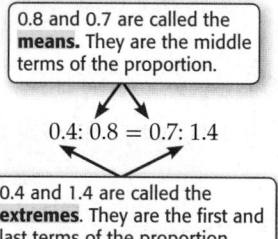

0.8 and 0.7 are called the **means.** They are the middle terms of the proportion.

$$0.4: 0.8 = 0.7: 1.4$$

0.4 and 1.4 are called the **extremes.** They are the first and last terms of the proportion.

Vocabulary Link

Extremes

Everyday Use something at one end or the other of a range, as in extremes of heat and cold

Math Use the first and last terms of a proportion

KEY CONCEPT — *Means–Extremes Property of Proportion*

Words In a proportion, the product of the extremes is equal to the product of the means.

Symbols If $\frac{a}{b} = \frac{c}{d}$, then $ad = bc$.

Examples Since $\frac{2}{4} = \frac{1}{2}$, $2(2) = 4(1)$ or $4 = 4$.

Another way to determine whether two ratios form a proportion is to use cross products. If the cross products are equal, then the ratios form a proportion.

EXAMPLE Use Cross Products

Study Tip

Cross Products
When you find cross products, you are said to be *cross multiplying*.

2 Use cross products to determine whether each pair of ratios forms a proportion.

a. $\frac{0.4}{0.8}, \frac{0.7}{1.4}$

$\frac{0.4}{0.8} \stackrel{?}{=} \frac{0.7}{1.4}$ Write the equation.

$0.4(1.4) \stackrel{?}{=} 0.8(0.7)$ Find the cross products.

$0.56 = 0.56$ Simplify.

The cross products are equal, so the ratios form a proportion.

b. $\frac{6}{8}, \frac{24}{28}$

$\frac{6}{8} \stackrel{?}{=} \frac{24}{28}$ Write the equation.

$6(28) \stackrel{?}{=} 8(24)$ Find the cross products.

$168 \neq 192$ Simplify.

The cross products are not equal, so the ratios do not form a proportion.

✓CHECK Your Progress

2A. $\frac{0.2}{1.8}, \frac{1}{0.9}$ no

2B. $\frac{15}{36}, \frac{35}{42}$ no

Intervention

Preventing Errors Point out that the definitions of extremes and means are not arbitrary. In the proportion $\frac{a}{b} = \frac{c}{d}$, a and d are the extremes, and b and c are the means. Remind students that the ratios can be written in the form $x{:}y$. If the proportions above are rewritten in this form, they are $a{:}b = c{:}d$. Looking at this proportion, a and d are the extremes because they are on the outside, and *extreme* is a synonym for outside. Similarly, b and c are the means because they are in the middle, and *mean* is often a synonym for middle.

Solve Proportions To solve proportions that involve a variable, use cross products and the techniques used to solve other equations.

Concepts in MOtion
Interactive Lab ca.algebra1.com

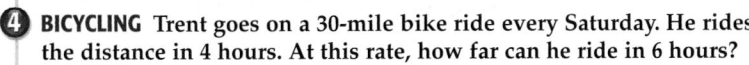

EXAMPLE Solve a Proportion

3 Solve the proportion $\frac{n}{15} = \frac{24}{16}$.

$\frac{n}{15} = \frac{24}{16}$	Original equation
$16(n) = 15(24)$	Find the cross products.
$16n = 360$	Simplify.
$\frac{16n}{16} = \frac{360}{16}$	Divide each side by 16.
$n = 22.5$	Simplify.

CHECK Your Progress

Solve each proportion. If necessary, round to the nearest hundredth.

3A. $\frac{r}{8} = \frac{25}{40}$ 5

3B. $\frac{3.2}{4} = \frac{2.6}{n}$ 3.25

The ratio of two measurements having different units of measure is called a **rate**. For example, a price of $1.99 per dozen eggs, a speed of 55 miles per hour, and a salary of $30,000 per year are all rates. Proportions are often used to solve problems involving rates.

Real-World EXAMPLE

4 **BICYCLING** Trent goes on a 30-mile bike ride every Saturday. He rides the distance in 4 hours. At this rate, how far can he ride in 6 hours?

Explore Let m represent the number of miles Trent can ride in 6 hours.

Plan Write a proportion for the problem using rates.

miles → $\frac{30}{4} = \frac{m}{6}$ ← miles
hours → ← hours

Solve Estimate: If he rides 30 miles in 4 hours, then he would ride 60 miles in 8 hours. So, in 6 hours, he would ride between 30 and 60 miles.

$\frac{30}{4} = \frac{m}{6}$	Original proportion
$30(6) = 4(m)$	Find the cross products.
$180 = 4m$	Simplify.
$\frac{180}{4} = \frac{4m}{4}$	Divide each side by 4.
$45 = m$	Simplify.

Check Check the reasonableness of the solution. If Trent rides 30 miles in 4 hours, he rides 7.5 miles in 1 hour. So, in 6 hours, Trent can ride 6 × 7.5 or 45 miles. The answer is correct.

Study Tip

To ensure that the proportion is set up correctly, you should label the units. For example,
$\frac{15 \text{ mi}}{2 \text{ hrs}} = \frac{25 \text{ mi}}{x \text{ hrs}}$.

Math Online Extra Examples at ca.algebra1.com

Focus on Mathematical Content

Proportions One way to determine if two ratios form a proportion is to use cross products. In a proportion, the product of the extremes is equal to the product of the means.

Solve Proportions

Example 3 shows how to solve a proportion involving a variable using the techniques used to solve other equations. **Example 4** shows how to write and solve a proportion for a problem involving rates (the ratio of two measurements having different units of measure). **Example 5** shows how to write and solve a problem using a ratio or rate called a scale.

ADDITIONAL EXAMPLES

3 Solve the proportion $\frac{n}{12} = \frac{3}{8}$.
$n = 4.5$

4 **BICYCLING** The gear on a bicycle is 8:5. This means that for every 8 turns of the pedals, the wheel turns 5 times. Suppose the bicycle wheel turns about 2435 times during a trip. How many times would you have to crank the pedals during the trip? about 3896 times

5 **MAP** In a road atlas, the scale for the map of Connecticut is 5 inches = 41 miles. The scale for the map of Texas is 5 inches = 144 miles. What are the distances in miles represented by $2\frac{1}{2}$ inches on each map? Connecticut $20\frac{1}{2}$ mi; Texas 72 mi

It is important for students to have a good understanding of writing and solving proportions before studying the next few lessons. If you have any doubt that your students have mastered the concept of proportions, place students in small groups to work through the Check Your Understanding problems. Have a student from each group report on that group's progress and areas in which the group may need assistance.

3 Practice

✓ Formative Assessment

Use Exercises 1–8 to check for understanding.

Use the chart below to customize assignments for your students.

Odd/Even Assignments

Exercises 9–30 are structured so that students practice the same concepts whether they are assigned odd or even problems.

⚠ Exercise Alert!
Use the Distributive Property
Exercises 31–33 require students to use cross products and the Distributive Property to solve for the variable. Suggest students write each product with grouping symbols before multiplying.

Real-World Connection

For Exercise 34, have students count how many students in their math class have pets. Then have students calculate, using the ratio given by the research study, how many of those students they would expect to have bought their pets from breeders. Finally, have them determine the actual ratio.

---

4. **EXERCISE** It takes 7 minutes for Isabella to walk around the track twice. At this rate, how many times can she walk around the track in a half hour? **about 8.6 times**

 **Personal Tutor at** ca.algebra1.com

A ratio or rate called a **scale** compares the size of a model to the actual size of the object using a proportion. Maps and blueprints are two common scale drawings.

🌐 Real-World EXAMPLE

5 **CRATER LAKE** The scale of a map for Crater Lake National Park is 2 inches = 9 miles. The distance between Discovery Point and Phantom Ship Overlook on the map is about $1\frac{3}{4}$ inches. What is the distance d between these two places?

Real-World Link
Crater Lake is a volcanic crater in Oregon that was formed by an explosion 42 times the blast of Mount St. Helens.

Source: travel.excite.com

$$\text{scale} \rightarrow \quad \frac{2}{9} = \frac{1\frac{3}{4}}{d} \quad \leftarrow \text{scale}$$
$$\text{actual} \rightarrow \qquad\qquad\quad \leftarrow \text{actual}$$

$$2(d) = 9\left(1\frac{3}{4}\right) \qquad \text{Find the cross products.}$$

$$2d = \frac{63}{4} \qquad \text{Simplify.}$$

$$2d \div 2 = \frac{63}{4} \div 2 \qquad \text{Divide each side by 2.}$$

$$d = \frac{63}{8} \text{ or } 7\frac{7}{8} \qquad \text{Simplify.}$$

The actual distance is about $7\frac{7}{8}$ miles.

COncepts in MOtion
BrainPOP®
ca.algebra1.com

5. **AIRPLANES** On a model airplane, the scale is 5 centimeters = 2 meters. If the wingspan of the model is 28.5 centimeters, what is the wingspan of the actual airplane? **11.4 m**

✓ CHECK Your Understanding

Examples 1, 2 (pp. 105–106)	Determine whether each pair of ratios forms a proportion. Write *yes* or *no*.

1. $\frac{4}{11}, \frac{12}{33}$ **yes**   2. $\frac{16}{17}, \frac{8}{9}$ **no**   3. $\frac{2.1}{3.5}, \frac{0.5}{0.7}$ **no**

Example 3 (p. 107)

Solve each proportion. If necessary, round to the nearest hundredth.

4. $\frac{3}{4} = \frac{6}{x}$ **8**   5. $\frac{a}{45} = \frac{5}{15}$ **15**   6. $\frac{0.6}{1.1} = \frac{n}{8.47}$ **4.62**

Example 4 (p. 107)

7. **TRAVEL** The Lehmans' minivan requires 5 gallons of gasoline to travel 120 miles. How much gasoline will they need for a 350-mile trip? **about 14.6 gal**

Example 5 (p. 108)

8. **BLUEPRINTS** On a blueprint for a house, 2.5 inches equals 10 feet. If the length of a wall is 12 feet, how long is the wall on the blueprint? **3 in.**

108 Chapter 2 Solving Linear Equations

DIFFERENTIATED HOMEWORK OPTIONS			
Level	**Assignment**	**Two-Day Option**	
BL Basic	9–30, 37, 38, 40–56	9–29 odd, 41, 42	10–30 even, 37, 38, 40, 43–56
OL Core	9–33 odd, 34–38, 40–56	9–30, 41, 42	31–38, 40, 43–56
AL Advanced /Pre-AP	31–52 (optional: 53–56)		

Exercises

HOMEWORK HELP

For Exercises	See Examples
9–14	1, 2
15–26	3
27, 28	4
29, 30	5

Exercise Levels
A: 9–30
B: 31–36
C: 37–40

Determine whether each pair of ratios forms a proportion. Write yes or no.

9. $\dfrac{3}{2}, \dfrac{21}{14}$ **yes**

10. $\dfrac{8}{9}, \dfrac{12}{18}$ **no**

11. $\dfrac{2.3}{3.4}, \dfrac{3.0}{3.6}$ **no**

12. $\dfrac{5}{2}, \dfrac{4}{1.6}$ **yes**

13. $\dfrac{21.1}{14.4}, \dfrac{1.1}{1.2}$ **no**

14. $\dfrac{4.2}{5.6}, \dfrac{1.68}{2.24}$ **yes**

Solve each proportion. If necessary, round to the nearest hundredth.

15. $\dfrac{4}{x} = \dfrac{2}{10}$ **20**

16. $\dfrac{1}{y} = \dfrac{3}{15}$ **5**

17. $\dfrac{6}{5} = \dfrac{x}{15}$ **18**

18. $\dfrac{20}{28} = \dfrac{n}{21}$ **15**

19. $\dfrac{6}{8} = \dfrac{7}{a}$ **$9\dfrac{1}{3}$**

20. $\dfrac{16}{7} = \dfrac{9}{b}$ **$3\dfrac{15}{16}$**

21. $\dfrac{w}{2} = \dfrac{4.5}{6.8}$ **1.32**

22. $\dfrac{t}{0.3} = \dfrac{1.7}{0.9}$ **0.57**

23. $\dfrac{2}{0.21} = \dfrac{8}{n}$ **0.84**

24. $\dfrac{2.4}{3.6} = \dfrac{s}{1.8}$ **1.2**

25. $\dfrac{1}{0.19} = \dfrac{12}{n}$ **2.28**

26. $\dfrac{7}{1.066} = \dfrac{z}{9.65}$ **63.37**

27. **WORK** Jun earns \$152 in 4 days. At that rate, how many days will it take him to earn \$532? **14 days**

28. **DRIVING** Lanette drove 248 miles in 4 hours. At that rate, how long will it take her to drive an additional 93 miles? **$1\dfrac{1}{2}$ hr**

29. **MODELS** A collector's model racecar is scaled so that 1 inch on the model equals $6\dfrac{1}{4}$ feet on the actual car. If the model is $\dfrac{2}{3}$ inch high, how high is the actual car? **$4\dfrac{1}{6}$ ft**

30. **GEOGRAPHY** On a map of Illinois, the distance between Chicago and Algonquin is 3.2 centimeters. If 2 centimeters = 40 kilometers, what is the approximate distance between the two cities? **64 km**

Solve each proportion. If necessary, round to the nearest hundredth.

31. $\dfrac{6}{14} = \dfrac{7}{x-3}$ **19.33**

32. $\dfrac{5}{3} = \dfrac{6}{x+2}$ **1.6**

33. $\dfrac{3-y}{4} = \dfrac{1}{9}$ **2.56**

34. **PETS** A research study shows that three out of every twenty pet owners bought their pets from breeders. Of the 122 animals cared for by a veterinarian, how many would you expect to have been bought from breeders? **18**

35–36. See Ch. 2 Answer Appendix.

ANALYZE TABLES For Exercises 35 and 36, use the table.

35. Write a ratio of the number of gold medals won to the total number of medals won for each country.

All-Time Summer Olympic Medal Standings, 1896–2004				
Country	**Gold**	**Silver**	**Bronze**	**Total**
United States	907	697	615	2219
USSR/UT/Russia	525	436	409	1370
Germany/E. Ger/W. Ger	388	408	434	1230
Great Britain	189	242	237	668
France	199	202	230	631
Italy	189	154	168	511
Sweden	140	157	179	476

Source: infoplease.com and athens2004.com

EXTRA PRACTICE
See pages 721, 745.

Math online
Self-Check Quiz at
ca.algebra1.com

36. Do any two of the ratios you wrote for Exercise 35 form a proportion? If so, explain the real-world meaning of the proportion.

BL = Below Grade Level
OL = On Grade Level
AL = Above Grade Level
ELL = English Language Learner

Additional pages not shown:
CRM Lesson Reading Guide, p. 41 **BL** **OL** **ELL**
CRM Skills Practice, p. 44 **BL** **OL**

Study Guide and Intervention
CRM pp. 42–43 **BL** **OL** **ELL**

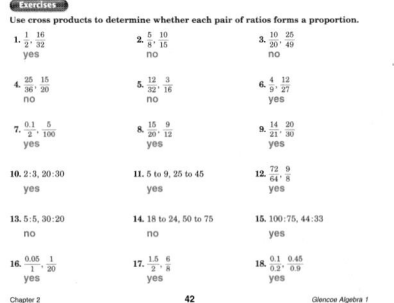

Practice
CRM p. 45 **OL** **AL**

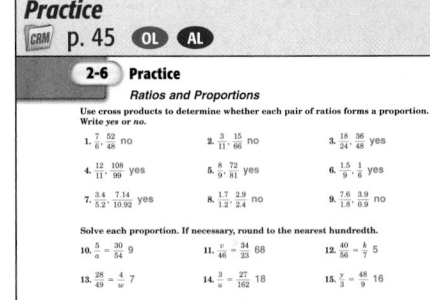

Word Problem Practice
CRM p. 46 **OL** **AL**

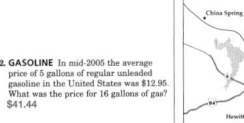

Enrichment
CRM p. 47 **OL** **AL**

2-6 Enrichment

Angles of a Triangle

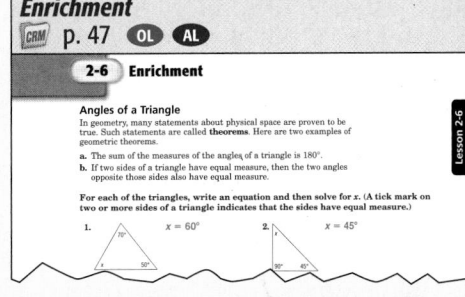

Ticket Out the Door Make several copies each of five different ratios. Give one ratio to each student. As students leave the room, ask them to tell you two ratios that form a proportion with the ratio they were given.

FOLDABLES Study Organizer **Foldables™ Follow-Up**
Have students choose problems from Exercises 15–26 and write the problems and the steps needed to solve them on index cards. Tell them to store the cards in the fourth pocket of the Foldable™, and label it "2-6: Ratios and Proportions."

Additional Answers

38. A ratio is a comparison of two numbers and a proportion is an equation of two equal ratios.

40. Sample answer: Ratios are used to determine how much of each ingredient to use for a given number of servings. To determine how much honey is needed if you use 3 eggs, write and solve the proportion $2:\frac{3}{4} = 3:h$, where h is the amount of honey. To alter the recipe to get 5 servings, multiply each amount by $1\frac{1}{4}$.

49. Sample answer:

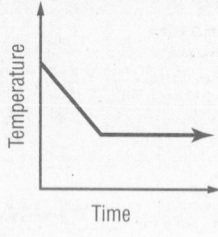

---

37. OPEN ENDED Find an example of ratios used in an advertisement. Analyze the ratios and describe how they are used to sell the product. **See students' wor**

38. REASONING Explain the difference between a ratio and a proportion. **See margi**

39. CHALLENGE Consider the proportion $a{:}b{:}c = 3{:}1{:}5$. What is the value of $\frac{2a + 3b}{4b + 3c}$? (*Hint*: Choose different values of a, b, and c for which the proportion is true and evaluate the expression.) $\frac{9}{19}$

40. *Writing in Math* Use the information about recipes on page 105 to explain how ratios are used in recipes. Include an explanation of how to use a proportion to determine how much honey is needed if you use 3 eggs, and a description of how to alter the recipe to get 5 servings. **See margi**

STANDARDS PRACTICE 6NS1.3

41. In the figure, $x{:}y = 2{:}3$ and $y{:}z = 3{:}5$. If $x = 10$, find the value of z. **C**

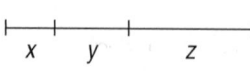

A 15

B 20

C 25

D 30

42. REVIEW If $\triangle LMN$ is similar to $\triangle LPO$, what is the length of side z? **G**

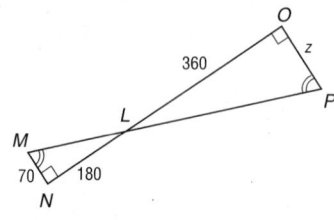

F 240 units   H 120 units

G 140 units   J   70 units

Spiral Review

Solve each equation. Then check your solution. (Lessons 2-4 and 2-5)

43. $8y - 10 = -3y + 2$ $1\frac{1}{11}$

44. $17 + 2n = 21 + 2n$ **no solution**

45. $-6(d - 3) = -d$ $3\frac{3}{5}$

46. $5 - 9w = 23$ **−2**

47. $\frac{m}{-5} + 6 = 31$ **−125**

48. $\frac{z - 7}{5} = -3$ **−8**

49. Sketch a reasonable graph for the temperature in the following statement. *In August, Joel enters his house and turns on the air conditioner.* (Lesson 1-9) **See margin.**

Evaluate each expression. (Lesson 1-2)

50. $12(5) - 6(4)$ **36**

51. $7(0.2 + 0.5) - 0.6$ **4.3**

52. $[6^2 - 3(2 + 5)] \div 5$ **3**

GET READY for the Next Lesson

PREREQUISITE SKILL Find each percent. (Pages 702–703)

53. Eighteen is what percent of 60? **30%**

54. What percent of 14 is 4.34? **31%**

55. Six is what percent of 15? **40%**

56. What percent of 2 is 8? **400%**

Main Ideas

- Find percents of increase and decrease.
- Solve problems involving percents of change.

 Standard 5.0 Students solve multistep problems, including word problems, involving linear equations and linear inequalities **in one variable and provide justification for each step.** (Key, CAHSEE)

New Vocabulary

percent of change
percent of increase
percent of decrease

GET READY for the Lesson

Phone companies began using area codes in 1947. The graph shows the number of area codes in use in different years. The growth in the number of area codes can be described by using a percent of change.

Area Codes on the Rise

84 1947 · 171 1996 · 285 1999 · 298 2004

Source: Associated Press

Percent of Change When an increase or decrease is expressed as a percent, the percent is called the **percent of change**. If the new number is greater than the original number, the percent of change is a **percent of increase**. If the new number is less than the original, the percent of change is a **percent of decrease**.

Review Vocabulary

Percent Proportion
percent proportion:

$$\frac{\text{part}}{\text{base}} = \frac{\text{percent}}{100}$$

(page 702)

EXAMPLE Find Percent of Change

 State whether each percent of change is a percent of increase or a percent of decrease. Then find each percent of change.

a. original: $25
new: $28

Since the new amount is greater than the original, this is a percent of increase. Find the *amount* of change.

$$28 - 25 = 3$$

Use the original number, 25, as the base.

$$\text{change} \rightarrow \frac{3}{25} = \frac{r}{100} \leftarrow \text{original amount}$$
$$3(100) = 25(r)$$
$$300 = 25r$$
$$\frac{300}{25} = \frac{25r}{25}$$
$$12 = r$$

The percent of increase is 12%.

b. original: 30
new: 12

This is a percent of decrease because the new amount is less than the original. Find the amount of change.

$$30 - 12 = 18$$

Use the original number, 30, as the base.

$$\text{change} \rightarrow \frac{18}{30} = \frac{r}{100} \leftarrow \text{original amount}$$
$$18(100) = 30(r)$$
$$1800 = 30r$$
$$\frac{1800}{30} = \frac{30r}{30}$$
$$60 = r$$

The percent of decrease is 60%.

Lesson 2-7 Percent of Change **111**

---

1 Focus

Standards Alignment

Before Lesson 2-7
Convert fractions to decimals and percents from Standard 7NS1.3

Lesson 2-7
Solve multi-step problems involving linear equations and inequalities from Standard 5.0

After Lesson 2-7
Solve rate problems, work problems, and percent mixture problems from Standard 15.0

2 Teach

Scaffolding Questions

Have students read *Get Ready for the Lesson.*

Ask:

- What do the numbers 84, 171, 285 and 298 represent on the graph? The number 84 represents the number of area codes in 1947, 171 was the number in 1996, 285 was the number in 1999, and 298 was the number in 2004.

- Are these numbers percents? Why do you think so? No, these numbers are not percents because they are not followed by the percent sign.

Lesson 2-7 Resources

Chapter 2 Resource Masters

Lesson Reading Guide, p. 48 **BL OL ELL**
Study Guide and Intervention, pp. 49–50
BL OL ELL
Skills Practice, p. 51 **BL OL**
Practice, p. 52 **OL AL**
Word Problem Practice, p. 53 **OL AL**
Enrichment, p. 54 **OL AL**
Spreadsheet, p. 55 **OL AL**
Quiz 3, p. 74

Transparencies

5-Minute Check Transparency 2-7

Additional Print Resources

Noteables™ Interactive Study Notebook with Foldables™
Teaching Algebra with Manipulatives

Technology

ca.algebra1.com
Interactive Classroom CD-ROM
AssignmentWorks CD-ROM
Graphing Calculator Easy Files

Percent of Change

Example 1 shows how to determine if a percent of change is a percent of increase or a percent of decrease and how to find the percent of change.
Example 2 shows how to write a percent proportion and use it to solve a real-world problem.

 Formative Assessment

Use the Check Your Progress exercises after each example to determine students' understanding of concepts.

Additional Examples are also in:

• Noteables™ Interactive Study Notebook with Foldables™

• Interactive Classroom PowerPoint® Presentations

🌐 **Real-World Link**

On November 12, 1892, the Allegheny Athletic Association paid William "Pudge" Heffelfinger $500 to play football. This game is considered the start of professional football.

Source: *World Book Encyclopedia*

Cross-Curricular Project

🌐 **Math nline** A percent of increase or decrease can be used to describe trends in populations. Visit ca.algebra1.com to continue work on your project.

 ✓ CHECK Your Progress   1A. dec.; 55%   1B. inc.; 23%
1A. original: 66; new: 30   **1B.** original: 9.8; new: 12.1

🌐 **Real-World EXAMPLE**   Find the Missing Value

2 FOOTBALL The National Football League's (NFL) fields are 120 yards long. The Canadian Football League's (CFL) fields are 25% longer. How long is a CFL field?

Let ℓ = the length of a CFL field. Since 25% is a percent of increase, an NFL field is shorter than a CFL field. Therefore, $\ell - 120$ represents the change.

$$\begin{array}{ll} \text{change} \rightarrow \\ \text{original amount} \rightarrow \end{array} \dfrac{\ell - 120}{120} = \dfrac{25}{100} \qquad \text{Percent proportion}$$

$$(\ell - 120)(100) = 120(25) \qquad \text{Find the cross products.}$$

$$100\ell - 12,000 = 3000 \qquad \text{Distributive Property}$$

$$100\ell - 12,000 + 12,000 = 3000 + 12,000 \qquad \text{Add 12,000 to each side.}$$

$$100\ell = 15,000 \qquad \text{Simplify.}$$

$$\dfrac{100\ell}{100} = \dfrac{15,000}{100} \qquad \text{Divide each side by 100.}$$

$$\ell = 150 \qquad \text{Simplify.}$$

The length of the field used by the CFL is 150 yards.

 ✓ CHECK Your Progress

2. TUITION A recent percent of increase in tuition at Northwestern University was 5.4%. If the new cost is $29,940 per year, find the original cost per year. **$28,406**

🌐 **Personal Tutor at** ca.algebra1.com

Solve Problems Sales tax is a tax that is added to the cost of the item. It is an example of a percent of increase.

🌐 **Real-World EXAMPLE**

3 SALES TAX A concert ticket costs $45. If the sales tax is 6.25%, what is the total price of the ticket?

The tax is 6.25% of the price of the ticket.

6.25% of $45 = 0.0625 × 45   6.25% = 0.0625

= 2.8125   Use a calculator.

Round $2.8125 to $2.81. Add this amount to the original price.

$45.00 + $2.81 = $47.81   The total price of the ticket is $47.81.

✓ CHECK Your Progress

3. TAXES A new DVD costs $24.99. If the sales tax is 7.25%, what is the total cost? **$26.80**

Discount is the amount by which the regular price of an item is reduced. It is an example of a percent of decrease.

Pre-AP Activity   Use after Example 4

A DVD with an original price of $10 is in the 20% off bin. If another reduction of 50% is taken at the cash register, is the total reduction 70%? If not, find the actual reduction. No, the reduction is not 70%, it is an actual reduction of 40% off.

Real-World EXAMPLE

4 **DISCOUNT** A sweater is on sale for 35% off the original price. If the original price of the sweater is $38, what is the discounted price?

The discount is 35% of the original price.

35% of $38 = 0.35 × 38   35% = 0.35
            = 13.30   Use a calculator.

Subtract $13.30 from the original price.

$38.00 − $13.30 = $24.70   The discounted price of the sweater is $24.70.

✓CHECK Your Progress

4. **SALES** A picture frame originally priced at $14.89 is on sale for 40% off. What is the discounted price? **$8.93**

★ indicates multi-step problem

✓CHECK Your Understanding

State whether each percent of change is a percent of increase or a percent of decrease. Then find each percent of change. Round to the nearest whole percent.

Example 1
(p. 111)

1. original: 72
new: 36 **dec.; 50%**

2. original: 45
new: 50 **inc.; 11%**

3. original: 14 books
new: 16 books **inc.; 14%**

4. original: 150 T-shirts
new: 120 T-shirts **dec.; 20%**

Example 2
(p. 112)

★ **5.** **GEOGRAPHY** The distance from El Monte to Fresno is 211 miles. The distance from El Monte to Oakland is about 64.5% longer. To the nearest mile, what is the distance from El Monte to Oakland? **347 mi**

Find the total price of each item.

Example 3
(p. 112)

6. software: $39.50
sales tax: 6.5% **$42.07**

7. compact disc: $15.99
sales tax: 5.75% **$16.91**

Example 4
(p. 113)

Find the discounted price of each item.

8. jeans: $45.00
discount: 25% **$33.75**

9. book: $19.95
discount: 33% **$13.37**

Exercises

HOMEWORK HELP	
For Exercises	See Examples
10–17	1
18, 19	2
20–25	3
26–31	4

Exercise Levels
A: 10–31   B: 32–38
C: 39–42

State whether each percent of change is a percent of increase or a percent of decrease. Then find each percent of change. Round to the nearest whole percent.

10. original: 50
new: 70 **inc.; 40%**

11. original: 25
new: 18 **dec.; 28%**

12. original: 58
new: 152 **inc.; 162%**

13. original: 13.7
new: 40.2 **inc.; 193%**

14. original: 15.6 meters
new: 11.4 meters **dec.; 27%**

15. original: 132 students
new: 150 students **inc.; 14%**

16. original: $85
new: $90 **inc.; 6%**

17. original: 40 hours
new: 32.5 hours **dec.; 19%**

Math Online Extra Examples at ca.algebra1.com

Lesson 2-7 Percent of Change   **113**

Solve Problems

Example 3 shows how to solve real-world problems that deal with a percent of increase, such as sales tax. **Example 4** shows how to solve real-world problems that deal with a percent of decrease, such as a discounted price.

ADDITIONAL EXAMPLES

3 **SALES TAX** A meal for two at a restaurant costs $32.75. If the sales tax is 5%, what is the total price of the meal? $34.39

4 **DISCOUNT** A dog toy is on sale for 20% off the original price. If the original price of the toy is $3.80, what is the discounted price? $3.04

Preventing Errors

Remind students that to change a percent to a decimal they should move the decimal point two places to the left and drop the percent sign.

3 Practice

✓ Formative Assessment

Use Exercises 1–9 to check for understanding.

Use the chart at the bottom of this page to customize assignments for your students.

Odd/Even Assignments

Exercises 10–31 are structured so that students practice the same concepts whether they are assigned odd or even problems.

DIFFERENTIATED HOMEWORK OPTIONS

Level	Assignment	Two-Day Option	
BL Basic	10–31, 40–57	11–31 odd, 43, 44	10–30 even, 40–42, 45–57
OL Core	11–33 odd, 35–38, 40–57	10–31, 43, 44	32–38, 40–42, 45–57
AL Advanced /Pre-AP	32–44 (optional: 45–57)		

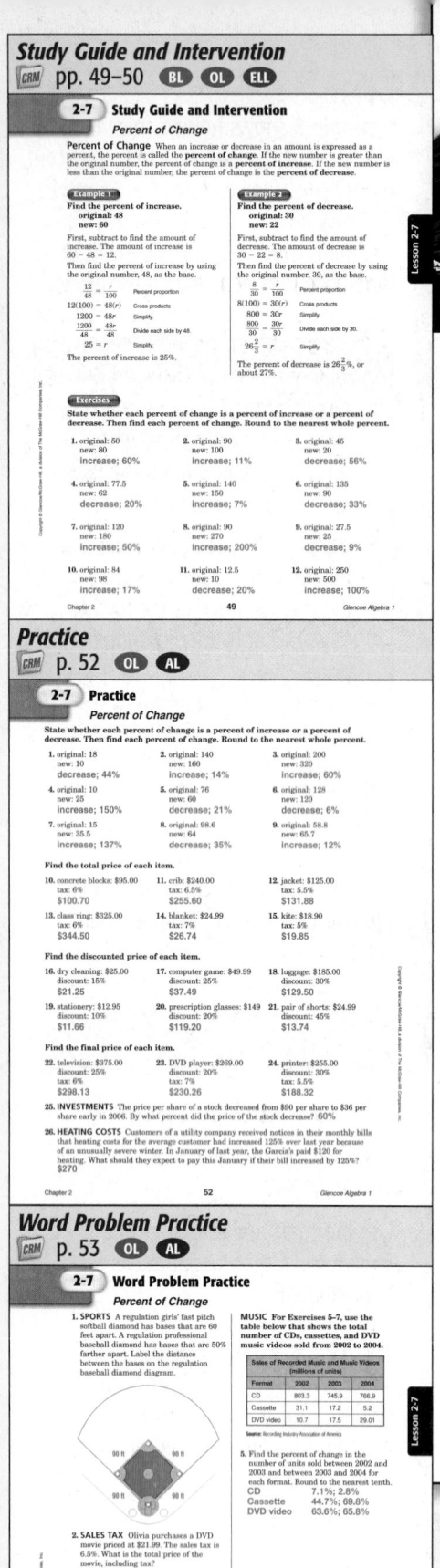

★ **18. EDUCATION** According to the Census Bureau, the average income of a person with a high school diploma is $27,351. The income of a person with a bachelor's degree is about 57% higher. What is the average income of a person with a bachelor's degree? **$42,941**

★ **19. BOATS** A 36-foot sailboat that is new costs 86% more than the same boat in good used condition. What is the cost of a new 36-foot sailboat? **$130,200**

Buying a Sailboat	
Type of Boat	**Cost ($)**
Used	70,000
New	x

Find the total price of each item.

20. umbrella: $14.00
tax: 5.5% **$14.77**

21. backpack: $35.00
tax: 7% **$37.45**

22. candle: $7.50
tax: 5.75% **$7.93**

23. hat: $18.50
tax: 6.25% **$19.66**

24. clock radio: $39.99
tax: 6.75% **$42.69**

25. sandals: $29.99
tax: 5.75% **$31.71**

Find the discounted price of each item.

26. shirt: $45.00
discount: 40% **$27.00**

27. socks: $6.00
discount: 20% **$4.80**

28. watch: $37.55
discount: 35% **$24.41**

29. gloves: $24.25
discount: 33% **$16.25**

30. suit: $175.95
discount: 45% **$96.77**

31. coat: $79.99
discount: 30% **$55.99**

Find the final price of each item.

★ **32.** lamp: $120.00
discount: 20%
tax: 6% **$101.76**

★ **33.** dress: $70.00
discount: 30%
tax: 7% **$52.43**

★ **34.** camera: $58.00
discount: 25%
tax: 6.5% **$46.33**

★ **35. MILITARY** In 2000, the United States had 2.65 million active-duty military personnel. In 2004, there were 1.41 million active-duty military personnel. What was the percent of decrease? Round to the nearest whole percent. **47%**

★ **36. THEME PARKS** In 2003, 162.3 million people visited theme parks in the United States. In 2004, the number of visitors increased by about 4%. About how many people visited theme parks in the United States in 2004? **168.8 million**

★ **37. ANALYZE TABLES** What are the projected 2050 populations for each country in the table? Which is projected to be the most populous? **China: about 1.52 billion people; India: about 1.53 billion people; United States: about 0.39 billion people; India**

Country	1997 Population (billions)	Projected Percent of Increase for 2050
China	1.24	22.6%
India	0.97	57.8%
United States	0.27	44.4%

Source: USA TODAY

38. RESEARCH Use the Internet or other reference to find the tuition for the last several years at a college of your choice. Find the percent of change for the tuition during these years. Predict the tuition for the year you plan to graduate from high school. **See students' work.**

H.O.T. Problems

39. CHALLENGE Is the following equation *sometimes*, *always*, or *never* true? Explain your reasoning. **See margin.**
$$x\% \text{ of } y = y\% \text{ of } x$$

40. OPEN ENDED Give a counterexample to the statement *The percent of change must always be less than 100%*. **See margin.**

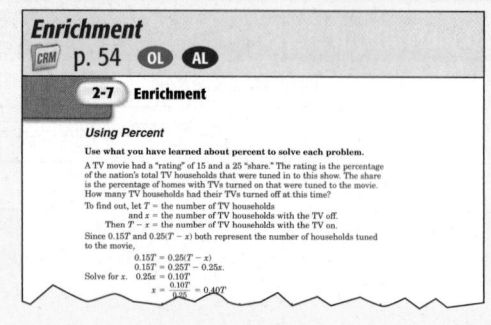

41. FIND THE ERROR Laura and Cory are writing proportions to find the percent of change if the original number is 20 and the new number is 30. Who is correct? Explain your reasoning.

Laura
Amount of change: 30 - 20 = 10
$\dfrac{10}{20} = \dfrac{r}{100}$

Cory
Amount of change: 30 - 20 = 10
$\dfrac{10}{30} = \dfrac{r}{100}$

42. *Writing in Math* Use the data on page 111 to find the percent of increase in the number of area codes from 1999 to 2004. Explain why knowing a percent of change can be more informative than knowing how much the quantity changed. **See margin.**

 **STANDARDS PRACTICE** 7NS1.6, 7MG2.1

43. The number of students at Franklin High School increased from 840 to 910 over a 5-year period. What was the percent of increase? **A**

  A 8.3%   **C** 18.5%

  B 14.0%   **D** 92.3%

44. REVIEW The rectangle has a perimeter of P centimeters. Which equation could be used to find the length of the rectangle? **J**

 2.4 cm

  F $P = 2.4\ell$ **H** $P = 2.4 + 2\ell$

  G $P = 4.8 + \ell$ **J** $P = 4.8 + 2\ell$

Spiral Review

Solve each proportion. (Lesson 2-6)

45. $\dfrac{a}{45} = \dfrac{3}{15}$ **9**   **46.** $\dfrac{2}{3} = \dfrac{8}{d}$ **12**   **47.** $\dfrac{5.2}{10.4} = \dfrac{t}{48}$ **24**

Solve each equation. Check your solution. (Lesson 2-5)

48. $6n + 3 = -3$ **−1**   **49.** $7 + 5c = -23$ **−6**   **50.** $18 = 4a - 2$ **5**

51. SALES As a salesperson, Mr. Goetz is paid a monthly salary and a commission on sales, as shown in the table. How much must Mr. Goetz sell to earn $2000 this month? (Lesson 2-4) **$75,000**

Mr. Goetz's Income	
Monthly salary	$500
Commission on sales	2%

Evaluate each expression. (Lesson 1-2)

52. $(3 + 6) \div 3^2$ **1**   **53.** $6(12 - 7.5) - 7$ **20**   **54.** $20 \div 4 \cdot 8 \div 10$ **4**

GET READY for the Next Lesson

PREREQUISITE SKILL Solve each equation. Check your solution. (Lesson 2-5)

55. $7y + 7 = 3y - 5$ **−3**   **56.** $7(d - 3) - 2 = 5$ **4**   **57.** $-8 = 4 - 2(a - 5)$ **11**

Additional Answers

39. always; $x\%$ of $y \Rightarrow \dfrac{x}{100} = \dfrac{P}{y}$ or $P = \dfrac{xy}{100}$; $y\%$ of $x \Rightarrow \dfrac{y}{100} = \dfrac{P}{x}$ or $P = \dfrac{xy}{100}$

40. Sample answer: If the original number is 10 and the new number is 30, the percent proportion is $\dfrac{30 - 10}{10} = \dfrac{r}{100}$ and the percent of change is 200%, which is greater than 100%.

Additional Answer

42. Sample answer: Find the amount of change and express this change as a percent of the original number. To find the percent of increase, first find the amount of increase. Then find what percent the amount of increase is of the original number. The percent of increase from 1996 to 1999 is about 5%. An increase of 100 is a very large increase if the original number is 50, but a very small increase if the original number is 100,000. The percent of change will indicate whether the change is large or small relative to the original.

READING MATH

1 Focus

Ask:
What words can act as clues that help you to translate a word problem into an equation? *Sample answers: sum, difference, product, dividend, more than, less than, etc.*

2 Teach

Using Clue Words Emphasize that the clue words *is* and *of* tell **how** to write the equation in the sentence method for solving percent problems. In the proportion method, the clue words tell **where** to place the numbers.

Have students work through the example. Point out that clue words such as *percent of decrease* or *percent of increase* indicate a percent of change problem, so they would use the proportion method to solve the problem. Ask students to identify other clue words or phrases that provide important information in the example.

Have students complete Exercises 1–3.

3 Assess

Ask students to summarize each method and discuss which they prefer.

ELL English Language Learners may benefit from working in small groups. Have one member of each group explain the key concepts in his or her native language. Have the other members then explain the key concepts in English.

Sentence Method and Proportion Method

Standard 5.0 Students solve multistep problems, including word problems, involving **linear equations** and linear inequalities **in one variable and provide justification for each step.** (Key, CAHSEE)

Recall that you can solve percent problems using two different methods. With either method, it is helpful to use "clue" words such as *is* and *of*. In the sentence method, *is* means equals and *of* means multiply. With the proportion method, the "clue" words indicate where to place the numbers in the proportion.

Sentence Method

15% of 40 is what number?

$0.15 \cdot 40 = ?$

Proportion Method

15% of 40 is what number?

$$\frac{(is)\ P}{(of)\ B} = \frac{R(percent)}{100} \rightarrow \frac{P}{40} = \frac{15}{100}$$

You can use the proportion method to solve percent of change problems. In this case, use the proportion $\frac{difference}{original} = \frac{\%}{100}$. When reading a percent of change problem, or any other word problem, look for the important numerical information.

Example In life skills class, Kishi heated <u>20 milliliters of water</u>. She let the water boil for 10 minutes. Afterward, only <u>17 milliliters of water remained</u>, due to evaporation. What is the <u>percent of decrease</u> in the amount of water?

$$\frac{difference}{original} = \frac{\%}{100} \rightarrow \frac{20 - 17}{20} = \frac{r}{100} \quad \text{Percent proportion}$$

$$\frac{3}{20} = \frac{r}{100} \quad \text{Simplify.}$$

$$3(100) = 20(r) \quad \text{Find the cross products.}$$

$$300 = 20r \quad \text{Simplify.}$$

$$\frac{300}{20} = \frac{20r}{20} \quad \text{Divide each side by 20.}$$

$$15 = r \quad \text{Simplify.}$$

There was a 15% decrease in the amount of water.

Reading to Learn

Give the original number and the amount of change. Then write and solve a percent proportion.

1. Monsa needed to lose weight for wrestling. At the start of the season, he weighed 166 pounds. By the end of the season, he weighed 158 pounds. What is the percent of decrease in Monsa's weight? **about 5%**

2. On Carla's last Algebra test, she scored 94 points out of 100. On her first Algebra test, she scored 75 points out of 100. What is the percent of increase in her score? **about 25%**

3. An online bookstore tracks daily book sales. A certain book sold 12,476 copies on Monday. After the book was mentioned on a national news program, sales were 37,884 on Tuesday. What is the percent of increase from Monday to Tuesday? **204%**

Main Ideas

- Solve equations for given variables.
- Use formulas to solve real-world problems.

Standard 5.0 Students solve multistep problems, including word problems, involving linear equations and linear inequalities in one variable and provide justification for each step. (Key, CAHSEE)

New Vocabulary

dimensional analysis

> **GET READY for the Lesson**

Suppose the designer of the Magnum XL-200 decided to adjust the height of the second hill so that the coaster would have a speed of 49 feet per second when it reached the top. If we ignore friction, the equation $g(195 - h) = \frac{1}{2}v^2$ can be used to find the height of the second hill. In this equation, g represents the acceleration due to gravity (32 feet per second squared), h is the height of the second hill, and v is the velocity of the coaster when it reaches the top of the second hill.

Solve for Variables Some equations such as the one above contain more than one variable. It is often useful to solve these equations for one of the variables.

> **EXAMPLE** Solve an Equation for a Specific Variable

1 Solve $3x - 4y = 7$ for y.

$3x - 4y = 7$	Original equation
$3x - 4y - 3x = 7 - 3x$	Subtract $3x$ from each side.
$-4y = 7 - 3x$	Simplify.
$\dfrac{-4y}{-4} = \dfrac{7 - 3x}{-4}$	Divide each side by -4.
$y = \dfrac{7 - 3x}{-4}$ or $\dfrac{3x - 7}{4}$	Simplify.

The value of y is $\dfrac{3x - 7}{4}$.

> **CHECK Your Progress**

Solve each equation for the variable indicated.

1A. $15 = 3n + 6p$, for n $5 - 2p$ **1B.** $\dfrac{k - 2}{5} = 11j$, for k $55j + 2$

It is sometimes helpful to use the Distributive Property to isolate the variable for which you are solving an equation or formula.

1 Focus

Standards Alignment

Before Lesson 2-8
Write an expression, an equation, an inequality, or a system that represents a verbal description from Standard 7AF1.1

Lesson 2-8
Solve multi-step problems involving linear equations and inequalities from Standard 5.0

After Lesson 2-8
Solve equations and inequalities involving absolute value from Standard 2A1.0

2 Teach

Scaffolding Questions Have students read *Get Ready for the Lesson.*
Ask:

- What are the known quantities in the roller coaster equation? *g* is the acceleration due to gravity; *v* is the velocity of the roller coaster at the top of the second hill
- What is the unknown quantity in the roller coaster equation? *h*, the height of the second hill
- Can the problem about the height of the second hill be solved with the given information? Yes, the problem can be solved because the values for *g* and *v* are given.

Lesson 2-8 Resources

Chapter 2 Resource Masters

Lesson Reading Guide, p. 56 **BL** **OL** **ELL**
Study Guide and Intervention, pp. 57–58 **BL** **OL** **ELL**
Skills Practice, p. 59 **BL** **OL**
Practice, p. 60 **OL** **AL**
Word Problem Practice, p. 61 **OL** **AL**
Enrichment, p. 62 **OL** **AL**

Transparencies

5-Minute Check Transparency 2-8

Additional Print Resources

Noteables™ Interactive Study Notebook with Foldables™
Teaching Algebra with Manipulatives

Technology

ca.algebra1.com
Interactive Classroom CD-ROM
AssignmentWorks CD-ROM
Graphing Calculator Easy Files

Solve For Variables

Example 1 shows how to solve an equation with more than one variable for a specific variable. **Example 2** shows how the Distributive Property can be used to isolate the variable for which you are solving an equation or formula.

 Formative Assessment

Use the Check Your Progress exercises after each example to determine students' understanding of concepts.

ADDITIONAL EXAMPLES

1 Solve $5b + 12c = 9$ for b.

$b = \dfrac{9 - 12c}{5}$

2 Solve $7x - 2z = 4 - xy$ for x.

$x = \dfrac{4 + 2z}{7 + y}$

Additional Examples are also in:

- Noteables™ Interactive Study Notebook with Foldables™
- Interactive Classroom PowerPoint Presentations®

Use Formulas

Example 3 shows how to solve for a specific variable in a formula for solving a real-world problem. **Example 4** shows how to use dimensional analysis when using a formula to solve a real-world problem.

ADDITIONAL EXAMPLE

3 **FUEL ECONOMY** A car's fuel economy E (miles per gallon) is given by the formula $E = \dfrac{m}{g}$, where m is the number of miles driven and g is the number of gallons of fuel used.

a. Solve the formula for m.

$m = Eg$

b. If Claudia's car has an average fuel consumption of 30 miles per gallon and she used 9.5 gallons, how far did she drive?

285 mi

---

2 Solve $2m - t = sm + 5$ for m.

$2m - t = sm + 5$	Original equation
$2m - t - sm = sm + 5 - sm$	Subtract sm from each side.
$2m - t - sm = 5$	Simplify.
$2m - t - sm + t = 5 + t$	Add t to each side.
$2m - sm = 5 + t$	Simplify.
$m(2 - s) = 5 + t$	Use the Distributive Property.
$\dfrac{m(2 - s)}{2 - s} = \dfrac{5 + t}{2 - s}$	Divide each side by $2 - s$.
$m = \dfrac{5 + t}{2 - s}$	Simplify.

The value of m is $\dfrac{5 + t}{2 - s}$. Since division by 0 is undefined, $2 - s \neq 0$ or $s \neq 2$.

✓CHECK Your Progress

Solve each equation for the variable indicated.

2A. $\dfrac{5c + 1}{2}$ **2A.** $d + 5c = 3d - 1$, for d **2B.** $6q - 18 = qr + s$, for q $\dfrac{18 + s}{6 - r}$

Personal Tutor at ca.algebra1.com

Use Formulas Sometimes solving a formula for a specific variable will help you solve the problem.

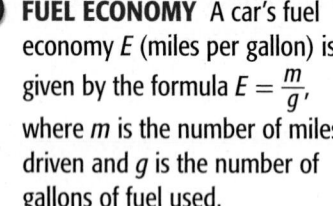

Real-World Link

The largest yo-yo in the world is 32.7 feet in circumference. It was launched by crane from a height of 189 feet.

Source: www.guinnessworldrecords.com

Real-World EXAMPLE

3 **YO-YOS** Use the information about the largest yo-yo at the left. The formula for the circumference of a circle is $C = 2\pi r$, where C represents circumference and r represents radius.

a. Solve the formula for r.

$C = 2\pi r$	Circumference formula
$\dfrac{C}{2\pi} = \dfrac{2\pi r}{2\pi}$	Divide each side by 2π.
$\dfrac{C}{2\pi} = r$	Simplify.

b. Find the radius of the yo-yo.

$\dfrac{C}{2\pi} = r$	Formula for radius
$\dfrac{32.7}{2\pi} = r$	$C = 32.7$
$5.2 \approx r$	The yo-yo has a radius of about 5.2 feet.

✓CHECK Your Progress

The formula for the volume of a rectangular prism is $V = \ell w h$, where ℓ is the length, w is the width, and h is the height.

3A. Solve the formula for w. $\dfrac{V}{\ell h} = w$

3B. Find the width of a rectangular prism that has a volume of 79.04 cubic centimeters, a length of 5.2 centimeters, and a height of 4 centimeters. **3.8 cm**

Tips for New Teachers

Preventing Errors

Sometimes it is helpful for students to circle or highlight the term containing the requested variable so they can remember which variable they are trying to isolate.

Additional Answer (Check Your Progress)

4A. $v = \dfrac{s - \frac{1}{2}at^2}{t}$.

When using formulas, you may want to use **dimensional analysis**, which is the process of carrying units throughout a computation.

Real-World EXAMPLE

4 PHYSICAL SCIENCE The formula $s = \frac{1}{2}at^2$ represents the distance s that a free-falling object will fall near a planet or the Moon in a given time t. In the formula, a represents the acceleration due to gravity.

a. Solve the formula for a.

$s = \frac{1}{2}at^2$ Original formula

$\frac{2}{t^2}(s) = \frac{2}{t^2}\left(\frac{1}{2}at^2\right)$ Multiply each side by $\frac{2}{t^2}$.

$\frac{2s}{t^2} = a$ Simplify.

b. A free-falling object near the Moon drops 20.5 meters in 5 seconds. What is the value of a for the Moon?

$a = \frac{2s}{t^2}$ Formula for a

$= \frac{2(20.5\text{ m})}{(5\text{ s})^2}$ $s = 20.5$ m and $t = 5$ s.

$= \frac{1.64\text{ m}}{s^2}$ or 1.64 m/s^2 Use a calculator.

Acceleration due to gravity on the Moon is 1.64 meters per second squared.

✓CHECK Your Progress

The formula $s = vt + \frac{1}{2}at^2$ represents the distance s an object travels with an initial velocity v, time t, and constant rate of acceleration a.

4A. Solve the formula for v. **See margin.**

4B. A sports car accelerates at a rate of 8 ft/s^2 and travels 100 feet in about 2.8 seconds. What is the initial velocity to the nearest tenth? **24.5 ft/s**

★ indicates multi-step problem

✓CHECK Your Understanding

Examples 1, 2
(pp. 117–118)

Solve each equation or formula for the variable specified.

1. $-3x + b = 6x$, for x $x = \frac{b}{9}$

2. $4z + b = 2z + c$, for z $z = \frac{c - b}{2}$

3. $\frac{y + a}{3} = c$, for y $y = 3c - a$

4. $p = a(b + c)$, for a $a = \frac{p}{b + c}$

Example 3
(p. 118)

GEOMETRY For Exercises 5 and 6, use the formula for the area of a triangle.

5. Solve the formula for h. $h = \frac{2A}{b}$

6. What is the height of a triangle with an area of 28 square feet and a base of 8 feet? **7 ft**

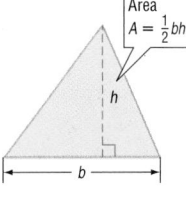
Area
$A = \frac{1}{2}bh$

Example 4
(p. 119)

7. SWIMMING A swimmer swims about one third of a lap per minute. At this rate, how many minutes would it take to swim 8 laps? (*Hint:* Use $d = rt$.) **24 min**

Lesson 2-8 Solving for a Specific Variable   **119**

Lesson 2-8 Solving for a Specific Variable   **119**

ADDITIONAL EXAMPLE

4 GEOMETRY The formula for the volume of a cylinder is $V = \pi r^2 h$, where r is the radius of the cylinder and h is the height.

a. Solve the formula for h.

$h = \frac{V}{\pi r^2}$

b. What is the height of a cylindrical swimming pool that has a radius of 12 feet and a volume of 1810 cubic feet? about 4 ft

Tips for New Teachers   **Preventing Errors**

Encourage students to write the units for values they are substituting into an equation. Writing the units will help them to determine the reasonableness of an answer. If the problem asks for "miles" and they have "hours," they will know something is wrong.

Focus on Mathematical Content

Using Formulas Many real-world problems require the use of formulas. Solving a formula for a specific variable may help to solve the problem.

3 Practice

✓ Formative Assessment

Use Exercises 1–7 to check for understanding.

Use the chart at the bottom of this page to customize assignments for your students.

Odd/Even Assignments

Exercises 8–25 are structured so that students practice the same concepts whether they are assigned odd or even problems.

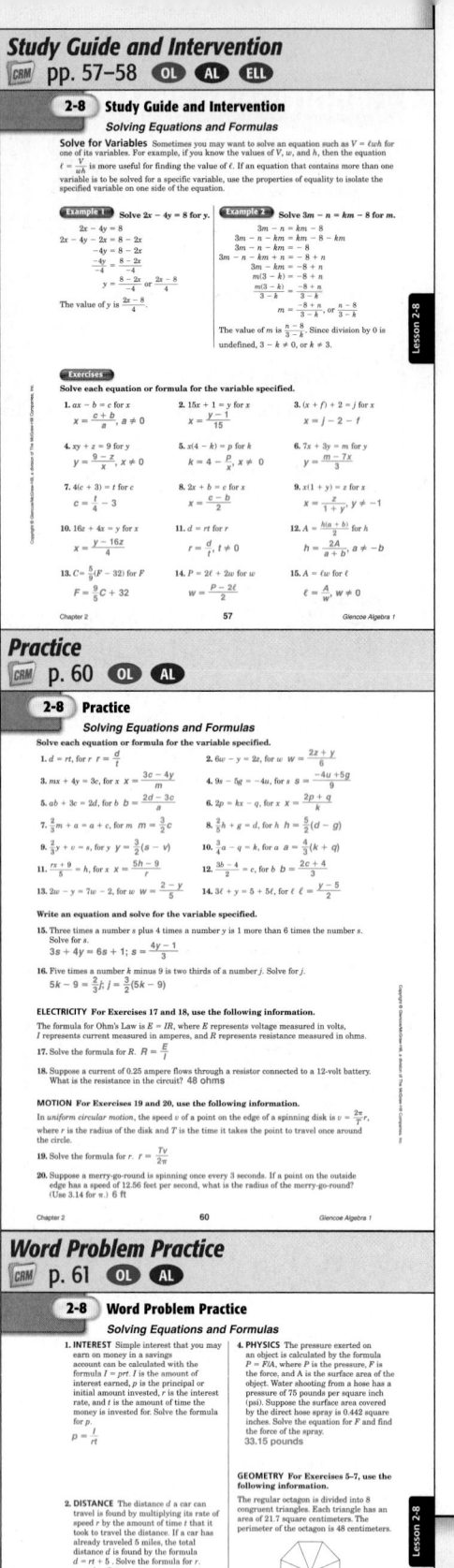

Solve each equation or formula for the variable specified.

HOMEWORK HELP	
For Exercises	See Examples
8–15	1
16–21	2
22–25	3, 4

Exercise Levels
A: 8–25
B: 26–34
C: 35–38

8. $y = mx + b$, for m $m = \dfrac{y - b}{x}$

9. $v = r + at$, for a $a = \dfrac{v - r}{t}$

10. $km + 5x = 6y$, for m **See margin.**

11. $4b - 5 = -t$, for b **See margin.**

12. $c = \dfrac{3}{4}y + b$, for y $y = \dfrac{4}{3}(c - b)$

13. $\dfrac{3}{5}m + a = b$, for m $m = \dfrac{5}{3}(b - a)$

14. $\dfrac{3ax - n}{5} = -4$, for x $x = \dfrac{n - 20}{3a}$

15. $\dfrac{by + 2}{3} = c$, for y $y = \dfrac{3c - 2}{b}$

16. $5g + h = g$, for g $g = -\dfrac{h}{4}$

17. $8t - r = 12t$, for t $t = -\dfrac{r}{4}$

18. $3y + z = am - 4y$, for y **See margin.**

19. $9a - 2b = c + 4a$, for a $a = \dfrac{2b + c}{5}$

20. $at + b = ar - c$, for a $a = \dfrac{c + b}{r - t}$

21. $2g - m = 5 - gh$, for g $g = \dfrac{5 + m}{2 + h}$

GEOMETRY For Exercises 22 and 23, use the formula for the area of a trapezoid.

22. Solve the formula for h. $h = \dfrac{2A}{a + b}$

23. What is the height of a trapezoid with an area of 60 square meters and bases of 8 meters and 12 meters?   **6 m**

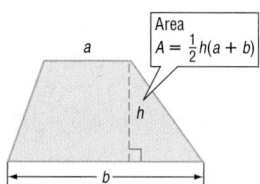

Area $A = \dfrac{1}{2}h(a + b)$

WORK For Exercises 24 and 25, use the following information.

The formula $s = \dfrac{w - 10e}{m}$ is often used by placement services to find keyboarding speeds. In the formula, s represents the speed in words per minute, w represents the number of words typed, e represents the number of errors, and m represents the number of minutes typed.

24. Solve the formula for e. $e = \dfrac{w - sm}{10}$

25. If Mateo typed 410 words in 5 minutes and received a keyboard speed of 76 words per minute, how many errors did he make?   **3 errors**

Solve each equation or formula for the variable specified.   **26–28. See margin.**

26. $S = \dfrac{n}{2}(A + t)$, for A

27. $p(t + 1) = -2$, for t

28. $\dfrac{5x + y}{a} = 2$, for a

Write an equation and solve for the variable specified.

29. Seven less than a number t equals another number r plus 6. Solve for t.   **See mar**

30. Five minus twice a number p equals 6 times another number q plus 1. Solve for p. $5 - 2p = 6q + 1$; $p = 2 - 3q$

31. Five eighths of a number x is 3 more than one half of another number y. Solve for y. $\dfrac{5}{8}x = \dfrac{1}{2}y + 3$; $y = \dfrac{5}{4}x - 6$

DANCING For Exercises 32 and 33, use the following information.

The formula $P = \dfrac{1.2W}{H^2}$ represents the amount of pressure exerted on the floor by a dancer's heel. In this formula, P is the pressure in pounds per square inch, W is the weight of a person wearing the shoe in pounds, and H is the width of the heel of the shoe in inches.

32. Solve the formula for W. $W = \dfrac{H^2 P}{1.2}$

33. Find the weight of the dancer if the heel is 3 inches wide and the pressure exerted is 30 pounds per square inch.   **225 lb**

120   Chapter 2 Solving Linear Equations

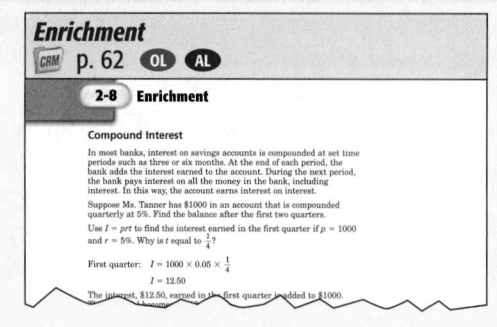

BL = *Below Grade Level*
OL = *On Grade Level*
AL = *Above Grade Level*
ELL = *English Language Learner*

Additional pages not shown:

CRM **Lesson Reading Guide**, p. 56   BL OL ELL

CRM **Skills Practice**, p. 59   BL OL

EXTRA **PRACTICE**
See pages 722, 745.
Math Online
Self-Check Quiz at
ca.algebra1.com

34. PACKAGING The Yummy Ice Cream Company wants to package ice cream in cylindrical containers that have a volume of 5453 cubic centimeters. The marketing department decides the diameter of the base of the containers should be 20 centimeters. How tall should the containers be? (Hint: $V = \pi r^2 h$) **about 17.4 cm**

Volume = 5453 cm³
20 cm

H.O.T. Problems

35. CHALLENGE Write a formula for the area of the arrow. Describe how you found it. **See margin.**

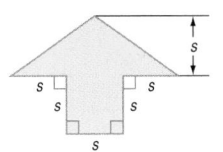

36. *t* can be any number except 2 because the denominator cannot equal zero.

36. REASONING Describe the possible values of *t* if $s = \dfrac{r}{t-2}$. Explain your reasoning.

37. Sample answer for a triangle:
$A = \frac{1}{2}bh$; $b = \dfrac{2A}{h}$

37. OPEN ENDED Write a formula for *A*, the area of a geometric figure such as a triangle or rectangle. Then solve the formula for a variable other than *A*.

38. *Writing in Math* Use the information on page 117 to explain how equations are used to design roller coasters. Include a list of steps you could use to solve the equation for *h*, and the height of the second hill of the roller coaster. **See margin.**

STANDARDS PRACTICE 5.0, 7MG2.1

39. If $2x + y = 5$, what is the value of $4x$? **B**

  A $10 - y$

  B $10 - 2y$

  C $\dfrac{5-y}{2}$

  D $\dfrac{10-y}{2}$

40. REVIEW What is the base of the triangle if the area is 56 meters squared? **H**

  F 4 m

  G 8 m

  H 16 m

  J 28 m

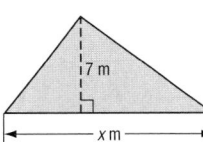
7 m
x m

Spiral Review

★ **41. FOOD** In order for a food to be marked "reduced fat," it must have at least 25% less fat than the same full-fat food. If one ounce of reduced-fat cheese has 7.5 grams of fat, what is the least amount of fat in one ounce of regular cheese? (Lesson 2-7) **10 g**

Solve each proportion. (Lesson 2-6)

42. $\dfrac{2}{9} = \dfrac{5}{a}$ **22.5**

43. $\dfrac{15}{32} = \dfrac{t}{8}$ **3.75**

44. $\dfrac{x+1}{8} = \dfrac{3}{4}$ **5**

GET READY for the Next Lesson

PREREQUISITE SKILL Use the Distributive Property to rewrite each expression without parentheses. (Lesson 1-5) **47.** $-21a - 7b$

45. $6(2-t)$ **12 − 6t**
46. $(5+2m)3$ **15 + 6m**
47. $-7(3a+b)$
48. $\frac{2}{3}(6h-9)$ **4h − 6**

Ticket Out the Door Have students pick a formula that was not used in this lesson, perhaps from science class, and explain the variables in the formula and what the formula is used to find. Have students solve the formula for a different variable.

FOLDABLES **Foldables™**
Study Organizer **Follow-Up**
Have students use the index cards to record notes on what they have learned about solving equations and formulas. Students should include information like that found in the lesson examples.

Additional Answers

10. $m = \dfrac{6y - 5x}{k}$

11. $b = \dfrac{5-t}{4}$

18. $y = \dfrac{am - z}{7}$

26. $A = \dfrac{2S - nt}{n}$

27. $t = \dfrac{-2 - p}{p}$

28. $a = \dfrac{5x + y}{2}$

29. $t - 7 = r + 6$; $t = r + 13$

35. Sample answer: $A = \frac{5}{2}s^2$; the area of the square is s^2 and the area of the triangle is $\frac{1}{2}(3s)(s)$ or $\frac{3}{2}s^2$. So, the total area is $s^2 + \frac{3}{2}s^2$ or $\frac{5}{2}s^2$.

38. Sample answer: Equations from physics can be used to determine the height needed to produce the desired results. Use the following steps to solve for *h*. (1) Use the Distributive Property to write the equation in the form $195g - hg = \frac{1}{2}mv^2$. (2) Subtract $195g$ from each side. (3) Divide each side by $-g$. The second hill should be 157 ft.

Pre-AP Activity Use as an Extension

Write $\dfrac{1}{R} = \dfrac{1}{a} + \dfrac{1}{b}$ on the board. Tell students that the total resistance *R* in an electrical circuit consisting of two resistances of *a* ohms and *b* ohms connected in parallel is given by this equation. Ask students to explain how to solve this formula for *R*.

Multiply each side by *R*. $R\left(\dfrac{1}{R}\right) = \left(\dfrac{1}{a} + \dfrac{1}{b}\right)R$. Divide each side by $\dfrac{1}{a} + \dfrac{1}{b}$. $R = \dfrac{1}{\frac{1}{a} + \frac{1}{b}}$ or $\dfrac{ab}{b + a}$

 **Weighted Averages**

1 Focus

Standards Alignment

Before Lesson 2-9
Solve multi-step problems involving rate, speed, distance and time from ⊶ Standard 7AF4.2

Lesson 2-9
Solve rate, work and percent mixture problems from Standard 15.0

After Lesson 2-9
Can recognize and graph a circle, ellipse, parabola, or hyperbola. from Standard 2A17.0

2 Teach

Scaffolding Questions Have students read *Get Ready for the Lesson.*
Ask:

- How would you find the unweighted average of the two scores? Add the two scores and divide the sum by the number of scores (2).
- What is the unweighted average? 5.65
- How is the weighted average similar to adding another score? Since the score for the long program is counted twice and the sum is divided by three, it is as if a third score has been added before the average is taken.

(continued on the next page)

Lesson 2-9 Resources

Chapter 2 Resource Masters
Lesson Reading Guide, p. 63
Study Guide and Intervention, pp. 64–65
Skills Practice, p. 66
Practice, p. 67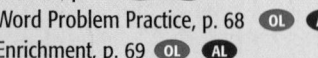
Word Problem Practice, p. 68 OL AL
Enrichment, p. 69 OL AL
Quiz 4, p. 74

Transparencies
5-Minute Check Transparency 2-9
Additional Print Resources
Noteables™ Interactive Study Notebook with Foldables™
Teaching Algebra with Manipulatives

Technology
ca.algebra1.com
Interactive Classroom CD-ROM
AssignmentWorks CD-ROM
Graphing Calculator Easy Files

Main Ideas
- Solve mixture problems.
- Solve uniform motion problems.

 Standard 15.0 Students apply algebraic techniques to solve rate problems, work problems, and percent mixture problems. (Key, CAHSEE)

New Vocabulary
weighted average
mixture problem
uniform motion problem

 GET READY for the Lesson

In an individual figure skating competition, the score for the long program is worth twice the score for the short program. Suppose a skater scores 5.5 in the short program and 5.8 in the long program. The final score is determined using a weighted average.

$$\frac{5.5(1) + 5.8(2)}{1 + 2} = \frac{5.5 + 11.6}{3}$$

$$= \frac{17.1}{3} \text{ or } 5.7 \quad \text{The final score would be 5.7.}$$

Mixture Problems The skater's average score is an example of a weighted average. The **weighted average** M of a set of data is the sum of the product of the number of units and the value per unit divided by the sum of the number of units. **Mixture problems**, in which two or more parts are combined into a whole, are solved using weighted averages.

Real-World EXAMPLE Prices

1 **TRAIL MIX** How many pounds of mixed nuts selling for $4.75 per pound should be mixed with 10 pounds of dried fruit selling for $5.50 per pound to obtain a trail mix that sells for $4.95 per pound?

Let $w =$ the number of pounds of mixed nuts. Make a table.

	Units (lb)	Price per Unit (lb)	Total Price
Dried Fruit	10	$5.50	5.50(10)
Mixed Nuts	w	$4.75	4.75w
Trail Mix	10 + w	$4.95	4.95(10 + w)

Price of dried fruit	plus	price of nuts	equals	price of trail mix.
5.50(10)	+	4.75w	=	4.95(10 + w)

$5.50(10) + 4.75w = 4.95(10 + w)$	Original equation
$55.00 + 4.75w = 49.50 + 4.95w$	Distributive Property
$55.00 + 4.75w - 4.75w = 49.50 + 4.95w - 4.75w$	Subtract 4.75w from each side.
$55.00 = 49.50 + 0.20w$	Simplify.
$55.00 - 49.50 = 49.50 + 0.20w - 49.50$	Subtract 49.50 from each side.
$5.50 = 0.20w$	Simplify.
$\dfrac{5.50}{0.20} = \dfrac{0.20w}{0.20}$	Divide each side by 0.20.
$27.5 = w$	Simplify.

27.5 pounds of mixed nuts should be used for the trail mix.

1. **COFFEE** How many pounds of coffee beans that sell for $9.50 per pound should be mixed with 2 pounds of coffee beans that sell for $11.75 per pound to obtain a mix that sells for $10 per pound? **7 lb**

Percent problems can also be solved using weighted averages.

 Real-World EXAMPLE **Percent Mixture Problems**

2 **SCIENCE** A chemistry experiment calls for a 30% solution of copper sulfate. Kendra has 40 milliliters of 25% solution. How many milliliters of 60% solution should she add to make a 30% solution?

Let x = the amount of 60% solution to be added. Make a table.

	Amount of Solution (mL)	Amount of Copper Sulfate
25% Solution	40	0.25(40)
60% Solution	x	0.60x
30% Solution	40 + x	0.30(40 + x)

Write and solve an equation using the information in the table.

Amount of copper sulfate in 25% solution	plus	amount of copper sulfate in 60% solution	equals	amount of copper sulfate in 30% solution.
0.25(40)	+	0.60x	=	0.30(40 + x)

$0.25(40) + 0.60x = 0.30(40 + x)$	Original equation
$10 + 0.60x = 12 + 0.30x$	Distributive Property
$10 + 0.60x - 0.30x = 12 + 0.30x - 0.30x$	Subtract 0.30x from each side.
$10 + 0.30x = 12$	Simplify.
$10 - 0.30x - 10 = 12 - 10$	Subtract 10 from each side.
$0.30x = 2$	Simplify.
$\dfrac{0.30x}{0.30} = \dfrac{2}{0.30}$	Divide each side by 0.30.
$x \approx 6.67$	Simplify.

Kendra should add 6.67 milliliters of the 60% solution to the 40 milliliters of the 25% solution. Check by substituting 6.67 for x in the original equation.

 **2. 60 gal of 40% glycol, 40 gal of 60% glycol**

2. **ANTIFREEZE** One type of antifreeze is 40% glycol, and another type of antifreeze is 60% glycol. How much of each kind should be used to make 100 gallons of antifreeze that is 48% glycol?

 Personal Tutor at ca.algebra1.com

Uniform Motion Problems Motion problems are another application of weighted averages. **Uniform motion problems** are problems where an object moves at a certain speed, or rate. The formula $d = rt$ is used to solve these problems. In the formula, d represents distance, r represents rate, and t represents time.

Math nline Extra Examples at ca.algebra1.com

Making a Connection

Once students have learned the concept of weighted average, challenge them to describe a weighted average in terms of weights on a balance. How do the weights help to "tip" the balance?

• Did the weighted average help or hurt the skater's score? Would this always be the case? Because the skater scored higher in the long program than in the short, the weighted average made his average score higher. If the skater had scored lower in the long program, the weighted average would have hurt his score. If the skater scored the same in both programs, the weighted average would have had no effect.

Mixture Problems

Example 1 shows how to solve a real-world mixture problem using weighted averages. **Example 2** shows how to solve a real-world mixture problem expressed in terms of percents using weighted averages.

 Formative Assessment

Use the Check Your Progress exercises after each example to determine students' understanding of concepts.

ADDITIONAL EXAMPLES

1 **PETS** Jeri feeds her cat gourmet cat food that costs $1.75 per pound. She combines it with cheaper food that costs $0.50 per pound. How many pounds of cheaper food should Jeri buy to go with 5 pounds of gourmet food, if she wants the average price to be $1.00 per pound? 7.5 lb of cheaper food

2 **AUTO MAINTENANCE** A car's radiator should contain a solution of 50% antifreeze. Darryl has 2 gallons of 35% antifreeze. How many gallons of 100% antifreeze should he add to his solution to produce a solution of 50% antifreeze? 0.6 gal of 100% antifreeze

Additional Examples are also in:
• Noteables™ Interactive Study Notebook with Foldables™
• Interactive Classroom PowerPoint® Presentations

Uniform Motion Problems

Example 3 shows how to solve a real-world, uniform-motion problem using weighted averages. **Example 4** shows how to solve a real-world, uniform motion problem using weighted averages and making a table.

ADDITIONAL EXAMPLES

3 **AIR TRAVEL** Mirasol took a non-stop flight to visit her grandmother. The 750-mile trip took three hours and 45 minutes. Because of bad weather, the return trip took four hours and 45 minutes. What was her average speed for the round trip? The average speed for the round trip was about 176 mph.

4 **RESCUE** A railroad switching operator has discovered that two trains are heading toward each other on the same track. Currently, the trains are 53 miles apart. One train is traveling at 75 miles per hour and the other 40 miles per hour. The faster train will require 5 miles to stop safely, and the slower train will require 3 miles to stop safely. About how many minutes does the operator have to warn the train engineers to stop their trains? about 23 min

Focus on Mathematical Content

Uniform Motion If an object moves without changing its speed, it is said to be in uniform motion. Uniform motion problems are solved using this formula:
Distance = rate × time
$$d = r \times t$$

Real-World EXAMPLE Speed of One Vehicle

3 **TRAVEL** On Alberto's drive to his aunt's house, the traffic was light and he drove the 45-mile trip in one hour. However, the return trip took him two hours. What was his average speed for the round trip?

To find the average speed for each leg of the trip, rewrite $d = rt$ as $r = \frac{d}{t}$.

Going

$r = \frac{d}{t}$

$= \frac{45 \text{ miles}}{1 \text{ hour}}$ or 45 miles per hour

Returning

$r = \frac{d}{t}$

$= \frac{45 \text{ miles}}{2 \text{ hours}}$ or 22.5 miles per hour

You may think that the average speed of the trip would be $\frac{45 + 22.5}{2}$ or 33.75 miles per hour. However, Alberto did not drive at these speeds for equal amounts of time. You must find the weighted average for the trip.

Round Trip   Let M = the average speed.

$M = \frac{45(1) + 22.5(2)}{1 + 2}$ Definition of weighted average

$= \frac{90}{3}$ or 30   Simplify.

Alberto's average speed was 30 miles per hour.

CHECK Your Progress

3. EXERCISE Austin jogged 2.5 miles in 16 minutes and then walked 1 mile in 10 minutes. What was his average speed? about 0.135 mi/min

COncepts in MOtion
Animation
ca.algebra1.com

Real-World Link
Under ideal conditions, a siren can be heard from up to 440 feet. However, under normal conditions, a siren can be heard from only 125 feet.

Source: U.S. Department of Transportation

Real-World EXAMPLE Speeds of Two Vehicles

4 **SAFETY** Use the information about sirens at the left. A car and an emergency vehicle are heading toward each other. The car is traveling at a speed of 30 miles per hour or about 44 feet per second. The emergency vehicle is traveling at a speed of 50 miles per hour or about 74 feet per second. If the vehicles are 1000 feet apart and the conditions are ideal, in how many seconds will the driver of the car first hear the siren?

Draw a diagram. The driver can hear the siren when the total distance traveled by the two vehicles equals 1000 − 440 or 560 feet.

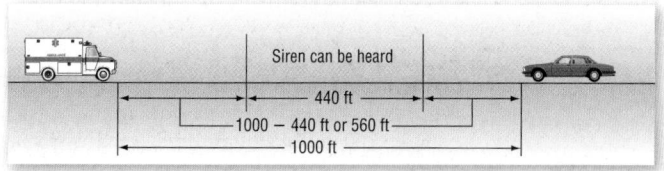

Let t = the number of seconds until the driver can hear the siren.

	r	t	$d = rt$
Car	44	t	44t
Emergency Vehicle	74	t	74t

124   Chapter 2 Solving Linear Equations

Differentiated Instruction

Logical   Some students will appreciate the way in which weighted averages can be used to manipulate data. Challenge these students to create additional example problems using weighted averages. Share these problems with the class.

124   Chapter 2 Solving Linear Equations

Write and solve an equation.

Distance traveled by car	plus	distance traveled by emergency vehicle	equals	560 feet.
44t	+	74t	=	560

$44t + 74t = 560$ Original equation

$118t = 560$ Simplify.

$\dfrac{118t}{118} = \dfrac{560t}{118}$ Divide each side by 118.

$t \approx 4.75$ The driver will hear the siren in about 4.75 seconds.

✓CHECK Your Progress

4. $\frac{1}{6}$ h or 10 min

4. CYCLING Two cyclists begin traveling in opposite directions on a circular bike trail that is 5 miles long. One cyclist travels 12 miles per hour, and the other travels 18 miles per hour. How long will it be before they meet?

★ indicates multi-step problem

✓CHECK Your Understanding

Example 1
(p. 122)

★ **BUSINESS** For Exercises 1–3, use the following information.
The Candle Supply Store sells votive wax for $0.90 a pound and low-shrink wax for $1.04 a pound. How many pounds of low-shrink wax should be mixed with 8 pounds of votive wax to obtain a blend that sells for $0.98 a pound?

1. Copy and complete the table representing the problem.

	Number of Pounds	Price per Pound	Total Price
Votive Wax	8	$0.90	0.90(8)
Low-Shrink Wax	p	$1.04	$1.04p
Blend	8 + p	$0.98	$0.98(8 + p)

2. Write an equation to represent the problem. $0.9(8) + 1.04p = 0.98(8 + p)$

3. How many pounds of low-shrink wax should be mixed with 8 pounds of votive wax? $10\frac{2}{3}$ lb

★ **4. COFFEE** A specialty coffee store wants to create a special mix using two coffees, one priced at $6.40 per pound and the other priced at $7.28 per pound. How many pounds of the $7.28 coffee should be mixed with 9 pounds of the $6.40 coffee to sell the mixture for $6.95 per pound? 15 lb

Example 2
(p. 123)

★ **FOOD** For Exercises 5–7, use the following information.
How many quarts of pure pineapple juice should Theo add to a 20% pineapple drink to create 5 quarts of a 50% pineapple juice mixture?

5. Copy and complete the table representing the problem.

	Quarts	Total Amount of Juice
20% Juice	5 − n	0.20(5 − n)
100% Juice	n	1.00n
50% Juice	5	0.50(5)

6. Write an equation to represent the problem. $0.20(5 − n) + 1.00n = 0.50(5)$

7. $1\frac{7}{8}$ qt; $3\frac{1}{8}$ qt

7. How much pure pineapple juice and 20% juice should Theo use?

Lesson 2-9 Weighted Averages **125**

Odd/Even Assignments

Exercises 13–34 are structured so that students practice the same concepts whether they are assigned odd or even problems.

★ 8. **METALS** An alloy of metals is 25% copper. Another alloy is 50% copper. How much of each should be used to make 1000 grams of an alloy that is 45% copper? **200 g of 25% alloy, 800 g of 50% alloy**

Example 3
(p. 124)

★ 9. **TRAVEL** A boat travels 16 miles due north in 2 hours and 24 miles due west in 2 hours. What is the average speed of the boat? **10 mph**

★ 10. **EXERCISE** Felisa jogged 3 miles in 25 minutes and then jogged 3 more miles in 30 minutes. What was her average speed in miles per minute? **about 0.11 mi/min**

Example 4
(pp. 124–125)

★ 11. **CYCLING** A cyclist begins traveling 18 miles per hour. At the same time and place, an in-line skater follows the cyclist's path and begins traveling 6 miles per hour. After how long will they be 24 miles apart? **2 h**

★ 12. **RESCUE** A fishing boat radioed the Coast Guard for a helicopter to pick up a sick crew member. At the time of the message, the boat is 660 kilometers from the helicopter and heading toward it. The average speed of the boat is 30 kilometers per hour, and the average speed of the helicopter is 300 kilometers per hour. How long will it take the helicopter to reach the boat? **2 h**

Exercises

HOMEWORK HELP	
For Exercises	**See Examples**
13–24	1
25, 26	2
27, 28	3
29–34	4

Exercise Levels
A: 13-34
B: 35-36
C: 37-39

★ 13. **GRADES** In Ms. Martinez's science class, a test is worth three times as much as a quiz. If a student has test grades of 85 and 92 and quiz grades of 82, 75, and 95, what is the student's average grade? **87**

★ 14. **ANALYZE TABLES** At Westbridge High School, a student's grade point average (GPA) is based on the student's grade and the class credit rating. Brittany's grades for this quarter are shown. Find Brittany's GPA if a grade of A equals 4 and a B equals 3. **about 3.67**

Class	Credit Rating	Grade
Algebra 1	1	A
Science	1	A
English	1	B
Spanish	1	A
Music	$\frac{1}{2}$	B

METALS For Exercises 15–18, use the following information.

In 2005, the international price of gold was $432 per ounce, and the international price of silver was $7.35 per ounce. Suppose gold and silver were mixed to obtain 15 ounces of an alloy worth $177.21 per ounce.

15. Copy and complete the table representing the problem.

	Number of Ounces	Price per Ounce	Value
Gold	g	$432	432g
Silver	$15 - g$	$7.35	$7.35(15 - g)$
Alloy	15	$177.21	177.21(15)

16. Write an equation to represent the problem. $432g + 7.35(15 - g) = 177.21(15)$

17. How much gold was used in the alloy? **6 oz**

18. How much silver was used in the alloy? **9 oz**

★ 19. **FUND-RAISING** The Madison High School marching band sold solid-color gift wrap for $4 per roll and print gift wrap for $6 per roll. The total number of rolls sold was 480, and the total amount of money collected was $2340. How many rolls of each kind of gift wrap were sold?
270 rolls of solid wrap, 210 rolls of print wrap

DIFFERENTIATED HOMEWORK OPTIONS

Level	Assignment	Two-Day Option	
BL Basic	13–34, 37, 39–47	13–33 odd, 40, 41	14–34 even, 37, 39, 42–47
OL Core	13–33 odd, 35–37, 39–47	13–34, 40, 41	35–37, 39, 42–47
AL Advanced /Pre-AP	35–47		

BUSINESS For Exercises 20–23, use the following information.

Party Supplies Inc. sells metallic balloons for $2 each and helium balloons for $3.50 per dozen. Yesterday, they sold 36 more metallic balloons than dozens of helium balloons. The total sales for both types of balloons were $281.00.

20. Copy and complete the table representing the problem.

	Number	Price	Total Price
Metallic Balloons	b	$2.00	$2.00b$
Dozens of Helium Balloons	$b - 36$	$3.50	$3.50(b - 36)$

21. Write an equation to represent the problem. $2.00b + 3.50(b - 36) = 281.00$

22. How many metallic balloons were sold? **74**

23. How many dozen helium balloons were sold? **38 doz**

24. MONEY Lakeisha spent $4.57 on color copies and black-and-white copies for her project. She made 7 more black-and-white copies than color copies. How many color copies did she make?

Type of Copy	Cost Per Page
color	$0.44
black-and-white	$0.07

8 color copies

25. FOOD Refer to the graphic at the left. How much whipping cream and 2% milk should be mixed to obtain 35 gallons of milk with 4% butterfat?

26. CHEMISTRY Hector is performing a chemistry experiment that requires 140 milliliters of a 30% copper sulfate solution. He has a 25% copper sulfate solution and a 60% copper sulfate solution. How many milliliters of each solution should he mix to obtain the needed solution?

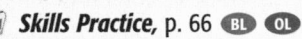

25. 10 gal of cream, 25 gal of 2% milk
26. 120 mL of 25% solution, 20 mL of 60% solution

27. TRAVEL A boat travels 36 miles in 1.5 hours and then 14 miles in 0.75 hour. What is the average speed of the boat? **22.2 mph**

28. EXERCISE An inline skater skated 1.5 miles in 28 minutes and then 1.2 more miles in 10 minutes. What was the average speed in miles per minute? **about 0.07 mi per min**

TRAVEL For Exercises 29–31, use the following information.

Two trains leave Smithville at the same time, one traveling east and the other west. The eastbound train travels at 40 miles per hour, and the westbound train travels at 30 miles per hour. Let h represent the hours since departure.

29. Copy and complete the table representing the situation.

30. Write an equation to determine when the trains will be 245 miles apart. $40h + 30h = 245$

	r	t	$d = rt$
Eastbound Train	40	h	$40h$
Westbound Train	30	h	$30h$

31. In how many hours will the trains be 245 miles apart? $3\frac{1}{2}$ h

ANIMALS For Exercises 32–34, use the graphic at the right.

Let t represent the number of seconds until the cheetah catches its prey.

32. Copy and complete the table representing the situation.

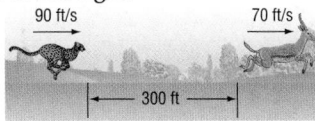

33. Write an equation to determine when the cheetah will catch its prey. $90t = 70t + 300$

34. When will the cheetah catch its prey? **15 s**

	r	t	$d = rt$
Cheetah	90	t	$90t$
Prey	70	t	$70t$

Lesson 2-9 Weighted Averages **127**

BL = Below Grade Level
OL = On Grade Level
AL = Above Grade Level
ELL = English Language Learner

Additional pages not shown:

📕 **Lesson Reading Guide,** p. 63 **BL OL ELL**

📕 **Skills Practice,** p. 66 **BL OL**

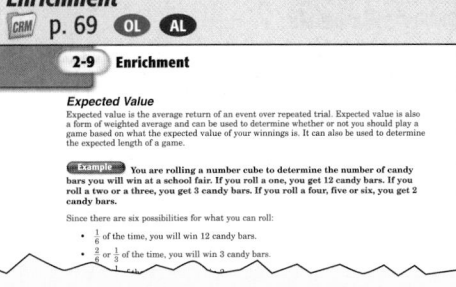

---

4 Assess

Name the Math Have students tell what mathematical procedures they would use to solve Exercise 23.

 Formative Assessment

Check for student understanding of concepts in Lessons 2-8 and 2-9
[CRM] Quiz 4 on p. 74

Additional Answers

35. No; it takes the sprinter $\frac{200}{8.2} \approx$ 24.39 s to run 200 m and it takes his opponent $\frac{200}{8} = 25$ s to run 200 m. Since the sprinter lost 1 second at the start his time would be 25.39, which is 0.39 second slower than his opponent's time.

38. Sample answer: how many grams of salt must be added to 40 grams of a 28% salt solution to obtain a 40% salt solution?

39. Sample answer: A weighted average is used to determine a skater's average. The score of the short program is added to twice the score of the long program.

The sum is divided by 3.
$$\frac{4.9(1) + 5.2(2)}{1 + 2} = 5.1$$

EXTRA PRACTICE
See pages 722, 745.
Math Online
Self-Check Quiz at
ca.algebra1.com

★ **35. TRACK AND FIELD** A sprinter has a bad start, and his opponent is able to start 1 second before him. If the sprinter averages 8.2 meters per second and his opponent averages 8 meters per second, will he be able to catch his opponent before the end of the 200-meter race? Explain. **See margin.**

★ **36. TRAVEL** A subway travels 60 miles per hour from Glendale to Midtown. Another subway, traveling at 45 miles per hour, takes 11 minutes longer for the same trip. How far apart are Glendale and Midtown? **33 mi**

H.O.T. Problems
37. Sample answer: grade point average
38. See margin.

37. OPEN ENDED Describe a real-world example of a weighted average.

38. CHALLENGE Write a mixture problem for $1.00x + 0.28(40) = 0.40(x + 40)$.

39. *Writing in Math* Use the information on page 122 to explain how scores are calculated in a figure-skating competition. Include an explanation of how a weighted average can be used to find a skating score and a demonstration of how to find the weighted average of a skater who received a 4.9 in the short program and a 5.2 in the long program. **See margin.**

STANDARDS PRACTICE 7NS1.7, 15.0

40. REVIEW Eula Jones is investing $6000, part at 4.5% interest and the rest at 6% interest. If d represents the amount invested at 4.5%, which expression represents the amount of interest earned in one year by the account paying 6%? **D**

A $0.06d$

B $0.06(d - 6000)$

C $0.06(d + 6000)$

D $0.06(6000 - d)$

41. Todd drove from Boston to Cleveland, a distance of 616 miles. His breaks, gasoline, and food stops took 2 hours. If his trip took 16 hours altogether, what was his average speed? **H**

F 38.5 mph   **H** 44 mph

G 40 mph   **J** 47.5 mph

Spiral Review

Solve each equation for the variable specified. (Lesson 2-8)

42. $a + 6 = \frac{b-1}{4}$, for b $b = 4a + 25$

43. $3t - 4 = 6t - s$, for t $t = \frac{s-4}{3}$

State whether each percent of change is a percent of increase or a percent of decrease. Then find the percent of change. Round to the nearest whole percent. (Lesson 2-7)

44. original: $25
new: $14 **decrease; 44%**

45. original: 35
new: 42 **increase; 20%**

46. original: 244
new: 300 **increase; 23%**

★ **47. MONEY** Tyler had $80 in his savings account. After his mother made a deposit, his new balance was $115. Write and solve an equation to find the amount of the deposit. (Lesson 2-2) **Sample answer: $80 + d = 115$; $35**

Cross-Curricular Project

Algebra and Social Studies

You're Only as Old as You Feel! It's time to complete your project. Use the information and data you have gathered about living to be 100 to prepare a portfolio or Web page. Be sure to include graphs and/or tables in the presentation.

 Cross-Curricular Project at ca.algebra1.com

Pre-AP Activity   **Use after the Exercises**

In many high schools, a special weight is assigned to the grades received in Advanced Placement classes when a student's GPA is calculated (A = 5 points; B = 4 points; C = 3 points). Have students pretend that one of their classes is an Advanced Placement class with a grade having the special weight assigned to it. Have them use their current grades to calculate their GPAs. Ask students to explain how the class chosen as an Advanced Placement class made their GPA higher.

Spreadsheet Lab
Finding a Weighted Average

Standard 15.0 **Students apply algebraic techniques to solve rate problems, work problems,** and **percent mixture problems.** (Key, CAHSEE)

You can use a spreadsheet to calculate weighted averages. It allows you to make calculations and print almost anything you can organize in a table.

The basic unit in a spreadsheet is called a cell. A cell may contain numbers, words, or a formula. Each cell is named by the column and row that describe its location. For example, cell B4 is in column B, row 4.

EXAMPLE

Greta Norris manages a sales firm. Each of her employees earns a different rate of commission. She has entered the commission rate and the sales for each employee for October in a spreadsheet. What was the average commission rate?

Commission ▢ ▱ ☒

◇	A	B	C	D
1	Employee	Rate	Sales	Commission
2	Mark	0.05	1588	=C2*B2
3	Andrea	0.075	1800	=C3*B3
4	Tamika	0.1	2008	=C4*B4
5	Daniel	0.1	2105	=C5*B5
6	Lasanda	0.05	1725	=C6*B6
7	Diego	0.06	1988	=C7*B7
8	Total		=SUM(C2:C7)	=SUM(D2:D7)
9	Weighted Average Commission Rate	=D8 / C8		
10				

◀ ◀ ▶ ▶ Sheet 1 / Sheet 2 / Sheet 3 /

The spreadsheet shows the formula to calculate the weighted average. It multiplies the rate of commission by the amount of sales and finds the total amount of sales and amount of commission. Then it divides the amount of commission by the amount of sales. To the nearest tenth, the average rate of commission is 7.4%.

2. It increases by $1.00. It increases by 10%.

EXERCISES

For Exercises 1–3, use the table at the right.

1. What is the average price of a pound of coffee? **$11.72**

2. How does the November weighted average change if all of the coffee prices are increased by $1.00? by 10%?

3. Find the weighted average of a pound of coffee if the shop sold 50 pounds of each type of coffee. How does the weighted average compare to the average of the per-pound coffee prices? Explain. **See margin.**

November Coffee Sales

Product	Pounds Sold	Price Per Pound ($)
Hawaiian Cafe	56	16.95
Mocha Java	97	12.59
House Blend	124	10.75
Decaf Espresso	71	10.15
Breakfast Blend	69	11.25
Italian Roast	45	9.95

Extend 2-9 Spreadsheet Lab: Finding a Weighted Average **129**

Additional Answer

3. The average of the prices per pound is the same as the weighted average if the same number of pounds of each type are sold. This is because each price is multiplied by the same weight, and then that weight is divded out.

Extend 2-9

Lesson Notes

1 Focus

Materials
• computer
• spreadsheet software

2 Teach

Working in Cooperative Groups
Have students work in pairs and take turns reading the data aloud.

Explain that the spreadsheet shows the formulas to calculate the income. Point out that they can click on the cell instead of typing the cell name.

Make sure that students type an equal sign at the beginning of any cell that contains a calculation formula. This ensures that the spreadsheet calculates a formula correctly.

Practice Have students complete Exercises 1–3.

3 Assess

✓ **Formative Assessment**

Use Exercises 1–3 to assess whether students understand the difference between an average of a set of numbers and a weighted average.

From Concrete to Abstract

Ask: What are the advantages of spreadsheets over pen-and-paper calculations? Sample answer: You can input and organize data faster than with a pen-and-paper. Multiple and large calculations can be done quickly. Calculations can be repeated easily when changes are needed.

CHAPTER 2 Study Guide and Review

STUDY TO GO — Download Vocabulary Review from ca.algebra1.com

Dinah Zike's Foldables™

Have students look through the chapter to make sure they have included examples for each lesson of the chapter in their Foldables.

Suggest that students keep their Foldables handy while completing the Study Guide and Review pages. Point out that their Foldables can serve as a quick review took for studying for the Chapter Test.

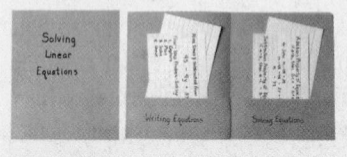

Formative Assessment

Key Vocabulary The page reference after each word denotes where that term was first introduced. If students have difficulty answering questions 1–7, remind them that they can use the page references to refresh their memories.

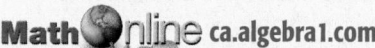

Math Online ca.algebra1.com

Vocabulary PuzzleMaker improves students' mathematics vocabulary using four puzzle formats—crossword, scramble, word search using a word list, and word search using clues. Students can work online or from a printed worksheet.

FOLDABLES™ Study Organizer — GET READY to Study

Be sure the following Key Concepts are noted in your Foldable.

Solving Linear Equations

Key Concepts

Writing Equations (Lesson 2-1)
- Four-Step Problem Solving Plan:
  - Step 1 Explore the problem.
  - Step 2 Plan the solution.
  - Step 3 Solve the problem.
  - Step 4 Check the solution.

Solving Equations (Lessons 2-2 to 2-5)
- Addition and Subtraction Properties of Equality: If an equation is true and the same number is added to or subtracted from each side, the resulting equation is true.

- Multiplication and Division Properties of Equality: If an equation is true and each side is multiplied by the same number or divided by the same non-zero number, the resulting equation is true.

- Steps for Solving Equations:
  - Step 1 Use the Distributive Property if necessary.
  - Step 2 Simplify expressions on each side.
  - Step 3 Use the Addition and/or Subtraction Properties of Equality to get the variables on one side and the numbers without variables on the other side.
  - Step 4 Simplify the expression on each side of the equals sign.
  - Step 5 Use the Multiplication or Division Property of Equality to solve.

Ratios and Proportions (Lesson 2-6)
- The Means-Extremes Property of Proportion states that in a proportion, the product of the extremes is equal to the product of the means.

Key Vocabulary

consecutive integers (p. 94)
defining a variable (p. 71)
dimensional analysis (p. 119)
equivalent equations (p. 79)
extremes (p. 106)
formula (p. 72)
four-step problem solving plan (p. 71)
identity (p. 99)
means (p. 106)
mixture problem (p. 122)

multi-step equations (p. 92)
number theory (p. 94)
percent of change (p. 111)
percent of decrease (p. 111)
percent of increase (p. 111)
proportion (p. 105)
rate (p. 107)
ratio (p. 105)
scale (p. 108)
solve an equation (p. 79)
uniform motion problem (p. 123)
weighted average (p. 122)

Vocabulary Check

State whether each sentence is *true* or *false*. If *false*, replace the underlined word or number to make a true sentence.

1. An example of <u>consecutive integers</u> is −10 and −9. **true**

2. A comparison of two numbers by division is called a <u>ratio</u>. **true**

3. In the proportion 1:4 = x:2, 4 and x are called the <u>means</u>. **true**

4. Equations with more than one operation are called <u>equivalent</u> equations. **false; multi-step**

5. <u>Dimensional analysis</u> is the process of carrying units throughout a computation. **true**

6. Mixture problems are solved using <u>number theory</u>. **false; weighted average**

7. An equation that is true for every value of the variable is called an <u>identity</u>. **true**

Math Online Vocabulary Review at ca.algebra1.com

Summative Assessment

CRM Vocabulary Test, p. 76

Lesson-by-Lesson Review

2-1 **Writing Equations** (pp. 70–76)

Translate each sentence into an equation.

8. The sum of z and one fifth of w is ninety-six. $z + \frac{1}{5}w = 96$

9. The product of m and n is as much as three times the sum of m and 8. $mn = 3(m + 8)$

10. The difference of p and thirteen is identical to the square of p. $p - 13 = p^2$

Translate each equation into a verbal sentence.

11. $\frac{56}{g} = 7 - 3g$ **12.** $8 + 2k = \frac{1}{4}k$

13. DESERTS One third of Earth's land surface is desert. There are 50 million square kilometers of desert. Define a variable and then write and solve an equation to find the total number of square kilometers of land surface.

Example 1 Translate the following sentence into an equation.

Forty-one increased by twice a number m is the same as three times the sum of a number m and seven.

$41 + 2m = 3(m + 7)$

Example 2 Translate $2y - 5 = \frac{1}{2}y$ into a verbal sentence.

Twice a number y minus five equals one half y.

11. Sample answer: The quotient of 56 and g equals seven minus three times g.

12. Sample answer: The sum of eight and twice a number k equals one fourth k.

13. Sample answer: Let $s =$ the millions of sq. km of land surface on Earth; $\frac{1}{3}s = 50$; $s = 150$ million km^2

2-2 **Solving Equations by Using Addition and Subtraction** (pp. 78–84)

Solve each equation.

14. $h - 15 = -22$ -7 **15.** $\frac{3}{5} = \frac{2}{3} + a$ $-\frac{1}{15}$

16. $16 - (-q) = 83$ 67 **17.** $-55 = x + (-7)$ -48

Write an equation for each problem. Then solve the equation and check your solution.

18. Nine subtracted from a number equals -15. Find the number. $x - 9 = -15$; -6

19. The sum of a number and -71 is 29. What is the number? $x + (-71) = 29$; 100

20. CANS The can opener was invented in 1858. That was 48 years after cans were first introduced. Write and solve an equation to determine in what year the can was introduced. $x + 48 = 1858$; 1810

Example 3 Solve $13 + p = -5$.

$13 + p = -5$ Original equation

$13 + p - 13 = -5 - 13$ Subtract 13 from each side.

$p = -18$ Check this result.

Example 4 Write an equation for the problem below. Then solve the equation.

The difference of a number and 62 is -47. What is the number?

$x - 62 = -47$ Original equation

$x - 62 + 62 = -47 + 62$ Add 62 to each side.

$x = 15$ Check this result.

Lesson-by-Lesson Review
Intervention If the given examples are not sufficient to review the topics covered by the questions, remind students that the page references tell them where to review that topic in their textbooks.

Two-Day Option Have students complete the Lesson-by-Lesson Review on pages 131–134. Once they have, use ExamView® Assessment Suite to customize another review worksheet that practices all of those objectives of this chapter or only those objectives for which your students need more help.

For more information on ExamView® Assessment Suite, see p. 68C.

Differentiated Instruction
Super DVD: MindJogger Videoquizzes
Use this DVD as an alternative format of review for the test. For more information on this game show format, see p. 68D.

2-3 Solving Equations by Using Multiplication and Division (pp. 85–90)

Solve each equation. Check your solution.

21. $\frac{a}{-7} = -29$ **203**   **22.** $-18 = \frac{3}{5}m$ **−30**

23. $14p = 42$ **3**   **24.** $\frac{y}{32} = \frac{5}{-8}$ **−20**

Write an equation for each problem. Then solve the equation.

25. Three eighths of a number equals 9. What is the number? $\frac{3}{8}n = 9$; **24**

26. The quotient of a number and -4 is -72. Find the number. $\frac{n}{-4} = -72$; **288**

27. DINING China produces 45 billion chopsticks per year from 25 million trees. Write and solve an equation to find the number of chopsticks that can be produced from 1 tree.

Example 5 Solve $\frac{k}{-3} = -9$.

$$\frac{k}{-3} = -9 \qquad \text{Original equation}$$

$$\frac{k}{-3}(-3) = -9(-3) \qquad \text{Multiply each side by } -3.$$

$$k = 27 \qquad \text{Check this result.}$$

Example 6 Write an equation for the problem below. Then solve the equation.

48 is negative twelve times a number. Find the number.

$$48 = -12n \qquad \text{Original equation}$$

$$\frac{48}{-12} = \frac{-12n}{-12} \qquad \text{Divide each side by } -12.$$

$$-4 = n \qquad \text{Check this result.}$$

27. $25{,}000{,}000x = 45{,}000{,}000{,}000$; $x = 1800$ chopsticks

2-4 Solving Multi-Step Equations (pp. 92–97)

Solve each equation. Check your solution.

28. $5 = 4t - 7$ **3**   **29.** $6 + \frac{y}{3} = -45$ **−153**

30. $9 = \frac{d+5}{8}$ **67**   **31.** $\frac{c}{-4} - 2 = -36$ **136**

Write an equation and solve each problem.

32. 22 increased by six times a number is -20. What is the number? $22 + 6n = -20$; **−7**

33. Find three consecutive odd integers with a sum of 39. $n + (n + 2) + (n + 4) = 39$; **11, 13, and 15**

34. THEATER Each row in a theater has eight more seats than the previous row. If the first row has 14 seats, which row has 46 seats? **fifth row**

Example 7 Write and solve an equation to find three consecutive even integers with a sum of 150.

Let $n =$ the least even integer.
Then $n + 2 =$ the next greater even integer and $n + 4 =$ the greatest of the three even integers.

$$n + (n + 2) + (n + 4) = 150 \qquad \text{Original equation}$$

$$3n + 6 = 150 \qquad \text{Simplify.}$$

$$3n = 144 \qquad \text{Subtract 6 from each side.}$$

$$n = 48 \qquad \text{Divide each side by 3.}$$

The integers are 48, 50, and 52.

Mixed Problem Solving
For mixed problem-solving practice,
see page 745.

2–5 **Solving Equations with the Variable on Each Side** (pp. 98–103)

Solve each equation. Check your solution.

35. $5b + 3 = 9b - 17$ **5**

36. $\frac{2}{3}n - 3 = \frac{1}{3}(2n - 9)$ **all numbers**

37. **160 cans**

37. FUND-RAISING The Band Boosters pay $200 to rent a concession stand at a university football game. They purchase cans of soft drinks for $0.25 each and sell them at the game for $1.50 each. How many cans of soft drinks must they sell to break even?

Example 8 Solve $7x + 56 = 5x - 11$.

$7x + 56 = 5x - 11$	Original equation
$7x + 56 - 5x = 5x - 11 - 5x$	Subtract 5x from each side.
$2x + 56 = -11$	Simplify.
$2x + 56 - 56 = -11 - 56$	Subtract 56 from each side.
$2x = -67$	Simplify.
$\frac{2x}{2} = \frac{-67}{2}$	Divide each side by 2.
$x = -33.5$	Check this result.

2–6 **Ratios and Proportions** (pp. 105–110)

Solve each proportion. If necessary, round to the nearest hundredth.

38. $\frac{14}{x} = \frac{20}{8}$ **5.6**   **39.** $\frac{0.47}{6} = \frac{1.41}{m}$ **18**

40. WORLD RECORDS Dustin drank 14 ounces of tomato juice through a straw in 33 seconds. At this rate, approximately how long would it take him to drink a bottle of water that contains 16.9 ounces? **about 39.8 s**

Example 9 Solve the proportion $\frac{h}{15} = \frac{7}{21}$.

$\frac{h}{15} = \frac{7}{21}$	Original equation
$h(21) = 15(7)$	Find the cross products.
$21h = 105$	Distributive Property
$\frac{21h}{21} = \frac{105}{21}$	Divide each side by 21.
$h = 5$	Simplify.

2–7 **Percent of Change** (pp. 111–115)

State whether each percent of change is a percent of increase or a percent of decrease. Then find each percent of change. Round to the nearest whole percent.

41. original: 54   **42.** original: 17
new: 46   new: 33
dec.; 15%   **inc.; 94%**

43. TIPS Felicia's meal cost $23.74. How much money should she leave for a 15% tip? **$3.56**

Example 10 Find the total price of a CD that costs $18.75 with 6.5% sales tax.

6.5% of $\$18.75 = 0.065 \times 18.75$ 6.5% = 0.065
$\qquad\qquad\qquad = 1.21875$ Multiply.

Round $1.21875 to $1.22. Add this amount to the original price.

$\$18.75 + \$1.22 = \$19.97$

The total price of the CD is $19.97.

Problem Solving Review

For additional practice in problem solving for Chapter 2, see the Mixed Problem Solving Appendix, p. 745 in the Student Handbook section.

Anticipation Guide

Have students complete the Anticipation Guide, p. 3, and discuss how their responses have changed now that they have completed Chapter 2.

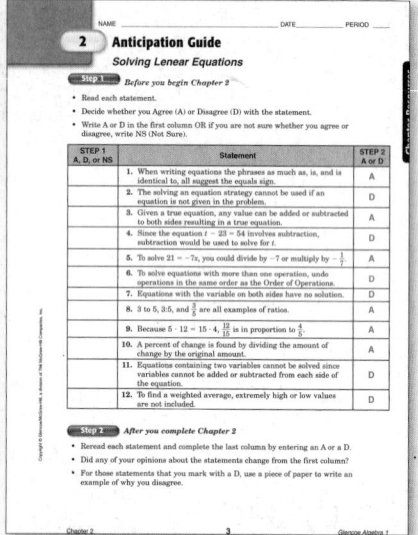

Additional Answer

45. $k = \frac{4}{7}(s + g)$ or $k = \frac{4(s + g)}{7}$

or $k = \frac{4s + 4g}{7}$

2-8 **Solving for a Specific Variable** (pp. 117–121)

Solve each equation or formula for the variable specified.

44. $d = 5v + m$, for v $v = \dfrac{d - m}{5}$

45. $\frac{7}{4}k - g = s$, for k See margin.

46. $\dfrac{ac - 3}{6} = w$, for c $c = \dfrac{6w + 3}{a}$

47. $9h + z = pq + 2h$, for h $h = \dfrac{pq - z}{7}$

48. TRAVEL In the formula $d = rt$, d is the distance, r is the rate, and t is the time spent traveling. Solve this equation for r. Then find Aida's rate if she drove 219 miles in $3\frac{3}{4}$ hours. $r = \dfrac{d}{t}$; 58.4 mi/h

Example 11 Solve $8q + 3b = 12$ for b.

$8q + 3b = 12$	Original equation
$8q + 3b - 8q = 12 - 8q$	Subtract $8q$ from each side.
$3b = 12 - 8q$	Simplify.
$\dfrac{3b}{3} = \dfrac{12 - 8q}{3}$	Divide each side by 3.
$b = \dfrac{12 - 8q}{3}$	Simplify.

The value of b is $\dfrac{12 - 8q}{3}$.

2-9 **Weighted Averages** (pp. 122–128)

49. COFFEE Jerome blends Brand A of coffee that sells for $9.50 a pound with Brand B of coffee that sells for $12.00 a pound. If the 45 pounds of blend sells for $10.50 a pound, how many pounds of each type of coffee did Jerome use?   **27 lb Brand A, 18 lb Brand B**

50. PUNCH Raquel is mixing lemon-lime soda and a fruit juice blend that is 45% juice. If she uses 3 quarts of soda, how many quarts of fruit juice must be added to produce punch that is 30% juice?   **6 qt**

51. JOGGING Delmar ran 4 miles in 22 minutes, stopped and rested, and ran an additional 4 miles in 28 minutes. Find his average speed. $\frac{4}{25}$ mi/min or 0.16 mi/min

52. TRAVEL Connor is driving 65 miles per hour on the highway. Ed is 15 miles behind him driving at 70 miles per hour. After how many hours will Ed catch up to Connor?   **3 h**

Example 12 MANUFACTURING Percy mixes 750 liters of water with 250 liters of 2% bleach. What percent of bleach is in the resultant mixture?

Let $x =$ the percent of bleach in the resultant mixture. Make a table.

	Amount of Solution (L)	Amount of Resultant Mixture
Water (0% bleach)	750	750(0)
Bleach (2% bleach)	250	250(0.02)
Resultant Mixture (x% bleach)	1000	1000(x)

Write and solve an equation using the information in the table.

$750(0) + 250(0.02) = 1000(x)$	Original equation
$5 = 1000x$	Simplify.
$0.005 = x$	Divide each side by 1000.

There is 0.5% bleach in the resultant mixture.

Problem Solving Review

For additional practice in problem solving for Chapter 2, see the Mixed Problem Solving Appendix, p. 745 in the Student Handbook section.

Anticipation Guide

Have students complete the Anticipation Guide, p. 3, and discuss how their responses have changed now that they have completed Chapter 2.

Translate each sentence into an equation.

1. The sum of x and four times y is equal to twenty. $x + 4y = 20$

2. Two thirds of n is negative eight fifths. $\frac{2}{3}n = -\frac{8}{5}$

Solve each equation. Then check your solution.

3. $-15 + k = 8$ **23**
4. $k - 16 = -21$ **−5**
5. $-1.2x = 7.2$ **−6**
6. $5a = 125$ **25**
7. $\frac{t-7}{4} = 11$ **51**
8. $\frac{3}{4}y = 27$ **36**
9. $-12 = 7 - \frac{y}{3}$ **57**
10. $-\frac{2}{3}z = -\frac{4}{9}$ $\frac{2}{3}$

11. **MULTIPLE CHOICE** The perimeter of the larger square is 11.6 centimeters greater than the perimeter of the smaller square. What are the side lengths of the smaller square? **B**

7.1 cm x cm

A 1.1 cm   C 4.5 cm

B 4.2 cm   D 16.8 cm

Solve each equation. Then check your solution.

12. $-3(x + 5) = 8x + 18$ **−3**
13. $2p + 1 = 5p - 11$ **4**

14. **POSTAGE** What was the percent of increase in the price of a first-class stamp from 2001 to 2006? Round to the nearest whole percent. **15%**

First-Class Stamps	
Year	Cost of Stamp
2001	34¢
2006	39¢

15. **MULTIPLE CHOICE** If $\frac{4}{5}$ of $\frac{3}{4} = \frac{2}{5}$ of $\frac{x}{4}$, find the value of x. **G**

F 12

G 6

H 3

J $\frac{3}{2}$

Solve each proportion.

16. $\frac{2}{10} = \frac{1}{a}$ **5**
17. $\frac{3}{5} = \frac{24}{x}$ **40**
18. $\frac{n}{4} = \frac{3.25}{52}$ **0.25**
19. $\frac{5}{12} = \frac{10}{x-1}$ **25**

State whether each percent of change is a percent of increase or a percent of decrease. Then find the percent of change. Round to the nearest whole percent.

20. original: 45
    new: 9
    decrease; 80%
21. original: 12
    new: 20
    increase; 67%

Solve each equation or formula for the variable specified.

22. $h = at - 0.25vt^2$, for a $a = \frac{h + 0.25vt^2}{t}$
23. $a(y + 1) = b$, for y $y = \frac{b - a}{a}$

24. **SALES** At The Central Perk coffee shop, Destiny sold 30 more cups of cappuccino than espresso, for a total of $178.50 worth of espresso and cappuccino. How many cups of each were sold? **espresso: 23 cups; cappuccino: 53 cups**

Coffee	Cost per Cup ($)
espresso	2.00
cappuccino	2.50

25. **BOATING** *The Yankee Clipper* leaves the pier at 9:00 A.M. at 8 knots (nautical miles per hour). A half hour later, *The River Rover* leaves the same pier in the same direction traveling at 10 knots. At what time will *The River Rover* overtake *The Yankee Clipper*? **11:30 A.M.**

 Summative Assessment

CRM *Chapter 2 Resource Masters*

Leveled Chapter 2 Tests			
Form	Type	Level	Pages
1	MC	BL	77–78
2A	MC	OL	79–80
2B	MC	OL	81–82
2C	FR	OL	83–84
2D	FR	OL	85–86
3	FR	AL	87–88

MC = multiple-choice questions
FR = free-response questions
BL = below grade level
OL = on grade level
AL = above grade level

- Vocabulary Test, p. 76
- Extended-Response Test, p. 89
- Unit 1 Test, pp. 93–94

ExamView® Assessment Suite   Customize and create multiple versions of your chapter test and their answer keys. All of the questions from the leveled chapter tests in the *Chapter 2 Resource Masters* are also available on ExamView Assessment Suite with the California Standard that each item assesses.

Data-Driven Decision Making	Exercises	Lesson	Standard	**Resources for Review**
	16–19	2-6	15.0	**CRM** Study Guide and Intervention, pp. 42–43, 49–50, 57–58, 64–65
Diagnostic Teaching Based on the results of the Chapter 2 Practice Test, use the following to review concepts that students continue to find challenging.	14, 20–21	2-7	5.0	
	22–23	2-8	5.0	Math Online
	24–25	2-9	15.0	• Extra Examples • Personal Tutor • Concepts in Motion

California Standards Practice
Cumulative, Chapters 1–2

 Read each question. Then fill in the correct answer on the answer document provided by your teacher or on a sheet of paper.

1 Which statement represents the verbal expression for the algebraic expression $4p^2 + 6(q - r)$? **D**

   A four p times two plus six q minus r

   B four p times two plus six times the difference of q and r

   C four p squared plus six q minus r

   D four p squared plus six times the difference of q and r

2 $5(3 - 2x) + 11x =$ **H**

   F $16x$

   G $8 + 9x$

   H $15 + x$

   J $15 + 9x$

3 Brianne makes baby blankets for a baby store. She works on the blankets 30 hours per week. The store pays her $9.50 per hour plus 30% of what the blankets profit. If her hourly rate were to increase by $0.75 and her commission were raised to 40%, how much would she earn if a total of $300 in blankets were sold? **427.5**

4 Carla solved the equation $3(3x + 5) = 12$ using the following steps.

   Given: $3(3x + 5) = 12$

   Step 1: $9x + 15 = 12$

   Step 2: $9x = -3$

   Step 3: $x = -\dfrac{1}{3}$

   To get from Step 2 to Step 3, Carla— **A**

   A divided both sides by 9.

   B subtracted 9 from both sides.

   C added 9 to both sides.

   D multiplied both sides by 9.

5 Which of the following is equivalent to $4(x + 5) - 3(x + 2) = 13$? **J**

   F $4x + 20 - 3x - 1 = 13$

   G $4x + 5 - 4x + 1 = 13$

   H $4x + 5 - 3x + 6 = 13$

   J $4x + 20 - 3x - 6 = 13$

6 A 160-foot-long piece of yarn is cut into 3 pieces. The second piece of yarn is four times as long as the first piece of yarn. The third piece of yarn is three times as long as the second piece of yarn. What is the length of the second piece of yarn to the nearest foot? **C**

   A 9 ft   C 38 ft

   B 20 ft   D 80 ft

7 Solve the equation. **112**

   $$\frac{1}{2}x + 12 = \frac{3}{4}x - 16$$

8 Solve: $3(x + 4) = 5x + 28$

   Step 1: $3x + 12 = 5x + 28$

   Step 2: $8x + 12 = 28$

   Step 3: $8x = 16$

   Step 4: $x = 2$

   Which is the first *incorrect* step in the solution shown above? **G**

   F Step 1

   G Step 2

   H Step 3

   J Step 4

9 Mr. Hiskey is making a doll-sized model of his house for his daughter. The model is $\dfrac{1}{16}$ the size of the actual house. If the door in the model is 6 inches tall, how many inches tall is the actual door on the house? **96**

 California Standards Practice at ca.algebra1.com

More California Standards Practice
For practice by standard, see pages CA1–CA43.

CHAPTER 2 California Standards Practice

10 Which of the following is equivalent to the equation shown below? **B**

$$\frac{15}{x} = \frac{5}{x - 3}$$

A $x(x - 3) = 65$

B $15(x - 3) = 5x$

C $15x = 5(x - 3)$

D $20 = x + (x - 3)$

11 Mr. Johnson can grade 180 tests in 60 minutes. His student aide can grade 180 tests in 90 minutes. Working together, how many minutes will it take them to grade 135 tests? **F**

F 27

G 36

H 42

J 75

12 Identify the hypothesis and conclusion for the statement below. **C**

> If $7x + 5 = 33$, then $x = 4$.

A H: $7x + 5$
  C: 33

B H: 33
  C: $7x + 5$

C H: $7x + 5 = 33$
  C: $x = 4$

D H: $x = 4$
  C: $7x + 5 = 33$

13 Which equation is equivalent to $6(3 - 4x) = 5 - 2(3 - x)$? **J**

F $-5x = 7$

G $3x = 19$

H $21x = 9$

J $26x = 19$

14 Maya is selling T-shirts to raise money for the student council. She makes $6.75 for every T-shirt that she sells. If she wants to raise $800 selling the T-shirts, what is a reasonable number of shirts she should sell? **B**

A 100

B 120

C 500

D 5400

Pre-AP/Anchor Problem

Record your answer on a sheet of paper. Show your work.

15 The Carsons have found three options for renting a minivan for their vacation. Which option would you choose? Explain.

Option #1   Option #2; it is the least expensive.
ReadyRents has a weekly rate of $260. The Carsons receive a 20% discount from their motor club membership. Insurance is an additional $39.

Option #2
Rent-A-Ride's weekly rate is $220. The Carsons' motor club membership entitles them to a 10% discount and insurance is included.

Option #3
The weekly rate at Acme is $185. Insurance is $22.25 and no discounts are available.

TEST-TAKING TIP

Question 15 When answering open-ended questions, remember to read the problem carefully. Show all of your work. Then check to see that you have answered the question fully.

Item Analysis

Questions 3, 7, and 9 are griddable questions. In a griddable question, students arrive at an answer and then record it in a special grid by coloring the appropriate bubble under each digit of the answer.

Answer Sheet Practice

Have students simulate taking a standardized test by recording their answers on practice recording sheets.

[CRM] Student Recording Sheet, p. 71

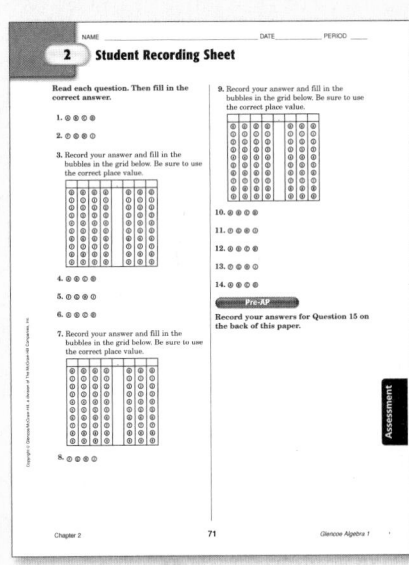

NEED EXTRA HELP?															
If You Missed Question...	1	2	3	4	5	6	7	8	9	10	11	12	13	14	15
Go to Lesson...	1-1	1-5	2-4	2-4	2-4	2-4	2-5	2-5	2-6	2-6	2-9	1-7	2-5	2-3	2-7
For Help with Standard...	7AF1.1	7AF1.2	7NS1.7	5.0	4.0	5.0	10.0	5.0	6NS1.3	4.0	15.0	24.2	4.0	5.0	NS1.7

Homework Option

Get Ready for Chapter 3 Assign students the exercises on page 139 as homework to assess whether they possess the prerequisite skills needed for the next chapter.

53. Sample answer: Both properties can be used to solve equations. The Multiplication Property of Equality says you can multiply each side of an equation by the same number. The Division Property of Equality says you can divide each side of an equation by the same number. Dividing each side of an equation by a number is the same as multiplying each side of the equation by the number's reciprocal.

54. Sample answer: One method is to solve the equation for y. Then substitute the value of y into the expression; 12. Another method is to use the Multiplicative Property of Equality. Since $3(6y - 7) = 18y - 21$, then $3(4) = 12$.

Page 103, Lesson 2-5

55.

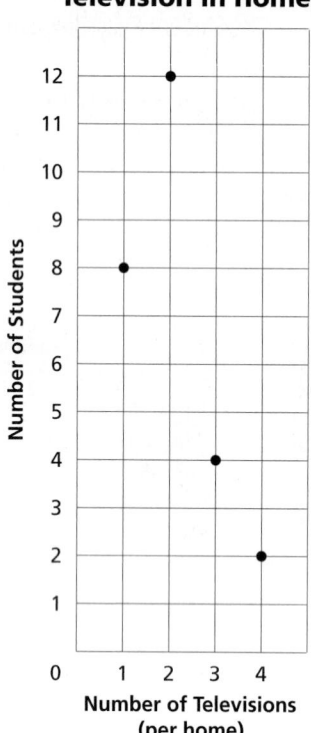

Television in Homes

Number of Students (y-axis)

Number of Televisions (per home) (x-axis)

Page 109, Lesson 2-6

35. USA: $\dfrac{907}{2219}$; USSR/UT/Russia: $\dfrac{525}{1370}$; Germany: $\dfrac{388}{1230}$; GB: $\dfrac{189}{668}$;

France: $\dfrac{199}{631}$; Italy: $\dfrac{189}{511}$; Sweden: $\dfrac{140}{476}$

36. No; if two of these ratios formed a proportion, the two countries would have the same part of their medals as gold medals.

Chapter 2 Answer Appendix

UNIT 2
Notes

Introduction

In this unit, students learn to recognize relations and determine whether a relation is a function. They explore data to determine if a linear relationship exists. They also learn to represent a linear relationship as points on a coordinate plane and as an equation representing a line. Students analyze how a linear equation and its graph are related.

Systems of equations are solved algebraically and graphically. The unit concludes with solving inequalities and open sentences involving absolute value.

Assessment Options

Unit 2 Test Pages 81–82 of the *Chapter 6 Resource Masters* may be used as a test or review for Unit 2. This assessment contains both multiple-choice and short answer items.

ExamView®
Assessment Suite

Create additional customized Unit Tests and review worksheets for differentiated instruction.

UNIT 2
Linear Functions

Focus
Use linear functions and inequalities to represent and model real-world situations.

CHAPTER 3
Functions and Patterns
BIG Idea   Understand the concepts of a relation and a function, and determine whether a given relation defined by a graph, a set of ordered pairs, or a symbolic expression is a function.

CHAPTER 4
Analyzing Linear Equations
BIG Idea   Graph a linear equation, compute an equation's x- and y-intercepts, and derive linear equations by using the point-slope formula.

CHAPTER 5
Solving Systems of Linear Equations
BIG Idea   Solve a system of two linear equations in two variables algebraically and interpret the answer graphically.

CHAPTER 6
Solving Linear Inequalities
BIG Idea   Solve absolute value inequalities, multistep problems involving linear inequalities in one variable, and solve a system of two linear inequalities in two variables.

138 Unit 2

Real-Life Math Videos *Real-Life Math Videos* engage students by showing them how math is used in everyday situations. Use Video 2 with this unit.

Cross-Curricular Project

Algebra and Sports

The Spirit of the Games The first Olympic Games featured only one event–a foot race. In 2004, the Olympic Games featured thousands of competitors in about 300 events. The 2004 summer games were held in Athens, Greece. In this project, you will explore how linear functions can be used to represent times in Olympic events.

Math Online **Log on to** ca.algebra1.com **to begin.**

Cross-Curricular Project

Algebra and Sports

The Spirit of the Games This Cross-Curricular Project is an online project in which students do research on the Internet, gather data, and make presentations using word processing, graphing, page-making, or presentation software. In each chapter, students advance to the next step in their project. At the end of Chapter 6, the project culminates with a presentation of their findings.

Math Online
ca.algebra1.com Log on for teaching suggestions and sample answers for this project.

Team Teaching You can use this Cross-Curricular Project with your students' social studies or physical education teacher to make the connections from mathematics to the sports and history of the Olympic Games your students are studying.

Chapter Overview

Functions and Patterns

Standards-Based Lesson Plan		Pacing Your Lessons	
LESSONS AND OBJECTIVES	California Standards	40–50 Minute Periods	90-Minute Periods
Explore 3-1 Modeling Relations (p. 142) • Use manipulatives to investigate a geometric pattern. **3-1 Representing Relations** (pp. 143–148) • Represent relations as sets of ordered pairs, tables, mappings, and graphs. • Find the inverse of a relation.	16.0, 17.0, 24.3, 25.1	2	1.5
3-2 Representing Functions (pp. 149–154) • Determine whether a relation is a function. • Find functional values.	16.0, 18.0, 24.3, 25.1	2	0.5
3-3 Linear Functions (pp. 155–161) • Identify linear equations, intercepts, and zeros. • Graph linear equations. **Extend 3-3 Graphing Linear Functions** (pp. 162–163) • Use a graphing calculator to graph linear equations.	6.0, 7.0, 16.0, 17.0	2	1.5
3-4 Arithmetic Sequences (pp. 165–170) • Recognize arithmetic sequences. • Extend and write formulas for arithmetic sequences.	7AF3.4	2	1
3-5 Proportional and Nonproportional Relationships (pp. 172–176) • Write an equation for a proportional relationship. • Write an equation for a nonproportional relationship.	16.0, 24.1	2	0.5
REVIEW		1	0.5
ASSESSMENT		1	0.5*
TOTAL		12	6

*The complete **Assessment Planner** for Chapter 3 is provided on p. 139.*

* *Begin Chapter 4 in the second half of the period.*

Professional Development

California Standards Vertical Alignment

Before Chapter 3

Related Topics from Grade 7

- Represent and interpret graphic relationships
  Standard 7AF1.5

- Graph functions of the form $y = nx^2$ and $y = nx^3$ and use in solving problems Standard 7AF3.1

- Graph linear functions and recognize the slope
  Standard 7AF3.3

Chapter 3

Related Topics from Algebra I

- Understand the concepts of a relation
- Determine the domain and range
- Determine whether a relation is a function

See individual lessons for the specific Standards covered.

After Chapter 3

Preparation for Algebra II

- Solve problems involving functional concepts
  Standard 2A24.0

- Solve and graph quadratic and complex equations
  Standard 2A8.0

- Solve problems involving arithmetic and geometric series
  Standard 2A22.0

- Derive the summation formulas for arithmetic series and geometric series Standard 2A23.0

Back-Mapping

California Algebra 1 was conceived and developed with the final result in mind, student success in Algebra I and beyond. The authors, using the California Mathematics Standards as their guide, developed this brand-new series by "back-mapping" from the desired result of student success in Algebra I and beyond. McGraw-Hill's *California Geometry, California Algebra 2,* and *California Algebra Readiness* were developed utilizing the same philosophy.

What the Research Says...

Hines et al (2001) found that reasoning with tables provides opportunities to deepen understanding.

- In Lesson 3-1, tables are used to determine properties of relations.

- In Lesson 3-3, tables are used to solve equations.

- In Lessons 3-4 and 3-5, students use patterns in tables to identify sequences and write equations based on the patterns.

 Professional Development

Targeted professional development has been articulated throughout the *California Mathematics: Concepts, Skills, and Problem Solving* series. The **McGraw-Hill Professional Development Video Library** provides short videos that support the Key Standards. For more information, visit ca.algebra1.com.

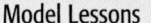

| Model Lessons | Instructional Strategies |

TeacherWorks™ All-in-One Planner and Resource Center

All of the print materials from the Classroom Resource Masters are available on your TeacherWorks™ CD-ROM.

BL = Below Grade Level **OL** = On Grade Level **AL** = Above Grade Level **ELL** = English Language Learner

Chapter Resource Masters						3-1	3-2	3-3	3-4	3-5
BL	OL		ELL	Lesson Reading Guide		5	12	19	27	34
BL	OL		ELL	Study Guide and Intervention*		6	13	20	28	35
BL	OL			Skills Practice*		8	15	22	30	37
	OL	AL		Practice*		9	16	23	31	38
	OL	AL		Word Problem Practice*		10	17	24	32	39
	OL	AL		Enrichment		11	18	25	33	40
	OL	AL		Calculator and Spreadsheet Activities				26		
	OL	AL		Chapter Assessments*		41–62				
BL	OL	AL		5-Minute Check Transparencies		✓	✓	✓	✓	✓
BL	OL			Teaching Mathematics with Manipulatives		✓	✓	✓		✓

*Also available in Spanish.

AssignmentWorks

Differentiated Assignments, Answers, and Solutions

- Print a customized assignment worksheet using the Student Edition exercises along with an answer key or worked-out solutions.
- Use default lesson assignments as outlined in the Differentiated Homework Options in the Teacher Wraparound Edition.
- Includes modified questions from the Student Edition.

Interactive Classroom

This CD-ROM is a customizable Microsoft® PowerPoint® presentation that includes:

- In-Class Examples
- Your Turn Exercises*
- 5-Minute Check Transparencies*
- Links to Online Study Tools
- Concepts in Motion

*compatible with response pad technology

Example 4b
Graph the preimage and its image.
Answer:
The preimage is trapezoid *EFGH*.
The image is trapezoid *E'F'G'H'*.
Notice that the image has sides that are twice the length of the sides of the original figure.

ExamView®Assessment Suite

ExamView® Assessment Suite lets you

- Create, edit, and customize tests and worksheets
- Create multiple versions
- Translate from English to Spanish and vice versa
- Build tests aligned with your state standards
- Track students' progress using the Teacher Management System

Student Resources

StudentWorks™ Plus

Textbook, Audio, Workbooks, and more

This CD-ROM is a valuable resource for students to access content online and use online resources to continue learning Chapter 3 concepts. Includes:

• Complete Student Editions in both English and Spanish
• English audio integrated throughout the text
• Links to Concepts in Motion, Personal Tutor, and other online resources
• Access to all student worksheets
• Daily Assignments and Grade Log

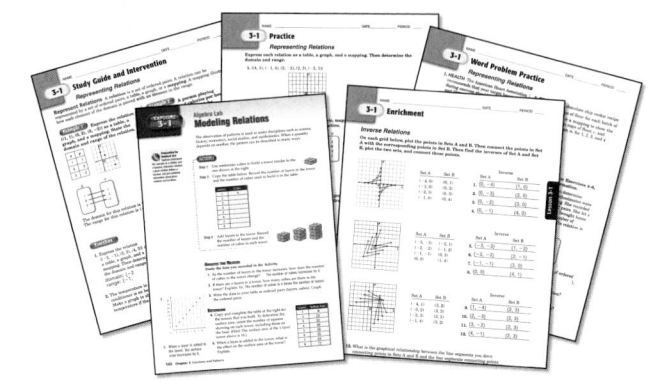

Super DVD

The Super DVD contains two Glencoe multimedia products.

MindJogger Plus An alternative review of concepts in which students work as teams in a game show format to gain points for correct answers.

What's Math Got to Do With It? Real Life Math Videos Engaging video that shows students how math is used in everyday situations

Unit 2 Theme: Linear Functions

Internet Resources

Math Online ca.algebra1.com

TEACHER	PARENT	STUDENT	
			Online Study Tools
	•	•	Online Student Edition
•	•	•	Multilingual Glossary
			Lesson Resources
	•	•	BrainPOP®
•	•	•	Concepts in Motion
•	•	•	Extra Examples
	•	•	Other Calculator Keystrokes
•			Problem of the Week Cards
	•	•	Real-World Careers
	•	•	Self-Check Quizzes
			Chapter Resources
	•	•	Chapter Readiness
	•	•	Chapter Test
	•	•	Standardized Test Practice
	•	•	Vocabulary Review/Chapter Review Activities
			Unit Resources
•		•	Cross-Curricular Internet Project
			Other Resources
•			Dinah Zike's Foldables
	•	•	Hotmath Homework Help
•			Key Concepts
•	•	•	Meet the Authors
	•	•	Personal Tutor
•			Project CRISS™
	•	•	Scavenger Hunts and Answer Sheets
•			Vocabulary PuzzleMakers

Focus on Mathematical Content

Big Idea for Chapter 3:
Functions and Patterns

A function represents a dependence of one quantity on another and can be described in a variety of ways. The idea of representing a function as a table, a graph, or a mapping is used from algebra to beyond calculus. Explore 3-1 on page 140 uses concrete objects to help students understand that a pattern can be described in many ways. Centimeter cubes are used to build a tower. As each layer is added, the number of cubes used changes accordingly. An algebraic expression to describe the relationship is written, a table of values is made, and a set of ordered pairs is written. The ordered pairs are graphed on a coordinate grid.

Why It's Important

For This Chapter
The lessons in this chapter use the properties and attributes of functions to represent them in different ways and translate among their various representations.
- What four ways can a relation be represented? (Lesson 3-1)
- How can you determine if a relation is a function? (Lesson 3-2)
- How do you know if an equation is a linear equation? (Lesson 3-3)
- How can you find a specific term in an arithmetic sequence? (Lesson 3-4)
- When a number pattern leads to a general rule and the relationship between the domain and range of the relation is linear, what type of equation best describes the relationship? (Lesson 3-5)

After This Chapter
- In Chapter 4, students examine more closely the equations that represent the linear functions they graph in this chapter.
- In algebra, situations modeled by functions that are not linear are also studied.
- Throughout mathematics, functions are used to model many real-world situations that relate two variables.

3-1 Representing Relations

A relation can be represented as a set of ordered pairs (Lesson 1-9). Relations can also be represented in several other ways: a table, a mapping, or a graph.

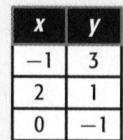

x	y
−1	3
2	1
0	−1

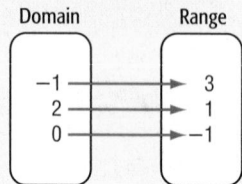

- A table lists the set of x-coordinates in the first column and their corresponding y-coordinates in the second column.

- Each ordered pair is graphed on a coordinate plane.

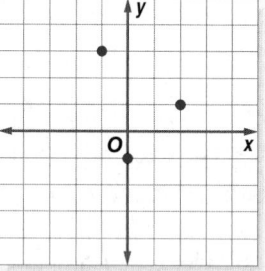

- A mapping lists the x–values in set X and the y–values in set Y. An arrow is drawn from each x–value in X to its corresponding y–value in Y.

The inverse of a relation is found by switching the coordinates in each ordered pair. In other words, the domain values become the range values and the range values become the domain values.

3-2 Representing Functions

A function is a relation in which each element of the range is paired with exactly one element of the domain. This means that an x-coordinate cannot be repeated. You can use a vertical line test to check if a graph is a function. Draw vertical lines on a graph, if the graph does not touch any vertical line more than once, it is a function.

Using function notation, if x represents the independent quantity (elements of the domain) then $f(x)$ represents the dependent quantity (elements of the range). Equations that are functions can be written using function notation. Solve the equation for the dependent variable, then replace that variable with f(independent variable), such as $f(x)$. For example, $y = x + 1$ becomes $f(x) = x + 1$ written in function notation.

Linear Functions

Linear equations can be written in the form $Ax + By = C$, the standard form of a linear equation. An equation is linear if the Properties of Equality can be applied to rewrite it in standard form.

The graph of a linear function has at most one x-intercept (where the graph crosses the x-axis) and one y-intercept (where the graph crosses the y-axis). You can find the intercepts by alternately replacing x and y with 0. If you graph these two points and then draw the line that connects them, all of the ordered pairs that lie on that line are solutions of the equation. Values of x for which $f(x) = 0$ are called zeros of the function. A zero of a function is an x-intercept. A graph that is a horizontal or vertical line has only one intercept.

 ## Arithmetic Sequences

A sequence is a set of numbers in a specific order. The numbers in a sequence are called terms. If the terms of a sequence increase or decrease at a constant rate, it is called an arithmetic sequence. The difference between successive terms of an arithmetic sequence is called the common difference, d. Any term of an arithmetic sequence can be found by adding the common difference to the preceding term.

The formula that can be used to find a specific term in an arithmetic sequence is $a_n = a_1 + (n - 1)d$. This means to find a specific term, a_n, find the sum of the first term, a_1, and the product of the common difference, times one less than n, the number of the specific term.

 ## Proportional and Nonproportional Relationships

When you solve a problem by making a conclusion based on a pattern, you are using inductive reasoning. Often patterns in sequences of figures or of numbers can be found. Sometimes these patterns can lead to a general rule for the pattern. If the relationship between the domain and range of a relation is linear, a linear equation can be used to describe the relationship.

Some linear relationships are proportional and can be modeled with an equation of the form $y + kx$. Others are non-proportional.

To write an equation for a pattern that exhibits a linear relationship and is made up of a set of data with two variables (x and y) follow these steps:

- Use a ratio to compare the common difference of the range values to the common difference of the domain values. This ratio should be a constant ratio.
- Then, write the equation as: dependent variable = constant ratio x independent variable. That is, $y =$ (constant ratio)x
- Check to be sure this equation works for the set of data. If it does not, then check to see if the difference between the value obtained for the y using your equation and the given value of y is the same for each pair of x and y values in the pattern. If so, add that difference to one side of the equation to correctly describe the relation.

CHAPTER 3

Differentiated Instruction

Options for Chapter 3 Lessons

ELL = English Language Learner	**AL** = Above Grade Level	**SS** = Struggling Students	**SN** = Special Needs

Connecting Mathematics to Music **SS** **SN**

Use with Lesson 3-1

If students have difficulty with the concept of a mapping, have those who are familiar with music make a mapping of the relation between different notes and the number of beats the notes contain. For example, a whole note has 4 beats, and a half note has 2 beats. In this case, the notes would be the domain and the number of beats would be the range.

Using Interpersonal Skills **ELL**

Use with Lesson 3-2

Have pairs of students write a relation that is a function and a relation that is not a function. Students can write each relation as a table, a set of ordered pairs, or an equation.

Connecting Mathematics with Nature **AL**

Use with Lesson 3-4

Sequences are often visible in nature. Have students research different sequences in nature, and determine whether the sequence is arithmetic. One particular sequence, called Fibonacci series, appears in reproduction rates, the arrangement of seeds in a sunflower head, the arrangement of leaves, and many other natural phenomena. Students can use an Internet search engine and the words "Fibonacci series nature" to find numerous references.

Noteables™ Interactive Study Notebook with Foldables™

Noteables™ Interactive Study Notebook with Foldables™ is a study organizer that provides helpful steps for students to follow to organize their notes for Chapter 3.

- Students use Noteables to record notes and to complete their Foldables as you present the material for each lesson.
- Noteables correspond to the Examples in the *Teacher Wraparound Edition* and *Interactive Classroom CD-ROM.*

Intervention

Quick Review Math Handbook*

is Glencoe's mathematical handbook for students and parents.

Hot Words includes a glossary of terms.

Hot Topics consists of two parts:

- explanations of key mathematical concepts
- exercises to check students' understanding.

Lesson	Hot Topics Section	Lesson	Hot Topics Section
3-1	6.7	3-4	6.7
3-2	1.5, 2.3, 6.7	3-5	6.1
3-3	6.4, 6.7;6.2, 6.7		

*Also available in Spanish

Teacher to Teacher

Berchie Holliday
Former Mathematics Teacher
Northwest Local School District
Cincinnati, Ohio

USE BEFORE LESSON 3-2

❝ I introduce the concept of *function* with three different mappings of favorite colors.

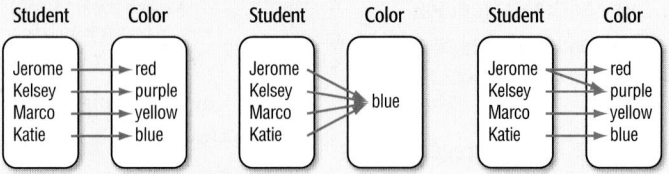

The first two mappings illustrate functions: each student can have a different favorite color or many students can have the same favorite color. However, the third mapping is *not* a function, because one student (Jerome) cannot have more than one favorite color. ❞

Reading and Writing in Mathematics

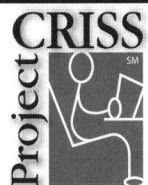

CRISS SM Project

STUDY SKILL

Students can use a free-form map to create their own representation of the concepts they are learning. Free-form mapping is done as a cooperative activity after students have read about and discussed a lesson or chapter.

Give groups of students large sheets of paper and markers. Have them present the important ideas from the lesson or chapter on paper using words, pictures, graphs, and diagrams.

The free-form map at the right represents the concepts in Lessons 3-1 and 3-2.

Representing Relations and Functions

Ordered Pairs Sample
(−1, 3)
(2, 1)
(0, −1)

Table Sample

x	y
−1	3
2	1
0	1

Graph Sample

Mapping
Each element of the domain is paired with an element of the range.
Sample

−1 → 3
2 → 1
0 → −1

CReating **I**ndependence through **S**tudent-owned **S**trategies

CHAPTER 3 Notes

Dinah Zike's Foldables™

Focus Students write about graphing relations and functions as these concepts are presented in the lessons of this chapter.

Teach Have students make and label the tabs for each lesson of their Foldables as illustrated.

Have students use the appropriate tabs as they cover each lesson in this chapter. Point out that the last tab is for their vocabulary words.

When to Use It Encourage students to write descriptive paragraphs about their experiences and graph examples in their Foldables. A version of a completed Foldable is shown on p. 177.

Differentiated Instruction

[CRM] Student-Built Glossary, pp. 1–2 Students should complete the chart by providing the definition of each term and an example as they progress through Chapter 3. This study tool can also be used to review for the chapter test.

Materials Needed for Chapter 3

- centimeter cubes (Explore 3-1)
- colored pencils (Lesson 3-1)
- graphing calculator (Extend 3-3)

CHAPTER 3

Functions and Patterns

BIG Ideas

- **Standard 16.0** Students understand the concepts of a relation and a function, determine whether a given relation defines a function, and give pertinent information about given relations and functions.

- **Standard 17.0** Students determine the domain of independent variables and the range of dependent variables defined by a graph, a set of ordered pairs, or a symbolic expression.

Key Vocabulary
arithmetic sequence (p. 165)

function (p. 149)

inverse (p. 145)

y-intercept (p. 156)

🌐 Real-World Link
Currency A function is a rule or a formula. You can use a function to describe real-world situations like converting between currencies. For example, in Japan, an item that costs 10,000 yen is equivalent to about 87 U.S. dollars.

FOLDABLES Study Organizer

Functions and Patterns Make this Foldable to help you organize your notes about graphing relations and functions. Begin with three sheets of notebook paper.

1 **Fold** each sheet of paper in half from top to bottom.

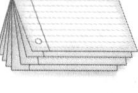

2 **Cut** along fold. Staple the six half-sheets together to form a booklet.

3 **Cut** tabs into margin. The top tab is 2 lines deep, the next tab is 6 lines deep, and so on.

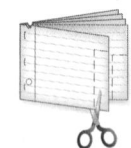

4 **Label** each of the tabs with a lesson number. Use the last page for vocabulary.

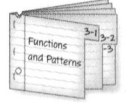

GET READY for Chapter 3

Diagnose Readiness You have two options for checking Prerequisite Skills.

Option 1

Take the Quick Check below. Refer to the Quick Review for help.

Option 2

Mathnline Take the Online Readiness Quiz at ca.algebra1.com.

QUICK Check

(Used in Lessons 3-1 through 3-4)

Evaluate each expression if $a = -1$, $b = 4$, and $c = -3$. (Lesson 1-2)

1. $a + b - c$ **6**
2. $2c - b$ **−10**
3. $3a - 6b - 2c$ **−21**
4. $6a + 8b + \frac{2}{3}c$ **24**

5. **FOOD** Noah is buying a sandwich with 1 type of meat, 2 types of cheese, and 2 types of vegetable. Each topping costs $1.55, $0.65, and $0.85 respectively. How much will Noah spend on the sandwich? **$4.55**

(Used in Lessons 3-1 through 3-5)

Solve each equation for y. 9. $y = -\frac{2}{3}x + 3$ (Lesson 2-8)

6. $2x + y = 1$
   $y = 1 - 2x$
7. $x = 8 - y$
   $y = 8 - x$
8. $6x - 3y = 12$
   $y = 2x - 4$
9. $2x + 3y = 9$
10. $9 - \frac{1}{2}y = 4x$
    $y = 18 - 8x$
11. $\frac{y + 5}{3} = x + 2$
    $y = 3x + 1$

(Used in Lessons 3-1 through 3-3)

Graph each ordered pair on a coordinate grid. (Lesson 1-9)

12. $(3, 0)$
13. $(-2, 1)$ **12–17.**
14. $(-3, 3)$ **See Ch. 3**
15. $(-5, 5)$ **Answer**
16. $(0, 6)$ **Appendix.**
17. $(2, -1)$

18. **MAPS** Taylor is looking at a map and needs to go 3 blocks east and 2 blocks south from where he is standing now. If he is standing at $(0, 0)$, what will his coordinates be when he arrives at his destination? **(3, −2)**

QUICK Review

EXAMPLE 1

Evaluate $a + 2b + 3c$ if $a = -1$, $b = 4$, and $c = -3$.

$a + 2b + 3c$ Original expression

$= (-1) + 2(4) + 3(-3)$ Substitute −1 for a, 4 for b, and −3 for c.

$= -1 + 8 - 9$ Multiply.

$= -2$ Simplify.

EXAMPLE 2

Solve $x - 2 = \frac{y}{3}$ for y.

$x - 2 = \frac{y}{3}$ Original equation

$3(x - 2) = (3)\frac{y}{3}$ Multiply each side by 3.

$3x - 6 = y$ Simplify.

EXAMPLE 3

Graph $(5, -3)$ on a coordinate grid.

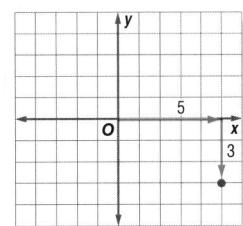

Start at the origin. Since the x-coordinate is 5, move 5 units to the right.

Since the y-coordinate is −3, move down 3 units. Draw a dot.

Diagnostic Assessment

Exercises	California Standards	Intervention
1–5	7AF1.1	SE Review Lesson 1-2, pp. 10–14
6–11	5.0	SE Review Lesson 2-8, pp. 117–121
12–18	5AF1.4	SE Review Lesson 1-9, pp. 53–58

✓ Formative Assessment

CRM Anticipation Guide, pp. 3–4
Spotting Preconceived Ideas
Students complete this survey to determine prior knowledge about ideas from Chapter 3. Revisit this worksheet after completing the chapter. Also see p. 180.

TWE Lesson Activities
- Ticket Out the Door, p. 161
- Crystal Ball, pp. 154, 170
- Name the Math, p. 176
- Yesterday's News, p. 148

Chapter Checkpoints

SE Mid-Chapter Quiz, p. 164
SE Study Guide and Review, pp. 177–180
SE California Standards Practice, pp. 182–183
CRM Quizzes, pp. 43 and 44
CRM Standardized Test Practice, pp. 60–62

Mathnline **ca.algebra1.com**
- Self-Check Quizzes
- Practice Test
- Standardized Test Practice

✓ Summative Assessment

SE Chapter Practice Test, p. 181
CRM Mid-Chapter Test, p. 45
CRM Vocabulary Test, p. 46
CRM Extended-Response Test, p. 59
CRM Leveled Chapter Tests, pp. 47–58
⊙ ExamView® Assessment Suite

KEY
CRM *Chapter 3 Resource Masters*
SE Student Edition
TWE Teacher Wraparound Edition
⊙ CD-ROM

EXPLORE 3-1 Lesson Notes

 **Focus**

Materials

• centimeter cubes

Teaching Tip Before students begin this lab, point out that they are going to investigate the relationship between two quantities—the number of layers of cubes in a tower and the number of cubes used to build the tower.

2 Teach

Working in Cooperative Groups
Put students in groups of 2 or 3, mixing abilities. Have groups complete the Activity, Analyze the Results 1–3, and Extension 4. For Extension 4, remind students that they need to count the squares on each side and on the top and bottom of the tower to determine surface area.

Practice Have students complete Extension 5.

3 Assess

 Formative Assessment

Use Analyze the Results 3 to assess whether students can identify the pattern shown in the scatter plot. Have them look at their graphs.

Ask:
As the number of layers increases, how does the number of cubes in the tower change? Sample answer: The number of cubes increases.

From Concrete to Abstract
Ask:
If there are n layers in a tower, what is the surface area of the tower? $8(n + 1)$

EXPLORE 3-1 Algebra Lab
Modeling Relations

The observation of patterns is used in many disciplines such as science, history, economics, social studies, and mathematics. When a quantity depends on another, the pattern can be described in many ways.

 Preparation for Standard 16.0 Students understand the concepts of a relation and a function, determine whether a given relation defines a function, and give pertinent information about given relations and functions.

ACTIVITY

Step 1 Use centimeter cubes to build a tower similar to the one shown at the right.

Step 2 Copy the table below. Record the number of layers in the tower and the number of cubes used to build it in the table.

Layers	Cubes
1	4
2	
3	
4	
5	
6	
7	
8	

Step 3 Add layers to the tower. Record the number of layers and the number of cubes in each tower.

  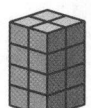

ANALYZE THE RESULTS
Study the data you recorded in the Activity.

1. As the number of layers in the tower increases, how does the number of cubes in the tower change?   **The number of cubes increases by 4.**

2. If there are n layers in a tower, how many cubes are there in the tower? Explain. **$4n$; The number of cubes is 4 times the number of layers.**

3. Write the data in your table as ordered pairs (layers, cubes). Graph the ordered pairs.

3.

[Scatter plot with y-axis labeled 4, 8, 12, 16, 20, 24, 28, 32 and x-axis labeled 0 through 8, with points plotted showing a linear increasing pattern]

EXTENSION

4. Copy and complete the table at the right for the towers that you built. To determine the surface area, count the number of squares showing on each tower, including those on the base. (Hint: The surface area of the 1-layer tower above is 16.)

5. When a layer is added to the tower, what is the effect on the surface area of the tower? Explain.

Layers	Surface Area
1	16
2	24
3	32
4	40
5	48
6	56
7	64
8	72

5. When a layer is added to the tower, the surface area increases by 8.

142 Chapter 3 Functions and Patterns

Representing Relations

Main Ideas

- Represent relations as sets of ordered pairs, tables, mappings, and graphs.
- Find the inverse of a relation.

 Preparation for Standard 16.0 Students understand the concepts of a relation and a function, determine whether a given relation defines a function, and give pertinent information about given relations and functions.

Standard 17.0 Students determine the domain of independent variables and the range of dependent variables defined by a graph, a set of ordered pairs, or a symbolic expression.

New Vocabulary

mapping
inverse

GET READY for the Lesson

Ken Griffey, Jr.'s batting statistics for home runs and strikeouts can be represented as a set of ordered pairs. The number of home runs are the first coordinates, and the number of strikeouts are the second coordinates.

You can plot the ordered pairs on a graph to look for patterns.

Ken Griffey, Jr.		
Year	Home Runs	Strikeouts
1998	56	121
1999	48	108
2000	40	117
2001	22	72
2002	8	39
2003	13	44
2004	20	67

Source: baseball-reference.com

Represent Relations Recall that a *relation* is a set of ordered pairs. A relation can also be represented by a table, a graph, or a mapping. A **mapping** illustrates how each element of the domain is paired with an element in the range.

Ordered Pairs

(1, 2)
(−2, 3)
(0, −3)

Table

x	y
1	2
−2	3
0	−3

Graph

Mapping

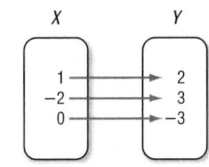

Study Tip

Look Back

To review **relations**, see Lesson 1-9.

CONcepts in MOtion

Animation ca.algebra1.com

EXAMPLE   Represent a Relation

1 **a.** Express the relation {(3, 2), (−1, 2), (0, −3), (−2, −2)} as a table, a graph, and a mapping.

Table

List the *x*-coordinates in the first column and the corresponding *y*-coordinates in the second column.

x	y
3	2
−1	2
0	−3
−2	−2

Graph

Graph each ordered pair on a coordinate plane.

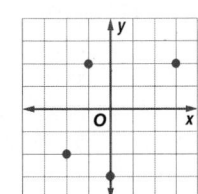

Mapping

List the *x*-values in set *X* and the *y*-values in set *Y*. Draw arrows from the *x*-values in *X* to the corresponding *y*-values.

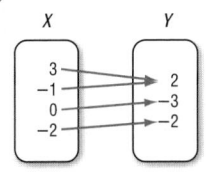

(continued on the next page)

Lesson 3-1 Representing Relations   **143**

---

1 Focus

Standards Alignment

Before Lesson 3-1
Represent and interpret quantitative relationships graphically from Standard 7AF1.5

Lesson 3-1
Understand the concepts of a relation and a function, and determine the domain and range from Standards 16.0 and 17.0

After Lesson 3-1
Solve problems involving functional concepts from Standard 2A24.0

2 Teach

Scaffolding Questions
Have students read *Get Ready for the Lesson*.

Ask:
- Give an example of an ordered pair from the data table shown. Sample answer: (56, 121)
- Why might plotting the data on a graph help a person analyze this data? Sample answer: Looking at the

(continued on the next page)

Lesson 3-1 Resources

Chapter 3 Resource Masters

Lesson Reading Guide, p. 5 **BL** **OL** **ELL**
Study Guide and Intervention, pp. 6–7
BL **OL** **ELL**
Skills Practice, p. 8 **BL** **OL**
Practice, p. 9 **OL** **AL**
Word Problem Practice, p. 10 **OL** **AL**
Enrichment, p. 11 **OL** **AL**

Transparencies

5-Minute Check Transparency 3-1

Additional Print Resources

Noteables™ Interactive Study Notebook with Foldables™

Technology

ca.algebra1.com
Interactive Classroom CD-ROM
AssignmentWorks CD-ROM
Graphing Calculator Easy Files

data graphically might reveal patterns that are not easy to detect when looking at the numbers in the table.

• **How do the number of strike-outs change as the number of home runs increase?** The number of strikeouts increase.

Represent Relations

Example 1 shows how to represent a relation as a table, a graph, and a mapping. **Example 2** shows how to solve a real-world problem in which the scales used on the axes may not be 1 and may not begin with 0.

✓ Formative Assessment

Use the Check Your Progress exercises after each example to determine students' understanding of concepts.

ADDITIONAL EXAMPLE

a. Express the relation {(4, 3), (−2, −1), (−3, 2), (2, −4), (0, −4)} as a table, a graph, and a mapping.

x	y
4	3
−2	−1
−3	2
2	−4
0	−4

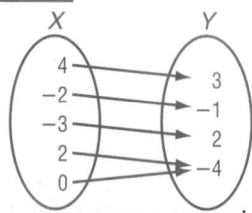

b. Determine the domain and range. D = {−3, −2, 0, 2, 4}; R = {−4, −1, 2, 3}

Additional Examples are also in:

• Noteables™ Interactive Study Notebook with Foldables™

• Interactive Classroom PowerPoint® Presentations

Real-World Link

An average student between the ages of 12 and 17 spends 10.3 hours per week with friends outside of school and about 7.8 hours per week talking to friends using the telephone, E-mail, instant messaging, or text messaging.

Source: www.pewinternet.org

---

b. Determine the domain and range.

The domain for this relation is {−2, −1, 0, 3}.

The range is {−3, −2, 2}.

✓ CHECK Your Progress

1A. Express the relation {(−4, 8), (−1, 9), (−4, 7), (6, 9)} as a table, a graph, and a mapping. **See margin.**

1B. Determine the domain and range of the relation. D = {−4, −1, 6}; R = {7, 8

Recall that the domain of a relation is the set of values of the independent variable and the range is the set of values of the dependent variable. This is useful when using relations that represent real-life situations.

🌐 Real-World EXAMPLE

2 **ANALYZE TABLES** The table shows the results of a recent survey in which students were asked about their use of text messaging.

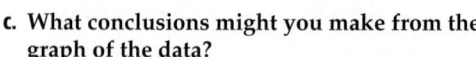

Percent of Students Who Use Text Messaging						
Age of Students	12	13	14	15	16	17
Percent	17	30	34	45	46	54

Source: www.pewinternet.org

a. Determine the domain and range of the relation.

The domain is {12, 13, 14, 15, 16, 17} because age is the independent variable. It is unaffected by the percents.

The range is {17, 30, 34, 45, 46, 54} because the percent of teens who use text messaging depends on the age of the teens.

b. Graph the data.

• The values of the x-axis need to go from 12 to 17. It is not practical to begin the scale at 0. Begin at 12 and extend to 17 to include all of the data. The units can be 1 unit per grid square.

• The values on the y-axis need to go from 17 to 54. In this case, you can begin the scale at 0 and extend to 60. You can use units of 10.

c. What conclusions might you make from the graph of the data?

There is a steady increase in the percent of students who use text messaging as the students get older.

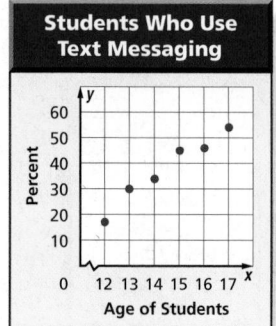

Students Who Use Text Messaging

✓ CHECK Your Progress

MONEY Leticia earns $7 for walking 1 dog, $28 for walking 4 dogs, $42 for walking 6 dogs, and $49 for walking 7 dogs.

2A. Determine the domain and range of the relation. D: {1, 4, 6, 7};
R: {7, 28, 42, 49}

2B. Graph the data. **See Ch. 3 Answer Appendix.**

🌐 **Personal Tutor** at ca.algebra1.com

144   Chapter 3 Functions and Patterns

Additional Answer

1A.

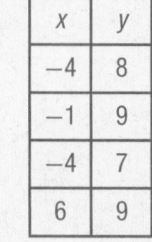

x	y
−4	8
−1	9
−4	7
6	9

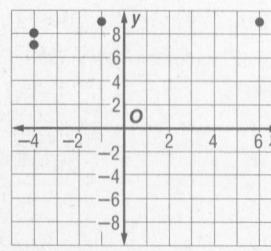

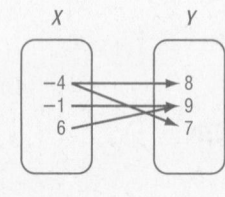

Inverse Relations The **inverse** of any relation is obtained by switching the coordinates in each ordered pair. The domain of a relation becomes the range of the inverse and the range of a relation becomes the domain of the inverse.

KEY CONCEPT *Inverse of a Relation*

Relation Q is the inverse of relation S if and only if for every ordered pair (a, b) in S, there is an ordered pair (b, a) in Q.

Relation	Inverse of Relation
$\{(0, 2), (-5, 4)\}$	$\{(2, 0), (4, -5)\}$

EXAMPLE Inverse Relation

3 Express the relation shown in the mapping as a set of ordered pairs. Then write the inverse of the relation.

Relation Notice that both 2 and 3 in the domain are paired with −4 in the range. $\{(2, -4),$ $(3, -4), (5, -7), (6, -8)\}$

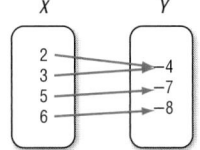

Inverse Exchange x and y in each ordered pair to write the inverse relation. $\{(-4, 2),$ $(-4, 3), (-7, 5), (-8, 6)\}$

The mapping of the inverse is shown at the right. Compare this to the mapping of the relation.

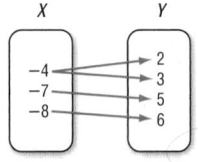

Study Tip

Functions The relation in Example 3 is a function, but the inverse of the relation is not. You will learn more about functions in Lesson 3-2.

✓**CHECK Your Progress**

3. Express the relation shown in the table as a set of ordered pairs. Then write the inverse of the relation.

x	1	3	5	7
y	2	4	6	8

$\{(1, 2), (3, 4), (5, 6), (7, 8)\}; \{(2, 1), (4, 3), (6, 5), (8, 7)\}$

ALGEBRA LAB

Relations and Inverses

• Graph the relation $\{(3, 4), (-2, 5), (-4, -3), (5, -6), (-1, 0), (0, 2)\}$ on grid paper using a colored pencil. Connect the points in order.

• Use a different colored pencil to graph the inverse of the relation, connecting the points in order.

• Fold the grid paper so that the positive y-axis lies on top of the positive x-axis. Hold the paper up to a light to view the points.

ANALYZE 3–4. See margin.

1. What do you notice about the location of the points? matches the point.

2. Unfold the paper. Describe the transformation of each point and its inverse.

2. reflections across the fold

3. What do you think are the ordered pairs that represent the points on the fold line? Describe these in terms of x and y.

4. How could you graph the inverse of a function without writing ordered pairs first?

---

2 **OPINION POLLS** The table shows the percent of students satisfied with their grades at the time of the survey.

Year	1996	1999	2002	2005
Percent Satisfied	21	32	60	51

a. Determine the domain and range of the relation.

D = {1996, 1999, 2002, 2005}; R = {21, 32, 51, 60}

b. Graph the data. See bottom margin.

c. What conclusions might you make from the graph of the data? Satisfaction increased from 1996 to 2002 but decreased from 2002 to 2005.

Inverse Relations

Example 3 shows how to find the inverse of a relation.

ADDITIONAL EXAMPLE

3 Express the relation shown in the mapping as a set of ordered pairs. Write the inverse of the relation.

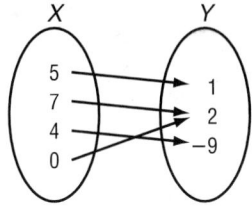

Relation: $\{(5, 1), (7, 2), (4, -9), (0, 2)\}$

Inverse: $\{(1, 5), (2, 7), (-9, 4), (2, 0)\}$

Additional Answers (Algebra Lab)

3. Sample ordered pairs: $(-1, -1)$, $(0, 0)$, $(2, 2)$; for each (x, y), $x = y$

4. Reflect the points across the line in which the x-coordinate equals the y-coordinate.

Answer for Additional Example 2b.

Percent Satisfied with Grades

(graph: Percent Satisfied vs. Year; points at 1996≈21, 1999≈32, 2002≈60, 2005≈51)

Algebra Lab

Students will need grid paper and colored pencils. After students have created the graph, explain that the fold they are to make is along a line through the center of quadrant I, the origin, and quadrant III. You could have students place patty paper over the grid paper and then have them graph.

Inverse Relations The inverse of a relation has the same number of ordered pairs as the relation. The *x*- and *y*-coordinates in each ordered pair of the relation have been reversed to make the inverse of the relation.

3 Practice

Formative Assessment

Use Exercises 1–7 to check for understanding.

Use the chart at the bottom of this page to customize assignments for your students.

Reading Tip
Point out to students that the letters D and R are often used to name the sets of numbers that represent the *domain* and *range*.

Odd/Even Assignments
Exercises 8–27 are structured so that students practice the same concepts whether they are assigned odd or even problems.

Additional Answers

14. Sample answer: (1996, 10), (2000, 4.4), (2002, 4.1)

15. {1992, 1993, 1994, 1995, 1996, 1997, 1998, 1999, 2000, 2001, 2002}

17. There are fewer students per computer in more recent years. So, the number of computers in schools has increased.

✓ CHECK Your Understanding

Example 1
(pp. 143–144)

Express each relation as a table, a graph, and a mapping. Then determine the domain and range. 1–2. Ch. 3 Answer Appendix.

1. {(5, −2), (8, 3), (−7, 1)}   **2.** {(6, 4), (3, −3), (−1, 9), (5, −3)}

Example 2
(p. 144)

COOKING For Exercises 3 and 4, use the table. Recipes often have different cooking times for high altitudes because water boils at a lower temperature.

3. Determine the domain and range of the relation and then graph the data. See Ch. 3 Answer Appendix.

4. Use your graph to estimate the boiling point of water at an altitude of 7000 feet.
Sample answer: 199°F

Altitude (feet)	Boiling Point of Water (°F)
0	212.0
1000	210.2
2000	208.4
3000	206.5
5000	201.9
10,000	193.7

Source: Stevens Institute of Technology

Example 3
(p. 145)

Express the relation shown in each table, mapping, or graph as a set of ordered pairs. Then write the inverse of the relation.

5. {(3, −2), (−6, 7), (4, 3), (−6, 5)}; {(−2, 3), (7, −6), (3, 4), (5, −6)}

5.

x	y
3	−2
−6	7
4	3
−6	5

6.
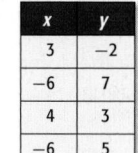

7.
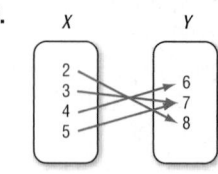

6. {(2, 8), (3, 7), (4, 6), (5, 7)}; {(8, 2), (7, 3), (6, 4), (7, 5)}
7. {(−1, 2), (2, 4), (3, −3), (4, −1)}; {(2, −1), (4, 2), (−3, 3), (−1, 4)}

Exercises

HOMEWORK HELP	
For Exercises	See Examples
8–13	1
14–21	2
22–27	3

Exercise Levels
A: 8–27
B: 28–33
C: 34–36

Express each relation as a table, a graph, and a mapping. Then determine the domain and range. 8–13. See Ch. 3 Answer Appendix.

8. {(0, 0), (6, −1), (5, 6), (4, 2)}   **9.** {(3, 8), (3, 7), (2, −9), (1, −9)}
10. {(4, −2), (3, 4), (1, −2), (6, 4)}   **11.** {(0, 2), (−5, 1), (0, 6), (−1, 9)}
12. {(3, 4), (4, 3), (2, 2), (5, −4), (−4, 5)}
13. {(7, 6), (3, 4), (4, 5), (−2, 6), (−3, 2)}

ANALYZE GRAPHS For Exercises 14–17, use the graph of the average number of students per computer in U.S. public schools. 14–15, 17. See margin.

14. Name three ordered pairs from the graph.

15. Determine the domain of the relation.

16. What are the least and greatest range values? 3.9; 18

17. What conclusions can you make from the graph of the data?

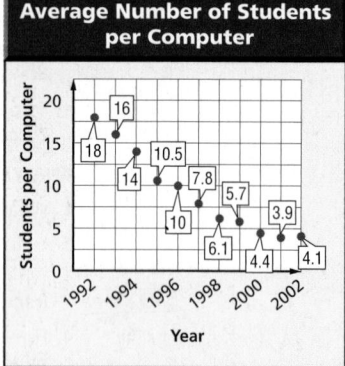

Average Number of Students per Computer

Source: Quality Education Data

DIFFERENTIATED HOMEWORK OPTIONS

Level	Assignment	Two-Day Option	
BL Basic	8–27, 35–45	9–27 odd, 37, 38	8–26 even, 35, 36, 39–45
OL Core	9–29 odd, 30–33, 35–45	8–27, 37, 38	28–33, 35, 36, 39–45
AL Advanced /Pre-AP	28–42, (optional: 43–45)		

18. Sample answer:
D = {2007, 2008, 2009, 2010, 2011, 2012, 2013, 2014};
R = {10.4, 10.7, 11.0, 11.3, 11.5, 11.8, 12.1, 12.4}
19. 2007; 2014
20. Sample answer: The production seems to increase at a steady rate every year.

FOOD For Exercises 18–21, use the graph that shows the projected annual production of apples from 2007–2014.

18. Estimate the domain and range.

19. Which year is projected to have the lowest production? the highest?

20. Describe any patterns that you see.

21. What is a reasonable range value for a domain value of 2015? Explain what this ordered pair represents.

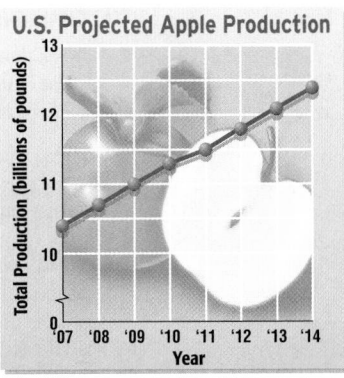

U.S. Projected Apple Production

Source: National Food and Agricultural Policy Project Outlook

Express the relation shown in each table, mapping, or graph as a set of ordered pairs. Then write the inverse of the relation. 22–27. See Ch. 3 Answer Appendix.

22.

x	y
0	3
−5	2
4	7
−8	2

23.

x	y
0	0
4	7
8	10.5
12	18
16	14.5

24.
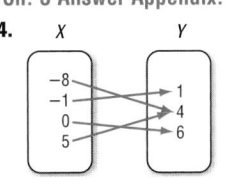

25.
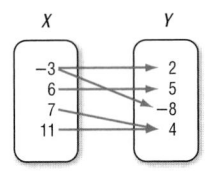

26.
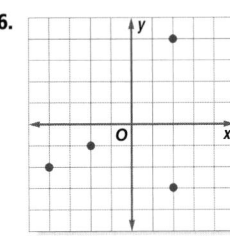

27.
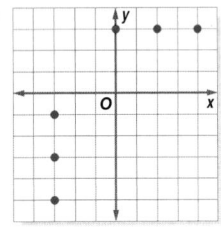

Real-World Link
Studies have shown that students who own fish score higher on both math and verbal SATs, with a combined score 200 points higher than non-pet owners.

Source: diveintofish.com/media/med_facts.html

21. Sample answer: 13.0; This means that the production of apples is projected to be 13.0 billion pounds in the year 2015.

Express each relation as a set of ordered pairs and describe the domain and range. Then write the inverse of the relation. 28–29. See Ch. 3 Answer Appendix.

28.

Buying Aquarium Fish	
Number of Fish	Total Cost ($)
1	2.50
2	5.50
5	10.00
8	18.75

29.
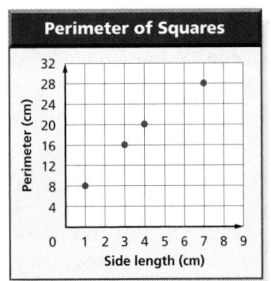

Perimeter of Squares

BIOLOGY For Exercises 30–33, use the fact that a person typically has about 2 pounds of muscle for each 5 pounds of body weight.

30. Make a table to show the relation between body and muscle weight for people weighing 100, 105, 110, 115, 120, 125, and 130 pounds.

31. State the domain and range and then graph the relation.

32. What are the domain and range of the inverse?

33. Graph the inverse relation.
30–33. See Ch. 3 Answer Appendix.

EXTRA PRACTICE
See pages 723, 746.

Math Online
Self-Check Quiz at
ca.algebra1.com

Lesson 3-1 Representing Relations **147**

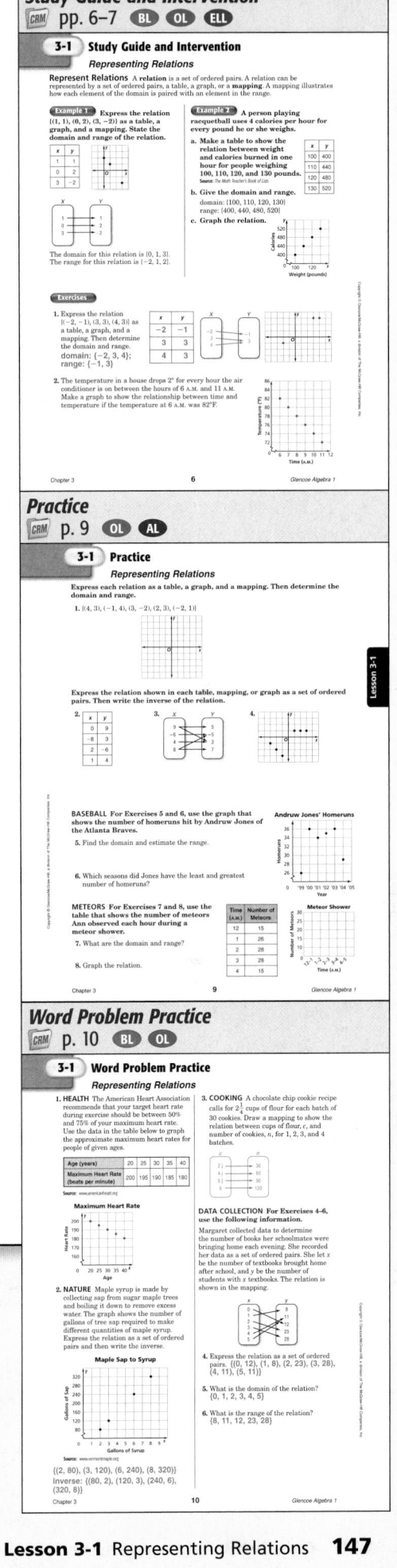

Study Guide and Intervention
CRM pp. 6–7 BL OL ELL

3-1 Study Guide and Intervention
Representing Relations

Practice
CRM p. 9 OL AL

3-1 Practice
Representing Relations

Word Problem Practice
CRM p. 10 BL OL

3-1 Word Problem Practice
Representing Relations

BL = *Below Grade Level*

OL = *On Grade Level*

AL = *Above Grade Level*

ELL = *English Language Learner*

Additional pages not shown:

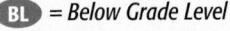 **Lesson Reading Guide,** p. 5 BL OL ELL

 **Skills Practice,** p. 8 BL OL

Enrichment
CRM p. 11 OL AL

3-1 Enrichment

Inverse Relations

On each grid below, plot the points in Sets A and B. Then connect the points in Set A with the corresponding points in Set B. Then find the inverses of Set A and Set B, plot the two sets, and connect those points.

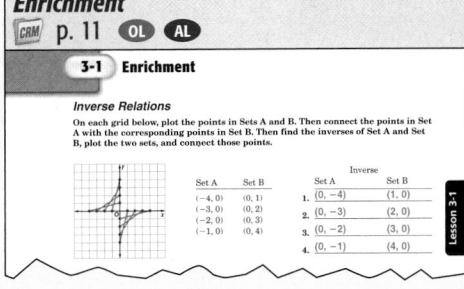

Additional Answers

34. Sample answer: $F = \{(-1, 1), (-2, 2), (-3, 3)\}$, $G = \{(1, -2), (2, -3), (3, -1)\}$; the elements in the domain and range of F should be paired differently in G.

35. Sample answer: The number of movie tickets bought and the total cost of the tickets can be represented using a relation. The total cost depends on the number of tickets bought.
$\{(0, 0), (1, 9), (2, 18), (3, 27)\}$

Number of Tickets	Total Cost
0	$0.00
1	$9.00
2	$18.00
3	$27.00

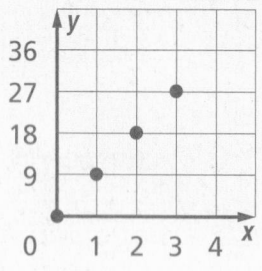

H.O.T. Problems

34. CHALLENGE Find a counterexample to disprove the following. 34–35. See margin.

The domain of relation F contains the same elements as the range of relation G. The range of relation F contains the same elements as the domain of relation G. Therefore, relation G must be the inverse of relation F.

35. OPEN ENDED Describe a real-life situation that can be represented using a relation and discuss how one of the quantities in the relation depends on the other. Then give an example of such a relation in three different ways.

36. *Writing in Math* Use the information about batting statistics on page 143 to explain how relations can be used to represent baseball statistics. Include a graph of the relation of the number of Ken Griffey, Jr.'s, home runs and his strikeouts. Describe the relationship between the quantities.
See Ch. 3 Answer Appendix.

STANDARDS PRACTICE 17.0, 7NS1.7

37. What is the domain of the function that contains the points at (0, -3), (−2, 4), (4, −3), and (−3, 1)? **D**

A $\{-3, -2\}$

B $\{-3, 1, 4\}$

C $\{-3, -2, 0, 1\}$

D $\{-3, -2, 0, 4\}$

38. REVIEW Kara deposited $2000 into a savings account that pays 1.5% interest compounded annually. If she does not deposit any more money into her account, how much will she earn in interest at the end of one year? **F**

F $30

G $35

H $300

J $350

Spiral Review

39. CHEMISTRY Jamaal has 20 milliliters of a 30% solution of nitric acid. How many milliliters of a 15% solution should he add to obtain a 25% solution of nitric acid? (Lesson 2-9) **10 mL**

Solve each equation or formula for the variable specified. (Lesson 2-8)

40. $3x + b = 2x + 5$ for x **$x = 5 - b$**

41. $6w - 3h = b$ for h **$h = \dfrac{6w - b}{3}$**

42. HOURLY PAY Dominique earned $9.75 per hour before her employer increased her hourly rate to $10.15 per hour. What was the percent of increase in her salary? (Lesson 2-7) **4.1%**

GET READY for the Next Lesson

PREREQUISITE SKILL Evaluate each expression. (Lesson 1-2)

43. $12 \div 4 + 15 \cdot 3$ **48**   **44.** $12(19 - 15) - 3 \cdot 8$ **24**   **45.** $(25 - 4) \div (2^2 - 1)$ **7**

148 Chapter 3 Functions and Patterns

Pre-AP Activity Use as an Extension

Write $y = \dfrac{1}{x}$ on the board. Ask the following questions:

- Does $x = 2$ and $y = \dfrac{1}{2}$ makes this equation a true statement? yes
- What value for x makes this equation undefined? $x \neq 0$
- What value could y never equal? $y \neq 0$

Representing Functions

Main Ideas

- Determine whether a relation is a function.
- Find function values.

 Standard 16.0 Students understand the concepts of a relation and a function, determine whether a given relation defines a function, and give pertinent information about given relations and functions.

Standard 18.0 Students determine whether a relation defined by a graph, a set of ordered pairs, or a symbolic expression is a function and justify the conclusion.

New Vocabulary

function
vertical line test
function notation
function value

Study Tip

Look Back
To review **relations and functions,** see Lesson 1-9.

1. Yes; each element of the domain is paired with exactly one element of the range.

▷ GET READY **for the Lesson**

The table shows barometric pressures and temperatures recorded by the National Climatic Data Center over a three-day period.

Pressure (millibars)	1013	1006	997	995	995	1000	1006	1011	1016	1019
Temperature (C)	3	4	10	13	8	4	1	−2	−6	−9

Notice that when the pressure is 995 and 1006 millibars, there is more than one value for the temperature.

Identify Functions Recall that relations in which each element of the domain is paired with exactly one element of the range are called **functions**.

KEY CONCEPT *Function*

A function is a relation in which each element of the domain is paired with *exactly* one element of the range.

EXAMPLE Identify Functions

① **Determine whether each relation is a function. Explain.**

a.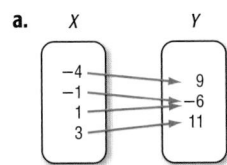

For each element of the domain, there is only one corresponding element in the range. So, this mapping represents a function. It does not matter if two elements of the domain are paired with the same element in the range.

b.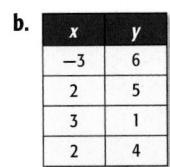

x	y
−3	6
2	5
3	1
2	4

The element 2 in the domain is paired with both 5 and 4 in the range. So, if *x* is 2, there are two possible values for *y*. The relation in this table does not represent a function.

✓ CHECK **Your Progress**

1. {(−2, 4), (1, 5), (3, 6), (5, 8), (7, 10)}

Lesson 3-2 Representing Functions **149**

---

① Focus

Standards Alignment

Before Lesson 3-2
Graph functions of the form $y = nx^2$ and $y = nx^3$ and use in solving problems from Standard 7AF3.1

Lesson 3-2
Determine whether a relation is a function from Standards 16.0 and 18.0

After Lesson 3-2
Solve problems involving functional concepts from Standard 2A24.0

② Teach

Scaffolding Questions

Have students read *Get Ready for the Lesson.*

Ask:

- Looking at the data as a set of ordered pairs, could it be represented by a linear equation? Explain. No, because the ordered pairs do not form a straight line when graphed.

(continued on the next page)

Lesson 3-2 Resources

Chapter 3 Resource Masters

Lesson Reading Guide, p. 12 **BL OL ELL**
Study Guide and Intervention, pp. 13–14
BL OL ELL
Skills Practice, p. 15 **BL OL**
Practice, p. 16 **OL AL**
Word Problem Practice, p. 17 **OL AL**
Enrichment, p. 18 **OL AL**
Quiz 1, p. 43

Transparencies

5-Minute Check Transparency 3-2

Additional Print Resources

Noteables™ Interactive Study Notebook with Foldables™
Science and Mathematics Lab Manual, pp. 139–144

Technology

ca.algebra1.com
Interactive Classroom CD-ROM
AssignmentWorks CD-ROM
Graphing Calculator Easy Files

- If you represented the ordered pairs as a mapping with temperature being domain and pressure being range, what would the mapping reveal? There are fewer range values than domain values.

Identifying Functions

Example 1 shows how to determine if a relation is a function. **Example 2** shows how to determine if an equation is a function by graphing and using the vertical line test.

 Formative Assessment

Use the Check Your Progress exercises after each example to determine students' understanding of concepts.

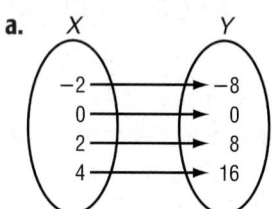
You can use the **vertical line test** to see if a graph represents a function. If no vertical line can be drawn that intersects the graph more than once, then the graph is a function. If a vertical line can be drawn so that it intersects the graph at two or more points, the graph is not a function.

Function 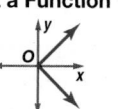 **Not a Function** 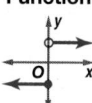 **Function**

COncepts in MOtion
Animation
ca.algebra1.com

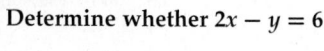

EXAMPLE Equations as Functions

❷ Determine whether $2x - y = 6$ represents a function.

Make a table and plot points to graph the equation.

Since the equation is in the form $Ax + By = C$, the graph of the equation will be a line. Place a pencil at the left of the graph to represent a vertical line. Slowly move the pencil to the right across the graph.

For each value of x, this vertical line passes through no more than one point on the graph. Thus, the graph represents a function.

x	1	2	3
y	−4	−2	0

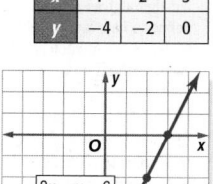

CHECK Your Progress

2. Determine whether $x = -2$ is a function. no

Review Vocabulary

Independent/ Dependent Variables

In a function, the value of the dependent variable depends on the value of the independent variable. (Lesson 1-9)

Function Values Equations that are functions can be written in a form called **function notation**. For example, consider $y = 3x - 8$.

equation	function notation
$y = 3x - 8$	$f(x) = 3x - 8$

In a function, x represents the independent quantity, or the elements of the domain and $f(x)$ represents the dependent quantity, or the elements of the range. For example, $f(5)$ is the element in the range that corresponds to the element 5 in the domain. We say that $f(5)$ is the **function value** of f for $x = 5$.

Reading Math

Function Notation The symbol $f(x)$ is read f of x. The symbol $f(5)$ is read f of 5.

EXAMPLE Function Values

❸ If $f(x) = 2x + 5$, find each value.

a. $f(-2)$

$f(-2) = 2(-2) + 5$ Replace x with −2.
$= -4 + 5$ Multiply.
$= 1$ Add.

b. $f(1) + 4$

$f(1) + 4 = [2(1) + 5] + 4$ Replace x with 1.
$= 7 + 4$ Simplify.
$= 11$ Add.

 CHECK Your Progress

3A. $f(3)$ 11

3B. $2 - f(0)$ −3

Math Online Extra Examples at ca.algebra1.com

Additional Example

2.

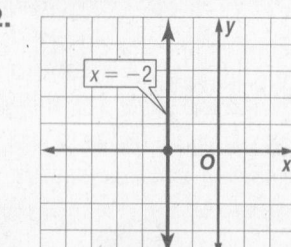

Functions Other
letters such as *g* and *h*
can be used to
represent functions.
For example, *g*(*x*) is
read *g of x* and *h*(*t*) is
read *h of t*.

EXAMPLE Nonlinear Function Values

④ **PHYSICS** The function $h(t) = -16t^2 + 68t + 2$ represents the height $h(t)$ of a football in feet t seconds after it is kicked. Find each value.

a. $h(4)$

$h(4) = -16(4)^2 + 68(4) +$ Replace *t* with 4.

$\quad\quad = -256 + 272 + 2$ Multiply.

$\quad\quad = 18$ Simplify.

b. $2[h(g)]$

$2[h(g)] = 2[-16(g)^2 + 68(g) +]$ Evaluate *h*(*g*) by replacing *t* with *g*.

$\quad\quad = 2(-16g^2 + 68g +)$ Simplify.

$\quad\quad = -32g^2 + 136g + 4$ Multiply the value of *h*(*g*) by 2.

✓CHECK **Your Progress** If $f(t) = 2t^3$, find each value.

4A. $f(4)$ **128**   **4B.** $3[f(t)]$ $6t^3$

Functions
When representing
functions, determine
the values of the
domain and range
that make sense for
the given situation.

STANDARDS EXAMPLE 18.0

⑤ The algebraic form of a function is $s = 9h$, where s is Barbara's weekly salary and h is the number of hours that she works in a week. Which of the following represents the same function?

A For every week Barbara works, she earns $9.

C $f(h) = 9$

B

h	s
0	0
2	18
4	36

D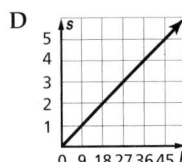

Read the Item

The independent variable is h and the dependent variable is s.

Solve the Item

Choices A and C both represent a constant weekly salary of $9. This is incorrect because the salary depends on the number of hours worked.

Choice D represents $s = \frac{1}{9}h$, which is incorrect. In choice B, the salary equals the number of hours times 9, which is correct. The answer is B.

✓CHECK **Your Progress**

5. Which statement represents the function that is described below? **F**

For every minute that Beatriz walks, she walks 0.1 mile.

F $f(t) = 0.1t$ **G** $f(t) = t + 0.1$ **H** $f(t) = 0.1 - t$ **J** $f(t) = t - 0.1$

Online **Personal Tutor at** ca.algebra1.com

Function Values

Example 3 shows how to find the element in the range that corresponds to a given element in the domain of a linear function. **Example 4** shows how to find the element in the range of a real-world problem that corresponds to a given element in the domain of a nonlinear function. **Example 5** shows how to recognize different representations for a function given on a standardized test.

ADDITIONAL EXAMPLES

③ If $f(x) = 3x - 4$, find each value.

a. $f(4)$ 8

b. $f(-5)$ -19

④ **PHYSICS** The function $h(t) = 1248 - 160t - 16t^2$ represents the height of an object ejected downward at a rate of 160 feet per second from an airplane flying at 1248 feet. Find each value.

a. $h(3)$ 624

b. $h(2z)$ $1248 - 320z - 64z^2$

⑤ **STANDARDS EXAMPLE** The algebraic form of a function is $m = 5d$, where d is the number of dollars customers of Mike's Car Rental donate to a charity and m is the donation made by Mike's Car Rental. Which of the following represents the same function? D

A For every $2 dollars donated, Mike's Car Rental donates $7.

B $f(d) = 5m$

C

d	m
0	00
10	2
60	12

D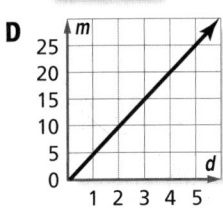

Focus on Mathematical Content

Functions The set of *x*-values is the domain, and the corresponding set of *y*-values is the range. A function is a relation in which each element of the domain is paired with exactly one element of the range.

Tips for New Teachers   **Preventing Error**

Function notation is sometimes difficult for students to comprehend. Stress that $f(x)$ does *not* mean "*f* times *x*".

Practice

Formative Assessment

Use Exercises 1–14 to check for understanding.

Use the chart at the bottom of this page to customize assignments for your students.

Odd/Even Assignments

Exercises 15–44 are structured so that students practice the same concepts whether they are assigned odd or even problems.

Real-World Connections

For Exercises 39–42, explain to students that the Greek word *meteorol* refers to something that occurs high in the sky. Thus the word "meteorologist" means someone who studies the atmosphere.

Additional Answers

13. $f(x) = 0.25x$; $1.25, $3.00; It costs $1.25 to send 5 photos and $3.00 to send 12 photos.

14. Sample answer: $\{(0, 0), (1, 0.25), (2, 0.5), (3, 0.75) \ldots\}$;

x	y
0	0
1	0.25
2	0.50
3	0.75

48. a; The cost is the same for 0–1 hour, excluding 0. Then it jumps after 1 hour and remains the same up to 2 hours. So the line is constant for x values between 0 and 1, then it jumps at 1. This trend continues at each hourly interval until 5 hours; then the cost is constant. The graph represents a function since it passes the vertical line test.

✓ CHECK Your Understanding

Example 1
(p. 149)

Determine whether each relation is a function.

1. 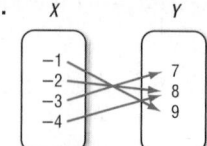 yes

2. 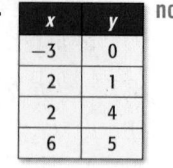 no

3. $\{(-4, 1), (-1, 4), (3, -2), (-4, 5)\}$ no

4. $y = x + 3$ yes

Example 2
(p. 150)

5. 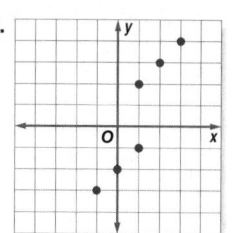 no

6. 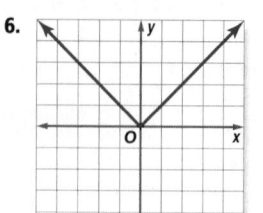 yes

Examples 3, 4
(pp. 150–151)

If $f(x) = 4x - 5$ and $g(x) = x^2 + 1$, find each value.

7. $f(2)$ 3

8. $f(c)$ $4c - 5$

9. $f(x + 5)$ $4x + 15$

10. $g(-1)$ 2

11. $g(t) - 4$ $t^2 - 3$

12. $g(3n)$ $9n^2 + 1$

13. **CELL PHONE PICTURES** The cost of sending cell phone pictures is given by $y = 0.25x$, where x is the number of pictures that you send. Write the equation in function notation and then find $f(5)$ and $f(12)$. What do these values represent? **See margin.**

Example 5
(p. 151)
18.0

14. **STANDARDS PRACTICE** Represent the function described in Exercise 13 in two different ways. **See margin.**

Exercises

Determine whether each relation is a function.

HOMEWORK HELP	
For Exercises	See Examples
15–22	1
23–26	2
27–38	3, 4
39–44	5

Exercise Levels
A: 15–44
B: 45–48
C: 49–51

15. no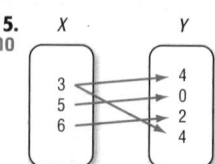

16. yes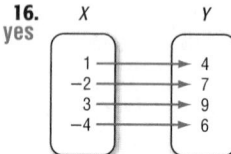

17. yes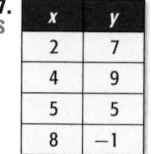

x	y
2	7
4	9
5	5
8	-1

18. no

x	y
-9	-5
-4	0
3	6
7	1
6	-5
3	2

19. yes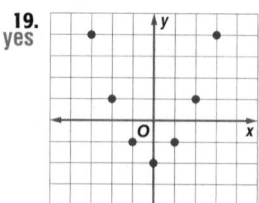

20. yes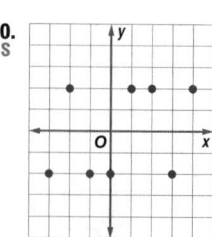

DIFFERENTIATED HOMEWORK OPTIONS

Level	Assignment	Two-Day Option	
BL Basic	15–44, 50–60	15–43 odd, 52, 53	16–44 even, 50, 51, 54–60
OL Core	15–47 odd, 48, 50–60	15–44, 52, 53	45–48, 50, 51, 54–60
AL Advanced /Pre-AP	45–56, (optional: 57–60)		

Real-World Career
Meteorologist

Meteorologists study the physical characteristics of the atmosphere using instruments and tools such as weather balloons. This information is used to interpret and predict trends in the weather.

Math Online
For more information, go to ca.algebra1.com.

Determine whether each relation is a function. 21. yes

21. $\{(5, -7), (6, -7), (-8, -1), (0, -1)\}$ 22. $\{(4, 5), (3, -2), (-2, 5), (4, 7)\}$ no

23. $y = -8$ yes   24. $x = 15$ no

25. $y = 3x - 2$ yes   26. $y = 3x + 2y$ yes

If $f(x) = 3x + 7$ and $g(x) = x^2 - 2x$, find each value.

27. $f(3)$ 16   28. $f(-2)$ 1   29. $g(5)$ 15

30. $g(0)$ 0   31. $g(-3) + 1$ 16   32. $f(8) - 5$ 26

33. $g(2c)$ $4c^2 - 4c$ 34. $g(4n)$ $16n^2 - 8n$ 35. $f(k + 2)$ $3k + 13$

36. $f(a - 1)$ $3a + 4$ 37. $3[f(r)]$ $9r + 21$ 38. $2[g(t)]$ $2t^2 - 4t$

METEOROLOGY For Exercises 39–42, use the following information.
The temperature of the atmosphere decreases about 5°F for every 1000 feet increase in altitude. Thus, if the temperature at ground level is 77°F, the temperature at an altitude of h feet is found by using $t = 77 - 0.005h$.

39. Write the equation in function notation. Then find $f(100)$, $f(200)$,
★ and $f(1000)$. $f(h) = 77 - 0.005h$; 76.5, 76, 72

40. Suppose the temperature at ground level was less than 77°F. Describe how the range values in Exercise 39 would change. Explain.

41. Graph the function. See Ch. 3 Answer Appendix.

42. Use the graph of the function to estimate the temperature at 4000 feet. 57°

40. The range values would decrease because the starting temperature is lower, but the amount by which the temperature decreases stays the same.

EDUCATION For Exercises 43 and 44, use the following information.
The average national math test scores $f(s)$ for 17-year-olds can be represented as a function of the national science scores s by $f(s) = 0.8s + 72$.

43. Graph this function. See Ch. 3 Answer Appendix.

44. What is the science score that corresponds to a math score of 308? 295

Determine whether each relation is a function.

45. 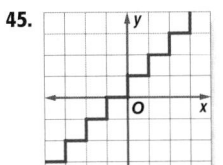 no   46. 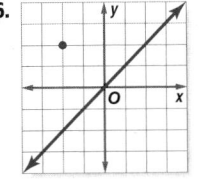 no   47. 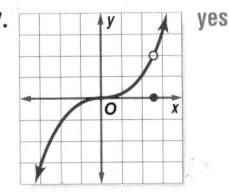 yes

48. **PARKING** A parking garage charges $2.00 for the first hour, $2.75 for the second, $3.50 for the third, $4.25 for the fourth, and $5.00 for any time over four hours. Choose the graph that best represents the information and determine whether the graph represents a function. Explain. See margin.

a.    b. 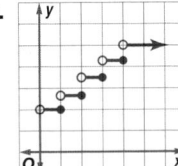   c.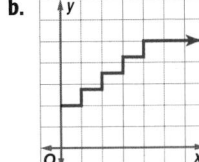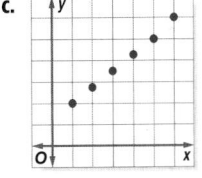

Lesson 3-2 Representing Functions **153**

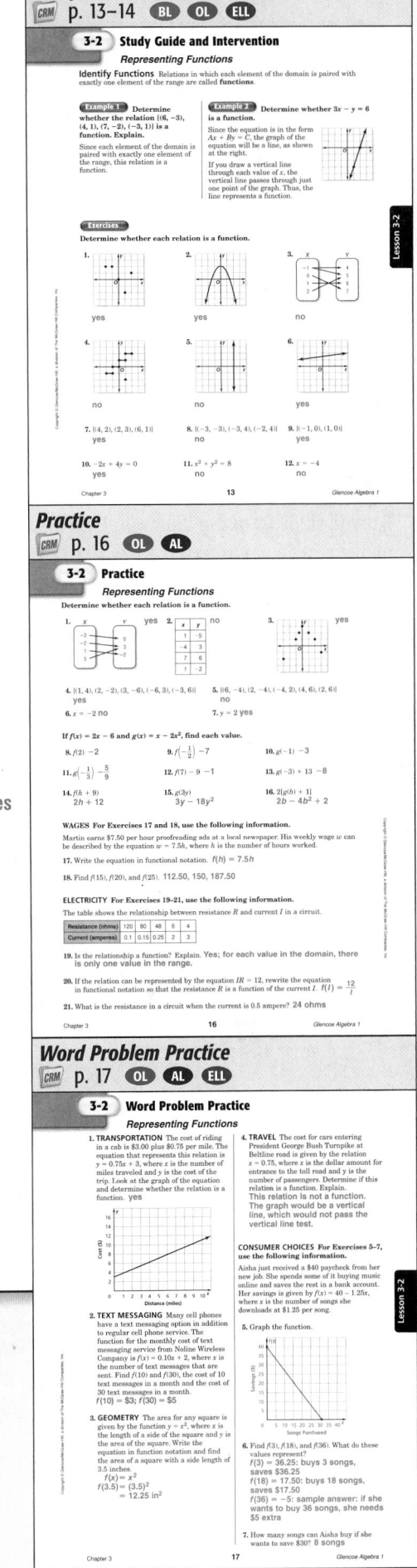
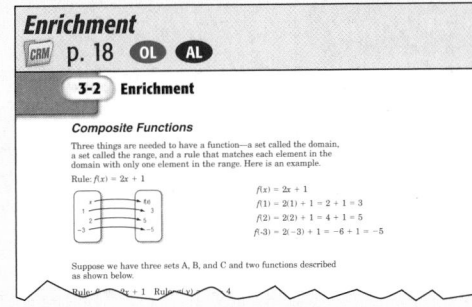

Crystal Ball Tell students that the next lesson they will study is titled Linear Functions. Ask them to write how they think what they have learned today about functions will connect with the next lesson.

 Formative Assessment

Check for student understanding of concepts in Lessons 3-1 and 3-2.

 Quiz 1, p. 43

 **Foldables™ Follow-Up**

Remind students to use the second tab on their Foldables to record notes on what they have learned about relations and functions.

Additional Answers

51. Sometimes; if each domain value is paired with a different range value, then the inverse is also a function. If two or more domain values are paired with the same range value, then the inverse is not a function.

53. Sample answer: Functions can be used in meteorology to determine if there is a relationship between certain weather conditions. This can help to predict future weather patterns. As barometric pressure decreases, temperature increases. As barometric pressure increases, temperature decreases. The relation is not a function since there is more than one temperature for a given barometric pressure. However, there is still a pattern in the data and the two variables are related.

H.O.T. Problems

REASONING For Exercises 49 and 50, refer to the following information.
The ordered pairs (0, 1), (3, 2), (3, −5), and (5, 4) are on the graph of a relation between x and y.

49. Determine whether y is a function of x. Explain. **No; one member of the domain is paired with two different members of the range.**

50. Determine whether x is a function of y. Explain. **Yes; each of the y-values is paired with one x-value.**

51. CHALLENGE State whether the following is *sometimes*, *always*, or *never* true. Explain your reasoning. *The inverse of a function is also a function.* **See margin.**

52. OPEN ENDED Disprove the following statement by finding a counterexample. *All linear equations are functions.*
Sample answer: $x = c$, where c is any constant

53. *Writing in Math* Use the information on page 149 to explain how functions are used in meteorology. Describe the relationship between pressure and temperature, and investigate whether the relation is a function. **See margin.**

STANDARDS PRACTICE 16.0, 7AF1.2

54. Which relation is a function? **D**

A {(−5, 6), (4, −3), (2, −1), (4, 2)}

B {(3, −1), (3, −5), (3, 4), (3, 6)}

C {(−2, 3), (0, 3), (−2, −1), (−1, 2)}

D {(−5, 6), (4, −3), (2, −1), (4, 2)}

55. REVIEW If $a = −4$ and $b = 8$, then $3a(b + 2) + a = $ **F**

F −124

G −98

H −26

J 18

Spiral Review

56. Express the relation shown in the table as a set of ordered pairs. Then write the inverse of the relation. (Lesson 3-1) **{(−4, 9), (2, 5), (−2, −2), (11, 12)}; {(9, −4), (5, 2), (−2, −2), (12, 11)}**

★ **57. AIRPLANES** At 1:30 P.M., an airplane leaves San José for Atlanta, a distance of 2109 miles. The plane flies at 281 miles per hour. A second airplane leaves San José at 2:15 P.M. and is scheduled to land in Atlanta 15 minutes before the first airplane. At what rate must the second airplane travel to arrive on schedule? (Lesson 2-9) **about 324.5 mph**

x	y
−4	9
2	5
−2	−2
11	12

56. RUNNING Lacey can run a 10K race (about 6.2 miles) in 45 minutes. If she runs a 26-mile marathon at the same pace, how long will it take her to finish? (Lesson 2-6) **approximately 3 h and 9 min**

GET READY for the Next Lesson

PREREQUISITE SKILL Solve each equation. (Lesson 2-4)

59. $r − 9 = 12$ **21**

60. $−4 = 5n + 6$ **−2**

61. $3 − 8w = 35$ **−4**

62. $\frac{g}{4} + 2 = 5$ **12**

Pre-AP Activity Use as an Extension

Write $f(x) = x^2 + 2$ and $f(x) = x + 2$ on the board. Ask students to name the coordinates of the point having the least y-value for each equation. **(0, 2); There is no least y-value for $f(x) = x + 2$.**

Main Ideas

- Identify linear equations, intercepts, and zeros.
- Graph linear equations.

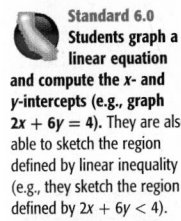 **Standard 6.0 Students graph a linear equation and compute the *x*- and *y*-intercepts (e.g., graph 2*x* + 6*y* = 4). They are also able to sketch the region defined by linear inequality (e.g., they sketch the region defined by 2*x* + 6*y* < 4). (Key, CAHSEE)**

Standard 7.0 Students verify that a point lies on a line, given an equation of the line. Students are able to derive linear equations by using the point-slope formula. (Key, CAHSEE)

New Vocabulary

linear equation
standard form
x-intercept
y-intercept
zero

GET READY for the Lesson

It is recommended that no more than 30% of a person's daily caloric intake come from fat. Since each gram of fat contains 9 Calories, the most grams of fat f that you should have each day is given by $f = 0.3\left(\frac{C}{9}\right)$ or $f = \frac{C}{30}$. C is the total number of Calories C that you consume. The graph of this equation shows the maximum number of grams of fat you should consume based on the total number of Calories you consume.

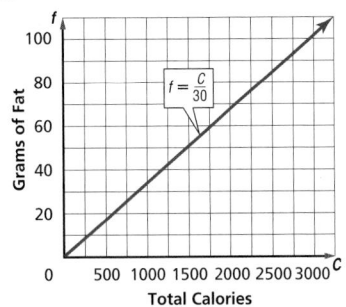

Identify Linear Equations, Intercepts, and Zeros A **linear equation** is the equation of a line. Linear equations can be written in the form $Ax + By = C$. This is called the **standard form** of a linear equation.

> **KEY CONCEPT**   *Standard Form of a Linear Equation*
>
> The standard form of a linear equation is
>
> $$Ax + By = C,$$
>
> where $A \geq 0$, A and B are not both zero, and A, B, and C are integers with a greatest common factor of 1.

EXAMPLE   Identify Linear Equations

1 Determine whether each equation is a linear equation. If so, write the equation in standard form.

a. $y = 5 - 2x$

Rewrite the equation so that both variables are on the same side of the equation.

$y = 5 - 2x$	Original equation
$y + 2x = 5 - 2x + 2x$	Add 2x to each side.
$2x + y = 5$	Simplify.

The equation is now in standard form where $A = 2$, $B = 1$, and $C = 5$. This is a linear equation.

Lesson 3-3 Linear Functions   **155**

1 Focus

Standards Alignment

Before Lesson 3-3
Graph linear functions and recognize the slope from Standard 7AF3.3

Lesson 3-3
Graph a linear equation or inequality from Standard 6.0
Verify that a point lies on a line from Standard 7.0

After Lesson 3-3
Solve and graph quadratic and complex equations from Standard 2A8.0

2 Teach

Scaffolding Questions

Have students read *Get Ready for the Lesson.*

Ask:

- If a person consumes an average of 2000 Calories per day, how many grams of fat should the person consume? about 67 g
- How can you use the graph to answer the question? Find 2000 on the *C*-axis. Look to where it meets the line. Move to the *f*-axis to read the value.

Lesson 3-3 Resources

Chapter 3 Resource Masters
Lesson Reading Guide, p. 19 **BL OL ELL**
Study Guide and Intervention, pp. 20–21 **BL OL ELL**
Skills Practice, p. 22 **BL OL**
Practice, p. 23 **OL AL**
Word Problem Practice, p. 24 **OL AL**
Enrichment, p. 25 **OL AL**
Graphing Calculator, p. 26
Quiz 2, p. 43

Transparencies
5-Minute Check Transparency 3-3
Additional Print Resources
Noteables™ Interactive Study Notebook with Foldables™

Technology
ca.algebra1.com
Interactive Classroom CD-ROM
AssignmentWorks CD-ROM
Graphing Calculator Easy Files

Identify Linear Equations, Intercepts, and Zeros

Example 1 shows how to identify a linear equation and write it in standard form. **Examples 2–3** show how to determine and describe what the x- and y-intercepts mean and how to determine the zeros for real-world problems.

 Formative Assessment

Use the Check Your Progress exercises after each example to determine students' understanding of concepts.

ADDITIONAL EXAMPLES

1 Determine whether each equation is linear. If so, write the equation in standard form.

a. $5x + 3y = z + 2$ not linear

b. $\frac{3}{4}x = y + 8$ linear;
  $3x - 4y = 32$

2 **WATER STORAGE** A valve on a tank is opened and the water is drained, as shown in the graph.

Water Drainage

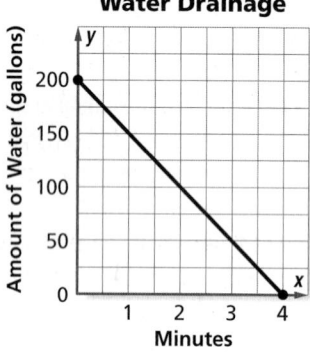

a. Determine the x-intercept, y-intercept, and zero. 4; 200; 4

b. Describe what the intercepts mean. y-intercept: 200 gal at 0 min; x-intercept: 0 gal at 4 min

Additional Examples are also in:

- Noteables™ Interactive Study Notebook with Foldables™
- Interactive Classroom PowerPoint® Presentations

---

b. $2xy - 5y = 6$

Since the term $2xy$ has two variables, the equation cannot be written in the form $Ax + By = C$. Therefore, this is not a linear equation.

✓**CHECK Your Progress**

Determine which functions are linear.

1A. $\frac{1}{3}y = -1$ yes; $y = -3$ **1B.** $y = x^2 + 3$ no

Study Tip

Linear Functions

The graph of a linear function has at most one x-intercept and one y-intercept, unless it is the function $f(x) = 0$, in which case every point of the graph is an x-intercept.

The x-coordinate of the point at which the graph of an equation crosses the x-axis is an **x-intercept**. The y-coordinate of the point at which the graph crosses the y-axis is called a **y-intercept**.

Values of x for which $f(x) = 0$ are called **zeros** of the function f. The zero of a linear function is its x-intercept.

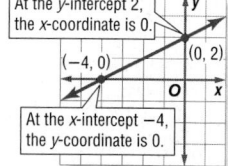
At the y-intercept 2, the x-coordinate is 0.
$(-4, 0)$ $(0, 2)$
At the x-intercept -4, the y-coordinate is 0.

Real-World EXAMPLE

2 **ANALYZE GRAPHS** High school students in Palo Alto, California, can buy ticket booklets for lunch, as shown in the graph.

a. Determine the x-intercept, y-intercept, and zero.

The x-intercept is 20 because it is the x-coordinate of the point where the line crosses the x-axis. The zero of the function is also 20.

The y-intercept is 60 because it is the y-coordinate of the point where the line crosses the y-axis.

Study Tip

Intercepts

Usually, the individual coordinates are called the x- and y-intercepts.

- The x-intercept 20 is located at (20, 0).
- The y-intercept 60 is located at (0, 60).

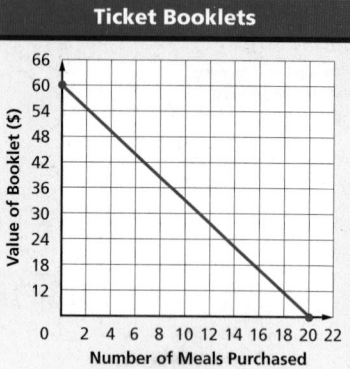
Ticket Booklets

b. Describe what the intercepts mean.

The x-intercept 20 means that after 20 meals are purchased, the meal ticket booklet has a value of $0.

The y-intercept 60 means before any meals are purchased, the booklet has a value of $60.

✓**CHECK Your Progress**

HEALTH Use the graph at the right that shows the cost of a gym membership.

2A. Determine the x-intercept, y-intercept, and zero. none; 150; none

2B. Describe what the intercept(s) mean. The y-intercept 150 means that the initial cost of the gym membership is $150.

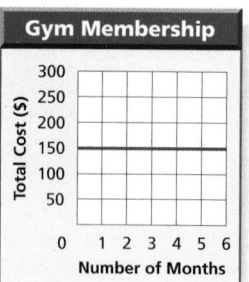
Gym Membership

🌐 **Personal Tutor at** ca.algebra1.com

156 Chapter 3 Functions and Patterns

Preventing Error

Tips for New Teachers

Point out that there are no restrictions on the value of B. This means that B could be negative. So, an equation like $3x - 4y = 7$ is a linear equation.

Focus on Mathematical Content

Linear Functions The standard form of a linear equation is $Ax + By = C$. If the properties of equality can be applied to an equation to rewrite it in standard form, then the equation is linear.

Study Tip

Defining Variables

Time is the *independent* variable, and volume of water is the *dependent* variable.

3 **ANALYZE TABLES** It is recommended that a swimming pool be drained at a maximum rate of 720 gallons per hour. The table shows the function relating the volume of water in a pool and the time in hours that the pool has been draining.

Draining a Pool	
Time, x (h)	Volume, y (gal)
0	10,080
2	8640
6	5760
10	2880
12	1440
14	0

a. Determine the *x*-intercept, *y*-intercept, and zero of the graph of the function.

x-intercept $= 14$ 14 is the value of *x* when $y = 0$.

y-intercept $= 10{,}080$ 10,080 is the value of *y* when $x = 0$.

zero $= 14$ The zero of the function is the *x*-intercept of the graph.

b. Describe what the intercepts mean.

The *x*-intercept 14 means that after 14 hours, the water in the pool has a volume of 0 gallons, or the pool is completely drained.

The *y*-intercept 10,080 means that the pool contained 10,080 gallons of water at time 0, or before it started to drain. This is shown in the graph.

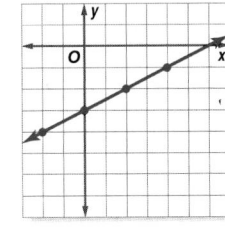

Draining a Pool

✓CHECK Your Progress

3. Use the table to determine the *x*-intercept, *y*-intercept, and zero of the graph of the function.

x	−3	−2	−1	0	1
y	2	0	−2	−4	−6

$x = -2, y = -4, x = -2$

COncepts in MOtion

Animation
ca.algebra1.com

Graph Linear Equations The graph of an equation represents all of its solutions. So, every ordered pair that satisfies the equation represents a point on the line. An ordered pair that does not satisfy the equation represents a point *not* on the line.

EXAMPLE Graph by Making a Table

4 Graph $y = \frac{1}{2}x - 3$.

Select values from the domain and make a table. Then graph the ordered pairs. The domain is all real numbers, so there are infinitely many solutions. Draw a line through the points.

Study Tip

Rewriting Equations

When appropriate, first solve an equation for *y* in order to find values for *y* more easily.

$3x + y = -1 \rightarrow$
$y = -1 - 3x$

x	$\frac{1}{2}x - 3$	y	(x, y)
−2	$\frac{1}{2}(-2) - 3$	−4	(−2, −4)
0	$\frac{1}{2}(0) - 3$	−3	(0, −3)
2	$\frac{1}{2}(2) - 3$	−2	(2, −2)
4	$\frac{1}{2}(4) - 3$	−1	(4, −1)

This line represents all of the solutions of $y = \frac{1}{2}x - 3$.

✓CHECK Your Progress Graph each equation. 4A–4B. See margin.

4A. $3x + y = -1$ **4B.** $y = -2$

 Math nline Extra Examples at ca.algebra1.com

Lesson 3-3 Linear Functions   **157**

ADDITIONAL EXAMPLE

3 **ANALYZE TABLES** A box of peanuts is poured into bags at the rate of 4 ounces per second. The table shows the function relating the weight of peanuts in the box and the time in seconds the peanuts have been pouring out of the box.

Pouring Peanuts	
Time (s) x	Weight (oz) y
0	2000
125	1500
250	1000
375	500
500	0

a. Determine the *x*-intercept, *y*-intercept, and zero of the graph of the function. 500; 2000; 500

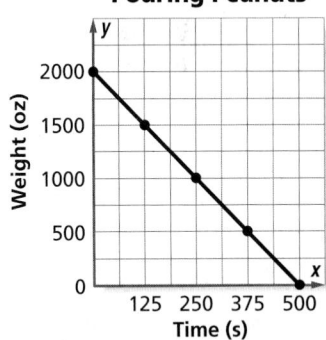

Pouring Peanuts

b. Describe what the intercepts mean. *x*-intercept: 0 oz after 500 s; *y*-intercept: 2000 oz before pouring began

Graph Linear Equations

Example 4 shows how to graph an equation by making a table. **Example 5** shows how to graph a linear equation using the *x*- and *y*-intercepts.

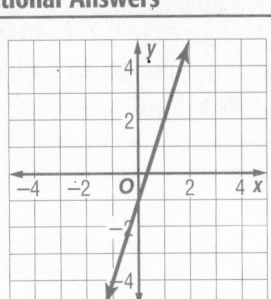
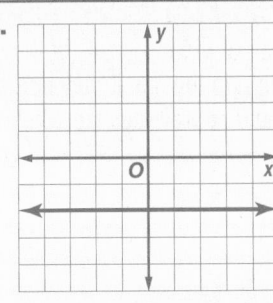

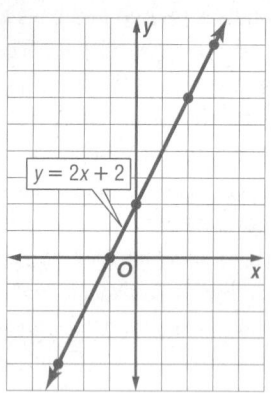
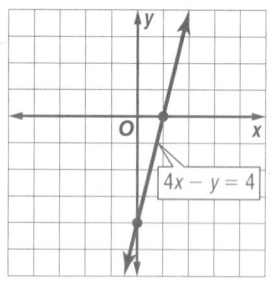
 Practice

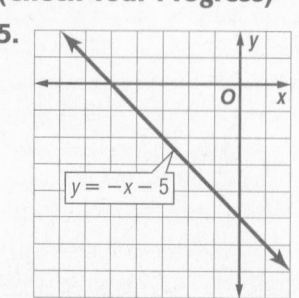

EXAMPLE Graph by Using Intercepts

5 Graph $3x + 2y = 9$ using the x-intercept and y-intercept.

COncepts in MOtion
Interactive Lab
ca.algebra1.com

To find the x-intercept, let $y = 0$.	To find the y-intercept, let $x = 0$.
$3x + 2y = 9$ Original equation	$3x + 2y = 9$ Original equation
$3x + 2(0) = 9$ Replace y with 0.	$3(0) + 2y = 9$ Replace x with 0.
$3x = 9$ Divide each side by 3.	$2y = 9$ Divide each side by 2.
$x = 3$	$y = 4.5$

The x-intercept is 3, so the graph intersects the x-axis at (3, 0). The y-intercept is 4.5, so the graph intersects the y-axis at (0, 4.5). Plot these points. Then draw the line through them.

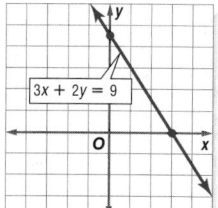

✓ **CHECK Your Progress**

5. Graph $y = -x - 5$ using the x- and y-intercepts. **See margin.**

★ indicates multi-step problem

✓ **CHECK Your Understanding**

Example 1 Determine whether each equation is a linear equation. If so, write the
(pp. 155–156) equation in standard form.   **2. yes;** $3y = -2$ **3. yes;** $3x - 2y = 25$
   1. $x + y^2 = 25$ **no**   **2.** $3y + 2 = 0$ **3.** $\frac{3}{5}x - \frac{2}{5}y = 5$

Examples 2, 3 Determine the x-intercept and y-intercept of each linear function and
(pp. 156–157) describe what the intercepts mean. **4–5. See Ch. 3 Answer Appendix.**

4.

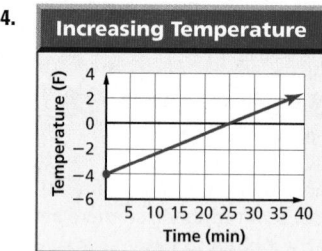

5.

Position of Scuba Diver	
Time, x (s)	Depth, y (m)
0	−24
3	−18
6	−12
9	−6
12	0

6. What are the zeros of the functions represented in Exercises 4 and 5? **25; 12**

Example 4 Graph each equation by making a table. **7–8. See Ch. 3 Answer Appendix.**
(p. 157)   **7.** $x - y = 0$ **8.** $x = 3$

Example 5 Graph each equation by using the x- and y-intercepts. **9–10. See Ch. 3 Answer**
(p. 158)   **9.** $y = -3 - x$ **10.** $x + 4y = 10$ **Appendix.**

11. RODEOS Tickets for a rodeo cost $5 for children and $10 for adults. The equation $5x + 10y = 60$ represents the number of children x and adults y who can attend the rodeo for $60. Use the x- and y-intercepts to graph the equation. What do these values mean? **See Ch. 3 Answer Appendix.**

Intervention

Intercepts If students find that one of the intercepts of the graph they are making is not a whole number, they may find it easier to graph the line if they find another point on the line that is a solution of the equation in which both coordinates are whole numbers.

Exercises

HOMEWORK HELP

For Exercises	See Examples
12–17	1
18–23	2, 3
24–38	4, 5

Exercise Levels
A: 12–38
B: 39–40
C: 51–56

Determine whether each equation is a linear equation. If so, write the equation in standard form. **13.** yes; $2x + y = 6$

12. $3x = 5y$ yes; $3x - 5y = 0$ **13.** $6 - y = 2x$ **14.** $6xy + 3x = 4$ no

15. $y + 5 = 0$ yes; $y = -5$ **16.** $7y = 2x + 5x$ **17.** $y = 4x^2 - 1$ no
yes; $x - y = 0$

Determine the x-intercept, y-intercept, and zero of each linear function.

18. 3, 4, 3   **19.** $-2, 2, -2$

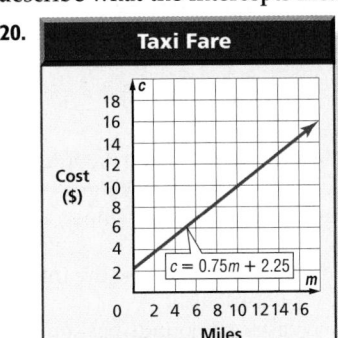

x	y
-3	-1
-2	0
-1	1
0	2
1	3

Determine the x-intercept and y-intercept of each linear function and describe what the intercepts mean. **20–23. See margin.**

20.

Taxi Fare
$c = 0.75m + 2.25$

21.

Descent of Eagle

22.

Swimming to Burn Calories

Time, x (min)	Calories Burned, y
0	0
10	106
15	159
20	212
30	318

23.

Eva's Distance from Home

Time, x (min)	Distance, y (mi)
0	4
2	3
4	2
6	1
8	0

Graph each equation. **24–32. See Ch. 3 Answer Appendix.**

24. $y = -1$ **25.** $y = 2x$ **26.** $y = x - 6$

27. $y = 5 - x$ **28.** $y = 4 - 3x$ **29.** $x = 3y$

30. $x = 4y - 6$ **31.** $x - y = -3$ **32.** $4x + 6y = 8$

METEOROLOGY For Exercises 33–35, use the following information.
The distance d in miles that the sound of thunder travels in t seconds is given by the equation $d = 0.21t$. **33–34. See Ch. 3 Answer Appendix.**

33. Make a table of values.

34. Graph the equation.

35. Use the graph to estimate how long it will take you to hear thunder from a storm that is 3 miles away. **about 14 s**

EXTRA PRACTICE
See pages 723, 746.

Math Online
Self-Check Quiz at
ca.algebra1.com

Real-World Connections For Check Your Understanding 11, explain that the term *rodeo* comes from the Spanish word "rodear" meaning "to surround." The rodeo tradition began in Mexico in the mid-sixteenth century.

Real-World Connections For Exercises 33–35, you may wish to point out that thunder is the sound of lightning moving rapidly through the atmosphere. The air expands then compresses violently, producing sound waves.

Additional Answers

20. -3, 2.25; The x-intercept does not make sense in the context of this situation because it is negative. The y-intercept represents the base fare, not including the charge per mile.

21. 6, 20; The x-intercept represents the number of seconds that it takes the eagle to land. The y-intercept represents the initial height of the eagle.

22. 0, 0; The intercepts mean that 0 Calories are burned when the time spent swimming is 0.

23. 8, 4; The x-intercept 8 means that it took Eva 8 minutes to get home. The y-intercept 4 means that Eva was initially 4 miles from home.

37. 7.5, 15; No; the x-intercept 7.5 means that the length would be 7.5 inches if the width were 0. The y-intercept means that the width would be 7.5 inches if the length were 0. A rectangle cannot have only a length or only a width, so these values do not make sense in the context of the problem.

38.

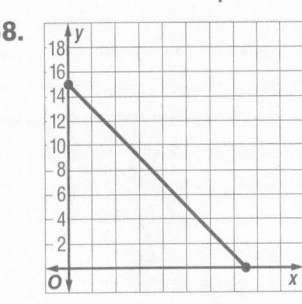

DIFFERENTIATED HOMEWORK OPTIONS

Level	Assignment	Two-Day Option	
BL Basic	12–38, 55–58, 60–75	13–37 odd, 61–63	12–38 even, 55–58, 60, 64–75
OL Core	13–53 odd, 54–58, 69–75	12–38, 61–63	39–58, 60, 64–75
AL Advanced /Pre-AP	39–71, (optional: 72–75)		

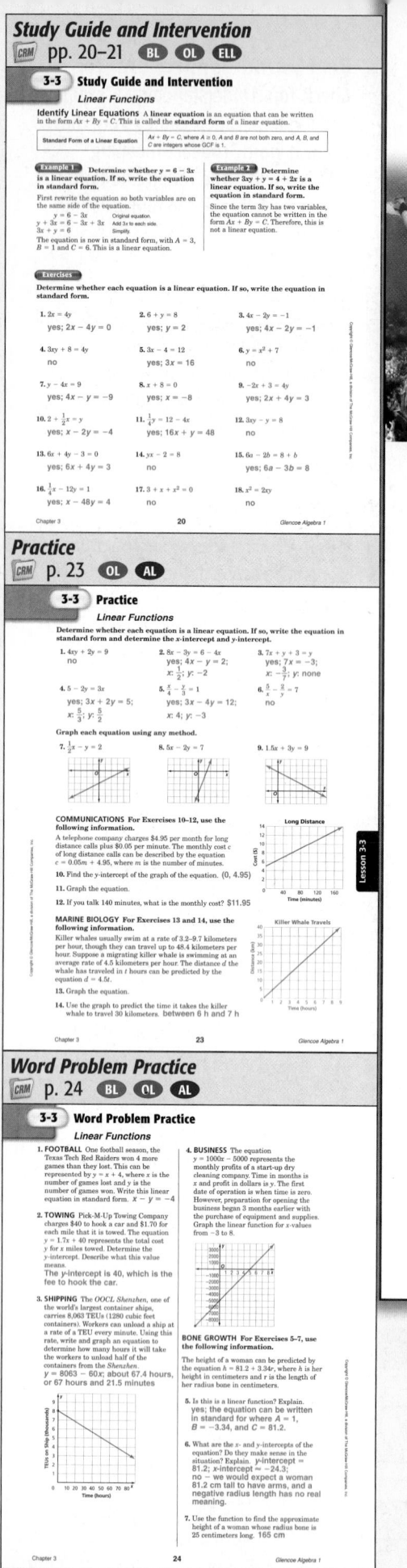

Study Guide and Intervention
CRM pp. 20–21 BL OL ELL

3-3 Study Guide and Intervention
Linear Functions

Identify Linear Equations A linear equation is an equation that can be written in the form $Ax + By = C$. This is called the **standard form** of a linear equation.

Standard Form of a Linear Equation	$Ax + By = C$, where $A \geq 0$, and A and B are not both zero, and A, B, and C are integers whose GCF is 1.

Example 1 Determine whether $y = 6 - 3x$ is a linear equation. If so, write the equation in standard form.

First rewrite the equation so both variables are on the same side of the equation.
$y = 6 - 3x$ Original equation
$y + 3x = 6 - 3x + 3x$ Add 3x to each side.
$3x + y = 6$ Simplify.
The equation is now in standard form, with $A = 3$, $B = 1$ and $C = 6$. This is a linear equation.

Example 2 Determine whether $3xy + y = 4 + 2x$ is a linear equation. If so, write the equation in standard form.

Since the term $3xy$ has two variables, the equation cannot be written in the form $Ax + By = C$. Therefore, this is not a linear equation.

Exercises

Determine whether each equation is a linear equation. If so, write the equation in standard form.

1. $2x = 4y$ yes; $2x - 4y = 0$
2. $6 + y = 8$ yes; $y = 2$
3. $4x - 2y = -1$ yes; $4x - 2y = -1$
4. $3xy + 8 = 4y$ no
5. $3x - 4 = 12$ yes; $3x = 16$
6. $y = x^2 + 7$ no
7. $y - 4x = 9$ yes; $4x - y = -9$
8. $x + 8 = 0$ yes; $x = -8$
9. $-2x + 3 = 4y$ yes; $2x + 4y = 3$
10. $2 + \frac{1}{2}x = y$ yes; $x - 2y = -4$
11. $\frac{1}{4}y = 12 - 4x$ yes; $16x + y = 48$
12. $3xy - y = 8$ no
13. $6x + 4y - 3 = 0$ yes; $6x + 4y = 3$
14. $yx - 2 = 8$ no
15. $6a - 2b = 8 + b$ yes; $6a - 3b = 8$
16. $\frac{1}{4}x - 12y = 1$ yes; $x - 48y = 4$
17. $3 + x + x^2 = 0$ no
18. $x^2 = 2xy$ no

Chapter 3   20   Glencoe Algebra 1

Practice
CRM p. 23 OL AL

3-3 Practice
Linear Functions

Determine whether each equation is a linear equation. If so, write the equation in standard form and determine the x-intercept and y-intercept.

1. $4xy + 2y = 9$ no
2. $8x - 3y = 6 - 4x$ yes; $4x - y = 2$; $x: \frac{1}{2}$; $y: -2$
3. $7x + y + 3 = y$ yes; $7x = -3$; $x: -\frac{3}{7}$; $y:$ none
4. $5 - 2y = 3x$ yes; $3x + 2y = 5$; $x: \frac{5}{3}$; $y: \frac{5}{2}$
5. $\frac{x}{4} - \frac{y}{3} = 1$ yes; $3x - 4y = 12$; $x: 4$; $y: -3$
6. $\frac{5}{x} - \frac{2}{y} = 7$ no

Graph each equation using any method.

7. $\frac{1}{2}x - y = 2$
8. $5x - 2y = 7$
9. $1.5x + 3y = 9$

COMMUNICATIONS For Exercises 10–12, use the following information.
A telephone company charges $4.95 per month for long distance calls plus $0.05 per minute. The monthly cost c of long distance calls can be described by the equation $c = 0.05m + 4.95$, where m is the number of minutes.

10. Find the y-intercept of the graph of the equation. (0, 4.95)
11. Graph the equation.
12. If you talk 140 minutes, what is the monthly cost? $11.95

MARINE BIOLOGY For Exercises 13 and 14, use the following information.
Killer whales usually swim at a rate of 3.2–9.7 kilometers per hour, though they can travel up to 48.4 kilometers per hour. Suppose a migrating killer whale is swimming at an average rate of 4.5 kilometers per hour. The distance d the whale has traveled in t hours can be predicted by the equation $d = 4.5t$.

13. Graph the equation.
14. Use the graph to predict the time it takes the killer whale to travel 30 kilometers. between 6 h and 7 h

Chapter 3   23   Glencoe Algebra 1

Word Problem Practice
CRM p. 24 BL OL AL

3-3 Word Problem Practice
Linear Functions

1. **FOOTBALL** One football season, the Texas Tech Red Raiders won 4 more games than they lost. This can be represented by $y = x + 4$, where x is the number of games lost and y is the number of games won. Write this linear equation in standard form. $x - y = -4$

2. **TOWING** Pick-M-Up Towing Company charges $40 to hook a car and $1.70 for each mile that it is towed. The equation $y = 1.7x + 40$ represents the total cost y for x miles towed. Determine the y-intercept. Describe what this value means. The y-intercept is 40, which is the fee to hook the car.

3. **SHIPPING** The OOCL Shenzhen, one of the world's largest container ships, carries 8,063 TEUs (1280 cubic feet containers). Workers can unload a ship at a rate of a TEU every minute. Using this rate, write and graph an equation to determine how many hours it will take the workers to unload half of the containers from the Shenzhen. $y = 8063 - 60x$; about 67.4 hours, or 67 hours and 21.5 minutes

4. **BUSINESS** The equation $y = 1000x - 5000$ represents the monthly profits of a start-up dry cleaning company. Time in months is x and profit in dollars is y. The first date of operation when time is zero. However, preparation for opening the business began 3 months earlier with the purchase of equipment and supplies. Graph the linear function for x-values from −3 to 8.

BONE GROWTH For Exercises 5–7, use the following information.
The height of a woman can be predicted by the equation $h = 81.2 + 3.34r$, where h is her height in centimeters and r is the length of her radius bone in centimeters.

5. Is this a linear function? Explain. yes; the equation can be written in standard for where $A = 1$, $B = -3.34$, and $C = 81.2$.

6. What are the x- and y-intercepts of the equation? Do they make sense in the situation? Explain. y-intercept = 81.2; x-intercept = −24.3; no — we would expect a woman 81.2 cm tall to have arms, and a negative radius length has no real meaning.

7. Use the function to find the approximate height of a woman whose radius bone is 25 centimeters long. 165 cm

Chapter 3   24   Glencoe Algebra 1

GEOMETRY For Exercises 36–38, refer to the figure at right.
The perimeter P of a rectangle is given by $2\ell + 2w = P$, where ℓ is the length of the rectangle and w is the width.

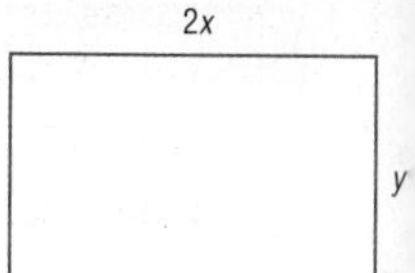

(Figure: rectangle with top side labeled $2x$ and right side labeled y)

36. If the perimeter of the rectangle is 30 inches, write an equation for the perimeter in standard form. $2x + y = 15$

37. What are the x- and y-intercepts of the graph? Do they make sense in this problem? Explain. **See margin.**

38. Graph the equation. **See margin.**

Determine whether each equation is a linear equation. If so, write the equation in standard form.

39. $x + \frac{1}{y} = 7$ **no**
40. $\frac{x}{2} = 10 + \frac{2y}{3}$ **yes; $3x - 4y = 60$**
41. $7n - 8m = 4 - 2m$ **yes; $6m - 7n = -4$**
42. $3a + b - 2 = b$ **yes; $3a = 2$**
43. $2r - 3rs + 5s = 1$ **no**
44. $\frac{3m}{4} = \frac{2n}{3} - 5$ **yes; $9m - 8n = -60$**

Graph each equation. **45–50. See Ch. 3 Answer Appendix.**

45. $1.5x + y = 4$
46. $75 = 2.5x + 5y$
47. $\frac{4x}{3} = \frac{3y}{4} + 1$
48. $y + \frac{1}{3} = \frac{1}{4}x - 3$
49. $\frac{1}{2}x + y = 4$
50. $1 = x - \frac{2}{3}y$

★ 51. Find the x- and y-intercepts of the graph of $4x - 7y = 14$. $\frac{7}{2}, -2$

52. Graph $5x + 3y = 15$. Where does the line intersect the x-axis? Where does the line intersect the y-axis? What is the slope? $3; 5; -\frac{5}{3}$; See margin for graph.

OCEANOGRAPHY For Exercises 53 and 54, use the information at left and below. **53–54. See Ch. 3 Answer Appendix.**

Under water, pressure increases 4.3 pounds per square inch (psi) for every 10 feet you descend. This can be expressed by the equation $p = 0.43d + 14.7$, where p is the pressure in pounds per square inch and d is the depth in feet.

53. Graph the equation and find the y-intercept.

54. Divers cannot work at depths below about 400 feet. Given this information, determine a reasonable domain and range for this situation.

55. **REASONING** Verify that the point at $(-4, 2)$ lies on the line with the equation $y = \frac{1}{2}x + 4$.

OPEN ENDED Describe a linear equation in the form $Ax + By = C$ for each condition.

56. $A = 0$ Sample answer: $y = 8$
57. $B = 0$ Sample answer: $x = 5$
58. $C = 0$ Sample answer: $x - y = 0$

59. **CHALLENGE** Demonstrate how you can determine whether a point at (x, y) is above, below, or on the line given by $2x - y = 8$ without graphing it. Give an example of each. **See Ch. 3 Answer Appendix.**

60. *Writing in Math* Use the information about nutrition on page 155 to explain how linear equations can be used in nutrition. Explain how you could use the Nutrition Information labels on packages to limit your fat intake. **See Ch. 3 Answer Appendix.**

Real-World Link
How heavy is air? The atmospheric pressure is a measure of the weight of air. At sea level, air pressure is 14.7 pounds per square inch.
Source: www.brittanica.com

H.O.T. Problems

55.
$2 \stackrel{?}{=} \frac{1}{2}(-4) + 4$
$2 \stackrel{?}{=} -2 + 4$
$2 = 2$
Since substituting the ordered pair in the equation yields a true equation, the point lies on the line.

Enrichment
CRM p. 25 OL AL

3-3 Enrichment

Translating Linear Graphs
Linear graphs can be **translated** on the coordinate plane. This means that the graph moves up, down, right, or left without changing its direction.

Translating the graphs up or down affects the y-coordinate for a given x value. Translating the graph right or left affects the x-coordinate for a given y value.

Example Translate the graph of $y = 2x + 3$, 3 units up.

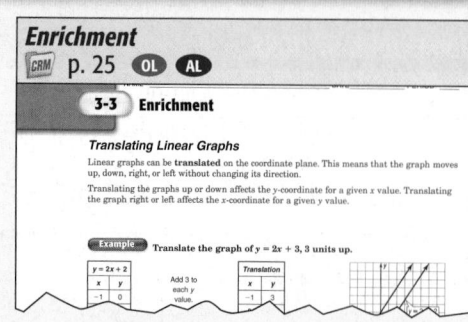

$y = 2x + 2$	
x	y
−1	

Add 3 to each y value.

Translation	
x	y
−1	

BL = Below Grade Level
OL = On Grade Level
AL = Above Grade Level
ELL = English Language Learner

Additional pages not shown:
CRM **Lesson Reading Guide**, p. 19 BL OL ELL
CRM **Skills Practice**, p. 22 BL OL

61. What are the *x*- and *y*-intercept points of the function graphed? **A**

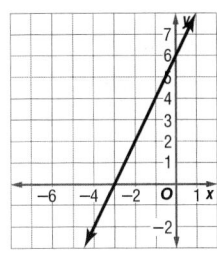

A $(-3, 0)$ and $(0, 6)$

B $(-3, 0)$ and $(6, 0)$

C $(0, -3)$ and $(0, 6)$

D $(0, -3)$ and $(6, 0)$

62. Which is the best estimate for the *x*-intercept of the graph of the linear function represented in the table? **H**

x	y
0	5
1	3
2	1
3	−1
4	−3

F between 0 and 1

G between 1 and 2

H between 2 and 3

J between 3 and 4

63. REVIEW A candle is 24 centimeters high and burns 3 centimeters per hour, as shown in the graph. **D**

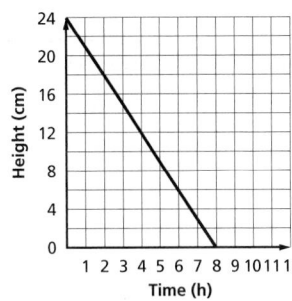

If the height of the candle is 8 centimeters, approximately how long has the candle been burning?

A 0 hours

B 24 minutes

C 64 minutes

D $5\frac{1}{2}$ hours

Spiral Review

If $f(x) = 3x - 2$ and $g(x) = x^2 - 5$, find each value. (Lesson 3-2)

64. $f(4)$ **10**

65. $g(-3)$ **4**

66. $2[f(6)]$ **32**

★ **67. NUTRITION** The cost of buying energy bars for a camping trip is given by $y = 2.25x$. Write the equation in function notation and then find $f(4)$ and $f(7)$. What do these values represent? (Lesson 3-2) **See margin.**

Solve each equation. Then check your solution. (Lesson 2-5)

68. $3n - 12 = 5n - 20$ **4**

69. $6(x + 3) = 3x$ **−6**

70. $2(x - 2) = 3x - (4x - 5)$ **3**

71. BALLOONS Brandon slowly fills a deflated balloon with air. Without tying the balloon, he lets it go. Draw a graph to represent this situation. (Lesson 1-9) **See margin.**

GET READY for the Next Lesson

PREREQUISITE SKILL Find each difference.

72. $12 - 16$ **−4**

73. $-5 - (-8)$ **3**

74. $16 - (-4)$ **20**

75. $-9 - 6$ **−15**

Ticket Out the Door Make several copies of five different linear equations. Give one equation to each student. As students leave the room, ask them to identify the *x*- and *y*-intercepts.

 Formative Assessment

Check for student understanding of Lesson 3-3.

CRM Quiz 2, p. 43

 **Foldables™ Follow-Up**

Remind students to use the third tab on their Foldables to record notes on what they have learned about linear functions.

Additional Answers

For answers to 37 and 38, see p. 159.

52.

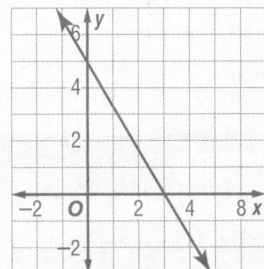

67. $f(x) = 2.25x$; $9.00, $15.75; It costs $9.00 to buy 4 energy bars and $15.75 to buy 7 energy bars.

71.

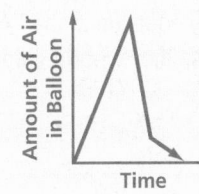

Pre-AP Activity Use as an Extension

Explain to students that the graph of a linear equation is called a *continuous graph.* It extends beyond the endpoints in each direction and represents all solutions of the linear equation. Every ordered pair on a continuous line satisfies the equation. When the variables in an equation must be whole numbers, the points cannot be connected with a line. This type of graph is a *discrete graph.* Ask students to think of an example of when a discrete graph would be used. Sample answer: if *x* stood for the number of boys in a class and *y* stood for the number of girls in a class

 **1 Focus**

Materials

• graphing calculator

Teaching Tips

• The graphing calculator has the ability to make graphs appear differently on the screen. The symbol before each Y= entry shows how the line will appear. Highlight the symbol and press ENTER repeatedly until the line type you want appears.

• The standard viewing window is selected by pressing ZOOM 6. This is a $[-10, 10]$ by $[-10, 10]$ screen with scales, Xscl and Yscl, of 1.

• You can keep an equation in the Y= list and have it not appear on the graphing screen by highlighting the = sign and pressing ENTER.

2 Teach

Working in Cooperative Groups

Put students in groups of 3 or 4, mixing abilities. Have groups help each other to complete Activities 1–2.

Make sure students have cleared or suppressed any equation in the Y= list other than those they wish to graph.

 EXTEND 3-3 **Graphing Calculator Lab**
Graphing Linear Functions

Standard 6.0 Students graph a linear equation and compute the *x*- and *y*-intercepts (e.g., graph $2x + 6y = 4$). They are also able to sketch the region defined by linear inequality (e.g., they sketch the region defined by $2x + 6y < 4$). (Key, CAHSEE)

The power of a graphing calculator is the ability to graph different types of equations accurately and quickly. Often linear equations are graphed in the standard viewing window. The **standard viewing window** is $[-10, 10]$ by $[-10, 10]$ with a scale of 1 on each axis. To quickly choose the standard viewing window on a TI-83/84 Plus, press ZOOM 6.

ACTIVITY 1

Graph $2x - y = 3$ on a TI-83/84 Plus graphing calculator.

Step 1 Enter the equation in the Y= list.

• The Y= list shows the equation or equations that you will graph.

• Equations must be entered with the y isolated on one side of the equation. Solve the equation for y, then enter it into the calculator.

$$2x - y = 3 \qquad \text{Original equation}$$
$$2x - y - 2x = 3 - 2x \qquad \text{Subtract } 2x \text{ from each side.}$$
$$-y = -2x + 3 \qquad \text{Simplify.}$$
$$y = 2x - 3 \qquad \text{Multiply each side by } -1.$$

KEYSTROKES: Y= 2 X,T,θ,*n* — 3

Step 2 Graph the equation in the standard viewing window.

KEYSTROKES: ZOOM 6

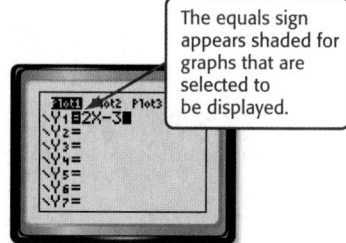

The equals sign appears shaded for graphs that are selected to be displayed.

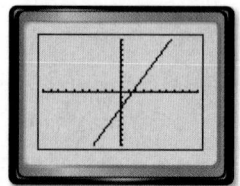

$[-10, 10]$ scl: 1 by $[-10, 10]$ scl: 1

Sometimes a complete graph is not displayed using the standard viewing window. A **complete graph** includes all of the important characteristics of the graph on the screen. These include the origin and the *x*- and *y*-intercepts. Notice that the graph of $2x - y = 3$ is a complete graph because all of these points are visible.

When a complete graph is not displayed using the standard viewing window, you will need to change the viewing window to accommodate these important features. You can use what you have learned about intercepts to help you choose an appropriate viewing window.

162 Chapter 3 Functions and Patterns

 Math Online **Other Calculator Keystrokes at** ca.algebra1.com

ACTIVITY 2

Graph $y = 3x - 15$ on a graphing calculator.

Step 1 Enter the equation in the Y= list and graph in the standard viewing window.

Clear the previous equation from the Y= list. Then enter the new equation and graph.

KEYSTROKES: Y= CLEAR 3 X,T,θ,n − 15 ZOOM 6

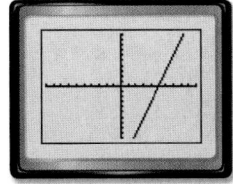

[−10, 10] scl: 1 by [−10, 10] scl: 1

Step 2 Modify the viewing window and graph again.

The origin and the x-intercept are displayed in the standard viewing window. But notice that the y-intercept is outside of the viewing window. Find the y-intercept.

$$y = 3x - 15 \quad \text{Original equation}$$
$$= 3(0) - 15 \quad \text{Replace } x \text{ with 0.}$$
$$= -15 \quad \text{Simplify.}$$

Since the y-intercept is -15, choose a viewing window that includes a number less than -15. The window $[-10, 10]$ by $[-20, 5]$ with a scale of 1 on each axis is a good choice.

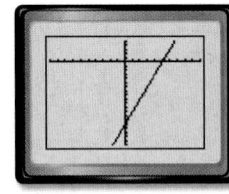

[−10, 10] scl: 1 by [−20, 5] scl: 1

KEYSTROKES: WINDOW −10 ENTER 10 ENTER 1 ENTER
−20 ENTER 5 ENTER 1 GRAPH

EXERCISES

Graph each linear equation in the standard viewing window. Determine whether the graph is complete. If the graph is not complete, choose a viewing window that will show a complete graph and graph the equation again. **1–5. See margin.**

1. $y = x + 2$ **2.** $y = 4x + 5$ **3.** $y = 6 - 5x$ **4.** $2x + y = 6$

5. $x + y = -2$ **6.** $x - 4y = 8$ **7.** $y = 5x + 9$ **8.** $y = 10x - 6$

9. $y = 3x - 18$ **10.** $3x - y = 12$ **11.** $4x + 2y = 21$ **12.** $3x + 5y = -45$
6–12. See Ch. 3 Answer Appendix.

For Exercises 13–15, consider the linear equation $y = 2x + b$.

13. Choose several different positive and negative values for b. Graph each equation in the standard viewing window. **See students' work.**

14. For which values of b is the complete graph in the standard viewing window? **−10 < b < 10**

15. How is the value of b related to the y-intercept of the graph of $y = 2x + b$? **b is the y-intercept of the graph.**

Extend 3-3 Graphing Calculator Lab: Graphing Linear Functions **163**

3 Assess

✓ Formative Assessment

- Ask students to summarize what belonging to a family of graphs means.

- Use Exercise 1 to assess whether students understand how changing b affects the graphs in a family of linear functions.

- Use Exercise 3 to assess whether students understand how changing m affects the graphs in a family of linear functions.

From Concrete to Abstract
Ask: How can the graph of $y = mx + b$ be drawn from the graph of $y = mx$? Sample answer: Shift the graph of $y = mx$ up b units if b is positive and down b units if b is negative.

Additional Answers

1.
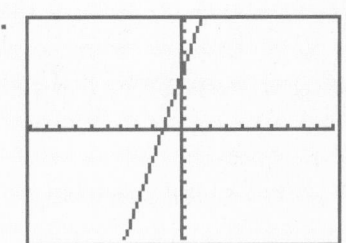

2.
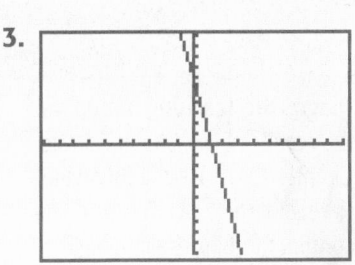

3.

4.
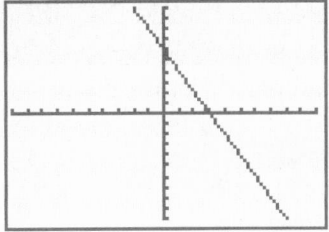

5.
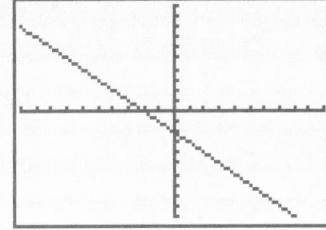

Formative Assessment

Use the Mid-Chapter Quiz to assess students' progress in the first half of the chapter.

For problems answered incorrectly, have students review the lessons indicated in parentheses.

Summative Assessment

 Mid-Chapter Test, p. 45

 Customize and create multiple versions of your Mid-Chapter Test and their answer keys.

FOLDABLES **Foldables™**
Study Organizer **Follow-Up**

Before students complete the Mid-Chapter Quiz, encourage them to review the information for Lessons 3-1 through 3-3 in their Foldables.

Additional Answers

1. D = {1, 2, 4}; R = {3, 5, 6};
   I = {(3, 1), (6, 4), (3, 2), (5, 1)}

2. D = {−5, −1, 2, 6}; R = {0, 3, 4,
   7, 8}; I = {(8, −5), (0, −1),
   (4, −1), (7, 2), (3, 6)}

3. D = {−8, 11, 15}; R = {3, 5, 22,
   31}; I = {(5, 11), (3, 15), (22, −8),
   (31, 11)}

4. D = {−2, 0, 2, 4, 6}; R = {0, 1, 2,
   3, 4}; I = {(4, −2), (3, 0), (2, 2),
   (1, 4), (0, 6)}

8, 19–20. See Ch. 3 Answer Appendix.

State the domain, range, and inverse of each relation. (Lesson 3-1) **1–4. See margin.**

1. {(1, 3), (4, 6), (2, 3), (1, 5)}
2. {(−5, 8), (−1, 0), (−1, 4), (2, 7), (6, 3)}
3.

x	y
11	5
15	3
−8	22
11	31

4.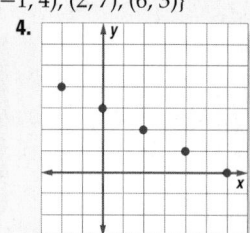

5. **MULTIPLE CHOICE** What are the domain and range of the relation? (Lesson 3-1) **B**

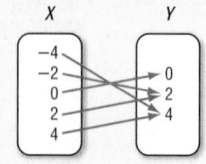

A D = {0, 2, 4}; R ={−4, −2, 0, 2, 4}
B D = {−4, −2, 0, 2, 4}; R = {0, 2, 4}
C D = {0, 2, 4}; R = {−4, −2, 0}
D D = {−4, −2, 0, 2, 4}; R ={−4, −2, 0, 2, 4}

CHEERLEADING For Exercises 6–8, use the following information.

The cost of a cheerleading camp is shown in the table. (Lesson 3-1)

Number of Cheerleaders	Total Cost ($)
1	70
2	140
3	210
4	280

6. Determine the domain and range of the relation. **D = {1, 2, 3, 4}; R = {70, 140, 210, 280}**

7. Graph the data. **See Ch. 3 Answer Appendix.**

8. Describe the independent and dependent quantities in this situation. **See margin.**

If f(x) = 3x + 5, find each value. (Lesson 3-2)

9. f(−4) **−7** 10. f(2a) 11. f(x + 2)
                    6a + 5   **3x + 11**

164 Chapter 3 Functions and Patterns

Determine whether each relation is a function. (Lesson 3-2)

12. {(3, 4), (5, 3), (−1, 4), (6, 2)} **yes**
13. {(−1, 4), (−2, 5), (7, 2), (3, 9), (−2, 1)} **no**

14. **MULTIPLE CHOICE** Which is a true statement about the relation? (Lesson 3-2) **H**

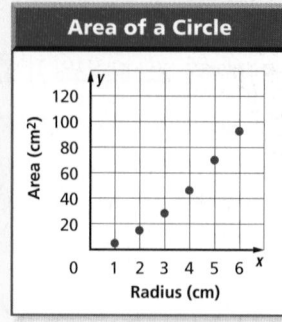

F As the radius increases, the area decreases.
G The relation is a linear function.
H The area is a function of the radius.
J The relation is not a function.

15–16. See Ch. 3
Graph each equation. (Lesson 3-3) **Answer Appendix.**
15. y = x − 2   16. 3x + 2y = 6

17. **MULTIPLE CHOICE** If (a, −7) is a solution to the equation 8a + 3b = 3, what is a? (Lesson 3-3) **B**

A 2   B 3   C 3.5   D −6.5

ENTERTAINMENT For Exercises 18–20, use the following information.

The equation 200x + 80y = 600 represents the number of premium tickets x and the number of discount tickets y to a car race that can be bought with $600. (Lesson 3-3) **See Ch. 3 Answer**

18. Graph the function.   **Appendix.**

19. Describe a domain and range that makes sense for this situation. Explain.

20. Describe what the x-and y-intercepts represent in the context of this situation.

19–20. See margin.

Data-Driven Decision Making	Exercises	Lesson	🔖 Standard	Resources for Review
Diagnostic Teaching Based on the results of the Chapter 3 Mid-Chapter Quiz, use the following to review concepts that students continue to find challenging.	1–8	3–1	17.0	CRM Study Guide and Intervention pp. 6–7, 13–14, 20–21 Math Online • Extra Examples • Personal Tutor • Concepts in Motion
	9–14	3–2	18.0	
	15–20	3–3	6.0	

Arithmetic Sequences

Main Ideas

- Recognize arithmetic sequences.
- Extend and write formulas for arithmetic sequences

 Reinforcement of Standard 7AF3.4 Plot the values of quantities whose ratios are always the same (e.g., cost to the number of an item, feet to inches, circumference to diameter of a circle). Fit a line to the plot and understand that the slope of the line equals the quantities. (Key, CAHSEE)

New Vocabulary

sequence
terms
arithmetic sequence
common difference

GET READY for the Lesson

A probe to measure air quality is attached to a hot-air balloon. The probe has an altitude of 6.3 feet after the first second, 14.5 feet after the next second, 22.7 feet after the third second, and so on. You can make a table and look for a pattern in the data.

Time (s)	1	2	3	4	5	6	7	8
Altitude (ft)	6.3	14.5	22.7	30.9	39.1	47.3	55.5	63.7

+ 8.2   + 8.2   + 8.2   + 8.2   + 8.2   + 8.2   + 8.2

Recognize Arithmetic Sequences A **sequence** is a set of numbers, called **terms,** in a specific order. If the difference between successive terms is constant, then it is called an **arithmetic sequence**. The difference between the terms is called the **common difference**.

KEY CONCEPT — Arithmetic Sequence

An arithmetic sequence is a numerical pattern that increases or decreases at a constant rate or value called the common difference.

Study Tip

Ellipsis
The three dots after the last number in a sequence are called an *ellipsis*. The ellipsis indicates that there are more terms in the sequence that are not listed.

EXAMPLE — Identify Arithmetic Sequences

① Determine whether each sequence is arithmetic. Explain.

a. 1, 2, 4, 8, …

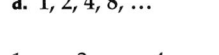

1   2   4   8

+ 1   + 2   + 4

This is not an arithmetic sequence because the difference between terms is not constant.

b. $\frac{1}{2}, \frac{1}{4}, 0, -\frac{1}{4}, \ldots$

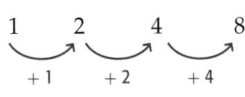

$\frac{1}{2}$ $\frac{1}{4}$ 0 $-\frac{1}{4}$

$-\frac{1}{4}$ $-\frac{1}{4}$ $-\frac{1}{4}$

This is an arithmetic sequence because the difference between terms is constant.

✓ **CHECK Your Progress** 1A–1B. See margin.

1A. $-26, -22, -18, -14, \ldots$ **1B.** $1, 4, 9, 25, \ldots$

---

1 Focus

Standards Alignment

Before Lesson 3-4
Represent quantitative relationships graphically from Standard 7AF1.5

Lesson 3-4
Plot the values of quantities whose ratios are always the same and fit a line to the plot from 🔑 Standard 7AF3.4

After Lesson 3-4
Derive the summation formulas for arithmetic and geometric series from 🔑 Standards 2A22.0 and 2A23.0

2 Teach

Scaffolding Questions
Have students read *Get Ready for the Lesson.*

Ask:
- What pattern do you see in the data table? After the first second, the balloon rises 8.2 feet every second.
- Why might the balloon not have risen 8.2 feet in the first second? Sample answer: Perhaps overcoming the force of gravity initially caused it not to rise as far in the first second.

(continued on the next page)

Lesson 3-4 Resources

Chapter 3 Resource Masters

Lesson Reading Guide, p. 27 BL OL ELL
Study Guide and Intervention, pp. 28–29 BL OL ELL
Skills Practice, p. 30 BL OL
Practice, p. 31 OL AL
Word Problem Practice, p. 32 OL AL
Enrichment, p. 33 OL AL
Quiz 3, p. 44

Transparencies

5-Minute Check Transparency 3-4

Additional Print Resources

Noteables™ Interactive Study Notebook with Foldables™

Technology

ca.algebra1.com
Interactive Classroom CD-ROM
AssignmentWorks CD-ROM
Graphing Calculator Easy Files

- What will the altitude of the balloon be after 9 seconds? **71.9 feet**
- How can you find the altitude of the balloon after 12 seconds? **Sample answer: 63.7 + 4(8.2)**

Recognize Arithmetic Sequences

Example 1 shows how to determine whether a sequence is arithmetic.

 Formative Assessment

Use the Check Your Progress exercises after each example to determine students' understanding of concepts.

ADDITIONAL EXAMPLE

1 Determine whether each sequence is arithmetic. Explain.

a. $-15, -13, -11, -9, \ldots$
  arithmetic sequence; the difference is constant

b. $\frac{7}{8}, \frac{5}{8}, \frac{1}{8}, -\frac{5}{8}, \ldots$
  not an arithmetic sequence; the difference is not constant

Additional Examples are also in:
- Noteables™ Interactive Study Notebook with Foldables™
- Interactive Classroom PowerPoint® Presentations

Write Arithmetic Sequences

Example 2 shows how to solve a real-world problem by extending an arithmetic sequence. **Example 3** shows how to write an equation for an arithmetic sequence to solve a real-world problem.

ADDITIONAL EXAMPLE

2 **TEMPERATURE** The arithmetic sequence $-8, -11, -14, -17, \ldots$ represents the daily low temperature in °F. Find the next three terms. $-20, -23, -26$

Write Arithmetic Sequences You can use the common difference of an arithmetic sequence to find the next term in the sequence.

KEY CONCEPT — Writing Arithmetic Sequences

Words	Each term of an arithmetic sequence after the first term can be found by adding the common difference to the preceding term.
Symbols	An arithmetic sequence, $a_1, a_2, \ldots$ can be found as follows: $$a_1, a_2 = a_1 + d, a_3 = a_2 + d, a_4 = a_3 + d, \ldots$$ where d is the common difference, a_1 is the first term, a_2 is the second term, and so on.

Real-World EXAMPLE

2 **MONEY** The arithmetic sequence 74, 67, 60, 53, ... represents the amount of money that Tiffany owes her mother at the end of each week. Find the next three terms.

Find the common difference by subtracting successive terms.

74   67   60   53   ?   ?   ?
  −7   −7   −7   −7   −7   −7

The common difference is −7.

Add −7 to the last term of the sequence to get the next term in the sequence. Continue adding −7 until the next three terms are found.

53   46   39   32   The next three terms are 46, 39, 32.
  −7   −7   −7

CHECK Your Progress 15.5, 17.0, 18.5

2. Find the next four terms of the arithmetic sequence 9.5, 11.0, 12.5, 14.0, …

Each term in an arithmetic sequence can be expressed in terms of the first term a_1 and the common difference d.

Study Tip

Formulas The formula for the nth term of an arithmetic sequence is called a *recursive formula*. This means that each succeeding term is formulated from one or more of the previous terms.

Term	Symbol	In Terms of a_1 and d	Numbers
first term	a_1	a_1	8
second term	a_2	$a_1 + d$	$8 + 1(3) = 11$
third term	a_3	$a_1 + 2d$	$8 + 2(3) = 14$
fourth term	a_4	$a_1 + 3d$	$8 + 3(3) = 17$
⋮	⋮	⋮	⋮
nth term	a_n	$a_1 + (n-1)d$	$8 + (n-1)(3)$

This leads to the formula that can be used to find any term in an arithmetic sequence.

 Extra Examples at ca.algebra1.com

Additional Answers

1A. Yes, the difference between terms is constant.

1B. No, the difference between terms is not constant.

Building on Prior Knowledge

Tips for New Teachers Ask a volunteer to count from zero by twos. Ask another to count from zero by threes. Ask a third to count from zero by fives. Explain to students that when they count by a certain number, whether 1, 2, 3, 5, or $\frac{1}{8}$, they are using an arithmetic sequence because there is a common difference.

Real-World EXAMPLE

3 SHIPPING The arithmetic sequence 12, 23, 34, 45, ... represents the total number of ounces that a box weighs after each additional book is added.

a. Write an equation for the nth term of the sequence.

In this sequence, the first term, a_1, is 12. Find the common difference.

12   23   34   45
  + 11 + 11 + 11

The common difference is 11.

Use the formula for the nth term to write an equation.

$a_n = a_1 + (n - 1)d$ ⟶ Formula for nth term

$\quad = 12 + (n - 1)11$ ⟶ $a_1 = 12, d = 11$

$\quad = 12 + 11n - 11$ ⟶ Distributive Property

$\quad = 11n + 1$ ⟶ Simplify.

b. Find the 10th term in the sequence.

$a_n = 11n + 1$ ⟶ Equation for the nth term

$a_{10} = 11(10) + 1$ ⟶ Replace n with 10.

$a_{10} = 111$ ⟶ Simplify.

Study Tip

Graph of a Sequence
Notice that the points on the graph fall on a line. The graph of an arithmetic sequence is linear.

c. Graph the first five terms of the sequence.

n	$11n + 1$	a_n	(n, a_n)
1	$11(1) + 1$	12	(1, 12)
2	$11(2) + 1$	23	(2, 23)
3	$11(3) + 1$	34	(3, 34)
4	$11(4) + 1$	45	(4, 45)
5	$11(5) + 1$	56	(5, 56)

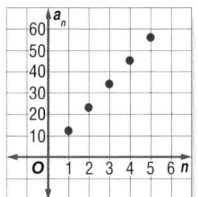

✓CHECK Your Progress

Consider the arithmetic sequence 3, −10, −23, −36, ...

3A. Write an equation for the nth term of the sequence. $a_n = -13n + 16$

3B. Find the 15th term in the sequence. −179

3C. Graph the first five terms of the sequence. **See margin.**

 Personal Tutor at ca.algebra1.com

Additional Answer

3C.

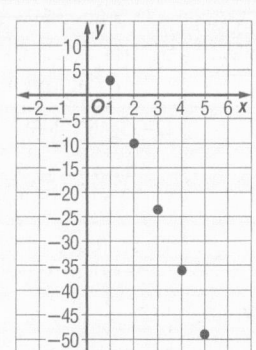

ADDITIONAL EXAMPLE

3 MONEY The arithmetic sequence 1, 10, 19, 28, … represents the total number of dollars Erin has in her account after her weekly allowance is added.

a. Write an equation for the nth term of the sequence.
$a_n = 9n - 8$

b. Find the 12th term in the sequence. $a_{12} = 100$

c. Graph the first five terms of the sequence.

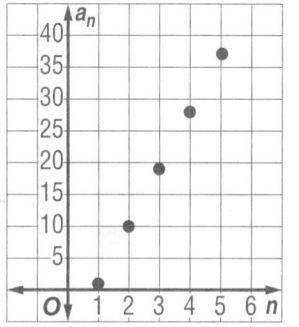

Tips for New Teachers

Preventing Error

Make sure students carefully keep track of the variables in the equation $a_n = a_1 + (n-1)d$ as it is easy to substitute for the wrong variable when using this equation.

3 Practice

Formative Assessment

Use Exercises 1–11 to check for understanding.

Use the chart at the bottom of this page to customize assignments for your students.

Odd/Even Assignments

Exercises 12–33 are structured so that students practice the same concepts whether they are assigned odd or even problems.

Preventing Errors

Before students work Exercises 20 and 21, remind them that the perimeter of a figure is the sum of the lengths of its sides. However, point out that the perimeter does not include the touching sides when two or more figures are combined to make one figure.

Additional Answers

10. $a_n = 6n$

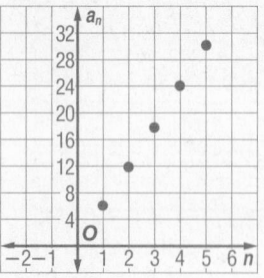

11. $a_n = 5.1n + 7$

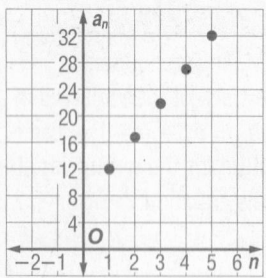

47. Yes; $4x + 5 - (2x + 5) = 2x$, $6x + 5 - (4x + 5) = 2x$, $8x + 5 - (6x + 5) = 2x$. The common difference is $2x$.

✓ CHECK Your Understanding

Example 1
(p. 165)

Determine whether each sequence is an arithmetic sequence. If it is, state the common difference.

1. 24, 16, 8, 0, … yes; −8

2. $3\frac{1}{4}, 6\frac{1}{2}, 13, 26, …$ no

Example 2
(p. 166)

Find the next three terms of each arithmetic sequence.

3. 7, 14, 21, 28, … **35, 42, 49**

4. −34, −29, −24, −19, … **−14, −9, −4**

Example 3
(p. 167)

Find the nth term of each arithmetic sequence described.

5. $a_1 = 3, d = 4, n = 8$ **31**

6. $a_1 = 10, d = -5, n = 21$ **−90**

7. 23, 25, 27, 29, … for $n = 12$ **45**

8. −27, −19, −11, −3, … for $n = 17$ **101**

9. FITNESS Latisha is beginning an exercise program that calls for 20 minutes of walking each day for the first week. Each week thereafter, she has to increase her walking by 7 minutes a day. Which week of her exercise program will be the first one in which she will walk over an hour a day? **the seventh week**

Write an equation for the nth term of each arithmetic sequence. Then graph the first five terms of the sequence. **10–11. See margin.**

10. 6, 12, 18, 24, …

11. 12.1, 17.2, 22.3, 27.4, …

Exercises

HOMEWORK HELP	
For Exercises	**See Examples**
12–15	1
16–19	2
20–33	3

Exercise Levels
A: 12–33
B: 34–45
C: 46–49

Determine whether each sequence is an arithmetic sequence. If it is, state the common difference.

12. 7, 6, 5, 4, … yes; −1

13. 10, 12, 15, 18, … no

14. −15, −11, −7, −3, … yes; 4

15. −0.3, 0.2, 0.7, 1.2, … yes; 0.5

Find the next three terms of each arithmetic sequence.

16. 4, 7, 10, 13, … **16, 19, 22**

17. 18, 24, 30, 36, … **42, 48, 54**

18. −66, −70, −74, −78, … **−82, −86, −90**

19. −31, −22, −13, −4, … **5, 14, 23**

GEOMETRY For Exercises 20 and 21, use the diagram below that shows the perimeter of the pattern consisting of trapezoids.

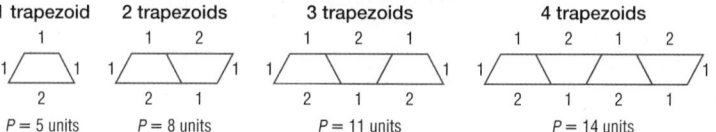

1 trapezoid	2 trapezoids	3 trapezoids	4 trapezoids
$P = 5$ units	$P = 8$ units	$P = 11$ units	$P = 14$ units

20. Write a formula that can be used to find the perimeter of a pattern containing n trapezoids. $P(n) = 3n + 2$

21. What is the perimeter of the pattern containing 12 trapezoids? **38**

Find the nth term of each arithmetic sequence described.

22. $a_1 = 8, d = 3, n = 16$ **53**

23. $a_1 = 52, d = 12, n = 102$ **1264**

24. $a_1 = \frac{5}{8}, d = \frac{1}{8}, n = 22$ **$3\frac{1}{4}$**

25. −9, −7, −5, −3, … for $n = 18$ **25**

26. −7, −3, 1, 5, … for $n = 35$ **129**

27. 0.5, 1, 1.5, 2, … for $n = 50$ **25**

168   **Chapter 3** Functions and Patterns

DIFFERENTIATED HOMEWORK OPTIONS			
Level	**Assignment**	**Two-Day Option**	
BL Basic	12–33, 46, 48–61	13–33 odd, 50–52	12–32 even, 46, 48, 49, 53–61
OL Core	13–39 odd, 40–46, 48–61	12–33, 50–52	34–46, 48, 49, 53–61
AL Advanced	34–57, (optional: 58–61)		

THEATER For Exercises 28 and 29, use the following information.
The Coral Gables Actors' Playhouse has 7 rows of seats in the orchestra section. The number of seats in each row forms an arithmetic sequence, as shown in the table. On opening night, 368 tickets were sold for the orchestra section.

Row	Number of Seats
7	76
6	68
5	60

28. Write a formula to find the number of seats in any given row of the orchestra section of the theater. $a_n = 8n + 20$

29. How many seats are in the first row? Was this section oversold?
28; yes, by 4 seats

Write an equation for the nth term of the arithmetic sequence. Then graph the first five terms in the sequence. **30–33. See Ch. 3 Answer Appendix.**

30. $-3, -6, -9, -12, \ldots$
31. $8, 9, 10, 11, \ldots$
32. $2, 8, 14, 20, \ldots$
33. $-18, -16, -14, -12, \ldots$

Real-World Link

The open-air theaters of ancient Greece held about 20,000 people. They became the models for amphitheaters, Roman coliseums, and modern sports arenas.

Source: encarta.msn.com

Find the next three terms of each arithmetic sequence.

34. $2\frac{1}{3}, 2\frac{2}{3}, 3, 3\frac{1}{3}, \ldots$ $3\frac{2}{3}, 4, 4\frac{1}{3}$
35. $\frac{7}{12}, 1\frac{1}{3}, 2\frac{1}{12}, 2\frac{5}{6}$ $3\frac{7}{12}, 4\frac{1}{3}, 5\frac{1}{12}$

36. 200 is the ___?___ th term of $24, 35, 46, 57\ldots$ **17**

37. -34 is the ___?___ th term of $30, 22, 14, 6, \ldots$ **9**

38. Find the value of y that makes $y + 4, 6, y, \ldots$ an arithmetic sequence. **4**

39. Find the value of y that makes $y + 8, 4y + 6, 3y, \ldots$ an arithmetic sequence. **-1**

ANALYZE TABLES For Exercises 40–43, use the following information.
Taylor and Brooklyn are recording how far a ball rolls down a ramp during each second. The table shows the data they have collected.

Time (s)	1	2	3	4	5	6
Distance traveled (cm)	9	13	17	21	25	29

40. Do the distances traveled by the ball form an arithmetic sequence? Justify your answer. **Yes, the constant difference between terms is 4.**

41. Write an equation for the sequence. How far will the ball have traveled after 35 seconds? $a_n = 4n + 5$; **145 cm**

42. Graph the sequence. **See Ch. 3 Answer Appendix.**

43. Suppose that for each second, the ball rolls twice the distance shown in the table. Is the graph representing this sequence linear? If so, describe how its rate of change is different from the rate of change shown in your original graph. **Sample answer: Yes; the rate of change is greater.**

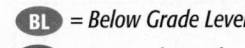

EXTRA PRACTICE
See pages 724, 746.

Math Online
Self-Check Quiz at
ca.algebra1.com

GAMES For Exercises 44 and 45, use the following information.
Contestants on a game show win money by answering 10 questions. The value of each question increases by $1500. **44. $16,000**

44. If the first question is worth $2500, find the value of the 10th question.

45. If the contestant answers all 10 questions correctly, how much money will he or she win? **$92,500**

H.O.T. Problems

46. **OPEN ENDED** Create an arithmetic sequence with a common difference of -10. **Sample answer: 2, -8, -18, -28, \ldots**

47. **CHALLENGE** Is $2x + 5, 4x + 5, 6x + 5, 8x + 5, \ldots$ an arithmetic sequence? Explain your reasoning. **See margin.**

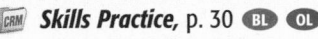

BL = Below Grade Level
OL = On Grade Level
AL = Above Grade Level
ELL = English Language Learner

Additional pages not shown:

Lesson Reading Guide, p. 27 **BL OL ELL**

Skills Practice, p. 30 **BL OL**

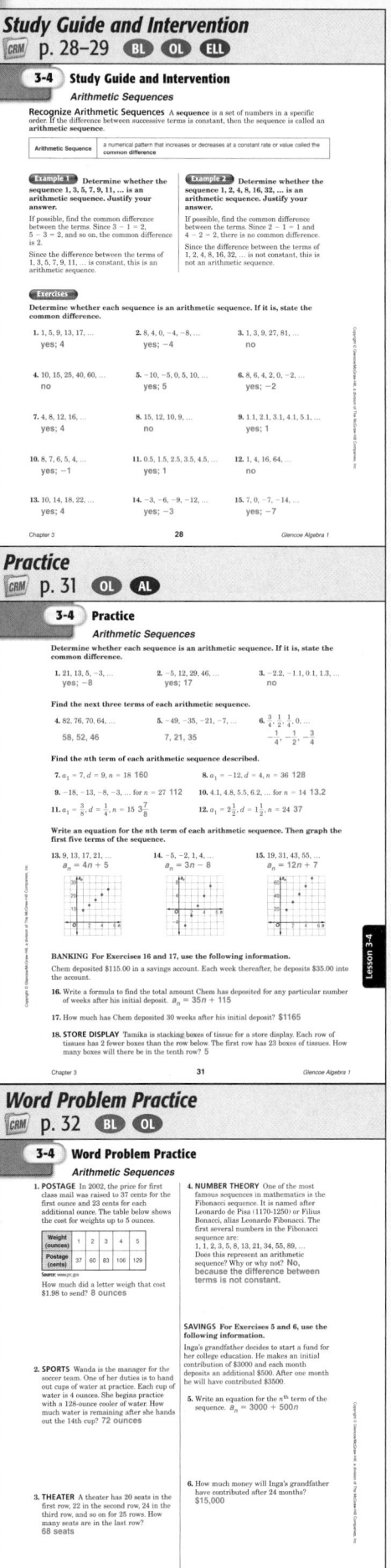

Exercise Alert!

Find the Error For Exercise 48, the common difference is found by subtracting the first term in the sequence from the second term. Suggest students check the arithmetic to make sure Marisela and Richard correctly subtracted the negative amount.

4 Assess

Crystal Ball Have students write how they think today's lesson will connect to tomorrow's lesson, Describing Number Patterns.

Formative Assessment

Check for student understanding of the concepts in Lesson 3-4.

[CRM] Quiz 3, p. 44

Additional Answers

48. Marisela; to find the common difference, subtract the first term from the second term.

49. Sample answer: The formula $a_t = 8.2t - 1.9$ represents the altitude a_t of the probe after t seconds. Replace t with 15 in the equation for a_t to find that the altitude of the probe after 15 seconds is 121.1 feet.

58–61.

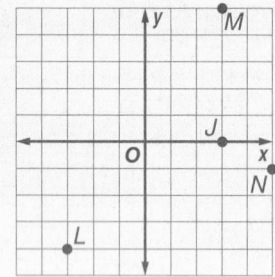

---

48. FIND THE ERROR Marisela and Richard are finding the common difference for the arithmetic sequence -44, -32, -20, -8. Who is correct? Explain. **See margin.**

Marisela	Richard
$-32 - (-44) = 12$	$-44 - (-32) = -12$
$-20 - (-32) = 12$	$-32 - (-20) = -12$
$-8 - (-20) = 12$	$-20 - (-8) = -12$

49. *Writing in Math* Refer to the data about measuring air quality on page 165. Write a formula for the arithmetic sequence that represents the altitude of the probe after each second, and an explanation of how you could use this information to predict the altitude of the probe after 15 seconds. **See margin.**

STANDARDS PRACTICE   6AF1.1, 7.0, 7MG3.2

50. REVIEW Luis deposits $25 each week into a savings account from his part-time job. If he has $350 in savings now, how much will he have in 12 weeks? **C**

   A $600   C $650

   B $625   D $675

51. What is the slope of a line that contains the point at $(1, -5)$ and has the same y-intercept as $2x - y = 9$? **J**

   F -9 H 2

   G -7 J 4

52. REVIEW Which is a true statement about the relation graphed? **C**

   A As the side length of a cube increases, the surface area decreases.

Surface Area of Cube

(graph: Surface Area (sq cm) on y-axis from 0 to 50, Side Length (cm) on x-axis from 1 to 5)

   B Surface area is the independent quantity.

   C The surface area of a cube is a function of the side length.

   D The relation is not a function.

Spiral Review

Determine whether each equation is a linear equation. If so, write the equation in standard form. (Lesson 3-3)

53. $x^2 + 3x - y = 8$ **no**

54. $y - 8 = 10 - x$ **yes; $x + y = 18$**

55. $2y = y + 2x - 3$ **yes; $2x - y = 3$**

56. TAX The amount of sales tax in California is given by $y = 0.0725x$, where x is the cost of an item that you buy. Write the equation in function notation and then find $f(40)$. What does this value represent? (Lesson 3-2)
$f(x) = 0.0725x$; **2.9;** The amount of tax on a $40 purchase is $2.90.

57. Translate the sentence *The sum of twice r and three times s is identical to thirteen* into an algebraic equation. (Lesson 2-1) **$2r + 3s = 13$**

GET READY for the Next Lesson

PREREQUISITE SKILL Graph each point on the same coordinate plane. (Lesson 1-9)

58. $J(3, 0)$ **59.** $L(-3, -4)$ **60.** $M(3, 5)$ **61.** $N(5, -1)$

■ 58–61. See margin.

Pre-AP Activity   Use after Exercises 36 and 37

Tell students that you applied a procedure that determines an arithmetic sequence in which the 4th term is 27 and the 8th term is 59. Ask students to find the starting number and the common difference. (Hint: Let the 4th term temporarily be the 1st term, which in turn makes the 8th term the 4th term.) $a_1 = 3$, $d = 8$

READING MATH

Inductive and Deductive Reasoning

 Standard 24.1 Students explain the difference between inductive and deductive reasoning and identify and provide examples of each.

Throughout your life, you have used reasoning skills, possibly without even knowing it. As a child, you used inductive reasoning to conclude that your hand would hurt if you touched the stove while it was hot. Now, you use inductive reasoning when you decide, after many trials, that one of the worst ways to prepare for an exam is by studying only an hour before you take it. **Inductive reasoning** is used to derive a general rule after observing many individual events.

Inductive reasoning involves:
- observing many examples
- looking for a pattern
- making a conjecture
- checking the conjecture
- discovering a likely conclusion

With **deductive reasoning**, you use a general rule to help you decide about a specific event. You come to a conclusion by accepting facts. There is no conjecturing involved. Read the two statements below.

1) If a person wants to play varsity sports, he or she must have a C average in academic classes.

2) Jolene is playing on the varsity tennis team.

If these two statements are accepted as facts, then the obvious conclusion is that Jolene has at least a C average in her academic classes. This is an example of deductive reasoning.

Reading to Learn 1–6. See margin.

1. Explain the difference between inductive and deductive reasoning. Then give an example of each.

2. When Sherlock Holmes reaches a conclusion about a murderer's height because he knows the relationship between a man's height and the distance between his footprints, what kind of reasoning is he using? Explain.

3. When you examine a sequence of numbers and decide that it is an arithmetic sequence, what kind of reasoning are you using? Explain.

4. Once you have found the common difference for an arithmetic sequence, what kind of reasoning do you use to find the 100th term in the sequence?

5. **a.** Copy and complete the following table.

3^1	3^2	3^3	3^4	3^5	3^6	3^7	3^8	3^9
3	9	27	81	243	729	2187	6561	19,683

b. Write the sequence of numbers representing the numbers in the ones place.

c. Find the number in the ones place for the value of 3100. Explain your reasoning. State the type of reasoning that you used.

6. A sequence contains all numbers less than 50 that are divisible by 5. You conclude that 35 is in the sequence. Is this an example of inductive or deductive reasoning? Explain.

Reading Math Inductive and Deductive Reasoning **171**

---

1 Focus

Ask students to explain the types of thoughts they have when they solve a problem. If students have trouble coming up with ideas, give them a situation. Ask them how they would solve the problem of opening a locked door if they had a key ring with 100 keys on it.

2 Teach

Induce Explain to students that the root of inductive is *induce.* Induce is a verb that means to call forth or bring about by influence, or to cause the formation of. After students read the description of inductive reasoning, have them relate the principle of inductive reasoning to the definition of the word induce.

Deduce The root of deductive is *deduce.* Deduce is a verb that means to infer from a general principle. Ask students to relate the principle of deductive reasoning to the definition of the word deduce.

3 Assess

Reading to Learn Ask students whether predicting the next term in a sequence of numbers is done by trial and error, or by interpreting given information with a set of rules.

ELL English Language Learners may benefit from writing key concepts from this activity in their Study Notebooks in their native language and then in English.

For answers 1–6, see p. 183G.

 **3-5** Lesson Notes

 **3-5** # Proportional and Nonproportional Relationships

1 Focus

Standards Alignment

Before Lesson 3-5
Represent quantitative relationships graphically from Standard 7AF1.5

Lesson 3-5
Determine whether a given relation defines a function from Standard 16.0

After Lesson 3-5
Derive the summation formulas for arithmetic and geometric series from ⚷ Standards 2A22.0 and 2A23.0

2 Teach

Scaffolding Questions
Have students read *Get Ready for the Lesson*.
Ask:
- Are the volumes of water in the table, 11, 22, 33, 44, etc., an arithmetic sequence? Explain. Yes, the common difference is 11.
- Are the volumes of ice in the table, 12, 24, 36, 48, etc., an arithmetic sequence? Explain. Yes, the common difference is 12.

(continued on the next page)

Main Ideas
- Write an equation for a proportional relationship.
- Write an equation for a nonproportional relationship.

 Standard 16.0 Students understand the concepts of a relation and a function, determine whether a given relation defines a function, and give pertinent information about given relations and functions.

New Vocabulary
inductive reasoning

GET READY for the Lesson

Water is one of the few substances that expands when it freezes. The table shows volumes of water and the corresponding volumes of ice.

Volume of Water (ft³)	11	22	33	44	55
Volume of Ice (ft³)	12	24	36	48	60

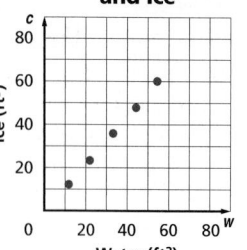
Volume of Water and Ice

The relation in the table can be represented by a graph. Let w represent the volume of water, and let c represent the volume of ice. When the ordered pairs are graphed, they form a linear pattern. This pattern can be described by an equation.

Proportional Relationships Using a pattern to find a general rule utilizes **inductive reasoning**. If the relationship between the domain and range of a relation is linear, the relationship can be described by a linear equation. If the equation is of the form $y = kx$, then the relationship is proportional. In a proportional relationship, the graph will pass through $(0, 0)$.

Real-World EXAMPLE   Proportional Relationships

1 **FUEL ECONOMY** The table below shows the average amount of gas Rogelio's car uses, depending on how many miles he drives.

Gallons of gasoline	1	2	3	4	5
Miles driven	28	56	84	112	140

a. Graph the data. What conclusion can you make about the relationship between the number of gallons used and the number of miles driven?

The graph shows a linear relationship between the number of gallons used g and the number of miles driven m.

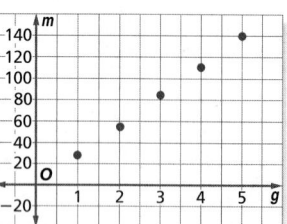

Lesson 3-5 Resources

Transparencies
5-Minute Check Transparency 3-5
Additional Print Resources
Noteables™ Interactive Study Notebook with Foldables™

Technology
ca.algebra1.com
Interactive Classroom CD-ROM
AssignmentWorks CD-ROM
Graphing Calculator Easy Files

Real-World Link
Hybrid cars have a small, fuel-efficient gas engine combined with an electric motor. The electric motor is powered by batteries that recharge automatically while the car is being driven.

Source: artheasy.com/live_hybrid_cars.htm

b. Write an equation to describe this relationship.

Look at the relationship between the values in the domain and range to find a pattern that can be described by an equation.

	+1	+1	+1	+1

Gallons of gasoline	1	2	3	4	5
Miles driven	28	56	84	112	140

+28   +28   +28   +28

The difference of the values for g is 1, and the difference of the values for m is 28. This suggests that $m = 28g$. Check to see if this equation is correct by substituting values of g into the equation.

CHECK   If $g = 1$, then $m = 28(1)$ or 28. ✔
If $g = 2$, then $m = 28(2)$ or 56. ✔
If $g = 3$, then $m = 28(3)$ or 84. ✔

The equation checks. Since this relation is a function, we can write the equation as $f(g) = 28g$, where $f(g)$ represents the number of miles driven.

✓ CHECK Your Progress

FUND-RAISING The table shows the cost of buying Spanish Club T-shirts.

Number of T-shirts	1	2	3	4
Total Cost ($)	7.50	15.00	22.50	30.00

1A. Graph the data and describe the relationship between the number of T-shirts bought and the amount spent. **See margin.**

1B. Write an equation to describe this relationship. $f(x) = 7.5x$, where x is the number of T-shirts.

Nonproportional Relationships Some linear relationships are nonproportional. In the equation of a nonproportional situation, a constant must be added or subtracted from the variable expression.

EXAMPLE Nonproportional Relationships

2 Write an equation in function notation for the relation graphed at the right.

Make a table of ordered pairs.

Study Tip

Nonproportional Relationships
The x- and y-values in Example 2 do not have a proportional relationship because $\frac{x}{y}$ is not always the same; for example, $\frac{1}{5} \neq \frac{2}{7}$.

	+1	+1	+1	+1

x	1	2	3	4	5
y	5	7	9	11	13

+2   +2   +2   +2

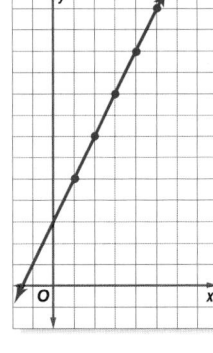

The difference of the x values is 1, and the difference of the y values is 2. The difference in y values is twice the difference of x values. This suggests that $y = 2x$.

(continued on the next page)

 Math Online Extra Examples at ca.algebra1.com

Lesson 3-5 Proportional and Nonproportional Relationships   **173**

Additional Answer

1A. The graph shows a linear relationship between the number of T-shirts bought and the amount spent.

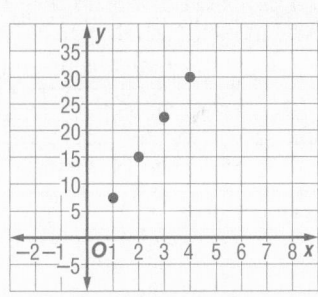

Scaffolding Questions continued
• Based on your answers to the two questions above, do you think there might be a way to predict the volume of ice that will form from a given volume of water? Yes, because there is a pattern to the increase in volumes in the table. So predicting the increase should be possible.

✓ Formative Assessment

Use the Check Your Progress exercises after each example to determine students' understanding of concepts.

Proportional Relationships
Example 1 shows how to write an equation for a real-world problem, given a table of data.

Nonproportional Relationships
Example 2 shows how to write an equation in function notation, given a graph of a relation.

ADDITIONAL EXAMPLE

1 **ENERGY** The table shows the number of miles driven for each hour of driving.

Hours	1	2	3	4
Miles	50	100	150	250

a. Graph the data. What conclusion can you make about the relationship between the number of hours of driving h and the number of miles driven m?

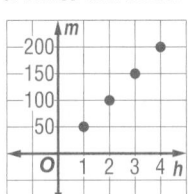

There is a linear relationship between hours of driving and miles driven.

b. Write an equation to describe this relationship. $f(h) = 50h$

2 Write an equation in function notation for the relation graphed below.

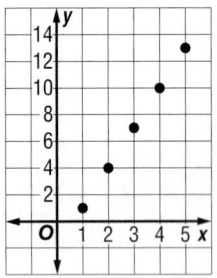

First make a table of ordered pairs, find the domain and range differences, and finally write an equation in function notation.

x	1	2	3	4	5
y	1	4	7	10	13

The pattern suggests that y is always 2 less than 3 times x. So, the equation is $f(x) = 3x - 2$

Additional Examples are also in:

• Noteables™ Interactive Study Notebook with Foldables™

• Interactive Classroom PowerPoint® Presentations

---

3 Practice

Formative Assessment

Use Exercises 1–7 to check for understanding.

Use the chart at the bottom of this page to customize assignments for your students.

Odd/Even Assignments

Exercises 8–22 are structured so that students practice the same concepts whether they are assigned odd or even problems.

CHECK Suppose the equation is $y = 2x$. If $x = 1$, then $y = 2(1)$ or 2. But the y-value for $x = 1$ is 5. This is a difference of 3. Try some other values in the domain to see if the same difference occurs.

x	1	2	3	4	5	
2x	2	4	6	8	10	y is always 3 more than 2x.
y	5	7	9	11	13	

This pattern suggests that 3 should be added to one side of the equation in order to correctly describe the relation. Check $y = 2x + 3$.

If $x = 2$, then $y = 2(2) + 3$ or 7.
If $x = 3$, then $y = 2(3) + 3$ or 9.

Thus, $y = 2x + 3$ correctly describes this relation. Since this relation is a function, the equation in function notation is $f(x) = 2x + 3$.

 CHECK Your Progress

2. Write an equation in function notation for the relation shown in the table. $f(x) = -x + 4$

x	1	2	3	4
y	3	2	1	0

 Personal Tutor at ca.algebra1.com

CHECK Your Understanding

Example 1
(pp. 172–173)

Write an equation in function notation for each relation.

1.

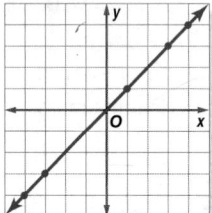

$f(x) = x$

2.

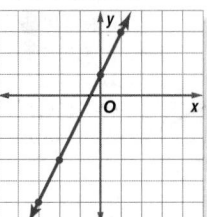

$f(x) = 2x + 1$

GEOMETRY For Exercises 3 and 4, use the table below that shows the perimeter of a square with sides of a given length.

Side length (in)	1	2	3	4	5
Perimeter (in)	4	8	12	16	20

3. See Ch. 3 Answer Appendix for graph; the length and the perimeter are proportional.

3. Graph the data. What can you conclude about the relationship between side length and perimeter?

4. Write an equation to describe the relationship. $p = 4s$

Example 2
(pp. 173–174)

ANALYZE TABLES For Exercises 5–7, use the table below that shows the underground temperature of rocks at various depths below Earth's surface.

Depth (km)	1	2	3	4	5	6
Temperature (°C)	55	90	125	160	195	230

5. Graph the data. See Ch. 3 Answer Appendix.

6. Write an equation in function notation for the relation. $f(x) = 35x + 20$

7. Find the temperature of a rock that is 10 kilometers below the surface. 370°C

174 Chapter 3 Functions and Patterns

DIFFERENTIATED HOMEWORK OPTIONS			
Level	Assignment	Two-Day Option	
BL Basic	8–20, 26–36	9–19 odd, 28, 29	18–20 even, 26, 27, 30–36
OL Core	9–23 odd, 24, 26–36	8–20, 28, 29	21–24, 26, 27, 30–36
AL Advanced /Pre-AP	21–36		

Exercises

HOMEWORK HELP	
For Exercises	See Examples
14, 15	1
16–22	2

Exercise Levels
A: 8–22
B: 23–24
C: 25–27

Find the next three terms in each sequence.

8. 0, 2, 6, 12, 20, … **30, 42, 56**

9. 9, 7, 10, 8, 11, 9, 12, … **10, 13, 11**

10. 1, 4, 9, 16, … **25, 36, 49**

11. 0, 2, 5, 9, 14, 20, … **27, 35, 44**

12. $a + 1, a + 2, a + 3, \ldots$ **$a + 4, a + 5, a + 6$**

13. $x + 1, 2x + 1, 3x + 1, \ldots$ **$4x + 1, 5x + 1, 6x + 1$**

Write an equation in function notation for each relation.

14.

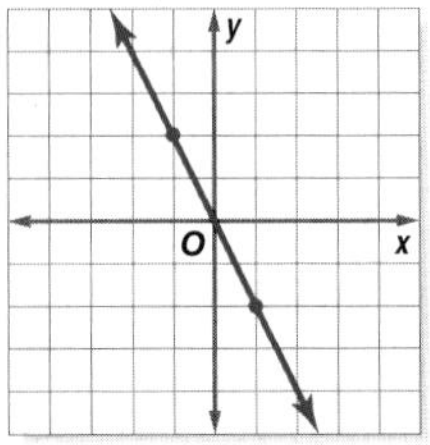

$f(x) = -2x$

15.

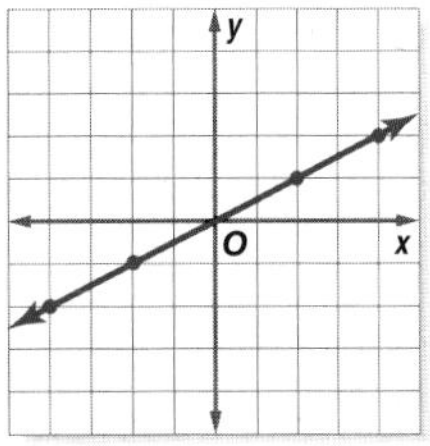

$f(x) = \frac{1}{2}x$

16.

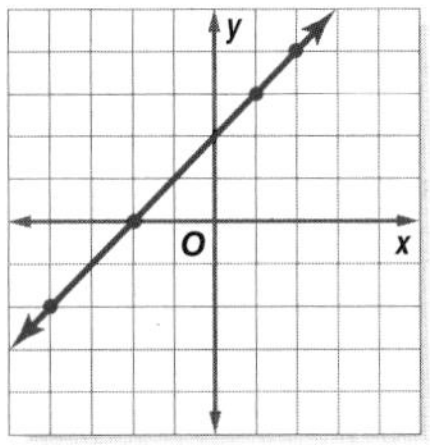

$f(x) = x + 2$

17.

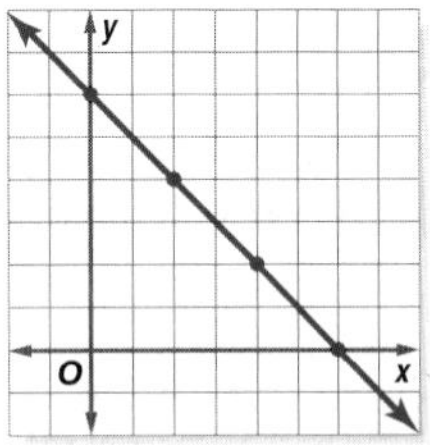

$f(x) = 6 - x$

18. TRAVEL On an island cruise in Hawaii, each passenger is given a lei. A crew member hands out 3 red, 3 blue, and 3 green leis in that order. If this pattern is repeated, what color lei will the 50th person receive? **blue**

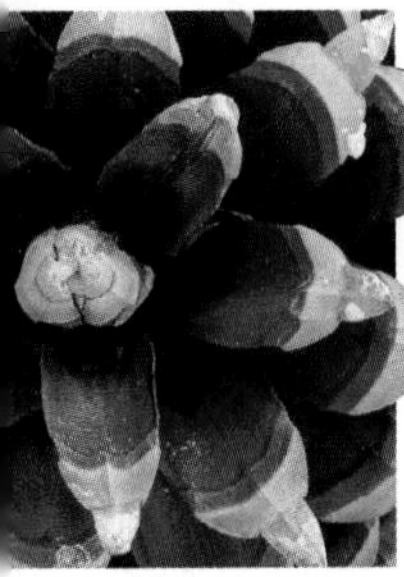

Real-World Link

Fibonacci numbers occur in many areas of nature, including pine cones, shell spirals, flower petals, branching plants, and many fruits and vegetables.

Source: mathworld.wolfram.com

NUMBER THEORY For Exercises 19 and 20, use the following information.
In 1201, Leonardo Fibonacci introduced his now famous pattern of numbers called the Fibonacci sequence.

1, 1, 2, 3, 5, 8, 13, …

Notice the pattern in this sequence. After the second number, each number in the sequence is the sum of the two numbers that precede it. That is, $2 = 1 + 1$, $3 = 2 + 1$, $5 = 3 + 2$, and so on.

19. Write the first 12 terms of the Fibonacci sequence.

20. Notice that every third term is divisible by 2. What do you notice about every fourth term? every fifth term?
Every fourth term is divisible by 3; every fifth term is divisible by 5.

19. 1, 1, 2, 3, 5, 8, 13, 21, 34, 55, 89, 144

Write an equation in function notation for each relation.

21.

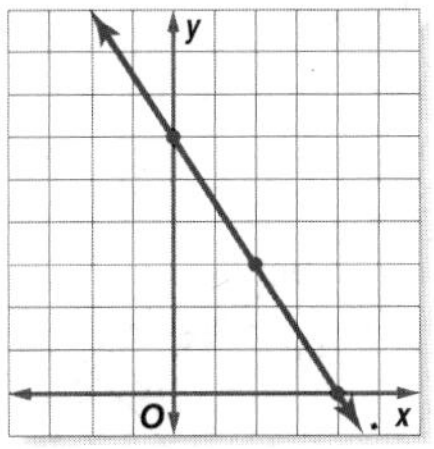

21. $f(x) = -\frac{3}{2}x + 6$

22.

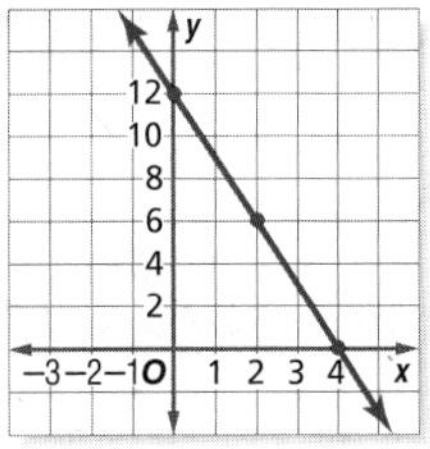

$f(x) = 12 - 3x$

Study Guide and Intervention
CRM pp. 35–36 BL OL ELL

3-5 Study Guide and Intervention
Describing Number Patterns

Look for Patterns A very common problem-solving strategy is to **look for a pattern**. Arithmetic sequences follow a pattern, and other sequences can follow a pattern.

Example 1 **Find the next three terms in the sequence 3, 9, 27, 81, … .**
Study the pattern in the sequence.
3 9 27 81 (×3, ×3, ×3)
Successive terms are found by multiplying the last given term by 3.
81 243 729 2187 (×3, ×3, ×3)
The next three terms are 243, 729, 2187.

Example 2 **Find the next three terms in the sequence 10, 6, 11, 7, 12, 8, … .**
Study the pattern in the sequence.
10 6 11 7 12 8 (−4, +5, −4, +5, −4)
Assume that the pattern continues.
8 13 9 14 (+5, −4, +5)
The next three terms are 13, 9, 14.

Exercises

1. Give the next two items for the pattern below.

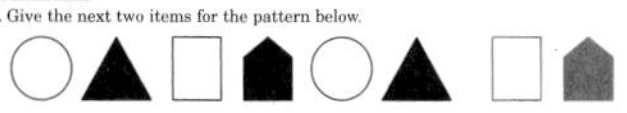

Give the next three numbers in each sequence.

2. 2, 12, 72, 432, … 2592, 15,552, 93,312
3. 7, −14, 28, −56, … 112, −224, 448
4. 0, 10, 5, 15, 10, … 20, 15, 25
5. 0, 1, 3, 6, 10, … 15, 21, 28
6. $x - 1, x - 2, x - 3, \ldots$ $x - 4, x - 5, x - 6$
7. $x, \frac{x}{2}, \frac{x}{3}, \frac{x}{4}, \ldots$ $\frac{x}{5}, \frac{x}{6}, \frac{x}{7}$

Lesson 3-5

Chapter 3 35 Glencoe Algebra 1

Practice
CRM p. 38 OL AL

3-5 Practice
Describing Number Patterns

1. Give the next two items for the pattern. Then find the 21st figure in the pattern.

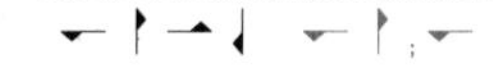

Find the next three terms in each sequence

2. −5, −2, −3, 0, −1, 2, 1, 4, … 3, 6, 5
3. 0, 1, 3, 6, 10, 15, … 21, 28, 36
4. 0, 1, 8, 27, … 64, 125, 216
5. 3, 2, 4, 3, 5, 4, … 6, 5, 7
6. $a + 1, a + 4, a + 9, \ldots$ $a + 16, a + 25, a + 36$
7. $3d - 1, 4d - 2, 5d - 3, \ldots$ $6d - 4, 7d - 5, 8d - 6$

Write an equation in function notation for each relation.

8.

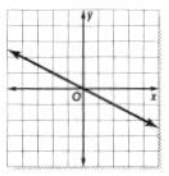

$f(x) = -\frac{1}{2}x$

9.

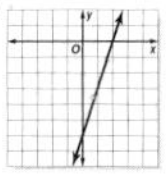

$f(x) = 3x - 6$

10.

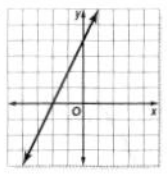

$f(x) = 2x + 4$

BIOLOGY For Exercises 11 and 12, use the following information.
Male fireflies flash in various patterns to signal location and perhaps to ward off predators. Different species of fireflies have different flash characteristics, such as the intensity of the flash, its rate, and its shape. The table below shows the rate at which a male firefly is flashing.

Time (seconds)	1	2	3	4	5
Number of Flashes	2	4	6	8	10

11. Write an equation in function notation for the relation. $f(t) = 2t$, where t is the time in seconds and $f(t)$ is the number of flashes
12. How many times will the firefly flash in 20 seconds? 40
13. **GEOMETRY** The table shows the number of diagonals that can be drawn from one vertex in a polygon. Write an equation in function notation for the relation and find the number of diagonals that can be drawn from one vertex in a 12-sided polygon. $f(s) = s - 3$, where s is the number of sides and $f(s)$ is the number of diagonals; 9

Sides	3	4	5	6
Diagonals	0	1	2	3

Chapter 3 38 Glencoe Algebra 1

Word Problem Practice
CRM p. 39 OL AL

3-5 Word Problem Practice
Describing Number Patterns

1. **GEOMETRY** A number that can be represented by a triangular array is called a triangular number.

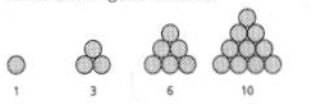

What are the next three numbers in the pattern? 15, 21, 28

2. **FOOD** It takes about four pounds of grapes to produce one pound of raisins. The graph shows the relation for the number of pounds of grapes needed, x, to make y pounds of raisins. Write an equation in function notation for the relation shown.

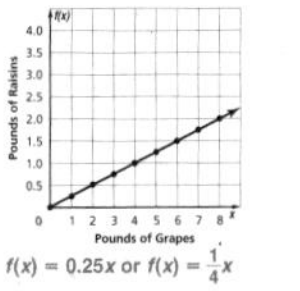

$f(x) = 0.25x$ or $f(x) = \frac{1}{4}x$

3. **TECHNOLOGY** Gordon wrote a computer program to control the lighting for a deejay. He sets the lighting so that only one color is on at a time. The lighting pattern is red, blue, violet, green, and rose. The pattern repeats and colors change every 10 seconds. After 1 minute, what color light is on? blue

4. **MUSIC** A measure of music contains the same number of beats throughout the song. The table shows the relation for the number of beats counted after a certain number of measures have been played in the six-eight time. Write an equation to describe this relationship.

Measures Played (x)	1	2	3	4	5	6
Total Number of Beats (y)	6	12	18	24	30	36

Source: www.sheetmusicusa.com

$y = 6x$

GEOMETRY For Exercises 5–7, use the following information.
A fractal is a pattern containing parts which are identical to the overall pattern. The following geometric pattern is a fractal.

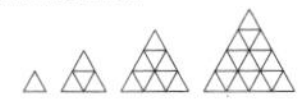

5. Complete the table.

Term	x	1	2	3	4
Number of Smaller Triangles	y	1	4	9	16

6. What are the next three numbers in the pattern? 25, 36, 49
7. Write an equation in function notation for the pattern. $f(x) = x^2$

Lesson 3-5

Chapter 3 39 Glencoe Algebra 1

BL = Below Grade Level
OL = On Grade Level
AL = Above Grade Level
ELL = English Language Learner

Additional pages not shown:

Lesson Reading Guide, p. 34 BL OL ELL
Skills Practice, p. 37 BL OL

Enrichment
CRM p. 40 OL AL

3-5 Enrichment

Taxicab Graphs

You have used a rectangular coordinate system to graph equations such as $y = x - 1$ on a coordinate plane. In a coordinate plane, the numbers in an ordered pair (x, y) can be any two real numbers.

A **taxicab plane** is different from the usual coordinate plane. The only points allowed are those that exist along the horizontal and vertical grid lines. You may think of the points as taxicabs that must stay on the streets.

The taxicab graph shows the equations $y = -2$ and $y = x - 1$. Notice that one of the graphs is no longer a straight line. It is now a collection of separate points.

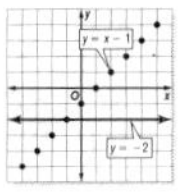

Graph these equations on the taxicab plane at the right.

1. $y = $ … 2. … $-2x + 3$

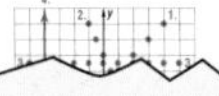

Assess

Name the Math On a coordinate grid, have students draw a line that has whole number *x*- and *y*-intercepts. Have them write an equation in function notation for the relation.

 Formative Assessment

Check for student understanding of concepts in Lesson 3-5.

 Quiz 4, p. 44

Additional Answers

27. Sample answer: In scientific experiments you try to find a relationship or develop a formula from observing the results of your experiment. For every 11 cubic feet the volume of water increases, the volume of ice increases 12 cubic feet.

33.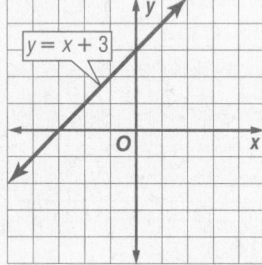

34.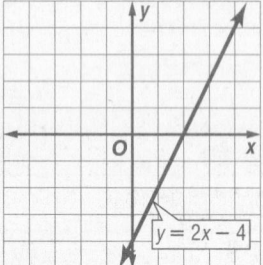

35.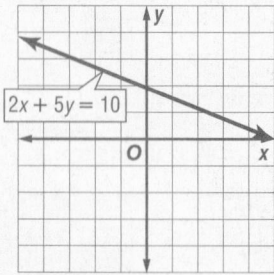

EXTRA PRACTICE
See pages 724, 746
Math Online
Self-Check Quiz at
ca.algebra1.com

FITNESS For Exercises 23 and 24, use the table below that shows the maximum heart rate to maintain during aerobic activities such as biking.

Age (yr)	20	30	40	50	60	70
Pulse rate (beats/min)	175	166	157	148	139	130

Source: Ontario Association of Sport and Exercise Sciences

23. Write an equation in function notation for the relation. $f(a) = -0.9a + 193$

24. What would be the maximum heart rate to maintain in aerobic training for a 10-year-old? an 80-year-old? **184 beats/min; 121 beats/min**

H.O.T. Problems

25. CHALLENGE Describe how inductive reasoning can be used to write an equation from a pattern. **Once you recognize a pattern, you can find a general rule that can be written as an algebraic expression.**

26. OPEN ENDED Create a number sequence in which the first term is 4. Explain the pattern that you used. **Sample answer: 4, 8, 16, 32, 64, …; each successive term doubles.**

27. *Writing in Math* Use the information about science on page 172 to explain how writing equations from patterns is important in science. Explain the relationship between the volumes of water and ice. **See margin.**

STANDARDS PRACTICE 4.0, 7AF4.2

28. The table below shows the cost *C* of renting a pontoon boat for *h* hours.

Hours	1	2	3
Cost	7.25	14.50	21.75

Which equation best represents the data? **A**

A $C = 7.25h$

B $C = h + 7.25$

C $C = 21.75 - 7.25h$

D $C = 7.25h + 21.75$

29. REVIEW Donald can ride 8 miles on his bicycle in 30 minutes. At this rate, how long would it take him to ride 30 miles? **J**

F 8 hours

G 6 hours 32 minutes

H 2 hours

J 1 hour 53 minutes

Spiral Review

Find the next three terms of each arithmetic sequence. (Lesson 3-4)

30. 9, 5, 1, −3, … **−7, −11, −15**

31. −25, −19, −13, −7, … **−1, 5, 11**

32. 22, 34, 46, 58, … **70, 82, 94**

Graph each equation. (Lesson 3-3) **33–35. See margin.**

33. $y = x + 3$

34. $y = 2x - 4$

35. $2x + 5y = 10$

36. IN THE MEDIA The following statement appeared on a news Web site shortly after a giant lobster named Bubba was found near Nantucket, Massachusetts. Approximately how much did Bubba weigh? (Lesson 2-3) **about 23 lb**

"At Tuesday's price of $14.98 a pound, Bubba would retail for about $350."

Source: cnn.com

176 Chapter 3 Functions and Patterns

Pre-AP Activity Use after Exercise 25

Write 1, 2, 3, 4, 5, 6, 7, 8, 9, 10 on the board. Ask students to find the sum of the first 10 integers and then use inductive reasoning to find the sum of the first 100 integers. (Hint: sum = 10 + (9 + 1) + (8 + 2) + (7 + 3) + (6 + 4) + 5) **55; 5050**

CHAPTER 3
Study Guide and Review

Download Vocabulary
Review from ca.algebra1.com

CHAPTER 3
Study Guide and Review

GET READY to Study

Be sure the following Key Concepts are noted in your Foldable.

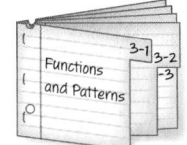
Functions and Patterns 3-1 3-2 -3

Key Concepts

Representing Relations and Functions
(Lessons 3-1 and 3-2)

- Relation Q is the inverse of relation S if, and only if, for every ordered pair (a, b) in S, there is an ordered pair (b, a) in Q.

- A function is a relation in which each element of the domain is paired with *exactly* one element of the range.

Linear Functions (Lesson 3-3)

- The standard form of a linear equation is $Ax + By = C$, where $A \geq 0$, A and B are not both zero, and A, B, and C are integers with the greatest common factor of 1.

Arithmetic Sequences (Lesson 3-4)

- An arithmetic sequence is a numerical pattern that increases or decreases at a constant rate or value called the common difference.

- The nth term a_n of an arithmetic sequence with first term a_1 and common difference d is given by $a_n = a_1 + (n - 1)d$, where n is a positive integer.

Number Patterns (Lesson 3-5)

- When you make a conclusion based on a pattern of examples, you are using inductive reasoning.

Key Vocabulary

arithmetic sequence (p. 165)	mapping (p. 143)
common difference (p. 165)	sequence (p. 165)
function (p. 149)	standard form (p. 155)
function notation (p. 150)	terms (p. 165)
function value (p. 150)	vertical line test (p. 150)
inductive reasoning (p. 172)	x-intercept (p. 156)
inverse (p. 144)	y-intercept (p. 156)
linear equation (p. 155)	zero (p. 156)

Vocabulary Check

State whether each sentence is *true* or *false*. If *false*, replace the underlined word or number to make a true sentence.

1. The mapping of a relation is obtained by switching the coordinates of each ordered pair. **false; inverse**

2. The function value of $g(x)$ for $x = 8$ is $g(8)$. **true**

3. To determine if a graph represents a function, you can use the vertical line test.

4. A relation is a set of ordered pairs. **true**

5. In a function, $f(x)$ represents the elements of the domain. **false; range**

6. The x-coordinate of the point at which a graph of an equation crosses the x-axis is an x-intercept. **true**

7. A linear equation is the equation of a line.

8. The difference between the terms of an arithmetic sequence is called the inverse.

9. The regular form of a linear equation is $Ax + By = C$. **false; standard form**

10. Values of x for which $f(x) = 0$ are called zeros of the function f. **true**

3, 7, 8. See margin.

Summative Assessment

Vocabulary Test, p. 46

Additional Answers

3. true

7. true

8. false; common difference

FOLDABLES
Study Organizer

Dinah Zike's Foldables™

Have students look through the chapter to make sure they have included examples in their Foldables for each lesson of the chapter.

Suggest that students keep their Foldables handy while completing the Study Guide and Review pages. Point out that their Foldables can serve as a quick review when studying for the Chapter Test.

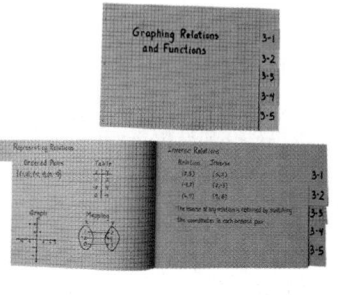

Formative Assessment

Key Vocabulary The page reference after each word denotes where that term was first introduced. If students have difficulty answering questions 1–10, remind them that they can use these page references to refresh their memories about the vocabulary terms.

ca.algebra1.com

Vocabulary PuzzleMaker improves students' mathematics vocabulary using four puzzle formats—crossword, scramble, word search using a word list, and word search using clues. Students can work online or from a printed worksheet.

Lesson-by-Lesson Review

Intervention If the given examples are not sufficient to review the topics covered by the questions, remind students that the page references tell them where to review that topic in their textbooks.

Two-Day Option Have students complete the Lesson-by-Lesson Review on pp. 178–180. Then you can use ExamView® Assessment Suite to customize another review worksheet that practices all the objectives of this chapter or only the objectives on which your students need more help.

For more information on ExamView® Assessment Suite, see p. 140C.

Differentiated Instruction

Super DVD: MindJogger Videoquizzes Use this DVD as an alternative format of review for the test. For more information on this game show format, see p. 140D.

Additional Answers

11.

x	y
−2	6
3	−2
3	0
4	6

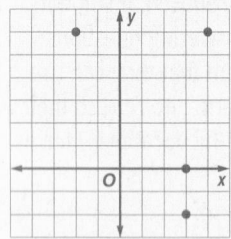

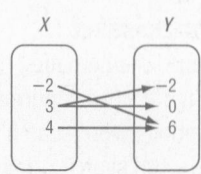

D = {−2, 3, 4}, R = {−2, 0, 6}

Lesson-by-Lesson Review

3–1 **Representing Relations** (pp. 143–148)

Express each relation as a table, a graph, and a mapping. Then determine the domain and range. **11–12. See margin.**

11. {(−2, 6), (3, −2), (3, 0), (4, 6)}

12. {(2, 5), (−3, 1), (4, −2), (2, 3)}

RIDES For Exercises 13 and 14, use the table. It shows the angles of descent and the vertical drops for five roller coasters. **13–14. See margin.**

Angle of Descent (°)	Vertical Drop (ft)
45	72
52	137
55	118
60	195
80	300

13. Determine the domain and range.

14. Graph the data. What conclusions might you make from the graph?

Example 1 Express the relation {(3, 2), (5, 3), (4, 3), (5, 2)} as a table, a graph, and a mapping. Then determine the domain and range.

Table	
x	y
3	2
5	3
4	3
5	2

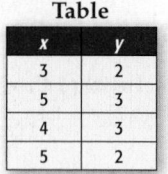

Graph

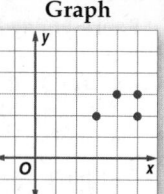

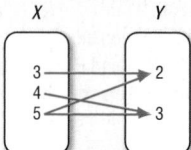

Mapping

The domain is {3, 4, 5}. The range is {2, 3}.

3–2 **Representing Functions** (pp. 149–154)

Determine whether each relation is a function.

15. {(5, 3), (1, 4), (−6, 5), (1, 6), (−2, 7)} **no**

16. {(2, 3), (−3, −4), (−1, 3), (6, 7)} **yes**

If $f(x) = x^2 − x + 1$, find each value.

17. $f(−1)$ **3** **18.** $f(5)$ − 3 **18** **19.** $f(a)$
$a^2 − a + 1$

20. DOLPHINS The amount of food that an adult bottlenose dolphin eats per day can be approximated by $y = 0.05x$, where x is the dolphin's body weight in pounds. Write the equation in function notation and then find $f(460)$. What does this value represent? **See margin.**

Example 2 Determine whether the relation shown is a function. Explain.

x	y
0	−4
1	−1
2	2
6	3

Since each element of the domain is paired with exactly one element of the range, the relation is a function.

Example 3 If $g(x) = 2x − 1$, find $g(−6)$.

$g(−6) = 2(−6) − 1$ Replace x with −6.
$= −12 − 1$ Multiply.
$= −13$ Subtract.

178 Chapter 3 Functions and Patterns

12.

x	y
2	5
−3	1
4	−2
2	3

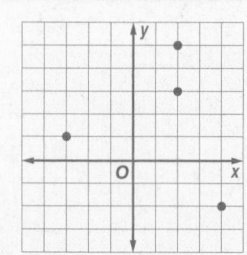

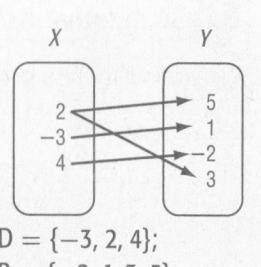

D = {−3, 2, 4};
R = {−2, 1, 3, 5}

Mixed Problem Solving
For mixed problem-solving practice,
see page 746.

CHAPTER
3 **Study Guide and Review**

3-3 Linear Functions (pp. 155–161)

Determine the x-intercept, y-intercept, and zero of each linear function.

21.

x	y
−8	0
−4	3
0	6
4	9

−8, 6, −8

22.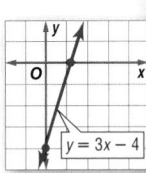

3, −2, 3

Graph each equation. 23–26. See margin.

23. $y = -x + 2$ **24.** $x + 5y = 4$

25 $2x - 3y = 6$ **26.** $5x + 2y = 10$

27. SOUND The distance d in kilometers that sound waves travel through water is given by $d = 1.6t$, where t is the time in seconds. Graph the equation. Estimate how far sound can travel through water in 7 seconds. **about 11 km**

See margin for graph.

Example 4 Graph $3x - y = 4$ by using the x- and y-intercepts.

Find the x-intercept.	Find the y-intercept.
$3x - y = 4$	$3x - y = 4$
$3x - 0 = 4$ Let $y = 0$.	$3(0) - y = 4$ Let $x = 0$.
$3x = 4$	$-y = 4$
$x = \frac{4}{3}$	$y = -4$

x-intercept: $\frac{4}{3}$, y-intercept: -4

The graph intersects the x-axis at $\left(\frac{4}{3}, 0\right)$ and the y-axis at $(0, -4)$. Plot these points. Then draw the line through them.

$y = 3x - 4$

3-4 Arithmetic Sequences (pp. 165–170)

Find the next three terms of each arithmetic sequence.

28. 6, 11, 16, 21, … **26, 31, 36**

29. 1.4, 1.2, 1.0, 0.8, … **0.6, 0.4, 0.2**

30. −3, −11, −19, −27, … **−35, −43, −51**

Find the nth term of each arithmetic sequence described.

31. $a_1 = 6, d = 5, n = 11$ **56**

32. 28, 25, 22, 19, … for $n = 8$ **7**

33. MONEY The table represents Tiffany's income. Write an equation for this sequence and use the equation to find her income if she works 20 hours.

Hours Worked	1	2	3	4
Income ($)	20.50	29	37.50	46

$a_n = 12 + 8.5n$; $182

Example 5 Find the next three terms of the arithmetic sequence 10, 23, 36, 49, ….

Find the common difference.

10 23 36 49
 +13 +13 +13

So, $d = 13$.

Add 13 to the last term of the sequence. Continue adding 13 until the next three terms are found.

49 62 75 88
 +13 +13 +13

The next three terms are 62, 75, and 88.

13. D = {45, 52, 55, 60, 80};
R = {72, 137, 118, 195, 300}

14.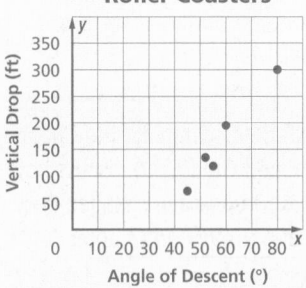

Roller Coasters

Sample answer: Generally, as the angles of descent increase, the vertical drops increase.

20. $f(x) = 0.05x$; 23; A dolphin that weighs 460 lb eats about 23 lb of food per day.

23.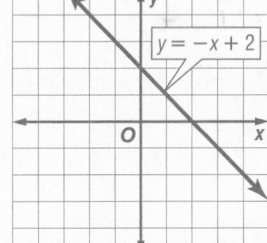
$y = -x + 2$

24.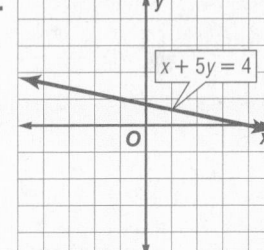
$x + 5y = 4$

25.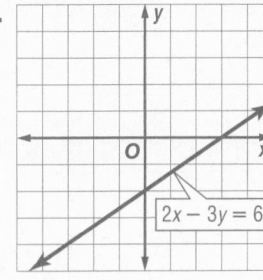
$2x - 3y = 6$

26.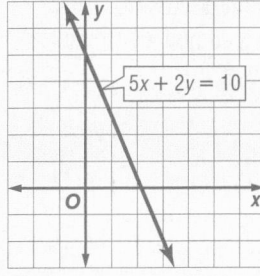
$5x + 2y = 10$

27. **Speed of Sound**

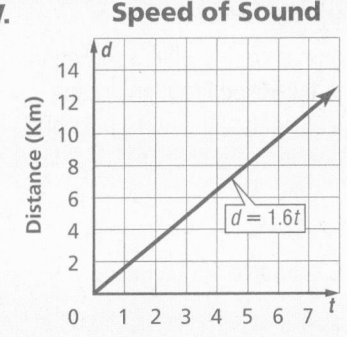
$d = 1.6t$

time (s)

Problem Solving Review

For additional practice in problem solving for Chapter 3, see the Mixed Problem Solving Appendix, p. 746, in the Student Handbook section.

Anticipation Guide

Have students complete the Chapter 3 Anticipation Guide and discuss how their responses have changed now that they have completed Chapter 3.

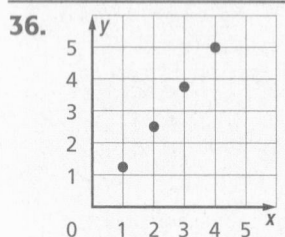

Additional Answer

36.

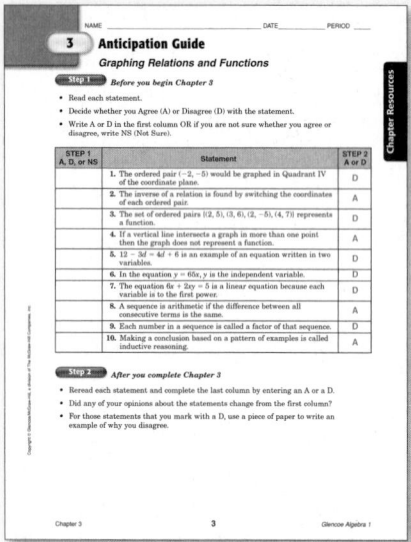

3-5 Proportional and Nonproportional Relationships (pp. 172–176)

Write an equation in function notation for each relation.

34. 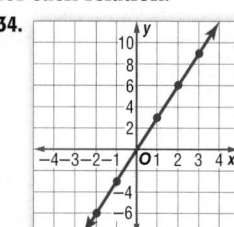 $f(x) = 3x$

35. 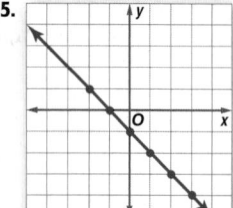 $f(x) = -x - 1$

ANALYZE TABLES For Exercises 36–38, use the table below that shows the cost of picking your own strawberries at a local farm.

Number of Pounds	1	2	3	4
Total Cost ($)	1.25	2.50	3.75	5.00

36. Graph the data. **See margin.**

37. Write an equation in function notation to describe this relationship. $f(x) = 1.25x$

38. How much would 6 pounds of strawberries cost if you picked them yourself? **$7.50**

Example 6 Write an equation in function notation for the relation graphed at the right.

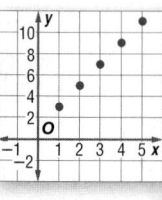

Make a table of ordered pairs for several points on the graph.

x	1	2	3	4	5
y	3	5	7	9	11

The difference in y-values is twice the difference of x-values. This suggests that $y = 2x$. However, $3 \neq 2(1)$. Compare the values of y to the values of $2x$.

x	1	2	3	4	5
2x	2	4	6	8	10
y	3	5	7	9	11

y is always 1 more than $2x$.

The difference between y and $2x$ is always 1. So the equation is $y = 2x + 1$. Since this relation is also a function, it can be written as $f(x) = 2x + 1$.

Problem Solving Review

For additional practice in problem solving for Chapter 3, see the Mixed Problem Solving Appendix, p. 746, in the Student Handbook section.

Anticipation Guide

Have students complete the Chapter 3

Anticipation Guide and discuss how their responses have changed now that they have completed Chapter 3.

Express the relation shown in each table, mapping, or graph as a set of ordered pairs. Then write the inverse of the relation.

1.

x	f(x)
0	−1
2	4
4	5
6	10

2.

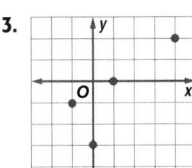

1–2. See margin.

3.

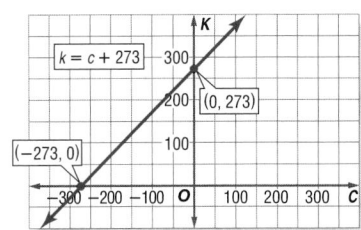

$\{(-1, -1), (0, -3),$
$(1, 0), (4, 2)\}$ I =;
$\{(-1, -1), (-3, 0),$
$(0, 1), (2, 4)\}$

Determine whether each relation is a function.

4. $\{(2, 4), (3, 2), (4, 6), 5, 4)\}$ **yes**

5. $\{(3, 1), (2, 5), (4, 0), (3, -2)\}$ **no**

6. $8y = 7 + 3x$ **yes**

If $f(x) = -2x + 5$ and $g(x) = x^2 - 4x + 1$, find each value.

7. $g(-2)$ **13**

8. $f\left(\frac{1}{2}\right)$ **4**

9. $g(3a) + 1$
$9a^2 - 12a + 2$

10. $f(x + 2)$ **−2x + 1**

TEMPERATURE The equation to convert Celsius temperature C to Kelvin temperature K is shown in the graph. **11–12. See margin.**

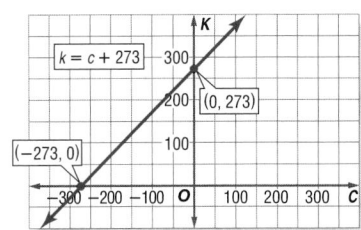

11. State the independent and dependent variables. Explain.

12. Determine the x-intercept and y-intercept and describe what the intercepts mean.

13. MULTIPLE CHOICE If $f(x) = 3x - 2$, find $f(8) - f(-5)$. **D**

A 7   C 37

B 9   D 39

Graph each equation. **14–17. See Ch. 3 Answer Appendix.**

14. $y = x + 2$ **15.** $y = 4x$

16. $x + 2y = -1$ **17.** $-3x = 5 - y$

Find the next three terms in each sequence.

18. 5, −10, 15, −20, 25, … **−30, 35, −40**

19. 5, 5, 6, 8, 11, 15, … **20, 26, 33**

BIOLOGY For Exercises 20 and 21, use the following information.
The amount of blood in the body can be predicted by the equation $y = 0.07w$, where y is the number of pints of blood and w is the weight of a person in pounds.

20. Graph the equation. **See Ch. 3 Answer Appendix.**

21. Predict the weight of a person whose body holds 12 pints of blood. **about 171 lb**

Determine whether each sequence is an arithmetic sequence. If it is, state the common difference.

22. −40, −32, −24, −16, … **yes; 8**

23. 0.75, 1.5, 3, 6, 12, … **no**

24. 5, 17, 29, 41, … **yes; 12**

25. MULTIPLE CHOICE In each figure, only one side of each regular pentagon touches. Each side of each pentagon is 1 centimeter. If the pattern continues, what is the perimeter of a figure that has 6 pentagons? **H**

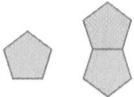 

F 15 cm   H 20 cm

G 25 cm   J 30 cm

✓ **Summative Assessment**

CRM **Chapter 3 Resource Masters**

Leveled Chapter 3 Tests			
Form	**Type**	**Level**	**Pages**
1	MC	BL	47–48
2A	MC	OL	49–50
2B	MC	OL	51–52
2C	FR	OL	53–54
2D	FR	OL	55–56
3	FR	AL	57–58

MC = multiple-choice questions
FR = free-response questions
BL *= below grade level*
OL *= on grade level*
AL *= above grade level*

• Vocabulary Test, p. 46

• Extended-Response Test, p. 59

 Customize and create multiple versions of your chapter tests and their answer keys. All of the questions from the leveled chapter tests in the *Chapter 3 Resource Masters* are also available on ExamView Assessment Suite with the California Standard that each item assesses.

Additional Answers

1. $\{(0, -1), (2, 4), (4, 5), (6, 10)\};$
   $I = \{(-1, 0), (4, 2), (5, 4), (10, 6)\}$

2. $\{(-1, 2), (-2, -2), (-3, 2)\};$
   $I = \{(2, -1), (-2, -2), (2, -3)\}$

11–12. See Ch. 3 Answer Appendix.

Data-Driven Decision Making	**Exercises**	**Lesson**	⬥ **Standard**	**Resources for Review**
Diagnostic Teaching Based on the results of the Chapter 3 Practice Test, use the following to review concepts that students continue to find challenging.	18–19, 22–24	3–4	**Reinforcement of 7AF3.4**	CRM Study Guide and Intervention pp. 28–29, 35–36 Math Online • Extra Examples • Personal Tutor • Concepts in Motion
	20–21, 25	3–5	16.0	

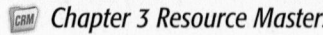

Read each question. Then fill in the correct answer on the answer document provided by your teacher or on a sheet of paper.

1 The chart below shows an expression evaluated for four different values of x.

x	1	3	4	5
$x^2 + 2x + 7$	10	22	31	42

Jordan concluded that for all positive values of x, $x^2 + 2x + 7$ produces a even number. Which value of x serves as a counterexample to prove Jordan's conclusion false? **C**

A 1

B 3

C 4

D 5

2 What is the domain of the function shown on the graph below? **J**

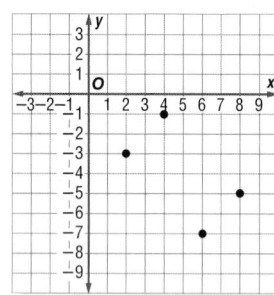

F $\{-1, -3, -5, -7\}$

G $\{-2, -4, -6, -8\}$

H $\{1, 3, 5, 7\}$

J $\{2, 4, 6, 8\}$

3 A chemist mixed some 15% saline solution with some 20% saline solution to obtain 200 mL of an 18% saline solution. How many milliliters of the 15% saline solution did the chemist use in the mixture? **80**

4 What is the y-intercept of the line $4x - 2y = 8$? **A**

A $(0, -4)$

B $(0, -2)$

C $(0, 2)$

D $(0, 4)$

5 Which equation is equivalent to $4x - 3(x + 2) = 10x$? **F**

F $x - 6 = 10x$

G $x + 2 = 10x$

H $x + 6 = 10x$

J $5x - 1 = 10x$

6 Solve $-2.25r + 1 = -17$. **C**

A $r = -20.25$

B $r = -8$

C $r = 8$

D $r = 20.25$

7 Lauren has $35 to spend on beads for making necklaces. If she spends $15 for string and each bead costs $2.50, solve the inequality $2.50n + 15 \leq 35$ to determine how many beads she can buy. **J**

F more than 14

G less than 14

H more than 8

J less than 8

More California
Standards Practice
For practice by standard,
see pages CA1–CA43.

CHAPTER 3

California Standards Practice

8 For which graph below are all the *y*-values negative? **A**

A
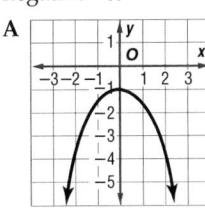

B
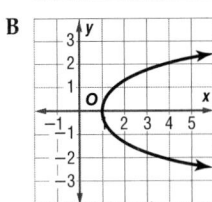

C
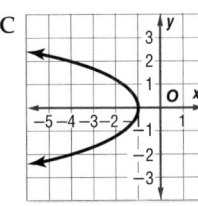

D
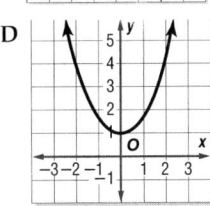

9 Find the value of *p* in $\frac{1}{13} \cdot p = 1$ and name the property that is used. **F**

F 13; Multiplicative Inverse Property

G −13; Multiplicative Inverse Property

H 13; Multiplicative Identity Property

J $\frac{1}{13}$; Multiplicative Identity Property

10 What are the coordinates of the *x*-intercept of the line $3x + 5y = 15$? **D**

A $(0, 3)$

B $(3, 0)$

C $(0, 5)$

D $(5, 0)$

11 Connor is redecorating his living room. He has budgeted $1200 for the project, and has already spent $400 on paint. If he wants to spend the rest of the money on curtains to cover 5 windows, which expression represents the maximum amount *w* he can spend on each window? **H**

F $1200 = 400 - 5w$

G $400 = 1200 + 5w$

H $1200 = 400 + 5w$

J $400 = 1200 + 5 - w$

Pre-AP/Anchor Problem

**Record your answer on a sheet of paper.
Show your work.**

12 A car company lists the stopping distances of a car at different speeds.

Speed (ft/s)	Minimum Stopping Distance (ft)
10	2
20	8
40	31
60	70
100	194

a. Does the table of values represent a function? Justify your reasoning.

b. Is this a proportional relationship? Explain.

12a. Yes, because each element of the domain is paired with exactly one element of the range.

12b. No, because the relationship cannot be described by a function of the form $y = kx$.

Item Analysis
Questions 3 and 7 are griddable questions. In a griddable question, students arrive at an answer and then record it in a special grid by coloring the appropriate bubble under each digit of the answer.

Answer Sheet Practice
Have students simulate taking a standardized test by recording their answers on practice recording sheets.

CRM Student Recording Sheet, p. 41

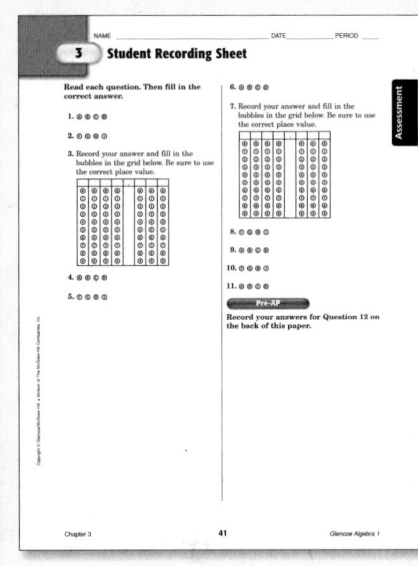

NEED EXTRA HELP?

If You Missed Question...	1	2	3	4	5	6	7	8	9	10	11	12
Go to Lesson...	3-2	3-2	2-9	3-3	2-5	2-4	1-5	3-2	1-4	3-3	1-3	3-5
For Help with Standard...	24.3	17.0	15.0	6.0	4.0	7AF4.1	5.0	17.0	1.0	6.0	7AF1.1	16.0

Homework Option

Get Ready for Chapter 4 Assign students the exercises on p. 141 as homework to assess whether they possess the prerequisite skills needed for the next chapter.

Page 141, Getting Started

12.
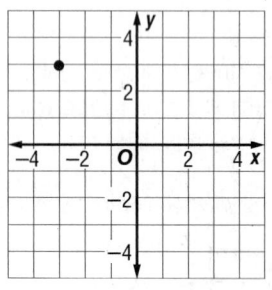

13.
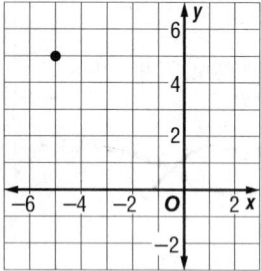

14.
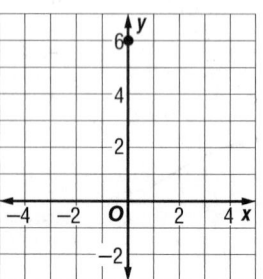

15.
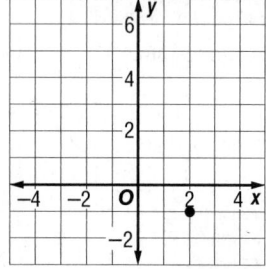

16.

17.

Page 144, Lesson 3-1

2B.
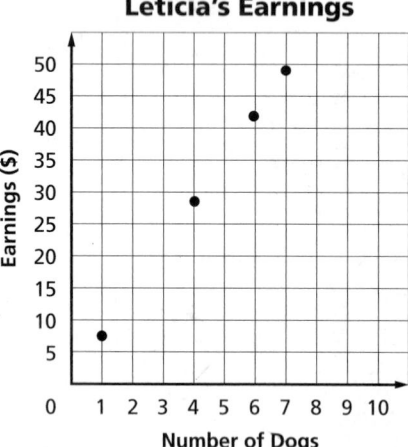

Leticia's Earnings

Pages 146–148, Lesson 3-1

1.

x	y
5	−2
8	3
−7	1

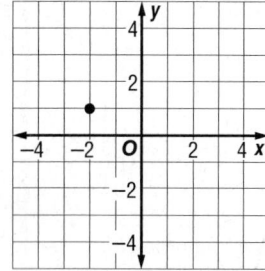

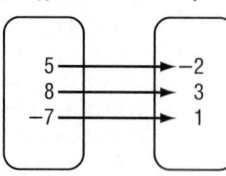

D = {−7, 5, 8}; R = {−2, 1, 3}

2.

x	y
6	4
3	−3
−1	9
5	−3

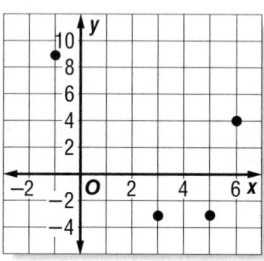

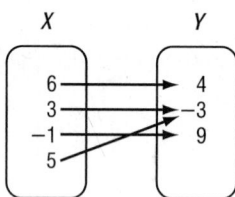

D = {−1, 3, 5, 6}; R = {−3, 4, 9}

3. D = {0, 1000, 2000, 3000, 5000, 10,000};
R = {212.0, 210.2, 208.4, 206.5, 201.9, 193.7}

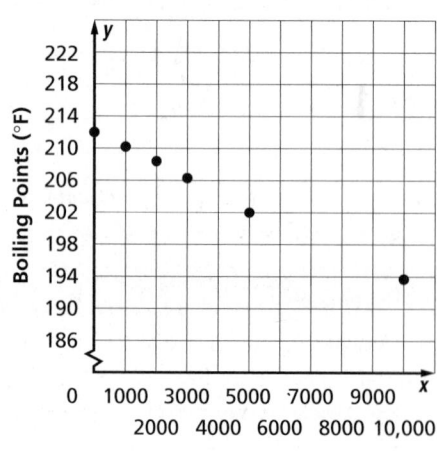

8.

x	y
0	0
6	−1
5	6
4	2

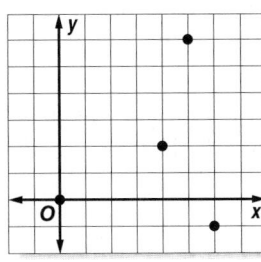

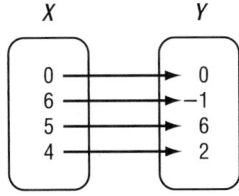

D = {0, 4, 5, 6}; R = {−1, 0, 2, 6}

9.

x	y
3	8
3	7
2	−9
1	−9

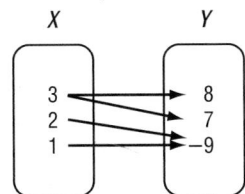

D = {1, 2, 3}; R = {−9, 7, 8}

10.

x	y
4	−2
3	4
1	−2
6	4

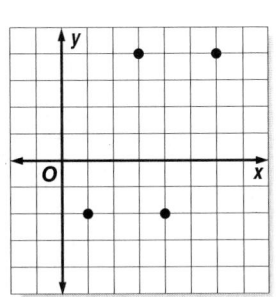

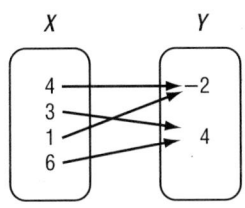

D = {1, 3, 4, 6}; R = {−2, 4}

11.

x	y
0	2
−5	1
0	6
−1	9

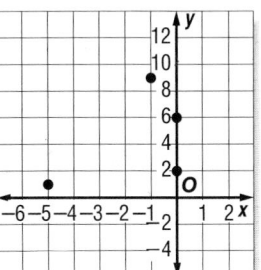

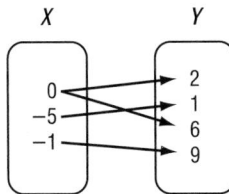

D = {−5, −1, 0}; R = {1, 2, 6, 9}

12.

x	y
3	4
4	3
2	2
5	−4
−4	5

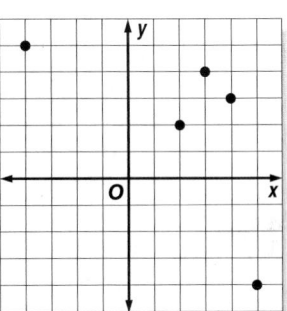

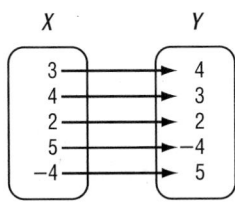

D = {−4, 2, 3, 4, 5}; R = {−4, 2, 3, 4, 5}

13.

x	y
7	6
3	4
4	5
−2	6
−3	2

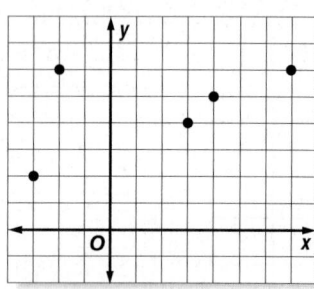

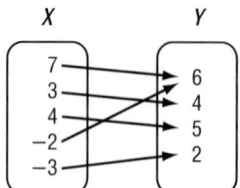

D = {−3, −2, 3, 4, 7}; R = {2, 4, 5, 6}

18. Sample answer: D = {2007, 2008, 2009, 2010, 2011, 2012, 2013, 2014}; R = {10.4, 10.7, 11.0, 11.3, 11.5, 11.8, 12.1, 12.4}

19. 2007; 2014

20. Sample answer: The production seems to increase at a steady rate every year.

21. Sample answer: 13.0; this means that the production of apples is projected to be 13.0 billion pounds in the year 2015.

22. {(0, 3), (−5, 2), (4, 7), (−8, 2)}; {(3, 0), (2, −5), (7, 4), (2, −8)}

23. {(0, 0), (4, 7), (8, 10.5), (12, 18), (16, 14.5)}; {(0, 0), (7, 4), (10.5, 8), (18, 12), (14.5, 16)}

24. {(−8, 4), (−1, 1), (0, 6), (5, 4)}; {(4, −8), (1, −1), (6, 0), (4, 5)}

25. {(−3, 2), (−3, −8), (6, 5), (7, 4), (11, 4)}; {(2, −3), (−8, −3), (5, 6), (4, 7), (4, 11)}

26. {(−4, −2), (−2, −1), (2, 4), (2, −3)}; {(−2, −4), (−1, −2), (4, 2), (−3, 2)}

27. {(−3, −1), (−3, −3), (−3, −5), (0, 3), (2, 3), (4, 3)}; {(−1, −3), (−3, −3), (−5, −3), (3, 0), (3, 2), (3, 4)}

28. {(1, 2.50), (2, 5.50), (5, 10.00), (8, 18.75)}; D = {1, 2, 5, 8}; R = {2.50, 5.50, 10.00, 18.75}; {(2.50, 1), (5.50, 2), (10.00, 5), (18.75, 8)}

29. {(1, 8), (3, 16), (4, 20), (7, 28)}; D = {1, 3, 4, 7}; R = {8, 16, 20, 28}; {(8, 1), (16, 3), (20, 4), (28, 7)}

30.

Body Weight (lb)	100	105	110	115	120	125	130
Muscle Weight (lb)	40	42	44	46	48	50	52

31. D = {100, 105, 110, 115, 120, 125, 130}; R = {40, 42, 44, 46, 48, 50, 52}

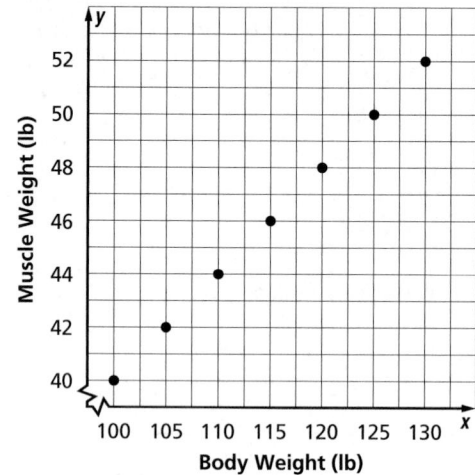

32. D = {40, 42, 44, 46, 48, 50, 52}; R = {100, 105, 110, 115, 120, 125, 130}

33.

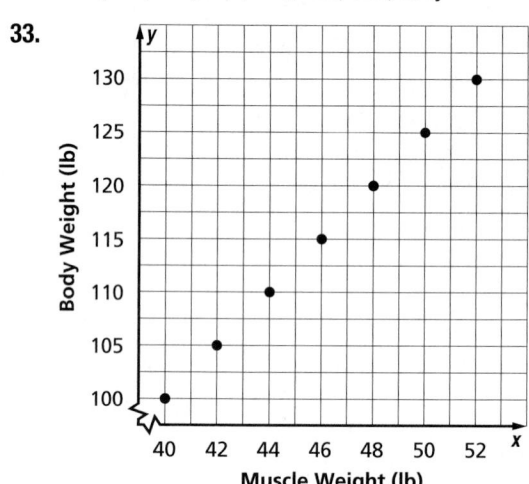

36. Sample answer: Expressing real-world data as relations shows how the members of a domain relate to the members of the range. For example, a table helps to organize the data or a graph may show a pattern in the data. Following is a graph that shows the number of homeruns and strikeouts.

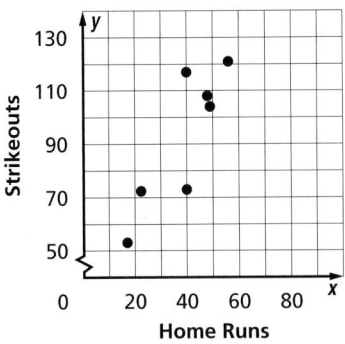

There seems to be a positive relationship between these sets of data. In years where Griffey hit more home runs, he also struck out more.

Page 153, Lesson 3–2

41.

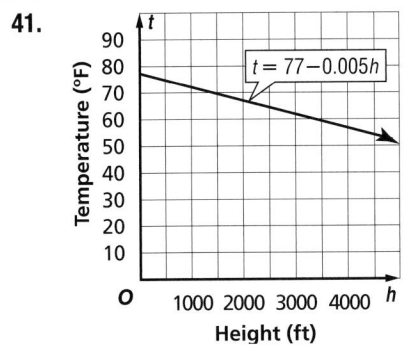

43.

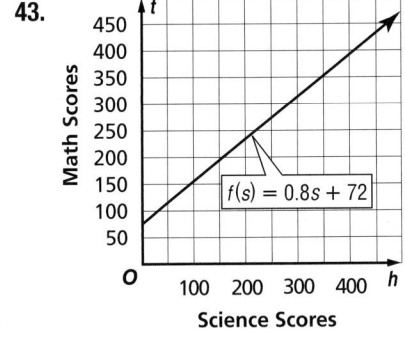

Pages 158–160, Lesson 3-3

4. 25, -4; The x-intercept 25 means that after 25 minutes, the temperature is 0°F. The y-intercept -4 means that at time 0, the temperature is -4°F.

5. 12; -24; The x-intercept 12 means that after 12 seconds, the scuba diver is at a depth of 0 meters, or at the surface. The y-intercept -24 means that at time 0, the scuba diver is at a depth of -24 meters, or 24 meters below sea level.

7.
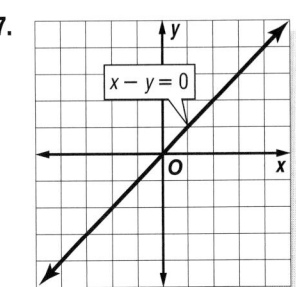

8.
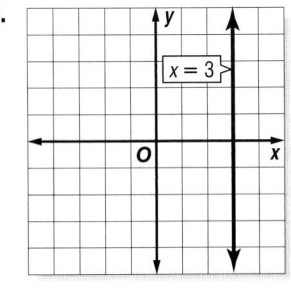

9.
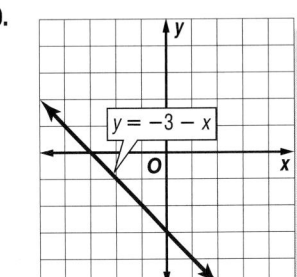

10.
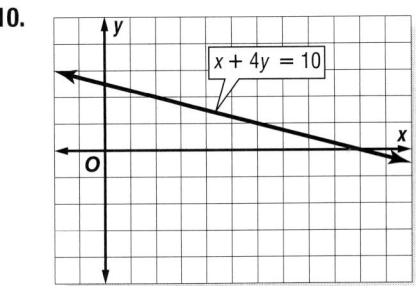

11.
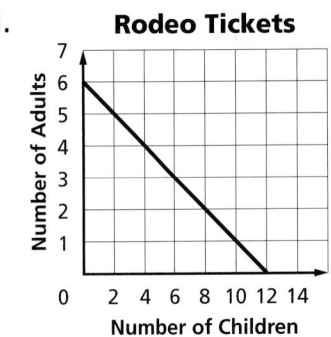

The x-intercept 12 means that 12 children could attend the rodeo if there are 0 adults attending. The y-intercept 6 means that 6 adults and 0 children could attend the rodeo.

24.

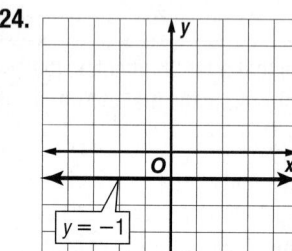

$y = -1$

34.

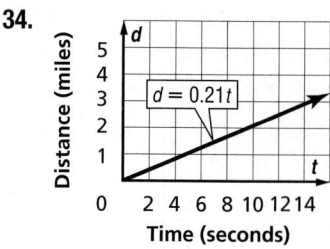

$d = 0.21t$

Distance (miles)

Time (seconds)

25.

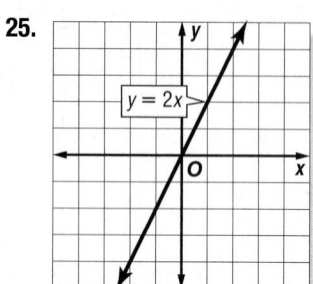

$y = 2x$

26.

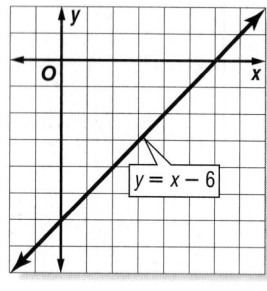

$y = x - 6$

45.

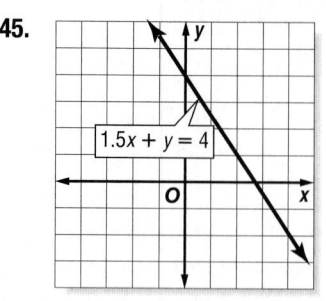

$1.5x + y = 4$

46.

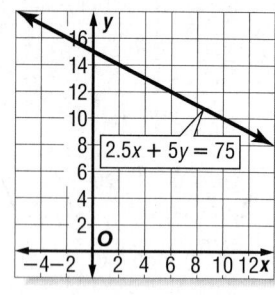

$2.5x + 5y = 75$

27.

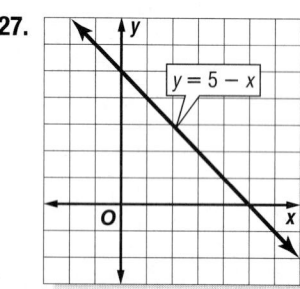

$y = 5 - x$

28.

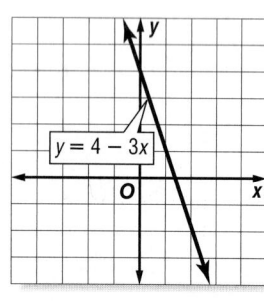

$y = 4 - 3x$

47.

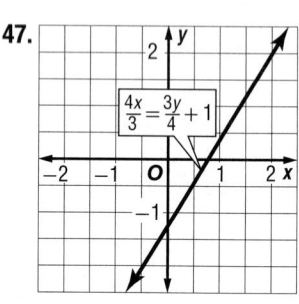

$\frac{4x}{3} = \frac{3y}{4} + 1$

48.

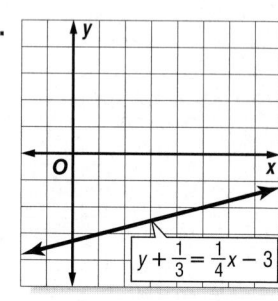

$y + \frac{1}{3} = \frac{1}{4}x - 3$

29.

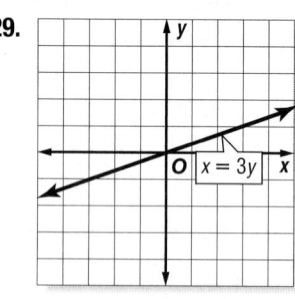

$x = 3y$

30.

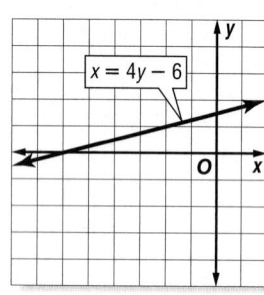

$x = 4y - 6$

49.

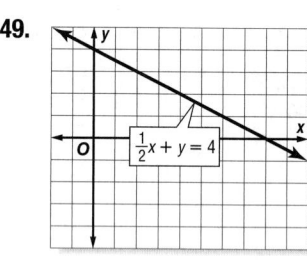

$\frac{1}{2}x + y = 4$

50.

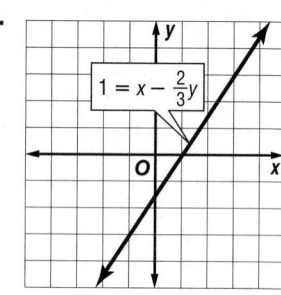

$1 = x - \frac{2}{3}y$

31.

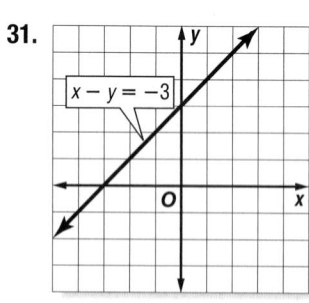

$x - y = -3$

32.

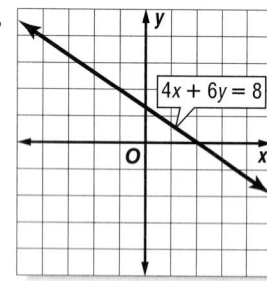

$4x + 6y = 8$

53.

14.7

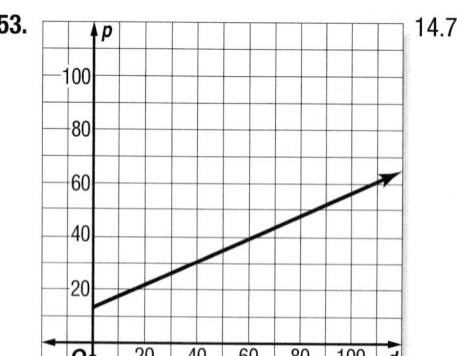

33.

t	d	t	d
0	0	10	2.10
2	0.42	12	2.52
4	0.84	14	2.94
6	1.26	16	3.36
8	1.68		

54. A reasonable domain for this situation is the set of real numbers from 0 to 400 feet. A reasonable range is the set of real numbers from 14.7 to 186.7 psi.

59. Substitute the values for x and y into the equation $2x - y = 8$. If the value of $2x - y$ is less than 8, then the point lies *above* the line. If the value of $2x - y$ is greater than 8, then the point lies *below* the line. If the value of $2x - y$ equals 8, then the point lies *on* the line. Sample answers: (1, 5) lies above the line, (5, 1) lies below the line, (6, 4) lies on the line.

60. Sample answer: You can graph an equation that represents how many Calories and nutrients your diet should contain. Since your diet is different every day, it is easier to use the graph to determine your goal instead of making calculations every day. Nutrition information labels provide facts about how many grams of fat are in each serving and/or how many Calories are from fat.

Pages 162–163, Extend 3-3

6–12. Sample answers given.

6.
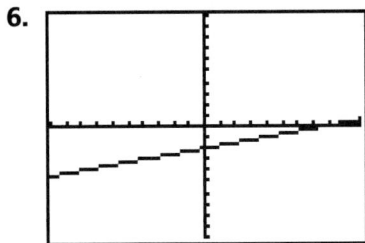

7.
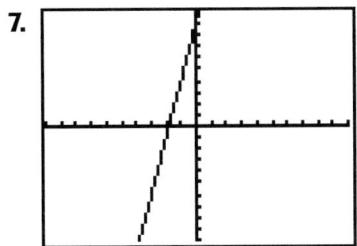

8.
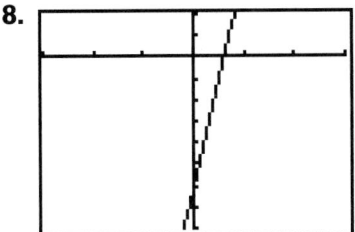

9.
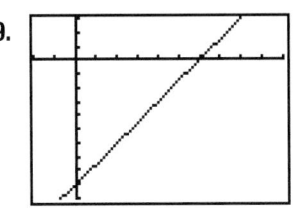

10.
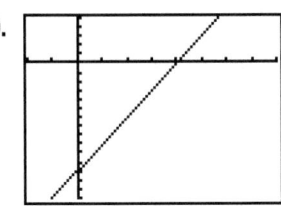

11.
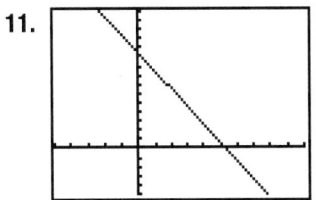

12.
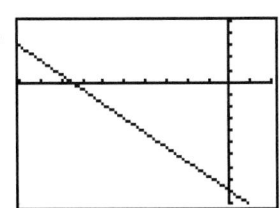

Page 164, Mid-Chapter Quiz

7.
Cheerleading Camp
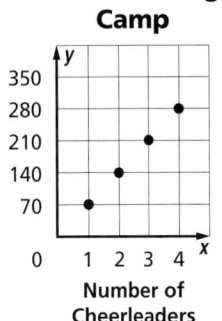

15.
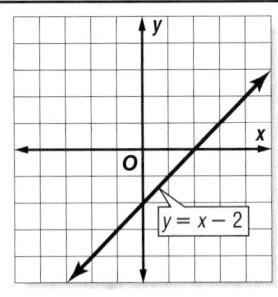
$y = x - 2$

8. The number of cheerleaders is the independent quantity. The total cost is the dependent quantity because it depends on the number of cheerleaders.

16.
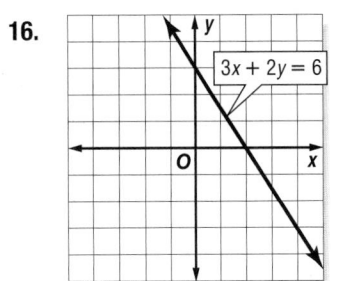
$3x + 2y = 6$

18.
Car Race Tickets
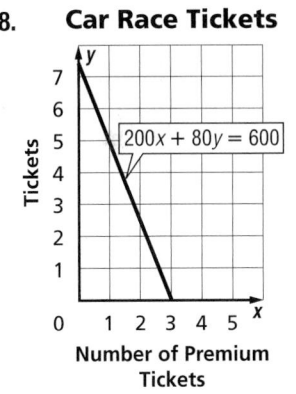
$200x + 80y = 600$

19. A reasonable domain is {0, 1, 2, 3}. A reasonable range is {0, 1, 2, 3, 4, 5, 6, 7}. Only whole number values make sense since partial tickets cannot be bought.

20. The x-intercept 3 means that 3 premium tickets could be bought if no discount tickets are bought. The y-intercept 7.5 means that 7.5 discount tickets could be bought if no premium tickets are bought. Since there cannot be partial tickets, only 7 discount tickets could be bought.

30. $a_n = -3n$

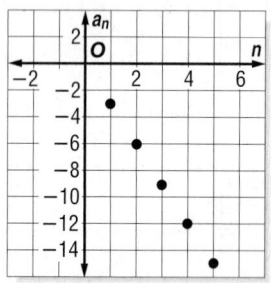

31. $a_n = n + 7$

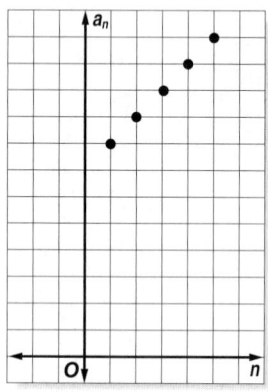

32. $a_n = 6n - 4$

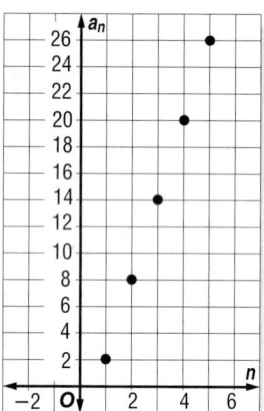

33. $a_n = 2n - 20$

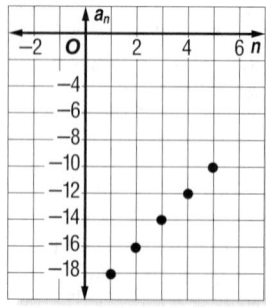

42.

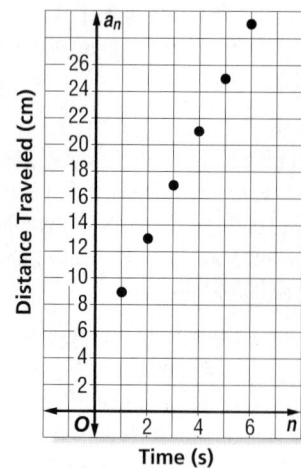

Page 171, Reading Math

1. Sample answer: Inductive reasoning uses examples or past experience to make conclusions; deductive reasoning uses rules to make conclusions. Looking at a pattern of numbers to decide the next number in an example of inductive reasoning. Using the formula $A = \ell w$ and the length and width of a rectangle to find the area of a rectangle is an example of deductive reasoning.
2. Deductive reasoning; he is applying a general rule about men's heights to a specific case.
3. Inductive reasoning; you are observing specific pairs of terms and discovering a common difference, and you conclude that the common difference applies to the sequence in general.
4. Deductive reasoning; you are using the general formula for the nth term and applying it to a particular series.
5b. $3, 9, 7, 1, 3, 9, 7, 1, 3, \ldots$
5c. 1; 100 is divisible by 4. According to the pattern, all powers with exponents divisible by 4 have 1 in the ones place. Inductive reasoning.
6. Deductive reasoning; the conclusion was based on a given rule.

Page 174, Lesson 3-5

3.

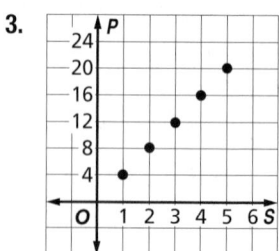

5.

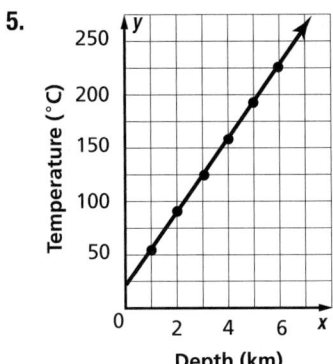

Page 181, Practice Test

11. Independent: C, dependent: K; Kelvin temperature depends on Celsius temperature.

12. x-int.: $(-273, 0)$; $-273°C$ equal to 0 K. y-int.: $(0, 273)$; $0°C$ equal to $273°K$.

14.

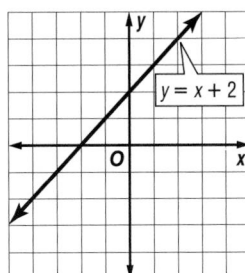

15.

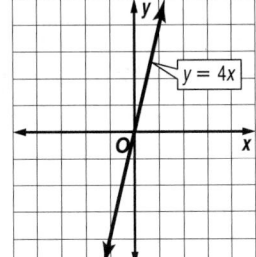

16.

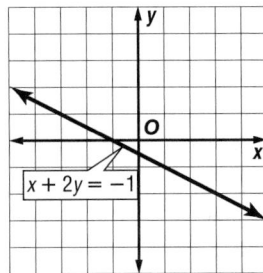

17.

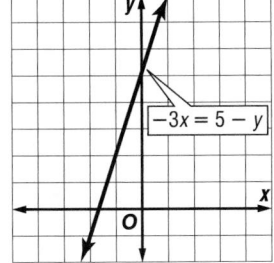

20.

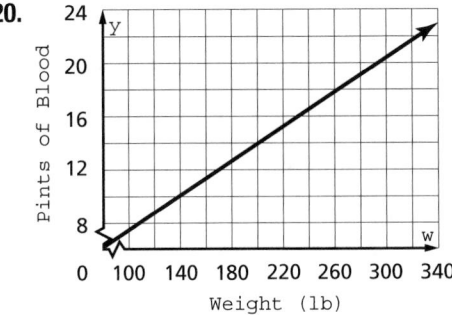

Chapter Overview

Analyzing Linear Equations

Standards-Based Lesson Plan	Pacing Your Lessons		
LESSONS AND OBJECTIVES	California Standards	40–50 Minute Periods	90-Minute Periods
Explore 4-1 Algebra Lab: Steepness of a Line (p. 186) **4-1 Rate of Change and Slope** (pp. 187–195) • Use rate of change to solve problems. • Find the slope of a line.	7AF3.3 7AF3.4	2	1.5
4-2 Slope and Direct Variation (pp. 196–202) • Write and graph direct variation equations. • Solve problems involving direct variation.	7AF4.2	2	1
Explore 4-3 Graphing Calculator Lab: Investigating Slope-Intercept Form (p. 203) **4-3 Graphing Equations in Slope-Intercept Form** (pp. 204–209) • Write and graph linear equations in slope-intercept form. • Model real-world data with an equation in slope-intercept form. **Extend 4-3 Graphing Calculator Lab: The Family of Linear Graphs** (pp. 210–211)	7AF1.5 6.0	3	1.5
4-4 Writing Equations in Slope-Intercept Form (pp. 213–218) • Write an equation of a line given the slope and one point on a line. • Write an equation of a line given two points on the line.	7AF1.1	2	1
4-5 Writing Equations in Point-Slope Form (pp. 219–225) • Write the equation of a line in point-slope form. • Write linear equations in different forms.	7.0	2	1
4-6 Statistics: Scatter Plots and Lines of Fit (pp. 227–233) • Interpret points on a scatter plot. • Use lines of fit to make and evaluate predictions. **Extend 4-6 Graphing Calculator Lab: Regression and Median-Fit Lines** (pp. 234–235)	PS8.0, APPS12.0, APPS 13.0	2	1.5
4-7 Geometry: Parallel and Perpendicular Lines (pp. 236–241) • Write an equation of the line that passes through a given point, parallel to a given line. • Write an equation of the line that passes through a given point, perpendicular to a given line.	8.0	2	0.5
REVIEW		1	0.5
ASSESSMENT		1	0.5*
TOTAL		17	9

*The complete **Assessment Planner** for Chapter 4 is provided on p. 185*

* Begin Chapter 5 in the second half of the period.

Professional Development

California Standards Vertical Alignment

Before Chapter 4

Related Topics from Grade 7

- Graph linear functions and recognize the slope of a graph
  ⟿ Standard 7AF3.3

- Represent and describe two numerical variables on a scatterplot Standard 7SDAP1.2

Chapter 4

Topics from Algebra I

- Graph a linear equation or inequality ⟿
- Verify that a point lies on a line and derive linear equations ⟿

See individual lessons for the specific Standards covered.

After Chapter 4

Preparation for Algebra II

- Prove theorems by using coordinate geometry
  ⟿ Standard G17.0

- Solve systems of linear equations and inequalities
  ⟿ Standard 2A2.0

- Compute the variance and the standard deviation of a distribution of data Standard 2APS7.0

Back-Mapping

California Algebra 1 was conceived and developed with the final result in mind, student success in Algebra I and beyond. The authors, using the California Mathematics Standards as their guide, developed this brand-new series by "back-mapping" from the desired result of student success in Algebra I and beyond. McGraw-Hill's *California Geometry, California Algebra 2,* and *California Algebra Readiness* were developed utilizing the same philosophy.

What the Research Says...

Good questioning includes challenging students to think about the main ideas in the lesson and go beyond simple recall or parroting of what has just been said. Questioning also increases student-to-student interaction so that students' ideas, expressed in their terminology, are shared with the class. (Hiebert et al, 1997)

- Stress that the concept of slope in Lesson 4-1 is one that is used widely in mathematics through calculus.

- Understanding what slope represents will help students easily master skills in Lessons 4-2 and 4-7.

[Source: Heibert, J., Carpenter, T.P., Fennema, E., Fuson, K.C., Murray, H., Olivier, A., Human, P., and Wearner, D. (1997) *Making Sense: Teaching and Learning Mathematics with Understanding,* Portsmouth, New Hampshire, Heinemann.]

Mc Graw Hill Professional Development

Targeted professional development has been articulated throughout the *California Mathematics: Concepts, Skills, and Problem Solving* series. The **McGraw-Hill Professional Development Video Library** provides short videos that support the ⟿ Key Standards. For more information, visit ca.algebra1.com.

Model Lessons	Instructional Strategies

CHAPTER 4

Technology Solutions

Teacher Resources

TeacherWorks™ All-in-One Planner and Resource Center

All of the print materials from the Classroom Resource Masters are available on your TeacherWorks™ CD-ROM.

BL = Below Grade Level **OL** = On Grade Level **AL** = Above Grade Level **ELL** = English Language Learner

Chapter Resource Masters					4-1	4-2	4-3	4-4	4-5	4-6	4-7
BL	OL		ELL	Lesson Reading Guide	5	12	19	26	33	41	49
BL	OL		ELL	Study Guide and Intervention*	6	13	20	27	34	42	50
BL	OL			Skills Practice*	8	15	22	29	36	44	52
	OL	AL		Practice*	9	16	23	30	37	45	53
	OL	AL		Word Problem Practice*	10	17	24	31	38	46	54
	OL	AL		Enrichment	11	18	25	32	39	47	55
	OL	AL		Calculator and Spreadsheet Activities						40	48	
	OL	AL		Chapter Assessments*	57–78						
BL	OL	AL		5-Minute Check Transparencies	✓	✓	✓	✓	✓	✓	✓
BL	OL			Teaching Mathematics with Manipulatives	✓		✓		✓	✓	✓

Also available in Spanish.

AssignmentWorks

Differentiated Assignments, Answers, and Solutions

- Print a customized assignment worksheet using the Student Edition exercises along with an answer key or worked-out solutions.
- Use default lesson assignments as outlined in the Differentiated Homework Options in the Teacher Wraparound Edition.
- Includes modified questions from the Student Edition.

Interactive Classroom

This CD-ROM is a customizable Microsoft® PowerPoint® presentation that includes:

- In-Class Examples
- Your Turn Exercises*
- 5-Minute Check Transparencies*
- Links to Online Study Tools
- Concepts in Motion

compatible with response pad technology

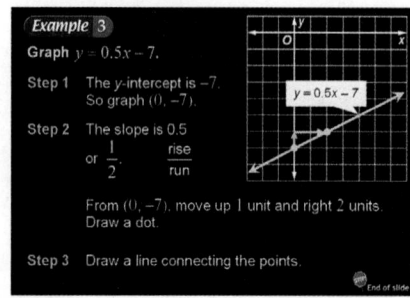

ExamView®Assessment Suite

 lets you

- Create, edit, and customize tests and worksheets using QuickTest Wizard
- Create multiple versions of tests and modify them for a desired level of difficulty
- Translate from English to Spanish and vice versa
- Build tests aligned with your state standards
- Track students' progress using the Teacher Management System

Student Resources

StudentWorks™ Plus

Textbook, Audio, Workbooks, and more

This CD-ROM is a valuable resource for students to access content online and use online resources to continue learning Chapter 4 concepts. Includes:

- Complete Student Editions in both English and Spanish
- English audio integrated throughout the text
- Links to Concepts in Motion, Personal Tutor, and other online resources
- Access to all student worksheets
- Daily Assignments and Grade Log

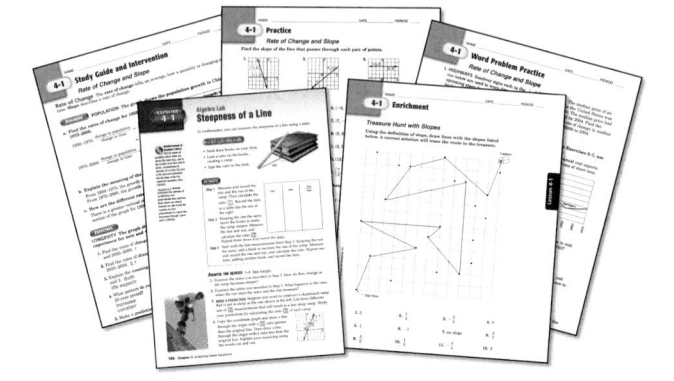

Super DVD

The Super DVD contains two Glencoe multimedia products.

MindJogger Plus An alternative review of concepts in which students work as teams in a game show format to gain points for correct answers.

What's Math Got to Do With It? Real Life Math Videos Engaging video that shows students how math is used in everyday situations

Unit 2 Theme: Linear Functions

Internet Resources

Math ca.algebra1.com

TEACHER	PARENT	STUDENT	**Online Study Tools**
	●	●	Online Student Edition
●	●	●	Multilingual Glossary
			Lesson Resources
	●	●	BrainPOP®
●	●	●	Concepts in Motion
●	●	●	Extra Examples
	●	●	Other Calculator Keystrokes
●			Problem of the Week Cards
	●	●	Real-World Careers
	●	●	Self-Check Quizzes
			Chapter Resources
	●	●	Chapter Readiness
	●	●	Chapter Test
	●	●	Standardized Test Practice
	●	●	Vocabulary Review/Chapter Review Activities
			Unit Resources
●		●	Cross-Curricular Internet Project
			Other Resources
●			Dinah Zike's Foldables
	●	●	Hotmath Homework Help
●			Key Concepts
●	●	●	Meet the Authors
	●	●	Personal Tutor
●			Project CRISS℠
	●	●	Scavenger Hunts and Answer Sheets
●			Vocabulary PuzzleMakers

Focus on Mathematical Content

Big Idea for Chapter 4:
Slope and Rate of Change

Slope is more than the result of plugging in x- and y-coordinates into a formula to find a rational number. The idea of describing how a line changes from point to point carries over into calculus. Explore 4-1 on page 186 examines slope in terms of steepness of a ramp. The height of the books does not change, but as the position of the books changes, it makes the ramp steeper or less steep. The slope varies accordingly. The closer the stack of books moves to the point where the ruler is taped down, the larger the slope. As you move the stack father away from that point the slope decreases, approaching zero.

Why It's Important

For This Chapter
The lessons in this chapter use slope and the meaning of what slope represents to explore many facets of linear equations.
- What does slope mean when a graph represents real-world data? (Lesson 4-1)
- What does slope mean in connection to direct variation? (Lesson 4-2)
- Once an equation is written in $y = mx + b$ form, how can you identify the slope? (Lesson 4-3)
- How can you use slope and a point on the line to write the equation of a line? (Lesson 4-4)
- What if you only have two points on a line—how can you determine the slope to write the equation of the line? (Lessons 4-4 and 4-5)
- When can a line be used to describe a trend in a set of data? (Lesson 4-6)
- Is there a special relationship between the slopes of lines and whether they are parallel or perpendicular? (Lesson 4-7)

After This Chapter
- In Chapter 5, slope can help you determine if a system of equations has a solution or many solutions.
- In geometry, slope can help you classify a figure graphed on a coordinate plane.
- In calculus, the concept of slope is applied to analyzing graphs that are not linear.

 Rate of Change and Slope

Rate of change is a ratio that describes how one quantity changes with respect to another. Slope can be used to describe rate of change.

The slope of a line is the ratio of the vertical change in the line to the horizontal change in the line. The slope can be expressed in several ways.

- slope $= \dfrac{\text{rise}}{\text{run}}$

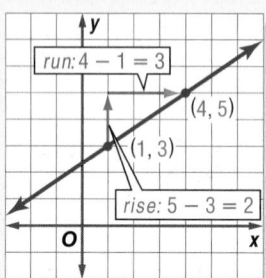

This can be observed from graphed lines and works well for whole number increments for the rise and run.

- $m = \dfrac{y_2 - y_1}{x_2 - x_1}$

This algebraic formula represents slope m using the coordinates of two points on a line (x_1, y_1) and (x_2, y_2). You can use this formula to determine the slope of a line without a graph if you know two points on the line.

4-2 Slope and Direct Variation

The concept of direct variation grows from the meaning of ratio (Lesson 2-6). If the ratio of two variables is a constant, then direct variation is the way of expressing the relationship between the two variables. That is, $\dfrac{y}{x} = k$, where y and x are variables and k is the constant (number) of variation. Multiply each side of the equation by x and you get $y = kx$. This represents an equation of a line. The k is the same value as the slope of the line. So, when you graph a direct variation, you are graphing lines with slope k. All of these lines pass through the origin. In real-world applications, most direct variation graphs are found in the first quadrant.

Graphing Equations in Slope-Intercept Form

An equation of the form $y = mx + b$, where m is the slope and b is the y-value where the graph of the equation crosses the y-axis, is said to be in slope-intercept form. The slope-intercept form offers two ways to graph a line.

- Select any two values for x, substitute the values into the equation, and then calculate the corresponding values of y to create two ordered pairs that can be graphed. Draw the line that contains these two points.

- Graph the y-intercept, use it as a starting point, and then use the slope to determine the distance and direction you go up/down and right/left to find another point on the line. Then draw the line.

To graph a linear equation that is not in the form $y = mx + b$, solve the equation for y to write the equation in slope-intercept form, then graph.

 ## Writing Equations in Slope-Intercept Form

It is important to understand what an equation represents and how to use it as a tool. The general expression for slope-intercept form is $y = mx + b$. This is the starting point for creating an equation from different types of information given.

- Given slope, m, and one point (x, y)

Step 1 Substitute the values of m, x, and y into the slope-intercept form and solve for b.

Step 2 Write the slope-intercept form using the values of m and b.

- Given two points

Step 1 Use the two points to find the slope.

Step 2 Choose one of the two points to use.

Step 3 Follow the steps for writing an equation given the slope and one point.

 ## Writing Equations in Point-Slope Form

Point-slope form is derived from the definition of slope using the coordinates of two points on a line. Suppose the two points on a line are given as (x, y) and (x_1, y_1). Using the definition of the slope, you get $m = \dfrac{y - y_1}{x - x_1}$. If you multiply each side by $(x - x_1)$, you get $y - y_1 = m(x - x_1)$, which is the point-slope form of a linear equation.

This form is the starting point for writing an equation when you are given the slope and a point on the line. When the slope is undefined, as in vertical lines, the equation cannot be written in point-slope form.

Linear equations in point-slope form can be manipulated to express them in slope-intercept form, $y = mx + b$, (Lesson 4-3) or in standard form, $Ax + By = C$ (Lesson 3-3).

 ## Statistics: Scatter Plots and Lines of Fit

A scatter plot consists of graphs of ordered pairs (x, y) that belong to a set in which the x-coordinate represents one real-world measurement and the y-coordinate represents another. Scatter plots can be used to visually investigate relationships between the two real-world quantities, identify trends if they exist, and determine how strong that trend is.

If a set of data exhibits a linear trend, a line of fit can be drawn to summarize the data. Once the line is drawn, an equation for the line can be found. This equation for the line of fit can be used to make predictions. It should be understood that predictions are totally dependent on the line drawn.

 ## Geometry: Parallel and Perpendicular Lines

This is a part of mathematics often called *coordinate geometry* or *analytic geometry*. In coordinate geometry, graphing and properties of graphs are used to prove geometric concepts. When two distinct lines lie in the same plane and have the same slope, they are parallel. When two lines intersect, we know they do not have the same slope. If the lines intersect at right angles the slopes of the two lines are negative reciprocals of each other.

Using the equation-writing skills presented in previous lessons and the information about the slopes of parallel and perpendicular lines, you can write the equation of a line that is parallel to or perpendicular to a given line.

CHAPTER 4

Differentiated Instruction

Options for Chapter 4 Lessons

ELL = English Language Learner   **AL** = Above Grade Level   **SS** = Struggling Students   **SN** = Special Needs

Using Movement **ELL** **SS**

Use with Lesson 4-1

Use floor tiles as a grid or use masking tape on the floor to create a grid. Have students walk the path from one point to another on the floor, allowing only one horizontal and one vertical path. Ask them to describe their trip in terms of positive and negative movement and the number of squares traveled in each direction. Then have them write the description of their movement as the slope of the line connecting the two points.

Using Interpersonal Skills **AL**

Use with Lesson 4-2

Have small groups of students use a triple-beam balance and 4 stacks of identical washers. Each stack should contain a different number of washers tied together so students cannot weigh just one washer. Record the number of washers n in each stack. Have students weigh one stack and then predict the weights W of the other stacks. How do they think this relates to the equation $W = kn$? See students' work. What does k represent? the weight of each washer

Using Verbal Skills **ELL** **SS** **SN**

Use with Lesson 4-5

Give students several exercises that ask them to write a particular type of equation. Have them describe or write how they would solve each type of problem. Then have them summarize the technique they think works best for each given situation (point and slope, two points, rewriting equations in various forms).

Noteables™ Interactive Study Notebook with Foldables™

Noteables™ Interactive Study Notebook with Foldables™ is a study organizer that provides helpful steps for students to follow to organize their notes for Chapter 4.

- Students use Noteables to record notes and to complete their Foldables as you present the material for each lesson.

- Noteables correspond to the Examples in the *Teacher Wraparound Edition* and *Interactive Classroom CD-ROM*.

Intervention

Quick Review Math Handbook*

is Glencoe's mathematical handbook for students and parents.

Hot Words includes a glossary of terms.

Hot Topics consists of two parts:

- explanations of key mathematical concepts
- exercises to check students' understanding.

Lesson	Hot Topics Section	Lesson	Hot Topics Section
4-1	2.4, 6.8	4-5	6.8
4-2	6.4, 6.8	4-6	4.3
4-3	6.7, 6.8	4-7	6.8
4-4	1.5, 6.8		

Also available in Spanish

Teacher to Teacher

Barbara A. Kevil
Teacher
Schindewolf I.S., Klein ISD
Spring, TX

USE WITH LESSON 4-2

❝ I teach this lesson by first graphing $y = x$ using a table of values. Then I ask students to hold their left arms in front of their faces, with their noses being the origin, and show me $y = x$. I then ask them to use their arms and show me the graph of $y = 2x$. They guess, and then we graph the equation on a graphing calculator. I repeat this activity with equations like $y = 5x$ and $y = \frac{1}{2}x$ until they make conclusions about the relationship between the coefficient of x and the steepness of the line. You can vary this activity for negative coefficients by having students use their right arms. ❞

Reading and Writing in Mathematics

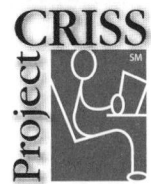

CRISS Project SM

STUDY SKILL

A point-by-point format and example can be used to help students better understand the steps of many mathematical processes. In order to explain a process, they must understand how to perform a step as well as the reasoning behind each step.

Provide students with the description at the right as an example of using point-by-point format to explain how to write an equation of a line when two points are given. After reading L4-4, have students write a description of how to write an equation of a line when a point and the slope are given.

Main Idea	Point-by-Point Steps	Example for the Points: (1, 5), (−1, 1)
Find an equation of a line when two point on the line are given.	1. Find the slope of the line containing the points.	$m = \dfrac{y_2 - y_1}{x_2 - x_1}$ $m = \dfrac{1 - 5}{-1 - 1}$ $m = \dfrac{-4}{-2}$ or 2
	2. Choose one of the points and find the y-intercept.	$y = mx + b$ $1 = 2(-1) + b$ $3 = b$
	3. Write the slope-intercept form of the equation using the slope and y-intercept.	Using $m = 2$ and $b = 3$, $y = mx + b$ $y = 2x + 3$

CReating **I**ndependence through **S**tudent-owned **S**trategies

Notes

 **Dinah Zike's Foldables™**

Focus At the end of each lesson, students write notes about the concepts, computation of skills, and graphs presented.

Teach Have students make and label the tabs for each lesson of their Foldables as illustrated.

Have students use the appropriate tabs as they cover each lesson in this chapter. Point out that the last tab is for their vocabulary words.

When to Use It Encourage students to write descriptive paragraphs about their experiences and graph examples in their Foldables as they work through the chapter. These notes may be used to review for the chapter test.

A version of a completed Foldable is shown on p. 242.

Differentiated Instruction

[CRM] Student-Built Glossary, pp. 1–2 Students should complete the chart by providing a definition and example of each term as they progress through Chapter 4. This study tool can also be used to review for the chapter test.

Analyzing Linear Equations

 **BIG Ideas**

- **Standard 7.0** Students verify that a point lies on a line, given an equation of the line. Students are able to derive linear equations by using the point-slope formula. (Key, CAHSEE)

Key Vocabulary

point-slope form (p. 220)

rate of change (p. 187)

slope (p. 189)

slope-intercept form (p. 204)

🌐 **Real-World Link**

Space Exploration Linear equations are used to model a variety of real-world situations, including the cost of the U.S. space program.

 **FOLDABLES Study Organizer**

Analyzing Linear Equations Make this Foldable to help you organize information about writing linear equations. Begin with four sheets of grid paper.

1 **Fold** each sheet of grid paper in half along the width. Then cut along the crease.

2 **Staple** the eight half-sheets together to form a booklet.

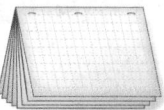

3 **Cut** seven lines from the bottom of the top sheet, six lines from the second sheet, and so on.

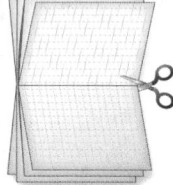

4 **Label** each of the tabs with a lesson number. The last tab is for the vocabulary.

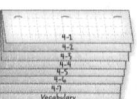

Materials Needed for Chapter 4

- rulers (Explore 4-1, Lessons 4-1, 4-6, 4-7)
- piece of tape (Explore 4-1)
- books (Explore 4-1)
- Internet (Lessons 4-1, 4-6)
- graphing calculator (Lesson 4-2, Extend 4-3, Extend 4-6)
- plastic sandwich bag (Explore 4-3)
- data collection device and force sensor (Explore 4-3)
- washers (Explore 4-3)
- scissors (Lesson 4-7)
- centimeter or meterstick (Lesson 4-6)

GET READY for Chapter 4

Diagnose Readiness You have two options for checking Prerequisite Skills.

Option 2

Math⬤nline Take the Online Readiness Quiz at ca.algebra1.com.

Option 1

Take the Quick Check below. Refer to the Quick Review for help.

QUICKCheck

Simplify. (Prerequisite Skill) (Used in Lesson 4-1)

1. $\frac{2}{10}$ $\frac{1}{5}$
2. $\frac{8}{12}$ $\frac{2}{3}$
3. $\frac{2}{-8}$ $-\frac{1}{4}$
4. $\frac{-4}{8}$ $\frac{-1}{2}$
5. $\frac{-5}{-15}$ $\frac{1}{3}$
6. $\frac{-7}{-28}$ $\frac{1}{4}$
7. $\frac{9}{3}$ 3
8. $\frac{18}{12}$ $1\frac{1}{2}$
9. $-\frac{26}{10}$ $-2\frac{3}{5}$

Evaluate $\frac{a-b}{c-d}$ for the values given.
(Lesson 1-2) (Used in Lesson 4-2)

10. $a = 6, b = 5, c = 8, d = 4$ $\frac{1}{4}$

11. $a = -2, b = 1, c = 4, d = 0$ $-\frac{3}{4}$

12. $a = -3, b = -3, c = 4, d = 7$ 0

13. **CELL PHONES** The average cost per minute of using a cell phone decreased $0.44 between 1996 and 2004. On average, how much did the cost decrease each year? (Lesson 1-2) (Used in Lesson 4-2)
    $0.055

Write the ordered pair for each point.
(Lesson 1-9) (Used in Lessons 4-3 through 4-7)

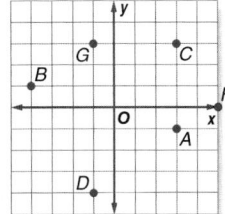

14. A (3, −1)
15. B (−4, 1)
16. C (3, 3)
17. D (−1, −4)
18. F (5, 0)
19. G (−1, 3)

QUICKReview

EXAMPLE 1

Simplify $-\frac{4}{28}$.

$-\frac{4}{28} = \frac{-4 \div 4}{28 \div 4}$ Divide −4 and 28 by their GCF, 4.

$= \frac{-1}{7}$ or $-\frac{1}{7}$ Simplify. Since the signs are different, the quotient is negative.

EXAMPLE 2

Evaluate $\frac{a-b}{c-d}$ if $a = 2, b = 5, c = -3, d = -12$.

$\frac{a-b}{c-d}$ Original expression

$= \frac{2-5}{(-3)-(-12)}$ Substitute 2 for a, 5 for b, −3 for c, and −12 for d.

$= \frac{-3}{9}$ Simplify.

$= \frac{-3 \div 3}{9 \div 3}$ Divide −3 and 9 by their GCF, 3.

$= \frac{-1}{3}$ or $-\frac{1}{3}$ Simplify. The signs are different, so the quotient is negative.

EXAMPLE 3

Write the ordered pair for A.

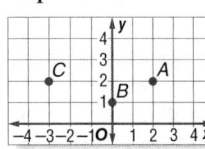

Step 1 Begin at point A.
Step 2 Follow along a vertical line through the point to find the x-coordinate on the x-axis. The x-coordinate is 2.
Step 3 Follow along a horizontal line through the point to find the y-coordinate on the y-axis. The y-coordinate is 2.
The ordered pair for point A is (2, 2).

✓ Diagnostic Assessment

Exercises	California Standards	Intervention
1–9	7NS1.1	[SE] Prerequisite Skill, pp. 700–701 *Prerequisite Skills Workbook* • Simplifying Fractions, pp. 39–40
10–13	7AF1.1	[SE] Review Lesson 1–2, pp. 10–14
14–19	5AF1.4	[SE] Review Lesson 1–9, pp. 53–58

✓ Formative Assessment

[CRM] Anticipation Guide, pp. 3–4
Spotting Preconceived Ideas
Students complete this survey to determine prior knowledge about ideas from Chapter 4. Revisit this worksheet after completing the chapter. Also see p. 246.

[TWE] **Lesson Activities**
• Ticket Out the Door, pp. 195, 241
• Crystal Ball, p. 202
• Name the Math, pp. 209, 225
• Yesterday's News, pp. 218, 233

Chapter Checkpoints

[SE] Mid-Chapter Quiz, p. 212

[SE] Study Guide and Review, pp. 242–246

[SE] California Standards Practice, pp. 248–249

[CRM] Quizzes, pp. 59 and 60

[CRM] Standardized Test Practice, pp. 76–78

Math⬤nline ca.algebra1.com

• Self-Check Quizzes
• Practice Test
• Standardized Test Practice

✓ Summative Assessment

[SE] Chapter Practice Test, p. 247

[CRM] Mid-Chapter Test, p. 61

[CRM] Vocabulary Test, p. 62

[CRM] Extended-Response Test, p. 75

[CRM] Leveled Chapter Tests, pp. 63–74

⊙ ExamView® Assessment Suite

KEY

[CRM] Chapter 4 Resource Masters

[SE] Student Edition

[TWE] Teacher Wraparound Edition

⊙ ExamView® Assessment Suite

Algebra Lab

Steepness of a Line

In mathematics, you can measure the steepness of a line using a ratio.

Objective Investigate the slope of a line using concrete objects.

Materials
- 2 rulers
- 3 books
- a large piece of tape

Easy-To-Make Manipulatives
Teaching Algebra with Manipulatives

Template for grid paper, p. 1

Working in Cooperative Groups
Put students in groups of 3 or 4, mixing abilities. Have groups complete the Activity and Exercises 1 and 2.

Ask:
- Which measurement, rise or run, changes as you move the books? run
- In Exercise 2, which measurement changes when you add a third book? rise

Practice Have students complete Exercise 3.

✓ Formative Assessment

Use Exercise 4 to assess whether students comprehend how to find slope from a coordinate graph.

From Concrete to Abstract
Give students a piece of uncooked spaghetti and a coordinate grid. Have them place the spaghetti on the grid and record the slope of the represented line. Repeat this activity 5 times.

Reinforcement of Standard 7AF3.4 Plot the values of quantities whose ratios are always the same (e.g., cost to the number of an item, feet to inches, circumference to diameter of a circle). Fit a line to the plot and understand that the slope of the line equals the quantities. (Key, CAHSEE)

Standard 8.0 Students understand the concepts of parallel lines and perpendicular lines and how those slopes are related. Students are able to find the equation of a line perpendicular to a given line that passes through a given point. (CAHSEE)

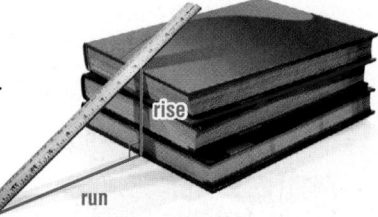

▶ SET UP the Lab

- Stack three books on your desk.
- Lean a ruler on the books, creating a ramp.
- Tape the ruler to the desk.

ACTIVITY

Step 1 Measure and record the rise and the run of the ramp. Then calculate the ratio $\frac{\text{rise}}{\text{run}}$. Record the data in a table like the one at the right.

rise	run	$\frac{\text{rise}}{\text{run}}$

Step 2 Keeping the rise the same, move the books to make the ramp steeper. Measure the rise and run, and calculate the ratio $\frac{\text{rise}}{\text{run}}$. Repeat three times and record the data.

Step 3 Start with the last measurements from Step 2. Keeping the run the same, add a book to increase the rise of the ramp. Measure and record the rise and run, and calculate the ratio. Repeat one time, adding another book, and record the data.

ANALYZE THE RESULTS 1–4. See margin.

1. Examine the ratios you recorded in Step 2. How do they change as the ramp becomes steeper?

2. Examine the ratios you recorded in Step 3. What happens to the ratio when the run stays the same and the rise increases?

3. **MAKE A PREDICTION** Suppose you want to construct a skateboard ramp that is not as steep as the one shown at the left. List three different sets of $\frac{\text{rise}}{\text{run}}$ measurements that will result in a less steep ramp. Verify your predictions by calculating the ratio $\frac{\text{rise}}{\text{run}}$ of each ramp.

4. Copy the coordinate graph and draw a line through the origin with a $\frac{\text{rise}}{\text{run}}$ ratio greater than the original line. Then draw a line through the origin with a ratio less than the original line. Explain your reasoning using the words *rise* and *run*.

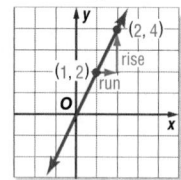

186 Chapter 4 Analyzing Linear Equations

Extending the Concept
Ask:
- Is the slope always a fraction? Slope can always be expressed as a fraction, even if it appears to be an integer.
- Can slope be negative? When? yes; when the line slopes down from left to right

Additional Answers

1. The ratios increased

2. The slope increased.

3. Sample answer:

$$\frac{12 \text{ in.}}{24 \text{ in.}} = \frac{1}{2}, \frac{18 \text{ in.}}{27 \text{ in.}} = \frac{2}{3}, \frac{6 \text{ in.}}{18 \text{ in.}} = \frac{1}{3}$$

4. See students' work.

Rate of Change and Slope

Main Ideas

- Use rate of change to solve problems.
- Find the slope of a line.

 Reinforcement of Standard 7AF3.3 Graph linear functions, noting that the vertical change (change in *y*-value) per unit of horizontal change (change in *x*-value) is always the same and know that the ratio ("rise over run") is called the slope of a graph. (Key, CAHSEE)

New Vocabulary

rate of change
slope

Study Tip

Independent Quantities

Rates of change often include *time* as the independent variable.

▶ **GET READY** for the Lesson

Houses in the north have steeper roofs so that snow does not pile up. A roof *pitch* describes how steep it is. It is the number of units the roof rises for each unit of run. In the photo, the roof rises 8 feet for each 12 feet of run.

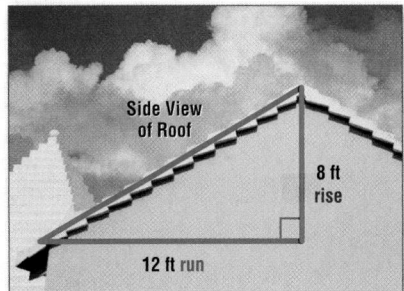

Side View of Roof

8 ft rise

12 ft run

$$\frac{rise}{run} = \frac{8}{12} \text{ or } \frac{2}{3}$$

Rate of Change Rate of change is a ratio that describes, on average, how much one quantity changes with respect to a change in another quantity. If *x* is the independent variable and *y* is the dependent variable, then

$$\text{rate of change} = \frac{\text{change in } y}{\text{change in } x}.$$

The table at the right shows the distance a person has walked for various amounts of time.

Time Walking (s)	Distance Walked (ft)
x	*y*
1	4
2	8
3	12

+1, +1 (on left) ; +4, +4 (on right)

$$\text{rate of change} = \frac{\text{change in } y}{\text{change in } x}$$

$$= \frac{\text{change in distance}}{\text{change in time}}$$

$$= \frac{4}{1} \quad \leftarrow \text{feet} \atop \leftarrow \text{seconds}$$

Each time *x* increases by 1 second, *y* increases by 4 feet.

The rate of change is $\frac{4}{1}$. This means that the person walked 4 feet per second.

▶ **Real-World EXAMPLE**

1 **ENTERTAINMENT** Use the table to find the rate of change. Explain the meaning of the rate of change.

Each time *x* increases by 2 games, *y* increases by $78.

Number of Computer Games	Total Cost ($)
x	*y*
2	78
4	156
6	234

(continued on the next page)

1 FOCUS

Standards Alignment

Before Lesson 4-1
Identify and graph ordered pairs in the coordinate plane from ⚷ Standard 5AF1.4

Lesson 4-1
Graph linear functions and recognize the slope of a graph from ⚷ Standard 7AF3.3

After Lesson 4-1
Prove theorems by using coordinate geometry from ⚷ Standard G17.0

2 Teach

Scaffolding Questions

Have students observe the diagram and the definition of slope in *Get Ready for the Lesson.*

Ask:

- What is the slope of the roof if the rise is 10 and the run is 6? $\frac{10}{6}$ or $\frac{5}{3}$
- What might the rise and run be for a roof with a slope of 2?

Sample answers: $\frac{10}{5}, \frac{6}{3}, \frac{2}{1}, \frac{-4}{-2}$

(continued on the next page)

Lesson 4-1 Resources

Chapter 4 Resource Masters

Lesson Reading Guide, p. 5 ⬤BL ⬤OL ⬤ELL
Study Guide and Intervention, pp. 6–7
⬤BL ⬤OL ⬤ELL
Skills Practice, p. 8 ⬤BL ⬤OL
Practice, p. 9 ⬤OL ⬤AL
Word Problem Practice, p. 10 ⬤OL ⬤AL
Enrichment, p. 11 ⬤OL ⬤AL

Transparencies

5-Minute Check Transparency 4-1

Additional Print Resources

Noteables™ Interactive Study Notebook with Foldables™
Teaching Algebra with Manipulatives

Technology

ca.algebra1.com
Interactive Classroom CD-ROM
AssignmentWorks CD-ROM
Graphing Calculator Easy Files

- Which has a steeper slope, a roof with a slope of $\frac{1}{2}$ or a roof with a slope of $\frac{5}{2}$? Why? $\frac{5}{2}$, because the rise is greater than in $\frac{1}{2}$ and both have the same run.

- What does a slope of $-\frac{1}{2}$ mean? Explain. $-\frac{1}{2} = \frac{-1}{2} = \frac{1}{-2}; \frac{-1}{2}$ means down 1 and right 2 and $\frac{1}{-2}$, means up 1 and left 2. The line goes from upper left to lower right.

Rate of Change

Example 1 shows how to find the rate of change given a table of values for a real-world situation. **Example 2** shows how to describe the rate of change for a real-world problem in which the difference between two *y*-values divided by the difference between their corresponding *x*-values is not constant.

 Formative Assessment

Use the Check Your Progress exercises after each example to determine students' understanding of concepts.

ADDITIONAL EXAMPLE

1 **DRIVING TIME** Use the table to find the rate of change. Explain the meaning of the rate of change. $\frac{38}{1}$; this means the car is traveling at a rate of 38 miles per hour.

Time Driving (h)	Distance Traveled (mi)
x	*y*
2	76
4	152
6	228

Additional Examples are also in:

- Noteables™ Interactive Study Notebook with Foldables™
- Interactive Classroom PowerPoint® Presentations

1B. 16 square inches of surface is tiled for each floor tile that is used.

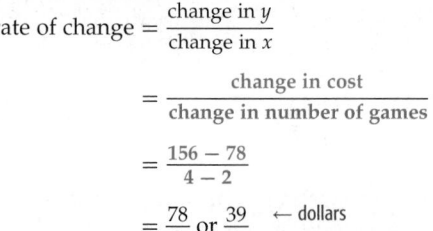

Real-World Link

One of the most visited theme parks in California is the Disneyland® Resort in Anaheim. An estimated 400 million people have visited the park since 1955.

Source: beachcalifornia.com

$$\text{rate of change} = \frac{\text{change in } y}{\text{change in } x}$$

$$= \frac{\text{change in cost}}{\text{change in number of games}}$$

$$= \frac{156 - 78}{4 - 2}$$

$$= \frac{78}{2} \text{ or } \frac{39}{1} \quad \begin{array}{l} \leftarrow \text{dollars} \\ \leftarrow \text{games} \end{array}$$

The rate of change is $\frac{39}{1}$. This means that it costs \$39 per game.

 CHECK Your Progress

REMODELING The table shows how the area changes with the number of floor tiles.
1A. Find the rate of change. $\frac{16}{1}$
1B. Explain the meaning of the rate of change.

Floor Tiles	Area (in²)
x	*y*
3	48
6	96
9	144

So far, you have seen rates of change that are *constant*. Many real-world situations involve rates of change that are not constant.

Real-World EXAMPLE

2 **ENTERTAINMENT** The graph shows the number of people who visited U.S. theme parks in recent years.

a. Find the rates of change for 1996–1998 and 2000–2002.

$$\text{rate of change}$$
$$= \frac{\text{change in attendance}}{\text{change in time}} \quad \begin{array}{l} \leftarrow \text{people} \\ \leftarrow \text{years} \end{array}$$

Theme Park Attendance

Attendance (millions)

92.4 · 84.6 · 81.8 · 78.8

92 · 88 · 84 · 80

1996 1998 2000 2002
Year

Source: tia.org

1996–1998:

$$\frac{\text{change in attendance}}{\text{change in time}} = \frac{81.8 - 78.8}{1998 - 1996} \quad \text{Substitute.}$$

$$= \frac{3}{2} \text{ or } 1.5 \quad \text{Simplify.}$$

Theme park attendance increased by 3 million in a 2-year period for a rate of change of 1.5 million per year.

2000–2002:

$$\frac{\text{change in attendance}}{\text{change in time}} = \frac{92.4 - 84.6}{2002 - 2000} \quad \text{Substitute.}$$

$$= \frac{7.8}{2} \text{ or } 3.9 \quad \text{Simplify.}$$

Over this 2-year period, attendance increased by 7.8 million, for a rate of change of 3.9 million per year.

188 Chapter 4 Analyzing Linear Equations

Tips for New Teachers **Geometry Concept**

The fact that the slope of a line is the same regardless of which pair of points of the line are used for its definition depends on the considerations of similar triangles. This small gap in the logical development should be made clear to students, with the added assurance that they will learn the concept in geometry.

b. Explain the meaning of the rate of change in each case.

For 1996–1998, on average, 1.5 million more people went to a theme park each year than the last.

For 2000–2002, on average, 3.9 million more people attended theme parks each year than the last.

c. How are the different rates of change shown on the graph?

There is a greater vertical change for 2000–2002 than for 1996–1998. Therefore, the section of the graph for 2000–2002 is steeper.

 CHECK Your Progress

1998–2000; Attendance increased 1.4 million per year.

2. Refer to the graph. Without calculating, find the 2-year period that has the least rate of change. Then calculate to verify your answer.

Online **Personal Tutor at** ca.algebra1.com

Find Slope The **slope** of a line is the ratio of the change in the *y*-coordinates (rise) to the change in the *x*-coordinates (run) as you move in the positive direction.

Slope can be used to describe a rate of change. This number describes how steep the line is. The greater the absolute value of the slope, the steeper the line.

Vocabulary Link
Slope
Everyday Use A hill used for snow skiing is often called a slope.

Math Use Slope is used to describe steepness.

The graph shows a line that passes through (1, 3) and (4, 5).

$$\text{slope} = \frac{\text{rise}}{\text{run}}$$

$$= \frac{\text{change in } y\text{-coordinates}}{\text{change in } x\text{-coordinates}}$$

$$= \frac{5-3}{4-1} \text{ or } \frac{2}{3}$$

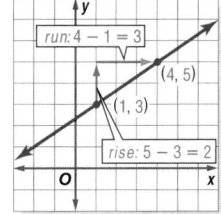

So, the slope of the line is $\frac{2}{3}$.

Any two points on a line can be used to determine the slope.

KEY CONCEPT   *Slope*

Words   The slope of a line is the ratio of the rise to the run.

Symbols   The slope *m* of a nonvertical line through any two points, (x_1, y_1) and (x_2, y_2), can be found as follows.

$$m = \frac{y_2 - y_1}{x_2 - x_1} \quad \begin{array}{l} \leftarrow \text{ change in } y \\ \leftarrow \text{ change in } x \end{array}$$

Graph

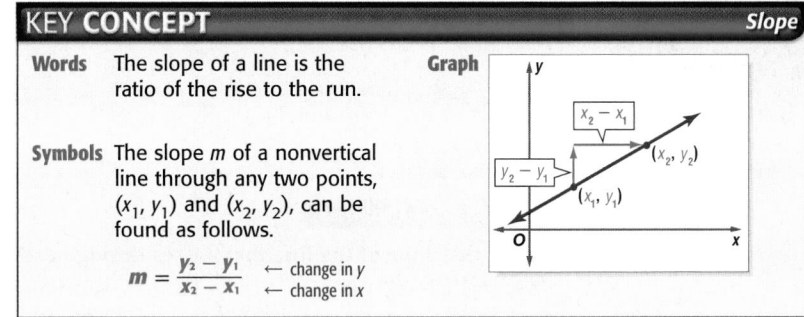

Math
Online **Extra Examples at** ca.algebra1.com

Lesson 4-1 Rate of Change and Slope   **189**

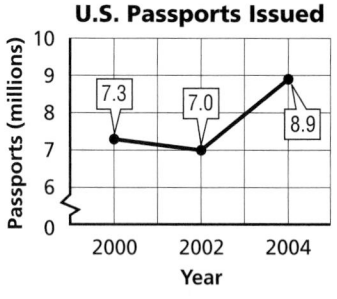

ADDITIONAL EXAMPLE

2 **TRAVEL** The graph below shows the number of U.S. passports issued in 2000, 2002, and 2004.

U.S. Passports Issued

a. Find the rates of change for 2000–2002 and 2002–2004.
−150,000/yr; 900,000/yr

b. Explain the meaning of the rate of change in each case.
For 2000–2002, there was an average annual drop of 150,000 in passports issued. However, between 2002 and 2004, there was an average yearly increase of 900,000 passports issued.

c. How are the different rates of change shown on the graphs?
The first rate of change is negative, and the line goes down on the graph; the second rate of change is positive, and the graph goes upward.

Find Slope
Examples 3–6 show the four types of slope that are possible for the graph of a line. **Example 7** shows how to use algebraic manipulation to find a missing coordinate when the slope is known.

The slope of a line can be positive, negative, zero, or undefined.

EXAMPLE Positive Slope

3 Find the slope of the line that passes through $(-1, 2)$ and $(3, 4)$.

Let $(-1, 2) = (x_1, y_1)$ and $(3, 4) = (x_2, y_2)$.

$$m = \frac{y_2 - y_1}{x_2 - x_1} \qquad \frac{\text{rise}}{\text{run}}$$

$$= \frac{4 - 2}{3 - (-1)} \qquad \text{Substitute.}$$

$$= \frac{2}{4} \text{ or } \frac{1}{2} \qquad \text{Simplify.}$$

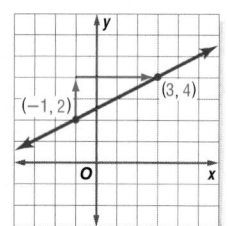

CHECK Your Progress

Find the slope of the line that passes through each set of points.

3A. $(3, 6), (4, 8)$ 2
3B. $(-4, 2), (2, 10)$ $\frac{4}{3}$

EXAMPLE Negative Slope

4 Find the slope of the line that passes through $(-1, -2)$ and $(-4, 1)$.

Let $(-1, -2) = (x_1, y_1)$ and $(-4, 1) = (x_2, y_2)$.

$$m = \frac{y_2 - y_1}{x_2 - x_1} \qquad \frac{\text{rise}}{\text{run}}$$

$$= \frac{1 - (-2)}{-4 - (-1)} \qquad \text{Substitute.}$$

$$= \frac{3}{-3} \text{ or } -1 \qquad \text{Simplify.}$$

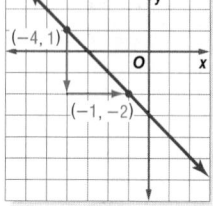

CHECK Your Progress

Find the slope of the line that passes though each set of points.

4A. $(-2, 2), (-6, 4)$ $-\frac{1}{2}$
4B. $(4, 3), (-1, 11)$ $-\frac{8}{5}$

EXAMPLE Zero Slope

5 Find the slope of the line that passes through $(1, 2)$ and $(-1, 2)$.

Let $(1, 2) = (x_1, y_1)$ and $(-1, 2) = (x_2, y_2)$.

$$m = \frac{y_2 - y_1}{x_2 - x_1} \qquad \frac{\text{rise}}{\text{run}}$$

$$= \frac{2 - 2}{-1 - 1} \qquad \text{Substitute.}$$

$$= \frac{0}{-2} \text{ or } 0 \qquad \text{Simplify.}$$

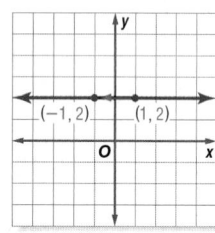

Real-World Link

A flat roof has a slope of zero.

CHECK Your Progress

Find the slope of the line that passes through each set of points.

5A. $(6, 7), (-2, 7)$ 0
5B. $(-4, -2), (0, -2)$ 0

190 Chapter 4 Analyzing Linear Equations

Intervention

Computing Slope Many students automatically assume that the left-most point has to be (x_1, y_1) and the point farther right is (x_2, y_2). The designation of (x_1, y_1) and (x_2, y_2) is arbitrary. However, it is possible that one way may make the subtraction easier than the other.

Slope and Improper Fractions Slope is usually expressed as a fraction or an integer because it gives information about the direction of the line. A mixed number would not reveal that information.

EXAMPLE Undefined Slope

6 Find the slope of the line that passes through $(1, -2)$ and $(1, 3)$.

Let $(1, -2) = (x_1, y_1)$ and $(1, 3) = (x_2, y_2)$.

$$m = \frac{y_2 - y_1}{x_2 - x_1} \quad \frac{\text{rise}}{\text{run}}$$

$$= \frac{3 - (-2)}{1 - 1} \text{ or } \cancel{\frac{5}{0}}$$

Since division by zero is undefined, the slope is undefined.

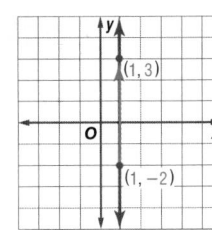

✓CHECK Your Progress

Find the slope of the line that passes through each set of points.
6A. $(3, 2), (3, -1)$ undefined   **6B.** $(-2, -1), (-2, 5)$ undefined

---

KEY CONCEPT   *Slope*

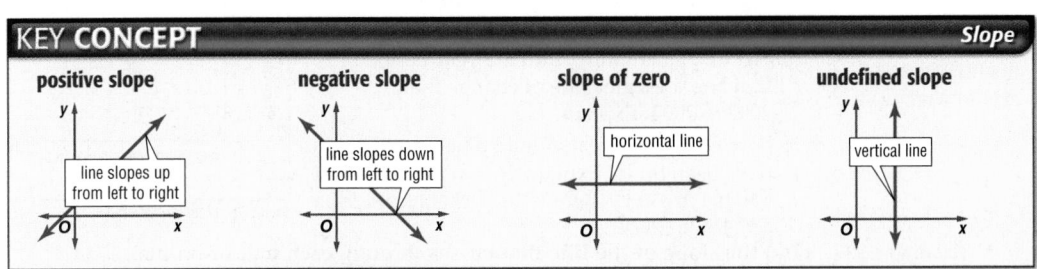

positive slope	negative slope	slope of zero	undefined slope
line slopes up from left to right	line slopes down from left to right	horizontal line	vertical line

---

Given the slope of a line and one point on the line, you can find other points on the line.

EXAMPLE Find Coordinates Given Slope

7 Find the value of r so that the line through $(r, 6)$ and $(10, -3)$ has a slope of $-\dfrac{3}{2}$.

$$m = \frac{y_2 - y_1}{x_2 - x_1} \quad \text{Slope Formula}$$

$$-\frac{3}{2} = \frac{-3 - 6}{10 - r} \quad \text{Let } (r, 6) = (x_1, y_1) \text{ and } (10, -3) = (x_2, y_2).$$

$$-\frac{3}{2} = \frac{-9}{10 - r} \quad \text{Subtract.}$$

$$-3(10 - r) = 2(-9) \quad \text{Find the cross products.}$$

$$-30 + 3r = -18 \quad \text{Simplify.}$$

$$3r = 12 \quad \text{Add 30 to each side and simplify.}$$

$$r = 4 \quad \text{Divide each side by 3 and simplify.}$$

So, the line goes through $(4, 6)$.

✓CHECK Your Progress

Find the value of r so the line that passes through each pair of points has the given slope.
7A. $(1, 4), (-1, r); m = 2$ 0   **7B.** $(r, -6), (5, -8); m = -8$ 4.75

Lesson 4-1 Rate of Change and Slope   **191**

Focus on Mathematical Content

Undefined Slope Undefined slope is not the same as slope of 0. The slope of a vertical line is undefined because the formula yields an expression with 0 as the denominator, and division by zero is undefined.

ADDITIONAL EXAMPLES

6 Find the slope of the line that passes through $(-2, -4)$ and $(-2, 3)$. undefined

7 Find the value of r so that the line through $(6, 3)$ and $(r, 2)$ has a slope of $\dfrac{1}{2}$. 4

Tips for New Teachers   **Preventing Errors**

As students work through Example 7, watch for those who try to find the cross product mentally and forget to multiply both 10 and $-r$ by -3.

3 Practice

✓ Formative Assessment

Use Exercises 1–13 to check for understanding.

Use the chart at the bottom of this page to customize your assignments for your students.

Odd/Even Assignments

Exercises 14–35 are structured so that students practice the same concepts whether they are assigned odd or even problems.

Pacing

Because slope is an important concept throughout this chapter, students should have a good understanding of it. If you are uncertain that your students have mastered the concept of slope, consider spending an extra day on this lesson.

Real-World Connection
For Exercise 19, determine what percent of students have a cell phone and then determine what percent had a cell phone two years ago. Have students find the annual rate of change in the percent of students with cell phones from two years ago to this year.

✓ CHECK Your Understanding

Example 1
(pp. 187–188)

Find the rate of change represented in each table or graph.

1. 4

x	y
3	−6
5	2
7	10
9	18
11	26

2. $-\frac{1}{2}$

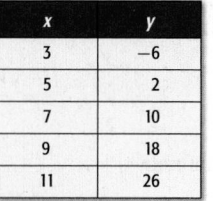

(−1, −3)
(3, −5)

3. 2.005; There was an average increase in ticket price of $2.005 per year.

Example 2
(pp. 188–189)

SPORTS For Exercises 3–5, use the graph at the right.

4. Sample answer: 1998–2000; A steeper segment means a greater rate of change.

★ **3.** Find the rate of change for prices from 2002 to 2004. Explain the meaning of the rate of change.

4. Without calculating, find a 2-year period that had a greater rate of change than 2002 to 2004. Explain.

★ **5.** Between which years might a new stadium have been built? Explain your reasoning. Sample answer: 1998–2000; Ticket prices show a sharp increase.

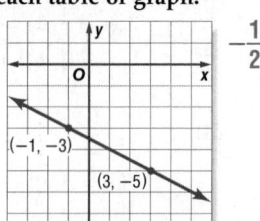

Houston Astros Tickets Average Price

Source: *Team Marketing Report*

Examples 3–6
(pp. 190–191)

Find the slope of the line that passes through each pair of points.

6. (1, 1), (3, 4) $\frac{3}{2}$

7. (0, 0), (5, 4) $\frac{4}{5}$

8. (−2, 2), (−1, −2) −4

9. (9, −4), (7, −1) $-\frac{3}{2}$

10. (3, 5), (−2, 5) 0

11. (−1, 3), (−1, 0) undefined

Example 7
(p. 191)

Find the value of r so the line that passes through each pair of points has the given slope.

12. (6, −2), (r, −6), m = 4 5

13. (9, r), (6, 3), m = −$\frac{1}{3}$ 2

Exercises

HOMEWORK HELP

For Exercises	See Examples
14–17	1
18–19	2
20–31	3–6
32–35	7

Exercise Levels
A: 16–35
B: 36–58
C: 59–63

Find the rate of change represented in each table or graph.

14. $\frac{1}{5}$

x	y
5	2
10	3
15	4
20	5

15. −6

x	y
1	15
2	9
3	3
4	−3

16. $\frac{3}{4}$

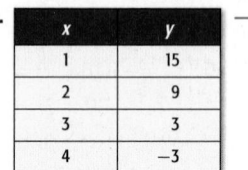

(2, −1)
(−2, −4)

17. $-\frac{1}{3}$

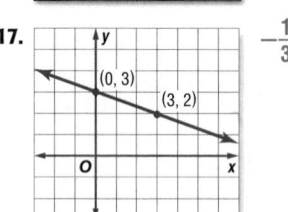

(0, 3)
(3, 2)

192 Chapter 4 Analyzing Linear Equations

DIFFERENTIATED HOMEWORK OPTIONS

Level	Assignment	Two-Day Option	
BL Basic	14–35, 60, 62–76	15–35 odd, 64, 65	14–34 even, 60, 62, 63, 66–76
OL Core	15–37 odd, 39–43, 45, 47–58, 60, 62–76	14–35, 64, 65	35–58, 60, 62, 63, 66–76
AL Advanced /Pre-AP	36–72, (optional: 73–76)		

18. 1812.5; There was an average increase of 1812.5 women per year competing in triathlons.

19. 12.75%; There was an average increase of 12.75% per year of teens who had cell phones.

24. undefined

★ **18. SPORTS** What was the annual rate of change from 1995 to 2003? Explain the meaning of the rate of change.

Women Competing in Triathlons	
Year	Number of Women
1995	4600
2003	19,100

★ **19. CELL PHONES** In 2000, 5% of 13- to 17-year-olds had cell phones. By 2004, 56% of teens had cell phones. Find the annual rate of change in the percent of teens with cell phones from 2000 to 2004. Describe what the rate of change means.

Find the slope of the line that passes through each pair of points.

20. $(2, 3), (9, 7)$ $\frac{4}{7}$
21. $(-3, 6), (2, 4)$ $-\frac{2}{5}$
22. $(2, 6), (-1, 3)$ 1
23. $(-3, 3), (1, 3)$ 0
24. $(-2, 1), (-2, 3)$
25. $(-3, 9), (-7, 6)$ $\frac{3}{4}$
26. $(5, 7), (-2, -3)$ $\frac{10}{7}$
27. $(2, -1), (5, -3)$ $-\frac{2}{3}$
28. $(-4, -1), (-3, -3)$ -2
29. $(-3, -4), (5, -1)$ $\frac{3}{8}$
30. $(-2, 3), (8, 3)$ 0
31. $(-5, 4), (-5, -1)$ undefined

Find the value of r so the line that passes through each pair of points has the given slope.

32. $(6, 2), (9, r), m = -1$ -1
33. $(r, -5), (3, 13), m = 8$ $\frac{3}{4}$
34. $(5, r), (2, -3), m = \frac{4}{3}$ 1
35. $(-2, 8), (r, 4), m = -\frac{1}{2}$ 6

Find the slope of the line that passes through each pair of points.

36.

x	y
4.5	−1
5.3	2

$\frac{15}{4}$

37.

x	y
0.75	1
0.75	−1

undefined

38.

x	y
$2\frac{1}{2}$	$-1\frac{1}{2}$
$-\frac{1}{2}$	$\frac{1}{2}$

$-\frac{2}{3}$

39. DRIVING When driving up a certain hill, you rise 15 feet for every 1000 feet you drive forward. What is the slope of the road? $\frac{3}{200}$

CONSTRUCTION Use a ruler to estimate the slope of each object.

40.
Sample answer: $-\frac{8}{11}$

41.
Sample answer: $\frac{1}{3}$

42. Find the slope of the line that passes through the origin and (r, s). $\frac{s}{r}$, if $r \neq 0$

43. What is the slope of the line that passes through (a, b) and $(a, -b)$? undefined

Find the value of r so the line that passes through each pair of points has the given slope.

44. $\left(\frac{1}{2}, -\frac{1}{4}\right), \left(r, -\frac{5}{4}\right), m = 4$ $\frac{1}{4}$
45. $\left(\frac{2}{3}, r\right), \left(1, \frac{1}{2}\right), m = \frac{1}{2}$ $\frac{1}{3}$
46. $(4, r), (r, 2), m = -\frac{5}{4}$ 12
47. $(r, 5), (-2, r), m = -\frac{2}{9}$ 7

Lesson 4-1 Rate of Change and Slope **193**

BL = Below Grade Level
OL = On Grade Level
AL = Above Grade Level
ELL = English Language Learner

Additional pages not shown:
CRM Lesson Reading Guide, p. 5 BL OL ELL
CRM Skills Practice, p. 8 BL OL

Exercise Alert!

Internet Exercise 58 requires the use of the Internet or other reference materials.

Additional Answers

48.

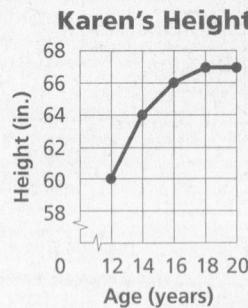

Karen's Height

55.

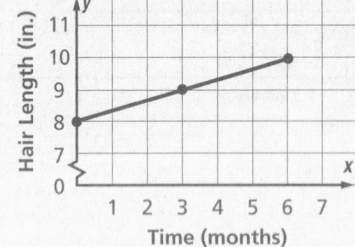

59. $(-4, -5)$ is in Quadrant III and $(4, 5)$ is in Quadrant I. The segment connecting them goes from lower left to upper right, which is a positive slope.

ANALYZE TABLES For Exercises 48–50, use the table that shows Karen's height at various ages.

Age (years)	12	14	16	18	20
Height (inches)	60	64	66	67	67

48. Make a broken-line graph of the data. **See margin.**

★ **49.** Use the graph to determine in which two-year period Karen grew the fastest. Explain your reasoning. **12–14; steepest part of the graph**

50. Discuss the rate of change associated with the horizontal section of the graph. **There was no change in height during those two years.**

ANALYZE GRAPHS For Exercises 51–53, use the graph that shows public school enrollment.

★ **51.** For which 5-year period was the rate of change the greatest? the least? **'90–'95; '80–'85**

52. Find the rate of change from 1985 to 1990. **−0.22**

53. Explain the meaning of the part of the graph with a negative slope. **a decline in enrollment**

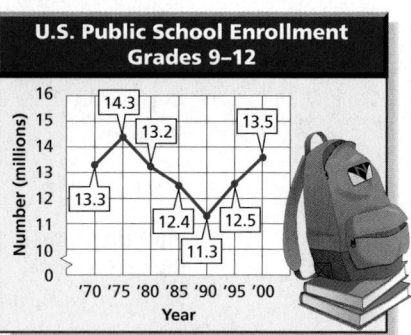

U.S. Public School Enrollment Grades 9–12

GROWTH RATE For Exercises 54–56, use the following information.
After her last haircut, May's hair was 8 inches long. In three months, it grew another inch. Assume that the hair growth continues at the same rate.

54. Make a table that shows May's hair length for each of the three months and for the next three months.

55. Draw a graph showing the relationship between May's hair length and time in months. **See margin.**

★ **56.** What is the slope of the graph? What does it represent?

54.

Time (months)	Hair Length (in.)
0	8
3	9
6	10

56. $\frac{1}{3}$; a rate of growth of 1 inch every 3 months or $\frac{1}{3}$ inch per month

EXTRA PRACTICE
See pages 724, 747.

Math Online
Self-Check Quiz at
ca.algebra1.com

H.O.T. Problems

57. CONSTRUCTION The slope of a stairway determines how easy it is to climb the stairs. Suppose the vertical distance between two floors is 8 feet 9 inches. Find the total run of the ideal stairway in feet and inches. (*Hint:* Do not include any part of the top or bottom floor in the run.) **12 ft 10 in.**

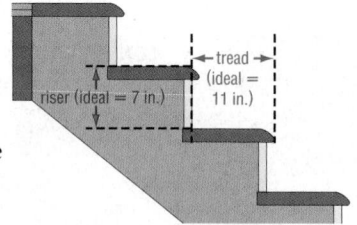

58. RESEARCH Use the Internet or another reference to find the population of your city or town in 1930, 1940, ..., 2000. Between which two decades was the rate of change the greatest? Explain. **See students' work.**

59. CHALLENGE Develop a strategy for determining whether the slope of the line through $(-4, -5)$ and $(4, 5)$ is positive or negative without calculating. **See margin.**

60. OPEN ENDED Integrate what you know about rate of change to describe the function at the right. **See students' work. The rate of change is $2\frac{1}{4}$ inches of growth per week.**

Time (wk)	Height of Plant (in.)
4	9.0
6	13.5
8	18.0

194 Chapter 4 Analyzing Linear Equations

61. No, they do not. Slope of $\overline{QR}$ is $\frac{4}{3}$ and slope of $\overline{RS}$ is $\frac{1}{3}$. If they lie on the same line, the slopes should be the same.

61. CHALLENGE Determine whether $Q(2, 3)$, $R(-1, -1)$, and $S(-4, -2)$ lie on the same line that passes through $(-2, -2)$ and $(4, 0)$. Explain your reasoning.

62. FIND THE ERROR Carlos and Allison are finding the slope of the line that passes through $(2, 6)$ and $(5, 3)$. Who is correct? Explain your reasoning. **See margin.**

Carlos
$$\frac{3-6}{5-2} = \frac{-3}{3} \text{ or } -1$$

Allison
$$\frac{6-3}{5-2} = \frac{3}{3} \text{ or } 1$$

63. *Writing in Math* Discuss how to find the slope of a roof and compare the appearance of roofs with different slopes. **See margin.**

STANDARDS PRACTICE 7AF1.1, 6NS1.3

64. A music store has x CDs in stock. If 350 are sold and $3y$ are added to stock, which expression represents the number of CDs in stock? **B**

A $350 + 3y - x$

B $x - 350 + 3y$

C $x + 350 + 3y$

D $3y - 350 - x$

65. REVIEW A recipe for fruit punch calls for 2 ounces of orange juice for every 8 ounces of lemonade. If Jennifer uses 64 ounces of lemonade, which proportion can she use to find x, the number of ounces of orange juice she should add to make the fruit punch? **H**

F $\frac{2}{x} = \frac{64}{6}$

G $\frac{8}{x} = \frac{64}{2}$

H $\frac{2}{8} = \frac{x}{64}$

J $\frac{6}{2} = \frac{x}{64}$

Spiral Review

Write an equation in function notation for each relation. (Lesson 3-5)

66.

Number of Lunches	1	2	3	4	5
Total Cost ($)	5	10	15	20	25

$f(x) = 5x$

67.

Time (s)	7	9	11	14	16
Altitude (ft)	4	2	0	-3	-5

$f(x) = 11 - x$

Find the next three terms of each arithmetic sequence. (Lesson 3-4)

68. $8, 20, 32, 44, \dots$ **56, 68, 80**

69. $-9, -6, -3, 0, \dots$ **3, 6, 9**

70. $35, 31, 27, 23, \dots$ **19, 15, 11**

71. $-56, -47, -38, -29, \dots$ **-20, -11, -2**

★ **72. FOOD** Garrett is making $\frac{1}{3}$-pound hamburgers. One pound of hamburger costs $3.19. How much will it cost to make 18 hamburgers? (Lesson 2-3) **$19.14**

GET READY for the Next Lesson

PREREQUISITE SKILL Find each quotient. (Pages 690–691)

73. $6 \div \frac{2}{3}$ **9**

74. $\frac{3}{4} \div \frac{1}{6}$ **$4\frac{1}{2}$**

75. $\frac{3}{4} \div 6$ **$\frac{1}{8}$**

76. $18 \div \frac{7}{8}$ **$20\frac{4}{7}$**

Pre-AP Activity Use after the Exercises

The road sign on a hill says 5% grade. The elevation of the road at that point is 1200 feet. Make a drawing of this situation. What would be the elevation of the road at an additional 2000 horizontal feet from the road sign? **1300 ft**

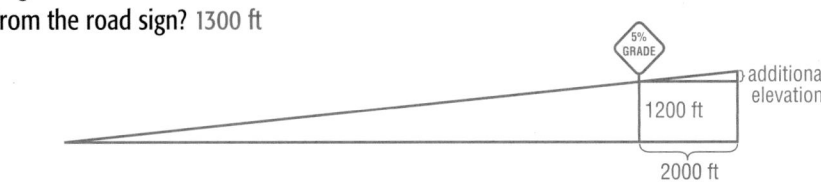

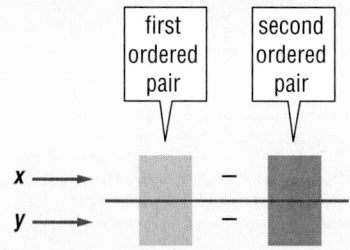

first ordered pair   second ordered pair

$x \longrightarrow$
$y \longrightarrow$

4 Assess

Ticket Out the Door Make several copies of five different lines graphed on a coordinate plane. Give one graph to each student. As the students leave the room, ask them to tell you the slopes of the lines they possess.

 **Foldables™**
Study Organizer **Follow-Up**
Remind students to use the first flap in their Foldables to record notes on what they have learned about analyzing linear equations.

Additional Answers

62. Carlos; Allison switched the order of the x-coordinates, resulting in an incorrect sign.

63. Sample answer: Analysis of the slope of a roof might help to determine the materials of which it should be made and its functionality. To find the slope of the roof, find a vertical line that passes through the peak of the roof and a horizontal line that passes through the eave. Find the distances from the intersection of those two lines to the peak and to the eave. Use those measures as the rise and run to calculate the slope. A roof that is steeper than one with a rise of 6 and a run of 12 would be one with a rise greater than 6 and the same run. A roof with a steeper slope appears taller than one with a less steep slope.

4-2 | # Slope and Direct Variation

1 Focus

Standards Alignment

Before Lesson 4-2
Identify and graph ordered pairs in the coordinate plane from
Standard 5AF1.4

Lesson 4-2
Solve multistep problems involving rate, speed, distance, and time from Standard 7AF4.2

After Lesson 4-2
Prove theorems by using coordinate geometry from Standard G17.0

2 Teach

Scaffolding Questions Have students read *Get Ready for the Lesson.*
Ask:
• What is the value of *y* if *x* = 5? $11.25
• What is the value of *x* if *y* = $18.00? 8
• What could you do to change the value of the slope in the total-cost-of-ring-tones equation? Increase or decrease the cost of a ring tone.

Direct Variation

Example 1 shows how the constant of variation for an equation is related to the slope of the line.

Main Ideas

• Write and graph direct variation equations.

• Solve problems involving direct variation.

 Reinforcement of Standard 7AF4.2 Solve multistep problems involving rate, average speed, distance, and time or a direct variation. (Key, CAHSEE)

New Vocabulary

direct variation
constant of variation
family of graphs
parent graph

Study Tip

Constant of Variation
Compare the constants of variation with the slopes of the graphs. What is the slope of the graph of $y = kx$?

It costs $2.25 per ringtone that you download for your cell phone. If you graph the ordered pairs, the slope of the line is 2.25.

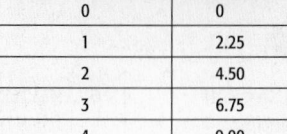

Number of Ringtones	Total Cost ($)
x	*y*
0	0
1	2.25
2	4.50
3	6.75
4	9.00

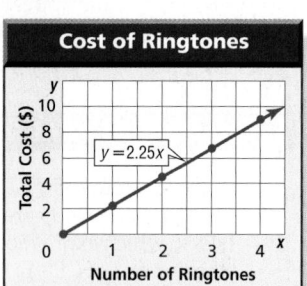

Cost of Ringtones

The total cost *y* depends *directly* on the number of ringtones that you download *x*. The rate of change is constant.

Direct Variation A **direct variation** is described by an equation of the form $y = kx$, where $k \neq 0$. The equation $y = kx$ represents a constant rate of change and k is the **constant of variation.**

EXAMPLE Slope and Constant of Variation

① Name the constant of variation for each equation. Then find the slope of the line that passes through each pair of points.

a.
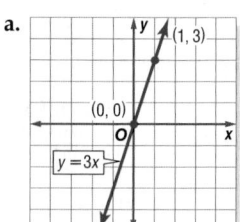

b.
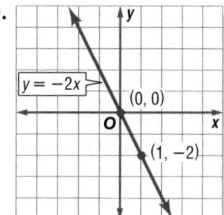

The constant of variation is 3.

$m = \dfrac{y_2 - y_1}{x_2 - x_1}$ Slope formula

$= \dfrac{3 - 0}{1 - 0}$ $(x_1, y_1) = (0, 0)$
          $(x_2, y_2) = (1, 3)$

$= 3$ The slope is 3.

The constant of variation is −2.

$m = \dfrac{y_2 - y_1}{x_2 - x_1}$ Slope formula

$= \dfrac{-2 - 0}{1 - 0}$ $(x_1, y_1) = (0, 0)$
          $(x_2, y_2) = (1, -2)$

$= -2$ The slope is −2.

✓ **CHECK Your Progress**

1. Name the constant of variation for $y = \frac{1}{4}x$. Then find the slope of the line that passes through (0, 0) and (4, 1). $\frac{1}{4}$; $\frac{1}{4}$

Lesson 4-2 Resources

Chapter 4 Resource Masters
Lesson Reading Guide, p. 12 **BL** **OL** **ELL**
Study Guide and Intervention, pp. 13–14
BL **OL** **ELL**
Skills Practice, p. 15 **BL** **OL**
Practice, p. 16 **OL** **AL**
Word Problem Practice, p. 17 **OL** **AL**
Enrichment, p. 18 **OL** **AL**
Quiz 1, p. 59

Transparencies
5-Minute Check Transparency 4-2

Additional Print Resources
Noteables™ Interactive Study Notebook with Foldables™
Science and Mathematics Lab Manual, pp. 145–148

Technology
ca.algebra1.com
Interactive Classroom CD-ROM
AssignmentWorks CD-ROM
Graphing Calculator Easy Files

Since $(0, 0)$ is a solution of $y = kx$, the graph of $y = kx$ always passes through the origin.

EXAMPLE Graph a Direct Variation

2 Graph each equation.

a. $y = 4x$

Step 1 Write the slope as a ratio.

$$4 = \frac{4}{1} \quad \frac{\text{rise}}{\text{run}}$$

Step 2 Graph $(0, 0)$.

Step 3 From the point $(0, 0)$, move up 4 units and right 1 unit. Draw a dot.

Step 4 Draw a line containing the points.

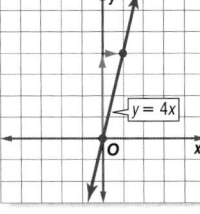

b. $y = -\frac{1}{3}x$

Step 1 Write the slope as a ratio.

$$-\frac{1}{3} = \frac{-1}{3} \quad \frac{\text{rise}}{\text{run}}$$

Step 2 Graph $(0, 0)$.

Step 3 From the point $(0, 0)$, move down 1 unit and right 3 units. Draw a dot.

Step 4 Draw a line containing the points.

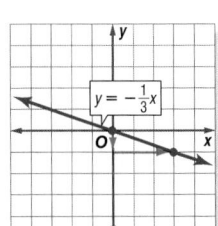

2. Sample answer: $y = 5x$; See students' graphs.

4. The graphs have a y-intercept of 0. The slopes are all positive, but they are all different.

✓**CHECK Your Progress** Graph each equation. 2A–2D. See margin.

2A. $y = 6x$ **2B.** $y = \frac{2}{3}x$ **2C.** $y = -5x$ **2D.** $y = -\frac{3}{4}x$

A **family of graphs** includes graphs and equations of graphs that have at least one characteristic in common. The **parent graph** is the simplest graph in a family.

ALGEBRA LAB

Graphs of $y = mx$

Graph $y = x$, $y = 2x$, and $y = 4x$ on the same piece of graph paper.

THINK AND DISCUSS

1. All the graphs pass through the origin. None of the graphs have the same slope.

1. Describe any similarities and differences among the graphs.

2. Write an equation with a graph that has a steeper slope than $y = 4x$. Check your answer by graphing $y = 4x$ and your equation.

3. Write an equation with a graph that lies between the graphs of $y = x$ and $y = 2x$. Check your answer by graphing the equations.

4. What characteristics do the graphs have in common? How are they different?

5. These equations are all of the form $y = mx$. How does the graph change as the absolute value of m increases? As $|m|$ increases, the graph becomes steeper.

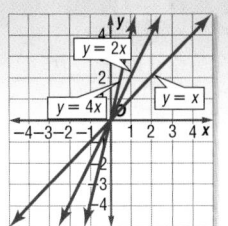

3. Sample answer: $y = \frac{3}{2}x$

ADDITIONAL EXAMPLE

1 Name the constant of variation for each equation. Find the slope of the line that passes through each pair of points.

a.

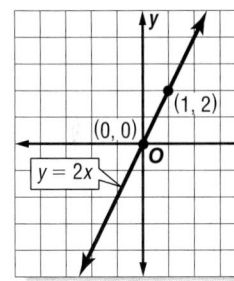

constant of variation: 2; slope: 2

b.

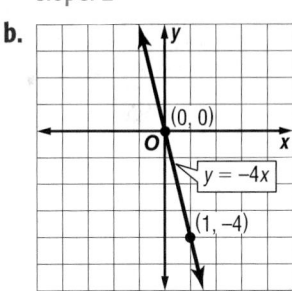

constant of variation: -4; slope: -4

Additional Answers

2A.

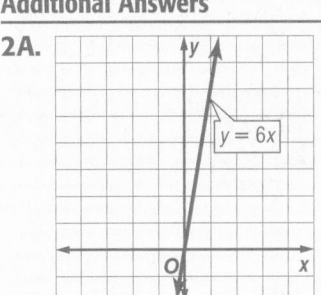

2B.

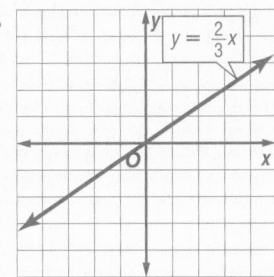

2C.

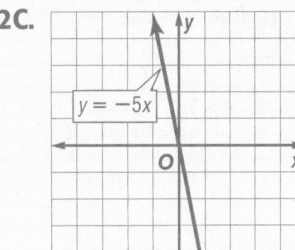

2D.

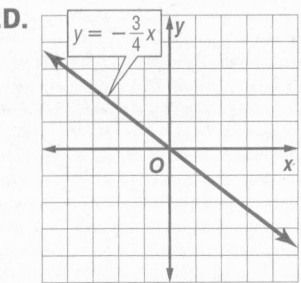

Algebra Lab

Students will need graph paper and a straightedge for this lab. Graphing the lines on the same plane allows students to analyze the slopes of each equation.

The results of the Graphing Calculator Lab lead to some general observations about the graphs of direct variation equations.

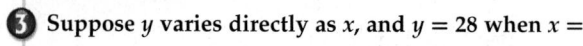

CONCEPT SUMMARY   *Direct Variation Graphs*

- Direct variation equations are of the form $y = kx$, where $k \neq 0$.
- The graph of $y = kx$ always passes through the origin.
- The slope is positive if $k > 0$.   • The slope is negative if $k < 0$.

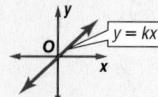   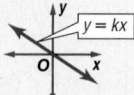

If you know that y varies directly as x, you can write a direct variation equation that relates the two quantities.

EXAMPLE Write and Solve a Direct Variation Equation

3 Suppose y varies directly as x, and $y = 28$ when $x = 7$.

  a. **Write a direct variation equation that relates x and y.**

   Find the value of k.

   $y = kx$ Direct variation formula

   $28 = k(7)$ Replace y with 28 and x with 7.

   $\dfrac{28}{7} = \dfrac{k(7)}{7}$ Divide each side by 7.

   $4 = k$ Simplify.

   Therefore, the direct variation equation is $y = 4x$.

  b. **Use the direct variation equation to find x when $y = 52$.**

   $y = 4x$ Direct variation equation

   $52 = 4x$ Replace y with 52.

   $\dfrac{52}{4} = \dfrac{4x}{4}$ Divide each side by 4.

   $13 = x$ Simplify.

   Therefore, $x = 13$ when $y = 52$.

CHECK Your Progress

Suppose y varies directly as x, and $y = 6$ when $x = -18$.

3A. Write a direct variation equation that relates x and y. $y = -\dfrac{1}{3}x$

3B. Find y when $x = -2$. $\dfrac{2}{3}$

Solve Problems One of the most common applications of direct variation is the formula $d = rt$. Distance d varies directly as time t, and the rate r is the constant of variation.

 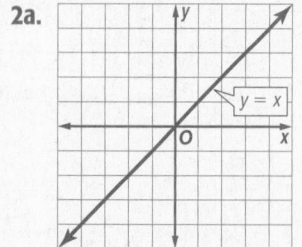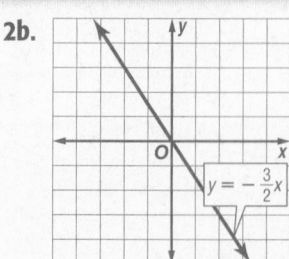

④ **BIOLOGY** The migration of snow geese varies directly as the number of hours. A flock of snow geese migrated 375 miles in 7.5 hours.

a. Write a direct variation equation for the distance d flown in time t.

Words	Distance	equals	rate	times	time.
▼					
Variable	Let r = rate.				
▼					
Equation	375 mi	=	r	×	7.5 h

Solve for the rate.

$$375 = r(7.5) \quad \text{Original equation}$$

$$\frac{375}{7.5} = \frac{r(7.5)}{7.5} \quad \text{Divide each side by 7.5.}$$

$$50 = r \quad \text{Simplify.}$$

Therefore, the direct variation equation is $d = 50t$. What does the 50 represent? **rate of change; slope; 50 mi/h; speed**

b. Graph the equation.

The graph of $d = 50t$ passes through the origin with slope 50.

$$m = \frac{50}{1} \quad \frac{\text{rise}}{\text{run}}$$

Migration of Snow Geese

c. Estimate how many hours of flying time it would take the geese to migrate 3000 miles.

$$d = 50t \quad \text{Original equation}$$

$$3000 = 50t \quad \text{Replace } d \text{ with 3000.}$$

$$\frac{3000}{50} = \frac{50t}{50} \quad \text{Divide each side by 50.}$$

$$t = 60 \quad \text{Simplify.}$$

At this rate, it would take 60 hours of flying time to migrate 3000 miles.

✓CHECK Your Progress

HOT AIR BALLOONS A hot air balloon's ascent varies directly as the number of minutes. A hot air balloon ascended 350 feet in 5 minutes.

4A. Write a direct variation for the distance d ascended in time t. $d = 70t$

4B. Graph the equation. **See margin.**

4C. Estimate how many minutes it would take the hot air balloon to ascend 2100 feet. **30 min**

🌐 **Personal Tutor at** ca.algebra1.com

Solve Problems

Example 4 shows how to use a direct variation equation to solve a real-world problem.

ADDITIONAL EXAMPLE

④ **TRAVEL** The Ramirez family is driving cross-country on vacation. They drive 330 miles in 5.5 hours.

a. Write a direct variation equation to find the distance driven for any number of hours. $d = 60t$

b. Graph the equation.

Travel Time

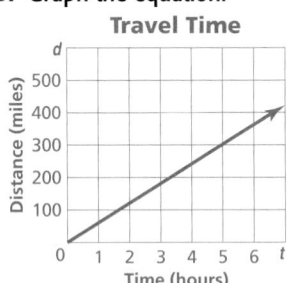

c. Estimate how many hours it would take to drive 600 miles. **10 h**

Tips for New Teachers

Preventing Errors

Be sure students do not interchange the values of x and y when substituting them into an equation.

Additional Answer

4B.

Hot Air Balloon Ascent

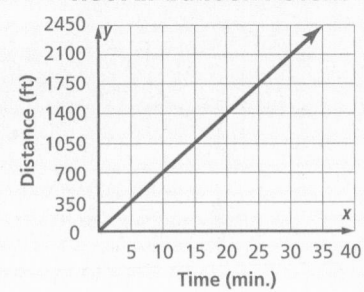

Pre-AP Activity Use as an Extension

Write $y = kx^2$ on the board. Tell students that y varies directly as the *square* of x, and $y = 48$ when $x = 4$. Ask students to find y when $x = 10$. Since $k = 3$, $y = 300$.

3 Practice

✓ Formative Assessment

Use Exercises 1–11 to check for understanding.

Use the chart at the bottom of this page to customize your assignments for students.

Odd/Even Assignments
Exercises 12–31 are structured so that students practice the same concepts whether they are assigned odd or even problems.

Real-World Connections
For Exercises 30 and 31, tell students an object's weight is a measure of the pull of gravity between the object and the body on which it stands. Have students talk about the different types of units used to measure an object's weight.

Additional Answers

10.

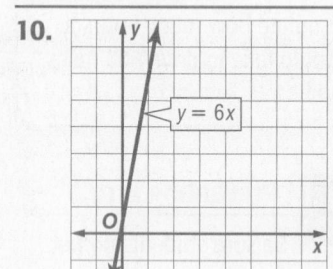

30.
Golf Ball Distance at High Altitudes

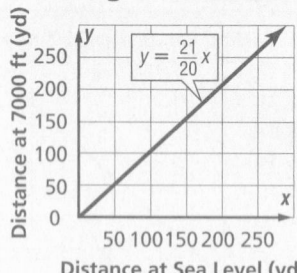

✓ CHECK Your Understanding

Example 1 (p. 196)
Name the constant of variation for each equation. Then find the slope of the line that passes through each pair of points.

1.
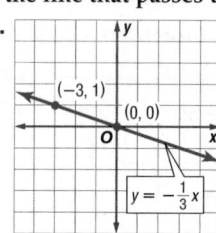
$-\frac{1}{3}$; $-\frac{1}{3}$

2.
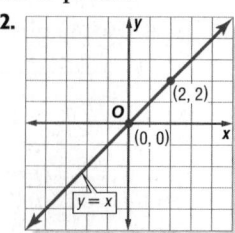
1; 1

Example 2 (p. 197)
Graph each equation. 3–6. See Ch. 4 Answer Appendix.

3. $y = 2x$
4. $y = \frac{1}{2}x$
5. $y = -3x$
6. $y = -\frac{5}{3}x$

Example 3 (p. 198)
Suppose y varies directly as x. Write a direct variation equation that relates x and y. Then solve.

7. If $y = 27$ when $x = 6$, find x when $y = 45$. $y = \frac{9}{2}x$; 10
8. If $y = -7$ when $x = 14$, find y when $x = -16$. $y = -\frac{1}{2}x$; 8

Example 4 (pp. 198–199)
JOBS For Exercises 9–11, use the following information.
Suppose your pay varies directly as the number of hours you work. Your pay for 7.5 hours is $45.

$y = 6x$

9. Write a direct variation equation relating your pay to the hours worked.
10. Graph the equation. **See margin.**
11. Find your pay if you work 30 hours. **$180**

Exercises
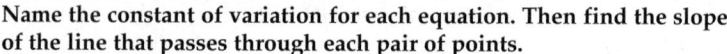

HOMEWORK HELP	
For Exercises	**See Examples**
12–17	1
18–25	2
26–29	3
30, 31	4

Exercise Levels
A: 12–31
B: 32–49
C: 50–53

12. 2; 2
13. 4; 4
14. $-\frac{1}{2}$; $-\frac{1}{2}$
15. -1; -1
16. $\frac{3}{2}$; $\frac{3}{2}$
17. $-\frac{1}{4}$; $-\frac{1}{4}$

Name the constant of variation for each equation. Then find the slope of the line that passes through each pair of points.

12.
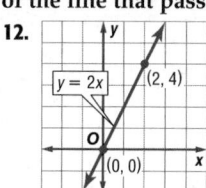

13.
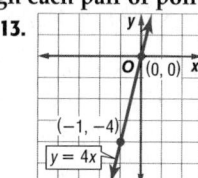

14.
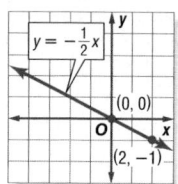

15.

16.

17.

Graph each equation. 18–25. See Ch. 4 Answer Appendix.

18. $y = 3x$
19. $y = -x$
20. $y = -4x$
21. $y = \frac{5}{2}x$
22. $y = \frac{1}{5}x$
23. $y = -\frac{2}{3}x$
24. $y = -\frac{4}{3}x$
25. $y = -\frac{9}{2}x$

200 Chapter 4 Analyzing Linear Equations

DIFFERENTIATED HOMEWORK OPTIONS

Level	Assignment	Two-Day Option	
BL Basic	12–31, 50, 51, 53–62	13–31 odd, 54, 55	12–30 even, 50, 51, 53, 56–62
OL Core	13–31 odd, 32, 33, 35–45 odd, 46–51, 53–62	12–31, 54, 55	32–51, 53, 56–62
AL Advanced /Pre-AP	32–59, (optional: 60–62)		

Suppose y varies directly as x. Write a direct variation equation that relates x and y. Then solve.

★ **26.** If $y = 8$ when $x = 4$, find y when $x = 5$. $y = 2x$; 10

★ **27.** If $y = -16$ when $x = 4$, find x when $y = 20$. $y = -4x$; -5

★ **28.** If $y = 4$ when $x = 12$, find y when $x = -24$. $y = \frac{1}{3}x$; -8

★ **29.** If $y = 12$ when $x = 15$, find x when $y = 21$. $y = \frac{4}{5}x$; 26.25

SPORTS For Exercises 30 and 31, use the following information.

The distance a golf ball travels at an altitude of 7000 feet varies directly with the distance the ball travels at sea level, as shown in the table.

Hitting a Golf Ball		
Altitude (ft)	0 (sea level)	7000
Distance (yd)	200	210

★ **30.** Write and graph an equation that relates the distance a golf ball travels at an altitude of 7000 feet y with the distance at sea level x. **See margin.**

31. What would be a person's average driving distance at 7000 feet if his average driving distance at sea level is 180 yards? **189 yd**

ANALYZE TABLES For Exercises 32 and 33, use the following information.

Most animals age more rapidly than humans do. The chart shows equivalent ages for horses and humans.

Horse age (x)	0	1	2	3	4	5
Human age (y)	0	3	6	9	12	15

32. Write an equation that relates human age to horse age. $y = 3x$

33. Find the equivalent horse age for a human who is 16 years old. **5 yr 4 mo**

Suppose y varies directly as x. Write a direct variation equation that relates x and y. Then solve.

34. If $y = 2.5$ when $x = 0.5$, find y when $x = 20$. $y = 5x$; 100

35. If $y = -6.6$ when $x = 9.9$, find y when $x = 6.6$. $y = -\frac{2}{3}x$; -4.4

36. If $y = 2\frac{2}{3}$ when $x = \frac{1}{4}$, find y when $x = 1\frac{1}{8}$. $y = \frac{32}{3}x$; 12

37. If $y = 6$ when $x = \frac{2}{3}$, find x when $y = 12$. $y = 9x$; $\frac{4}{3}$

ANALYZE GRAPHS Which line in the graph represents the sprinting speed of each animal?

38. elephant, 25 mph **4**

39. reindeer, 32 mph **2**

40. lion, 50 mph **1**

41. grizzly bear, 30 mph **3**

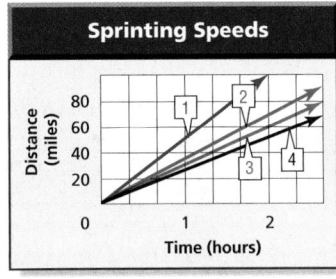

Sprinting Speeds

Write a direct variation equation that relates the variables. Then graph the equation. 42–45. See Ch. 4 Answer Appendix for graphs.

42. GEOMETRY The circumference C of a circle is about 3.14 times the diameter d.

43. GEOMETRY The perimeter P of a square is 4 times the length of a side s.

44. RETAIL The total cost is C for n yards of ribbon priced at $0.99 per yard.

45. RETAIL Kona coffee beans are $14.49 per pound. The cost of p pounds is C.

42. $C = 3.14d$
43. $P = 4s$
44. $C = 0.99n$
45. $C = 14.49p$

Lesson 4-2 Slope and Direct Variation **201**

Real-World Career

Veterinarian

A veterinarian uses math to compare the age of an animal to the age of a human on the basis of bone and tooth growth and to determine the amount of medicine to prescribe based on the weight of the animal.

Math Online

For more information, go to ca.algebra1.com.

Additional pages not shown:

CRM **Lesson Reading Guide**, p. 12 **BL** **OL** **ELL**

CRM **Skills Practice**, p. 15 **BL** **OL**

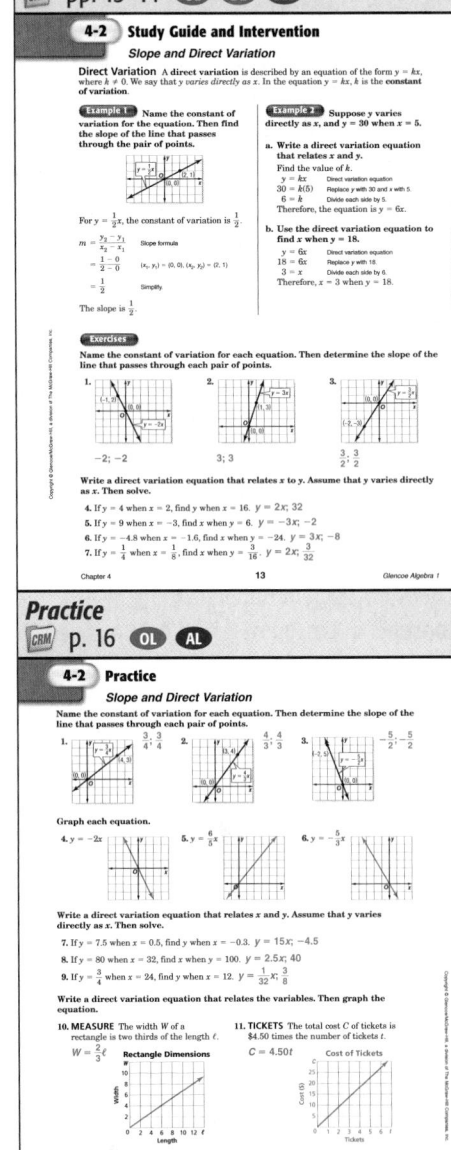

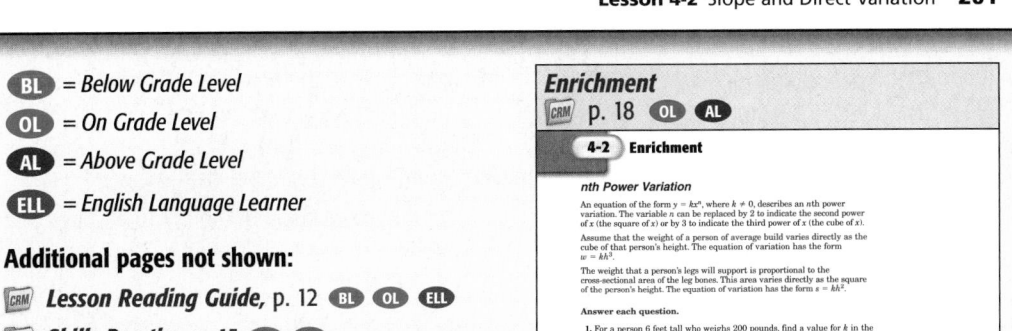

Graphing Calculator Students will need a graphing calculator to answer Exercises 46 through 49.

 Assess

Crystal Ball Tell students that the next lesson they will study is about writing a linear equation in slope-intercept form. Ask them to write how they think today's lesson on the equation for direct variation will connect with the next lesson they study.

 Formative Assessment

Check for student understanding of concepts in Lessons 4-1 and 4-2.

CRM Quiz 1, p. 59

Additional Answers

46.

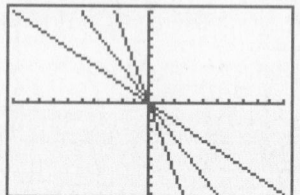

49. Sample answer: Find the absolute value of k in each equation. The one with the greatest value of $|k|$ has the steeper slope.

50. $z = \frac{1}{9}x$; It is the only equation that is a direct variation.

51. Sample answer: $y = 0.50x$ represents the cost of x apples.

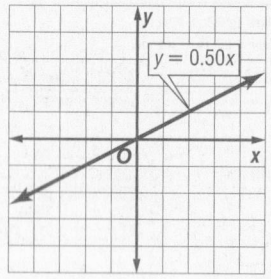

The rate of change, 0.50, is the cost per apple.

GRAPHING CALCULATOR Consider the graphs of $y = -1x$, $y = -2x$, and $y = -4x$.

46. Graph these three equations on the same screen. **See margin.**

EXTRA PRACTICE
See pages 725, 747.
Math Online
Self-Check Quiz at
ca.algebra1.com

47. Describe the similarities and differences between these graphs and the graphs in the Graphing Calculator Lab on page 195.

48. Write an equation whose graph is steeper than the graph of $y = -4x$.

49. Make a conjecture about how you can determine without graphing which of two direct variation equations has the graph with a steeper slope.
See margin.

H.O.T. Problems

47. Sample answer: They all pass through (0, 0), but these have negative slopes.

48. Sample answer: $y = -5x$

50–53. See margin.

50. Which One Doesn't Belong? Identify the equation that does not belong with the other three. Explain your reasoning.

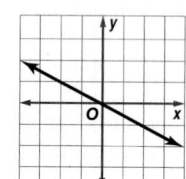

51. OPEN ENDED Model a real-world situation using a direct variation equation. Graph the equation and describe the rate of change.

52. CHALLENGE Suppose y varies directly as x. If the value of x is doubled, what can you conclude about the value of y? Explain your reasoning.

53. *Writing in Math* Write an equation that relates the total cost y to the number of ringtones x for ringtones that cost $1.50 each. Compare the steepness of the graph of this equation to the graph at the top of page 196.

STANDARDS PRACTICE 6.0, 7NS1.7

54. Which equation *best* represents the graph?

A $y = 2x$

B $y = -2x$

C $y = \frac{1}{2}x$

D $y = -\frac{1}{2}x$

D

55. REVIEW Roberto receives an employee discount of 12%. If he spent $355 at the store, how much was his discount to the nearest dollar? **J**

F $3 **H** $30

G $4 **J** $43

Spiral Review

56. Find the value of r so that the line that passes through $(1, 7)$ and $(r, 3)$ has a slope of 2. (Lesson 4-1) **−1**

Write an equation in function notation for the relation shown in each table. (Lesson 3-5)

57.

x	0	1	2	3	4	5
y	1	5	9	13	17	21

$f(x) = 4x + 1$

58.

x	2	4	6	8	10	12
y	8	6	4	2	0	−2

$f(x) = -x + 10$

59. BASKETBALL A school purchased five new basketballs for $149.95. At that rate, how much more money will it cost the school to have 12 new basketballs in all? (Lesson 2-6) **$209.93**

GET READY for the Next Lesson

PREREQUISITE SKILL Solve each equation for y. (Lesson 2-8)

60. $4x = y + 3$ $y = 4x - 3$

61. $2y = 4x + 10$ $y = 2x + 5$

62. $9x + 3y = 12$ $y = -3x + 4$

---

52. It also doubles. If $\frac{y}{x} = k$, and x is multiplied by 2, y must also be multiplied by 2 to maintain the value of k.

53. The slope of the equation that relates number of ringtones and total cost is the cost of each ringtone; $y = 1.5x$; The graph of this equation is less steep; the slope is less than the slope of the graph on page 196.

Graphing Calculator Lab
Investigating Slope-Intercept Form

Reinforcement of Standard 7AF1.5 Represent quantitative relationships graphically and interpret the meaning of a specific part of a graph in the situation represented by the graph. (CAHSEE)

▶ SET UP the Lab

• Cut a small hole in a top corner of a plastic sandwich bag. Hang the bag from the end of the force sensor.

• Connect the force sensor to your data collection device.

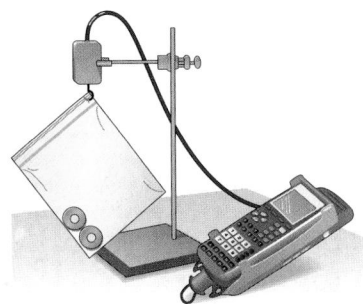

ACTIVITY

Step 1 Use the sensor to collect the weight with 0 washers in the bag. Record the data pair in the calculator.

Step 2 Place one washer in the plastic bag. Wait for the bag to stop swinging, then measure and record the weight.

Step 3 Repeat the experiment, adding different numbers of washers to the bag. Each time, record the data.

ANALYZE THE RESULTS

1. The domain contains values represented by the independent variable, washers. The range contains values represented by the dependent variable, weight. Use the graphing calculator to create a scatterplot using the ordered pairs (washers, weight). **See students' work.**

2. Write a sentence that describes the points on the graph.

3. Describe the position of the point on the graph that represents the trial with no washers in the bag. **It is the *y*-intercept.**

4. The rate of change can be found by using the formula for slope.

$$\frac{\text{rise}}{\text{run}} = \frac{\text{change in weight}}{\text{change in number of washers}}$$

See students' work.
Sample answer: 0.025

Find the rate of change in the weight as more washers are added.

5. Explain how the rate of change is shown on the graph.

2. Sample answer: It is a linear pattern.

5. The slope represents the rate of change.

6. Sample answer: The graph is the same as the one shown, shifted upward so that the *y*-intercept is at (0, 0.8).

7. Sample answer: The graph has the same *y*-intercept, but the rate of change is greater.

8. Sample answer: The graph has the same *y*-intercept, but the rate of change is less.

The graph shows sample data from a washer experiment. Describe the graph for each situation.

6. A bag that hangs weighs 0.8 N when empty and increases in weight at the rate of the sample.

7. A bag that has the same weight when empty as the sample and increases in weight at a faster rate.

[0, 20] scl: 2 by [0, 1] scl: 0.25

8. A bag that has the same weight when empty as the sample and increases in weight at a slower rate.

Explore 4-3 Graphing Calculator Lab: Investigating Slope-Intercept Form **203**

---

1 Focus

Objective Use a graphing calculator to create a scatter plot and describe rate of change for an experiment with washers.

Materials
• graphing calculator
• data collection device and force sensor
• plastic sandwich bag
• washers

Teaching Tip
Point out to students the features of the data collection device and show them how to weigh the washers. Urge students to record their data carefully. One careless recording will prevent students from seeing a pattern.

2 Teach

Working in Cooperative Groups
Have students work in groups of 2 or 3, mixing abilities. Have groups complete the Activity and Analyze the Results 1–5. In Step 1 suggest that students enter the number of washers in L1 and the corresponding weights in L2. In Analyze the Results 3, point out that the weight with no washers is the weight of the bag.

Practice Have students complete Analyze the Results 6–8.

3 Assess

✓ Formative Assessment

Use Exercise 4 to assess whether students can calculate the rate of change correctly. Use Exercise 7 to assess whether students understand that the rate of change is the slope of the line connecting the points.

From Concrete to Abstract
• Ask students what they think the graph would look like if a bag had the same weight when empty as the sample and increased in weight at a slower and slower rate. Sample answer: the same *y*-intercept but the rate of change would be less and less.

• Ask what the graph would look like if the slope were close to 0. Sample answer: a linear pattern that is close to horizontal.

Graphing Equations in Slope-Intercept Form

1 Focus

Standards Alignment

Before Lesson 4-3
Graph linear functions and recognize the slope of a graph
Standard 7AF3.3

Lesson 4-3
Graph a linear equation or inequality from Standard 6.0

After Lesson 4-3
Solve systems of linear equations and inequalities from Standard 2A2.0

2 Teach

Scaffolding Questions Have students read *Get Ready for the Lesson.*
Ask:
• Does the line have a positive slope or a negative slope? positive
• What do *x* and *y* represent in the equation $y = 0.99x + 3$? *x* is number of books; *y* is total cost.
• **BANKING** A checking plan offered by a bank includes a $10 monthly service fee and $0.20 per check for accounts with an average daily balance of less than $2000. What equation describes this plan?
$P = 0.20c + 10$

Main Ideas
• Write and graph linear equations in slope-intercept form.
• Model real-world data with an equation in slope-intercept form.

Standard 6.0 Students graph a linear equation and compute the *x*- and *y*-intercepts (e.g., graph $2x + 6y = 4$). They are also able to sketch the region defined by linear inequality (e.g., they sketch the region defined by $2x + 6y < 4$). (Key, CAHSEE)

New Vocabulary
slope-intercept form

COncepts in MOtion
BrainPOP®
ca.algebra1.com

GET READY for the Lesson

An online store charges $3 per order plus $0.99 per book for shipping.

Number of Books	Shipping Cost
1	3.99
2	4.98
3	5.97
4	6.96
5	7.95
6	8.94
7	9.93

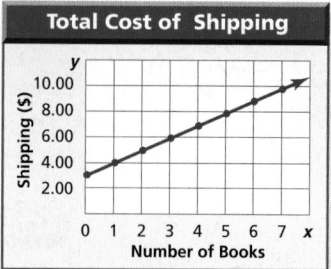
Total Cost of Shipping

The slope of the line is 0.99. It crosses the *y*-axis at (0, 3).
The equation of the line is $y = 0.99x + 3$.
charge per book, $0.99   flat fee, $3.00

Slope-Intercept Form An equation of the form $y = mx + b$, where *m* is the slope and *b* is the *y*-intercept, is in **slope-intercept form**.

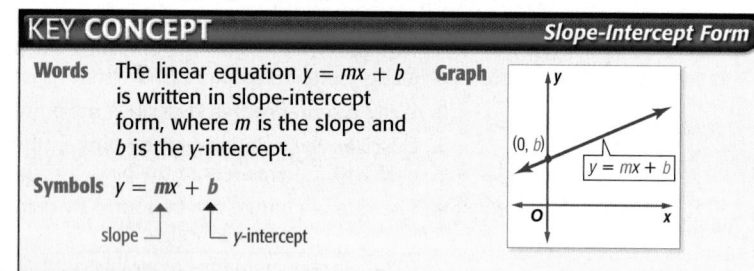

KEY CONCEPT *Slope-Intercept Form*

Words The linear equation $y = mx + b$ is written in slope-intercept form, where *m* is the slope and *b* is the *y*-intercept.

Symbols $y = mx + b$
slope   *y*-intercept

Graph
(0, *b*) $y = mx + b$

EXAMPLE Write an Equation Given Slope and *y*-Intercept

1 Write an equation in slope-intercept form of the line with a slope of 3 and a *y*-intercept of −5.

$y = mx + b$ Slope-intercept form
$y = 3x + (-5)$ Replace *m* with 3 and *b* with −5.
$y = 3x - 5$ Rewrite.

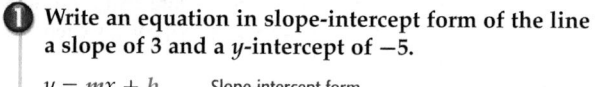
CHECK Your Progress
1. Write an equation of the line with a slope of $-\frac{1}{2}$ and a *y*-intercept of 3. $y = -\frac{1}{2}x + 3$

204 Chapter 4 Analyzing Linear Equations

Lesson 4-3 Resources

Chapter 4 Resource Masters
Lesson Reading Guide, p. 19 **BL** **OL** **ELL**
Study Guide and Intervention, pp. 20–21
BL **OL** **ELL**
Skills Practice, p. 22 **BL** **OL**
Practice, p. 23 **OL** **AL**
Word Problem Practice, p. 24 **OL** **AL**
Enrichment, p. 25 **OL** **AL**

Transparencies
5-Minute Check Transparency 4-3
Additional Print Resources
Noteables™ Interactive Study Notebook with Foldables™
Teaching Algebra with Manipulatives

Technology
ca.algebra1.com
Interactive Classroom CD-ROM
AssignmentWorks CD-ROM
Graphing Calculator Easy Files

EXAMPLE Write an Equation From a Graph

2 Write an equation in slope-intercept form of the line shown in the graph.

Step 1 Find the slope using two points on the line. Let $(x_1, y_1) = (0, 3)$ and $(x_2, y_2) = (2, -1)$.

$$m = \frac{y_2 - y_1}{x_2 - x_1} \qquad \frac{\text{rise}}{\text{run}}$$

$$= \frac{-1 - 3}{2 - 0} \qquad \begin{matrix} x_1 = 0, x_2 = 2 \\ y_1 = 3, y_2 = -1 \end{matrix}$$

$$= \frac{-4}{2} \text{ or } -2 \qquad \text{Simplify.}$$

The slope is -2.

Step 2 The line crosses the y-axis at $(0, 3)$. So, the y-intercept is 3.

Step 3 Finally, write the equation.

$$y = mx + b \qquad \text{Slope-intercept form}$$

$$y = -2x + 3 \qquad \text{Replace } m \text{ with } -2 \text{ and } b \text{ with } 3.$$

The equation of the line is $y = -2x + 3$.

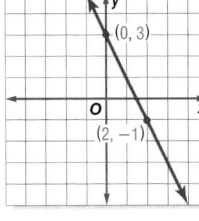

CHECK Your Progress

2. Write an equation in slope-intercept form of the line shown at the right. $y = \frac{1}{4}x - 1$

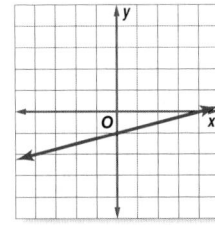

nline **Personal Tutor at** ca.algebra1.com

EXAMPLE Graph Equations

3 Graph each equation.

a. $y = -\frac{2}{3}x + 1$

Step 1 The y-intercept is 1. So, graph $(0, 1)$.

Step 2 The slope is $-\frac{2}{3}$ or $\frac{-2}{3}$. $\frac{\text{rise}}{\text{run}}$

From $(0, 1)$, move down 2 units and right 3 units. Draw a dot.

Step 3 Draw a line through the points.

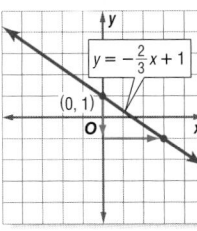

b. $5x - 3y = 6$

Step 1 Solve for y to write the equation in slope-intercept form.

$$5x - 3y = 6 \qquad \text{Original equation}$$

$$5x - 3y - 5x = 6 - 5x \qquad \text{Subtract } 5x \text{ from each side.}$$

$$-3y = 6 - 5x \qquad \text{Simplify.}$$

$$-3y = -5x + 6 \qquad 6 - 5x = 6 + (-5x) \text{ or } -5x + 6$$

$$\frac{-3y}{-3} = \frac{-5x + 6}{-3} \qquad \text{Divide each side by } -3.$$

$$\frac{-3y}{-3} = \frac{-5x}{-3} + \frac{6}{-3} \qquad \text{Divide each term in the numerator by } -3.$$

$$y = \frac{5}{3}x - 2 \qquad \text{Simplify.}$$

(continued on the next page)

 Math nline **Extra Examples at** ca.algebra1.com

Lesson 4-3 Graphing Equations in Slope-Intercept Form **205**

Study Tip

Vertical Lines
The equation of a vertical line *cannot* be written in slope-intercept form. *Why?*

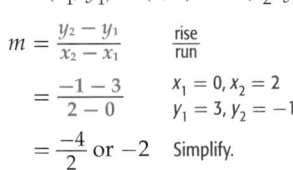

Horizontal Lines
The equation of a horizontal line *can* be written in slope-intercept form as $y = 0x + b$ or $y = b$.

Slope-Intercept Form

Example 1 shows how to write a linear equation given the slope and y-intercept. **Example 2** shows how to write a linear equation given its graph. **Example 3** shows how to graph a linear equation given in slope-intercept form.

✓ Formative Assessment

Use the Check Your Progress exercises after each example to determine students' understanding of concepts.

ADDITIONAL EXAMPLES

1 Write an equation in slope-intercept form of the line with a slope of $\frac{1}{4}$ and a y-intercept of -6. $y = \frac{1}{4}x - 6$

2 Write an equation in slope-intercept form of the line shown in the graph.

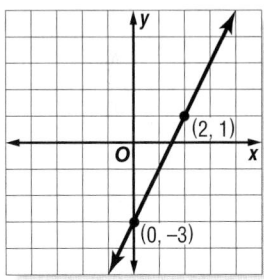

$y = 2x - 3$

3 Graph each equation.

a. $y = 0.5x - 7$

b. $5x + 4y = 8$

See bottom margin for graphs.

Additional Examples are also in:

• Noteables™ Interactive Study Notebook with Foldables™

• Interactive Classroom PowerPoint® Presentations

Answers for Additional Examples

3a.

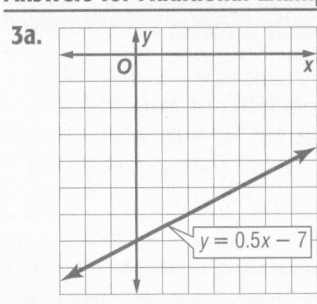

3b.

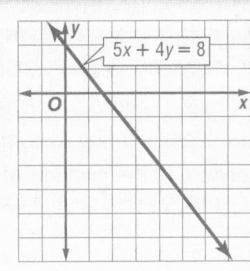

 **Preventing Errors**

Remind students that b can be negative, so equations may not always have positive constants.

Lesson 4-3 Graphing Equations in Slope-Intercept From **205**

Slope-Intercept Form The slope-intercept form of a linear equation is $y = mx + b$. The b in this form represents the y-intercept of the graph, the point where the line crosses the y-axis. The m represents the slope of the line.

Model Real-World Data

Example 4 shows how to model real-world data with an equation in slope-intercept form and then use that equation to solve a problem.

4 **HEALTH** The ideal maximum heart rate for a 25-year-old exercising to burn fat is 117 beats per minute. For every 5 years older than 25, that ideal rate drops 3 beats per minute.

a. Write a linear equation to find the ideal maximum heart rate for anyone over 25 who is exercising to burn fat.
$R = -\frac{3}{5}a + 117$, where R is the ideal heart rate and a is the number of years older than 25

Ideal Heart Rates

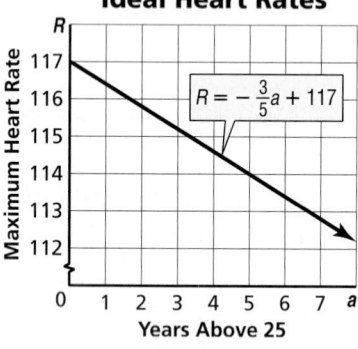

$R = -\frac{3}{5}a + 117$

b. Graph the equation.

c. Find the ideal maximum heart rate for a 55-year-old person exercising to burn fat. 99 beats per minute

---

Step 2 The y-intercept of $y = \frac{5}{3}x - 2$ is -2. So, graph $(0, -2)$.

Step 3 The slope is $\frac{5}{3}$. From $(0, -2)$, move up 5 units and right 3 units. Draw a dot.

Step 4 Draw a line containing the points.

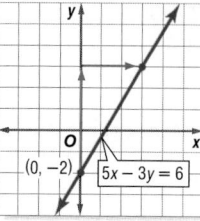
$(0, -2)$ $5x - 3y = 6$

✓ CHECK Your Progress

Graph each equation. **3A–3B. See margin.**

3A. $y = 2x - 3$ **3B.** $y = \frac{1}{4}x + 5$ **3C.** $4x + 3y = -12$ **3D.** $2x - 3y = 6$

3C–3D. See Ch. 4 Answer Appendix.

Model Real-World Data If a quantity changes at a constant rate over time, it can be modeled by a linear equation. The y-intercept represents a starting point, and the slope represents the rate of change.

Real-World EXAMPLE

4 **SPORTS** Use the information at the left about high school sports.

a. The number of girls competing in high school sports has increased by an average of 0.06 million per year since 1997. Write a linear equation to find the number of girls in high school sports in any year after 1997.

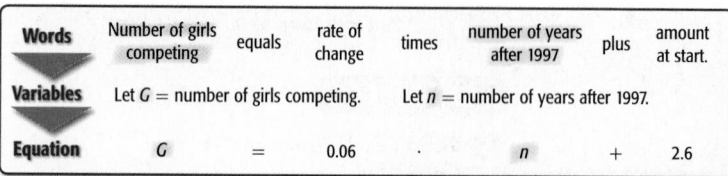

Words	Number of girls competing	equals	rate of change	times	number of years after 1997	plus	amount at start.
Variables	Let G = number of girls competing.				Let n = number of years after 1997.		
Equation	G	=	0.06	·	n	+	2.6

b. Graph the equation.
The graph passes through $(0, 2.6)$ with slope 0.06.

c. Find the number of girls competing in 2007.
The year 2007 is 10 years after 1997.

$G = 0.06n + 2.6$ Write the equation.

$= 0.06(10) + 2.6$ Replace n with 10.

$= 3.2$ Simplify.

So, 3.2 million girls competed in high school sports in 2007.

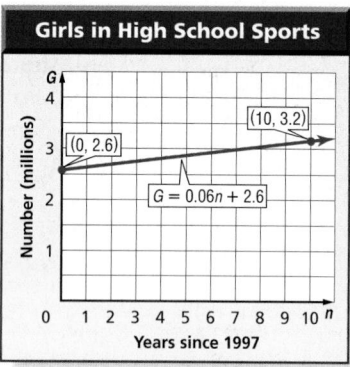

Girls in High School Sports
$(0, 2.6)$ $(10, 3.2)$ $G = 0.06n + 2.6$
Number (millions) Years since 1997

Real-World Link
In 1997, 2.6 million girls competed in high school sports.
Source: www.nfhs.org

✓ CHECK Your Progress

FUND-RAISERS The band boosters are selling submarine sandwiches for $5 each. The cost of the ingredients to make the sandwiches was $1160.

4A. Write an equation for the profit P made on s sandwiches. $P = 5s - 1160$

4B. Graph the equation. See margin.

4C. Find the total profit if 1400 sandwiches are sold. $5840

Differentiated Instruction

Visual/Spatial Learners Word problems may be difficult for some students because they cannot picture what the problem is trying to communicate. Sometimes it is easier for those students to graph or draw a picture of the given information before writing the equation. For Additional Example 4, you may wish to have students do part **b** first by using the starting point and the rate of change to determine other points on the graph. Then have students write the equation that describes the line formed.

★ indicates multi-step problem

✓ CHECK Your Understanding

Example 1
(p. 204)

Write an equation in slope-intercept form of the line with the given slope and *y*-intercept.

1. slope: -3, *y*-intercept: 1
$y = -3x + 1$

2. slope: 4, *y*-intercept: -2
$y = 4x - 2$

Example 2
(p. 205)

Write an equation in slope-intercept form of the line shown in each graph.

3. 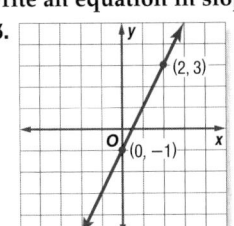 $y = 2x - 1$

4. 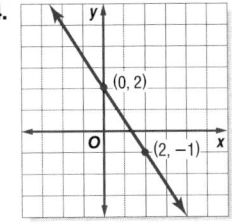 $y = -\dfrac{3}{2}x + 2$

Example 3
(p. 205)

Graph each equation. **5–8. See Ch.4 Answer Appendix.**

5. $y = 2x - 3$

6. $y = -3x + 1$

7. $2x + y = 5$

8. $3x - 2y = 2$

Example 4
(p. 206)

MONEY For Exercises 9–11, use the following information.
Suppose you have already saved $50 toward the cost of a new television. You plan to save $5 more each week for the next several weeks.

9. Write an equation for the total amount T that you will have w weeks from now. $T = 50 + 5w$

10. Graph the equation. **See Ch.4 Answer Appendix.**

11. Find the total amount saved after 7 weeks. **$85**

Exercises

HOMEWORK HELP	
For Exercises	See Examples
12–17	1
18–23	2
24–32	3
33–38	4

Exercise Levels
A: 12–38
B: 39–44
C: 45–47

18. $y = 3x + 1$

19. $y = \dfrac{3}{2}x - 4$

20. $y = -4x + 2$

Write an equation in slope-intercept form of the line with the given slope and *y*-intercept.   12. $y = -2x + 6$ 14. $y = \dfrac{1}{2}x + 3$

12. slope: -2, *y*-intercept: 6

13. slope: 3, *y*-intercept: -5 $y = 3x - 5$

14. slope: $\dfrac{1}{2}$, *y*-intercept: 3

15. slope: $-\dfrac{3}{5}$, *y*-intercept: 12 $y = -\dfrac{3}{5}x + 12$

16. slope: 0, *y*-intercept: 3 $y = 3$

17. slope: -1, *y*-intercept: 0 $y = -x$

Write an equation in slope-intercept form of the line shown in each graph.

18.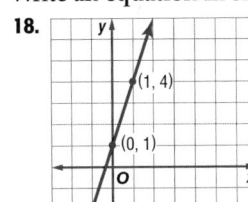

19.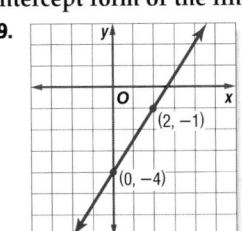

20.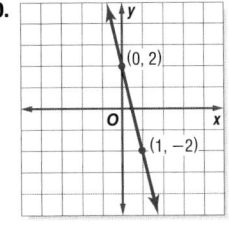

 Practice

✓ Formative Assessment

Use Exercises 1–11 to check for understanding.

Use the chart at the bottom of this page to customize assignments for your students.

Odd/Even Assignments
Exercises 12–38 are structured so that students practice the same concepts whether they are assigned odd or even problems.

Real-World Connections For Exercises 33 and 34, you may want to point out that in some countries, walking and bicycling are normal parts of daily life. Have students talk about how popular walking and bicycling was in places they have lived or vacationed.

Additional Answers

3A.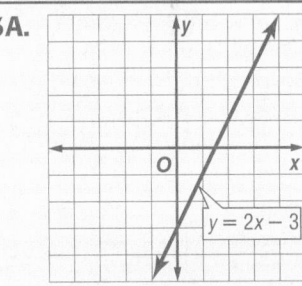

3B.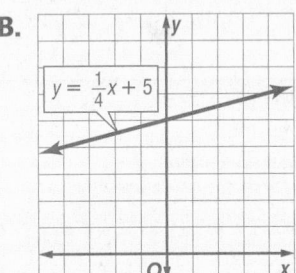

4B.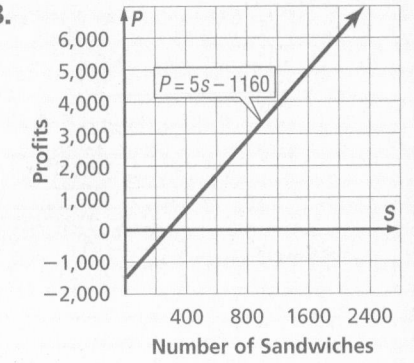

DIFFERENTIATED HOMEWORK OPTIONS

Level	Assignment	Two-Day Option	
BL Basic	12–38, 46–58	13–37 odd, 48, 49	12–38 even, 46, 47, 50–58
OL Core	13–43 odd, 46–58	12–38, 48, 49	39–44, 46, 47, 50–58
AL Advanced /Pre-AP	39–55, (optional: 56–58)		

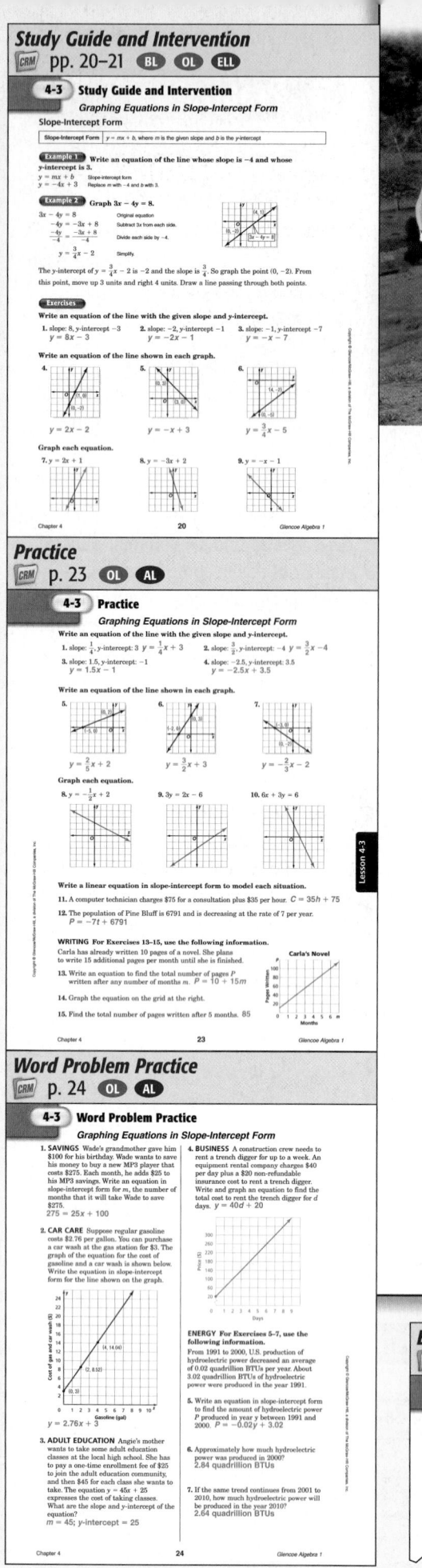

🌐 **Real-World Link**·····★

More than 3 million teens participate in mountain bicycling each year.

Source: *Statistical Abstract of the United States*

42.
$y = -1.5x - 0.25$

EXTRA PRACTICE
See pages 725, 747.

Math Online
Self-Check Quiz at
ca.algebra1.com

H.O.T. Problems·······

45. They all have a *y*-intercept of 3.

Write an equation in slope-intercept form of the line shown in each graph.

21.
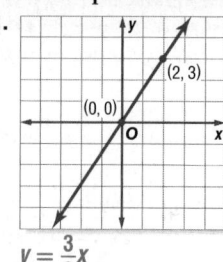
(2, 3)
(0, 0)
$y = \frac{3}{2}x$

22.
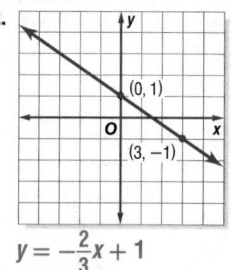
(0, 1)
(3, −1)
$y = -\frac{2}{3}x + 1$

23.
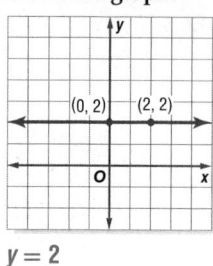
(0, 2) (2, 2)
$y = 2$

Graph each equation. 24–32. See Ch. 4 Answer Appendix.

24. $y = x - 2$
25. $y = 3x + 1$
26. $y = -4x + 1$
27. $y = \frac{1}{2}x + 4$
28. $y = -\frac{1}{3}x - 3$
29. $3x + y = -2$
30. $2x - y = -3$
31. $3y = 2x + 3$
32. $2x + 3y = 6$

BICYCLES For Exercises 33 and 34, use the following information.
A rental company on Padre Island charges $8 per hour for a mountain bicycle plus a $5 fee for a helmet.

33. Write a linear equation in slope-intercept form for the total rental cost for a helmet and bicycle for *t* hours. Then graph the equation. $y = 8t + 5$

34. Find the cost of a 2-hour rental. $21

ANALYZE GRAPHS For Exercises 35 and 36, use the following information.
In 2003, book sales in the United States totaled $23.4 billion. Suppose sales continue to increase by about $1.2 billion each year. $S = 23.4 + 1.2t$

35. Write an equation in slope-intercept form to find the total sales *S* for the number of years *t* since 2003.

36. If the trend continues, what will sales be in 2007? $28.2 billion

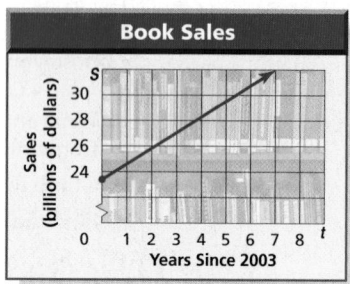

Book Sales

Source: Association of American Publishers

COLLEGE For Exercises 37 and 38, use the following information
For California residents, the average tuition and fees per year at the University of California at Berkeley is approximately $232.31 per credit hour of classes plus $11,968 for room and board. 37. $T = 232.31c + 11,968$

37. Write an equation in slope-intercept form for the tuition *T* for *c* credit hours.

38. Find the cost of tuition in a year for a student taking 32 credit hours. $19,401.90

Write an equation of the line with the given slope and *y*-intercept.

39. slope: −1, *y*-intercept: 0 $y = -x$
40. slope: 0.5; *y*-intercept: 7.5 $y = 0.5x + 7.5$
41. slope: 0, *y*-intercept: 7 $y = 7$
42. slope: −1.5, *y*-intercept: −0.25

43. Write an equation of a horizontal line that crosses the *y*-axis at (0, −5). $y = -5$
44. Write an equation of a line that passes through the origin with slope 3. $y = 3x$

45. **CHALLENGE** Summarize the characteristic that the graphs of $y = 2x + 3$, $y = 4x + 3$, $y = -x + 3$, and $y = -10x + 3$ have in common.

46. **OPEN ENDED** Draw a graph representing a real-world linear function and write an equation for the graph. Describe verbally what the graph represents, including the slope and *y*-intercept. **See margin.**

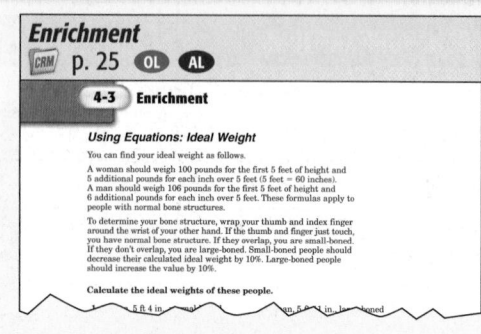
BL = *Below Grade Level*
OL = *On Grade Level*
AL = *Above Grade Level*
ELL = *English Language Learner*

Additional pages not shown:

CRM *Lesson Reading Guide*, p. 19 BL OL ELL
CRM *Skills Practice*, p. 22 BL OL

47. *Writing in Math* Use the data about online shipping costs on page 204 to explain how y-intercepts can be used to describe real-world costs. Write a description of a situation in which the y-intercept of its graph is $25. **See margin.**

Name the Math Have students summarize how they can draw the graph of an equation without finding points that satisfy the equation.

STANDARDS PRACTICE 7AF1.5, 7AF1.1

48. Which statement is *most* strongly supported by the graph? **B**

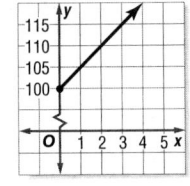

A You have $100 and plan to spend $5 each week.

B You have $100 and plan to save $5 each week.

C You need $100 for a new CD player and plan to save $5 each week.

D You need $100 for a new CD player and plan to spend $5 each week.

49. REVIEW Sam is going to put a border around a poster he is making for a class project. x represents the poster's width, and y represents the poster's length. Which equation represents how much border Sam will use if he doubles both the length and the width of the poster? **G**

F $4xy$

G $4(x + y)$

H $(x + y)^4$

J $16(x + y)$

Additional Answers

46. Sample answer:

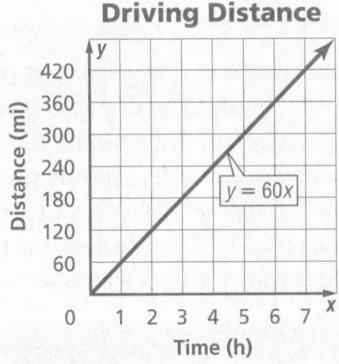

This graph represents the distance traveled in y in x hours. The slope 60 represents the speed in miles per hour. The y-intercept 0 represents 0 miles traveled at time 0.

47. Sample answer: The y-intercept is the flat fee in an equation that represents a price. If a mechanic charges $25 plus $40 per hour to work on your car, the graph representing this situation would have a y-intercept of $25.

Spiral Review

Suppose y varies directly as x. Write a direct variation equation that relates x and y. Then solve. (Lesson 4-2)

50. If $y = -54$ when $x = 9$, find x when $y = -42$. $y = -6x$; 7

51. If $y = 45$ when $x = 60$, find x when $y = 8$. $y = \frac{3}{4}x$, $10\frac{2}{3}$

Find the rate of change represented in each table or graph. (Lesson 4-1)

52. 3

x	y
1	4
2	7
3	10
4	13
5	16

53. $-\frac{1}{4}$

(0, 0)
(4, −1)

54. −2

x	y
8	50
13	40
18	30
23	20
28	10

★ **55. LIFE SCIENCE** A *Laysan albatross* tracked by biologists flew more than 24,843 miles in just 90 days in flights across the North Pacific to find food for its chick. At this rate, how far could the bird fly in a week? (Lesson 2-6) **1932.2 mi**

GET READY for the Next Lesson

PREREQUISITE SKILL Find the slope of the line that passes through each pair of points. (Lesson 4-1)

56. $(-1, 2)$, $(1, -2)$ **−2**

57. $(-3, -1)$, $(2, 3)$ $\frac{4}{5}$

58. $(5, 8)$, $(-2, 8)$ **0**

Lesson 4-3 Graphing Equations in Slope-Intercept Form **209**

Pre-AP Activity Use as an Extension

Write $3x + 2y = 8$ and $-3x + 2y = 8$ on the board. Remind students that these equations are in the standard form for the equation of a line. Ask students to tell how the equations are alike and how they are different. Then, ask students to tell how the graphs of these two equations are alike and how they are different. The coefficients of x are additive inverses; the coefficients of y are the same and the constant after the equals sign in each equation is the same. The slopes, $-\frac{3}{2}$ and $\frac{3}{2}$, are additive inverses of each other; they both have the same y-intercept, 4.

1 Focus

Objective Use a graphing calculator to investigate families of linear functions.

Materials
• graphing calculator

Teaching Tip The graphing calculator has the ability to make graphs appear differently on the screen. The symbol before each Y= entry shows how the line will appear. Highlight the symbol and press ENTER repeatedly until the type of line you want appears.

2 Teach

Working in Cooperative Groups
Have students work in groups of 2 or 3, mixing abilities. Have groups complete Activities 1–3 and Exercises 1–9.

• If necessary, remind students how to enter equations into the Y= list. Point out that by highlighting the = sign and pressing ENTER, an equation will remain in the list but not appear on the screen.
• The standard viewing window is a [–10, 10] by [–10, 10] screen with X Scl and Y Scl of 1. It is selected by pressing ZOOM 6.
• Before starting Activity 1, make sure students have cleared or suppressed any equations in the Y= list other than those they wish to graph.

Practice Have students complete Exercises 10–15.

Additional Answers

3A. The graphs with negative values of m slopes downward from left to right. Graphs with a positive m slope upward from left to right.

The Family of Linear Graphs

Standard 6.0 Students graph a linear equation and compute the x- and y-intercepts (e.g., graph $2x + 6y = 4$). They are also able to sketch the region defined by linear inequality (e.g., they sketch the region defined by $2x + 6y < 4$). (Key, CAHSEE)

A family of people is a group related by birth, marriage, or adoption. Recall that a *family of graphs* includes graphs with at least one characteristic in common.

You can use a graphing calculator to investigate how changing the parameters m and b in $y = mx + b$ affects the graphs in the family of linear functions.

COncepts in MOtion
Animation ca.algebra1.com

ACTIVITY 1 Changing b in $y = mx + b$

Graph $y = x$, $y = x + 4$, and $y = x - 2$ in the standard viewing window.

Enter the equations in the Y= list as Y1, Y2, and Y3. Then graph the equations.

KEYSTROKES: *Review graphing on pages 162 and 163.*

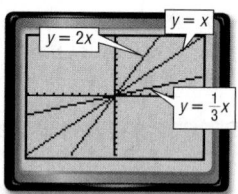
$y = x + 4$
$y = x$
$y = x - 2$

1A. How do the slopes of the graphs compare? **They have the same slope.**
1B. Compare the graph of $y = x + 4$ and the graph of $y = x$. How would you obtain the graph of $y = x + 4$ from the graph of $y = x$? **Shift the graph of $y = x$ up 4 units.**
1C. How would you obtain the graph of $y = x - 2$ from the graph of $y = x$? **Shift the graph of $y = x$ down 2 units.**

Changing m in $y = mx + b$ affects the graphs in a different way than changing b. First, investigate positive values of m.

ACTIVITY 2 Changing m in $y = mx + b$, Positive Values

Graph $y = x$, $y = 2x$, and $y = \frac{1}{3}x$ in the standard viewing window.

Enter the equations in the Y= list and graph.

$y = x$
$y = 2x$
$y = \frac{1}{3}x$

2A. How do the y-intercepts of the graphs compare? **They have the same y-intercept.**
2B. Compare the graphs of $y = 2x$ and $y = x$. **The graph of $y = 2x$ is steeper than the graph of $y = x$.**
2C. Which is steeper, the graph of $y = \frac{1}{3}x$ or the graph of $y = x$? **The graph of $y = x$ is steeper.**

Does changing m to a negative value affect the graph differently than changing it to a positive value?

Math Online Other Calculator Keystrokes at ca.algebra1.com

1.
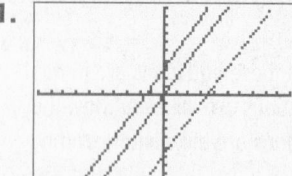
They have the same slope, but different intercepts.

2.
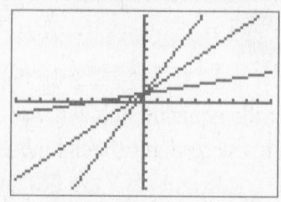
They have the same y-intercept, but different slopes.

ACTIVITY 3 — Changing m in $y = mx + b$, Negative Values

Graph $y = x$, $y = -x$, $y = -3x$, and $y = -\frac{1}{2}x$ in the standard viewing window.

Enter the equations in the Y= list and graph.

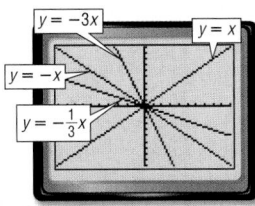

3A. How are the graphs with negative values of m different than graphs with a positive m?
See margin.

3B. Compare the graphs of $y = -x$, $y = -3x$, and $y = -\frac{1}{2}x$. Which is steepest? $y = -3x$

ANALYZE THE RESULTS

Graph each set of equations on the same screen. Describe the similarities or differences among the graphs. 1–6. **See margin.**

1. $y = 2x$
$y = 2x + 3$
$y = 2x - 7$

2. $y = x + 1$
$y = 2x + 1$
$y = \frac{1}{4}x + 1$

3. $y = x + 4$
$y = 2x + 4$
$y = 0.75x + 4$

4. $y = \frac{1}{2}x + 2$
$y = \frac{1}{2}x - 5$
$y = \frac{1}{2}x + 4$

5. $y = -2x - 2$
$y = -4x - 2$
$y = -\frac{1}{3}x - 2$

6. $y = 3x$
$y = 3x + 6$
$y = 3x - 7$

7. Families of graphs have common characteristics. What do the graphs of all equations of the form $y = mx + b$ have in common? **They are all lines.**

8. How does the value of b affect the graph of $y = mx + b$?
The value of b determines the y-intercept.

9. What is the result of changing the value of m on the graph of $y = mx + b$ if m is positive? if m is negative? **See Ch. 4 Answer Appendix.**

10. How can you determine which graph is steepest by examining the following equations?
$y = 3x$, $y = -4x - 7$, $y = \frac{1}{2}x + 4$
The graph of $y = -4x - 7$ is steepest because the absolute value of m is greatest.

11. Explain how knowing about the effects of m and b can help you sketch the graph of an equation. **See margin.**

Nonlinear functions can also be defined in terms of a family of graphs. Graph each set of equations on the same screen. Describe the similarities or differences among the graphs. 12–15. **See Ch. 4 Answer Appendix.**

12. $y = x^2$
$y = -3x^2$
$y = (-3x)^2$

13. $y = x^2$
$y = x^2 + 3$
$y = (x - 2)^2$

14. $y = x^2$
$y = 2x^2 + 4$
$y = (3x)^2 - 5$

15. Describe the similarities and differences in the classes of functions $f(x) = x^2 + c$ and $f(x) = (x + c)^2$, where c is any real number.

Extend 4-3 Graphing Calculator Lab: The Family of Linear Graphs **211**

3.

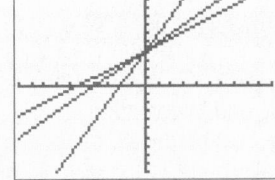

They have the same y-intercept, but different slopes.

4.

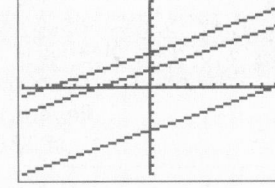

They have the same slope, but different y-intercepts.

---

③ Assess

✓ Formative Assessment

Ask students to summarize what belonging to a family of graphs means.

- Use Exercise 1 to assess whether students understand how changing b affects the graphs in a family of linear functions.

- Use Exercises 3 and 5 to assess whether students understand how changing m affects the graphs in a family of linear functions.

From Concrete to Abstract
Ask:
How can the graph of $y = mx + b$ be drawn from the graph of $y = mx$?
Sample answer: Shift the graph of $y = mx$ up b units if b is positive and down b units if b is negative.

Additional Answers

5.

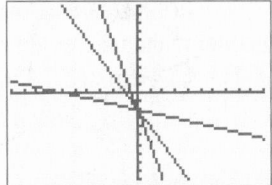

They have the same y-intercept, but different slopes.

6.

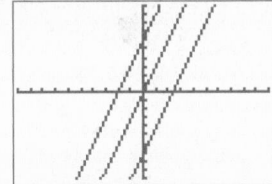

They have the same slope, but different y-intercepts.

11. The value of m tells you how much steeper the graph should be than the graph of $y = x$ and the value of b tells you how many units to shift the graph up or down.

✓ Formative Assessment

Use the Mid-Chapter Quiz to assess students' progress in the first half of the chapter.

For problems answered incorrectly, have students review the lessons indicated in parentheses.

✓ Summative Assessment

CRM Mid-Chapter Test, p. 61

ExamView® Customize and
Assessment Suite create multiple
versions of your Mid-Chapter Test and their answer keys.

FOLDABLES **Foldables™**
Study Organizer **Follow-Up**

Before students complete the Mid-Chapter Quiz, encourage them to review the information under the tabs for Lessons 4-1 through 4-3 in their Foldables.

Additional Answers

5. The slope of 0.026 means that there has been an increase of population. A look at the graph shows that the increase is constant throughout the years without decrease.

Find the slope of the line that passes through each pair of points. (Lesson 4-1)

1. $(-4, 6)$, $(-3, 8)$ **2**   2. $(8, 3)$, $(-11, 3)$ **0**

POPULATION GROWTH For Exercises 3–5, use the following information.

The graph shows the population growth in the USA for 1960 through 2005. (Lesson 4-1)

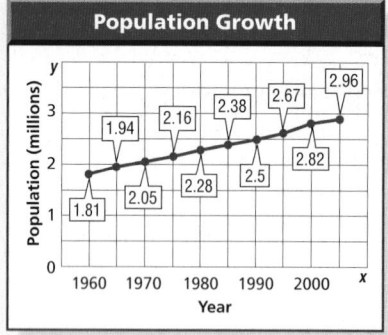

Population Growth

Source: U.S. Census Bureau

3. For which 5-year time period was the rate of change the greatest? the least?

4. Find the rate of change from 1980 to 1990.

5. Explain the meaning of the slope from 1960 to 2005. **See margin.**

   3. **1990 to 1995; 1980 to 1985**   4. **0.022**

6. What is the slope of the *line* containing the points shown in the table? (Lesson 4-1) $\frac{3}{2}$

x	y
-4	-3
2	6
6	12

7. Find the value of r so the line that passes through $(5, -3)$ and $(r, -5)$ has slope 2. (Lesson 4-1) **4**

8. Suppose that y varies directly as x, and $y = 24$ when $x = 8$. Write a direct variation equation that relates x and y. Use the equation to find y when $x = -3$. (Lesson 4-2)
   $y = 3x$; **−9**

   9–11. See Ch. 4 Answer Appendix.
Graph each equation. (Lessons 4–2 and 4–3)

9. $y = -7x$ 10. $y = \frac{3}{4}x + 2$ 11. $x - y = 5$

212 Chapter 4 Analyzing Linear Equations

---

12. **MULTIPLE CHOICE** Megan works at a sporting goods store, and her salary is shown in the graph. Which is a valid conclusion that can be made from the graph? (Lesson 4-2) **A**

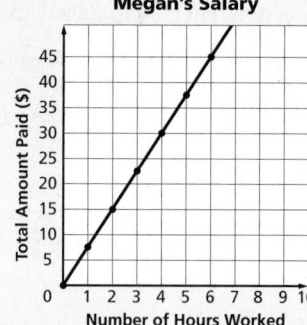

Megan's Salary

A Megan earns about $7 per hour.

B Megan earns about $30 for every 2 hours that she works.

C Megan earns about $52 per week.

D Megan earns about $60 for each shift that she works.

For Exercises 13–15, use the following information.

Suppose you have already saved $75 toward the cost of a new television. You plan to save $5 more each week for the next several weeks. (Lesson 4-3) **13. $T = 75 + 5w$**

13. Write an equation for the total amount T you will have w weeks from now.

14. Graph the equation. **See Ch. 4 Answer App.**

15. Find the total amount saved after 10 weeks.
    $125

16. **MULTIPLE CHOICE** Which equation describes a line that has a y-intercept of 3 and a slope of 2? (Lesson 4-3) **F**

   F $y = 3 + 2x$

   G $y = (3 + x)2$

   H $y = 3x + 2$

   J $y = (3x + 1)2$

Data-Driven Decision Making	**Exercises**	**Lesson**	🌐 **Standard**	**Resources for Review**
Diagnostic Teaching Based on the results of the Chapter 4 Mid-Chapter Quiz, use the following to review concepts that students continue to find challenging.	1–7	4–1	**Reinforcement of 7AF3.3**	**CRM** Study Guide and Intervention pp. 6–7, 13–14, 20–21 **Math Online** • Extra Examples • Personal Tutor • Concepts in Motion
	8–12	4–2	**Reinforcement of 7AF4.2**	
	9–11, 13–16	4–3	**6.0**	

4-4

Writing Equations in Slope-Intercept Form

Main Ideas

- Write an equation of a line given the slope and one point on a line.
- Write an equation of a line given two points on the line.

Reinforcement of Standard 7AF1.1 Use variables and appropriate operations to write an expression, an equation, an inequality, or a system of equations or inequalities that represents a verbal description (e.g., three less than a number, half as large as area A). (CAHSEE)

New Vocabulary

linear extrapolation

▶ GET READY **for the Lesson**

In 2006, the population of a city was about 263 thousand. At that time, the population was growing at a rate of about 7 thousand per year.

Year	Population (thousands)
2005	256
2006	263
2007	270

If you could write an equation based on the slope, 7 (thousand), and the point (2006, 263), you could predict the population for another year.

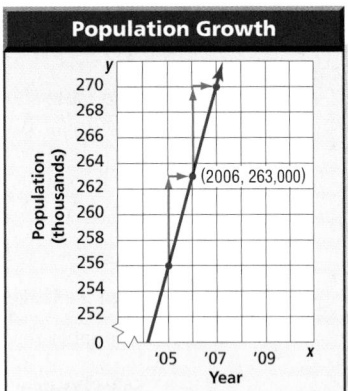

Population Growth

(2006, 263,000)

Write an Equation Given the Slope and One Point You have learned how to write an equation of a line when you know the slope and a specific point, the *y*-intercept. The following example shows how to write an equation when you know the slope and any point on the line.

EXAMPLE Write an Equation Given Slope and One Point

1 Write an equation of a line that passes through (1, 5) with slope 2.

Step 1 Find the *y*-intercept by replacing *m* with 2 and (*x*, *y*) with (1, 5) in the slope-intercept form and solving for *b*.

$y = mx + b$ Slope-intercept form

$5 = 2(1) + b$ Replace *m* with 2, *y* with 5, and *x* with 1.

$5 = 2 + b$ Multiply.

$5 - 2 = 2 + b - 2$ Subtract 2 from each side.

$3 = b$ Simplify.

Step 2 Write the slope-intercept form using $m = 2$ and $b = 3$.

$y = mx + b$ Slope-intercept form

$y = 2x + 3$ Replace *m* with 2 and *b* with 3.

Therefore, an equation of the line is $y = 2x + 3$.

(continued on the next page)

4-4

Lesson Notes

1 Focus

Standards Alignment

Before Lesson 4-4
Solve problems involving linear functions from ⚷ Standard 6AF1.5

Lesson 4-4
Write an expression, an equation, an inequality, or a system that represents a verbal description from Standard 7AF1.1

After Lesson 4-4
Prove theorems by using coordinate geometry from ⚷ Standard G17.0

2 Teach

Scaffolding Questions

Have students read *Get Ready for the Lesson*.

Ask:

- How do you know that the slope is 7000? The *y*-values increase 7000 for each unit of the *x*-axis.

- **BIOLOGY** A population of bacteria has an average growth of 200 bacteria per hour. Describe the graph that demonstrates the growth. The line would have a slope of 200 and begin at (0, *p*), where *p* is the initial population.

Lesson 4-4 Resources

Write an Equation Given the Slope and One Point

Example 1 shows how to write an equation for a line given the slope and any one point on the line.

Write an Equation Given Two Points

Example 2 shows how to write an equation for a line given any two points on the line. **Example 3** shows how to solve a real-world problem by writing an equation for a line given two points on the line. **Example 4** shows how to use a linear equation to predict values for a real-world problem.

CHECK You can check your result by graphing.

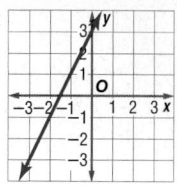

Write an Equation Given Two Points If you know two points on a line, first find the slope. Then follow the steps in Example 1.

 STANDARDS EXAMPLE Write an Equation Given Two Points

2 The table shows the coordinates of two points on the graph of a linear function. Which equation describes the function?

x	y
–3	–1
6	–4

A $y = -\frac{1}{3}x - 2$

B $y = 3x - 2$

C $y = -\frac{1}{3}x + 2$

D $y = \frac{1}{3}x - 2$

Read the Item

The table represents the ordered pairs (–3, –1) and (6, –4).

Solve the Item

Step 1 Find the slope of the line containing the points.

$m = \frac{y_2 - y_1}{x_2 - x_1}$ Slope formula

$= \frac{-4 - (-1)}{6 - (-3)}$ $(x_1, y_1) = (-3, -1)$ and $(x_2, y_2) = (6, -4)$

$= \frac{-3}{9}$ or $-\frac{1}{3}$ Simplify.

Step 2 Use the slope and one of the two points to find the y-intercept.

$y = mx + b$ Slope-intercept form

$-4 = -\frac{1}{3}(6) + b$ Replace m with $-\frac{1}{3}$, x with 6, and y with –4.

$-4 = -2 + b$ Multiply.

$-2 = b$ Add 2 to each side.

Step 3 Write the slope-intercept form using $m = -\frac{1}{3}$ and $b = -2$.

$y = mx + b$ Slope-intercept form

$y = -\frac{1}{3}x - 2$ Replace m with $-\frac{1}{3}$, and b with –2. The answer is A.

Real-World Link
In 2005, J. D. Drew played a total of 72 games.

Source: MLB.com

③ BASEBALL After 22 games in 2005, J. D. Drew of the Los Angeles Dodgers had 10 runs batted in. After 36 games, he had 15 runs batted in. Write a linear equation to estimate the number of runs batted in for any number of games that season.

Explore You know the number of runs batted in after 22 and 36 games.

Plan Let x represent the number of games. Let y represent the number of runs batted in. Write an equation of the line that passes through (22, 10) and (36, 15).

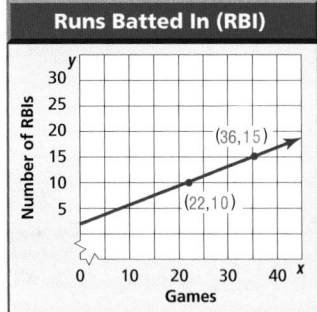

Runs Batted In (RBI)

Solve Find the slope.

$m = \dfrac{y_2 - y_1}{x_2 - x_1}$ Slope formula

$= \dfrac{15 - 10}{36 - 22}$ Let $(x_1, y_1) = (22, 10)$ and $(x_2, y_2) = (36, 15)$.

$= \dfrac{5}{14}$ or about 0.357   Simplify.

Choose (36, 15) and find the y-intercept of the line.

$y = mx + b$ Slope-intercept form

$15 = 0.357(36) + b$ Replace m with 0.357, x with 36, and y with 15.

$15 = 12.852 + b$ Multiply.

$2.148 = b$ Subtract 12.852 from each side and simplify.

Write the slope-intercept form using $m = 0.357$, and $b = 2.148$.

$y = mx + b$ Slope-intercept form

$y = 0.357x + 2.148$ Replace m with 0.357 and b with 2.148.

Therefore, the equation is $y = 0.357x + 2.148$.

Check Check your result by substituting the coordinates of the point not chosen, (22, 10), into the equation.

$y = 0.357x + 2.148$ Original equation

$10 \overset{?}{=} 0.357(22) + 2.148$ Replace y with 10 and x with 22.

$10 \approx 10.002$ Simplify.

The slope was rounded, so the answers vary slightly. The answer checks.

CHECK Your Progress

3. MONEY As a part-time job, Ethan makes deliveries for a caterer. In addition to his weekly salary, he is also paid $16 per delivery. Last week, he made 5 deliveries and his total salary was $215. Write a linear equation to find Ethan's total weekly salary S if he makes d deliveries. $S = 16d + 135$

Focus on Mathematical Content

Slope-Intercept Form When only the coordinates of two points on a line are known, use the two points to find the slope. Substitute the slope and the values of one of the points into $y = mx + b$ and solve for b, the y-intercept.

ADDITIONAL EXAMPLE

③ ECONOMY In 2005, Tim's cost for self-serve regular gasoline was $2.60 on the first of June and $2.82 on the first of July. Write a linear equation to predict Tim's cost of gasoline the first of any month in 2005, using 1 to represent January.
$y = 0.22x + 1.28$

Student Misconceptions

Remind students that the x and y in an equation represent any pairs of x- and y-values that satisfy the equation. The coordinates of the given point are one pair of these values.

Make sure students understand that while two points can be used to write an equation, real-life prediction equations involve many more data points.

Pre-AP Activity   Use as an Extension

Write (3, 4) and (5, 4) on the board. Ask students to find b, the y-intercept, for the equation of the line through these two points. After they have done this, write (3, 5) and (3, 4) on the board and ask students to find b for the equation of the line through these two points and have them explain. $b = 4$; there is no y-intercept. Since these two points are on a vertical line, there is no y-intercept.

3 Practice

✓ Formative Assessment

Use Exercises 1–9 to check for understanding.

Use the chart at the bottom of this page to customize assignments for your students.

Odd/Even Assignments

Exercises 10–29 are structured so that students practice the same concepts whether they are assigned odd or even problems.

Real-World Connection

For Exercises 26 and 27, have students use the enrollment numbers for your school in two different years to write an equation in slope-intercept form. Ask students to predict the enrollment number for next year.

Additional Answers

30. $y = \frac{3}{2}x - 9\frac{1}{2}$

31. $y = -\frac{1}{4}x + \frac{11}{16}$

32. $y = -x - \frac{7}{12}$

For the answer to 37, see p. 218.

When you use a linear equation to predict values that are beyond the range of the data, you are using **linear extrapolation**.

 Vocabulary Link
Extra
Everyday Use
beyond or outside, as in extracurricular activities
Math Use beyond the range of data

Real-World EXAMPLE

④ **SPORTS** Use the equation in Example 3 and the information in the margin to estimate Drew's runs batted in during the 2005 season.

$$y = 0.357x + 2.148 \qquad \text{Original equation}$$

$$= 0.357(72) + 2.148 \qquad \text{Replace } x \text{ with 72.}$$

$$\approx 28 \qquad \text{Simplify.}$$

Using the equation, an estimate for the number of RBIs is 28.

✓ CHECK Your Progress

4. MONEY Use the equation that you wrote in Check Your Progress 3 to predict how much money Ethan will earn in a week if he makes 8 deliveries. **$263**

Be cautious when making a prediction or an estimate using just two given points. The model may be *approximately* correct, but still give inaccurate predictions. For example, in 2005, J. D. Drew had 36 runs batted in, which was 8 more than the estimate.

★ indicates multi-step problem

✓ CHECK Your Understanding

Example 1
(p. 213)

Write an equation of the line that passes through each point with the given slope.

1. $(4, -2), m = 2$
$y = 2x - 10$

2. $(3, 7), m = -3$
$y = -3x + 16$

3. $(-3, 5), m = -1$
$y = -x + 2$

Example 2
(p. 214)

Write an equation of the line that passes through each pair of points.

4. $(5, 1), (8, -2)$
$y = -x + 6$

5. $(6, 0), (0, 4)$
$y = -\frac{2}{3}x + 4$

6. $(5, 2), (-7, -4)$
$y = \frac{1}{2}x - \frac{1}{2}$

7.0 ★ 7. **STANDARDS PRACTICE** The table of ordered pairs shows the coordinates of the two points on the graph of a line. Which equation describes the line? **A**

A $y = x + 7$
B $y = x - 7$
C $y = -5x + 2$
D $y = 5x + 2$

x	y
−5	2
0	7

Examples 3 and 4
(pp. 215–216)

CANOE RENTAL For Exercises 8 and 9, use the information at the right and below.
Ilia and her friends rented a canoe for 3 hours and paid a total of $45. **8.** $C = 10h + 15$

8. Write a linear equation to find the total cost C of renting the canoe for h hours.

9. How much would it cost to rent the canoe for 8 hours? **$95**

CANOE RENTALS
DAILY RATE PLUS
$10 PER HOUR

216 Chapter 4 Analyzing Linear Equations

For Exercises	See Examples
10–17	1
18–25	2
26–29	3, 4

HOMEWORK HELP

Exercise Levels
A: 10–29
B: 30–35
C: 36–40

Write an equation of the line that passes through each point with the given slope.

10. 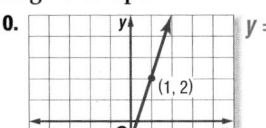 $y = 3x - 1$ **11.** 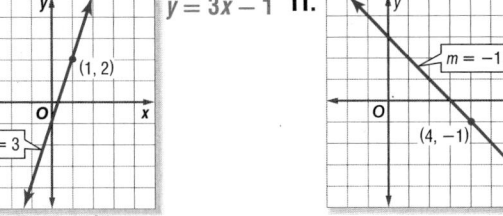 $y = -x + 3$

(1, 2) $m = 3$ $m = -1$ (4, −1)

12. $(5, -2), m = 3$ **13.** $(5, 4), m = -5$ **14.** $(3, 0), m = -2$

15. $(5, 3), m = \frac{1}{2}$ **16.** $(-3, -1), m = -\frac{2}{3}$ **17.** $(-3, -5), m = -\frac{5}{3}$

12. $y = 3x - 17$
13. $y = -5x + 29$
14. $y = -2x + 6$
15. $y = \frac{1}{2}x + \frac{1}{2}$
16. $y = -\frac{2}{3}x - 3$
17. $y = -\frac{5}{3}x - 10$

Write an equation of the line that passes through each pair of points.

18. $(4, 2), (-2, -4)$ $y = x - 2$ **19.** $(3, -2), (6, 4)$ $y = 2x - 8$

20. $(-1, 3), (2, -3)$ $y = -2x + 1$ **21.** $(2, -2), (3, 2)$ $y = 4x - 10$

22. $(7, -2), (-4, -2)$ $y = -2$ **23.** $(0, 5), (-3, 5)$ $y = 5$

24. $(1, 1), (7, 4)$ $y = \frac{1}{2}x + \frac{1}{2}$ **25.** $(5, 7), (0, 6)$ $y = \frac{1}{5}x + 6$

POPULATION For Exercises 26 and 27, use the data at the top of page 213.

★ **26.** Write a linear equation to find the city's population P for any year t.

27. Predict what the city's population will be in 2010. **about 312 thousand or 312,000**

26. $P = 7t - 13,758$

DOGS For Exercises 28 and 29, refer to the information below.
In 2001, there were about 62.5 thousand golden retrievers registered in the United States. In 2002, the number was 56.1 thousand.

★ **28.** Write a linear equation to predict the number of golden retrievers G that will be registered in year t. $G = -6.4t + 12,868.9$

29. Predict the number of golden retrievers that will be registered in 2007. **24.1 thousand or 24,100**

30–32. See margin.

Write an equation of the line that passes through each pair of points.

30. $(5, -2), (7, 1)$ **31.** $\left(-\frac{5}{4}, 1\right), \left(-\frac{1}{4}, \frac{3}{4}\right)$ **32.** $\left(\frac{5}{12}, -1\right), \left(-\frac{3}{4}, \frac{1}{6}\right)$

33. $y = \frac{5}{3}x + 5$

33. Write an equation of the line that has an x-intercept -3 and a y-intercept 5.

For Exercises 34 and 35, consider line ℓ that passes through $(14, 2)$ and $(28, 6)$.

★ **34.** Write an equation for line ℓ and describe the slope. $y = \frac{2}{7}x - 2; \frac{2}{7}$

35. Where does line ℓ intersect the x-axis? the y-axis? $(7, 0), (0, -2)$

EXTRA PRACTICE
See pages 725, 747.

Math Online
Self-Check Quiz at
ca.algebra1.com

H.O.T. Problems

36. CHALLENGE The x-intercept of a line is p, and the y-intercept is q. Use symbols to describe an equation of the line. $y = -\frac{q}{p}x + q$

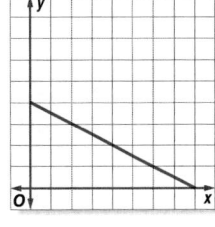

37. OPEN ENDED Create a real-world situation that fits the graph at the right. Then draw and label the graph to represent this situation. Define the two quantities and describe the functional relationship between them. Write an equation to represent this relationship and describe what the slope and y-intercept mean.
See margin.

BL = Below Grade Level
OL = On Grade Level
AL = Above Grade Level
ELL = English Language Learner

Additional pages not shown:

CRM Lesson Reading Guide, p. 26 **BL OL ELL**

CRM Skills Practice, p. 29 **BL OL**

Study Guide and Intervention
CRM pp. 27–28 **BL OL ELL**

4-4 Study Guide and Intervention
Writing Equations in Slope-Intercept Form

Write an Equation Given the Slope and One Point

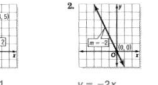

Example 1 Write an equation of a line that passes through $(-4, 2)$ with slope 3.

The line has slope 3. To find the y-intercept, replace m with 3 and (x, y) with $(-4, 2)$ in the slope-intercept form. Then solve for b.

$y = mx + b$ Slope-intercept form
$2 = 3(-4) + b$ $m = 3, y = 2,$ and $x = -4$
$2 = -12 + b$ Multiply.
$14 = b$ Add 12 to each side.
Therefore, the equation is $y = 3x + 14$.

Example 2 Write an equation of the line that passes through $(-2, -1)$ with slope $\frac{1}{4}$.

The line has slope $\frac{1}{4}$. Replace m with $\frac{1}{4}$ and (x, y) with $(-2, -1)$ in the slope-intercept form.

$y = mx + b$ Slope-intercept form
$-1 = \frac{1}{4}(-2) + b$ $m = \frac{1}{4}, y = -1,$ and $x = -2$
$-1 = -\frac{1}{2} + b$ Multiply.
$-\frac{1}{2} = b$ Add $\frac{1}{2}$ to each side.
Therefore, the equation is $y = \frac{1}{4}x - \frac{1}{2}$.

Exercises

Write an equation of the line that passes through each point with the given slope.

1. $y = 2x - 1$ **2.** $y = -2x$ **3.** 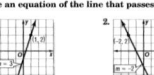 $y = \frac{1}{2}x + 3$

4. $(8, 2), m = -\frac{3}{4}$ **5.** $(-1, -3), m = 5$ **6.** $(4, -5), m = -\frac{1}{2}$
$y = -\frac{3}{4}x + 8$ $y = 5x + 2$ $y = -\frac{1}{2}x - 3$

7. $(-5, 4), m = 0$ **8.** $(2, 2), m = \frac{1}{2}$ **9.** $(1, -4), m = -6$
$y = 4$ $y = \frac{1}{2}x + 1$ $y = -6x + 2$

10. Write an equation of a line that passes through the y-intercept -3 with slope 2.
$y = 2x - 3$

11. Write an equation of a line that passes through the x-intercept 4 with slope -3.
$y = -3x + 12$

12. Write an equation of a line that passes through the point $(0, 350)$ with slope $\frac{1}{5}$.
$y = \frac{1}{5}x + 350$

Practice
CRM p. 30 **OL AL**

4-4 Practice
Writing Equations in Slope-Intercept Form

Write an equation of the line that passes through each point with the given slope.

1. $y = 3x - 1$ **2.** $y = -2x - 2$ **3.** $y = -x - 4$

4. $(-5, 4), m = -3$ **5.** $(4, 3), m = \frac{4}{9}$ **6.** $(1, -5), m = -\frac{3}{2}$
$y = -3x - 11$ $y = \frac{1}{2}x + 1$ $y = -\frac{3}{2}x - \frac{7}{2}$

Write an equation of the line that passes through each pair of points.

7. $y = x - 6$ **8.** $y = -x + 5$ **9.** $y = -2x - 5$

10. $(0, -4), (5, -4)$ **11.** $(-4, -2), (4, 0)$ **12.** $(-2, -3), (4, 5)$
$y = -4$ $y = \frac{1}{4}x - 1$ $y = \frac{4}{3}x - \frac{1}{3}$

13. $(0, 1), (5, 3)$ **14.** $(-3, 0), (1, -6)$ **15.** $(1, 0), (5, -1)$
$y = \frac{2}{5}x + 1$ $y = -\frac{3}{2}x - \frac{9}{2}$ $y = -\frac{1}{4}x + \frac{1}{4}$

Write an equation of the line that has each pair of intercepts.

16. x-intercept: 2, y-intercept: -5 **17.** x-intercept: 2, y-intercept: 10
$y = \frac{5}{2}x - 5$ $y = -5x + 10$

18. x-intercept: 12, y-intercept: 1   **19.** x-intercept: -4, y-intercept: -3
$y = \frac{1}{12}x + 1$ $y = -\frac{3}{4}x - 3$

20. DANCE LESSONS The cost for 7 dance lessons is $82. The cost for 11 lessons is $122. Write a linear equation to find the total cost C for ℓ lessons. Then use the equation to find the cost of 4 lessons. $C = 10\ell + 12$; $52

21. WEATHER It is 76°F at the 6000-foot level of a mountain, and 49°F at the 12,000-foot level of the mountain. Write a linear equation to find the temperature T at an elevation e on the mountain, where e is in thousands of feet. $T = -4.5e + 103$

Word Problem Practice
CRM p. 31 **OL AL**

4-4 Word Problem Practice
Writing Equations in Slope-Intercept Form

1. FUND-RAISING Yvonne and her friends held a bake sale to benefit a shelter for homeless people. The friends sold 22 cakes on the first day and 15 cakes on the second day of the bake sale. They collected $88 on the first day and $60 on the second day. Let x represent the number of cakes sold and y represent the amount of money made. Find the slope of the line that would pass through the points. **4**

2. JOBS Mr. Kimball receives a $3000 annual salary increase on the anniversary of his hiring if he receives a satisfactory performance review. His starting salary was $41,250. Write an equation to show x, Mr. Kimball's salary after y years at this company if his performance reviews are always satisfactory.
$s = 3000y + 41,250$

3. CENSUS The population of Laredo, Texas, was about 197,500 in 2003. It was about 123,000 in 1990. If we assume that the population growth is constant and y represents the number of years after 1990, write a linear equation to find p, Laredo's population for any year after 1990.
$p = 5731y + 123,000$

4. WATER Mr. Williams pays $40 a month for city water, no matter how many gallons of water he uses in a given month. Let x represent the number of gallons of water used per month. Let y represent the monthly cost of the city water in dollars. What is the equation of the line that represents this information? What is the slope of the line?
$y = 40$; slope is 0. The line is horizontal.

SHOE SIZES For Exercises 5–7, use the following information.
The table shows how women's shoe sizes in the United Kingdom compare to women's shoe sizes in the United States.

Women's Shoe Sizes							
U.K.	3	3.5	4	4.5	5	5.5	6
U.S.	5.5	6	6.5	7	7.5	8	8.5

Source: www.daveappel.uk.com/shen

5. Write a linear equation to determine any U.S. size if you are given the U.K. size.
$y = x + 2.5$

6. What is the slope and y-intercept of the line?
Slope = 1; y-intercept = 2.5

7. Is the y-intercept a valid data point for the given information? No. It is not likely a valid data point because the U.K. sizing probably does not include zero. However, the point is the y-intercept of the line represented by the data if the data were to continue indefinitely in both directions.

Enrichment
CRM p. 32 **OL AL**

4-4 Enrichment

Tangent to a Curve
A tangent line is a line that intersects a curve at a point with the same rate of change, or slope, as the rate of change of the curve at that point.

For quadratic functions (functions of the form $ax^2 + bx + c$), the equation of the tangent line can be found. This is based on the fact that the slope through any two points on the curve is equal to the slope of the line tangent to the curve at the point whose x-value is halfway between the x-values of the other two points.

Example To find the equation of a tangent line to the curve $y = x^2 + 3x + 2$ through the point $(2, 12)$, first find two points on the curve whose x-values are equidistant from the x-value of the point the tangent needs to pass through.

Step 1: Find two more points. Use $x = 1$ and $x = 3$.
When $x = 1, y = 1^2 + 3(1) + 2$, or 6.

Yesterday's News Have students write how yesterday's lesson helped them with writing equations in slope-intercept form today.

Formative Assessment

Check for student understanding of concepts in Lessons 4-3 and 4-4.

CRM Quiz 2, p. 59

Foldables™ Follow-Up

Remind students to use the fourth flap in their Foldables to record notes on what they have learned about writing equations in slope-intercept form. Students should include the steps given in the Concept Summary on p. 214.

Additional Answers

37. Sample answer: Let y represent the quarts of water in a pitcher and let x represent the time in seconds.

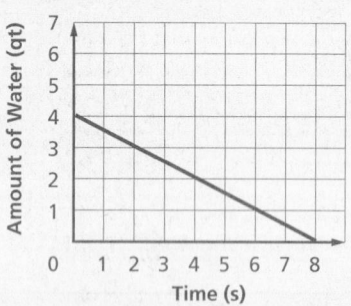

As the time increases by 1 second, the amount of water in the pitcher decreases by $\frac{1}{2}$ quart. An equation is $y = -\frac{1}{2}x + 4$. The slope $-\frac{1}{2}$ represents the rate at which the water is emptying from the pitcher, $\frac{1}{2}$ quart per second. The y-intercept 4 represents the initial amount of water in the pitcher, 4 quarts.

H.O.T. Problems

38. Sometimes; if the x- and y-intercepts are both zero, you cannot write the equation of the graph.

38. REASONING Tell whether the statement is *sometimes*, *always*, or *never* true. Explain your reasoning.
You can write the equation of a line given its x- and y-intercepts.

39. Writing in Math Use the information about population on page 213 to explain how the slope-intercept form can be used to make predictions. Discuss how slope-intercept form is used in linear extrapolation.
See margin.

STANDARDS PRACTICE 7.0, 7MG2.1

40. Which equation *best* describes the relationship between the values of x and y shown in the table? **B**

A $y = x - 5$
B $y = 2x - 5$
C $y = 3x - 7$
D $y = x^2 - 7$

x	y
−1	−7
0	−5
2	−1
4	3

41. REVIEW Mrs. Aguilar's bedroom is shaped like a rectangle that measures 13 feet by 11 feet. She wants to purchase carpet for the bedroom that costs $2.95 per square foot, including tax. How much will it cost to carpet her bedroom? **J**

F $70.80   H $145.95
G $141.60   J $421.85

Spiral Review

Graph each equation. (Lesson 4-3) **42–44. See Ch. 4 Answer Appendix.**

42. $y = 3x - 2$ **43.** $x + y = 6$ **44.** $x + 2y = 8$

45. HEALTH Each time your heart beats, it pumps 2.5 ounces of blood. Write a direct variation equation that relates the total volume of blood V with the number of times your heart beats b. (Lesson 4-2) $V = 2.5b$

Determine the x-intercept and y-intercept of each linear function and describe what the intercepts mean. (Lesson 3-3) **46–47. See Ch. 4 Answer Appendix.**

46.

Kwame's Bike Ride	
Time, x (min)	Distance, y (mi)
0	0
5	1
10	2
15	3

47.

Tara's Walk Home	
Time, x (min)	Distance, y (mi)
0	3
15	2
30	1
45	0

Determine the domain and range of each relation. (Lesson 3-1)

48. $\{(0, 8), (9, -2), (4, 2)\}$
D = {0, 4, 9}; R = {−2, 2, 8}

49. $\{(-2, 1), (5, 1), (-2, 7), (0, -3)\}$
D = {−2, 0, 5}; R = {−3, 1, 7}

GET READY for the Next Lesson

PREREQUISITE SKILL Find each difference. (Pages 688–689)

50. $4 - 7$ −3   **51.** $5 - 12$ −7   **52.** $2 - (-3)$ 5   **53.** $-1 - 4$ −5

39. Sample answer: Linear extrapolation is when you use a linear equation to predict values that are outside of the given points on the graph. You can use the slope-intercept form of the equation to find the y-value for any requested x-value.

Main Ideas

- Derive linear equations by using the point-slope formula.
- Write linear equations in different forms.

 Standard 7.0 Students verify that a point lies on a line, given an equation of the line. **Students are able to derive linear equations by using the point-slope formula.** (Key, CAHSEE)

New Vocabulary

point-slope form

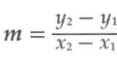 **GET READY** for the Lesson

The graph shows a line with slope 2. One point on the line is (3, 4). Another point on the line is (x, y).

$$m = \frac{y_2 - y_1}{x_2 - x_1} \qquad \text{Slope formula}$$

$$2 = \frac{y - 4}{x - 3} \qquad \begin{array}{l}(x_2, y_2) = (x, y) \\ (x_1, y_1) = (3, 4)\end{array}$$

$$2(x - 3) = \frac{y - 4}{x - 3}(x - 3) \qquad \begin{array}{l}\text{Multiply each side} \\ \text{by } (x - 3).\end{array}$$

$$2(x - 3) = y - 4 \qquad \text{Simplify.}$$

$$y - 4 = 2(x - 3) \qquad \text{Symmetric Property of Equality}$$

↑   ↑   ↑
y-coordinate   slope x-coordinate

Point-Slope Form The equation above was generated using the coordinates of a known point and the slope of the line. It is written in **point-slope form.**

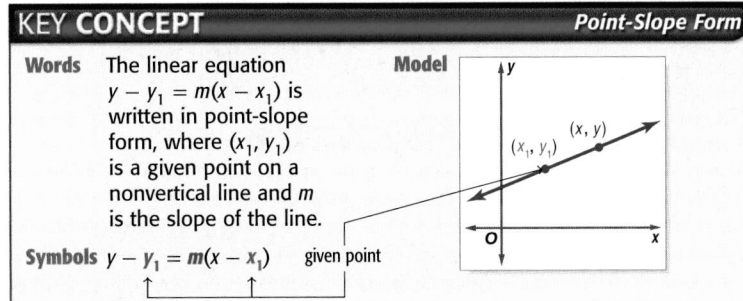

KEY CONCEPT   *Point-Slope Form*

Words   The linear equation $y - y_1 = m(x - x_1)$ is written in point-slope form, where (x_1, y_1) is a given point on a nonvertical line and m is the slope of the line.

Model

Symbols $y - y_1 = m(x - x_1)$ given point

EXAMPLE   Write an Equation Given Slope and a Point

1 Write the point-slope form of an equation for the line that passes through $(-1, 5)$ with slope -3.

$$y - y_1 = m(x - x_1) \qquad \text{Point-slope form}$$
$$y - 5 = -3[x - (-1)] \qquad (x_1, y_1) = (-1, 5)$$
$$y - 5 = -3(x + 1) \qquad \text{Simplify.}$$

CHECK Your Progress

1. Write the point-slope form of an equation for the line that passes through $(1, -4)$ with slope $-\frac{8}{3}$. $y + 4 = -\frac{8}{3}(x - 1)$

Lesson 4-5 Writing Equations in Point-Slope Form   **219**

---

1 Focus

 Standards Alignment

Before Lesson 4-5
Solve problems involving linear functions from ⊶ Standard 6AF1.5

Lesson 4-5
Verify that a point lies on a line and derive linear equations from Standard 7.0

After Lesson 4-5
Prove theorems by using coordinate geometry from ⊶ Standard G17.0

2 Teach

Scaffolding Questions
Have students read *Get Ready for the Lesson*.

Ask:
- How does the final form of the equation relate to the given slope and point? Sample answer: The slope and each coordinate appear as numbers.
- How would the equation change if the given point were at $(4, 6)$? $y - 6 = 2(x - 4)$

(continued on the next page)

Lesson 4-5 Resources

Chapter 4 Resource Masters
Lesson Reading Guide, p. 33 **BL** **OL** **ELL**
Study Guide and Intervention, pp. 34–35 **BL** **OL** **ELL**
Skills Practice, p. 36 **BL** **OL**
Practice, p. 37 **OL** **AL**
Word Problem Practice, p. 38 **OL** **AL**
Enrichment, p. 39 **OL** **AL**
Graphing Calculator, p. 40

Transparencies
5-Minute Check Transparency 4-5

Additional Print Resources
Noteables™ Interactive Study Notebook with Foldables™
Teaching Algebra with Manipulatives

Technology
ca.algebra1.com
Interactive Classroom CD-ROM
AssignmentWorks CD-ROM
Graphing Calculator Easy Files

- What equation do you get if you substitute x_1, y_1, and m for the numerical values in the final form of the equation? $y - y_1 = m(x - x_1)$

Point-Slope Form

Examples 1–2 show how to write an equation in point-slope form when the slope and a point on the line are known.

 Formative Assessment

Use the Check Your Progress exercises after each example to determine students' understanding of concepts.

ADDITIONAL EXAMPLES

1 Write the point-slope form of an equation for a line that passes through $(-2, 0)$ with slope $-\frac{3}{2}$. $y = -\frac{3}{2}(x + 2)$

2 Charlie is flying from San Diego, California, to Washington D.C., for vacation. After 1.5 hours, his plane has traveled 810 miles. If the average speed of travel is 540 miles per hour, write the equation of the line in point-slope. $y - 810 = 540(x - 1.5)$

3 Write the point-slope form of an equation for a horizontal line that passes through $(0, 5)$. $y - 5 = 0$

Additional Examples are also in:
- Noteables™ Interactive Study Notebook with Foldables™
- Interactive Classroom PowerPoint® Presentations

Teaching Tip

In Example 2, note that since $(0, 0)$ lies on the line, the equation can also be written as $y - 0 = 65(x - 0)$ or $y = 65x$.

220 Chapter 4 Analyzing Linear Equations

 Real-World EXAMPLE

2 Candace and her family are visiting her grandmother. After 2.5 hours in the car, they had traveled 162.5 miles. If the average speed of travel is 65 miles per hour, write the equation of the line in point-slope form.

Let x represent hours and y represent miles. The average speed of travel is the slope, so $m = 65$. Let $(x_1, y_1) = (2.5, 162.5)$.

$$y - y_1 = m(x - x_1)$$
$$y - 162.5 = 65(x - 2.5)$$
$$y - 162.5 = 65(x - 2.5)$$

The equation $y - 162.5 = 65(x - 2.5)$ represents their trip.

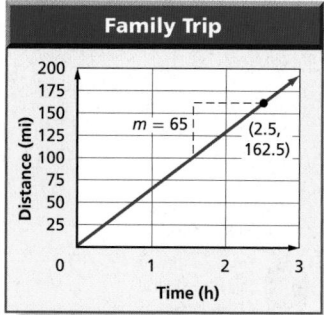

Family Trip

✓ **CHECK Your Progress**

2. The sales for a company were \$25 million in the 2nd quarter and \$35 million in the 4th quarter. Write a linear equation to represent this data. Assume the rate of change is constant. $y - 25 = 5(x - 2)$

EXAMPLE Write an Equation of a Horizontal Line

3 Write the point-slope form of an equation for the horizontal line that passes through $(6, -2)$.

$$y - y_1 = m(x - x_1) \quad \text{Point-slope form}$$
$$y - (-2) = 0(x - 6) \quad (x_1, y_1) = (6, -2)$$
$$y + 2 = 0 \quad \text{Simplify.}$$

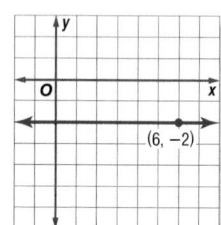

✓ **CHECK Your Progress**

3. Write the point-slope form of an equation for the horizontal line that passes through $(-4, 4)$. $y - 4 = 0$

Study Tip

Vertical and Horizontal Lines

Vertical lines cannot be written in point-slope form because the slope is undefined. Horizontal lines can be written in point-slope form because their slope is 0.

Study Tip

Look Back

To review **standard form**, see Lesson 3–5.

Forms of Linear Equations You have learned how to write linear equations given the slope and one point or two points.

CONCEPT SUMMARY   *Writing Equations*

Given the Slope and One Point	Given Two Points
Step 1 Substitute the values of m, x, and y into the slope-intercept form and solve for b. Or use the point-slope form. Substitute the value of m and let x and y be (x_1, y_1).	**Step 1** Find the slope.
	Step 2 Choose one of the two points to use.
Step 2 Write the slope-intercept form using the values of m and b.	**Step 3** Follow the steps for writing an equation given the slope and one point.

Linear equations in point-slope form can be written in slope-intercept or standard form.

 Math Online Extra Examples at ca.algebra1.com

Focus on Mathematical Content

Point-Slope Form In general, if the point (x_1, y_1) is on a line with a slope of m, the definition of slope can be used to write an equation for all points (x, y).

$$m = \frac{y - y_1}{x - x_1}$$

Multiply both sides of the equation by $(x - x_1)$. $y - y_1 = m(x - x_1)$

This form of the equation of a line is known as the point-slope form.

EXAMPLE — Write an Equation in Standard Form

4 Write $y + 5 = -\frac{5}{4}(x - 2)$ in standard form.

In standard form, both variables are on the left side of the equation. The equation is of the form, $Ax + By = C$, where A, B, and C are all integers.

$y + 5 = -\frac{5}{4}(x - 2)$	Original equation
$4(y + 5) = 4\left(-\frac{5}{4}\right)(x - 2)$	Multiply each side by 4 to eliminate the fraction.
$4y + 20 = -5(x - 2)$	Distributive Property
$4y + 20 = -5x + 10$	Distributive Property
$4y + 20 - 20 = -5x + 10 - 20$	Subtract 20 from each side.
$4y = -5x - 10$	Simplify.
$4y + 5x = -5x - 10 + 5x$	Add 5x to each side.
$5x + 4y = -10$	Simplify.

The standard form of the equation is $5x + 4y = -10$.

✓ CHECK Your Progress

4. Write $y - 1 = 7(x + 5)$ in standard form. $\ 7x - y = -36$

EXAMPLE — Write an Equation in Slope-Intercept Form

5 Write $y - 2 = \frac{1}{2}(x + 5)$ in slope-intercept form.

$y - 2 = \frac{1}{2}(x + 5)$	Original equation
$y - 2 = \frac{1}{2}x + \frac{5}{2}$	Distributive Property
$y - 2 + 2 = \frac{1}{2}x + \frac{5}{2} + 2$	Add 2 to each side.
$y = \frac{1}{2}x + \frac{9}{2}$	$2 = \frac{4}{2}$ and $\frac{4}{2} + \frac{5}{2} = \frac{9}{2}$

The slope-intercept form of the equation is $y = \frac{1}{2}x + \frac{9}{2}$.

✓ CHECK Your Progress

5. Write $y + 6 = -3(x - 4)$ in slope-intercept form. $\ y = -3x + 6$

EXAMPLE — Write an Equation in Point-Slope Form

6 **GEOMETRY** The figure shows right triangle ABC.

Study Tip

Hypotenuse
The *hypotenuse* is the side of a right triangle opposite the right angle.

a. Write the point-slope form of the line containing hypotenuse $\overline{AB}$.

Step 1 First, find the slope of $\overline{AB}$.

$m = \frac{y_2 - y_1}{x_2 - x_1}$ — Slope formula

$= \frac{4 - 1}{6 - 2}$ or $\frac{3}{4}$ — $(x_1, y_1) = (2, 1)$ and $(x_2, y_2) = (6, 4)$

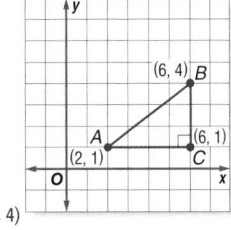

Forms of Linear Equations

Example 4 shows how to write an equation in standard form when given an equation in point-slope form.

ADDITIONAL EXAMPLE

4 Write $y = \frac{3}{4}x - 5$ in standard form. $3x - 4y = 20$

Tips for New Teachers — **Preventing Error**

Emphasize that in standard form, A, B, and C are all integers. Example 3 is an exercise in algebraic manipulation.

Tips for New Teachers — **Multiplication Facts**

Another way for students to write the equation in Example 5 in slope-intercept form is to identify the slope m of the line and let $x = 0$ to find the y-intercept. Solve for y. This value is the value of b for the equation in slope-intercept form.

Example 5 shows how to write an equation in slope-intercept form when given an equation in point-slope form.

ADDITIONAL EXAMPLE

5 Write $y - 5 = \frac{4}{3}(x - 3)$ in slope-intercept form. $y = \frac{4}{3}x + 1$

Intervention

Slope of Horizontal Lines Some students will have trouble remembering whether a vertical line or a horizontal line has a slope of 0. Tell students the word *horizontal* has an o to remind them of 0. A h<u>o</u>rizontal line has a slope of **0**.

Example 6 shows how to use the point-slope form to write equations for the lines making up a geometric figure.

6 **GEOMETRY** The figure shows trapezoid $ABCD$, with bases $\overline{AB}$ and $\overline{CD}$.

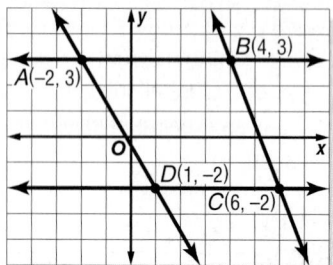

a. Write the point-slope form of the lines containing the bases of the trapezoid.
$\overline{AB}$: $y - 3 = 0$; $\overline{CD}$: $y + 2 = 0$

b. Write each equation in standard form. $y = 3$, $y = -2$

---

3 Practice

 Formative Assessment

Use Exercises 1–13 to check for understanding.

Use the chart at the bottom of this page to customize assignments for your students.

⚠ **Exercise Alert!**
Find the Error For Exercise 56, students may assume that one of the two examples has to be incorrect. Point out that this is not necessarily the case.

Step 2 You can use either point for (x_1, y_1) in the point-slope form.

Method 1 Use (6, 4).	**Method 2** Use (2, 1).
$y - y_1 = m(x - x_1)$	$y - y_1 = m(x - x_1)$
$y - 4 = \frac{3}{4}(x - 6)$	$y - 1 = \frac{3}{4}(x - 2)$

Study Tip

Standard Form
Regardless of which point is used to find the point-slope form, the standard form results in the same equation.

b. Write each equation in standard form.

$y - 4 = \frac{3}{4}(x - 6)$	Original equation	$y - 1 = \frac{3}{4}(x - 2)$
$4(y - 4) = 4\left(\frac{3}{4}\right)(x - 6)$	Multiply each side by 4.	$4(y - 1) = 4\left(\frac{3}{4}\right)(x - 2)$
$4y - 16 = 3(x - 6)$	Multiply.	$4y - 4 = 3(x - 2)$
$4y - 16 = 3x - 18$	Distributive Property	$4y - 4 = 3x - 6$
$4y = 3x - 2$	Add to each side.	$4y = 3x - 2$
$-3x + 4y = -2$	Subtract 3x from each side.	$-3x + 4y = -2$
$3x - 4y = 2$	Multiply each side by −1.	$3x - 4y = 2$

✓ **CHECK Your Progress** 6A. $y - 2 = 5(x - 1)$ or $y + 3 = 5x$

GEOMETRY Triangle JKL has vertices $J(1, 2,)$ $K(0, -3)$, and $L(-4, 1)$.
6A. Write the point-slope form of the line containing side $\overline{JK}$.
6B. Write the standard form of the line containing $\overline{JK}$. $5x - y = 3$

Online Personal Tutor at ca.algebra1.com

★ indicates multi-step problem

✓ **CHECK Your Understanding**

Examples 1, 3
(pp. 219–220)
Write the point-slope form of an equation for the line that passes through each point with the given slope.

1.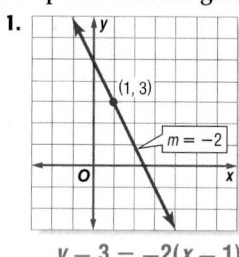
$y - 3 = -2(x - 1)$

2.
$y + 1 = \frac{3}{2}(x + 4)$

3.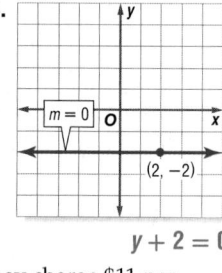
$y + 2 = 0$

Example 2
(p. 220)
4. A coffee company sells ground coffee by the pound. They charge $11 per pound so a 2-pound package costs $22. Write an equation of a line to represent the cost, y, in terms of pounds of coffee sold, x, using the point-slope form. $y - 22 = 11(x - 2)$

5. Jasmine is saving to buy an MP3 player. She already has $50 saved and she plans to save $25 per month. Use the point-slope form to write an equation of a line to represent this situation. $y - 50 = 25(x - 0)$

Example 4
(p. 221)
Write each equation in standard form.

6. $y - 5 = 4(x + 2)$
$4x - y = -13$

7. $y + 3 = -\frac{3}{4}(x - 1)$
$3x + 4y = -9$

8. $y + 2 = \frac{5}{3}(x + 6)$
$5x - 3y = -24$

222 **Chapter 4** Analyzing Linear Equations

DIFFERENTIATED HOMEWORK OPTIONS

Level	Assignment	Two-Day Option	
BL Basic	12–41, 50, 51, 53–70	13–41 odd, 54, 55	12–40 even, 50, 51, 53, 56–70
OL Core	13–49 odd, 50, 51, 53–70	12–41, 54, 55	42–51, 53, 56–70
AL Advanced /Pre-AP	42–64 (optional: 65–70)		

Example 5
(p. 221)

Write each equation in slope-intercept form.

9. $y + 6 = 2(x - 2)$
$y = 2x - 10$

10. $y + 3 = -\frac{2}{3}(x - 6)$
$y = -\frac{2}{3}x + 1$

11. $y - 9 = x + 4$
$y = x + 13$

Example 6
(pp. 221–222)

GEOMETRY For Exercises 12 and 13, use parallelogram *ABCD*.

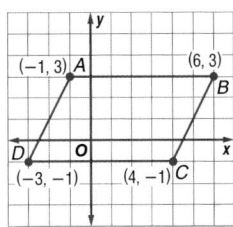

12. Write the point-slope form of the line containing $\overline{AD}$. $y - 3 = 2(x + 1)$

13. Write the standard form of the line containing $\overline{AD}$. $2x - y = -5$

HOMEWORK HELP

For Exercises	See Examples
14–21	1, 3
22–25	2
26–33	4
34–41	5
42–47	6

Exercise Levels
A: 14–47
B: 48–55
C: 56–61

Write the point-slope form of an equation for the line that passes through each point with the given slope.

14. $(6, 1)$, $m = -4$ $y - 1 = -4(x - 6)$ **15.** $(-4, -3)$, $m = 1$ $y + 3 = x + 4$

16. $(9, -5)$, $m = 0$ $y + 5 = 0$ **17.** $(-7, 6)$, $m = 0$ $y - 6 = 0$

18. $(-4, 8)$, $m = \frac{7}{2}$ $y - 8 = \frac{7}{2}(x + 4)$ **19.** $(1, -3)$, $m = -\frac{5}{8}$ $y + 3 = -\frac{5}{8}(x - 1)$

20. Write the point-slope form of an equation for the horizontal line that passes through $(5, -9)$. $y + 9 = 0$

21. A horizontal line passes through $(0, 7)$. Write the point-slope form of its equation. $y - 7 = 0$

22. HIKING Manny and his friends are hiking at an average rate of 4 miles per hour. After $1\frac{1}{2}$ hours they had hiked 6 miles. Use the point-slope form to write an equation of a line to represent this situation. $y - 6 = 4(x - 1.5)$

23. JOBS Carlotta works at a store after school. After working 22 hours she earned $176. She earned $304 for working 38 hours. Use the point-slope form to write an equation of a line to represent this situation.
$y - 176 = 8(x - 22)$ or $y - 304 = 8(x - 38)$

24. SALES The manager of a retail store keeps track of the sales for each month. The total sales for January were $3600. In April, the total sales were $4500. Assume that the sales rate is constant. Write an equation of a line using the point-slope form to represent this situation.
$y - 3600 = 300(x - 1)$ or $y - 4500 = 300(x - 4)$

25. SWIMMING The Olympic record for the 1500 meter freestyle event in the men's swimming competition is held by Grant Hackett of Australia. His time for the event is 14 minutes 43.4 seconds. He swam at an average rate of about 1.7 meters per second. Use the point-slope form to write an equation of the line representing this situation. $y - 883.4 = 1.7(x - 1500)$

Write each equation in standard form.

26. $y - 13 = 4(x - 2)$ $4x - y = -5$ **27.** $y - 5 = -2(x + 6)$ $2x + y = -7$

28. $y + 3 = -5(x + 1)$ $5x + y = -8$ **29.** $y + 7 = \frac{1}{2}(x + 2)$ $x - 2y = 12$

30. $y - 1 = \frac{5}{6}(x - 4)$ $5x - 6y = 14$ **31.** $y - 2 = -\frac{2}{5}(x - 8)$ $2x + 5y = 26$

32. $2y + 3 = -\frac{1}{3}(x - 2)$ $x + 6y = -7$ **33.** $4y - 5x = 3(4x - 2y + 1)$ $17x - 10y = -3$

Odd/Even Assignments
Exercises 12–41 are structured so that students practice the same concepts whether they are assigned odd or even problems.

Real-World Connection For Exercises 45–47, tell students that in 1907, the average movie ticket cost $0.05. Use that cost and the price of a movie ticket today to write the point-slope form of an equation to find the cost of a movie ticket *y* for any year *x*. Ask students to predict the cost of a movie ticket in the year they graduate from high school.

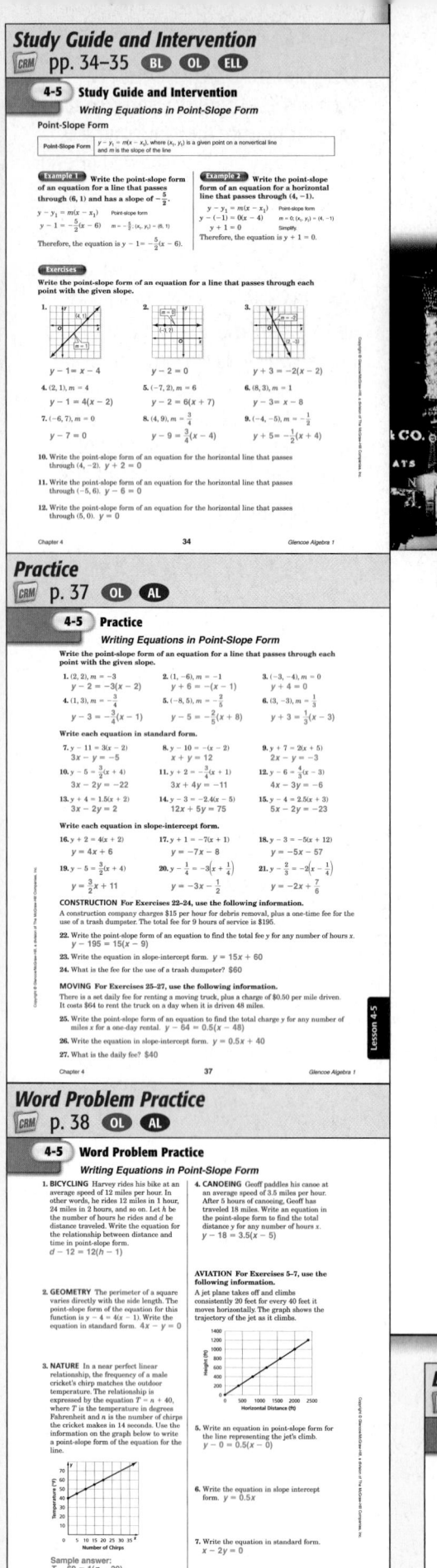

Study Guide and Intervention
CRM pp. 34–35 BL OL ELL

Practice
CRM p. 37 OL AL

Word Problem Practice
CRM p. 38 OL AL

Write each equation in slope-intercept form.

34. $y - 2 = 3(x - 1)$ $y = 3x - 1$ **35.** $y - 5 = 6(x + 1)$ $y = 6x + 11$

36. $y + 2 = -2(x - 5)$ $y = -2x + 8$ **37.** $y + 3 = \frac{1}{2}(x + 4)$ $y = \frac{1}{2}x - 1$

38. $y - 1 = \frac{2}{3}(x + 9)$ $y = \frac{2}{3}x + 7$ **39.** $y + 3 = -\frac{1}{4}(x + 2)$ $y = -\frac{1}{4}x - \frac{7}{2}$

40. $y + 3 = -\frac{1}{3}(2x + 6)$ $y = -\frac{2}{3}x - 5$ **41.** $y + 4 = 3(3x + 3)$ $y = 9x + 5$

BUSINESS For Exercises 42–44, use the following information.
A home security company provides security systems for $5 per week, plus an installation fee. The total cost for installation and 12 weeks of service is $210.

42. Write the point-slope form of an equation to find the total fee y for any number of weeks x. (*Hint:* The point (12, 210) is a solution to the equation.)

43. Write the equation in slope-intercept form. $y = 5x + 150$

44. What is the flat fee for installation? $150

42. $y - 210 = 5(x - 12)$

MOVIES For Exercises 45–47, use the following information.
Between 2001 and 2003, the number of movie screens in the United States increased an average of 410 each year. In 2001, there were about 35,170 movie screens.

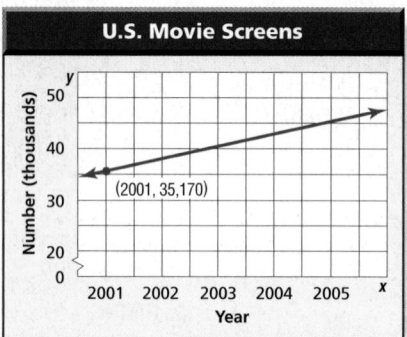

U.S. Movie Screens

(2001, 35,170)

Source: National Association of Theatre Owners

45. Write the point-slope form of an equation to find the total number of screens y for any year x.

46. Write the equation in slope-intercept form. $y = 410x - 785,240$

47. Predict the number of movie screens in the United States in 2007. 37,630

45. $y - 35{,}170 = 410(x - 2001)$

Real-World Link
In 1907, movie theaters were called nickelodeons. There were about 5000 movie screens, and the average movie ticket cost 5 cents.

Source: National Association of Theatre Owners

Write each equation in standard form.

48. $y + 4 = -\frac{1}{3}(x - 12)$ **49.** $y - 3 = 2.5(x + 1)$ **50.** $y - 6 = 1.7(x + 7)$

$x + 3y = 0$ $5x - 2y = -11$ $17x - 10y = -179$

Write each equation in slope-intercept form. 52. $y = \frac{1}{2}x + \frac{3}{2}$ 53. $y = -3x - \frac{7}{4}$

51. $y + \frac{1}{2} = x - \frac{1}{2}$ $y = x - 1$ **52.** $y - \frac{7}{2} = \frac{1}{2}(x - 4)$ **53.** $y + \frac{1}{4} = -3\left(x + \frac{1}{2}\right)$

EXTRA PRACTICE
See pages 726, 747.

Math Online
Self-Check Quiz at ca.algebra1.com

54. Write the point-slope form, slope-intercept form, and standard form of an
★ equation for a line that passes through (5, −3) with slope 10. See margin.

55. Line ℓ passes through (1, −6) with slope $\frac{3}{2}$. Write the point-slope form,
★ slope-intercept form, and standard form of an equation for line ℓ.

55. $y + 6 = \frac{3}{2}(x - 1)$; $y = \frac{3}{2}x - \frac{15}{2}$; $3x - 2y = 15$

H.O.T. Problems

56. FIND THE ERROR Tanya and Akira wrote the point-slope form of an equation for a line that passes through (−2, −6) and (1, 6). Tanya says that Akira's equation is wrong. Tanya says they are both correct. Who is correct? Explain.
See margin.

Tanya
$y + 6 = 4(x + 2)$

Akira
$y - 6 = 4(x - 1)$

224 Chapter 4 Analyzing Linear Equations

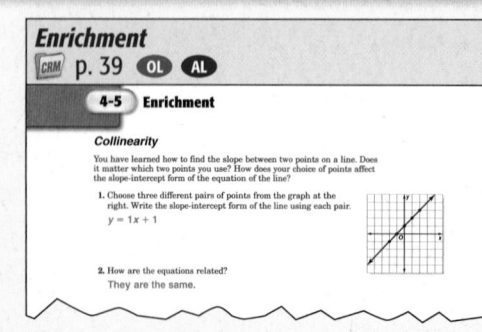

Enrichment
CRM p. 39 OL AL

4-5 Enrichment

Collinearity

You have learned how to find the slope between two points on a line. Does it matter which two points you use? How does your choice of points affect the slope-intercept form of the equation of the line?

1. Choose three different pairs of points from the graph at the right. Write the slope-intercept form of the line using each pair.
$y = 1x + 1$

2. How are the equations related?
They are the same.

BL = *Below Grade Level*
OL = *On Grade Level*
AL = *Above Grade Level*
ELL = *English Language Learner*

Additional pages not shown:

CRM **Lesson Reading Guide**, p. 33 BL OL ELL

CRM **Skills Practice**, p. 36 BL OL

57. OPEN ENDED Compose a real-life scenario that has a constant rate of change and whose value at a particular time is (x, y). Represent this situation using an equation in slope-intercept form and an equation in point-slope form.

58. REASONING Find an equation for the line that passes through $(-4, 8)$ and $(3, -7)$. What is the slope? Where does the line intersect the x-axis? the y-axis?

59. REASONING Barometric pressure is a linear function of altitude. At an altitude of 2 kilometers, the barometric pressure is 600 mmHg, At 7 kilometers, the barometric pressure is 300 mmHg. Find a formula for the barometric pressure as a function of altitude. $f(x) = -60x + 720$

60. CHALLENGE A line contains the points $(9, 1)$ and $(5, 5)$. Make a convincing argument that the same line intersects the x-axis at $(10, 0)$. **See margin.**

61. *Writing in Math* Demonstrate how you can use the slope formula to write the point-slope form of an equation of a line. **See margin.**

STANDARDS PRACTICE 7.0, 7AF3.3

62. What is the equation of the line that passes through $(0, 1)$, and that has a slope of 3? **D**

A $y = 3x - 1$

B $y = 3x - 2$

C $y = 3x + 4$

D $y = 3x + 1$

63. REVIEW What is the slope of the line that passes through $(1, 3)$ and $(-3, 1)$? **H**

F -2

G $-\frac{1}{2}$

H $\frac{1}{2}$

J 2

Spiral Review

Write the slope-intercept form of an equation of the line that satisfies each condition. (Lessons 4-3 and 4-4)

64. passes through $(2, -4)$ and $(0, 6)$ $y = -5x + 6$

65. a horizontal line through $(1, -1)$ $y = -1$

66. slope -2 and y-intercept -5 $y = -2x - 5$

67. passes through $(-2, 4)$ with slope 3 $y = 3x + 10$

68. WATER The table shows the number of gallons of water that a standard showerhead uses. Write an equation in function notation to describe the relation. (Lesson 3-5) $f(x) = 6x$

Number of Minutes	1	2	3	4
Number of Gallons	6	12	18	24

Solve each equation. (Lesson 2-3)

69. $4a - 5 = 15$ **5**

70. $7 + 3c = -11$ **−6**

71. $\frac{2}{9}v - 6 = 14$ **90**

72. Evaluate $(25 - 4) \div (2^2 - 1^3)$. (Lesson 1-3) **7**

GET READY for the Next Lesson

PREREQUISITE SKILL Write the slope-intercept form of an equation for the line that passes through each pair of points. (Lesson 4-3)

73. $(5, -1), (-3, 3)$ $y = -\frac{1}{2}x + \frac{3}{2}$

74. $(0, 2), (8, 0)$ $y = -\frac{1}{4}x + 2$

75. $(2, 1), (3, -4)$ $y = -5x + 11$

---

4 Assess

Name the Math Prepare two paper bags containing pieces of paper. One bag will contain a value for the slope on each slip of paper; the other will contain an ordered pair on each slip of paper. Have students select both a slope and an ordered pair or two ordered pairs. Ask students to write equations in the three forms discussed in this lesson.

FOLDABLES Study Organizer **Foldables™ Follow-Up**
Remind students to use the sixth flap in their Foldables to record notes on what they have learned about writing equations in point-slope form.

Additional Answers

54. $y + 3 = 10(x - 5)$; $y = 10x - 53$; $10x - y = 53$

56. Tanya; $(-2, -6)$ and $(1, 6)$ are both on the line, so either could be substituted into point-slope form to find a correct equation.

60. Sample answer: The point-slope form of the equation is $y - 1 = -(x - 9)$. Let $x = 10$ and $y = 0$. The equation becomes $0 - 1 = -(10 - 9)$ or $-1 = -1$. Since the equation holds true, $(10, 0)$ is a point on the line passing through $(9, 1)$ and $(5, 5)$.

61. Write the definition of the slope using (x, y) as one point and (x_1, y_1) as the other. Then solve the equation so that the y's are on one side and the slope and x's are on the other.

Pre-AP Activity Use as an Extension

Write $4x + 3y = 8$ on the board. Ask students to rewrite the equation in slope-intercept form. Have students name the slope and then draw a conclusion about the values of A and B when an equation is written in standard form, $Ax + By = C$. $y = -\frac{4}{3}x + \frac{8}{3}$; $-\frac{4}{3}$; Sample answer: A is the negative of the numerator of the slope, and B is the denominator of the slope.

1 Focus

Ask students where one of your state parks is located. Some students may say, for example, that the park is in the middle of the northwest portion of the state. Others may give specific directions to the park.

Point out that both answers explain where the park is located, so the better answer depends on what the question means. Do you want to know the geographic location of the park or how to reach it?

2 Teach

Clarifying Meaning Explain to students that answering a question properly requires understanding what kind of information is desired. Point out that words like *describe, explain, compare, contrast* and *justify* act as clue words, identifying the kind of information, or level of response, needed to answer the question. Tell students that recognizing the level of response required by a question will help them in mathematics, English, social studies, and everyday activities.

Have students complete Exercises 1–4.

ELL Students may be interested in seeing the words *describe, explain, compare and contrast*, and *justify* in a language other than English. Ask volunteers to write these words on the board in their native languages and then in English.

3 Assess

Ask students to summarize what they have learned about the levels of response required by questions.

READING MATH

> **Standard 7.0** Students verify that a point lies on a line, given an equation of the line. **Students are able to derive linear equations by using the point-slope formula.** (Key, CAHSEE)

Understanding the Questions

Describe what canyon hiking is.

- hiking in a deep narrow valley that has steep sides

Explain what canyon hiking involves.

- Depending on the canyon, the hike may require a rope and training in basic rope work, or advanced training in rope work, rappelling, setting up anchors, and so on to descend canyon walls safely.

Notice that both responses above give information about canyon hiking. However, the second response provides more in-depth information than the first. Often in mathematics you are asked to *describe, explain, compare and contrast*, or *justify* statements. As in the situation above, these terms require different levels of response.

Question	What Your Answer Should Show
Describe	**KNOWLEDGE:** recalling information
Explain	**COMPREHENSION:** understanding information
Compare and Contrast	**ANALYSIS:** taking apart information
Justify	**EVALUATION:** making choices based on information

Reading to Learn 1–2. See margin.

1. Describe the information that is needed to write an equation of a line. Explain the steps that you can take to write an equation of a line.

2. Compare and contrast equations that are written in slope-intercept form, point-slope form, and standard form.

3. The graph shows the number of members in U.S. Lacrosse.
   a. Describe the trend.
   b. Explain possible reasons for the trend.
   c. Use the graph to justify a city's decision to have a lacrosse field included in a new sports complex.

   3–4. See Ch. 4 Answer Appendix.

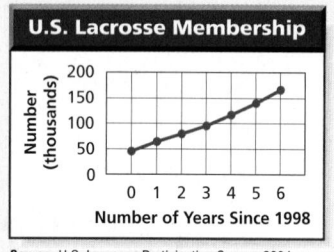

U.S. Lacrosse Membership

Source: U.S. Lacrosse Participation Survey, 2004

4. *Distinguish, summarize, define, predict*, and *demonstrate* are other terms used in mathematics. Write a brief definition of each term as it applies to mathematics and determine whether it requires an answer that shows knowledge, comprehension, analysis, or evaluation.

226 Chapter 4 Analyzing Linear Equations

Additional Answers

1. Sample answer: the slope and the coordinates of a point on a line, or two points on the line; if you know the slope and one point, replace the known values for m, x, and y in $y = mx + b$. Then solve the equation for b. Next, replace the known values for m and b into $y = mx + b$.

2. Sample answer: When an equation is written in slope-intercept form, you can easily determine the slope and y-intercept of the line. An equation written in point-slope form shows the slope and a point on the line. If an equation is written in standard form, the slope and a point on the line must be calculated.

Statistics: Scatter Plots and Lines of Fit

Main Ideas

- Interpret points on a scatter plot.
- Use lines of fit to make and evaluate predictions.

 Probability and Statistics Standard 8.0
Students organize and describe distributions of data by using a number of different methods, including frequency tables, histograms, standard line and bar graphs, stem-and-leaf displays, **scatterplots,** and box-and-whisker plots.

New Vocabulary

scatter plot
line of fit
best-fit line
linear interpolation

GET READY for the Lesson

The points of a set of real-world data do not always lie on one line. But, you may be able to draw a line that seems to be close to all the points. The line in the graph shows a linear relationship between the year x and the number of whooping cranes sighted in January of each year, y. Generally, as the years increase, the number of whooping cranes also increases.

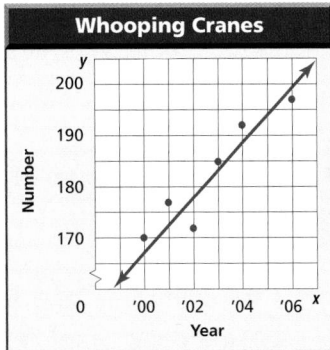

Whooping Cranes

Interpret Points On a Scatter Plot A **scatter plot** is a graph in which two sets of data are plotted as ordered pairs in a coordinate plane. Scatter plots are used to investigate a relationship between two quantities. If the pattern in a scatter plot is linear, you can draw a line to summarize the data. This can help identify trends in the data and the type of correlation.

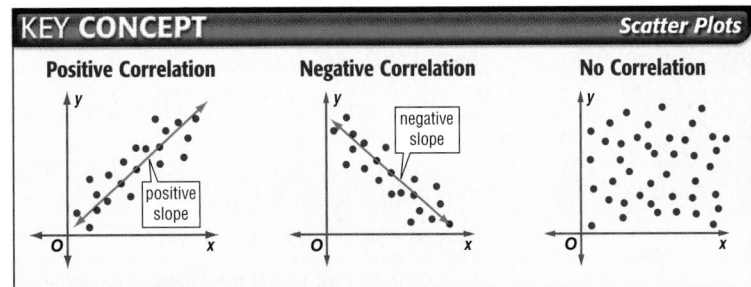

KEY CONCEPT — *Scatter Plots*

Positive Correlation — positive slope

Negative Correlation — negative slope

No Correlation

Real-World EXAMPLE

1 **NUTRITION** Determine whether the graph shows a *positive correlation,* a *negative correlation,* or *no correlation.* If there is a positive or negative correlation, describe its meaning in the situation.

The graph shows a positive correlation. As the number of fat grams increases, the number of Calories increases.

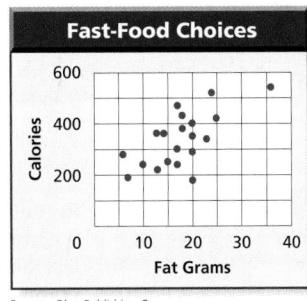

Fast-Food Choices

Source: Olen Publishing Co.

Lesson 4-6 Statistics: Scatter Plots and Lines of Fit **227**

1 Focus

Standards Alignment

Before Lesson 4-6
Represent and describe two numerical variables on a scatterplot from Standard 7SDAP1.2

Lesson 4-6
Students organize and describe distributions of data by using a number of different methods from Standard CA PS8.0

After Lesson 4-6
Compute the variance and the standard deviation of a distribution of data from Standard 2APS7.0

2 Teach

Scaffolding Questions
Have students read *Get Ready for the Lesson.*
Ask:
- Does the line have a positive or negative slope? positive
- What would you do to find the equation of that line? Use two points on the line to write the equation.

Lesson 4-6 Resources

Chapter 4 Resource Masters
Lesson Reading Guide, p. 41 **BL OL ELL**
Study Guide and Intervention, pp. 42–43
BL OL ELL
Skills Practice, p. 44 **BL OL**
Practice, p. 45 **OL AL**
Word Problem Practice, p. 46 **OL AL**
Enrichment, p. 47 **OL AL**
Spreadsheet, p. 48
Quiz 3, p. 60

Transparencies
5-Minute Check Transparency 4-6

Additional Print Resources
Noteables™ Interactive Study Notebook with Foldables™
Teaching Algebra with Manipulatives

Technology
ca.algebra1.com
Interactive Classroom CD-ROM
AssignmentWorks CD-ROM
Graphing Calculator Easy Files

228 Chapter 4 Analyzing Linear Equations

Scaffolding Questions continued

- **TRAVEL** What type of graph would show that the longer you drive, the less gas is left in your gas tank? *a line with a negative slope*

Interpret Points on a Scatter Plot

Example 1 shows how to determine whether the graph of real-world data shows a *positive correlation*, a *negative correlation*, or *no correlation*.

 Formative Assessment

Use the Check Your Progress exercises after each example to determine students' understanding of concepts.

ADDITIONAL EXAMPLE

1 **TECHNOLOGY** The graph shows the average number of students per computer in Maria's school. Determine whether the graph shows a *positive correlation*, a *negative correlation*, or *no correlation*. If there is a positive or negative correlation, describe it.

Computer Sharing in Maria's School

(graph: Students per Computer vs Year)

Negative correlation; each year, Maria's school has more computers, making the students-per-computer rate smaller.

Additional Examples are also in:

- Noteables™ Interactive Study Notebook with Foldables™
- Interactive Classroom PowerPoint® Presentations

Study Tip

Correlations

positive: as *x* increases, *y* increases

negative: as *x* increases, *y* decreases

no correlation: no relationship between *x* and *y*

✓CHECK **Your Progress**

1. **CARS** The graph shows the weight and the highway gas mileage of selected cars. Determine whether the graph shows a *positive correlation*, a *negative correlation*, or *no correlation*. If there is a positive or negative correlation, describe its meaning in the situation.
The graph shows a negative correlation. As the weight of the automobile increases, the gas mileage decreases.

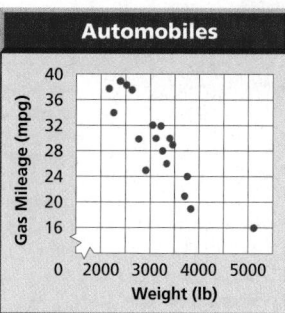

Automobiles

Source: Yahoo!

Is there a relationship between the length of a person's foot and his or her height? Make a scatter plot and then look for a pattern.

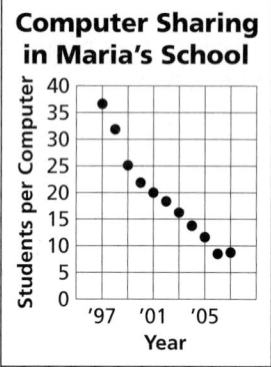

ALGEBRA LAB

Making Predictions

COLLECT AND ORGANIZE THE DATA

- Measure your partner's foot and height in centimeters. Then trade places.
- Add the points (foot length, height) to a class scatter plot.

ANALYZE THE DATA 1–3. See students' work.

1. Is there a correlation between foot length and height for the members of your class? If so, describe it.

2. Draw a line that summarizes the data and shows how the height changes as the foot length changes.

MAKE A CONJECTURE

3. Use the line to predict the height of a person whose foot length is 25 centimeters. Explain your method.

Make and Evaluate Predictions If the data points do not all lie on a line, but are close to a line, you can draw a **line of fit.** This line describes the trend of the data. Once you have a line of fit, you can find an equation of the line.

In this lesson, you will use a graphical method to find a line of fit. In Extend Lesson 4-6, you will use a graphing calculator to find a line of fit. The calculator uses a statistical method to find the line that most closely approximates the data. This line is called the **best-fit line.**

 Math Online Extra Examples at ca.algebra1.com

Algebra Lab Each pair of students will need a centimeter ruler or meterstick and grid paper. You could give pairs of students identical grids on transparencies and then place all the grids together on an overhead projector to get a quick compilation of the data points. If students are uncomfortable having their feet measured, allow them to skip this activity.

2 **ROLLER COASTERS** The table shows the largest vertical drops of nine roller coasters in the United States and the number of years after 1988 that they were opened.

Years since 1988	1	3	5	8	12	12	12	13	15
Vertical Drop (ft)	151	155	225	230	306	300	255	255	400

Source: ultimaterollercoaster.com

a. **Draw a scatter plot and determine what relationship exists, if any, in the data.**

As the number of years increases, the vertical drop of roller coasters increases. There is a positive correlation between the variables.

b. **Draw a line of fit.**

No one line will pass through all of the data points. Draw a line that passes close to the points. One line of fit is shown in the scatter plot.

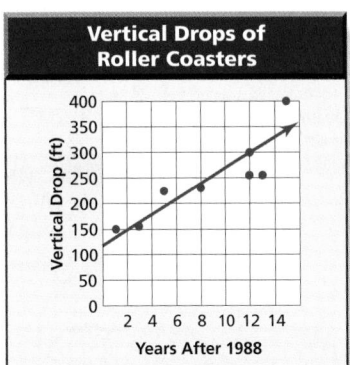

Vertical Drops of Roller Coasters

c. **Write the slope-intercept form of an equation for the line of fit.**

The line of fit shown above passes through (2, 150) and (12, 300).

Step 1 Find the slope.

$$m = \frac{y_2 - y_1}{x_2 - x_1} \quad \text{Slope formula}$$

$$= \frac{300 - 150}{12 - 2} \quad \begin{array}{l}(x_1, y_1) = (2, 150),\\ (x_2, y_2) = (12, 300)\end{array}$$

$$= \frac{150}{10} \text{ or } 15 \quad \text{Simplify.}$$

Step 2 Use $m = 15$ and either the point-slope form or the slope-intercept form to write the equation of the line of fit.

$$y - y_1 = m(x - x_1)$$
$$y - 150 = 15(x - 2)$$
$$y - 150 = 15x - 30$$
$$y = 15x + 120$$

A slope of 15 means that the vertical drops increased an average of 15 feet per year. A y-intercept of 120 means that a roller coaster that opened in 1988 has a vertical drop of approximately 120 feet.

✓ **CHECK Your Progress**

EAGLES The table shows an estimate for the number of bald eagle pairs in the United States for certain years since 1985.

Year since 1985	3	5	7	9	11	14	15
Bald Eagle Pairs	2500	3000	3700	4500	5000	5800	6500

Source: U.S. Fish and Wildlife Service

2A. Draw a scatter plot and determine what relationship exists, if any, in the data. **2A–2B. See Ch. 4 Answer Appendix.**

2B. Draw a line of fit for the scatter plot.

2C. Write the slope-intercept form of an equation for the line of fit. **2C. $y = 312.5x + 1562.5$**

online Personal Tutor at ca.algebra1.com

Study Tip

Lines of Fit
When you use the graphical method, the line of fit is an approximation. So, you may draw another line of fit using other points that is equally valid. Some valid lines of fit may not contain any of the data points.

Real-World Link
The difference in height between the top of the hill and the bottom is the vertical drop.

Source: ultimaterollercoaster.com

COncepts in MOtion
Interactive Lab
ca.algebra1.com

Make and Evaluate Predictions
Example 2 shows how to draw a scatter plot for real-world data, draw a line of fit, and then write the slope-intercept form of an equation for the line of fit. **Example 3** shows how to use the equation for the line of fit to predict values inside the range of the data for a real-world situation.

ADDITIONAL EXAMPLE

2 **POPULATION** The table shows the world population growing at a rapid rate.

Year	Populations (millions)
1650	500
1850	1000
1930	2000
1975	4000
2004	6400

a. Draw a scatter plot and determine what relationship exists, if any, in the data.
There is a positive correlation between years and population.

b. Draw a line of fit.

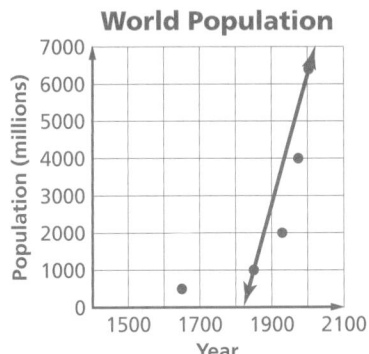

World Population

c. Write the slope-intercept form of an equation for the line of fit using (1850, 1000) and (2004, 6400).
$y = 35.1x - 63,935$

🔍 **Focus on Mathematical Content**

Scatter Plot A scatter plot has points unconnected by a line. These points can show trends in the relationship between two sets of data. If the points show a linear trend, you can draw a line of fit to model that trend. Once a line is drawn, you can find an equation of the line and use that equation to make predictions.

ADDITIONAL EXAMPLE

3 Use the equation for the line of fit in Additional Example 2 to predict the world's population in 2010. **6616 million**

Student Misconception

Remind students that predictions are only as valid as the equations used to find them. Therefore, there are as many predictions as there are equations that can be written from pairs of points.

3 Practice

Formative Assessment

Use Exercises 1–7 to check for understanding.

Use the chart at the bottom of this page to customize assignments for your students.

Odd/Even Assignments

Exercises 8–27 are structured so that students practice the same concepts whether they are assigned odd or even problems.

Additional Answers

3–4. positive

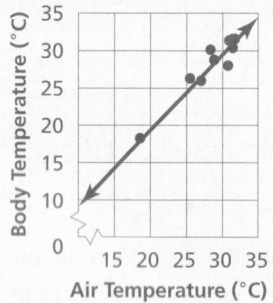

5. Sample answer: Using (31.2, 31.0) and (26.2, 25.6), $y = 1.08x - 2.696$.

6. Sample answer: 40.7°C

Linear extrapolation is used to predict values that are *outside* the range of the data. You can also use a linear equation to predict values that are *inside* the range of the data. This is called **linear interpolation**.

Study Tip
Limits of the Model
Notice that the equation cannot be used in extreme cases. For example, it is not reasonable that a roller coaster be 1000 feet tall.

Real-World EXAMPLE

3 ROLLER COASTERS Use the equation for the line of fit in Example 2. Estimate the largest vertical drop of a roller coaster that is opened in 2007.

$y = 15x + 120$ Original equation

$\quad = 15(19) + 120$ Replace x with 2007 − 1988 or 19.

$\quad = 405$ Simplify.

In 2007, the largest vertical drop is estimated to be 405 feet.

CHECK Your Progress

3. EAGLES Use the equation for the line of fit in Check Your Progress 2B on page 229 to estimate the number of bald eagle pairs in 2008.
about 8750

★ indicates multi-step problem

CHECK Your Understanding

1. Positive; the longer you study, the better your test score.
2. Negative; the more TV you watch, the less you exercise.

Example 1
(p. 228)

Determine whether each graph shows a *positive correlation*, a *negative correlation*, or *no correlation*. If there is a positive or negative correlation, describe its meaning in the situation.

1.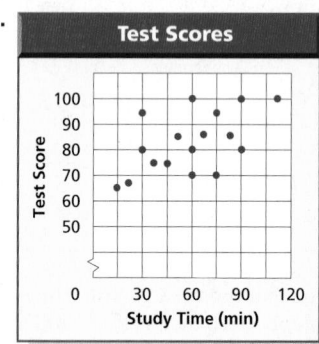

2.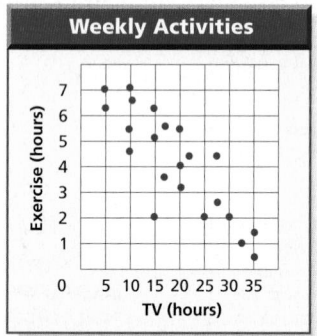

BIOLOGY For Exercises 3–7, use the table that shows the average body temperature in degrees Celsius of nine insects at a given air temperature.

Temperature (°C)								
Air	25.7	30.4	28.7	31.2	31.5	26.2	30.1	31.5	18.2
Body	27.0	31.5	28.9	31.0	31.5	25.6	28.4	31.7	18.7

Example 2
(p. 229)

3. ★ Draw a scatter plot and determine what relationship exists, if any, in the data.

4. Draw a line of fit for the scatter plot. **3–6. See margin.**

5. Write the slope-intercept form of an equation for the line of fit.

Example 3
(p. 230)

6. Predict the body temperature of an insect if the air temperature is 40.2°C.

7. ★ Suppose the air temperature is −50°C. According to your judgment, do you think the equation can give a reasonable estimate for the body temperature of an insect? Explain. **No; at this temperature, there would be no insects.**

230 Chapter 4 Analyzing Linear Equations

DIFFERENTIATED HOMEWORK OPTIONS

Level	Assignment	Two-Day Option	
BL Basic	8–27, 32, 33, 35–47	9–27 odd, 36, 37	8–26 even, 32, 33, 35, 38–47
OL Core	9–27 odd, 28–33, 35–47	8–27, 36, 37	28–33, 35, 38–47
AL Advanced/Pre-AP	28–42 (optional: 43–47)		

Exercises

HOMEWORK HELP	
For Exercises	**See Examples**
8–11	1
12–27	2, 3

Exercise Levels
A: 8–27
B: 28–31
C: 32–35

8. Negative; as time goes by, fewer people return their census forms.

9. no correlation

10. Positive; as time goes on, more people use electronic tax returns.

11. Positive; the higher the sugar content, the more Calories.

14. No; using the equation would give −330 cranes in 1900, which is not a reasonable estimate. The equation can be used to make reasonable estimates only within a narrow span of time.

Cross-Curricular Project

Math You can use
Online a line of fit to describe the trend in winning Olympic times. Visit ca.algebra1.com to continue work on your project.

Determine whether each graph shows a *positive correlation*, a *negative correlation*, or *no correlation*. If there is a positive or negative correlation, describe its meaning in the situation.

8.
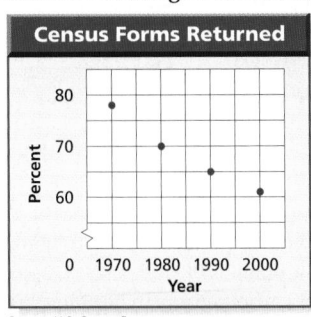
Census Forms Returned
Source: U.S. Census Bureau

9.
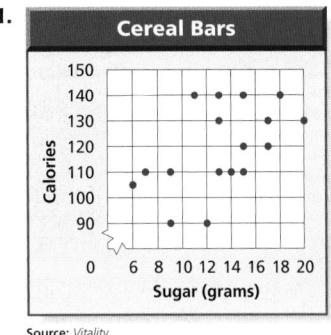
Atlantic Hurricanes
Source: USA TODAY

10.
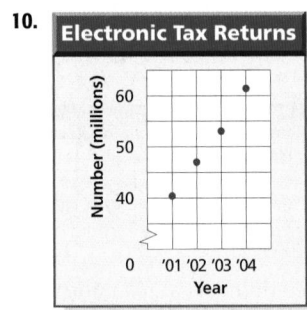
Electronic Tax Returns
Source: IRS

11.
Cereal Bars
Source: Vitality

BIRDS For Exercises 12–14, refer to the graph at the top of page 227 about whooping cranes. **12.** $y = 5x - 9830$

12. Use the points (2000, 170) and (2003, 185) to write an equation for a line of fit.

13. Predict the number of whooping cranes in 2008. **about 210**

★ **14.** Is it reasonable to use the equation to estimate the number of whooping cranes in any year, such as in 1900? Explain.

USED CARS For Exercises 15–17, use the scatter plot that shows the ages and prices of used cars from classified ads.

15. Use the points (2, 9600) and (5, 6000) to write the slope-intercept form of an equation for the line of fit shown in the scatter plot. $y = -1200x + 12,000$

16. Predict the price of a car that is 7 years old. **$3600**

★ **17.** Can you use the equation to make a decision about buying a used car that is 50 years old? Explain. **See margin.**

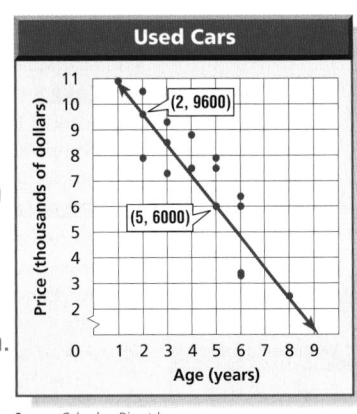
Used Cars
Source: Columbus Dispatch

Lesson 4-6 Statistics: Scatter Plots and Lines of Fit   **231**

Real-World Connections For Exercises 15–17, have students choose a used car from your local classified ads and substitute its price into the equation for line of fit. Ask students to compare the age given in the ad and the age derived from the equation.

⚠ **Exercise Alert!**
Internet Exercise 29 requires the use of the Internet or other reference materials.

Additional Answer

17. No; the equation would give a price of −$48,000. In reality, this car would be an antique and would more than likely be valuable.

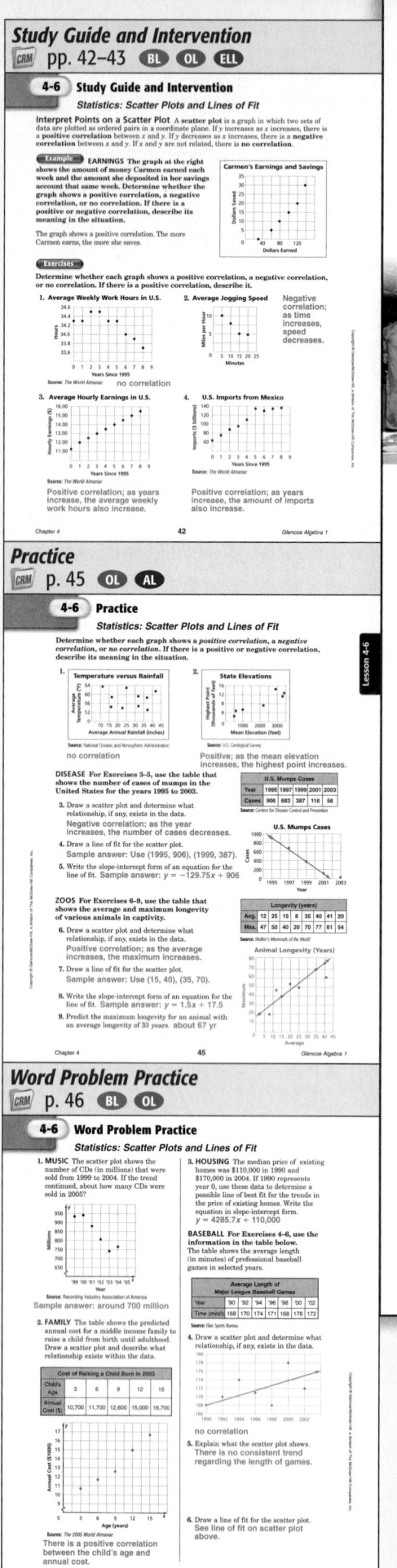

Study Guide and Intervention

CRM pp. 42–43 **BL** **OL** **ELL**

4-6 Study Guide and Intervention

Statistics: Scatter Plots and Lines of Fit

Interpret Points on a Scatter Plot A scatter plot is a graph in which two sets of data are plotted as ordered pairs in a coordinate system. If *y* increases as *x* increases, there is a **positive** correlation between *x* and *y*. If *y* decreases as *x* increases, there is a **negative** correlation between *x* and *y*. If *x* and *y* are not related, there is **no correlation**.

Example EARNINGS The graph at the right shows the amount of money Carmen earned each week and the amount she deposited in her savings account that same week. Determine whether the graph shows a positive correlation, a negative correlation, or no correlation. If there is a positive or negative correlation, describe its meaning in the situation.

The graph shows a positive correlation. The more Carmen earns, the more she saves.

Exercises

Determine whether each graph shows a positive correlation, a negative correlation, or no correlation. If there is a positive correlation, describe it.

1. Average Weekly Work Hours in U.S. — no correlation

2. Average Jogging Speed — Negative correlation; as time increases, speed decreases.

3. Average Hourly Earnings in U.S. — Positive correlation; as years increase, the average weekly work hours also increase.

4. U.S. Imports from Mexico — Positive correlation; as years increase, the amount of imports also increase.

Chapter 4   42   Glencoe Algebra 1

Practice

CRM p. 45 **OL** **AL**

4-6 Practice

Statistics: Scatter Plots and Lines of Fit

Determine whether each graph shows a *positive correlation, a negative correlation,* or *no correlation.* If there is a positive or negative correlation, describe its meaning in the situation.

1. Temperature versus Rainfall — no correlation

2. State Elevations — Positive; as the mean elevation increases, the highest point increases.

DISEASE For Exercises 3–5, use the table that shows the number of cases of mumps in the United States for the years 1995 to 2003.

3. Draw a scatter plot and determine what relationship, if any, exists in the data. Negative correlation; as the year increases, the number of cases decreases.

4. Draw a line of fit for the scatter plot. Sample answer: Use (1995, 906), (1999, 387).

5. Write the slope-intercept form of an equation for the line of fit. Sample answer: $y = -129.75x + 906$

ZOOS For Exercises 6–9, use the table that shows the average and maximum longevity of various animals in captivity.

6. Draw a scatter plot and determine what relationship, if any, exists in the data. Positive correlation; as the average increases, the maximum increases.

7. Draw a line of fit for the scatter plot. Sample answer: Use (15, 40), (35, 70).

8. Write the slope-intercept form of an equation for the line of fit. Sample answer: $y = 1.5x + 17.5$

9. Predict the maximum longevity for an animal with an average longevity of 33 years. about 67 yr

Chapter 4   45   Glencoe Algebra 1

Word Problem Practice

CRM p. 46 **BL** **OL**

4-6 Word Problem Practice

Statistics: Scatter Plots and Lines of Fit

1. MUSIC The scatter plot shows the number of CDs (in millions) that were sold from 1999 to 2004. If the trend continued, about how many CDs were sold in 2005? Sample answer: around 700 million

2. FAMILY The table shows the predicted annual cost for a middle income family to raise a child from birth until adulthood. Draw a scatter plot and describe what relationship exists within the data. no correlation

3. HOUSING The median price of existing homes was $110,000 in 1990 and $170,000 in 2004. If 1990 represents year 0, use these data to determine a possible line of best fit for the trends in the price of existing homes. Write the equation in slope-intercept form. $y = 4285.7x + 110,000$

BASEBALL For Exercises 4–6, use the information in the table below. The table shows the average length (in minutes) of professional baseball games in selected years.

4. Draw a scatter plot and determine what relationship, if any, exists in the data.

5. Explain what the scatter plot shows. There is no consistent trend regarding length of games.

6. Draw a line of fit for the scatter plot. See the line of fit on scatter plot above.

There is a weak positive correlation between the child's age and annual cost.

Chapter 4   46   Glencoe Algebra 1

232 Chapter 4 Analyzing Linear Equations

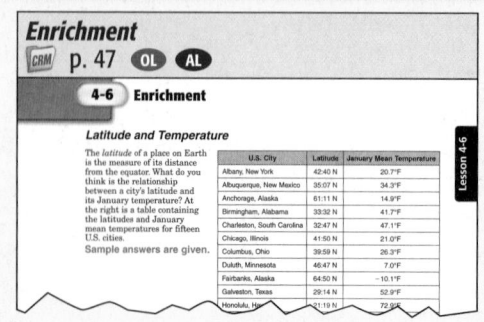

Real-World Career

Aerospace Engineers
Aerospace engineers specialize in a type of aircraft such as commercial airplanes, military aircraft, and spacecraft.

Math Online
For more information, go to ca.algebra1.com.

28. Sample answer: Cities with greater northern latitudes have lower January temperatures.

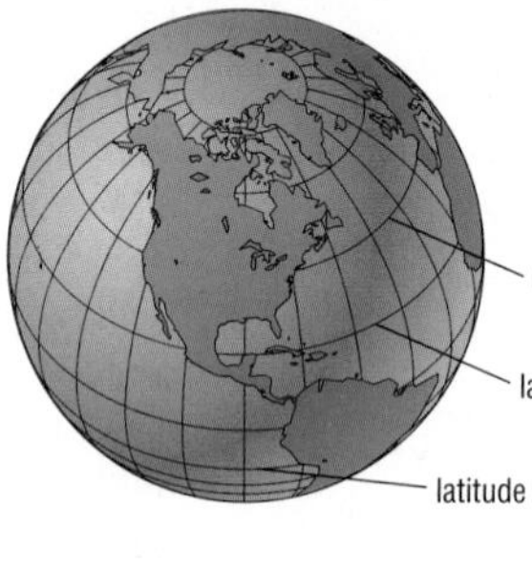

EXTRA PRACTICE
See pages 726, 747.

Math Online
Self-Check Quiz at ca.algebra1.com

---

20. Sample answer: $y = 37x - 153$

21. Sample answer: 32°C

PHYSICAL SCIENCE For Exercises 18–22, use the following information.

Hydrocarbons are composed of only carbon and hydrogen atoms. The table gives the number of carbon atoms and the boiling points for several hydrocarbons.

Hydrocarbons			
Name	Formula	Number of Carbon Atoms	Boiling Point (°C)
Ethane	C_2H_6	2	−89
Propane	C_3H_8	3	−42
Butane	C_4H_{10}	4	−1
Hexane	C_6H_{12}	6	69
Octane	C_8H_{18}	8	126

18. Draw a scatter plot comparing the numbers of carbon atoms to the boiling points. **18–19. See Ch. 4 Answer Appendix.**

19. Draw a line of fit for the data.

20. Write the slope-intercept form of an equation for the line of fit.

21. Predict the boiling point for pentane (C_5H_{12}), which has 5 carbon atoms.

22. The boiling point of heptane is 98.4°C. Use the equation of the line of fit to predict the number of carbon atoms in heptane. **Sample answer: 7**

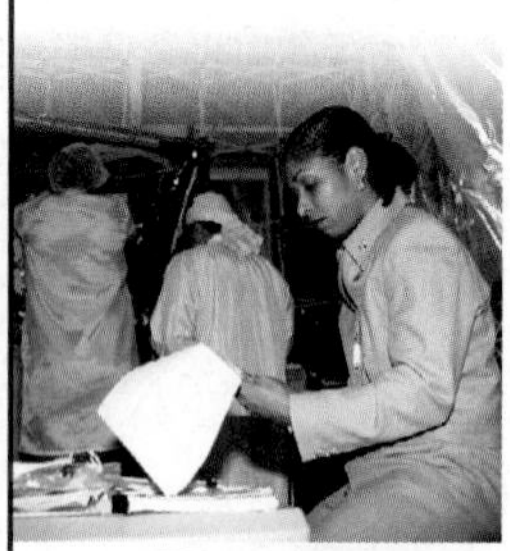

SPACE For Exercises 23–27, use the table that shows the amount the United States government has spent on space and other technologies in selected years.

Federal Spending on Space and Other Technologies									
Year	1980	1985	1990	1995	1996	1997	1998	1999	2004
Spending (billions of dollars)	4.5	6.6	11.6	12.6	12.7	13.1	12.9	12.4	15.4

Source: U.S. Office of Management and Budget

★ 23. Draw a scatter plot and determine what relationship, if any, exists in the data.

24. Draw a line of fit for the scatter plot. **23–24. See Ch. 4 Answer Appendix.**

25. Let *x* represent the number of years since 1980. Let *y* represent spending in billions of dollars. Write the slope-intercept form of the equation for the line of fit. **Sample answer: Using (0, 4.5) and (16, 12.7), $y = 0.5125x + 4.5$.**

26. Predict the amount that will be spent on space and other technologies in 2007. **Sample answer: about $18.3 billion**

27. Make a critical judgment about the amount that will be spent on space and other technologies in the next century. Would the equation that you wrote be a useful model? **See Ch. 4 Answer Appendix.**

GEOGRAPHY For Exercises 28–31, use the following information.
The *latitude* of a place on Earth is the measure of its distance from the equator.

28. **MAKE A CONJECTURE** What do you think is the relationship between a city's latitude and its January temperature?

29. **RESEARCH** Use the Internet or other reference to find the latitude of 15 cities in the northern hemisphere and the corresponding January mean temperatures. **See students' work.**

30. Make a scatter plot and draw a line of fit for the data. **See students' work.**

★ 31. Write an equation for the line of fit. **See students' work.**

latitude 40° N
latitude 20° N
latitude 20° S

232 Chapter 4 Analyzing Linear Equations

Enrichment

CRM p. 47 **OL** **AL**

4-6 Enrichment

Latitude and Temperature

The *latitude* of a place on Earth is the measure of its distance from the equator. What do you think is the relationship between a city's latitude and its January temperature? At the right is a table containing the latitudes and January mean temperatures for fifteen U.S. cities.

Sample answers are given.

U.S. City	Latitude	January Mean Temperature
Albany, New York	42.40 N	20.7°F
Albuquerque, New Mexico	35.07 N	34.3°F
Anchorage, Alaska	61.11 N	14.9°F
Birmingham, Alabama	33.32 N	41.7°F
Charleston, South Carolina	32.47 N	47.1°F
Chicago, Illinois	41.50 N	21.0°F
Columbus, Ohio	39.59 N	26.3°F
Duluth, Minnesota	46.47 N	7.0°F
Fairbanks, Alaska	64.50 N	−10.1°F
Galveston, Texas	29.14 N	52.9°F
Honolulu, Hawaii	21.19 N	72.6°F

BL = Below Grade Level

OL = On Grade Level

AL = Above Grade Level

ELL = English Language Learner

Additional pages not shown:

CRM *Lesson Reading Guide*, p. 41 **BL** **OL** **ELL**

CRM *Skills Practice*, p. 44 **BL** **OL**

H.O.T. Problems

33. Linear extrapolation predicts values outside the range of the data set. Linear interpolation predicts values inside the range of the data.

32. OPEN ENDED Sketch scatter plots that have each type of correlation: positive, negative, and none. Associate each graph with a real-life situation. **See Ch. 4 Answer Appendix.**

33. REASONING Compare and contrast interpolation and extrapolation.

34. CHALLENGE A test contains 20 true-false questions. Draw a scatter plot that shows the relationship between the number of correct answers x and the number of incorrect answers y. **See margin.**

35. *Writing in Math* Draw a scatter plot that shows a person's height and his or her age, with a description of any trends. Explain how you could use the scatter plot to predict a person's age given his or her height. How can the information from a scatter plot be used to identify trends and make decisions? **See margin.**

STANDARDS PRACTICE 7PS1.2, 7.0

36. REVIEW Mr. Hernandez collected data on the heights and average stride lengths of a random sample of students in grades 8, 9, and 10. He then graphed the data on a scatter plot. What correlation did he most likely see? **A**

   A positive   **C** constant

   B negative   **D** no correlation

37. Which equation *best* fits the data in the table? **G**

x	y
1	5
2	7
3	7
4	11

   F $y = x + 4$

   G $y = 2x + 3$

   H $y = 7$

   J $y = 4x - 5$

Spiral Review

Write the point-slope form of an equation for the line that passes through each point with the given slope. (Lesson 4-5)

38. $(1, -2); m = 3$
$y + 2 = 3(x - 1)$

39. $(-2, 3); m = -2$
$y - 3 = -2(x + 2)$

40. $(-3, -3); m = 1$
$y + 3 = x + 3$

★ **41. COMMUNICATION** A calling plan charges a rate per minute plus a flat fee. A 10-minute call to the Czech Republic costs $3.19. A 15-minute call costs $4.29. Write a linear equation in slope-intercept form to represent the total cost C of an m-minute call. Then find the cost of a 12-minute call. (Lesson 4-4)
$C = 0.22m + 0.99; \$3.63$

★ **42. EXERCISE** The statement below was found in *Healthy Fun* magazine.

A typical 100-pound kid can burn more than 350 calories per hour riding a bike.

At this rate, about how many Calories would be burned riding a bike 25 minutes? (Lesson 2-6) **about 145.8 Calories**

GET READY for the Next Lesson

PREREQUISITE SKILL Write the multiplicative inverse of each number. (Pages 698–699)

43. 10 $\frac{1}{10}$ **44.** -1 -1 **45.** $\frac{2}{3}$ $\frac{3}{2}$ **46.** $-\frac{1}{9}$ -9 **47.** $\frac{3}{4}$ $-\frac{4}{3}$

Pre-AP Activity   Use after the Exercises

Write $(1, 10.1)$, $(2, 9.8)$, $(3, 10)$, $(4, 10.5)$, $(5, 10.4)$, $(6, 10.8)$, and $(7, 10.3)$ on the board. As a class, graph these data points on two separate graphs. Make the scale on the first graph such that the result is a scatter plot with no correlation. Make the scale on the second graph such that the result is a scatter plot with a positive correlation. Discuss how graphs can be manipulated to show different trends.

---

4 Assess

Yesterday's News Ask students to write how yesterday's lesson on writing an equation in point-slope form helped them with today's lesson.

 **Formative Assessment**

Check for student understanding of concepts in Lessons 4-5 and 4-6.

CRM Quiz 3, p. 60

FOLDABLES Foldables™
Study Organizer Follow-Up

Remind students to use the sixth flap in their Foldables to record notes on what they have learned about drawing lines of fit. Students should include examples of the graphs given in the Key Concept box on page 225.

Additional Answers

34.

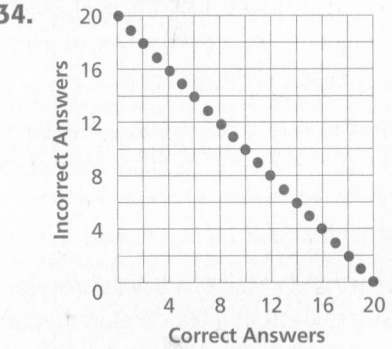

35. Sample answer: You can visualize a line to determine whether the data has a positive or negative correlation. The graph below shows the ages and heights of people. To predict a person's age given his or her height, write a linear equation for the line of fit. Then substitute the person's height and solve for the corresponding age. You can use the pattern in the scatter plot to make decisions.

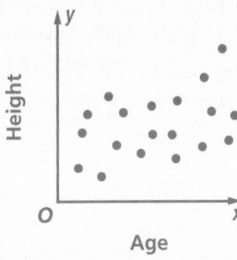

Graphing Calculator Lab
Regression and Median-Fit Lines

Preparation for Advanced Placement Probability and Statistics Standards 12.0 Students find the line of best fit to a given distribution of data by using least squares regression.
Standard 13.0 Students know what the *correlation coefficient of two variables* means and are familiar with the coefficient's properties.

One type of equation of best-fit you can find is a linear **regression equation**.

ACTIVITY 1

MUSIC The table shows the percent of music sales that were made on the Internet in the United States for the period 1997–2004.

Year	1997	1998	1999	2000	2001	2002	2003	2004
Sales	0.3	1.1	2.4	3.2	2.9	3.4	5.0	5.9

Source: Recording Industry Association of America

Find and graph a linear regression equation. Then predict the percent of music sales that will be made on the Internet in 2010.

Step 1   Find a regression equation.

Enter the years in L1 and the earnings in L2. Find the regression equation.

KEYSTROKES: STAT   ENTER 1997 ENTER …
▶ 0.3 ENTER …   STAT ▶ 4
ENTER

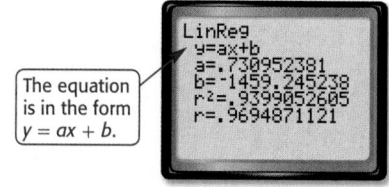

The equation is in the form $y = ax + b$.

The equation is about $y = 0.73x - 1459.25$.

r is the **linear correlation coefficient**. The closer the absolute value of r is to 1, the better the equation models the data.

Step 2   Graph the regression equation.

Use STAT PLOT to graph the scatter plot.

KEYSTROKES: 2nd [STAT] ENTER   ENTER

Copy the equation to the Y= list and graph.

KEYSTROKES: Y=   VARS 5 ▶ ▶ 1 GRAPH

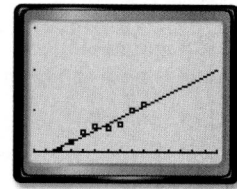

[1995, 2010] scl: 1 by [0, 15] scl: 5

Step 3   Predict using the regression equation.

Find y when $x = 2010$.

KEYSTROKES: 2nd [CALC] 1 2010 ENTER

According to the regression equation, in 2010 about 9.97% of music sales will be made on the Internet.

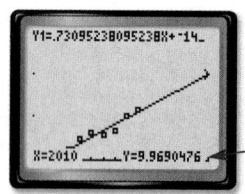

The graph and the coordinates of the point are shown.

Math Online Other Calculator Keystrokes at ca.algebra1.com

Objective Use a graphing calculator to investigate linear regression and median-fit lines.

Materials
• graphing calculator

Teaching Tip The TI-83/84 Plus graphing calculator has two methods to compute the equation of a best-fit line:

LinReg(ax + b) linear regression

Med-Med median-fit line

The linear regression method uses a least-squares fit method to determine the values for *a* and *b*. This utilizes calculus involving the distance each point is from the best-fit line. The median-fit method calculates the medians of the coordinates of the data points.

The calculator also displays values for r^2 and r, where r is the linear correlation coefficient. The closer $|r|$ is to 1, the better the equation fits the data.

If the r and r^2 values are not displayed, have students turn these features on. To do that, press 2nd [CATALOG]. Then scroll down to Diagnostic On and press ENTER   ENTER .

2 Teach

Working in Cooperative Groups
Put students in groups of 2 or 3, mixing abilities. Have groups complete Activities 1–2.

For both Activities, make sure that students understand the keystrokes for the STAT menu. Make sure students have cleared the **L1** and **L2** lists before entering new data.

Practice Have students complete Analyze the Results 1–3.

A second type of best-fit line that can be found using a graphing calculator is a **median-fit line.** The equation of a median-fit line is calculated using the medians of the coordinates of the data points.

ACTIVITY 2

Find and graph a median-fit equation for the data on music sales. Then predict the percent of sales that will be made on the Internet in 2010. Compare this prediction to the one made using the regression equation.

Step 1 Find a median-fit equation.

The data are already in Lists 1 and 2. Find the median-fit equation by using *Med-Med* on the STAT CALC menu.

KEYSTROKES: STAT ▶ 3 ENTER

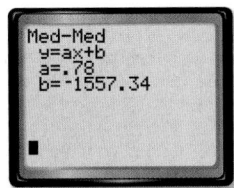

The median-fit equation is $y = 0.78x - 1557.34$.

Step 2 Graph the median-fit equation.

Copy the equation to the Y= list and graph.

KEYSTROKES: Y= CLEAR VARS 5 ▶ ▶
1 GRAPH

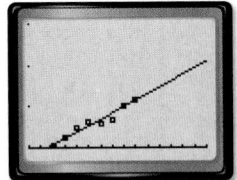

[1995, 2010] scl: 1 by [0, 15] scl: 5

Step 3 Predict using the median-fit equation.

KEYSTROKES: 2nd [CALC] 1 2010 ENTER

According to the median-fit equation, about 10.46% of music sales will be made on the Internet in 2010. This is slightly more than the predicted value found using the regression equation.

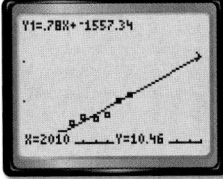

ANALYZE THE RESULTS

Refer to the data on roller coasters in Example 2 on page 229.

1. Find regression and median-fit equations for the data.
   regression: $y = 14.02x + 126.64$; median-fit: $y = 15.86x + 99.32$

2. What is the correlation coefficient of the regression equation? What does it tell you about the data?
   0.8923298033; The regression equation is a fairly good fit for the data.

3. Use the regression and median-fit equations to predict the largest vertical drop for a roller coaster in 2007. Compare these to the number found in Example 3 on page 230. regression: 393 ft; median-fit: 401 ft; Both estimates are close to but less than the prediction.

Extend 4-6 Graphing Calculator Lab: Regression and Median-Fit Lines   **235**

✓ **Formative Assessment**

Use Exercise 3 to assess whether students are able to determine the regression and median-fit equations and use them to make predictions.

From Concrete to Abstract Ask:

• When should you use linear regression or the median-fit method to create a model for a set of data? Sample answer: Use either method when the data in a scatterplot shows a linear pattern.

4-7 **Geometry: Parallel and Perpendicular Lines**

 Standards Alignment

Before Lesson 4-7
Identify perpendicular and parallel lines from 🔑 Standard 5MG2.1

Lesson 4-7
Understand the concepts of parallel and perpendicular lines from Standard 8.0

After Lesson 4-7
Prove theorems by using coordinate geometry from 🔑 Standard G17.0

2 Teach

Scaffolding Questions
Have students read *Get Ready for the Lesson*.
Ask:
- How would the graph of $y = x + 5$ relate to the graphs shown? It would be parallel to them.
- How would the appearance of the lines change if the slopes were 2? The lines would be steeper, but they would still be parallel.
- **Geometry** Describe the slopes of the sides of a rectangle whose vertices are $A(0, 0)$, $B(2, 0)$, $C(2, 6)$, and $D(0, 6)$. $\overline{AB}$ and $\overline{CD}$ have slope 0 and are parallel. $\overline{AD}$ and $\overline{BC}$ are vertical, so their slope is undefined. They are also parallel.

Lesson 4-7 Resources

Chapter 4 Resource Masters
Lesson Reading Guide, p. 49 (BL) (OL) (ELL)
Study Guide and Intervention, pp. 50–51 (BL) (OL) (ELL)
Skills Practice, p. 52 (BL) (OL)
Practice, p. 53 (OL) (AL)
Word Problem Practice, p. 54 (OL) (AL)
Enrichment, p. 55 (OL) (AL)
Quiz 4, p. 60

Transparencies
5-Minute Check Transparency 4-7
Additional Print Resources
Noteables™ Interactive Study Notebook with Foldables™
Teaching Algebra with Manipulatives

Technology
ca.algebra1.com
Interactive Classroom CD-ROM
AssignmentWorks CD-ROM
Graphing Calculator Easy Files

Main Ideas
- Write an equation of the line that passes through a given point, parallel to a given line.
- Write an equation of the line that passes through a given point, perpendicular to a given line.

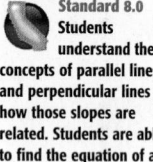 **Standard 8.0**
Students understand the concepts of parallel lines and perpendicular lines and how those slopes are related. Students are able to find the equation of a line perpendicular to a given line that passes through a given point. (CAHSEE)

New Vocabulary
parallel lines
perpendicular lines

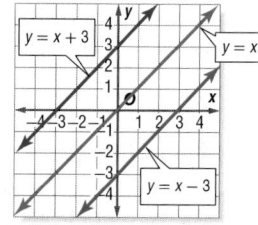

The graph shows a family of linear graphs whose slope is 1. Note that the lines do not appear to intersect.

Parallel Lines Lines in the same plane that do not intersect are called **parallel lines**. Parallel lines have the same slope.

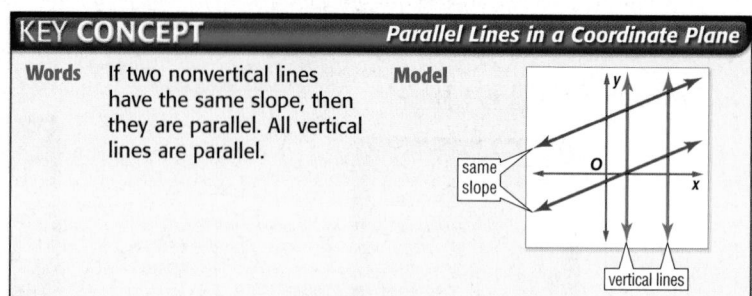

KEY CONCEPT   *Parallel Lines in a Coordinate Plane*

Words	Model
If two nonvertical lines have the same slope, then they are parallel. All vertical lines are parallel.	

You can write the equation of a line parallel to a given line if you know a point on the line and an equation of the given line.

EXAMPLE   Parallel Line Through a Given Point

① Write the slope-intercept form of an equation for the line that passes through $(-1, -2)$ and is parallel to the graph of $y = -3x - 2$.

The line parallel to $y = -3x - 2$ has the same slope, -3. Replace m with -3, and (x_1, y_1) with $(-1, -2)$ in the point-slope form.

$y - y_1 = m(x - x_1)$ Point-slope form

$y - (-2) = -3[x - (-1)]$ Replace m with -3, y_1 with -2, and x_1 with -1.

$y + 2 = -3(x + 1)$ Simplify.

$y + 2 = -3x - 3$ Distributive Property

$y + 2 - 2 = -3x - 3 - 2$ Subtract 2 from each side.

$y = -3x - 5$ Write the equation in slope-intercept form.

✓ CHECK **Your Progress**

1. Write the point-slope form of an equation for the line that passes through $(4, -1)$ and is parallel to the graph of $y = \frac{1}{4}x + 7$.

$$y + 1 = \frac{1}{4}(x - 4)$$

Perpendicular Lines Lines that intersect at right angles are called **perpendicular lines.** There is a relationship between the slopes of perpendicular lines.

Example 1 shows how to write the slope-intercept form of an equation for a line that passes through a particular coordinate and is parallel to a given line.

ALGEBRA LAB

Perpendicular Lines

- A scalene triangle is one in which no two sides are equal in length. Cut out a scalene right triangle *ABC* so that ∠*C* is a right angle. Label the vertices and the sides as shown.

- Draw a coordinate plane on grid paper. Place △*ABC* on the coordinate plane so that *A* is at the origin and side *b* lies along the positive *x*-axis.

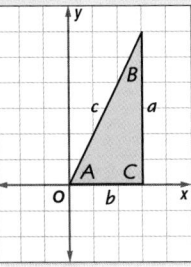

ANALYZE THE RESULTS

1. Name the coordinates of *B*. (3, 6)

2. What is the slope of side *c*? 2

3. Rotate the triangle 90° counterclockwise so that *A* is still at the origin and side *b* is along the positive *y*-axis. Name the coordinates of *B*. (−6, 3)

4. What is the slope of side *c*? $-\frac{1}{2}$

5. Repeat the activity for two other scalene right triangles. See students' work.

6. For each triangle and its rotation, what is the relationship between the first position of side *c* and the second? They are perpendicular.

7. For each triangle and its rotation, describe the relationship between the coordinates of *B* in the first and second positions.

8. Describe the relationship between the slopes of *c* in each position.

MAKE A CONJECTURE

8. They are opposite reciprocals.

9. Their product is −1.

9. Describe the relationship between the slopes of any two perpendicular lines.

Study Tip

Look Back

To review **rotations on the coordinate plane,** see Lesson 3-2.

7. The *x*- and *y*-coordinates are reversed and the *x*-coordinate is multiplied by −1.

The results of the Algebra Lab suggests an important property of perpendicular lines.

Review Vocabulary

Reciprocals $\frac{1}{4}$ and 4 are reciprocals because their product is 1. (Lesson 1-4)

KEY CONCEPT — *Perpendicular Lines in a Coordinate Plane*

Words If the product of the slopes of two nonvertical lines is −1, then the lines are perpendicular. In this case, the slopes are *opposite reciprocals* of each other. Vertical lines and horizontal lines are also perpendicular.

Model
$m = -\frac{1}{2}$
$m = 2$
horizontal line
vertical line

 Formative Assessment

Use the Check Your Progress exercises after each example to determine students' understanding of concepts.

ADDITIONAL EXAMPLE

1. Write the slope-intercept form of an equation for the line that passes through (4, −2) and is parallel to the graph of $y = \frac{1}{2}x - 7$. $y = \frac{1}{2}x - 4$

Additional Examples are also in:

- Noteables™ Interactive Study Notebook with Foldables™
- Interactive Classroom PowerPoint® Presentations

Perpendicular Lines

Example 2 shows how to determine whether two line segments in a real-world situation are perpendicular. **Example 3** shows how to write an equation, in slope-intercept form, of a line perpendicular to a given line if you know a point on the line and the equation of the given line. **Example 4** shows how to write an equation of a line perpendicular to a given line if you know the *x*-intercept and the equation of the given line.

Algebra Lab

Give each student or groups of students grid paper and scissors. To save time, you may want to provide students with scalene triangles cut from lightweight cardboard. If students are not familiar with the term *negative reciprocal*, point out that another name for multiplicative inverse is *reciprocal*.

Intervention

Slope of Lines   Remind students that all vertical lines are parallel, and all horizontal lines are parallel. All vertical lines are perpendicular to all horizontal lines and therefore, all horizontal lines are perpendicular to all vertical lines.

Focus on Mathematical Content

Parallel and Perpendicular Lines

All vertical lines are parallel and all horizontal lines are parallel. All vertical lines are perpendicular to all horizontal lines, and vice versa. Two nonvertical lines are parallel if their slopes are the same. They are perpendicular if the product of their slopes is –1.

ADDITIONAL EXAMPLES

2 **GEOMETRY** The height of a trapezoid is measured on a segment that is perpendicular to a base. In trapezoid $ARTP$, $\overline{AP}$ and $\overline{RT}$ are bases. Can $\overline{EZ}$ be used to measure the height of the trapezoid? Explain.

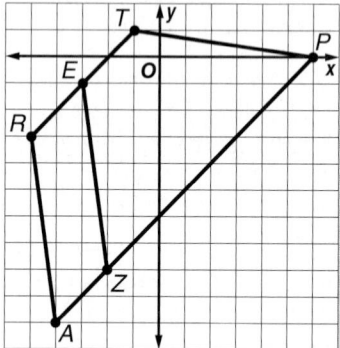

No, the slope of $\overline{RT}$ is 1, and the slope of $\overline{EZ}$ is –7. Since $1(-7) \neq 1$, $\overline{EZ}$ is not perpendicular to $\overline{RT}$. So, it cannot be used to measure height.

3 Write the slope-intercept form for an equation of a line that passes through $(4, -1)$ and is perpendicular to the graph of $7x - 2y = 3$. $y = -\frac{2}{7}x + \frac{1}{7}$

Tips for New Teachers — Preventing Errors

Encourage students to understand the process used instead of simply the mechanics. For example, what do they know from the given information? What do they know about perpendicular lines? What do they need to know to write a new equation?

Real-World EXAMPLE   Determine Whether Lines are Perpendicular

2 **DESIGN** The outline of a new company logo is shown on a coordinate plane. Is $\angle DFE$ a right angle?

If $\overline{BE}$ and $\overline{AD}$ are perpendicular, then $\angle DFE$ is a right angle. Find the slopes of $\overline{BE}$ and $\overline{AD}$.

slope of $\overline{BE}$: $m = \dfrac{1-3}{7-2}$ or $-\dfrac{2}{5}$

slope of $\overline{AD}$: $m = \dfrac{6-1}{4-2}$ or $\dfrac{5}{2}$

The line segments are perpendicular because $-\dfrac{2}{5} \cdot \dfrac{5}{2} = -1$. Therefore, $\angle DFE$ is a right angle.

CHECK Your Progress   Slope of $\overline{QR} = \dfrac{6}{5}$, slope of $\overline{ST} = \dfrac{1}{5}$; they are not perpendicular.

2. CONSTRUCTION On the plans for a tree house, a beam represented by $\overline{QR}$ has endpoints $Q(-6, 2)$ and $R(-1, 8)$. A beam represented by $\overline{ST}$ has endpoints $S(-3, 6)$ and $T(-8, 5)$. Are the beams perpendicular? Explain.

You can write the equation of a line perpendicular to a given line if you know a point on the line and the equation of the given line.

EXAMPLE   Perpendicular Line Through a Given Point

3 Write the slope-intercept form of an equation for the line that passes through $(-3, -2)$ and is perpendicular to the graph of $x + 4y = 12$.

Step 1 Find the slope of the given line.

$x + 4y = 12$	Original equation
$x + 4y - x = 12 - x$	Subtract $1x$ from each side.
$4y = -1x + 12$	Simplify.
$\dfrac{4y}{4} = \dfrac{-1x + 12}{4}$	Divide each side by 4.
$y = -\dfrac{1}{4}x + 3$	Simplify.

Step 2 The slope of the given line is $-\dfrac{1}{4}$. So, the slope of the line perpendicular to this line is the opposite reciprocal of $-\dfrac{1}{4}$, or 4.

Step 3 Use the point-slope form to find the equation.

$y - y_1 = m(x - x_1)$	Point-slope form
$y - (-2) = 4[x - (-3)]$	$(x_1, y_1) = (-3, -2)$ and $m = 4$
$y + 2 = 4(x + 3)$	Simplify.
$y + 2 = 4x + 12$	Distributive Property
$y + 2 - 2 = 4x + 12 - 2$	Subtract 2 from each side.
$y = 4x + 10$	Simplify.

CHECK Your Progress

3. Write the slope-intercept form of an equation for the line that passes through $(4, 7)$ and is perpendicular to the graph of $y = \dfrac{2}{3}x - 1$. $y = -\dfrac{3}{2}x + 13$

Online Personal Tutor at ca.algebra1.com

Intervention

Parallel and Perpendicular Lines Students may be familiar with the terms *parallel* and *perpendicular*. However, before covering the examples, you may want students to use rulers to draw parallel and perpendicular lines on graph paper.

Write an equation in slope-intercept form for a line perpendicular to the graph of $y = -\frac{1}{3}x + 2$ that passes through the x-intercept of that line.

Step 1 Find the slope of the perpendicular line. The slope of the given line is $-\frac{1}{3}$, therefore a perpendicular line has slope 3.

Step 2 Find the x-intercept of the given line.

$$y = -\frac{1}{3}x + 2 \qquad \text{Original equation}$$

$$0 = -\frac{1}{3}x + 2 \qquad \text{Replace } y \text{ with 0.}$$

$$-2 = -\frac{1}{3}x \qquad \text{Subtract 2 from each side.}$$

$$6 = x \qquad \text{Multiply each side by } -3.$$

The x-intercept is at $(6, 0)$.

Step 3 Substitute the slope and the given point into the point-slope form of a linear equation. Then write in slope-intercept form.

$$y - y_1 = m(x - x_1) \quad \text{Point-slope form}$$

$$y - 0 = 3(x - 6) \quad \text{Replace } x_1 \text{ with 6, } y_1 \text{ with 0, and } m \text{ with 3.}$$

$$y = 3x - 18 \quad \text{Distributive Property}$$

CHECK Your Progress $y = \frac{2}{3}x + 4$

4. Write an equation in slope-intercept form for a line perpendicular to the graph of $3x + 2y = 8$ that passes through the y-intercept of that line.

★ indicates multi-step problem

CHECK Your Understanding

Example 1
(pp. 236–237)

Write the slope-intercept form of an equation for the line that passes through the given point and is parallel to the graph of each equation.

1.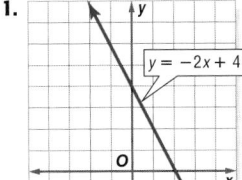

2.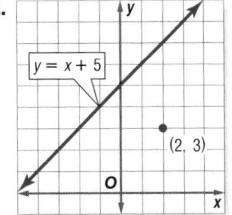

6. $y = -3x - 8$

7. $y = -\frac{5}{3}x + 8$

8. $y = \frac{1}{2}x - 3$

9. $y = -\frac{1}{6}x + \frac{1}{6}$

3. $(1, -3), y = 2x - 1$ $y = 2x - 5$ **4.** $(-2, 2), -3x + y = 4$ $y = 3x + 8$

Example 2
(p. 238)

★ **5. GARDENS** A garden is in the shape of a quadrilateral with vertices $A(-2, 1)$, $B(3, -3)$, $C(5, 7)$, and $D(-3, 4)$. Two paths represented by $\overline{AC}$ and $\overline{BD}$ cut across the garden. Are the paths perpendicular? Explain. **See margin.**

Example 3
(p. 238)

Write the slope-intercept form of an equation for the line that passes through the given point and is perpendicular to the graph of the equation.

6. $(-3, 1), y = \frac{1}{3}x + 2$ **7.** $(6, -2), y = \frac{3}{5}x - 4$ **8.** $(2, -2), 2x + y = 5$

Example 4
(p. 239)

9. Write the slope-intercept form for an equation of a line that is perpendicular to the graph of $y = 6x - 6$ and passes through the x-intercept of that line.

Lesson 4-7 Geometry: Parallel and Perpendicular Lines   **239**

ADDITIONAL EXAMPLE

 Write the slope-intercept form for an equation of a line perpendicular to the graph of $2y + 5x = 2$ that passes through $(0, 6)$. $y = \frac{2}{5}x + 6$

3 Practice

Formative Assessment

Use Exercises 1–9 to check for understanding.

Use the chart at the bottom of this page to customize assignments for your students.

Odd/Even Assignments

Exercises 10–27 are structured so that students practice the same concepts whether they are assigned odd or even problems.

Additional Answer

5. Slope of $\overline{AC} = \frac{1 - 7}{-2 - 5}$ or $\frac{6}{7}$; slope of $\overline{BD} = \frac{-3 - 4}{3 - (-3)}$ or $-\frac{7}{6}$; the paths are perpendicular.

 Geometry Concept

The fact that two nonvertical lines are perpendicular if and only if the product of their slopes is -1 depends on the considerations of similar triangles. This should be made clear to students, with the added assurance that they will learn the concept in geometry.

DIFFERENTIATED HOMEWORK OPTIONS

Level	Assignment	Two-Day Option	
BL Basic	10–27, 34–43	11–27 odd, 36, 37	10–26 even, 34, 35, 38–43
OL Core	11–31 odd, 32, 34–43	10–27, 36, 37	28–32, 34, 35, 38–43
AL Advanced /Pre-AP	28–43		

Study Guide and Intervention

CRM pp. 50–51 BL OL ELL

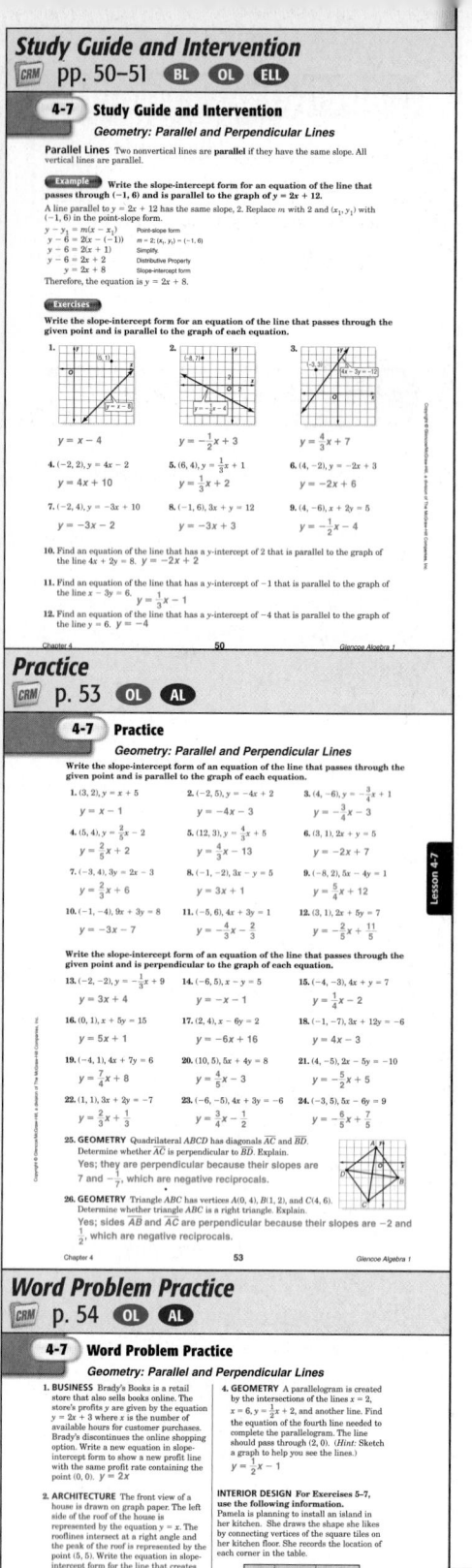

4-7 Study Guide and Intervention

Geometry: Parallel and Perpendicular Lines

Parallel Lines Two nonvertical lines are **parallel** if they have the same slope. All vertical lines are parallel.

Example **Write the slope-intercept form for an equation of the line that passes through (−1, 6) and is parallel to the graph of $y = 2x + 12$.**

A line parallel to $y = 2x + 12$ has the same slope, 2. Replace m with 2 and (x_1, y_1) with (−1, 6) in the point-slope form.

$y - y_1 = m(x - x_1)$	Point-slope form
$y - 6 = 2(x - (-1))$	$m = 2$; $(x_1, y_1) = (-1, 6)$
$y - 6 = 2(x + 1)$	Simplify.
$y - 6 = 2x + 2$	Distributive Property
$y = 2x + 8$	Slope-intercept form

Therefore, the equation is $y = 2x + 8$.

Exercises

Write the slope-intercept form for an equation of the line that passes through the given point and is parallel to the graph of each equation.

1. 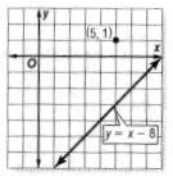

$y = x - 4$

2. 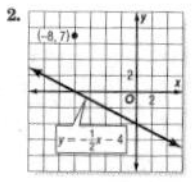

$y = -\frac{1}{2}x + 3$

3. 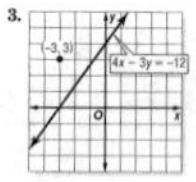

$y = \frac{4}{3}x + 7$

4. $(-2, 2)$, $y = 4x - 2$ $y = 4x + 10$
5. $(6, 4)$, $y = \frac{1}{3}x + 1$ $y = \frac{1}{3}x + 2$
6. $(4, -2)$, $y = -2x + 3$ $y = -2x + 6$
7. $(-2, 4)$, $y = -3x + 10$ $y = -3x - 2$
8. $(-1, 6)$, $3x + y = 12$ $y = -3x + 3$
9. $(4, -6)$, $x + 2y = 5$ $y = -\frac{1}{2}x - 4$
10. Find an equation of the line that has a y-intercept of 2 that is parallel to the graph of the line $4x + 2y = 8$. $y = -2x + 2$
11. Find an equation of the line that has a y-intercept of −1 that is parallel to the graph of the line $x - 3y = 6$. $y = \frac{1}{3}x - 1$
12. Find an equation of the line that has a y-intercept of −4 that is parallel to the graph of the line $y = 6$. $y = -4$

Chapter 4 50 Glencoe Algebra 1

Practice

CRM p. 53 OL AL

4-7 Practice

Geometry: Parallel and Perpendicular Lines

Write the slope-intercept form of an equation of the line that passes through the given point and is parallel to the graph of each equation.

1. $(3, 2)$, $y = x + 5$ $y = x - 1$
2. $(-2, 5)$, $y = -4x + 2$ $y = -4x - 3$
3. $(4, -6)$, $y = -\frac{3}{4}x + 1$ $y = -\frac{3}{4}x - 3$
4. $(5, 4)$, $y = \frac{2}{5}x - 2$ $y = \frac{2}{5}x + 2$
5. $(12, 3)$, $y = \frac{4}{3}x + 5$ $y = \frac{4}{3}x - 13$
6. $(3, 1)$, $2x + y = 5$ $y = -2x + 7$
7. $(-3, 4)$, $3y = 2x - 3$ $y = \frac{2}{3}x + 6$
8. $(-1, -2)$, $3x - y = 5$ $y = 3x + 1$
9. $(-8, 2)$, $5x - 4y = 1$ $y = \frac{5}{4}x + 12$
10. $(-1, -4)$, $9x + 3y = 8$ $y = -3x - 7$
11. $(-5, 6)$, $4x + 3y = 1$ $y = -\frac{4}{3}x - \frac{2}{3}$
12. $(3, 1)$, $2x + 5y = 7$ $y = -\frac{2}{5}x + \frac{11}{5}$

Write the slope-intercept form of an equation of the line that passes through the given point and is perpendicular to the graph of each equation.

13. $(-2, -2)$, $y = -\frac{1}{3}x + 9$ $y = 3x + 4$
14. $(-6, 5)$, $x - y = 5$ $y = -x - 1$
15. $(-4, -3)$, $4x + y = 7$ $y = \frac{1}{4}x - 2$
16. $(0, 1)$, $x + 5y = 15$ $y = 5x + 1$
17. $(2, 4)$, $x - 6y = 2$ $y = -6x + 16$
18. $(-1, -7)$, $3x + 12y = -6$ $y = 4x - 3$
19. $(-4, 1)$, $4x + 7y = 6$ $y = \frac{7}{4}x + 8$
20. $(10, 5)$, $5x + 4y = 8$ $y = \frac{4}{5}x - 3$
21. $(4, -5)$, $2x - 5y = -10$ $y = -\frac{5}{2}x + 5$
22. $(1, 1)$, $3x + 2y = -7$ $y = \frac{2}{3}x + \frac{1}{3}$
23. $(-6, -5)$, $4x + 3y = -6$ $y = \frac{3}{4}x - \frac{1}{2}$
24. $(-3, 5)$, $5x - 6y = 9$ $y = -\frac{6}{5}x + \frac{7}{5}$
25. **GEOMETRY** Quadrilateral $ABCD$ has diagonals $\overline{AC}$ and $\overline{BD}$. Determine whether $\overline{AC}$ is perpendicular to $\overline{BD}$. Explain.
Yes; they are perpendicular because their slopes are 7 and $-\frac{1}{7}$, which are negative reciprocals.

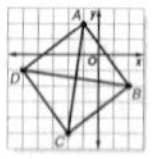

26. **GEOMETRY** Triangle ABC has vertices $A(0, 4)$, $B(1, 2)$, and $C(4, 6)$. Determine whether triangle ABC is a right triangle. Explain.
Yes; sides $\overline{AB}$ and $\overline{AC}$ are perpendicular because their slopes are −2 and $\frac{1}{2}$, which are negative reciprocals.

Chapter 4 53 Glencoe Algebra 1

Word Problem Practice

CRM p. 54 OL AL

4-7 Word Problem Practice

Geometry: Parallel and Perpendicular Lines

1. **BUSINESS** Brady's Books is a retail store that also sells books online. The store's profits y are given by the equation $y = 2x + 3$ where x is the number of available hours for customer purchases. Brady's discontinues the online shopping option. Write a new equation in slope-intercept form to show a new profit line with the same profit rate containing the point (0, 0). $y = 2x$

2. **ARCHITECTURE** The front view of a house is drawn on graph paper. The left side of the roof of the house is represented by the equation $y = x$. The rooflines intersect at a right angle and the peak of the roof is represented by the point (5, 5). Write the equation in slope-intercept form for the line that creates the right side of the roof.

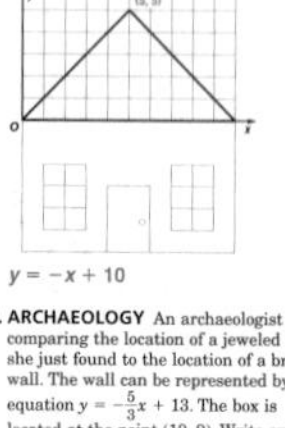

$y = -x + 10$

3. **ARCHAEOLOGY** An archaeologist is comparing the location of a jeweled box she just found to the location of a brick wall. The wall can be represented by the equation $y = -\frac{5}{3}x + 13$. The box is located at the point (10, 9). Write an equation representing a line that is perpendicular to the wall and that passes through the location of the box.
$y = \frac{3}{5}x + 3$

4. **GEOMETRY** A parallelogram is created by the intersections of the lines $x = 2$, $x = 6$, $y = \frac{1}{2}x + 2$, and another line. Find the equation of the fourth line needed to complete the parallelogram. The line should pass through (2, 0). (*Hint:* Sketch a graph to help you see the lines.)
$y = \frac{1}{2}x - 1$

INTERIOR DESIGN For Exercises 5–7, use the following information.
Pamela is planning to install an island in her kitchen. She draws the shape she likes by connecting vertices of the square tiles on her kitchen floor. She records the location of each corner in the table.

Corner	Distance from West Wall (tiles)	Distance from South Wall (tiles)
A	5	4
B	3	8
C	7	10
D	11	7

5. How many pairs of parallel sides are there in the shape she designed? Explain.
1 pair: $\overline{BC}$ and $\overline{AD}$ are parallel because their slopes are both 0.5.
6. How many pairs of perpendicular sides are there in the shape she designed? Explain.
2 pairs: $\overline{BC} \perp \overline{AB}$ and $\overline{AB} \perp \overline{AD}$ because $\overline{AB}$ has a slope of −2, which is the opposite reciprocal of the slopes of $\overline{BC}$ and $\overline{AD}$, 0.5.
7. What is the shape of her new island?
a trapezoid

Chapter 4 54 Glencoe Algebra 1

Exercises

HOMEWORK HELP	
For Exercises	**See Examples**
10–16	1
18, 19	2
17, 20–25	3
26, 27	4

Exercise Levels
A: 10–27
B: 28–30
C: 31–33

Write the slope-intercept form of an equation for the line that passes through the given point and is parallel to the graph of each equation.

10. $(-3, 2)$, $y = x - 6$ $y = x + 5$
11. $(2, -1)$, $y = 2x + 2$ $y = 2x - 5$
12. $(-5, -4)$, $y = \frac{1}{2}x + 1$ $y = \frac{1}{2}x - \frac{3}{2}$
13. $(3, 3)$, $y = \frac{2}{3}x - 1$ $y = \frac{2}{3}x + 1$
14. $(-4, -3)$, $y = -\frac{1}{3}x + 3$ $y = -\frac{1}{3}x - \frac{13}{3}$
15. $(-1, 2)$, $y = -\frac{1}{2}x - 4$ $y = -\frac{1}{2}x + \frac{3}{2}$
16. **GEOMETRY** A *parallelogram* is a quadrilateral in which opposite sides are parallel. Determine whether $ABCD$ is a parallelogram. Explain your reasoning.

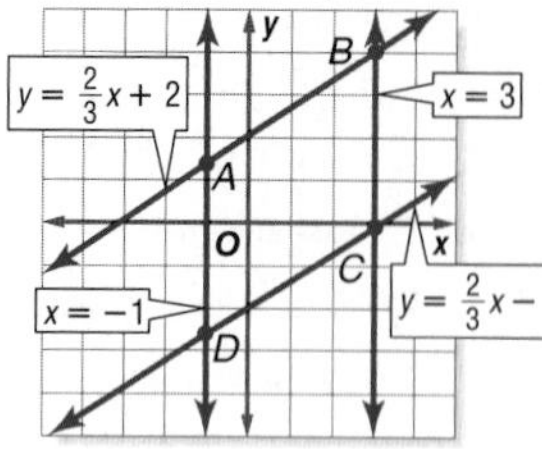

16. The lines for $x = 3$ and $x = -1$ are parallel because all vertical lines are parallel. The lines for $y = \frac{2}{3}x + 2$ and $y = \frac{2}{3}x - 3$ are parallel because they have the same slope. Thus, both pairs of opposite sides are parallel and the figure is a parallelogram.

★ 17. **GEOMETRY** The line with equation $y = 3x - 4$ contains side $\overline{AC}$ of right triangle ABC. If the vertex of the right angle C is at (3, 5), what is an equation of the line that contains side $\overline{BC}$? $y = -\frac{1}{3}x + 6$

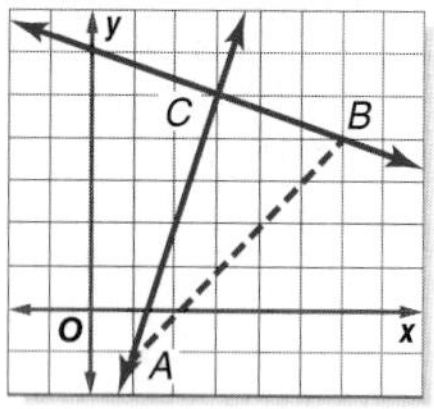

★ 18. Determine whether $y = -6x + 4$ and $y = \frac{1}{6}x$ are perpendicular. Explain. Yes; the slopes are −6 and $\frac{1}{6}$.

★ 19. **MAPS** On a map, Elmwood Drive passes through $R(4, -11)$ and $S(0, -9)$ and Taylor Road passes through $J(6, -2)$ and $K(4, -5)$. If they are straight lines, are the two streets perpendicular? Explain. No; the slopes are $-\frac{1}{2}$ and $\frac{3}{2}$.

Write the slope-intercept form of an equation for the line that passes through the given point and is perpendicular to the graph of the equation.

20. $(-2, 0)$, $y = x - 6$ $y = -x - 2$
21. $(1, 1)$, $y = 4x + 6$ $y = -\frac{1}{4}x + \frac{5}{4}$
22. $(-3, 1)$, $y = -3x + 7$ $y = \frac{1}{3}x + 2$
23. $(1, -3)$, $y = \frac{1}{2}x + 4$ $y = -2x - 1$

★ 24. $(-2, 7)$, $2x - 5y = 3$ $y = -\frac{5}{2}x + 2$
25. $(4, 7)$, $3y - 2x = -3$ $y = -\frac{3}{2}x + 13$

★ 26. Find an equation for the line that has a y-intercept of −2 and is perpendicular to the graph of $3x + 6y = 2$. $y = 2x - 2$

27. Write an equation of the line that is perpendicular to the line through (9, 10) and (3, −2) and passes through the x-intercept of that line. $y = -\frac{1}{2}x + 2$

Determine whether the graphs of each pair of equations are *parallel*, *perpendicular*, or *neither*.

★ 28. $y = -2x + 11$; $y + 2x = 23$ parallel
29. $3y = 2x + 14$; $2x - 3y = 2$ parallel
30. $y = -5x$; $y = 5x - 18$ neither

31. **GEOMETRY** Determine the relationship between the diagonals $\overline{AC}$ and $\overline{BD}$ of square $ABCD$ with $A(1, 3)$, $B(3, -1)$, $C(-1, -3)$ and $D(-3, 1)$. ★

31. They are perpendicular because the slopes are 3 and $-\frac{1}{3}$.

32. Write an equation of the line that is parallel to the graph of $y = 7x - 3$ and passes through the origin. $y = 7x$ ★

EXTRA PRACTICE
See pages 726, 747.
Math Online
Self-Check Quiz at ca.algebra1.com

Enrichment

CRM p. 55 OL AL

4-7 Enrichment

Pencils of Lines

All of the lines that pass through a single point in the same plane are called a **pencil of lines**.

All lines with the same slope, but different intercepts, are also called a "pencil," a **pencil of parallel lines**.

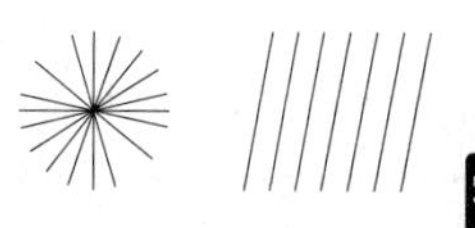

Graph some of the lines in each pencil.

1. A pencil of lines through the
2. A pencil of lines described by

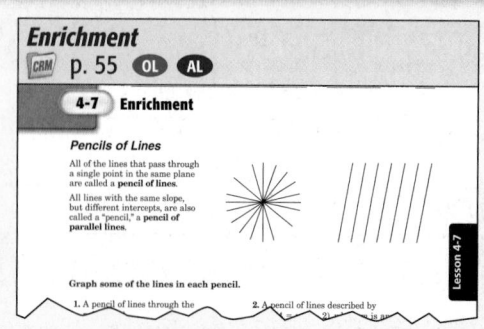

BL = *Below Grade Level*
OL = *On Grade Level*
AL = *Above Grade Level*
ELL = *English Language Learner*

Additional pages not shown:

CRM ***Lesson Reading Guide,*** p. 49 BL OL ELL
CRM ***Skills Practice,*** p. 52 BL OL

H.O.T. Problems

33. CHALLENGE The line that passes through the points $(3a, 4)$ and $(-1, 2)$ is parallel to the graph of $-4x + 2y = 6$. Find the value of a. **0**

34. OPEN ENDED Draw two segments on the coordinate plane that appear to be perpendicular. Describe how you could check your accuracy without measuring. **See students' drawings.**
Find the slopes to see if the lines are perpendicular.

35. *Writing in Math* Illustrate how you can determine whether two lines are parallel or perpendicular. Write an equation for a graph parallel to the line graphed at the right, and an equation with a graph perpendicular to the line graphed. Explain. **See margin.**

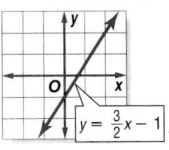
$y = \frac{3}{2}x - 1$

---

36. Which equation represents a line that is perpendicular to the graph and passes through the point at $(2, 0)$? **C**

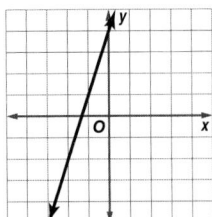

  A $y = 3x - 6$

  B $y = -3x + 6$

  C $y = -\frac{1}{3}x + \frac{2}{3}$

  D $y = \frac{1}{3}x - \frac{2}{3}$

37. REVIEW If $\triangle JKL$ is similar to $\triangle JNM$ what is the length of side a? **G**

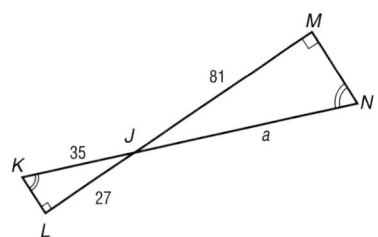

  F 62.5 units

  G 105 units

  H 125 units

  J 155.5 units

Spiral Review

38. TECHNOLOGY Would a scatter plot showing the relationship between the year and the amount of memory available on a personal computer manufactured that year show a *positive*, *negative*, or *no* correlation? (Lesson 4-6) **positive**

Write the point-slope form of an equation for the line that passes through each point with the given slope. (Lesson 4-5)

39. $(3, 5)$, $m = -2$
$y - 5 = -2(x - 3)$

40. $(-4, 7)$, $m = 5$
$y - 7 = 5(x + 4)$

41. $(-1, -3)$, $m = -\frac{1}{2}$
$y + 3 = -\frac{1}{2}(x + 1)$

42. ARCHITECTURE An architect is building a scale model of a sports complex. If the tallest building of the complex is 160 feet and the scale is 1 inch = 8 feet, how tall is the highest point of the scale model? (Lesson 2-6) **20 in.**

43. Solve $\frac{6c - t}{7} = b$ for c. (Lesson 2-8) $c = \frac{7b + t}{6}$

Real-World Connection For Exercise 31, many students will think that drawing a figure with four equal sides makes the figure a square. Point out that if the two diagonals are perpendicular and consecutive sides are perpendicular, the figure is a square. Have students determine that the consecutive sides of square *ABCD* are perpendicular to each other.

4 Assess

Ticket Out the Door Ask students to write and graph a line whose equation is of the form $Ax + By = C$. Have students draw two lines parallel to this line and describe the characteristics of those lines in terms of A, B, and C.

✓ Formative Assessment

Check for student understanding of concepts in Lesson 4-7.

[CRM] Quiz 4, p. 60

Additional Answer

35. Sample answer: If two equations have the same slope, then the lines are parallel. If the product of their slopes equals -1, then the lines are perpendicular. The graph of $y = \frac{3}{2}x$ is parallel to the graph of $y = \frac{3}{2}x + 1$ because their slopes both equal $\frac{3}{2}$. The graph of $y = -\frac{2}{3}x$ is perpendicular to the graph of $y = \frac{3}{2}x + 1$ because the slopes are negative reciprocals of each other.

Pre-AP Activity   Use after the Exercises

Write $A(-4, -1)$, $B(1, 4)$, $C(4, 1)$, and $D(-1, -4)$ on the board. Ask students to determine what geometric figure is made by connecting these points. Ask students to justify their answer. Rectangle; the slope of $\overline{AB}$ is 1. The slope of $\overline{CD}$ is 1. So $\overline{AB}$ is parallel to $\overline{CD}$. The slope of $\overline{AD}$ is -1. The slope of $\overline{BC}$ is -1. So $\overline{AD}$ is parallel to $\overline{BC}$. This makes the figure a parallelogram. Since the slopes of $\overline{AB}$ and $\overline{BC}$ are negative reciprocals of each other, $\overline{AB}$ and $\overline{BC}$ are perpendicular. This makes the figure a rectangle. The diagonals are not perpendicular so the figure is not a square. Therefore, the figure is a rectangle.

FOLDABLES™
Study Organizer

Dinah Zike's Foldables™

Have students look through the chapter to make sure they have included examples in their Foldables for each tab.

Suggest that students keep their Foldables handy while completing the Study Guide and Review pages. Point out that their Foldables can serve as a quick review tool for studying for the Chapter Test.

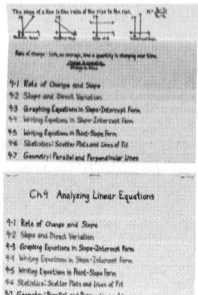

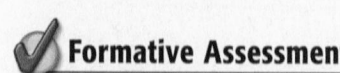

✔ Formative Assessment

Key Vocabulary The page references after each word denote where that term was first introduced. If students have difficulty answering questions 1–10, remind them that they can use these page references to refresh their memories about the vocabulary terms.

Math Online ca.algebra1.com

Vocabulary PuzzleMaker improves students' mathematics vocabulary using four puzzle formats—crossword, scramble, word search using a word list, and word search using clues. Students can work online or from a printed worksheet.

FOLDABLES™
Study Organizer   GET READY to Study

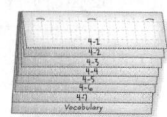
Be sure the following Key Concepts are noted in your Foldable.

Key Concepts

Rate of Change and Slope (Lesson 4-1)

- If x is the independent variable and y is the dependent variable, then rate of change equals $\dfrac{\text{change in } y}{\text{change in } x}$.

- The slope of a line is the ratio of the rise to the run; $m = \dfrac{y_2 - y_1}{x_2 - x_1}$.

Slope and Direct Variation (Lesson 4-2)

- A direct variation is described by an equation of the form $y = kx$, where $k \neq 0$.

Linear Equations in Slope-Intercept and Point-Slope Form (Lessons 4-3, 4-4, 4-5)

- The linear equation $y = mx + b$ is in slope-intercept form, where $m = $ slope and $b = y$-intercept.

- The linear equation $y - y_1 = m(x - x_1)$ is in point-slope form, where (x_1, y_1) is a point on a nonvertical line and m is the slope.

Scatter Plots and Lines of Fit (Lesson 4-6)

- A line of fit describes the trend of the data, and its equation can be used to make predictions.

- The correlation between x and y is positive if as x increases, y increases, and negative if as x increases, y decreases. There is no correlation between x and y if no relationship exists between x and y.

Parallel and Perpendicular Lines (Lesson 4-7)

- Two nonvertical lines are parallel if they have the same slope. Two nonvertical lines are perpendicular if the product of their slopes is -1.

✔ Sumative Assessment

 Vocabulary Test, p. 62

Key Vocabulary

best-fit line (p. 228)	parent graph (p. 197)
constant of variation (p. 196)	perpendicular lines (p. 237)
direct variation (p. 196)	point-slope form (p. 219)
family of graphs (p. 197)	rate of change (p. 187)
linear extrapolation (p. 216)	scatter plot (p. 227)
linear interpolation (p. 230)	slope (p. 189)
line of fit (p. 228)	slope-intercept form (p. 204)
parallel lines (p. 236)	

Vocabulary Check   3, 4, 6, 9. See margin.

State whether each sentence is *true* or *false*. If *false*, replace the underlined word or number to make a true sentence.

1. Any two points on a line can be used to determine the <u>slope</u>. **true**

2. The equation $y - 2 = -3(x - 1)$ is written in <u>point-slope form</u>. **true**

3. The equation of a vertical line can be written in <u>slope-intercept form</u>.

4. When you use a linear equation to predict values that are beyond the range of the data, you are using <u>linear interpolation</u>.

5. The lines with equations $y = -5x + 7$ and $y = -5x - 6$ are <u>perpendicular</u>. **false; parallel**

6. The lines with the equations $4x - y = 8$ and $y = -\dfrac{1}{4}x$ are <u>parallel</u>.

7. The slope of the line $y = 5$ is <u>5</u>. **false; 0**

8. The line that most closely approximates a set of data is called a <u>best-fit line</u>. **true**

9. An equation of the form $y = kx$, where $k \neq 0$, describes a <u>linear extrapolation</u>.

10. The <u>y-intercept</u> of the equation $3x - 2y = 24$ is $\dfrac{3}{2}$. **false, slope**

 Math Online Vocabulary Review at ca.algebra1.com

Additional Answers

3. false; standard form

4. false; linear extrapolation

6. false; perpendicular

9. false; direct variation

Lesson-by-Lesson Review

4-1 Rate of Change and Slope (pp. 187–195)

Find the rate of change represented in each table or graph.

11.
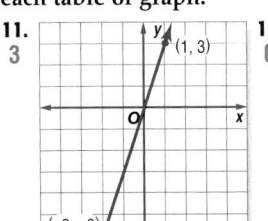
3

12.
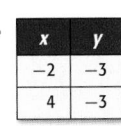
0

x	y
−2	−3
4	−3

Find the slope of the line that passes through each pair of points.

13. $(0, 5), (6, 2)$ $-\frac{1}{2}$ **14.** $(-6, 4), (-6, -2)$ **undefined**

15. DIGITAL CAMERAS The average cost of using an online photo finisher decreased from $0.50 per print to $0.27 per print between 2002 and 2005. Find the average rate of change in the cost. Explain what the rate of change means.

Example 1 Find the slope of the line that passes through $(0, -4)$ and $(3, 2)$.

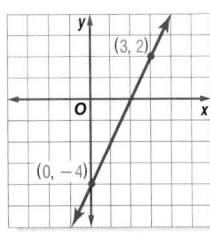

Let $(0, -4) = (x_1, y_1)$ and $(3, 2) = (x_2, y_2)$.

$m = \frac{y_2 - y_1}{x_2 - x_1}$ Slope formula

$= \frac{2 - (-4)}{3 - 0}$ $x_1 = 0, x_2 = 3, y_1 = -4, y_2 = 2$

$= \frac{6}{3}$ or 2   Simplify.

15. 0.08; an average decrease in cost of $0.08 per year

4-2 Slope and Direct Variation (pp. 196–202)

Graph each equation. **16–18. See margin.**
16. $y = x$ **17.** $y = \frac{4}{3}x$ **18.** $y = -2x$

Suppose y varies directly as x. Write a direct variation equation that relates x and y. Then solve.

19. If $y = 15$ when $x = 2$, find y when $x = 8$.

20. $y = -6$ when $x = 9$, find x when $y = -3$.

21. $y = 4$ when $x = -4$, find y when $x = 7$.
$y = -x; y = -7$

22. JOBS Suppose you earn $127 for working 20 hours. Write a direct variation equation relating your earnings to the number of hours worked. $y = 6.35x$

Example 2 Suppose y varies directly as x, and $y = -24$ when $x = 8$. Write a direct variation equation that relates x and y.

Find the constant of variation.

$y = kx$ Direct variation equation

$-24 = k(8)$ Replace y with −24 and x with 8.

$\frac{-24}{8} = \frac{k(8)}{8}$ Divide each side by 8.

$-3 = k$ Simplify.

So, the direct variation equation is $y = -3x$.

19. $y = 7.5x; y = 60$

20. $y = -\frac{2}{3}x; x = 4\frac{1}{2}$

Lesson-by-Lesson Review
Intervention If the given examples are not sufficient to review the topics covered by the questions, remind students that the page references tell them where to review that topic in their textbooks.

Two-Day Option Have students complete the Lesson-by-Lesson Review on pages 243–246. Then you can use ExamView® Assessment Suite to customize another review worksheet that practices all the objectives of this chapter or only the objectives on which your students need more help.

ExamView Assessment Suite — For more information on ExamView® Assessment Suite, see p. 184C.

Differentiated Instruction
Super DVD: MindJogger Videoquizzes Use this DVD as an alternative format of review for the test. For more information on this game show format, see p. 184D.

Additional Answers
16.
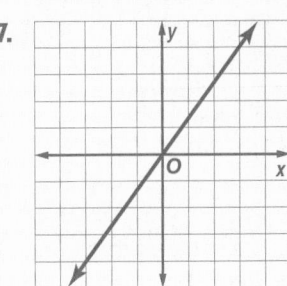

17.

18.
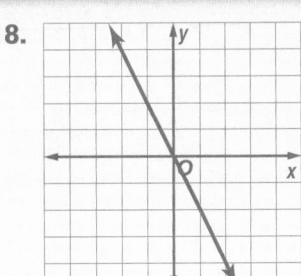

Additional Answers

27.
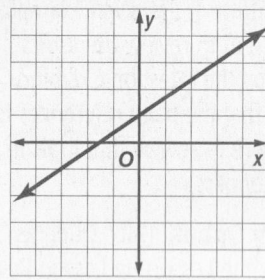

28.
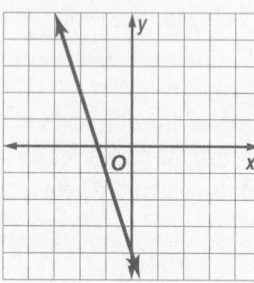

29.
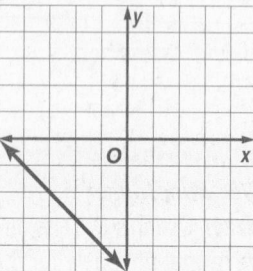

30.
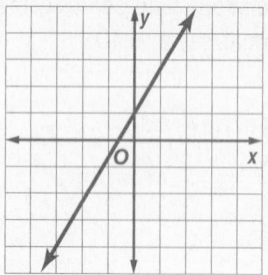

4-3 **Slope-Intercept Form** (pp. 204–209)

Write an equation in slope-intercept form of the line with the given slope and y-intercept.

23. slope: 3, y-intercept: 2 $y = 3x + 2$

24. slope: 1, y-intercept: -3 $y = x - 3$

25. slope: 0, y-intercept: 4 $y = 0x + 4$ or $y = 4$

26. slope: $\frac{1}{3}$, y-intercept: 2 $y = \frac{1}{3}x + 2$

Graph each equation. 27–30. See margin.

27. $y = \frac{2}{3}x + 1$ **28.** $6x + 2y = -8$

29. $y = -x - 5$ **30.** $5x - 3y = -3$

31. WIRELESS PHONES A wireless phone-service provider charges a \$0.35 daily fee plus \$0.10 per minute. Write a linear equation to find the daily cost y for any number of minutes x.
$y = 0.35 + 0.10x$

Example 3 Graph $-3x + y = -1$.

Write in slope-intercept form.

$$-3x + y = -1 \quad \text{Original equation}$$
$$-3x + y + 3x = -1 + 3x \quad \text{Add } 3x \text{ to each side.}$$
$$y = 3x - 1 \quad \text{Simplify.}$$

Step 1 The y-intercept is -1. So, graph $(0, -1)$.

Step 2 The slope is 3 or $\frac{3}{1}$. From $(0, -1)$, move up 3 units and right 1 unit. Then draw a line.

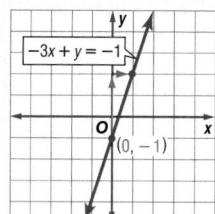

4-4 **Writing Equations in Slope-Intercept Form** (pp. 213–218)   **33.** $y = -\frac{3}{5}x - \frac{3}{5}$

Write an equation of the line that passes through each point with the given slope.

32. $(-3, 3)$, $m = 1$ **33.** $(4, -3)$, $m = -\frac{3}{5}$
    $y = x + 6$

34. $(8, -1)$, $m = 0$ **35.** $(0, 6)$, $m = -2$
    $y = -1$ $y = -2x + 6$

Write an equation of the line that passes through each pair of points.

36. $(-4, 2)$, $(1, 12)$ **37.** $(5, 0)$, $(4, 5)$
    $y = 2x + 10$ $y = -5x + 25$

38. MUSIC The table shows the average time Americans spent annually listening to recorded music. Write an equation to predict the number of hours h for any year y.

Year	Amount of Time (h)
1999	290
2006	195

$y = -13.6x + 27{,}476.6$

Example 4 Write an equation of the line that passes through $(-2, -3)$ with slope $\frac{1}{2}$.

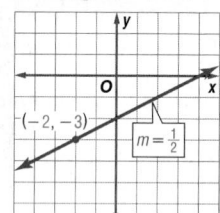

$$y = mx + b \quad \text{Slope-intercept form}$$
$$-3 = \frac{1}{2}(-2) + b \quad \text{Replace } m \text{ with } \frac{1}{2}, y \text{ with } -3, \text{ and } x \text{ with } -2.$$
$$-3 = -1 + b \quad \text{Multiply.}$$
$$-3 + 1 = -1 + b + 1 \quad \text{Add 1 to each side.}$$
$$-2 = b \quad \text{Simplify.}$$

Therefore, the equation is $y = \frac{1}{2}x - 2$.

Mixed Problem Solving
For mixed problem-solving practice,
see page 747.

CHAPTER
4 Study Guide
and Review

see page 747.

4–5 **Writing Equations in Point-Slope Form** (pp. 219–225)

Write the point-slope form of an equation for the line that passes through each point with the given slope.

39. 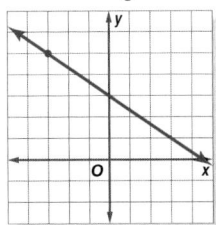 $y - 5 = -\frac{2}{3}(x + 3)$

40. $(4, 6)$, $m = 5$ $y - 6 = 5(x - 4)$

41. $(5, -3)$, $m = \frac{1}{2}$ $y + 3 = \frac{1}{2}(x - 5)$

42. $\left(\frac{1}{4}, -2\right)$, $m = 0$ $y + 2 = 0\left(x - \frac{1}{4}\right)$

Write each equation in standard form.

43. $y + 4 = 1.5(x - 4)$ $3x - 2y = 20$

44. $y - 6 = \frac{2}{3}(x + 9)$ $2x - 3y = -36$

Write each equation in slope-intercept form.

45. $y - 1 = 2(x + 1)$ $y = 2x + 3$

46. $y + 3 = \frac{1}{2}(x - 5)$ $y = \frac{1}{2}x - \frac{11}{2}$

47. **LAWN CARE** A lawn care company charges $25 per month for lawn maintenance, plus an initial service fee. The total cost for service fee and 8 months of maintenance is $165. Write the point-slope form of an equation to find the total cost y for any number of months x. (*Hint:* (8, 165) is a solution of the equation.) $y - 165 = 25(x - 8)$

Example 5 Write the point-slope form of an equation for a line that passes through $(-2, 5)$ with slope 3.

$y - y_1 = m(x - x_1)$ Point-slope form

$y - 5 = 3[x - (-2)]$ $(x_1, y_1) = (-2, 5)$

$y - 5 = 3(x + 2)$ Subtract.

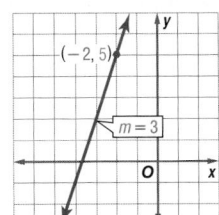

Example 6 Write $y + 4 = \frac{1}{2}(x - 6)$ in slope-intercept form and in standard form.

$y + 4 = \frac{1}{2}(x - 6)$ Original equation

$2(y + 4) = 2\left(\frac{1}{2}\right)(x - 6)$ Multiply each side by 2 to eliminate the fraction.

$2y + 8 = x - 6$ Distributive Property

$2y = x - 14$ Subtract 8 from each side.

$\frac{2y}{2} = \frac{x - 14}{2}$ Divide each side by 2.

$y = \frac{1}{2}x - 7$ Simplify.

The slope-intercept form is $y = \frac{1}{2}x - 7$.

$2y = x - 14$ Return to equation.

$2y - x = x - 14 - x$ Subtract x from each side.

$-x + 2y = -14$ Simplify.

$\frac{-x + 2y}{-1} = \frac{-14}{-1}$ Divide each side by -1.

$x - 2y = 14$ Simplify.

The standard form is $x - 2y = 14$.

Study Guide and Review

Problem Solving Review

For additional practice in problem solving for Chapter 4, see the Mixed Problem Solving Appendix, p. 747 in the Student Handbook section.

Anticipation Guide

Have students complete the Chapter 4 Anticipation Guide and discuss how their responses have changed now that they have completed Chapter 4.

CRM Anticipation Guide, p. 3

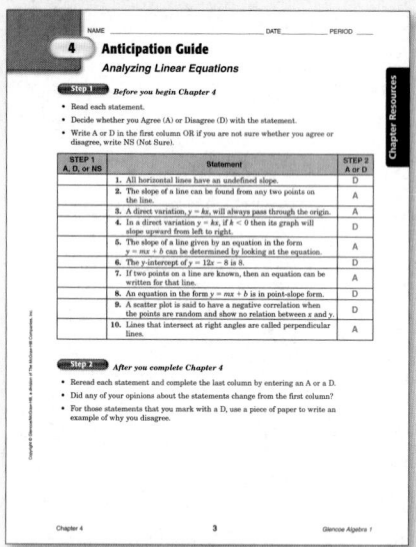

Additional Answers

48–49.

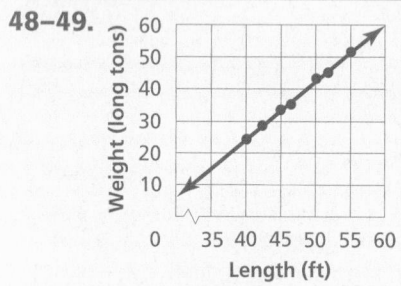

Additional Answers (Practice Test)

21–22.

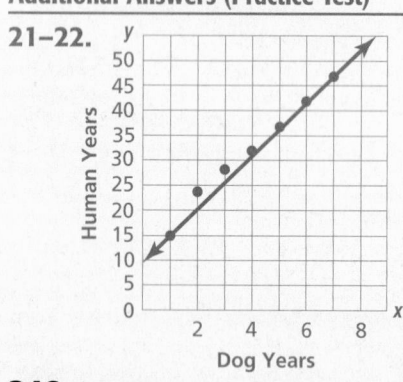

23. using (1, 15) and (7, 47),
$$y = \frac{16}{3}x + \frac{29}{3}$$

25. No, because dogs do not typically live to be 20 years old.

4-6 **Statistics: Scatter Plots and Lines of Fit** (pp. 227–233)

USE TABLES For Exercises 48–52, use the table that shows the length and weight of several humpback whales.

Length (ft)	40	42	45	46	50	52	55
Weight (long tons)	25	29	34	35	43	45	51

48. Draw a scatter plot with length on the x-axis and weight on the y-axis. **See margin.**

49. Draw a line of fit for the data. **See graph.**

50. Write the slope-intercept form of an equation for the line of fit. $y - 25 = \frac{26}{15}(x - 40)$

51. Predict the weight of a 48-foot humpback whale. **38.9 long tons**

52. Most newborn humpback whales are about 12 feet in length. Use the equation of the line of fit to predict the weight of a newborn humpback whale. Do you think your prediction is accurate? Explain. **About −23.5 long tons; this answer cannot be accurate because weight cannot be negative.**

Example 7 Use the table shown to draw a scatter plot and predict the future stock price.

Month	1	5	10	15	20	48
Price	$7	$17	$23	$35	$47	?

Step 1 Draw the scatter plot and find the line of fit.

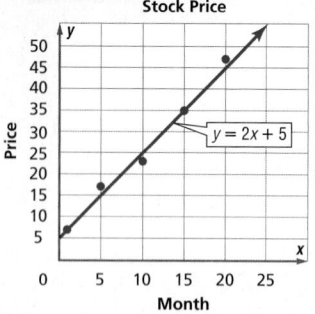

Stock Price

Step 2 Use line of fit to make predictions.

$y = 2x + 5$ Line of fit equation

$= 2(48) + 5$ Substitute 48 for x.

$= 96 + 5$ or 101 Simplify.

If the trend continues, the price will be $101.

4-7 **Geometry: Parallel and Perpendicular Lines** (pp. 236–241) **56.** $y = \frac{1}{2}x - 3$

Write the slope-intercept form of an equation for the line that passes through the given point and satisfies each condition.

53. (4, 6); parallel to $y = 3x - 2$ $y = 3x - 6$

54. (3, 0); parallel to $3x + 9y = 1$ $y = -\frac{1}{3}x + 1$

55. (2, −5); perpendicular to $5y = -x + 1$ $y = 5x - 15$

56. (0, −3); perpendicular to $y = -2x - 7$

57. GEOMETRY Determine if triangle ABC with vertices $A(-2, 0)$, $B(3, 3)$, and $C(-5, 5)$ is a right triangle. Explain. **Yes, $\overline{AC} \perp \overline{AB}$.**

Example 8 Write the slope-intercept form of an equation for a line that passes through (5, −2) and is parallel to $y = 2x + 7$.

The line parallel to $y = 2x + 7$ has the same slope, 2.

$y - y_1 = m(x - x_1)$ Point-slope form

$y - (-2) = 2(x - 5)$ Replace m with 2, y_1 with −2, and x_1 with 5.

$y + 2 = 2x - 10$ Simplify.

$y = 2x - 12$ Subtract 2 from each side.

Find the slope of the line that passes through each pair of points.

1. $(5, 8), (-3, 7)$ $\frac{1}{8}$ **2.** $(5, -2), (3, -2)$ 0

3. $(-4, 7), (8, -1)$ $-\frac{2}{3}$ **4.** $(6, -3), (6, 4)$ undefined

5. MULTIPLE CHOICE Which is the slope of the linear function shown in the graph? **B**

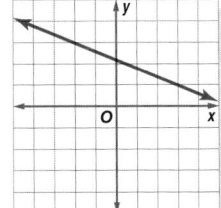

A $-\frac{5}{2}$

B $-\frac{2}{5}$

C $\frac{5}{2}$

D $\frac{2}{5}$

6. BUSINESS A Web design company advertises that it will design and maintain a Website for your business for $9.95 per month. Write a direct variation equation to find the total cost C for any number of months m.
$C = 9.95m$

Graph each equation.   **7–10. See Ch. 4 Answer Appendix.**

7. $y = 3x - 1$ **8.** $y = 2x + 3$

9. $2x + 3y = 9$ **10.** $4y - 2x = 12$

Suppose y varies directly as x. Write a direct variation equation that relates x and y.

11. $y = 6$ when $x = 9$ $y = \frac{2}{3}x$

12. $y = -8$ when $x = 8$ $y = -x$

13. $y = -5$ when $x = -2$ $y = \frac{5}{2}x$

14. $y = 2$ when $x = -12$ $y = -\frac{1}{6}x$

15. Write the point-slope form of an equation for a line that passes through $(-4, 3)$ with slope -2. $y - 3 = -2(x + 4)$

16. MULTIPLE CHOICE The temperature is 80°F at noon and is expected to rise 4° each hour during the afternoon. Which equation could be used to determine h, the number of hours it will take to reach a temperature of 96°? **H**

F $96 = 4 + 80h$

G $96 = 4(h + 80)$

H $96 = 80 + 4h$

J $96 = (4 + 80)h$

18. $y = \frac{1}{5}x - 4\frac{3}{5}$

Write the slope-intercept form of an equation of the line that satisfies each condition.

17. has slope -4 and y-intercept 3 $y = -4x + 3$

18. passes through $(-2, -5)$ and $(8, -3)$

19. parallel to $3x + 7y = 4$ and passes through $(5, -2)$ $y = -\frac{3}{7}x + \frac{1}{7}$

20. perpendicular to the graph of $5x - 3y = 9$ and passes through the origin $y = -\frac{3}{5}x$

ANALYZE TABLES For Exercises 21–25, use the table that shows the relationship between dog years and human years.

Dog Years	1	2	3	4	5	6	7
Human Years	15	24	28	32	37	42	47

21. Draw a scatter plot and determine what relationship, if any, exists in the data.

22. Draw a line of fit for the scatter plot.

23. Write the slope-intercept form of an equation for the line of fit.

24. Determine how many human years are comparable to 13 dog years. **79**

25. Is it reasonable to use the equation for the line of fit to estimate the age in human years of a dog 20 years old? Explain.
21–23, 25. See margin.

✓ Summative Assessment

 *Chapter 4 Resource Masters*

Leveled Chapter 4 Tests			
Form	Type	Level	Pages
1	MC	**BL**	63–64
2A	MC	**OL**	65–66
2B	MC	**OL**	67–68
2C	FR	**OL**	69–70
2D	FR	**OL**	71–72
3	FR	**AL**	73–74

MC = multiple-choice questions
FR = free-response questions
BL = below grade level
OL = on grade level
AL = above grade level

- Vocabulary Test, p. 62
- Extended Response Test, p. 74

 Customize and create multiple versions of your chapter tests and their answer keys. All of the questions from the leveled chapter tests in the *Chapter 4 Resource Masters* are also available on ExamView Assessment Suite with the California Standard that each item assesses.

For Exercises 21–23, and 25, see Ch. 4 Answer Appendix.

Data-Driven Decision Making	Exercises	Lesson	✏ Standard	**Resources for Review**
Diagnostic Teaching Based on the results of the Chapter 4 Mid-Chapter Quiz, use the following to review concepts that students continue to find challenging.	17–18	4–4	**Reinforcement of 7AF1.1**	🖳 Study Guide and Intervention pp. 27–28, 34–35, 42–43, 50–51
	15–16	4–5	7.0	**Math** nline
	21–25	4–6	**Probability and Statistics 8.0**	• Extra Examples • Personal Tutor
	19–20	4–7	8.0	• Concepts in Motion

 Read each question. Then fill in the correct answer on the answer document provided by your teacher or on a sheet of paper.

1 Which point lies on the line defined by $4x + 12y = 3$? **C**

A $\left(0, \dfrac{3}{4}\right)$

B $\left(0, \dfrac{4}{3}\right)$

C $\left(1, -\dfrac{1}{12}\right)$

D $\left(1, -\dfrac{1}{6}\right)$

2 The data in the table show the cost of renting a boat by the hour, including a deposit.

Renting a Boat

Hours (h)	1	3	5
Cost in dollars (c)	30	60	90

If hours h were graphed on the horizontal axis and cost c were graphed on the vertical axis, what would be the equation of the line that fits the data? **J**

F $c = 15h$

G $c = \dfrac{1}{15}h + 15$

H $c = 15h - 15$

J $c = 15h + 15$

3 What is the equation of the line that has a slope of -2 and passes through the point $(4, -11)$? **C**

A $y = -2x - 19$

B $y = -2x + 19$

C $y = -2x - 3$

D $y = -2x + 3$

4 Which of the following could be the equation of a line parallel to the line graphed below? **F**

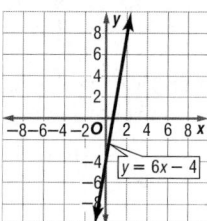

F $y = 6x + 4$

G $y = \dfrac{1}{6}x - 4$

H $y = -6x - 4$

J $y = -\dfrac{1}{6}x - 4$

5 Roberto runs 5 miles each Friday. If he doubles his usual speed, he can run the 5 miles in 30 minutes less than his usual speed. What is his usual speed in miles per hour? **5**

6 What is the equation of the line shown below? **A**

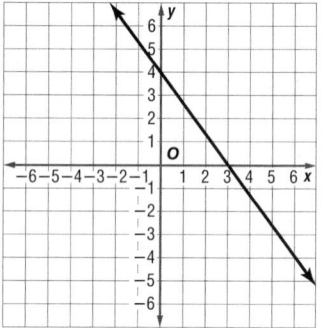

A $y = -\dfrac{4}{3}x + 4$

B $y = -\dfrac{3}{4}x + 4$

C $y = -\dfrac{4}{3}x + 3$

D $y = -\dfrac{3}{4}x + 3$

 Math Online California Standards Practice at ca.algebra1.com

More California
Standards Practice
For more standards practice,
see pages CA1–CA43.

7 What is the y-intercept of the graph of
$6x + 3y = 18$? **G**

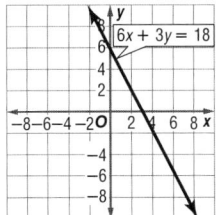

F -2

G 6

H 9

J 18

8 Which missing value for y would make this
relation a linear relation? **1**

x	y
1	-3
2	-1
3	?
4	3

9 Which of the following statements describes
perpendicular lines? **B**

A Perpendicular lines have the same slope.

B Perpendicular lines have opposite
reciprocal slopes.

C Perpendicular lines have opposite slopes.

D Perpendicular lines have reciprocal slopes.

10 Find a counterexample to the statement
below. **G**

> If $8x - 13 \geq 35$, then $x > 7$.

F 4

G 6

H 8

J 10

Pre-AP/Anchor Problem

**Record your answers on a sheet of paper.
Show your work.** a. **Plan 1: C = 0.59m;
Plan 2: 10 + 0.39m Plan 3: C = 59.95**

11 A friend wants to enroll for cellular phone
service. Three different plans are available.

Plan 1 charges $0.59 per minute.

Plan 2 charges a monthly fee of $10, plus
$0.39 per minute.

Plan 3 charges a monthly fee of $59.95.

a. For each plan, write an equation that
represents the monthly cost C for m
number of minutes per month.

b. Graph each of the three equations.

c. Your friend expects to use 100 minutes
per month. In which plan do you think
that your friend should enroll? Explain.

11b. See Margin.

**11c. Plan 2 since 100 minutes would cost $59
for plan 1, $49 for plan 2 and $59.95 for
plan 3**

Item Analysis
Questions 5 and 8 are griddable
questions. In a griddable question,
students arrive at an answer and then
record it in a special grid by coloring
the appropriate bubble under each digit
of the answer.

Answer Sheet Practice
Have students simulate taking a
standardized test by recording their
answers on practice recording sheets.

CRM Student Recording Sheet, p. 57

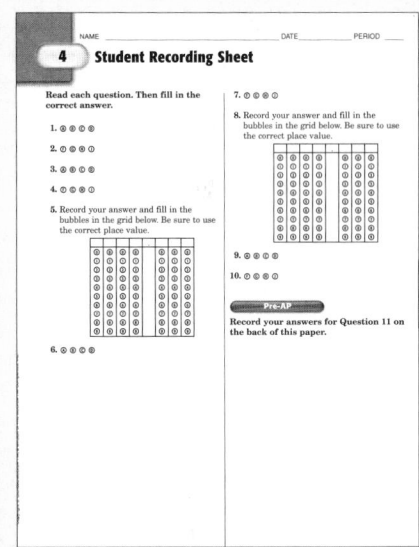

Additional Answers

11b.

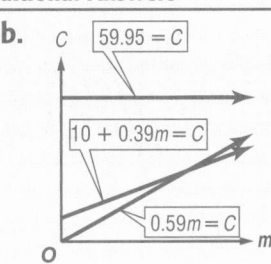

NEED EXTRA HELP?											
If You Missed Question...	1	2	3	4	5	6	7	8	9	10	11
Go to Lesson...	4-5	4-6	4-5	4-7	2-9	4-3	3-3	3-4	4-7	1-7	4-3
For Help with Standard	7.0	7.0	7.0	8.0	15.0	6.0	6.0	16.0	8.0	25.1	6.0

Homework Option

Get Ready for Chapter 5   Assign students the exercises on p. 251 as homework to assess whether
they possess the prerequisite skills for the next chapter.

Pages 200–202, Lesson 4-2

3.
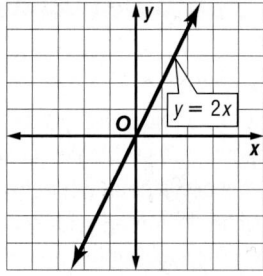

4.
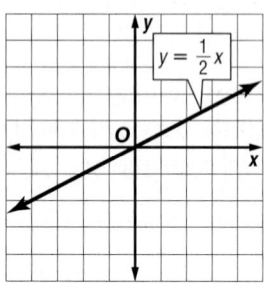

5.
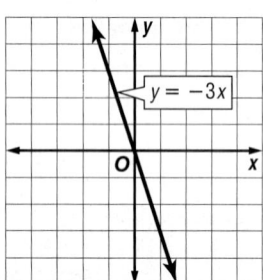

6.
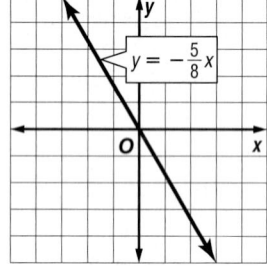

18.
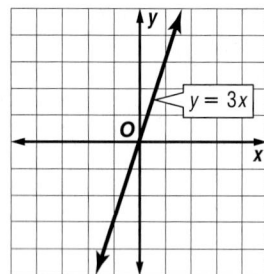

19.
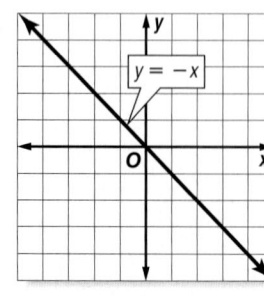

20.
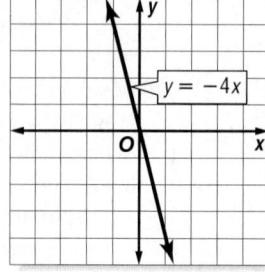

21.
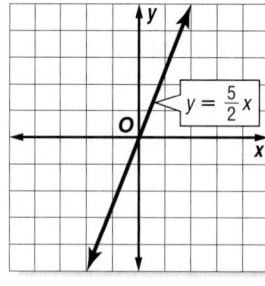

22.
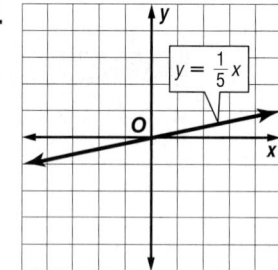

23.
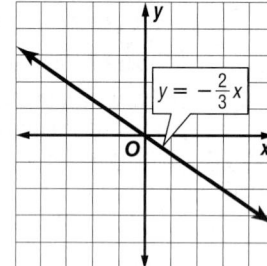

24.
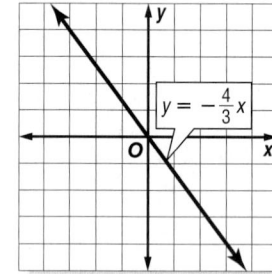

25.
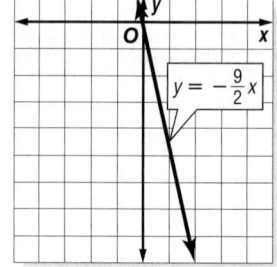

42.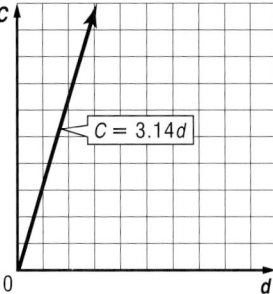

$C = 3.14d$

43.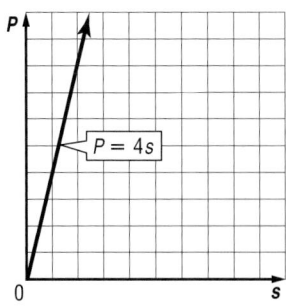

$P = 4s$

44.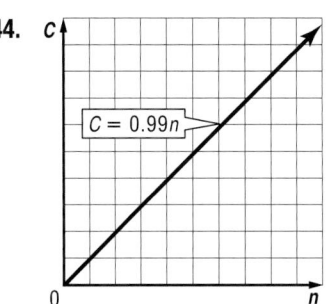

$C = 0.99n$

45.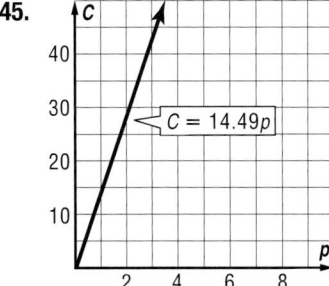

$C = 14.49p$

Pages 206–209, Lesson 4-3

3C.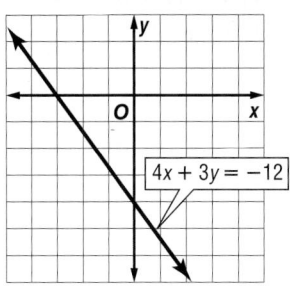

$4x + 3y = -12$

3D.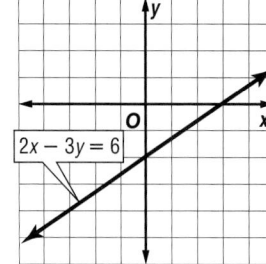

$2x - 3y = 6$

5.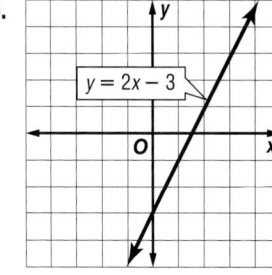

$y = 2x - 3$

6.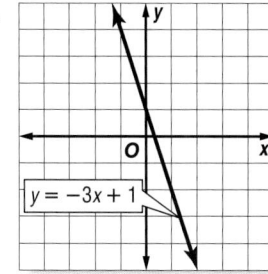

$y = -3x + 1$

7.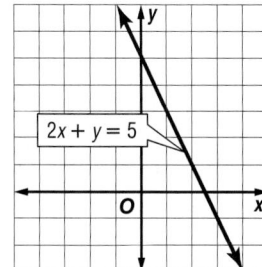

$2x + y = 5$

8.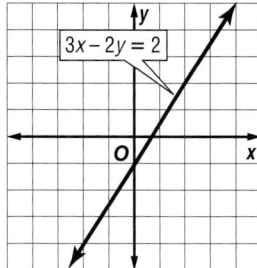

$3x - 2y = 2$

10.

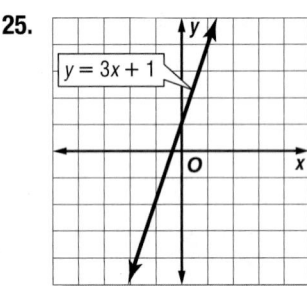

$T = 50 + 5w$

24.

$y = x - 2$

25.

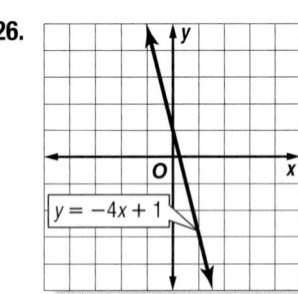

$y = 3x + 1$

26.

$y = -4x + 1$

27.

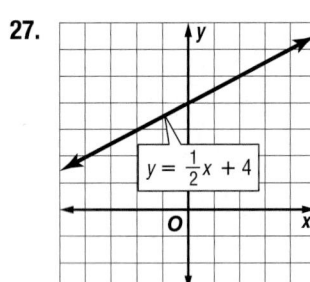

$y = \frac{1}{2}x + 4$

28.

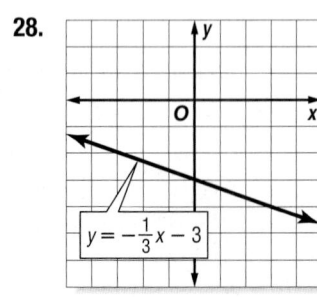

$y = -\frac{1}{3}x - 3$

29.

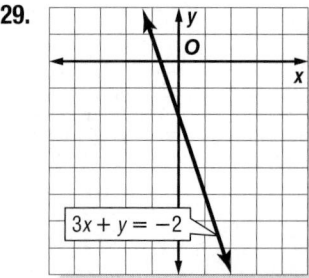

$3x + y = -2$

30.

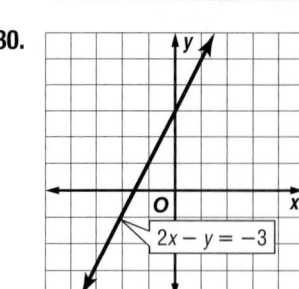

$2x - y = -3$

31.

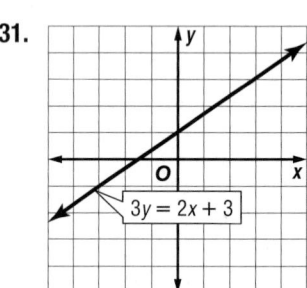

$3y = 2x + 3$

32.

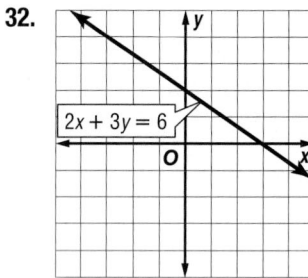

$2x + 3y = 6$

Page 211, Extend 4-3

9. Changing the value of m changes the slope of the graph. If m is positive, the line goes up from left to right. If m is negative, the line goes down from left to right. The greater the value of m, the steeper the graph.

12.

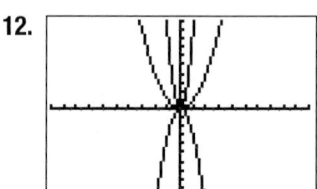

The graphs have the same y-intercept, but different widths.

13.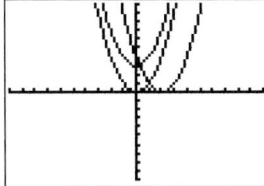

The widths of the graphs are the same, but are shifted horizontally and vertically.

14.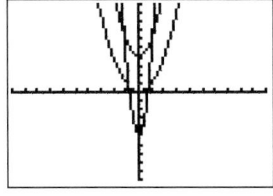

The graphs have different widths and different intercepts.

15. In the graph of $f(x) = x^2 + c$, the graph is the same as $f(x) = x^2$, shifted vertically c units. In the graph of $f(x) = (x + c)^2$, the graph is the same as $f(x) = x^2$, shifted horizontally c units.

Page 212, Mid-Chapter Quiz

9.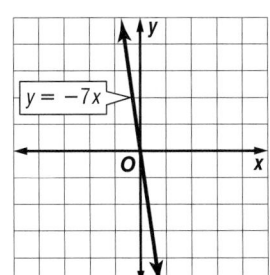

10.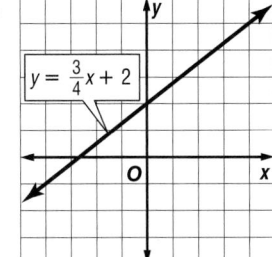

11.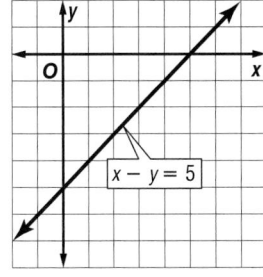

14.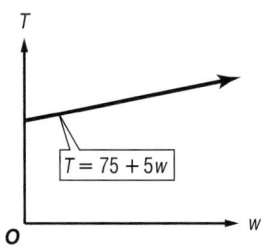

Page 218, Lesson 4-4

42.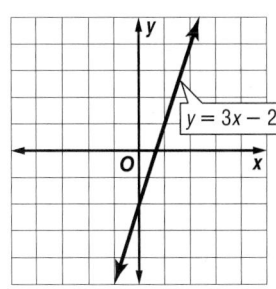

43.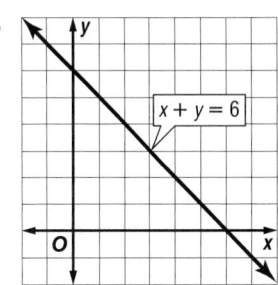

44.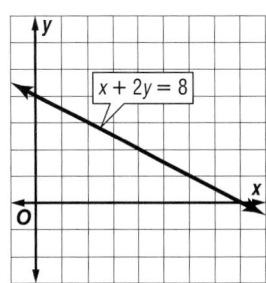

46. 0, 0; The intercept means that 0 miles are traveled when the time spent riding is 0 minutes.

47. 45, 3; The x-intercept 45 means that it took Tara 45 minutes to walk home. The y-intercept 3 means that she was initially 3 miles from her home.

Page 226, Reading Math

3a. Since 1998, the number of members in U.S. Lacrosse has steadily increased.

3b. Sample answer: As more people became familiar with the sport through its visibility in the media, the sport has attracted more participants.

3c. Sample answer: Since the number of participants in the sport has steadily increased, it can be reasonably assumed that the number will continue to increase and that the need for a lacrosse field will be greater.

4. Sample answer: distinguish: to perceive a difference in, analysis; summarize: to cover the main points succinctly, comprehension; define: to identify the meaning of, knowledge; predict: to foretell on the basis of observation, evaluation; demonstrate: to make clear by reasoning or evidence, comprehension

Page 229, Lesson 4-6

2A–2B.

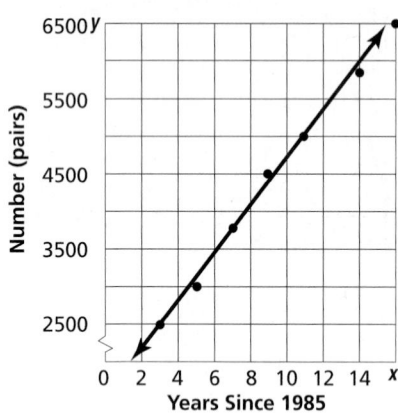

Bald Eagle Pairs

Pages 232–233, Lesson 4-6

18–19.

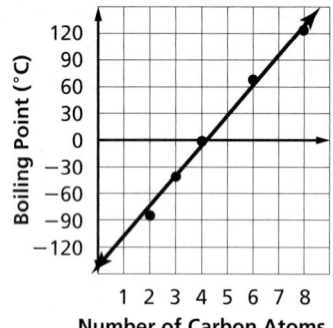

23–24. positive

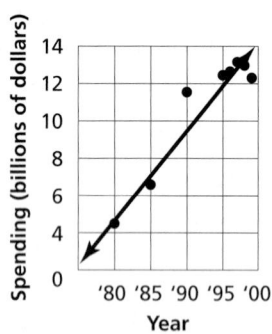

27. Sample answer: The amount spent will probably not increase at a constant rate, so the linear equation that is useful in making predictions in the near future would not be useful for making predictions in the distant future.

32. Sample answer:

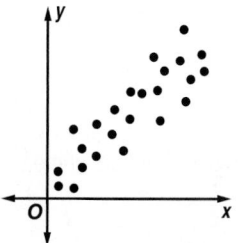

positive: age and height of students

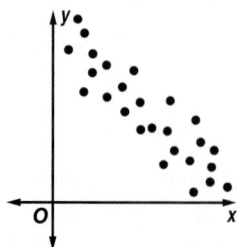

negative: number of minutes after football game and number of people in the stadium

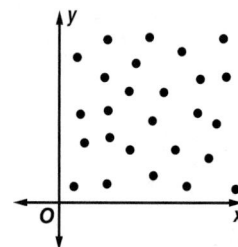

none: age and birth month of students

Page 247, Practice Test

7.

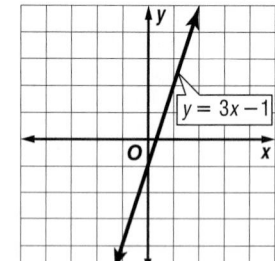

$y = 3x - 1$

8.

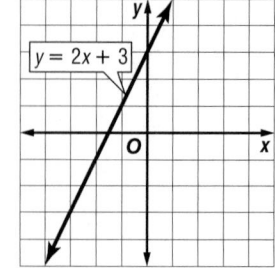

$y = 2x + 3$

9.

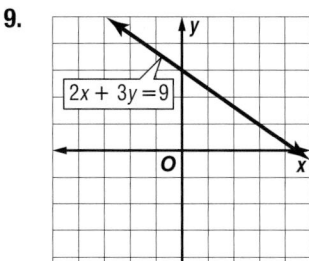

$2x + 3y = 9$

10.

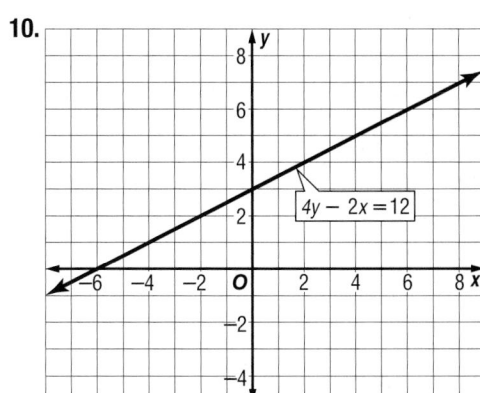

$4y - 2x = 12$

CHAPTER 5

Chapter Overview

Solving Systems of Linear Equations

Standards-Based Lesson Plan		Pacing Your Lessons	
LESSONS AND OBJECTIVES	California Standards	40-50 Minute Periods	90-Minute Periods
Explore 5-1 **Spreadsheet Lab: Systems of Equations** (p. 252) • Use a spreadsheet to investigate when the values of two expressions are equal.	6.0, 7.0,	3	2
5-1 **Graphing Systems of Equations** (pp. 253–258) • Determine whether a system of linear equations has no, one, or infinitely many solutions. • Solve systems of equations by graphing.	8.0, 9.0,		
Extend 5-1 **Graphing Calculator Lab: Systems of Equations** (p. 259) • Use a graphing calculator to solve a system of equations.	25.3		
5-2 **Substitution** (pp. 260–265) • Solve systems of equations by using substitution. • Solve real-world problems involving systems of equations.	9.0, 15.0, 25.2	2	1
5-3 **Elimination Using Addition and Subtraction** (pp. 266–270) • Solve systems of equations by using elimination with addition. • Solve systems of equations by using elimination with subtraction.	9.0	2.5	1
5-4 **Elimination Using Multiplication** (pp. 272–278) • Solve systems of equations by using elimination with multiplication. • Solve real-world problems involving systems of equations.	9.0, 15.0, 25.2	2.5	1
5-5 **Applying Systems of Linear Equations** (pp. 280–284) • Determine the best method for solving systems of equations. • Apply systems of linear equations.	9.0	3	1
REVIEW		1	0.5
ASSESSMENT		1	0.5*
TOTAL		15	7

*The complete **Assessment Planner** for Chapter 5 is provided on p. 251*

* Begin Chapter 6 in the second half of the period.

Professional Development

California Standards Vertical Alignment

Before Chapter 5

Related Topics from Grade 7
- Write an expression, an equation, an inequality, or a system that represents a verbal description.

   Standard 7AF1.1

Chapter 5

Topics from Algebra I
- Solve a system of two linear equations or inequalities in two variables algebraically and graphically.

See individual lessons for the specific Standards covered.

After Chapter 5

Preparation for Algebra II
- Solve systems of linear equations and inequalities by substitution, with graphs, or with matrices.

  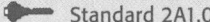 Standard 2A1.0

What the Research Says...

According to Smith (1997), current technology allows readily accessible representations of systems of equations in algebraic, numeric, and geometric forms. Integrating these different representations into the curriculum helps students to think more critically about systems, to foster new perspectives, and to feel more confident in their results.

- In Lesson 5-1A, students examine a system of equations numerically using a spreadsheet.
- In Lesson 5-1B, students use graphing calculators to visualize systems, based on concepts discussed in Lesson 5-1.
- Throughout Chapter 5, algebraic methods for solving systems are related to graphical representations.

[Source: Smith, K.B. (1997). "Exploration and Visualization: Making Critical Connections About Linear Systems of Equations," *School Science and Mathematics*, 97(1), pp. 13–19.]

Back-Mapping

California Algebra 1 was conceived and developed with the final result in mind, student success in Algebra I and beyond. The authors, using the California Mathematics Standards as their guide, developed this brand-new series by "back-mapping" from the desired result of student success in Algebra I and beyond. McGraw-Hill's *California Geometry, California Algebra 2,* and *California Algebra Readiness* were developed utilizing the same philosophy.

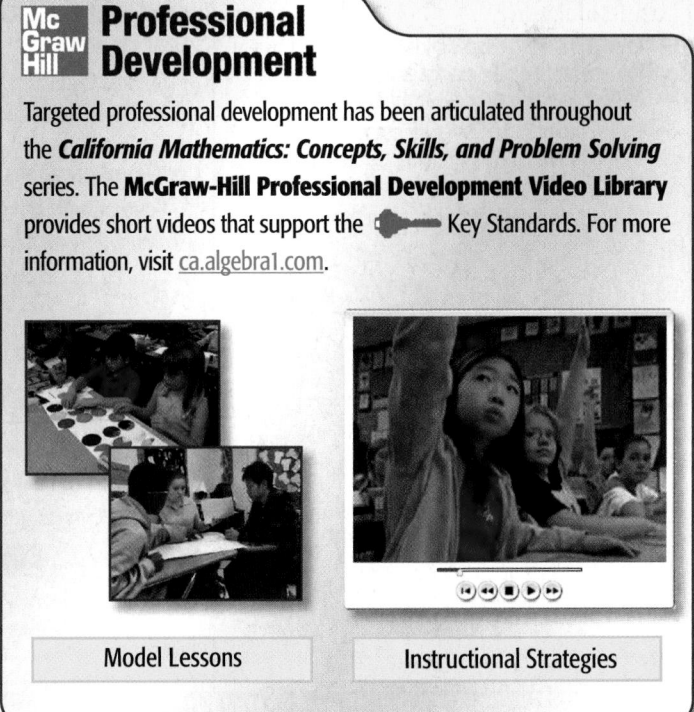

Professional Development

Targeted professional development has been articulated throughout the *California Mathematics: Concepts, Skills, and Problem Solving* series. The **McGraw-Hill Professional Development Video Library** provides short videos that support the Key Standards. For more information, visit ca.algebra1.com.

| Model Lessons | Instructional Strategies |

CHAPTER 5

Technology Solutions

Teacher Resources

TeacherWorks™ All-in-One Planner and Resource Center

All of the print materials from the Classroom Resource Masters are available on your TeacherWorks™ CD-ROM.

BL = Below Grade Level **OL** = On Grade Level **AL** = Above Grade Level **ELL** = English Language

Chapter Resource Masters					5-1	5-2	5-3	5-4	5-5
BL	OL		ELL	Lesson Reading Guide	5	13	20	27	34
BL	OL		ELL	Study Guide and Intervention*	6	14	21	28	35
BL	OL			Skills Practice*	8	16	23	30	37
	OL	AL		Practice*	9	17	24	31	38
	OL	AL		Word Problem Practice*	10	18	25	32	39
	OL	AL		Enrichment	11	19	26	33	40
	OL	AL		Calculator and Spreadsheet Activities	12				
	OL	AL		Chapter Assessments*	41–62				
BL	OL	AL		5-Minute Check Transparencies	✓	✓	✓	✓	✓
BL	OL			Teaching Mathematics with Manipulatives	✓	✓	✓		

Also available in Spanish.

AssignmentWorks

Differentiated Assignments, Answers, and Solutions

- Print a customized assignment worksheet using the Student Edition exercises along with an answer key or worked-out solutions.
- Use default lesson assignments as outlined in the Differentiated Homework Options in the Teacher Wraparound Edition.
- Include modified questions from the Student Edition.

Interactive Classroom

This CD-ROM is a customizable Microsoft® PowerPoint® presentation that includes:

- In-Class Examples
- Your Turn Exercises*
- 5-Minute Check Transparencies*
- Links to Online Study Tools
- Concepts in Motion

compatible with response pad technology

Your Turn

Solve the system of inequalities by graphing.
$$2x + y \leq 4$$
$$x + 2y > -4$$

$2x + y = 4$

Answer:

$x + 2y = -4$

End of slide

ExamView®Assessment Suite

ExamView® Assessment Suite lets you

- Create, edit, and customize tests and worksheets using QuickTest Wizard
- Create multiple versions of tests and modify them for a desired level of difficulty
- Translate from English to Spanish and vice versa
- Build tests aligned with your state standards
- Track students' progress using the Teacher Management System

Student Resources

StudentWorks™ Plus

Textbook, Audio, Workbooks, and more

This CD-ROM is a valuable resource for students to access content online and use online resources to continue learning Chapter 5 concepts. Includes:

- Complete Student Editions in both English and Spanish
- English audio integrated throughout the text
- Links to Concepts in Motion, Personal Tutor, and other online resources
- Access to all student worksheets
- Daily Assignments and Grade Log

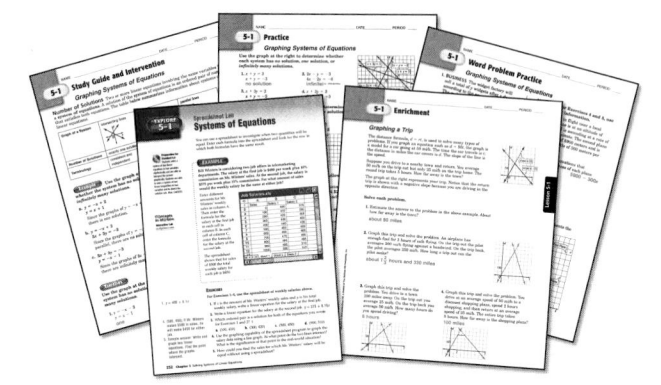

Super DVD

The Super DVD contains two Glencoe multimedia products.

MindJogger Plus An alternative review of concepts in which students work as teams in a game show format to gain points for correct answers.

What's Math Got to Do With It? Real Life Math Videos
Engaging video that shows students how math is used in everyday situations

Unit 2 Theme: Linear Function

Internet Resources

Math Online ca.algebra1.com

TEACHER	PARENT	STUDENT	**Online Study Tools**
	•	•	Online Student Edition
•	•	•	Multilingual Glossary
			Lesson Resources
	•	•	BrainPOP®
•	•	•	Concepts in Motion
•	•	•	Extra Examples
	•	•	Other Calculator Keystrokes
•			Problem of the Week Cards
	•	•	Real-World Careers
	•	•	Self-Check Quizzes
			Chapter Resources
	•	•	Chapter Readiness
	•	•	Chapter Test
	•	•	Standardized Test Practice
	•	•	Vocabulary Review/Chapter Review Activities
			Unit Resources
•		•	Cross-Curricular Internet Project
			Other Resources
•			Dinah Zike's Foldables
	•	•	Hotmath Homework Help
•			Key Concepts
•	•	•	Meet the Authors
	•	•	Personal Tutor
•			Project CRISS℠
	•	•	Scavenger Hunts and Answer Sheets
•			Vocabulary PuzzleMakers

Focus on Mathematical Content

Big Idea for Chapter 5:
Solving Systems of Linear Equations

Systems of equations can be used to model many real-world situations. The method of solution of these systems often determines the exactness of the solution. Explore 5-1 on page 252 examines how a spreadsheet can be used to determine when two quantities are equal. Solving a system of equations by graphing allows for a visual model of the situation and its solution, but can be inaccurate. The algebraic methods of substitution and elimination provide a more accurate and often quicker solution. However, once a system of linear equations is solved, the solution needs to be analyzed in terms of the situation.

Why It's Important

For This Chapter
The lessons in this chapter explore the various methods of solving systems of linear equations and their application to problem situations.
- How many solutions can a system of linear equations have? (Lesson 5-1)
- How can a system of equations be solved using substitution? (Lesson 5-2)
- When should a system of equations be solved by elimination using addition or subtraction? (Lesson 5-3)
- What if addition or subtraction of the equations won't eliminate a variable—how can you use multiplication to solve real-world problems? (Lesson 5-4)
- What method is best to use? How can this method be used to solve a real-world problem? (Lessons 5-5)

After This Chapter
- In Chapter 6, systems of inequalities are solved by graphing.
- In Algebra 2, matrices are used to solve systems of equations.
- In Algebra 2 and beyond, systems of nonlinear equations are solved.

5-1 Graphing Systems of Equations

A system of equations can be solved by graphing the equations on the same coordinate plane. A solution of a system of two linear equations is an ordered pair that satisfies both equations in the system. A system of two linear equations can have one, no, or an infinite number of solutions.

- One solution
  The graphs of the equations intersect. The lines will intersect at one point. This system is said to be consistent and independent.

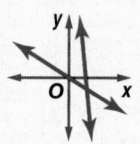

Intersecting Lines

- No solution
  The graphs of the equations are parallel. There are no ordered pairs that satisfy both equations. This system is said to be inconsistent.

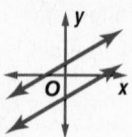

Parallel Lines

- Infinite number of solutions
  The graphs of the equations are the same line. An infinite number of points will satisfy both equations. This system is said to be consistent and dependent.

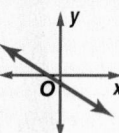

Same Line

5-2 Substitution

Determining the exact solution to a system of equations from a graph can be difficult at times. When an exact solution is needed, algebraic methods can be used. One of these methods is called substitution. To use the method of substitution,

- begin by solving one of the equations for one of the variables in terms of the other variable.

- Next, substitute this expression into the other equation, thus eliminating one of the variables.

- Solve the resulting equation for the remaining variable.

- This value is then substituted into either equation to find the value of the other variable.

The solution to the system is the two values written as an ordered pair. This ordered pair represents the point at which the two lines would intersect if graphed.

If solving the system of equations results in a true statement (an identity such as $3 = 3$), the system has an infinite number of solutions. There is no solution if the result of solving the system is a false statement (such as $-2 = 4$). Should either statement occur, stop solving the system and write either infinite number of solutions or no solutions.

5-3 Elimination Using Addition and Subtraction

Another algebraic method used in solving a system of equations is elimination using addition and subtraction. When using this method, the two equations are combined to eliminate one of the variables. You can add or subtract one equation from the other because of the Addition and Subtraction Properties of Equality that state that equal amounts can be added to or subtracted from each side of an equation. To use the method of elimination using addition and subtraction,

- add the two equations if the coefficients of one of the variables are additive inverses, or opposites, of each other.

- subtract the two equations if the coefficients of one of the variables are the same.

After eliminating one of the variables, solve for the remaining variable. Then substitute this value back into either original equation and find the value of the eliminated variable. The solution to the system is the two values written as an ordered pair.

5-4 Elimination Using Multiplication

Elimination using multiplication is used when the coefficients of one of the variables aren't additive inverses or the same. Solving a system of equations with this method requires that either one or both equations be changed by applying the Multiplication Property of Equality.

To use the method of elimination using multiplication, multiply each term of one equation by the same number, or, multiply both equations by different numbers in order to have one of the variables have coefficients that are additive inverses of each other or the same number. Once this has been done, solve the system by following the steps for solving a system by elimination using addition or subtraction.

5-5 Applying Systems of Linear Equations

The previous lessons in the chapter have covered five methods of solving systems of equations. Systems of equations can be solved by graphing or by algebraic methods.

- Graphing can be used when an estimate of the solution is needed. An exact solution is often not available when graphing.

- Substitution is used when one of the variables in either equation has a coefficient of 1 or -1.

- Elimination using addition is used if the coefficients of one of the variables are additive inverses, opposites, of each other in the two equations.

- Elimination using subtraction is used if the coefficients of one of the variables are the same in the two equations.

- Elimination using multiplication is used if none of the coefficients are 1 or -1 and neither of the variables can be eliminated by adding or subtracting the equations.

When systems of equations are used to solve real-world problems, it is important to check each solution in the context of the situation.

Differentiated Instruction

Options for Chapter 5 Lessons

ELL = English Language Learner   **AL** = Above Grade Level   **SS** = Struggling Students   **SN** = Special Needs

Using Interpersonal Skills SS SN

Use with Lesson 5-2

If students have difficulty solving systems of equations by using substitution, ask them to indicate where they get confused in the process before doing another example. Encourage them to think through each step.

Using Movement ELL SS

Use with Lesson 5-4

If students have difficulty solving systems of equations by using elimination, have them write the terms of the equations on pieces of paper. Then, when they eliminate one of the variables, have them remove the papers with eliminated terms. The act of removing the terms should help cement the concept in students' minds.

Using Verbal Skills AL

Use with Lesson 5-4

Place students in pairs or small groups and assign systems of equations for them to solve. Tell students to use the Concept Summary on p. 280 to discuss which method is best to use to solve the system of equations they have been assigned. Make sure all group members participate in the discussion.

Noteables™ Interactive Study Notebook with Foldables™

Noteables™ Interactive Study Notebook with Foldables™ is a study organizer that provides helpful steps for students to follow to organize their notes for Chapter 5.

- Students use Noteables to record notes and to complete their Foldables as you present the material for each lesson.

- Noteables correspond to the Examples in the *Teacher Wraparound Edition* and *Interactive Classroom CD-ROM.*

Intervention

Quick Review Math Handbook*

is Glencoe's mathematical handbook for students and parents.

Hot Words includes a glossary of terms.

Hot Topics consists of two parts:

- explanations of key mathematical concepts
- exercises to check students' understanding.

Lesson	Hot Topics Section	Lesson	Hot Topics Section
5.1	6.4	5.3	6.2
5.2	6.2	5.4	6.6

*Also available in Spanish

Teacher to Teacher

Lou Jane Tynan
Sacred Heart Model School
Louisville, KY

USE BEFORE LESSON 5-3

❝ Many students will forget to distribute the negative sign over the entire equation being subtracted in Example 3. I require my students to change the signs of the equation being subtracted and then add the two equations. **❞**

$$5s + 2t = 6 \qquad\qquad 5s + 2t = 6$$
$$(-)9s + 2t = 22 \qquad (+)\ -9s - 2t = -22$$

Reading and Writing in Mathematics

STUDY SKILL

Students may find it helpful to organize information they are learning in a frame. A sample concept frame that shows the major concepts about systems of two liner equations is shown at the right. Have students complete this sample or develop their own frames to explain other concepts from Chapter 5.

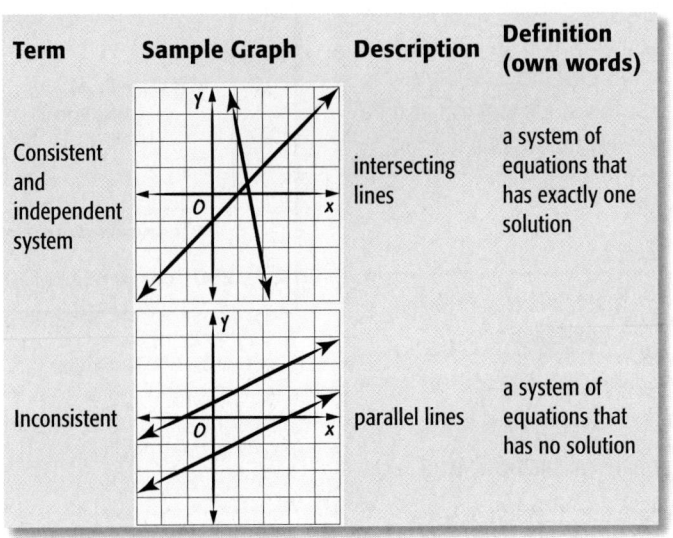

Term	Sample Graph	Description	Definition (own words)
Consistent and independent system		intersecting lines	a system of equations that has exactly one solution
Inconsistent		parallel lines	a system of equations that has no solution

Notes

Dinah Zike's Foldables™

Focus Students create a visualization journal in which they write notes and create visuals (graphs, diagrams, charts) about solving systems of equations and inequalities for each lesson in this chapter.

Teach Have students make and label their Foldables as illustrated. Have them label the top of each front page with a lesson number. Under the appropriate tabs of their Foldables, students should take notes on the concepts presented in each lesson.

When to Use It At the end of each lesson, ask students to design a visual (graph, diagram, picture, chart) that presents the lesson information in a concise, easy-to-study format. Encourage students to label their visuals clearly.

A version of a completed Foldable is shown on p. 285.

Differentiated Instruction

CRM Student-Built Glossary, pp. 1–2

Students should complete the chart by providing a definition and example of each term as they progress through Chapter 5. This study tool can also be used to review for the Chapter test.

Materials Needed for Chapter 5

- computer with spreadsheet software (Explore 5-1)
- graphing calculator (Extend 5-1)
- algebra tiles (Lesson 5-2)
- equation mat (Lesson 5-2)
- Internet (Lesson 5-2)

Solving Systems of Linear Equations

BIG Idea

- **Standard 9.0** Students solve a system of two linear equations in two variables algebraically and are able to interpret the answer graphically. Students are able to solve a system of two linear inequalities in two variables and to sketch the solution sets. (Key, CAHSEE)

Key Vocabulary

elimination (p. 266)
substitution (p. 260)
system of equations (p. 253)

🌐 Real-World Link

TREES The tallest redwood trees in the world are in Humboldt County, California. The tallest redwood tree is 370 feet tall. In ideal conditions, a redwood tree could grow to a height of 420 feet. The height of these trees can be modeled by systems of linear equations.

FOLDABLES Study Organizer

Solving Systems of Linear Equations Make this Foldable to record information about solving systems of equations and inequalities. Begin with five sheets of grid paper.

1 **Fold** each sheet in half along the width.

2 **Unfold** and cut four rows from left side of each sheet, from the top to the crease.

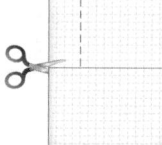

3 **Stack** the sheets and staple to form a booklet.

4 **Label** each page with a lesson number and title.

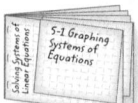

GET READY for Chapter 5

Diagnose Readiness You have two options for checking Prerequisite Skills.

Option 1

Take the Quick Check below. Refer to the Quick Review for help.

Option 2

Math [online] Take the Online Readiness Quiz at **ca.algebra1.com**.

QUICK Check

(Used in Lesson 5-1.)

Graph each equation. (Lesson 3-3)

1. $y = 1$ 1–6. See Ch. 5
2. $y = -2x$
   Answer Appendix.
3. $y = 4 - x$
4. $y = 2x + 3$
5. $y = 5 - 2x$
6. $y = \frac{1}{2}x + 2$

7. **HOUSES** The number on Craig's house is 7. The numbers of the houses on his block increase by 2. Graph the equation that models the house numbers on Craig's block. **See Ch. 5 Answer Appendix.**

(Used in Lesson 5-2.)

Solve each equation or formula for the variable specified. (Lesson 2-8)

8. $4x + a = 6x$, for x $x = \dfrac{a}{2}$
9. $8a + y = 16$, for a $a = \dfrac{16 - y}{8}$
10. $\dfrac{7bc - d}{10} = 12$, for b $b = \dfrac{120 + d}{7c}$
11. $\dfrac{7m + n}{q} = 2m$, for q $q = \dfrac{7m + n}{2m}$

(Used in Lessons 5-3 and 5-4.)

Simplify each expression. If not possible, write *simplified*. (Lesson 1-6)

12. $(3x + y) - (2x + y)$ x
13. $(7x - 2y) - (7x + 4y)$ $-6y$

14. **MOWING** Jake and his brother charge x dollars to cut and y dollars to weed an average lawn. Simplify the expression that gives the total amount that their business earns in a weekend if Jake cuts and weeds 7 lawns and his brother cuts and weeds 10 lawns. $17x + 17y$

QUICK Review

EXAMPLE 1

Graph $y = \dfrac{3}{4}x - 3$.

Step 1 The y-intercept is -3. So, graph $(0, -3)$.

Step 2 The slope is $\dfrac{3}{4}$. From $(0, -3)$, move up 3 units and right 4 units. Draw a dot.

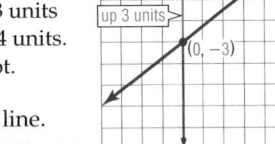

Step 3 Draw the line.

EXAMPLE 2

Solve $\dfrac{2y}{3s} = \dfrac{2y}{13x}$ for x.

$\dfrac{2y}{3s} = \dfrac{2y}{13x}$ Original equation

$2y \cdot 13x = 3s \cdot 2y$ Find the cross products.

$26yx = 6sy$ Simplify.

$x = \dfrac{6sy}{26y}$ Divide each side by $26y$.

$x = \dfrac{3s}{13}$ Simplify.

EXAMPLE 3

Simplify $3(x - y) - (x - y)$. If not possible, write *simplified*.

$3(x - y) - (x - y)$ Original expression

$= 3x - 3y - x + y$ Distributive Property

$= 2x - 2y$ Combine like terms.

$= 2(x - y)$ Factor out a 2.

Chapter 5 Get Ready For Chapter 5 **251**

✓ Formative Assessment

[CRM] Anticipation Guide, pp. 3–4
Spotting Preconceived Ideas
Students complete this survey to determine prior knowledge about ideas from Chapter 5. Revisit this worksheet after completing the chapter. Also see p. 288.

[TWE] **Lesson Activities**
- Ticket Out the Door, pp. 258, 270
- Crystal Ball, p. 278
- Name the Math, p. 265
- Yesterday's News, p. 284

Chapter Checkpoints

[SE] Mid-Chapter Quiz, p. 271

[SE] Study Guide and Review, pp. 285–288

[SE] California Standards Practice, pp. 290–291

[CRM] Quizzes, pp. 43 and 44

[CRM] Standardized Test Practice, pp. 60–62

Math [online] **ca.algebra1.com**

- Self-Check Quizzes
- Practice Test
- Standardized Test Practice

✓ Summative Assessment

[SE] Chapter Practice Test, p. 289

[CRM] Mid-Chapter Test, p. 45

[CRM] Vocabulary Test, p. 46

[CRM] Extended-Response Test, p. 59

[CRM] Leveled Chapter Tests, pp. 47–58

⊙ ExamView® Assessment Suite

✓ Diagnostic Assessment

Exercises	California Standards	Intervention
1–7	7AF3.3	[SE] Review Lesson 3-3, pp. 155–161
8–11	5.0	[SE] Review Lesson 2-8, pp. 117–121
12–14	4.0	[SE] Review Lesson 1-6, pp. 33–37

1 Focus

Objective

Solve a system of equations using a computer spreadsheet.

Materials

- computer
- spreadsheet software

Teaching Tip Once the spreadsheet formulas are entered for one sales amount, those formulas can be dragged to copy for all the other sales amounts. Have the students take their time creating the first formulas as any errors will be duplicated to all the other cells.

Teaching Tip This technique of solving systems of equations using a table can also be applied using the TABLE feature or CellSheet application on a TI-83/84 Plus graphing calculator.

2 Teach

Working in Cooperative Groups

Put students in groups of 2 or 3, mixing abilities. Have groups enter the data from the Example and complete Exercises 1–3.

- Remind students that spreadsheet software cannot interpret an expression such as 0.1x. It must typed as 0.1 * x.

- Urge students not to assume that the software will apply the order of operations. Students should use parentheses to ensure that operations are performed in the correct order.

- If the students use Microsoft Excel™, they can create a graph by using the Chart Wizard button on the standard toolbar.

Practice Have students complete Exercises 4 and 5.

252 Chapter 5 Solving Systems of Linear Equations

Preparation for Standard 9.0 Students solve a system of two linear equations in two variables algebraically and are able to interpret the answer graphically. Students are able to solve a system of two linear inequalities in two variables and to sketch the solution sets. (Key, CAHSEE)

COncepts in MOtion

Interactive Lab
ca.algebra1.com

1. $y = 400 + 0.1x$

4. (500, 450); If Mr. Winters makes $500 in sales, he will make $450 for either job.

5. Sample answer: Write and graph two linear equations. Find the point where the graphs intersect.

Spreadsheet Lab

Systems of Equations

You can use a spreadsheet to investigate when two quantities will be equal. Enter each formula into the spreadsheet and look for the row in which both formulas have the same result.

EXAMPLE

Bill Winters is considering two job offers in telemarketing departments. The salary at the first job is $400 per week plus 10% commission on Mr. Winters' sales. At the second job, the salary is $375 per week plus 15% commission. For what amount of sales would the weekly salary be the same at either job?

Enter different amounts for Mr. Winters' weekly sales in column A. Then enter the formula for the salary at the first job in each cell in column B. In each cell of column C, enter the formula for the salary at the second job.

Job Salaries.xls

◇	A	B	C	
1	Sales	Salary 1	Salary 2	
2	0	400	375	
3	100	410	390	
4	200	420	405	
5	300	430	420	
6	400	440	435	
7	500	450	450	
8	600	460	465	
9	700	470	480	
10	800	480	495	
11	900	490	510	
12	1000	500	525	

Sheet 1 / Sheet 2 / Sheet 3

The spreadsheet shows that for sales of $500 the total weekly salary for each job is $450.

EXERCISES

For Exercises 1–4, use the spreadsheet of weekly salaries above.

1. If x is the amount of Mr. Winters' weekly sales and y is his total weekly salary, write a linear equation for the salary at the first job.

2. Write a linear equation for the salary at the second job. $y = 375 + 0.15x$

3. Which ordered pair is a solution for both of the equations you wrote for Exercises 1 and 2? c
   a. (100, 410) **b.** (300, 420) **c.** (500, 450) **d.** (900, 510)

4. Use the graphing capability of the spreadsheet program to graph the salary data using a line graph. At what point do the two lines intersect? What is the significance of that point in the real-world situation?

5. How could you find the sales for which Mr. Winters' salary will be equal without using a spreadsheet?

252 Chapter 5 Solving Systems of Linear Equations

---

3 Assess

 Formative Assessment

Use Exercises 1 and 2 to determine whether students can write the correct expressions to translate the real-world situation into an algebraic representation. Use Exercise 3 to determine whether students can translate between a mathematical solution and its real-world meaning.

From Concrete to Abstract Have students explain the mathematical meaning of the point of intersection of two lines in Exercise 4. Sample answer: The point of intersection is an ordered pair which is a solution to both equations.

Main Ideas

- Determine whether a system of linear equations has no, one, or infinitely many solutions.
- Solve systems of equations by graphing.

Standard 9.0 Students solve a system of two linear equations in two variables algebraically **and are able to interpret the answer graphically.** Students are able to solve a system of two linear inequalities in two variables and to sketch the solution sets. (Key, CAHSEE)

New Vocabulary

system of equations
consistent
independent
dependent
inconsistent

Reading Math

Simultaneous Equations
Systems of equations are also known as *simultaneous equations*, because a solution consists of values for the variables that satisfy all of the equations at the same time, or *simultaneously*.

COncepts in MOtion
Animation
ca.algebra1.com

▶ **GET READY** for the Lesson

If x is the number of years since 2000 and y is units sold in millions, the following equations represent the sales of CD singles and music videos.

CD singles: $y = 34.2 - 14.9x$
music videos: $y = 3.3 + 4.7x$

The point at which the graphs of the two equations intersect represents the time when the CD units sold equaled the music videos sold. The ordered pair of this point is a solution of both equations.

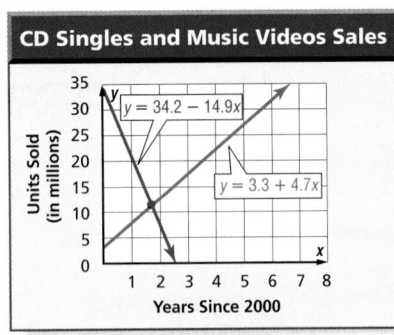

CD Singles and Music Videos Sales

Source: The Recording Industry Association of America

Number of Solutions Two equations, such as $y = 34.2 - 14.9x$ and $y = 3.3 + 4.7x$, together are called a **system of equations**. A solution of a system is an ordered pair that satisfies both equations. A system of two linear equations can have no, one, or an infinite number of solutions.

- If the graphs intersect or coincide, the system of equations is **consistent**. That is, it has at least one ordered pair that satisfies both equations.

- If a consistent system has exactly one solution, it is **independent**. If it has infinite solutions, it is **dependent**.

- If the graphs are parallel, the system of equations is said to be **inconsistent**. There are *no* ordered pairs that satisfy both equations.

KEY CONCEPT		Graphing Systems of Equations	
Graph of a System			
Number of Solutions	exactly one solution	infinitely many	no solutions
Terminology	consistent and independent	consistent and dependent	inconsistent

---

(continued on the next page)

1 Focus

Standards Alignment

Before Lesson 5-1
Write an expression, an equation, an inequality, or a system that represents a verbal description from Standard 7AF1.1

Lesson 5-1
Solve a system of two linear equations or inequalities in two variables algebraically and graphically from ◄— Standard 9.0

After Lesson 5-1
Solve systems of linear equations and inequalities from ◄— Standard 2A1.0

2 Teach

Scaffolding Questions
Have students read *Get Ready for the Lesson.*
Ask:
- The graph that is sloping downward represents sales of which product? CD singles
- The graph that is sloping upward represents sales of which product? music videos
- During what year were the sales equal? 2001

Lesson 5-1 Resources

Chapter 5 Resource Masters

Lesson Reading Guide, p. 5 BL OL ELL
Study Guide and Intervention, pp. 6–7 ELL BL OL
Skills Practice, p. 8 BL OL
Practice, p. 9 OL AL
Word Problem Practice, p. 10 OL AL
Enrichment, p. 11 OL AL
Graphing Calculator, p. 12

Transparencies

5-Minute Check Transparency 5-1

Additional Print Resources

Noteables™ Interactive Study Notebook with Foldables™
Teaching Algebra with Manipulatives

Technology

ca.algebra1.com
Interactive Classroom CD-ROM
AssignmentWorks CD-ROM
Graphing Calculator Easy Files

- You are told to assume that the sales are linear functions. What does this mean? It means that sales either increase or decrease by the same amount every year. Also, the graphs of linear functions are straight lines.

Number of Solutions

Example 1 shows how to determine the number of solutions of a system of equations.

 Formative Assessment

Use the Check Your Progress exercises after each example to determine students' understanding of concepts.

ADDITIONAL EXAMPLE

1 Use the graph to determine whether each system has *no* solution, *one* solution, or *infinitely many* solutions.

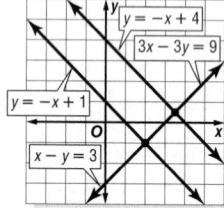

a. $y = -x + 1$
$y = -x + 4$
The graphs are parallel, so there are no solutions.

b. $3x - 3y = 9$
$y = -x + 1$
The graphs are intersecting lines, so there is *one* solution.

Additional Examples are also in:

- Noteables™ Interactive Study Notebook with Foldables™

- Interactive Classroom PowerPoint® Presentations

Solving by Graphing

Example 2 shows how to solve a system of equations by graphing.
Example 3 shows how to use a system of equations to solve a real-world problem.

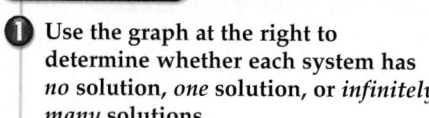 **Number of Solutions**

1 Use the graph at the right to determine whether each system has *no* solution, *one* solution, or *infinitely many* solutions.

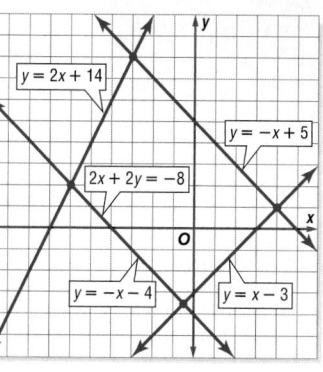

a. $y = -x + 5$
$y = x - 3$

Since the graphs are intersecting lines, there is one solution.

b. $y = -x + 5$
$2x + 2y = -8$

Since the graphs are parallel, there are no solutions.

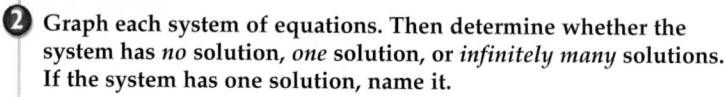 **Your Progress**

1A. $2x + 2y = -8$
$y = -x - 4$ infinitely many

1B. $y = 2x + 14$
$y = -x + 5$ one

Solve By Graphing One method of solving systems of equations is to carefully graph the equations on the same coordinate plane.

EXAMPLE Solve a System of Equations

2 Graph each system of equations. Then determine whether the system has *no* solution, *one* solution, or *infinitely many* solutions. If the system has one solution, name it.

a. $y = -x + 8$
$y = 4x - 7$

The graphs appear to intersect at (3, 5). Check by replacing x with 3 and y with 5.

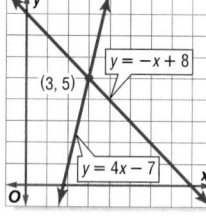

CHECK	$y = -x + 8$	$y = 4x - 7$
	$5 \stackrel{?}{=} -3 + 8$	$5 \stackrel{?}{=} 4(3) - 7$
	$5 = 5$ ✓	$5 = 5$ ✓

The solution is (3, 5).

b. $x + 2y = 5$
$2x + 4y = 2$

The graphs are parallel lines. Since they do not intersect, there are no solutions to this system of equations. Notice that the lines have the same slope but different y-intercepts. *Recall that a system of equations that has no solution is said to be inconsistent.*

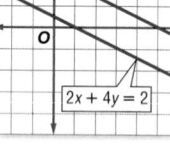

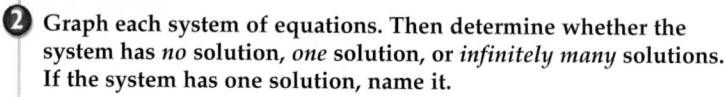 **Your Progress**

2A. $x - y = 2$
$3y + 2x = 9$

2B. $y = -2x - 3$
$2x + y = -3$

Online Personal Tutor at ca.algebra1.com

Study Tip

Look Back

To review **graphing linear equations,** see Lesson 3-3.

Pre-AP Activity   Use after Example 1

Write a system of three equations and two unknowns on the board. Have the students determine if the system has *one* solution, *no* solution, or *infinitely many* solutions. If it has one solution, name it. For example,

$x + y = 2$
$x - y = 0$
$\quad\;\; y = -2$

has *no* solution because the three lines do not intersect at one point.

Real-World EXAMPLE Write and Solve a System of Equations

3 SPORTS The number of girls participating in high school soccer and track and field has steadily increased during the past few years. Use the information in the table to predict the year in which the number of girls participating in these two sports will be the same.

High School Sport	Number of Girls Participating in 2004 (thousands)	Average Rate of Increase (thousands per year)
soccer	309	8
track and field	418	3

Source: National Federation of State High School Associations

Words	Number of girls participating	equals	rate of increase	times	number of years after 2004	plus	number participating in 2004.
Variables	Let y = number of girls competing.				Let x = number of years after 2004.		
Equations	soccer: y	=	8	×	x	+	309
	track and field: y	=	3	×	x	+	418

Graph the equations $y = 8x + 309$ and $y = 3x + 418$. The graphs appear to intersect at (22, 485). Check by replacing x with 22 and y with 485 in each equation.

CHECK

$y = 8x + 309$ $y = 3x + 418$

$485 = 8(22) + 309$ $485 = 3(22) + 418$

$485 = 485$ ✓ $485 \approx 484$ ✓

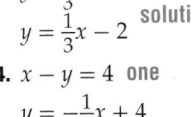

The solution means that approximately 22 years after 2004, or in 2026, the number of girls participating in high school soccer and track and field will be the same, about 485,000.

CHECK Your Progress

3. GARDENS A rectangular garden has a border around it consisting of 60 bricks. The width of the border has $\frac{2}{3}$ the number of bricks as the length. How many bricks are along one length of the garden? **18**

★ indicates multi-step problem

CHECK Your Understanding

Example 1 (p. 254)   Use the graph to determine whether each system has *no* solution, *one* solution, or *infinitely many* solutions.

1. $y = x - 4$ **one**
$y = \frac{1}{3}x - 2$

2. $y = \frac{1}{3}x + 2$ **no solution**
$y = \frac{1}{3}x - 2$

3. $x - y = 4$
$y = x - 4$
infinitely many

4. $x - y = 4$ **one**
$y = -\frac{1}{3}x + 4$

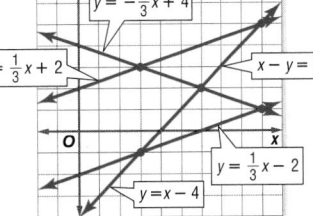

Differentiated Instruction

Kinesthetic Learners Students may benefit from solving systems of equations using elimination using concrete models. Have students write the terms of the equation on pieces of paper or use algebra tiles or other models to represent the equations. Then when they eliminate one of the variables, have them remove the model for that variable. The act of removing the terms should help them remember eliminating the variable.

ADDITIONAL EXAMPLES

2 Graph each system of equations. Determine whether the system has *no* solution, *one* solution, or *infinitely many* solutions. If the system has one solution, name it.

a. $2x - y = -3$
$8x - 4y = -12$ infinitely many solutions

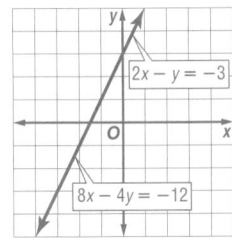

b. $x - 2y = 4$
$x - 2y = -2$ no solution

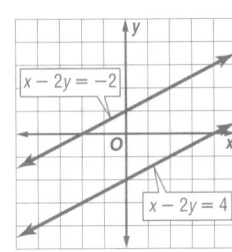

3 BICYCLING Tyler and Pearl went on a 20-kilometer bike ride that lasted 3 hours. Because of the steep hills on the ride, they had to walk for most of the trip. Their walking speed was 4 kilometers per hour. Their riding speed was 12 kilometers per hour. How much time did they spend walking? Let r = the number of hours they rode and w = the number of hours they walked.

$r + w = 3$
$12r + 4w = 20$

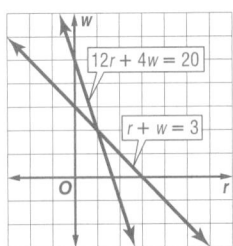

They walked for 2 hours.

3 Practice

✓ **Formative Assessment**

Use Exercises 1–9 to check for understanding.

Use the chart at the bottom of the next page to customize assignments for your students.

Odd/Even Assignments

Exercises 10–31 are structured so that students practice the same concepts whether they are assigned odd or even problems.

Additional Answer

39.

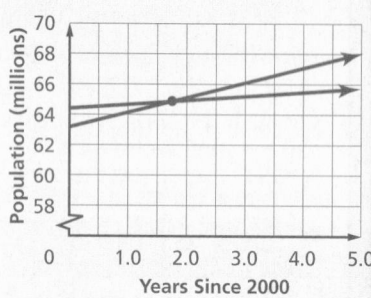

The solution (1.75, 65) means that 1.75 years after 2000, or in 2002, the population of the West and the Midwest were approximately equal, 65 million.

Example 2
(p. 254)

Graph each system of equations. Then determine whether the system has *no* solution, *one* solution, or *infinitely many* solutions. If the system has one solution, name it. **5–8. See Ch. 5 Answer Appendix for graphs.**

5. $y = 3x - 4$ one; (0, −4)
$y = -3x - 4$

6. $x + y = 2$ one; (−1, 3)
$y = 4x + 7$

7. $x + y = 4$ no solution
$x + y = 1$

8. $2x + 4y = 2$ infinitely many
$3x + 6y = 3$

Example 3 ★ **9. GEOMETRY** The length of the rectangle is 1 meter
(p. 255) less than twice its width. What are the dimensions of the rectangle? **13 m by 7 m**

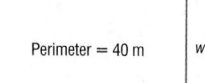

Exercises

HOMEWORK	
For Exercises	**See Examples**
10–15	1
16–27	2
28–31	3

Exercise Levels:
A: 10–31
B: 32–39
C: 40–43

12. infinitely many
13. no solution

Use the graph to determine whether each system has *no* solution, *one* solution, or *infinitely many* solutions.

10. $x = -3$
$y = 2x + 1$ one

11. $y = -x - 2$
$y = 2x - 4$ one

12. $y = 2x + 1$
$2y - 4x = 2$

13. $y = 2x + 1$
$y = 2x - 4$

14. $y + x = -2$
$y = -x - 2$
infinitely many

15. $2y - 4x = 2$
$y = 2x - 4$
no solutions

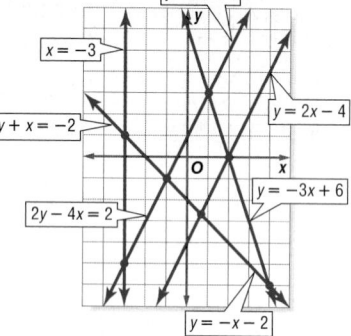

Graph each system of equations. Then determine whether the system has *no* solution, *one* solution, or *infinitely many* solutions. If the system has one solution, name it. **16–27. See Ch. 5 Answer Appendix for graphs.**

16. $y = -6$ one; (2, −6)
$4x + y = 2$

17. $x = 2$ one; (2, −2)
$3x - y = 8$

18. $y = \frac{1}{2}x$ one, (4, 2)
$2x + y = 10$

19. $y = -x$ one; (2, −2)
$y = 2x - 6$

20. $y = 2x + 6$ one;
$y = -x - 3$ (−3, 0)

21. $x - 2y = 2$ one;
$3x + y = 6$ (2, 0)

22. $x + y = 2$ one; (−2, 4)
$2y - x = 10$

23. $3x + 2y = 12$ no
$3x + 2y = 6$ solution

24. $2x + 3y = 4$
$-4x - 6y = -8$
infinitely many

25. $2x + y = -4$ one;
$5x + 3y = -6$ (−6, 8)

26. $4x + 3y = 24$ one;
$5x - 8y = -17$ (3, 4)

27. $3x + y = 3$
$2y = -6x + 6$
infinitely many

SAVINGS For Exercises 28 and 29, use the following information.
Monica and Max Gordon each want to buy a scooter. Monica has already saved $25 and plans to save $5 per week until she can buy the scooter. Max has $16 and plans to save $8 per week.

28. In how many weeks will Monica and Max have saved the same amount of money? **3 weeks**

29. How much will each person have saved at that time? **$40**

256 Chapter 5 Solving Systems of Linear Equations

DIFFERENTIATED HOMEWORK OPTIONS

Level	Assignment	Two-Day Option	
BL Basic	10–31, 41–51	9–31 odd, 44, 45	10–30 even, 41–43, 46–51
OL Core	9–33 odd, 34–39, 41–51	10–31, 44, 45	32–39, 41–51
AL Advanced /Pre-AP	32–48 (optional: 49–51)		

BALLOONING For Exercises 30 and 31, use the information in the graphic at the right.

30. In how many minutes will the balloons be at the same height? **4 min**

31. How high will the balloons be at that time? Is your answer reasonable? Explain. **70 m; yes, 70 m is a reasonable height for balloons to fly.**

Graph each system of equations. Then determine whether the system has *no solution, one* solution, or *infinitely many* solutions. If the system has one solution, name it. **32–33. See Ch. 5 Answer Appendix for graphs.**

32. $y = 0.6x - 5$
$2y = 1.2x$
no solution

33. $6 - \frac{3}{8}y = x$
$\frac{2}{3}x + \frac{1}{4}y = 4$
infinitely many

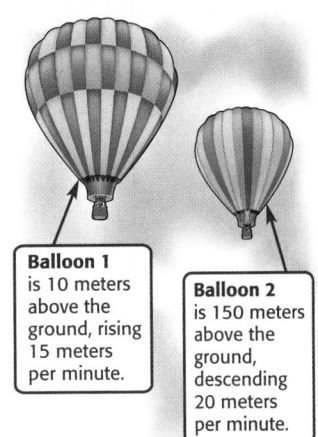

Balloon 1 is 10 meters above the ground, rising 15 meters per minute.

Balloon 2 is 150 meters above the ground, descending 20 meters per minute.

ANALYZE GRAPHS For Exercises 34–36, use the graph at the right.

34. Which company had the greater profit during the ten years? **Widget Co.**

35. Which company had a greater rate of growth? **neither**

★ **36.** If the profit patterns continue, will the profits of the two companies ever be equal? Explain. **No; the graphs are parallel so the lines will never meet. There is no year when the profits will be equal.**

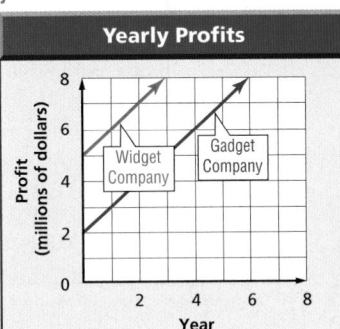

Yearly Profits

40. $A = 4$, $B = -4$; Substitute 2 for x and -3 for y into the first equation to find that $A = 4$. Then substitute these values into the second equation to find that $B = -4$.

POPULATION For Exercises 37–39, use the following information.

The U.S. Census Bureau divides the country into four sections. They are the Northeast, the Midwest, the South, and the West. The populations and rates of growth for the Midwest and the West are shown in the table.

Section	2000 Population (millions)	Average Rate of Increase (millions per year)
Midwest	64.4	0.3
West	63.2	1.0

Source: U.S. Census Bureau

37. Write an equation to represent the population of the Midwest for the years since 2000. $p = 64.4 + 0.3t$

38. Write an equation to represent the population of the West for the years since 2000. $p = 63.2 + 1t$ or $p = 63.2 + t$

★ **39.** Graph the population equations. Assume that the rate of growth of each of these areas remained the same. Estimate the solution and interpret what it means. **See margin.**

H.O.T. Problems

40. CHALLENGE The solution of the system of equations $Ax + y = 5$ and $Ax + By = 20$ is $(2, -3)$. What are the values of A and B? Justify your reasoning.

41. OPEN ENDED Write three equations such that they form a system of equations with $y = 5x - 3$. The systems should have *no, one,* and *infinitely many* solutions, respectively. **Sample answer:** $y = 5x + 3$, $y = -x - 3$, $2y = 10x - 6$

Lesson 5-1 Graphing Systems of Equations **257**

Enrichment
CRM p. 11 **OL** **AL**

5-1 Enrichment

Graphing a Trip

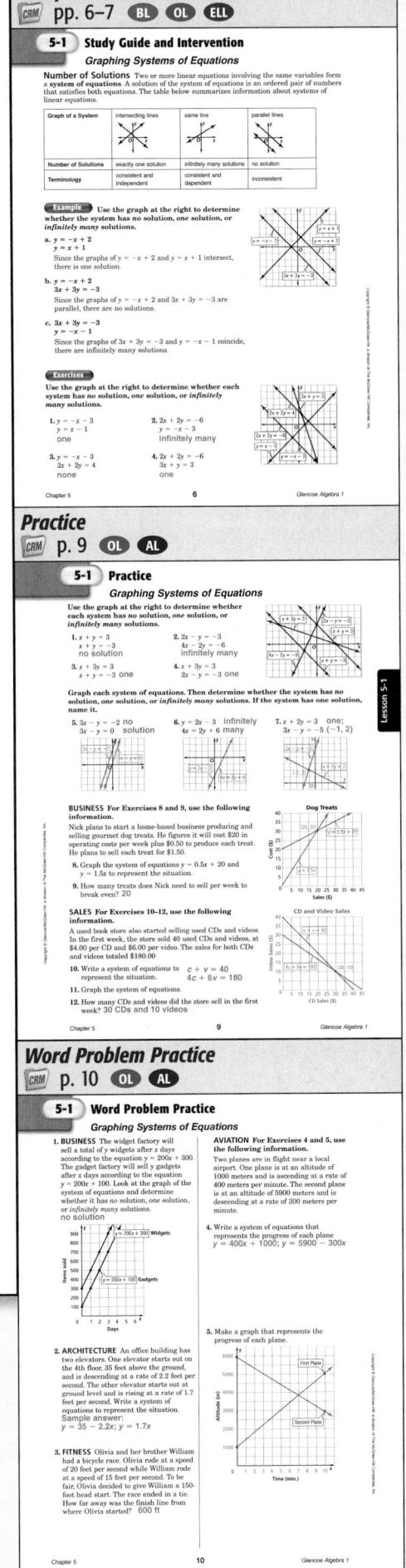

4 Assess

Ticket Out the Door Give each student a small piece of grid paper. Have each student draw a graph that represents a system of equations with no solution.

FOLDABLES **Foldables™ Follow-Up**
Study Organizer

Under the tab for this lesson have students record the three kinds of graphs that occur when graphing a system of equations. Ask them to tell the number of solutions that can occur and whether the system is consistent or inconsistent and independent or dependent. Students should include information like that in the Concept Summary on p. 253.

Additional Answers

42. Always; if the system of linear equations has 2 solutions, their graphs are the same line and there are infinitely many solutions.

43. Graphs can show when the units sold of one item is greater than the units sold of the other item and when the units sold of the items are equal. The units sold of CD singles equaled the units sold of music videos in about 1.5 years, or between 2001 and 2002.

48.

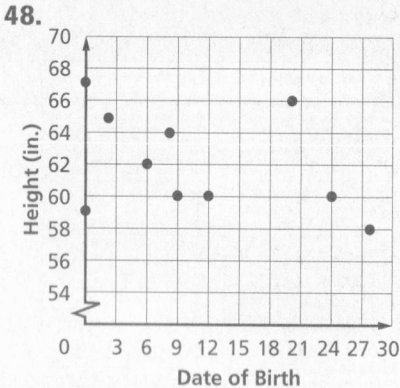

No correlation; height is not dependent on dates of birth.

---

42. REASONING Determine whether a system of two linear equations with (0, 0) and (2, 2) as solutions *sometimes*, *always*, or *never* has other solutions. Explain. See margin.

43. *Writing in Math* Use the information on page 253 to explain how graphs can be used to compare the sales of two products. Include an estimate of the year in which the CD units sold equaled the music videos sold. Then determine the reasonableness of your solution in the context of the problem. See margin.

 STANDARDS PRACTICE 9.0, 6AF1.1

44. A buffet restaurant has one price for adults and another price for children. The Taylor family has two adults and three children, and their bill was $40.50. The Wong family has three adults and one child. Their bill was $38. Which system of equations could be used to determine the buffet price for an adult and the price for a child? **C**

A $x + y = 40.50$
  $x + y = 38$

B $2x + 3y = 40.50$
  $x + 3y = 38$

C $2x + 3y = 40.50$
  $3x + y = 38$

D $2x + 2y = 40.50$
  $3x + y = 38$

45. REVIEW Francisco has 3 dollars more than $\frac{1}{4}$ the number of dollars that Kayla has. Which expression represents how much money Francisco has? **H**

F $3\left(\frac{1}{4}k\right)$

G $3 - \frac{1}{4}k$

H $\frac{1}{4}k + 3$

J $\frac{1}{4} + 3k$

Spiral Review

Write the slope-intercept form of an equation for the line that passes through the given point and is parallel to the graph of each equation. (Lesson 4-7)

46. 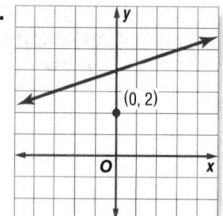 $y = \frac{1}{3}x + 2$

47. 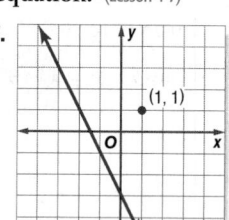 $y = -2x + 3$

★ **48. BIOLOGY** The table shows the date of the month that 10 students were born, and their heights. Draw a scatter plot and determine what relationship exists, if any, in the data. Explain. (Lesson 4-6) See margin.

Date of Birth	12	28	24	15	3	11	20	5	3	9
Height (in.)	60	58	62	60	59	64	66	65	67	62

▶ **GET READY for the Next Lesson**

PREREQUISITE SKILL Solve each equation for the variable specified. (Lesson 2-8)

49. $12x - y = 10x$, for y
   $y = 2x$

50. $6a + b = 2a$, for a
   $a = -\frac{1}{4}b$

51. $\frac{7m - n}{q} = 10$, for q
   $q = \frac{7m - n}{10}$

EXTEND 5-1

Graphing Calculator Lab
Systems of Equations

Standard 9.0 Students solve a system of two linear equations in two variables algebraically **and are able to interpret the answer graphically.** Students are able to solve a system of two linear inequalities in two variables and to sketch the solution sets. (Key, CAHSEE)

You can use a graphing calculator to solve a system of equations.

EXAMPLE

Solve the system of equations. State the decimal solution to the nearest hundredth.

$2.93x + y = 6.08$

$8.32x - y = 4.11$

Step 1 Solve each equation for y. Enter them into the calculator.

$2.93x + y = 6.08$	First equation
$2.93x + y - 2.93x = 6.08 - 2.93x$	Subtract $2.93x$ from each side.
$y = 6.08 - 2.93x$	Simplify.
$8.32x - y = 4.11$	Second equation
$8.32x - y - 8.32x = 4.11 - 8.32x$	Subtract $8.32x$ from each side.
$-y = 4.11 - 8.32x$	Simplify.
$(-1)(-y) = (-1)(4.11 - 8.32x)$	Multiply each side by -1.
$y = -4.11 + 8.32x$	Simplify.

Step 2 Enter these equations in the Y= list and graph.

    KEYSTROKES: *Review on pages 162–163.*

Step 3 Use the CALC menu to find the point of intersection.

    KEYSTROKES: 2nd [CALC] 5 ENTER ENTER ENTER

The solution is approximately (0.91, 3.43).

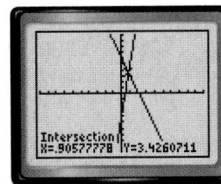

[−10, 10] scl: 1 by [−10, 10] scl: 1

EXERCISES

Use a graphing calculator to solve each system of equations. Write decimal solutions to the nearest hundredth. 9. (−2.35, 5.44)

1. $y = 3x - 4$ (2.86, 4.57)
$y = -0.5x + 6$

2. $y = 2x + 5$
$y = -0.2x - 4$
  (−4.09, −3.18)

3. $x + y = 5.35$ (2.28, 3.08)
$3x - y = 3.75$

4. $0.35x - y = 1.12$
$2.25x + y = -4.05$
  (−1.13, −1.51)

5. $1.5x + y = 6.7$
$5.2x - y = 4.1$ (1.61, 4.28)

6. $5.4x - y = 1.8$
$6.2x + y = -3.8$
  (−0.17, −2.73)

7. $5x - 4y = 26$
$4x + 2y = 53.3$ (10.2, 6.25)

8. $2x + 3y = 11$
$4x + y = -6$ (−2.9, 5.6)

9. $0.22x + 0.15y = 0.30$
$-0.33x + y = 6.22$

 **Other Calculator Keystrokes at** ca.algebra1.com

Extend 5-1 Graphing Calculator Lab   **259**

EXTEND 5-1

Lesson Notes

① Focus

Objective
Use a graphing calculator to solve a system of equations.

Materials
• graphing calculator

Teaching Tip Remind students that the equations must be solved for y before they are entered in the calculator.

② Teach

Working in Cooperative Groups

Put students in groups of 2 or 3, mixing abilities. Have groups follow the example and complete Exercises 1–6.

• In Step 2, remind students to clear all previous equations from the Y=LIST 1. Have students graph each system using the standard viewing window. If the intersection is not visible, have them adjust the window to an area suggested by the directions of the lines.

• In Step 3, point out that the **GUESS** feature that appears after the second ENTER gives students an opportunity to use the arrow keys to estimate the solution to the system and then check their estimates by pressing ENTER the third time.

• Discuss how students can use the calculator's feature to solve systems of equations by examining the x- and y-values for both equations.

Practice Have students complete Exercises 7–9.

---

③ Assess

✓ Formative Assessment

Use Exercise 6 to see whether students can use graphing calculators to solve systems of equations.

From Concrete to Abstract Ask students how they can verify if their solutions are correct. Sample answer: Substitute the values into the original equation to see if they make both equations true.

Extending the Concept
Ask: When would a system of two linear equations not have a point of intersection? Sample answer: Two linear equations will not have a point of intersection if their graphs are parallel.

Lesson 5-1 Graphing Calculator Lab   **259**

5-2 Lesson Notes

5-2 Substitution

1 Focus

Standards Alignment

Before Lesson 5-2
Write an expression, an equation, an inequality, or a system that represents a verbal description *from Standard 7AF1.1*

Lesson 5-2
Solve a system of two linear equations or inequalities in two variables algebraically and graphically *from Standard 9.0*

After Lesson 5.2
Solve systems of linear equations and inequalities *from Standard 2A1.0*

2 Teach

Scaffolding Questions Have students read *Get Ready for the Lesson.*
Ask:
- Which is changing at a greater rate: the number of newspaper readers or people online? number of people online
- According to the graph, in about what year will the number of hours online per person equal time spent reading newspapers? in about 2003

(continued on the next page)

Main Ideas
- Solve systems of equations algebraically by using substitution.
- Solve real-world problems involving systems of equations.

Standard 9.0
Students solve a system of two linear equations in two variables algebraically and are able to interpret the answer graphically. Students are able to solve a system of two linear ineqalities in two variables and to sketch the solution sets. (Key, CAHSEE)

New Vocabulary
substitution

▶ GET READY for the Lesson

Americans spend more time online than they spend reading daily newspapers. If x represents the number of years since 2000 and y represents the average number of hours per person per year, the following system represents the situation.

reading daily newspapers: $y = -2.8x + 150.4$
online: $y = 14.4x + 102.8$

The solution of the system represents the year that the number of hours spent on each activity will be the same. To solve this system, you could graph the equations and find the point of intersection. However, the exact coordinates of the point would be very difficult to determine from the graph. You could find a more accurate solution by using algebraic methods.

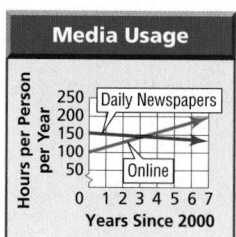

Substitution The exact solution of a system of equations can be found by using algebraic methods. One such method is called **substitution**.

ALGEBRA LAB

Using Substitution
Use algebra tiles and an equation mat to solve the system of equations. $3x + y = 8$ and $y = x - 4$

MODEL AND ANALYZE
Since $y = x - 4$, use 1 positive x-tile and 4 negative 1-tiles to represent y. Use algebra tiles to represent $3x + y = 8$.

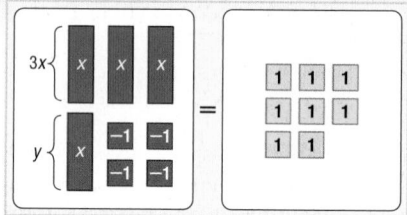

1. Use what you know about equation mats to solve for x. What is the value of x? **3**
2. Use $y = x - 4$ to solve for y. **−1**
3. What is the solution of the system of equations? **(3, −1)**
4. **MAKE A CONJECTURE** Explain how to solve the following system of equations using algebra tiles. $4x + 3y = 10$ and $y = x + 1$
5. Why do you think this method is called substitution?
   You substitute a representation of y for y.

4. On an equation mat, use algebra tiles to model $4x + 3y = 10$ using 1 positive x-tile and 1 positive 1-tile to represent each y. Use what you know about equation mats to solve for x. Use the value of x and $y = x + 1$ to solve for y. The solution is (1, 2).

Lesson 5-2 Resources

Chapter 5 Resource Masters
Lesson Reading Guide, p. 13 **BL OL ELL**
Study Guide and Intervention, pp. 14–15 **ELL BL OL**
Skills Practice, p. 16 **BL OL**
Practice, p. 17 **OL AL**
Word Problem Practice, p. 18 **OL AL**
Enrichment, p. 19 **OL AL**
Quiz 1, p. 43

Transparencies
5-Minute Check Transparency 5-2
Additional Print Resources
Noteables™ Interactive Study Notebook with Foldables™
Teaching Algebra with Manipulatives
Science and Mathematics Lab Manual, pp. 149–152

Technology
ca.algebra1.com
Interactive Classroom CD-ROM
AssignmentWorks CD-ROM
Graphing Calculator Easy Files

1 Use substitution to solve each system of equations.

a. $y = 3x$

$x + 2y = -21$

Since $y = 3x$, substitute $3x$ for y in the second equation.

$$x + 2y = -21 \quad \text{Second equation}$$
$$x + 2(3x) = -21 \quad y = 3x$$
$$x + 6x = -21 \quad \text{Simplify.}$$
$$7x = -21 \quad \text{Combine like terms.}$$
$$x = -3 \quad \text{Divide each side by 7 and simplify.}$$

Use $y = 3x$ to find the value of y.

$$y = 3x \quad \text{First equation}$$
$$y = 3(-3) \text{ or } -9 \quad x = -3$$

The solution is $(-3, -9)$.   Check the solution by graphing.

b. $x + 5y = -3$

$3x - 2y = 8$

Solve the first equation for x since the coefficient of x is 1.

$$x + 5y = -3 \quad \text{First equation}$$
$$x + 5y - 5y = -3 - 5y \quad \text{Subtract 5y from each side.}$$
$$x = -3 - 5y \quad \text{Simplify.}$$

Find the value of y by substituting $-3 - 5y$ for x in the second equation.

$$3x - 2y = 8 \quad \text{Second equation}$$
$$3(-3 - 5y) - 2y = 8 \quad x = -3 - 5y$$
$$-9 - 15y - 2y = 8 \quad \text{Distributive Property}$$
$$-9 - 17y = 8 \quad \text{Combine like terms.}$$
$$-9 - 17y + 9 = 8 + 9 \quad \text{Add 9 to each side.}$$
$$-17y = 17 \quad \text{Simplify.}$$
$$\frac{-17y}{-17} = \frac{17}{-17} \quad \text{Divide each side by } -17.$$
$$y = -1 \quad \text{Simplify.}$$

Substitute -1 for y in either equation to find the value of x.

$$x + 5y = -3 \quad \text{First equation}$$
$$x + 5(-1) = -3 \quad y = -1$$
$$x - 5 = -3 \quad \text{Simplify.}$$
$$x = 2 \quad \text{Add 5 to each side.}$$

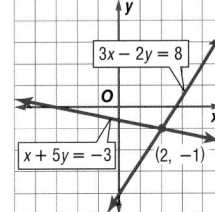

The solution is $(2, -1)$. The graph verifies the solution.

✓ **CHECK Your Progress**

1A. $4x + 5y = 11$

$y = 3x - 13$ $(4, -1)$

1B. $x - 3y = -9$

$5x - 2y = 7$ $(3, 4)$

Math Online Extra Examples at ca.algebra1.com

Lesson 5-2 Substitution   **261**

Study Tip

Looking Back

To review **solving linear equations,** see Lesson 2-5.

Study Tip

Substituting

When substituting to find the value of the second variable, choose the equation that is easier to solve.

• If the two equations weren't labeled, how would you tell them apart? The one with negative slope represents newspaper readers because the reading time is declining.

Substitution

Example 1 shows how to solve a system of equations using substitution. **Example 2** shows how to solve one of the equations for one variable and then substitute to solve the system of equations.

 Formative Assessment

Use the Check Your Progress exercises after each example to determine students' understanding of concepts.

Algebra Lab

Students will need algebra tiles and an equation mat for the activities on p. 260. Remind them that anything they add to one side of the mat must also be added to the other side. Also, remind them that the purpose is to eliminate zero pairs. Once a value for x is found, have students use that value to find y.

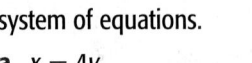
ADDITIONAL EXAMPLE

1 Use substitution to solve each system of equations.

a. $x = 4y$

$4x - y = 75$ $(20, 5)$

b. $4x + y = 12$

$-2x - 3y = 14$ $(5, -8)$

Focus on Mathematical Content

Substitution Method This method works well when one of the equations of the system gives one variable in terms of the other. For example, if one of the equations is solved for y as in $y = 3x$, you can substitute $3x$ for y in the second equation and solve for x. If this is not the case, solve one of the equations for one of the variables, substitute, and then solve the other equation. Once one of the values has been found, substitute that value into either of the original equations to find the other value.

Preventing Error

Point out that if neither of the equations gives one variable in terms of the other, you must solve for one variable first. The easiest choice in Example 16 is to solve the first equation for *x* by subtracting 5*y* from both sides.

ADDITIONAL EXAMPLE

 Use substitution to solve the system of equations.

$2x + 2y = 8$

$x + y = -2$ no solution

Additional Examples are also in:

- Noteables™ Interactive Study Notebook with Foldables™
- Interactive Classroom PowerPoint® Presentations

Real World Problems

Example 3 shows how to write and solve a system of equations for a real-world problem that can be solved by substitution.

ADDITIONAL EXAMPLE

3 **GOLD** Gold is alloyed with different metals to make it hard enough to be used in jewelry. The amount of gold present in a gold alloy is measured in 24ths, called *karats*. 24-karat gold is 24/24 or 100% gold. Similarly, 18-karat gold is 18/24 or 75% gold. How many ounces of 18-karat gold should be added to an amount of 12-karat gold to make 4 ounces of 14-karat gold?

$1\frac{1}{3}$ ounces of 18-karat gold and $2\frac{2}{3}$ ounces of 12-karat gold

---

In general, if you solve a system of linear equations and the result is a true statement (an identity such as $-4 = -4$), the system has an infinite number of solutions. If the result is a false statement (such as $-4 = 5$), there is no solution.

EXAMPLE   Infinitely Many or No Solutions

2 Use substitution to solve the system of equations.

$6x - 2y = -4$

$y = 3x + 2$

Since $y = 3x + 2$, substitute $3x + 2$ for y in the first equation.

$6x - 2y = -4$	First equation
$6x - 2(3x + 2) = -4$	$y = 3x + 2$
$6x - 6x - 4 = -4$	Distributive Property
$-4 = -4$	Simplify.

The statement $-4 = -4$ is true. So, there are infinitely many solutions.

> **Study Tip**
>
> **Dependent Systems** There are infinitely many solutions of the system in Example 2, because the slope-intercept form of both equations is $y = 3x + 2$. That is, the equations are equivalent, and they have the same graph.

✓CHECK Your Progress

2A. $2x - y = 8$
      $y = 2x - 3$ no solution

2B. $4x - 3y = 1$
      $6y - 8x = -2$ infinitely many solutions

Real-World Problems Sometimes it is helpful to organize data tables, charts, graphs, or diagrams before solving a problem.

EXAMPLE   Write and Solve a System of Equations

3 **METAL ALLOYS** A metal alloy is 25% copper. Another metal alloy is 50% copper. How much of each alloy should be used to make 1000 grams of a metal alloy that is 45% copper?

Let $a =$ the number of grams of the 25% copper alloy and $b =$ the number of grams of the 50% copper alloy. Use a table to organize the information.

> **Study Tip**
>
> **Alternative Method** Using a system of equations is an alternative method for solving the weighted average problems that you studied in Lesson 2-9.

	25% Copper	50% Copper	45% Copper	
Total Grams	a	b	1000	→ $a + b = 1000$
Grams of Copper	$0.25a$	$0.50b$	$0.45(1000)$	→ $0.25a + 0.5b = 0.45(1000)$

$a + b = 1000$	First equation
$a + b - b = 1000 - b$	Subtract b from each side.
$a = 1000 - b$	Simplify.

$0.25a + 0.50b = 0.45(1000)$	Second equation
$0.25(1000 - b) + 0.50b = 0.45(1000)$	$a = 1000 - b$
$250 - 0.25b + 0.50b = 450$	Distributive Property
$250 + 0.25b = 450$	Combine like terms.
$250 + 0.25b - 250 = 450 - 250$	Subtract 250 from each side.
$0.25b = 200$	Simplify.
$\dfrac{0.25b}{0.25} = \dfrac{200}{0.25}$	Divide each side by 0.25.
$b = 800$	Simplify.

262   Chapter 5 Solving Systems of Linear Equations

(**Focus on Mathematical Content**)

Infinitely Many or No Solutions   If solving a system of equations results in a true sentence (such as $3 = 3$), then the system has infinitely many solutions. This happens when the two equations represent the same line. When solving a system of equations results in a false sentence (such as $3 = 2$), the system has no solution. The equations represent two parallel lines. If both equations are solved for *y*, the equations will have the same slope but different *y*-intercepts.

$$a + b = 1000 \quad \text{First equation}$$
$$a + 800 = 1000 \quad b = 800$$
$$a = 200 \quad \text{Subtract 800 from each side and simplify.}$$

200 grams of the 25% alloy and 800 grams of the 50% alloy should be used.

 **CHECK Your Progress**   Yankees: 26; Reds: 5

3. BASEBALL The New York Yankees and the Cincinnati Reds together have won a total of 31 World Series. The Yankees have won 5.2 times as many as the Reds. How many World Series did each team win?

 **Personal Tutor at** ca.algebra1.com

★ indicates multi-step problem

CHECK Your Understanding

Examples 1–2
(pp. 261–262)

Use substitution to solve each system of equations. If the system does *not* have exactly one solution, state whether it has *no* solution or *infinitely many* solutions.

1. $2x + 7y = 3$ $(5, -1)$
   $x = 1 - 4y$

2. $6x - 2y = -4$ infinitely
   $y = 3x + 2$ many

3. $y = \frac{3}{5}x$ no solution
   $3x - 5y = 15$

4. $x + 3y = 12$ $(9, 1)$
   $x - y = 8$

5. $a + b = 1$ $(-2, 3)$
   $5a + 3b = -1$

6. $\frac{1}{3}x - y = 2$ infinitely many
   $x - 3y = 6$

Example 3 ★ **7. TRANSPORTATION** The Thrust SSC is the world's fastest land vehicle. Suppose the driver of a car with a top speed of 200 miles per hour requests a race against the SSC. The car gets a head start of one-half hour. If there is unlimited space to race, at what distance will the SSC pass the car? **about 135.5 mi**

Thrust SSC top speed is 763 mph.

Exercises

HOMEWORK HELP	
For Exercises	See Examples
8–19	1–2
20, 21	3

Exercise Levels
A: 8-21
B: 22-30
C: 31-34

Review Vocabulary

Supplementary Angles two angles with measures that have the sum of 180 degrees

Use substitution to solve each system of equations. If the system does *not* have exactly one solution, state whether it has *no* solution or *infinitely many* solutions. **10.** $(-23, -7)$ **13.** infinitely many   **14.** no solution

8. $y = 5x$ $(2, 10)$
   $2x + 3y = 34$

9. $x = 4y$ $(16, 4)$
   $2x + 3y = 44$

10. $x = 4y + 5$
   $x = 3y - 2$

11. $y = 2x + 3$ $(2, 7)$
   $y = 4x - 1$

12. $4c = 3d + 3$ $(6, 7)$
   $c = d - 1$

13. $x = \frac{1}{2}y + 3$
   $2x - y = 6$

14. $8x + 2y = 13$
   $4x + y = 11$

15. $2x - y = -4$ $(13, 30)$
   $-3x + y = -9$

16. $3x - 5y = 11$ $(7, 2)$
   $x - 3y = 1$

17. $2x + 3y = 1$ $(-4, 3)$
   $-x + \frac{1}{3}y = 5$

18. $c - 5d = 2$ $(2, 0)$
   $2c + d = 4$

19. $5r - s = 5$ $(2, 5)$
   $-4r + 5s = 17$

20. GEOMETRY Angles X and Y are supplementary, and the measure of angle X is 24 degrees greater than the measure of angle Y. Find the angle measures. $m\angle X = 102, m\angle Y = 78$

Lesson 5-2 Substitution   **263**

DIFFERENTIATED HOMEWORK OPTIONS

Level	Assignment	Two-Day Option	
BL Basic	8–21, 31, 33–48	9–21 odd, 35–37	8–20 even, 31, 33, 34, 38–48
OL Core	9–25 odd, 26–30, 31, 33–48	8–21, 35–37	22–31, 33, 34, 38–48
AL Advanced /Pre-AP	22–42, (Optional: 43–48)		

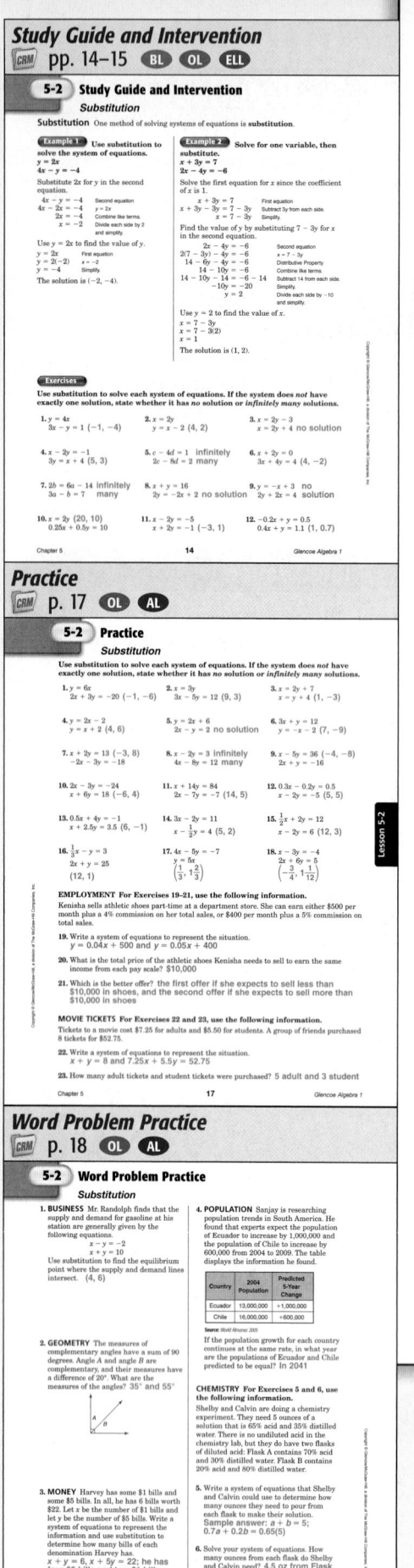

Study Guide and Intervention
pp. 14–15 · BL · OL · ELL

5-2 Study Guide and Intervention
Substitution

Practice
p. 17 · OL · AL

5-2 Practice
Substitution

Word Problem Practice
p. 18 · OL · AL

5-2 Word Problem Practice
Substitution

---

21. CHEMISTRY MX Labs needs to make 500 gallons of a 34% acid solution. The only solutions available are a 25% acid solution and a 50% acid solution. How many gallons of each solution should be mixed to make the 34% solution? **320 gal of 25% acid, 180 gal of 50% acid**

Use substitution to solve each system of equations. If the system does *not* have exactly one solution, state whether it has *no* solutions or *infinitely many* solutions.

22. $x - 3y = 0$ $\left(2\dfrac{1}{10}, \dfrac{7}{10}\right)$
$3x + y = 7$

23. $-0.3x + y = 0.5$ **(5, 2)**
$0.5x - 0.3y = 1.9$

24. $0.5x - 2y = 17$ **(50, 4)**
$2x + y = 104$

25. $y = \dfrac{1}{2}x + 3$ $\left(2\dfrac{2}{3}, 4\dfrac{1}{3}\right)$
$y = 2x - 1$

JOBS For Exercises 26 and 27, use the following information.
Shantel Jones has a job offer in which she will receive $600 per month plus a commission of 2% of the total price of the cars she sells. At her current job, she receives $1000 per month plus a commission of 1.5% of her total sales.

26. What is the total price of the cars that Ms. Jones must sell each month to make the same income from either dealership? **$80,000**

27. How much must Ms. Jones sell to make the new job a better deal? **See margin.**

28. LANDSCAPING A blue spruce grows an average of 6 inches per year. A hemlock grows an average of 4 inches per year. If a blue spruce is 4 feet tall and a hemlock is 6 feet tall, write a system of equations to represent their growth. Find and interpret the solution in the context of the situation. **See margin.**

29. ANALYZE TABLES The table shows the approximate number of tourists in two areas during a recent year and the average rates of change in tourism. If the trends continue, in how many years would you expect the number of tourists to the regions to be equal? **23 yr**

Destination	Number of Tourists	Average Rates of Change in Tourists (millions per year)
South America and the Caribbean	40.3 million	increase of 0.8
Middle East	17.0 million	increase of 1.8

30. RESEARCH Use the Internet or other resource to find the pricing plans for various cell phones. Determine the number of minutes you would need to use the phone for two plans to cost the same amount of money. **See students' work.**

31. FIND THE ERROR In the system $a + b = 7$ and $1.29a + 0.49b = 6.63$, a represents the pounds of apples bought and b represents pounds of bananas. Josh and Lydia are finding and interpreting the solution. Who is correct? Explain. **See margin.**

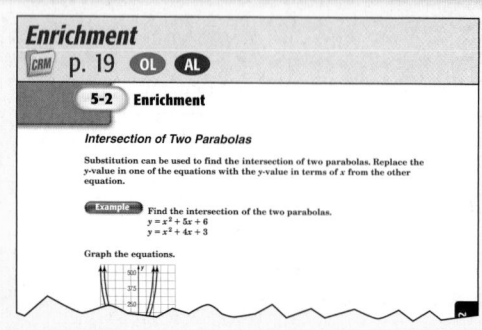

Josh
$1.29a + 0.49b = 6.63$
$1.29a + 0.49(7 - a) = 6.63$
$1.29a + 3.43 - 0.49a = 6.63$
$0.8a = 3.2$
$a = 4$

$a + b = 7$, so $b = 3$. The solution (4, 3) means that 4 apples and 3 bananas were bought.

Lydia
$1.29a + 0.49b = 6.63$
$1.29(7 - b) + 0.49b = 6.63$
$9.03 - 1.29b + 0.49b = 6.63$
$-0.8b = -2.4$
$b = 3$

The solution $b = 3$ means that 3 apples and 3 bananas were bought.

264 **Chapter 5** Solving Systems of Linear Equations

Real-World Career

Chemist
Many chemists study the properties and composition of substances. This research can be applied to the develpment of products including cosmetics, pharmaceuticals, and cleaning products.

Math Online
For more information, go to ca.algebra1.com.

EXTRA PRACTICE
See pages 727, 748.

Math Online
Self-Check Quiz at
ca.algebra1.com

H.O.T. Problems

Enrichment
p. 19 · OL · AL

5-2 Enrichment

Intersection of Two Parabolas

Substitution can be used to find the intersection of two parabolas. Replace the y-value in one of the equations with the y-value in terms of x from the other equation.

Example Find the intersection of the two parabolas.
$y = x^2 + 5x + 6$
$y = x^2 + 4x + 3$

Graph the equations.

BL = *Below Grade Level*
OL = *On Grade Level*
AL = *Above Grade Level*
ELL = *English Language Learner*

Additional pages not shown:
Lesson Reading Guide, p. 13 · BL · OL · ELL
Skills Practice, p. 16 · BL · OL

264 Chapter 5 Solving Systems of Linear Equations

32. CHALLENGE Solve the system of equations below. Write the solution as an ordered triple of the form (x, y, z). Describe the steps that you used.
$$2x + 3y - z = 17 \qquad y = -3z - 7 \qquad 2x = z + 2$$
$(-1, 5, -4)$

33. OPEN ENDED Create a system of equations that has one solution. Illustrate how the system could represent a real-world situation and describe the significance of the solution in the context of the situation. **See Ch. 5 Answer Appendix.**

34. *Writing in Math* Use the data about the time Americans spend online and reading newspapers on page 260 to explain how substitution can be used to analyze problems. Then solve the system and interpret its meaning in the situation. **See Ch. 5 Answer Appendix.**

STANDARDS PRACTICE 9.0, 7AF4.1

35. The debate team plans to make and sell trail mix for a fundraiser.

Item	Cost Per Pound
sunflower seeds	$4.00
raisins	$1.50

The number of pounds of raisins in the mix is to be 3 times the pounds of sunflower seeds. If they can spend $34, which system can be used to find r, the pounds of raisins, and s, pounds of sunflower seeds, they should buy? **A**

A $3s = r$
$4s + 1.5r = 34$

C $3s = r$
$4r + 1.5s = 34$

B $3r = s$
$4s + 1.5r = 34$

D $3r = s$
$4r + 1.5s = 34$

36. What is the solution to this system of equations? **G**
$$\begin{cases} x + 4y = 1 \\ 2x - 3y = -9 \end{cases}$$

F $(2, -8)$

G $(-3, 1)$

H no solution

J infinitely many solutions

37. REVIEW What is the value of x if $4x - 3 = -2x$? **C**

A -2

B $-\dfrac{1}{2}$

C $\dfrac{1}{2}$

D 2

Spiral Review

Graph each system of equations. Then determine whether the system has *no* solution, *one* solution, or *infinitely many* solutions. If the system has one solution, name it. (Lesson 5-1) **38–40. See Ch. 5 Answer Appendix.**

38. $x + y = 3$
$x + y = 4$

39. $x + 2y = 1$
$2x + y = 5$

40. $2x + y = 3$
$4x + 2y = 6$

41. Draw a scatter plot that shows a positive correlation. (Lesson 4-7) **See Ch. 5 Answer Appendix.**

42. RECYCLING When a pair of blue jeans is made, the leftover denim scraps can be recycled. One pound of denim is left after making every fifth pair of jeans. How many pounds of denim would be left from 250 pairs of jeans? (Lesson 2-6) **50 lb**

GET READY for the Next Lesson

PREREQUISITE SKILL Simplify each expression. (Lesson 1-5)

43. $6a - 9a$ $-3a$

44. $8t + 4t$ $12t$

45. $-7g - 8g$ $-15g$

46. $7d - (2d + b)$
$5d - b$

47. $(2x + 5y) + (x - 2y)$
$3x + 3y$

48. $(3m + 2n) - (5m + 7n)$
$-2m - 5n$

Lesson 5-2 Substitution **265**

Pre-AP Activity Use after the Exercises

Have students write a system of equations that produces one solution using $y = \dfrac{1}{3}x - 2$ as one of the equations. Ask them to solve the system. Sample answer: Using the equation $2x - y = 7$, the solution is $(3, -1)$.

5-3 Elimination Using Addition and Subtraction

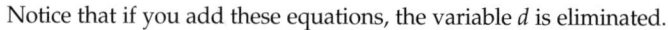

1 Focus

Standards Alignment

Before Lesson 5-3
Write an expression, an equation, an inequality, or a system that represents a verbal description from Standard 7AF1.1

Lesson 5-3
Solve a system of two linear equations or inequalities in two variables algebraically and graphically from 🔑 Standard 9.0

After Lesson 5-3
Solve systems of linear equations and inequalities from 🔑 Standard 2A1.0

2 Teach

Scaffolding Questions Have students read *Get Ready for the Lesson.* **Ask:**

• If $2n = 36$, then how many hours of darkness are there in Seward, Alaska, on the winter solstice? 18 hours
• Since you know n is 18, how can you find the value of d? Use substitution.
• How many hours of daylight are there in Seward, Alaska, on the winter solstice? 6 hours

(continued on the next page)

Lesson 5-3 Resources

Chapter 5 Resource Masters
Lesson Reading Guide, p. 20 **BL OL ELL**
Study Guide and Intervention, pp. 21–22 **BL OL ELL**
Skills Practice, p. 23 **BL OL**
Practice, p. 24 **OL AL**
Word Problem Practice, p. 25 **OL AL**
Enrichment, p. 26 **OL AL**
Quiz 2, p. 44

Transparencies
5-Minute Check Transparency 5-3
Additional Print Resources
Noteables™ Interactive Study Notebook with Foldables™
Teaching Algebra with Manipulatives

Technology
ca.algebra1.com
Interactive Classroom CD-ROM
AssignmentWorks CD-ROM
Graphing Calculator Easy Files

Main Ideas
• Solve systems of equations algebraically by using elimination with addition.
• Solve systems of equations algebraically by using elimination with subtraction.

 Standard 9.0 Students solve a system of two linear equations in two variables algebraically and are able to interpret the answer graphically. Students are able to solve a system of two linear inequalities in two variables and to sketch the solution sets. (Key, CAHSEE)

New Vocabulary
elimination

Study Tip

Look Back
To review the **Addition Property of Equality**, see Lesson 2-2.

▶ **GET READY for the Lesson**

The winter solstice marks the shortest day and longest night of the year in the Northern Hemisphere. On that day in Seward, Alaska, the difference between the number of hours of darkness n and the number of hours of daylight d is 12. The following system of equations represents the situation.

$$n + d = 24$$
$$n - d = 12$$

Notice that if you add these equations, the variable d is eliminated.

$$\begin{array}{r} n + d = 24 \\ (+)\ n - d = 12 \\ \hline 2n \quad\quad = 36 \end{array}$$

Elimination Using Addition Sometimes using the Addition Property of Equality to add two equations together will eliminate one variable. Using this step to solve a system of equations is called **elimination**.

EXAMPLE Elimination Using Addition

① Use elimination to solve the system of equations.

$$3x - 5y = -16$$
$$2x + 5y = 31$$

Since the coefficients of the y-terms, -5 and 5, are additive inverses, you can eliminate these terms by adding the equations.

$$\begin{array}{r} 3x - 5y = -16 \\ (+)\ 2x + 5y = 31 \\ \hline 5x \quad\quad = 15 \end{array}$$ Write the equations in column form and add.

The y variable is eliminated.

$$\frac{5x}{5} = \frac{15}{5}$$ Divide each side by 5.

$$x = 3$$ Simplify.

Now substitute 3 for x in either equation to find the value of y.

$$3x - 5y = -16$$ First equation

$$3(3) - 5y = -16$$ Replace x with 3.

266 Chapter 5 Solving Systems of Linear Equations

$$9 - 5y = -16 \qquad \text{Simplify.}$$
$$9 - 5y - 9 = -16 - 9 \qquad \text{Subtract 9 from each side.}$$
$$-5y = -25 \qquad \text{Simplify.}$$
$$\frac{-5y}{-5} = \frac{-25}{-5} \qquad \text{Divide each side by } -5.$$
$$y = 5 \qquad \text{Simplify.}$$

The solution is $(3, 5)$.

✓**CHECK Your Progress**

Use elimination to solve each system of equations.

1A. $-4x + 3y = -3$ $(0, -1)$
$\quad\ \ 4x - 5y = 5$

1B. $4y + 3x = 22$
$\quad\ \ 3x - 4y = 14$ $(6, 1)$

Study Tip

Eliminating Variables

When solving systems by elimination, be sure to add like terms.

EXAMPLE Write and Solve a System of Equations

2 Twice one number added to another number is 18. Four times the first number minus the other number is 12. Find the numbers.

Let x represent the first number and y represent the second number.

Twice one number	added to	another number	is	18.
$2x$	$+$	y	$=$	18

Four times the first number	minus	the other number	is	12.
$4x$	$-$	y	$=$	12

Use elimination to solve the system.

$$\begin{array}{r} 2x + y = 18 \\ (+)\ 4x - y = 12 \\ \hline 6x \quad\ = 30 \end{array}$$

Write the equations in column form and add.

The variable y is eliminated.

$$\frac{6x}{6} = \frac{30}{6} \qquad \text{Divide each side by 6.}$$
$$x = 5 \qquad \text{Simplify.}$$

Now substitute 5 for x in either equation to find the value of y.

$$4x - y = 12 \qquad \text{Second equation}$$
$$4(5) - y = 12 \qquad \text{Replace } x \text{ with 5.}$$
$$20 - y = 12 \qquad \text{Simplify.}$$
$$-y = -8 \qquad \text{Simplify.}$$
$$\frac{-y}{-1} = \frac{-8}{-1} \qquad \text{Divide each side by } -1.$$
$$y = 8$$

The numbers are 5 and 8.

✓**CHECK Your Progress**

2. The sum of two numbers is -10. Negative three times the first number minus the second number equals 2. Find the numbers. $4, -14$

 **Personal Tutor at** ca.algebra1.com

---

Focus on Mathematical Content

Elimination Using Addition Solving a system of equations by using elimination with addition requires adding the two equations together to eliminate one of the variables. The resulting equation is then solved for the remaining variable. Once the value of one variable is known, it can be substituted into one of the original equations to determine the value of the other variable. In order to use this method, the coefficients of either the x or y need to be additive inverses.

Elimination Using Subtraction

Example 3 shows how to solve a system of equations using elimination with subtraction.

 **Focus on Mathematical Content**

Elimination Using Subtraction
Solving a system of equations by subtraction requires subtracting one equation from the other to eliminate one of the variables. The coefficients of either the x or y must be the same in order to use this method.

 Tips for New Teachers

Preventing Errors
When using elimination with subtraction to solve systems of equations, many students forget to distribute the negative sign over the entire equation that is subtracted. Since subtraction is the same as adding the inverse, you might suggest that students change the signs of the terms and then add to eliminate the variable.

3 Practice

Formative Assessment

Use Exercises 1–6 to check for understanding.

Use the chart at the bottom of this page to customize assignments for your students.

Odd/Even Assignments

Exercises 7–24 are structured so that students practice the same concepts whether they are assigned odd or even problems.

Study Tip

Look Back
To review the **Subtraction Property of Equality,** see Lesson 2-2.

Elimination Using Subtraction Sometimes using the Subtraction Property of Equality to subtract one equation from another will eliminate one variable.

 **EXAMPLE** Elimination Using Subtraction

3 Use elimination to solve the system of equations.

$5s + 2t = 6$

$9s + 2t = 22$

Since the coefficients of the t-terms, 2 and 2, are the same, you can eliminate the t-terms by subtracting the equations.

$$\begin{array}{rl} 5s + 2t = & 6 \\ (-)\ 9s + 2t = & 22 \\ \hline -4s\ \ \ \ \ = & -16 \end{array}$$ Write the equations in column form and subtract.
The variable t is eliminated.

$$\frac{-4s}{-4} = \frac{-16}{-4}$$ Divide each side by -4.

$$s = 4$$ Simplify.

Now substitute 4 for s in either equation to find the value of t.

$$5s + 2t = 6$$ First equation

$$5(4) + 2t = 6$$ $s = 4$

$$20 + 2t = 6$$ Simplify.

$$2t = -14$$ Subtract 20 from each side and simplify.

$$\frac{2t}{2} = -\frac{14}{2}$$ Divide each side by 2.

$$t = -7$$ The solution is $(4, -7)$.

CHECK Your Progress

Use elimination to solve each system of equations.

3A. $8b + 3c = 11$
$\quad\ \ 8b + 7c = 7$ (1.75, −1)

3B. $12n - m = -14$
$\quad\ \ 6n - m = -8$ (2, −1)

★ indicates multi-step problem

CHECK Your Understanding

Examples 1, 3
(pp. 266–268)

Use elimination to solve each system of equations.

1. $2a - 3b = -11$ (−1, 3)
$\quad\ a + 3b = 8$

2. $4x + y = -9$ (−2, −1)
$\quad\ 4x + 2y = -10$

3. $6x + 2y = -10$ (0, −5)
$\quad\ 2x + 2y = -10$

4. $-4m + 2n = 6$ (−2.5, −2)
$\quad\ -4m + n = 8$

Example 2
(p. 267)

5. The sum of two numbers is 24. Five times the first number minus the second number is 12. What are the two numbers? **6, 18**

★ **6. FOOTBALL** In 2003, Rich Gannon, the Oakland Raiders quarterback, earned about $4 million more than Charles Woodson, the Raiders cornerback. Together they cost the Raiders approximately $9 million. How much did each make?
Gannon: $6.5 million; Woodson: $2.5 million

 Math Online Extra Examples at ca.algebra1.com

DIFFERENTIATED HOMEWORK OPTIONS

Level	Assignment	Two-Day Option	
BL Basic	7–24, 30, 32–45	7–23 odd, 33, 34	8–24 even, 30, 32, 35–45
OL Core	7–23 odd, 25–30, 32–45	7–24, 33, 34	25–29, 30, 32, 35–45
AL Advanced /Pre-AP	25–41 (optional: 42–45)		

Exercises

HOMEWORK HELP

For Exercises	See Examples
7–18	1, 3
19–24	2

Exercise Levels
A: 7–24
B: 25–29
C: 30–32

Use elimination to solve each system of equations.

7. $x + y = -3$ $(-1, -2)$
$x - y = 1$

8. $s - t = 4$ $(3, -1)$
$s + t = 2$

9. $3m - 2n = 13$ $(5, 1)$
$m + 2n = 7$

10. $-4x + 2y = 8$ $(-1, 2)$
$4x - 3y = -10$

11. $3a + b = 5$ $(-5, 20)$
$2a + b = 10$

12. $2m - 5n = -6$ $(7, 4)$
$2m - 7n = -14$

13. $3r - 5s = -35$ $(-5, 4)$
$2r - 5s = -30$

14. $13a + 5b = -11$
$13a + 11b = 7$ $(-2, 3)$

15. $3x - 5y = 16$ $(2, -2)$
$-3x + 2y = -10$

16. $6s + 5t = 1$ $(1, -1)$
$6s - 5t = 11$

17. $4x - 3y = 12$ $(4.5, 2)$
$4x + 3y = 24$

18. $a - 2b = 5$ $(2, -1.5)$
$3a - 2b = 9$

★ **19.** The sum of two numbers is 48, and their difference is 24. What are the numbers? **36, 12**

★ **20.** Find the two numbers whose sum is 51 and whose difference is 13. **32, 19**

★ **21.** Three times one number added to another number is 18. Twice the first number minus the other number is 12. Find the numbers. **6, 0**

★ **22.** One number added to twice another number is 13. Four times the first number added to twice the other number is −2. What are the numbers?
−5, 9

★ **23.** **PARKS** A youth group traveling in two vans visited Mammoth Cave in Kentucky. The number of people in each van and the total cost of a tour of the cave are shown in the table. Find the adult price and the student price of the tour. **adult: $16; student: $9**

Van	Number of Adults	Number of Students	Total Cost
A	2	5	$77
B	2	7	$95

★ **24.** **ARCHITECTURE** The total height of an office building b and the granite statue that stands on top of it g is 326.6 feet. The difference in heights between the building and the statue is 295.4 feet. How tall is the statue? **15.6 ft**

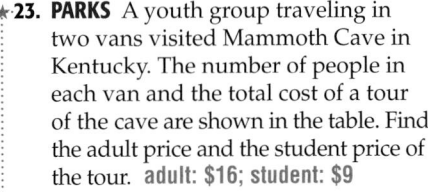

Real-World Link

On average, 2 million people visit Mammoth Cave National Park each year. On a busy summer day, about 5000 to 7000 people come to the park.

Source: Mammoth Cave National Park

ANALYZE GRAPHS For Exercises 25–27, use the information in the graph. **26.** $y = 0.0116x + 1.05$

25. Let x represent the number of years since 2000 and y represent population in billions. Write an equation to represent the population of China. $y = 0.0022x + 1.28$

26. Write an equation to represent the population of India.

★ **27.** Use elimination to find the solution to the system of equations. Interpret the solution.

27. Sample answer: The solution (23, 1.33) means that 23 years after 2002, or in 2025, the populations of China and India are predicted to be the same, 1.33 billion.

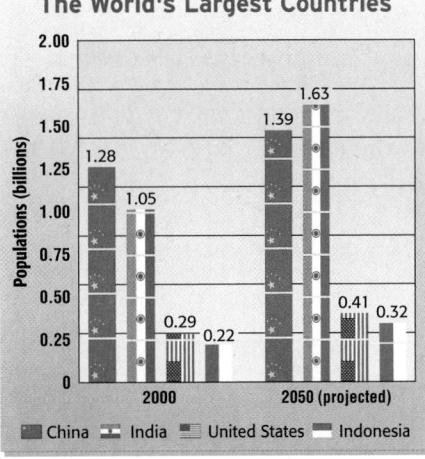

The World's Largest Countries

Populations (billions)

2000: China 1.28, India 1.05, United States 0.29, Indonesia 0.22
2050 (projected): China 1.39, India 1.63, United States 0.41, Indonesia 0.32

■ China ■ India ■ United States ▢ Indonesia

Source: Population Reference Bureau

BL = Below Grade Level
OL = On Grade Level
AL = Above Grade Level
ELL = English Language Learner

Additional pages not shown:

 Lesson Reading Guide, p. 20 **BL** **OL** **ELL**

Skills Practice, p. 23 **BL** **OL**

Real-World Connections

For Exercise 23, tell students that Mammoth Cave National Park is located in central Kentucky. The park was authorized as a national park in 1926. It consists of 52,830 acres and contains the longest recorded cave system in the world, with more than 348 miles explored and mapped.

The park is opened year round with the highest visitation in June, July, and August and the lowest in January.

Assess

Ticket Out the Door Have students write a system that can be solved by elimination using subtraction.

Formative Assessment

Check for student understanding of concepts in Lesson 5-3.

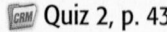 Quiz 2, p. 43

FOLDABLES™
Study Organizer **Follow-Up**

Under the tab for Lesson 5-3, have students record a system solved by elimination using addition and a system solved by elimination using subtraction.

Additional Answers

28. $y = 7440 + 1293x$ and $y = 3805 - 1364x$

29. $(-1.4, 5630)$; About 1.4 years before 2004, or in 2002, the number of online catalogs and the number of print catalogs were both 5630.

30. Sample answer: $2a + b = 5$; $a - b = 4$; a system that can be solved by using addition to eliminate one variable must have one variable with coefficients that are additive inverses.

ONLINE CATALOGS For Exercises 28 and 29, use the table that shows the number of online catalogs and print catalogs in 2004 and the growth rates of each type.

Catalogs	Number in 2004	Growth Rate (number per year)
Online	7440	1293
Print	3805	−1364

Source: MediaPost Publications

EXTRA PRACTICE
See pages 727, 748.

Math Online
Self-Check Quiz at ca.algebra1.com

H.O.T. Problems

28. Let x represent the number of years since 2004 and y represent the number of catalogs. Write a system of equations to represent this situation. **See margin.**

★**29.** Solve the system of equations. Analyze the solution in terms of the situation. Determine the reasonableness of the solution. **See margin.**

30. OPEN ENDED Create a system of equations that can be solved by adding to eliminate a variable. Formulate a general rule for creating such systems. **See margin.**

31. CHALLENGE The graphs of $Ax + By = 15$ and $Ax - By = 9$ intersect at $(2, 1)$. Find A and B and describe the steps that you used to find the values. **See Ch. 5 Answer Appendix.**

32. *Writing in Math* Use the information on page 266 to explain how to use elimination to solve a system of equations. Include a step-by-step solution of the Seward daylight problem. **See Ch. 5 Answer Appendix.**

STANDARDS PRACTICE 9.0, 7AF4.2

33. What is the solution to this system of equations? **B**

$2x - 3y = -9$
$-x + 3y = 6$

A $(3, 3)$ C $(-3, 3)$

B $(-3, 1)$ D $(1, -3)$

34. REVIEW Rhiannon is paid $52 for working 4 hours. At this rate, how many hours of work will it take her to earn $845? **G**

F 13 hours   H 3380 hours

G 65 hours   J 10,985 hours

Spiral Review

Use substitution to solve each system of equations. If the system does *not* have exactly one solution, state whether it has *no solution* or *infinitely many* solutions. (Lesson 5-2)

35. $y = 5x$ (2, 10)   **36.** $x = 2y + 3$ (1, −1)   **37.** $2y - x = -5$ (−9, −7)
    $x + 2y = 22$ $3x + 4y = -1$ $4y - 3x = -1$

38–40. See Ch. 5 Answer Appendix.

Graph each system of equations. Then determine whether the system has *no* solution, *one* solution, or *infinitely many* solutions. If the system has one solution, name it. (Lesson 5-1)

38. $x - y = 3$ **39.** $2x - 3y = 7$ **40.** $4x + y = 12$
    $3x + y = 1$ $3y = 7 + 2x$ $x = 3 - \frac{1}{4}y$

41. PHYSICAL SCIENCE If x cubic centimeters of water is frozen, the ice that is formed has a volume of $\left(x + \frac{1}{11}x\right)$ cubic centimeters. Simplify the expression for the volume of the ice. (Lesson 1-5) $\frac{12}{11}x$ or $1\frac{1}{11}x$

GET READY for the Next Lesson

PREREQUISITE SKILL Rewrite each expression without parentheses. (Lesson 1-5)

42. $2(3x + 4y)$ **43.** $6(2a - 5b)$ **44.** $-3(-2m + 3n)$ **45.** $-5(4t - 2s)$
    $6x + 8y$ $12a - 30b$ $6m - 9n$ $-20t + 10s$

270 Chapter 5 Solving Systems of Linear Equations

Pre-AP Activity Use as an Extension.

Write two equations on the board with the constants missing. Have students find the missing constants that ensure the given solution. For example, write the system

$3x + 2y = ?$; then tell students that the solution is (1.5, 0.25).
$5x - 2y = ?$
$3x + 2y = 5, 5x - 2y = 7$

Graph each system of equations. Then determine whether the system has *no solution*, *one* solution, or *infinitely many* solutions. If the system has one solution, name it. (Lesson 5-1)

1. $y = -x - 1$
$y = x + 5$

2. $x + y = 3$
$x - y = 1$

3. $3x - 2y = -6$
$3x - 2y = 6$

4. $3x + 2y = 4$
$6x + 4y = 8$

1–4. See margin.

WORLD RECORDS For Exercises 5 and 6, use the following information.

A swimmer broke a world record by crossing the Atlantic Ocean on a raft. He traveled about 44 miles each day by swimming *s* hours and floating on a raft *f* hours. The rates that he traveled are shown in the table. (Lesson 5-1)

Activity	Rate
swimming	3 mph
floating	1 mph

5. Write a system of equations to represent this situation. $s + f = 24$ and $3s + f = 44$

6. Graph the system. Describe what the solution means in the context of the problem.
See Ch. 5 Answer Appendix.

7. MULTIPLE CHOICE The graphs of the linear equations $y = -\frac{1}{2}x + 4$ and $y = x - 2$ are shown below. If $-\frac{1}{2}x + 4 = x - 2$, what is the value of x? (Lesson 5-1) **B**

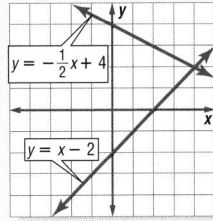

A 2
B 4
C 6
D 8

Use substitution to solve each system of equations. If the system does *not* have exactly one solution, state whether it has *no solution* or *infinitely many* solutions. (Lesson 5-2)

8. $y = 6x$
$4x + y = 10$ **(1, 6)**

9. $c + d = 0$
$3c + d = -8$ **(-4, 4)**

10. $x - 2y = 5$
$3x - 5y = 8$
(-9, -7)

11. $x + y = 2$
$y = 2 - x$
infinitely many

12. MULTIPLE CHOICE Sydney has $115 and she is earning $50 per week at her summer job. Felipe has $130 and is earning $50 per week at his summer job. Which is a true statement about the system of equations that represents this situation? (Lesson 5-2) **J**

F The system has 1 solution, which represents their hourly rates.

G The system has 1 solution, which represents the number of weeks in which they will have earned the same amount of money.

H The system has infinitely many solutions.

J The system has no solution.

Use elimination to solve each system of equations. (Lesson 5-3)

13. $a + b = 9$ **(8, 1)**
$a - b = 7$

14. $3x + y = 1$ **(-1, 4)**
$-6x + y = 10$

15. $5x + 4y = 2$
$3x - 4y = 14$
(2, -2)

16. $2s - 3t = 13$ **(2, -3)**
$2s + 2t = -2$

WATER PARKS For Exercises 17 and 18, use the following information. 17–18. See margin.

The cost of two groups going to a water park is shown in the table. (Lesson 5-3)

Group	Total Cost ($)
2 adults, 1 child	68.97
2 adults, 4 children	125.94

17. Define variables and write a system of equations that you can use to find the admission cost of an adult and a child.

18. Solve the system of equations and explain what the solution means.

 **Formative Assessment**

Use the Mid-Chapter Quiz to assess student progress in the first half of the chapter.

For the problems answered incorrectly, have students review the lessons indicated in parentheses.

 **Summative Assessment**

CRM Mid-Chapter Test, p. 45

ExamView® Assessment Suite

ExamView
Assessment Suite Customize and create multiple versions of your Mid-Chapter Test and their answer keys.

FOLDABLES **Foldables™**
Study Organizer **Follow-Up**

Before students complete the Mid-Chapter Quiz, encourage them to review the information under the tabs for Lessons 5-1 through 5-3 on their Foldables.

Additional Answers

1.

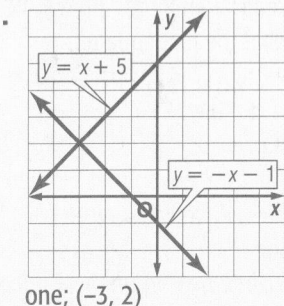

one; (-3, 2)

For Exercises 2–4, 17, and 18, see Ch. 5 Answer Appendix.

Data-Driven Decision Making	Exercises	Lesson	Standard	Resources for Review
Diagnostic Teaching Based on the results of the Chapter 5 Mid-Chapter Quiz, use the following to review concepts that students continue to find challenging.	1–7	5–1	9.0	CRM Study Guide and Intervention pp. 6–7, 14–15, 21–22 Math Online • Extra Examples • Personal Tutor • Concepts in Motion
	8–12	5–2	9.0	
	13–18	5–3	9.0	

 **5-4** Elimination Using Multiplication

1 Focus

Standards Alignment

Before Lesson 5-4
Write an expression, an equation, an inequality, or a system that represents a verbal description from Standard 7AF1.1

Lesson 5-4
Solve a system of two linear equations or inequalities in two variables algebraically and graphically from ⚷ Standard 9.0

After Lesson 5-4
Solve systems of linear equations and inequalities from ⚷ Standard 2A1.0

2 Teach

Scaffolding Questions Have students read *Get Ready for the Lesson.*
Ask:
- How much preparation time is allowed per batch of cookies and per loaf of bread? 20 minutes; 10 minutes
- Explain what the first equation represents. It represents preparation time because the cookies take 20 minute to prepare, the bread takes 10 minutes, and the bakery has allotted 800 minutes of employee time for preparation.

(continued on the next page)

Lesson 5-4 Resources

Chapter 5 Resource Masters
Lesson Reading Guide, p. 27 BL OL ELL
Study Guide and Intervention, pp. 28–29
BL OL ELL
Skills Practice, p. 30 BL OL
Practice, p. 31 OL AL
Word Problem Practice, p. 32 OL AL
Enrichment, p. 33 OL AL
Quiz 3, p. 44

Transparencies
5-Minute Check Transparency 5-4
Additional Print Resources
Noteables™ Interactive Study Notebook with Foldables™

Technology
ca.algebra1.com
Interactive Classroom CD-ROM
AssignmentWorks CD-ROM
Graphing Calculator Easy Files

Main Ideas

- Solve systems of equations algebraically by using elimination with multiplication.
- Solve real-world problems involving systems of equations.

Standard 9.0 Students solve a system of two linear equations in two variables algebraically and are able to interpret the answer graphically. Students are able to solve a system of two linear inequalities in two variables and to sketch the solution sets. (Key, CAHSEE)

Study Tip

Look Back
To review the **Multiplication Property of Equality,** see Lesson 2-3.

GET READY for the Lesson

The Finneytown Bakery is making peanut butter cookies and loaves of quick bread. The preparation and baking times for each are shown.

For these two items, the management has allotted 800 minutes of employee time and 900 minutes of oven time. The following system of equations can be used to determine how many of each to bake.

$20c + 10b = 800$
$10c + 30b = 900$

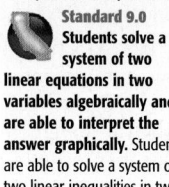

	Cookies (per batch)	Bread (per loaf)
Preparation	20 min	10 min
Baking	10 min	30 min

Elimination Using Multiplication Neither variable in the system above can be eliminated by simply adding or subtracting the equations. However, you can use the Multiplication Property of Equality so that adding or subtracting eliminates one of the variables.

EXAMPLE Multiply One Equation to Eliminate

① Use elimination to solve the system of equations.

$3x + 4y = 6$
$5x + 2y = -4$

Multiply the second equation by -2 so the coefficients of the y-terms are additive inverses. Then add the equations.

$3x + 4y = 6$ $3x + 4y = 6$
$5x + 2y = -4$ Multiply by -2. $(+) -10x - 4y = 8$
                                          $-7x \quad\quad = 14$ Add the equations.
                                          $x = -2$ Divide each side by -7.

Now substitute -2 for x in either equation to find the value of y.

$3x + 4y = 6$ First equation
$3(-2) + 4y = 6$ $x = -2$
$-6 + 4y = 6$ Simplify.
$4y = 12$ Add 6 to each side and simplify.
$\dfrac{4y}{4} = \dfrac{12}{4}$ Divide each side by 4 and simplify.
$y = 3$ The solution is $(-2, 3)$.

CHECK Your Progress

Use elimination to solve each system of equations.

1A. $6x - 2y = 10$
$\quad\ 3x - 7y = -19$ (3, 4)

1B. $9p + q = 13$
$\quad\ 3p + 2q = -4$ (2, -5)

Sometimes you have to multiply each equation by a different number in order to solve the system.

EXAMPLE Multiply Both Equations to Eliminate

② Use elimination to solve the system of equations. $3x + 4y = -25$
    $2x - 3y = 6$

Method 1 Eliminate x.

$3x + 4y = -25$ Multiply by 2. $6x + 8y = -50$
$2x - 3y = 6$ Multiply by -3. $(+) -6x + 9y = -18$
                                        $17y = -68$ Add the equations.
                                        $\dfrac{17y}{17} = \dfrac{-68}{17}$ Divide each side by 17.
                                        $y = -4$ Simplify.

Now substitute -4 for y in either equation to find the value of x.

$2x - 3y = 6$ Second equation
$2x - 3(-4) = 6$ $y = -4$
$2x + 12 = 6$ Simplify.
$2x + 12 - 12 = 6 - 12$ Subtract 12 from each side.
$2x = -6$ Simplify.
$\dfrac{2x}{2} = \dfrac{-6}{2}$ Divide each side by 2 and simplify.
$x = -3$ The solution is $(-3, -4)$.

Method 2 Eliminate y.

$3x + 4y = -25$ Multiply by 3. $9x + 12y = -75$
$2x - 3y = 6$ Multiply by 4. $(+) 8x - 12y = 24$
                                        $17x = -51$ Add the equations.
                                        $\dfrac{17x}{17} = \dfrac{-51}{17}$ Divide each side by 17.
                                        $x = -3$ Simplify.

Now substitute -3 for x in either equation to find the value of y.

$2x - 3y = 6$ Second equation
$2(-3) - 3y = 6$ $x = -3$
$-6 - 3y = 6$ Simplify.
$-6 - 3y + 6 = 6 + 6$ Add 6 to each side.
$-3y = 12$ Simplify.
$\dfrac{-3y}{-3} = \dfrac{12}{-3}$ Divide each side by -3.
$y = -4$ Simplify.

The solution is $(-3, -4)$, which matches the result obtained with Method 1.

 CHECK Your Progress

Use elimination to solve each system of equations.

2A. $5x - 3y = 6$ **2B.** $6a + 2b = 2$
    $2x - 5y = 10$ $(0, -2)$ $4a + 3b = 8$ $(-1, 4)$

 Math Online Extra Examples at ca.algebra1.com   **Lesson 5-4** Elimination Using Multiplication   **273**

Study Tip

Using Multiplication

There are many other combinations of multipliers that could be used to solve the system in Example 2. For instance, the first equation could be multiplied by -2 and the second by 3.

Scaffolding Questions continued

• Explain what the second equation in the system of equations represents. The second equation represents baking time because the cookies take 10 minutes to bake, the bread takes 30 minutes to bake, and the bakery has allotted 900 minutes of oven time for baking.

Elimination Using Multiplication

Example 1 shows how to multiply one equation of a system by a number to use elimination. **Example 2** shows how to multiply both equations of a system by numbers to use elimination. **Example 3** shows how to answer a multiple choice test item on writing a system of equations. **Example 4** shows how to write and solve a system of equations by elimination for a real-world situation.

 Formative Assessment

Use the Check Your Progress exercises after each example to determine students' understanding of concepts.

ADDITIONAL EXAMPLES

① Use elimination to solve the system of equations.
    $2x + y = 23$
    $3x + 2y = 37$ $(9, 5)$

② Use elimination to solve the system of equations.
    $4x + 3y = 8$
    $3x - 5y = -23$ $(-1, 4)$

Additional Examples are also in:

• Noteables™ Interactive Study Notebook with Foldables™

• Interactive Classroom PowerPoint® Presentations

Focus on Mathematical Content

Elimination Using Multiplication This method of solving a system must be used when neither x nor y can be eliminated by adding or subtracting the two equations. The Multiplication Property of Equality is used in order to add or subtract the equations to eliminate one of the variables. Multiply one or both of the equations by numbers so that a variable will be eliminated when the equations are added or subtracted.

③ STANDARDS EXAMPLE John has 30 science-fiction and mystery books. Four times the number of science-fiction books minus the number of mystery books is 5. Which system of equations can be used to find how many science-fiction, f, and mystery, m, books he has? **B**

A $f + m = 30$
$\quad f - 4m = 5$

C $f + m = 30$
$\quad f + 4m = 5$

B $f + m = 30$
$\quad 4f - m = 5$

D $f + m = 30$
$\quad 4f + m = 5$

④ TRANSPORTATION A fishing boat travels 10 miles downstream in 30 minutes. The return trip takes the boat 40 minutes. Find the rate of the boat in still water.
17.5 mi/h

Common Errors

When using elimination with multiplication, many students forget to multiply each term on both sides of the equation by the number. Suggest that they include an extra step in the solutions that shows the multiplication:

$3x + 2y = 7 \Rightarrow 2(3x + 2y) = 2(7)$

$2x - 7y = -12 \Rightarrow$
$-3(2x - 7y) = -3(-12)$

Test-Taking Tip

Checking the Complete Answer Since choices A and B both have $a + b = 28$ as one of the equations, be careful to choose the answer with the correct second equation.

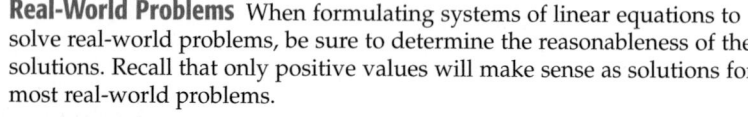

Real-World Link

About 203 million tons of freight are transported on the Ohio River each year, making it the second most used commercial river in the United States.

Source: *World Book Encyclopedia*

③ Anita has a total of 28 e-mail addresses of family and friends stored on her PDA. Twice the number of family addresses minus the number of friends' addresses is 2. Which system of equations can be used to find how many e-mail addresses of family a and friends b that Anita has stored?

A $a + b = 28$
$\quad 2a - b = 2$

B $a + b = 28$
$\quad 2a + b = 2$

C $a - b = 28$
$\quad 2a - b = 2$

D $a - b = 28$
$\quad a - 2b = 2$

Read the Item

You are asked to find a system of equations to represent this situation using a, the number of family addresses, and b, the number of friends' addresses.

Solve the Item

Represent the situation algebraically by writing two equations.

The total of family's and friends' e-mail addresses is 28.
$$a \quad + \quad b \qquad\qquad = 28$$

One equation is $a + b = 28$.

Twice the number of family addresses minus the number of friends' addresses is 2.
$$2a \qquad - \qquad\qquad\qquad b \qquad = 2$$

The second equation is $2a - b = 2$.

The system of equations that represents this situation is $a + b = 28$ and $2a - b = 2$. The answer is A.

✓CHECK Your Progress

3. The cost of 4 notebooks and 5 pens is $20. The cost of 6 notebooks and 2 pens is $19. Which system of equations can be used to find the cost of a notebook n and the cost of a pen p? **H**

F $4n + 5p = 20$
$\quad 2n + 6p = 19$

G $5n + 4p = 20$
$\quad 6n + 2p = 19$

H $4n + 5p = 20$
$\quad 6n + 2p = 19$

J $5n + 4p = 20$
$\quad 2n + 6p = 19$

 **Personal Tutor at** ca.algebra1.com

Real-World Problems When formulating systems of linear equations to solve real-world problems, be sure to determine the reasonableness of the solutions. Recall that only positive values will make sense as solutions for most real-world problems.

EXAMPLE Write and Solve a System of Equations

④ TRANSPORTATION A coal barge on the Ohio River travels 24 miles upstream in 3 hours. The return trip takes the barge only 2 hours. Find the rate of the barge in still water.

ESTIMATE The average speed upstream is $\frac{24}{3}$, or 8 mph. The average speed downstream is $\frac{24}{2}$ or 12 mph. So, the rate in still water should be between 8 and 12 miles per hour.

WORDS   You know the distance traveled each way and the times spent traveling.

VARIABLES   Let b = the rate of the barge in still water and c = the rate of the current. Use the formula rate × time = distance, or $rt = d$.

EQUATIONS

	r	t	d	rt = d	
Downstream	$b + c$	2	24	$(b + c)2 = 24$	→ $2b + 2c = 24$
Upstream	$b - c$	3	24	$(b - c)3 = 24$	→ $3b - 3c = 24$

Use elimination with multiplication to solve this system. Since the problem asks for b, eliminate c.

$2b + 2c = 24$ Multiply by 3. $6b + 6c = 72$
$3b - 3c = 24$ Multiply by 2.   (+) $6b - 6c = 48$
                                        $12b = 120$ Add the equations.

$$\frac{12b}{12} = \frac{120}{12}$$ Divide each side by 12.

$$b = 10$$ Simplify.

The rate of the barge in still water is 10 miles per hour. This solution is between 8 and 12 miles per hour. So, the solution is reasonable.

CHECK Your Progress

4. **CANOEING** A canoe travels 4 miles upstream in 1 hour. The return trip takes the canoe 1.5 hours. Find the rate of the boat in still water. $3\frac{1}{3}$ mi/h

★ indicates multi-step problem

CHECK Your Understanding

Use elimination to solve each system of equations.

Examples 1
(p. 272)

1. $2x - y = 6$
$3x + 4y = -2$ $(2, -2)$

2. $2x + 7y = 1$
$x + 5y = 2$ $(-3, 1)$

Example 2
(p. 273)

3. $4x + 7y = 6$
$6x + 5y = 20$ $(5, -2)$

4. $9a - 2b = -8$
$-7a + 3b = 12$ $(0, 4)$

Example 3
(p. 274)

5. **STANDARDS PRACTICE** At a restaurant, the cost for 2 burritos and 1 tortilla salad is $20.57. The cost for 3 burritos and 3 tortilla salads is $36.24. Which pair of equations can be used to determine b, the cost of a burrito, and t, the cost of a tortilla salad? **B**

A $b + t = 20.57$
$3b + 3t = 36.24$

C $2b + t = 20.57$
$b + t = 36.24$

B $2b + t = 20.57$
$3b + 3t = 36.24$

D $b + 2t = 20.57$
$b + t = 36.24$

Example 4
(pp. 274–275)

★ **6. BUSINESS** The owners of the River View Restaurant have hired enough servers to handle 17 tables of customers, and the fire marshal has approved the restaurant for a limit of 56 customers. How many two-seat tables and how many four-seat tables should the owners purchase?
6 two-seat tables, 11 four-seat tables

Lesson 5-4 Elimination Using Multiplication   **275**

3 Practice

Formative Assessment

Use Exercises 1–6 to check for understanding.

Use the chart at the bottom of this page to customize assignments for your students.

Odd/Even Assignments

Exercises 7–18 are structured so that students practice the same concepts whether they are assigned odd or even problems.

DIFFERENTIATED HOMEWORK OPTIONS

Level	Assignment	Two-Day Option	
BL Basic	7–18, 29–31, 33–48	7–17 odd, 34–36	8–18 even, 29–31, 33–48
OL Core	7–21 odd, 23–31, 33–48	7–18, 34–36	19–28, 29–31, 33–48
AL Advanced /Pre-AP	19–45 (optional: 46–48)		

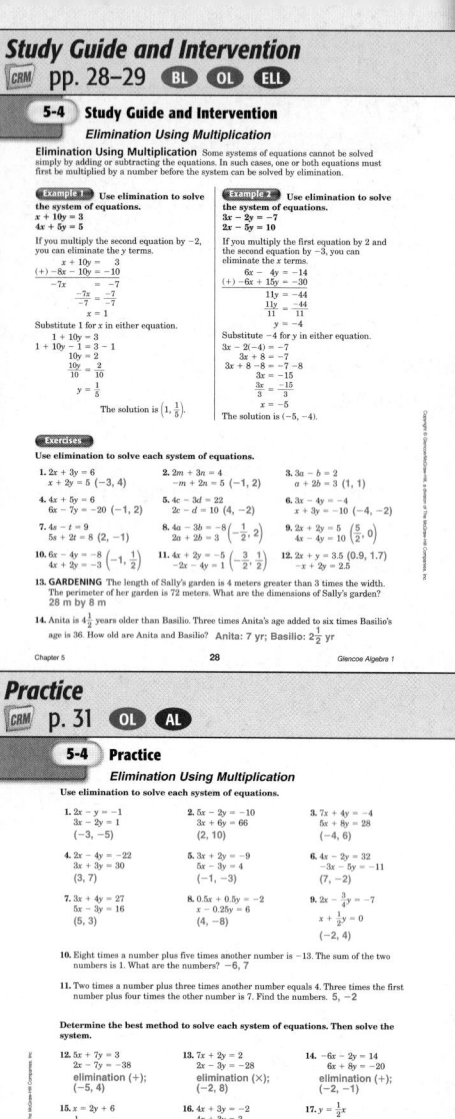

HOMEWORK	
For Exercises	See Examples
7–14	1, 2
15, 16	4
17, 18	3

Exercise Levels
A: 7–18
B: 19–28
C: 29–33

Use elimination to solve each system of equations.

7. $x + y = 3$
$2x - 3y = 16$ **(5, −2)**

8. $-5x + 3y = 6$
$x - y = 4$ **(−9, −13)**

9. $2x + y = 5$
$3x - 2y = 4$ **(2, 1)**

10. $4x - 3y = 12$
$x + 2y = 14$ **(6, 4)**

11. $8x - 3y = -11$
$2x - 5y = 27$ **(−4, −7)**

12. $5x - 2y = -15$
$3x + 3y = 12$ **(−1, 5)**

13. $4x - 7y = 10$
$3x + 2y = -7$ **(−1, −2)**

14. $2x - 3y = 2$
$5x + 4y = 28$ **(4, 2)**

15. $12x - 3y = -3$
$6x + y = 1$ **(0, 1)**

16. $-4x + 2y = 0$
$10x + 3y = 8$ $\left(\frac{1}{2}, 1\right)$

★ **17. NUMBER THEORY** Seven times a number plus three times another number equals negative one. The sum of the two numbers is negative three. What are the numbers? **2, −5**

★ **18. BASKETBALL** In basketball, a free throw is 1 point and a field goal is either 2 or 3 points. In a recent season, Tim Duncan of the San Antonio Spurs scored a total of 1342 points. The total number of 2-point field goals and 3-point field goals was 517, and he made 305 of the 455 free throws that he attempted. Find the number of 2-point field goals and 3-point field goals Duncan made that season. **514 2-point field goals; 3 3-point field goals**

Use elimination to solve each system of equations.

19. $1.8x - 0.3y = 14.4$
$x - 0.6y = 2.8$ **(10, 12)**

20. $0.4x + 0.5y = 2.5$
$1.2x - 3.5y = 2.5$ **(5, 1)**

21. $3x - \frac{1}{2}y = 10$
$5x + \frac{1}{4}y = 8$ **(2, −8)**

22. $2x + \frac{2}{3}y = 4$
$x - \frac{1}{2}y = 7$ **(4, −6)**

★ **23. NUMBER THEORY** The sum of the digits of a two-digit number is 14. If the digits are reversed, the new number is 18 less than the original number. Find the original number. **86**

ANALYZE TABLES For Exercises 24 and 25, use the information below.
At an entertainment center, two groups of people bought batting tokens and miniature golf games, as shown in the table. **24–25. See margin.**

Group	Number of Batting Tokens	Number of Miniature Golf Games	Total Cost
A	16	3	$30
B	22	5	$43

24. Define variables and formulate a system of linear equations from this situation.

★ **25.** Solve the system of equations and explain what the solution represents in terms of the situation.

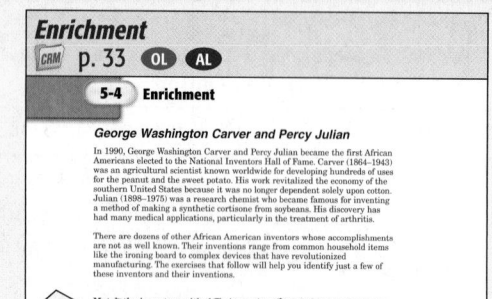

Additional pages not shown:

CRM **Lesson Reading Guide,** p. 27 BL OL ELL

CRM **Skills Practice,** p. 30 BL OL

BL = *Below Grade Level*
OL = *On Grade Level*
AL = *Above Grade Level*
ELL = *English Language Learner*

★ **26. TRANSPORTATION** Traveling against the wind, a plane flies 1080 miles from Omaha, Nebraska, to San Diego, California, in the time shown at right. On the return trip, the plane is traveling with a wind that is twice as fast. Find the rate of the plane in still air. **486 mph**

Trip	Time
traveling against the wind	2 h 30 min
traveling with the wind	2 h

★ **27. GEOMETRY** The graphs of $x + 2y = 6$ and $2x + y = 9$ contain two of the sides of a triangle. A vertex of the triangle is at the intersection of the graphs. What are the coordinates of the vertex? **(4, 1)**

EXTRA PRACTICE
See pages 728, 748.

Math Online
Self-Check Quiz at
ca.algebra1.com

★ **28. TESTS** Mrs. Henderson discovered that she had accidentally reversed the digits of a test score and shorted a student 36 points. Mrs. Henderson told the student that the sum of the digits was 14 and agreed to give the student his correct score plus extra credit if he could determine his actual score without looking at his test. What was his actual score on the test? **95**

H.O.T. Problems

29. REASONING Explain why multiplication is sometimes needed to solve a system of equations by elimination. **See margin.**

30. David; in order to eliminate the r-terms, you must multiply the second equation by 2 and then subtract, or multiply the equation by -2 and then add.

30. FIND THE ERROR David and Yoomee are solving a system of equations. Who is correct? Explain your reasoning.

David
$$2r + 7s = 11 \Rightarrow$$
$$r - 9s = -7 \Rightarrow$$
$$2r + 7s = 11$$
$$(-) \; 2r - 18s = -14$$
$$\overline{25s = 25}$$
$$s = 1$$

$$2r + 7s = 11$$
$$2r + 7(1) = 11$$
$$2r + 7 = 11$$
$$2r = 4$$
$$\frac{2r}{2} = \frac{4}{2}$$
$$r = 2$$
The solution is (2, 1).

Yoomee
$$2r + 7s = 11$$
$$(-) \; r - 9s = -7$$
$$\overline{r \quad = 18}$$

$$2r + 7s = 11$$
$$2(18) + 7s = 11$$
$$36 + 7s = 11$$
$$7s = -25$$
$$\frac{7s}{7} = \frac{25}{7}$$
$$s = -3.6$$
The solution is (18, -3.6).

31. OPEN ENDED Formulate a system of equations that could be solved by multiplying one equation by 5 and then adding the two equations together to eliminate one of the variables. **Sample answer: $3x + 2y = 5$, $5x - 10y = -6$**

32. CHALLENGE The solution of the system $4x + 5y = 2$ and $6x - 2y = b$ is $(3, a)$. Find the values of a and b. Discuss the steps that you used. **See margin.**

33. *Writing in Math* Use the information about the bakery on page 272 to explain how a manager can use a system of equations to plan employee time. Include a demonstration of how to solve the system of equations given in the problem and an explanation of how a restaurant manager would schedule oven and employee time. **See Ch. 5 Answer Appendix.**

Lesson 5-4 Elimination Using Multiplication **277**

⚠ Exercise Alert!
Find the Error Tell students to look at the original system of equations before they evaluate David's and Yoomee's work. Did they multiply one of the equations by a number to eliminate r?

Additional Answers

24. Let $x =$ the cost of a batting token and let $y =$ the cost of a miniature golf game; $16x + 3y = 30$ and $22x + 5y = 43$.

25. (1.5, 2); A batting token costs $1.50 and a game of miniature golf costs $2.00.

29. If one of the variables cannot be eliminated by adding or subtracting the equations, you must multiply one or both of the equations by numbers so that a variable will be eliminated when the equations are added or subtracted.

32. $a = -2, b = 22$; Substitute 3 for x and a for y in the first equation and then solve for a to get $a = -2$. Then substitute 3 for x and -2 for y in the second equation and simplify to get $b = 22$.

Pre-AP Activity Use after Exercises 7–16.

Have students solve this system or a similar system using elimination.
$$\frac{1}{2}x - \frac{2}{3}y = \frac{7}{3}$$
$$\frac{3}{2}x + 2y = -25$$
$(-6, -8)$

Crystal Ball Have students write how they think what they learned today about solving a system with elimination using multiplication will help them in the next lesson, Applying Systems of Equations.

Formative Assessment

Check for student understanding of concepts in Lesson 5-4.

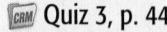 Quiz 3, p. 44

 **Foldables™ Follow-Up**

Under the tab for this lesson, have students record two examples: a system that needs to be multiplied by one number to eliminate a variable and a system that requires each equation to be multiplied by a number to eliminate a variable.

STANDARDS PRACTICE 9.0, 7MG2.3

34. If $5x + 3y = 12$ and $4x - 5y = 17$, what is the value of y? **A**

A -1 C $(-1, 3)$

B 3 D $(3, -1)$

35. What is the solution to the system of equations? **J**

$x + 2y = -1$

$2x + 4y = -2$

F $(-1, -1)$

G $(2, 1)$

H no solution

J infinitely many solutions

36. REVIEW What is the surface area of the rectangular solid shown below? **C**

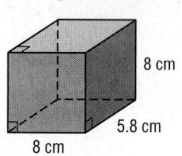

A 249.6 cm^2

B 278.4 cm^2

C 313.6 cm^2

D 371.2 cm^2

Spiral Review

Use elimination to solve each system of equations. (Lesson 5-3)

37. $x + y = 8$ **(6, 2)**
$x - y = 4$

38. $2r + s = 5$ **(2, 1)**
$r - s = 1$

39. $x + y = 18$ **(11, 7)**
$x + 2y = 25$

Use substitution to solve each system of equations. If the system does *not* have exactly one solution, state whether it has *no* solution or *infinitely many* solutions. (Lesson 5-2) **42. infinitely many**

40. $2x + 3y = 3$ **(3, −1)**
$x = -3y$

41. $x + y = 0$ **(−4, 4)**
$3x + y = -8$

42. $x - 2y = 7$
$-3x + 6y = -21$

★ **43. PAINTING** A ladder reaches a height of 16 feet on a wall. If the bottom of the ladder is placed 4 feet away from the wall, what is the slope of the ladder as a positive number? Explain the meaning of the slope. (Lesson 4-1)

4; For every 4-feet increase in height, there is a 1-foot increase in horizontal distance.

Determine the *x*-intercept, *y*-intercept, and zero of each linear function. (Lesson 3-3)

44.

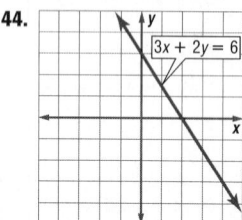

2, 3, 2

45.

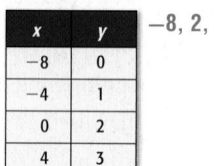

$-8, 2, -8$

x	y
−8	0
−4	1
0	2
4	3

GET READY for the Next Lesson

PREREQUISITE SKILL Solve each equation. (Lesson 2-4)

46. $3(x + 5) - x = 1$ -7

47. $14 = 5(n - 1) + 9$ 2

48. $y - 2(y + 8) = 6$
-22

Additional Answers (Page 279)

1. There are two types of systems of equations, consistent and inconsistent. Consistent systems have one or more solutions and inconsistent systems have no solutions. If consistent systems have one solution, they are called independent. If consistent systems have infinite solutions, they are called dependent.

2. Use substitution if an expression for one variable is given or if the coefficient of a variable is ± 1. Otherwise, use elimination. Sample answers:

system to solve using substitution	system to solve using elimination
$y = 3x + 3$	$4x + 3y = 9$
$5x + 2y = 6$	$6x - y = 10$

READING MATH

 Standard 9.0 Students solve a system of two linear equations in two variables algebraically and are able to interpret the answer graphically. Students are able to solve a system of two linear inequalities in two variables and to sketch the solution sets. (Key, CAHSEE)

Making Concept Maps

After completing a chapter, it is wise to review each lesson's main topics and vocabulary. In Lesson 5-1, the new vocabulary words were *system of equations, consistent, inconsistent, independent,* and *dependent.* They are all related in that they explain how many and what kind of solutions a system of equations has.

A graphic organizer called a *concept map* is a convenient way to show these relationships. A concept map is shown below for the vocabulary words for Lesson 5-1. The main ideas are placed in boxes. Any information that describes how to move from one box to the next is placed along the arrows.

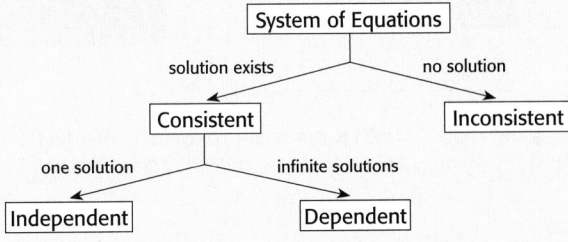

Concept maps are used to organize information. They clearly show how ideas are related to one another. They also show the flow of mental processes needed to solve problems.

Reading to Learn

Review Lessons 5-2, 5-3, and 5-4. **1–4. See margin.**

1. Write a couple of sentences describing the information in the concept map above.

2. How do you decide whether to use substitution or elimination? Give an example of a system that you would solve using each method.

3. How do you decide whether to multiply an equation by a factor?

4. How do you decide whether to add or subtract two equations?

5. Copy and complete the concept map at the right for solving systems of equations by using either substitution or elimination.
   See Ch. 5 Answer Appendix.

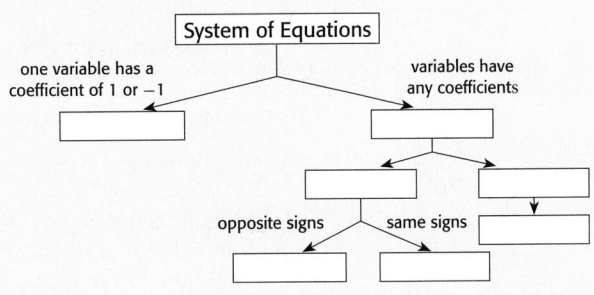

---

1 Focus

Ask students how they organize information when they study for tests. After a few minutes of discussion, ask students if they think a visual arrangement of information might help them to remember information better than lists or notes.

2 Teach

Creating Concept Maps After students have reviewed the sample concept map shown on this page, have them draw their own concept maps. Ask them to create a map for tasks not related to mathematics, such as the start of class procedures or the school lunch menu. Have them share their maps with the class.

Once students have reviewed Lessons 5-2, 5-3, and 5-4, have them complete Reading to Learn 1–4. For Exercise 5, draw the concept map on the board and ask volunteers to fill in the boxes.

ELL English Language Learners may benefit from working in small groups as they create their maps. Have each team discuss the key concepts of their maps in their native language and then fill in their maps in English.

3 Assess

Ask students to summarize what they have learned about concept maps.

Additional Answers

3. Multiply by a factor if neither variable has the same or opposite coefficients in the two equations.

4. Add if one of the variables has opposite coefficients in the two equations. Subtract if on of the variables has the same coefficient in the two equations.

5-5 Lesson Notes

5-5 Applying Systems of Linear Equations

1 Focus

Standards Alignment

Before Lesson 5-5
Write an expression, an equation, an inequality, or a system that represents a verbal description from Standard 7AF1.1

Lesson 5-5
Solve a system of two linear equations or inequalities in two variables algebraically and graphically from Standard 9.0

After Lesson 5-5
Solve systems of linear equations and inequalities from Standard 2A1.0

2 Teach

Scaffolding Questions Have students read *Get Ready for the Lesson.*
Ask:

• What do the variables *x* and *y* represent in the problem? The depth of Mr. Mercer's tour is represented by *x* and the depth of the current tour by *y*.

• Formulate a system of equations that could be used to solve this system.
$x + y = 160; y = 4x$

Lesson 5-5 Resources

Chapter 5 Resource Masters

Lesson Reading Guide, p. 34 **BL** **OL** **ELL**
Study Guide and Intervention, pp. 35–36 **BL** **OL** **ELL**
Skills Practice, p. 37 **BL** **OL**
Practice, p. 38 **OL** **AL**
Word Problem Practice, p. 39 **OL** **AL**
Enrichment, p. 40 **OL** **AL**
Quiz 4, p. 44

Main Ideas

• Determine the best method for solving systems of equations.
• Apply systems of linear equations.

Standard 9.0
Students solve a system of two linear equations in two variables algebraically and are able to interpret the answer graphically. Students are able to solve a system of two linear inequalities in two variables and to sketch the solution sets. (Key, CAHSEE)

GET READY for the Lesson

Northern California is home to several caves and caverns. Mercer Caverns is in Calaveras County near Murphys. Walter J. Mercer discovered the cavern in 1885. He descended to the base of the first chamber. Tours are currently offered at the caverns that descend approximately 4 times the depth that Mr. Mercer descended initially.

Tour	Depth (ft)
Mr. Mercer's tour	x
Current tour	y

The total depth of both tours is approximately 160 feet. How could you use a system of equations to determine the depth of each tour?

Determine the Best Method You have learned five methods for solving systems of linear equations. The table summarizes the methods and the systems for which each method works best.

KEY CONCEPT	*Solving Systems of Equations*
Method	**The Best Time to Use**
Graphing	to estimate the solution, since graphing usually does not give an exact solution
Substitution	if one of the variables in either equation has a coefficient of 1 or −1
Elimination Using Addition	if one of the variables has opposite coefficients in the two equations
Elimination Using Subtraction	if one of the variables has the same coefficient in the two equations
Elimination Using Multiplication	if none of the coefficents are 1 or −1 and neither of the variables can be eliminated by simply adding or subtracting the equations

For an exact solution, an algebraic method is best. It is also usually a quicker method for solving linear equations than graphing. Graphing, with or without technology, is a good way to estimate solutions.

Transparencies

5-Minute Check Transparency 5-5

Additional Print Resources

Noteables™ Interactive Study Notebook with Foldables™

Technology

ca.algebra1.com
Interactive Classroom CD-ROM
AssignmentWorks CD-ROM
Graphing Calculator Easy Files

Real-World EXAMPLE Determine the Best Method

1 **SHOPPING** At a sale, Sarah bought 4 T-shirts and 3 pairs of jeans for $181. Jenna bought 1 T-shirt and 2 pairs of jeans for $94. The T-shirts were all the same price and the jeans were all the same price, so the following system of equations represents this situation. Determine the best method to solve the system of equations. Then solve the system.

$$4x + 3y = 181$$
$$x + 2y = 94$$

- Since neither the coefficients of x nor the coefficients of y are the same or additive inverses, you cannot add or subtract to eliminate.

- Since the coefficient of x in the second equation is 1, you can use the substitution method. You could also use elimination using multiplication.

The following solution uses substitution.   Which method would you prefer?

$x + 2y = 94$	Second equation
$x + 2y - 2y = 94 - 2y$	Subtract $2y$ from each side.
$x = 94 - 2y$	Simplify.
$4x + 3y = 181$	First equation
$4(94 - 2y) + 3y = 181$	$x = 94 - 2y$
$376 - 8y + 3y = 181$	Distributive Property
$376 - 5y = 181$	Combine like terms.
$376 - 5y - 376 = 181 - 376$	Subtract 376 from each side.
$-5y = -195$	Simplify.
$y = 39$	Divide each side by -5 and simplify.
$x + 2y = 94$	Second equation
$x + 2(39) = 94$	$y = 39$
$x + 78 = 94$	Simplify.
$x + 78 - 78 = 94 - 78$	Subtract 78 from each side.
$x = 16$	Simplify.

The solution is $(16, 39)$. This means that the cost of a T-shirt was $16 and the cost of a pair of jeans was $39.

> **Study Tip**
>
> **Alternative Method**
> This system could also be solved easily by multiplying the second equation by 4 and then subtracting the equations.

✓CHECK Your Progress

Determine the best method to solve each system of equations. Then solve the system.

1A. $5x + 7y = 2$ elimination $(-)$;
$-2x + 7y = 9$ $(-1, 1)$

1B. $3x - 4y = -10$ elimination $(\times)$;
$5x + 8y = -2$ $(-2, 1)$

Apply Systems of Linear Equations When applying systems of linear equations to problem situations, it is important to analyze each solution in the context of the situation.

 Extra Examples at ca.algebra1.com

Lesson 5-5 Applying Systems of Linear Equations   **281**

Determine the Best Method

Example 1 shows how to determine the best method to use in solving a real-world problem involving a system of equations.

✓ Formative Assessment

Use the Check Your Progress exercises after each example to determine students' understanding of concepts.

ADDITIONAL EXAMPLE

1 **FUND-RAISING** At a Boy Scout fund-raising dinner, Mr. Jones bought 2 adult meals and 3 child meals for $23. Mrs. Gomez bought 4 adult meals and 2 child meals for $34. All adult meals are the same price and all child meals are the same price. The following system can be used to represent this situation.

$$2x + 3y = 23$$
$$4x + 2y = 34$$

Determine the best method to solve the system of equations. Solve the system. The best method is elimination using multiplication. The solution is $(7, 3)$. This means an adult meal is $7 and a child meal is $3.

Additional Examples are also in:
- Noteables™ Interactive Study Notebook with Foldables™
- Interactive Classroom PowerPoint® Presentations

 Planning Tips

Encourage students to take the time to plan their solution strategies before they start their calculations. Point out that taking this time may provide them with insight into which method of solution would be best.

Apply Systems of Linear Equations

Example 2 shows how to solve a real-world problem by writing and solving a system of equations.

Focus on Mathematical Content

Best Method for Solving a System of Equations Systems of equations can be solved by graphing, substitution, or elimination. Graphing can be used to approximate a solution and to provide a visual model of the problem. To find an exact solution, substitution or elimination should be used. Use substitution if one of the variables has a 1 or -1 for its coefficient. Use elimination with addition if the coefficients of one of the variables are opposites. Use eliminators with subtraction if the coefficients of one of the variables are the same. Use elimination with multiplication in all other situations.

Lesson 5-5 Applying Systems of Linear Equations   **281**

2 CAR RENTAL Ace Car Rental rents a car for $45 a day and $0.25 per mile. Star Car Rental rents a car for $35 per day and $0.30 per mile. How many miles would a driver need to drive before the cost of renting a car at Ace Car Rental and renting a car at Star Car Rental were the same?

Let x = number of miles and y = cost of renting car.

$45 + 0.25x = y$
$35 + 0.30x = y$

The solution is (200, 95). This means that when the car has been driven 200 miles, the cost of renting a car will be the same ($95) at both rental companies.

Intervention

Applying Systems Students often have trouble writing the necessary equations for a system in a real-world situation. Give them these steps to help them explore, plan, solve, and check.

- Determine the question.
- Describe the variables used for the unknowns.
- Translate the conditions in the problem into two equations.
- Solve the system by the best method.
- Analyze the solution in the context of the situation.

3 Practice

✓ Formative Assessment

Use Exercises 1–5 to check for understanding.

Use the chart at the bottom of this page to customize assignments for your students.

Odd/Even Assignments

Exercises 6–13 are structured so that students practice the same concepts whether they are assigned odd or even problems.

Real-World Link
Digital photography can trace its roots back almost 40 years, when NASA needed a technology for spacecraft to send images back to Earth.
Source: technology.com

Real-World EXAMPLE

2 PHOTOGRAPHY Since 2000, the number of film cameras sold has decreased at an average rate of 2.5 million per year. At the same time, the number of digital cameras sold has increased at an average rate of 2.6 million per year. Use the table to estimate the year in which the sales of digital cameras equaled the sales of film cameras.

Cameras Sold in 2000	
Type of Camera	Number Sold (millions)
film	20.0
digital	4.7

Source: Mediamark Research, Inc.

Explore You know the number of each type of camera sold in 2000 and the rates of change in numbers sold.

Plan Write an equation to represent the number of cameras sold for each type of camera. Then solve.

Solve Let x = the number of years after 2000 and let y = the total number of cameras sold.

		number sold		number sold in 2000		rate of change times number of years after 2000
film cameras	y	=	20.0	+		$-2.5x$
digital cameras	y	=	4.7	+		$2.6x$

You can use elimination by subtraction to solve this system.

$$y = 20.0 + -2.5x$$
$$(-)\ y = 4.7 + 2.6x$$

Write the equations in column form and subtract.

$$0 = 15.3 - 5.1x$$ The variable y is eliminated.
$$5.1x = 15.3$$ Add $5.1x$ to each side and simplify.
$$x = 3$$ Divide each side by 5.1 and simplify.

This means that 3 years after 2000, or in 2003, the sales of digital cameras equaled the sales of film cameras.

Check Does this solution make sense in the context of the problem? After 1 year, the number of film cameras would be about $20 - 3$ or 17. The number of digital cameras would be about $4.7 + 3$ or 7.7. Continue estimating.

Check by sketching a graph of the equations. The graphs appear to intersect at (3, 12.5), which verifies the solution of $x = 3$.

In 2003, approximately 12.5 million film and digital cameras were sold.

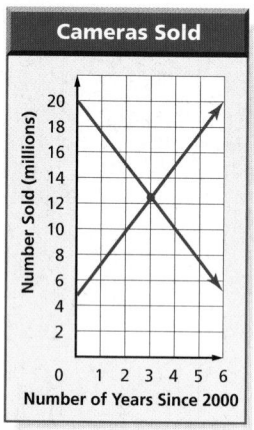

Cameras Sold

Number Sold (millions) / Number of Years Since 2000

✓ CHECK Your Progress
 $y = 50 + 3x$, $y = 5x$; 25 weeks

2. VOLUNTEERING Jared has volunteered 50 hours and plans to continue volunteering 3 hours each week. Clementine just started volunteering 5 hours each week. Find the number of weeks in which Jared and Clementine will have both volunteered the same number of hours.

 Personal Tutor at <u>ca.algebra1.com</u>

Study Tip

Elimination
Equations do not have to be written in standard form to use elimination by addition or subtraction.

DIFFERENTIATED HOMEWORK OPTIONS			
Level	**Assignment**	**Two-Day Option**	
BL Basic	6–13, 19–26	7–13 odd, 22	6–12 even, 19–21, 23–26
OL Core	7–15 odd, 17–26	6–13, 22	14–16, 17–26
AL Advanced /Pre-AP	14–26		

★ indicates multi-step problem

Example 1
(p. 281)

Determine the best method to solve each system of equations. Then solve the system.

1. $4x + 3y = 19$ elimination (×);
$3x - 4y = 8$ **(4, 1)**

2. $3x - 7y = 6$ elimination (+);
$2x + 7y = 4$ **(2, 0)**

3. $y = 4x + 11$ substitution;
$3x - 2y = -7$ **(−3, −1)**

4. $5x - 2y = 12$ elimination (−);
$3x - 2y = -2$ **(7, 11.5)**

Example 2
(p. 282)

★ **5. FUND-RAISING** For a Future Teachers of America fund-raiser, Denzell sold subs and pizzas as shown in the table. He sold 11 more subs than pizzas and earned a total of $233. Write and solve a system of equations to represent this situation. Then describe what the solution means. **Sample answer: $3s + 5p = 233$ and $s = p + 11$; Denzell sold 25 pizzas and 36 subs.**

Item	Selling Price
pizza	$5.00
sub	$3.00

Exercises

Determine the best method to solve each system of equations. Then solve the system.

HOMEWORK HELP	
For Exercises	See Examples
6–11	1
12–13	2

Exercise Levels
A: 6–13
B: 14–18
C: 19–21

6. $9x - 8y = 42$ elimination
$4x + 8y = -16$ **(+); (2, −3)**

7. $y = 3x$ substitution;
$3x + 4y = 30$ **(2, 6)**

8. $x = 4y + 8$
$2x - 8y = -3$

8. substitution; no solution

9. $x - y = 2$ elimination (×)
$5x + 3y = 18$ or substitution; **(3, 1)**

10. $y = 2x + 9$
$2x - y = -9$

10. substitution; infinitely many solutions

11. $6x - y = 9$
$6x - y = 11$

11. elimination (−); no solution

★**12. ENTERTAINMENT** Miranda has a total of 40 DVDs of movies and television shows. The number of movies is 4 less than 3 times the number of television shows. Write and solve a system of equations to find how many movies and television shows that she has on DVD.
$x + y = 40$ and $y = 3x - 4$; 29 movies, 11 television shows

★**13. YEARBOOKS** The *break-even point* is the point at which income equals expenses. McGuffey High School is paying $13,200 for the writing and research of their yearbook, plus a printing fee of $25 per book. If they sell the books for $40 each, how many will they have to sell to break even? Explain. **See Ch. 5 Answer Appendix.**

Determine the best method to solve each system of equations. Then solve the system.
16. elimination (−); (16, 8)

14. $2.3x - 1.9y = -2.5$
$x - 0.4y = 3.6$
substitution; (8, 11)

15. $1.6x - 0.7y = -11$
$3.2x + 2.1y = -15$
elimination (×); (−6, 2)

16. $\frac{1}{2}x - \frac{1}{4}y = 6$
$\frac{5}{8}x - \frac{1}{4}y = 8$

For Exercises 17 and 18, use the table and the information at the right.

Mara and Ling each recycled aluminum cans and newspaper, as shown in the table. Mara earned $3.77 and Ling earned $4.65. **17. See Ch. 5 Answer Appendix.**

Material	Pounds Recycled	
	Mara	Ling
aluminum cans	9	9
newspaper	26	114

17. Define variables and formulate a system of linear equations from this situation.

★**18.** What was the price per pound of aluminum? Determine the reasonableness of your solution. **$0.39**

EXTRA PRACTICE
See pages 728, 748.
Math online
Self-Check Quiz at ca.algebra1.com

Lesson 5-5 Applying Systems of Linear Equations **283**

BL = Below Grade Level
OL = On Grade Level
AL = Above Grade Level
ELL = English Language Learner

Additional pages not shown:

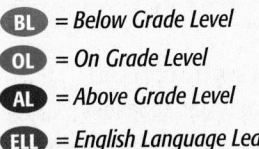
CRM Lesson Reading Guide, p. 34 BL OL ELL

CRM Skills Practice, p. 37 BL OL

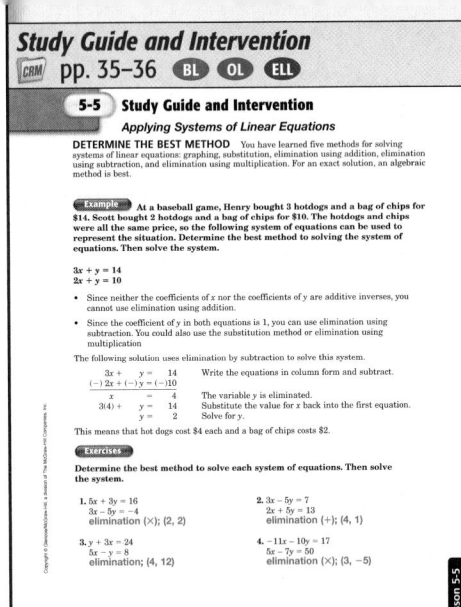
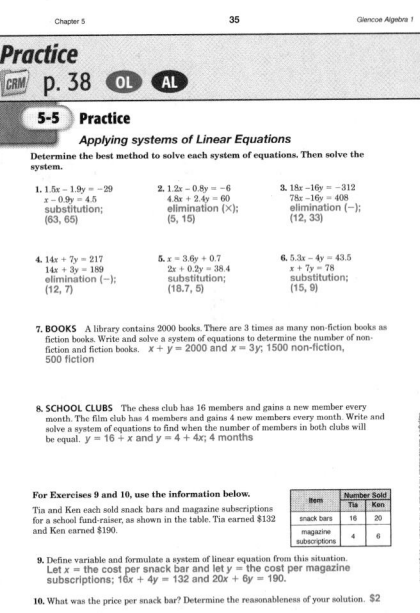
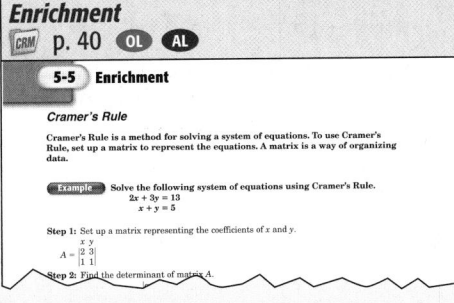

 Assess

Yesterday's News Have students write how yesterday's concept of using elimination with multiplication to solve systems of equations helped them with today's concept of determining the best method for solving systems of equations.

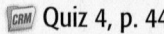 **Formative Assessment**

Check for student understanding of concepts in Lesson 5-5.

CRM Quiz 4, p. 44

Additional Answers

19. Sample answer: $x + y = 12$ and $3x + 2y = 29$, where x represents the cost of a student ticket for the football game and y represents the cost of an adult ticket; substitution could be used to solve the system; $(5, 7)$ means the cost of a student ticket is $5 and the cost of an adult ticket is $7.

21. Sample answer: You should always check that the answer makes sense in the context of the original problem. If it does not, you may have made an incorrect calculation. If $(1, -7)$ was the solution, then it is probably incorrect since distance in this case cannot be a negative number. The solution should be recalculated.

H.O.T. Problems

19. OPEN ENDED Formulate a system of equations that represents a situation in your school. Describe the method that you would use to solve the system. Then solve the system and explain what the solution means. **See margin.**

20. $y = x - 4$ and $y = \frac{2}{x}$ because it is the only system that has one equation that is nonlinear.

20. Which One Doesn't Belong? Identify the system of equations that is not the same as the other three. Explain your reasoning.

$$\begin{array}{cccc} x - y = 3 & -x + y = 0 & y = x - 4 & y = x + 1 \\ x + \frac{1}{2}y = 1 & 5x = 2y & y = \frac{2}{x} & y = 3x \end{array}$$

21. *Writing in Math* Suppose that in a system of equations, x represents the time spent riding a bike, y represents the distance traveled, and you determine the solution to be $(1, -7)$. Use this problem to discuss the importance of analyzing solutions in the context of real-world problems.
See margin.

STANDARDS PRACTICE 9.0

22. Marcus descends at a rate of 2 feet per second from the surface of the ocean. Toshiko is 45 feet below sea level and she is rising to the surface at a rate of 3 feet per second. Which graph represents when the two divers will be at the same depth? **C**

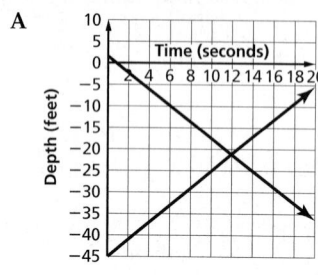
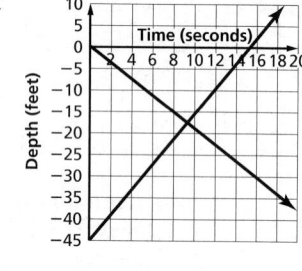
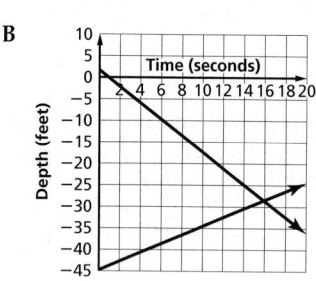
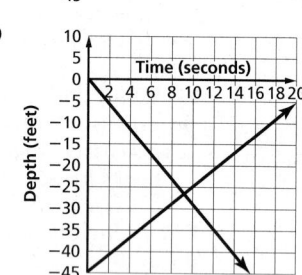

Spiral Review

Use elimination to solve each system of equations. (Lesson 5-4)

23. $x + y = -3$ $(0, -3)$
$3x + 2y = -6$

24. $4x - 5y = 22$ $(8, 2)$
$3x - 10y = 4$

25. $2x - 7y = -3$
$5x + 2y = -27$
$(-5, -1)$

★**26. BUSINESS** In 2003, the United States produced about 2 million more motor vehicles than Japan. Together, the two countries produced about 22 million motor vehicles. How many vehicles were produced in each country? (Lesson 5-3) **U.S.: about 12 million vehicles; Japan: about 10 million vehicles**

Pre-AP Activity Use as an Extension.

Have students make up their own real-world problem that can be solved using a system of linear equations. This will help all students understand the concept of solving systems of linear equations.

CHAPTER 5
Study Guide and Review

 FOLDABLES™ Study Organizer GET READY to Study

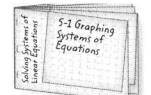

Be sure the following Key Concepts are noted in your Foldable.

Key Concepts

Graphing Systems of Equations (Lesson 5-1)
- A system of intersecting lines has exactly one solution and is consistent and independent.

- A system whose graphs coincide has infinitely many solutions and is consistent and dependent.

- A system of parallel lines has no solution and is inconsistent.

- Graphing is best used to estimate the solution of a system of equations, since graphing usually does not give an exact solution.

Solving Systems of Equations Using Algebra (Lessons 5-2, 5-3, 5-4, and 5-5)
- Substitution is best used if one of the variables in either equation has a coefficient of 1 or −1.

- Elimination using addition is best used if one of the variables has opposite coefficients in the two equations.

- Elimination using subtraction is best used if one of the variables has the same coefficient in the two equations.

- Elimination using multiplication is best used if none of the coefficients are 1 or −1 and neither of the variables can be eliminated by simply adding or subtracting the equations.

Key Vocabulary

consistent (p. 253)
dependent (p. 253)
elimination (p. 266)
inconsistent (p. 253)
independent (p. 253)
substitution (p. 260)
system of equations (p. 253)

Vocabulary Check

2, 5, 10. See margin.

State whether each sentence is *true* or *false*. If *false*, replace the underlined word or phrase to make a true sentence.

1. Two or more equations together are called a <u>system of equations</u>. **true**

2. The best method for solving the system $3x - y = 9$ and $6x + y = 12$ is to use <u>elimination using subtraction</u>.

3. The system $2x + y = 5$ and $4x + 2y = 10$ is <u>dependent</u>. **true**

4. If the graphs of the equations in a system have the same slope and different y-intercepts, the graph of the system is a pair of <u>intersecting lines</u>. **false; parallel lines**

5. If a system has infinitely many solutions, it is <u>inconsistent and independent</u>.

6. The best method for solving the system $x = 4y$ and $2x + 3y = 6$ is to use <u>substitution</u>. **true**

7. The system $y = 3x - 1$ and $y = 3x + 4$ is <u>consistent</u>. **false; inconsistent**

8. Adding or subtracting two equations to solve a system of equations is known as <u>substitution</u>. **false; elimination**

9. A system of equations whose solution is $(3, -5)$ is said to be <u>independent</u>. **true**

10. If the graphs of the equations in a system have the same slope and y-intercept(s), the system has <u>exactly</u> one solution.

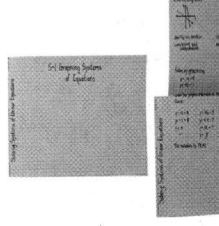 FOLDABLES™ Study Organizer **Dinah Zike's Foldables**

Have students look through the chapter to make sure they have included examples in their Foldables for each method of solving systems of equations.

Suggest that students keep their Foldables handy while completing the Study Guide and Review pages. Point out that their Foldables can serve as a quick review tool for studying for the Chapter Test.

 Formative Assessment

Key Vocabulary The page reference after each word denotes where that term was first introduced. If students have difficulty answering questions 1–10, remind them that they can use these page references to refresh their memories.

 Math Online ca.algebra1.com

Vocabulary PuzzleMaker improves students' mathematics vocabulary using four puzzle formats— crossword, scramble, word search using a word list, and word search using clues. Students can work online or from a printed worksheet.

Chapter 5 Study Guide and Review **285**

Additional Answers

2. false; elimination using addition

5. false; consistent and dependent

10. false; infinitely many

Summative Assessment

CRM Vocabulary Test, p. 46

Lesson-by-Lesson Review

Intervention If the given examples are not sufficient to review the topics covered by the questions, remind students that the page references tell them where to review that topic in their textbooks.

Two-Day Option Have students complete the Lesson-by-Lesson Review on pp. 286–288. Then you can use ExamView® Assessment Suite to customize another review worksheet that practices all the objectives of this chapter or only the objectives on which your students need more help.

For more information on ExamView® Assessment Suite, see p. 250C.

Differentiated Instruction
Super DVD: MindJogger Videoquizzes Use this DVD as an alternative format of review for the test. For more information on this game show format, see p. 250D.

Additional Answers

11.
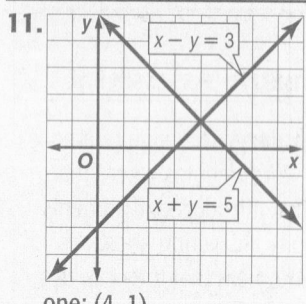
one; (4, 1)

12.
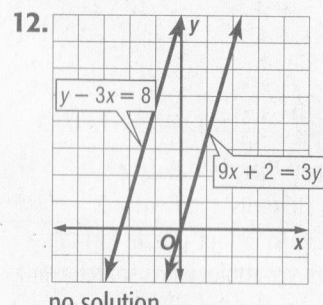
no solution

Lesson-by-Lesson Review

5–1 **Graphing Systems of Equations** (pp. 253–258)

Graph each system of equations. Then determine whether the system has *no* solution, *one* solution, or *infinitely many* solutions. If the system has one solution, name it. **11–14. See margin.**

11. $x - y = 3$
$x + y = 5$

12. $9x + 2 = 3y$
$y - 3x = 8$

13. $2x - 3y = 4$
$6y = 4x - 8$

14. $3x - y = 8$
$3x = 4 - y$

15. RACE In a race, Pablo is 3 miles behind Marc. Pablo increases his speed to 5 miles per hour, while Marc continues to run at 4 miles per hour. At this rate, how many miles will Pablo have to run to catch up to Marc? How long will this take? **15 mi; 3 h**

Example 1 Graph the system of equations. Then determine whether the system has *no* solution, *one* solution, or *infinitely many* solutions. If the system has one solution, name it.

$3x + y = -4$
$6x + 2y = -8$

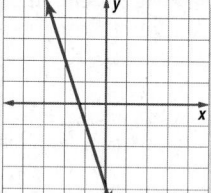

When the lines are graphed, they coincide. There are infinitely many solutions.

5–2 **Substitution** (pp. 260–265)

Use substitution to solve each system of equations. If the system does *not* have exactly one solution, state whether it has *no* solution or *infinitely many* solutions.

16. $2m + n = 1$
$m - n = 8$ **(3, −5)**

17. $x = 3 - 2y$
$2x + 4y = 6$ **infinitely many**

18. $3x - y = 1$
$-12x + 4y = 3$ **no solution**

19. $6m - 2n = 24$
$n = 12 - 3m$ **(4, 0)**

20. PHONES The table shows the long-distance plans of Companies A and B. For how many minutes is the cost the same for the two long-distance companies? **290 min**

Company	Flat Fee	Rate
A	$0	$0.06/minute
B	$5.80	$0.04/minute

Example 2 Use substitution to solve the system of equations.

$y = x - 1$
$4x - y = 19$

Since $y = x - 1$, substitute $x - 1$ for y in the second equation.

$4x - y = 19$	Second equation
$4x - (x - 1) = 19$	$y = x - 1$
$4x - x + 1 = 19$	Distributive Property
$3x + 1 = 19$	Combine like terms.
$3x = 18$	Subtract 1 from each side.
$x = 6$	Divide each side by 3.

You can find the value of y by replacing x with 6 in the first equation.

$y = x - 1$	First equation
$= 6 - 1$	$x = 6$
$= 5$	The solution is (6, 5).

13.
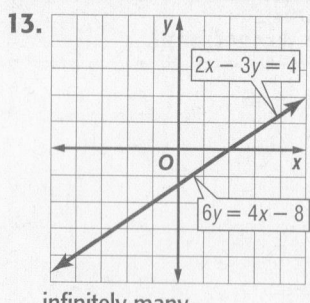
infinitely many

14.
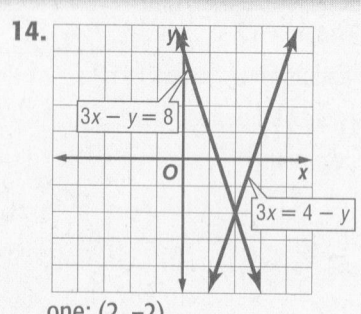
one; (2, −2)

Mixed Problem Solving
For mixed problem-solving practice,
see page 748.

CHAPTER
5 Study Guide
and Review

5-3 **Elimination Using Addition and Subtraction** (pp. 266–270)

Use elimination to solve each system of equations.

21. $x + 2y = 6$
$x - 3y = -4$ **(2, 2)**

22. $2m - n = 5$
$2m + n = 3$ **(2, −1)**

23. $3x - y = 11$
$x + y = 5$ **(4, 1)**

24. $3x + 1 = -7y$
$6x + 7y = -16$
(−5, 2)

25. AIRPORTS The Detroit Wayne County Airport and the Denver International Airport appeared in the top 20 rankings of busiest airports by number of passengers. The sum of their rankings was 29, and the difference was 9. If Denver was busier than Detroit, what were their rankings?
Denver: 10th; Detroit: 19th

Example 3 Use elimination to solve the system of equations.

$2m - n = 4$
$m + n = 2$

Eliminate the n-terms by adding the equations.

$2m - n = 4$ Write the equations in column
$(+)\ m + n = 2$ form and add.
$\overline{\quad\ 3m = 6}$ Notice the variable n is eliminated.
$\quad\ m = 2$ Divide each side by 3.

Substitute 2 for m in either equation to find n.

$m + n = 2$ Second equation
$2 + n = 2$ Replace m with 2.
$n = 0$ Subtract 2 from each side.

The solution is (2, 0).

5-4 **Elimination Using Multiplication** (pp. 272–278)

Use elimination to solve each system of equations.

26. $x - 5y = 0$
$2x - 3y = 7$ **(5, 1)**

27. $x - 2y = 5$
$3x - 5y = 8$
(−9, −7)

28. $2x + 3y = 8$
$x - y = 2$ **(2.8, 0.8)**

29. $-5x + 8y = 21$
$10x + 3y = 15$
(0.6, 3)

30. ENTERTAINMENT The cost for tickets to see a play are shown in the table. A group of 11 adults and students bought tickets for the play. If the total cost was $156, how many of each type of ticket did they buy?

Ticket	Cost
adult	$15
student	$12

8 adult tickets, 3 student tickets

Example 4 Use elimination to solve the system of equations.

$x + 2y = 7$
$3x + y = 1$

Multiply the second equation by −2 so the coefficients of the y-terms are additive inverses. Then add the equations.

$x + 2y = 7$ Multiply $x + 2y = 7$
$3x + y = 1$ by −2. $(+)\ -6x - 2y = -2$
$\overline{\qquad\qquad -5x = 5}$
$\dfrac{-5x}{-5} = \dfrac{5}{-5}$
$x = -1$

$x + 2y = 7$ First equation
$-1 + 2y = 7$ $x = -1$
$2y = 8$ Add 1 to each side.
$\dfrac{2y}{2} = \dfrac{8}{2}$ Divide each side by 2.
$y = 4$ Simplify.

The solution is (−1, 4).

Problem Solving Review

For additional practice in problem solving for Chapter 5, see the Mixed Problem Solving Appendix, p. 748 in the Student Handbook section.

Anticipation Guide

Have students complete the Chapter 5 Anticipation Guide and discuss how their responses have changed now that they have completed Chapter 5.

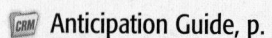 Anticipation Guide, p. 3

| NAME | | DATE | PERIOD |

5 Anticipation Guide

Solving Systems of Linear Equations

Step 1 *Before you begin Chapter 5*

- Read each statement.
- Decide whether you Agree (A) or Disagree (D) with the statement.
- Write A or D in the first column OR if you are not sure whether you agree or disagree, write NS (Not Sure).

STEP 1 A, D, or NS	Statement	STEP 2 A or D
	1. A solution of a system of equations is any ordered pair that satisfies one of the equations	D
	2. A system of equations of parallel lines will have no solutions.	A
	3. A system of equations of two perpendicular lines will have infinitely many solutions.	D
	4. It is not possible to have exactly two solutions to a system of linear equations.	A
	5. The most accurate way to solve a system of equations is to graph the equations to see where they intersect.	D
	6. To solve a system of equations, such as $2x - y = 21$ and $3y = 2x - 6$, by substitution, solve one of the equations for one variable and substitute the result into the other equation.	A
	7. When solving a system of equations, a result that is a true statement, such as $-5 = -5$, means the equations do not share a common solution.	D
	8. Mutually exclusive events are events that cannot happen Adding the equations $3x - 4y = 8$ and $2x + 4y = 7$ results in a 0 coefficient for y.	A
	9. The equation $7x - 2y = 12$ can be multiplied by 2 so that the coefficient of y is -4.	A
	10. The result of multiplying $-7x - 3y = 11$ by -3 is $-1x + 9y = 11$.	D

Step 2 *After you complete Chapter 5*

- Reread each statement and complete the last column by entering an A or a D.
- Did any of your opinions about the statements change from the first column?
- For those statements that you mark with a D, use a piece of paper to write an example of why you disagree.

Additional Answers

31. substitution; (1.6, 3.2)

32. elimination ($\times$); (-3, 4)

33. substitution or elimination ($-$); (0, 0)

34. elimination ($-$); (13, -2)

5–5 **Applying Systems of Linear Equations** (pp. 280–284)

Determine the best method to solve each system of equations. Then solve the system. **31–34. See margin.**

31. $y = 2x$
$x + 2y = 8$

32. $9x + 8y = 5$
$18x + 15y = 6$

33. $3x + 5y = 2x$
$x + 3y = y$

34. $2x + y = 3x - 15$
$x + 5 = 4y + 2x$

35. **SAVINGS** Raul invests $1500 into two savings accounts, one earning 4% annual interest and the other earning 6% annual interest. At the end of one year, Raul has earned $72 in interest. How much did he invest at each rate? **$900 at 4% and $600 at 6%**

Example 5 Determine the best method to solve the system. Then solve the system.

$4x - 3y = 7$
$3x + 1 = y$

Since the coefficient of y in the second equation is 1, you can use the substitution method.

$4x - 3y = 7$	First equation
$4x - 3(3x + 1) = 7$	$y = 3x + 1$
$4x - 9x - 3 = 7$	Distributive Property
$-5x - 3 = 7$	Combine like terms.
$-5x - 3 + 3 = 7 + 3$	Add 3 to each side.
$-5x = 10$	Simplify.
$\dfrac{-5x}{-5} = \dfrac{10}{-5}$	Divide each side by -5.
$x = -2$	Simplify.
$3x + 1 = y$	Second equation
$3(-2) + 1 = y$	$x = -2$
$-5 = y$	Simplify.

The solution is $(-2, -5)$.

Problem Solving Review

For additional practice in problem solving for Chapter 5, see the Mixed Problem Solving Appendix, p. 748 in the Student Handbook section.

Anticipation Guide

Have students complete the Chapter 5

Anticipation Guide and discuss how their responses have changed now that they have completed Chapter 5.

 Anticipation Guide, p. 3

Graph each system of equations. Then determine whether the system has *no* solution, *one* solution, or *infinitely many* solutions. If the system has one solution, name it. **1–3. See margin.**

1. $y = x + 2$
$y = 2x + 7$

2. $x + 2y = 11$
$x = 14 - 2y$

3. $3x + y = 5$
$2y - 10 = -6x$

4. MULTIPLE CHOICE Which graph represents a system of equations with no solution? **B**

A
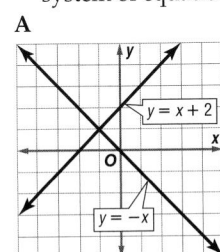

C
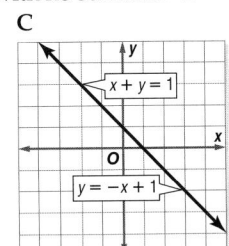

B
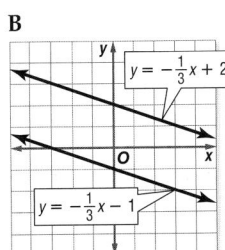

D
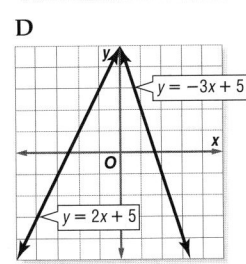

Use substitution or elimination to solve each system of equations.

5. $2x + 5y = 16$ **(3, 2)**
$5x - 2y = 11$

6. $y + 2x = -1$ **no solution**
$y - 4 = -2x$

7. $2x + y = -4$ **(−6, 8)**
$5x + 3y = -6$

8. $y = 7 - x$ **(2, 5)**
$x - y = -3$

9. $x = 2y - 7$ **(5, 6)**
$y - 3x = -9$

10. $x + y = -10$ **(−6, −4)**
$x - y = -2$

11. $3x + y = 10$ **(4, −2)**
$3x - 2y = 16$

12. $5x - 3y = 12$ **(3, 1)**
$-2x + 3y = -3$

13. MULTIPLE CHOICE The units digit of a two-digit number exceeds twice the tens digit by 1. The sum of its digits is 10. Find the number. **H**

F 7   H 37

G 19   J 39

14. GEOMETRY The difference between the length and width of a rectangle is 7 centimeters. Find the dimensions of the rectangle if its perimeter is 50 centimeters. **16 cm by 9 cm**

15. FINANCE Last year, Evelina invested $10,000, part at 6% annual interest and the rest at 8% annual interest. If she received $760 in interest at the end of the year, how much did she invest at each rate? **$2000 at 6%, $8000 at 8%**

GEOMETRY For Exercises 16 and 17, use the graphs of $y = 2x + 6$, $3x + 2y = 19$, and $y = 2$, which contain the sides of a triangle.

16. Find the coordinates of the vertices of the triangle. **(−2, 2), (5, 2), (1, 8)**

17. Find the area of the triangle. **21 units²**

18. MULTIPLE CHOICE At a movie theater, the costs for various amounts of popcorn and hot pretzels are shown below.

Boxes of Popcorn	Hot Pretzels	Total Cost
1	1	$6.25
2	4	$18.00

Which pair of equations can be used to find p, the cost of a box of popcorn, and z, the cost of a hot pretzel? **C**

A $p + z = 6.25$
   $2p + 2z = 18$

C $p + z = 6.25$
   $2p + 4z = 18$

B $p + z = 6.25$
   $4p + 4z = 18$

D $p + z = 6.25$
   $4p + 2z = 18$

Summative Assessment

CRM *Chapter 5 Resource Masters*

Leveled Chapter 5 Tests			
Form	Type	Level	Pages
1	MC	BL	47–48
2A	MC	OL	49–50
2B	MC	OL	51–52
2C	FR	OL	53–54
2D	FR	OL	55–56
3	FR	AL	57–58

MC = multiple-choice questions
FR = free-response questions
BL = below grade level
OL = on grade level
AL = above grade level

- Vocabulary Test, p. 46
- Extended-Response Test, p. 59

ExamView **Assessment Suite** Customize and create multiple versions of your chapter tests and their answer keys. All of the questions from the leveled chapter tests in the *Chapter 5 Resource Masters* are also available on ExamView® Assessment Suite with the California Standard that each item assesses.

For Exercises 1–3, see Ch. 5 Answer Appendix.

Data-Driven Decision Making	Exercises	Lesson	Standard	**Resources for Review**
Diagnostic Teaching Based on the results of the Chapter 5 Practice Test, use the following to review concepts that students continue to find challenging.	5–13	5–4	9.0	**CRM** Study Guide and Intervention pp. 28–29, 35–36 **Math online** • Extra Examples • Personal Tutor • Concepts in Motion
	14–18	5–5	9.0	

California Standards Practice
Cumulative, Chapters 1–5

Formative Assessment

You can use these two pages to benchmark student progress. The California Standards are listed with each question.

Chapter 5 Resource Masters
• Standardized Test Practice, pp. 260–262

Create practice worksheets or tests that align to the California Standards, as well as TIMSS and NAEP tests.

Read each question. Then fill in the correct answer on the answer document provided by your teacher or on a sheet of paper.

1 What is the solution to this system of equations? **D**

$$y = -4x - 5$$
$$12x + 3y = -15$$

A $(-9, 1)$

B $(12, 3)$

C no solution

D infinitely many solutions

TEST-TAKING TIP

Question 1 When solving a system of equations, make sure that your answer satisfies both equations in the system.

2 Which graph represents the system of equations shown below? **F**

$$y = -x + 2$$
$$y = x + 2$$

F 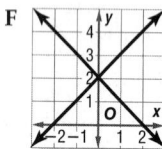   H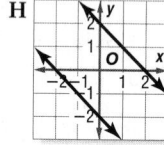

G 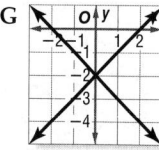   J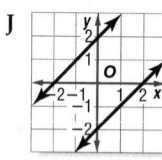

---

3 Allen's average driving speed for a 6-hour trip was 55 miles per hour. During the first 4 hours he drove 65 miles per hour. What was his average speed in miles per hour for the last 2 hours of his trip? **35**

4 For which of the graphs below is the x-intercept -4 and the y-intercept 2? **C**

A 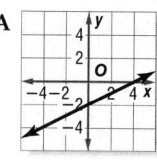   C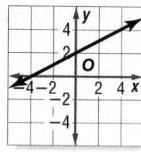

B 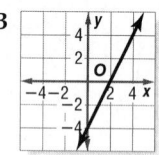   D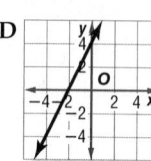

5 The equation of line m is $3y + 4x = -6$, and the equation of line n is $4y - 3x = 12$. Which statement about the two lines is true? **J**

F Lines m and n have the same y-intercept.

G Lines m and n have the same x-intercept.

H Lines m and n are parallel.

J Lines m and n are perpendicular.

6 Which of the following points lies on the line $6x + 3y = 18$? **B**

A $(0, 3)$

B $(0, 6)$

C $(3, 6)$

D $(6, 3)$

 California Standards Practice at ca.algebra1.com

More California Standards Practice
For practice by standard, see pages CA1–CA43.

CHAPTER 5 California Standards Practice

7 For a science project, Kelsey measured the height of a plant grown from seed. She made the bar graph below to show the height of the plant at the end of each week. Which is the most reasonable estimate of the plant's height at the end of the sixth week? **G**

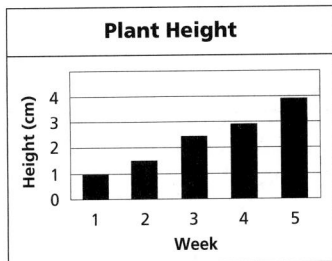

Plant Height

F 2 to 3.5 cm
G 4 to 5.5 cm
H 6 to 7 cm
J 8 to 8.5 cm

8 What is the slope of a line perpendicular to the line below? **3**

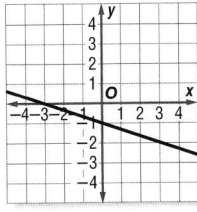

9 What is the domain of the function shown on the graph below? **B**

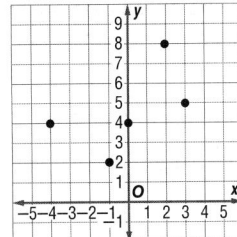

A $\{0, 1, 2, 3, 4\}$
B $\{-4, -1, 0, 2, 3\}$
C $\{2, 4, 5, 8\}$
D $\{-4, 2, 4, 5, 8\}$

Pre-AP/Anchor Problem

Record your answer on a sheet of paper. Show your work.

10 The manager of a movie theater found that Saturday's sales were $3675. He knew that a total of 650 tickets were sold Saturday. Adult tickets cost $7.50 and children's tickets cost $4.50.

  a. Write equations to represent the number of tickets sold and the amount of money collected.

  b. How many of each kind of ticket were sold? Show your work. Include all steps.

    a. $7.5a + 4.5c = 3675$ and $a + c = 650$
    b. $a = 250$, $c = 400$

Item Analysis
Questions 3 and 8 are griddable questions. In griddable questions, students arrive at an answer and then record it in a special grid by coloring the appropriate bubble under each digit of the answer.

Answer Sheet Practice
Have students simulate taking a standardized test by recording their answers on practice recording sheets.

CRM Student Recording Sheet, p. 41

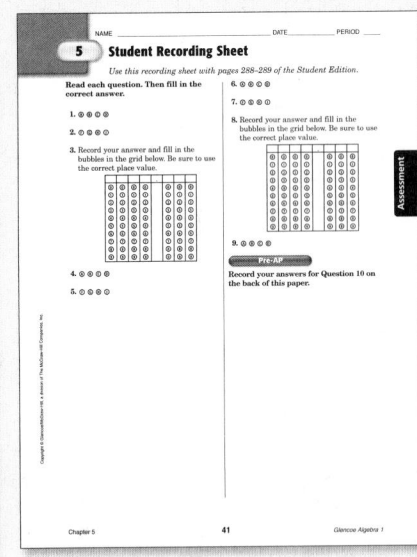

Need extra help?										
If You Missed Question...	1	2	3	4	5	6	7	8	9	10
Go to Lesson...	5-4	5-1	2-9	3-3	4-7	4-3	1-9	4-7	3-1	5-2
For Help with Standard...	9.0	9.0	15.0	6.0	8.0	7.0	16.0	8.0	17.0	9.0

Chapter 5 California Standards Practice **291**

Homework Option

Get Ready for Chapter 6 Assign students the exercises on p. 293 as homework to assess whether they possess the prerequisite skills for the next chapter.

Page 251, Get Ready for Chapter 5

1.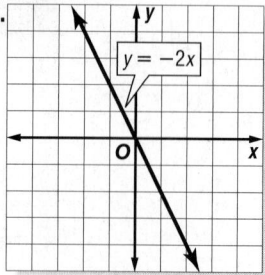

2.

3.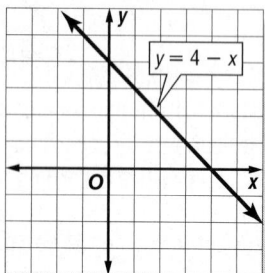

4.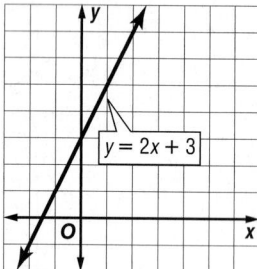

5.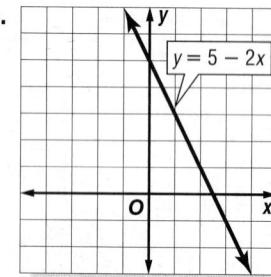

6.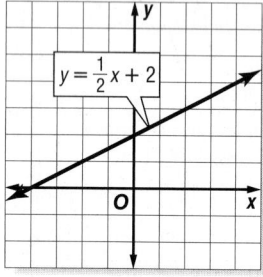

7.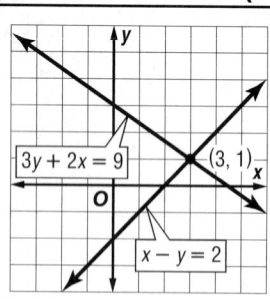

Page 254, Lesson 5-1 (Check Your Progress)

2A.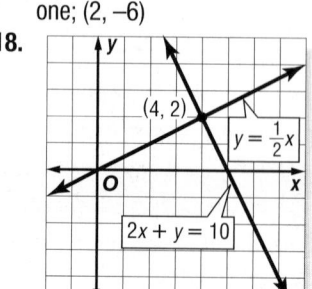

one; (3, 1)

2B.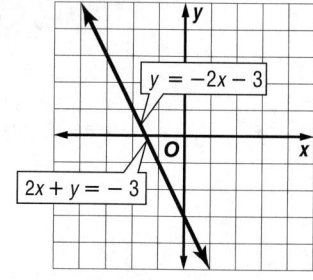

infinitely many

Page 256, Lesson 5-1

5.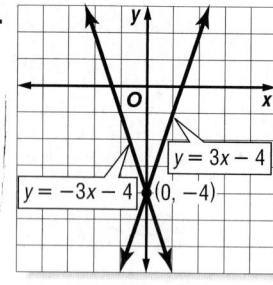

6.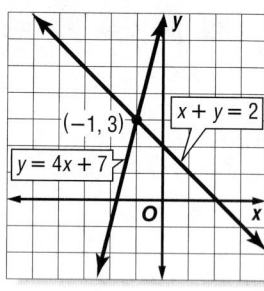

7.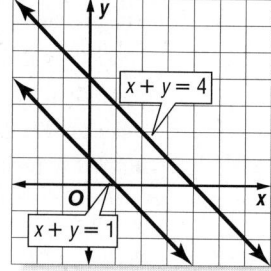

8.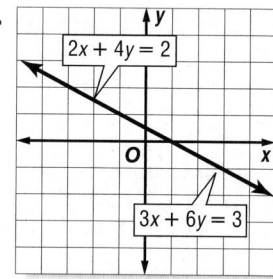

16.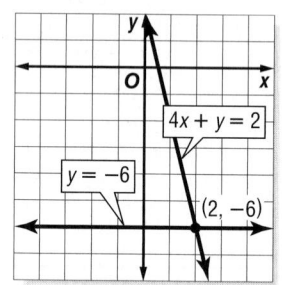

one; (2, −6)

17.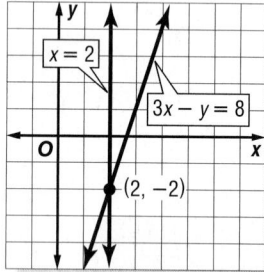

one; (2, −2)

18.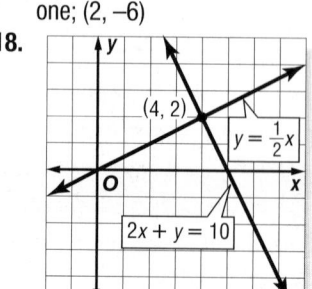

one; (4, 2)

19.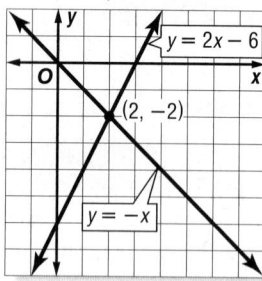

one; (2, −2)

20.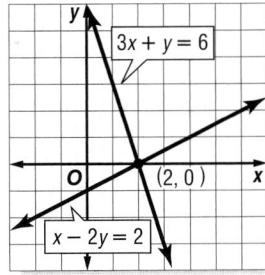

one; (−3, 0)

21.

one; (2, 0)

22.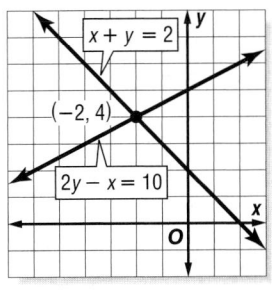

one; (−2, 4)

23.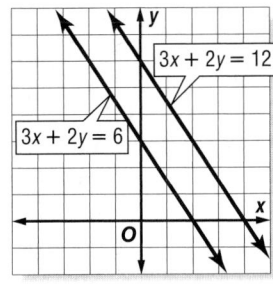

no solution

24.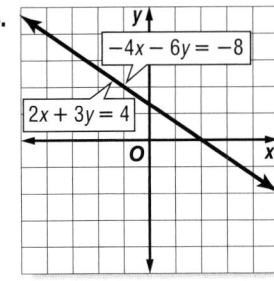

infinitely many

25.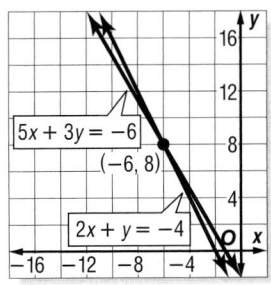

one; (−6, 8)

26.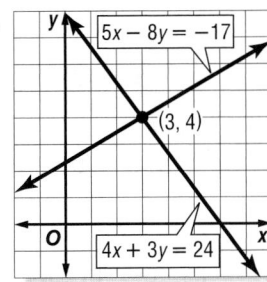

one; (3, 4)

27.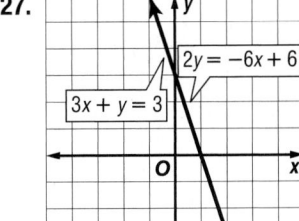

infinitely many

32.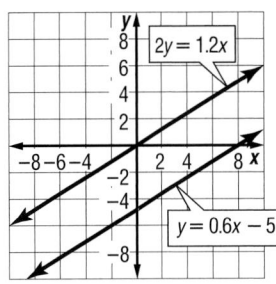

33.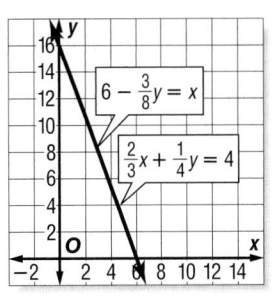

33. Sample answer:

$x + y = 3$

$3x + 2y = 6$

Discount movie tickets for one adult and one child cost $3. The cost for 3 adults and two children is $6. The solution (2, 1) means that an adult ticket costs $2 and a child's ticket costs $1.

34. Sample answer: When problems involve a system of equations, the problem can be solved by substitution. To solve a system of equations using substitution, solve one equation for one unknown. Substitute this value for the unknown in the other equation and solve the equation. Use this number to find the other unknown. For the problem at the top of page 254, the solution (2.8, 143) means that the number of hours spent doing the activities was the same, 143 hours, about 2.8 years after 2000, or in 2002.

38.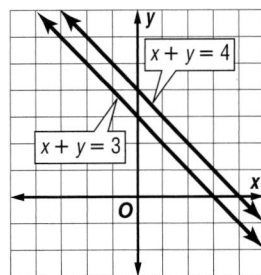

no solution

39.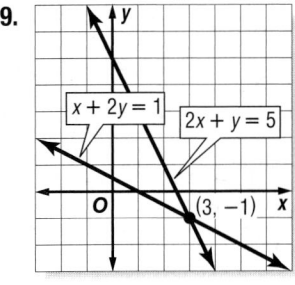

one; (3, −1)

40.

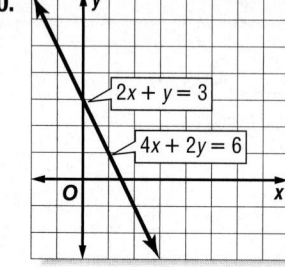

2x + y = 3

4x + 2y = 6

infinitely many

41. Sample answer:

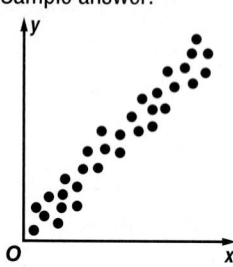

Pages 269–270, Lesson 5-3

31. $A = 6$, $B = 3$; In each equation, replace x with 2 and y with 1 to get $2A + B = 15$ and $2A - B = 9$. Next, eliminate the B variables by adding the equations to get $4A = 24$. Divide each side by 4 to get $A = 6$. Now substitute 6 for A in either equation to get $B = 3$.

32. Sample answer: Elimination can be used to solve problems about meteorology if the coefficients of one variable are the same or are additive inverses. The two equations in the system of equations are added or subtracted so that one of the variables is eliminated. You then solve for the remaining variable. This number is substituted into one of the original equations, and that equation is solved for the other variable. Solve the Seward daylight problem by using the following steps.

$$n + d = 24 \quad \text{Write the equations in column form and add.}$$
$$\underline{(+) \; n - d = 12}$$
$$2n = 36 \quad \text{The d variable is eliminated.}$$
$$\frac{2n}{2} = \frac{36}{2} \quad \text{Divide each side by 2.}$$
$$n = 18 \quad \text{Simplify.}$$
$$n + d = 24 \quad \text{First equation}$$
$$18 + d = 24 \quad n = 18$$
$$18 + d - 18 = 24 - 18 \quad \text{Subtract 18 from each side.}$$
$$d = 6 \quad \text{Simplify.}$$

On the winter solstice, Seward, Alaska, has 18 hours of nighttime and 6 hours of daylight.

38.

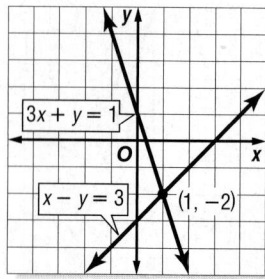

3x + y = 1

x − y = 3

(1, −2)

one; (1, −2)

39.

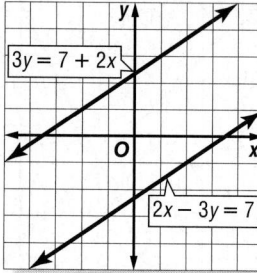

3y = 7 + 2x

2x − 3y = 7

no solution

40.

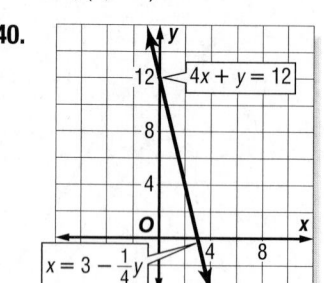

4x + y = 12

$x = 3 - \frac{1}{4}y$

infinitely many

Page 271, Mid-Chapter Quiz

2.

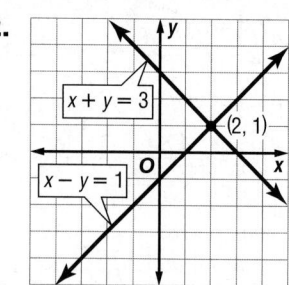

x + y = 3

x − y = 1

(2, 1)

one; (2, 1)

3.

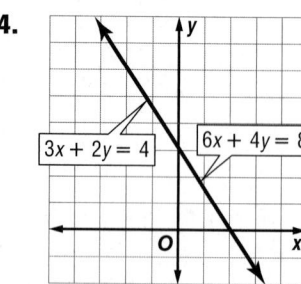

3x − 2y = −6

3x − 2y = 6

no solution

4.

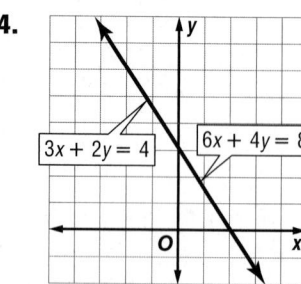

3x + 2y = 4

6x + 4y = 8

infinitely many

6.

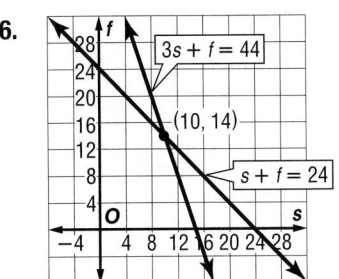

The solution means that each day, he spent 10 hours swimming and 14 hours floating.

17. Let $x =$ the cost of an adult
and let $y =$ the cost of a child;
$2x + y = 68.97$,
$2x + 4y = 125.94$.

18. (24.99, 18.99); The cost of admission for 1 adult is
$24.99 and the cost for a
child is $18.99.

Pages 275–278, Lesson 5-4

33. Sample answer: By having two equations that represent the time restraints, a manager can determine the best use of employee time. The following is a solution to the system of equations on top of page 272.

$$\begin{aligned}
20c + 10b = 800 &\rightarrow & 20c + 10b = & 800 \\
10c + 30b = 900 &\rightarrow & -20c - 60b = & -1800 \\
\hline
& & -50b = & -1000 \\
& & \frac{-50b}{-50} = & \frac{-1000}{-50} \\
& & b = & 20
\end{aligned}$$

$$\begin{aligned}
20c + 10b &= 800 \\
20c + 10(20) &= 800 \\
20c + 200 &= 800 \\
20c + 200 - 200 &= 800 - 200 \\
20c &= 600 \\
\frac{20c}{20} &= \frac{600}{20} \\
c &= 30
\end{aligned}$$

In order to make the most of the employee and oven time, the manager should make assignments to bake 30 batches of cookies and 20 loaves of bread.

5.

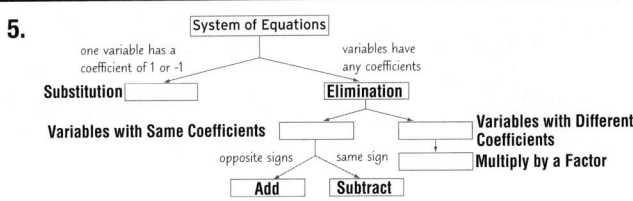

Page 283, Lesson 5-5

13. 880 books; If they sell this number, then their income and expenses both equal $35,200

17. Let $x =$ the cost per pound of aluminum cans and let $y =$ the cost per pound of newspaper;
$9x + 9y = 3.77$ and $26x + 114y = 4.65$.

Page 289, Practice Test

1.

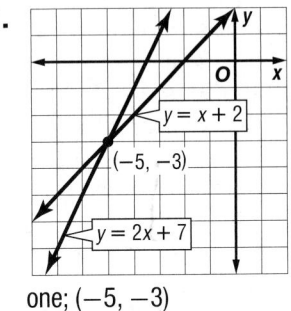

one; $(-5, -3)$

2.

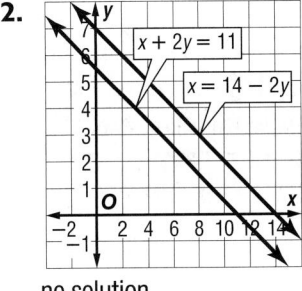

no solution

3.

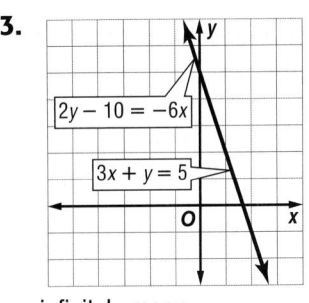

infinitely many

Solving Linear Inequalities

Standards-Based Lesson Plan			Pacing Your Lessons	
LESSONS AND OBJECTIVES		California Standards	40-50 Minute Periods	90-Minute Periods
6-1 Solving Inequalities by Addition and Subtraction (pp. 294–299) • Solve linear inequalities by using addition. • Solve linear inequalities by using subtraction.		4.0, 5.0, 25.3	2	1
Explore 6-2 Solving Inequalities (p. 300) **6-2 Solving Inequalities by Multiplication and Division** (pp. 301–307) • Solve linear inequalities by using multiplication. • Solve linear inequalities by using division.		4.0, 5.0, 24.3, 25.1, 25.2	2	1
6-3 Solving Multi-Step Inequalities (pp. 308–312) • Solve linear inequalities involving more than one operation. • Solve linear inequalities involving the Distributive Property.		4.0, 5.0	2	1
6-4 Solving Compound Inequalities (pp. 315–320) • Solve compound inequalities containing the word *and* and graph their solution sets. • Solve compound inequalities containing the word *or* and graph their solution sets.		4.0, 5.0	2.5	1
6-5 Solving Open Sentences Involving Absolute Value (pp. 322–327) • Solve absolute value equations. **Extend 6-5 Graphing Absolute Value Functions** (p. 328)		3.0, 25.3 17.0	1.5	0.5
6-6 Solving Inequalities Involving Absolute Value (pp. 330–333) • Solve absolute value inequalities.		3.0, 25.3	1	0.5
6-7 Graphing Inequalities in Two Variables (pp. 334–339) • Graph inequalities on the coordinate plane. • Solve real-world problems involving linear inequalities. **Extend 6-7 Graphing Inequalities** (p. 340)		6.0	2.5	1
6-8 Graphing Systems of Inequalities (pp. 341–345) • Solve systems of inequalities by graphing. • Solve real-world problems involving systems of inequalities.		6.0, 9.0	2.5	1
REVIEW			1	0.5
ASSESSMENT			1	0.5*
*The complete **Assessment Planner** for Chapter 6 is provided on p. 291*		**TOTAL**	18	8

* Begin Chapter 7 in the second half of the period.

Professional Development

California Standards Vertical Alignment

Before Chapter 6

Related Topics from Grade 7

- Solve two-step linear equations and inequalities in one variable over the rational numbers ◆━ Standard 7AF4.1

- Understand the meaning of absolute value of a number ◆━ Standard 7NS2.5

- Write an expression, an equation, an inequality, or a system that represents a verbal description Standard 7AF1.1

Chapter 6

Topics from Algebra I

- Students solve equations and inequalities involving absolute values

- Solve multi-step problems involving linear equations and inequalities and provide justification for each step ◆━

- Graph a linear equation or inequality ◆━

- Solve a system of two linear equations or inequalities ◆━

See individual lessons for the specific standards covered.

After Chapter 6

Preparation for Algebra II

- Solve systems of linear equations and inequalities by substitution, with graphs, or with matrices ◆━ Standard 2A2.0

- Solve equations and inequalities involving absolute value ◆━ Standard 2A1.0

Back-Mapping

California Algebra 1 was conceived and developed with the final result in mind, student success in Algebra I and beyond. The authors, using the California Mathematics Standards as their guide, developed this brand-new series by "back-mapping" from the desired result of student success in Algebra I and beyond. McGraw-Hill's *California Geometry, California Algebra 2,* and *California Algebra Readiness* were developed utilizing the same philosophy.

What the Research Says...

According to Pimm (1981), confusion can occur as a result of differing linguistic usage with the teacher speaking mathematical English while the student interprets it as ordinary English. Mathematics is notorious for attaching specialized meanings to everyday words. It is important to make the distinction between the different usages.

- In the Reading Mathematics feature in Chapter 6, the mathematical use of the words *and* and *or* is discussed. This use of language is then applied in the remainder of the chapter.

[Source: Pimm, D. (1981). "Mathematics? I Speak It Fluently," in Ann Floyd (Ed.) *Developing Mathematical Thinking*. Addison-Wesley, pp. 139-150.]

Professional Development

Targeted professional development has been articulated throughout the *California Mathematics: Concepts, Skills, and Problem Solving* series. The **McGraw-Hill Professional Development Video Library** provides short videos that support the ◆━ Key Standards. For more information, visit ca.algebra1.com.

| Model Lessons | Instructional Strategies |

CHAPTER 6

Technology Solutions

Teacher Resources

TeacherWorks™ All-in-One Planner and Resource Center

All of the print materials from the Classroom Resource Masters are available on your TeacherWorks™ CD-ROM.

BL = Below Grade Level   **OL** = On Grade Level   **AL** = Above Grade Level   **ELL** = English Language Learner

Chapter Resource Masters				6-1	6-2	6-3	6-4	6-5	6-6	6-7	6-8
BL **OL**		**ELL**	Lesson Reading Guide	5	12	19	26	33	40	48	56
BL **OL**		**ELL**	Study Guide and Intervention*	6	13	20	27	34	41	49	57
BL **OL**			Skills Practice*	8	15	22	29	36	43	51	59
	OL	**AL**	Practice*	9	16	23	30	37	44	52	60
	OL	**AL**	Word Problem Practice*	10	17	24	31	38	45	53	61
	OL	**AL**	Enrichment	11	18	25	32	39	46	54	62
	OL	**AL**	Calculator and Spreadsheet Activities						47	55	63–64
	OL	**AL**	Chapter Assessments*	59–80							
BL **OL** **AL**			5-Minute Check Transparencies	✓	✓	✓	✓	✓	✓	✓	
BL **OL**			Teaching Mathematics with Manipulatives	✓	✓		✓	✓	✓	✓	

Also available in Spanish.

AssignmentWorks

Differentiated Assignments, Answers, and Solutions

- Print a customized assignment worksheet using the Student Edition exercises along with an answer key or worked-out solutions.
- Use default lesson assignments as outlined in the Differentiated Homework Options in the Teacher Wraparound Edition.
- Includes modified questions from the Student Edition.

Interactive Classroom

This CD-ROM is a customizable Microsoft® PowerPoint® presentation that includes:

- In-Class Examples
- Your Turn Exercises*
- 5-Minute Check Transparencies*
- Links to Online Study Tools
- Concepts in Motion

compatible with response pad technology

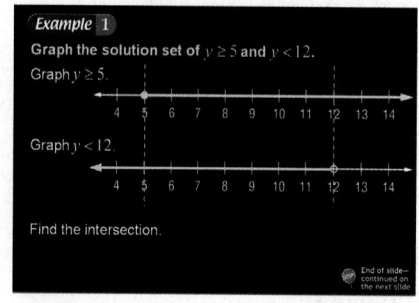

ExamView® Assessment Suite

 lets you

- Create, edit, and customize tests and worksheets using QuickTest Wizard
- Create multiple versions of tests and modify them for a desired level of difficulty
- Translate from English to Spanish and vice versa
- Build tests aligned with your state standards
- Track students' progress using the Teacher Management System

Student Resources

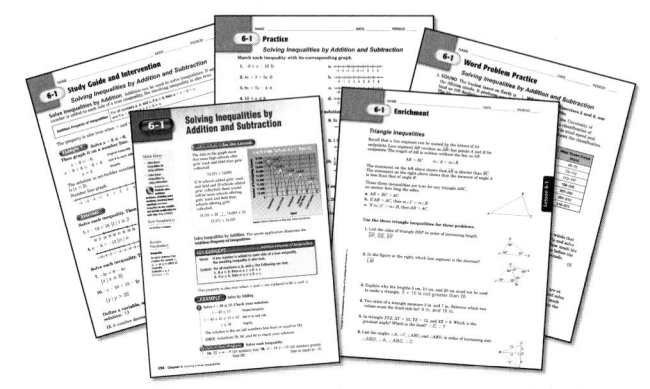

Internet Resources

Math Online ca.algebra1.com

TEACHER	PARENT	STUDENT	
			Online Study Tools
	●	●	Online Student Edition
●	●	●	Multilingual Glossary
			Lesson Resources
	●	●	BrainPOP®
●	●	●	Concepts in Motion
●	●	●	Extra Examples
	●	●	Other Calculator Keystrokes
●			Problem of the Week Cards
	●	●	Real-World Careers
	●	●	Self-Check Quizzes
			Chapter Resources
	●	●	Chapter Readiness
	●	●	Chapter Test
	●	●	Standardized Test Practice
	●	●	Vocabulary Review/Chapter Review Activities
			Unit Resources
●		●	Cross-Curricular Internet Project
			Other Resources
●			Dinah Zike's Foldables
	●	●	Hotmath Homework Help
●			Key Concepts
●	●	●	Meet the Authors
	●	●	Personal Tutor
●			Project CRISS℠
	●	●	Scavenger Hunts and Answer Sheets
●			Vocabulary PuzzleMakers

Focus on Mathematical Content

Big Idea for Chapter 6:
Solving Linear Inequalities

Inequalities are used to represent various real-world situations in which a quantity must fall within a range of values. The properties that are used to solve them are similar to those that are used to solve equations. Properties such as the Addition, Subtraction, Multiplication, and Division Properties of Inequality are used to solve single-step, multi-step, and compound inequalities.

Why It's Important

For This Chapter
The lessons in this chapter use a variety of methods to solve linear inequalities and analyze the solutions in terms of the situation.

- How is using addition and subtraction to solve an inequality similar to solving equations using addition and subtraction? (Lesson 6-1)
- How is using multiplication and division to solve an inequality different from solving equations using multiplication and division? (Lesson 6-2)
- What is the solution set when the inequality results in a false statement? (Lesson 6-3)
- How does the graph of a compound inequality containing *and* differ from one containing *or*? (Lesson 6-4)
- How do absolute value equations/inequalities relate to compound sentences/inequalities? (Lessons 6-5 and 6-6)
- What does a dashed line, open circle, and shading mean when solving a real-world inequality? (Lesson 6-7)
- Where on a graph would you find the solution to a system of inequalities? (Lesson 6-8)

After This Chapter
- In future mathematics courses, students solve and graph inequalities of other types of functions, such as quadratic functions.
- In Algebra 2, students apply solving inequalities to linear programming.
- In Calculus, the concept of inequalities is applied to analyzing the area between curves.

6-1 Solving Inequalities by Addition and Subtraction

To solve an equation, you isolate the variable so that it has a coefficient of 1 on one side of the equals sign (Lesson 2-2). An inequality is solved the same way. The Addition and Subtraction Properties of Inequality are used in the same way as the Addition and Subtraction Properties of Equality. If any number is added to or subtracted from each side of a true inequality, the result is a true inequality.

The solutions to inequalities can be expressed in more than one way.

- The solutions can be written in set builder notation, for example:
  $\{x \mid x < 7\}$. This is read as *the set of all numbers x such that x is less than 7*. Since the inequality is $<$, the number 7 is a boundary that is not included in the solution.

- The solutions can be graphed on a number line, for example:

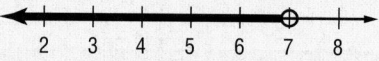

  The circle at 7 shows that 7 is *not* included in the solution of the inequality. The darkened line and arrow pointing to the left shows that the solution of the inequality includes all numbers less than 7.

If the inequality is $\geq$ or $\leq$, the boundary number is included in the solution. A solid dot is placed at the point on the number line. If an arrow is drawn to the right of a boundary number, it indicates the solutions are greater than the boundary.

6-2 Solving Inequalities by Multiplication and Division

Inequalities that include multiplication or division of the variable can also be solved. The same principles as found in the Multiplication and Division Properties of Equality (Lesson 2-3) are used, with one main difference. When you multiply or divide each side of an inequality by the same negative number, you must reverse the direction of the inequality symbol. You multiply or divide by a negative number only if the coefficient of the variable is negative.

Solving Multi-Step Inequalities

You can solve multi-step inequalities with the same process used for solving multi-step equations (Lesson 2-4). Work backward, using inverse operations to undo the operations. After each side is simplified using the Distributive Property and/or by combining like terms, work in the opposite order of the order of operations. The Addition and Subtraction Properties of Inequality are applied first, followed by the Multiplication or Division Property of Inequalities.

If the solution is an untrue statement, such as $4 > 8$, the solution is the empty set $\varnothing$, which has no members. If the solution results in a statement that is always true, such as $5 > 3$, then the solution is the set of all real numbers.

 ## Solving Compound Inequalities

If two simple inequalities are joined by the words *and* or *or*, the result is a compound inequality. The solution to a compound inequality that contains the word *and* must be a solution to both simple inequalities. The graph of the solution is the intersection of the graphs of the two simple inequalities.

If the compound inequality contains the word *or*, the solution must be a solution to *one* or *both* simple inequalities. The graph of the solution is the *union* of the two inequalities.

The properties used to solve compound inequalities are the same as those used to solve simple linear inequalities.

 ## Solving Open Sentences Involving Absolute Value

The *absolute value* of a number is the distance the number is from zero on a number line. An absolute value open sentence can be an equation or an inequality. To solve an absolute value equation, it is important to keep in mind that the expression inside the absolute value symbols can be either positive or negative, so two cases must be considered.

Absolute value equations can be solved by graphing them on a number line or by writing them as a compound sentence using the word *or* and solving them algebraically.

 ## Solving Inequalities Involving Absolute Value

Absolute value inequalities can also be solved algebraically by writing them as compound inequalities. There are two possible cases.

- First Case: If the absolute value expression can be written in the form $|x| < n$ or $|x| \le n$, the compound sentence is written with *and*.

- Second Case: If the absolute value expression can be written in the form $|x| > n$ or $x \ge n$, the compound sentence is written with *or*.

 ## Graphing Inequalities in Two Variables

The solution set of a linear inequality, like that of a linear equation, is the set of all ordered pairs that make the statement true. Like the solution set of an equation in two variables (Lesson 3-3), the solution set of an inequality in two variables is graphed on a coordinate plane. However, the solution set of a linear inequality is not linear. The graph of a linear inequality has the following characteristics.

- It has a linear boundary.
  The inequality is first graphed as if it contained an equal sign like an equation. This determines the boundary line. Use a solid line if the inequality is $\le$ or $\ge$. Use a dashed line if the inequality is $<$ or $>$.

- It covers a region called a half-plane.
  Select a point in either half-plane determined by the line and test it in the inequality. If the resulting statement is true, shade the half-plane that contains that point. If the statement is false, shade the other half-plane.

 ## Graphing Systems of Inequalities

A solution of a system of inequalities is the set of all points that satisfy both inequalities. Use the methods learned in Lesson 6-6 to graph each inequality. The points that are solutions of both inequalities lie in the region where the graphs overlap, or intersect. There are two possibilities.

- A system of inequalities has *no* solution if the boundary lines are parallel and the shaded regions have no points in common.

- A system of inequalities has *infinitely many* solutions if the overlapping shaded region extends on indefinitely.

Differentiated Instruction

Options for Chapter 6 Lessons

ELL = English Language Learner	**AL** = Above Grade Level	**SS** = Struggling Students	**SN** = Special Needs

Using Verbal Skills **ELL** **SS** **SN**

Use with Lesson 6-1

If students are having difficulty choosing the correct symbol for the problem's wording, have them use the chart on p. 294 to write the common inequality phrases on the index cards and the appropriate inequality symbol on the back of each card. As students solve verbal problems such as Example 4 on p. 296, they can pick the card that has the same wording as the problem. The back of the card will reveal the appropriate inequality symbol to use.

Using Opposites **AL**

Use with Lesson 6-2

Have students write an inequality involving a negative coefficient of the variable on their paper, using a self-adhesive note for the inequality symbol, such as $-12x > 24$. Tell them that they are going to change all the signs in the inequality, so everything is its opposite. The expression becomes $+12x < -24$. Students now can divide without having to worry about the inequality sign.

Using Visual Learning **ELL** **SN**

Use with Lesson 6-4

Prepare a large number line with two dashed horizontal lines above it as a transparency or laminated sheet of paper. Give students a compound inequality written as two sentences. Have students use a dry-erase marker to plot the solution for each inequality on one of the dashed lines. If the inequality involves "and," have them wipe away any parts that are not on both dashed lines. This leaves a clear picture of what part of the number line should be used for the solution.

Noteables™ Interactive Study Notebook with Foldables™

Noteables™ Interactive Study Notebook with Foldables™ is a study organizer that provides helpful steps for students to follow to organize their notes for Chapter 6.

- Students use Noteables to record notes and to complete their Foldables as you present the material for each lesson.
- Noteables correspond to the Examples in the *Teacher Wraparound Edition* and *Interactive Classroom CD-ROM.*

Intervention

Quick Review Math Handbook*

is Glencoe's mathematical handbook for students and parents.

Hot Words includes a glossary of terms.

Hot Topics consists of two parts:

- explanations of key mathematical concepts
- exercises to check students' understanding.

Lesson	Hot Topics Section	Lesson	Hot Topics Section
6-1	6.4, 6.6	6-4	6.6
6-2	6.4, 6.6	6-5	6.4
6-3	6.6	6-7	6.4, 6.6

Also available in Spanish

Teacher to Teacher

Laurie Newton
Crossler M.S.,
Salem, OR

USE BEFORE LESSON 6-5

❝ To help students understand what their solution set to an absolute inequality represents, I have students check their work by testing numbers in all of the regions of the number line prescribed by the inequality. In Example 3, I have them test a number less than −14, −14 itself, a number greater than −14 and less than 4, 4 itself, and a number greater than 4. ❞

Reading and Writing in Mathematics

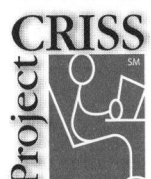

Project CRISSSM

STUDY SKILL

Taking good notes will help students become actively involved in the learning process. For each lesson have students read and then write notes about the topic.

You may wish to show them the sample notes for Lesson 6-6 at the right so they can use them as a guide. Then allow class time for students to discuss their notes. Encourage students to talk about the procedures used in the lesson for solving problems and how they addressed those procedures in their notes.

Lesson 6-6

Set up an absolute value inequality.

Example: $|x + 8| < 10$

Case 1: When the value inside the absolute value symbols is positive: $x + 8 < 10$.

Case 2: When the value inside the absolute value symbols is negative: $-(x + 8) < 10$.

CReating **I**ndependence through **S**tudent-owned **S**trategies

CHAPTER 6 Notes

FOLDABLES Study Organizer
Dinah Zike's Foldables™

Focus Students write about solving linear inequalities and open sentences involving absolute value as these concepts are presented in the lessons of this chapter.

Teach Have students make and label their Foldables as illustrated.

Suggest that students use their Foldables to take notes, record concepts, and define terms. They can also use them to record the direction and progress of learning, to describe positive and negative experiences during learning, to write about personal associations and experiences, and to list examples of ways in which this new knowledge has or will be used in their daily lives.

When to Use It As students read and study the chapter, have them fill the journal with notes, diagrams, and examples of linear inequalities.

A version of a completed Foldable is shown on p. 346.

Differentiated Instruction
[CRM] Student-Made Glossary, pp. 1–2

Students should complete the chart by providing a definition and an example of each term as they progress through Chapter 6. This study tool can also be used to review for the chapter test.

CHAPTER 6
Solving Linear Inequalities

BIG Ideas

- **Standard 3.0** Students solve equations and inequalities involving absolute values. (CAHSEE)

- **Standard 9.0** Students are able to solve a system of two linear inequalities in two variables and to sketch the solution sets. (Key, CAHSEE)

Key Vocabulary
compound inequality (p. 315)

intersection (p. 315)

set-builder notation (p. 295)

union (p. 316)

🌐 Real-World Link
Roller Coasters Inequalities are used to represent various real-world situations in which a quantity must fall within a range of possible values. For example, the cars on the Giant Dipper roller coaster at the Santa Cruz Beach Boardwalk must gain enough speed on the first hill to propel it through the entire ride.

FOLDABLES Study Organizer

Solving Linear Inequalities Make this Foldable to record information about solving linear inequalities. Begin with two sheets of notebook paper.

1. **Fold** one sheet in half along the width. Cut along the fold from the edges to margin.

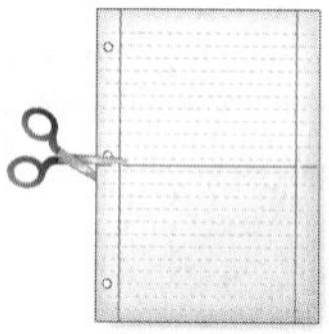

2. **Fold** the second sheet in half along the width. Cut along the fold between the margins.

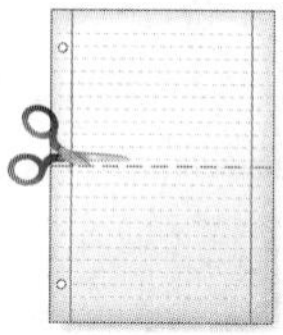

3. **Insert** the first sheet through the second sheet and align the folds.

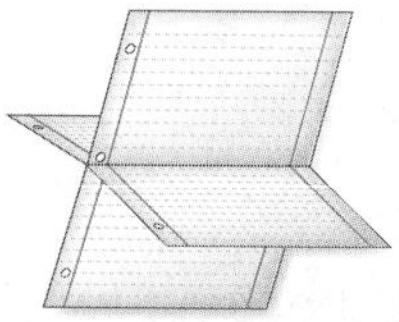

4. **Label** each page with a lesson number and title.

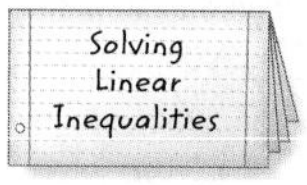

Solving Linear Inequalities

Materials Needed for Chapter 6	
• algebra tiles (Explore 6-2)	• internet (Lesson 6-4)
• equation mat (Explore 6-2)	• graph paper (Lessons 6-7, 6-8)
• graphing calculator (Extend 6-5, Extend 6-7)	

GET READY for Chapter 6

Diagnose Readiness You have two options for checking Prerequisite Skills.

Option 2

Math Online Take the Online Readiness Quiz at ca.algebra1.com.

Option 1

Take the Quick Check below. Refer to the Quick Review for help.

QUICK Check

(Used in Lessons 6-1 and 6-3.)
Solve each equation. (Lessons 2-4 and 2-5)

1. $18 = 27 + f$ -9

2. $d - \frac{2}{3} = \frac{1}{2}$ $1\frac{1}{6}$

3. $5m + 7 = 4m - 12$ -19

4. $3y + 4 = 16$ 4

5. $\frac{1}{2}k - 4 = 7$ 22

6. $4.3b + 1.8 = 8.25$ 1.5

7. $6s - 12 = 2(s + 2)$ 4

8. $n - 3 = \frac{n+1}{2}$ 7

9. **NUMBER THEORY** Three times the lesser of two consecutive integers is 4 more than 2 times the greater number. Find the integers. **6, 7**

(Used in Lessons 6-5 and 6-6.)
Find each value. (Prerequisite Skill)

10. $|20|$ **20**

11. $|-1.5|$ **1.5**

12. $|14 - 7|$ **7**

13. $|1 - 16|$ **15**

14. $|2 - 3|$ **1**

15. $|7 - 10|$ **3**

(Used in Lesson 6-7.)
Graph each equation. (Lesson 3-3)

16. $2x + 2y = 6$

17. $x - 3y = -3$

18. $y = 2x - 3$

19. $y = -4$

20. $x = -\frac{1}{2}y$

21. $3x - 6 = 2y$

22. $15 = 3(x + y)$

23. $2 - x = 2y$

16–23. See Ch. 6 Answer Appendix.

24. **CRAFTS** Rosa and Taylor are making scarves for the upcoming craft fair. Rosa can make x scarves per hour and Taylor can make y scarves per hour. Rosa can only work 8 hours and Taylor can only work 10. In total, they need to complete 25 scarves. Express Taylor's rate in terms of Rosa's rate.
$y = -\frac{4}{5}x + \frac{5}{2}$

QUICK Review

EXAMPLE 1

Solve $\frac{1}{2} = \frac{1}{8}t + 1$.

$\frac{1}{2} = \frac{1}{8}t + 1$	Original equation
$-\frac{1}{2} = \frac{1}{8}t$	Subtract 1 from each side.
$8\left(-\frac{1}{2}\right) = 8\left(\frac{1}{8}t\right)$	Multiply each side by 8.
$-4 = t$	Simplify.

EXAMPLE 2

Find the value of $|15 - 20|$.

$\begin{aligned}|15 - 20| &= |-5| \\ &= 5\end{aligned}$	Evaluate inside the absolute value. -5 is five units from zero in the negative direction.

EXAMPLE 3

Graph $y - x = 1$.

Step 1 Put the equation in slope intercept form.

$$y - x = 1 \rightarrow y = x + 1$$

Step 2 The y-intercept is 1. So, graph the point $(0, 1)$.

Step 3 The slope is 1 or $\frac{1}{1}$. $\frac{\text{rise}}{\text{run}}$
From $(0, 1)$, move up 1 unit and right 1 unit. Draw a dot.

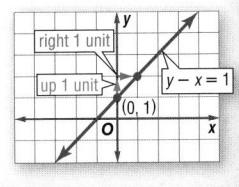

Step 4 Draw a line connecting the points.

✔ Formative Assessment

CRM Anticipation Guide, p. 3
Spotting Preconceived Ideas
Students complete this survey to determine prior knowledge about ideas from Chapter 6. Revisit this worksheet after completing the chapter. Also see p. 350.

TWE Lesson Activities

- Ticket out the Door, p. 307
- Crystal Ball, pp. 299, 327, 333, 339
- Name the Math, pp. 320, 345
- Yesterday's News, p. 313

Chapter Checkpoints

SE Mid-Chapter Quiz, p. 321

SE Study Guide and Review pp. 346–350

SE California Standards Practice, pp. 352–353

CRM Quizzes, pp. 67 and 68

CRM Standardized Test Practice, pp. 84–86

Math Online ca.algebra1.com

- Self-Check Quizzes
- Practice Test
- Standardized Test Practice

✔ Summative Assessment

SE Chapter Practice Test, p. 351

CRM Mid-Chapter Test, p. 69

CRM Vocabulary Test, p. 70

CRM Extended-Response Test, p. 83

CRM Leveled Chapter Tests, pp. 71–82

◉ ExamView® Assessment Suite

KEY

CRM *Chapter 6 Resource Masters*

SE Student Edition

TWE Teacher Wraparound Edition

◉ CD-ROM

✔ Diagnostic Assessment

Exercises	California Standards	Intervention
1–9	5.0	**SE** Review Lesson 2-4, pp. 92–97 **SE** Review Lesson 2-5, pp. 98–103
10–15	7NS2.5	Extra Examples, Chapter 1, at ca.gr7math.com
16–24	6.0	**SE** Review Lesson 3-3, pp. 155–161

 **Lesson Notes**

1 Focus

 Standards Alignment

Before Lesson 6-1
Solve two-step linear equations and inequalities in one variable from Standard 7AF4.1

Lesson 6-1
Students solve multi-step problems involving linear equations and inequalities from Standard 5.0

After Lesson 6-1
Solve systems of linear equations and inequalities by substitution, with graphs, or with matrices from Standard 2A2.0

2 Teach

Scaffolding Questions
Have students read *Get Ready for the Lesson.*
Ask:
- Is the number of schools offering volleyball greater or less than the number offering track and field? less than
- Suppose 1000 schools added track and field, and 1000 schools added volleyball. Would there be more schools offering track and field, or volleyball? track and field

(continued on the next page)

Lesson 6-1 Resources

Chapter 6 Resource Masters
Lesson Reading Guide, p. 5 **BL OL ELL**
Study Guide and Intervention, pp. 6–7 **BL OL ELL**
Skills Practice, p. 8 **BL OL**
Practice, p. 9 **OL AL**
Word Problem Practice, p. 10 **OL AL**
Enrichment, p. 11 **OL AL**

Transparencies
5-Minute Check Transparency 6-1
Additional Print Resources
Noteables™ Interactive Study Notebook with Foldables™

Technology
ca.algebra1.com
Interactive Classroom CD-ROM
AssignmentWorks CD-ROM
Graphing Calculator Easy Files

Main Ideas
- Solve linear inequalities by using addition.
- Solve linear inequalities by using subtraction.

 Standard 5.0 Students solve **multistep problems, including word problems, involving linear equations** and linear **inequalities in one variable and provide justification for each step.** (Key, CAHSEE)

New Vocabulary
set-builder notation

Review Vocabulary

Inequality
An open sentence that contains the symbol $<$, $\leq$, $>$, or $\geq$ is called an inequality.
Example: $x \geq 4$
(Lesson 1-3)

GET READY for the Lesson

The data in the graph show that more high schools offer girls' track and field than girls' volleyball.

$$15{,}151 > 14{,}083$$

If 20 schools added girls' track and field and 20 schools added girls' volleyball, there would still be more schools offering girls' track and field than schools offering girls' volleyball.

$$15{,}151 + 20 \;\underline{\;?\;}\; 14{,}083 + 20$$
$$15{,}171 > 14{,}103$$

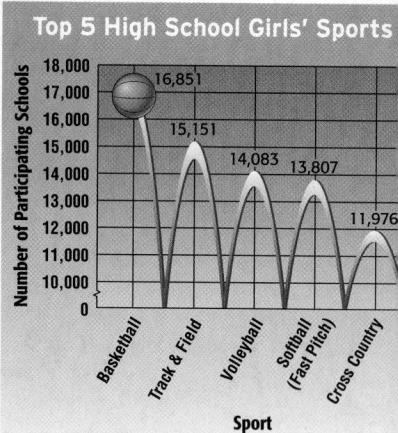

Top 5 High School Girls' Sports

Source: National Federation of State High School Associations

Solve Inequalities by Addition The sports application illustrates the **Addition Property of Inequalities**.

KEY **CONCEPT**	*Addition Property of Inequalities*
Words	If any number is added to each side of a true inequality, the resulting inequality is also true.
Symbols	For all numbers a, b, and c, the following are true. 1. If $a > b$, then $a + c > b + c$. 2. If $a < b$, then $a + c < b + c$.

This property is also true when $>$ and $<$ are replaced with $\geq$ and $\leq$.

EXAMPLE Solve by Adding

① Solve $t - 45 \leq 13$. Check your solution.

$$t - 45 \leq 13 \qquad \textit{Original inequality}$$
$$t - 45 + 45 \leq 13 + 45 \qquad \text{Add 45 to each side.}$$
$$t \leq 58 \qquad \text{Simplify.}$$

The solution is the set {all numbers less than or equal to 58}.

CHECK Substitute 58, 50, and 60 to check your solution.

 Your Progress Solve each inequality.
1A. $22 > m - 8$ {all numbers less than 30}
1B. $d - 14 \geq -19$ {all numbers greater than or equal to −5}

294 Chapter 6 Solving Linear Inequalities

The solution in Example 1 was expressed as a set. A more concise way of writing a solution set is to use **set-builder notation**. The solution in set-builder notation is $\{t \mid t \le 58\}$.

The solution can also be graphed on a number line.

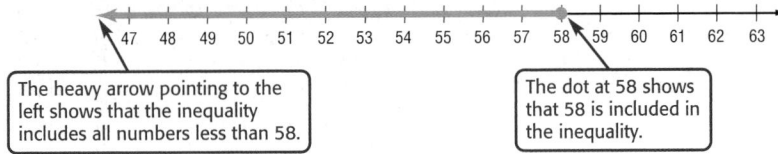

The heavy arrow pointing to the left shows that the inequality includes all numbers less than 58.

The dot at 58 shows that 58 is included in the inequality.

Solve Inequalities by Subtraction
Subtraction can also be used to solve inequalities.

KEY CONCEPT   *Subtraction Property of Inequalities*

Words   If any number is subtracted from each side of a true inequality, the resulting inequality is also true.

Symbols   For all numbers a, b, and c, the following are true.
1. If $a > b$, then $a - c > b - c$.
2. If $a < b$, then $a - c < b - c$.

This property is also true when $>$ and $<$ are replaced with $\ge$ and $\le$.

 Real-World EXAMPLE   Solve by Subtracting

2 **MUSIC** Josh added 19 more songs to his MP3 player, making the total number of songs more than 56. How many songs were originally on the player? Solve $s + 19 > 56$. Then graph the solution.

$s + 19 > 56$ Original inequality

$s + 19 - 19 > 56 - 19$ Subtract 19 from each side.

$s > 37$ Simplify.

The solution set is $\{s \mid s > 37\}$. So, Josh had more than 37 songs originally on the music player.

CHECK Your Progress

2. **TEMPERATURE** The temperature t in a swimming pool increased 4°F since this morning. The temperature is now less than 81°F. What was the temperature this morning? Solve $t + 4 < 81$. Then graph the solution. **$\{t \mid t < 77\}$; The temperature was less than 77° F.**

Terms with variables can also be subtracted from each side to solve inequalities.

Scaffolding Questions continued
• Would the order from greatest to least change in the graph if 50 schools removed basketball from their sports programs, 50 removed track and field, 50 removed volleyball, 50 removed softball, and 50 removed cross country? no

Solve Inequalities by Addition
Example 1 shows how to solve a linear inequality using the Addition Property of Inequalities.

✓ Formative Assessment
Use the Check Your Progress exercises after each example to determine students' understanding of concepts.

ADDITIONAL EXAMPLE

1 Solve $s - 12 > 65$. Check your solution. $s > 77$ or {all numbers greater than 77}

Additional Examples are also in:
• Noteables™ Interactive Study Notebook with Foldables™
• Interactive Classroom PowerPoint® Presentations

Solve Inequalities by Subtraction
Example 2 shows how to solve and graph a real-world linear inequality using the Subtraction Property of Inequality. **Example 3** shows how to solve and graph a linear inequality with variables on each side. **Example 4** shows how to write and solve a linear inequality from a problem.

Intervention

Rewriting Inequalities   An equation such as $x = 5$ can be written as $5 = x$ because of the Symmetric Property of Equality. Because of this property, students may incorrectly assume that they can rewrite an inequality such as $3 > y$ as $y > 3$. Remind students that the inequality sign always points to the smaller value. In $3 > y$, it points to y, so to write the expression with y on the left, use $y < 30$.

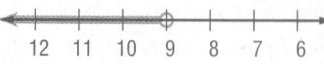
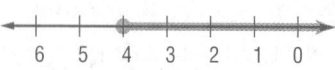
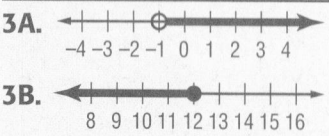

Preventing Errors

When students solve inequalities with variables on both sides, suggest that they subtract the term with the lesser coefficient from each side so that the remaining coefficient of the variable will be positive.

Preventing Errors

Ask students to identify one phrase they will never see in a verbal inequality problem. Sample answer: equals or is equal to

Additional Answers

3A.
-4 -3 -2 -1 0 1 2 3 4

3B.
8 9 10 11 12 13 14 15 16

EXAMPLE   Variables on Each Side

3 Solve $5p + 7 > 6p$. Then graph the solution.

$5p + 7 > 6p$	Original inequality
$5p + 7 - 5p > 6p - 5p$	Subtract $5p$ from each side.
$7 > p$	Simplify.

Since $7 > p$ is the same as $p < 7$, the solution set is $\{p \mid p < 7\}$.

-2 -1 0 1 2 3 4 5 6 7 8 9 10 11 12 13 14

CHECK Your Progress   3A–3B. See margin for graphs.

Solve each inequality. Graph the solution on a number line.
3A. $9n - 1 < 10n$ $\{n \mid n > -1\}$ **3B.** $5h \leq 12 + 4h$ $\{h \mid h \leq 12\}$

Here are some phrases that indicate inequalities in verbal problems.

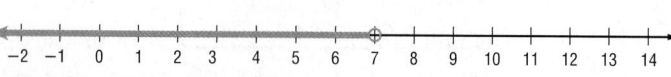

Inequalities			
<	>	≤	≥
less than	greater than	at most	at least
fewer than	more than	no more than	no less than
		less than or equal to	greater than or equal to

Real-World EXAMPLE   Write an Inequality to Solve a Problem

4 **OLYMPICS** Irina Tchachina scored a total of 107.325 points in the four events of rhythmic gymnastics. Alina Kabaera scored a total of 81.300 in the clubs, hoop, and ball events. How many points did she need to score in the ribbon event to get ahead of Tchachina and win the gold medal?

Words	Kabaera's total	is greater than	Tchachina's total.
Variable	Let r = Kabaera's score in the ribbon event.		
Inequality	$81.300 + r$	>	107.325

Solve the inequality.   **ESTIMATE:** $110 - 80 = 30$

$81.300 + r > 107.325$	Original inequality
$81.300 + r - 81.300 > 107.325 - 81.300$	Subtract 81.300 from each side.
$r > 26.025$	Simplify.

Kabaera needed to score more than 26.025 points to win the gold medal. The solution is close to the estimate, so the answer is reasonable.

Real-World Link

Alina Kabaera of the Russian Federation won the gold medal in rhythmic gymnastics at the 2004 Summer Olympics in Athens, and her teammate Irina Tchachina won the silver medal.

Source:
www.athens2004.com

CHECK Your Progress

4. SHOPPING Terrell has $65 to spend. He bought a T-shirt for $18 and a belt for $14. If Terrell still wants jeans, how much can he spend on the jeans? no more than $33

Online **Personal Tutor at** ca.algebra1.com

Focus on Mathematical Content

Producing Equivalent Inequalities You can substitute for either side of an inequality an expression equivalent to that side. For example, the inequality $2(3 + x) > 5$ is equivalent to the inequality $6 + 2x > 5$. You can also add (or subtract) the same real number to (or from) each side of an inequality.

★ indicates multi-step problem

Examples 1–3
(pp. 294–296)

Solve each inequality. Check your solution, and then graph it on a number line. **1–8. See Ch. 6 Answer Appendix.**

1. $t - 5 \geq 7$ $\{t \mid t \geq 12\}$
2. $-7 \geq -2 + x$ $\{x \mid x \leq -5\}$
3. $a + 4 < 2$ $\{a \mid a < -2\}$
4. $9 \leq b + 4$ $\{b \mid b \geq 5\}$
5. $10 > n - 1$ $\{n \mid n < 11\}$
6. $k + 24 > -5$ $\{k \mid k > -29\}$
7. $8r + 6 < 9r$ $\{r \mid r > 6\}$
8. $7p \leq 6p - 2$ $\{p \mid p \leq -2\}$

Example 4
(p. 296)

Define a variable, write an inequality, and solve each problem. Check your solution.

9. A number decreased by 8 is at most 14. **See margin.**
10. Twice a number is greater than −5 plus the number.
    Sample answer: Let n = the number, $2n > -5 + n$; $\{n \mid n > -5\}$.
11. **BIOLOGY** Adult Nile crocodiles weigh up to 2200 pounds. If a young Nile crocodile weighs 157 pounds, how many pounds might it be expected to gain in its lifetime? **no more than 2043 lb**

Exercises

HOMEWORK HELP	
For Exercises	**See Examples**
12–29	1–3
30–35	4

Exercise Levels
A: 12–35
B: 36–46
C: 47–50

Solve each inequality. Check your solution, and then graph it on a number line. **12–29. See Ch. 6 Answer Appendix for graphs. 19. $\{q \mid q \leq 7\}$**

12. $t + 14 \geq 18$ $\{t \mid t \geq 4\}$
13. $d + 5 \leq 7$ $\{d \mid d \leq 2\}$
14. $n - 7 < -3$ $\{n \mid n < 4\}$
15. $-5 + s > -1$ $\{s \mid s > 4\}$
16. $5 < 3 + g$ $\{g \mid g > 2\}$
17. $13 > 18 + r$ $\{r \mid r < -5\}$
18. $2 \leq -1 + m$ $\{m \mid m \geq 3\}$
19. $-23 \geq q - 30$
20. $11 + m \geq 15$
21. $h - 26 < 4$ $\{h \mid h < 30\}$
22. $8 \leq r - 14$ $\{r \mid r \geq 22\}$
23. $-7 > 20 + c$
24. $2y > -8 + y$ $\{y \mid y > -8\}$
25. $3f < -3 + 2f$ $\{f \mid f < -3\}$
26. $3b \leq 2b - 5$
27. $4w \geq 3w + 1$ $\{w \mid w \geq 1\}$
28. $6x + 5 \geq 7x$ $\{x \mid x \leq 5\}$
29. $-9 + 2a < 3a$
20. $\{m \mid m \geq 4\}$ 23. $\{c \mid c < -27\}$ 26. $\{b \mid b \leq -5\}$ $\{a \mid a > -9\}$

Define a variable, write an inequality, and solve each problem. Check your solution. **30–32. See margin.**

30. The sum of a number and 13 is at least 27.
31. A number decreased by 5 is less than 33.
32. Twice a number is more than the sum of that number and 14.
33. The sum of two numbers is at most 18, and one of the numbers is −7.
    Sample answer: Let n = the number, $n + (-7) \leq 18$; $\{n \mid n \leq 25\}$.

For Exercises 34–36, define a variable, write an inequality, and solve each problem. Then interpret your solution. **34–36. See margin.**

34. **BIOLOGY** There are 3500 species of bees and more than 600,000 species of insects. How many species of insects are not bees?

35. **TECHNOLOGY** A recent survey found that more than 21 million people between the ages of 12 and 17 use the Internet. Of those online teens, about 16 million said they use the Internet at school. How many teens who are online do not use the Internet at school?

36. **ANALYZE TABLES** Chapa is limiting her fat intake to no more than 60 grams per day. Today, she has had two breakfast bars and a slice of pizza. How many more grams of fat can she have today?

Food	Grams of Fat
breakfast bar	3
slice of pizza	21

Real-World Link
One common species of bees is the honeybee. A honeybee colony may have 60,000 to 80,000 bees.

Source: Penn State, Cooperative Extension Service

3 Practice

✓ **Formative Assessment**

Use Exercises 1–11 to check for understanding.

Use the chart at the bottom of this page to customize assignments for your students.

Odd/Even Assignments

Exercises 12–35 are structured so that students practice the same concepts whether they are assigned odd or even problems.

Additional Answers

9. Sample answer: Let n = the number, $n - 8 \leq 14$; $\{n \mid n \leq 22\}$.

30. Sample answer: Let n = the number, $n + 13 \geq 27$; $\{n \mid n \geq 14\}$.

31. Sample answer: Let n = the number, $n - 5 < 33$; $\{n \mid n < 38\}$

32. Sample answer: Let n = the number, $2n > n + 14$; $\{n \mid n > 14\}$.

34. Sample answer: Let s = the number of species of insects that are not bees, $s + 3500 > 600,000$; $\{s \mid s > 596,500\}$, more than 596,500 species of insects are not bees.

35. more than 5 million; $n + 16 \geq 21$

36. Sample answer: Let g = the number of grams of fat Chapa can have during the rest of the day, $2(3) + 21 + g \leq 60$; $\{g \mid g \leq 33\}$, Chapa can have no more than 33 grams of fat today.

DIFFERENTIATED HOMEWORK OPTIONS

Level	Assignment	Two-Day Option	
BL Basic	12–35, 47, 49–63	13–35 odd, 51–53	12–34 even, 47, 49, 50, 54–63
OL Core	13–35 odd, 36, 37, 39, 41–63	12–35, 51–53	36–47, 49, 50, 54–63
AL Advanced /Pre-AP	36–59, (optional: 60–63)		

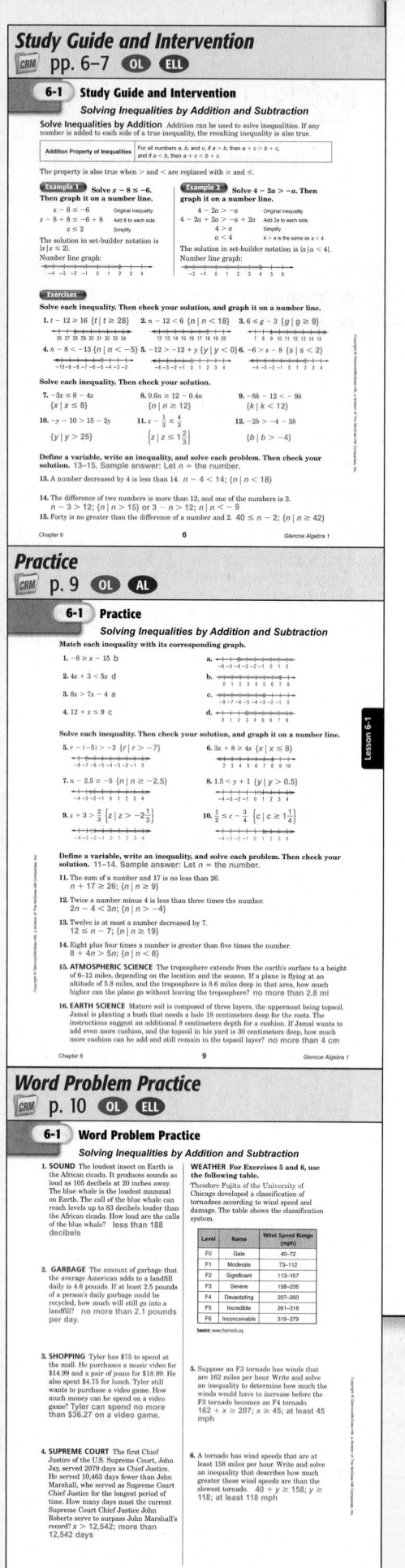

Solve each inequality. Check your solution, and then graph it on a number line. 37–40. See margin for graphs.

37. $y - (-2.5) > 8.1$ $\{y \mid y > 5.6\}$

38. $5.2r + 6.7 \geq 6.2r$ $\{r \mid r \leq 6.7\}$

39. $a + \frac{1}{4} > \frac{1}{8}$ $\left\{a \mid a > -\frac{1}{8}\right\}$

40. $\frac{3}{2}p - \frac{2}{3} \leq \frac{4}{9} + \frac{1}{2}p$ $\left\{p \mid p \leq 1\frac{1}{9}\right\}$

Define a variable, write an inequality, and solve each problem. Check your solution. 41. Sample answer: Let n = the number, $30 \leq n + (-8)$; $\{n \mid n \geq 38\}$.

41. Thirty is no greater than the sum of a number and −8.

42. Four times a number is less than or equal to the sum of 3 times the number and −2. Sample answer: Let n = the number, $4n \leq 3n + (-2)$; $\{n \mid n \leq -2\}$.

For Exercises 43 and 44, define a variable, write an inequality, and solve each problem. Then interpret your solution.

43. Sample answer: Let m = the amount of money in the account, $m - 1300 - 947 \geq 1500$; $\{m \mid m \geq 3747\}$, Mr. Hayashi must have at least $3747 in his account.

★ 43. **MONEY** City Bank requires a minimum balance of $1500 to maintain free checking services. If Mr. Hayashi is going to write checks for the amounts listed in the table, how much money should he have in his account before writing the checks in order to have free checking?

Check	Amount
750	$1300
751	$947

44. Sample answer: Let w = the number of wins to meet the goal, $w + 4 \geq 0.60(18)$; $\{w \mid w \geq 6.8\}$, the team must win at least 7 more games to reach their goal.

★ 44. **SOCCER** The Centerville High School soccer team has a goal of winning at least 60% of their 18 games this season. In the first three weeks, the team has won 4 games. How many more games must the team win to meet their goal?

★ 45. **GEOMETRY** The length of the base of the triangle is less than the height of the triangle. What are the possible values of x? Formulate a linear inequality to solve the problem. Determine whether your answers are reasonable. $12 < 4 + x$; more than 8 in.

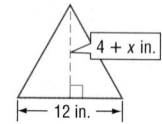

EXTRA PRACTICE
See pages 728, 749.

Math Online
Self-Check Quiz at
ca.algebra1.com

46. If $d + 5 \geq 17$, then complete each inequality.
   a. $d \geq \underline{\ ?\ }$ 12
   b. $d + \underline{\ ?\ } \geq 20$ 8
   c. $d - 5 \geq \underline{\ ?\ }$ 7

H.O.T. Problems

47. **REASONING** Compare and contrast the graphs of $a < 4$ and $a \leq 4$. See margin.

48. **CHALLENGE** Determine whether each statement is *always*, *sometimes*, or *never* true. Explain. 48a–c. See Ch. 6 Answer Appendix.
   a. If $a < b$ and $c < d$, then $a + c < b + d$.
   b. If $a < b$ and $c < d$, then $a + c \geq b + d$.
   c. If $a < b$ and $c < d$, then $a - c < b - d$.

49. **OPEN ENDED** Formulate three linear inequalities that are equivalent to $y < -3$.
   Sample answers: $y + 1 < -2$, $y - 1 < -4$, $y + 3 < 0$

50. *Writing in Math* Use the information about sports on page 294 to explain how inequalities can be used to describe school sports. Include an inequality describing the number of schools needed to add girls' track and field so that the number is greater than the number of schools currently participating in girls' basketball. See Ch. 6 Answer Appendix.

298 **Chapter 6** Solving Linear Inequalities

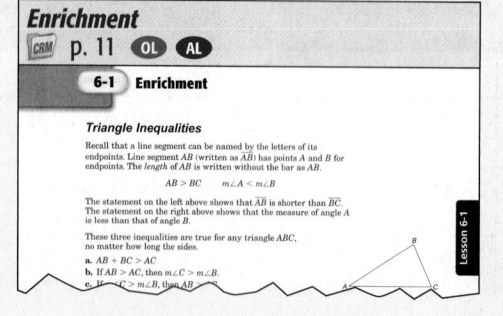

Enrichment
CRM p. 11 OL AL

6-1 **Enrichment**

Triangle Inequalities

Recall that a line segment can be named by the letters of its endpoints. Line segment AB (written as $\overline{AB}$) has points A and B for endpoints. The *length* of AB is written without the bar as AB.

$$AB > BC \qquad m\angle A < m\angle B$$

The statement on the left above shows that $\overline{AB}$ is shorter than $\overline{BC}$. The statement on the right above shows that the measure of angle A is less than that of angle B.

These three inequalities are true for any triangle ABC, no matter how long the sides.

a. $AB + BC > AC$
b. If $AB > AC$, then $m\angle C > m\angle B$.

BL = Below Grade Level
OL = On Grade Level
AL = Above Grade Level
ELL = English Language Learner

Additional pages not shown:
CRM **Lesson Reading Guide**, p. 5 BL OL ELL
CRM **Skills Practice**, p. 8 BL OL

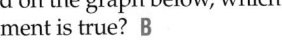
51. Based on the graph below, which statement is true? **B**

Sports Drinks Supply

A Maria started with 30 bottles of sports drinks.

B On day 10, Maria will have drunk 10 bottles of sports drinks.

C Maria will be out of sports drinks on day 14.

D Maria drank 5 bottles in the first 2 days.

52. What is the solution set to the inequality $7 + x < 5$? **G**

F $x < 2$ **H** $x > 2$

G $x < -2$ **J** $x > -2$

53. REVIEW Miss Miller wants to calculate the cost of buying tile to cover her rectangular kitchen floor. She knows the cost per square foot of tile, and she knows the dimensions of the kitchen. Which formula should she use to find the area of the floor? **A**

A $A = \ell w$ **C** $P = 2\ell + 2w$

B $V = Bh$ **D** $c^2 = a^2 + b^2$

Spiral Review

Determine the best method to solve each system of equations. Then solve the system. (Lesson 5-5) **56. elimination (×) (−4, 1)**

54. $4x - 3y = -1$ **elimination (+);**
$3x + 3y = 15$ **(2, 3)**

55. $x = 8y$ **substitution;**
$2x + 3y = 38$ **(16, 2)**

56. $2a + 5b = -3$
$3a + 4b = -8$

★ **57. NUTRITION** The costs for various items at a mall food court are shown in the table. What is the cost of an iced tea and a vegetable wrap? (Lesson 5-4) **$1.50; 3.75**

Number of Iced Teas	Number of Vegetable Wraps	Total Cost
2	2	$10.50
3	4	$19.50

VOLUNTEERING For Exercises 58 and 59, use the graph. It shows the total hours that Estella spent volunteering. (Lesson 3-5)

58. Write an equation in function notation for the relation. $f(x) = 3x$

59. What would be the total hours that Estella spent volunteering after 12 weeks? **36 h**

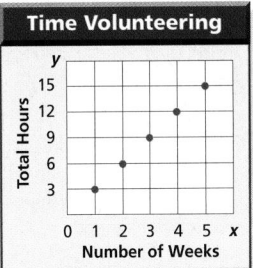

Time Volunteering

GET READY for the Next Lesson

PREREQUISITE SKILL Solve each equation. (Lesson 2-3)

60. $6g = 42$ **7**

61. $3m = 435$ **145**

62. $\frac{t}{9} = 14$ **126**

63. $\frac{2}{3}y = -14$ **−21**

Tips for New Teachers

Check Solutions

Students should always check their solutions but often omit this step in their hurry to finish their assignments. Remind students that checking their solutions is especially important with inequalities because the direction of the inequality sign often is changed when writing solutions in set-builder notation.

4 Assess

Crystal Ball Have students write how they think today's lesson will connect to the next lesson, *Solving Inequalities by Multiplication and Division*.

FOLDABLES Study Organizer **Foldables™ Follow-Up**

Remind students to use the page in their Foldables that corresponds to this lesson to take notes and show examples of using addition and subtraction to solve inequalities.

Additional Answers

37.

38.

39.

40.

47. In both graphs, the line is darkened to the left. In the graph of $a < 4$, there is a circle at 4 to indicate that 4 is not included in the graph. In the graph of $a \leq 4$, there is a dot at 4 to indicate that 4 is included in the graph.

Pre-AP Activity   **Use before Exercise 49**

Write these three linear inequalities on the board:

$$y > 3 \qquad y + 1 > 4 \qquad 5 < y + 2$$

Have students solve each linear inequality and compare the solutions. Ask students to formulate three more linear inequalities that are equivalent to $y > 3$.

1 Focus

Objective Use algebra tiles to model solving inequalities.

Materials

- algebra tiles and equation mats
- self-adhesive blank notes

Easy–to–Make Manipulatives

Teaching Algebra with Manipulatives
Templates for:

- algebra tiles, pp. 10–11
- equation mat, p. 16

Teaching Tip Have students use a self-adhesive note to cover the equals sign on the equation mat. Write a ≥ symbol on the note. This will allow students to model inequalities with the equation mat and algebra tiles.

2 Teach

Working in Cooperative Groups Put students in groups of 2 or 3 and demonstrate the example. Have groups complete Exercises 1 and 2.

- Make sure the inequality sign on the self-adhesive note is pointed in the correct direction to match the inequality.

- Once students have isolated the x-tiles, remind them to separate the 1-tiles into equal groups to correspond to the number of x-tiles.

- If the x-tiles end up on the right side of the inequality, students may rotate the mat 180 degrees to read the inequality with the variable on the left side.

Practice Have students complete Exercises 3–7.

 EXPLORE 6-2

Algebra Lab
Solving Inequalities

You can use algebra tiles to solve inequalities.

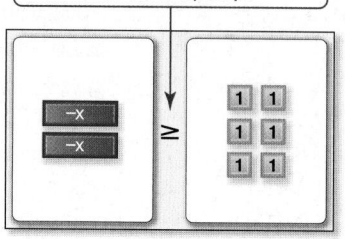

Concepts in MOtion
Animation
ca.algebra1.com

Preparation for Standard 5.0 Students solve multistep problems, including word problems, involving linear equations and linear inequalities in one variable and provide justification for each step. (Key, CAHSEE)

ACTIVITY Solve $-2x \geq 6$.

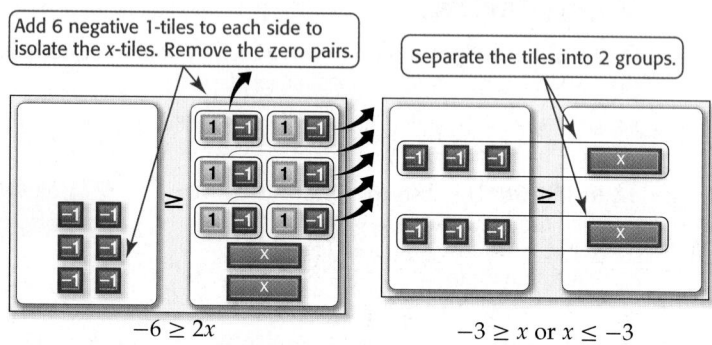

Step 1 Model the inequality.

Use a self-adhesive note to cover the equals sign on the equation mat. Then write a ≥ symbol on the note. Model the inequality.

$$-2x \geq 6$$

Step 2 Remove the zero pairs.

Since you do not want to solve for a negative x-tile, eliminate the negative x-tiles by adding 2 positive x-tiles to each side. Remove the zero pairs.

$$-2x + 2x \geq 6 + 2x$$

Step 3 Remove the zero pairs.

Add 6 negative 1-tiles to each side to isolate the x-tiles. Remove the zero pairs.

$$-6 \geq 2x$$

Step 4 Group the tiles.

Separate the tiles into 2 groups.

$$-3 \geq x \text{ or } x \leq -3$$

MODEL AND ANALYZE THE RESULTS

Use algebra tiles to solve each inequality.

1. $-4x < 12$
$\{x \mid x > -3\}$

2. $-2x > 8$
$\{x \mid x < -4\}$

3. $-3x \geq -6$
$\{x \mid x \leq 2\}$

4. $-5x \leq -5$
$\{x \mid x \geq 1\}$

5. In Exercises 1–4, is the coefficient of x in each inequality *positive* or *negative*? **negative**

6. Compare the inequality symbols and locations of the variable in Exercises 1–4 with those in their solutions. What do you find?

7. Model the solution for $2x \geq 6$. What do you find? How is this different than solving $-2x \geq 6$?

6. The symbols in the solutions point in the opposite direction with relationship to the variable than the symbols in the original problem.

7. There are no negative x-tiles, so the variable remains on the left and the symbol remains ≥.

300 Chapter 6 Solving Linear Inequalities

---

3 Assess

 Formative Assessment

Use Exercises 5 and 6 to assess whether students understand that when they multiply or divide both sides of an inequality by a negative number, the direction of the inequality sign changes.

From Concrete to Abstract

Ask: What happens to the inequality sign when you add or subtract from both sides of an inequality by a negative number? Sample answer: The direction of the inequality sign does not change.

Ask: What happens to the inequality sign when you multiply or divide both sides of an inequality by a negative number? Sample answer: The direction of the inequality sign changes.

Solving Inequalities by Multiplication and Division

Main Ideas

- Solve linear inequalities by using multiplication.
- Solve linear inequalities by using division.

Preparation for Standard 5.0 Students solve multistep problems, including word problems, involving linear equations and linear inequalities in one variable and provide justification for each step. (Key, CAHSEE)

Study Tip

Look Back
To review solving linear equations by multiplication, see Lesson 2-3.

> **GET READY for the Lesson**

Isabel Franco is stacking cases of drinks to sell at a basketball game. A case of bottled water is 8 inches high. A case of sports drinks is 10 inches high. Notice that 8 inches is less than 10 inches, or 8 in. < 10 in. How would the height of stacks of three cases of each compare?

 8 in.    10 in.

8 in. < 10 in.	The height of the water is less than the height of the sports drinks.
8 in. × 3 < 10 in. × 3	Multiply to find the height of 3 cases of each.
24 in. < 30 in.	The height of 3 cases of water is less than the height of 3 cases of sports drinks.

Solve Inequalities by Multiplication If each side of an inequality is multiplied by a positive number, the inequality remains true.

$8 > 5$	Original inequality	$5 < 9$	Original inequality
$8(2) \underline{\ ?\ } 5(2)$	Multiply each side by 2.	$5(4) \underline{\ ?\ } 9(4)$	Multiply each side by 4.
$16 > 10$	Simplify.	$20 < 36$	Simplify.

This is *not* true when multiplying by negative numbers.

$5 > 3$	Original inequality	$-6 < 8$	Original inequality
$5(-2) \underline{\ ?\ } 3(-2)$	Multiply each side by −2.	$-6(-5) \underline{\ ?\ } 8(-5)$	Multiply each side by −5.
$-10 < -6$	Simplify.	$30 > -40$	Simplify.

If each side of an inequality is multiplied by a negative number, the direction of the inequality symbol changes. These examples illustrate the **Multiplication Property of Inequalities**.

KEY CONCEPT   *Multiplying by a Positive Number*

Words   If each side of a true inequality is multiplied by the same positive number, the resulting inequality is also true.

Symbols   If a and b are any numbers and c is a positive number, the following are true.
If $a > b$, then $ac > bc$, and if $a < b$, then $ac < bc$.

This property also holds for inequalities involving ≥ and ≤.

1 Focus

 Standards Alignment

Before Lesson 6-2
Solve two-step linear equations and inequalities in one variable from ⚷ Standard 7AF4.1

Lesson 6-2
Students solve multi-step problems involving linear equations and inequalities from ⚷ Standard 5.0

After Lesson 6-2
Solve systems of linear equations and inequalities by substitution, with graphs, or with matrices from ⚷ Standard 2A2.0

2 Teach

Scaffolding Questions
Have students read *Get Ready for the Lesson.*
Ask:
- Compare the two cases. Both cases are rectangular; each case of water is 8 in. high and each case of sports drink is 10 in. high.
- By what number are both sides of the inequality 8 < 10 multiplied to yield 24 < 30? 3
- After you multiply both sides of the inequality 8 < 10 by the same number to yield 24 < 30, is the inequality still true? Explain. Yes, 24 is less than 30.

Lesson 6-2 Resources

Chapter 6 Resource Masters
Lesson Reading Guide, p. 12 **BL OL ELL**
Study Guide and Intervention, pp. 13–14 **BL OL ELL**
Skills Practice, p. 15 **BL OL**
Practice, p. 16 **OL AL**
Word Problem Practice, p. 17 **OL AL**
Enrichment, p. 18 **OL AL**
Quiz 1, p. 67

Transparencies
5-Minute Check Transparency 6-2
Additional Print Resources
Noteables™ Interactive Study Notebook with Foldables™

Technology
ca.algebra1.com
Interactive Classroom CD-ROM
AssignmentWorks CD-ROM
Graphing Calculator Easy Files

Solve Inequalities by Multiplication

Example 1 shows how to solve an inequality by multiplying each side by a positive number. **Example 2** shows how to solve an inequality by multiplying each side by a negative number.

 Formative Assessment

Use the Check Your Progress exercises after each example to determine students' understanding of concepts.

 **Focus on Mathematical Content**

Inequality Symbols The Multiplication Property of Inequalities also holds for inequalities involving ≤ and ≥ symbols.

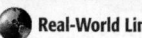 **Real-World Link**

More than 30,000 different orchid species flower in the wild on every continent except Antarctica.

Source: www.alohaorchid.com

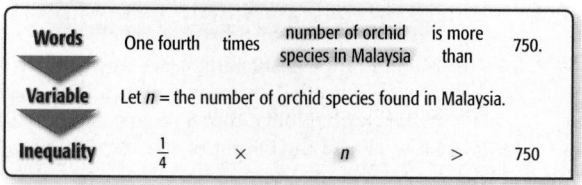 **Real-World EXAMPLE** Write and Solve an Inequality

1 **BIOLOGY** Mt. Kinabalue in Malaysia has the greatest concentration of wild orchids on Earth. It contains more than 750 species, which is approximately one fourth of all orchid species in Malaysia. How many orchid species are there in Malaysia?

Words	One fourth	times	number of orchid species in Malaysia	is more than	750.
Variable	Let n = the number of orchid species found in Malaysia.				
Inequality	$\frac{1}{4}$	×	n	>	750

$\frac{1}{4}n > 750$ Original inequality

$(4)\frac{1}{4}n > (4)750$ Multiply each side by 4 and do not change the inequality's direction.

$n > 3000$ Simplify.

The solution set is $\{n \mid n > 3000\}$. This means that there are more than 3000 orchid species in Malaysia.

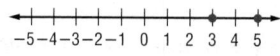 **Your Progress** **1B.** fewer than 63 employees

1A. **SURVEYS** Of the students surveyed at Madison High School, fewer than eighty-four said they have never purchased an item online. This is about three eighths of those surveyed. How many students were surveyed? **fewer than 224 students**

1B. **CANDY** Fewer than 42 employees at the factory stated that they preferred chocolate candy over fruit candy. This is about two thirds of the employees. How many employees are there?

Graph 3 and 5 on a number line.	Multiply each number by −1.
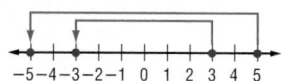	

Since 3 is to the left of 5, 3 < 5.

Since −3 is to the right of −5, −3 > −5

Notice that the numbers being compared switched positions as a result of being multiplied by a negative number. In other words, their order reversed. This suggests the following property.

KEY CONCEPT *Multiplying by a Negative Number*

Words If each side of a true inequality is multiplied by the same negative number, the direction of the inequality symbol must be *reversed* so that the resulting inequality is also true.

Symbols If a and b are any numbers and c is a negative number, the following are true.
If $a > b$, then $ac < bc$, and if $a < b$, then $ac > bc$.

This property also holds for inequalities involving ≥ and ≤ .

EXAMPLE Multiply by a Negative Number

2 Solve $-\frac{2}{5}p < -14$.

$$-\frac{2}{5}p < -14 \qquad \text{Original inequality}$$

$$\left(-\frac{5}{2}\right)\left(-\frac{2}{5}p\right) > \left(-\frac{5}{2}\right)(-14) \qquad \text{Multiply each side by } -\frac{5}{2} \text{ and change } < \text{ to } >.$$

$$p > 35 \qquad \text{Simplify.}$$

The solution set is $\{p|p > 35\}$.

CHECK Your Progress Solve each inequality.

2A. $-\frac{n}{6} \le 8$ $\{n|\, n \ge -48\}$ **2B.** $-\frac{4}{3}p > -10$ $\{p|\, p < 7.5\}$

Solve Inequalities By Division You can also solve an inequality by dividing each side by the same number. Consider the inequality $6 < 15$.

Divide each side by 3.

$$6 \;<\; 15$$

$$6 \div 3 \;\underline{\;?\;}\; 15 \div 3$$

$$2 \;<\; 5$$

> The direction of the inequality symbol remains the same.

Divide each side by -3.

$$6 \;<\; 15$$

$$6 \div (-3) \;\underline{\;?\;}\; 15 \div (-3)$$

$$-2 \;>\; -5$$

> The direction of the inequality symbol is reversed.

These examples illustrate the **Division Property of Inequalities**.

KEY CONCEPT — *Dividing by a Positive Number*

Words If each side of a true inequality is divided by the same positive number, the resulting inequality is also true.

Symbols If a and b are any numbers and c is a positive number, the following are true.

If $a > b$, then $\frac{a}{c} > \frac{b}{c}$, and if $a < b$, then $\frac{a}{c} < \frac{b}{c}$.

KEY CONCEPT — *Dividing by a Negative Number*

Words If each side of a true inequality is divided by the same negative number, the direction of the inequality symbol must be *reversed* so that the resulting inequality is also true.

Symbols If a and b are any numbers and c is a negative number, the following are true.

If $a > b$, then $\frac{a}{c} < \frac{b}{c}$, and if $a < b$, then $\frac{a}{c} > \frac{b}{c}$.

These properties also hold for inequalities involving $\ge$ and $\le$.

Study Tip

Common Misconception
You may be tempted to change the direction of the inequality when solving if there is a negative number anywhere in the inequality. Remember that you only change the direction of the inequality when multiplying or dividing by a negative.

 Math Online Extra Examples at ca.algebra1.com   **Lesson 6-2** Solving Inequalities by Multiplication and Division **303**

ADDITIONAL EXAMPLE

2 Solve $-\frac{3}{5}d \ge 6$. $\{d \mid d \le -10\}$

Solve Inequalities by Division

Example 3 shows how to solve an inequality by dividing each side by a positive number. **Example 4** shows how to solve an inequality by dividing each side by a negative number. **Example 5** shows how to write and solve an inequality.

Intervention

Relating Multiplication and Division Challenge students to explain how they might already know how to solve inequalities by division once they know how to solve inequalities by multiplication. Students should suggest that since they know how to solve inequalities by multiplying, and since division is the same as multiplying by the reciprocal, then they already know how to solve inequalities by division.

ADDITIONAL EXAMPLES

3 Solve each inequality.

a. $12s \geq 60$. $\{s \mid s \geq 5\}$

b. $-8q < 136$ $\{q \mid q > -17\}$

4 **STANDARDS EXAMPLE** Sports pennants are on sale for $2.50 each. Which inequality can be used to find how many sports pennants Amy can purchase for herself and her friends if she wants to spend no more than $15? B

A $2.50p \geq 15$ **C** $2.50 \leq 15p$

B $2.50p \leq 15$ **D** $2.50 \geq 15p$

Tips for New Teachers

Preventing Errors

Point out to students that it is easier to solve an inequality using division when the inequality involves whole numbers and easier to solve using multiplication by reciprocals when the inequality involves fractions.

Tips for New Teachers

Preventing Errors

Point out that the rules for the Division Property of Inequalities state that each side of an inequality can be divided by a positive or negative number. In neither case is zero included because division by zero is an undefined operation.

Study Tip

Alternate Method

Since dividing is the same as multiplying by the reciprocal, you could also solve $-5t \geq 275$ by multiplying each side by $-\frac{1}{5}$.

Test-Taking Tip

Clue Words

Always look for clue words like *no more than* in problems involving inequalities. They will indicate which symbol should be used.

EXAMPLE   Divide to Solve an Inequality

3 Solve each inequality.

a. $14h > 91$

$14h > 91$ Original inequality

$\dfrac{14h}{14} > \dfrac{91}{14}$ Divide each side by 14 and do not change the direction of the inequality sign.

$h > 6.5$ Simplify.

The solution set is $\{h \mid h > 6.5\}$.

b. $-5t \geq 275$

$-5t \geq 275$ Original inequality

$\dfrac{-5t}{-5} \leq \dfrac{275}{-5}$ Divide each side by -5 and change $\geq$ to $\leq$.

$t \leq -55$ Simplify.

The solution set is $\{t \mid t \leq -55\}$.

CHECK Your Progress

3A. $9r < 27$ $\{r \mid r < 3\}$ **3B.** $-15 \geq 3t$ $\{t \mid t \leq -5\}$

3C. $32 < -8k$ $\{k \mid k < -4\}$ **3D.** $-5g \geq 40$ $\{g \mid g \leq -8\}$

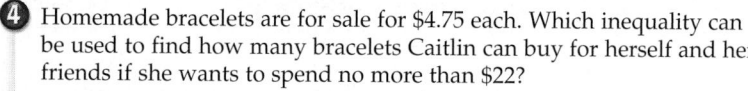

STANDARDS EXAMPLE   Write an Inequality 5.0

4 Homemade bracelets are for sale for $4.75 each. Which inequality can be used to find how many bracelets Caitlin can buy for herself and her friends if she wants to spend no more than $22?

A $4.75b \geq 22$ **C** $4.75 \leq 22b$

B $4.75b \leq 22$ **D** $4.75 \geq 22b$

Read the Item

You want to find the inequality that represents the number of bracelets that can be bought for $22 or less.

Solve the Item

If b represents the number of bracelets, then $4.75b$ represents the total cost of b bracelets. So, you can eliminate Choices C and D.

No more than $22 indicates less than or equal to 22, so the inequality that represents this situation is $4.75b \leq 22$. The answer is B.

CHECK Your Progress

4. Write an inequality for the sentence below.

Eighteen is greater than or equal to -9 times a number. **H**

F $-9n \geq 18$ **H** $18 \geq -9n$

G $-9 + n \geq 18$ **J** $18 \geq n - 9$

 **Personal Tutor at** ca.algebra1.com

---

Pre-AP Activity   **Use as an Extension**

Ask students to solve $2n + 4 \neq 12$. Have the students discuss the solution and write and solve a different inequality using the $\neq$ symbol. $\{n \mid n \neq 4\}$

✓ CHECK Your Understanding

Examples 1, 2
(pp. 302–303)

Solve each inequality. Check your solution.

1. $\frac{t}{9} < -12$ {$t | t < -108$}

2. $30 > \frac{1}{2}n$ {$n | n < 60$}

3. $-\frac{3}{4}r \leq -6$ {$r | r \geq 8$}

4. $-\frac{c}{8} \geq 7$ {$c | c \leq -56$}

Define a variable, write an inequality, and solve each problem. Then check your solution.

5. The opposite of four times a number is more than 12. **See margin.**

6. Half of a number is at least 26.
Sample answer: Let n = the number, $\frac{1}{2}n \geq 26$; {$n | n \geq 52$}.

★ **7.** **FUND-RAISING** The Jefferson High School Band Boosters raised more than $5500 for their Music Scholarship Fund. This money came from sales of their Marching Band Performances DVD, which sold for $15. How many DVDs did they sell? Define a variable and write an inequality to solve the problem. Interpret your solution. **See margin.**

Example 3
(pp. 303–304)

Solve each inequality. Check your solution.

8. $7m \geq 42$ {$m | m \geq 6$}

9. $12x > -60$ {$x | x > -5$}

10. $75 < -15g$ {$g | g < -5$}

11. $-21 \leq -3s$ {$s | s \leq 7$}

Example 4
(p. 304)

5.0

12. **STANDARDS PRACTICE** The area of the rectangle is less than 85 square feet. What is the width of the rectangle? **C**

20 ft

w ft

A $w > 4\frac{1}{4}$ ft   **B** $w \geq 4\frac{1}{4}$ ft   **C** $w < 4\frac{1}{4}$ ft   **D** $w \leq 4\frac{1}{4}$ ft

Exercises

HOMEWORK HELP

For Exercises	See Examples
13–20	1, 2
21–24	1
25–32	3
33, 34	4

Solve each inequality. Check your solution. **13–20. See margin.**

13. $\frac{1}{4}m < -17$

14. $\frac{b}{10} \leq 5$

15. $-7 > -\frac{r}{7}$

16. $-\frac{a}{11} > 9$

17. $\frac{5}{8}y \geq -15$

18. $6 > \frac{2}{3}v$

19. $-10 \geq \frac{x}{-2}$

20. $-\frac{3}{4}q \leq -33$

Define a variable, write an inequality, and solve each problem. Then check your solution. **21–24. See margin.**

21. Seven times a number is greater than 28.

22. Negative seven times a number is at least 14.

23. Twenty-four is at most a third of a number.

24. Two thirds of a number is less than −15.

Exercise Levels
A: 13–34
B: 35–50
C: 51–55

25. {$g | g \leq 24$}

26. {$t | t > 12$}

27. {$d | d \leq -6$}

28. {$n | n \leq -7$}

33. Sample answer: Let b = the number of bags of mulch, $2.5b \geq 2000$; {$b | b \geq 800$}, at least 800 bags.

Solve each inequality. Check your solution.

25. $6g \leq 144$

26. $84 < 7t$

27. $-14d \geq 84$

28. $14n \leq -98$

29. $32 > -2y$ {$y | y > -16$}

30. $-64 \geq -16z$ {$z | z \geq 4$}

31. $-26 < 26s$ {$s | s > -1$}

32. $-6x > -72$ {$x | x < 12$}

For Exercises 33 and 34, define a variable, write an inequality, and solve each problem. Then interpret your solution.

33. **FUND-RAISING** The Middletown High School girls basketball team wants to make at least $2000 on their annual mulch sale. The team makes $2.50 on each bag of mulch sold. How many bags of mulch should the team sell?

34. **EVENT PLANNING** Shaniqua is planning the prom. The hall does not charge a rental fee as long as at least $4000 is spent on food. If she has chosen a buffet that costs $28.95 per person, how many people must attend the prom to avoid a rental fee for the hall? Sample answer: Let p = the number of people, $28.95p \geq 4000$; {$p | p \geq 138.2$}, at least 139 people.

Lesson 6-2 Solving Inequalities by Multiplication and Division **305**

3 Practice

✓ Formative Assessment

Use Exercises 1–12 to check for understanding.

Use the chart at the bottom of this page to customize assignments for your students.

Odd/Even Assignments
Exercises 13–34 are structured so that students practice the same concepts whether they are assigned odd or even problems.

Additional Answers
5. Sample answer: Let n = the number, $-4n > 12$; {$n | n < -3$}.

7. Sample answer: Let n = the number of DVDs sold, $15n > 5500$; {$n | n \geq 366.6$}, they sold at least 367 DVDs.

13. {$m | m < -68$}

14. {$b | b \leq 50$}

15. {$r | r > 49$}

16. {$a | a < -99$}

17. {$y | y \geq -24$}

18. {$v | v < 9$}

19. {$x | x \geq 20$}

20. {$q | q \geq 44$}

21. Sample answer: Let n = the number, $7n > 28$; {$n | n > 4$}.

22. Sample answer: Let n = the number, $-7n \geq 14$; {$n | n \leq -2$}.

23. Sample answer: Let n = the number, $24 \leq \frac{1}{3}n$; {$n | n \geq 72$}.

24. Sample answer: Let n = the number, $\frac{2}{3}n < -15$; {$n | n < -22.5$}.

DIFFERENTIATED HOMEWORK OPTIONS

Level	Assignment	Two-Day Option	
BL Basic	13–34, 51, 52, 54–68	13–33 odd, 56, 57	14–34 even, 51, 52, 54, 55, 58–68
OL Core	13–43 odd, 44–52, 54–68	13–34, 56, 57	35–52, 54–68
AL Advanced /Pre-AP	35–63, (optional: 64–67)		

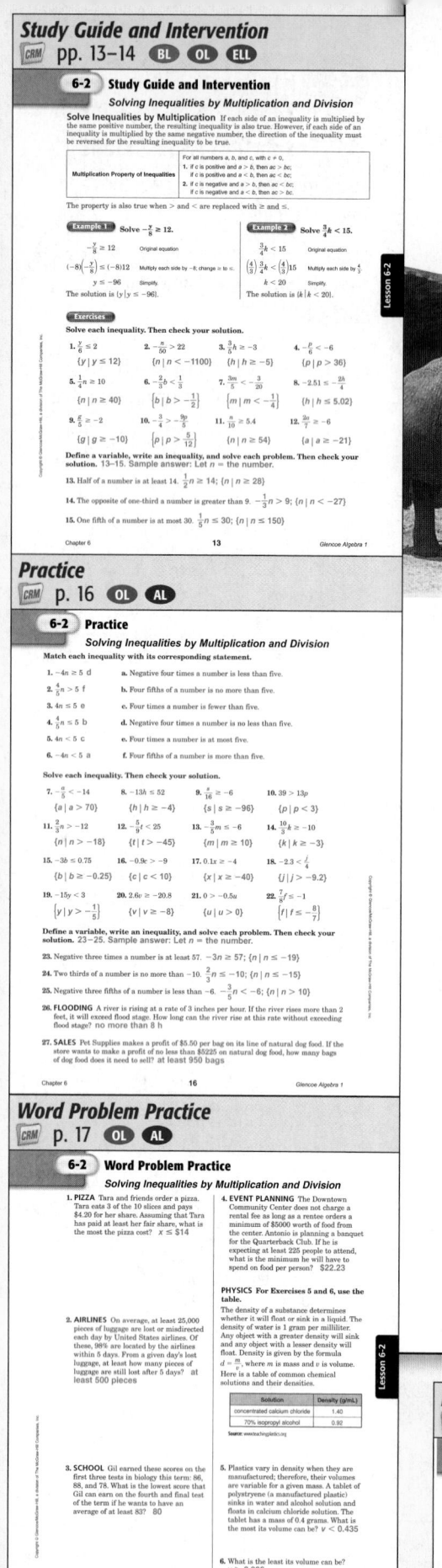

Study Guide and Intervention
CRM pp. 13–14 BL OL ELL

6-2 Study Guide and Intervention
Solving Inequalities by Multiplication and Division

Practice
CRM p. 16 OL AL

6-2 Practice
Solving Inequalities by Multiplication and Division

Word Problem Practice
CRM p. 17 OL AL

6-2 Word Problem Practice
Solving Inequalities by Multiplication and Division

Solve each inequality. Check your solution.

37. $\{w \mid w > -2.72\}$

39. $\left\{c \mid c < -\dfrac{1}{10}\right\}$

40. $\left\{m \mid m < -\dfrac{1}{4}\right\}$

35. $-\dfrac{2}{3}b \le -9$ $\{b \mid b \ge 13.5\}$

36. $25f \ge 9$ $\{f \mid f \ge 0.36\}$

37. $-2.5w < 6.8$

38. $-0.8s > 6.4$ $\{s \mid s < -8\}$

39. $\dfrac{15c}{-7} > \dfrac{3}{14}$

40. $\dfrac{4m}{5} < \dfrac{-3}{15}$

41. Solve $-\dfrac{m}{9} \le -\dfrac{1}{3}$. Then graph the solution.
$\{m \mid m \ge 3\}$; See Ch. 6 Answer Appendix for graph.

42. Solve $\dfrac{x}{4} > \dfrac{3}{16}$. Then graph the solution.
$\left\{x \mid x > \dfrac{3}{4}\right\}$; See Ch. 6 Answer Appendix for graph.

43. If $2a \ge 7$, then complete each inequality.

   a. $a \ge \underline{\ ?\ }$ 3.5
   b. $-4a \le \underline{\ ?\ }$ −14
   c. $\underline{\ ?\ }\ a \le -21$ −6

Define a variable, write an inequality, and solve each problem. Check your solution. 44–45. See margin.

44. Twenty-five percent of a number is greater than or equal to 90.

45. Forty percent of a number is less than or equal to 45.

★ 46. **GEOMETRY** The area of the triangle is greater than 100 square centimeters. What is the height of the triangle? Estimate the height first, and then determine whether your solution is reasonable. greater than 12.5 cm

16 cm

For Exercises 47–50, define a variable, write an inequality, and solve each problem. Then interpret your solution. 47–50. See margin.

47. **LANDSCAPING** Morris is planning a circular flower garden with a low fence around the border. If he can use up to 38 feet of fence, what radius can he use for the garden? (*Hint:* $C = 2\pi r$)

48. **DRIVING** Average speed is calculated by dividing distance by time. If the speed limit on the interstate is 65 miles per hour, how far can a person travel legally in $1\frac{1}{2}$ hours?

★ 49. **ANALYZE TABLES** The annual membership to the San Diego Zoo for 2 adults and 2 children is $128. The regular admission to the zoo is shown in the table. How many times should such a family plan to visit the zoo in a year to make a membership less expensive than paying regular admission?

Regular Admission	
Visitor	**Price**
adult	$19.50
child	$11.75

50. **CITY PLANNING** A city parking lot can have no more than 20% of the parking spaces limited to compact cars. If a certain parking lot has 35 spaces for compact cars, how many spaces must the lot have to conform to the code?

Real-World Link
Dr. Harry Wegeforth founded the San Diego Zoo in 1916 with just 50 animals. Today, the zoo has over 4000 animals.
Source:
www.sandiegozoo.org

EXTRA PRACTICE
See pages 729, 749.

Math Online
Self-Check Quiz at
ca.algebra1.com

H.O.T. Problems

51. **REASONING** Explain why you can use either the Multiplication Property of Inequalities or the Division Property of Inequalities to solve $-7r \le 28$. See margin.

52. **OPEN ENDED** Describe a real-life situation that can be represented by the inequality $\dfrac{3}{4}a > 9$. Sample answer: The weight of three fourths of a bag of apples is greater than 9 pounds.

53. **CHALLENGE** Give a counterexample to show that each statement is not always true. See margin.
   a. If $a > b$, then $a^2 > b^2$.
   b. If $a < b$ and $c < d$, then $ac < bd$.

306 Chapter 6 Solving Linear Inequalities

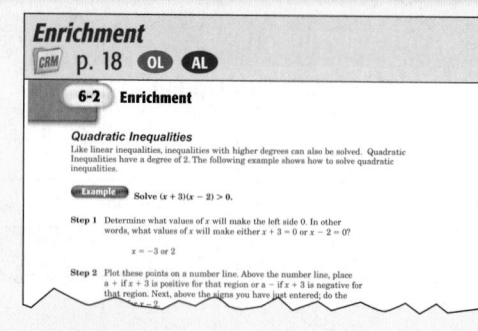

Enrichment
CRM p. 18 OL AL

6-2 Enrichment

Quadratic Inequalities

BL = Below Grade Level
OL = On Grade Level
AL = Above Grade Level
ELL = English Language Learner

Additional pages not shown:
CRM Lesson Reading Guide, p. 12 BL OL ELL
CRM Skills Practice, p. 15 BL OL

54. FIND THE ERROR Ilonia and Zachary are solving $-9b \leq 18$. Who is correct? Explain your reasoning. **Ilonia; when you divide each side of an inequality by a negative number, you must reverse the direction of the inequality symbol.**

Ilonia	Zachary
$-9b \leq 18$	$-9b \leq 18$
$\dfrac{-9b}{-9} \geq \dfrac{18}{-9}$	$\dfrac{-9b}{-9} \leq \dfrac{18}{-9}$
$b \geq -2$	$b \leq -2$

55. *Writing in Math* Use the information about the cases of beverages on page 301 to explain how inequalities can be used in storage. Include an inequality representing a stack of cases of water or sports drinks that can be no higher than 3 feet and an explanation of how to solve the inequality. **See margin.**

STANDARDS PRACTICE 5.0, 6PS3.3

56. Juan's long-distance phone company charges 9¢ for each minute. Which inequality can be used to find how long can he talk to his friend if he does not want to spend more than $2.50 on the call? **D**

A $0.09 \geq 2.50m$

B $0.09 \leq 2.50m$

C $0.09m \geq 2.50$

D $0.09m \leq 2.50$

57. REVIEW The table shows the results of a number cube being rolled. What is the experimental probability of rolling a 3? **J**

Outcome	Frequency
1	4
2	8
3	2
4	0
5	5
6	1

F $\dfrac{2}{3}$ G $\dfrac{1}{3}$ H 0.2   J 0.1

Spiral Review

58–60. See Ch. 6 Answer Appendix for graphs.

Solve each inequality. Check your solution, and graph it on a number line. (Lesson 6-1)

58. $s - 7 < 12$ {$s \mid s < 19$}

59. $g + 3 \leq -4$ {$g \mid g \leq -7$}

60. $7 > n + 2$ {$n \mid n < 5$}

★ **61. GYMS** To join a gym, Cristina paid an initial fee of $120, plus $10 per month. Jackson pays $20 per month without an initial fee. After how many months will they have paid the same amount? How much will it be? (Lesson 5-5) **12 months, $240**

Write an equation in standard form for a line that passes through each pair of points. (Lesson 4-4)

62. $(-1, 3), (2, 4)$ $x - 3y = -10$

63. $(5, -2), (-1, -2)$ $y = -2$

64. $(3, 3), (-1, 2)$ $x - 4y = -9$

GET READY for the Next Lesson

PREREQUISITE SKILL Solve each equation. (Lessons 2-4 and 2-5)

65. $5x - 3 = 32$ **7**

66. $14g + 5 = 54$ **3.5**

67. $6y - 1 = 4y + 23$ **12**

68. $2(p - 4) = 7(p + 3)$ **−5.8**

---

50. Sample answer: Let $s =$ the number of parking spaces, $35 \leq 0.2s$; {$s \mid s \geq 175$}, at least 175 spaces.

51. You could solve the inequality by multiplying each side by $-\dfrac{1}{7}$ or by dividing each side by -7. In either case, you must reverse the direction of the inequality symbol.

53a. Sample answer: $2 > -3$, but $4 < 9$.

53b. Sample answer: $-1 < 2$ and $-3 < -2$, but $3 > -4$.

55. Sample answer: Inequalities can be used to compare the heights of cases of beverages. If x represents the number of cases of water and the cases must be no higher than 3 ft or 36 in., then $8x \leq 36$. To solve this inequality, divide each side by 8 and do not change the direction of the inequality. The solution is $x \leq 4.5$. This means that the stack must be 4 cases high or fewer.

 Exercise Alert!
Find the Error Tell students to look first at the solutions from Ilonia and Zachary. The only difference is the inequality symbol. Since the solution involves division by a negative number, the inequality symbol of the solution must be reversed from the original inequality.

4 Assess

Ticket Out the Door Have students write a short statement about what they think is the most important thing to remember about solving inequalities by multiplication and division.

 Formative Assessment
Check for student understanding of concepts in Lessons 6-1 and 6-2.

CRM Quiz 1, p. 67

 FOLDABLES **Foldables™**
Study Organizer **Follow-Up**
Make sure students have filled in their Foldables with notes and examples of solving inequalities using addition, subtraction, multiplication, and division.

Additional Answers

44. Sample answer: Let $n =$ the number, $0.25n \geq 90$; {$n \mid n \geq 360$}.

45. Sample answer: Let $n =$ the number, $0.40n \leq 45$; {$n \mid n \leq 112.5$}.

47. Sample answer: Let $r =$ the radius of the flower garden, $2\pi r \leq 38$; {$r \mid r \leq 6.04$}, up to about 6 ft.

48. Sample answer: Let $d =$ the distance, $d \leq 65 \cdot 1\dfrac{1}{2}$; $\left\{d \mid d \leq 97\dfrac{1}{2}\right\}$, no more than $97\dfrac{1}{2}$ mi.

49. Sample answer: Let $v =$ the number of visits to the zoo, $128 < v(2 \cdot 19.50 + 2 \cdot 11.75)$; {$v \mid v > 2.05$}, at least 3 times.

 **6-3** # Solving Multi-Step Inequalities

1 Focus

 Standards Alignment

Before Lesson 6-3
Solve two-step linear equations and inequalities in one variable from ◗━ Standard 7AF4.1

Lesson 6-3
Students simplify expressions before solving multi-step problems involving linear equations from ◗━ Standards 4.0 and 5.0

After Lesson 6-3
Solve systems of linear equations and inequalities by substitution, with graphs, or with matrices from ◗━ Standard 2A2.0

2 Teach

Scaffolding Questions
Have students read *Get Ready for the Lesson.*

Ask:

• What would the inequality $F > 97.7$ represent? the body temperature of a camel in the morning (in degrees Fahrenheit) if it has no water

• What expression was substituted for F to represent the normal body temperature of a camel at noon in degrees Celsius? $\frac{9}{5}C + 32$

Lesson 6-3 Resources

Chapter 6 Resource Masters
Lesson Reading Guide, p. 19 **BL** **OL** **ELL**
Study Guide and Intervention, pp. 20–21 **BL** **OL** **ELL**
Skills Practice, p. 22 **BL** **OL**
Practice, p. 23 **OL** **AL**
Word Problem Practice, p. 24 **OL** **AL**
Enrichment, p. 25 **OL** **AL**

Transparencies
5-Minute Check Transparency 6-3

Additional Print Resources
Noteables™ Interactive Study Notebook with Foldables™

Technology
ca.algebra1.com
Interactive Classroom CD-ROM
AssignmentWorks CD-ROM
Graphing Calculator Easy Files

Main Ideas

• Solve linear inequalities involving more than one operation.

• Solve linear inequalities involving the Distributive Property.

 Standard 4.0 Students simplify expressions before solving linear equations and **inequalities in one variable, such as 3(2x − 5) + 4(x − 2) = 12.** (Key, CAHSEE) **Standard 5.0 Students solve multistep problems, including word problems, involving** linear equations and **linear inequalities in one variable and provide justification for each step.** (Key, CAHSEE)

▶ GET READY for the Lesson

The normal body temperature of a camel is 97.7°F in the morning. If it has had no water by noon, its body temperature can be greater than 104°F. If F represents temperature in degrees Fahrenheit, the inequality $F > 104$ represents the temperature of a camel at noon.

If C represents degrees Celsius, then $F = \frac{9}{5}C + 32$. You can solve $\frac{9}{5}C + 32 > 104$ to find the temperature in degrees Celsius of a camel at noon.

Solve Multi-Step Inequalities The inequality $\frac{9}{5}C + 32 > 104$ involves more than one operation. It can be solved by undoing the operations in the same way you would solve a multi-step equation.

 Real-World EXAMPLE Multi-Step Inequality

① SCIENCE Find the body temperature in degrees Celsius of a camel that has had no water by noon.

$$\frac{9}{5}C + 32 > 104 \qquad \text{Original inequality}$$

$$\frac{9}{5}C + 32 - 32 > 104 - 32 \qquad \text{Subtract 32 from each side.}$$

$$\frac{9}{5}C > 72 \qquad \text{Simplify.}$$

$$\left(\frac{5}{9}\right)\frac{9}{5}C > \left(\frac{5}{9}\right)(72) \qquad \text{Multiply each side by } \frac{5}{9}.$$

$$C > 40 \qquad \text{Simplify.}$$

The body temperature of a camel that has had no water by noon is greater than 40°C.

✓ CHECK Your Progress

1. **MONEY** ABC Cellphones advertises a plan with 400 minutes per month for less than the competition. The price includes the $3.50 local tax. If the competition charges $43.50, what does ABC Cellphones charge for each minute? less than 10¢

EXAMPLE Inequality Involving a Negative Coefficient

2 Solve $-7b + 19 < -16$.

$-7b + 19 < -16$	Original inequality
$-7b + 19 - 19 < -16 - 19$	Subtract 19 from each side.
$-7b < -35$	Simplify.
$\dfrac{-7b}{-7} > \dfrac{-35}{-7}$	Divide each side by -7 and change $<$ to $>$.
$b > 5$	The solution set is $\{b \mid b > 5\}$.

CONcepts in MOtion
BrainPOP®
ca.algebra1.com

✓ CHECK Your Progress Solve each inequality.

2A. $23 \geq 10 - 2w$ $\{w \mid w \geq -6.5\}$ **2B.** $43 > -4y + 11$ $\{y \mid y > -8\}$

EXAMPLE Write and Solve an Inequality

3 Define a variable, write an inequality, and solve the problem below. Then check your solution. *Three times a number minus eighteen is at least five times the number plus twenty-one.*

Three times a number	minus	eighteen	is at least	five times the number	plus	twenty-one.
$3n$	$-$	18	$\geq$	$5n$	$+$	21

$-2n - 18 \geq 21$	Subtract $5n$ from each side.
$-2n \geq 39$	Add 18 to each side.
$n \leq -19.5$	Divide each side by -2 and change $\geq$ to $\leq$.

The solution set is $\{n \mid n \leq -19.5\}$.   Check your solution.

✓ CHECK Your Progress

3. Write an inequality for the sentence below. Then solve the inequality. *Two more than half of a number is greater than twenty-seven.*

3. Sample answer: Let $n =$ the number, $\frac{1}{2}n + 2 > 27$; $\{n \mid n > 50\}$.

 Online Personal Tutor at ca.algebra1.com

Solve Inequalities Involving the Distributive Property When solving equations that contain grouping symbols, first use the Distributive Property to remove the grouping symbols.

EXAMPLE Distributive Property

4 Solve each inequality.

a. $-3(2 + 3b) \leq 2$

$-3(2 + 3b) \leq 2$	Original inequality
$-6 - 3b \leq 2$	Distributive Property
$-6 - 3b + 6 \leq 2 + 6$	Add 6 to each side.
$-3b \leq 8$	Simplify.
$\dfrac{-3b}{-3} \geq \dfrac{8}{-3}$	Divide each side by -3 and change $\leq$ to $\geq$.
$b \geq -\dfrac{8}{3}$	Simplify.

The solution set is $\left\{b \mid b \geq -\dfrac{8}{3}\right\}$.

Solve Multi-Step Inequalities

Example 1 shows how to solve a multi-step inequality. **Example 2** shows how to solve a multi-step inequality involving a negative coefficient. **Example 3** shows how to write and solve an inequality.

✓ Formative Assessment

Use the Check Your Progress exercises after each example to determine students' understanding of concepts.

ADDITIONAL EXAMPLES

1 **SCIENCE** The inequality $F > 212$ represents the temperature in degrees Fahrenheit for which water is a gas (steam). The inequality $\frac{9}{5}C + 32 > 212$ represents the temperature in degrees Celsius for which water is a gas. Find the temperatures in degrees Celsius for which water is a gas. Water is a gas for all temperatures greater than 100°C.

2 Solve $13 - 11d \geq 79$.
$\{d \mid d \leq -6\}$

3 Define a variable, write an inequality, and solve the problem. Check your solution. *Four times a number plus twelve is less than a number minus three.* Let $n =$ the number; $4n + 12 < n - 3$; $\{n \mid n < -5\}$.

Additional Examples are also in:

• Noteables™ Interactive Study Notebook with Foldables™

• Interactive Classroom PowerPoint® Presentations

Solving Inequalities Involving the Distributive Property

Example 4 shows how to use the Distributive Property to solve a multi-step inequality. **Example 5** shows how to solve an inequality that results in a statement that is never true.

ADDITIONAL EXAMPLES

4 Solve each inequality.
a. $3(-2x + 4) > -12$
   $\{x \mid x < 4\}$
b. $6c + 3(2 - c) \geq -2c + 1$
   $\{c \mid c \geq -1\}$

5 Solve each inequality.
a. $-7(s + 4) + 11s \geq 8s - 2(2s + 1).$ $\varnothing$
b. $4d - 3 > 2d + 3(d + 3) - (d + 12)$
   $\{d \mid d$ is a real number.$\}$

Student Misconceptions

Tips for New Teachers

Students may incorrectly assume that the solution of all inequalities in which the variable has been eliminated is the empty set. Remind students that they must simplify the inequality to determine whether it is a true statement. If the inequality is true, the solution set is the set of all real numbers. Only when the inequality is untrue is the solution the empty set.

b. $3d - 2(8d - 9) > -2d - 4$

$3d - 2(8d - 9) > -2d - 4$	Original inequality
$3d - 16d + 18 > -2d - 4$	Distributive Property
$-13d + 18 > -2d - 4$	Combine like terms.
$-13d + 18 + 13d > -2d - 4 + 13d$	Add $13d$ to each side.
$18 > 11d - 4$	Simplify.
$18 + 4 > 11d - 4 + 4$	Add 4 to each side.
$22 > 11d$	Simplify.
$\dfrac{22}{11} > \dfrac{11d}{11}$	Divide each side by 11.
$2 > d$	The solution set is $\{d \mid d < 2\}$.

✓**CHECK Your Progress** Solve each inequality.

4A. $6(5z - 3) \leq 36z$ $\{z \mid z \geq -3\}$ **4B.** $2(h + 6) > -3(8 - h)$ $\{h \mid h < 36\}$

If solving an inequality results in a statement that is always true, the solution set is the set of all real numbers. This is written as $\{x \mid x$ is a real number$\}$. If solving an inequality results in a statement that is never true, the solution set is the empty set, written as the symbol $\varnothing$. The empty set has no members.

EXAMPLE Empty Set and All Reals

5 Solve each inequality.

a. $8(t + 2) - 3(t - 4) < 5(t - 7) + 8$

$8(t + 2) - 3(t - 4) < 5(t - 7) + 8$	Original inequality
$8t + 16 - 3t + 12 < 5t - 35 + 8$	Distributive Property
$5t + 28 < 5t - 27$	Combine like terms.
$5t + 28 - 5t < 5t - 27 - 5t$	Subtract $5t$ from each side.
$28 < -27$	Simplify.

Since the inequality results in a false statement, the solution is the empty set $\varnothing$.

b. $3(p + 4) - p + 12 \leq 2(p + 12)$

$3(p + 4) - p + 12 \leq 2(p + 12)$	Original inequality
$3p + 12 - p + 12 \leq 2p + 24$	Distributive Property
$2p + 24 \leq 2p + 24$	Combine like terms.
$2p + 24 - 24 \leq 2p + 24 - 24$	Subtract 24 from each side.
$2p \leq 2p$	Simplify.
$\dfrac{2p}{2} \leq \dfrac{2p}{2}$	Divide each side by 2.
$p \leq p$	Simplify.

Since the inequality is always true, the solution set is $\{p \mid p$ is a real number$\}$.

✓**CHECK Your Progress** Solve each inequality.

5A. $18 - 3(8c + 4) \geq -6(4c - 1)$ **5B.** $46 \leq 8m - 4(2m + 5)$ $\varnothing$
$\{c \mid c$ is a real number$\}$.

Pre-AP Activity   Use before the Exercises

Ask students to explain how you can use the graph of $y = -2x + 6$ to solve the inequality $-2x + 6 < 0$. Sample explanation: The x-intercept ($x = 3$) is the value of x where $-2x + 6 = 0$. All values of x that are less than the x-intercept are solutions of $-2x + 6 < 0$. So, $x < 3$.

★ indicates multi-step problem

Examples 1, 2
(pp. 308–309)

Solve each inequality. Check your solution.

1. $6h - 10 \geq 32$ $\{h | h \geq 7\}$
2. $-3 \leq \frac{2}{3}r + 9$ $\{r | r \geq -18\}$
3. $-4y - 23 < 19$ $\{y | y > -10.5\}$
4. $7b + 11 > 9b - 13$ $\{b | b < 12\}$

5. **CANOEING** A certain canoe was advertised as having an "800 pound capacity," meaning that it can hold at most 800 pounds. If four people plan to use the canoe and take 60 pounds of supplies, write and solve an inequality to find the average weight per person.
$4n + 60 \leq 800$; $n \leq 185$; less than 185 lb

Example 3
(p. 309)

6. Define a variable, write an inequality, and solve the problem below. Then check your solution.
Seven minus two times a number is less than three times the number plus thirty-two.
Sample answer: Let $n =$ the number, $7 - 2n < 3n + 32$; $\{n | n > -5\}$.

Examples 4, 5
(p. 310)

Solve each inequality. Check your solution.

7. $-6 \leq 3(5v - 2)$
$\{v | v \geq 0\}$
8. $-5(g + 4) > 3(g - 4)$
$\{g | g < -1\}$
9. $3 - 8x \geq 9 + 2(1 - 4x)$
$\varnothing$

Exercises

HOMEWORK HELP	
For Exercises	**See Examples**
10–19	1, 2
20–25	3
26–33	4, 5

Exercise Levels
A: 10–33
B: 34–47
C: 48–52

Solve each inequality. Check your solution.

10. $5b - 1 \geq -11$ $\{b | b \geq -2\}$
11. $21 > 15 + 2a$ $\{a | a < 3\}$
12. $-9 \geq \frac{2}{5}m + 7$ $\{m | m \leq -40\}$
13. $\frac{w}{8} - 13 > -6$ $\{w | w > 56\}$
14. $-3t + 6 \leq -3$ $\{t | t \geq 3\}$
15. $59 > -5 - 8f$ $\{f | f > -8\}$
16. $-2 - \frac{d}{5} < 23$ $\{d | d > -125\}$
17. $-\frac{3}{2}a + 4 > 10$ $\{a | a < -4\}$
18. $9r + 15 \leq 24 + 10r$ $\{r | r \geq -9\}$
19. $13k - 11 > 7k + 37$ $\{k | k > 8\}$

Define a variable, write an inequality, and solve each problem. Then check your solution. 20–23. See margin.

20. One eighth of a number decreased by five is at least thirty.
21. Two thirds of a number plus eight is greater than twelve.
22. Negative four times a number plus nine is no more than the number minus twenty-one.
23. Ten is no more than 4 times the sum of twice a number and three.

For Exercises 24 and 25, define a variable, write an inequality, and solve each problem. Then interpret your solution. 24–25. See margin.

24. **SALES** A salesperson is paid $22,000 a year plus 5% of the amount of sales made. What is the amount of sales needed to have an annual income greater than $35,000?

25. **ANIMALS** Keith's dog weighs 90 pounds. The veterinarian told him that a healthy weight for his dog would be less than 75 pounds. If Keith's dog can lose an average of 1.25 pounds per week on a certain diet, how long will it take the dog to reach a healthy weight?

Solve each inequality. Check your solution. 29. $\{b | b$ is a real number.$\}$

26. $5(2h - 6) > 4h$ $\{h | h > 5\}$
27. $21 \geq 3(a - 7) + 9$ $\{a | a \leq 11\}$
28. $2y + 4 > 2(3 + y)$ $\varnothing$
29. $3(2 - b) < 10 - 3(b - 6)$
30. $7 + t \leq 2(t + 3) + 2$ $\{t | t \geq -1\}$
31. $8a + 2(1 - 5a) \leq 20$ $\{a | a \geq -9\}$

Lesson 6-3 Solving Multi-Step Inequalities **311**

✓ **Formative Assessment**

Use Exercises 1–9 to check for understanding.

Use the chart at the bottom of this page to customize assignments for your students.

Odd/Even Assignments

Exercises 10–33 are structured so that students practice the same concepts whether they are assigned odd or even problems.

Additional Answers

20. Sample answer: Let $n =$ the number, $\frac{1}{8}n - 5 \geq 30$; $\{n | n \geq 280\}$.

21. Sample answer: Let $n =$ the number, $\frac{2}{3}n + 8 > 12$; $\{n | n > 6\}$.

22. Sample answer: Let $n =$ the number, $-4n + 9 \leq n - 21$; $\{n | n \geq 6\}$.

23. Sample answer: Let $n =$ the number, $10 \leq 4(2n + 3)$; $\left\{n | n \geq -\frac{1}{4}\right\}$.

24. Sample answer: Let $s =$ the amount of sales made, $22,000 + 0.05s > 35,000$; $\{x | x > 260,000\}$, the amount of sales must be more than $260,000.

25. Sample answer: Let $w =$ the number of weeks, $1.25w > 90 - 75$; $\{w | w > 12\}$, it will take more than 12 weeks for the dog to reach a healthy weight.

DIFFERENTIATED HOMEWORK OPTIONS

Level	Assignment	Two-Day Option	
BL Basic	10–33, 48, 50–67	11–33 odd, 53, 54	10–32 even, 48, 50–52, 55–67
OL Core	11–33 odd, 34–39, 41, 43–47 odd, 48, 50–67	10–33, 53, 54	34–48, 50–52, 55–67
AL Advanced /Pre-AP	35–63 (optional: 64–67)		

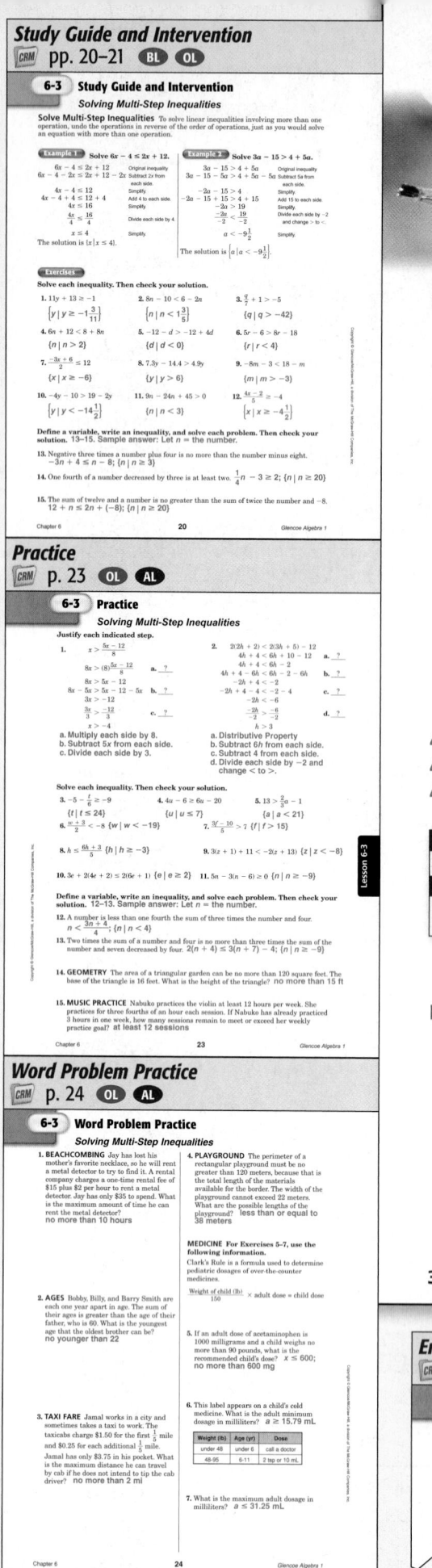

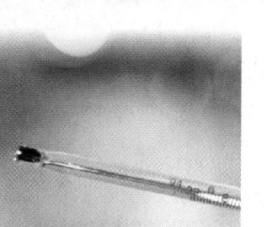

Real-World Link

Mercury is a metal that is a liquid at room temperature. In fact, its melting point is −38°C. Mercury is used in thermometers because it expands evenly as it is heated.

Source: *World Book Encyclopedia*

32. Solve $4(t - 7) \leq 2(t + 9)$. Show each step and justify your work. See Ch. 6 Answer Appendix.

33. Solve $-5(k + 4) > 3(k - 4)$. Show each step and justify your work. See Ch. 6 Answer Appendix.

SCHOOL For Exercises 34–36, use the following information.

Carmen's scores on three math tests are shown in the table. The fourth and final test of the grading period is tomorrow. She needs an average (mean) of at least 92 to receive an A for the grading period.

Test	Score
1	91
2	95
3	88

34. $\dfrac{91 + 95 + 88 + s}{4} \geq 92$

34. If s is her score on the fourth test, write an inequality to represent the situation.

35. If Carmen wants an A in math, what must she score on the test? **at least 94**

36. Is 150 a solution to the inequality that you wrote in Exercise 35? Is this a reasonable solution to the problem? Explain your reasoning. **See margin.**

37. ★ **MONEY** Nicholas has $13 to order a pizza. The pizza costs $7.50 plus $1.25 per topping. He plans to tip 15% of the total cost of the pizza. Write and solve an inequality to find how many toppings he can order. **See margin.**

38. **PHYSICAL SCIENCE** The melting point for an element is the temperature where the element changes from a solid to a liquid. If C represents degrees Celsius and F represents degrees Fahrenheit, then $C = \dfrac{5(F - 32)}{9}$. Refer to the information at the left to write and solve an inequality that can be used to find the temperatures in degrees Fahrenheit for which mercury is a solid. **See Ch. 6 Answer Appendix.**

Solve for x in each case.

39. $3x - 6 > 2 + 4(x - 2)$ $x < 0$

40. $2(x - 4) \leq 2 + 3(x - 6)$ $x \geq 8$

41. $3x - 6 = 3(2 + 2(3 + x) + 4) - 1$ $-\dfrac{41}{3}$

42. $\dfrac{3}{3x - 6} = \dfrac{4}{2x + 4}$ **6**

43. **NUMBER THEORY** Find all sets of two consecutive positive odd integers with a sum no greater than 18. 7, 9; 5, 7; 3, 5; 1, 3

Solve each inequality. Check your solution.

44. $\dfrac{5b + 8}{3} < 3b$

45. $3.1v - 1.4 \geq 1.3v + 6.7$

46. $0.3(d - 2) - 0.8d > 4.4$

47. Define a variable, write an inequality, and solve the problem below. Then check your solution.
Three times the sum of a number and seven is greater than five times the number less thirteen. $3(n + 7) > 5n - 13; \{n \mid n < 17\}$

EXTRA PRACTICE
See pages 729, 749.

Math Online
Self-Check Quiz at ca.algebra1.com

H.O.T. Problems

48. **REASONING** Explain how you could solve $-3p + 7 \geq 2$ without multiplying or dividing each side by a negative number. **See margin.**

49. **CHALLENGE** Create a multi-step inequality that has no solution and one that has infinitely many solutions. Investigate the best method for solving each one. **Sample answers:** $2x + 5 < 2x + 3$; $2x + 5 > 2x + 3$

50. **OPEN ENDED** Create a multi-step inequality with the solution graphed below. Explain how you know. **See margin.**

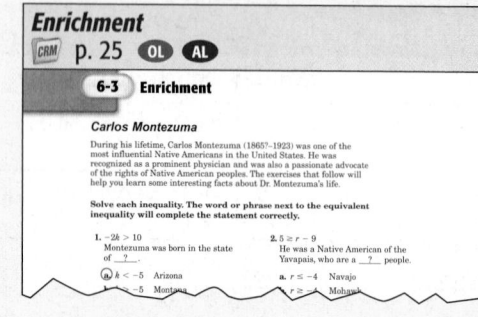

BL = *Below Grade Level*
OL = *On Grade Level*
AL = *Above Grade Level*
ELL = *English Language Learner*

Additional pages not shown:
CRM **Lesson Reading Guide,** p. 19 BL OL ELL
CRM **Skills Practice,** p. 22 BL OL

51. Which One Doesn't Belong? Identify the inequality that does not belong with the other three. Explain. **See margin.**

| $4y + 9 > -3$ | $3y - 4 > 5$ | $2y + 1 > 7$ | $-5y + 2 < -13$ |

52. *Writing in Math* Use the information about camels on page 308 to explain how linear inequalities can be used in science. **Sample answer: Inequalities can be used to describe the different body temperatures of animals.**

 **STANDARDS PRACTICE**   5.0, 7MG2.3

53. What is the solution set of the inequality $4t + 2 < 8t - (6t - 10)$? **C**

A $t < -6.5$

B $t > -6.5$

C $t < 4$

D $t > 4$

54. REVIEW What is the volume of the triangular prism? **H**

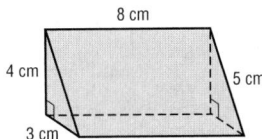

F 120 cm³

G 96 cm³

H 48 cm³

J 30 cm³

Spiral Review

55. BUSINESS The charge per mile for a compact rental car is $0.12. Mrs. Ludlow must rent a car for a business trip. She has a budget of $50 for mileage charges. How many miles can she travel without going over her budget? (Lesson 6-2) **up to 416 mi**

Solve each inequality. Check your solution, and then graph it on a number line. (Lesson 6-1) **56–58. See margin.**

56. $d + 13 \geq 22$ **57.** $t - 5 < 3$ **58.** $4 > y + 7$

Write the standard form of an equation of the line that passes through the given point and has the given slope. (Lesson 4-5)

59. $(1, -3), m = 2$ $2x - y = 5$ **60.** $(-2, -1), m = -\frac{2}{3}$ $2x + 3y = -7$ **61.** $(3, 6), m = 0$ $y - 6 = 0$

CABLE TV For Exercises 62 and 63, use the graph at the right. (Lesson 4-1) **62–63. See margin.**

62. Find the rate of change for 2001–2003. Explain the meaning of the rate of change.

63. Without calculating, find a 2-year period that had a greater rate of change than 2001–2003. Explain.

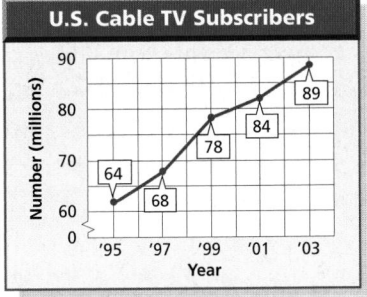

U.S. Cable TV Subscribers

GET READY for the Next Lesson

PREREQUISITE SKILL Graph each set of numbers on a number line. (Lesson 1-8)
64–67. See margin.

64. $\{-1, 0, 3, 4\}$

65. $\{-5, -4, -1, 1\}$

66. {integers less than 5}

67. {integers between 1 and 6}

---

58. $\{y \mid y < -3\}$

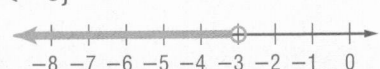

62. $\frac{5}{2}$ or 2.5; an increase of 2.5 million subscribers per year

63. Sample answer: '97–'99; A steeper segment means greater rate of change.

64.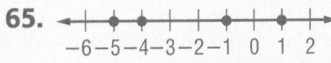

65.

66.

67.

Real-World Connections
For Exercises 37 and 38, point out that there are other real-world situations in both the areas of personal finance and physical science. Have students talk about how linear inequalities could be connected to these areas. Examples could be banking with interest-bearing accounts or chemistry.

4 Assess

Yesterday's News Have students write an explanation of how the different methods they learned for solving multi-step linear inequalities relate to the methods learned in previous lessons, such as solving multi-step linear equations and using the Distributive Property.

Additional Answers

36. Yes; it is not a reasonable solution to the problem because 100 is the highest score that Carmen can receive on a test.

37. Sample answer: $7.5 + 1.25x + 0.15(7.5 + 1.25x) < 13$; 3 or fewer toppings

48. Add $3p$ and subtract 2 from each side. The inequality becomes $5 \geq 3p$. Then divide each side by 3 to get $\frac{5}{3} \geq p$.

50. Sample answer: $2x + 4 > 2$; If 4 is subtracted from each side of the inequality, the result is $2x > -2$. Dividing each side by 2 gives $x > -1$, which is the solution that is graphed.

51. $4y + 9 > -3$; it is the only inequality that does not have a solution set of $\{y \mid y > 3\}$

56. $\{d \mid d \geq 9\}$

57. $\{t \mid t < 8\}$

READING MATH

READING MATH

Standard 1.1 Students use properties of numbers to demonstrate whether assertions are true or false.

1 Focus

On the board, write the word *rowboat*.

Ask:

Who can tell me what a compound word is?

Students should note that a compound word is a word made up of two or more words (row + boat).

2 Teach

Sentence Structure Ask students to recall the definition of a compound sentence from their language arts studies. Students should know that a compound sentence is a sentence made up of two independent clauses joined by a coordinating conjunction, punctuation mark, or both.

Explain that the compound statements in this activity are made up of two independent clauses joined by *and* or *or*. Be sure students understand that *or* is inclusive in mathematics. Emphasize that a compound statement using *or* is true if one or the other or both independent clauses of the statement are true. It is false only if both independent clauses are false.

ELL English Language Learners may benefit from working in small groups. Have one member of the group give the statement in a native language. Have the other members of the group discuss the statement and then give the answer in English.

3 Assess

Ask students to summarize what they have learned about compound statements. Be sure that they note that *or* is inclusive.

Compound Statements

Two simple statements connected by the words *and* or *or* form a compound statement. Before you can determine whether a compound statement is true or false, you must understand what the words *and* and *or* mean. Consider the statement below.

A triangle has three sides, and a hexagon has five sides.

For a compound statement connected by the word *and* to be true, both simple statements must be true. In this case, it is true that a triangle has three sides. However, it is false that a hexagon has five sides; it has six. Thus, the compound statement is false.

A compound statement connected by the word *or* may be *exclusive* or *inclusive*. For example, the statement "With your dinner, you may have soup *or* salad," is exclusive. In everyday language, *or* means one or the other, but not both. However, in mathematics, *or* is inclusive. It means one or the other or both. Consider the statement below.

A triangle has three sides, or a hexagon has five sides.

For a compound statement connected by the word *or* to be true, at least one of the simple statements must be true. Since it is true that a triangle has three sides, the compound statement is true.

Triangle

Square

Pentagon

Hexagon

Octagon

Reading to Learn

Determine whether each compound statement is *true* or *false*. Explain your answer.

1. A hexagon has six sides, *or* an octagon has seven sides. true; true or false
2. An octagon has eight sides, *and* a pentagon has six sides. false; true and false
3. A pentagon has five sides, *and* a hexagon has six sides. true; true and true
4. A triangle has four sides, *or* an octagon does *not* have seven sides. true; false or true
5. A pentagon has three sides, *or* an octagon has ten sides. false; false or false
6. A square has four sides, *or* a hexagon has six sides. true; true or true
7. $5 < 4$ or $8 < 6$ false; false or false
8. $-1 > 0$ and $1 < 5$ false; false and true
9. $4 > 0$ and $-4 < 0$ true; true and true
10. $0 = 0$ or $-2 > -3$ true; true or true
11. $5 \neq 5$ or $-1 > -4$ true; false or true
12. $0 > 3$ and $2 > -2$ false; false and true

314 Chapter 6 Solving Linear Inequalities

Main Ideas

- Solve compound inequalities containing the word *and* and graph their solution sets.

- Solve compound inequalities containing the word *or* and graph their solution sets.

 Standard 4.0 Students simplify expressions before solving linear equations and inequalities in one variable, such as $3(2x - 5) + 4(x - 2) = 12$. (Key, CAHSEE)

Standard 5.0 Students solve multistep problems, including word problems, involving linear equations and linear inequalities in one variable and provide justification for each step. (Key, CAHSEE)

New Vocabulary

compound inequality
intersection
union

Reading Math

Compound Inequalities
The statement $-2 \leq x < 3$ can be read *negative 2 is less than or equal to x, which is less than 3.*

> ▶ **GET READY** for the Lesson

The V2: Vertical Velocity Roller Coaster at Six Flags Marine World in San Francisco is a suspended spiraling impulse coaster. To ride this coaster, you must be at least 54 inches tall and no more than 75 inches.

Let h represent the height of a rider. You can write two inequalities to represent the height restrictions.

at least 54 inches	no more than 75 inches
$h \geq 54$	$h \leq 75$

The inequalities $h \geq 54$ and $h \leq 75$ can be combined and written without using *and*.

$$54 \leq h \leq 75$$

Inequalities Containing *and* When considered together, two inequalities such as $w \geq 40$ and $w \leq 250$ form a **compound inequality**. A compound inequality containing *and* is true only if both inequalities are true. Its graph is the **intersection** of the graphs of the two inequalities. In other words, the solution must be a solution of *both* inequalities.

The intersection can be found by graphing each inequality and then determining where the graphs overlap.

> **EXAMPLE** Graph an Intersection

1 Graph the solution set of $x < 3$ and $x \geq -2$.

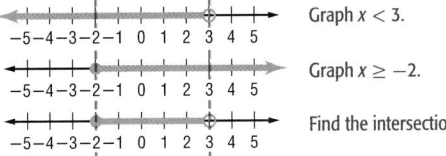

The solution set is $\{x | -2 \leq x < 3\}$. Note that the graph of $x \geq -2$ includes the point -2. The graph of $x < 3$ does *not* include 3.

✓ **CHECK Your Progress** 1A–1B. See Ch. 6 Answer Appendix.

Graph the solution set of each compound inequality.
1A. $a > -5$ and $a < 0$ **1B.** $p \leq 6$ and $p > 2$

Standards Alignment

Before Lesson 6-4
Solve two-step linear equations and inequalities in one variable from Standard 7AF4.1

Lesson 6-4
Students simplify expressions before solving multi-step problems involving linear equations from Standards 4.0 and 5.0

After Lesson 6-4
Solve systems of linear equations and inequalities by substitution and with graphs from Standard 9.0

2 Teach

Scaffolding Questions
Have students read *Get Ready for the Lesson*.
Ask:
- What inequality symbol represents the term *at least* when we say that a rider must be at least 54 inches? $\geq$
- What is the minimum height a rider could be? 54 in.
- What is the maximum height a rider could be? 75 in.
- Could a rider who is 60 inches tall ride? Explain. Yes, because that rider would be more than 54 in. but less than 75 in.

Lesson 6-4 Resources

Chapter 6 Resource Masters
Lesson Reading Guide, p. 26 BL OL ELL
Study Guide and Intervention, pp. 27–28
BL OL ELL
Skills Practice, p. 29 OL AL
Practice, p. 30 OL AL
Word Problem Practice, p. 31 OL AL
Enrichment, p. 32 OL AL
Quiz 2, p. 67

Transparencies
5-Minute Check Transparency 6-4
Additional Print Resources
Noteables™ Interactive Study Notebook with Foldables™

Technology
ca.algebra1.com
Interactive Classroom CD-ROM
AssignmentWorks CD-ROM
Graphing Calculator Easy Files

Inequalities Containing *and*

Example 1 shows how to graph the intersection of a compound inequality containing *and*. **Example 2** shows how to solve a compound inequality containing *and* and then graph the solution set.

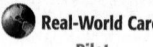
Inequalities Containing *or*

Example 3 shows how to write and graph a compound inequality containing *or* for a real-world situation. **Example 4** shows how to solve and graph the union of two inequalities.

Reading Math

Keywords

When solving problems involving inequalities,

- **within** is meant to be inclusive. Use $\le$ or $\ge$.
- **between** is meant to be exclusive. Use $<$ or $>$.

 EXAMPLE   Solve and Graph an Intersection

2 Solve $-5 < x - 4 < 2$. Then graph the solution set.

First express $-5 < x - 4 < 2$ using *and*. Then solve each inequality.

$-5 < x - 4$	and	$x - 4 < 2$	Write the inequalities.
$-5 + 4 < x - 4 + 4$		$x - 4 + 4 < 2 + 4$	Add 4 to each side.
$-1 < x$		$x < 6$	Simplify.

The solution set is $\{x \mid -1 < x < 6\}$. Now graph the solution set.

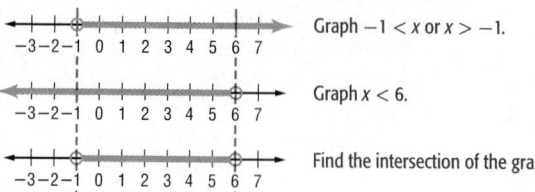

Graph $-1 < x$ or $x > -1$.

Graph $x < 6$.

Find the intersection of the graphs.

 **CHECK Your Progress**   2A–2B. See Ch. 6 Answer Appendix.

Solve each compound inequality. Then graph the solution set.

2A. $y - 3 \ge -11$ and $y - 3 \le -8$ **2B.** $6 \le r + 7 < 10$

Personal Tutor at ca.algebra1.com

Inequalities Containing *or* Another type of compound inequality contains the word *or*. A compound inequality containing *or* is true if one or more of the inequalities is true. Its graph is the **union** of the graphs of the two inequalities. In other words, its solution is a solution of *either* inequality, not necessarily both. The union can be found by graphing each inequality.

Real-World Career

Pilot
A pilot uses math to calculate the altitude that will provide the smoothest flight.

Math Online
For more information, go to ca.algebra1.com.

Real-World EXAMPLE   Write and Graph a Compound Inequality

3 **AVIATION** A pilot flying at 30,000 feet is told by the control tower that he should increase his altitude to at least 33,000 feet or decrease his altitude to no more than 26,000 feet to avoid turbulence. Write and graph a compound inequality that describes the optimum altitude.

Words	The plane's altitude	is at least	33,000 feet	or	the altitude	is no more than	26,000 feet.
Variable	Let a be the plane's altitude.						
Inequality	a	$\ge$	33,000	or	a	$\le$	26,000

Now, graph the solution set.

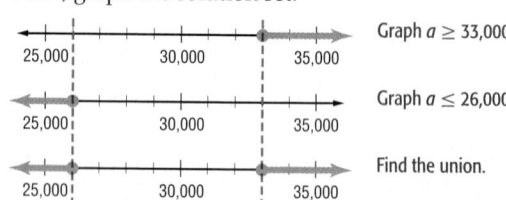

Graph $a \ge 33,000$.

Graph $a \le 26,000$.

Find the union.

The compound inequality $a \ge 33,000$ or $a \le 26,000$ is graphed above.

Intervention

Intersection and Union Symbols

Point out that the symbol for intersection is $\cap$. The solution set for Example 1 could be written as $\{x \mid x < 3\} \cap \{x \mid x \ge -2\}$. The symbol for union is $\cup$. The solution set for Example 4 could be written as $\{h \mid h > -5\} \cup \{h \mid h > 3\}$.

Focus on Mathematical Content

Conjunctions When the word *and* is used to join two inequalities to form a compound inequality, the resulting sentence is called a *conjunction*. To solve a conjunction, find the values of the variable for which *both* sentences are true.

3. **SHOPPING** A store is offering a $30 mail-in rebate on all color printers. Luisana is looking at different color printers that range in price from $175 to $260. How much can she expect to spend after the mail-in rebate? **$145 to $230**

 Personal Tutor at ca.algebra1.com

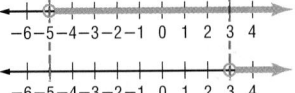 **EXAMPLE** Solve and Graph a Union

④ Solve $-3h + 4 < 19$ or $7h - 3 > 18$. Then graph the solution set.

$-3h + 4 < 19$	or $\qquad 7h - 3 > 18$	Write the inequalities.
$-3h + 4 - 4 < 19 - 4$	$7h - 3 + 3 > 18 + 3$	Add or subtract.
$-3h < 15$	$7h > 21$	Simplify.
$\dfrac{-3h}{-3} > \dfrac{15}{-3}$	$\dfrac{7h}{7} > \dfrac{21}{7}$	Divide.
$h > -5$	$h > 3$	Simplify.

Graph $h > -5$.

Graph $h > 3$.

Find the union.

Notice that the graph of $h > -5$ contains every point in the graph of $h > 3$. So, the union is the graph of $h > -5$. The solution set is $\{h \mid h > -5\}$.

 CHECK Your Progress 4A–4B. See Ch. 6 Answer Appendix.

Solve each compound inequality. Then graph the solution set.

4A. $a + 1 < 4$ or $a - 1 \geq 3$ **4B.** $x \leq 9$ or $2 + 4x < 10$

COncepts in MOtion
Animation
ca.algebra1.com

★ indicates multi-step problem

 **CHECK Your Understanding**

Example 1 (p. 315)

Graph the solution set of each compound inequality. 1–2. See margin.

1. $a \leq 6$ and $a \geq -2$ **2.** $y < 12$ and $y > 9$

3–6. See Ch. 6 Answer Appendix.

Examples 2, 4 (pp. 316–317)

Solve each compound inequality. Then graph the solution set.

3. $6 < w + 3$ and $w + 3 < 11$ **4.** $n - 7 \leq -5$ or $n - 7 \geq 1$

5. $3z + 1 < 13$ or $z \leq 1$ **6.** $-8 < x - 4 \leq -3$

Example 3 (pp. 316–317)

★ **7. BIKES** The recommended air pressure for the tires of a mountain bike is at least 35 pounds per square inch (psi), but no more than 80 pounds per square inch. If a bike's tires have 24 pounds per square inch, what increase in air pressure is needed so the tires are in the recommended range? **11 psi $\leq x \leq$ 56 psi**

Math Online Extra Examples at ca.algebra1.com   **Lesson 6-4** Solving Compound Inequalities   **317**

Additional Answers

1.

2.

 Reading

Tips for New Teachers   Students may confuse the meaning of the words *intersection* and *union*. Have them compare the definitions of these two words in real-world situations. For intersection, students may suggest two roads overlapping at an intersection. For union, they might suggest the 50 states coming together to form a union.

③ Practice

Formative Assessment

Use Exercises 1–7 to check for understanding.

Use the chart at the bottom of the next page to customize assignments for your students.

Odd/Even Assignments

Exercises 8–25 are structured so that students practice the same concepts whether they are assigned odd or even problems.

Lesson 6-4 Solving Compound Inequalities   **317**

Additional Answers

8.
0 1 2 3 4 5 6 7 8 9

9.
−10−9−8−7−6−5−4−3−2−1 0

10.
0 1 2 3 4 5 6 7 8 9 10

11.
−7−6−5−4−3−2−1 0 1 2 3

12.
2 3 4 5 6 7 8 9 10 11 12

13.
−5−4−3−2−1 0 1 2 3 4 5

14. $\{k \mid 10 < k \le 16\}$
8 9 10 11 12 13 14 15 16 17 18

15. $\{f \mid −13 \le f \le −5\}$
−14−13−12−11−10−9−8−7−6−5−4

16. $\{d \mid d \le 5 \text{ or } d > 7\}$
0 1 2 3 4 5 6 7 8 9 10

17. $\{h \mid h < −1\}$
−5−4−3−2−1 0 1 2 3 4 5

18. $\{x \mid 3 < x < 9\}$
-2 -1 0 1 2 3 4 5 6 7 8

19. $\{y \mid 3 < y < 6\}$
0 1 2 3 4 5 6 7 8 9 10

20. ∅
−5−4−3−2−1 0 1 2 3 4 5

21. $\{q \mid −1 < q < 6\}$
−3−2−1 0 1 2 3 4 5 6 7

22. $\{x \mid x \text{ is a real number.}\}$
−5−4−3−2−1 0 1 2 3 4 5

23. $\{n \mid n \le 4\}$
0 1 2 3 4 5 6 7 8 9 10

Exercises

HOMEWORK HELP	
For Exercises	See Examples
8–13	1
14–23	2, 4
24–25	3

Exercise Levels
A: 8–25
B: 26–46
C: 47–50

Graph the solution set of each compound inequality. 8–13. See margin.

8. $x > 5$ and $x \le 9$ **9.** $s < −7$ and $s \le 0$

10. $r < 6$ or $r > 6$ **11.** $m \ge −4$ or $m > 6$

12. $7 < d < 11$ **13.** $−1 \le g < 3$

14–23.
Solve each compound inequality. Then graph the solution set. See margin.

14. $k + 2 > 12$ and $k + 2 \le 18$ **15.** $f + 8 \le 3$ and $f + 9 \ge −4$

16. $d − 4 > 3$ or $d − 4 \le 1$ **17.** $h − 10 < −21$ or $h + 3 < 2$

18. $3 < 2x − 3 < 15$ **19.** $4 < 2y − 2 < 10$

20. $3t − 7 \ge 5$ and $2t + 6 \le 12$ **21.** $8 > 5 − 3q$ and $5 − 3q > −13$

22. $−1 + x \le 3$ or $−x \le −4$ **23.** $3n + 11 \le 13$ or $−3n \ge −12$

24. ANALYZE TABLES The Fujita Scale (F-scale) is the official classification system for tornado damage. One factor used to classify a tornado is wind speed. Use the information in the table to write an inequality for the range of wind speeds of an F3 tornado. $158 \le w \le 206$

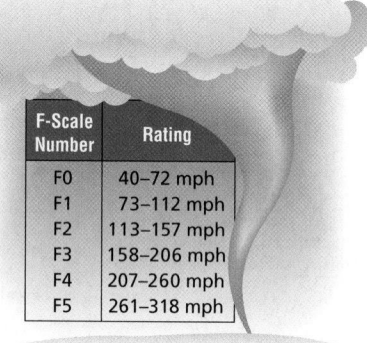

F-Scale Number	Rating
F0	40–72 mph
F1	73–112 mph
F2	113–157 mph
F3	158–206 mph
F4	207–260 mph
F5	261–318 mph

Real-World Link

The average life span of a shark is 25 years, but some sharks can live to be 100.

Source: about.com

25. BIOLOGY Each type of fish thrives in a specific range of temperatures. The optimum temperatures for sharks range from 18°C to 22°C, inclusive. Write an inequality to represent temperatures where sharks will *not* thrive. (*Hint:* The word *inclusive* means that 18°C and 22°C are included in the optimum temperature range.) $t < 18$ or $t > 22$

Write a compound inequality for each graph.

26.
−5−4−3−2−1 0 1 2 3 4 5
$−2 \le x \le 2$

27.
−10−9−8−7−6−5−4−3−2−1 0
$−7 < x < −3$

28.
9 10 11 12 13 14 15 16 17 18 19
$x \le 12$ or $x > 15$

29.
−10−9−8−7−6−5−4−3−2−1 0
$x \le −7$ or $x \ge −6$

30.
−9−8−7−6−5−4−3−2−1 0 1
$x = 0$ or $x \le −4$

31.
−1 0 1 2 3 4 5 6 7 8 9
$x = 2$ or $x > 5$

32–35. See Ch. 6 Answer Appendix.
Solve each compound inequality. Then graph the solution set.

32. $2p − 2 \le 4p − 8 \le 3p − 3$ **33.** $3g + 12 \le 6 − g \le 3g − 18$

34. $4c < 2c − 10$ or $−3c < −12$ **35.** $0.5b > −6$ or $3b + 16 < −8 + b$

★ **36. HEALTH** About 20% of the time you sleep is spent in rapid eye movement (REM) sleep, which is associated with dreaming. If an adult sleeps 7 to 8 hours, how much time is spent in REM sleep? **between 1.4 and 1.6 hours inclusive**

DIFFERENTIATED HOMEWORK OPTIONS

Level	Assignment	Two-Day Option	
BL Basic	8–25, 47, 48, 50–68	9–25 odd, 51–53	8–24 even, 47, 48, 50, 54–68
OL Core	9–35 odd, 36–48, 50–68	8–25, 51–53	26–48, 50, 54–68
AL Advanced /Pre-AP	26–60 (optional: 61–68)		

★ **37. FUND-RAISING** Rashid is selling potted flowers for his school's fund-raiser. He can earn prizes depending on how much he sells. So far, he has sold $70 worth of flowers. How much more does he need to sell to earn a prize in category D? **between $51 and $110 inclusive**

Sales ($)	Prize
0–25	A
26–60	B
61–120	C
121–180	D
180+	E

Define a variable, write an inequality, and solve each problem. Then check your solution. 38–40. See Ch. 6 Answer Appendix.

38. Eight less than a number is no more than 14 and no less than 5.

39. The sum of 3 times a number and 4 is between −8 and 10.

40. The product of −5 and a number is greater than 35 or less than 10.

41. One half a number is greater than 0 and less than or equal to 1.
Sample answer: Let n = the number, $0 < \frac{1}{2}n \le 1$; $\{n \mid 0 < n \le 2\}$.

HEARING For Exercises 42–44, use the table.

42. Write a compound inequality for the hearing range of humans and one for the hearing range of dogs.

43. What is the union of the two graphs? the intersection? $\{h \mid 15 \le h \le 50{,}000\}$; $\{h \mid 20 \le h \le 20{,}000\}$

44. Write an inequality or inequalities for the range of sounds that dogs can hear, but humans cannot. $15 \le h < 20$ or $20{,}000 < h \le 50{,}000$

What Humans and Dogs Can Hear	
Species	**Sound Waves (hertz)**
humans	20–20,000
dogs	15–50,000

Real-World Link
A dog's sense of smell is about 1000 times better than a human's, but its eyesight is not as good.

Source: about.com

42. $20 \le h \le 20{,}000$; $15 \le d \le 50{,}000$

45. RESEARCH Use the Internet or other resource to find the altitudes in miles of the layers of Earth's atmosphere, troposphere, stratosphere, mesosphere, thermosphere, and exosphere. Write inequalities for the range of altitudes for each layer. **See Ch. 6 Answer Appendix.**

46. RESEARCH Use the Internet or another resource to find the everyday meaning of each term. Give an example of the everyday meaning of each term and compare to the math meaning of each term. **See Ch. 6 Answer Appendix.**
  a. intersection **b.** union

H.O.T. Problems

47. OPEN ENDED Create an example of a compound inequality containing *and* that has no solution. **Sample answer:** $x < -2$ and $x > 3$

48. REASONING Formulate a compound inequality to represent *$7 is less than t, which is less than $12.* Interpret what the solution means.
$7 < t < 12$; Sample answer: Lunch will cost between $7 and $12.

EXTRA PRACTICE
See pages 729, 749.

Math Online
Self-Check Quiz at ca.algebra1.com

49. CHALLENGE Select compound inequalities that represent the values of x which make the following expressions *false.*
  a. $x < 5$ or $x > 8$ **b.** $x \le 6$ and $x \ge 1$
  $x \ge 5$ and $x \le 8$ $x > 6$ or $x < 1$

50. *Writing in Math* Use the information about the roller coaster on page 315 to explain how compound inequalities can be used to describe weight restrictions at amusement parks. Include a compound inequality describing a possible height restriction for riders of the roller coaster. Describe what this represents. **See Ch. 6 Answer Appendix.**

Lesson 6-4 Solving Compound Inequalities **319**

BL = Below Grade Level
OL = On Grade Level
AL = Above Grade Level
ELL = English Language Learner

Additional pages not shown:
CRM **Lesson Reading Guide,** p. 26 BL OL ELL
CRM **Skills Practice,** p. 29 BL OL

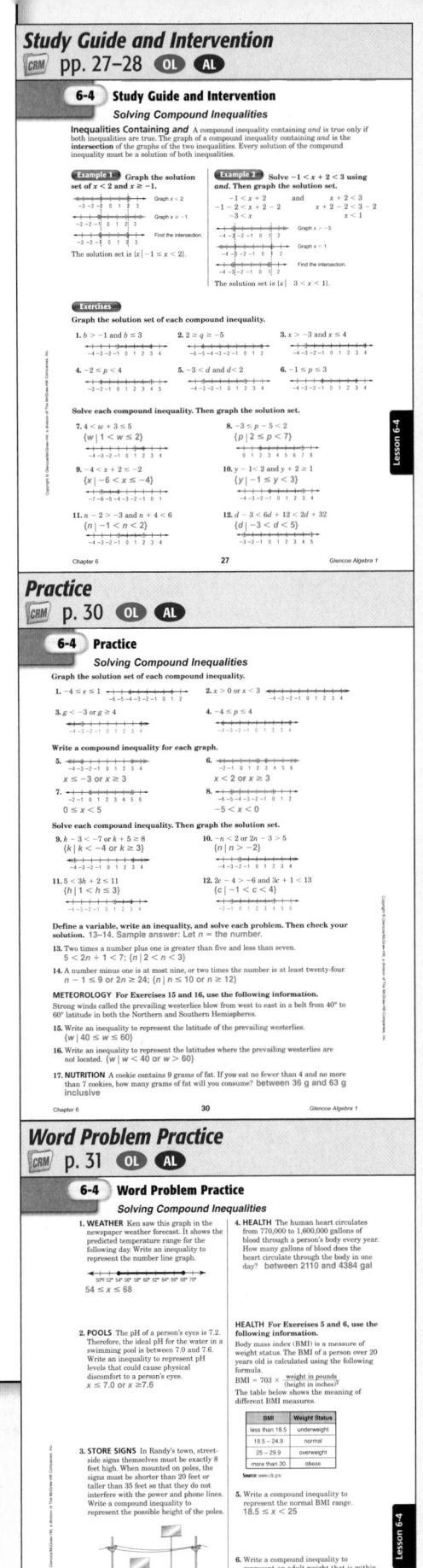

Study Guide and Intervention
CRM pp. 27–28 OL AL

6-4 Study Guide and Intervention
Solving Compound Inequalities

Practice
CRM p. 30 OL AL

6-4 Practice
Solving Compound Inequalities

Word Problem Practice
CRM p. 31 OL AL

6-4 Word Problem Practice
Solving Compound Inequalities

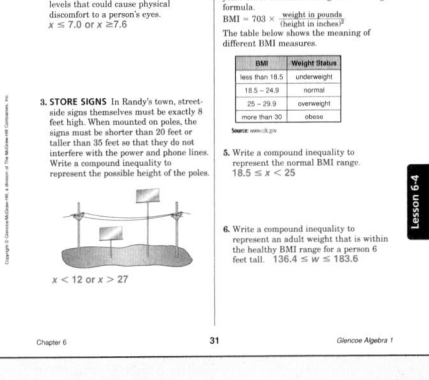

Enrichment
CRM p. 32 OL AL

6-4 Enrichment

Some Properties of Inequalities

The two expressions on either side of an inequality symbol are sometimes called the *first* and *second* members of the inequality.

If the inequality symbols of two inequalities point in the same direction, the inequalities have the same sense. For example, $a < b$ and $c < d$ have the same sense; $a < b$ and $c > d$ have opposite senses.

In the problems on this page, you will explore some properties of inequalities.

Three of the four statements below are true for all numbers a and b (or a, b, c, and d). Write each statement in algebraic form. If the statement is true for all numbers, prove it. If it is not true, give an example to show that it is false.

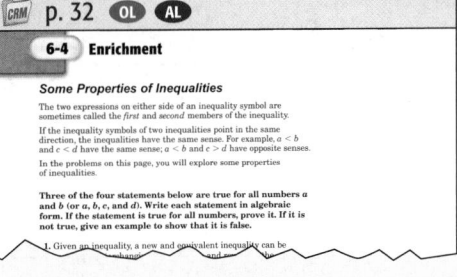

Lesson 6-4 Solving Compound Inequalities **319**

4 Assess

Name the Math Have each student tell a partner the difference between a compound inequality that contains *or* and a compound inequality that contains *and*.

✓ Formative Assessment

Check for student understanding of concepts in Lessons 6-3 and 6-4.

[CRM] Quiz 2, p. 67

STANDARDS PRACTICE   7AF4.2, 5.0, 7PS1.2

51. REVIEW Ten pounds of fresh tomatoes make about 15 cups of cooked tomatoes. How many cups does one pound of tomatoes make? **A**

   A $1\frac{1}{2}$ cups

   B 5 cups

   C 3 cups

   D 4 cups

52. What is the solution set of the inequality $-7 < x + 2 < 4$? **G**

   F $-5 < x < 6$

   G $-9 < x < 2$

   H $-5 < x < 2$

   J $-9 < x < 6$

53. REVIEW The scatterplot below shows the number of hay bales used by the Crosley farm during the last year.

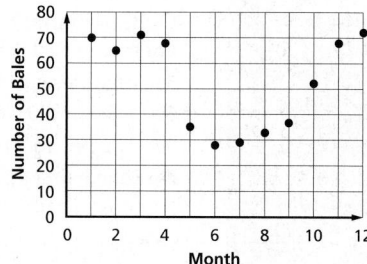

Hay Bales Used

Which is an invalid conclusion? **D**

   A The Crosleys used less hay in the summer than they did in the winter.

   B The Crosleys used a total of 629 bales of hay.

   C The Crosleys used about 52 bales each month.

   D The Crosleys used the most hay in February.

Spiral Review

54. MONEY In the summer, Richard earns $200 per month at his part-time job at a restaurant, plus an average of $18 for each lawn that he mows. If his goal is to earn at least $280 this month, how many lawns will he have to mow? (Lesson 6-3) **at least 5 lawns**

Solve each inequality. Check your solution. (Lesson 6-2)

55. $18d \geq 90$
{$d|d \geq 5$}

56. $-7v < 91$
{$v|v > -13$}

57. $\frac{t}{13} < 13$
{$t|t < 169$}

58. $-\frac{3}{8}b > 9$
{$b|b < -24$}

Solve. Assume that y varies directly as x. (Lesson 5-2)

59. If $y = -8$ when $x = -3$, find x when $y = 6$. **2.25**

60. If $y = 2.5$ when $x = 0.5$, find y when $x = 20$. **100**

▷ GET READY for the Next Lesson

PREREQUISITE SKILL Solve each equation. (Lesson 2-4)

61. $3n - 14 = 1$ **5**   **62.** $2t + 5 = 7$ **1**   **63.** $8w - 13 = 3$ **2**   **64.** $5d + 9 = -6$ **−3**

65. $12 = 3n + 15$ **−1** **66.** $17 = 4p - 3$ **5**   **67.** $-3 = 4x + 5$ **−2**   **68.** $-14 = 4 + 3w$ **−6**

320   Chapter 6 Solving Linear Inequalities

Pre-AP Activity   Use after Exercise 49

Find a value of k so that the solution set of $k - 5 \leq x - 6 \leq 3$ is {$x \mid 6 \leq x < 9$} **5**

1. **MULTIPLE CHOICE** Which graph represents all the values of m such that $m + 3 > 7$? (Lesson 6-1) **A**

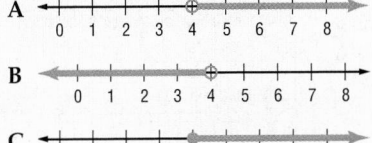

2–7. See margin.

Solve each inequality. Check your solution, then graph it on a number line. (Lesson 6-1)

2. $8 + x < 9$ 3. $h - 16 > -13$

4. $r + 3 \le -1$ 5. $4 \ge p + 9$

6. $-3 < a - 5$ 7. $7g \le 6g - 1$

8. **MULTIPLE CHOICE** Which inequality does NOT have the same solution as $-14w < 14$? (Lesson 6-2) **J**

F $8w > -8$ H $\dfrac{w}{5} > -\dfrac{1}{5}$

G $11 > -11w$ J $-\dfrac{3}{2} < \dfrac{2}{3}w$

Solve each inequality. Check your solution.
(Lesson 6-2)

9. $12 \ge 3a$ $\{a \,|\, a \le 4\}$ 10. $15z \ge 105$ $\{z \,|\, z \ge 7\}$

11. $\dfrac{v}{5} < 4$ $\{v \,|\, v < 20\}$ 12. $-\dfrac{3}{7}q > 15$ $\{q \,|\, q < -35\}$

13. $-156 < 12r$ 14. $-\dfrac{2}{5}w \le -\dfrac{1}{2}$ $\left\{w \,\middle|\, w \ge \dfrac{5}{4}\right\}$
    $\{r \,|\, r > -13\}$

15. **MONEY** Javier is saving $175 each month to buy a used all-terrain vehicle. How long will it take him to save at least $2900? Define a variable and write an inequality to solve the problem. Interpret your solution. (Lesson 6-2) **See margin.**

Solve each inequality. Check your solution.
(Lesson 6-3)

16. $5 - 4b > -23$ 17. $\dfrac{1}{2}n + 3 \ge -5$
   $\{b \,|\, b < 7\}$ $\{n \,|\, n \ge -16\}$

18. $3(t + 6) < 9$ 19. $9x + 2 > 20$ $\{x \,|\, x > 2\}$
   $\{t \,|\, t < -3\}$

20. $2m + 5 \le 4m - 1$ 21. $a < \dfrac{2a - 15}{3}$ $\{a \,|\, a < -15\}$
   $\{m \,|\, m \ge 3\}$

22. **MULTIPLE CHOICE** What is the first step in solving $\dfrac{y - 5}{9} \ge 13$? (Lesson 6-3) **D**

A Add 5 to each side.

B Subtract 5 from each side.

C Divide each side by 9.

D Multiply each side by 9.

23. **PHYSICAL SCIENCE** Chlorine is a gas for all temperatures greater than $-31°F$. If F represents temperature in degrees Fahrenheit, the inequality $F > -31$ represents the temperatures for which chlorine is a gas. Solve $\dfrac{9}{5}C + 32 > -31$ to find the temperatures in degrees Celsius for which chlorine is a gas. (Lesson 6-3) **$C > -35°C$**

Write a compound inequality for each graph.
(Lesson 6-4)

24. 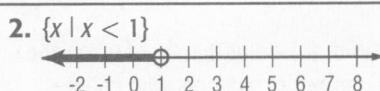 $-3 < x \le 1$

25. 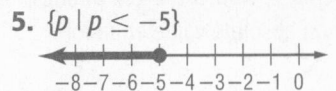 $x \le -1$ or $x \ge 5$

26. **MULTIPLE CHOICE** Some parts of a state get less than 9 inches of annual rainfall. Other parts of the state get more than 57 inches. Which inequality represents this situation? (Lesson 6-4) **H**

F $9 < r < 57$

G $9 > r > 57$

H $r < 9$ or $r > 57$

J $r < 9$ and $r > 57$

Solve each compound inequality. Then graph the solution set. (Lesson 6-4) **27–30. See margin.**

27. $x - 2 < 7$ and $x + 2 > 5$

28. $2b + 5 \le -1$ or $b - 4 \ge -4$

29. $4m - 5 > 7$ or $4m - 5 < -9$

30. $a - 4 < 1$ and $a + 2 > 1$

CHAPTER 6 Mid-Chapter Quiz

✓ Formative Assessment

Use the Mid-Chapter Quiz to assess students' progress in the first half of the chapter.

For problems answered incorrectly, have students review the lessons indicated in parenthesis.

✓ Summative Assessment

CRM Mid-Chapter Test, p. 69

⊙ ExamView® Assessment Suite

ExamView *Assessment Suite* Customize and create multiple versions of your own Mid-Chapter Tests and their answer keys.

FOLDABLES *Study Organizer* **Foldables™ Follow-Up**

Before students complete the Mid-Chapter Quiz, encourage them to review the information under the appropriate labels on their Foldables.

Additional Answers

2. $\{x \,|\, x < 1\}$

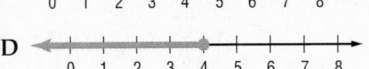

3. $\{h \,|\, h > 3\}$

4. $\{r \,|\, r \le -4\}$

5. $\{p \,|\, p \le -5\}$

6–7, 15, 27–30. See Ch. 6 Answer Appendix.

Data-Driven Decision Making	Exercises	Lesson	Standard	Resources for Review
Diagnostic Teaching Based on the results of the Chapter 6 Mid-Chapter Quiz, use the following to review concepts that students continue to find challenging.	1–7	6-1	5.0	**CRM** Study Guide and Intervention, pp. 6–7, 13–14, 20–21, 27–28
	8–15	6-2	5.0	**Math⊙nline**
	16–23	6-3	4.0	• Extra Examples • Personal Tutor
	24–30	6-4	5.0	• Concepts in Motion

 **Lesson Notes**

1 Focus

Standards Alignment

Before Lesson 6-5
Understand, interpret and determine the absolute value of real numbers from ➡ Standard 7NS2.5

Lesson 6-5
Students solve equations and inequalities involving absolute values from Standard 3.0

After Lesson 6-5
Solve equations and inequalities involving absolute value from ➡ Standard 2A1.0

2 Teach

Scaffolding Questions
Have students read *Get Ready for the Lesson.*

Ask:
- Which technology is the least important to the students surveyed?
  digital cameras
- With a 3-point margin of error, the number of students who chose notebook computers as the most important technology could be as high as what percent? As low as what percent? 28%; 22%
- How would you represent the maximum or minimum percent of students, *x*, who chose cell phones, with an absolute value equation?
  $|x - 52| = 3$

Lesson 6-5 Resources

Chapter 6 Resource Masters
Lesson Reading Guide, p. 33 **BL OL ELL**
Study Guide and Intervention, pp. 34–35 **BL OL ELL**
Skills Practice, p. 36 **OL AL**
Practice, p. 37 **OL AL**
Word Problem Practice, p. 38 **OL AL**
Enrichment, p. 39 **OL AL**

Main Ideas
- Solve absolute value equations.
- Graph absolute value functions.

 Standard 3.0
Students solve equations and inequalities **involving absolute values.** (CAHSEE)

New Vocabulary
absolute value
absolute value function
piecewise function

Study Tip

Absolute Value
Since distance cannot be less than zero, absolute values are always greater than or equal to zero.

Transparencies
5-Minute Check Transparency 6-6

Additional Print Resources
Noteables™ Interactive Study Notebook with Foldables™

Technology
ca.algebra1.com
Interactive Classroom CD-ROM
Answer Key Maker Plus CD-ROM
Graphing Calculator Easy Files

▶ **GET READY** for the Lesson

In an international survey of students from 25 high schools in 9 different countries, 52% of those surveyed chose cell phones as the technology that is most important to them.

Suppose the survey had a 3-point margin of error. This means that the result may be 3 percentage points higher or lower. So, the number of students favoring cell phones over other technology may be as high as 55% or as low as 49%.

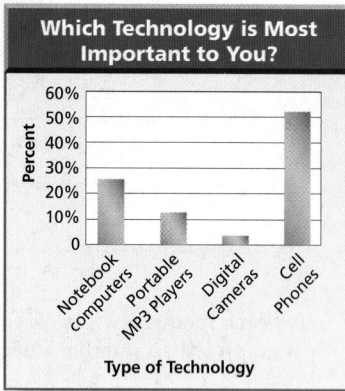
Which Technology is Most Important to You?
Source: www.ucdsb.on.ca/athens/surveys.index.htm

Absolute Value Equations The margin of error of the data in the bar graph is an example of absolute value. The distance between 52 and 55 on a number line is the same as the distance between 49 and 52.

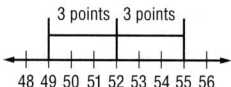

The **absolute value** of any number *n* is its distance from zero on a number line. The absolute value of *n* is written as $|n|$. There are three types of open sentences involving absolute value. They are $|x| = n, |x| < n, and |x| > n$. Consider the first type. $|x| = 5$ means the distance between 0 and *x* is 5 units.

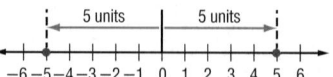

If $|x| = 5$, then $x = -5$ or $x = 5$. The solution set is $\{-5, 5\}$.

KEY CONCEPT   *Solving Absolute Value Equations*

When solving equations that involve absolute value, there are two cases to consider.

Case 1 The expression inside the absolute value symbols is positive.

Case 2 The expression inside the absolute value symbols is negative.

---

322 Chapter 6 Solving Linear Inequalities

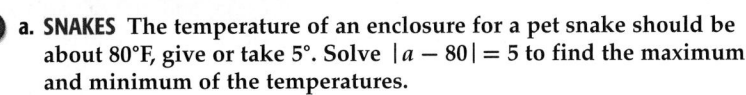 **Real-World EXAMPLE** Solve an Absolute Value Equation

1 **a. SNAKES** The temperature of an enclosure for a pet snake should be about 80°F, give or take 5°. Solve $|a - 80| = 5$ to find the maximum and minimum of the temperatures.

Method 1 Graphing

$|a - 80| = 5$ means that the distance between a and 80 is 5 units. To find a on the number line, start at 80 and move 5 units in either direction.

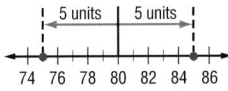

The distance from 80 to 75 is 5 units.
The distance from 80 to 85 is 5 units.
The solution set is {75, 85}.

Method 2 Compound Sentence

Write $|a - 80| = 5$ as $a - 80 = 5$ or $a - 80 = -5$.

Case 1	Case 2
$a - 80 = 5$	$a - 80 = -5$
$a - 80 + 80 = 5 + 80$ Add 80 to each side.	$a - 80 + 80 = -5 + 80$
$a = 85$ Simplify.	$a = 75$

The solution set is {75, 85}. The maximum and minimum temperatures are 85°F and 75°F.

b. Solve $|b - 1| = -3$.

$|b - 1| = -3$ means that the distance between b and 1 is −3. Since distance cannot be negative, the solution is the empty set ∅.

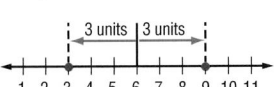 **Your Progress**

Solve each open sentence. Then graph the solution set. **1A–1B. See margin.**
1A. $|y + 2| = 4$ {−6, 2}   **1B.** $|3n - 4| = -1$ ∅

 **EXAMPLE** Write an Absolute Value Equation

2 Write an open sentence involving absolute value for the graph.

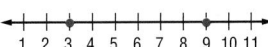

Find the point that is the same distance from 3 and from 9. This is the midpoint between 3 and 9, which is 6.

The distance from 6 to 3 is 3 units.
The distance from 6 to 9 is 3 units.

So, an equation is $|x - 6| = 3$.

 Your Progress

2. Write an open sentence involving absolute value for the graph. **See margin.**

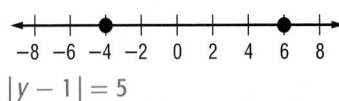 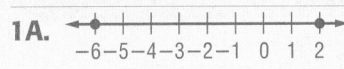

Study Tip

Absolute Value
Since $|a| = 3$ means $a = 3$ or $-a = 3$, the second equation can be written as $a = -3$. So, $|a - 4| = 3$ means $a - 4 = 3$ or $-(a - 4) = 3$. These can be written as $a - 4 = 3$ or $a - 4 = -3$.

Daily Intervention

Absolute Value Equations Some students may respond better to rewriting absolute value equations by applying the two situations (positive and negative) to the expression within the absolute value symbols. For example, $|x| = 4$ can be written as $x = 4$ or as $-x = 4$, which yields $x = -4$.

Absolute Value Inequalities

Example 3 shows how to graph absolute value equations in the form $f(x) = |x|$ using piece-wise functions.

Focus on Mathematical Content
Piecewise Functions

Piecewise functions are sometimes called *multi-part* functions or *split-domain* functions. For example, the absolute value function is the same as $y = x$ over one part of its domain, and $y = -x$ over another.

ADDITIONAL EXAMPLE

3 **a.** Graph $f(x) = |x + 3|$.

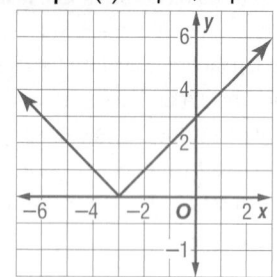

b. Graph $f(x) = |x - 5|$.

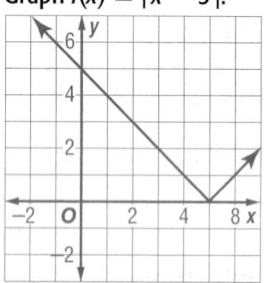

Additional Examples are also in:

• Noteables™ Interactive Study Notebook with Foldables™

• Interactive Classroom PowerPoint® Presentations

Graphing Absolute Value Functions An **absolute value function** is a function written as $f(x) = |x|$, when $f(x) \geq 0$ for all values of x. To graph $f(x) = |x|$, make a table of values and plot the ordered pairs on a coordinate plane. Notice that for negative values of x, the slope of the line is -1. When the x-values are positive, the slope of the line is 1. An absolute value function can be written using two or more expressions. This is an example of a **piecewise function.**

$f(x) = |x|$	
x	$f(x)$
-3	3
-2	2
-1	1
-0	0
-1	1
-2	2
-3	3

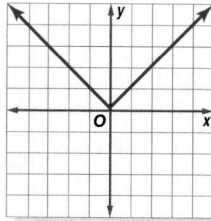

The absolute value function $f(x) = |x|$ can be written as $f(x) = \begin{cases} -x \text{ if } x < 0 \\ x \text{ if } x \geq 0 \end{cases}$.

EXAMPLE Graphing Absolute Value Functions

3 Graph $f(x) = |x - 4|$.

First, find the minimum point on the graph. Since $f(x)$ cannot be negative, the minimum point of the graph is where $f(x) = 0$.

$f(x) = |x - 4|$ Original function

$0 = x - 4$ Set $f(x) = 0$.

$4 = x$ Add 4 to each side.

The minimum point of the graph is at $(4, 0)$.

Next fill out a table of values. Include values for $x > 4$ and $x < 4$.

$f(x) = |x - 4|$	
x	$f(x)$
-2	6
0	4
2	2
4	0
5	1
6	2
7	3
8	4

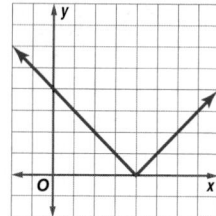

> **Study Tip**
>
> **Absolute Value**
> When plotting points on a graph, choose values of x that are less than and that are greater than the minimum point of the graph.

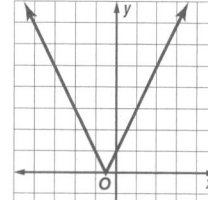

✓**CHECK Your Progress**

3. Graph $f(x) = |2x + 1|$.

324 **Chapter 6** Solving Linear Inequalities

> **Tips for New Teachers**
>
> ## Preventing Errors
>
> If students are having difficulty understanding the split-domain of piecewise functions, have them draw dashed vertical lines where the domain splits. In this way, students can more clearly see which sections of the graph are defined by each function.

✓ CHECK Your Understanding

Example 1
(p. 323)

Solve each open sentence. Then graph the solution set.

1. $|r + 3| = 10$ **2.** $|2x - 8| = 6$ **3.** $|4n - 1| = -6$

1–3. See margin.

4. Write an open sentence involving absolute value for the graph. $|x - 1| = 3$

Example 2
(p. 323)

Examples 3
(p. 324)

Graph each function.

5. $f(x) = |x - 3|$ **6.** $g(x) = |2x + 4|$

5–6. See Ch. 6 Answer Appendix.

Exercises

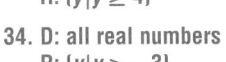

For Exercises	See Examples
7–18	1
19–22	2
23–30	3

Exercise Levels
A: 7–30
B: 31–38
C: 39–46

7–18. See Ch. 6
Answer Appendix.

Solve each open sentence. Then graph the solution set.

7. $|x - 5| = 8$ **8.** $|b + 9| = 2$ **9.** $|v - 2| = -5$

10. $|2p - 3| = 17$ **11.** $|5c - 8| = 12$ **12.** $|6y - 7| = -1$

13. $\left|\frac{1}{2}x + 5\right| = -3$ **14.** $|-2x + 6| = 6$ **15.** $\left|\frac{3}{4}x - 3\right| = 9$

16. $\left|-\frac{1}{2}x - 2\right| = 10$ **17.** $|-4x + 6| = 12$ **18.** $|5x - 3| = 12$

Write an open sentence involving absolute value for each graph.

19.
$|x| = 5$

20.
$|x| = 4$

21.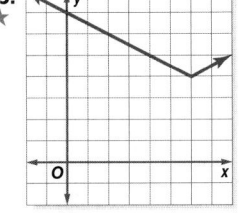
$|x - 3| = 5$

22.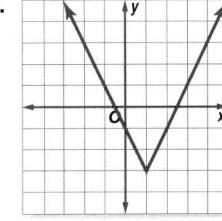
$|x - 1| = 4$

Graph each function.

23. $f(x) = |2x - 1|$ **24.** $f(x) = |x + 5|$ **25.** $g(x) = |-3x - 5|$

26. $g(x) = |-x - 3|$ **27.** $f(x) = \left|\frac{1}{2}x - 2\right|$ **28.** $f(x) = \left|\frac{1}{3}x + 2\right|$

29. $g(x) = |x + 2| + 3$

30. $g(x) = |2x - 3| + 1$ 23–30. See Ch. 6 Answer Appendix.

Solve for x.

31. $2|x| - 3 = 8$ 5.5, −5.5 **32.** $4 - 3|x| = 10$ no solution

Determine the domain and range for each absolute value function.

33. D: all real numbers R: $\{y | y \geq 4\}$

34. D: all real numbers R: $\{y | y \geq -3\}$

35. D: all real numbers R: $\{y | y \geq 1\}$

36. D: all real numbers R: $\{y | y \geq -3\}$

33.

★ 34.

35.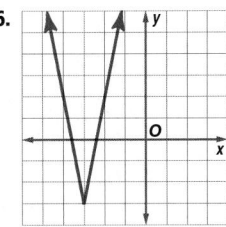

★ 36.

3 Practice

✓ Formative Assessment

Use Exercises 1–6 to check for understanding.

Then use the chart at the bottom of this page to customize assignments for your students.

Odd/Even Assignments

Exercises 7-30 are structured so that students practice the same concepts whether they are assigned odd or even problems.

Real-World Connections

For Exercise 37, you may wish to survey your class and compare the results with that of the textbook. Tell students that the moon's average distance from the earth is 238,855 miles and its minimum and maximum surface temperatures range from −387°F to 253°F. Discuss how these facts may create obstacles in living on the moon.

⚠ Exercise Alert!

Find the Error Suggest that students determine whether Leslie and Holly are considering the correct two cases for each absolute value. Students should notice that Holly's second case, $x - 3 = 2$, is incorrect. It should be noted that if Holly's second case equation was $-x - 3 = 2$, she would come up with the correct solution.

Additional Answers

1. $\{-13, 7\}$

2. $\{1, 7\}$

3. ∅

DIFFERENTIATED HOMEWORK OPTIONS

Level	Assignment	Two-Day Option	
BL Basic	7–30, 41–45, 47–70	7–29 odd, 49–51	8–30 even, 41–45, 47, 48, 52–70
OL Core	7–35 odd, 37–45, 47–70	7–30, 49–51	31–45, 47, 48, 52–70
AL Advanced /Pre-AP	31–64, (optional: 65–70)		

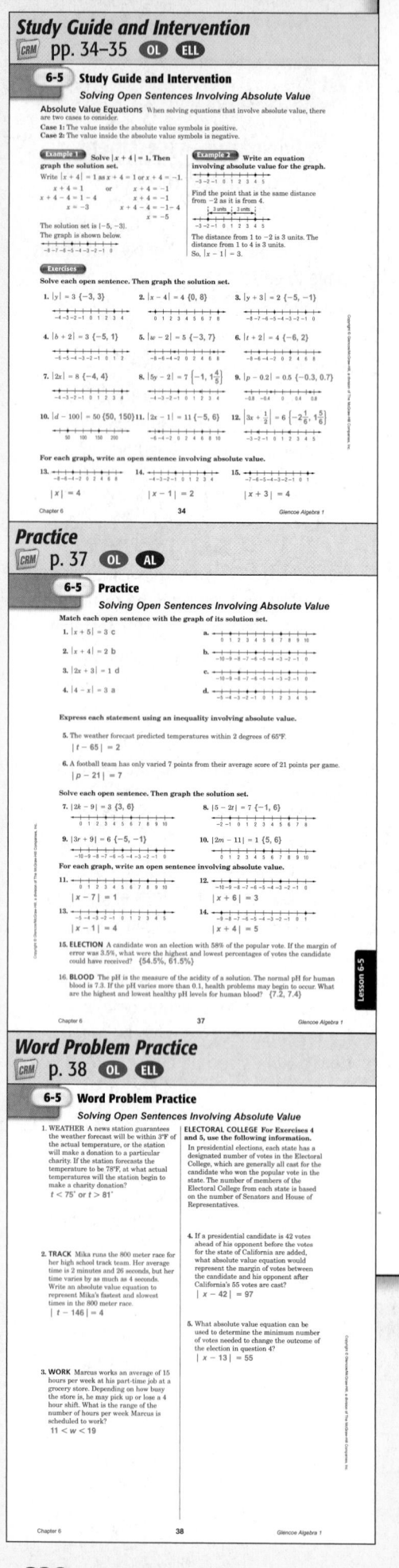

★ **37. ANALYZE GRAPHS** The circle graph at the right shows the results of a survey that asked teens "When do you think humans will be able to live on the moon?" If the margin of error is ±3 percentage points, what is the range of the percent of teens who say humans will live on the moon in 2100? **45–51%**

When Will Humans Live on the Moon?

8% 2005
25% 2010
48% 2100
32% Never

Source: Global Teen Surveys

★ **38. PHYSICS** As part of a physics lab, Tiffany and Curtis determined that an object was traveling at 25 miles per hour. If the margin of error is 6%, determine the slowest and the fastest rate of the object. **23.5 mph, 26.5 mph**

PING PONG For Exercises 39 and 40, use the following information.
Esmerelda dropped a ping pong ball from a height of 4 feet. She tracked the height of the ball and the elapsed time. The ball hit the floor at 2 seconds and then bounced. At 4 seconds, the height was 4 feet.

39. Draw a graph of the path of the ping pong ball, assuming that the ball traveled at a constant rate. Let the x-axis represent the time and the y-axis represent the height.

40. Write a piecewise function to describe the path of the ping pong ball. **39–40. See Ch. 6 Answer Appendix.**

EXTRA PRACTICE
See pages 729, 749.

Math **Online**
Self-Check Quiz at
ca.algebra1.com

H.O.T. Problems

41. OPEN ENDED Describe a real-world situation that could be represented by the absolute value equation $|x - 4| = 10$. **Sample answer: Let $x =$ the time in minutes to run one mile. Then the time to run one mile is 10 ± 4.**

REASONING Determine whether the following statements are *sometimes*, *always*, or *never* true, where c is a whole number. Explain your reasoning.

42. The value of $|x + 1|$ is greater than zero. **Sometimes; when $x =$ – the value is zero.**

43. The solution of $|x + c| = 0$ is greater than 0.

43. Sometimes; when c is a negative value, x is a positive value.

44. The inequality $|x| + c < 0$ has no solution.

44. Sometimes; when c is a negative value, the inequality is true.

45. The value of $|x + c| + c$ is greater than zero. **Sometimes; when $c < 0$ and $0 < x < -2$, then the expression is less than 0.**

46. CHALLENGE Use the sentence $x = 3 \pm 1.2$.
  a. Describe the values of x. **{1.8, 4.2}**
  b. Translate the sentence into an expression involving absolute value. $|x - 3| = 1.2$

47. FIND THE ERROR Leslie and Holly are solving $|x + 3| = 2$. Who is correct? Explain your reasoning.

47. Leslie; you need to consider the case when the value inside the absolute value symbols is positive and the case when the value inside the absolute value symbols is negative. So $x + 3 = 2$ or $x + 3 = -2$

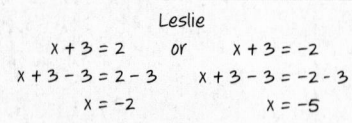

Leslie
$x + 3 = 2$ or $x + 3 = -2$
$x + 3 - 3 = 2 - 3$ $x + 3 - 3 = -2 - 3$
$x = -2$ $x = -5$

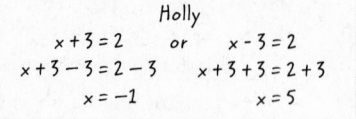

Holly
$x + 3 = 2$ or $x - 3 = 2$
$x + 3 - 3 = 2 - 3$ $x + 3 + 3 = 2 + 3$
$x = -1$ $x = 5$

48. *Writing in Math* Use the data about the technology survey on page 322 to explain how absolute value is used in surveys. **See margin.**

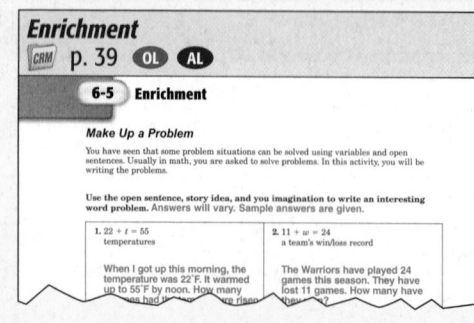

BL = *Below Grade Level*
OL = *On Grade Level*
AL = *Above Grade Level*
ELL = *English Language Learner*

Additional pages not shown:

CRM *Lesson Reading Guide,* p. 33 **BL** **OL** **ELL**

CRM *Skills Practice,* p. 36 **BL** **OL**

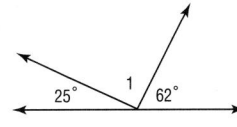
49. Assume n is an integer and solve for n.
$$|2n - 3| = 5 \text{ C}$$

A $\{-4, -1\}$ C $\{-1, 4\}$

B $\{1, 1\}$ D $\{4, 4\}$

50. If p is an integer, which of the following is the solution set for $2|p| = 16$? **G**

F $\{0, 8\}$

G $\{-8, 8\}$

H $\{-8, 0\}$

J $\{-8, 0, 8\}$

51. REVIEW What is the measure of $\angle 1$ in the figure shown below? **D**

A $83°$

B $87°$

C $90°$

D $93°$

Spiral Review

★ **52. FITNESS** To achieve the maximum benefits from aerobic activity, your heart rate should be in your target zone. Your target zone is the range between 60% and 80% of your maximum heart rate. If Rafael's maximum heart rate is 190 beats per minute, what is his target zone? (Lesson 6-4)
between 114 and 152 beats per min

Solve each inequality. Check your solution. (Lesson 6-3)

53. $2m + 7 > 17$ $\{m \mid m > 5\}$ **54.** $-2 - 3x \geq 2$ $\left\{x \mid x \leq -1\frac{1}{3}\right\}$ **55.** $\frac{2}{3}w - 3 \leq 7$ $\{w \mid w \leq 15\}$

Find the slope and y-intercept of each equation. (Lesson 4-4)

56. $2x + y = 4$ $-2; 4$ **57.** $2y - 3x = 4$ $\frac{3}{2}; 2$ **58.** $\frac{1}{2}x + \frac{3}{4}y = 0$ $-\frac{2}{3}; 0$

Express the relation shown in each mapping as a set of ordered pairs. Then state the domain, range, and inverse. (Lesson 4-3) **59–61. See margin.**

59.

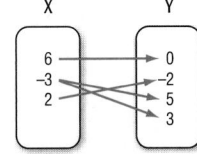

60.

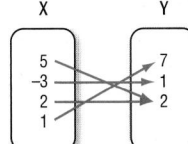

61.

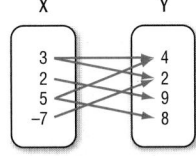

Solve each equation for the variable specified. (Lesson 2-8)

62. $I = prt$, for r $r = \frac{I}{pt}$ **63.** $ex - 2y = 3z$, for x $x = \frac{3z + 2y}{e}$ **64.** $\frac{a + 5}{3} = 7x$, for x $x = \frac{a + 5}{21}$

GET READY for the Next Lesson

PREREQUISITE SKILL Solve each inequality. Check your solution. (Lesson 6-1)

65. $m + 4 \geq 6$ $m \geq 2$ **66.** $p - 3 < 2$ $p < 5$ **67.** $z + 5 \leq 11$ $z \leq 6$

68. $8 + w < -12$ $w < -20$ **69.** $4 - r \geq -3$ $r \leq 7$ **70.** $6 - v \geq -2$ $v \leq 8$

⚠️ **Exercise Alert!**

Find the Error Suggest that students determine whether Leslie and Holly are considering the correct two cases for each absolute value. Students should notice that Holly's second case, $x - 3 = 2$, is incorrect. It should be noted that if Holly's second case equation was $-x - 3 = 2$, she would come up with the correct solution.

4 Assess

Crystal Ball Ask students to write a sentence predicting how learning to solve and graph absolute value equations will help them to learn to solve and graph absolute value inequalities in the next lesson.

FOLDABLES Study Organizer **Foldables™ Follow-Up**

At the end of this lesson, remind students to take notes and show examples of absolute value equations.

Additional Answers

48. Sample answer: Inequalities involving absolute value are used to represent margin of error. The inequality representing the percent of students who say that notebook computers are the most important technology to them is $|x - 25| \leq 3$. To solve this inequality, find the intersection of $x - 25 \leq 3$ and $x - 25 \geq -3$. To solve these inequalities, add 25 to each side of each inequality. The solution set is $\{x \mid 22 \leq x \leq 28\}$. The percent of students who say that notebook computers are the most important technology to them can be between 22% and 28%.

59. $\{(6, 0), (-3, 5), (2, -2), (-3, 3)\}; \{-3, 2, 6\};$ $\{-2, 0, 3, 5\}; \{(0, 6), (5, -3), (-2, 2), (3, -3)\}$

---

60. $\{(5, 2), (-3, 1), (2, 2), (1, 7)\}; \{-3, 1, 2, 5\};$ $\{1, 2, 7\}; \{(2, 5), (1, -3), (2, 2), (7, 1)\}$

61. $\{(3, 4), (3, 2), (2, 9), (5, 4) (5, 8), (-7, 2)\};$ $\{-7, 2, 3, 5\}; \{2, 4, 8, 9\}; \{(4, 3), (2, 3), (9, 2), (4, 5), (8, 5), (2, -7)\}$

Graphing Calculator Lab
Graphing Absolute Value Functions

Standard 17.0 Students determine the domain of independent variables and the range of dependent variables defined by a graph, a set of ordered pairs, **or** a symbolic expression.

The absolute value function $y = |x|$ is the parent function of the family of absolute value functions. The graphs of absolute value functions are similar to the graphs of linear functions.

ACTIVITY 1

Graph $y = |x|$ in the standard viewing window.

Enter the equation in the Y= list. Then graph the equation.

KEYSTROKES: [Y=] [MATH] [▶] 1 [X,T,θ,n] [)] [ZOOM] 6

1A. How does the graph of $y = |x|$ compare to the graph of $y = x$?

1B. What are the domain and range of the function $y = |x|$? Explain.
1A–1B. See Ch. 6 Answer Appendix.

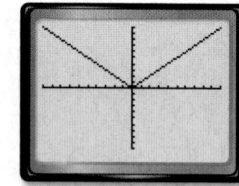
[−10, 10] scl: 1 by [−10, 10] scl: 1

The graphs of absolute value functions are affected by changes in parameters in a way similar to the way changes in parameters affect the graphs of linear functions.

ACTIVITY 2

Graph $y = |x| - 3$ and $y = |x| + 1$ in the standard viewing window.

Enter the equations in the Y= list. Then graph.

KEYSTROKES: [Y=] [MATH] [▶] 1 [X,T,θ,n] [)] [−] 3 [ENTER] [MATH] [▶] 1 [X,T,θ,n] [)] [+] 1 [ZOOM] 6

2A. Compare and contrast the graphs to the graph of $y = |x|$.

2B. How does the value of c affect the graph of $y = |x| + c$?
2A–2B. See Ch. 6 Answer Appendix.

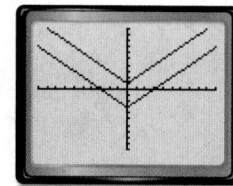
[−10, 10] scl: 1 by [−10, 10] scl: 1

ANALYZE THE RESULTS

1. Write the function shown in the graph. $y = |x| + 4$

2. Graph $y = -|x|$ in the standard viewing window. How is this graph related to the graph of $y = |x|$? **See Ch. 6 Answer Appendix.**

3. **MAKE A CONJECTURE** Describe the transformation of the parent graph $y = |x + c|$. Use a graphing calculator with different values of c to test your conjecture. **See Ch. 6 Answer Appendix.**

[−10, 10] scl: 1 by [−10, 10] scl: 1

4. Determine whether the following statement is *always, sometimes,* or *never* true. Justify your answer. The y-values of the function $y = -|x - 1| - 1$ are negative. **Always; the maximum of the graph is (1, −1).**

328 Chapter 6 Solving Linear Inequalities

Math Online Other Calculator Keystrokes at ca.algebra1.com

1 Focus

Objective Use a a graphing calculator to explore graphs of absolute value functions.

Materials
• TI 83/84 Plus graphing calculator

Teaching Tip Students will use the MATH menu to graph the absolute value function. Remind students to use closing parentheses at the end of the expression **abs(**.

2 Teach

Working in Cooperative Groups
Put students in groups of 2 or 3, mixing abilities. Students should follow the keystrokes for graphing absolute value functions in Activities 1 and 2.

• Students should understand that they can take the absolute value of any number but that the resulting absolute value is always non-negative.

• For Activity 2, Exercise 2b, students should enter different values of c and describe the effect of c on the graph of the function $y = |x| + c$.

• For Exercise 3, students should enter different values of c and describe the effect of c on the graph of the function $y = |x + c|$.

• Be sure that students understand the notational differences between $y = |x| + c$ and $y = |x + c|$.

Practice Have students complete Analyze the Results 1–4.

3 Assess

 Formative Assessment

Use Exercise 1B of Activity 1 to assess whether students understand that the absolute value function always gives non-negative real numbers.

From Concrete to Abstract Ask students to describe the similarities and differences of the transformations of the parent graphs $y = |x| + c$ and $y = |x + c|$. Sample answer: Both transformations shift $y = |x|$, but the shape of the graph does not change. The first function shifts $y = |x|$ vertically, and the second function shifts $y = |x|$ horizontally.

6-6 Solving Inequalities Involving Absolute Value

Main Ideas

- Solve absolute value inequalities.
- Apply absolute value inequalities in real-world problems.

 Standard 3.0 Students solve equations and **inequalities involving absolute values.** (CAHSEE)

GET READY for the Lesson

To make baby carrots for snacks, long carrots are sliced into 2-inch sections and then peeled. If the machine that slices the carrots is accurate to within $\frac{1}{8}$ of an inch, the length of a baby carrot ranges from $1\frac{7}{8}$ inch to $2\frac{1}{8}$ inch.

Absolute Value Inequalities Consider the inequality $|x| < n$. $|x| < 5$ means that the distance from 0 to x is less than 5 units.

Therefore, $x > -5$ and $x < 5$. The solution set is $\{x \mid -5 < x < 5\}$. When solving inequalities of the form $|x| < n$, consider the two cases.

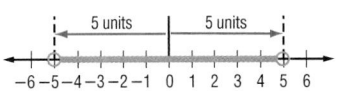

Case 1 The expression inside the absolute value symbols is positive.

Case 2 The expression inside the absolute value symbols is negative.

To solve, find the *intersection* of the solutions of these two cases.

EXAMPLE · Solve an Absolute Value Inequality ($<$)

1 Solve each open sentence. Then graph the solution set.

a. $|t + 5| < 9$

Write $|t + 5| < 9$ as $t + 5 < 9$ and $-(t + 5) < 9$.

Case 1 $t + 5$ is positive.	**Case 2** $t + 5$ is negative.
$t + 5 < 9$	$-(t + 5) < 9$
$t + 5 - 5 < 9 - 5$	$t + 5 > -9$
$t < 4$	$t + 5 - 5 > -9 - 5$
	$t > -14$

Study Tip

Less Than

When an absolute value is on the left and the inequality symbol is $<$ or $\le$, the compound sentence uses *and*.

Therefore, $t < 4$ and $t > -14$.

The solution set is $\{t \mid -14 < t < 4\}$.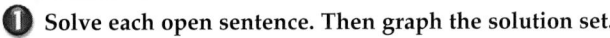

b. $|x + 2| < -1$

Since $|x + 2|$ cannot be negative, $|x + 2|$ cannot be less than -1. So, the solution set is the empty set $\varnothing$.

1A–1B. See Ch. 6 Answer Appendix.

CHECK Your Progress

1A. $|n - 8| \le 2$ **1B.** $|2c - 5| < -3$

1 Focus

Standards Alignment

Before Lesson 6-6
Understand, interpret and determine the absolute value of real numbers from ← Standard 7NS2.5

Lesson 6-6
Students solve equations and inequalities involving absolute values from ← Standard 1A3.0

After Lesson 6-6
Solve equations and inequalities involving absolute value from ← Standard 2A1.0

2 Teach

Scaffolding Questions
Have students read *Get Ready for the Lesson.*

Ask:

- How would you represent the length of a baby carrot, *x*, sliced by the machine with an absolute value inequality? $|x - 2| \le \frac{1}{8}$
- What graph would represent the length of baby carrots sliced by the machine?

1.75   1.875   2   2.125   2.25

- If the accuracy of the machine were within $\frac{1}{4}$ of an inch, would the margin of error be less or greater? greater

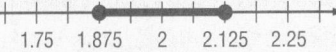
Chapter 6 Resource Masters
Lesson Reading Guide, p. 40 BL OL ELL
Study Guide and Intervention, pp. 41–42 BL OL ELL
Skills Practice, p. 43 OL AL
Practice, p. 44 OL AL
Word Problem Practice, p. 45 OL AL
Enrichment, p. 46 OL AL
Quiz 3, p. 68

Transparencies
5-Minute Check Transparency 6-6

Additional Print Resources
Noteables™ Interactive Study Notebook with Foldables™

Technology
Glencoe Online Learning Center:
ca.algebra1.com
Interactive Classroom CD-ROM
AssignmentWorks CD-ROM
Graphing Calculator Easy Files

Absolute Value Inequalities

Example 1 shows how to solve an absolute value inequality in the form $|x| < n$.

ADDITIONAL EXAMPLE

1

Solve each open sentence. Then graph the solution set.

a. $|s - 3| \leq 12$

b. $|x + 6| < -8$

Additional Examples are also in:

- Noteables™ Interactive Study Notebook with Foldables™
- Interactive Classroom PowerPoint® Presentations

Focus on Mathematical Content

Conjunction or Disjunction
When $b > 0$, inequalities of the form $|x| < b$ are equivalent to the conjunction $x < b$ and $x > -b$. Inequalities of the form $|x| > b$ are equivalent to the disjunction $x > b$ or $x < -b$.

Focus on Mathematics

Absolute Value Inequalities
Example 2 shows how to solve an absolute value inequality in the form of $|x| > n$. **Example 3** shows how to solve an absolute value inequality involving a real-world situation.

Consider the inequality $|x| > n$. $|x| > 5$ means that the distance from 0 to x is greater than 5 units.

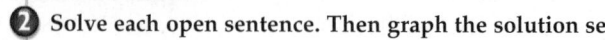

Therefore, $x < -5$ or $x > 5$. The solution set is $\{x \mid x < -5 \text{ or } x > 5\}$.

When solving inequalities of the form $|x| > n$, consider the two cases.

Case 1 The expression inside the absolute value symbols is positive.

Case 2 The expression inside the absolute value symbols is negative.

To solve, find the *union* of the solutions of these two cases.

EXAMPLE   Solve an Absolute Value Inequality (>)

2 Solve each open sentence. Then graph the solution set.

a. $|2x + 8| \geq 6$

Study Tip

Greater Than
When the absolute value is on the left and the inequality symbol is > or ≥, the compound sentence uses *or*.

    Case 1 $2x + 8$ is positive.

$2x + 8 \geq 6$	Definition of Absolute Value
$2x + 8 - 8 \geq 6 - 8$	Subtract 8 from each side.
$2x \geq -2$	Simplify.
$\dfrac{2x}{2} \geq \dfrac{-2}{2}$	Divide each side by 2.
$x \geq -1$	Simplify.

    Case 2 $2x + 8$ is negative.

$-(2x + 8) \geq 6$	Definition of Absolute Value
$2x + 8 \leq -6$	Divide each side by −1 and reverse the symbol.
$2x + 8 - 8 \leq -6 - 8$	Subtract 8 from each side.
$2x \leq -14$	Simplify.
$\dfrac{2x}{2} \leq \dfrac{-14}{2}$	Divide each side by 2.
$x \leq -7$	Simplify.

The solution set is $\{x \mid x \leq -7 \text{ or } x \geq -1\}$.

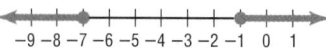

b. $|2y - 1| \geq -4$

Since $|2y - 1|$ is always greater than or equal to 0, the solution set is $\{y \mid y \text{ is a real number}\}$. Its graph is the entire number line.

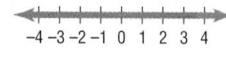

✓ CHECK Your Progress   2A–2B. See Ch. 6 Answer Appendix.

2A. $|2k + 1| > 7$ **2B.** $|r - 6| \geq -5$

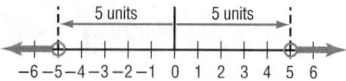 **Personal Tutor at** ca.algebra1.com

---

Student Misconceptions

Students may be confused about why $|t + 5| < 9$ is rewritten as $t + 5 < 9$ and $t + 5 > -9$. Tell them that an alternative method is to rewrite the inequality as $t + 5 < 9$ and $(t + 5) < 9$ and multiply each side of the second inequality by −1 to yield $t + 5 > -9$. This method makes the switch of the direction of the inequality more obvious, as students must make the switch when they divide each side by −1.

In general, there are three rules to remember when solving equations and inequalities involving absolute value.

CONCEPT SUMMARY   *Absolute Value Equations and Inequalities*

If $|x| = n$, then $x = -n$ or $x = n$.

If $|x| < n$, then $x < n$ and $x > -n$.

If $|x| > n$, then $x > n$ or $x < -n$.

These properties are also true when $>$ or $<$ is replaced with $\geq$ or $\leq$.

Applying Absolute Value Inequalities Many situations can be represented using an absolute value inequality.

Real-World EXAMPLE

3   **BIOLOGY** The pH is a measure of the acidity of a solution. The pH of a healthy human stomach is about 2.5 and is within 0.5 pH of this value. Find the range of pH levels of a healthy stomach.

The difference between the actual pH of a stomach and the ideal pH of a stomach is less than or equal to 0.5. Let x be the actual pH of a stomach. Then $|x - 2.5| \leq 0.5$.

Solve each case of the inequality.

Case 1	Case 2
$x - 2.5 \leq 0.5$	$-(x - 2.5) \leq 0.5$
$x - 2.5 + 2.5 \leq 0.5 + 2.5$	$x - 2.5 \geq -0.5$
$x \leq 3.0$	$x - 2.5 + 2.5 \geq -0.5 + 2.5$
	$x \geq 2.0$

The range of pH levels of a healthy stomach is $\{x \mid 2.0 \leq x \leq 3.0\}$.

CHECK Your Progress

3. CHEMISTRY The melting point of ice is 0° Celsius. During a chemistry experiment, Jill observed ice melting within 2 degrees. Write the range of temperatures that Jill observed ice melting. $\{x \mid -2 \leq x \leq 2\}$

CHECK Your Understanding

Examples 1, 2
(p. 330)

Solve each open sentence. Then graph the solution set.

1. $|c - 2| < 6$ **2.** $|x + 5| \leq 3$ **3.** $|m - 4| \leq -3$

4. $|10 - w| > 15$ **5.** $|2g + 5| \geq 7$ **6.** $|3p + 2| \geq -8$
1–6. See Ch. 6 Answer Appendix.

Example 3
(p. 331)

7. MANUFACTURING A manufacturer produces bolts which must have a diameter within 0.001 centimeter of 1.5 centimeters. What are the acceptable measurements for the diameter of the bolts? $\{d \mid 1.499 \leq d \leq 1.501\}$

greatest acceptable diameter
1.5 cm
least acceptable diameter

Lesson 6-6 Solving Inequalities Involving Absolute Value   **331**

ADDITIONAL EXAMPLES

2 Solve each open sentence. Then graph the solution set.

a. $|3y - 3| > 9$
$\{y \mid y < -2 \text{ or } y > 4\}$

$-3 -2 -1 \ 0 \ 1 \ 2 \ 3 \ 4 \ 5$

b. $|2x + 7| \geq -11$
$\{x \mid x \text{ is a real number}\}$

$-5 -4 -3 -2 -1 \ 0 \ 1 \ 2 \ 3 \ 4 \ 5$

3 The average annual rainfall in California for the last 100 years is 23 inches. However, the annual rainfall can differ by 10 inches from the 100 year average. What is the range of annual rainfall for California? $13 \leq x \leq 33$

3 Practice

Formative Assessment

Use Exercises 1-7 to check for understanding.

Then use the chart at the bottom of this page to customize assignments for your students.

Odd/Even Assignments
Exercises 8-18 are structured so that students practice the same concepts whether they are assigned odd or even problems.

Real-World Connections
For Exercise 17, you may wish to tell students that the pressure of a scuba tank is not a measure of the size or volume of a tank. For example, a small scuba tank may contain 6 cubic feet of air while a large tank may contain as much as 80 cubic feet of air. Both tanks will have the same fill pressure of 2500 psi $\pm$ 500 psi.

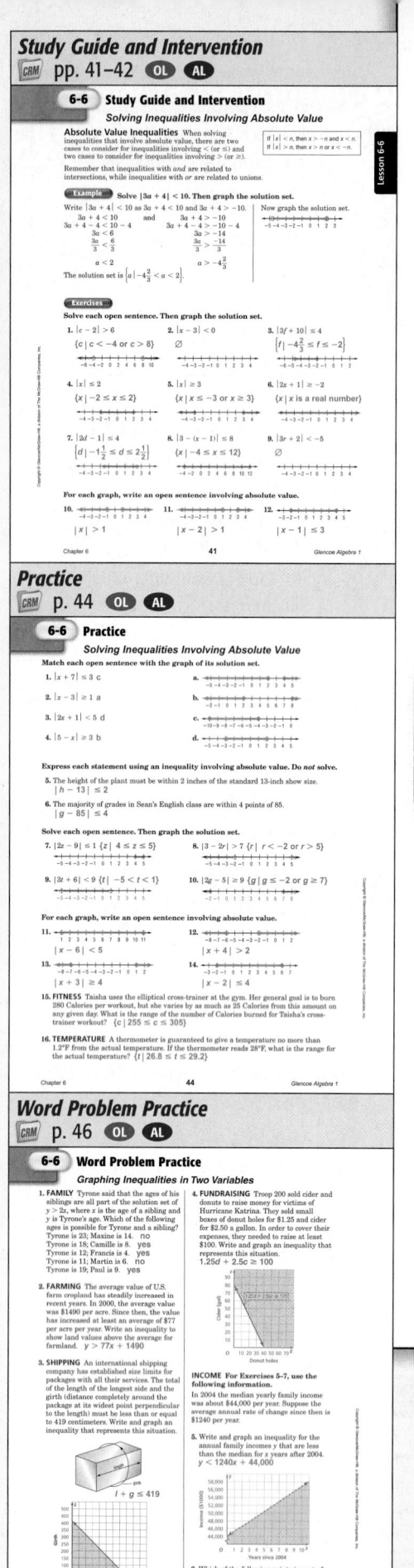

Exercises

<table>
<tr><td colspan="2">HOMEWORK HELP</td></tr>
</table>

For Exercises	See Examples
8–6	1, 2
17, 18, 31–34	3

Exercise Levels
A: 8–18
B: 19–30
C: 35–38

19. $|x| \leq 3$
20. $|x + 3| < 4$

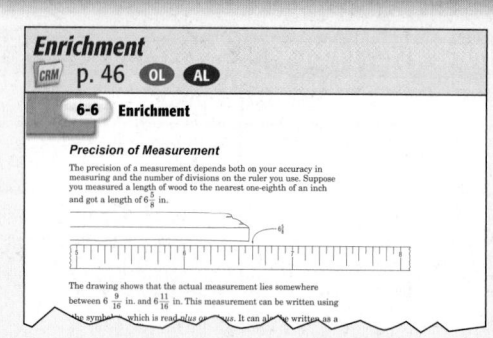

Real-World Link

Always inflate your tires to the pressure that is recommended by the manufacturer. The pressure stamped on the tire is the *maximum* pressure and should only be used under certain circumstances.

Source: www.etires.com

EXTRA PRACTICE
See pages 730, 749.

Math Online
Self-Check Quiz at
ca.algebra1.com

Solve each open sentence. Then graph the solution set.

8. $|z - 2| \leq 5$ 9. $|t + 8| < 2$ 10. $|6 - d| \leq -4$
11. $|v + 3| > 1$ 12. $|w - 6| \geq 3$ 13. $|3a - 9| > -2$
14. $|3k + 4| \geq 8$ 15. $|2n + 1| < 9$ 16. $|4q + 7| \leq -13$

8–16. See Ch. 6 Answer Appendix.

17. **SCUBA DIVING** The pressure of a typical scuba tank should be within 500 pounds per square inch (psi) of 2500 psi. Write the range of optimum pressures for scuba tanks. $\{p \mid 2000 < p < 3000\}$

18. **ANIMALS** A sheep's normal body temperature is 39°C. However, a healthy sheep may have body temperatures 1°C above or below this temperature. What is the range of body temperatures for a sheep? $\{t \mid 38 \leq t \leq 40\}$

Write an open sentence involving absolute value for each graph.

19. 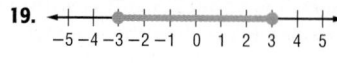   20.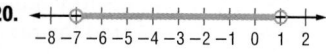

21.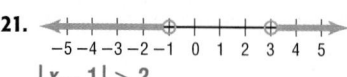
$|x - 1| > 2$

22.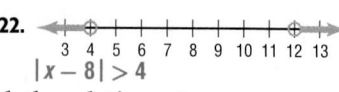
$|x - 8| > 4$

Solve each open sentence. Then graph the solution set.

23. $\left|\dfrac{5h + 2}{6}\right| = 7$ 24. $\left|\dfrac{2 - 3x}{5}\right| \geq 2$

25. $|3s + 2| > -7$ 26. $|6r + 8| < -4$

23–26. See Ch. 6 Answer Appendix.

Express each statement using an inequality involving absolute value. Do *not* solve. 27. $|p - 7.5| \leq 0.3$ 28. $|t - 38| \leq 1.5$

27. The pH of a swimming pool must be within 0.3 of a pH of 7.5.
28. The temperature inside a refrigerator should be within 1.5 degrees of 38°F.
29. Ramona's bowling score was within 6 points of her average score of 98.
30. The cruise control of a car set at 55 miles per hour should keep the speed within 3 miles per hour of 55. $|s - 55| \leq 3$

29. $|s - 98| \leq 6$

31. **DRIVING** Tires should be kept within 2 pounds per square inch (psi) of the manufacturer's recommended tire pressure. If the recommendation for a tire is 30 psi, what is the range of acceptable pressures? $\{p \mid 28 \leq p \leq 32\}$

32. **PHYSICAL SCIENCE** Li-Cheng must add 3.0 milliliters of sodium chloride to a solution. The sodium chloride must be within 0.5 milliliter of the required amount. How much sodium chloride can she add and obtain the correct results? $\{a \mid 2.5 \leq a \leq 3.5\}$

33. **MINIATURE GOLF** Ginger played miniature golf. Her score was within 5 strokes of her average score of 52. Determine the range of scores for Ginger's game. $|g - 52| \leq 5$

34. **MUSIC DOWNLOADS** Carlos is allowed to download $10 worth of music each month. This month he has spent within $3 of his allowance. What is the range of money he has spent on music downloads this month?
$|d - 10| \leq 3$

Enrichment
CRM p. 46 OL AL

6-6 Enrichment

Precision of Measurement

The precision of a measurement depends both on your accuracy in measuring and the number of divisions on the ruler you use. Suppose you measured a length of wood to the nearest one-eighth of an inch and got a length of $6\frac{5}{8}$ in.

The drawing shows that the actual measurement lies somewhere between $6\frac{9}{16}$ in. and $6\frac{11}{16}$ in. This measurement can be written using the symbol ± which is read *plus or minus*. It can also be written as a

BL = Below Grade Level
OL = On Grade Level
AL = Above Grade Level
ELL = English Language Learner

Additional pages not shown:
CRM **Lesson Reading Guide,** p. 40 BL OL ELL
CRM **Skills Practice,** p. 43 BL OL

H.O.T. Problems

35–38.
See Ch. 6
Answer Appendix.

35. REASONING Compare and contrast the solution of $|x - 2| > 6$ and the solution of $|x - 2| < 6$.

36. OPEN ENDED Formulate an absolute value inequality to represent a real-world situation and graph its solution set. Interpret the solution.

37. CHALLENGE Translate the inequality $x < 2 \pm 0.3$ into an absolute value inequality.

38. *Writing in Math* Refer to the information on page 329. Describe how the definition of absolute value can be applied to manufacturing baby carrots. Write an absolute value inequality to represent the range of lengths for a baby carrot.

STANDARDS PRACTICE 3.0, 5.0, 7MG2.3

39. What is the solution to the inequality $-6 < |x| < 6$? **C**

A $-x \geq 0$ C $-x < 6$

B $x \leq 0$ D $-x > 6$

40. Which inequality *best* represents the statement below?
A jar contains 832 gumballs. Amanda's guess was within 46 pieces. **F**

F $|g - 832| \leq 46$ H $|g - 832| \geq 46$

G $|g + 832| \leq 46$ J $|g + 832| \geq 46$

41. REVIEW An 84-centimeter piece of wire is cut into equal segments and then attached at the ends to form the edges of a cube. What is the volume of the cube? **B**

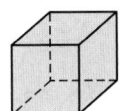

A 294 cm^3 C 1158 cm^3

B 343 cm^3 D 2744 cm^3

Spiral Review

Solve each open sentence. Then graph the solution set. (Lesson 6-5)

42–44. See Ch. 6 Answer Appendix.

42. $|x + 3| = 5$ **43.** $|2x + 3| = -4$ **44.** $|3x - 2| = 4$

45. SHOPPING A catalog company varies the costs to ship merchandise based on the amount of the order. The cost for shipping is shown in the table. Write a compound inequality for each shipping cost. (Lesson 6-4)
$0 \leq x \leq 25; 25.01 \leq x \leq 50$

Shipping Costs	
Merchandise	**Shipping**
$0–$25	$5
$25.01–$50	$8

Write an equation in slope-intercept form of the line with the given slope and y-intercept. (Lesson 4-3)

46. slope: -3, y-intercept: 4
$y = -3x + 4$

47. slope: $\frac{1}{2}$, y-intercept: $\frac{3}{4}$ $y = \frac{1}{2}x + \frac{3}{4}$

GET READY for the Next Lesson

PREREQUISITE SKILL Graph each equation. (Lesson 3-3) 48–51. See Ch. 6 Answer Appendix.

48. $y = 3x + 4$ **49.** $x + y = 3$ **50.** $y - 2x = -1$ **51.** $2y - x = -6$

Lesson 6-6 Solving Inequalities Involving Absolute Value **333**

4 Assess

Crystal Ball Have students write how they think what they learned in today's lesson will connect to the next lesson *Graphing Inequalities in Two Variables.*

 Formative Assessment

Check for student understanding of concepts in Lessons 6-5 and 6-6.

[CRM] Quiz 3, p. 68

 Foldables™ Follow-Up

At the end of this lesson, remind students to take notes and show examples of absolute value inequalities.

Pre-AP Activity   Use after Exercise 26

Draw a number line on the board or overhead. Have a student use your number line to create the graph of an absolute value inequality. Ask the rest of the class to write the inequality that the graph models.

1 Focus

Standards Alignment

Before Lesson 6-7
Solve two-step linear equations and inequalities in one variable from ☛ Standard 7AF4.1

Lesson 6-7
Graph a linear equation or inequality from ☛ Standard 6.0

After Lesson 6-7
Solve systems of linear equations and inequalities by substitution, with graphs, or with matrices from ☛ Standard 2A2.0

2 Teach

Scaffolding Questions

Have students read *Get Ready for the Lesson.*

Ask:

- What does the 3 in the quantity $3x$ represent? $3; her average cost of a cafeteria lunch

- What does the 4 in the quantity $4y$ represent? a $4 restaurant lunch

- Why can't this problem be represented with an inequality containing only one variable? It cannot be represented this way because the amount Hannah spends on cafeteria lunches and the amount she spends on restaurant lunches is not the same.

Lesson 6-7 Resources

Chapter 6 Resource Masters

Lesson Reading Guide, p. 48 **BL** **OL** **ELL**
Study Guide and Intervention, pp. 49–50
BL **OL** **ELL**
Skills Practice, p. 51 **BL** **OL**
Practice, p. 52 **OL** **AL**
Word Problem Practice, p. 53 **OL** **AL**
Enrichment, p. 54 **OL** **AL**
Spreadsheet, p. 55 **BL** **OL** **AL**

Transparencies

5-Minute Check Transparency 6-6

Additional Print Resources

Noteables™ Interactive Study Notebook with Foldables™

Technology

ca.algebra1.com
Interactive Classroom CD-ROM
AssignmentWorks CD-ROM
Graphing Calculator Easy Files

Main Ideas

- Graph inequalities on the coordinate plane.
- Solve real-world problems involving linear inequalities.

Standard 6.0
Students graph a linear equation and compute the *x*- and *y*-intercepts (e.g., graph $2x + 6y = 4$). **They are also able to sketch the region defined by linear inequality (e.g., they sketch the region defined by $2x + 6y < 4$).** (Key, CAHSEE)

New Vocabulary

half-plane
boundary

▶ GET READY **for the Lesson**

Hannah budgets $30 a month for lunch. On most days, she brings her lunch. She can also buy lunch at the cafeteria or at a fast-food restaurant. She spends an average of $3 for lunch at the cafeteria and an average of $4 for lunch at a restaurant. How many times a month can Hannah buy her lunch and remain within her budget?

	My Monthly Budget
○	Lunch (school days) $30
	Entertainment $55
○	Clothes $50
	Fuel $60

There are many solutions for this inequality. Each solution represents a different combination of lunches bought in the cafeteria and in a restaurant.

Words	The cost of eating in the cafeteria	plus	the cost of eating in a restaurant	is less than or equal to	$30.
Variables	Let x = the number of days she buys lunch at the cafeteria.		Let y = the number of days she buys lunch at a restaurant.		
Inequality	$3x$	+	$4y$	≤	30

Graph Linear Inequalities The solution set for an inequality in two variables contains many ordered pairs when the domain and range are the set of real numbers. The graphs of all of these ordered pairs fill a region on the coordinate plane called a **half-plane**. An equation defines the **boundary** or edge for each half-plane.

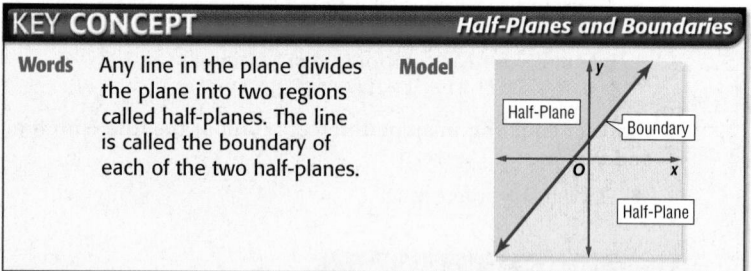

KEY **CONCEPT** *Half-Planes and Boundaries*

Words Any line in the plane divides the plane into two regions called half-planes. The line is called the boundary of each of the two half-planes.

Model

The boundary may or may not be included in the graph of an inequality. Graphing the boundary is the first step in graphing a linear inequality.

Consider the graph of $y > 4$. First determine the boundary by graphing $y = 4$, the equation you obtain by replacing the inequality sign with an equals sign. Since the inequality involves y-values greater than 4, but not equal to 4, the line should be dashed. The boundary divides the coordinate plane into two half-planes.

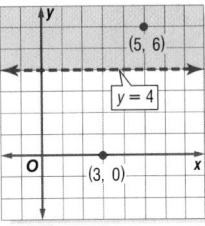

To determine which half-plane contains the solution, choose a point from each half-plane and test it in the inequality.

Try $(3, 0)$.   Try $(5, 6)$.

$y > 4$ $y = 0$ $y > 4$ $y = 6$

$0 > 4$ false $6 > 4$ true

The half-plane that contains $(5, 6)$ contains the solution. Shade that half-plane.

EXAMPLE Graph an Inequality

1 Graph $y - 2x \le -4$.

Step 1 Solve for y in terms of x.

$y - 2x \le -4$ Original inequality

$y - 2x + 2x \le -4 + 2x$ Add $2x$ to each side.

$y \le 2x - 4$ Simplify.

Step 2 Graph $y = 2x - 4$. Since $y \le 2x - 4$ means $y < 2x - 4$ or $y = 2x - 4$, the boundary is included in the solution set. The boundary should be drawn as a solid line.

Step 3 Select a point in one of the half-planes and test it. Let's use $(0, 0)$.

$y - 2x \le -4$ Original inequality

$0 - 2(0) \le -4$ $x = 0, y = 0$

$0 \le -4$ false

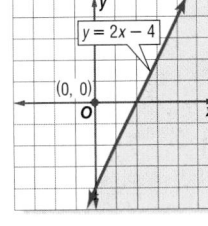

Since the statement is false, the half-plane containing the origin is not part of the solution. Shade the other half-plane.

CHECK Test a point in the other half plane, for example, $(3, -3)$.

$y - 2x \le -4$ Original inequality

$-3 - 2(3) \le -4$ $x = 3, y = -3$

$-9 \le -4$ ✔   Simplify.

Since the statement is true, the half-plane containing $(3, -3)$ should be shaded. The graph of the solution is correct.

CHECK Your Progress Graph each inequality. 1A–1B. See margin.

1A. $x \le -1$ **1B.** $y > \frac{1}{2}x + 3$

Graph Linear Inequalities

Example 1 shows how to graph an inequality by first graphing the equation that defines the boundary for each half-plane.

Formative Assessment

Use the Check Your Progress exercises after each example to determine students' understanding of concepts.

Tips for New Teachers **Preventing Errors**

Students may need a quick refresher on slope-intercept form before they graph inequalities. Remind students that slope-intercept form is $y = mx + b$.

ADDITIONAL EXAMPLE

1 Graph $2y - 4x > 6$.

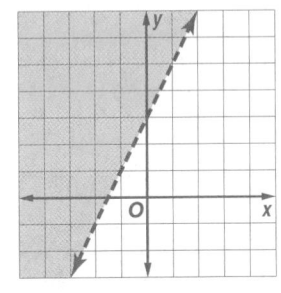

Additional Examples are also in:

• Noteables™ Interactive Study Notebook with Foldables™

• Interactive Classroom PowerPoint® Presentations

Additional Answers

1A.

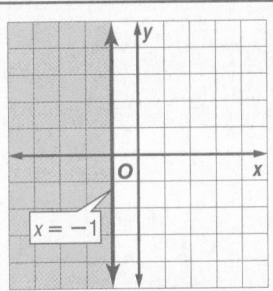

1B.

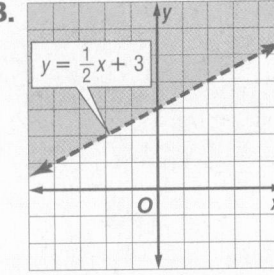

Solve Real-World Problems

Example 2 shows how to write, solve, and graph an inequality involving a real-world situation.

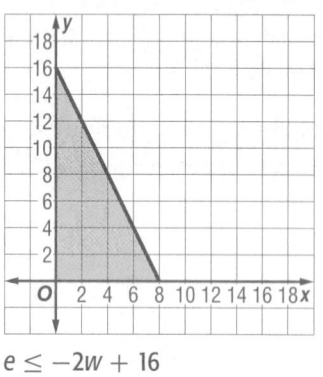
Solve Real-World Problems

Solve Real-World Problems When solving real-world inequalities, the domain and range of the inequality are often restricted to nonnegative numbers or whole numbers.

Real-World EXAMPLE   Write and Solve an Inequality

2 **ADVERTISING** Rosa Padilla sells radio advertising in 30-second and 60-second time slots. During every hour, there are up to 15 minutes available for commercials. How many commercial slots can she sell for one hour of broadcasting?

Explore   You know the length of the time slots in seconds and the number of minutes each hour available for commercials.

Plan   Let $x =$ the number of 30-second commercials. Let $y =$ the number of 60-second or 1-minute commercials. Write an open sentence representing this situation.

$\frac{1}{2}$ min	times	the number of 30-s commercials	plus	1 min	times	the number of 1-min commercials	is up to	15 min.
$\frac{1}{2}$	$\cdot$	x	$+$	1	$\cdot$	y	$\leq$	15

Solve   Solve for y in terms of x.

$$\frac{1}{2}x + y \leq 15 \qquad \text{Original inequality}$$

$$\frac{1}{2}x + y - \frac{1}{2}x \leq 15 - \frac{1}{2}x \qquad \text{Subtract } \tfrac{1}{2}x \text{ from each side.}$$

$$y \leq 15 - \frac{1}{2}x \qquad \text{Simplify.}$$

Since the open sentence includes the equation, graph $y = 15 - \frac{1}{2}x$ as a solid line. Test a point in one of the half-planes, for example $(0, 0)$. Shade the half-plane containing $(0, 0)$ since

$$0 \leq 15 - \frac{1}{2}(0) \text{ is true.}$$

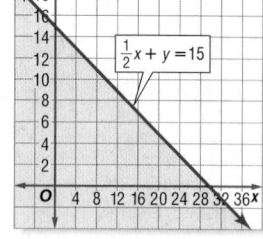

Check   Examine the solution.
- Rosa cannot sell a negative number of commercials. Therefore, the domain and range contain only nonnegative numbers.
- She also cannot sell half of a commercial. Thus, only points in the shaded half-plane with x- and y-coordinates that are whole numbers are possible solutions.

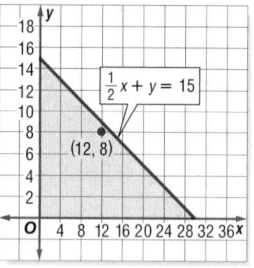

One solution is $(12, 8)$. This represents twelve 30-second commercials and eight 60-second commercials in a one hour period.

Additional Answer (Check Your Progress)   **2.**

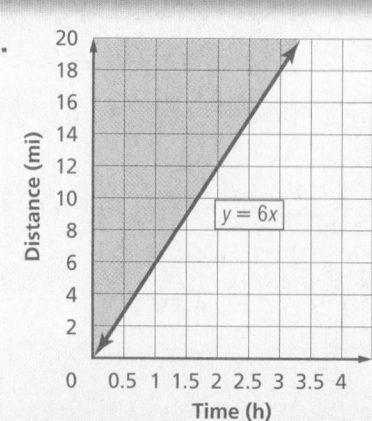

✓ CHECK Your Progress

2. **MARATHONS** Neil wants to run a marathon at a pace of at least 6 miles per hour. Write an inequality for the miles y he will run in x hours and graph the solution set. $y \geq 6x$; See margin for graph.

Online Personal Tutor at ca.algebra1.com

★ indicates multi-step problem

✓ CHECK Your Understanding

Example 1
(p. 335)

Graph each inequality. 1–6. See Ch. 6 Answer Appendix.

1. $y \geq 4$
2. $y \leq 2x - 3$
3. $y > x + 3$
4. $4 - 2x < -2$
5. $1 - y > x$
6. $x + 2y \leq 5$

Example 2
(pp. 336–337)

★ **7. ENTERTAINMENT** Coach Washington wants to take her softball team out for pizza and soft drinks after the last game of the season. She doesn't want to spend more than $60. Write an inequality that represents this situation and graph the solution set. **See margin.**

 Welcome to Angelo's Pizza!

Large Pizza $12

Pitcher of soft drink $3

Exercises

HOMEWORK HELP	
For Exercises	See Examples
8–17	1
18–21	2

Exercise Levels
A: 8–17
B: 23–37
C: 38–41

Cross-Curricular Project

Math Online A linear inequality can be used to represent trends in Olympic times. Visit ca.algebra1.com to continue work on your project.

Graph each inequality. 8–17. See Ch. 6 Answer Appendix.

8. $y < -3$
9. $x \geq 2$
10. $5x + 10y > 0$
11. $y < x$
12. $2y - x \leq 6$
13. $6x + 3y > 9$
14. $3y - 4x \geq 12$
15. $y \leq -2x - 4$
16. $8x - 6y < 10$
17. $3x - 1 \geq y$

POSTAGE For Exercises 18 and 19, use the following information.
The U.S. Postal Service limits the size of packages. The length of the longest side plus the distance around the thickest part must be less than or equal to 108 inches.

18. Write an inequality that represents this situation. $\ell + d \leq 108$

19. Are there any restrictions on the domain or range? Explain.
The solution set is limited to pairs of positive numbers.

ANALYZE TABLES For Exercises 20–22, use the table.
A delivery truck with a 4000-pound weight limit is transporting televisions and microwaves.

Item	Weight (lb)
television	77
microwave	55

★ 20. Define variables and write an inequality for this situation. **20–22. See margin.**

21. Will the truck be able to deliver 35 televisions and 25 microwaves at once?

★ 22. Write two possible solutions to the inequality. Are there solutions that make the inequality mathematically true, but are not reasonable in the context of the problem? Explain.

Lesson 6-7 Graphing Inequalities in Two Variables **337**

3 Practice

✓ Formative Assessment

Use Exercises 1–7 to check for understanding.

Use the chart at the bottom of this page to customize assignments for your students.

Odd/Even Assignments
Exercises 8–17 are structured so that students practice the same concepts whether they are assigned odd or even problems.

Additional Answers

7. $12x + 3y \leq 60$

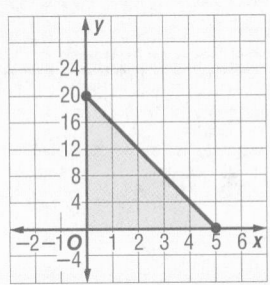

20. Sample answer: Let $t =$ the weight of a television and let $m =$ the weight of a microwave; $77t + 55m \leq 4000$.

21. No, the weight will be greater than 4000 pounds.

22. Sample answer: (5, 10) and (20, 20); yes, $(-10, -8)$ is a solution that makes the inequality true, but it does make sense to have a negative number of items. So, $(-10, -8)$ is not a solution for this problem.

DIFFERENTIATED HOMEWORK OPTIONS			
Level	Assignment	Two-Day Option	
BL Basic	8–21, 37–39, 41–59	9–17 odd, 42, 43	8–16 even, 37–39, 41, 44–59
OL Core	9–33 odd, 35–39, 41–59	8–17, 42, 43	18–39, 41, 44–59
AL Advanced /Pre-AP	18–56 (optional: 57–59)		

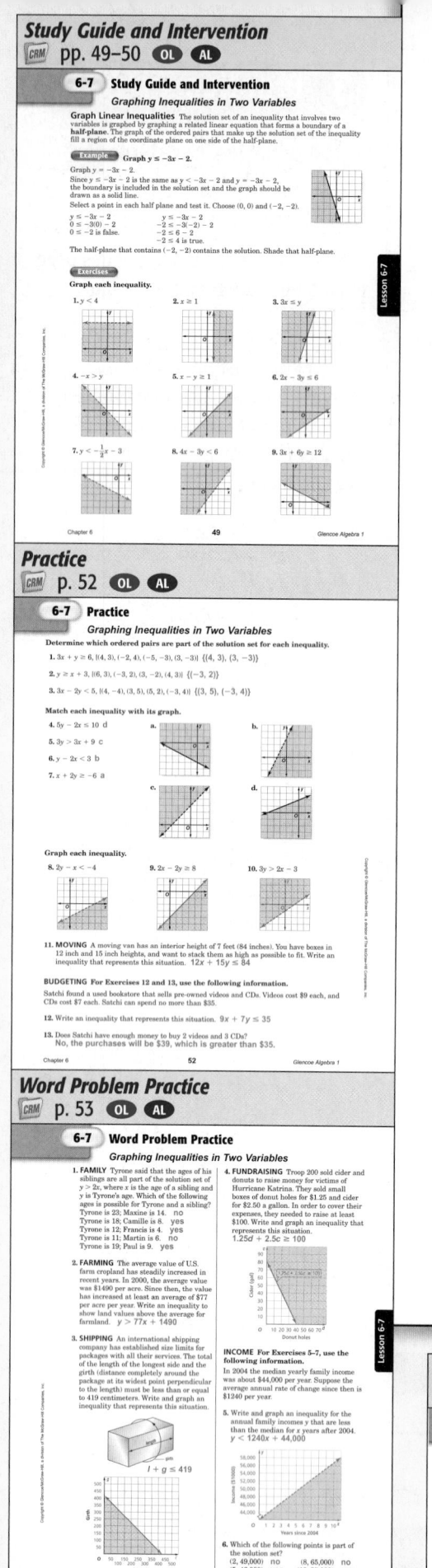

Study Guide and Intervention — pp. 49–50

Practice — p. 52

Word Problem Practice — p. 53

Enrichment — p. 54

Determine which ordered pairs are part of the solution set for each inequality.

23. $y \le 3 - 2x$, $\{(0, 4), (-1, 3), (6, -8), (-4, 5)\}$ $\{(-1, 3), (-4, 5)\}$

24. $y < 3x$, $\{(-3, 1), (-3, 2), (1, 1), (1, 2)\}$ $\{(1, 1), (1, 2)\}$

25. $x + y < 11$, $\{(5, 7), (-13, 10), (4, 4), (-6, -2)\}$ $\{(-13, 10), (4, 4), (-6, -2)\}$

26. $2x - 3y > 6$, $\{(3, 2), (-2, -4), (6, 2), (5, 1)\}$ $\{(-2, -4), (5, 1)\}$

Match each inequality with its graph.

a.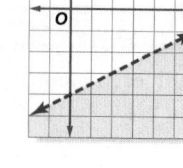

b.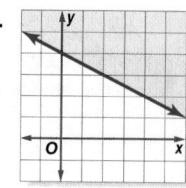

27. $2y + x \le 6$ c

28. $\frac{1}{2}x - y > 4$ a

29. $y > 3 + \frac{1}{2}x$ d

30. $4y + 2x \ge 16$ b

Determine which ordered pairs are part of the solution set for each inequality.

c.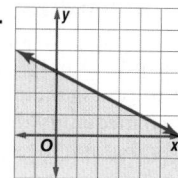

d.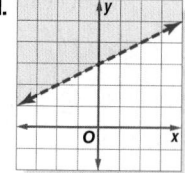

31. $|x - 3| \ge y$, $\{(6, 4), (-1, 8), (-3, 2), (5, 7)\}$ $\{(-3, 2)\}$

32. $|y + 2| < x$, $\{(2, -4), (-1, -5), (6, -7), (0, 0)\}$ $\{(6, -7)\}$

Graph each inequality. 33–34. See Ch. 6 Answer Appendix.

33. $3(x + 2y) > -18$

34. $\frac{1}{2}(2x + y) < 2$

MUSEUMS For Exercises 35 and 36, use the table at the right. **35.** $8x + 4y \le 96$
A Cub Scout troop plans to visit a flight museum. The troop leaders can spend up to $96 on admission.

Flight Museum	
Visitor	**Admission Cost**
adult	$8.00
children 6–12 years old	$4.00

35. Write an inequality for this situation.

36. Will the entire troop be able to go to the museum if there are 3 adults and 16 Cub Scouts who are all under 12 years old? Explain.
Yes; the admission cost of 3 adults and 16 children is $88, which is less than $96.

37. REASONING Compare and contrast the graph of $y = x + 2$ and the graph of $y < x + 2$.

38. OPEN ENDED Create a linear inequality in two variables and graph it.
Sample answer: $x > y$; See Ch. 6 Answer Appendix for graph.

39. REASONING Explain why it is usually only necessary to test one point when graphing an inequality. See margin.

40. CHALLENGE Graph the intersection of the graphs of $y \le x - 1$ and $y \ge -x$.
See Ch. 6 Answer Appendix.

41. *Writing in Math* Use the information about budgets on page 334 to explain how inequalities are used in finances. Include an explanation of the restrictions placed on the domain and range of the inequality that describes the number of times Hannah can buy lunch. Describe three possible solutions of the inequality. See margin.

H.O.T. Problems

37. The graph of $y = x + 2$ is a line. The graph of $y < x + 2$ does not include the boundary $y = x + 2$, and it includes all ordered pairs in the half-plane that contains the origin.

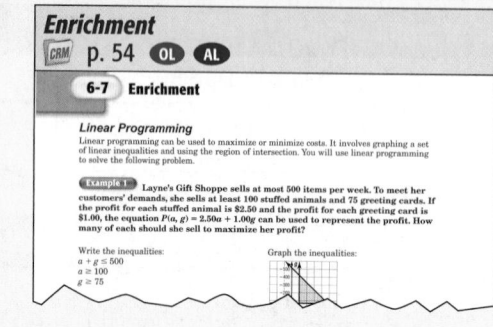

42. Which inequality is shown on the graph at the right? **B**

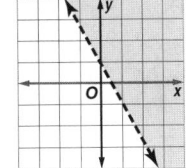

A $2x + y < 1$

B $2x + y > 1$

C $2x + y \leq 1$

D $2x + y \geq 1$

43. REVIEW The perimeters of two similar polygons are 250 centimeters and 300 centimeters, respectively. What is the scale factor of the two polygons? **F**

F $\frac{5}{6}$

G $\frac{3}{4}$

H $\frac{1}{2}$

J $\frac{1}{4}$

Spiral Review

BIOLOGY For Exercises 44 and 45, use the following information.
The *average* length of a human pregnancy is 280 days. However, a healthy, full-term pregnancy can be 14 days longer or shorter. (Lesson 6-6)

44. If d is the length in days, write an absolute value inequality for the length of a full-term pregnancy. $|d - 280| \leq 14$

45. Solve the inequality for the length of a full-term pregnancy. $\{d \mid 266 \leq d \leq 294\}$

Solve each open sentence. Then graph the solution. (Lesson 6-4) **46–47. See margin.**

46. $|y + 0.5| = 6.5$

47. $|m - 0.5| = 2.5$

Write an equation in slope-intercept form of the line that passes through the given point and is parallel to the graph of each equation. (Lesson 4-7)

48. $(1, -3); y = 3x - 2$
$y = 3x - 6$

49. $(0, 4); x + y = -3$
$y = -x + 4$

50. $(-1, 2); 2x - y = 1$
$y = 2x + 4$

Find the next two terms in each sequence. (Lesson 3-4)

51. $7, 13, 19, 25, \ldots$
$31, 37$

52. $243, 81, 27, 9, \ldots$
$3, 1$

53. $3, 6, 12, 24, \ldots$
$48, 96$

State whether each percent of change is a percent of *increase* or *decrease*. Then find the percent of change. Round to the nearest whole percent. (Lesson 2-7)

54. original: 200
new: 172
decrease; 14%

55. original: 100
new: 142
increase; 42%

56. original: 53
new: 75
increase; 42%

GET READY for the Next Lesson

PREREQUISITE SKILL Graph each equation. (Lesson 4-3) **57–59. See Ch. 6 Answer Appendix.**

57. $y = 3x + 1$

58. $x - y = -4$

59. $5x + 2y = 6$

---

4 Assess

Crystal Ball Have students write how they think what they learned today about graphing inequalities will connect to the next lesson on graphing systems of linear inequalities.

FOLDABLES Study Organizer **Foldables™ Follow-Up**
Remind students to record notes about and examples of graphing inequalities in two variables in their Foldables.

Additional Answers

39. If the test point results in a true statement, shade the half-plane that contains the point. If the test point results in a false statement, shade the other half-plane.

41. The amount of money spent in each category must be less than or equal to the budgeted amount. How much you spend on individual items can vary. The domain and range must be positive integers. Sample answers: Hannah could buy 5 cafeteria lunches and 3 restaurant lunches, 2 cafeteria lunches and 5 restaurant lunches, or 8 cafeteria lunches and 1 restaurant lunch.

46. $\{-7, 6\}$

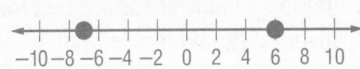

47. $\{-2, 3\}$

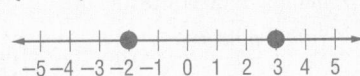

Pre-AP Activity Use as an Extension

Challenge students to write an inequality for the graph whose boundary passes through the points at $(4, -2)$ and $(-3, -2)$ and whose solution set contains the boundary and all the points above the boundary. $y \geq -2$

1 Focus

Objective Use a graphing calculator to investigate the graphs of inequalities.

Materials
• graphing calculator

Teaching Tip Have students enter the keystrokes [2nd] [DRAW] 1 [ENTER] to clear any stored drawings. You may also need students to reset the viewing windows. Have them enter ZOOM 6 to graph in the standard viewing window.

2 Teach

Working in Cooperative Groups
Put students in groups of 2 or 3, mixing abilities. Have groups complete the Activity and Exercise 1.

• Point out that when using the DRAW menu instruction Shade the first boundary entered is always the lower boundary. The comma separates the lower and upper boundaries.

• An alternative method to graphing inequalities is to enter the function in the Y= table editor at $Y_1=$. Then highlight the symbol in front of the Y_1 entry and press [ENTER] until either shading above or below the symbol appears.

Practice Have students complete Exercises 2 and 3.

Additional Answers

1. $y \leq 3x + 1$ is shaded below the line $y = 3x + 1$. $y \geq 3x + 1$ is shaded above the line $y = 3x + 1$.

2a. $y = -2x + 4$; Ymax or 10

2b. Sample answer: $\{(0, 4), (-1, 7), (2, 6), (4.2, -1.5)\}$

3b. $y \geq -x + 10$; $y \leq -0.5x + 10$

340 **Chapter 6** Solving Linear Inequalities

Graphing Inequalities

Standard 6.0 Students graph a linear equation and compute the *x*- and *y*-intercepts (e.g., graph 2*x* + 6*y* = 4). **They are also able to sketch the region defined by linear inequality (e.g., they sketch the region defined by 2*x* + 6*y* < 4).** (Key, CAHSEE)

To graph inequalities, graphing calculators shade between two functions. Enter a lower boundary as well as an upper boundary for each inequality.

ACTIVITY 1 Graph two different inequalities on your graphing calculator.

Step 1 Graph $y \leq 3x + 1$.

• Clear all functions from the Y= list.

KEYSTROKES: [Y=] [CLEAR]

• Graph $y \leq 3x + 1$ in the standard window.

KEYSTROKES: [2nd] [DRAW] 7 −10 [,] 3 [X,T,θ,n] [+] 1 [)] [ENTER]

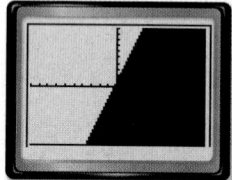

[−10, 10] scl: 1 by [−10, 10] scl: 1

The lower boundary is Ymin or −10. The upper boundary is $y = 3x + 1$. All ordered pairs for which *y* is *less than or equal to* $3x + 1$ lie *below or on* the line and are solutions.

Step 2 Graph $y - 3x \geq 1$.

• Clear the drawing that is displayed.

KEYSTROKES: [2nd] [DRAW] 1

• Rewrite $y - 3x \geq 1$ as $y \geq 3x + 1$ and graph it.

KEYSTROKES: [2nd] [DRAW] 7 3 [X,T,θ,n] [+] 1 [,] 10 [)] [ENTER]

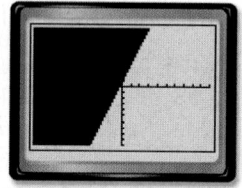

[−10, 10] scl: 1 by [−10, 10] scl: 1

The lower boundary is $y = 3x + 1$. The upper boundary is Ymax or 10. All ordered pairs for which *y* is *greater than or equal to* $3x + 1$ lie *above or on* the line and are solutions.

EXERCISES

1. Compare and contrast the two graphs shown above. **See margin.**

2. Graph the inequality $y \geq -2x + 4$ in the standard viewing window.
   a. What functions do you enter as the lower and upper boundaries? **See margin.**
   b. Using your graph, name four solutions of the inequality. **See margin.**

3. Suppose student movie tickets cost $4 and adult movie tickets cost $8. You would like to buy at least 10 tickets, but spend no more than $80.
   a. Let x = number of student tickets and y = number of adult tickets. Write two inequalities, one representing the total number of tickets and the other representing the total cost of the tickets. $x + y \geq 10$; $4x + 8y \leq 80$
   b. Which inequalities would you use as the lower and upper boundaries? **See margin.**
   c. Graph the inequalities. Use the viewing window [0, 20] scl: 1 by [0, 20] scl: 1.
   d. Name four possible combinations of student and adult tickets.
      3c–3d. See Ch. 6 Answer Appendix.

340 **Chapter 6** Solving Linear Inequalities

 Math Online Other Calculator Keystrokes at ca.algebra1.com

---

3 Assess

 Formative Assessment

Use Exercise 2 to assess whether students understand that the coordinates of all the points on the line or in the shaded region are solutions of the inequality.

From Concrete to Abstract
Ask: Why do the ordered pairs that lie on the line belong to the solution set of the inequality for Exercise 2? Sample answer: The equal sign is included with the inequality.

Graphing Systems of Inequalities

Main Ideas

- Solve systems of inequalities by graphing.
- Solve real-world problems involving systems of inequalities.

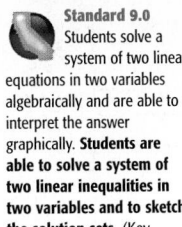 **Standard 9.0** Students solve a system of two linear equations in two variables algebraically and are able to interpret the answer graphically. **Students are able to solve a system of two linear inequalities in two variables and to sketch the solution sets.** (Key, CAHSEE)

New Vocabulary

system of inequalities

GET READY for the Lesson

Joshua's doctor recommends the following.
- Get between 60 and 80 grams of protein per day.
- Keep daily fat intake between 60 and 75 grams.

The green section of the graph indicates the appropriate amounts of protein and fat for Joshua.

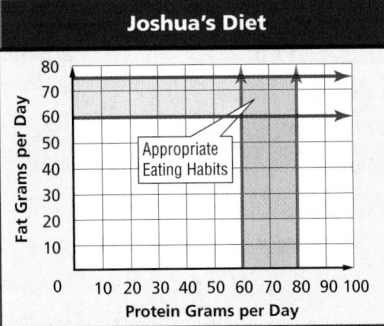

Joshua's Diet

Appropriate Eating Habits

Systems of Inequalities A **system of inequalities** is a set of two or more inequalities with the same variables. To solve a system of inequalities like the one above, find the ordered pairs that satisfy all the inequalities. The solution set is represented by the intersection, or overlap, of the graphs.

EXAMPLE   Solve by Graphing

 Solve each system of inequalities by graphing.

a. $y < -x + 1$
$y \leq 2x + 3$

The solution includes the ordered pairs in the intersection of the graphs of $y < -x + 1$ and $y \leq 2x + 3$. This region is shaded in green at the right. The graph of $y = -x + 1$ is dashed and is *not* included in the graph of $y < -x + 1$. The graph of $y = 2x + 3$ is solid and *is* included in the graph of $y \leq 2x + 3$.

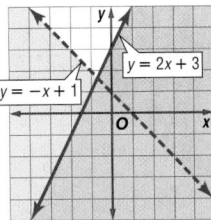

$y = -x + 1$ $y = 2x + 3$

b. $x - y < -1$
$x - y > 3$

The graphs of $x - y = -1$ and $x - y = 3$ are parallel lines. Because the two regions have no points in common, the system of inequalities has no solution.

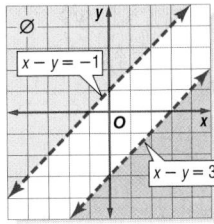

$x - y = -1$ $x - y = 3$

Concepts in MOtion
Animation ca.algebra1.com

 CHECK Your Progress

1A–1B. See Ch. 6 Answer Appendix.

1A. $y \leq 3$
$x + y \geq 1$

1B. $2x + y \geq 2$
$2x + y < 4$

Online Personal Tutor at ca.algebra1.com

1 Focus

Standards Alignment

Before Lesson 6-8
Write an expression, an equation, an inequality, or a system that represents a verbal description from Standard 7AF1.1

Lesson 6-8
Solve a system of two linear equations or inequalities in two variables algebraically and graphically from ━ Standard 9.0

After Lesson 6-8
Solve systems of linear equations and inequalities by substitution, with graphs, or with matrices from ━ Standard 2A2.0

2 Teach

Scaffolding Questions

Have students read *Get Ready for the Lesson*.

Ask:
- Does Joshua need to eat the exact same amount of protein and fat each day? Explain. No, but his protein and fat intake should be within the area of the graph labeled "Appropriate Eating Habits."
- Suppose Joshua eats 65 grams of protein one day, but only 55 grams of fat. Is this an appropriate intake of protein and fat? Why? no, because it does not fall within the area labeled "Appropriate Eating Habits"

Lesson 6-8 Resources

Chapter 6 Resource Masters

Lesson Reading Guide, p. 56 BL OL ELL
Study Guide and Intervention, pp. 57–58
BL OL ELL
Skills Practice, p. 59 BL OL
Practice, p. 60 OL AL
Word Problem Practice, p. 61 OL AL
Enrichment, p. 62 OL AL
Graphing Calculator, p. 63

Spreadsheet, p. 64
Quiz 4, p. 68

Transparencies

5-Minute Check Transparency 6-7

Additional Print Resources

Noteables™ Interactive Study Notebook with Foldables™

Technology

ca.algebra1.com
Interactive Classroom CD-ROM
AssignmentWorks Plus CD-ROM
Graphing Calculator Easy Files

Systems of Inequalities

Example 1 shows how to solve a system of inequalities by graphing.

ADDITIONAL EXAMPLE

1 Solve the system of inequalities by graphing.

a. $y < 2x + 2$
   $y \geq -x - 3$

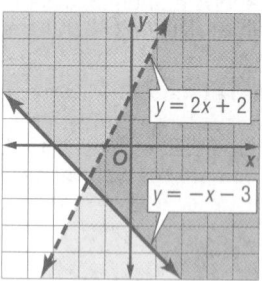

b. $y \geq -3x + 1$
   $y \leq -3x - 2$ ∅

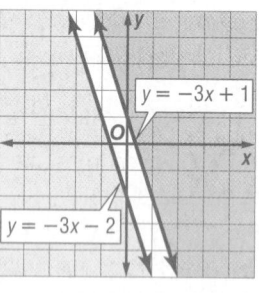

Additional Examples are also in:

• Noteables™ Interactive Study Notebook with Foldables™

• Interactive Classroom PowerPoint® Presentations

Real-World Link

The average first-year student at University of Massachusetts Amherst had a high school GPA of 3.38.

Source: umass.edu/oir

Real-World Problems In real-world problems involving systems of inequalities, sometimes only whole-number solutions make sense.

Real-World EXAMPLE Use a System of Inequalities

2 **COLLEGE** The middle 50% of first-year students attending the University of Massachusetts at Amherst scored between 520 and 630, inclusive, on the math portion of the SAT. They scored between 510 and 620, inclusive, on the critical reading portion of the test. Graph the scores that a student would need to be in the middle 50% of first year students.

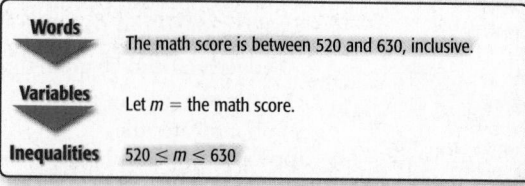

Words	The math score is between 520 and 630, inclusive.
Variables	Let m = the math score.
Inequalities	$520 \leq m \leq 630$

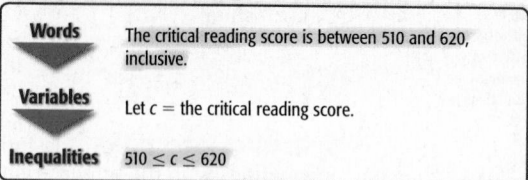

Words	The critical reading score is between 510 and 620, inclusive.
Variables	Let c = the critical reading score.
Inequalities	$510 \leq c \leq 620$

The solution is the set of all ordered pairs that are in the intersection of the graphs of these inequalities. However, since SAT scores are whole numbers, only whole-number solutions make sense in this problem.

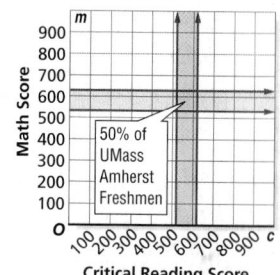

Critical Reading Score

✓ CHECK Your Progress

2A. **HEALTH** The LDL or "bad" cholesterol of a teenager should be less than 110. The HDL or "good" cholesterol of a teenager should be between 35 and 59. Make a graph showing appropriate levels of cholesterol for a teenager. **2A. See Ch. 6 Answer Appendix.**

2B. **COOKING** Marisol wants to make a vinaigrette for a salad. She has two different recipes for the salad dressing. The table below gives the amounts of oil and vinegar needed for each recipe and the amount of each that she has available. Make a graph showing how much salad dressing she can make using each recipe.

2B. See Ch. 6 Answer Appendix.

	Recipe 1	Recipe 2	Amount Available
Oil	1 c	$\frac{3}{4}$ c	4 c
Vinegar	$\frac{1}{2}$ c	1 c	4 c

 Extra Examples at ca.algebra1.com

Differentiated Instruction

Visual Learners If students have difficulty graphing systems of inequalities, suggest that they graph each inequality on a separate coordinate graph and then put the two graphs together on the same coordinate graph by copying them over or tracing them.

★ indicates multi-step problem

✓ CHECK Your Understanding

Example 1
(p. 341)

Solve each system of inequalities by graphing. 1–4. See Ch. 6 Answer Appendix.

1. $x > 5$
   $y \le 4$

2. $y > 3$
   $y > -x + 4$

3. $y \le -x + 3$
   $y \le x + 3$

4. $2x + y \ge 4$
   $y \le -2x - 1$

Example 2
(p. 342)

HEALTH For Exercises 5 and 6, use the following information.
Natasha exercises every day by walking and jogging at least 3 miles. Natasha walks at a rate of 4 miles per hour and jogs at a rate of 8 miles per hour. Suppose she only has a half-hour to exercise today.

5. Draw a graph showing the possible amount of time she can spend walking and jogging. **See Ch. 6 Answer Appendix.**

6. List three possible solutions. **Sample answers: walk 15 min, jog 15 min; walk 10 min, jog 20 min; walk 5 min, jog 25 min**

Exercises

HOMEWORK HELP	
For Exercises	**See Examples**
7–18	1
19–22	2

Exercise Levels
A: 7–22
B: 23–32
C: 33–36

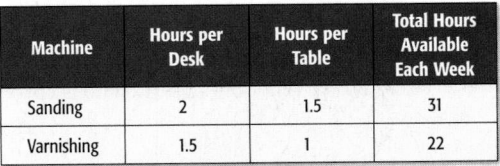

Real-World Career

Visual Artist
A visual artist uses math to create art to communicate ideas. The work of fine artists is made for display. Illustrators and graphic designers produce art for clients.

Math Online
For more information, go to ca.algebra1.com.

Solve each system of inequalities by graphing. 7–18. See Ch. 6 Answer Appendix.

7. $y < 0$
   $x \ge 0$

8. $x > -4$
   $y \le -1$

9. $y \ge -2$
   $y - x < 1$

10. $x \ge 2$
    $y + x \le 5$

11. $x \le 3$
    $x + y > 2$

12. $y \ge 2x + 1$
    $y \le -x + 1$

13. $y < 2x + 1$
    $y \ge -x + 3$

14. $y - x < 1$
    $y - x > 3$

15. $y - x < 3$
    $y - x \ge 2$

16. $2x + y \le 4$
    $3x - y \ge 6$

17. $3x - 4y < 1$
    $x + 2y \le 7$

18. $x + y > 4$
    $-2x + 3y < -12$

MANUFACTURING For Exercises 19 and 20, use the following information.
The Natural Wood Company has machines that sand and varnish desks and tables. The table below gives the time requirements of the machines.

Machine	Hours per Desk	Hours per Table	Total Hours Available Each Week
Sanding	2	1.5	31
Varnishing	1.5	1	22

19. Make a graph showing the number of desks and the number of tables that can be made in a week. **See Ch. 6 Answer Appendix.**

20. List three possible solutions.
    Sample answers: 8 desks, 10 tables; 6 desks, 12 tables; 4 desks, 14 tables

★ **ART** For Exercises 21 and 22, use the following information.
A painter has 32 units of yellow dye and 54 units of blue dye for mixing to make two shades of green. The units needed to make a gallon of light green and a gallon of dark are shown in the table.

Color	Units of Yellow Dye	Units of Blue Dye
light green	4	1
dark green	1	6

21. Make a graph showing the numbers of gallons of the two greens she can make. **See Ch.6 Answer Appendix.**

22. List three possible solutions. **See margin.**

Lesson 6-8 Graphing Systems of Inequalities **343**

Real-World Problems

Example 2 shows how to use a system of inequalities to solve a real-world problem.

ADDITIONAL EXAMPLE

2 **SERVICE** A college service organization requires that its members maintain at least a 3.0 grade point average and volunteer at least 10 hours a week. Graph these requirements.

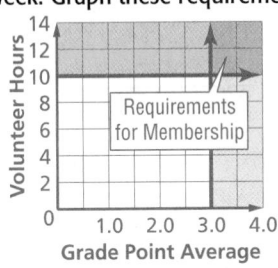

3 Practice

✓ Formative Assessment

Use Exercises 1–6 to check for understanding.

Use the chart at the bottom of this page to customize assignments for your students.

Odd/Even Assignments
Exercises 7–22 are structured so that students practice the same concepts whether they are assigned odd or even problems.

Real-World Connections For Exercises 21 and 22, have students talk about any painting their families have done, how many gallons were necessary to complete the jobs, and if any colors used were the result of mixing different colors to get the desired color. Ask students to estimate how many units of each color were required to make the required colors.

Additional Answer

22. Sample answers: 2 light, 8 dark; 6 light, 8 dark; 7 light, 4 dark

DIFFERENTIATED HOMEWORK OPTIONS

Level	Assignment	Two-Day Option	
BL Basic	7–22, 33, 35–50	7–21 odd, 37, 38	8–22 even, 33, 35, 36, 39–50
GT Core	7–27 odd, 28–33, 35–50	7–22, 37, 38	23–33, 35, 36, 39–50
SL Advanced /Pre-AP	23–50		

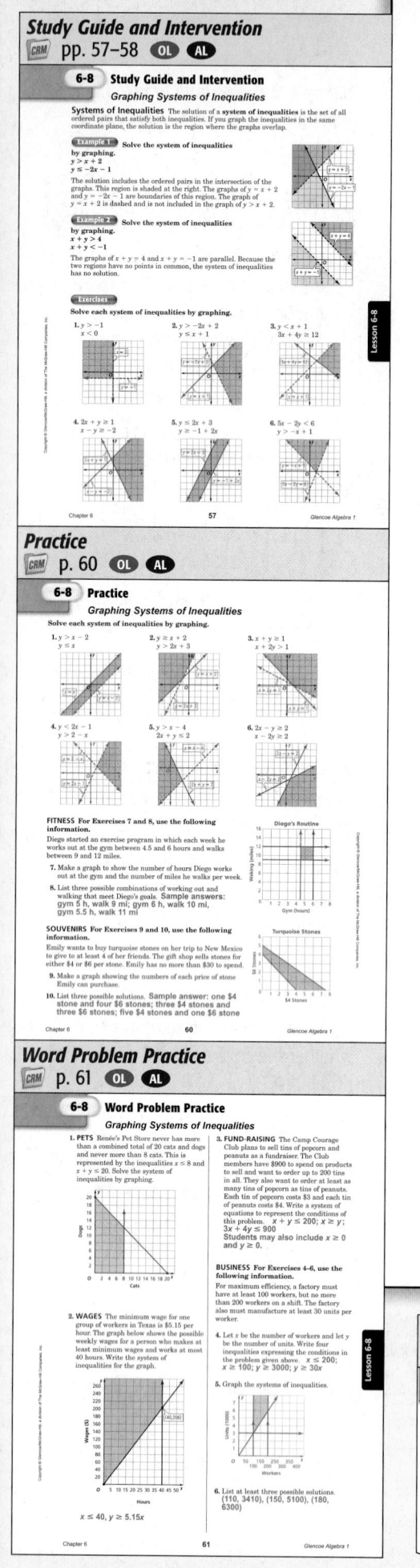

Study Guide and Intervention
CRM pp. 57–58 **OL** **AL**

6-8 Study Guide and Intervention
Graphing Systems of Inequalities

Practice
CRM p. 60 **OL** **AL**

6-8 Practice
Graphing Systems of Inequalities

Word Problem Practice
CRM p. 61 **OL** **AL**

6-8 Word Problem Practice
Graphing Systems of Inequalities

Solve each system of inequalities by graphing. 23–25. See Ch. 6 Answer Appendix.

★ **23.** $x \geq 0$
$x - 2y \leq 2$
$3x + 4y \leq 12$

★ **24.** $y \leq x + 3$
$2x - 7y \leq 4$
$3x + 2y \leq 6$

★ **25.** $x < 2$
$4y > x$
$2x - y < -9$
$x + 3y < 9$

Write a system of inequalities for each graph.

26.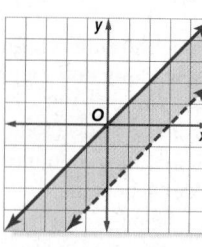

$y \leq x, \ y > x - 3$

27.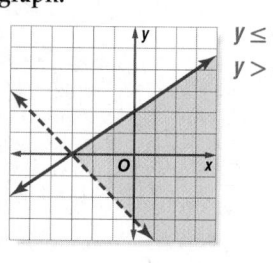

$y \leq \frac{2}{3}x + 2,$
$y > -x - 3$

AGRICULTURE For Exercises 28 and 29, use the following information.
To ensure a growing season of sufficient length, Mr. Hobson has at most 16 days left to plant his corn and soybean crops. He can plant corn at a rate of 250 acres per day and soybeans at a rate of 200 acres per day.

28. If he has at most 3500 acres available, make a graph showing how many acres of each type of crop he can plant. 28–29. See Ch. 6 Answer Appendix.

29. Name one solution and explain what it means.

Sketch the region in the plane that satisfies both inequalities.

30. $3x - y \leq 6$
$x - y \geq -1$

31. $3y - x \geq 6$
$y < -2x - 1$

32. $3y - x \leq 9$
$4y + x \leq 12$

30–32. See Ch. 6 Answer Appendix.

33. OPEN ENDED Draw the graph of a system of inequalities that has no solution. See Ch. 6 Answer Appendix.

34. CHALLENGE Create a system of inequalities equivalent to $|x| \leq 4$.
$x \geq -4$ and $x \leq 4$

35. FIND THE ERROR Jocelyn and Sonia are solving the system of inequalities $x + 2y \geq -2$ and $x - y > 1$. Who is correct? Explain your reasoning.

Jocelyn
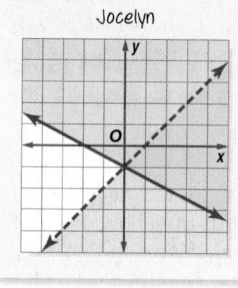

Sonia
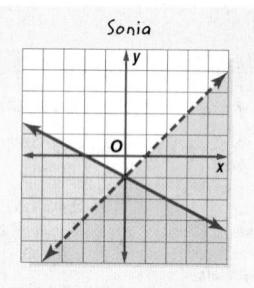

35. Jocelyn; the graph of $x + 2y \geq -2$ is the region representing $x + 2y = -2$ and the half-plane above it.

36. Writing in Math Use the information about nutrition on page 341 to explain how you can use a system of inequalities to plan a sensible diet. Include two appropriate protein and fat intakes for a day and the system of inequalities that is represented by the graph. See Ch. 6 Answer Appendix.

Enrichment
CRM p. 62 **OL** **AL**

6-8 Enrichment

Describing Regions

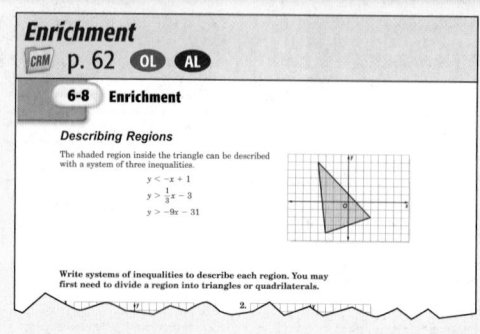

BL = Below Grade Level
OL = On Grade Level
AL = Above Grade Level
ELL = English Language Learner

Additional pages not shown:
CRM Lesson Reading Guide, p. 56 **BL** **OL** **ELL**
CRM Skills Practice, p. 59 **BL** **OL**

37. Which system of inequalities is *best* represented by the graph? **A**

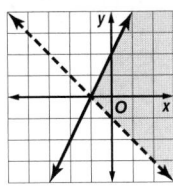

A $y \leq 2x + 2$
$y > -x - 1$

B $y \geq 2x + 2$
$y < -x - 1$

C $y < 2x + 2$
$y \leq -x - 1$

D $y > 2x + 2$
$y \leq -x - 1$

38. REVIEW The table shows the cost of organic wheat flour, depending on the amount purchased. Which conclusion can be made based on the information in the table? **G**

Number of Pounds	Cost ($)
2	3.40
10	16.00
25	37.50
50	75.00

F The cost of 4 pounds of flour would be more than $7.

G The cost of 100 pounds of flour would be less than $150.

H The cost of flour is always more than $1.60 per pound.

J The cost of flour is always less than $1.50 per pound.

Spiral Review

Graph each inequality. (Lesson 6-7) **39–41. See margin.**

39. $y < \frac{1}{2}x - 4$

40. $2y + x \leq 6$

41. $x + 2y \geq 8$

42. FISH The temperature of a freshwater tropical fish tank should be within 1.5 degrees of 76.5°F. Express this using an inequality involving absolute value. (Lesson 6-6) $|t - 76.5| \leq 1.5$

Use elimination to solve each system of equations. (Lesson 5-4)

43. $2x + 3y = 1$
$4x - 5y = 13$
$(2, -1)$

44. $5x - 2y = -3$
$3x + 6y = -9$
$(-1, -1)$

45. $-3x + 2y = 12$
$2x - 3y = -13$
$(-2, 3)$

46. $6x - 2y = 4$
$5x - 3y = -2$
$(2, 4)$

Determine whether each relation is a function. (Lesson 3-2)

47. $y = -15$ yes

48. $x = 5$ no

49. $\{(1, 0), (1, 4), (-1, 1)\}$ no

50. $\{(6, 3), (5, -2), (2, 3)\}$ yes

Cross-Curricular Project

Math and Science

The Spirit of the Games It's time to complete your project. Use the information and data you have gathered about the Olympics to prepare a portfolio or Web page. Be sure to include graphs and/or tables in the presentation.

Math Online Cross-Curricular Project at ca.algebra1.com

Find the Error

First have the students identify the differences between the two graphs. Once they have found that one graph is shaded above the line representing $x + 2y = 2$ and the other is shaded below the line, they can determine which is correct.

4 Assess

Name the Math Have each student write the method for determining whether to shade above or below the line when graphing an inequality and how to determine the common solutions when graphing a system of inequalities.

Formative Assessment

Check for student understanding of concepts in Lessons 6-7 and 6-8.

CRM Quiz 4, p. 68

Additional Answers

39.

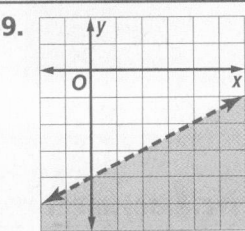

40.

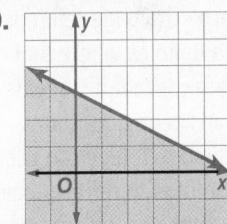

41.

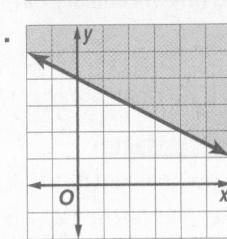

Have students graph $2 \leq x \leq 5$ and $1 \leq y \leq 4$ on the same coordinate plane. Have them describe what polygon is formed by their intersection. a square with vertices at (2, 4), (5, 4), (2, 1) and (5, 1)

Download Vocabulary Review from ca.algebra1.com

FOLDABLES™
Study Organizer

Dinah Zike's Foldables™

Have students look through the chapter to make sure they have included examples in their Foldables for each type of inequality they learned to solve.

Suggest that students keep their Foldables handy while completing the Study Guide and Review pages. Point out that their Foldables can serve as a quick review tool for studying for the chapter test.

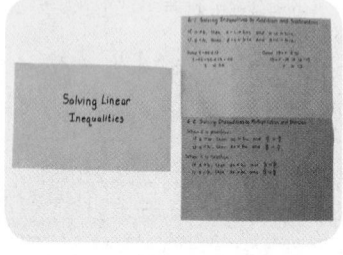

Solving Linear Inequalities

 Formative Assessment

Key Vocabulary The page reference after each word denotes where that term was first introduced. If students have difficulty answering questions 1–10, remind them that they can use these page references to refresh their memories about the vocabulary terms.

 ca.algebra1.com

Vocabulary PuzzleMaker
improves students' mathematics vocabulary using four puzzle formats—crossword, scramble, word search using a word list, and word search using clues. Students can work online or from a printed worksheet.

FOLDABLES™
Study Organizer
GET READY to Study

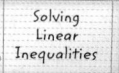
Solving Linear Inequalities

Be sure the following Key Concepts are noted in your Foldable.

Key Concepts

Solving Inequalities by Adding, Subtracting, Multiplying, or Dividing (Lessons 6-1 and 6-2)

- If any number is added to or subtracted from each side of a true inequality, the resulting inequality is also true.

- If each side of a true inequality is multiplied or divided by the same positive number, the resulting inequality is also true.

Multi-Step and Compound Inequalities (Lessons 6-3 and 6-4)

- If each side of a true inequality is multiplied or divided by the same negative number, the direction of the inequality symbol must be *reversed* so that the resulting inequality is also true.

Absolute Value Equations and Inequalities (Lessons 6-5 and 6-6)

- The absolute value of any number n is its distance from zero on a number line and is written as $|n|$.

- If $|x| = n$, then $x = -n$ or $x = n$.
  If $|x| < n$, then $x < n$ or $x > -n$.
  If $|x| > n$, then $x > n$ or $x < -n$.

Inequalities in Two Variables (Lesson 6-7)

- Any line in the plane divides the plane into two regions called *half-planes*. The line is called the boundary of each of the two half-planes.

Systems of Inequalities (Lesson 6-8)

- A system of inequalities is a set of two or more inequalities with the same variables.

 Summative Assessment

CRM Vocabulary Test, p. 70

Key Vocabulary

boundary (p. 334)
compound inequality (p. 315)
half-plane (p. 334)
intersection (p. 315)
piecewise function (p. 324)
set-builder notation (p. 295)
system of inequalities (p. 341)
union (p. 316)

Vocabulary Check

State whether each sentence is *true* or *false*. If *false*, replace the underlined word or phrase to make a true sentence.

1. The edge of a half-plane is called a <u>boundary</u>. **true**

2. The symbol ∅ means <u>intersection</u>. **empty set**

3. The phrase <u>at least</u> is represented by the same symbol as the phrase <u>greater than</u>.

4. To solve a <u>system of inequalities</u>, find the ordered pairs that satisfy all the inequalities involved. **true**

5. The <u>union</u> can be found by graphing each inequality and then determining where the graphs overlap. **false; intersection**

6. The solution $\{x \mid x < 5\}$ is written in <u>set-builder notation</u>. **true**

7. A compound inequality containing <u>and</u> is true if one or more of the inequalities is true. **false; or**

8. When solving $4x > -12$, the direction of the inequality symbol <u>should</u> be reversed.

9. The graph of $y > 3x - 6$ has a <u>dashed</u> line boundary. **true**

10. A <u>union</u> is formed when a line in the plane divides the plane into two regions. **false; half-plane**

3. false; greater than or equal to   8. false; should not

 Vocabulary Review at ca.algebra1.com

Lesson-by-Lesson Review

6–1 **Solving Inequalities by Addition and Subtraction** (pp. 294–299)

Solve each inequality. Check your solution, and then graph it on a number line. 11–14. See margin.

11. $x - 9 < 16$ **12.** $-11 \geq -5 + p$

13. $12w + 4 \leq 13w$ **14.** $8g > 7g - 1$

15–16. See margin.

For Exercises 15 and 16, define a variable, write an inequality, and solve each problem. Check your solution.

15. Sixteen is less than the sum of a number and 31.

16. **TOMATOES** There are more than 10,000 varieties of tomatoes. One seed company produces seed packages for 200 varieties of tomatoes. For how many varieties do they not provide seeds?

Example 1 Solve $-2 \leq h + 17$. Check your solution, and then graph it on a number line.

$-2 \leq h + 17$ Original inequality

$-2 - 17 \leq h + 17 - 17$ Subtract 17 from each side.

$-19 \leq h$ Simplify.

Since $-19 \leq h$ is the same as $h \geq -19$, the solution set is $\{h \mid h \geq -19\}$.

$-21\ -20\ -19\ -18\ -17\ -16\ -15\ -14\ -13\ -12$

6–2 **Solving Inequalities by Multiplication and Division** (pp. 301–307)

Solve each inequality. Check your solution.

17. $15v > 60$
$\{v \mid v > 4\}$

18. $3 \leq -\dfrac{d}{13}$
$\{d \mid d \leq -39\}$

19. $-9m < 99$
$\{m \mid m > -11\}$

20. $-15 \geq \dfrac{3}{5}k$
$\{k \mid k \leq -25\}$

For Exercises 21 and 22, define a variable, write an inequality, and solve the problem. Check your solution.

21. Eighty percent of a number is greater than or equal to 24. See margin.

22. **FISHING** About 41.6 million tons of fish were caught in China in a recent year. If this is over 35% of the world's catch, how many fish were caught in the world that year? See margin.

Example 2 Solve $-14g \geq 126$.

$-14g \geq 126$ Original inequality

$\dfrac{-14g}{-14} \leq \dfrac{126}{-14}$ Divide each side by -14 and change $\geq$ to $\leq$.

$g \leq -9$ Simplify.

The solution set is $\{g \mid g \leq -9\}$.

Example 3 Solve $\dfrac{3}{4}w < 15$.

$\dfrac{3}{4}w < 15$ Original inequality

$\left(\dfrac{4}{3}\right)\dfrac{3}{4}w < \left(\dfrac{4}{3}\right)15$ Multiply each side by $\frac{4}{3}$.

$w < 20$ Simplify.

The solution set is $\{w \mid w < 20\}$.

22. Sample answer: Let $x =$ the millions of tons of fish caught in the world, $41.6 > 0.35x$; $\{x \mid x < 118.86\}$, less than 118.86 million tons.

Lesson-by-Lesson Review
Intervention If the given examples are not sufficient to review the topics covered by the questions, remind students that the page references tell them where to review that topic in their textbooks.

Two-Day Option Have students complete the Lesson-by-Lesson Review on pp. 347–350. Then you can use ExamView® Assessment Suite to customize another review worksheet that practices all the objectives of this chapter or only the objectives on which your students need more help.

For more information on ExamView® Assessment Suite, see p. 292C.

Differentiated Instruction
Super DVD: MindJogger Videoquizzes
Use this DVD as an alternative format of review for the test. For more information on this game show format, see p. 292D.

Additional Answers

11.
21 22 23 24 25 26 27 28 29

12.
$-1\ -2\ -3\ -4\ -5\ -6\ -7\ -8\ -9$

13.
0 1 2 3 4 5 6 7 8

14.
$-4\ -3\ -2\ -1\ 0\ 1\ 2\ 3\ 4$

15. Sample answer: Let $n =$ the number, $16 < n + 31$; $\{n \mid n > -15\}$.

16. Sample answer: Let $t =$ the number of tomato varieties they do not produce seeds for, $t + 200 > 10,000$; $\{t \mid t > 8000\}$.

21. Sample answer: Let $n =$ the number, $0.8n \geq 24$; $\{n \mid n \geq 30\}$.

Additional Answers

29. $\{y \mid y < -1 \text{ and } y < 3\}$

$$\overset{\ominus}{\underset{-4\ -3\ -2\ -1\ \ 0\ \ 1\ \ 2\ \ 3\ \ 4}{\longleftrightarrow}}$$

30. $\{a \mid -1 < a < 5\}$

$$\underset{10\ 11\ 12\ 13\ 14\ 15\ 16\ 17\ 18}{\longleftrightarrow}$$

31. $\{w \mid w \text{ is a real number.}\}$

$$\underset{-4\ -3\ -2\ -1\ \ 0\ \ 1\ \ 2\ \ 3\ \ 4}{\longleftrightarrow}$$

32. $\{p \mid -4 < p < 2\}$

$$\overset{\ominus \qquad\qquad \ominus}{\underset{-5\ -4\ -3\ -2\ -1\ \ 0\ \ 1\ \ 2\ \ 3}{\longleftrightarrow}}$$

6–3 **Solving Multi-Step Inequalities** (pp. 308–313)

Solve each inequality. Check your solution.

23. $5 - 6y > -19$ $\{y \mid y < 4\}$

24. $\dfrac{1 - 7n}{5} \geq 10$ $\{n \mid n \leq -7\}$

25. $-5x + 3 \leq 3x + 19$ $\{x \mid x \geq -2\}$

26. $7(g + 8) < 3(g + 2) + 4g$ $\varnothing$

For Exercises 27 and 28, define a variable, write an inequality, and solve the problem. Check your solution.

27. Two thirds of a number decreased by 27 is at least 9.

28. **CATS** Dexter has $20 to spend at the pet store. He plans to buy a toy for his cat that costs $3.75 and several bags of cat food. If each bag of cat food costs $2.99, what is the greatest number of bags that he can buy? **Sample answer: Let** $n =$ **the number of bags of cat food**, $3.75 + 2.99x < 20$; $\{x \mid x < 5.4\}$, **at most 5 bags.**

Example 4 Solve $4(n - 1) < 7n + 8$.

$4(n - 1) < 7n + 8$	Original Inequality
$4n - 4 < 7n + 8$	Distributive Property
$4n - 4 - 7n < 7n + 8 - 7n$	Subtract $7n$ from each side.
$-3n - 4 < 8$	Simplify.
$-3n - 4 + 4 < 8 + 4$	Add 4 to each side.
$-3n < 12$	Simplify.
$\dfrac{-3n}{-3} > \dfrac{12}{-3}$	Divide and change $<$ to $>$.
$n > -4$	Simplify.

The solution set is $\{n \mid n > -4\}$.

27. Sample answer: Let $n =$ the number, $\dfrac{2}{3}n - 27 \geq 9$; $\{n \mid n \geq 54\}$.

6–4 **Solving Compound Inequalities** (pp. 315–320)

Graph the solution set of each compound inequality. **29–32. See margin.**

29. $10 - 2y > 12$ and $7y < 4y + 9$

30. $a - 3 \leq 8$ or $a + 5 \geq 21$

31. $3w + 8 \leq 2$ or $w + 12 \geq 2 - w$

32. $-1 < p + 3 < 5$

33. **FAIRS** A vendor at the state fair is trying to guess Martin's age within 2 years. The vendor guesses that Martin is 35 years old. If m represents Martin's age, write a compound inequality that represents the possible range of m if the vendor is correct. Then graph the solution set. $33 \leq m \leq 37$

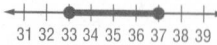

$$\underset{31\ 32\ 33\ 34\ 35\ 36\ 37\ 38\ 39}{\longleftrightarrow}$$

Example 5 Graph the solution set of $x \geq -1$ and $x > 3$.

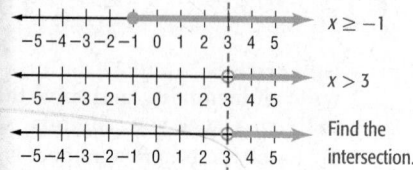

Example 6 Graph the solution set of $x \leq -2$ or $x > 4$.

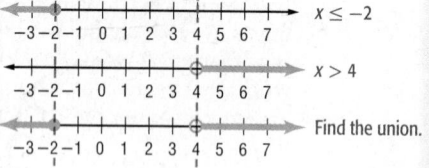

Mixed Problem Solving
For mixed problem-solving practice,
see page 749.

CHAPTER
6
**Study Guide
and Review**

6-5 **Solving Open Sentences Involving Absolute Value** (pp. 322–327)

Solve each open sentence. Then graph the solution set. **34–35. See margin.**

34. $|x + 4| = 3$ **35.** $|2x - 3| = 5$

36. TESTS Kent has an A in math class. If his score on the next test is 98%, plus or minus 2 percentage points, he will maintain an A average. Write an open sentence to find the highest and lowest scores he can earn on the next test. $|t - 98| = 2$; **96, 100**

37. CARS The stated capacity of a fuel tank in a passenger car is accurate within 3%. Write an open sentence to find the greatest and least capacity for a fuel tank if the stated capacity is 13.6 gallons. $|c - 13.6| = 0.408$; **14.008 gal, 13.192 gal**

Example 7 Solve $|x + 6| = 15$. Then graph the solution set.

$|x + 6| = 15$ is $x + 6 = 15$ or $x + 6 = -15$.

$$x + 6 = 15 \qquad\qquad x + 6 = -15$$
$$x + 6 - 6 = 15 - 6 \quad x + 6 - 6 = -15 - 6$$
$$x = 9 \qquad\qquad x = -21$$

The solution set is $\{-21, 9\}$.

6-6 **Solving Inequalities Involving Absolute Value** (pp. 329–333)

Solve each open sentence. Then graph the solution set. **38–43. See margin.**

38. $|3d + 8| < 23$ **39.** $|g + 2| \geq -9$

40. $|m - 1| > -6$ **41.** $|2x - 5| \geq 7$

42. $|4h - 3| < 13$ **43.** $|w + 8| \leq 11$

44. AIRPLANES For the average commercial airplane to take off from the runway, its speed should be within 10 miles per hour of 170 miles per hour. Define a variable, write an open sentence, and find this range of takeoff speeds.
Sample answer: Let t **represent the takeoff speed,** $|t - 170| \leq 10$; $\{t | 160 \leq t \leq 180\}$, **between 160 mph and 180 mph.**

Example 8 Solve $|2x - 3| < 5$. Then graph the solution set.

$|2x - 3| < 5$ is $2x - 3 < 5$ and $2x - 3 > -5$.

$$2x - 3 < 5 \qquad\qquad 2x - 3 > -5$$
$$2x - 3 + 3 < 5 + 3 \quad 2x - 3 + 3 > -5 + 3$$
$$2x < 8 \qquad\qquad 2x > -2$$
$$\frac{2x}{2} < \frac{8}{2} \qquad\qquad \frac{2x}{2} > \frac{-2}{2}$$
$$x < 4 \qquad\qquad x > -1$$

$x < 4$ and $x > -1$

The solution set is $\{x | -1 < x < 4\}$.

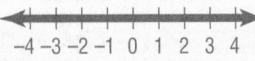

Additional Answers

34. $\{-7, -1\}$

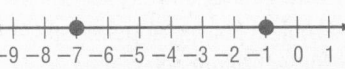

35. $\{4, -1\}$

38. $\left\{ d \mid -10\frac{1}{3} < d < 5 \right\}$

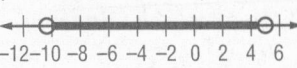

39. $\varnothing$

40. $\{m \mid m \text{ is a real number.}\}$

41. $\{x \mid x \leq -1 \text{ or } x \geq 6\}$

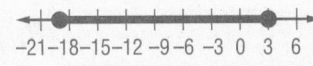

42. $\{-2.5, 4\}$

43. $\{w \mid -19 \leq w \leq 3\}$

Problem Solving Review

For additional practice in problem solving for Chapter 6, see the Mixed Problem Solving Appendix, p. 749 in the Student Handbook section.

Anticipation Guide

Have students complete the Chapter 6 Anticipation Guide and discuss how their responses have changed now that they have completed Chapter 6.

CRM Anticipation Guide, p. 3

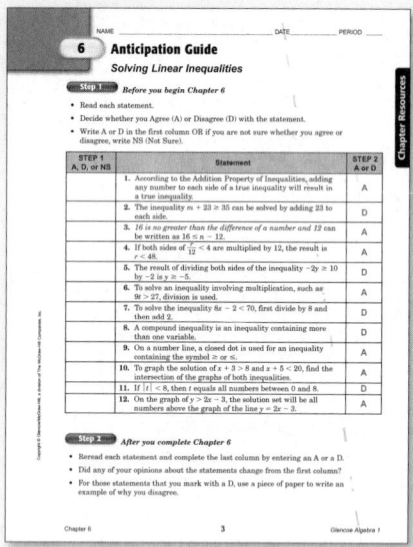

Additional Answers

50.

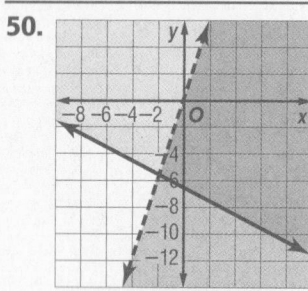

51.

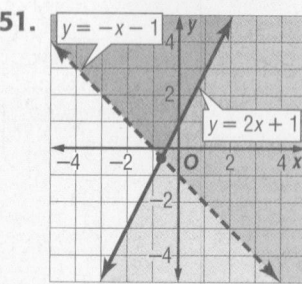

6–7 **Graphing Inequalities in Two Variables** (pp. 334–339)

Graph each inequality. 45–48. See Ch. 6 Answer Appendix.

45. $y - 2x < -3$ **46.** $x + 2y \geq 4$

47. $y \leq 5x + 1$ **48.** $2x - 3y > 6$

49. MOVING A moving company charges $95 an hour and $0.08 a mile to move items from Brianna's old apartment to her new house. If Brianna has only $500 for moving expenses, write an inequality for this situation. Can she afford to hire this moving company if she knows it will take 5 hours and the distance between houses is 75 miles? $95h + 0.08m \leq 500$; **Yes, Brenda can afford to hire this moving company.**

Example 9 Graph $y \geq x - 2$.

Since the boundary is included in the solution, draw a solid line.

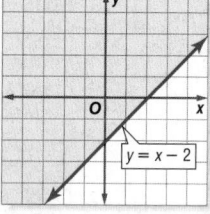

Test the point $(0, 0)$.

$y \geq x - 2$ Original inequality

$0 \geq 0 - 2$ $x = 0, y = 0$

$0 \geq -2$ true

The half-plane that contains $(0, 0)$ should be shaded.

6–8 **Graphing Systems of Inequalities** (pp. 341–345)

Solve each system of inequalities by graphing. 50–53. See margin.

50. $y < 3x$
$x + 2y \geq -21$

51. $y > -x - 1$
$y \leq 2x + 1$

52. $2x + y < 9$
$x + 11y < -6$

53. $y \geq 1$
$y + x \leq 3$

54. TREES Justin wants to plant peach and apple trees in his backyard. He can fit at most 12 trees. Each peach tree costs $60, and each apple tree costs $75. If he only has $800 to spend, make a graph showing the number of each kind of tree that he can buy. Then list three possible solutions.
See Ch. 6 Answer Appendix.

Example 10 Solve the system of inequalities by graphing.

$x \geq -3$

$y \leq x + 2$

The solution includes the ordered pairs in the intersection of the graphs $x \geq -3$ and $y \leq x + 2$. This region is shaded in green. The graphs of $x \geq -3$ and $y \leq x + 2$ are boundaries of this region.

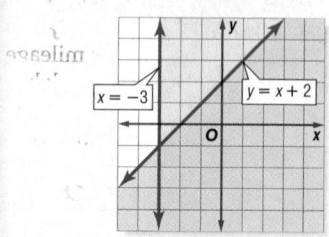

52.

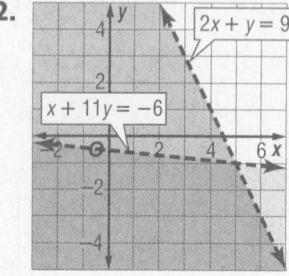

53.

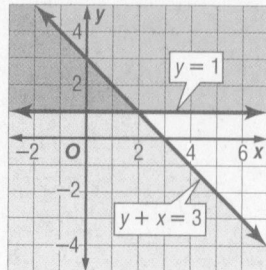

Solve each inequality. Check your solution.

1. $-23 \geq g - 6$
$\{g \mid g \leq -17\}$

2. $9p < 8p - 18$
$\{p \mid p < -18\}$

3. $4m - 11 \geq 8m + 7$
$\{m \mid m \leq -4.5\}$

4. $3(k - 2) > 12$
$\{k \mid k > 6\}$

5. **REAL ESTATE** A homeowner is selling her house. She must pay 7% of the selling price to her real estate agent after the house is sold. Define a variable and write and solve an inequality to find what the selling price of her house must be to have at least $140,000 after the agent is paid. Round to the nearest dollar. **See margin.**

6. Solve $6 + |r| = 3$. $\varnothing$

7. Solve $|d| > -2$. $\{d \mid d$ is a real number.$\}$

8–13. See Ch. 6 Answer Appendix for graphs.

Solve each compound inequality. Then graph the solution set.

8. $r + 3 > 2$ and $4r < 12$ $\{r \mid -1 < r < 3\}$

9. $3n + 2 \geq 17$ or $3n + 2 \leq -1$ $\{n \mid n \leq -1$ or $n \geq 5\}$

Solve each open sentence. Then graph the solution set.

10. $|4x + 3| = 9$ $\left\{\frac{3}{2}, -3\right\}$

11. $|6 - 4m| = 8$ $\left\{\frac{1}{2}, \frac{7}{2}\right\}$

12. $|2a - 5| < 7$ $\{a \mid -1 < a < 6\}$

13. $|7 - 3s| \geq 2$ $\left\{s \mid s \leq 1\frac{2}{3}$ or $s \geq 3\right\}$

For Exercises 14–17, define a variable, write an inequality, and solve each problem. Check your solution. 14. See margin.

14. One fourth of a number is no less than -3.

15. Three times a number subtracted from 14 is less than two. **See margin.**

16. Five less than twice a number is between 13 and 21. **Sample answer: Let $n =$ the number, $13 < 2n - 5 < 21$; $\{n \mid 9 < n < 13\}$.**

17. **TRAVEL** Mary's car gets the gas mileage shown in the table. If her car's tank holds 15 gallons, what is the range of distance that Mary can drive her car on one tank of gasoline? **See margin.**

Gas Mileage	Miles Per Gallon
minimum	18
maximum	21

Graph each inequality. 18–20. See Ch. 6 Answer Appendix.

18. $y \geq 3x - 2$

19. $2x + 3y < 6$

20. $x - 2y > 4$

21. **MULTIPLE CHOICE** Ricardo purchased x bottles of paint and y paint brushes. He spent less than $20, not including tax. If $3x + 2y < 20$ represents this situation, which point represents a reasonable number of bottles of paint and paint brushes that Ricardo could have purchased? **D**

Product	Cost
bottle of paint	$3.00
paint brush	$2.00

A $(2, 7)$

B $(5, 4)$

C $(2, 8)$

D $(5, 2)$

Solve each system of inequalities by graphing. 22–23. See Ch. 6 Answer Appendix.

22. $y > -4$
$y < -1$

23. $y \leq 3$
$y > -x + 2$

24. **MULTIPLE CHOICE** Which graph represents $y > 2x + 1$ and $y < -x - 2$? **J**

F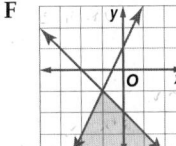

H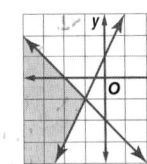

G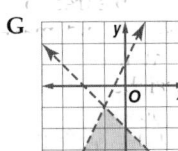

J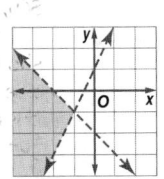

✓ Summative Assessment

CRM *Chapter 6 Resource Masters*

Leveled Chapter 6 Tests			
Form	**Type**	**Level**	**Pages**
1	MC	BL	71–72
2A	MC	OL	73–74
2B	MC	OL	75–76
2C	FR	OL	77–78
2D	FR	OL	79–80
3	FR	AL	81–82

MC = *multiple-choice questions*
FR = *free-response questions*
BL = *below grade level*
OL = *on grade level*
AL = *above grade level*

- Vocabulary Test, p. 70
- Extended-Response Test, p. 84
- Unit 2 Test, pp. 87–88

ExamView Assessment Suite Customize and create multiple versions of your chapter tests and their answer keys. All of the questions from the leveled chapter tests in the *Chapter 6 Resource Masters* are also available on ExamView® Assessment Suite with the California Standard that each item assesses.

Additional Answers

5. Sample answer: Let $p =$ the price of the house, $p - 0.07p > 140,000$; $\{p \mid p > 150,538\}$, at least $150,538.

14–17. See Ch. 6 Answer Appendix.

Data-Driven Decision Making	**Exercises**	**Lesson**	🌐 **Standard**	**Resources for Review**
Diagnostic Teaching Based on the results of the Chapter 6 Practice Test, use the following to review concepts that students continue to find challenging.	6, 10–11	6-5	3.0	**CRM** Study Guide and Intervention, pp. 34–35, 41–42, 49–50, 57–58
	7, 12–13	6-6	3.0	Math Online
	18–21	6-7	6.0	• Extra Examples
	22–24	6-8	9.0	• Personal Tutor • Concepts in Motion

Formative Assessment

You can use these two pages to benchmark student progress. The California Standards are listed with each question.

 Chapter 6 Resource Masters

• Standardized Test Practice, pp. 84–86

Create practice worksheets or tests that align to the California Standards, as well as TIMSS and NAEP tests.

 Read each question. Then fill in the correct answer on the answer document provided by your teacher or on a sheet of paper.

1 What is the solution set of the inequality $6 - |x + 3| \leq -3$? **D**

A $1 \geq x \geq 3$

B $x \leq 1$ or $x \geq 3$

C $6 \geq x \geq 12$

D $x \leq -12$ or $x \geq 6$

TEST-TAKING TIP

Questions 1, 4 When solving an equation or inequality involving absolute value, treat the absolute value bars as a grouping symbol.

2 Solve the system of equations. **J**

$$x - y = 4$$
$$2x + 7y = 35$$

F $(2, 6)$

G $(3, 7)$

H $(6, 2)$

J $(7, 3)$

3 Jonah has 80 sports trading cards. The number of baseball trading cards is 5 more than twice the number of basketball trading cards. Use the system of equations graphed below to determine how many basketball cards Jonah has. **25**

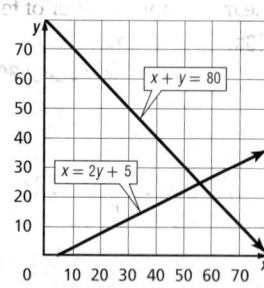

4 Which inequality is shown on the graph below? **B**

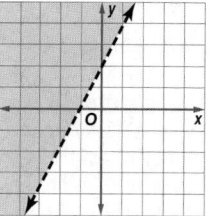

A $y < 2x + 2$

B $y > 2x + 2$

C $y \leq 2x + 2$

D $y \geq 2x + 2$

5 Which of the following is equivalent to $10 - 4x > 5(3x - 2)$? **J**

F $0 < 19x$

G $0 > 19x$

H $20 < 19x$

J $20 > 19x$

6 Which graph best represents the solution to this system of inequalities? **C**

$$3x \geq y + 2$$
$$-2x \geq -4y + 8$$

A
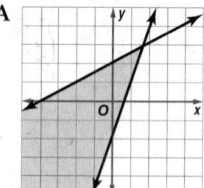

C
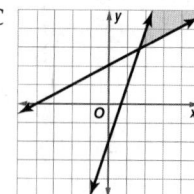

B
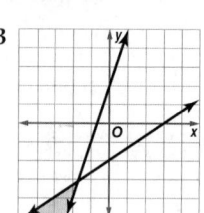

D
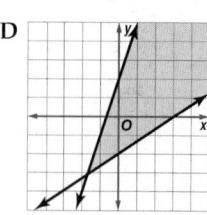

 **California Standards Practice at** ca.algebra1.com

More California
Standards Practice
For practice by standard,
see pages CA1–CA43.

CHAPTER
6

California
Standards Practice

7 What is the slope of a line perpendicular to the line graphed below? **F**

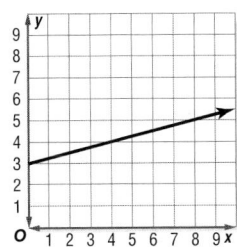

F −4

G $-\frac{1}{4}$

H $\frac{1}{4}$

J 3

8 Airplane A is descending from an altitude of 13,000 feet at a rate of 1300 feet per minute. Airplane B is ascending from the ground at a rate of 1000 feet per minute. Which graph below accurately represents the point when the airplanes will reach the same altitude? **A**

A
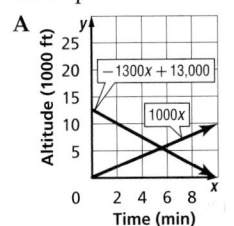

C
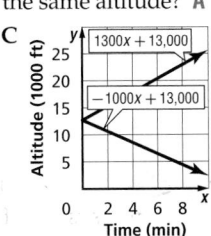

B
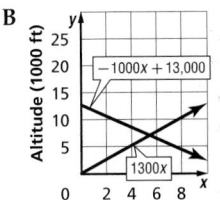

D
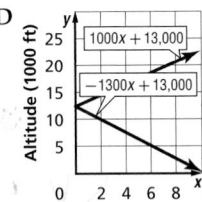

9 What is the algebraic expression for the verbal expression below? **H**

nine times the sum of four and the quotient of s and 2

F $9\left(\frac{4+s}{2}\right)$

G $9+4\left(\frac{s}{2}\right)$

H $9\left(4+\frac{s}{2}\right)$

J $(9+4)\frac{s}{2}$

Pre-AP/Anchor Problem

Record your answers on a sheet of paper. Show your work.

10 The Washington family is building a house on a lot that is 91 feet long and 158 feet wide.

a. Town law states that the sides of a house cannot be closer than 10 feet to the edges of a lot. Write an inequality for the possible lengths of the Washington family's house, and solve the inequality.

b. The Washington family wants their house to be at least 2800 square feet and no more than 3200 square feet. They also want their house to have the maximum possible length. Write an inequality for the possible widths of their house, and solve the inequality. Round your answer to the nearest whole number of feet.

10a. $0 < L < 71$

10b. $2800 < 71w < 3200$; $39 < w < 45$

Item Analysis
Question 3 is a griddable question. In griddable questions, students arrive at an answer and then record it in a special grid by coloring in the appropriate bubble under each digit of the answer.

Answer Sheet Practice
Have students simulate taking a standardized test by recording their answers on practice recording sheets.

[CRM] Student Recording Sheet, p. 59

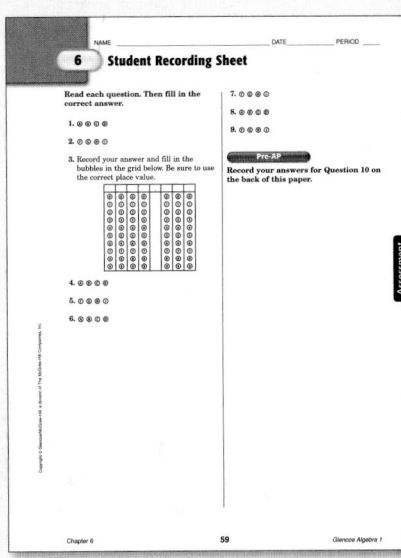

NEED EXTRA HELP?										
If You Missed Question...	1	2	3	4	5	6	7	8	9	10
Go to Lesson...	6-5	5-5	5-1	6-7	6-3	6-8	4-7	5-5	1-1	6-4
For Help with Standard...	3.0	9.0	9.0	6.0	4.0	9.0	8.0	9.0	7AF1.1	5.0

Homework Option

Get Ready for Chapter 7 Assign students the exercises on p. 357 as homework to assess whether they possess the prerequisite skills needed for the next chapter.

Page 293, Chapter 6: Get Ready for Chapter 6

16.

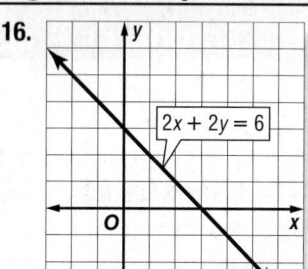

$2x + 2y = 6$

17.

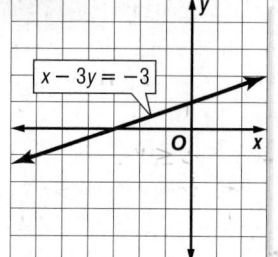

$x - 3y = -3$

18.

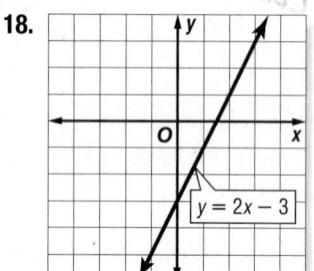

$y = 2x - 3$

19.

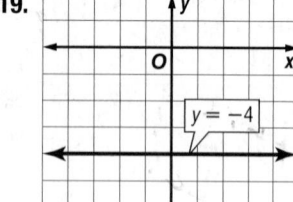

$y = -4$

20.

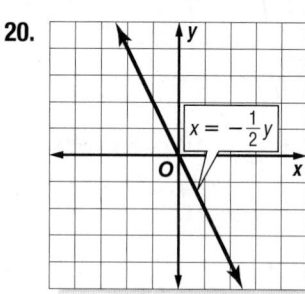

$x = -\frac{1}{2}y$

21.

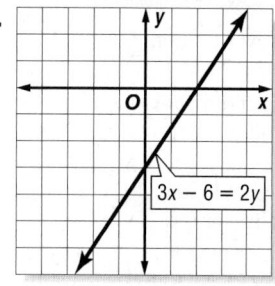

$3x - 6 = 2y$

22.

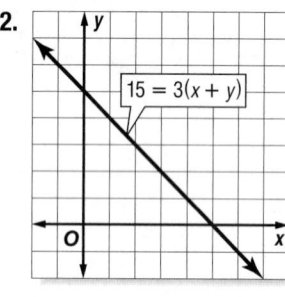

$15 = 3(x + y)$

23.

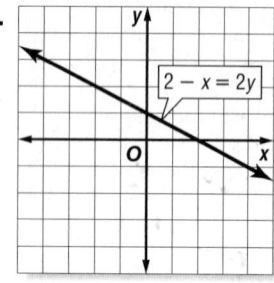

$2 - x = 2y$

Pages 297–298, Lesson 6-1

1. (number line: 0 2 4 6 8 10 12 14 16, closed circle at 12, shaded left)

2. (number line: −8−7−6−5−4−3−2−1 0, open circle at −6, shaded left)

3. (number line: −8−7−6−5−4−3−2−1 0, open circle at −3, shaded left)

4. (number line: 0 1 2 3 4 5 6 7 8, closed circle at 5, shaded left)

5. (number line: 7 8 9 10 11 12 13 14 15, open circle at 10, shaded left)

6. (number line: −33−32−31−30−29−28−27, open circle at −29, shaded left)

7. (number line: 0 1 2 3 4 5 6 7 8, open circle at 6, shaded right)

8. (number line: −4−3−2−1 0 1 2 3 4, closed circle at −2, shaded left)

12. (number line: 0 1 2 3 4 5 6 7 8, closed circle at 3, shaded both)

13. (number line: 0 1 2 3 4 5 6 7 8, closed circle at 2, shaded left)

14. (number line: 0 1 2 3 4 5 6 7 8, open circle at 4, shaded left)

15. (number line: 0 1 2 3 4 5 6 7 8, open circle at 3, shaded right)

16. (number line: 0 1 2 3 4 5 6 7 8, open circle at 2, shaded left)

17. (number line: −8−7−6−5−4−3−2−1 0, open circle at −5, shaded left)

18. (number line: 0 1 2 3 4 5 6 7 8, closed circle at 3, shaded right)

19. (number line: 0 1 2 3 4 5 6 7 8, closed circle at 6, shaded left)

20. (number line: 0 1 2 3 4 5 6 7 8, closed circle at 4, shaded both)

21. (number line: 26 27 28 29 30 31 32 33 34, open circle at 30, shaded left)

22. (number line: 18 19 20 21 22 23 24 25 26, closed circle at 21, shaded right)

23. (number line: −31 −29 −27 −25 −23, open circle at −27, shaded left)

24. (number line: −8−7−6−5−4−3−2−1 0, open circle at −8, shaded right)

25. (number line: −8−7−6−5−4−3−2−1 0, open circle at −3, shaded left)

26. (number line: −8−7−6−5−4−3−2−1 0, closed circle at −6, shaded left)

27. (number line: −4−3−2−1 0 1 2 3 4, closed circle at 1, shaded right)

28. (number line: 1 2 3 4 5 6 7 8 9, closed circle at 5, shaded left)

29. (number line: −13 −11 −9 −7 −5, open circle at −9, shaded right)

48a. Always; if $a < b$, then $a + c < b + c$ by the Addition Property of Inequalities. If $c < d$, then $b + c < b + d$ by the Addition Property of Inequalities. Since $a + c < b + c$ and $b + c < b + d$, it follows that $a + c < b + d$ by the Transitive Property of Inequalities.

48b. Never; if $x < y$ is always true, then $x \geq y$ is never true. In part a, it was shown that, if $a < b$ and $c < d$, the statement $a + c < b + d$ is always true. Therefore, the statement $a + c \geq b + d$ is never true.

48c. Sometimes; if $a = 1$, $b = 2$, $c = 3$, and $d = 5$, then $a - c = 1 - 3$ or -2, but $b - d = 2 - 5$ or -3. In this case, $a - c \neq b - d$. However, if $a = 1$, $b = 2$, $c = 3$, and $d = 4$, then $a - c = 1 - 3$ or -2, and $b - d = 2 - 4$ or -2. In this case, $a - c = b - d$.

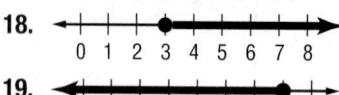

Chapter 6 Answer Appendix

50. Sample answer: Inequalities can be used to compare the number of schools participating in certain sports, to compare the number of participating schools if sports are added or discontinued in a certain number of schools, and to determine how many schools need to add a certain sport to surpass the number participating in another sport. To find how many schools must add girls track and field to surpass the current number of schools participating in girls' basketball, solve $16{,}851 < 15{,}151 + x$. More than 1700 schools must add girls' track and field.

Page 307, Lesson 6-2

41.
```
←——————●————————→
  0  1  2  3  4  5  6  7  8
```

42.
```
←—————○——————————→
 -4 -3 -2 -1  0  1  2  3  4
```

58.
```
←————————○————————→
 15 16 17 18 19 20 21 22 23
```

59.
```
←———●————————————→
 -8 -7 -6 -5 -4 -3 -2 -1  0
```

60.
```
←——————————○—————→
  0  1  2  3  4  5  6  7  8
```

Page 312, Lesson 6-3

32.

$4(t-7) \le 2(t+9)$	Original inequality
$4t - 28 \le 2t + 18$	Distributive Property
$4t - 28 - 2t \le 2t + 18 - 2t$	Subtract $2t$ from each side.
$2t - 28 \le 18$	Simplify.
$2t - 28 + 28 \le 18 + 28$	Add 28 to each side.
$2t \le 46$	Simplify.
$\dfrac{2t}{2} \le \dfrac{46}{2}$	Divide each side by 2.
$t \le 23$	Simplify.

$\{t \mid t \le 23\}$

33.

$-5(k+4) > 3(k-4)$	Original inequality
$-5k - 20 > 3k - 12$	Distributive Property
$-5k - 20 + 5k > 3k - 12 + 5k$	Add $5k$ to each side.
$-20 > 8k - 12$	Simplify.
$-20 + 12 > 8k - 12 + 12$	Add 12 to each side.
$-8 > 8k$	Simplify.
$\dfrac{-8}{8} > \dfrac{8k}{8}$	Divide each side by 8.
$-1 > k$	Simplify.

38. $\dfrac{5(F - 32)}{9} < -38$

1A.
```
←—○——————○——→
 -6-5-4-3-2-1 0  1  2
```

1B.
```
←——○—————————●——→
  0  1  2  3  4  5  6  7  8
```

2A. $\{y \mid -8 \le y \le -5\}$
```
←————●————●————→
-10-9-8-7-6-5-4-3-2
```

2B. $\{r \mid -1 \le r < 3\}$
```
←————●————○————→
 -3-2-1 0  1  2  3  4  5
```

4A. $\{a \mid a < 3 \text{ or } a \ge 4\}$
```
←————○——●—————→
  0  1  2  3  4  5  6  7  8
```

4B. $\{x \mid x \le 9\}$
```
←——————————●————→
  4  5  6  7  8  9 10 11 12
```

3. $\{w \mid 3 < w < 8\}$
```
←——————○————————○——→
  0  1  2  3  4  5  6  7  8  9 10
```

4. $\{n \mid n \le 2 \text{ or } n \ge 8\}$
```
←————●——————————●——→
  0  1  2  3  4  5  6  7  8  9 10
```

5. $\{z \mid z < 4\}$
```
←——————————○——————→
 -2-1 0  1  2  3  4  5  6  7  8
```

6. $\{x \mid -4 < x \le 1\}$
```
←————○——————————●————→
 -7-6-5-4-3-2-1 0  1  2  3
```

32. $\{p \mid 3 \le p \le 5\}$
```
←————●——●——————————→
  0  1  2  3  4  5  6  7  8  9 10
```

33. $\varnothing$
```
←——————————————————→
 -5-4-3-2-1 0  1  2  3  4  5
```

34. $\{c \mid c < -5 \text{ or } c > 4\}$
```
←○——————————————○—→
 -5-4-3-2-1 0  1  2  3  4  5
```

35. $\{b \mid b < -12 \text{ or } b > -12\}$
```
←————○—————————————→
-18-16-14-12-10-8-6-4-2 0  2
```

38. $5 \le n - 8 \le 14$; $\{x \mid 13 \le n \le 22\}$

39. Sample answer: Let n = the number, $-8 < 3n + 4 < 10$; $\{n \mid -4 < n < 2\}$.

40. Sample answer: Let n = the number, $-5n > 35$ or $-5n < 10$; $\{n \mid n < -7 \text{ or } n > -2\}$.

45. Sample answer: troposphere: $a \le 10$, stratosphere: $10 < a \le 30$, mesosphere: $30 < a \le 50$, thermosphere: $50 < a \le 400$, exosphere: $a > 400$

46a. Sample answer: An *intersection* is the place where two or more things overlap. The place where two streets cross is called an intersection. If the solution to a compound inequality is the intersection of the graphs, then the solution is the overlap of the graphs of each inequality.

46b. Sample answer: A *union* is the product of joining two or more different things together. A labor union brings people in the same profession together. If the solution to a compound inequality is the union of the graphs, then the solution is the graph of each inequality.

50. Sample answer: Compound inequalities can be used to show the least and greatest amounts that riders can weigh to go on the ride. A sample height restriction would be $42 \le x \le 80$. This would mean that a rider must be between 42 inches and 80 inches tall, inclusive.

Page 321, Mid-Chapter Quiz

6. $\{a \mid a > 2\}$

7. $\{g \mid g \le -1\}$

15. Sample answer: Let m = the number of months, $175m \ge 2900$; $\{m \mid m \ge 16.6\}$, it will take him at least 17 months to save $2900.

27. $\{x \mid 3 < x < 9\}$

28. $\{b \mid b \le -3 \text{ or } b \ge 0\}$

29. $\{m \mid m > 3 \text{ or } m < -1\}$

30. $\{a \mid -1 < a < 5\}$

Pages 325–327, Lesson 6-5

5.

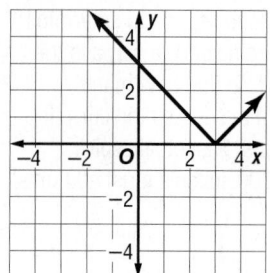

6.

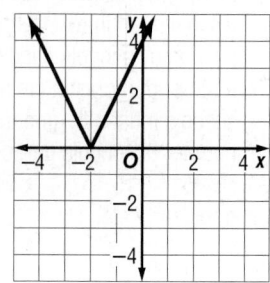

7. $\{-3, 13\}$

8. $\{-11, -7\}$

9. $\varnothing$

10. $\{-7, 10\}$

11. $\{-0.8, 4\}$

12. $\varnothing$

13. $\{-16, -4\}$

14. $\{0, 6\}$

15. $\{16, -8\}$

16. $\{-24, 16\}$

17. $\left\{-\dfrac{3}{2}, \dfrac{9}{2}\right\}$

18. $\left\{3, -\dfrac{9}{5}\right\}$

23.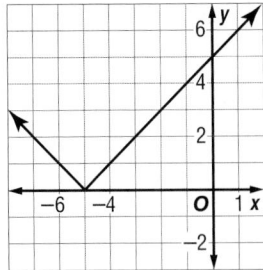

24.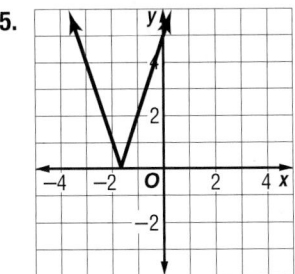

25.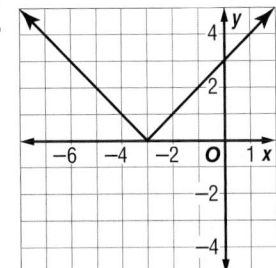

26.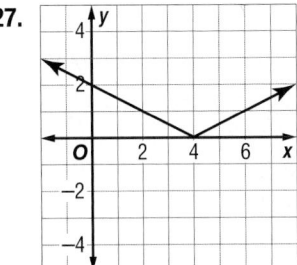

27.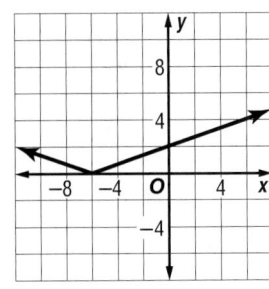

28.

29.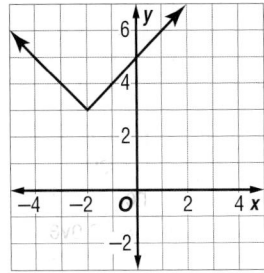

30.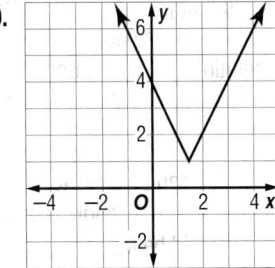

39.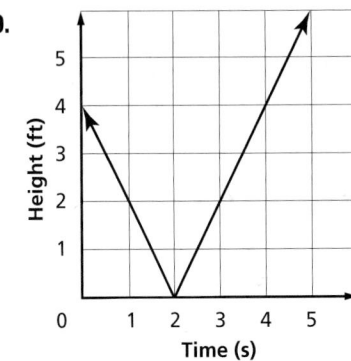

40. $f(x) = \begin{cases} -2x + 4 & \text{if } 2 \geq x \geq 0 \\ 2x - 4 & \text{if } x > 2 \end{cases}$

Page 328, Extend 6-5

1A. Sample answer: The graph of $y = |x|$ is a v-shape. The graph of $y = x$ is a line. The graphs coincide in the first quadrant.

1B. The domain is all real numbers. The range is nonnegative real numbers because the absolute value of a number is never negative.

2A. The graph of $y = |x| - 3$ is the graph of $y = |x|$, shifted 3 units down. The graph of $y = |x| + 1$ is the graph of $y = |x|$, shifted 1 unit up.

2B. Sample answer: The value of c shifts the graph up c units if $c > 0$ and down c units if $c < 0$.

2.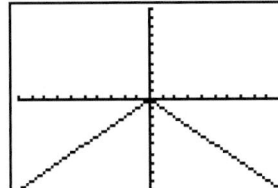

The graph is the reflection of $y = |x|$ over the x-axis.

3. Sample answer: The graph of $y = |x + c|$ is the graph of $y = |x|$ shifted c units left if $c < 0$ and c units right if $c > 0$.

Page 329, Check Your Progress

1A. $\{n \mid 6 \le n \le 10\}$

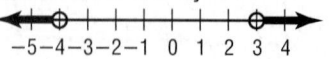

1B. $\varnothing$

Page 330, Check Your Progress

2A. $\{k \mid k < -4 \text{ or } k > 3\}$

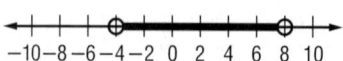

2B. $\{r \mid r \text{ is a real number}\}$

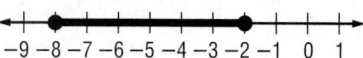

Pages 331–333, Lesson 6-6

1. $\{c \mid -4 < c < 8\}$

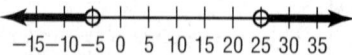

2. $\{x \mid -8 \le x \le 2\}$

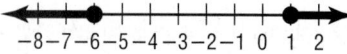

3. $\varnothing$

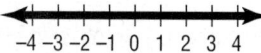

4. $\{w \mid w < -5 \text{ or } w > 25\}$

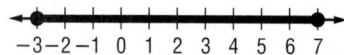

5. $\{g \mid g \le -6 \text{ or } g \ge 1\}$

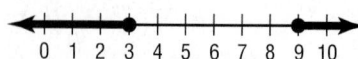

6. $\{p \mid p \text{ is a real number.}\}$

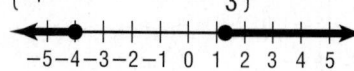

8. $\{z \mid -3 \le z \le 7\}$

9. $\{t \mid -10 < t < -6\}$

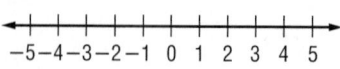

10. $\varnothing$

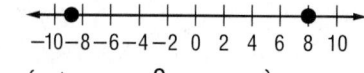

11. $\{v \mid v < -4 \text{ or } v > -2\}$

12. $\{w \mid w \le 3 \text{ or } w \ge 9\}$

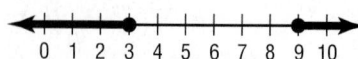

13. $\{a \mid a \text{ is a real number.}\}$

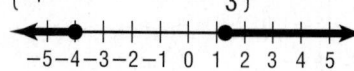

14. $\left\{k \mid k \le -4 \text{ or } k \ge 1\frac{1}{3}\right\}$

15. $\{n \mid -5 < n < 4\}$

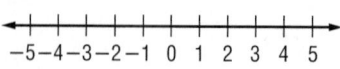

16. $\varnothing$

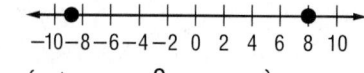

23. $\left\{-8\frac{4}{5}, 8\right\}$

24. $\left\{x \mid x \le -2\frac{2}{3} \text{ or } x \ge 4\right\}$

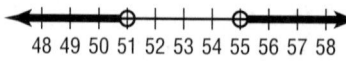

25. $\{s \mid s \text{ is a real number.}\}$

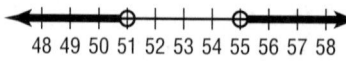

26. $\varnothing$

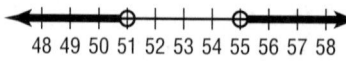

35. The solution of $|x - 2| > 6$ includes all values that are less than -4 or greater than 8. The solution of $|x - 2| < 6$ includes all values that are greater than -4 and less than 8.

36. Sample answer: $|x - 53| > 2$ means that the absolute value of the difference between a student's height x and the class average height, 53 inches, is more than two inches. The solution $\{x \mid x < 51 \text{ or } x > 55\}$ represents possible heights of the student, less than 51 inches or greater than 55 inches.

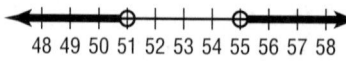

37. $|x - 2| < 0.3$

38. The absolute value of a number is the distance it is from zero on a number line. There is an allowable range of lengths for each baby carrot. Let $x =$ the length of a baby carrot,

$$|x - 2| \le \frac{1}{8}.$$

42. $\{-8, 2\}$

43. ∅

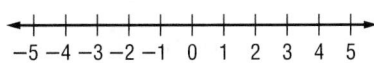

44. $\left\{-\dfrac{2}{3}, 2\right\}$

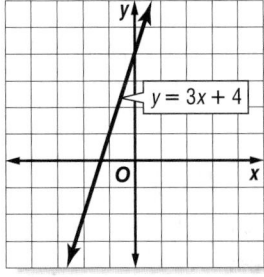

48.

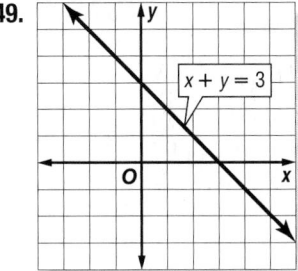

$y = 3x + 4$

49.

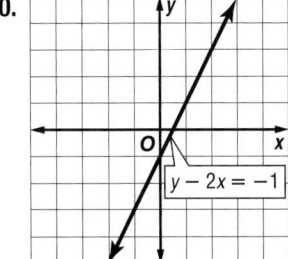

$x + y = 3$

50.

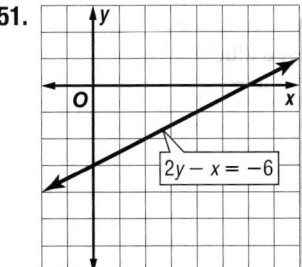

$y - 2x = -1$

51.

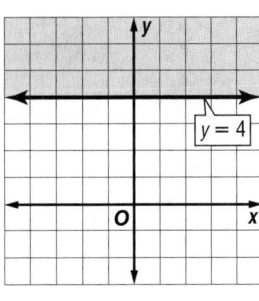

$2y - x = -6$

Pages 337–338, Lesson 6-7

1.

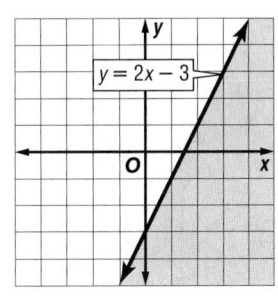

$y = 4$

2.

$y = 2x - 3$

3.

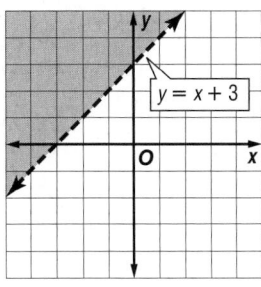

$y = x + 3$

4.

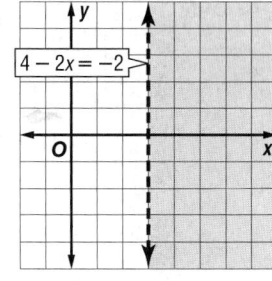

$4 - 2x = -2$

5.

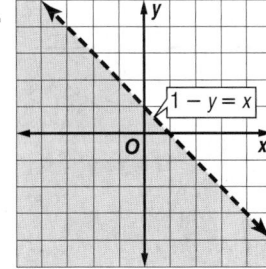

$1 - y = x$

6.

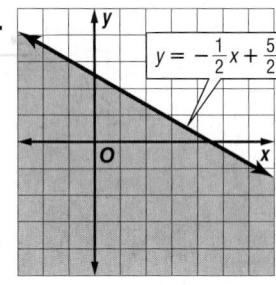

$y = -\dfrac{1}{2}x + \dfrac{5}{2}$

8.

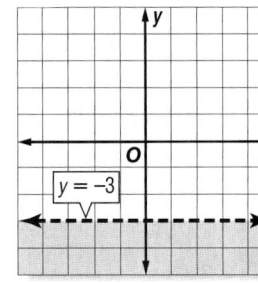

$y = -3$

9.

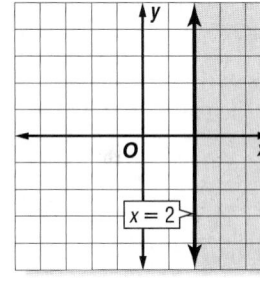

$x = 2$

10.

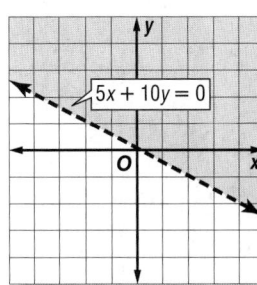

$5x + 10y = 0$

11.

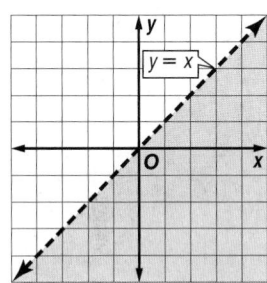

$y = x$

12.

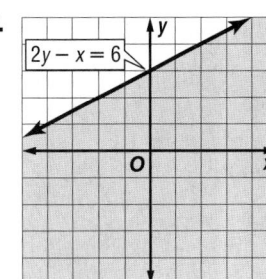

$2y - x = 6$

13.

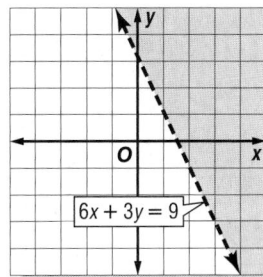

$6x + 3y = 9$

14.

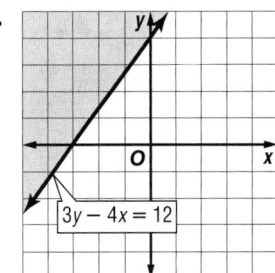

$3y - 4x = 12$

15.

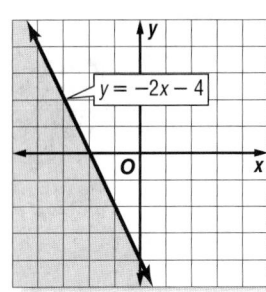

$y = -2x - 4$

16.
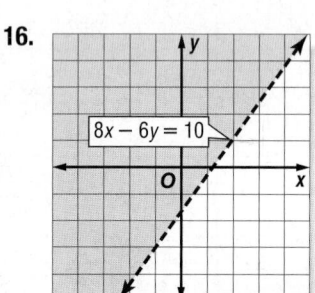

8x − 6y = 10

17.
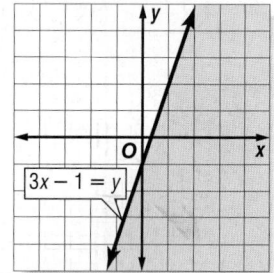

3x − 1 = y

33.
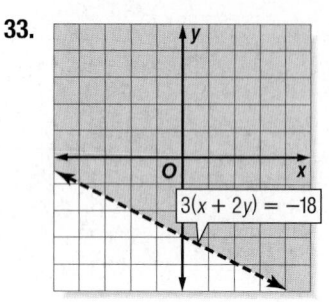

3(x + 2y) = −18

34.
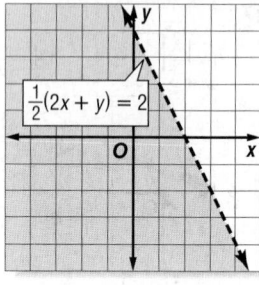

$\frac{1}{2}(2x + y) = 2$

38.
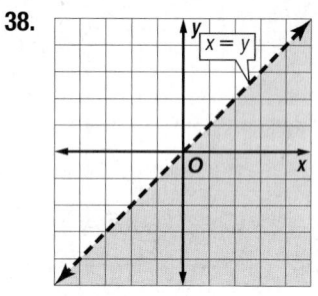

x = y

40.
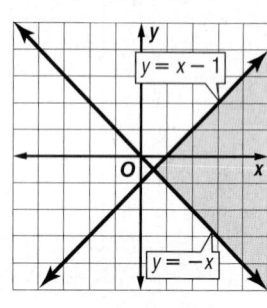

y = x − 1
y = −x

57.
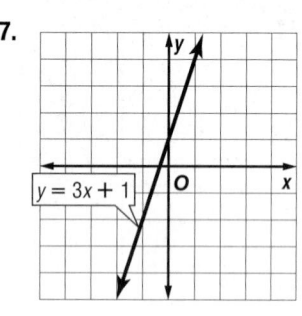

y = 3x + 1

58.
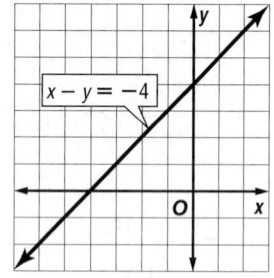

x − y = −4

59.
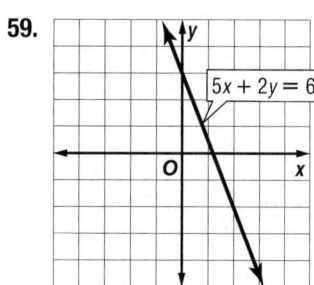

5x + 2y = 6

Page 340, Extend 6-7

3c.
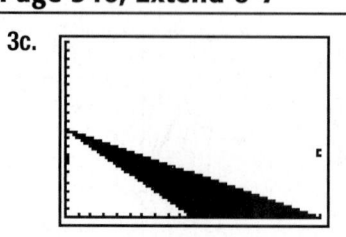

3d. Sample answer: {(8, 5), (10, 4), (14, 2), (20, 0)}

Pages 341–342, Lesson 6-8

1A.
y = 3
x + y = 1

1B.
2x + y = 2
2x + y = 4

2A. Appropriate Cholesterol Levels
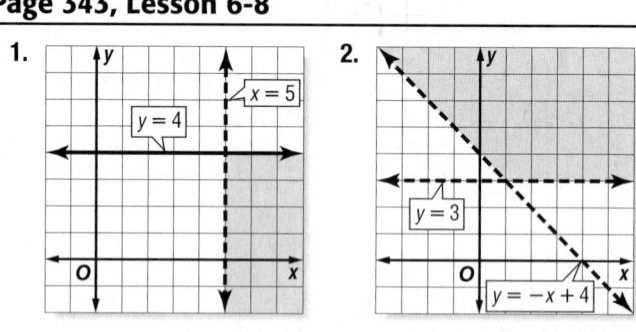
LDL

2B. Salad Dressing
$x + \frac{3}{4}y = 4$
$\frac{1}{2}x + y = 4$
Recipe 2 / Recipe 1

Page 343, Lesson 6-8

1. x = 5; y = 4

2. y = 3; y = −x + 4

3. y = −x + 3; y = x + 3

4. ∅; 2x + y = 4; y = −2x − 1

5. Natasha's Daily Exercise

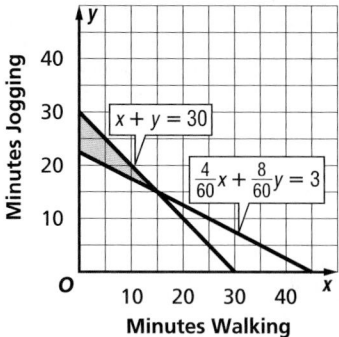

7.

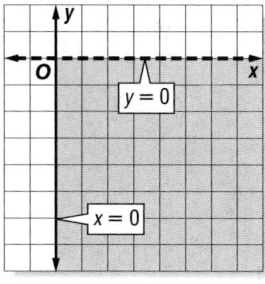

8.

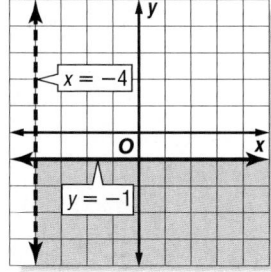

9.

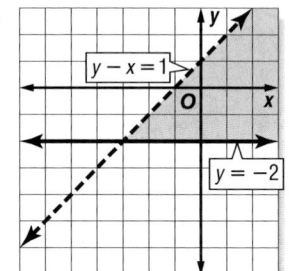

10.

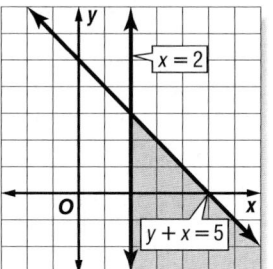

11.

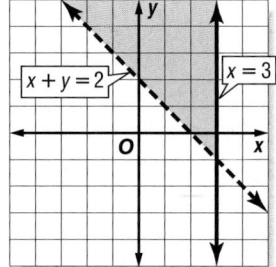

12.

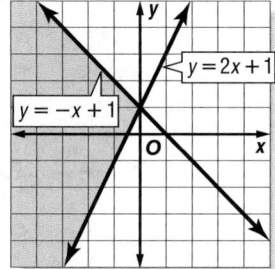

13.

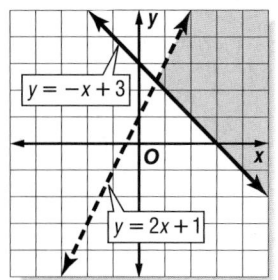

14.

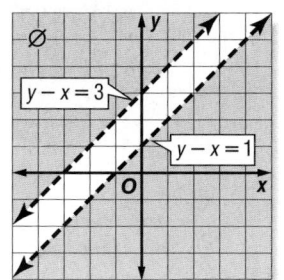

15.

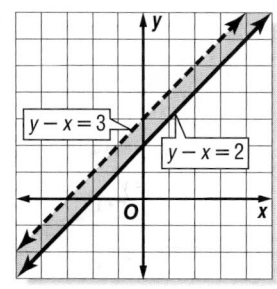

16.

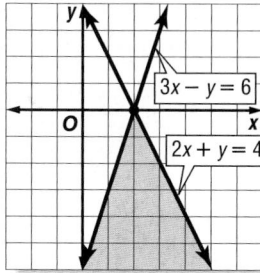

17.

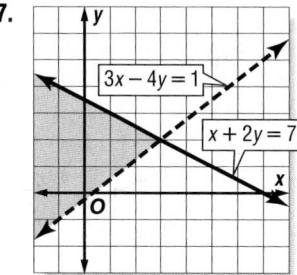

18.

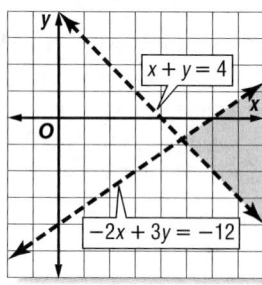

19. Furniture Manufacturing

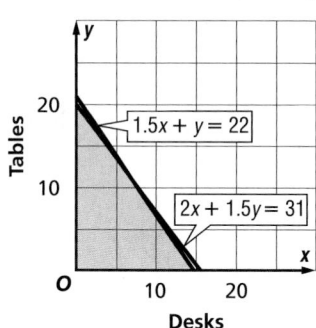

21.

Green Paint

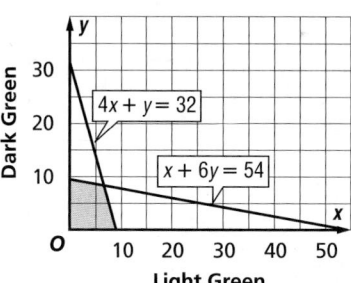

Page 344, Lesson 6-8

23.

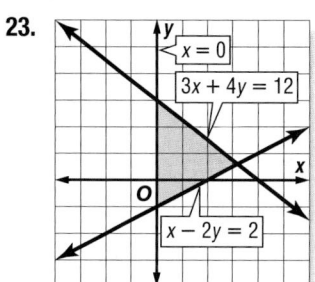

24.

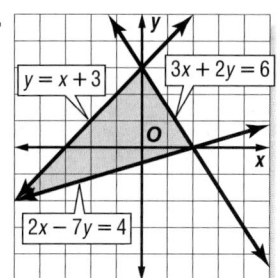

25.

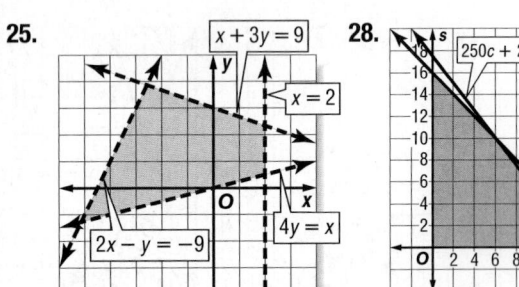

28.

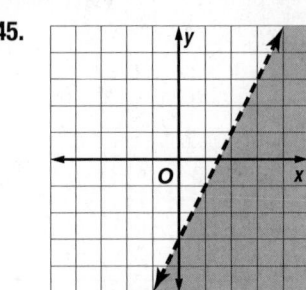

29. Any point in the shaded region is a possible solution. For example, since (7, 8) is a point in the region, Mr. Hobson could plant corn for 7 days and soybeans for 8 days. In this case, he would use 15 days to plant 250(7) or 1750 acres of corn and 200(8) or 1600 acres of soybeans.

30.

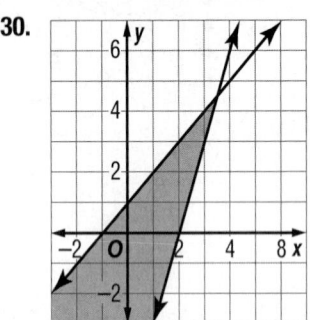

31.

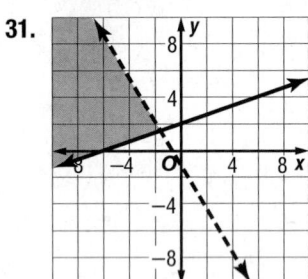

32.

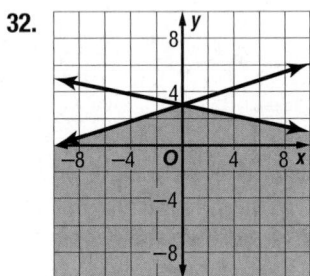

33. Sample answer:

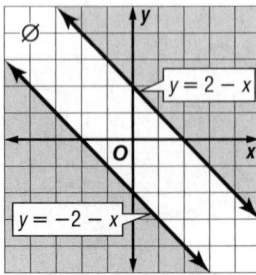

36. Sample answer: By graphing a system of equations, you can see the appropriate range of protein and fat intake. Two sample appropriate protein and fat intakes are 70 g of protein and 60 g of fat and 75 g of protein and 65 g of fat. The graph represents $60 \leq p \leq 80$ and $60 \leq f \leq 75$.

Pages 349–350, Study Guide and Review

45.

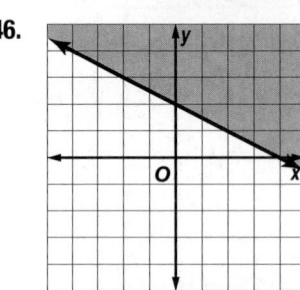

46.

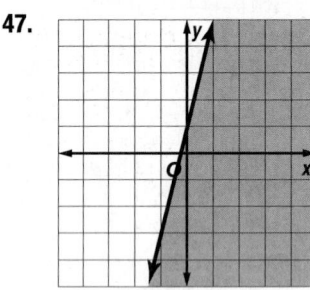

47.

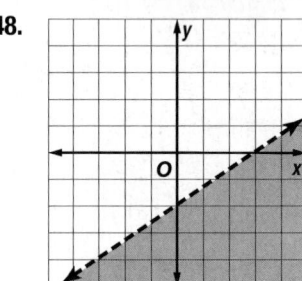

48.

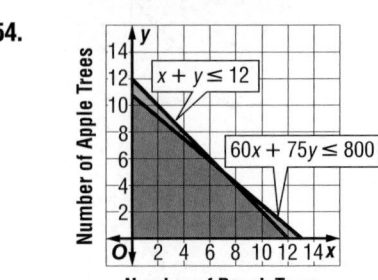

54.

Sample answer: 7 peach trees and 5 apple trees; 8 peach trees and 4 apple trees; 9 peach trees and 3 apple trees

8.
A number line from -5 to 5 with open circles at -2 and 3, segment shaded between.

9.
A number line from -3 to 7 with closed circles at 0 and 5, shaded outside (to the left of 0 and to the right of 5).

10.
A number line from -4 to 6 with closed circles at -3 and 1, shaded between.

11.
A number line from -3 to 7 with closed circles at 1 and 3, shaded between.

12.
A number line from -3 to 7 with open circles at -1 and 6, shaded between.

13.
A number line from -3 to 7 with closed circles at 1 and 2, shaded to the left.

14. Sample answer: Let $n =$ the number, $\frac{1}{4}n \geq -3$;
$\{n \mid n \geq -12\}$.

15. Sample answer: Let $n =$ the number, $14 - 3n < 2$;
$\{n \mid n > 4\}$.

17. Sample answer: Let $d =$ the distance, $18(15) \leq d \leq 21(15)$;
$\{d \mid 270 \leq d \leq 315\}$, between 270 mi and 315 mi.

18.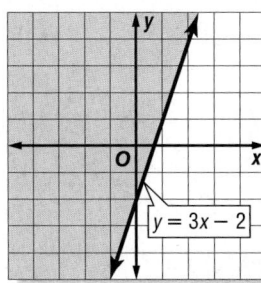
$y = 3x - 2$

19.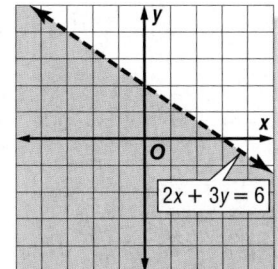
$2x + 3y = 6$

20.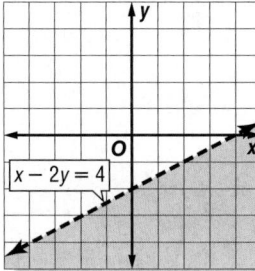
$x - 2y = 4$

22.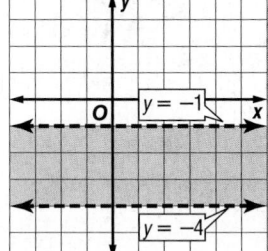
$y = -1$
$y = -4$

23.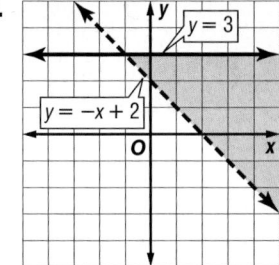
$y = 3$
$y = -x + 2$

Introduction

In this unit, students are introduced to nonlinear functions. Students first learn about polynomials and operations involving monomials and polynomials. They then examine various methods of factoring.

The unit concludes with instruction on the various methods of solving quadratic equations, which includes graphing, factoring, and the Quadratic Formula. Students end this unit with an introduction to exponential functions.

Assessment Options

Unit 3 Test Pages 71–72 of the *Chapter 9 Resource Masters* may be used as a test or review for Unit 3. This assessment contains both multiple-choice and short answer items.

ExamView®
Assessment Suite

Create additional customized Unit Tests and review worksheets for differentiated instruction.

UNIT 3
Polynomials and Nonlinear Functions

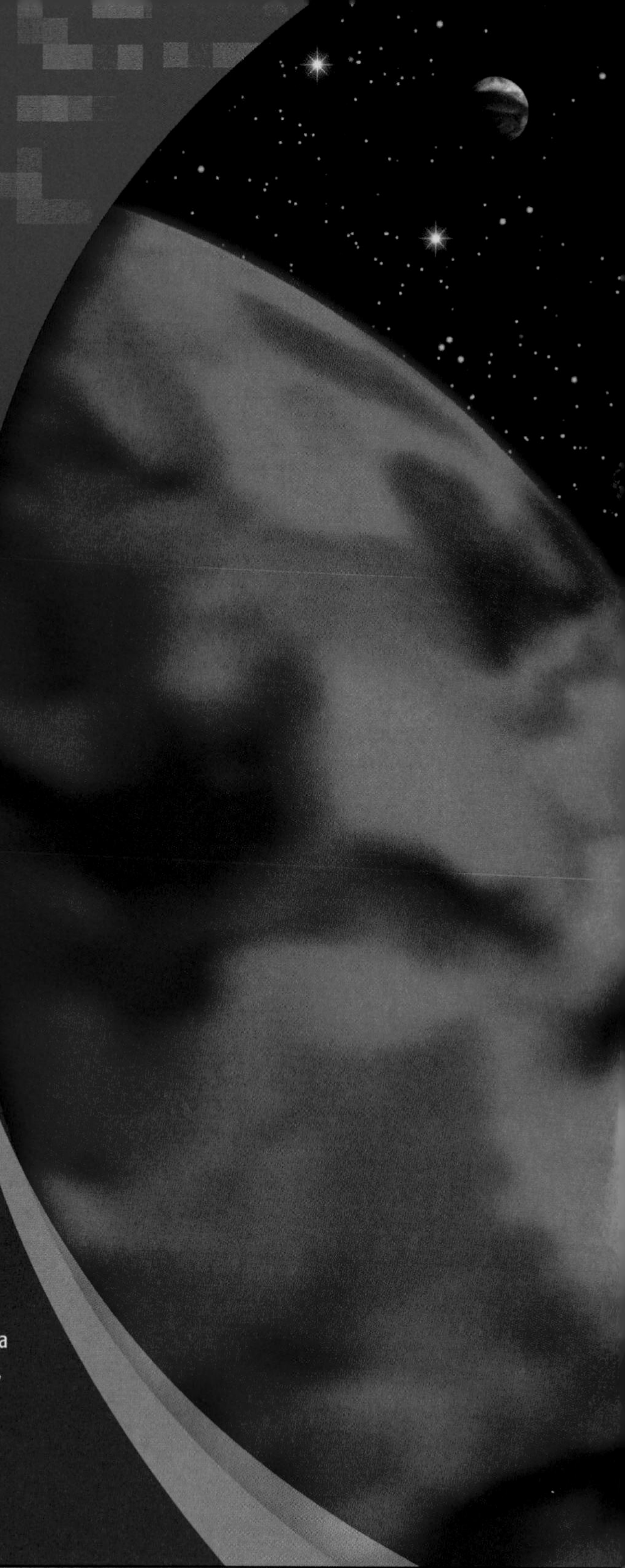

Focus
Use quadratic and other nonlinear functions to model and solve real-world problems.

CHAPTER 7   Polynomials
BIG Idea Use the rules of exponents.

BIG Idea Add, subtract, multiply, and divide monomials.

CHAPTER 8   Factoring
BIG Idea Apply basic factoring techniques to second- and simple third-degree polynomials.

CHAPTER 9
Quadratic and Exponential Functions
BIG Idea Solve a quadratic equation by factoring or completing the square.

BIG Idea Graph quadratic functions and know that their roots are the *x*-intercepts.

BIG Idea Determine whether the graph of a quadratic function will intersect the *x*-axis in zero, one, or two points.

354 Unit 3

Real-Life Math Videos *Real-Life Math Videos* engage students by showing them how math is used in everyday situations. Use Video 3 with this unit.

Algebra and Physical Science

Out of this World You can probably name the planets in the solar system, but can you name planets outside of our system? In recent years, planets in other systems have been discovered. In August, 2004, a team of astronomers discovered a small planet orbiting a star known as 55 Cancri. Star 55 Cancri has three other planets, making it the first known four-planet system outside our system. In this project, you will examine how exponents, factors, and graphs are useful in presenting information about planets.

Math Online Log on to ca.algebra1.com to begin.

Cross-Curricular Project

Algebra and Physical Science

Out of this World This Cross-Curricular Project is an online project in which students do research on the Internet, gather data, and make presentations using word processing, graphing, page-making, or presentation software. In each chapter, students advance to the next step in their project. At the end of Chapter 9, the project culminates with a presentation of their findings.

Math Online
ca.algebra1.com Log on for teaching suggestions and sample answers for this project.

Team Teaching You can use this Cross-Curricular Project with your students' science teacher to make the connection from mathematics to the astronomy and physics topics your students are studying.

Chapter Overview

Polynomials

Standards-Based Lesson Plan		Pacing Your Lessons	
LESSONS AND OBJECTIVES	California Standards	40-50 Minute Periods	90-Minute Periods
7-1 Multiplying Monomials (pp. 358–364) • Multiply monomials. • Simplify expressions involving powers of monomials. **Extend 7-1 Investigating Surface Area and Volume** (p. 365) • Use grid paper to investigate the surface area ratio and volume ratio of pairs of rectangular prisms.	2.0, 10.0	2	1.5
7-2 Dividing Monomials (pp. 366–373) • Simplify expressions involving the quotient of monomials. • Simplify expressions containing negative exponents.	2.0, 10.0	2	0.5
Explore 7-3 Polynomials (p. 375) • Use algebra tiles to model polynomials. **7-3 Polynomials** (pp. 376–381) • Find the degree of a polynomial. • Arrange the terms of a polynomial in ascending or descending order.	10.0	2	1
Explore 7-4 Adding and Subtracting Polynomials (pp. 382–383) • Use algebra tiles to add and subtract polynomials. **7-4 Adding and Subtracting Polynomials** (pp. 384–388) • Add polynomials. • Subtract polynomials.	10.0	2	1
7-5 Multiplying a Polynomial by a Monomial (pp. 390–395) • Find the product of a monomial and a polynomial. • Solve equations involving polynomials.	10.0	2	0.5
Explore 7-6 Multiplying Polynomials (pp. 396–397) • Use algebra tiles to multiply polynomials. **7-6 Multiplying Polynomials** (pp. 398–403) • Multiply two binomials by using the FOIL method. • Multiply two polynomials by using the Distributive Property.	10.0	2	1.5
7-7 Special Products (pp. 404–409) • Find squares of sums and differences. • Find the product of a sum and a difference.	10.0	1	1
REVIEW		1	0.5
ASSESSMENT		1	0.5*
*The complete **Assessment Planner** for Chapter 7 is provided on p. 357.*	**TOTAL**	15	8

Begin Chapter 8 in the second half of the period.

356A Chapter 7 Polynomials

Professional Development

California Standards Vertical Alignment

Before Chapter 7

Related Topics from Grade 7

- Multiply and divide monomials Standard 7AF2.2
- Simplify numerical expressions and justify the process used ⬤━ Standard 7AF1.3

Chapter 7

Topics from Algebra I

- Understand and use the rules of exponents ⬤━
- Add, subtract, multiply, and divide monomials and polynomials ⬤━

See individual lessons for the specific Standards covered.

After Chapter 7

Preparation for Algebra II

- Operations on polynomials, including long division ⬤━ Standard 2A3.0

What the Research Says...

Wenglinsky (2000) found that students whose teachers conduct hands-on learning activities outperform their peers by more than 70% of a grade level in mathematics on the National Assessment of Educational Progress (a study of over 7000 students).

- Lessons 7-1B, 7-3A, 7-4A, and 7-6A all involve activity-based investigations of polynomial properties.
- Algebra tiles are used in Lessons 7-3A, 7-4A, and 7-6A to provide students with concrete models for their understanding of polynomials.

[Source: Wenglinsky, H. (2000). *How Teaching Matters: Bringing the Classroom Back into Discussions of Teacher Quality*, Princeton, New Jersey: Educational Testing Service, p. 7.]

Back-Mapping

California Algebra 1 was conceived and developed with the final result in mind, student success in Algebra I and beyond. The authors, using the California Mathematics Standards as their guide, developed this brand-new series by "back-mapping" from the desired result of student success in Algebra I and beyond. McGraw-Hill's *California Geometry, California Algebra 2,* and *California Algebra Readiness* were developed utilizing the same philosophy.

Professional Development

Targeted professional development has been articulated throughout the *California Mathematics: Concepts, Skills, and Problem Solving* series. The **McGraw-Hill Professional Development Video Library** provides short videos that support the ⬤━ Key Standards. For more information, visit ca.algebra1.com.

| Model Lessons | Instructional Strategies |

CHAPTER 7
Technology Solutions

Teacher Resources

TeacherWorks™ All-in-One Planner and Resource Center

All of the print materials from the Classroom Resource Masters are available on your TeacherWorks™ CD-ROM.

BL = Below Grade Level **OL** = On Grade Level **AL** = Above Grade Level **ELL** = English Language Learner

Chapter Resource Masters			7-1	7-2	7-3	7-4	7-5	7-6	7-7
BL OL — ELL	Lesson Reading Guide		5	12	19	27	34	41	49
BL OL ELL	Study Guide and Intervention*		6	13	20	28	35	42	50
BL OL	Skills Practice*		8	15	22	30	37	44	52
OL AL	Practice*		9	16	23	31	38	45	53
OL AL	Word Problem Practice*		10	17	24	32	39	46	54
OL AL	Enrichment		11	18	25	33	40	47	55
OL AL	Calculator and Spreadsheet Activities				26			48	
OL AL	Chapter Assessments*		57–78						
BL OL AL	5-Minute Check Transparencies		✓	✓	✓	✓	✓	✓	✓
BL OL	Teaching Mathematics with Manipulatives		✓		✓	✓	✓	✓	✓

Also available in Spanish.

AssignmentWorks

Differentiated Assignments, Answers, and Solutions

- Print a customized assignment worksheet using the Student Edition exercises along with an answer key or worked-out solutions.
- Use default lesson assignments as outlined in the Differentiated Homework Options in the Teacher Wraparound Edition.
- Includes modified questions from the Student Edition.

Interactive Classroom

This CD-ROM is a customizable Microsoft® PowerPoint® presentation that includes:

- In-Class Examples
- Your Turn Exercises*
- 5-Minute Check Transparencies*
- Links to Online Study Tools
- Concepts in Motion

compatible with response pad technology

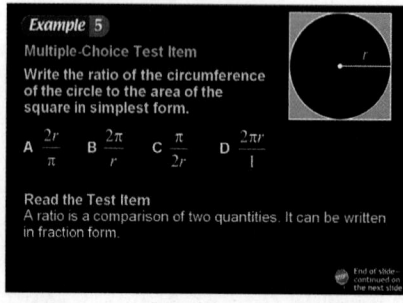

ExamView®Assessment Suite

 lets you

- Create, edit, and customize tests and worksheets using QuickTest Wizard
- Create multiple versions of tests and modify them for a desired level of difficulty
- Translate from English to Spanish and vice versa
- Build tests aligned with your state standards
- Track students' progress using the Teacher Management System

Student Resources

StudentWorks™ Plus

Textbook, Audio, Workbooks, and more

This CD-ROM is a valuable resource for students to access content online and use online resources to continue learning Chapter 7 concepts. Includes:

- Complete Student Editions in both English and Spanish
- English audio integrated throughout the text
- Links to Concepts in Motion, Personal Tutor, and other online resources
- Access to all student worksheets
- Daily Assignments and Grade Log

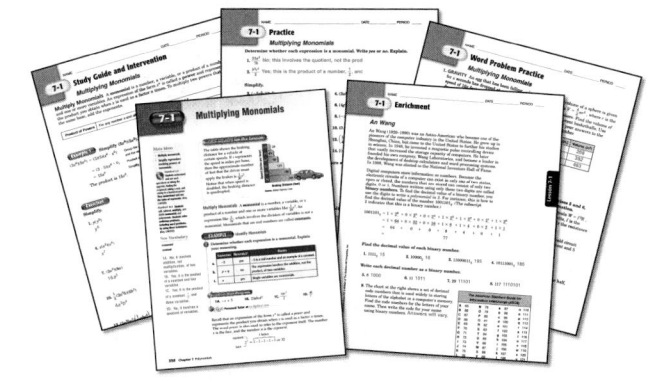

Super DVD

The Super DVD contains two Glencoe multimedia products.

MindJogger Plus An alternative review of concepts in which students work as teams in a game show format to gain points for correct answers.

What's Math Got to Do With It? Real Life Math Videos Engaging video that shows students how math is used in everyday situations

Internet Resources

Math Online ca.algebra1.com

TEACHER	PARENT	STUDENT	**Online Study Tools**
	•	•	Online Student Edition
•	•	•	Multilingual Glossary
			Lesson Resources
	•	•	BrainPOP®
•	•	•	Concepts in Motion
•	•	•	Extra Examples
	•	•	Other Calculator Keystrokes
•			Problem of the Week Cards
	•	•	Real-World Careers
	•	•	Self-Check Quizzes
			Chapter Resources
	•	•	Chapter Readiness
	•	•	Chapter Test
	•	•	Standardized Test Practice
	•	•	Vocabulary Review/Chapter Review Activities
			Unit Resources
•		•	Cross-Curricular Internet Project
			Other Resources
•			Dinah Zike's Foldables™
	•	•	Hotmath Homework Help
•			Key Concepts
•	•	•	Meet the Authors
	•	•	Personal Tutor
•			Project CRISS℠
	•	•	Scavenger Hunts and Answer Sheets
•			Vocabulary PuzzleMakers

Focus on Mathematical Content

Big Idea for Chapter 7:
Monomials and Polynomials

Many situations in the real world cannot be modeled with first-degree equations. They require the use of functions that are not linear. For example, in order to model the volumes of solids, it is necessary to use expressions that include exponents. A cube with side x has volume x^3; a cylinder with height h and radius r has volume $\pi r^2 h$. Such algebraic expressions, called monomials, are the building blocks of more complex algebraic expressions called *polynomials*. Before using monomials and polynomials to model real-world situations, the necessary algebraic skills required to simplify algebraic expressions must be acquired.

Why It's Important

For This Chapter
The lessons in this chapter help students to master operations with polynomials that form the foundation for solving equations that involve polynomials.

- What is a monomial? How can you multiply monomials and simplify expressions involving powers of monomials? (Lesson 7-1)
- How can you divide monomials and simplify expressions containing negative exponents? (Lesson 7-2)
- What is a polynomial? How do you find the degree of a polynomial? (Lesson 7-3)
- What methods can be used to add and subtract polynomials? (Lesson 7-4)
- What property is used when a polynomial is multiplied by a monomial? (Lesson 7-5)
- How do you use the FOIL method to multiply two polynomials? (Lesson 7-6)
- Which binomial products have patterns that make their multiplication simpler? (Lesson 7-7)

After This Chapter
- In Chapter 8, simplifying algebraic expressions can help students factor polynomials.
- In geometry, monomials and polynomials can help students model two- and three-dimensional figures.
- In calculus, polynomials are used to introduce the concept of finding the derivative of a function.

7-1 Multiplying Monomials

A *monomial* is a number, a variable, or a product of a number and one or more variables. An expression involving the division of variables is not a monomial. Monomials that are real numbers are called *constants*. When multiplying monomials, use the Commutative and Associative Properties to group constants together and group powers with the same base together.

- To multiply two powers with the same base, add the exponents.
- To find a power of a power, multiply the exponents.
- To find the power of a product, find the power of each factor and multiply.

A monomial expression is simplified when each base appears exactly once, there are no powers of powers, and all fractions are in simplest form.

7-2 Dividing Monomials

Monomials may also be divided.

- To divide two powers that have the same base, subtract the exponents.
- To find the power of a quotient, find the power of the numerator and the power of the denominator.
- Any nonzero number raised to the zero power is 1.
- Expressions can also have negative exponents.
- A nonzero number raised to a negative integer power is the reciprocal of the same number with the opposite, or positive, power.
- A fraction that has a negative exponent can be rewritten as its reciprocal with the opposite or positive power.
- An expression that has a variable raised to a negative exponent in the numerator is not a monomial.

Polynomials

A *polynomial* is a monomial or a sum (or difference) of monomials. The sum of two monomials is called a *binomial*, and the sum of three monomials is called a *trinomial*.

Polynomials with more than three monomials have no special names.

The degree of a polynomial is the greatest degree of any monomial in the polynomial. To find the degree of a monomial, add the exponents of all its variables. The degree of a polynomial should not be confused with the number of terms in the polynomial.

The terms of a polynomial are usually arranged so that the powers of one variable are in ascending (increasing) or descending (decreasing) order. This aids in reading and understanding the polynomial.

 Adding and Subtracting Polynomials

Polynomials may be added and subtracted by combining like terms. If the variable parts of two terms are exactly the same, the terms are called like terms.

- When adding polynomials, add the coefficients of like terms using the rules for adding real numbers.
- When subtracting polynomials, first replace each term of the polynomial being subtracted with its additive inverse. Then combine the like terms.
- There are two methods that can be used to add and subtract polynomials. You can group like terms horizontally, or you can write them in column form, aligning like terms.

 Multiplying a Polynomial by a Monomial

The Distributive Property is used to find the product of a monomial and a polynomial.

- Multiply each term of the polynomial by the monomial, using the rules for monomial multiplication.
- If the monomial is negative, don't forget to apply the rules for multiplying real numbers.
- Be sure to simplify the product by combining any like terms.

Many equations contain polynomials that must be added, subtracted, or multiplied before the equation can be solved. To solve such equations, first simplify each side. Then apply the rules for solving multi-step equations and equations with variables on both sides.

 Multiplying Polynomials

When multiplying two binomials, the Distributive Property is used twice.

- Multiply the first term of the first binomial by each term of the second binomial.
- Do the same with the second term of the first binomial.
- Then combine like terms.

A shortcut of the Distributive Property called the FOIL method can be used to multiply two binomials. To use the FOIL method, find the sum of the products of the First terms (F), the Outer terms (O), the Inner terms (I), and the Last terms (L).

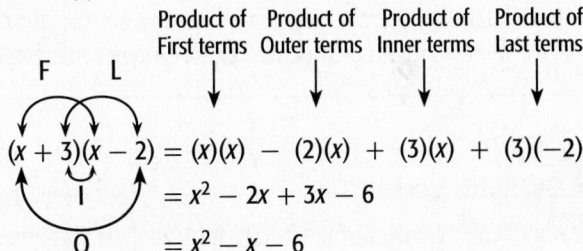

The Distributive Property can be used to multiply any two polynomials. Products are not in simplest form until all like terms have been combined.

 Special Products

While you can always use the Distributive Property or the FOIL method to multiply two binomials, some binomial products have patterns that make finding their products simpler.

- One pattern is the *square of a sum*, $(a + b)^2$. The resulting product is always of the form $a^2 + 2ab + b^2$.
- A second pattern is the *square of a difference*, $(a - b)^2$. The resulting product is always of the form $a^2 - 2ab + b^2$. Note that this product is the same as the square of a sum except for the sign of the middle term.
- A third pattern is the product of a sum and a difference of the same two terms, $(a + b)(a - b)$. The resulting product, $a^2 - b^2$, is called a *difference of squares*.

Being able to identify and use these patterns can make it easier to simplify these special products.

Differentiated Instruction

Options for Chapter 7 Lessons

ELL = English Language Learner	**AL** = Above Grade Level	**SS** = Struggling Students	**SN** = Special Needs

Using Logic **AL**

Use with Lesson 7-1

Give students a term such as $144a^{10}b^8$ and challenge them to write 20 unique combinations of monomials that would produce this product if multiplied.

Using Interpersonal Skills **ELL** **SN**

Use with Lesson 7-4

To reinforce the concepts of the lesson, place students in pairs and have the students take turns completing the Check for Understanding Exercises. As one student works the problem, have the other student offer guidance and suggestions. Make sure students offer constructive reinforcement to each other and that each student completes at least one exercise.

Connecting Mathematics to Music **SS**

Use with Lesson 7-6

Music can be a powerful memory tool. Suggest that groups of students make up a song or rap to explain how to use the FOIL method to multiply binomials. Have the groups perform their songs in front of the class when they are finished.

Noteables™ Interactive Study Notebook with Foldables™

Noteables™ Interactive Study Notebook with Foldables™ is a study organizer that provides helpful steps for students to follow to organize their notes for Chapter 7.

- Students use Noteables to record notes and to complete their Foldables as you present the material for each lesson.
- Noteables correspond to the Examples in the *Teacher Wraparound Edition* and *Interactive Classroom CD-ROM*.

Intervention

Quick Review Math Handbook*

is Glencoe's mathematical handbook for students and parents.

Hot Words includes a glossary of terms.

Hot Topics consists of two parts:

- explanations of key mathematical concepts
- exercises to check students' understanding.

Lesson	Hot Topics Section	Lesson	Hot Topics Section
7-1	2.1	7-4	6.2
7-2	3.4	7-5	6.2
7-3	6.2	7-6	3.2, 3.4

*Also available in Spanish

Teacher To Teacher

Cindy Anderson
Math Facilitator
Waco High School
Waco, Texas

USE WITH LESSON 7-6

❝ I have my students use the 'box method' to multiply polynomials. For example, to multiply $(2x + 5)(3x - 1)$, they start with a 2×2 grid and write the terms along the top and left side. Then they fill in the grid, one row at a time, and combine like terms along the diagonal.

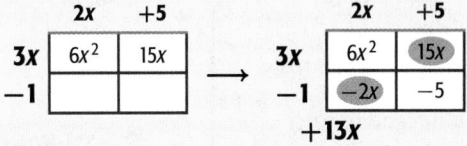

The product is $6x^2 + 13x - 5$. Students prefer this method because it is a good organizer. ❞

Reading and Writing in Mathematics

STUDY SKILL

Students often struggle with definitions and could benefit from making concept maps. These maps help students visualize the components of definitions.

A sample concept map on polynomials is shown at the right. You may wish to have students use this sample to develop their own maps to organize other definitions they will study in Chapter 7.

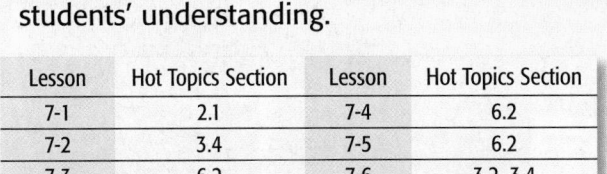

C R e a t i n g **I** n d e p e n d e n c e t h r o u g h **S** t u d e n t - o w n e d **S** t r a t e g i e s

Notes

 Dinah Zike's Foldables™

Focus Students create pages of tables on which they organize information about polynomials for each lesson in this chapter.

Teach Have students make their Foldables as illustrated. Have them label the rows and columns of their tables.

Students should include information in the appropriate rows and columns of the tables that will allow them to compare the different operations. Remind students that comparing involves determining a trait to be compared and then finding the similarities and differences in that trait.

When to Use It At the end of each lesson, ask students to take notes and write examples for each operation.

A version of a completed Foldable is shown on p. 410.

Differentiated Instruction

[CRM] Student-Built Glossary, pp. 1–2

Students should complete the chart by providing a definition and an example of each term as they progress through Chapter 7. This study tool can also be used to review for the chapter test.

Materials Needed for Chapter 7

- centimeter grid paper (Explore 7-1, Extend 7-1)
- scissors (Explore 7-1)
- tape (Explore 7-1)
- algebra tiles (Explore 7-3, Explore 7–4, Explore 7-6, Lessons 7-6, 7-7)
- product mat (Explore 7-6)

Polynomials

 **BIG Ideas**

- **Standard 2.0** Students understand and use such operations as taking the opposite, finding the reciprocal, taking a root, and raising to a fractional power. They understand and use the rules of exponents. (Key, CAHSEE)

- **Standard 10.0** Students add, subtract, multiply, and divide monomials and polynomials. Students solve multistep problems, including word problems, by using these techniques. (Key, CAHSEE)

Key Vocabulary

binomial (p. 376)

FOIL method (p. 399)

monomial (p. 358)

polynomial (p. 376)

🌐 Real-World Link

Running Polynomials can be used to model many real-world situations, such as the way that distance runners on a curved track should be staggered at the start of a race.

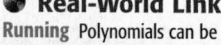 **FOLDABLES™**
Study Organizer

Polynomials Make this Foldable to help you organize information about polynomials. Begin with a sheet of 11" by 17" paper.

1 **Fold** in thirds lengthwise.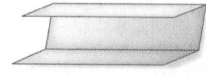

2 **Open** and fold a 2" tab along the width. Then fold the rest in fourths.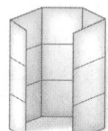

3 **Draw** lines along folds and label as shown.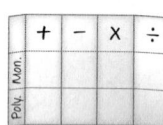

356 Chapter 7 Polynomials

Additional Answer (Get Ready for Chapter 7)

15. The probability of correctly guessing the outcome of a flipped penny six times in a row is $\frac{1}{64}$.

356 Chapter 7 Polynomials

GET READY for Chapter 7

Diagnose Readiness You have two options for checking Prerequisite Skills.

Option 1

Take the Quick Check below. Refer to the Quick Review for help.

Option 2

Math Online Take the Online Readiness Quiz at ca.algebra1.com.

QUICK Check

(Used in Lessons 7-1 and 7-3)
Write each expression using exponents. (Lesson 1-1)

1. $2 \cdot 2 \cdot 2 \cdot 2 \cdot 2$ 2^5
2. $3 \cdot 3 \cdot 3 \cdot 3$ 3^4
3. $5 \cdot 5$ 5^2
4. $x \cdot x \cdot x$ x^3
5. $a \cdot a \cdot a \cdot a \cdot a \cdot a$ a^6
6. $x \cdot x \cdot y \cdot y \cdot y$ $x^2 y^3$
7. $\frac{1}{2} \cdot \frac{1}{2} \cdot \frac{1}{2} \cdot \frac{1}{2} \cdot \frac{1}{2}$ $\left(\frac{1}{2}\right)^5$
8. $\frac{a}{b} \cdot \frac{a}{b} \cdot \frac{c}{d} \cdot \frac{c}{d} \cdot \frac{c}{d} \cdot \frac{c}{d}$ $\left(\frac{a}{b}\right)^2 \left(\frac{c}{d}\right)^4$

Evaluate each expression. (Lesson 1-1)
(Used in Lessons 7-1 and 7-2)

9. 3^2 9
10. 4^3 64
11. $(-6)^2$ 36
12. $(-3)^3$ -27
13. $\left(\frac{2}{3}\right)^4$ $\frac{16}{81}$
14. $\left(-\frac{7}{8}\right)^2$ $\frac{49}{64}$

15. **PROBABILITY** The probability of correctly guessing the outcome of a flipped penny six times is $\left(\frac{1}{2}\right)^6$. Express this probability as a fraction without exponents. **See margin.**

(Used in Lessons 7-1, 7-2, 7-4, 7-5, 7-6, 7-7)
Find the area or volume of each figure.
(Prerequisite Skill)

16. 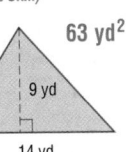 63 yd²   9 yd, 14 yd

17. 36π m² or about 113.04   6 m

18. 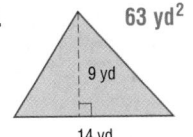 84 ft³   4 ft, 3 ft, 7 ft

19. 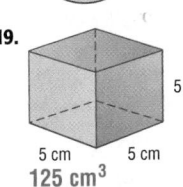 125 cm³   5 cm, 5 cm, 5 cm

QUICK Review

EXAMPLE 1

Express $6 \cdot 6 \cdot 6 \cdot x \cdot x + y \cdot y \cdot y \cdot y \cdot z$ using exponents.

3 factors of six is 6^3.   4 factors of y is y^4.

2 factors of x is x^2.   1 factor of z is z^1 or z.

So, $6 \cdot 6 \cdot 6 \cdot x \cdot x + y \cdot y \cdot y \cdot y \cdot z = 6^3 x^2 + y^4 z$.

EXAMPLE 2

Evaluate $\left(\frac{8}{11}\right)^2$.

$\left(\frac{8}{11}\right)^2$ Original expression

$= \frac{8^2}{11^2}$ Power of a Quotient Rule

$= \frac{64}{121}$ Simplify.

EXAMPLE 3

Find the volume of the figure.

4 ft, 3 ft, 2 ft

$V = \ell w h$ Volume formula

$= 3 \cdot 4 \cdot 2$ Substitute 3 for length, 4 for width, and 2 for height.

$= 24$ ft³   Evaluate volume.

The volume of the box is 24 cubic feet.

Diagnostic Assessment

Exercises	California Standards	Intervention
1–8	7AF1.1	SE Review Lesson 1-1, pp. 6–9
9–15	7AF1.1	SE Review Lesson 1-1, pp. 6–9
16–19	7MG2.1	SE Prerequisite Skill, pp. 706–707 SE Prerequisite Skill, p. 708

✓ Formative Assessment

CRM Anticipation Guide, pp. 3–4
Spotting Preconceived Ideas
Students complete this survey to determine prior knowledge about ideas from Chapter 7. Revisit this worksheet after completing the chapter. Also see p. 414.

TWE Lesson Activities
- Ticket Out the Door, pp. 364, 388, 409
- Crystal Ball, p. 395
- Name the Math, pp. 381, 403
- Yesterday's News, p. 373

Chapter Checkpoints

SE Mid-Chapter Quiz, p. 389
SE Study Guide and Review, pp. 410–414
SE California Standards Practice, pp. 416–417
CRM Quizzes, pp. 59 and 60
CRM Standardized Test Practice, pp. 76–78

Math Online ca.algebra1.com
- Self-Check Quizzes
- Practice Test
- Standardized Test Practice

✓ Summative Assessment

SE Chapter Practice Test, p. 415
CRM Mid-Chapter Test, p. 61
CRM Vocabulary Test, p. 62
CRM Extended-Response Test, p. 75
CRM Leveled Chapter Tests, pp. 63–74
💿 ExamView® Assessment Suite

Key

CRM *Chapter 7 Resource Masters*
SE Student Edition
TWE Teacher Wraparound Edition
💿 CD-ROM

 **Lesson Notes**

7-1 Multiplying Monomials

1 Focus

Standards Alignment

Before Lesson 7-1
Multiply and divide monomials from Standard 7AF2.2

Lesson 7-1
Understand and use the rules of exponents from 🔑 Standard 2.0
Add, subtract, multiply, and divide monomials from 🔑 Standard 1A10.0

After Lesson 7-1
Operations on polynomials, including long division from 🔑 Standard 2A3.0

2 Teach

Scaffolding Questions
Have students read *Get Ready for the Lesson.*
Ask:
- What does the term *quadrupled* mean? increased by 4 times, or multiplied by 4
- Why isn't the braking distance 4 times the speed? The expression for finding the braking distance, where *s* is speed in mph, is $\frac{1}{20}s^2$, not 4s.
- Based on the chart, what would be the braking distance for a car traveling 80 mph? 320 ft 120 mph? 720 ft

Lesson 7-1 Resources

Main Ideas

- Multiply monomials.
- Simplify expressions involving powers of monomials.

 Standard 2.0
Students understand and use such operations as taking the opposite, finding the reciprocal, taking a root, and raising to a fractional power. **They understand and use the rules of exponents.** (Key, CAHSEE)

Standard 10.0 Students add, subtract, **multiply,** and divide **monomials** and polynomials. **Students solve multistep problems, including word problems, by using these techniques.** (Key, CAHSEE)

New Vocabulary

monomial
constant

1A. No; it involves addition, not multiplication, of two variables.
1B. Yes; it is the product of a constant and four variables.
1C. Yes; it is the product of a constant, $\frac{1}{2}$, and three variables.
1D. No, it involves a quotient of variables.

▶ GET READY for the Lesson

The table shows the braking distance for a vehicle at certain speeds. If *s* represents the speed in miles per hour, then the approximate number of feet that the driver must apply the brakes is $\frac{1}{20}s^2$. Notice that when speed is doubled, the braking distance is quadrupled.

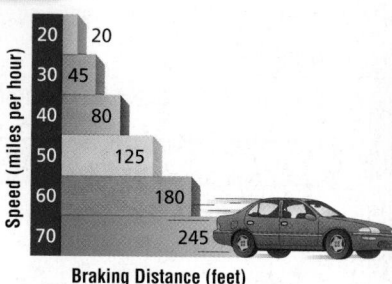

Speed (miles per hour)	Braking Distance (feet)
20	20
30	45
40	80
50	125
60	180
70	245

Source: *British Highway Code*

Multiply Monomials A **monomial** is a number, a variable, or a product of a number and one or more variables like $\frac{1}{20}s^2$. An expression like $\frac{x}{2y}$, which involves the division of variables is not a monomial. Monomials that are real numbers are called **constants.**

EXAMPLE   Identify Monomials

① Determine whether each expression is a monomial. Explain your reasoning.

	Expression	Monomial?	Reason
a.	-5	yes	-5 is a real number and an example of a constant.
b.	$p + q$	no	The expression involves the addition, not the product, of two variables.
c.	x	yes	Single variables are monomials.

✓CHECK Your Progress

1A. $-x + 5$ **1B.** $23abcd^2$ **1C.** $\frac{xyz^3}{2}$ **1D.** $\frac{ab}{c}$

Online Personal Tutor at ca.algebra1.com

Recall that an expression of the form x^n is called a *power* and represents the product you obtain when *x* is used as a factor *n* times. The word *power* is also used to refer to the exponent itself. The number *x* is the *base*, and the number *n* is the *exponent*.

$$\underset{\text{base}}{\overset{\text{exponent}}{2^5}} = \overset{\text{5 factors}}{\overbrace{2 \cdot 2 \cdot 2 \cdot 2 \cdot 2}} \text{ or } 32$$

Chapter 7 Resource Masters
Lesson Reading Guide, p. 5 **BL** **OL** **ELL**
Study Guide and Intervention, pp. 6–7 **BL** **OL** **ELL**
Skills Practice, p. 8 **BL** **OL**
Practice, p. 9 **OL** **AL**
Word Problem Practice, p. 10 **OL** **AL**
Enrichment, p. 11 **OL** **AL**

Transparencies
5-Minute Check Transparency 7-1

Additional Print Resources
Noteables™ Interactive Study Notebook with Foldables™
Teaching Algebra with Manipulatives

Technology
ca.algebra1.com
Interactive Classroom CD-ROM
AssignmentWorks CD-ROM
Graphing Calculator Easy Files

In the following examples, the definition of a power is used to find the products of powers. Look for a pattern in the exponents.

$$2^3 \cdot 2^5 = \overbrace{2 \cdot 2 \cdot 2}^{\text{3 factors}} \cdot \overbrace{2 \cdot 2 \cdot 2 \cdot 2 \cdot 2}^{\text{5 factors}} \text{ or } 2^8$$
$$\underbrace{}_{\text{3 + 5 or 8 factors}}$$

$$3^2 \cdot 3^4 = \overbrace{3 \cdot 3}^{\text{2 factors}} \cdot \overbrace{3 \cdot 3 \cdot 3 \cdot 3}^{\text{4 factors}} \text{ or } 3^6$$
$$\underbrace{}_{\text{2 + 4 or 6 factors}}$$

These examples suggest the property for multiplying powers.

KEY CONCEPT — Product of Powers

Words To multiply two powers that have the same base, add their exponents.

Symbols For any number a and all integers m and n, $a^m \cdot a^n = a^{m+n}$.

Example $a^4 \cdot a^{12} = a^{4+12}$ or a^{16}

EXAMPLE Product of Powers

2️⃣ Simplify each expression.

a. $(5x^7)(x^6)$

$(5x^7)(x^6) = (5)(1)(x^7)(x^6)$ Group the coefficients and the variables.

$= (5 \cdot 1)(x^{7+6})$ Product of Powers

$= 5x^{13}$ Simplify.

b. $(4ab^6)(-7a^2b^3)$

$(4ab^6)(-7a^2b^3) = (4)(-7)(a \cdot a^2)(b^6 \cdot b^3)$ Group the coefficients and the variables.

$= -28(a^{1+2})(b^{6+3})$ Product of Powers

$= -28a^3b^9$ Simplify.

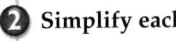 **Your Progress**

2A. $(3y^4)(7y^5)$ $21y^9$ **2B.** $(-4rs^2t^3)(-6r^5s^2t^3)$ $24r^6s^4t^6$

Study Tip

Power of 1

A variable with no exponent indicated can be written as a power of 1, for example, $x = x^1$ and $ab = a^1b^1$.

Powers of Monomials You can also look for a pattern to discover the property for finding the power of a power.

$$(4^2)^5 = \overbrace{(4^2)(4^2)(4^2)(4^2)(4^2)}^{\text{5 factors}}$$
$$= 4^{2+2+2+2+2}$$
$$= 4^{10}$$

Apply rule for Product of Powers.

$$(z^8)^3 = \overbrace{(z^8)(z^8)(z^8)}^{\text{3 factors}}$$
$$= z^{8+8+8}$$
$$= z^{24}$$

These examples suggest the property for finding the power of a power.

KEY CONCEPT — Power of a Power

Words To find the power of a power, multiply the exponents.

Symbols For any number a and all integers m and n, $(a^m)^n = a^{m \cdot n}$.

Example $(k^5)^9 = k^{5 \cdot 9}$ or k^{45}

Math Online Extra Examples at ca.algebra1.com

Lesson 7-1 Multiplying Monomials **359**

Multiply Monomials

Example 1 shows how to determine whether an expression is a monomial. **Example 2** shows how to find the product of powers.

 Formative Assessment

Use the Check Your Progress exercises after each example to determine students' understanding of concepts.

ADDITIONAL EXAMPLES

1️⃣ Determine whether each expression is a monomial. Explain your reasoning.

a. $17 - s$ This is not a monomial because it involves subtraction, not multiplication.

b. $8f^2g$ This is a monomial because it is the product of a number and two variables.

c. $\dfrac{3}{4}$ This is a monomial because it is a real number.

d. $\dfrac{5}{t}$ This is not a monomial because it involves division by a variable.

2️⃣ Simplify each expression.

a. $(r^4)(-12r^7)$ $-12r^{11}$

b. $(6cd^5)(5c^5d^2)$ $30c^6d^7$

Additional Examples are also in:

• Noteables™ Interactive Study Notebook with Foldables™

• Interactive Classroom PowerPoint® Presentations

Powers of Monomials

Example 3 shows how to find the power of a power. **Example 4** shows how to find the power of a product. **Example 5** shows how to simplify complex monomials by using the power and product rules.

Intervention

Variables with No Exponents A variable without an exponent can be rewritten as a power of 1. For example, x can be written as x^1 and ab can be written as a^1b^1. In order for students to find the products of powers correctly, suggest that they rewrite variables without exponents with an exponent of 1.

ADDITIONAL EXAMPLES

3 Simplify $[(2^3)^3]^2$. 2^{18} or 262,144

4 **GEOMETRY** Find the volume of a cube with side length $5xyz$.
$(5xyz)^3 = 125x^3y^3z^3$

Student Misconceptions

Students may simplify an expression such as $\frac{4}{6}(x^2y^5)^3[2(xy)^7]$ into $\frac{8}{6}x^{13}y^{22}$, not realizing that the simplification is incomplete because the fraction is not in the simplest form.

Study Tip

Look Back

To review **using a calculator to find a power of a number**, see Lesson 1-1.

EXAMPLE Power of a Power

3 Simplify $[(3^2)^3]^2$.

$$[(3^2)^3]^2 = (3^{2 \cdot 3})^2 \qquad \text{Power of a Power}$$
$$= (3^6)^2 \qquad \text{Simplify.}$$
$$= 3^{6 \cdot 2} \qquad \text{Power of a Power}$$
$$= 3^{12} \text{ or } 531,441 \quad \text{Simplify.}$$

 CHECK Your Progress

3. Simplify $[(2^2)^2]^4$. **65,536**

Look for a pattern in these examples.

$$(xy)^4 = (xy)(xy)(xy)(xy) \qquad\qquad (6ab)^3 = (6ab)(6ab)(6ab)$$
$$= (x \cdot x \cdot x \cdot x)(y \cdot y \cdot y \cdot y) \qquad = (6 \cdot 6 \cdot 6)(a \cdot a \cdot a)(b \cdot b \cdot b)$$
$$= x^4y^4 \qquad\qquad\qquad\qquad = 6^3a^3b^3 \text{ or } 216a^3b^3$$

These examples suggest the following property.

Study Tip

Powers of Monomials

Sometimes the rules for the Power of a Power and the Power of a Product are combined into one rule.
$(a^m b^n)^p = a^{mp}b^{np}$

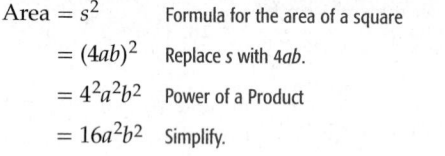

KEY CONCEPT *Power of a Product*

Words To find the power of a product, find the power of each factor and multiply.

Symbols For all numbers a and b and any integer m, $(ab)^m = a^m b^m$.

Example $(-2xy)^3 = (-2)^3 x^3 y^3$ or $-8x^3y^3$

EXAMPLE Power of a Product

4 **GEOMETRY** Express the area of the square as a monomial.

$$\text{Area} = s^2 \qquad \text{Formula for the area of a square}$$
$$= (4ab)^2 \qquad \text{Replace } s \text{ with } 4ab.$$
$$= 4^2a^2b^2 \qquad \text{Power of a Product}$$
$$= 16a^2b^2 \qquad \text{Simplify.}$$

The area of the square is $16a^2b^2$ square units.

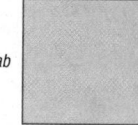

4ab

4ab

CHECK Your Progress

4. Express the area of a square with sides of length $2xy^2$ as a monomial.
$4x^2y^4$

CONCEPT SUMMARY *Simplifying Expressions*

To *simplify* an expression involving monomials, write an equivalent expression in which:

• each base appears exactly once,

• there are no powers of powers, and

• all fractions are in simplest form.

5 Simplify $(3xy^4)^2[(-2y)^2]^3$.

$$(3xy^4)^2[(-2y)^2]^3 = (3xy^4)^2(-2y)^6 \quad \text{Power of a Power}$$
$$= (3)^2x^2(y^4)^2(-2)^6y^6 \quad \text{Power of a Product}$$
$$= 9x^2y^8(64)y^6 \quad \text{Power of a Power}$$
$$= 9(64)x^2 \cdot y^8 \cdot y^6 \quad \text{Commutative Property}$$
$$= 576x^2y^{14} \quad \text{Product of Powers}$$

CHECK Your Progress

5. Simplify $\left(\frac{1}{2}a^2b^2\right)^3[(-4b)^2]^2$. $32a^6b^{10}$

★ indicates multi-step problem

CHECK Your Understanding

Example 1
(p. 358)

Determine whether each expression is a monomial. Write *yes* or *no*. Explain.

1. $5 - 7d$ 1–3. See margin. **2.** $\frac{4a}{3b}$ **3.** n

Examples 2, 3
(pp. 359–360)

Simplify.

4. $x(x^4)(x^6)$ x^{11} **5.** $(4a^4b)(9a^2b^3)$ $36a^6b^4$ **6.** $[(2^3)^2]^3$ 2^{18} or $262,144$

7. $[(3^2)^2]^2$ 3^8 or $6,561$ **8.** $(3y^5z)^2$ $9y^{10}z^2$ **9.** $(-2f^2g)^3$ $-8f^6g^3$

Example 4
(p. 360)

GEOMETRY Express the area of each triangle as a monomial.

★ **10.**
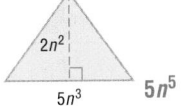
$5n^5$

★ **11.**
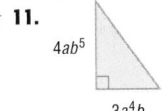
$6a^5b^6$

Example 5
(p. 361)

Simplify.

12. $(-2v^3w^4)^3(-3vw^3)^2$ $-72v^{11}w^{18}$ **13.** $(5x^2y)^2(2xy^3z)^3(4xyz)$ $800x^8y^{12}z^4$

14–19. See margin for explanations.

Exercises

Determine whether each expression is a monomial. Write *yes* or *no*. Explain.

14. 12 yes **15.** $4x^3$ yes **16.** $a - 2b$ no

17. $4n + 5m$ no **18.** $\frac{x}{y^2}$ no **19.** $\frac{1}{5}abc^{14}$ yes

Simplify.

20. $(ab^4)(ab^2)$ a^2b^6 **21.** $(p^5q^4)(p^2q)$ p^7q^5 **22.** $(-7c^3d^4)(4cd^3)$ $-28c^4d^7$

23. $(-3j^7k^5)(-8jk^8)$ $24j^8k^{13}$ **24.** $(9pq^7)^2$ $81p^2q^{14}$ **25.** $(7b^3c^6)^3$ $343b^9c^{18}$

26. $[(3^2)^4]^2$ 3^{16} or $43,046,721$ **27.** $[(4^2)^3]^2$ 4^{12} or $16,777,216$ **28.** $[(-2xy^2)^3]^2$ $64x^6y^{12}$

GEOMETRY Express the area of each figure as a monomial.

★ **29.**
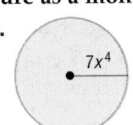
a^4b^2 units^2

★ **30.**
$(49x^8)\pi$ units^2

HOMEWORK HELP	
For Exercises	**See Examples**
14–19	1
20–23	2
24–28	3
29–30	4
31–34	5

Exercise Levels
A: 14–34
B: 35–55
C: 56–62

ADDITIONAL EXAMPLE

5 Simplify $[(8g^3h^4)^2]^2(2gh^5)^4$.
$65,536g^{16}h^{36}$

3 Practice

Formative Assessment

Use Exercises 1–13 to check for understanding.

Use the chart at the bottom of this page to customize assignments for your students.

Odd/Even Assignments

Exercises 14–34 are structured so that students practice the same concepts whether they are assigned odd or even problems.

Additional Answers

1. No; $5 - 7d$ shows subtraction, not multiplication.

2. No; $\frac{4a}{3b}$ shows division, not multiplication.

3. Yes; a single variable is a monomial.

14. 12 is a real number and therefore a monomial.

15. $4x^3$ is the product of a number and three variables.

16. $a - 2b$ shows subtraction, not multiplication of variables.

17. $4n + 5m$ shows addition, not multiplication of variables.

18. $\frac{x}{y^2}$ shows division, not multiplication of variables.

19. $\frac{1}{5}abc^{14}$ is the product of a number, $\frac{1}{5}$, and several variables.

DIFFERENTIATED HOMEWORK OPTIONS			
Level	**Assignment**	**Two-Day Option**	
BL Basic	14–34, 56, 60–90	15–33 odd, 63, 64	14–34 even, 56, 60–62, 65–90
OL Core	15–35 odd, 37, 38, 39–49 odd, 50–56, 60–90	14–34, 63, 64	35–56, 60–62, 65–90
AL Advanced /Pre-AP	35–82, (optional: 83–90)		

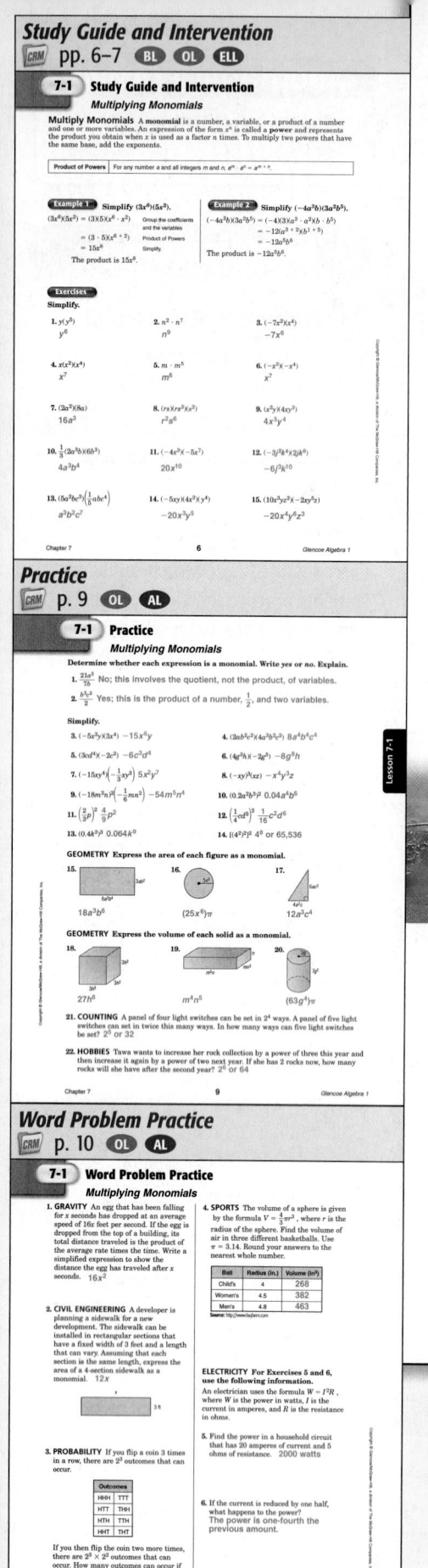

Study Guide and Intervention
CRM pp. 6-7 BL OL ELL

7-1 Study Guide and Intervention
Multiplying Monomials

Practice
CRM p. 9 OL AL

7-1 Practice
Multiplying Monomials

Word Problem Practice
CRM p. 10 OL AL

7-1 Word Problem Practice
Multiplying Monomials

Simplify.

31. $(4cd)^2(-3d^2)^3$ $-432c^2d^8$

32. $(-2x^5)^3(-5xy^6)^2$ $-200x^{17}y^{12}$

33. $(2ag^2)^4(3a^2g^3)^2$ $144a^8g^{14}$

34. $(2m^2n^3)^3(3m^3n)^4$ $648m^{18}n^{13}$

35. Simplify the expression $(-2b^3)^4 - 3(-2b^4)^3$. $40b^{12}$

36. Simplify the expression $2(-5y^3)^2 + (-3y^3)^3$. $50y^6 - 27y^9$

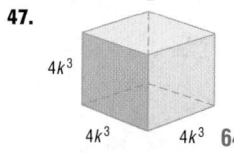
Cross-Curricular Project
Math Online You can use powers to write and compare the distances of the planets to the Sun. Visit ca.algebra1.com.

37. CHEMISTRY Lemon juice is 10^2 times as acidic as tomato juice. Tomato juice is 10^3 times as acidic as egg whites. How many times as acidic is lemon juice as egg whites? Write as a monomial. 10^5E

38. GEOLOGY The seismic waves of a magnitude 6 earthquake are 10^2 times as great as a magnitude 4 earthquake. The seismic waves of a magnitude 4 earthquake are 10 times as great as a magnitude 3 earthquake. How many times as great are the seismic waves of a magnitude 6 earthquake as those of a magnitude 3 earthquake? Write as a monomial. 10^3M_3

Simplify.

39. $(5a^2b^3c^4)(6a^3b^4c^2)$ $30a^5b^7c^6$

40. $(10xy^5z^3)(3x^4y^6z^3)$ $30x^5y^{11}z^6$

41. $(0.5x^3)^2$ $0.25x^6$

42. $(0.4h^5)^3$ $0.064h^{15}$

43. $\left(-\dfrac{3}{4}c\right)^3$ $-\dfrac{27}{64}c^3$ or $-0.421875c^3$

44. $\left(\dfrac{4}{5}a^2\right)^2$ $\dfrac{16}{25}a^4$ or $0.64a^4$

45. $(8y^3)(-3x^2y^2)\left(\dfrac{3}{8}xy^4\right)$ $-9x^3y^9$

46. $\left(\dfrac{4}{7}m\right)^2(49m)(17p)\left(\dfrac{1}{34}p^5\right)$ $8m^3p^6$

GEOMETRY Express the volume of each solid as a monomial.

★ **47.**
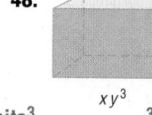
$64k^9$ units^3

48.
x^3y^5 units^3

★ **49.**
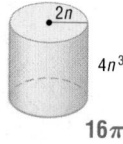
$16\pi n^5$ units^3

TELEPHONES For Exercises 50 and 51, use the following information.
The first transatlantic telephone cable has 51 amplifiers along its length. Each amplifier strengthens the signal on the cable 10^6 times.

50. After it passes through the second amplifier, the signal has been boosted $10^6 \cdot 10^6$ times. Simplify this expression. 10^{12} or 1 trillion

51. Represent the number of times the signal has been boosted after it has passed through the first four amplifiers as a power of 10^6. Then simplify the expression. $(10^6)^4$ or 10^{24}

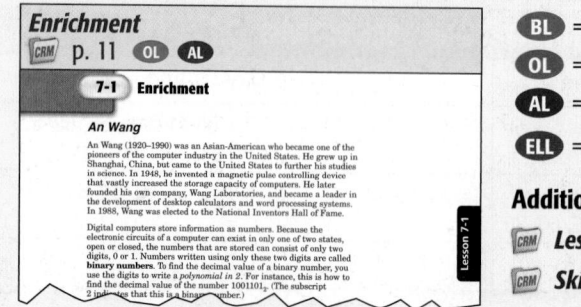

Real-World Link
In a demolition derby, the winner is not the car that finishes first but the last car still moving under its own power.

Source: *Smithsonian Magazine*

DEMOLITION DERBY For Exercises 52 and 53, use the following information.
When a car hits an object, the damage is measured by the collision impact. For a certain car, the collision impact I is given by $I = 2s^2$, where s represents the speed in kilometers per minute.

52. What is the collision impact if the speed of the car is 1 kilometer per minute? 2 kilometers per minute? 4 kilometers per minute? 2; 8; 32

53. As the speed doubles, explain what happens to the collision impact.
The collision impact quadruples, since $2(2s)^2$ is $4(2s^2)$.

362 Chapter 7 Polynomials

Enrichment
CRM p. 11 OL AL

7-1 Enrichment

An Wang

An Wang (1920–1990) was an Asian-American who became one of the pioneers of the computer industry in the United States. He grew up in Shanghai, China, and came to the United States to further his studies in science. In 1948, he invented a magnetic pulse controlling device that vastly increased the storage capacity of computers. He later founded his own company, Wang Laboratories, and became a leader in the development of desktop calculators and word processing systems. In 1988, Wang was elected to the National Inventors Hall of Fame.

Digital computers store information as numbers. Because the electronic circuits of a computer can exist in only one of two states, open or closed, the numbers that are stored can consist of only two digits, 0 or 1. Numbers written using only these two digits are called *binary numbers*. To find the decimal value of a binary number, you use the digits to write a polynomial in 2. For instance, this is how to find the decimal value of the number 1001101_2. (The subscript 2 indicates that this is a binary number.)

BL = Below Grade Level
OL = On Grade Level
AL = Above Grade Level
ELL = English Language Learner

Additional pages not shown:
CRM **Lesson Reading Guide**, p. 5 BL OL ELL
CRM **Skills Practice**, p. 8 BL OL

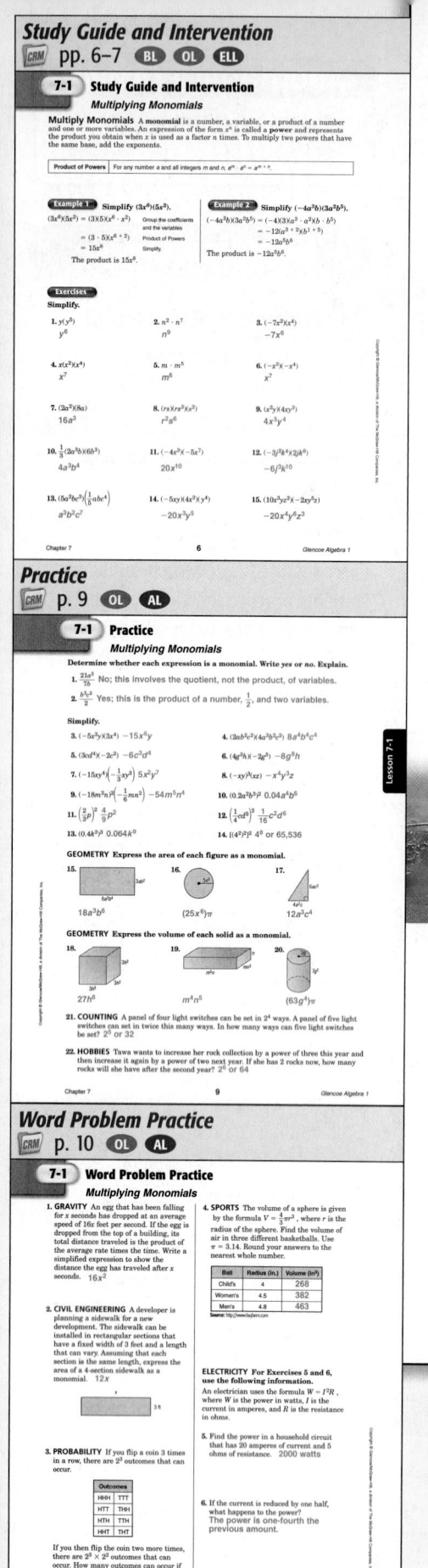

TESTING For Exercises 54 and 55, use the following information.

A history test covers two chapters. There are 2^{12} ways to answer the 12 true-false questions on the first chapter and 2^{10} ways to answer the 10 true-false questions on the second chapter. **54. 2^{22} or 4,194,304 ways**

54. How many ways are there to answer all 22 questions on the test?

55. If a student guesses on each question, what is the probability of answering all questions correctly? $\dfrac{1}{4,194,304}$

H.O.T. Problems

56. OPEN ENDED Write three different expressions that are equivalent to x^6.
Sample answers: $(x^2)^3$; $x(x^5)$; $(x^2)(x^4)$

CHALLENGE Determine whether each statement is *true* or *false*. If true, explain your reasoning. If false, give a counterexample. **58. See margin.**

57. For any real number a, $(-a)^2 = -a^2$.

58. For all real numbers a and b, and all integers m, n, and p, $(a^m b^n)^p = a^{mp} b^{np}$.

59. For all real numbers a, b, and all integers n, $(a + b)^n = a^n + b^n$.

57. False;
let $a = 2$. Then
$(-a)^2 = (-2)^2 =$
4 and $-a^2 = -2^2 =$
-4.

59. False; let $a = 3$,
$b = 4$, and $n = 2$.
Then $(a + b)^n =$
$(3 + 4)^2$ or 49 and
$a^n + b^n = 3^2 + 4^2$
or 25.

60. FIND THE ERROR Nathan and Poloma are simplifying $(5^2)(5^9)$. Who is correct? Explain your reasoning. **See margin.**

Nathan
$(5^2)(5^9) = (5 \cdot 5)^{2+9}$
$= 25^{11}$

Poloma
$(5^2)(5^9) = 5^{2+9}$
$= 5^{11}$

61. REASONING Compare each pair of monomials. Explain why each pair is or is not equivalent. **See margin.**

a. $5m^2$ and $(5m)^2$

b. $(yz)^4$ and $y^4 z^4$

c. $-3a^2$ and $(-3a)^2$

d. $2(c^7)^3$ and $8c^{21}$

62. *Writing in Math* Use the data about braking distances on page 358 to explain why doubling speed quadruples braking distance. **See margin.**

STANDARDS PRACTICE   10.0, 7MG3.2

63. The length of a rectangle is three times the width of the rectangle. If the width of the rectangle is y units, what is the area of the rectangle? **B**

A $3y$ units^2

B $3y^2$ units^2

C $y + 3$ units^2

D $3y(y + 3)$ units^2

64. REVIEW The vertices of $\triangle ABC$ have coordinates $A(4, 5)$, $B(1, 3)$, and $C(4, 0)$. What will the coordinates of A' be if the triangle is translated 3 units down and 2 units to the left? **G**

F $(1, 3)$

G $(2, 2)$

H $(7, 7)$

J $(8, 0)$

Exercise Alert!

Find the Error Both Nathan and Poloma added the exponents 2 and 9, which is the correct procedure when finding a product of powers. However, tell students to notice how Nathan and Poloma handled the bases. Suggest that students substitute a variable for 5 and then examine which method is correct.

Additional Answers

58. True;
$(a^m b^n)^p$
$= (a^m)^p (b^m)^p$ Power of a Product
$= a^{mp} b^{mp}$ Power of a Power

60. Poloma; when finding the product of powers with the same base, you keep the same base and add the exponents. You do not multiply the bases.

61a. no; $(5m)^2 = 25m^2$

61b. yes; the power of a product is the product of the powers.

61c. no; $(-3a)^2 = 9a^2$

61d. no; $2(c^7)^3 = 2c^{21}$

62. If s is replaced by $2s$ in the formula for the breaking distance required for a car traveling s miles per hour, the result is $\frac{1}{20}(2s)^2$. Using the Power of a Product and Power of a Power rules, this simplifies to $4 \cdot \left(\frac{1}{20}s^2\right)$. This means that doubling the speed of car multiplies the breaking distance by 4.

Pre-AP Activity   Use after Exercise 53.

Tell students that a sports car on a drag-racing strip can reach 100 miles per hour in a quarter mile. If s represents the speed in miles per hour, then the approximate number of feet that the driver must apply the brakes before stopping is $\frac{1}{20}s^2$. Calculate how far the car would travel on the drag strip, from start to stop, if the driver started braking when the car reached 100 miles per hour. A mile is 5280 feet. 1820 ft; the initial quarter mile (1320 ft) plus braking distance (500 ft)

4 Assess

Ticket Out the Door Make several copies each of five monomial expressions that need to be simplified. Give one expression to each student. As students leave the room, ask them to tell you the simplified versions of the expressions they possess.

 **Foldables™ Follow-Up**

At the end of this lesson, remind students to take notes and show examples in the row labeled *Monomials* and the column labeled ×.

Additional Answers

65.
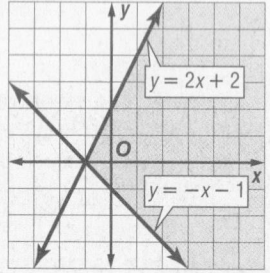

66.
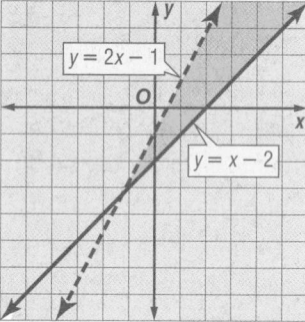

67.
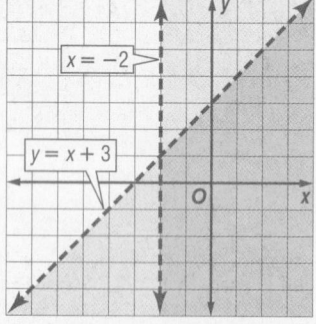

70. $\{h \mid h \leq -7 \text{ or } h \geq 1\}$

Spiral Review

Solve each system of inequalities by graphing. (Lesson 6-8) 65–67. See margin.

65. $y \leq 2x + 2$
$y \geq -x - 1$

66. $y \geq x - 2$
$y < 2x - 1$

67. $x > -2$
$y < x + 3$

Determine which ordered pairs are part of the solution set for each inequality. (Lesson 6-7)

68. $y \leq 2x$, $\{(1, 4), (-1, 5), (5, -6), (-7, 0)\}$ $\{(5, -6)\}$
69. $y < 8 - 3x$, $\{(-4, 2), (-3, 0), (1, 4), (1, 8)\}$ $\{(-4, 2), (-3, 0), (1, 4)\}$

Solve each compound inequality. Then graph the solution set. (Lesson 6-4) 70–73. See margin.

70. $4 + h \leq -3$ or $4 + h \geq 5$

71. $4 < 4a + 12 < 24$

72. $14 < 3h + 2$ and $3h + 2 < 2$

73. $2m - 3 > 7$ or $2m + 7 > 9$

Use elimination to solve each system of equations. (Lesson 5-4)

74. $-4x + 5y = 2$ (2, 2)
$x + 2y = 6$

75. $3x + 4y = -25$ (−3, −4)
$2x - 3y = 6$

76. $x + y = 20$
$4 = 0.4x + 0.15y$
(4, 16)

Write an equation in function notation for each relation. (Lesson 3-5)

77.
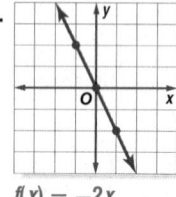
$f(x) = -2x$

78.
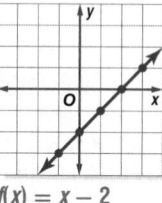
$f(x) = x - 2$

Express the relation shown in each table, mapping, or graph as a set of ordered pairs. Then write the inverse of the relation. (Lesson 3-1) 79–81. See margin.

79.

x	y
−5	2
−2	3
0	5
4	9

80.
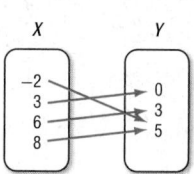

81.
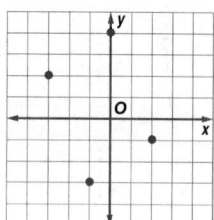

82. TRANSPORTATION Two trains leave Sacramento at the same time, one traveling north, the other south. The northbound train travels at 40 miles per hour and the southbound at 30 miles per hour. In how many hours will the trains be 245 miles apart? (Lesson 2-9) $3\frac{1}{2}$ h

GET READY for the Next Lesson

PREREQUISITE SKILL Simplify. (Pages 694–695)

83. $\frac{2}{6}$ $\frac{1}{3}$

84. $\frac{3}{15}$ $\frac{1}{5}$

85. $\frac{10}{5}$ 2

86. $\frac{27}{9}$ 3

87. $\frac{14}{36}$ $\frac{7}{18}$

88. $\frac{9}{48}$ $\frac{3}{16}$

89. $\frac{44}{32}$ $\frac{11}{8}$

90. $\frac{45}{18}$ $\frac{5}{2}$

364 Chapter 7 Polynomials

---

71. $\{a \mid -2 < a < 3\}$

72. ∅
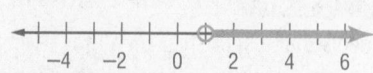

73. $\{m \mid m > 1\}$

79. $\{(-5, 2), (-2, 3), (0, 5), (4, 9)\}$;
$\{(2, -5), (3, -2), (5, 0), (9, 4)\}$

80. $\{(-2, 5), (3, 0), (6, 3), (8, 5))\}$;
$\{(5, -2), (0, 3), (3, 6), (5, 8)\}$

364 Chapter 7 Polynomials

EXTEND 7-1

Algebra Lab
Investigating Surface Area and Volume

 Preparation for Geometry Standard 11.0 Students determine how changes in dimensions affect the perimeter, area, and volume of common geometric figures and solids.

ACTIVITY

- Cut out the pattern shown from a sheet of centimeter grid paper. Fold along the dashed lines and tape the edges together to form a rectangular prism.
- Find the surface area SA of the prism by counting the squares on all the faces of the prism or by using the formula $SA = 2w\ell + 2wh + 2\ell h$, where w is the width, ℓ is the length, and h is the height of the prism. **62 cm^2**
- Find the volume V of the prism by using the formula $V = \ell wh$. **30 cm^3**
- Now construct another prism with dimensions that are 2 times each of the dimensions of the first prism, or 4 centimeters by 10 centimeters by 6 centimeters.
- Finally, construct a third prism with dimensions that are 3 times each of the dimensions of the first prism.

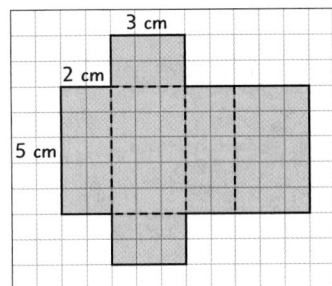

ANALYZE THE RESULTS

1. Copy and complete the table using the prisms you made.

Prism	Dimensions	Surface Area (cm^2)	Volume (cm^3)	Surface Area Ratio $\left(\dfrac{SA \text{ of New}}{SA \text{ of Original}}\right)$	Volume Ratio $\left(\dfrac{V \text{ of New}}{V \text{ of Original}}\right)$
Original	2 by 5 by 3	62	30	_____	_____
A	4 by 10 by 6	248	240	4	8
B	6 by 15 by 9	558	810	9	27

2. **MAKE A CONJECTURE** Suppose you multiply each dimension of a prism by 2. What is the ratio of the surface area of the new prism to the surface area of the original prism? What is the ratio of the volumes? **4; 8**

3. If you multiply each dimension of a prism by 3, what is the ratio of the surface area of the new prism to the surface area of the original? What is the ratio of the volumes? **9; 27**

4. Suppose you multiply each dimension of a prism by a. Make a conjecture about the ratios of surface areas and volumes. **a^2; a^3**

5. Repeat the activity using cylinders. To start, make a cylinder with radius 4 centimeters and height 5 centimeters. To compute surface area SA and volume V, use the formulas $SA = 2\pi r^2 + 2\pi rh$ and $V = \pi r^2 h$, where r is the radius and h is the height of the cylinder. Do the conjectures you made in Exercise 4 hold true for cylinders? Explain. **See margin.**

Extend 7-1 Algebra Lab: Investigating Surface Area and Volume **365**

Additional Answer (page 364)

81. $\{(-3, 2), (0, 4), (2, -1), (-1, -3)\}$;
$\{(2, -3), (4, 0), (-1, 2), (-3, -1)\}$

Additional Answer

5. Yes, the conjectures hold. If the ratio of the dimensions of two cylinders is a, then the ratio of the surface areas is a^2 and the ratio of the volumes is a^3.

EXTEND 7-1 | **Lesson Notes**

1 Focus

Objective Use grid paper to investigate the surface area ratio and volume ratio of pairs of rectangular prisms.

Materials
- centimeter grid paper
- scissors
- tape

Easy-to-Make Manipulatives
Teaching Algebra with Manipulatives
Templates for centimeter grid paper, p. 2

Teaching Tip Any size grid paper will work for this activity because the units are not important.

2 Teach

Working in Cooperative Groups
Put students in groups of 2 or 3, mixing abilities. Have students complete the Activity.

- Before students begin, direct their attention to the data table. Ask them to make conjectures about the surface area and volume of the prism when each dimension is multiplied by two and three. Write the predictions on the board to use in a discussion after the activity has been completed.

- Have students count the squares on the surface of their prisms to verify the formula for the surface area.

Practice Have students complete Exercises 1–5.

3 Assess

 Formative Assessment
Use Exercises 3 and 4 to assess whether students are able to determine the change in surface area and volume when the dimensions of the prism are multiplied by a whole number.

Extend 7-1 Algebra Lab: Investigating Surface Area and Volume **365**

1 Focus

Standards Alignment

Before Lesson 7-2
Multiply and divide monomials from Standard 7AF2.2

Lesson 7-2
Understand and use the rules of exponents from ➤ Standard 2.0
Divide monomials from ➤ Standard 1A10.0

After Lesson 7-2
Operations on polynomials, including long division from ➤ Standard 2A3.0

2 Teach

Scaffolding Questions

Have students read *Get Ready for the Lesson*.

Ask:

- Using the formula $c = \left(\frac{1}{10}\right)^{pH}$, what is the concentration of hydrogen ions in a solution with pH 1?
  0.1 mole/liter

- What is the concentration in a solution with pH 2? 0.01 mole/liter

- As the pH increases by 1, what happens to the concentration? It gets 10 times as small.

- Ammonia has a pH of 12. Would this indicate that ammonia has a very large or very small concentration?
  very small

Lesson 7-2 Resources

Main Ideas

- Simplify expressions involving the quotient of monomials.
- Simplify expressions containing negative exponents.

Standard 2.0
Students understand and use such operations as taking the opposite, finding the reciprocal, taking a root, and raising to a fractional power. **They understand and use the rules of exponents.** (Key, CAHSEE)

Standard 10.0 **Students** add, subtract, multiply, and **divide monomials** and polynomials. **Students solve multistep problems, including word problems, by using these techniques.** (Key, CAHSEE)

New Vocabulary

zero exponent

negative exponent

C○ncepts in M○tion
BrainPOP®
ca.algebra1.com

GET READY for the Lesson

To test whether a solution is a base or an acid, chemists use a pH test. This test measures the concentration c of hydrogen ions (in moles per liter) in the solution.

$$c = \left(\frac{1}{10}\right)^{pH}$$

The table gives examples of solutions with various pH levels. You can find the quotient of powers and use negative exponents to compare measures on the pH scale.

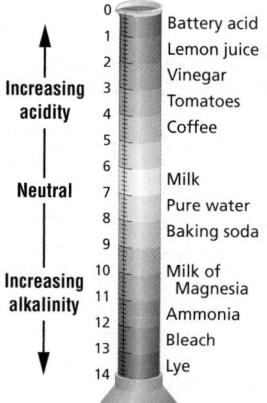

Source: U.S. Geological Survey

Quotients of Monomials Look for a pattern in the examples below.

5 factors

$$\frac{4^5}{4^3} = \frac{\overset{1}{\cancel{4}} \cdot \overset{1}{\cancel{4}} \cdot \overset{1}{\cancel{4}} \cdot 4 \cdot 4}{\underset{1}{\cancel{4}} \cdot \underset{1}{\cancel{4}} \cdot \underset{1}{\cancel{4}}} = 4 \cdot 4 \text{ or } 4^2$$

3 factors   5 − 3 or 2 factors

6 factors

$$\frac{3^6}{3^2} = \frac{\overset{1}{\cancel{3}} \cdot \overset{1}{\cancel{3}} \cdot 3 \cdot 3 \cdot 3 \cdot 3}{\underset{1}{\cancel{3}} \cdot \underset{1}{\cancel{3}}} = 3 \cdot 3 \cdot 3 \cdot 3 \text{ or } 3^4$$

2 factors   6 − 2 or 4 factors

KEY CONCEPT   *Quotient of Powers*

Words To divide two powers with the same base, subtract the exponents.

Symbols For all integers m and n and any nonzero number a, $\frac{a^m}{a^n} = a^{m-n}$.

Example $\frac{b^{15}}{b^7} = b^{15-7}$ or b^8

EXAMPLE   Quotient of Powers

1 Simplify $\frac{a^5 b^8}{ab^3}$. Assume that no denominator is equal to zero.

$$\frac{a^5 b^8}{ab^3} = \left(\frac{a^5}{a}\right)\left(\frac{b^8}{b^3}\right) \qquad \text{Group powers that have the same base.}$$

$$= \left(a^{5-1}\right), \left(b^{8-3}\right) \text{ or } a^4 b^5 \qquad \text{Quotient of Powers}$$

 CHECK Your Progress

1. Simplify $\frac{x^3 y^4}{x^2 y}$. Assume that no denominator is equal to zero. xy^3

Chapter 7 Resource Masters

Lesson Reading Guide, p. 12 **BL** **OL** **ELL**
Study Guide and Intervention, pp. 13–14
BL **OL** **ELL**
Skills Practice, p. 15 **BL** **OL**
Practice, p. 16 **OL** **AL**
Word Problem Practice, p. 17 **OL** **AL**
Enrichment, p. 18 **OL** **AL**
Quiz 1, p. 59

Transparencies

5-Minute Check Transparency 7-2

Additional Print Resources

Noteables™ Interactive Study Notebook with Foldables™

Technology

ca.algebra1.com
Interactive Classroom CD-ROM
AssignmentWorks CD-ROM
Graphing Calculator Easy Files

Look for a pattern in the example below.

$$\left(\frac{2}{5}\right)^3 = \underbrace{\left(\frac{2}{5}\right)\left(\frac{2}{5}\right)\left(\frac{2}{5}\right)}_{\text{3 factors}} = \frac{\overbrace{2 \cdot 2 \cdot 2}^{\text{3 factors}}}{\underbrace{5 \cdot 5 \cdot 5}_{\text{3 factors}}} \text{ or } \frac{2^3}{5^3}$$

KEY CONCEPT *Power of a Quotient*

Words To find the power of a quotient, find the power of the numerator and the power of the denominator.

Symbols For any integer m and any real numbers a and b, $b \neq 0$, $\left(\frac{a}{b}\right)^m = \frac{a^m}{b^m}$.

EXAMPLE Power of a Quotient

2 Simplify $\left(\frac{2p^2}{3}\right)^4$.

$\left(\frac{2p^2}{3}\right)^4 = \frac{\left(2p^2\right)^4}{3^4}$ Power of a Quotient

$= \frac{2^4\left(p^2\right)^4}{3^4}$ Power of a Product

$= \frac{16p^8}{81}$ Power of a Power

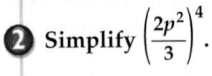 **Your Progress** Simplify each expression.

2A. $\left(\frac{3x^4}{4}\right)^3$ $\frac{27x^{12}}{64}$ **2B.** $\left(\frac{5x^5y}{6}\right)^2$ $\frac{25x^{10}y^2}{36}$

Negative Exponents A graphing calculator can be used to investigate expressions with 0 as an exponent and negative exponents.

ALGEBRA LAB

Zero Exponent and Negative Exponents

1. Copy and complete the table.

Power	2^4	2^3	2^2	2^1	2^0	2^{-1}	2^{-2}	2^{-3}	2^{-4}
Value	16	8	4	2	1	$\frac{1}{2}$	$\frac{1}{4}$	$\frac{1}{8}$	$\frac{1}{16}$

2. Describe the relationship between each pair of values.

    a. 2^4 and 2^{-4} **b.** 2^3 and 2^{-3} **c.** 2^2 and 2^{-2} **d.** 2^1 and 2^{-1}
    2a–d. They are reciprocals.
3. Make a conjecture as to the fractional value of 5^{-1}. $\frac{1}{5}$

4. What is the value of 5^0?   1

5. What happens when you evaluate 0^0?   An error message appears.

Intervention

Powers of Negative Numbers Students may assume that the expression -6^3 means $(-6)(-6)(-6)$. Explain that -6^3 means $-(6^3)$. To express -6 to the third power, they must use the parentheses, $(-6)^3$.

Example 1 shows how to find the quotient of powers. **Example 2** shows how to find the power of a quotient.

 Formative Assessment

Use the Check Your Progress exercises after each example to determine students' understanding of concepts.

ADDITIONAL EXAMPLES

 Simplify $\frac{x^7 y^{12}}{x^6 y^3}$. Assume that no denominator is equal to zero. xy^9

2 Simplify $\left(\frac{4c^3d^2}{5}\right)^3$. $\frac{64c^9d^6}{125}$

Additional Examples are also in:
- Noteables™ Interactive Study Notebook with Foldables™
- Interactive Classroom PowerPoint® Presentations

 **Preventing Errors**

Remind students not to forget to find the powers of the constant terms of the monomials.

Negative Exponents

Example 3 shows how to simplify expressions involving zero exponents. **Example 4** shows how to simplify expressions involving negative exponents. **Example 5** shows how to apply the properties of exponents in test-taking situations.

Algebra Lab

Make sure students understand that 2^4 and 2^{-4} are reciprocals of each other. After answering Exercise 5, ask students to write an expression involving division that will be equivalent to 0^0, for example, $\frac{0^6}{0^6}$. Show students that $\frac{0^6}{0^6} = \frac{0}{0}$ and remind them that division by zero is undefined.

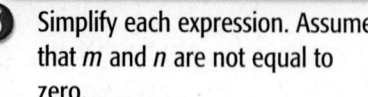
Study Tip

Alternative Method

Another way to look at the problem of simplifying $\dfrac{2^4}{2^4}$ is to recall that any nonzero number divided by itself is 1: $\dfrac{2^4}{2^4} = \dfrac{16}{16}$ or 1.

To understand why $2^0 = 1$, study the two methods used to simplify $\dfrac{2^4}{2^4}$.

Method 1

$\dfrac{2^4}{2^4} = 2^{4-4}$ Quotient of Powers

$= 2^0$ Subtract.

Method 2

$$\dfrac{2^4}{2^4} = \dfrac{\overset{1}{\cancel{2}} \cdot \overset{1}{\cancel{2}} \cdot \overset{1}{\cancel{2}} \cdot \overset{1}{\cancel{2}}}{\underset{1}{\cancel{2}} \cdot \underset{1}{\cancel{2}} \cdot \underset{1}{\cancel{2}} \cdot \underset{1}{\cancel{2}}}$$ Definition of powers

$= 1$ Simplify.

Since $\dfrac{2^4}{2^4}$ cannot have two different values, we can conclude that $2^0 = 1$.

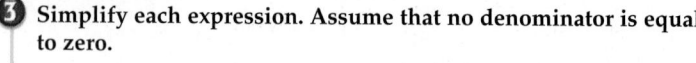

KEY CONCEPT   *Zero Exponent*

Words Any nonzero number raised to the zero power is 1.

Symbols For any nonzero number a, $a^0 = 1$.

Example $(-0.25)^0 = 1$

EXAMPLE Zero Exponent

3 Simplify each expression. Assume that no denominator is equal to zero.

a. $\left(-\dfrac{3x^5y}{8xy^7}\right)^0$

$\left(-\dfrac{3x^5y}{8xy^7}\right)^0 = 1$ $a^0 = 1$

b. $\dfrac{t^3s^0}{t}$

$\dfrac{t^3s^0}{t} = \dfrac{t^3(1)}{t}$ $a^0 = 1$

$= \dfrac{t^3}{t}$ Simplify.

$= t^2$ Quotient of Powers

CHECK Your Progress

3A. $\dfrac{x^0y^4}{y^2}$ y^2

3B. $\left(\dfrac{2x^3y^2z^5}{10xy^3z^4}\right)^0$ 1

To investigate the meaning of a negative exponent, we can simplify expressions like $\dfrac{8^2}{8^5}$ in two ways.

Method 1

$\dfrac{8^2}{8^5} = 8^{2-5}$ Quotient of Powers

$= 8^{-3}$ Subtract.

Method 2

$$\dfrac{8^2}{8^5} = \dfrac{\overset{1}{\cancel{8}} \cdot \overset{1}{\cancel{8}}}{\underset{1}{\cancel{8}} \cdot \underset{1}{\cancel{8}} \cdot 8 \cdot 8 \cdot 8}$$ Definition of powers

$= \dfrac{1}{8^3}$ Simplify.

Since $\dfrac{8^2}{8^5}$ cannot have two different values, we can conclude that $8^{-3} = \dfrac{1}{8^3}$.

Words	For any nonzero number a and any integer n, a^{-n} is the reciprocal of a^n. In addition, the reciprocal of a^{-n} is a^n.
Symbols	For any nonzero number a and any integer n, $a^{-n} = \dfrac{1}{a^n}$ and $\dfrac{1}{a^{-n}} = a^n$.
Examples	$5^{-2} = \dfrac{1}{5^2}$ or $\dfrac{1}{25}$ $\dfrac{1}{m^{-3}} = m^3$

An expression is simplified when it contains only positive exponents.

Study Tip

Common Misconception
Do not confuse a negative number with a number raised to a negative power.
$3^{-1} = \dfrac{1}{3}$ $-3 \neq \dfrac{1}{3}$

EXAMPLE Negative Exponents

4 Simplify each expression. Assume that no denominator is equal to zero.

a. $\dfrac{b^{-3}c^2}{d^{-5}}$

$\dfrac{b^{-3}c^c}{d^{-5}} = \left(\dfrac{b^{-3}}{1}\right)\left(\dfrac{c^2}{1}\right)\left(\dfrac{1}{d^{-5}}\right)$ Write as a product of fractions.

$= \left(\dfrac{1}{b^3}\right)\left(\dfrac{c^2}{1}\right)\left(\dfrac{d^5}{1}\right)$ $a^{-n} = \dfrac{1}{a^n}$

$= \dfrac{c^2d^5}{b^3}$ Multiply fractions.

b. $\dfrac{-3a^{-4}b^7}{21a^2b^7c^{-5}}$

$\dfrac{-3a^{-4}b^7}{21a^2b^7c^{-5}} = \left(\dfrac{-3}{21}\right)\left(\dfrac{a^{-4}}{a^2}\right)\left(\dfrac{b^7}{b^7}\right)\left(\dfrac{1}{c^{-5}}\right)$ Group powers with the same base.

$= \dfrac{-1}{7}\left(a^{-4-2}\right)\left(b^{7-7}\right)\left(c^5\right)$ Quotient of Powers and Negative Exponent Properties

$= \dfrac{-1}{7}a^{-6}b^0c^5$ Simplify.

$= \dfrac{-1}{7}\left(\dfrac{1}{a^6}\right)(1)c^5$ Negative Exponent and Zero Exponent Properties

$= -\dfrac{c^5}{7a^6}$ Multiply fractions.

c. $\dfrac{-3q^{-2}rs^4}{-12qr^{-3}s^{-5}}$

$\dfrac{-3q^{-2}rs^4}{-12qr^{-3}s^{-5}} = \left(\dfrac{-3}{-12}\right)\left(\dfrac{q^{-2}}{q}\right)\left(\dfrac{r}{r^{-3}}\right)\left(\dfrac{s^4}{s^{-5}}\right)$ Group powers with the same base.

$= \dfrac{1}{4}q^{-3}r^4s^9$ Simplify.

$= \dfrac{r^4s^9}{4q^3}$ Negative Exponent Property

✓CHECK Your Progress

4A. $\dfrac{r^{-5}s^4}{t^{-3}}$ $\dfrac{s^4t^3}{r^5}$

4B. $\dfrac{24x^{-2}y^4}{-6x^{-3}y^{-2}z^{-1}}$ $-4xy^6z$

 Preventing Errors

Have students look at the first step of the solution of Example 4. Point out that rewriting an expression as a product of fractions makes applying the Negative Exponent Property easier. Fractions that have negative exponents can be rewritten as their reciprocals.

ADDITIONAL EXAMPLE

 Simplify each expression. Assume that no denominator is equal to zero.

a. $\dfrac{x^{-4}y^9}{z^{-6}}$ $\dfrac{y^9z^6}{x^4}$

b. $\dfrac{75p^3q^{-5}}{15p^5q^{-4}r^{-8}}$ $\dfrac{5r^8}{p^2q}$

c. $\dfrac{-3x^{-6}y^5z}{30x^4y^{-2}z^5}$ $-\dfrac{y^7}{10x^{10}z^4}$

 Monomials

Point out to students that a variable with a negative exponent such as x^{-2} is not a monomial. A monomial does not involve division of variables and $x^{-2} = \dfrac{1}{x^2}$.

5 **STANDARDS EXAMPLE** Refer to the figure in Example 5. Write the ratio of the circumference of the circle to the area of the square in simplest form. C

A $\dfrac{2r}{\pi}$ C $\dfrac{\pi}{2r}$

B $\dfrac{2\pi}{r}$ D $\dfrac{2\pi r}{1}$

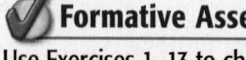

Preventing Errors

Make sure students realize that the diameter of the circle is the same measure as the length of one side of the square. It is important that students recognize that the area of the square is $(2r)^2$ and not $2r^2$.

3 Practice

Formative Assessment

Use Exercises 1–13 to check for understanding.

Use the chart at the bottom of the next page to customize assignments for your students.

Odd/Even Assignments

Exercises 14–30 are structured so that students practice the same concepts whether they are assigned odd or even problems.

Test-Taking Tip

Some problems can be solved using estimation. The area of the circle is less than the area of the square. Therefore, the ratio of the two areas must be less than 1. Use 3 as an approximate value for π to determine which of the choices is less than 1.

STANDARDS EXAMPLE Apply Properties of Exponents 2.0

5 Write the ratio of the area of the circle to the area of the square in simplest form.

A $\dfrac{\pi}{2}$ C $\dfrac{2\pi}{1}$

B $\dfrac{\pi}{4}$ D $\dfrac{\pi}{3}$

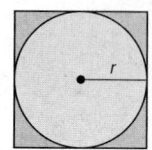

Read the Item

A ratio is a comparison of two quantities. It can be written in fraction form.

Solve the Item

• area of circle: πr^2

length of square: diameter of circle or $2r$

area of square: $(2r)^2$

• $\dfrac{\text{area of circle}}{\text{area of square}} = \dfrac{\pi r^2}{(2r)^2}$ Substitute.

$= \dfrac{\pi}{4} r^{2-2}$ Quotient of Powers

$= \dfrac{\pi}{4} r^0$ or $\dfrac{\pi}{4}$ $r^0 = 1$

The answer is B.

CHECK Your Progress

5. Write the ratio of the area of the circle to the area of the square in simplest form. H

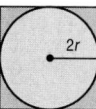

F $\dfrac{\pi}{3}$ G $\dfrac{\pi}{2}$ H $\dfrac{\pi}{4}$ J $\dfrac{3\pi}{2}$

Online **Personal Tutor at** ca.algebra1.com

★ indicates multi-step problem

CHECK Your Understanding

Simplify. Assume that no denominator is equal to zero.

Example 1
(p. 367)

1. $\dfrac{7^8}{7^2}$ 7^6 or 117,649   **2.** $\dfrac{x^8 y^{12}}{x^2 y^7}$ $x^6 y^5$ **3.** $\dfrac{5pq^7}{10p^6 q^3}$ $\dfrac{q^4}{2p^5}$

Example 2
(p. 367)

4. $\left(\dfrac{2c^3 d}{7z^2}\right)^3$ $\dfrac{8c^9 d^3}{343z^6}$ **5.** $\left(\dfrac{4a^2 b}{2c^3}\right)^2$ $\dfrac{4a^4 b^2}{c^6}$ **6.** $\left(\dfrac{3mn^3}{6n^2}\right)^2$ $\dfrac{m^2 n^2}{4}$

Example 3
(p. 369)

7. $y^0\left(y^5\right)\left(y^{-9}\right)$ $\dfrac{1}{y^4}$ **8.** $\dfrac{\left(4m^{-3} n^5\right)^0}{mn}$ $\dfrac{1}{mn}$ **9.** $\dfrac{\left(3x^2 y^5\right)^0}{\left(21x^5 y^2\right)^0}$ 1

Example 4
(p. 370)

10. 13^{-2} $\dfrac{1}{169}$ **11.** $\dfrac{c^{-5}}{d^3 g^{-8}}$ $\dfrac{g^8}{d^3 c^5}$ **12.** $\dfrac{(cd^{-2})^3}{(c^4 d^9)^{-2}}$ $c^{11} d^{12}$

370 Chapter 7 Polynomials

DIFFERENTIATED HOMEWORK OPTIONS

Level	Assignment	Two-Day Option	
BL Basic	14–30, 48, 49, 53–68	15–29 odd, 56, 57	14–30 even, 48, 49, 53–55, 58–68
OL Core	15–39 odd, 40–49, 53–68	14–30, 56, 57	31–49, 53–55, 58–68
AL Advanced /Pre-AP	31–65, (optional: 66–68)		

Example 5
(p. 370)

★ **13. STANDARDIZED TEST PRACTICE** Find the ratio of the volume of the cylinder to the volume of the sphere. **D**

A $\frac{1}{2}$ C $\frac{4}{3}$

B $\frac{3}{4}$ D $\frac{3}{2}$

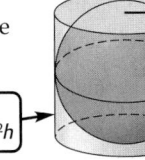

Volume of sphere = $\frac{4}{3}\pi r^3$

Volume of cylinder = $\pi r^2 h$

Exercises

Simplify. Assume that no denominator is equal to zero.

HOMEWORK HELP	
For Exercises	See Examples
14–17	1
18–19	2
20–21	3
22–28	4
29–30	5

Exercise Levels
A: 14–30
B: 31–47
C: 48–55

14. $\frac{4^{12}}{4^2}$ 4^{10} or 1,048,576   **15.** $\frac{3^{13}}{3^7}$ 3^6 or 729   **16.** $\frac{p^7n^3}{p^4n^2}$ p^3n

17. $\frac{y^3z^9}{yz^2}$ y^2z^7 **18.** $\left(\frac{5b^4n}{2a^6}\right)^2$ $\frac{25b^8n^2}{4a^{12}}$ **19.** $\left(\frac{3m^7}{4x^5y^3}\right)^4$ $\frac{81m^{28}}{256x^{20}y^{12}}$

20. $\left(\frac{r^{-2}t^5}{t^{-1}}\right)^0$ 1 **21.** $\left(\frac{4c^{-2}d}{b^{-2}c^3d^{-1}}\right)^0$ 1 **22.** 6^{-2} $\frac{1}{36}$

23. 5^{-3} $\frac{1}{125}$ **24.** $\left(\frac{4}{5}\right)^{-2}$ $\frac{25}{16}$ **25.** $\left(\frac{3}{2}\right)^{-3}$ $\frac{8}{27}$

26. $n^2\left(p^{-4}\right)\left(n^{-5}\right)$ $\frac{1}{n^3p^4}$ **27.** $\frac{28a^7c^{-4}}{7a^3b^0c^{-8}}$ $4a^4c^4$ **28.** $x^3y^0x^{-7}$ $\frac{1}{x^4}$

★ **29.** The area of the rectangle is $24x^5y^3$ square units. Find the length of the rectangle. $3x^2y$ units

★ **30.** The area of the triangle is $100a^3b$ square units. Find the height of the triangle. $10ab$ units

$8x^3y^2$

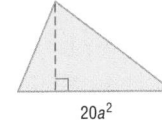

$20a^2$

Simplify. Assume that no denominator is equal to zero.

31. $\frac{-2a^3}{10a^8}$ $-\frac{1}{5a^5}$ **32.** $\frac{15b}{45b^5}$ $\frac{1}{3b^4}$ **33.** $\frac{30h^{-2}k^{14}}{5hk^{-3}}$ $\frac{6k^{17}}{h^3}$

34. $\frac{18x^3y^4z^7}{-2x^2yz}$ $-9xy^3z^6$ **35.** $\frac{-19y^0z^4}{-3z^{16}}$ $\frac{19}{3z^{12}}$ **36.** $\frac{\left(5r^{-2}\right)^{-2}}{\left(2r^3\right)^2}$ $\frac{1}{100r^2}$

37. $\frac{p^{-4}q^{-3}}{\left(p^5q^2\right)^{-1}}$ $\frac{p}{q}$ **38.** $\left(\frac{b^{-4}c^3}{b^{-1}}\right)^0$ 1 **39.** $\left(\frac{5b^{-2}n^4}{n^2z^{-3}}\right)^{-1}$ $\frac{b^2}{5n^2z^3}$

PROBABILITY For Exercises 40 and 41, use the following information.

If you toss a coin, the probability of getting heads is $\frac{1}{2}$. If you toss a coin 2 times, the probability of getting heads each time is $\frac{1}{2} \cdot \frac{1}{2}$ or $\left(\frac{1}{2}\right)^2$. **40.** $\left(\frac{1}{2}\right)^n$

40. Write an expression to represent the probability of tossing a coin n times and getting n heads.

41. Express your answer to Exercise 40 as a power of 2. 2^{-n}

Lesson 7-2 Dividing Monomials **371**

Pre-AP Activity   Use after Exercise 41.

Tell students that if you throw a die, the probability of getting a three is $\frac{1}{6}$. If you throw a die 2 times, the probability of getting a three each time is $\frac{1}{6} \cdot \frac{1}{6}$ or $\left(\frac{1}{6}\right)^2$. Ask them to write an expression using a negative exponent to represent the probability of throwing a die n times and getting n threes.

$\left(\frac{1}{6}\right)^n = 6^{-n}$

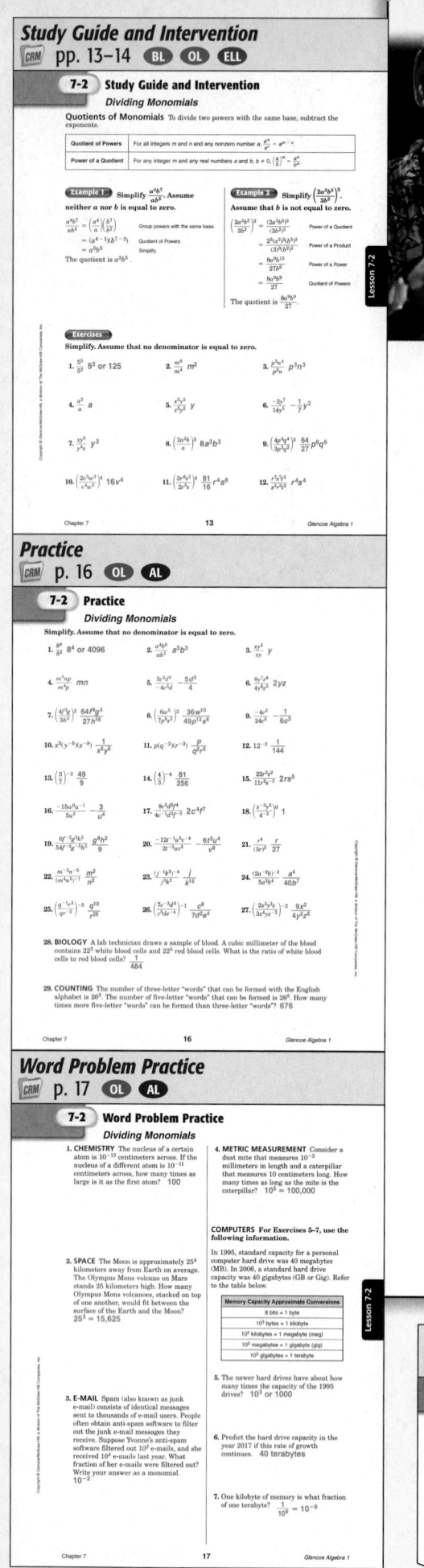

SOUND For Exercises 42–44, use the following information.
The intensity of sound can be measured in watts per square meter. The table gives the watts per square meter for some common sounds.

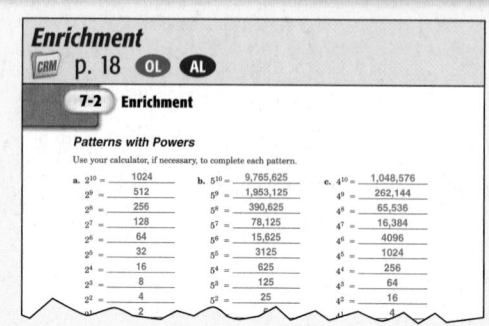

Watts per Square Meter	Common Sounds
10^2	jet plane (30 m away)
10^1	pain level
10^0	amplified music (2 m away)
10^{-2}	noisy kitchen
10^{-3}	heavy traffic
10^{-6}	normal conversation
10^{-7}	average home
10^{-9}	soft whisper
10^{-12}	barely audible

Real-World Link

Timbre is the quality of the sound produced by a musical instrument. Sound quality is what distinguishes the sound of a note played on a flute from the sound of the same note played on a trumpet with the same frequency and intensity.

Source: www.school.discovery.com

42. How many times more intense is the sound from heavy traffic than the sound from normal conversation? 10^3 or 1000

43. What sound is 10,000 times as loud as a noisy kitchen?   jet plane

44. How does the intensity of a whisper compare to that of normal conversation? $\frac{1}{1000}$

LIGHT For Exercises 45 and 46, use the table at the right.

45. Express the range of the wavelengths of visible light using positive exponents. Then evaluate each expression.

46. Express the range of the wavelengths of X rays using positive exponents. Then evaluate each expression. **See margin.**

45. $\frac{1}{10^5} - \frac{1}{10^4}$ cm; $\frac{1}{100,000} - \frac{1}{10,000}$ cm

Spectrum of Electromagnetic Radiation	
Region	**Wavelength (om)**
Radio	greater than 10
Microwave	10^1 to 10^{-2}
Infrared	10^{-2} to 10^{-5}
Visible	10^{-5} to 10^{-4}
Ultraviolet	10^{-4} to 10^{-7}
X rays	10^{-7} to 10^{-9}
Gamma Rays	less than 10^{-9}

EXTRA PRACTICE
See pages 731, 750.

Math Online
Self-Check Quiz at ca.algebra1.com

47. **COMPUTERS** In 1993, the processing speed of a desktop computer was about 10^8 instructions per second. By 2004, it had increased to 10^{10} instructions per second. How many times faster is the newer computer?   100

H.O.T. Problems

48. **OPEN ENDED** Name two monomials whose product is $54x^2 y^3$.
Sample answer: $9xy$ and $6xy^2$

49. **ALTERNATIVE METHODS** Describe a method of simplifying $\frac{a^3 b^5}{ab^2}$ using negative exponents instead of the Quotient of Powers Property.
$\frac{a^3 b^5}{ab^2} = a^3 a^{-1} b^5 b^{-2} = a^{3-1} b^{5-2} = a^2 b^3$

CHALLENGE Simplify. Assume that no denominator equals zero.

50. $a^n(a^3)$ a^{n+3}
51. $(5^{4x-3})(5^{2x+1})$ 5^{6x-2}
52. $\frac{c^{x+7}}{c^{x-4}}$ c^{11}

53. **REASONING** Write a convincing argument to show why $3^0 = 1$ using the following pattern: $3^5 = 243, 3^4 = 81, 3^3 = 27, 3^2 = 9$. **Since each number is obtained by dividing the previous number by 3, $3^1 = 3$ and $3^0 = 1$.**

BL = Below Grade Level
OL = On Grade Level
AL = Above Grade Level
ELL = English Language Learner

Additional pages not shown:
CRM Lesson Reading Guide, p. 12 **BL** **OL** **ELL**
CRM Skills Practice, p. 15 **BL** **OL**

54. Jamal; a factor is moved from the numerator of a fraction to the denominator or vice versa only if the exponent of the factor is negative; $-4 \neq \frac{1}{4}$.

54. FIND THE ERROR Jamal and Angelina are simplifying $\frac{-4x^3}{x^5}$. Who is correct? Explain your reasoning.

Jamal
$\frac{-4x^3}{x^5} = -4x^{3-5}$
$= -4x^{-2}$
$= \frac{-4}{x^2}$

Angelina
$\frac{-4x^3}{x^5} = \frac{x^{3-5}}{4}$
$= \frac{x^{-2}}{4}$
$= \frac{1}{4x^2}$

55. *Writing in Math* Use the information about pH levels on page 366 to explain how you can use the properties of exponents to compare measures on the pH scale. Demonstrate an example comparing two pH levels using the properties of exponents. **See margin.**

STANDARDS PRACTICE 2.0, 7MG2.3

56. How many times as great is the volume of the larger cube as the volume of the smaller cube? **C**

A 2
B 4
C 8
D 16

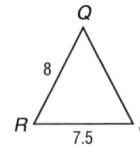

2x   x

57. REVIEW $\triangle QRS$ is similar to $\triangle TUV$. What is the length of $\overline{UV}$? **J**

Q
8
R ——— S
7.5

T
1.6 /\ 1.6
U   V

F 11.0   G 2.3   H 1.7   J 1.5

Spiral Review

Simplify. (Lesson 7-1)

58. $(m^3n)(mn^2)$ m^4n^3

59. $(3x^4y^3)(4x^4y)$ $12x^8y^4$

60. $(a^3x^2)^4$ $a^{12}x^8$

61. $(3cd^5)^2$ $9c^2d^{10}$

62. $[(2^3)^2]^2$ 2^{12} or 4096

63. $(-3ab)^3(2b^3)^2$ $-108a^3b^9$

NUTRITION For Exercises 64 and 65, use the following information.
Between the ages of 11 and 18, you should get at least 1200 milligrams of calcium each day. One ounce of mozzarella cheese has 147 milligrams of calcium, and one ounce of Swiss cheese has 219 milligrams. Suppose you want to eat no more than 8 ounces of cheese. (Lesson 6-8)

64. Draw a graph showing the possible amounts of each type of cheese you can eat and still get your daily requirement of calcium. Let x be the amount of mozzarella cheese and y be the amount of Swiss cheese. **See margin.**

65. List three possible solutions. **Sample answers: 3 oz of mozzarella, 4 oz of Swiss; 4 oz of mozzarella, 3 oz of Swiss; 5 oz of mozzarella, 3 oz of Swiss**

GET READY for the Next Lesson

PREREQUISITE SKILL Evaluate each expression when $a = 5$, $b = -2$, **and** $c = 3$. (Lesson 1-2)

66. $5b^2$ 20

67. $b^3 + 3ac$ 37

68. $-2b^4 - 5b^3 - b$ 10

4 Assess

Yesterday's News Ask students to write two ways in which the concepts of multiplying monomials helped them to understand dividing monomials.

Formative Assessment

Check for student understanding of concepts in Lessons 7-1 and 7-2.

[CRM] Quiz 1, p. 59

Additional Answers

46. $\frac{1}{10^7} - \frac{1}{10^9}$ cm;

$\frac{1}{10,000,000} - \frac{1}{1,000,000,000}$ cm

55. You can compare pH levels by finding the ratio of one pH to another written in terms of the concentration c of hydrogen ions, $c = \left(\frac{1}{10}\right)^{pH}$. Sample answer: To compare a pH of 8 with a pH of 9 requires simplifying the quotient of powers, $\frac{\left(\frac{1}{10}\right)^8}{\left(\frac{1}{10}\right)^9} = 10$. Thus, a pH of 8 is ten times more acidic than a pH of 9.

64.

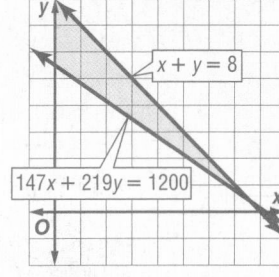

$x + y = 8$

$147x + 219y = 1200$

READING MATH

1 Focus

Ask:

What is the difference between a bicycle and a tricycle?

As students answer, write the words *two* and *three* on the board along with the words *bicycle* and *tricycle*.

2 Teach

Prefixes Explain to students that prefixes can be used to help them understand the meaning of many mathematical terms. Tell students that they can recall the meaning of terms readily by relating prefixes to everyday words.

Have student complete Exercises 1–3.

3 Assess

Ask students to summarize what they have learned about prefixes.

ELL English Language Learners may benefit from writing the key concepts from this activity in their native languages and then in English.

Preparation for Standard 10.0 Students add, subtract, multiply, and divide monomials and polynomials. Students solve multistep problems, including word problems, by using these techniques. (Key, CAHSEE)

Mathematical Prefixes and Everyday Prefixes

You may have noticed that many prefixes used in mathematics are also used in everyday language. You can use the everyday meaning of these prefixes to better understand their mathematical meaning. The table shows four mathematical prefixes along with their meaning and an example of an everyday word using that prefix.

Prefix	Everyday Meaning	Example
mono-	1. one; single; alone	**monologue** A continuous series of jokes or comic stories delivered by one comedian.
bi-	1. two 2. both 3. both sides, parts, or directions	**bicycle** A vehicle with two wheels behind one another.
tri-	1. three 2. occurring at intervals of three 3. occurring three times during	**trilogy** A group of three dramatic or literary works related in subject or theme.
poly-	1. more than one; many; much	**polygon** A closed plane figure bounded by three or more line segments.

Source: *The American Heritage Dictionary of the English Language*

You can use your everyday understanding of prefixes to help you understand mathematical terms that use those prefixes.

Reading to Learn

1. Give an example of a geometry term that uses one of these prefixes. Then define that term. **Sample answer: triangle; a three-sided polygon**

2. **MAKE A CONJECTURE** Given your knowledge of the meaning of the word monomial, make a conjecture as to the meaning of each of the following mathematical terms.

   a. binomial   **b.** trinomial   **c.** polynomial
   See students' work.

3. Research the following prefixes and their meanings.

   a. semi- half   **b.** hexa- six   **c.** octa- eight

   d. penta- five   **e.** tri- three   **f.** quad- four

374 Reading Math Polynomials

Additional Answers (Explore 7–3)

1. $-x^2$ $-x^2$

2. x x x x x -1 -1 -1 -1

Algebra Lab
Polynomials

Lesson Notes

Preparation for Standard 10.0 Students add, subtract, multiply, and divide monomials and polynomials. Students solve multistep problems, including word problems, by using these techniques. (Key, CAHSEE)

Algebra tiles can be used to model polynomials. A polynomial is a monomial or the sum of monomials. The diagram at the right shows the models.

Polynomial Models			
Polynomials are modeled using three types of tiles.	1	x	x^2
Each tile has an opposite.	−1	−x	$−x^2$

ACTIVITY

Use algebra tiles to model each polynomial.

- $4x$

  To model this polynomial, you will need 4 green x-tiles.

  | x | x | x | x |

- $2x^2 − 3$

  To model this polynomial, you will need 2 blue x^2-tiles and 3 red −1-tiles.

  | x^2 | x^2 | | −1 −1 −1 |

- $−x^2 + 3x + 2$

  To model this polynomial, you will need 1 red $−x^2$-tile, 3 green x-tiles, and 2 yellow 1-tiles.

  | $−x^2$ | x | x | x | | 1 1 |

MODEL AND ANALYZE

Use algebra tiles to model each polynomial. Then draw a diagram of your model. **1–4. See margin.**

1. $−2x^2$
2. $5x − 4$
3. $3x^2 − x$
4. $x^2 + 4x + 3$

Write an algebraic expression for each model.

5.

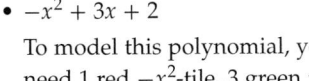

$3x^2 − 2x$

6.

$−x^2 + x + 4$

7.

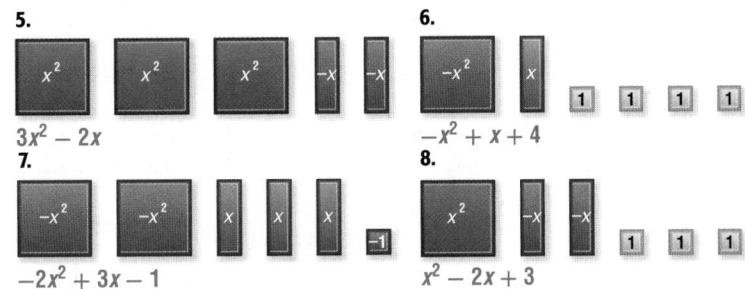

$−2x^2 + 3x − 1$

8.

$x^2 − 2x + 3$

9. **MAKE A CONJECTURE** Write a sentence or two explaining why algebra tiles are sometimes called *area tiles*.

   x^2 and 1 represent the areas of the tiles.

Explore 7-3 Algebra Lab: Polynomials **375**

1 Focus

Objective Use algebra tiles to model polynomials.

Materials
- algebra tiles

Easy-to-Make Manipulatives
Teaching Algebra with Manipulatives

Template for algebra tiles, pp. 10–11

2 Teach

Working in Cooperative Groups
Put students in groups of 2 or 3, mixing abilities. Have groups complete the Activity and Exercises 1 and 2.

- Make sure students understand that the number of x-tiles and x^2-tiles represent the coefficients of x and x^2, respectively. The number of 1-tiles represents the constant in the expression.

- Tell students to be careful to use the tiles with the correct signs. It is easy to substitute an x-tile for a $−x$-tile.

Practice Have students complete Exercises 3–9.

3 Assess

✓ Formative Assessment

Use Exercises 3–4 to assess whether students can use algebra to model a polynomial correctly.

Use Exercises 5–8 to assess whether students can write a polynomial from an algebra-tile model.

Additional Answers

3.

4.

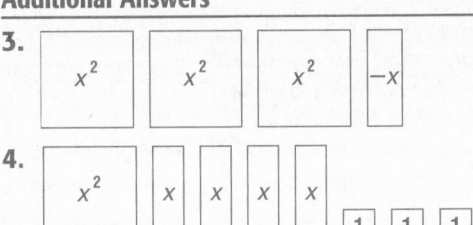

From Concrete to Abstract Place a set of tiles in a bag. Have each group of students draw 7 tiles from the bag and write an algebraic expression for the model.

Extending the Concept Ask student to use their tiles to model $x^2 + 3x$ and $x^2 + 2x$. Ask them to make conjectures about the sum of the two polynomials and to use their algebra tiles to support their conjectures.

7-3 Polynomials

1 Focus

Standards Alignment

Before Lesson 7-3
Simplify numerical expressions by applying properties of rational numbers from ⚷ Standard 7AF1.3

Lesson 7-3
Understand and use the rules of exponents from ⚷ Standard 2.0

After Lesson 7-3
Operations on polynomials, including long division from ⚷ Standard 2A3.0

2 Teach

Scaffolding Questions
Have students read *Get Ready for the Lesson.*
Ask:
- What is the value of *t* for the year 2002? 2 What would be the value of *t* for the year 2005? 5
- Using the equation, find the value of *H* for the year 2002. 89.5
- Why does the value of *H* for the year 2005 differ from the value in the table? The polynomial model approximates, but does not necessarily match, the real values exactly.

Present the Pre-AP Activity from the bottom of p. 381.

Lesson 7-3 Resources

Chapter 7 Resource Masters
Lesson Reading Guide, p. 19 BL OL ELL
Study Guide and Intervention, pp. 20–21 BL OL ELL
Skills Practice, p. 22 BL OL
Practice, p. 23 OL AL
Word Problem Practice, p. 24 OL AL
Enrichment, p. 25 OL AL
Graphing Calculator, p. 26

Main Ideas
- Find the degree of a polynomial.
- Arrange the terms of a polynomial in ascending or descending order.

Preparation for Standard 10.0
Students add, subtract, multiply, and divide monomials and polynomials. Students solve multistep problems, including word problems, by using these techniques. (Key, CAHSEE)

New Vocabulary
polynomial
binomial
trinomial
degree of a monomial
degree of a polynomial

▷ GET READY for the Lesson

The number of hours *H* spent per person per year playing video games from 2000 through 2005 is shown in the table. These data can be modeled by the equation

$$H = \frac{1}{4}(t^4 - 9t^3 + 24t^2 + 19t + 280),$$

where *t* is the number of years since 2000. The expression $t^4 - 9t^3 + 24t^2 + 19t + 280$ is an example of a polynomial.

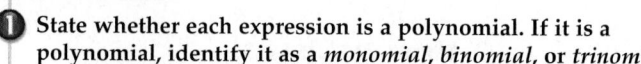
Video Game Usage

Year	Hours per Year
2000	70
2001	79
2002	90
2003	97
2004	103
2005	115

Source: U.S. Census Bureau

Degree of a Polynomial A **polynomial** is a monomial or a sum of monomials. Some polynomials have special names. A **binomial** is the sum of *two* monomials, and a **trinomial** is the sum of *three* monomials.

Monomial	Binomial	Trinomial
7	$3 + 4y$	$x + y + z$
$4ab^3c^2$	$7pqr + pq^2$	$3v^2 - 2w + ab^3$

EXAMPLE Identify Polynomials

① State whether each expression is a polynomial. If it is a polynomial, identify it as a *monomial, binomial,* or *trinomial.*

	Expression	Polynomial?	Monomial, Binomial, or Trinomial?
a.	$2x - 3yz$	Yes, $2x - 3yz = 2x + (-3yz)$, the sum of two monomials.	binomial
b.	$8n^3 + 5n^{-2}$	No. $5n^{-2} = \frac{5}{n^2}$, which is not a monomial.	none of these
c.	-8	Yes, -8 is a real number.	monomial
d.	$4a^2 + 5a + a + 9$	Yes, the expression simplifies to $4a^2 + 6a + 9$, so it is the sum of three monomials.	trinomial

✓CHECK Your Progress
1A. x monomial
1B. $-3y^2 - 2y + 4y - 1$ trinomial
1C. $5rs + 7tuv$ binomial
1D. $10x^{-4} - 8x^3$ none of these

Transparencies
5-Minute Check Transparency 7-3

Additional Print Resources
Noteables™ Interactive Study Notebook with Foldables™
Teaching Algebra with Manipulatives

Technology
ca.algebra1.com
Interactive Classroom CD-ROM
AssignmentWorks CD-ROM
Graphing Calculator Easy Files

EXAMPLE Write a Polynomial

2 **GEOMETRY** Write a polynomial to represent the area of the shaded region.

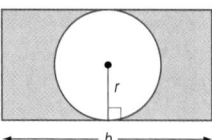

Words	The area of the shaded region is the area of the rectangle minus the area of the circle.
Variables	area of shaded region = A width of rectangle = $2r$ rectangle area = $b(2r)$ circle area = πr^2
	Area of shaded region = rectangle area − circle area.
Equation	$A = b(2r) - \pi r^2$ $A = 2br - \pi r^2$

The polynomial representing the area of the shaded region is $2br - \pi r^2$.

✓CHECK Your Progress

2. Write a polynomial to represent the area of the shaded region. **$6x^2$**

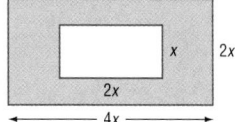

🌐 **Personal Tutor at** ca.algebra1.com

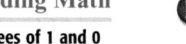
COncepts in MOtion
Interactive Lab
ca.algebra1.com

The **degree of a monomial** is the sum of the exponents of all its variables.

The **degree of a polynomial** is the greatest degree of any term in the polynomial. To find the degree of a polynomial, you must find the degree of each term.

Monomial	Degree
$8y^4$	4
$3a$	1
$-2xy^2z^3$	$1+2+3$ or 6
7	0

Reading Math

Degrees of 1 and 0
• Since $a = a^1$, the monomial $3a$ can be rewritten as $3a^1$. Thus $3a$ has degree 1.
• Since $x^0 = 1$, the monomial 7 can be rewritten as $7x^0$. Thus 7 has degree 0.

EXAMPLE Degree of a Polynomial

3 Find the degree of each polynomial.

	Polynomial	Terms	Degree of Each Term	Degree of Polynomial
a.	$5mn^2$	$5mn^2$	3	3
b.	$-4x^2y^2 + 3x^2 + 5$	$-4x^2y^2, 3x^2, 5$	4, 2, 0	4
c.	$3a + 7ab - 2a^2b + 16$	$3a, 7ab, -2a^2b, 16$	1, 2, 3, 0	3

✓CHECK Your Progress

3A. $7xy^5z$ **7**   **3B.** $12m^3n^2 - 8mn^2 + 3$ **5**   **3C.** $2rs - 3rs^2 - 7r^2s^2 - 13$ **4**

Write Polynomials in Order The terms of a polynomial are usually arranged so that the powers of one variable are in *ascending* (increasing) order or *descending* (decreasing) order.

 Math Online Extra Examples at ca.algebra1.com

Lesson 7-3 Polynomials **377**

Degree of a Polynomial
Example 1 shows how to determine whether an expression is a polynomial. **Example 2** shows how to write a polynomial. **Example 3** shows how to find the degree of a polynomial.

✓ Formative Assessment

Use the Check Your Progress exercises after each example to determine students' understanding of concepts.

ADDITIONAL EXAMPLES

1 State whether each expression is a polynomial. If it is a polynomial, identify it as a *monomial*, *binomial*, or *trinomial*.

a. $6 - 4$ yes, binomial

b. $x^2 + 2xy - 7$ yes, trinomial

c. $\dfrac{14d + 19e^3}{5d^4}$ no

d. $26b^2$ yes, monomial

2 **GEOMETRY** Write a polynomial to represent the area of the shaded region.

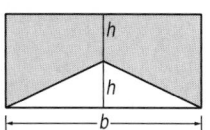

$2bh - \dfrac{1}{2}bh$

3 Find the degree of each polynomial.

a. $12 + 5b + 6bc + 8bc^2$ 3

b. $9x^2 - 2x - 4$ 2

c. $14g^2h^5j$ 8

Additional Examples are also in:

• Noteables™ Interactive Study Notebook with Foldables™

• Interactive Classroom PowerPoint® Presentations

Write Polynomials in Order
Example 4 shows how to arrange polynomials in ascending order.
Example 5 shows how to arrange polynomials in descending order.

ADDITIONAL EXAMPLES

4 Arrange the terms of each polynomial so that the powers of x are in ascending order.

a. $16 + 14x^3 + 2x - x^2$
$16 + 2x - x^2 + 14x^3$

b. $7y^2 + 4x^3 + 2xy^3 - x^2y^2$
$7y^2 + 2xy^3 - x^2y^2 + 4x^3$

5 Arrange the terms of each polynomial so that the powers of x are in descending order.

a. $8 + 7x^2 - 12xy^3 - 4x^3y$
$-4x^3y + 7x^2 - 12xy^3 + 8$

b. $a^4 + ax^2 - 2a^3xy^3 - 9x^4y$
$-9x^4y + ax^2 - 2a^3xy^3 + a^4$

Preventing Errors

For Exercise 2, remind students that monomials are the products of a number and one or more variables, so expressions such as $\frac{1}{b^2}$ are not monomials.

COncepts in MOtion
BrainPOP®
ca.algebra1.com

EXAMPLE Arrange Polynomials in Ascending Order

4 Arrange the terms of each polynomial so that the powers of x are in ascending order.

a. $7x^2 + 2x^4 - 11$

$7x^2 + 2x^4 - 11 = 7x^2 + 2x^4 - 11x^0 \quad x^0 = 1$

$= -11 + 7x^2 + 2x^4 \quad$ Compare powers of x: $0 < 2 < 4$.

b. $2xy^3 + y^2 + 5x^3 - 3x^2y$

$2xy^3 + y^2 + 5x^3 - 3x^2y$

$= 2x^1y^3 + y^2 + 5x^3 - 3x^2y^1 \quad x = x^1$

$= y^2 + 2xy^3 - 3x^2y + 5x^3 \quad$ Compare powers of x: $0 < 1 < 2 < 3$.

✓ CHECK Your Progress

4A. $3x^2y^4 + 2x^4y^2 - 4x^3y + x^5 - y^2$ **4B.** $7x^3 - 4xy^4 + 3x^2y^3 - 11x^6y$

$-y^2 + 3x^2y^4 - 4x^3y + 2x^4y^2 + x^5$ $-4xy^4 + 3x^2y^3 + 7x^3 - 11x^6y$

EXAMPLE Arrange Polynomials in Descending Order

5 Arrange the terms of each polynomial so that the powers of x are in descending order.

a. $6x^2 + 5 - 8x - 2x^3$

$6x^2 + 5 - 8x - 2x^3 = 6x^2 + 5x^0 - 8x^1 - 2x^3 \quad x^0 = 1$ and $x = x^1$

$= -2x^3 + 6x^2 - 8x + 5 \quad 3 > 2 > 1 > 0$

b. $3a^3x^2 - a^4 + 4ax^5 + 9a^2x$

$3a^3x^2 - a^4 + 4ax^5 + 9a^2x$

$= 3a^3x^2 - a^4x^0 + 4a^1x^5 + 9a^2x^1 \quad a = a^1, x^0 = 1,$ and $x = x^1$

$= 4ax^5 + 3a^3x^2 + 9a^2x - a^4 \quad 5 > 2 > 1 > 0.$

✓ CHECK Your Progress

5A. $4x^2 + 2x^3y + 5 - x$

$2x^3y + 4x^2 - x + 5$

5B. $x + 2x^7y - 5x^4y^8 - x^2y^2 + 3$

$2x^7y - 5x^4y^8 - x^2y^2 + x + 3$

★ indicates multi-step problem

✓ CHECK Your Understanding

Example 1
(p. 376)

State whether each expression is a polynomial. If the expression is a polynomial, identify it as a *monomial*, a *binomial*, or a *trinomial*.

1. $5x - 3xy + 2x$
yes; binomial

2. $\frac{2z}{5}$ yes; monomial

3. $9a^2 + 7a - 5$
yes; trinomial

Example 2
(p. 377)

★ **4. GEOMETRY** Write a polynomial to represent the area of the shaded region. $2cd - \pi d^2$

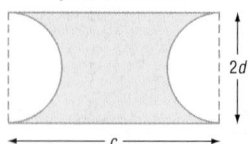

Example 3
(p. 377)

Find the degree of each polynomial.

5. 1   0

6. $3x + 2$ 1

7. $2x^2y^3 + 6x^4$ 5

Example 4
(p. 378)

Arrange the terms of each polynomial so that the powers of x are in ascending order.

8. $6x^3 - 12 + 5x$
$-12 + 5x + 6x^3$

9. $-7a^2x^3 + 4x^2 - 2ax^5 + 2a$
$2a + 4x^2 - 7a^2x^3 - 2ax^5$

Example 5
(p. 378)

Arrange the terms of each polynomial so that the powers of x are in descending order.

10. $2c^5 + 9cx^2 + 3x$
$9cx^2 + 3x + 2c^5$

11. $y^3 + x^3 + 3x^2y + 3xy^2$
$x^3 + 3x^2y + 3xy^2 + y^3$

Exercises

HOMEWORK HELP

For Exercises	See Examples
12–17	1
18–21	2
22–33	3
34–41	4
42–49	5

Exercise Levels
A: 12–49
B: 50–53
C: 54–58

State whether each expression is a polynomial. If the expression is a polynomial, identify it as a *monomial*, a *binomial*, or a *trinomial*.

12. 14   yes; monomial

13. $\frac{6m^2}{p} + p^3$ no

14. $7b - 3.2c + 8b$
yes; binomial

15. $\frac{1}{3}x^2 + x - 2$
yes; trinomial

16. $6gh^2 - 4g^2h + g$
yes; trinomial

17. $-4 + 2a + \frac{5}{a^2}$ no

GEOMETRY Write a polynomial to represent the area of each shaded region.

★ **18.**
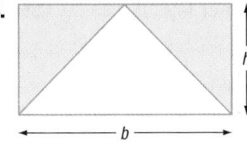
0.5bh

★ **19.**
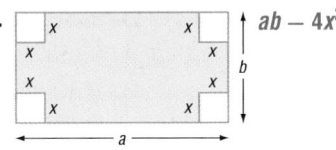
$ab - 4x^2$

★ **20.**
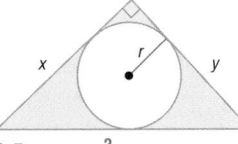
$0.5xy - \pi r^2$

★ **21.**
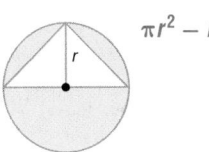
$\pi r^2 - r^2$

Find the degree of each polynomial.

22. $5x^3$ 3

23. $9y$ 1

24. $4ab$ 2

25. -13 0

26. $c^4 + 7c^2$ 4

27. $6n^3 - n^2p^2$ 4

28. $15 - 8ag$ 2

29. $3a^2b^3c^4 - 18a^5c$ 9

30. $2x^3 - 4y + 7xy$ 3

31. $3z^5 - 2x^2y^3z - 4x^2z$ 6

32. $7 + d^5 - b^2c^2d^3 + b^6$ 7

33. $11r^2t^4 - 2s^4t^5 + 24$ 9

Arrange the terms of each polynomial so that the powers of x are in ascending order.   **38.** $4 - 5a^7 + 2ax^2 + 3ax^5$ **39.** $5y^4 + 2x^2 + 10x^3y^2 - 3x^9y$

34. $2x + 3x^2 - 1$ $-1 + 2x + 3x^2$

35. $9x^3 + 7 - 3x^5$ $7 + 9x^3 - 3x^5$

36. $c^2x^3 - c^3x^2 + 8c$

37. $x^3 + 4a + 5a^2x^6$ $4a + x^3 + 5a^2x^6$

38. $4 + 3ax^5 + 2ax^2 - 5a^7$

39. $10x^3y^2 - 3x^9y + 5y^4 + 2x^2$

40. $3xy^2 - 4x^3 + x^2y + 6y$

41. $-8a^5x + 2ax^4 - 5 - a^2x^2$

36. $8c - c^3x^2 + c^2x^3$

40. $6y + 3xy^2 + x^2y - 4x^3$

41. $-5 - 8a^5x - a^2x^2 + 2ax^4$

EXTRA PRACTICE
See pages 731, 750.

Math Online
Self-Check Quiz at
ca.algebra1.com

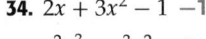

Lesson 7-3 Polynomials   **379**

✓ **Formative Assessment**

Use Exercises 1–11 to check for understanding.

Use the chart at the bottom of this page to customize assignments for your students.

Odd/Even Assignments

Exercises 12–49 are structured so that students practice the same concepts whether they are assigned odd or even problems.

DIFFERENTIATED HOMEWORK OPTIONS

Level	Assignment	Two-Day Option	
BL Basic	12–49, 55, 56, 59–78	13–49 odd, 60, 61	12–48 even, 55, 56, 59, 62–78
OL Core	13–49 odd, 50–56, 58–78	12–49, 60, 61	50–56, 58, 59, 62–78
AL Advanced /Pre-AP	50–74, (optional: 75–78)		

Study Guide and Intervention
CRM pp. 20–21

7-3 Study Guide and Intervention
Polynomials

Degree of a Polynomial A *polynomial* is a monomial or a sum of monomials. A *binomial* is the sum of two monomials, and a *trinomial* is the sum of three monomials. Polynomials with more than three terms have no special name. The **degree** of a monomial is the sum of the exponents of all its variables. The **degree of the polynomial** is the same as the degree of the monomial term with the highest degree.

Example State whether each expression is a polynomial. If the expression is a polynomial, identify it as a *monomial*, *binomial*, or *trinomial*. Then give the degree of the polynomial.

Expression	Polynomial?	Monomial, Binomial, or Trinomial?	Degree of the Polynomial
$3x - 7xyz$	Yes. $3x - 7xyz = 3x + (-7xyz)$, which is the sum of two monomials	binomial	3
-25	Yes. -25 is a real number.	monomial	0
$7n^3 + 3n^{-4}$	No. $3n^{-4} = \frac{3}{n^4}$, which is not a monomial	none of these	—
$9x^2 + x + x + 4 + 2x$	Yes. The expression simplifies to $9x^2 + 7x + 4$, which is the sum of three monomials	trinomial	3

Exercises

State whether each expression is a polynomial. If the expression is a polynomial, identify it as a *monomial*, *binomial*, or *trinomial*.

1. 36 yes; monomial
2. $\frac{3}{q^2} + 5$ no
3. $7x - x + 5$ yes; binomial
4. $8g^2h - 7gh + 2$ yes; trinomial
5. $\frac{1}{4y^3} + 5y - 8$ no
6. $6x + x^3$ yes; binomial

Find the degree of each polynomial.

7. $4x^3y^2z$ 6
8. $-2abc$ 3
9. $15m$ 1
10. $s + 5t$ 1
11. 22 0
12. $18x^2 + 4yz - 10y$ 2
13. $x^4 - 6x^2 - 2x^3 - 10$ 4
14. $2x^2y^3 - 4xy^3$ 5
15. $-2r^3s^4 + 7r^2s - 4r^3s^6$ 13
16. $9x^3 + yz^8$ 9
17. $8b + bc^3$ 6
18. $4x^4y - 8zx^3 + 2x^5$ 5
19. $4z^3 - 1$ 2
20. $9abc + bc - d^5$ 5
21. $h^2m + 6h^4m^2 - 7$ 6

Chapter 7 — 20 — Glencoe Algebra 1

Practice
CRM p. 23

7-3 Practice
Polynomials

State whether each expression is a polynomial. If the expression is a polynomial, identify it as a *monomial*, a *binomial*, or a *trinomial*.

1. $7a^2b + 3b^2 - a^2b$ yes; binomial
2. $\frac{1}{3}y^3 + y^2 - 9$ yes; trinomial
3. $6g^2h^3b$ yes; monomial

GEOMETRY Write a polynomial to represent the area of each shaded region.

4. $ab - b^2$
5. $d^2 - \frac{1}{4}\pi d^2$

Find the degree of each polynomial.

6. $x + 3x^4 - 21x^2 + x^3$ 4
7. $3g^2h^3 + g^3h$ 5
8. $-2x^2y + 3xy^3 + z^2$ 4
9. $5n^3m - 2m^3 + n^2m^4 + n^2$ 6
10. $a^3b^2c + 2a^3c + b^3c^2$ 6
11. $10a^2t^3 + 4at^2 - 5a^2t^2$ 5

Arrange the terms of each polynomial so that the powers of x are in ascending order.

12. $8x^2 - 15 + 5x^5$
$-15 + 8x^2 + 5x^5$
13. $10bx - 7b^2 + x^4 + 4b^4x^3$
$-7b^2 + 10bx + 4b^2x^3 + x^4$
14. $-3x^2y + 8y^2 + xy^4$
$8y^2 + xy^4 - 3x^2y$
15. $7ax - 12 + 3ax^2 + a^2x^2$
$-12 + 7ax + a^2x^2 + 3ax^2$

Arrange the terms of each polynomial so that the powers of x are in descending order.

16. $13x^2 - 5 + 6x^3 - x$
$6x^3 + 13x^2 - x - 5$
17. $4x + 2x^5 - 6x^3 + 2$
$2x^5 - 6x^3 + 4x + 2$
18. $g^3x - 3gx^3 + 7g^3 + 4g^2$
$-3gx^3 + 4x^3 + g^2x + 7g^3$
19. $-11x^2y^3 + 6y - 2xy + 2x^4$
$2x^4 - 11x^2y^3 - 2xy + 6y$
20. $7a^3x^2 + 17 - a^3x^3 + 2ax$
$-a^3x^3 + 7a^3x^2 + 2ax + 17$
21. $12zx^3 + 9z^4 + r^2z + 8z^6$
$8z^6 + 12zx^3 + r^2z + 9z^6$

22. **MONEY** Write a polynomial to represent the value of t ten-dollar bills, f fifty-dollar bills, and n one-hundred-dollar bills. $10t + 50f + 100h$

23. **GRAVITY** The height above the ground of a ball thrown up with a velocity of 96 feet per second from a height of 6 feet is $6 + 96t - 16t^2$ feet, where t is the time in seconds. According to this model, how high is the ball after 7 seconds? Explain. -106 ft; The height is negative because the model does not account for the ball hitting the ground when the height is 0 feet.

Chapter 7 — 23 — Glencoe Algebra 1

Word Problem Practice
CRM p. 24

7-3 Word Problem Practice
Polynomials

1. **PRIMES** Mei is trying to list as many prime numbers as she can for a challenge problem for her math class. She finds that the polynomial expression $n^2 - n + 41$ can be used to generate some, but not all, prime numbers. What is the degree of Mei's polynomial? 2

2. **PHONE CALLS** A long-distance telephone company charges a $19.95 standard monthly service fee plus $0.05 per minute of long-distance use. Write a polynomial to express the monthly cost of the phone plan if x minutes of long-distance time are used per month. What is the degree of the polynomial? $0.05x + 19.95$; 1

3. **COSTUMES** Jack's mother is sewing the cape of his costume for a charity masked ball. The pattern for the cape (lying flat) is shown below. The radius of the neck hole is 6 inches. What is the area, in square feet, of the finished cape? 27.5 ft²

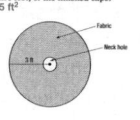
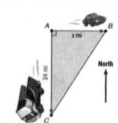

4. **ARCHITECTURE** Graphing the polynomial function $y = -x^2 + 3$ produces an accurate drawing of the shape of an archway inside a historical library, where x is the horizontal distance in meters from the base of the arch and y is the height of the arch. At $x = 0$, what is the height of the arch? 3 m

DRIVING For Exercises 5 and 6, use the following information.
A truck and a car leave an intersection. The truck travels south, and the car travels east. When the truck had gone 24 miles, the distance between the car and truck was four miles more than three times the distance traveled by the car heading east.

5. Suppose the truck stops at point C and the car stops at point B. Write a polynomial to express the sum of the distances traveled by the car and the truck. $x + 24$

6. Write a simplified polynomial to express the perimeter of triangle ABC. $4x + 28$ mi

Chapter 7 — 24 — Glencoe Algebra 1

Real-World Link

From 1980 to 1999, the number of triplet and higher births rose approximately 532% (from 1377 to 7321 births). This steep climb in multiple births coincides with the increased use of fertility drugs.

Source: National Center for Health and Statistics

49. $4x^3y - x^2y^3 + 3xy^4 + y^4$

H.O.T. Problems

57. True; for the degree of a binomial to be zero, the highest degree of both terms would need to be zero. Then the terms would be like terms. With these like terms combined, the expression is not a binomial, but a monomial. Therefore, the degree of a binomial can never be zero. Only a monomial can have a degree of zero.

Arrange the terms of each polynomial so that the powers of x are in descending order. 44. $2a^2x^3 + 4a^3x^2 - 5a$ 46. $cx^3 - 5c^3x^2 + 11x + c^2$

42. $5 + x^5 + 3x^3$ $x^5 + 3x^3 + 5$
43. $2x - 1 + 6x^2$ $6x^2 + 2x - 1$
44. $4a^3x^2 - 5a + 2a^2x^3$
45. $b^2 + x^2 - 2xb$ $x^2 - 2xb + b^2$
46. $c^2 + cx^3 - 5c^3x^2 + 11x$
47. $9x^2 + 3 + 4ax^3 - 2a^2x$
48. $8x - 9x^2y + 7y^2 - 2x^4$
49. $4x^3y + 3xy^4 - x^2y^3 + y^4$
47. $4ax^3 + 9x^2 - 2a^2x + 3$ 48. $-2x^4 - 9x^2y + 8x + 7y^2$

50. **MONEY** Write a polynomial to represent the value of q quarters, d dimes and n nickels. $0.25q + 0.10d + 0.05n$

51. **MULTIPLE BIRTHS** The rate of quadruplet births Q in the United States in recent years can be modeled by $Q = -0.5t^3 + 11.7t^2 - 21.5t + 218.6$, where t represents the number of years since 1992. For what values of t does this model no longer give realistic data? Explain your reasoning.
$t > 15$; For $t > 15$, the number of quadruplet births declines dramatically.

PACKAGING For Exercises 52 and 53, use the following information.
A convenience store sells milkshakes in cups with semispherical lids. The volume of a cylinder is the product of π, the square of the radius r, and the height h. The volume of a sphere is the product of $\frac{4}{3}$, π, and the cube of the radius.

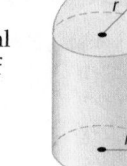
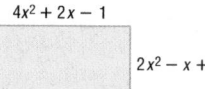

52. Write a polynomial that represents the volume of the container. $\pi r^2 h + \frac{2}{3}\pi r^3$

53. If the height of the container is 6 inches and the radius is 2 inches, find the volume of the container. about 92.15 in³

54. Write two polynomials that represent the perimeter and area of the rectangle shown at right.
$12x^2 + 2x + 4$; $(4x^2 + 2x - 1)(2x^2 - x + 3)$

[rectangle: $4x^2 + 2x - 1$, $2x^2 - x + 3$]

55. **OPEN ENDED** Give an example of a monomial of degree zero. Sample answer: -8

56. **REASONING** Explain why a polynomial cannot contain a variable term with a negative power. See margin.

57. **CHALLENGE** Tell whether the following statement is *true* or *false*. Explain your reasoning.
The degree of a binomial can never be zero.

58. **REASONING** Determine whether each statement is *true* or *false*. If false, give a counterexample.
   a. All binomials are polynomials. true
   b. All polynomials are monomials. false, $3x + 5$
   c. All monomials are polynomials. true

59. *Writing in Math* Use the information about video game usage on page 376 to explain how polynomials can be useful in modeling data. Include a discussion of the accuracy of the equation by evaluating the polynomial for $t = \{0, 1, 2, 3, 4, 5\}$ and an example of how and why someone might use this equation. See margin.

Enrichment
CRM p. 25 OL AL

7-3 Enrichment
Polynomial Functions

Suppose a linear equation such as $-3x + y = 4$ is solved for y. Then an equivalent equation, $y = 3x + 4$, is found. Expressed in this way, y is a function of x, or $f(x) = 3x + 4$. Notice that the right side of the equation is a binomial of degree 1.

Higher-degree polynomials in x may also form functions. An example is $f(x) = x^3 + 1$, which is a polynomial function of degree 3. You can graph this function using a table of ordered pairs, as shown at the right.

x	y
$-1\frac{1}{2}$	$-2\frac{3}{8}$
-1	0
0	1
1	2
$1\frac{1}{2}$	$4\frac{3}{8}$

For each of the following polynomial functions, make a table of values for x and $y = f(x)$, then draw the graph on the grid.

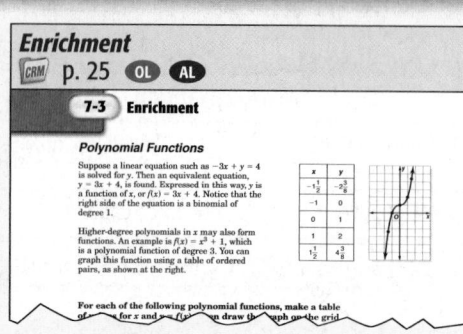

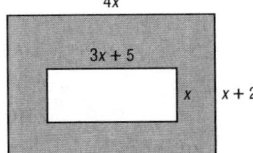
60. Which expression could be used to represent the area of the shaded region of the rectangle, reduced to simplest terms? **A**

A $3x^2 + 7x$ **C** $3x^2 - 7x$

B $4x^2 + 8x$ **D** $4x^2 + 7x$

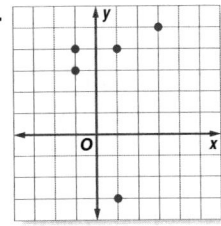

4x

3x + 5

x   x + 2

61. REVIEW Lawanda rolled a six-sided game cube 30 times and recorded her results in the table below. Each side of the cube is a different color. Which color has the same experimental probability and theoretical probability? **F**

F Purple

G Red

H White

J Orange

Color	Rolls
Red	4
Blue	8
White	4
Orange	3
Green	6
Purple	5

Spiral Review

Simplify. Assume that no denominator is equal to zero. (Lesson 7-2)

62. $a^0 b^{-2} c^{-1}$ $\dfrac{1}{b^2 c}$

63. $\dfrac{-5n^5}{n^8}$ $\dfrac{-5}{n^3}$

64. $\left(\dfrac{4x^3 y^2}{3z}\right)^2$ $\dfrac{16x^6 y^4}{9z^2}$

65. $\dfrac{(-y)^5 m^8}{y^3 m^{-7}}$ $-y^2 m^{15}$

Determine whether each expression is a monomial. Write *yes* or *no*. (Lesson 7-1)

66. $3a + 4b$ no

67. $\dfrac{6}{n}$ no

68. $\dfrac{v^2}{3}$ yes

Determine whether each relation is a function. (Lesson 3-6)

69.
no

70.
x	y
−2	−2
0	1
3	4
5	−2
yes

71. MAPS The scale of a road map is 0.5 inch = 75 miles. The distance between Chico and Santa Rosa by highway on the map is about 0.68 inch. What is the distance between these two cities? (Lesson 2-6)   **102 mi**

Find each square root. Round to the nearest hundredth if necessary. (Lesson 1-8)

72. $\pm\sqrt{121}$ ± 11

73. $\sqrt{3.24}$ ± 1.8

74. $-\sqrt{52}$ -7.21

GET READY for the Next Lesson

PREREQUISITE SKILL Simplify each expression, if possible. If not possible, write *in simplest form*. (Lesson 1-5)

75. $3n + 5n$ $8n$

76. $9a^2 + 3a - 2a^2$ $7a^2 + 3a$

77. $-3a + 5b + 4a - 7b$ $a - 2b$

78. $4x + 3y - 6 + 7x + 8 - 10y$
$11x - 7y + 2$

Pre-AP Activity   Use with *Get Ready for the Next Lesson*

Tell students the number of hours, *H*, spent per person per year playing video games from 1992 through 1997 can be modeled by the equation $H = \frac{1}{4}(t^4 - 9t^3 + 26t^2 - 18t + 76)$ where *t* is the number of years since 1992. For 2000 through 2005, the equation changes to $H = \frac{1}{4}(t^4 - 9t^3 + 26t^2 - 19t + 280)$ where *t* is the number of years since 2000. Ask students to discuss why the two equations might be different. In 1992, the number of hours *H* was only 19. In 2000, *H* is 70.

Name the Math Ask students to tell what mathematical procedures they would use to determine the degree of a polynomial.

Additional Answers

56. A variable with a negative power would indicate the quotient of a number, 1, and a variable. Monomials can only be a number, variable, or the product of a number and one or more variables. If one of the terms of an expression is not a monomial, then the expression is not a polynomial.

59. A polynomial model of a set of data can be used to predict future trends in data. Answers should include the following.

t	H	Actual Data Values
0	70	70
1	78.75	79
2	89.5	90
3	97.75	97
4	105	103
5	118.75	115

The polynomial function models the data almost exactly for the first three values of *t*, and then closely for the next three values.

Someone might point to this model as evidence that the time people spend playing video games is on the rise. This model may assist video game manufacturers in predicting production needs.

1 Focus

Objective Use algebra tiles to add and subtract polynomials.

Materials
• algebra tiles

Easy-to-Make Manipulatives
Teaching Algebra with Manipulatives

Template for algebra tiles, pp. 10–11

Teaching Tip Prior to the activity, discuss the concept of a zero pair. Have students form zero pairs using 1-tiles, x-tiles, and x^2-tiles.

2 Teach

Working in Cooperative Groups
Put students in groups of 2 or 3, mixing abilities. Have groups complete Activities 1–3 and Exercise 1.

• Talk about like terms in the context of the tiles. Tiles with the same shape and size represent like terms.

• For Activity 1, tell students that it is easier to model the polynomials if they arrange the tiles in the same order as the monomials within each polynomial. In this case, the monomials are arranged in descending order. Therefore, students should arrange the tiles in descending order from left to right.

• After groups have completed Activity 1, write the addition of the two polynomials vertically so students can see that the coefficients of like terms are added.

• For Activity 2, explain that adding a zero pair to the polynomial does not change its value because the zero pair is equal to zero.

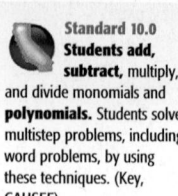 Standard 10.0 **Students add, subtract,** multiply, and divide monomials and **polynomials.** Students solve multistep problems, including word problems, by using these techniques. (Key, CAHSEE)

EXPLORE 7-4

Algebra Lab
Adding and Subtracting Polynomials

Monomials such as $5x$ and $-3x$ are called *like terms* because they have the same variable to the same power. When you use algebra tiles, you can recognize like terms because these tiles have the same size and shape as each other.

Polynomial Models	
Like terms are represented by tiles that have the same shape and size.	like terms
A *zero pair* may be formed by pairing one tile with its opposite. You can remove or add zero pairs without changing the value of the polynomial.	→ 0

ACTIVITY 1   Use algebra tiles to find $(3x^2 - 2x + 1) + (x^2 + 4x - 3)$.

Step 1 Model each polynomial.

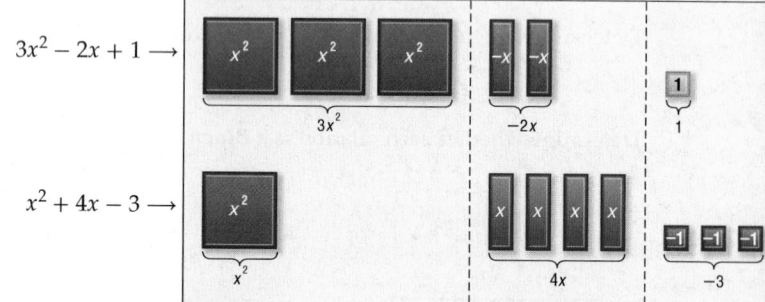

$3x^2 - 2x + 1 \longrightarrow$ $3x^2$ $-2x$ 1

$x^2 + 4x - 3 \longrightarrow$ x^2 $4x$ -3

Step 2 Combine like terms and remove zero pairs.

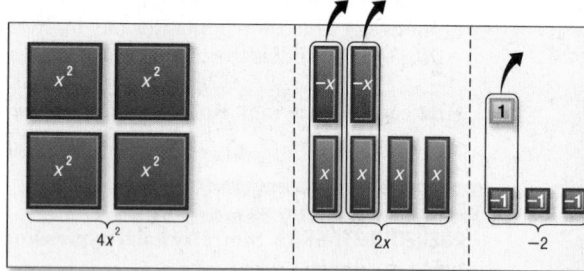

$4x^2$ $2x$ -2

Step 3 Write the polynomial for the tiles that remain.

$$(3x^2 - 2x + 1) + (x^2 + 4x - 3) = 4x^2 + 2x - 2$$

ACTIVITY 2 Use algebra tiles to find $(5x + 4) - (-2x + 3)$.

Step 1 Model the polynomial $5x + 4$.

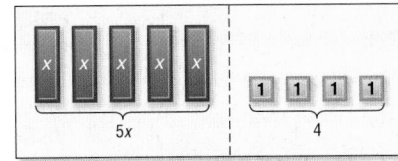

Step 2 To subtract $-2x + 3$, you must remove 2 $-x$-tiles and 3 1-tiles. You can remove the 1-tiles, but there are no $-x$-tiles. Add 2 zero pairs of x-tiles. Then remove the 2 $-x$-tiles.

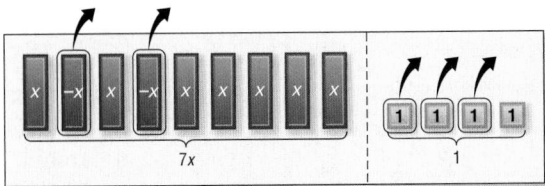

Step 3 The remaining tiles model $7x + 1$.

Recall that you can subtract a number by adding its additive inverse or opposite. Similarly, you can subtract a polynomial by adding its opposite.

ACTIVITY 3 Use algebra tiles and the additive inverse, or opposite, to find $(5x + 4) - (-2x + 3)$.

Step 1 To find the difference of $5x + 4$ and $-2x + 3$, add $5x + 4$ and the opposite of $-2x + 3$. The opposite of $-2x + 3$ is $2x - 3$.

Step 2 Write the polynomial for the tiles that remain.
$(5x + 4) - (-2x + 3) = 7x + 1$
Notice that this is the same answer as in Activity 2.

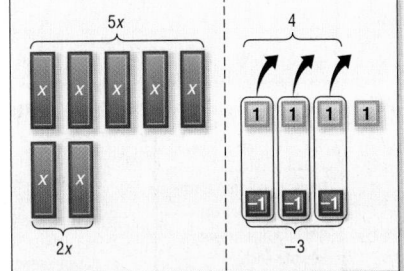

CONcepts in MOtion
Animation ca.algebra1.com

MODEL AND ANALYZE

Use algebra tiles to find each sum or difference. 1–6. See margin.

1. $(5x^2 + 3x - 4) + (2x^2 - 4x + 1)$ 2. $(2x^2 + 5) + (3x^2 + 2x + 6)$
3. $(-4x^2 + x) + (5x - 2)$ 4. $(3x^2 + 4x + 2) - (x^2 - 5x - 5)$
5. $(-x^2 + 7x) - (-x^2 + 3x)$ 6. $(8x + 4) - (6x^2 + x - 3)$

7. Find $(2x^2 - 3x + 1) - (2x + 3)$ using each method from Activities 2 and 3. Illustrate and explain how zero pairs are used in each case.
See Ch. 7 Answer Appendix.

Explore 7-4 Algebra Lab: Adding and Subtracting Polynomials **383**

- After groups complete Activity 2, write the difference vertically so students can see that coefficients of like terms are subtracted.

- For Activity 3, students may find that it is easier to add the additive inverse when using algebra tiles. By doing so, they can avoid adding zero pairs.

- Have groups rework the Activity 3 example using the subtraction method in Activity 2 to confirm their results.

Practice Have students complete Exercises 2–6.

3 Assess

✓ Formative Assessment

Use Exercise 7 to assess whether students can use models to compare polynomials.

From Concrete to Abstract

Write a polynomial addition or subtraction problem on the board. Have students determine the sum or difference without using tiles. If they answer incorrectly, have them use their tiles to help them find their errors.

Additional Answers

1. $7x^2 - x - 3$
2. $5x^2 + 2x + 11$
3. $-4x^2 + 6x - 2$
4. $2x^2 + 9x + 7$
5. $4x$
6. $-6x^2 + 7x + 7$

Lesson Notes

7-4

Adding and Subtracting Polynomials

Focus

Standards Alignment

Before Lesson 7-4
Simplify numerical expressions by applying properties of rational numbers from Standard 7AF1.3

Lesson 7-4
Add and subtract polynomials from Standard 10.0

After Lesson 7-4
Operations on polynomials, including long division from Standard 2A3.0

Teach

Scaffolding Questions

Have students read *Get Ready for the Lesson*.

Ask:

- Look at the polynomials for rap/hip-hop and country music sales. How many terms does each have? 4
- Compare the two polynomials. Are the terms like terms? yes
- How would you add the two polynomials? Combine the like terms.

Main Ideas

- Add polynomials.
- Subtract polynomials.

Standard 10.0
Students add, subtract, multiply, and divide **monomials and polynomials. Students solve multistep problems, including word problems, by using these techniques.**
(Key, CAHSEE)

GET READY for the Lesson

From 2000 to 2003, the amount of sales (in millions of dollars) of rap/hip-hop music R and country music C in the United States can be modeled by the following equations, where t is the number of years since 2000.

$$R = -132.32t^3 + 624.74t^2 - 773.61t + 1847.67$$
$$C = -3.42t^3 + 8.6t^2 - 94.95t + 1532.56$$

The total music sales T of rap/hip-hop and country music is $R + C$.

Add Polynomials To add polynomials, you can group like terms horizontally or write them in column form, aligning like terms. Adding polynomials involves adding like terms.

EXAMPLE Add Polynomials

1. Find $(3x^2 - 4x + 8) + (2x - 7x^2 - 5)$.

Method 1 Horizontal

$(3x^2 - 4x + 8) + (2x - 7x^2 - 5)$
$= [3x^2 + (-7x^2)] + (-4x + 2x) + [8 + (-5)]$ Group like terms.
$= -4x^2 - 2x + 3$ Add like terms.

Method 2 Vertical

$$\begin{array}{r} 3x^2 - 4x + 8 \\ (+) -7x^2 + 2x - 5 \\ \hline -4x^2 - 2x + 3 \end{array}$$

Notice that terms are in descending order with like terms aligned.

Study Tip

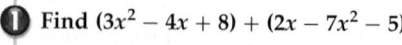

Adding Columns

When adding like terms in column form, remember that you are adding integers. Rewrite each monomial to eliminate subtractions. For example, you could rewrite $3x^2 - 4x + 8$ as $3x^2 + (-4x) + 8$.

CHECK Your Progress

1. Find $(5x^2 - 3x + 4) + (6x - 3x^2 - 3)$. $2x^2 + 3x + 1$

Subtract Polynomials Recall that you can subtract a real number by adding its opposite or additive inverse. Similarly, you can subtract a polynomial by adding its additive inverse.

To find the additive inverse of a polynomial, replace each term with its additive inverse.

Polynomial	Additive Inverse
$-5m + 3n$	$5m - 3n$
$2y^2 - 6y + 11$	$-2y^2 + 6y - 11$
$7a + 9b - 4$	$-7a - 9b + 4$

Lesson 7-4 Resources

Chapter 7 Resource Masters
Lesson Reading Guide, p. 27 BL OL ELL
Study Guide and Intervention, pp. 28–29 BL OL ELL
Skills Practice, p. 30 BL OL
Practice, p. 31 OL AL
Word Problem Practice, p. 32 OL AL
Enrichment, p. 33 OL AL
Quiz 2, p. 59

Transparencies
5-Minute Check Transparency 7-4

Additional Print Resources
Noteables™ Interactive Study Notebook with Foldables™
Teaching Algebra with Manipulatives

Technology
ca.algebra1.com
Interactive Classroom CD-ROM
AssignmentWorks CD-ROM
Graphing Calculator Easy Files

EXAMPLE Subtract Polynomials

2 Find $(3n^2 + 13n^3 + 5n) - (7n + 4n^3)$.

Method 1 Horizontal

Subtract $7n + 4n^3$ by adding its additive inverse.

$(3n^2 + 13n^3 + 5n) - (7n + 4n^3)$

$= (3n^2 + 13n^3 + 5n) + (-7n - 4n^3)$ The additive inverse of $7n + 4n^3$ is $-7n - 4n^3$.

$= 3n^2 + [13n^3 + (-4n^3)] + [5n + (-7n)]$ Group like terms.

$= 3n^2 + 9n^3 - 2n$ Combine like terms.

Method 2 Vertical

Align like terms in columns and subtract by adding the additive inverse.

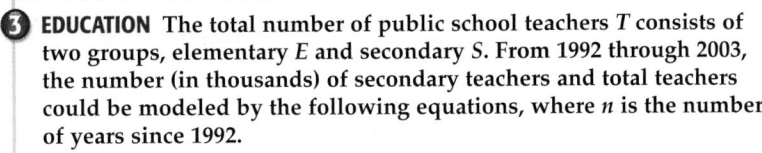

$$
\begin{array}{r}
3n^2 + 13n^3 + 5n \\
(-) \quad\quad 4n^3 + 7n \\
\hline
\end{array}
\qquad \text{Add the opposite.} \qquad
\begin{array}{r}
3n^2 + 13n^3 + 5n \\
(+) \quad\quad -4n^3 - 7n \\
\hline
3n^2 + 9n^3 - 2n
\end{array}
$$

Thus, $(3n^2 + 13n^3 + 5n) - (7n + 4n^3) = 3n^2 + 9n^3 - 2n$ or, arranged in descending order, $9n^3 + 3n^2 - 2n$.

✓CHECK Your Progress

2. Find $(4x^3 - 3x^2 + 6x - 4) - (-2x^3 + x^2 - 2)$. $6x^3 - 4x^2 + 6x - 2$

When polynomials are used to model real-world data, their sums and differences can have real-world meaning, too.

Real-World EXAMPLE

3 **EDUCATION** The total number of public school teachers T consists of two groups, elementary E and secondary S. From 1992 through 2003, the number (in thousands) of secondary teachers and total teachers could be modeled by the following equations, where n is the number of years since 1992.

$S = 29n + 949 \quad T = 58n + 2401$

a. Find an equation that models the number of elementary teachers E for this time period.

Subtract the polynomial for S from the polynomial for T.

$$
\begin{array}{ll}
\text{Total} & 58n + 2401 \\
- \text{ Secondary} & (-)\ 29n + 949 \\
\hline
\text{Elementary} &
\end{array}
\quad \text{Add the opposite.} \quad
\begin{array}{l}
58n + 2401 \\
(+) -29n - 949 \\
\hline
29n + 1452
\end{array}
$$

An equation is $E = 29n + 1452$.

b. Use the equation to predict the number of elementary teachers in 2015.

The year 2015 is $2015 - 1992$ or 23 years after the year 1992.

If this trend continues, the number of elementary teachers in 2015 would be $29(23) + 1452$ or about 2,119,000.

Add Polynomials

Example 1 shows how to add polynomials by grouping like terms.

✓ Formative Assessment

Use the Check Your Progress exercises after each example to determine students' understanding of concepts.

ADDITIONAL EXAMPLE

1 Find $(7y^2 + 2y - 3) + (2 - 4y + 5y^2)$. $12y^2 - 2y - 1$

Additional Examples are also in:
- Noteables™ Interactive Study Notebook with Foldables™
- Interactive Classroom PowerPoint® Presentations

Subtract Polynomials

Example 2 shows how to subtract a polynomial by adding its additive inverse. **Example 3** shows how to use subtraction of polynomials to model a real-world situation.

ADDITIONAL EXAMPLES

2 Find $(6y^2 + 8y^4 - 5y) - (9y^4 - 7y + 2y^2)$. $-y^4 + 4y^2 + 2y$

3 **VIDEO GAMES** The total amount of toy sales T (in billions of dollars) consists of two groups: sales of video games V and sales of traditional toys R. In recent years, the sales of traditional toys and total sales could be modeled by the following equations, where n is the number of years since 1996.

$R = 0.5n^3 - 1.9n^2 + 3n + 19$

$T = 0.45n^3 - 1.85n^2 + 4.4n + 22.6$

a. Find an equation that models the sales of video games V.
$V = -0.05n^3 + 0.05n^2 + 1.4n + 3.6$

b. What did this equation predict for the amount of video game sales in the year 1998?
6.2 billion dollars

3 Practice

Use Exercises 1–10 to check for understanding.

Use the chart at the bottom of this page to customize assignments for your students.

Odd/Even Assignments
Exercises 11–24 are structured so that students practice the same concepts whether they are assigned odd or even problems.

⚠ Exercise Alert!
Find the Error Have students check each step of Esteban and Kendra's work. Remind students that Esteban and Kendra need to add the additive inverse since this is a subtraction problem.

Additional Answers
1. $2p^2 + 6p$
2. $9y^2 - 3y - 1$
3. $10cd - 3d + 4c - 6$
4. $7x^2 - 2xy - 7y$
5. $11a^2 + 6a + 1$
6. $g^3 - 3g^2 + 3g + 6$
7. $3ax^2 - 9x - 9a + 8a^2x$
8. $3s^2 - rst - 8r^2s - 6rs^2$
11. $4n^2 + 5$
12. $13z - 10z^2$
13. $2a^2 - 6a + 8$
14. $-2n^2 + 7n + 5$
15. $5x + 2y + 3$
16. $5b^3 - 8b^2 - 4b$
17. $10d^2 + 8$
18. $2g^3 - 9g$
19. $-8y^3 - 3y^2 - y + 17$
20. $-2x - 3xy$
21. $-2x^2 + 8x + 8$
22. $3ab^2 + 11ab - 4$
36. Kendra; Esteban added the additive inverses of both polynomials when he should have added the opposite of the polynomial being subtracted.

---

3. **WIRELESS DEVICES** An electronics store sells cell phones and pagers. The equations below represent the monthly sales m of cell phones C and pagers P. Write an equation that represents the total monthly sales T of wireless devices. Use the equation to predict the number of wireless devices sold in 10 months.

$C = 7m + 137$ $P = 4m + 78$ $T = 11m + 215$; 325 wireless devices

online **Personal Tutor at** ca.algebra1.com

★ indicates multi-step problem

Examples 1, 2
(pp. 384, 385)

Find each sum or difference. 1–8. See margin.

1. $(4p^2 + 5p) + (-2p^2 + p)$
2. $(5y^2 - 3y + 8) + (4y^2 - 9)$
3. $(8cd - 3d + 4c) + (-6 + 2cd)$
4. $(-8xy + 3x^2 - 5y) + (4x^2 - 2y + 6xy)$
5. $(6a^2 + 7a - 9) - (-5a^2 + a - 10)$
6. $(g^3 - 2g^2 + 5g + 6) - (g^2 + 2g)$
7. $(3ax^2 - 5x - 3a) - (6a - 8a^2x + 4x)$
8. $(4rst - 8r^2s + s^2) - (6rs^2 + 5rst - 2s^2)$

Example 3
(p. 385)

POPULATION For Exercises 9 and 10, use the following information.
From 1980 through 2003, the female population F and the male population M of the United States (in thousands) are modeled by the following equations, where n is the number of years since 1980.

$F = 1,379n + 115,513$ $M = 1,450n + 108,882$

9. Find an equation that models the total population T of the United States in thousands for this time period. $T = 2,829n + 224,395$
10. If this trend continues, what will the population of the U. S. be in 2010? about 309,265,000

Exercises

HOMEWORK HELP	
For Exercises	See Examples
11–16	1
17–22	2
23–24	3

Exercise Levels
A: 11–24
B: 25–33
C: 34–40

Find each sum or difference. 11–22. See margin.

11. $(6n^2 - 4) + (-2n^2 + 9)$
12. $(9z - 3z^2) + (4z - 7z^2)$
13. $(3 + a^2 + 2a) + (a^2 - 8a + 5)$
14. $(-3n^2 - 8 + 2n) + (5n + 13 + n^2)$
15. $(x + 5) + (2y + 4x - 2)$
16. $(2b^3 - 4b + b^2) + (-9b^2 + 3b^3)$
17. $(11 + 4d^2) - (3 - 6d^2)$
18. $(4g^3 - 5g) - (2g^3 + 4g)$
19. $(-4y^3 - y + 10) - (4y^3 + 3y^2 - 7)$
20. $(4x + 5xy + 3y) - (3y + 6x + 8xy)$
21. $(3x^2 + 8x + 4) - (5x^2 - 4)$
22. $(5ab^2 + 3ab) - (2ab^2 + 4 - 8ab)$

GEOMETRY The measures of two sides of a triangle are given. If P is the perimeter, find the measure of the third side.

★ 23. $P = 7x + 3y$ $4x + 2y$

★ 24. $P = 10x^2 - 5x + 16$ $6x^2 - 15x + 12$

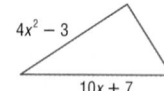

DIFFERENTIATED **HOMEWORK OPTIONS**

Level	Assignment	Two-Day Option	
BL Basic	11–24, 34–36, 40–59	11–23 odd, 41, 42	12–24 even, 34–36, 40, 43–59
OL Core	11–23 odd, 25, 27, 29–36, 40–59	11–26, 41, 42	25–36, 40, 43–59
AL Advanced /Pre-AP	25–53, (optional: 54–59)		

Real-World Link

In 2002, attendance at movie theaters was at its highest point in 40 years with 1.63 billion tickets sold for a record $9.52 billion in gross income.

Source: The National Association of Theatre Owners

Find each sum or difference.

25. $(3a + 2b - 7c) + (6b - 4a + 9c) + (-7c - 3a - 2b)$ $-4a + 6b - 5c$

26. $(5x^2 - 3) + (x^2 - x + 11) + (2x^2 - 5x + 7)$ $8x^2 - 6x + 15$

27. $(3y^2 - 8) + (5y + 9) - (y^2 + 6y - 4)$ $2y^2 - y + 5$

28. $(9x^3 + 3x - 13) - (6x^2 - 5x) + (2x^3 - x^2 - 8x + 4)$ $11x^3 - 7x^2 - 9$

MOVIES For Exercises 29 and 30, use the following information.
From 1995 to 2004, the number of indoor movie screens I and total movie screens T in the U.S. could be modeled by the following equations, where n is the number of years since 1995. **29.** $D = 1.8n^2 - 42n + 860$

$I = -194.8n^2 + 2,658n + 26,933$ $\qquad T = -193n^2 + 2,616n + 27,793$

29. Find an equation that models the number of outdoor movie screens D.

30. If this trend continues, how many outdoor screens will there be in 2010? **635 outdoor screens**

POSTAL SERVICE For Exercises 31–33, use the following information.
The U.S. Postal Service restricts the sizes of boxes shipped by parcel post. The sum of the length and the girth of the box must not exceed 108 inches.

Suppose you want to make an open box using a 60-by-40-inch piece of cardboard by cutting squares out of each corner and folding up the flaps. The lid will be made from another piece of cardboard. You do not know how big the squares should be, so for now call the length of the side of each square x.

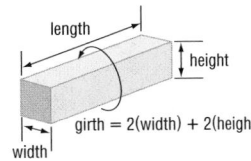

girth = 2(width) + 2(height)

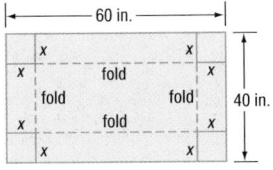

EXTRA PRACTICE
See pages 731, 750.

Math Online
Self-Check Quiz at
ca.algebra1.com

★ **31.** Write polynomials to represent the length, width, and girth of the box formed. **60 − 2x; 40 − 2x; 80 − 2x**

★ **32.** Write and solve an inequality to find the least possible value of x you could use in designing this box so it meets postal regulations.

33. What is the greatest integral value of x you could use to design this box if it does not have to meet regulations? **19 in.**

H.O.T. Problems

34. REASONING Explain why $5xy^2$ and $3x^2y$ are *not* like terms.

35. OPEN ENDED Write two polynomials with a difference of $2x^2 + x + 3$.

36. FIND THE ERROR Esteban and Kendra are finding $(5a - 6b) - (2a + 5b)$. Who is correct? Explain your reasoning. **See margin.**

32. $140 - 4x \le 108$; 8 in.

34. The powers of x and y are not the same.

35. Sample answer: $6x^2 + 4x + 7$ and $4x^2 + 3x + 4$

Esteban
$(5a - 6b) - (2a + 5b)$
$= (-5a + 6b) + (-2a - 5b)$
$= -7a + b$

Kendra
$(5a - 6b) - (2a + 5b)$
$= (5a - 6b) + (-2a - 5b)$
$= 3a - 11b$

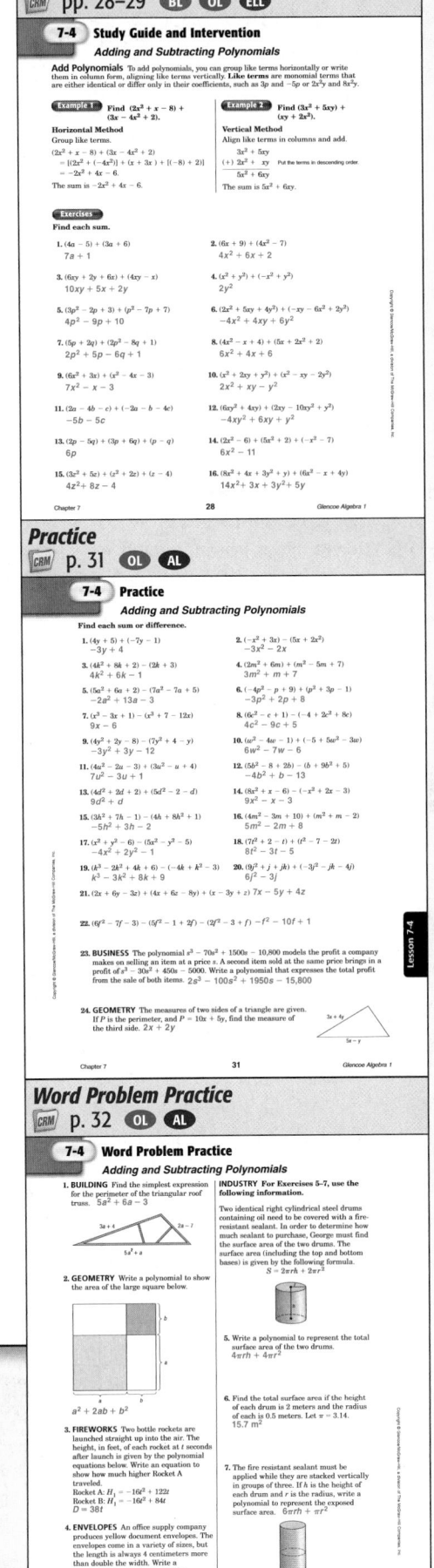

Additional pages not shown:

CRM **Lesson Reading Guide,** p. 27 **BL** **OL** **ELL**

CRM **Skills Practice,** p. 30 **BL** **OL**

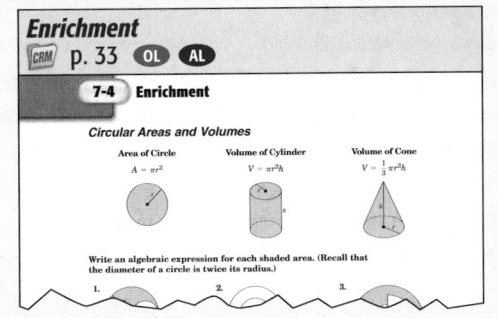

Ticket Out the Door Make several copies each of five polynomial expressions. Give one expression to each student. As the students leave the room, ask them to tell you the additive inverses of their expressions.

 Formative Assessment

Check for student understanding of concepts in Lessons 7-3 and 7-4.

[CRM] Quiz 2, p. 59

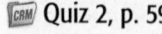  **Foldables™ Follow-Up**

At the end of this lesson, remind students to take notes and show examples in the row labeled *Polynomials* and the columns labeled $+$ and $-$.

Additional Answers

38. $\dfrac{x + (x + 1)}{2} = \dfrac{2x + 1}{2}$

$\qquad = \dfrac{2x}{2} + \dfrac{1}{2}$ or $x + \dfrac{1}{2}$

$x + (x + 1)$ when divided by 2 has a remainder of $\dfrac{1}{2}$; therefore, the sum of two consecutive integers is odd.

40. In order to find the sum of the video games sales and the traditional toy sales, you must add the two polynomial models V and R, which represent each of these sales from 1996 to 1999.

• $T = 0.45t^3 - 1.85t^2 + 4.4t + 22.6$

• If a person was looking to invest in a toy company, he or she might want to look at the trend in toy sales over the last several years and try to predict toy sales for the future.

CHALLENGE For Exercises 37–39, suppose x is an integer. **38.** See margin.

37. Write an expression for the next integer greater than x. $x + 1$

38. Show that the sum of two consecutive integers, x and the next integer after x, is always odd. (*Hint:* A number is considered even if it is divisible by 2.)

39. What is the least number of consecutive integers that must be added together to always arrive at an even integer? **4**

40. *Writing in Math* Use the information about music sales on page 384 to explain how you can use polynomials to model sales. Include an equation that models total music sales, and an example of how and why someone might use this equation in your answer. **See margin.**

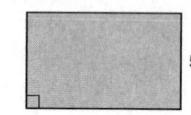 **STANDARDS PRACTICE** 2.0, 7MG2.3

41. The perimeter of the rectangle shown below is $16a + 2b$. Which expression represents the length of the rectangle? **A**

$5a - b$

A $3a + 2b$ **C** $2a - 3b$

B $10a + 2b$ **D** $6a + 4b$

42. REVIEW The scale factor of two similar polygons is 4:5. The perimeter of the larger polygon is 200 inches. What is the perimeter of the smaller polygon? **G**

F 250 inches   **H** 80 inches

G 160 inches   **J** 40 inches

Spiral Review

Find the degree of each polynomial. (Lesson 7-3)

43. $15t^3y^2$ **5**

44. 24 **0**

45. $m^2 + n^3$ **3**

46. $4x^2y^3z - 5x^3z$ **6**

Simplify. Assume no denominator is equal to zero. (Lesson 7-2)

47. $\dfrac{49a^4b^7c^2}{7ab^4c^3}$ $\dfrac{7a^3b^3}{c}$

48. $\dfrac{-4n^3p^{-5}}{n^{-2}}$ $-\dfrac{4n^5}{p^5}$

49. $\dfrac{(8n^7)^2}{(3n^2)^{-3}}$ $1728n^{20}$

KEYBOARDING For Exercises 50–53, use the table that shows keyboarding speeds of 12 students in words per minute (wpm) and weeks of experience. (Lesson 4-7)

Experience (weeks)	4	7	8	1	6	3	5	2	9	6	7	10
Keyboarding Speed (wpm)	33	45	46	20	40	30	38	22	52	44	42	55

50. Make a scatter plot of these data. Then draw a line of fit. **See Ch. 7 Answer Appendix.**

51. Find the equation of the line. **Sample answer:** $y = 4x + 17$

52. Use the equation to predict the speed of a student after a 12-week course. **about 65 wpm**

53. Why is this equation not used to predict the speed for any number of weeks of experience? **There's a limit as to how fast one can keyboard.**

▶ **GET READY for the Next Lesson**

PREREQUISITE SKILL. Simplify. (Lesson 1-5)

54. $6(3x - 8)$ $18x - 48$

55. $-2(b + 9)$ $-2b - 18$

56. $-7(-5p + 4q)$ $35p - 28q$

57. $9(3a + 5b - c)$ $27a + 45b - 9c$

58. $8(x^2 + 3x - 4)$ $8x^2 + 24x - 32$

59. $-3(2a^2 - 5a + 7)$ $-6a^2 + 15a - 21$

▶ **Pre-AP Activity** Use after the Exercises.

Tell students the equations for the monthly sales trends for CDs, C, and DVDs, D, are $C = 7m + 87$ and $D = 9m + 152$, where m represents time passed in months. Suppose the total monthly sales of CDs, DVDs, and videos, V, is represented by the equation $T = 15m + 248$. Write an equation that can be used to calculate monthly video sales (V). How many videos did the store sell in the sixth month when $m = 5$? $V = (-1)m + 9; 4$

Simplify. (Lesson 7-1)

1. $n^3(n^4)(n)$ n^8

2. $4ad(3a^3d)$ $12a^4d^2$

3. $(-2w^3z^4)^3(-4wz^3)^2$ $-128w^{11}z^{18}$

4. **MULTIPLE CHOICE** Ruby says that $(xy)^2 = x^2 + 2xy + y^2$ for every value of x and y, but Ebony disagrees. What does $(xy)^2$ really equal? (Lesson 7-1) **D**

   A $2x^2y$

   B $2xy$

   C xy^2

   D x^2y^2

5. **MULTIPLE CHOICE** Which expression represents the volume of the cube? (Lesson 7-1) **J**

   $5x$

   F $15x^3$

   G $25x^2$

   H $25x^3$

   J $125x^3$

Simplify. Assume that no denominator is equal to zero. (Lesson 7-2)

6. $\dfrac{25p^{10}}{15p^3}$ $\dfrac{5p^7}{3}$

7. $\left(\dfrac{6k^3}{7np^4}\right)^2$ $\dfrac{36k^6}{49n^2p^8}$

8. $\dfrac{4x^0y^2}{(3y^{-3}z^5)^{-2}}$ $\dfrac{36z^{10}}{y^4}$

9. $\dfrac{(m^2np^3)^{-3}}{(m^5n^3p^6)^{-4}}$ $m^{14}n^9p^{15}$

10. **GEOMETRY** The area of the rectangle is $66a^3b^5c^7$ square inches. Find the length of the rectangle. (Lesson 7-2)

    $6a^2b^3c$ in.

    $11ab^2c^6$ in.

11. **MULTIPLE CHOICE** The wavelength of a microwave is 10^{-2} centimeters, and the wavelength of an X ray is 10^{-8} centimeters. How many times greater is the length of a microwave than an X ray? (Lesson 7-3) **B**

    A 10^{10}

    B 10^6

    C 10^{-6}

    D 10^{-10}

Find the degree of each polynomial. (Lesson 7-3)

12. $5x^4$ 4

13. $-9n^3p^4$ 7

14. $7a^2 - 2ab^2$ 3

15. $-6 - 8x^2y^2 + 5y^3$ 4

GEOMETRY For Exercises 16 and 17, use the figure below. (Lesson 7-3)

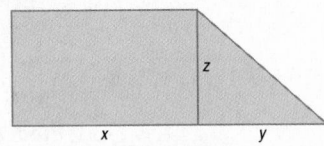

16. Write a polynomial that represents the area of the figure. $xz + \dfrac{1}{2}yz$

17. If $x = 7$ feet, $y = 3$ feet, and $z = 2$ feet, find the area of the figure. $17\ ft^2$

Arrange the terms of each polynomial so that the powers of x are in ascending order. (Lesson 7-4)

18. $4x^2 + 9x - 12 + 5x^3$ $-12 + 9x + 4x^2 + 5x^3$

19. $2xy^4 + x^3y^5 + 5x^5y - 13x^2$
    $2xy^4 - 13x^2 + x^3y^5 + 5x^5y$

20. **MULTIPLE CHOICE** If three consecutive integers are x, $x + 1$, and $x + 2$, what is the sum of these three integers? (Lesson 7-4) **G**

    F $2x + 3$

    G $3x + 3$

    H $x(x + 1)(x + 2)$

    J $x^3 + 3x^2 + 2x$

✔ Formative Assessment

Use the Mid-Chapter Quiz to assess students' progress in the first half of the chapter.

For problems answered incorrectly, have students review the lessons indicated in parentheses.

✔ Summative Assessment

CRM Mid-Chapter Test, p. 61

 **ExamView** Assessment Suite   Customize and create multiple versions of your Mid-Chapter Tests and their answer keys.

FOLDABLES Study Organizer **Foldables™ Follow-Up**

Before students complete the Mid-Chapter Quiz, encourage them to review the information in the rows and columns on their Foldables.

Data-Driven Decision Making	Exercises	Lesson	Standard	Resources for Review
Diagnostic Teaching Based on the results of the Chapter 7 Mid-Chapter Quiz, use the following to review concepts that students continue to find challenging.	1–5	7–1	10.0	CRM Study Guide and Intervention, pp. 6–7, 13–14, 20–21, 28–29
	6–10	7–2	10.0	Math Online
	11–17	7–3	Preparation for 10.0	• Extra Examples
	18–20	7–4	10.0	• Personal Tutor • Concepts in Motion

① Focus

Standards Alignment

Before Lesson 7-5
Multiply and divide monomials from Standard 7AF2.2

Lesson 7-5
Multiply monomials and polynomials from Standard 10.0

After Lesson 7-5
Operations on polynomials, including long division from Standard 2A3.0

② Teach

Scaffolding Questions

Have students read *Get Ready for the Lesson.*

Ask:

- What is the formula for finding the area of a rectangle? $A = \ell w$, where ℓ is the length and w is the width.
- What are ℓ and w for the rectangle shown? ℓ is $x + 3$ and w is $2x$.
- What is the area of the given rectangle? $2x^2 + 6$
- Substitute the given values for A, ℓ, and w to write an equation for the area of this rectangle.
  $2x^2 + 6x = (x + 3)(2x)$

Main Ideas

- Find the product of a monomial and a polynomial.
- Solve equations involving polynomials.

 **Standard 10.0**
Students add, subtract, **multiply, and divide monomials and polynomials. Students solve multistep problems, including word problems, by using these techniques.** (Key, CAHSEE)

Review Vocabulary

Distributive Property:
For any numbers a, b, and c,
$a(b + c) = ab + ac$
and
$a(b - c) = ab - ac$.
(Lesson 1–5)

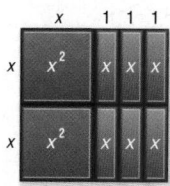

The algebra tiles shown are grouped together to form a rectangle with a width of $2x$ and a length of $x + 3$. Notice that the rectangle consists of 2 blue x^2-tiles and 6 green x-tiles. The area of the rectangle is the sum of these algebra tiles or $2x^2 + 6x$.

Product of Monomial and Polynomial The Distributive Property can be used to multiply a polynomial by a monomial.

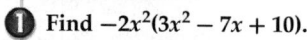 **EXAMPLE** Multiply a Polynomial by a Monomial

① Find $-2x^2(3x^2 - 7x + 10)$.

Method 1 Horizontal
$-2x^2(3x^2 - 7x + 10)$
$= -2x^2(3x^2) - (-2x^2)(7x) + (-2x^2)(10)$ Distributive Property
$= -6x^4 - (-14x^3) + (-20x^2)$ Multiply.
$= -6x^4 + 14x^3 - 20x^2$ Simplify.

Method 2 Vertical
$$3x^2 - 7x + 10$$
$$(\times) \qquad\qquad -2x^2$$ Distributive Property
$$\overline{-6x^4 + 14x^3 - 20x^2}$$ Multiply.

✓ **CHECK Your Progress**
1. Find $5a^2(-4a^2 + 2a - 7)$. $-20a^4 + 10a^3 - 35a^2$

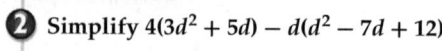 **EXAMPLE** Simplify Expressions

② Simplify $4(3d^2 + 5d) - d(d^2 - 7d + 12)$.

$4(3d^2 + 5d) - d(d^2 - 7d + 12)$
$= 4(3d^2) + 4(5d) + (-d)(d^2) - (-d)(7d) + (-d)(12)$ Distributive Property
$= 12d^2 + 20d + (-d^3) - (-7d^2) + (-12d)$ Product of Powers
$= 12d^2 + 20d - d^3 + 7d^2 - 12d$ Simplify.
$= -d^3 + (12d^2 + 7d^2) + (20d - 12d)$ Commutative and Associative Properties
$= -d^3 + 19d^2 + 8d$ Combine like terms.

✓ **CHECK Your Progress**
2. Simplify $3(5x^2 + 2x - 4) - x(7x^2 + 2x - 3)$. $-7x^3 + 13x^2 + 9x - 12$

Chapter 7 Resource Masters

Lesson Reading Guide, p. 34 BL OL ELL
Study Guide and Intervention, pp. 35–36
BL OL ELL
Skills Practice, p. 37 BL OL
Practice, p. 38 OL AL
Word Problem Practice, p. 39 OL AL
Enrichment, p. 40 OL AL

Transparencies

5-Minute Check Transparency 7-5

Additional Print Resources

Noteables™ Interactive Study Notebook with Foldables™
Teaching Algebra with Manipulatives

Technology

ca.algebra1.com
Interactive Classroom CD-ROM
AssignmentWorks CD-ROM
Graphing Calculator Easy Files

Real-World EXAMPLE

3 **PHONE SERVICE** Greg pays a fee of $20 a month for local calls. Long-distance rates are 6¢ per minute for in-state calls and 5¢ per minute for out-of-state calls. Suppose Greg makes 300 minutes of long-distance phone calls in January and m of those minutes are for in-state calls.

a. Find an expression for Greg's phone bill for January.

Words	Bill	=	service fee	+	in-state minutes	·	6¢ per minute	+	out-of-state minutes	·	5¢ per minute.

Variables If m = number of minutes of in-state calls, then $300 - m$ = number of minutes of out-of-state calls. Let B = phone bill for the month of January, expressed in dollars.

Equation	B	=	20	+	m	·	0.06	+	$(300 - m)$	·	0.05

$$B = 20 + m \cdot 0.06 + (300 - m) \cdot 0.05 \quad \text{Write the equation.}$$
$$= 20 + 0.06m + 300(0.05) - m(0.05) \quad \text{Distributive Property}$$
$$= 20 + 0.06m + 15 - 0.05m \quad \text{Simplify.}$$
$$= 35 + 0.01m \quad \text{Simplify.}$$

Greg's bill for January is $35 + 0.01m$ dollars for m minutes of in-state calls.

b. Evaluate the expression to find the cost if Greg had 37 minutes of in-state calls in January.

$$35 + 0.01m = 35 + 0.01(37) \quad m = 37$$
$$= 35 + 0.37 \quad \text{Multiply.}$$
$$= 35.37 \quad \text{Add.} \qquad \text{Greg's bill was \$35.37.}$$

✓CHECK Your Progress

3. A parking garage charges $30 per month plus $0.50 per daytime hour and $0.25 per hour during nights and weekends. Suppose Juana parks in the garage for 47 hours in January and h of those are night and weekend hours. Find an expression for her January bill. Then find the cost if Juana had 12 hours of night and weekend hours.
$B = 30 + 0.25(h) + 0.50(47 - h) = 53.50 - 0.25h$; $50.50

 Online Personal Tutor at ca.algebra1.com

Solve Equations with Polynomial Expressions Many equations contain polynomials that must be added, subtracted, or multiplied.

EXAMPLE Polynomials on Both Sides

4 Solve $y(y - 12) + y(y + 2) + 25 = 2y(y + 5) - 15$.

$$y(y - 12) + y(y + 2) + 25 = 2y(y + 5) - 15 \quad \text{Original equation}$$
$$y^2 - 12y + y^2 + 2y + 25 = 2y^2 + 10y - 15 \quad \text{Distributive Property}$$
$$2y^2 - 10y + 25 = 2y^2 + 10y - 15 \quad \text{Combine like terms.}$$
$$-10y + 25 = 10y - 15 \quad \text{Subtract } 2y^2 \text{ from each side.}$$
$$-20y + 25 = -15 \quad \text{Subtract } 10y \text{ from each side.}$$
$$-20y = -40 \quad \text{Subtract 25 from each side.}$$
$$y = 2 \quad \text{Divide each side by } -20.$$

Math Online Extra Examples at ca.algebra1.com

Product of Monomial and Polynomial

Example 1 shows how the Distributive Property can be used to multiply a polynomial by a monomial. **Example 2** shows how to simplify expressions by combining like terms. **Example 3** shows how to write and evaluate a polynomial expression for a real-world situation.

✓ Formative Assessment

Use the Check Your Progress exercises after each example to determine students' understanding of concepts.

ADDITIONAL EXAMPLES

 Find $6y(4y^2 - 9y - 7)$. $24y^3 - 54y^2 - 42y$

 Simplify $3(2t^2 - 4t - 15) + 6t(5t + 2)$. $36t^2 - 45$

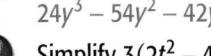 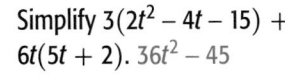 **ENTERTAINMENT** Admission to the Super Fun Amusement Park is $10. Once in the park, super rides are an additional $3 each, and regular rides are an additional $2. Sarita goes to the park and rides 15 rides, of which s of those 15 are super rides.

a. Find an expression for how much money Sarita spent at the park. $40 + s$

b. Evaluate the expression to find the cost if Sarita rode 9 super rides. $49

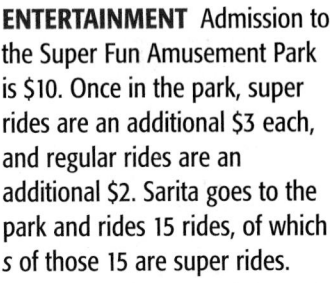

Additional Examples are also in:

- Noteables™ Interactive Study Notebook with Foldables™
- Interactive Classroom PowerPoint® Presentations

Solve Equations with Polynomial Expressions

Example 4 shows how to solve equations that contain polynomials on both sides.

ADDITIONAL EXAMPLE

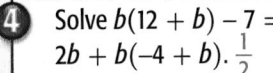 Solve $b(12 + b) - 7 = 2b + b(-4 + b)$. $\frac{1}{2}$

Focus on Mathematical Content

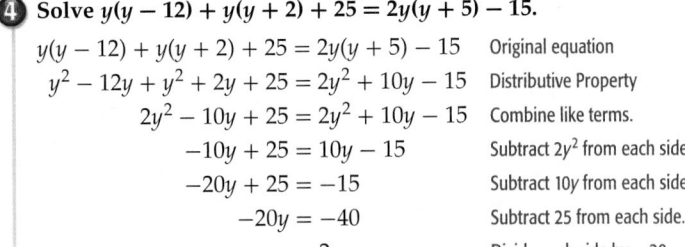

Order of Operations When simplifying expressions involving products of monomials and polynomials, the order of operations must be followed. Multiplication precedes addition, unless parentheses indicate otherwise.

✓ **Formative Assessment**

Use Exercises 1–15 to check for understanding.

Use the chart at the bottom of this page to customize assignments for your students.

Odd/Even Assignments

Exercises 16–43 are structured so that students practice the same concepts whether they are assigned odd or even problems.

 Tips for New Teachers

Multiplication Facts
In Exercises 16 through 31, some students may prefer using the horizontal method for multiplying a polynomial by a monomial. Others may prefer the vertical method. As these two methods are forms of the same method, either may be used.

Real-World Connections For Exercise 34, tell students the United States is the largest producer of corn in the world. In 2004, U.S. farmers planted corn on over 80 million acres of land.

Intervention

Multiplying by a Negative Monomial If students are having difficulty multiplying by a negative monomial, you may want to have them apply the negative first (by multiplying all terms by –1) and then multiply by the monomial in positive form.

CHECK $y(y-12) + y(y+2) + 25 = 2y(y+5) - 15$ Original equation

$2(2-12) + 2(2+2) + 25 \stackrel{?}{=} 2(2)(2+5) - 15$ $y = 2$

$2(-10) + 2(4) + 25 \stackrel{?}{=} 4(7) - 15$ Simplify.

$-20 + 8 + 25 \stackrel{?}{=} 28 - 15$ Multiply.

$13 = 13 \checkmark$ Add and subtract.

✓ **CHECK Your Progress**

4. Solve $2x(x+4) + 7 = (x+8) + 2x(x+1) + 12$. $\frac{13}{5}$

★ indicates multi-step problem

✓ CHECK Your Understanding

Example 1
(p. 390)

Find each product.

1. $-3y(5y+2)$ $-15y^2 - 6y$

2. $9b^2(2b^3 - 3b^2 + b - 8)$ $18b^5 - 27b^4 + 9b^3 - 72b^2$

3. $2x(4a^4 - 3ax + 6x^2)$ $8a^4x - 6ax^2 + 12x^3$

4. $-4xy(5x^2 - 12xy + 7y^2)$ $-20x^3y + 48x^2y^2 - 28xy^3$

Example 2
(p. 390)

Simplify.

5. $t(5t-9) - 2t$ $5t^2 - 11t$

6. $x(3x+4) + 2(7x-3)$ $3x^2 + 18x - 6$

7. $5n(4n^3 + 6n^2 - 2n + 3) - 4(n^2 + 7n)$ $20n^4 + 30n^3 - 14n^2 - 13n$

8. $4y^2(y^2 - 2y + 5) + 3y(2y^2 - 2)$ $4y^4 - 2y^3 + 20y^2 - 6y$

Example 3
(p. 391)

SAVINGS For Exercises 9–11, use the following information.
Matthew's grandmother left him \$10,000 for college. Matthew puts some of the money into a savings account earning 3% interest per year. With the rest, he buys a certificate of deposit (CD) earning 5% per year.

9. If Matthew puts x dollars into the savings account, write an expression to represent the amount of the CD. $10,000 - x$

10. Write an equation for the total amount of money T Matthew will have saved for college after one year. $10,500 - 0.02x$

11. If Matthew puts \$3000 in savings, how much money will he have in one year?   \$10,440

Example 4
(p. 391)

Solve each equation.

12. $-2(w+1) + w = 7 - 4w$ 3

13. $3(y-2) + 2y = 4y + 14$ 20

14. $a(a+3) + a(a-6) + 35 = a(a-5) + a(a+7)$ 7

15. $n(n-4) + n(n+8) = n(n-13) + n(n+1) + 16$ 1

Exercises

HOMEWORK HELP	
For Exercises	**See Examples**
16–25	1
26–31	2
32–35	3
36–43	4

Find each product.   **24.** $40x^3y + 16x^2y^3 - 24x^2y$ **25.** $-3cd^3 - 2c^3d^3 + 4c^2d^2$

16. $r(5r + r^2)$ $5r^2 + r^3$

17. $w(2w^3 - 9w^2)$

18. $-4x(8 + 3x)$

19. $5y(-2y^2 - 7y)$

20. $7ag(g^3 + 2ag)$

21. $-3np(n^2 - 2p)$

22. $-2b^2(3b^2 - 4b + 9)$

23. $6x^3(5 + 3x - 11x^2)$ $30x^3 + 18x^4 - 66x^5$

24. $8x^2y(5x + 2y^2 - 3)$

25. $-cd^2(3d + 2c^2d - 4c)$

17. $2w^4 - 9w^3$

18. $-32x - 12x^2$

19. $-10y^3 - 35y^2$

Simplify.   **28.** $20w^2 - 18w + 10$ **29.** $10n^4 + 5n^3 - n^2 + 44n$

26. $d(-2d + 4) + 15d$ $-2d^2 + 19d$

27. $-x(4x^2 - 2x) - 5x^3$ $-9x^3 + 2x^2$

28. $3w(6w - 4) + 2(w^2 - 3w + 5)$

29. $5n(2n^3 + n^2 + 8) + n(4 - n)$

30. $10(4m^3 - 3m + 2) - 2m(-3m^2 - 7m + 1)$ $46m^3 + 14m^2 - 32m + 20$

31. $4y(y^2 - 8y + 6) - 3(2y^3 - 5y^2 + 2)$ $-2y^3 - 17y^2 + 24y - 6$

20. $7ag^4 + 14a^2g^2$

21. $-3n^3p + 6np^2$

22. $-6b^4 + 8b^3 - 18b^2$

392 Chapter 7 Polynomials

DIFFERENTIATED HOMEWORK OPTIONS			
Level	**Assignment**	**Two-Day Option**	
BL Basic	16–43, 61, 65–90	17–43 odd, 66, 67	16–42 even, 61, 65, 68–90
OL Core	17–43 odd, 45–53 odd, 54–61, 65–90	16–43, 66, 67	44–61, 65, 68–90
AL Advanced /Pre-AP	44–84, (optional: 85–90)		

SAVINGS For Exercises 32 and 33, use the following information.
Marta has $6000 to invest. She puts x dollars of this money into a savings account that earns 2% interest per year. With the rest, she buys a certificate of deposit that earns 4% per year.

32. Write an equation for the amount of money T Marta will have in one year. $T = -0.02x + 6240$

★ **33.** Suppose at the end of one year, Marta has a total of $6210. How much money did Marta invest in each account?
savings account: $1500; certificate of deposit: $4500

★ **34. FARMING** A farmer plants corn in a field with a length to width ratio of 5:4. Next year, he plans to increase the field's area by increasing its length by 12 feet. Write an expression for this new area. $20x^2 + 48x$

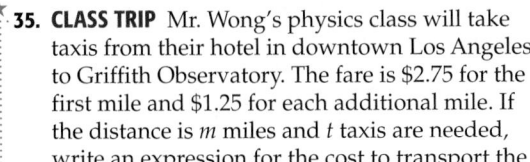

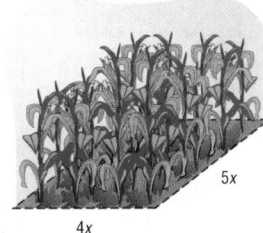
5x
4x

★ **35. CLASS TRIP** Mr. Wong's physics class will take taxis from their hotel in downtown Los Angeles to Griffith Observatory. The fare is $2.75 for the first mile and $1.25 for each additional mile. If the distance is m miles and t taxis are needed, write an expression for the cost to transport the group. $1.50t + 1.25mt$

Real-World Link
About two million people visit Griffith Observatory in Los Angeles each year. The purpose of the Griffith Observatory is to educate the public on astronomy.
Source: griffithobs.org

Solve each equation.

36. $2(4x - 7) = 5(-2x - 9) - 5$ -2 **37.** $4(3p + 9) - 5 = -3(12p - 5)$ $-\frac{1}{3}$

38. $d(d - 1) + 4d = d(d - 8)$ 0 **39.** $c(c + 3) - c(c - 4) = 9c - 16$ 8

40. $a(3a - 2) + 2a(a + 4) = a(a + 2) + 4a(a - 3) + 48$ 3

41. $3(4w - 2) + 6(w + 4) - 3 = 4w - 7(w + 2) + 5(3w + 7)$ 1

Expand and simplify.

42. $4(x + 2) - 6$ $4x + 2$ **43.** $3x - 2(x + 1)$ $x - 2$

Find each product. **44.** $-15hk^4 - \frac{15}{4}h^2k^2 + 6hk^2$ **45.** $4a^5b - \frac{8}{3}a^3b^2 + 6a^2b^3$

44. $-\frac{3}{4}hk^2(20k^2 + 5h - 8)$ **45.** $\frac{2}{3}a^2b(6a^3 - 4ab + 9b^2)$

46. $-5a^3b(2b + 5ab - b^2 + a^3)$ **47.** $4p^2q^2(2p^2 - q^2 + 9p^3 + 3q)$
$-10a^3b^2 - 25a^4b^2 + 5a^3b^3 - 5a^6b$ $8p^4q^2 - 4p^2q^4 + 36p^5q^2 + 12p^2q^3$

Simplify.

48. $-3c^2(2c + 7) + 4c(3c^2 - c + 5) + 2(c^2 - 4)$ $6c^3 - 23c^2 + 20c - 8$

49. $4x^2(x + 2) + 3x(5x^2 + 2x - 6) - 5(3x^2 - 4x)$ $19x^3 - x^2 + 2x$

Solve each equation.

50. $2n(n + 4) + 18 = n(n + 5) + n(n - 2) - 7$ -5

51. $3g(g - 4) - 2g(g - 7) = g(g + 6) - 28$ 7

GEOMETRY Find the area of each shaded region in simplest form.

★ **52.**
4x
3x
$3x + 2$ 2x
$6x^2 + 8x$

★ **53.**
5p
6
$2p - 1$ $3p + 4$
$15p^2 + 8p + 6$

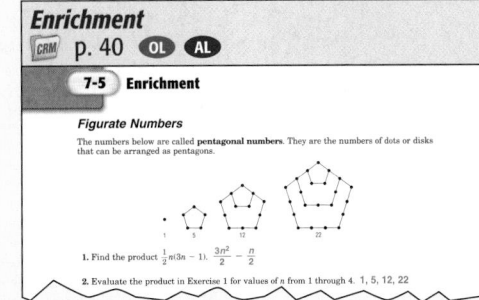

Lesson 7-5 Multiplying a Polynomial by a Monomial   **393**

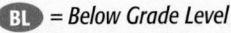

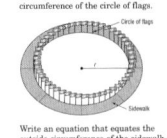
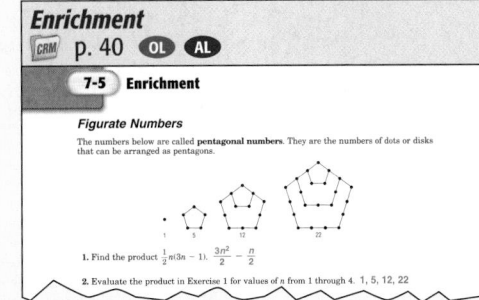

Real-World Link

Approximately one third of young people in grades 7–12 suggested that "working for the good of my community and country" and "helping others or volunteering" were important future goals.

Source: Primeday/Roper National Youth Opinion Survey

VOLUNTEERING For Exercises 54 and 55, use the following information.
Loretta is making baskets of apples and oranges for homeless shelters. She wants to place a total of 10 pieces of fruit in each basket. Apples cost 25¢ each, and oranges cost 20¢ each. **54.** $T = 2 + 0.05a$

54. If a represents the number of apples Loretta uses, write a polynomial model in simplest form for the total amount of money T Loretta will spend.

55. If Loretta uses 4 apples in each basket, find the total cost for fruit. **$2.20**

SALES For Exercises 56 and 57, use the following information.
A store advertises that all sports equipment is 30% off the retail price. In addition, the store asks customers to select and pop a balloon to receive a coupon for an additional n percent off one of their purchases. **56.** $0.7p - 0.7np$

56. Write an expression for the cost of a pair of inline skates with retail price p.

57. Use this expression to calculate the cost, not including sales tax, of a $200 pair of inline skates for an additional 10% off. **$126**

★ **58. SPORTS** You may have noticed that when runners race around a curved track, their starting points are staggered. This is so each contestant runs the same distance to the finish line.

Finish

$x + 12.5$

x

Start

If the radius of the inside lane is x and each lane is 2.5 feet wide, how far apart should the officials start the runners in the inside lane and the outside (6th) lane? (*Hint*: Circumference = $2\pi r$, where r is the radius of the circle)
12.5π or about 39.3 ft

NUMBER THEORY For Exercises 59 and 60, let x be an odd integer.

59. Write an expression for the next odd integer. $x + 2$

60. Find the product of x and the next odd integer. $x^2 + 2x$

61. OPEN ENDED Write a monomial and a trinomial involving one variable. Then find their product. **Sample answer:** $4x$ and $x^2 + 2x + 3$; $4x^3 + 8x^2 + 12x$

CHALLENGE For Exercises 62–64, use the following information.
An even number can be represented by $2x$, where x is any integer.

62. Show that the product of two even integers is always even. **See margin.**

63. Write a representation for an odd integer. $2x + 1$ or $2x - 1$

64. Show that the product of an even and an odd integer is always even. **See margin.**

65. *Writing in Math* Use the information about the area of a rectangle on page 390 to explain how the product of a monomial and a polynomial relate to finding the area of a rectangle. Include the product of $2x$ and $x + 3$ derived algebraically in your answer. **See margin.**

EXTRA PRACTICE
See pages 732, 750.

Math Online
Self-Check Quiz at ca.algebra1.com

H.O.T. Problems

66. A plumber charges $70 for the first thirty minutes of each house call plus $4 for each additional minute that she works. The plumber charges Ke-Min $122 for her time. What amount of time, in minutes, did the plumber work? **A**

 A 43

 B 48

 C 58

 D 64

67. REVIEW What is the slope of this line? **J**

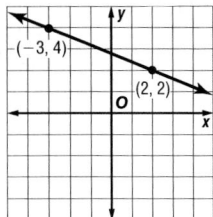

 F $-\dfrac{5}{2}$ G -2 H $-\dfrac{1}{2}$ J $-\dfrac{2}{5}$

Spiral Review

Find each sum or difference. (Lesson 7-4)

68. $(4x^2 + 5x) + (-7x^2 + x)$ $-3x^2 + 6x$

69. $(3y^2 + 5y - 6) - (7y^2 - 9)$ $-4y^2 + 5y + 3$

70. $(5b - 7ab + 8a) - (5ab - 4a)$ $5b - 12ab + 12a$

71. $(6p^3 + 3p^2 - 7) + (p^3 - 6p^2 - 2p)$
   $7p^3 - 3p^2 - 2p - 7$

State whether each expression is a polynomial. If the expression is a polynomial, identify it as a *monomial*, a *binomial*, or a *trinomial*. (Lesson 7-3)

72. $4x^2 - 10ab + 6$
   yes; trinomial

73. $4c + ab - c$
   yes; binomial

74. $\dfrac{7}{y} + y^2$ no

75. $\dfrac{n^2}{3}$ yes, monomial

Define a variable, write an inequality, and solve each problem. Then check your solution. (Lesson 6-3)   **76.** $6 + 10n < 9n$; $\{n \mid n < -6\}$

76. Six increased by ten times a number is less than nine times the number.

77. Nine times a number increased by four is no less than seven decreased by thirteen times the number. $9n + 4 \geq 7 - 13n$; $\left\{ n \mid n \geq \dfrac{3}{22} \right\}$

Write an equation of the line that passes through each pair of points. (Lesson 4-4)

78. $(-3, -8), (1, 4)$ $y = 3x + 1$ **79.** $(-4, 5), (2, -7)$ $y = -2x - 3$ **80.** $(3, -1), (-3, 2)$ $y = -\dfrac{1}{2}x + \dfrac{1}{2}$

Solve each equation. (Lesson 2-5)

81. $2(x + 3) + 3 = 4x - 5$ 7   **82.** $3(y - 3) - 6 = 9y - 15$ 0   **83.** $2(3a + 6) - 3 = 6a + 12$
   no solution

★ **84. BASKETBALL** Tremaine scored 54 three-point field goals, 84 two-point field goals, and 106 free throws in 23 games. How many points did he score on average per game? (Lesson 2-4)   **19 points per game**

GET READY for the Next Lesson

PREREQUISITE SKILL Simplify. (Lesson 7-1)

85. $(a)(a)$ a^2

86. $2x(3x^2)$ $6x^3$

87. $-3y^2(8y^2)$ $-24y^4$ **88.** $4y(3y) - 4y(6)$ $12y^2 - 24y$

89. $-5n(2n^2) - (-5n)(8n) + (-5n)(4)$
   $-10n^3 + 40n^2 - 20n$

90. $3p^2(6p^2) - 3p^2(8p) + 3p^2(12)$
   $18p^4 - 24p^3 + 36p^2$

Lesson 7-5 Multiplying a Polynomial by a Monomial   **395**

1 Focus

Objective Use algebra tiles to multiply polynomials.

Materials
- algebra tiles
- product mat

Easy-to-Make Manipulatives

Teaching Algebra with Manipulatives Templates for:

- algebra tiles, pp. 10–11
- product mat, p. 17

Teaching Tip Some students may benefit from laying tiles along the top and side of the product mat to model each expression. Have them remove the two factors before determining their final product.

2 Teach

Working in Cooperative Groups
Put students in groups of 2 or 3, mixing abilities. Have groups complete Activities 1–2 and Exercise 1.

- For Activity 1, make sure groups mark the dimensions properly on the product mat. Since *x*-tiles are rectangular, remind students that the long side is the correct side to use to mark a value of *x* on the mat.

- When students are filling in the mats with the tiles, remind them to look carefully at the horizontal and vertical dimensions of each tile on the product mat. If both dimensions have a value of *x*, then use an x^2-tile. If one dimension is *x* and the other is 1, then use an *x*-tile. If both dimensions are 1, then use a 1-tile.

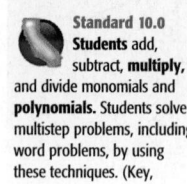

EXPLORE 7-6

Algebra Lab
Multiplying Polynomials

Standard 10.0 Students add, subtract, **multiply,** and divide monomials and **polynomials.** Students solve multistep problems, including word problems, by using these techniques. (Key, CAHSEE)

ACTIVITY 1 Use algebra tiles to find $(x + 2)(x + 5)$.

The rectangle will have a width of $x + 2$ and a length of $x + 5$. Use algebra tiles to mark off the dimensions on a product mat. Then complete the rectangle with algebra tiles.

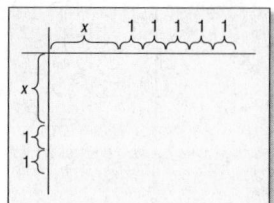  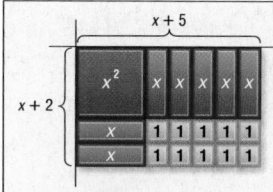

The rectangle consists of 1 blue x^2-tile, 7 green x-tiles, and 10 yellow 1-tiles. The area of the rectangle is $x^2 + 7x + 10$. Therefore, $(x + 2)(x + 5) = x^2 + 7x + 10$.

ACTIVITY 2 Use algebra tiles to find $(x - 1)(x - 4)$.

Step 1 The rectangle will have a width of $x - 1$ and a length of $x - 4$. Use algebra tiles to mark off the dimensions on a product mat. Then begin to make the rectangle with algebra tiles.

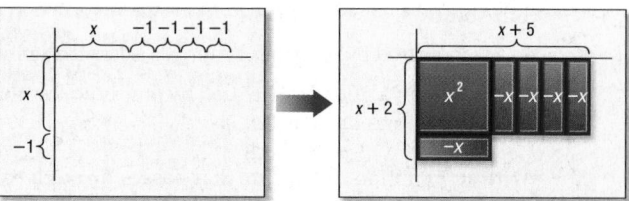

Step 2 Determine whether to use 4 yellow 1-tiles or 4 red −1-tiles to complete the rectangle. Remember that the numbers at the top and side give the dimensions of the tile needed. The area of each tile is the product of −1 and −1 or 1. This is represented by a yellow 1-tile. Fill in the space with 4 yellow 1-tiles to complete the rectangle.

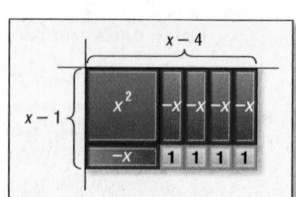

The rectangle consists of 1 blue x^2-tile, 5 red −x-tiles, and 4 yellow 1-tiles. The area of the rectangle is $x^2 - 5x + 4$. Therefore, $(x - 1)(x - 4) = x^2 - 5x + 4$.

ACTIVITY 3 Use algebra tiles to find $(x - 3)(2x + 1)$.

Step 1 The rectangle will have a width of $x - 3$ and a length of $2x + 1$. Mark off the dimensions on a product mat. Then make the rectangle.

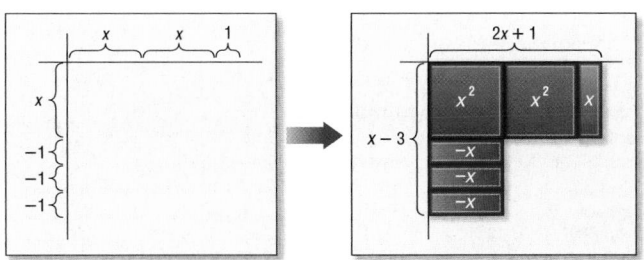

Step 2 Determine what color x-tiles and what color 1-tiles to use to complete the rectangle. The area of each $-x$-tile is the product of x and -1. This is represented by a red $-x$-tile. The area of the -1-tile is represented by the product of 1 and -1 or -1. This is represented by a red -1-tile. Complete the rectangle with 3 red $-x$-tiles and 3 red -1-tiles.

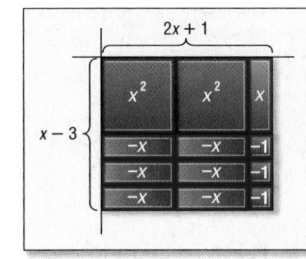

Step 3 Rearrange the tiles to simplify the diagram. Notice that a zero pair is formed by one positive and one negative x-tile.

There are 2 blue x^2-tiles, 5 red $-x$-tiles, and 3 red -1-tiles left. $(x - 3)(2x + 1) = 2x^2 - 5x - 3$.

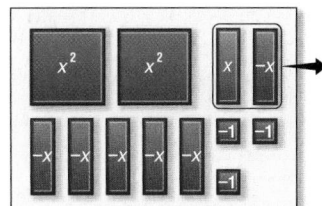

COncepts
in MOtion
Animation
ca.algebra1.com

MODEL

Use algebra tiles to find each product. 1. $x^2 + 5x + 6$ 2. $x^2 - 4x + 3$

1. $(x + 2)(x + 3)$ **2.** $(x - 1)(x - 3)$ **3.** $(x + 1)(x - 2)$ $x^2 - x - 2$

4. $(x + 1)(2x + 1)$ **5.** $(x - 2)(2x - 3)$ **6.** $(x + 3)(2x - 4)$
$2x^2 + 3x + 1$ $2x^2 - 7x + 6$ $2x^2 + 2x - 12$

ANALYZE THE RESULTS

7. You can also use the Distributive Property to find the product of two binomials. The figure at the right shows the model for $(x + 3)(x + 4)$ separated into four parts. Write a sentence or two explaining how this model shows the use of the Distributive Property. See margin.

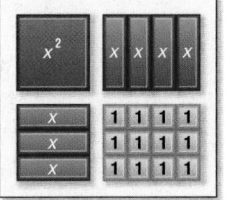

Explore 7-6 Algebra Lab: Multiplying Polynomials   **397**

Working in Cooperative Groups (continued)

- For Activity 2, have students pay close attention to whether the dimensions for each tile are positive or negative, as this affects which tile to use. If both dimensions are positive, then the tile is positive. If one is positive and the other is negative, the tile is negative. If both are negative, then the tile is positive.

- For Activity 3, as an alternative to removing zero pairs, have students write the expression based on the tiles without removing zero pairs. They can then simplify the expression by combining like terms.

Practice Have students complete Exercises 2–6.

3 Assess

✓ Formative Assessment

Use Exercise 6 to assess whether students can model a product correctly.

From Concrete to Abstract After students have completed Exercise 7, help them to see that when using the Distributive Property to multiply polynomials, each term from the first polynomial is multiplied by each term from the second polynomial.

Additional Answer

7. By the Distributive Property, $(x + 3)(x + 4) = x(x + 4) + 3(x + 4)$. The top row represents $x(x + 4)$ or $x^2 + 4x$. The bottom row represents $3(x + 4)$ or $3x + 12$.

7-6 # Multiplying Polynomials

1 Focus

Standards Alignment

Before Lesson 7-6
Multiply and divide monomials from Standard 7AF2.2

Lesson 7-6
Multiply polynomials from Standard 10.0

After Lesson 7-6
Operations on polynomials, including long division from Standard 2A3.0

2 Teach

Scaffolding Questions Have students read *Get Ready for the Lesson.*
Ask:

• Explain how the Distributive Property was used in the first step of this problem. The number 6 in 36 was multiplied by 20 and 4.

• Explain how the Distributive Property was used in the second step of this problem. The number 30 in 36 was multiplied by 20 and 4.

(continued on the next page)

Lesson 7-6 Resources

Main Ideas

• Multiply two binomials by using the FOIL method.

• Multiply two polynomials by using the Distributive Property.

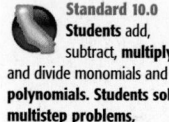 **Standard 10.0** **Students** add, subtract, **multiply,** and divide monomials and **polynomials. Students solve multistep problems, including word problems, by using these techniques.** (Key, CAHSEE)

New Vocabulary

FOIL method

> **GET READY for the Lesson**

To compute 24×36, we multiply each digit in 24 by each digit in 36, paying close attention to the place value of each digit.

Step 1	**Step 2**	**Step 3**
Multiply by the ones.	Multiply by the tens.	Add like place values.
$\begin{array}{r} 24 \\ \times\ 36 \\ \hline 144 \end{array}$	$\begin{array}{r} 24 \\ \times\ 36 \\ \hline 144 \\ 720 \end{array}$	$\begin{array}{r} 24 \\ \times\ 36 \\ \hline 144 \\ +\ 720 \\ \hline 864 \end{array}$

$6 \times 24 = 6(20 + 4)$
$\qquad = 120 + 24$ or 144

$30 \times 24 = 30(20 + 4)$
$\qquad = 600 + 120$ or 720

You can multiply two binomials in a similar way.

Multiply Binomials To multiply two binomials, apply the Distributive Property twice as you do when multiplying two-digit numbers.

> **EXAMPLE** The Distributive Property

1 Find $(x + 3)(x + 2)$.

Method 1 Vertical

Multiply by 2.	Multiply by x.	Combine like terms.
$\begin{array}{r} x + 3 \\ (\times)\ x + 2 \\ \hline 2x + 6 \end{array}$	$\begin{array}{r} x + 3 \\ (\times)\ x + 2 \\ \hline 2x + 6 \\ x^2 + 3x \\ \hline \end{array}$	$\begin{array}{r} x + 3 \\ (\times)\ x + 2 \\ \hline 2x + 6 \\ x^2 + 3x \\ \hline x^2 + 5x + 6 \end{array}$
$2(x + 3) = 2x + 6$	$x(x + 3) = x^2 + 3x$	

Method 2 Horizontal

$$(x + 3)(x + 2) = x(x + 2) + 3(x + 2) \qquad \text{Distributive Property}$$
$$= x(x) + x(2) + 3(x) + 3(2) \qquad \text{Distributive Property}$$
$$= x^2 + 2x + 3x + 6 \qquad \text{Multiply.}$$
$$= x^2 + 5x + 6 \qquad \text{Combine like terms.}$$

> **CHECK Your Progress**

Find each product.
1A. $(m + 4)(m + 5)$ $\ m^2 + 9m + 20$ **1B.** $(y - 2)(y + 8)$ $\ y^2 + 6y - 16$

Chapter 7 Resource Masters

Lesson Reading Guide, p. 41 **BL** **OL** **ELL**
Study Guide and Intervention, pp. 42–43
BL **OL** **ELL**
Skills Practice, p. 44 **BL** **OL**
Practice, p. 45 **OL** **AL**
Word Problem Practice, p. 46 **OL** **AL**
Enrichment, p. 47 **OL** **AL**
Spreadsheet, p. 48
Quiz 3, p. 60

Transparencies

5-Minute Check Transparency 7-6

Additional Print Resources

Noteables™ Interactive Study Notebook with Foldables™
Teaching Math with Manipulatives

Technology

ca.algebra1.com
Interactive Classroom CD-ROM
AssignmentWorks CD-ROM
Graphing Calculator Easy Files

There is a shortcut version of the Distributive Property called the **FOIL method.** You can use the FOIL method to multiply two binomials.

KEY CONCEPT   *FOIL Method*

Words   To multiply two binomials, find the sum of the products of

     F   the *First* terms,

     O   the *Outer* terms,

     I   the *Inner* terms, and

     L   the *Last* terms.

Example   Product of First Terms   Product of Outer Terms   Product of Inner Terms   Product of Last Terms

$(x + 3)(x - 2) = (x)(x) + (-2)(x) + (3)(x) + (3)(-2)$

$= x^2 - 2x + 3x - 6$

$= x^2 + x - 6$

EXAMPLE   FOIL Method

2 Find each product.

a. $(x - 5)(x + 7)$

$(x - 5)(x + 7) = (x)(x) + (x)(7) + (-5)(x) + (-5)(7)$ FOIL method

$= x^2 + 7x - 5x - 35$ Multiply.

$= x^2 + 2x - 35$ Combine like terms.

b. $(2y + 3)(6y - 7)$

$(2y + 3)(6y - 7)$

$= (2y)(6y) + (2y)(-7) + (3)(6y) + (3)(-7)$ FOIL method

$= 12y^2 - 14y + 18y - 21$ Multiply.

$= 12y^2 + 4y - 21$ Combine like terms.

CHECK Your Progress

2A. $(x + 3)(x - 4)$ $x^2 - x - 12$

2B. $(4a - 5)(3a + 2)$ $12a^2 - 7a - 10$

The FOIL method can be used to find an expression that represents the area of geometric shapes when the lengths of the sides are given as binomials.

• **How is the third step similar to combining like terms when working with polynomials?** The digits in each place value are combined: first the ones, then the tens, and finally the hundreds.

Multiply Binomials

Example 1 shows how to multiply two binomials using the Distributive Property. **Example 2** shows how to multiply two binomials using a shortcut of the Distributive Property called the FOIL method. **Example 3** shows how to use the FOIL method to solve a geometry problem.

 Formative Assessment

Use the Check Your Progress exercises after each example to determine students' understanding of concepts.

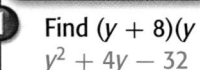 **ADDITIONAL EXAMPLES**

1 Find $(y + 8)(y - 4)$.
$y^2 + 4y - 32$

2 Find each product.

a. $(z - 6)(z - 12)$
$z^2 - 18z + 72$

b. $(5x - 4)(2x + 8)$
$10x^2 + 32x - 32$

Additional Examples are also in:

• Noteables™ Interactive Study Notebook with Foldables™

• Interactive Classroom PowerPoint® Presentations

Focus on Mathematical Content

Multiplying Other Polynomials The FOIL method only works for multiplying two binomials. To multiply any other polynomials, the Distributive Property must be used.

Intervention

Vertical Method for Multiplying Binomials   Students who are less familiar with the Distributive Property may wish to use the vertical method for multiplying binomials because it is similar to multiplying two-digit numbers. Suggest that students use the method with which they are most comfortable.

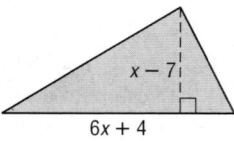
Multiply Polynomials

Example 4 shows how the Distributive Property can be used to multiply any two polynomials.

EXAMPLE FOIL Method

3 **GEOMETRY** The area *A* of a trapezoid is one half the height *h* times the sum of the bases, b_1 and b_2. Write an expression for the area of the trapezoid.

Explore Identify the height and bases.

$$h = x + 2$$
$$b_1 = 3x - 7$$
$$b_2 = 2x + 1$$

Plan Now write and apply the formula.

Area	equals	one-half	height	times	sum of bases.
A	$=$	$\frac{1}{2}$	h	$\cdot$	$(b_1 + b_2)$

Solve $A = \frac{1}{2}h(b_1 + b_2)$ Original formula

$\quad = \frac{1}{2}(x + 2)[(3x - 7) + (2x + 1)]$ Substitution

$\quad = \frac{1}{2}(x + 2)(5x - 6)$ Add polynomials in the brackets.

$\quad = \frac{1}{2}[x(5x) + x(-6) + 2(5x) + 2(-6)]$ FOIL Method

$\quad = \frac{1}{2}(5x^2 - 6x + 10x - 12)$ Multiply.

$\quad = \frac{1}{2}(5x^2 + 4x - 12)$ Combine like terms.

$\quad = \frac{5}{2}x^2 + 2x - 6$ Distributive Property

Check The area of the trapezoid is $\frac{5}{2}x^2 + 2x - 6$ square units.

CHECK Your Progress

3. Write an expression for the area of a triangle with a base of $2x + 3$ and a height of $3x - 1$. $3x^2 + \frac{7}{2}x - \frac{3}{2}$

Online Personal Tutor at ca.algebra1.com

Multiply Polynomials The Distributive Property can be used to multiply any two polynomials.

EXAMPLE The Distributive Property

4 Find each product.

a. $(4x + 9)(2x^2 - 5x + 3)$

$(4x + 9)(2x^2 - 5x + 3)$

$= 4x(2x^2 - 5x + 3) + 9(2x^2 - 5x + 3)$ Distributive Property

$= 8x^3 - 20x^2 + 12x + 18x^2 - 45x + 27$ Distributive Property

$= 8x^3 - 2x^2 - 33x + 27$ Combine like terms.

b. $(y^2 - 2y + 5)(6y^2 - 3y + 1)$

$(y^2 - 2y + 5)(6y^2 - 3y + 1)$

$= y^2(6y^2 - 3y + 1) - 2y(6y^2 - 3y + 1) + 5(6y^2 - 3y + 1)$

$= 6y^4 - 3y^3 + y^2 - 12y^3 + 6y^2 - 2y + 30y^2 - 15y + 5$

$= 6y^4 - 15y^3 + 37y^2 - 17y + 5$

 CHECK Your Progress   4A. $6x^3 + 11x^2 - 59x + 40$

4A. $(3x - 5)(2x^2 + 7x - 8)$ **4B.** $(m^2 + 2m - 3)(4m^2 - 7m + 5)$

$4m^4 + 1m^3 - 21m^2 + 31m - 15$

★ indicates multi-step problem

CHECK Your Understanding

Examples 1–2
(pp. 398–399)

Find each product.

1. $(y + 4)(y + 3)$ $y^2 + 7y + 12$ **2.** $(x - 2)(x + 6)$ $x^2 + 4x - 12$

3. $(a - 8)(a + 5)$ $a^2 - 3a - 40$ **4.** $(4h + 5)(h + 7)$ $4h^2 + 33h + 35$

5. $(9p - 1)(3p - 2)$ $27p^2 - 21p + 2$ **6.** $(2g + 7)(5g - 8)$ $10g^2 + 19g - 56$

Example 3
(p. 400)

★ **7. GEOMETRY** The area A of a triangle is half the product of the base b times the height h. Write a polynomial expression that represents the area of the triangle at the right. **See margin.**

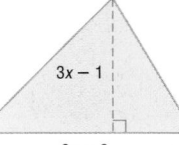
$3x - 1$
$2x + 3$

Example 4
(p. 400)

Find each product. **8–11. See margin.**

8. $(3k - 5)(2k^2 + 4k - 3)$ **9.** $(4x^2 - 2)(2x^2 + 6x + 1)$

10. $(y^2 - 5y + 3)(4y^2 + 2y - 6)$ **11.** $(3m^2 + 2m - 7)(5m^2 + m + 9)$

Exercises

HOMEWORK HELP	
For Exercises	**See Examples**
12–29	1, 2
30–33	3
34–41	4

Find each product. **12–29. See margin.**

12. $(b + 8)(b + 2)$ **13.** $(n + 6)(n + 7)$ **14.** $(x - 4)(x - 9)$

15. $(a - 3)(a - 5)$ **16.** $(y + 4)(y - 8)$ **17.** $(p + 2)(p - 10)$

18. $(2w - 5)(w + 7)$ **19.** $(k + 12)(3k - 2)$ **20.** $(8d + 3)(5d + 2)$

21. $(4g + 3)(9g + 6)$ **22.** $(7x - 4)(5x - 1)$ **23.** $(6a - 5)(3a - 8)$

24. $(2n + 3)(2n + 3)$ **25.** $(5m - 6)(5m - 6)$ **26.** $(10r - 4)(10r + 4)$

27. $(7t + 5)(7t - 5)$ **28.** $(8x + 2y)(5x - 4y)$ **29.** $(11a - 6b)(2a + 3b)$

Exercise Levels
A: 12–41
B: 42–48
C: 49–53

30. $2x^2 + 3x - 20$ units^2
31. $6x^2 - \frac{17}{2}x + 3$ units^2

GEOMETRY Write an expression to represent the area of each figure.

30.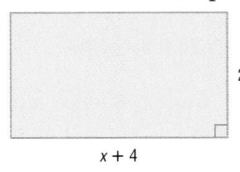
$2x - 5$
$x + 4$

31.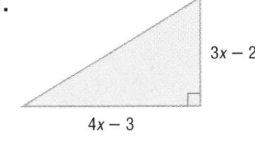
$3x - 2$
$4x - 3$

32.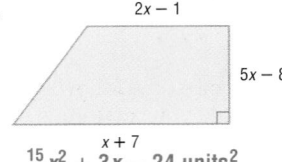
$2x - 1$
$5x - 8$
$x + 7$
$\frac{15}{2}x^2 + 3x - 24$ units^2

33.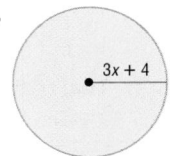
$3x + 4$
$9\pi x^2 + 24\pi x + 16\pi$ units^2

Lesson 7-6 Multiplying Polynomials   **401**

DIFFERENTIATED HOMEWORK OPTIONS

Level	Assignment	Two-Day Option	
BL Basic	12–41, 49, 50, 52–73	13–41 odd, 54, 55	12–40 even, 49, 50, 52, 53, 56–73
OL Core	13–41 odd, 43, 44–50, 52–73	12–41, 54, 55	42–50, 52, 53, 56–73
AL Advanced /Pre-AP	42–67, (optional: 68–73)		

 Practice

 **Formative Assessment**

Use Exercises 1–11 to check for understanding.

Use the chart at the bottom of this page to customize assignments for your students.

Odd/Even Assignments

Exercises 12–41 are structured so that students practice the same concepts whether they are assigned odd or even problems.

Common Errors

Tips for New Teachers When students multiply polynomials horizontally, they often try to combine terms that are not like terms. For students who are having difficulty finding the product in Exercises 12–29, suggest that they try multiplying the polynomials in vertical form, aligning like terms.

Additional Answers

12. $b^2 + 10b + 16$

13. $n^2 + 13n + 42$

14. $x^2 - 13x + 36$

15. $a^2 - 8a + 15$

16. $y^2 - 4y - 32$

17. $p^2 - 8p - 20$

18. $2w^2 + 9w - 35$

19. $3k^2 + 34k - 24$

20. $40d^2 + 31d + 6$

21. $36g^2 + 51g + 18$

22. $35x^2 - 27x + 4$

23. $18a^2 - 63a + 40$

24. $4n^2 + 12n + 9$

25. $25m^2 - 60m + 36$

26. $100r^2 - 16$

27. $49t^2 - 25$

28. $40x^2 - 22xy - 8y^2$

29. $22a^2 + 21ab - 18b^2$

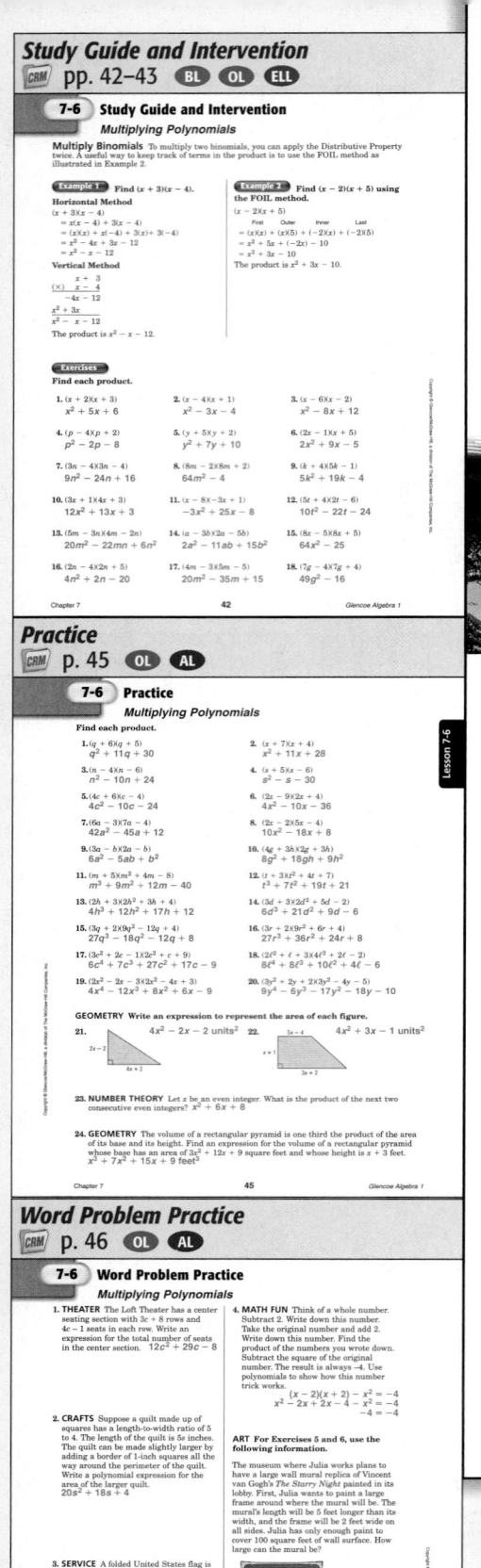

Study Guide and Intervention (CRM pp. 42–43), Practice (CRM p. 45), and Word Problem Practice (CRM p. 46) reproduced pages.

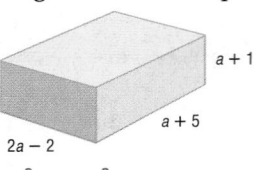

Find each product. 34–39. See margin.

34. $(p + 4)(p^2 + 2p - 7)$ **35.** $(a - 3)(a^2 - 8a + 5)$

36. $(2x - 5)(3x^2 - 4x + 1)$ **37.** $(3k + 4)(7k^2 + 2k - 9)$

38. $(n^2 - 3n + 2)(n^2 + 5n - 4)$ **39.** $(y^2 + 7y - 1)(y^2 - 6y + 5)$

Simplify.

40. $(m + 2)[(m^2 + 3m - 6) + (m^2 - 2m + 4)]$ $2m^3 + 5m^2 - 4$

41. $[(t^2 + 3t - 8) - (t^2 - 2t + 6)](t - 4)$ $5t^2 - 34t + 56$

GEOMETRY The volume V of a prism equals the area of the base B times the height h. Write an expression to represent the volume of each prism.

42.

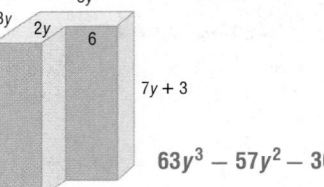

$2a^3 + 10a^2 - 2a - 10$ units³

★ **43.**

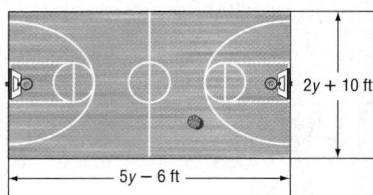

$63y^3 - 57y^2 - 36y$ units³

Real-World Link

More than 200 million people a year pay to see basketball games. That is more admissions than for any other American sport.

Source: *Compton's Encyclopedia*

44. BASKETBALL The dimensions of a professional basketball court are represented by a width of $5y - 6$ feet and a length of $2y + 10$ feet. Find an expression for the area of the court. $10y^2 + 38y - 60$ ft²

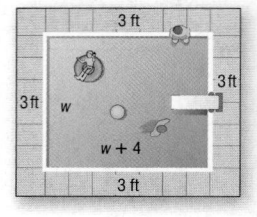

OFFICE SPACE For Exercises 45–47, use the following information.
LaTanya's modular office is square. Her office in the company's new building will be 2 feet shorter in one direction and 4 feet longer in the other.

45. Write expressions for the dimensions of LaTanya's new office. $x - 2$, $x + 4$

46. Write a polynomial expression for the area of her new office. $x^2 + 2x - 8$

47. Suppose her office is presently 9 feet by 9 feet. Will her new office be bigger or smaller than her old office and by how much? Explain. bigger; 10 sq

EXTRA PRACTICE
See pages 732, 750.

Math Online
Self-Check Quiz at ca.algebra1.com

48. POOL CONSTRUCTION A homeowner is installing a swimming pool in his backyard. He wants its length to be 4 feet longer than its width. Then he wants to surround it with a concrete walkway 3 feet wide. If he can only afford 300 square feet of concrete for the walkway, what should the dimensions of the pool be? 20 ft by 24 ft

H.O.T. Problems

49. REASONING Compare and contrast the procedure used to multiply a trinomial by a binomial using the vertical method with the procedure used to multiply a three-digit number by a two-digit number. **See margin.**

50. ALGEBRA TILES Draw a diagram to show how you would use algebra tiles to find the product of $2x - 1$ and $x + 3$. **See Ch. 7 Answer Appendix.**

51. CHALLENGE Determine whether the following statement is *sometimes*, *always*, or *never* true. Explain your reasoning. **See margin.**
The product of a binomial and a trinomial is a polynomial with four terms.

402 Chapter 7 Polynomials

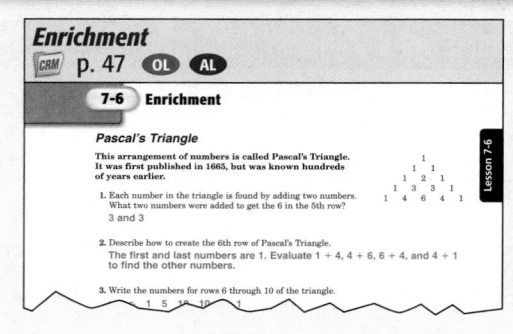

Enrichment (CRM p. 47) — 7-6 Enrichment, Pascal's Triangle, reproduced page.

BL = Below Grade Level

OL = On Grade Level

AL = Above Grade Level

ELL = English Language Learner

Additional pages not shown:

CRM **Lesson Reading Guide**, p. 41 **BL OL ELL**

CRM **Skills Practice**, p. 44 **BL OL**

52. OPEN ENDED Write a binomial and a trinomial involving a single variable. Then find their product. **Sample answer:** $(x + 2)$ and $(x^2 - 3x + 4)$; $x^3 - x^2 - 2x + 8$

53. *Writing in Math* Using the information about multiplying binomials on page 398 explain how multiplying binomials is similar to multiplying two-digit numbers. Include a demonstration of a horizontal method for multiplying 24×36 in your answer. **See Ch. 7 Answer Appendix.**

Spiral Review

Simplify. (Lesson 7-5) **56–57. See margin.**

56. $3x(2x - 4) + 6(5x^2 + 2x - 7)$

57. $4a(5a^2 + 2a - 7) - 3(2a^2 - 6a - 9)$

58. GEOMETRY The sum of the degree measures of the angles of a triangle is 180. (Lesson 7-4)

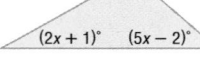
$(2x + 1)°$ $(5x - 2)°$

a. Write an expression to represent the measure of the third angle of the triangle. $(181 - 7x)°$

b. If $x = 15$, find the measures of the three angles of the triangle. $31°, 73°, 76°$

If $f(x) = 2x - 5$ and $g(x) = x^2 + 3x$, find each value. (Lesson 3-6)

59. $f(-4)$ -13

60. $g(-2) + 7$ 5

61. $f(a + 3)$ $2a + 1$

Solve each equation or formula for the variable specified. (Lesson 2-8)

62. $a = \frac{v}{t}$ for t $t = \frac{v}{a}$

63. $ax - by = 2cz$ for y $y = \frac{ax - 2cz}{b}$

64. $4x + 3y = 7$ for y $y = -\frac{4}{3}x + \frac{7}{3}$

Solve each equation. (Lesson 2-4)

65. $\frac{d - 2}{3} = 7$ 23

66. $3n + 6 = -15$ -7

67. $35 + 20h = 100$ 3.25

> **GET READY for the Next Lesson**

PREREQUISITE SKILL Simplify. (Lesson 7-1)

68. $(6a)^2$ $36a^2$

69. $(7x)^2$ $49x^2$

70. $(9b)^2$ $81b^2$

71. $(4y^2)^2$ $16y^4$

72. $(2v^3)^2$ $4v^6$

73. $(3g^4)^2$ $9g^8$

Lesson 7-6 Multiplying Polynomials **403**

> **Pre-AP Activity**   **Use after Exercise 53.**

Tell students that one way to multiply 25 and 18 mentally is to find $(20 + 5)$ and $(20 - 2)$. Have them show how the FOIL method can be used to find each product.

a. 35(19) $35(19) = (30 + 5)(10 + 9) = (30)(10) + (30)(9) + 5(10) + 5(9) =$
$300 + 270 + 50 + 45 = 665$

b. 67(102) $67(102) = (60 + 7)(100 + 2) = (60)(100) + (60)(2) + 7(100) + 7(2) =$
$6000 + 120 + 700 + 14 = 6834$

7-7 Special Products

2 Teach

Scaffolding Questions
Have students read *Get Ready for the Lesson.*
Ask:
• In the first example, why does using the FOIL method result in three terms instead of four? The *Outer* and *Inner* terms are like terms and combine to produce a trinomial product.
• In the second example, what sometimes happens when using the FOIL method to multiply binomials that produces a binomial product? The like *x* terms combine to produce a zero pair and drop out of the product.

Main Ideas
• Find squares of sums and differences.
• Find the product of a sum and a difference.

Standard 10.0 Students add, subtract, **multiply,** and divide monomials and polynomials. Students solve multistep problems, including word problems, by using these techniques. (Key, CAHSEE)

New Vocabulary
difference of two squares

▶ GET READY for the Lesson

In the previous lesson, you learned how to multiply two binomials using the FOIL method. You may have noticed that the *Outer* and *Inner* terms often combine to produce a trinomial product. This is not always the case, however. Notice that the product of $x + 3$ and $x - 3$ is a binomial.

$$(x + 5)(x - 3)$$
$$ F \quad O \quad I \quad L$$
$$= x^2 - 3x + 5x - 15$$
$$= x^2 + 2x - 15$$

$$(x + 3)(x - 3)$$
$$ F \quad O \quad I \quad L$$
$$= x^2 - 3x + 3x - 9$$
$$= x^2 + 0x - 9$$
$$= x^2 - 9$$

Squares of Sums and Differences While you can always use the FOIL method to find the product of two binomials, some pairs of binomials have products that follow a specific pattern. One such pattern is the *square of a sum*, $(a + b)^2$ or $(a + b)(a + b)$.

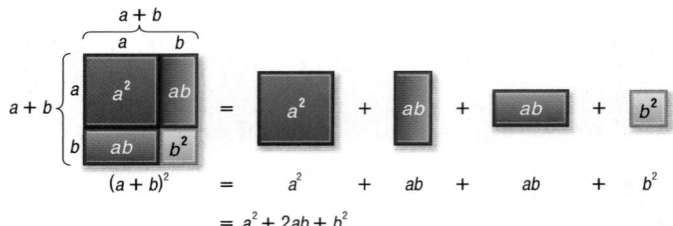

$$(a + b)^2 = a^2 + ab + ab + b^2$$
$$= a^2 + 2ab + b^2$$

KEY CONCEPT   *Square of a Sum*

Words   The square of $a + b$ is the square of a plus twice the product of a and b plus the square of b.

Symbols $(a + b)^2 = (a + b)(a + b) = a^2 + 2ab + b^2$

Example $(x + 7)^2 = x^2 + 2(x)(7) + 7^2 = x^2 + 14x + 49$

EXAMPLE   Square of a Sum

 Find $(4y + 5)^2$.

$$(a + b)^2 = a^2 + 2ab + b^2$$
$$(4y + 5)^2 = (4y)^2 + 2(4y)(5) + 5^2 \quad a = 4y \text{ and } b = 5$$
$$= 16y^2 + 40y + 25 \quad \text{Check by using FOIL.}$$

COncepts in MOtion
Animation
ca.algebra1.com

 Extra Examples at ca.algebra1.com

✓ **CHECK** Your Progress Find each product.

1A. $(8c + 3d)^2$ $64c^2 + 48cd + 9d^2$ **1B.** $(3x + 4y)^2$ $9x^2 + 24xy + 16y^2$

Study Tip

$(a + b)^2$

In the pattern for $(a + b)^2$, a and b can be numbers, variables, or expressions with numbers and variables.

To find the pattern for the *square of a difference*, $(a - b)^2$, write $a - b$ as $a + (-b)$ and square it using the square of a sum pattern.

$$(a - b)^2 = [a + (-b)]^2$$
$$= a^2 + 2(a)(-b) + (-b)^2 \quad \text{Square of a Sum}$$
$$= a^2 - 2ab + b^2 \quad \text{Simplify. Note that } (-b)^2 = (-b)(-b) \text{ or } b^2.$$

KEY CONCEPT   *Square of a Difference*

Words   The square of $a - b$ is the square of a minus twice the product of a and b plus the square of b.

Symbols $(a - b)^2 = (a - b)(a - b) = a^2 - 2ab + b^2$

Example $(x - 4)^2 = x^2 - 2(x)(4) + 4^2 = x^2 - 8x + 16$

EXAMPLE   Square of a Difference

② Find $(5m^3 - 2n)^2$.

$$(a - b)^2 = a^2 - 2ab + b^2$$
$$(5m^3 - 2n)^2 = (5m^3)^2 - 2(5m^3)(2n) + (2n)^2 \quad a = 5m^3 \text{ and } b = 2n$$
$$= 25m^6 - 20m^3n + 4n^2 \quad \text{Simplify.}$$

✓ **CHECK** Your Progress Find each product.

2A. $(6p - 1)^2$ $36p^2 - 12p + 1$ **2B.** $(a - 2b)^2$ $a^2 - 4ab + 4b^2$

Real-World EXAMPLE

③ **GENETICS** The Punnett square shows the possible gene combinations between two hamsters. Each hamster passes on one *dominant* gene G for golden coloring and one *recessive* gene g for cinnamon coloring.

Show how combinations can be modeled by the square of a binomial. Then determine what percent of the offspring will be pure golden, hybrid golden, and pure cinnamon.

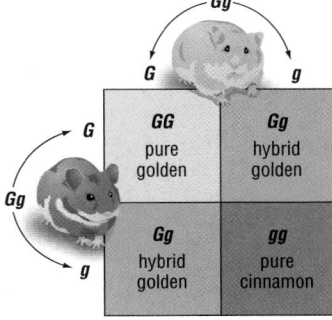

Each parent has half the genes necessary for golden coloring and half the genes necessary for cinnamon coloring. The makeup of each parent can be modeled by $0.5G + 0.5g$. Their offspring can be modeled by the product of $0.5G + 0.5g$ and $0.5G + 0.5g$ or $(0.5G + 0.5g)^2$.

Real-World Career
Geneticist
Laboratory geneticists work in medicine to find cures for disease, in agriculture to breed new crops and livestock, and in police work to identify criminals.

Math Online
For more information, go to ca.algebra1.com

Lesson 7-7 Special Products   **405**

Squares of Sums and Differences

Example 1 shows how to follow a specific pattern to find the square of a sum. **Example 2** shows how to find the square of a difference. **Example 3** shows how to use the square of the sum to write an expression that models a real–world situation.

✓ **Formative Assessment**

Use the Check Your Progress exercises after each example to determine students' understanding of concepts.

ADDITIONAL EXAMPLES

① Find $(7z + 2)^2$.
$49z^2 + 28z^2 + 4$

② Find $(3c - 4)^2$.
$9c^2 - 24c + 16$

③ **GEOMETRY** Write an expression that represents the area of a square that has a side length of $2x + 12$ units. $4x^2 + 48x + 144$ units^2

Additional Examples are also in:
• Noteables™ Interactive Study Notebook with Foldables™
• Interactive Classroom PowerPoint® Presentations

Tips for New Teachers

Alternative Method
Even though it is important to learn the special products, point out to students that they can always find these products using methods from previous lessons in the chapter.

Intervention

Squares of Sums and Differences   Since the square of a sum and the square of a difference are the same except for the sign of the middle term, the risk of making a careless mistake when finding the sum or difference of a square is high. Tell students to pay close attention to the signs when finding squares of sums or differences.

Use this product to determine possible colors of the offspring.

$$(a + b)^2 = a^2 + 2ab + b^2 \qquad \text{Square of a Sum}$$
$$(0.5G + 0.5g)^2 = (0.5G)^2 + 2(0.5G)(0.5g) + (0.5g)^2 \quad a = 0.5G \text{ and } b = 0.5g$$
$$= 0.25G^2 + 0.5Gg + 0.25g^2 \qquad \text{Simplify.}$$
$$= 0.25GG + 0.5Gg + 0.25gg \qquad G^2 = GG \text{ and } g^2 = gg$$

Thus, 25% of the offspring are GG or pure golden, 50% are Gg or hybrid golden, and 25% are gg or pure cinnamon.

 **Your Progress**

3. Andrew has a garden that is x feet long and x feet wide. He decides that he wants to add 3 feet to the length and the width in order to grow more vegetables. Show how the new area of the garden can be modeled by the square of a binomial. **See margin.**

Online Personal Tutor at ca.algebra1.com

Product of a Sum and a Difference You can use the diagram below to find the pattern for the product of the sum and difference of the *same two terms*, $(a + b)(a - b)$. Recall that $a - b$ can be rewritten as $a + (-b)$.

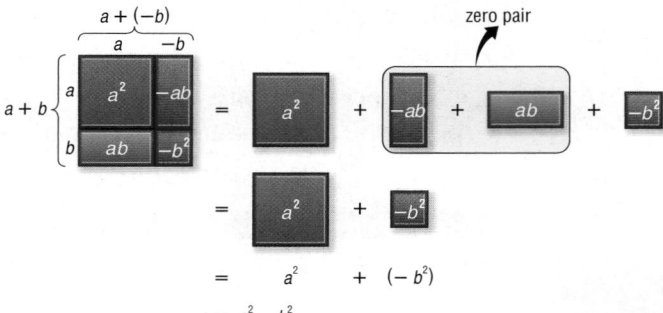

COncepts in MOtion

Animation
ca.algebra1.com

The resulting product, $a^2 - b^2$, is called the **difference of two squares.**

KEY CONCEPT   *Product of a Sum and a Difference*

Words   The product of $a + b$ and $a - b$ is the square of a minus the square of b.

Symbols $(a + b)(a - b) = (a - b)(a + b) = a^2 - b^2$

Example $(x + 9)(x - 9) = x^2 - 9^2 = x^2 - 81$

EXAMPLE   Product of a Sum and a Difference

4 Find $(11v - 8w^2)(11v + 8w^2)$.

$$(a - b)(a + b) = a^2 - b^2$$
$$(11v - 8w^2)(11v + 8w^2) = (11v)^2 - (8w^2)^2 \quad a = 11v \text{ and } b = 8w^2$$
$$= 121v^2 - 64w^4 \qquad \text{Simplify.}$$

Your Progress   Find each product.

4A. $(3n + 2)(3n - 2)$ $9n^2 - 4$ **4B.** $(4c - 7d)(4c + 7d)$ $16c^2 - 49d^2$

★ indicates multi-step problem

✓CHECK Your Understanding

Examples 1–2
(pp. 404–405)

Find each product. **1–6. See margin.**

1. $(a + 6)^2$
2. $(2a + 7b)^2$
3. $(3x + 9y)^2$
4. $(4n - 3)(4n - 3)$
5. $(x^2 - 6y)^2$
6. $(9 - p)^2$

Example 3
(pp. 405–406)

GENETICS For Exercises 7 and 8, use the following information.
Dalila has brown eyes and Bob has blue eyes. Brown genes B are dominant over blue genes b. A person with genes BB or Bb has brown eyes. Someone with genes bb has blue eyes. Suppose Dalila's genes for eye color are Bb.

7. $0.5Bb + 0.5b^2$

7. Write an expression for the possible eye coloring of Dalila and Bob's children.
8. What is the probability that a child of Dalila and Bob would have blue eyes?
$\frac{1}{2}$

Example 4
(p. 406)

Find each product.

9. $(8x - 5)(8x + 5)$
$64x^2 - 25$
10. $(3a + 7b)(3a - 7b)$
$9a^2 - 49b^2$
11. $(4y^2 + 3z)(4y^2 - 3z)$
$16y^4 - 9z^2$

Exercises

HOMEWORK HELP	
For Exercises	See Examples
12–14	1
15–17	2
18–19	3
20–22	4

Exercise Levels
A: 12–22
B: 23–47
C: 48–52

18. $0.25CF^2 +$
$0.5CFcf + 0.25cf^2$

Find each product. 12. $k^2 + 16k + 64$ 14. $4g^2 + 20g + 25$

12. $(k + 8)(k + 8)$
13. $(y + 4)^2$ $y^2 + 8y + 16$
14. $(2g + 5)^2$
15. $(a - 5)(a - 5)$
$a^2 - 10a + 25$
16. $(n - 12)^2$
$n^2 - 24n + 144$
17. $(7 - 4y)^2$
$49 - 56y + 16y^2$

GENETICS For Exercises 18 and 19, use the following information and the Punnett square.
Cystic fibrosis is inherited from parents only if both parents have the abnormal CF gene. Children of two parents with the CF gene will either be affected with the disease, a carrier but not affected, or not have the gene.

18. Write an expression for the genetic makeup of children of two parents that are carriers of cystic fibrosis.
19. What is the probability that a child will not be affected and not be a carrier? **25%**

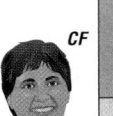

	CF	cf
CF	**CFCF** affected	**CFcf** carrier
cf	**CFcf** carrier	**cfcf** not carrier not affected

Find each product.

20. $(b + 7)(b - 7)$ $b^2 - 49$
21. $(c - 2)(c + 2)$ $c^2 - 4$
22. $(11r + 8)(11r - 8)$
$121r^2 - 64$

Find each product. **23–39. See margin.**

23. $(9x + 3)^2$
24. $(4 - 6h)^2$
25. $(12p - 3)(12p + 3)$
26. $(a + 5b)^2$
27. $(m + 7n)^2$
28. $(2x - 9y)^2$
29. $(3n - 10p)^2$
30. $(5w + 14)(5w - 14)$
31. $(4d - 13)(4d + 13)$
32. $(x^3 + 4y)^2$
33. $(3a^2 - b^2)^2$
34. $(8a^2 - 9b^3)(8a^2 + 9b^3)$
35. $(5x^4 - y)(5x^4 + y)$
36. $\left(\frac{2}{3}x - 6\right)^2$
37. $\left(\frac{4}{5}x + 10\right)^2$
38. $(2n + 1)(2n - 1)(n + 5)$
39. $(p + 3)(p - 4)(p - 3)(p + 4)$

Lesson 7-7 Special Products **407**

3 Practice

✓ Formative Assessment

Use Exercises 1–11 to check for understanding.

Use the chart at the bottom of this page to customize assignments for your students.

Odd/Even Assignment
Exercises 12–22 are structured so that students practice the same concepts whether they are assigned odd or even problems.

Additional Answers

1. $a^2 + 12a + 36$
2. $4a^2 + 28ab + 49b^2$
3. $9x^2 + 54xy + 81y^2$
4. $16n^2 - 24n + 9$
5. $x^4 - 12x^2y + 36y^2$
6. $81 - 18p + p^2$
23. $81x^2 + 54x + 9$
24. $16 - 48h + 36h^2$
25. $144p^2 - 9$
26. $a^2 + 10ab + 25b^2$
27. $m^2 + 14mn + 49n^2$
28. $4x^2 - 36xy + 81y^2$
29. $9n^2 - 60np + 100p^2$
30. $25w^2 - 196$
31. $16d^2 - 169$
32. $x^6 + 8x^3y + 16y^2$
33. $9a^4 - 6a^2b^2 + b^4$
34. $64a^4 - 81b^6$
35. $25x^8 - y^2$
36. $\frac{4}{9}x^2 - 8x + 36$
37. $\frac{16}{25}x^2 + 16x + 100$
38. $4n^3 + 20n^2 - n - 5$
39. $p^4 - 25p^2 + 144$

DIFFERENTIATED HOMEWORK OPTIONS

Level	Assignment	Two-Day Option	
BL Basic	12–22, 48–50, 52–73	13–21 odd, 53, 54	12–22 even, 48–50, 52, 55–73
OL Core	13–21 odd, 23–37 odd, 40–50, 52–73	12–22, 53, 54	23–50, 52, 55–73
AL Advanced /Pre-AP	23–73		

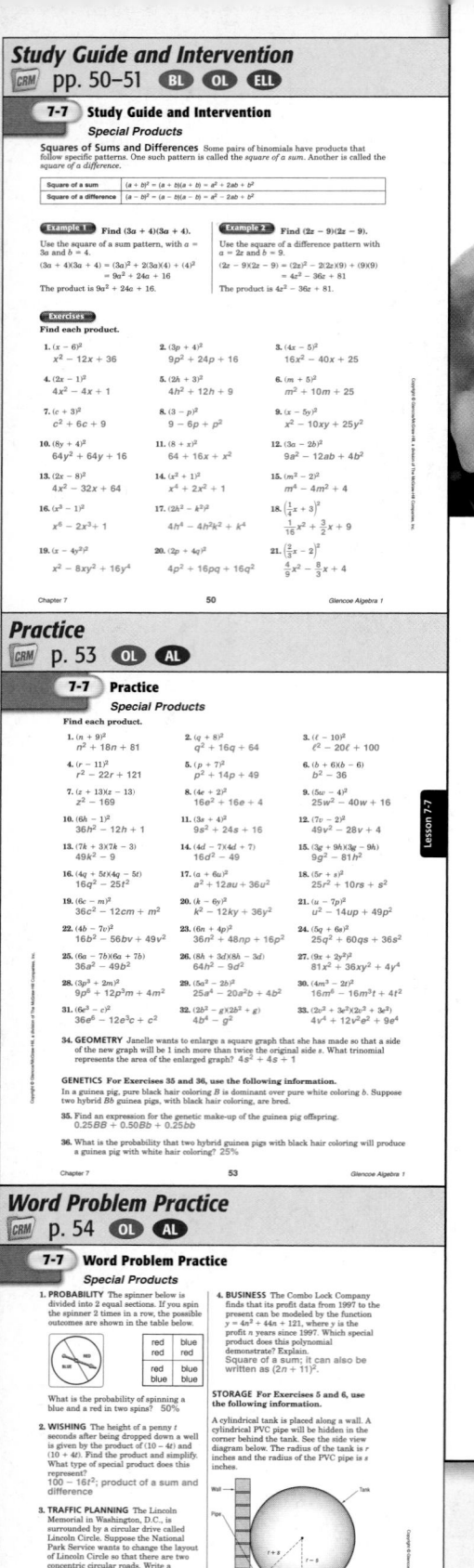

MAGIC TRICK For Exercises 40–43, use the following information.
Madison says that she can perform a magic trick with numbers. She asks you to pick an integer, any integer. Square that integer. Then, add twice your original number. Next add 1. Take the square root of the result. Finally, subtract your original number. Then Madison exclaims with authority, "Your answer is 1!"

42. $(a + 1)^2$

40. Pick an integer and follow Madison's directions. Is your result 1? **See students' work; yes.**

41. Let a represent the integer you chose. Then, find a polynomial representation for the first three steps of Madison's directions. $a^2 + 2a + 1$

42. The polynomial you wrote in Exercise 41 is the square of what binomial sum?

43. Take the square root of the perfect square you wrote in Exercise 42, then subtract a, your original integer. What is the result? **1**

44. $(3.14s^2 + 56.52s + 254.34)$ ft^2

WRESTLING For Exercises 44–46, use the following information.
A high school wrestling mat must be a square with 38-foot sides and contain two circles as shown. Suppose the inner circle has a radius of s feet, and the outer circle's radius is nine feet longer than the inner circle.

38 ft

44. Write an expression for the area of the larger circle.

45. Write an expression for the area of the square outside the circle. **$(1189.66 - 3.14s^2 - 56.52s)$ ft^2**

46. Use the expression to find the area if $s = 1$. **1130 ft^2**

★ **47. GEOMETRY** The area of the shaded region models the difference of two squares, $a^2 - b^2$. Show that the area of the shaded region is also equal to $(a - b)(a + b)$. (*Hint*: Divide the shaded region into two trapezoids as shown.) **See Ch. 7 Answer Appendix.**

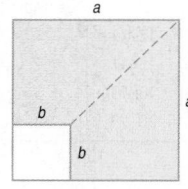

Real-World Link
Cael Sanderson of Iowa State University is the only wrestler in NCAA Division 1 history to be undefeated for four years. He compiled a 159–0 record from 1999–2002.
Source: www.teamsanderson.cc

H.O.T. Problems

48. REASONING Compare and contrast the pattern for the square of a sum with the pattern for the square of a difference. **See margin.**

49. ALGEBRA TILES Draw a diagram to show how you would use algebra tiles to model the product of $x - 3$ and $x - 3$, or $(x - 3)^2$. **See Ch. 7 Answer Appendix.**

50. OPEN ENDED Write two binomials whose product is a difference of squares. Then multiply to verify your answer. **Sample answer: $x - 1$ and $x + 1$**

51. CHALLENGE Does a pattern exist for the cube of a sum, $(a + b)^3$?
a. Investigate this question by finding the product of $(a + b)(a + b)(a + b)$.
b. Use the pattern you discovered in part a to find $(x + 2)^3$.
c. Draw a diagram of a geometric model for the cube of a sum. **See margin.**

52. *Writing in Math* Using the information about the product of two binomials on page 404 distinguish when the product of two binomials is also a binomial. Include an example of two binomials whose product is a binomial and an example of two binomials whose product is not a binomial in your answer. **See margin.**

408 Chapter 7 Polynomials

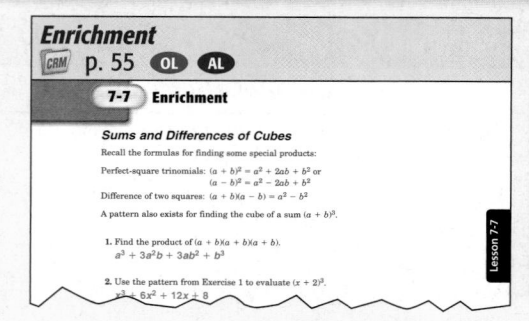

Enrichment
CRM p. 55 **OL** **AL**

7-7 Enrichment

Sums and Differences of Cubes
Recall the formulas for finding some special products:
Perfect-square trinomials: $(a + b)^2 = a^2 + 2ab + b^2$ or
$(a - b)^2 = a^2 - 2ab + b^2$
Difference of two squares: $(a + b)(a - b) = a^2 - b^2$
A pattern also exists for finding the cube of a sum $(a + b)^3$.

1. Find the product of $(a + b)(a + b)(a + b)$.
$a^3 + 3a^2b + 3ab^2 + b^3$

2. Use the pattern from Exercise 1 to evaluate $(x + 2)^3$.
$x^3 + 6x^2 + 12x + 8$

BL = Below Grade Level
OL = On Grade Level
AL = Above Grade Level
ELL = English Language Learner

Additional pages not shown:
CRM *Lesson Reading Guide*, p. 49 **BL** **OL** **ELL**
CRM *Skills Practice*, p. 52 **BL** **OL**

53. The base of a triangle is represented by $x - 4$, and the height is represented by $x + 4$. Which of the following represents the area of the triangle? **D**

A $x^2 - 16$

B $\frac{1}{2}x^2 + 4x - 8$

C $x^2 + 8x - 16$

D $\frac{1}{2}x^2 - 8$

54. REVIEW The sum of a number and 8 is -19. Which equation shows this relationship? **G**

F $8n = -19$

G $n + 8 = -19$

H $n - 8 = 19$

J $n - 19 = 8$

Spiral Review

Find each product. (Lesson 7-6) 57. $20y^2 - 29y + 6$

55. $(x + 2)(x + 7)$ $x^2 + 9x + 14$

56. $(c - 9)(c + 3)$ $c^2 - 6c - 27$

57. $(4y - 1)(5y - 6)$

58. $(3n - 5)(8n + 5)$
$24n^2 - 25n - 25$

59. $(x - 2)(3x^2 - 5x + 4)$
$3x^3 - 11x^2 + 14x - 8$

60. $(2k + 5)(2k^2 - 8k + 7)$
$4k^3 - 6k^2 - 26k + 35$

Solve. (Lesson 7-5)

61. $6(x + 2) + 4 = 5(3x - 4)$ **4**

62. $-3(3a - 8) + 2a = 4(2a + 1)$ $\frac{4}{3}$

63. $p(p + 2) + 3p = p(p - 3)$ **0**

64. $y(y - 4) + 2y = y(y + 12) - 7$ $\frac{1}{2}$

Use elimination to solve each system of equations. (Lesson 5-3, 5-4)

65. $\frac{3}{4}x + \frac{1}{5}y = 5$ **(0, 25)**

  $\frac{3}{4}x - \frac{1}{5}y = -5$

66. $2x - y = 10$ **(3, −4)**

  $5x + 3y = 3$

67. $2x = 4 - 3y$ **(5, −2)**

  $3y - x = -11$

Write the slope-intercept form of an equation that passes through the given point and is perpendicular to the graph of each equation. (Lesson 4-6)

68. $5x + 5y = 35$, $(-3, 2)$
$y = x + 5$

69. $2x - 5y = 3$, $(-2, 7)$
$y = -2.5x + 2$

70. $5x + y = 2$, $(0, 6)$
$y = \frac{1}{5}x + 6$

Find the nth term of each arithmetic sequence described. (Lesson 3-7)

71. $a_1 = 3, d = 4, n = 18$ **71**

72. $-5, 1, 7, 13, \ldots$ for $n = 12$ **61**

73. PHYSICAL FITNESS Mitchell likes to exercise regularly. He likes to warm up by walking two miles. Then he runs five miles. Finally, he cools down by walking another mile. Identify the graph that best represents Mitchell's heart rate as a function of time. (Lesson 1-9) **b**

a.
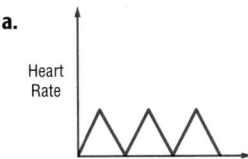

b.
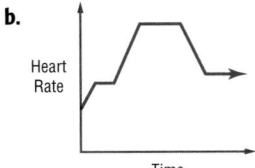

c.
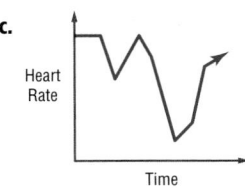

Pre-AP Activity   Use as an Extension.

A diagram of the Gwennap Pit is shown here. Tell students the historical Gwennap Pit, an outdoor amphitheater in southern England, consists of a circular stage surrounded by circular levels used for seating. Each seating level is about 1 meter wide. Suppose the radius of the stage is s meters.

a. Find binomial representations for the radii of the second and third seating levels. $s + 2, s + 3$

b. Find the area of the shaded region representing the third seating level. about $(6.3s + 15.7)$ m²

Algebra Tiles Students may want to use algebra tiles to model the product in Exercise 49.

④ Assess

Ticket Out the Door Make several copies each of five squares of sums that need to be multiplied. Give one expression to each student. As the students leave the room, ask them to tell you the products of the expressions.

Check for student understanding of concepts in Lesson 7–7.

📋 Quiz 4, p. 60

FOLDABLES **Foldables™**
Study Organizer **Follow-Up**

At the end of this lesson, remind students to take notes and show examples in the row labeled *Polynomials* and the column labeled ×.

Additional Answers

48. The patterns are the same except for their middle terms. The middle terms have different signs.

51a. $a^3 + 3a^2b + 3ab^2 + b^3$

51b. $x^3 + 6x^2 + 12x + 8$

51c. $(a + b)$

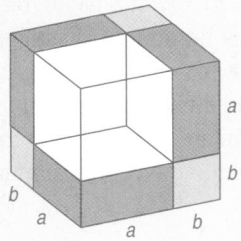

52. The product of two binomials is also a binomial when the two binomials are the sum and the difference of the same two terms. Answers should include the following.

• Sample answer:
  $(2x - 13)(2x + 13)$
• Sample answer:
  $(10x + 11)(10x + 11)$

Study Guide and Review

Dinah Zike's Foldables™

Have students look through the chapter to make sure they have included examples in their Foldables for each type of polynomial and monomial operation they learned.

Suggest that students keep their Foldables handy while completing the Study Guide and Review pages. Point out that their Foldables can serve as a review tool for studying for the Chapter Test.

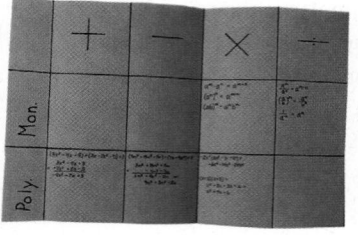

Formative Assessment

Key Vocabulary The page reference after each word denotes where that term was first introduced. If students have difficulty completing Exercises 1–10, remind them that they can use these page references to refresh their memories about the vocabulary terms.

 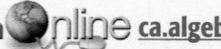

Vocabulary PuzzleMaker
improves students' mathematics vocabulary using four puzzle formats—crossword, scramble, word search using a word list, and word search using clues. Students can work online or from a printed worksheet.

CHAPTER 7 Study Guide and Review

Download Vocabulary Review from ca.algebra1.com

FOLDABLES Study Organizer **GET READY to Study**

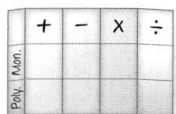

Be sure the following Key Concepts are noted in your Foldable.

Key Concepts

Multiplying Monomials (Lesson 7-1)
- To multiply two powers that have the same base, add exponents.
- To find the power of a power, multiply exponents.
- The power of a product is the product of the powers.

Dividing Monomials (Lesson 7-2)
- To divide two powers that have the same base, subtract the exponents.
- To find the power of a quotient, find the power of the numerator and the power of the denominator.
- Any nonzero number raised to the zero power is 1.
- For any nonzero number a and any integer n,

$$a^{-n} = \frac{1}{a^n} \text{ and } \frac{1}{a^{-n}} = a^n.$$

Polynomials (Lesson 7-3)
- The degree of a monomial is the sum of the exponents of all its variables.
- The degree of a polynomial is the greatest degree of any term. To find the degree of a polynomial, you must find the degree of each term.

Operations with Polynomials
(Lessons 7-4 to 7-7)
- The Distributive Property can be used to multiply a polynomial by a monomial.
- Square of a Sum: $(a + b)^2 = a^2 + 2ab + b^2$
- Square of a Difference: $(a - b)^2 = a^2 - 2ab + b^2$
- Product of a Sum and a Difference:
  $(a + b)(a - b) = (a - b)(a + b) = a^2 - b^2$

Summative Assessment

 Vocabulary Test, p. 62

Key Vocabulary

binomial (p. 376)
constant (p. 358)
degree of a monomial (p. 377)
degree of a polynomial (p. 377)
difference of two squares (p. 406)
FOIL method (p. 399)
monomial (p. 358)
negative exponent (p. 369)
polynomial (p. 376)
Power of a Power (p. 360)
Power of a Product (p. 360)
Power of a Quotient (p. 367)
Product of Powers (p. 359)
Quotient of Powers (p. 366)
trinomial (p. 376)
zero exponent (p. 368)

Vocabulary Check

Choose a term from the vocabulary list that best matches each example.

1. $4^{-3} = \frac{1}{4^3}$ negative exponent

2. $(n^3)^5 = n^{15}$ Power of a Power

3. $\frac{4x^2y}{8xy^3} = \frac{x}{2y^2}$ Quotient of Powers

4. $4x^2$ monomial

5. $x^2 - 3x + 1$ trinomial

6. $2^0 = 1$ zero exponent

7. $x^4 - 3x^3 + 3x^2 - 1$ polynomial

8. $x^2 + 2$ binomial

9. $(a^3b)(2ab^2) = 2a^4b^3$ Product of Powers

10. $(x + 3)(x - 4) = x^2 - 4x + 3x - 12$ FOIL method

  Vocabulary Review at ca.algebra1.com

Lesson-by-Lesson Review

7-1 **Multiplying Monomials** (pp. 358–364) 12–18. See margin.

Simplify.

11. $y^3 \cdot y^3 \cdot y$ y^7

12. $(3ab)(-4a^2b^3)$

13. $(-4a^2x)(-5a^3x^4)$

14. $(4a^2b)^3$

15. $(-3xy)^2(4x)^3$

16. $(-2c^2d)^4(-3c^2)^3$

17. $-\frac{1}{2}(m^2n^4)^2$

18. $(5a^2)^3 + 7(a^6)$

19. **GEOMETRY** A cone has a radius of $4x^3$ and a height of $3b^2$. Use the formula $V = \frac{1}{3}(\pi r^2 \ell)$ to find the volume of the cone. $16\pi x^6 b^2$

Example 1 Simplify $(2ab^2)(3a^2b^3)$.

$(2ab^2)(3a^2b^3)$

$= (2 \cdot 3)(a \cdot a^2)(b^2 \cdot b^3)$ Commutative Property

$= 6a^3b^5$ Product of Powers

Example 2 Simplify $(2x^2y^3)^3$.

$(2x^2y^3)^3 = 2^3(x^2)^3(y^3)^3$ Power of a Product

$= 8x^6y^9$ Power of a Power

7-2 **Dividing Monomials** (pp. 366–373) 25. $\frac{bx^3}{3ay^2}$

Simplify. Assume that no denominator is equal to zero.

20. $\frac{(3y)^0}{6a}$ $\frac{1}{6a}$

21. $\left(\frac{3bc^2}{4d}\right)^3$ $\frac{27b^3c^5}{64d^3}$

22. $x^{-2}y^0z^3$ $\frac{z^3}{x^2}$

23. $\frac{27b^{-2}}{14b^{-3}}$ $\frac{27b}{14}$

24. $\frac{(3a^3bc^2)^2}{18a^2b^3c^4}$ $\frac{a^4}{2b}$

25. $\frac{-16a^3b^2x^4y}{-48a^4bxy^3}$

26. $\frac{(-a)^5b^8}{a^5b^2}$ $-b^6$

27. $\frac{(4a^{-1})^{-2}}{(2a^4)^2}$ $\frac{1}{64a^6}$

28. $\left(\frac{5xy^{-2}}{35x^{-2}y^6}\right)^0$ 1

29. $\frac{12}{3}\left(\frac{m}{n^3}\right)\left(\frac{n^4}{m^3}\right)$ $\frac{4n}{m^2}$

30. **GEOMETRY** The area of a triangle is $50a^2b$ square feet. The base of the triangle is $5a$ feet. What is the height of the triangle? $20ab$

5a ft

Example 3 Simplify $\frac{2x^6y}{8x^2y^2}$. Assume that no denominator is equal to zero.

$\frac{2x^6y}{8x^2y^2} = \left(\frac{2}{8}\right)\left(\frac{x^6}{x^2}\right)\left(\frac{y}{y^2}\right)$ Group the powers with the same base.

$= \left(\frac{1}{4}\right)(x^{6-2})(y^{1-2})$ Quotient of Powers

$= \frac{x^4}{4y}$ Simplify.

Example 4 Simplify $\frac{m^{-4}n^3p^0}{mn^{-2}}$. Assume that no denominator is zero.

$\frac{m^{-4}n^3p^0}{mn^{-2}} = \left(\frac{m^{-4}}{m}\right)\left(\frac{n^3}{n^{-2}}\right)(p^0)$ Group the powers with the same base.

$= \left(m^{-4-1}\right)\left(n^{3+2}\right)$ Quotient of Powers and Zero Exponent

$= \frac{n^5}{m^5}$ Simplify.

Additional Answers

12. $-12a^3b^4$

13. $20a^5x^5$

14. $64a^6b^3$

15. $576x^5y^2$

16. $-432c^{14}d^4$

17. $-\frac{1}{2}m^4n^8$

18. $132a^6$

Additional Answers

36. $-4x^4 + 5x^3y^2 - 2x^2y^3 + xy - 27$

38. $-3x^3 + x^2 - 5x + 5$

39. $4x^2 - 5xy + 6y^2$

40. $4z^2 - 2z + 10$

41. $21m^4 - 10m - 1$

42. $16m^2n^2 + 10mn + 11$

43. $-7p^2 - 2p + 25$

7-3 **Polynomials** (pp. 376–381)

Find the degree of each polynomial.

31. $n - 2p^2$ **2**

32. $29n^2 + 17n^2t^2$ **4**

33. $4xy + 9x^3z^2 + 17rs^3$ **5**

34. $-6x^5y - 2y^4 + 4 - 8y^2$ **6**

Arrange the terms of each polynomial so that the powers of x are in descending order.

35. $3x^4 - x + x^2 - 5$ $3x^4 + x^2 - x - 5$

36. $-2x^2y^3 - 27 - 4x^4 + xy + 5x^3y^2$
See margin.

37. **CONSTRUCTION** Ben is building a brick patio with pavers using the drawing below. Write a polynomial to represent the area of the patio.
$2\pi x^2 + 12x + 5$

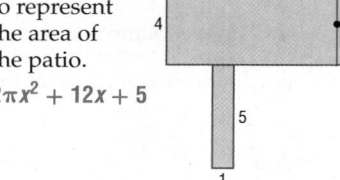

Example 5 Find the degree of $2xy^3 + x^2y$.

Polynomial:	$2xy^3 + x^2y$
Terms:	$2xy^3, x^2y$
Degree of Each Term:	4, 3
Degree of Polynomial:	4

Example 6 Arrange the terms of $4x^2 + 9x^3 - 2 - x$ so that the powers of x are in descending order.

$4x^2 + 9x^3 - 2 - x$

$= 4x^2 + 9x^3 - 2x^0 - x^1$ $x^0 = 1$ and $x = x^1$

$= 9x^3 + 4x^2 - x - 2$ $3 > 2 > 1 > 0$

7-4 **Adding and Subtracting Polynomials** (pp. 384–388) **38–43. See margin.**

Find each sum or difference.

38. $(2x^2 - 5x + 7) - (3x^3 + x^2 + 2)$

39. $(x^2 - 6xy + 7y^2) + (3x^2 + xy - y^2)$

40. $(7z^2 + 4) - (3z^2 + 2z - 6)$

41. $(13m^4 - 7m - 10) + (8m^4 - 3m + 9)$

42. $(11m^2n^2 + 4mn - 6) + (5m^2n^2 + 6mn + 17)$

43. $(-5p^2 + 3p + 49) - (2p^2 + 5p + 24)$

44. **GARDENING** Kyle is planting flowers around the perimeter of his rectangular garden. If the perimeter of his garden is $110x$ and one side measures $25x$, find the length of the other side. **$30x$**

Example 7 Find $(7r^2 + 9r) - (12r^2 - 4)$.

$(7r^2 + 9r) - (12r^2 - 4)$

$= 7r^2 + 9r + (-12r^2 + 4)$ The additive inverse of $12r^2 - 4$ is $-12r^2 + 4$.

$= (7r^2 - 12r^2) + 9r + 4$ Group like terms.

$= -5r^2 + 9r + 4$ Add like terms.

Mixed Problem Solving
For mixed problem-solving practice,
see page 750.

7-5 **Multiplying a Polynomial by a Monomial** (pp. 390–395)

Simplify. **47. $61y^3 - 16y^2 + 167y - 18$**

45. $b(4b - 1) + 10b$ $4b^2 + 9b$

46. $x(3x - 5) + 7(x^2 - 2x + 9)$ $10x^2 - 19x + 63$

47. $8y(11y^2 - 2y + 13) - 9(3y^3 - 7y + 2)$

48. $2x(x - y^2 + 5) - 5y^2(3x - 2)$
$2x^2 - 17xy^2 + 10x + 10y^2$

Solve each equation.

49. $m(2m - 5) + m = 2m(m - 6) + 16$ 2

50. $2(3w + w^2) - 6 = 2w(w - 4) + 10$ $1\frac{1}{7}$

51. **SHOPPING** Nicole bought x shirts for
$15.00 each, y pants for $25.72 each,
and z belts for $12.53 each. Sales tax
on these items was 7%. Write an
expression to find the total cost of
Nicole's purchases. $16.05x + 27.52y + 13.41z$

Example 8 Simplify $x^2(x + 2) + 3(x^3 + 4x^2)$.

$x^2(x + 2) + 3(x^3 + 4x^2)$
$= x^2(x) + x^2(2) + 3(x^3) + 3(4x^2)$
$= x^3 + 2x^2 + 3x^3 + 12x^2$ Multiply.
$= 4x^3 + 14x^2$ Combine like terms.

Example 9 Solve
$x(x - 10) + x(x + 2) + 3 = 2x(x + 1) - 7$.

$x(x - 10) + x(x + 2) + 3 = 2x(x + 1) - 7$
$x^2 - 10x + x^2 + 2x + 3 = 2x^2 + 2x - 7$
$2x^2 - 8x + 3 = 2x^2 + 2x - 7$
$-8x + 3 = 2x - 7$
$-10x = -10$
$x = 1$

7-6 **Multiplying Polynomials** (pp. 398–403)

Find each product.

52. $(r - 3)(r + 7)$ $r^2 + 4r - 21$

53. $(4a - 3)(a + 4)$ $4a^2 + 13a - 12$

54. $(5r - 7s)(4r + 3s)$ $20r^2 - 13rs - 21s^2$

55. $(3x + 0.25)(6x - 0.5)$ $18x^2 - 0.125$

56. $(2k + 1)(k^2 + 7k - 9)$ $2k^3 + 15k^2 - 11k - 9$

57. $(4p - 3)(3p^2 - p + 2)$ $12p^3 - 13p^2 + 11p - 6$

58. **MANUFACTURING** A company is
designing a box in the shape of a
rectangular prism for dry pasta. The
length is 2 inches more than twice the
width and the height is 3 inches more
than the length. Write an expression for
the volume of the box. $4w^3 + 14w^2 + 10w$

Example 10 Find $(3x + 2)(x - 2)$.

$$\begin{array}{c} \text{F} \quad \text{L} \\ (3x + 2)(x - 2) \\ \text{I} \\ \text{O} \end{array}$$

$$\begin{array}{cccc} \text{F} & \text{O} & \text{I} & \text{L} \end{array}$$
$= (3x)(x) + (3x)(-2) + (2)(x) + (2)(-2)$
$= 3x^2 - 6x + 2x - 4$ Multiply
$= 3x^2 - 4x - 4$ Combine like terms.

Example 11 Find $(2y - 5)(4y^2 + 3y - 7)$.

$(2y - 5)(4y^2 + 3y - 7)$
$= 2y(4y^2 + 3y - 7) - 5(4y^2 + 3y - 7)$
$= 8y^3 + 6y^2 - 14y - 20y^2 - 15y + 35$
$= 8y^3 - 14y^2 - 29y + 35$

Problem Solving Review

For additional practice in problem solving for Chapter 7, see the Mixed Problem Solving Appendix, p. 750 in the Student Handbook section.

Anticipation Guide

Have students complete the Chapter 7 Anticipation Guide and discuss how their responses have changed now that they have completed Chapter 7.

CRM **Anticipation Guide, p. 3**

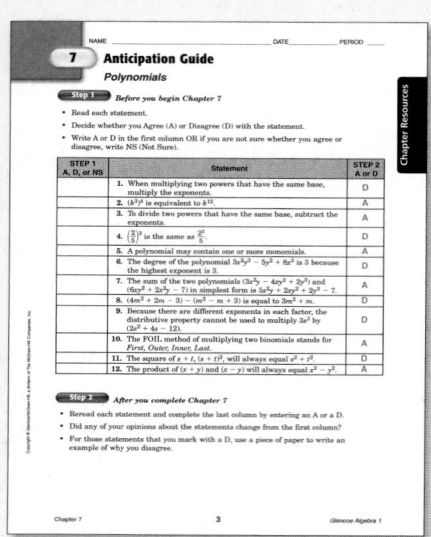

7-7 **Special Products** (pp. 404–409)

Find each product.

59. $(x - 6)(x + 6)$ $x^2 - 36$

60. $(4x + 7)^2$ $16x^2 + 56x + 49$

61. $(8x - 5)^2$ $64x^2 - 80x + 25$

62. $(5x - 3y)(5x + 3y)$ $25x^2 - 9y^2$

63. $(6a - 5b)^2$ $36a^2 - 60ab + 25b^2$

64. $(3m + 4n)^2$ $9m^2 + 24mn + 16n^2$

65. GENETICS Emily and Santos are both able to roll their tongues. Tongue rolling genes R are dominant over nonrolling genes r. A person with genes RR or Rr is able to roll their tongue. Someone with genes rr cannot roll their tongue. Suppose Emily's and Santos's genes for tongue rolling are Rr. Write an expression for the possible tongue-rolling abilities of Santos's and Emily's children. What is the probability that a child of Emily and Santos could not roll their tongue? $0.25RR + 0.5Rr + 0.25rr$; 0.25

Example 12 Find $(r - 5)^2$.

$(a - b)^2 = a^2 - 2ab + b^2$ Square of a Difference

$(r - 5)^2 = r^2 - 2(r)(5) + 5^2$ $a = r$ and $b = 5$

$= r^2 - 10r + 25$ Simplify.

Example 13 Find $(2c + 9)(2c - 9)$.

$(a + b)(a - b) = a^2 - b^2$

$(2c + 9)(2c - 9) = (2c)^2 - 9^2$ $a = 2c$ and $b = 9$

$= 4c^2 - 81$ Simplify.

414 **Chapter 7** Polynomials

Simplify. Assume that no denominator is equal to zero.

1. $(a^2b^4)(a^3b^5)$ a^5b^9

2. $(-12abc)(4a^2b^4)$ $-48a^3b^5c$

3. $\left(\dfrac{3}{5}m\right)^2$ $\dfrac{9}{25}m^2$

4. $(-3a)^4(a^5b)^2$ $81a^{14}b^2$

5. $(-5a^2)(-6b^3)^2$ $-180a^2b^6$

6. $\dfrac{mn^4}{m^3n^2}$ $\dfrac{n^2}{m^2}$

7. $\dfrac{9a^2bc^2}{63a^4bc}$ $\dfrac{c}{7a^2}$

8. $\dfrac{48a^2bc^5}{(3ab^3c^2)^2}$ $\dfrac{16c}{3b^5}$

Find the degree of each polynomial. Then arrange the terms so that the powers of y are in descending order.

9. $2y^2 + 8y^4 + 9y$ 4; $8y^4 + 2y^2 + 9y$

10. $5xy - 7 + 2y^4 - x^2y^3$ 5; $2y^4 - x^2y^3 + 5xy - 7$

Find each sum or difference.

11. $(5a + 3a^2 - 7a^3) + (2a - 8a^2 + 4)$

12. $(x^3 - 3x^2y + 4xy^2 + y^3)$ $-6x^3 - 4x^2y + 13xy^2$
$- (7x^3 + x^2y - 9xy^2 + y^3)$
11. $7a - 5a^2 - 7a^3 + 4$

13. GEOMETRY The measures of two sides of a triangle are given. If the perimeter is represented by $11x^2 - 29x + 10$, find the measure of the third side. $5x^2 - 23x - 23$

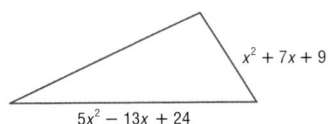

$x^2 + 7x + 9$
$5x^2 - 13x + 24$

14. MULTIPLE CHOICE What is the area of the square with sides that measure $x - 6$? **B**

A $4x - 24$

B $x^2 - 12x + 36$

C $x^2 + 12x + 36$

D $x^2 - 36$

Simplify.

15. $h^2 - 10h + 25$

15. $(h - 5)^2$

16. $(4x - y)(4x + y)$ $16x^2 - y^2$

17. $3x^2y^3(2x - xy^2)$

18. $(2a^2b + b^2)^2$

19. $(4m + 3n)(2m - 5n)$ $8m^2 - 14mn - 15n^2$

20. $(2c + 5)(3c^2 - 4c + 2)$ $6c^3 + 7c^2 - 16c + 10$

17. $6x^3y^3 - 3x^3y^5$ 18. $4a^4b^2 + 4a^2b^3 + b^4$

Solve each equation.

21. $2x(x - 3) = 2(x^2 - 7) + 2$ **2**

22. $3a(a^2 + 5) - 11 = a(3a^2 + 4)$ **1**

23. MULTIPLE CHOICE If $x^2 + 2xy + y^2 = 8$, find $3(x + y)^2$. **J**

F 2

H 12

G 4

J 24

GENETICS The Punnett square shows the possible gene combinations of a cross between two pea plants. Each plant passes on one dominant gene T for tallness and one recessive gene t for shortness.

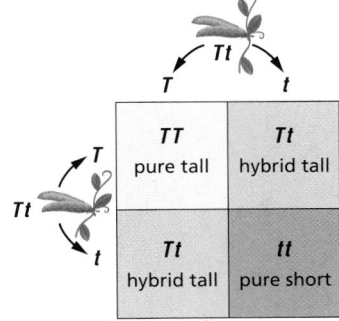

24. $(0.5T + 0.5t)^2 = 0.25T^2 + 0.5Tt + 0.25t^2$

24. Show how the possible combinations can be modeled by the square of a binomial.

25. What is the probability that the offspring will be pure tall (TT), hybrid tall (Tt), and pure short (tt)? **25% TT; 50% Tt; 25% tt**

 ✓ **Summative Assessment**

CRM Chapter 7 Resource Masters

Leveled Chapter 7 Tests

Form	Type	Level	Pages
1	MC	BL	63–64
2A	MC	OL	65–66
2B	MC	OL	67–68
2C	FR	OL	69–70
2D	FR	OL	71–72
3	FR	AL	73–74

MC = multiple-choice questions
FR = free-response questions

BL = below grade level
OL = on grade level
AL = above grade level

• Vocabulary Test, p. 62
• Extended-Response Test, p. 75

ExamView Assessment Suite Customize and create multiple versions of your chapter tests and their answer keys. All of the questions from the leveled chapter tests in the *Chapter 7 Resource Masters* are also available on ExamView Assessment Suite with the California Standard that each item assesses.

Data-Driven Decision Making	Exercises	Lesson	Standard	Resources for Review
Diagnostic Teaching Based on the results of the Chapter 7 Practice Test, use the following to review concepts that students continue to find challenging.	17, 21–22	7-5	10.0	**CRM** Study Guide and Intervention, pp. 35–36, 42–43, 50–51
	14, 16, 19–20	7-6	10.0	**Math Online** • Extra Examples
	15, 18, 23–25	7-7	10.0	• Personal Tutor • Concepts in Motion

 Read each question. Then fill in the correct answer on the answer document provided by your teacher or on a sheet of paper.

1 $\dfrac{4x^2}{12x^9} =$ **B**

A $3x^7$

B $\dfrac{1}{3x^7}$

C $\dfrac{1}{4x^7}$

D $\dfrac{x^7}{4}$

2 Ryan is 5 years older than his sister Rebecca. If the sum of their ages is 21, how old is Rebecca? **8**

3 Which expression is equivalent to x^4x^8? **J**

F x^2x^6

G x^3x^7

H x^4x^4

J x^5x^7

4 Simplify. **D**

$(x^2 - 4x + 2) - (x^2 + x - 5)$

A $x - 3$

B $-3x - 3$

C $-5x - 3$

D $-5x + 7$

5 If x is an integer, which of the following is the solution set for $4|x| = 24$? **G**

F $\{0, 6\}$

G $\{-6, 6\}$

H $\{-6, 0, 6\}$

J $\{0, 96\}$

6 The length of the rectangle below is 5 units longer than the width. Which expression could be used to represent the area of the rectangle? **A**

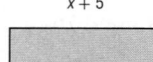

A $x^2 + 5x$

B $x^2 - 25$

C $x^2 + 5x + 5$

D $x^2 + 10x + 25$

7 Which of the following is equivalent to $2 - 3x > 4(x - 3)$? **J**

F $2 - 3x > 4x - 3$

G $2 - 3x > 4x - 6$

H $2 - 3x > 4x - 9$

J $2 - 3x > 4x - 12$

8 Solve $\dfrac{23 - r}{4} = 5$. **3**

 California Standards Practice at ca.algebra1.com

More California
Standards Practice
For practice by standard,
see pages CA1–CA43.

CHAPTER
7
California
Standards Practice

9 Which of the following is the graph of $y = \frac{3}{2}x + 3$? **A**

A
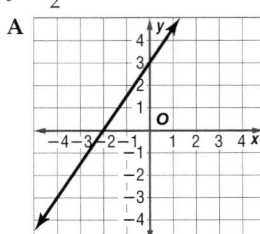

B
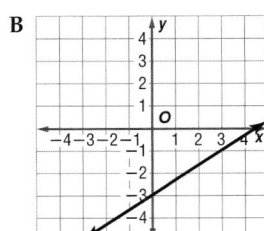

C
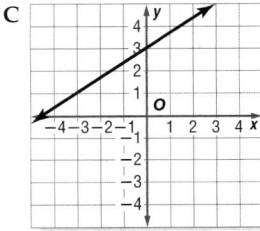

D
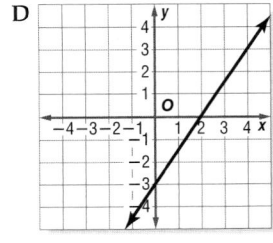

10 Which of the following points lies on the line $y = x$? **J**

F $(2, 0)$

G $(2, -2)$

H $(-2, 2)$

J $(-2, -2)$

11 What is the reciprocal of $\frac{ab^2}{c}$? **D**

A $-\frac{ab^2}{c}$

B $-\frac{c}{ab^2}$

C $\frac{ab^2}{c}$

D $\frac{c}{ab^2}$

Pre-AP/Anchor Problem

**Record your answer on a sheet of paper.
Show your work.**

12 Two cars leave at the same time and both drive to Sacramento. The cars' distance from Sacramento, in miles, can be represented by the two equations below, where t represents time in hours.

Car A: $A = 65t + 10$
Car B: $B = 55t + 20$

a. Which car is faster? Explain.

b. How far did Car B travel after 2 hours? **130 miles**

c. Find an expression that models the distance between the two cars. **$10t - 10$**

d. How far apart are the cars after $3\frac{1}{2}$ hours? **25 miles**

a. Car A is faster because it has a greater speed (slope).

Item Analysis

Exercises 2 and 8 are griddable questions. In a griddable question, students arrive at an answer and then record it in a special grid by coloring the appropriate bubble under each digit of the answer.

Answer Sheet Practice

Have students simulate taking a standardized test by recording their answers on practice recording sheets.

[CRM] Student Recording Sheet, p. 57

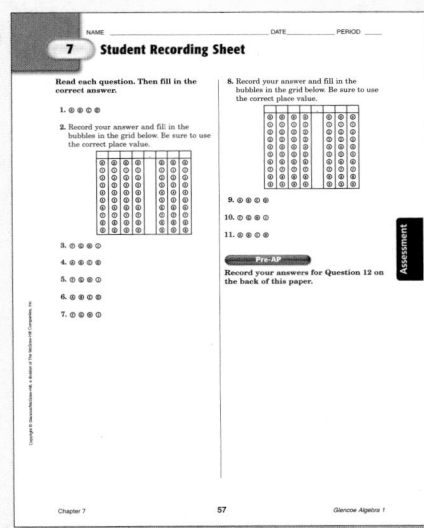

Homework Option

Get Ready for Chapter 8   Assign students the exercises on p. 419 as homework to assess whether they possess the prerequisite skills needed for the next chapter.

Page 383, Explore 7-4

7. Method from Activity 2:

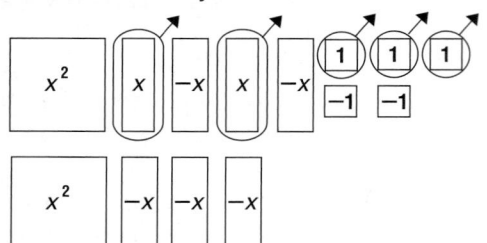

$$2x^2 - 5x - 2$$

You need to add zero pairs so that you can remove 2 green x-tiles and 3 yellow 1-tiles.

Method from Activity 3:

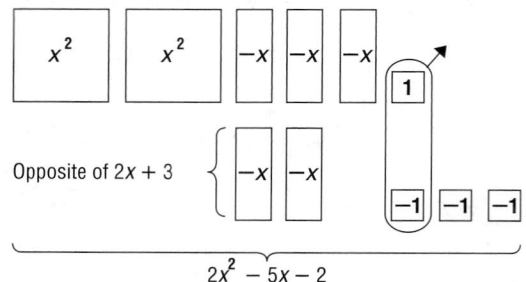

Opposite of $2x + 3$

$$2x^2 - 5x - 2$$

You remove all zero pairs to find the difference in simplest form.

Page 388, Lesson 7-4

50.

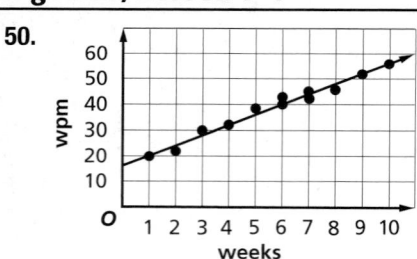

Pages 402–403, Lesson 7-6

50.

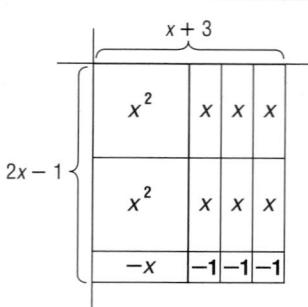

53. Multiplying binomials and two-digit numbers involves the use of the Distributive Property twice. Each procedure involves four multiplications and the addition of like terms.

$$
\begin{aligned}
24 \times 36 &= (4 + 20)(6 + 30) \\
&= (4 + 20)6 + (4 + 20)30 \\
&= (24 + 120) + (120 + 600) \\
&= 144 + 720 \\
&= 864
\end{aligned}
$$

The like terms in vertical 2-digit multiplication are digits with the same place value.

Page 408, Lesson 7-7

47.

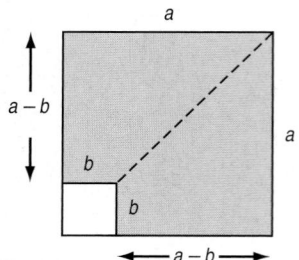

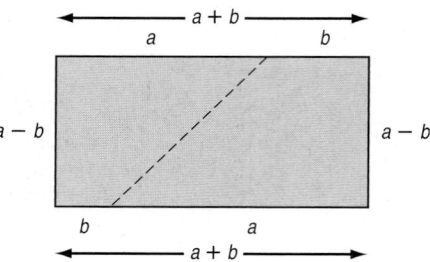

Area of rectangle $= (a - b)(a + b)$

or

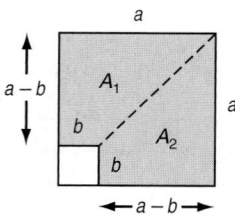

Area of a trapezoid $= \frac{1}{2}(\text{height})(\text{base 1} + \text{base 2})$

$A_1 = \frac{1}{2}(a - b)(a + b)$

$A_2 = \frac{1}{2}(a - b)(a + b)$

Total area of shaded region

$$
\begin{aligned}
&= \left[\frac{1}{2}(a - b)(a + b)\right] + \left[\frac{1}{2}(a - b)(a + b)\right] \\
&= (a - b)(a + b)
\end{aligned}
$$

49.

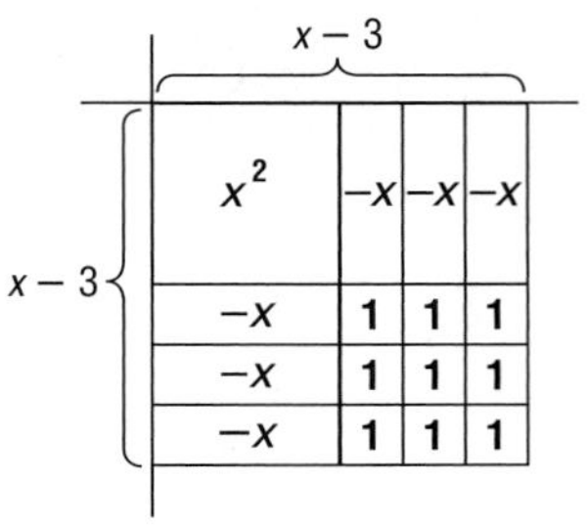

$x - 3$

$x - 3$

x^2	$-x$	$-x$	$-x$
$-x$	1	1	1
$-x$	1	1	1
$-x$	1	1	1

CHAPTER 8

Chapter Overview

Factoring

Standards-Based Lesson Plan	Pacing Your Lessons		
LESSONS AND OBJECTIVES	California Standards	40-50 Minute Periods	90-Minute Periods
8-1 Monomials and Factoring (pp. 420–424) • Find prime factorizations of monomials. • Find the greatest common factors of monomials.	11.0	2	0.5
Explore 8-2 Factoring Using the Distributive Property (p. 425) • Use algebra tiles to model using the Distributive Property to factor binomials. **8-2 Factoring Using the Distributive Property** (pp. 426–431) • Factor polynomials by using the Distributive Property. • Solve quadratic equations of the form $ax^2 + bx = 0$.	11.0	2	1.5
Explore 8-3 Factoring Trinomials (pp. 432–433) • Use algebra tiles to model factoring trinomials. **8-3 Factoring Trinomials: $x^2 + bx + c$** (pp. 434–439) • Factor trinomials of the form $x^2 + bx + c$. • Solve equations of the form $x^2 + bx + c = 0$.	11.0 14.0	2.5	1.5
8-4 Factoring Trinomials: $ax^2 + bx + c$ (pp. 441–446) • Factor trinomials of the form $ax^2 + bx + c$. • Solve equations of the form $ax^2 + bx + c = 0$.	11.0 14.0	2.5	1
8-5 Factoring Differences of Squares (pp. 447–452) • Factor binomials that are differences of squares. • Solve equations involving the differences of squares.	11.0 14.0	2	1
8-6 Perfect Squares and Factoring (pp. 454–460) • Factor perfect square trinomials. • Solve equations involving perfect squares.	11.0 14.0	2	0.5
REVIEW		1	0.5
ASSESSMENT		1	0.5*
TOTAL		15	7

The complete **Assessment Planner** for Chapter 8 is provided on p. 419

Begin Chapter 8 in the second half of the period.

The complete Assessment Planner for Chapter 8 is provided on p. 419.

Professional Development

California Standards Vertical Alignment

Before Chapter 8

Related Topics from Grade 7

• Multiply and divide monomials ◄━━ Standard 7AF2.2

Chapter 8

Topics from Algebra I

• Apply basic factoring techniques to second-and simple third-degree polynomials

• Solve a quadratic equation by factoring or completing the square

See individual lessons for the specific Standards covered

After Chapter 8

Preparation for Algebra II

• Factor special polynomials ◄━━ Standard 2A4.0

• Solve and graph quadratic equations in the complex number system ◄━━ Standard 2A8.0

What the Research Says…

In a meta-analysis of 60 research studies, Sowell (1989) found that for students of all ages, mathematics achievement is increased and students' attitudes toward mathematics are improved with the long-term use of manipulative materials.

• Lessons 8-2A and 8-3A continue the use of algebra tiles that was begun in Chapter 7. Tiles are used in these lessons to develop strategies for factoring polynomials.

• Algebra tiles can be used to help students who have difficulty with the factoring strategies presented throughout Chapter 8.

• Another type of manipulative activity, rearranging regions cut from paper, is used in Lesson 8-5 to examine factoring the differences of squares.

[Source: Sowell, E.J. (1989). "Effects of Manipulative Materials in Mathematics Instruction," *Journal for Research in Mathematics Education*, 20(5), pp. 498–505.]

Back-Mapping

California Algebra 1 was conceived and developed with the final result in mind, student success in Algebra I and beyond. The authors, using the California Mathematics Standards as their guide, developed this brand-new series by "back-mapping" from the desired result of student success in Algebra I and beyond. McGraw-Hill's *California Geometry, California Algebra 2,* and *California Algebra Readiness* were developed utilizing the same philosophy.

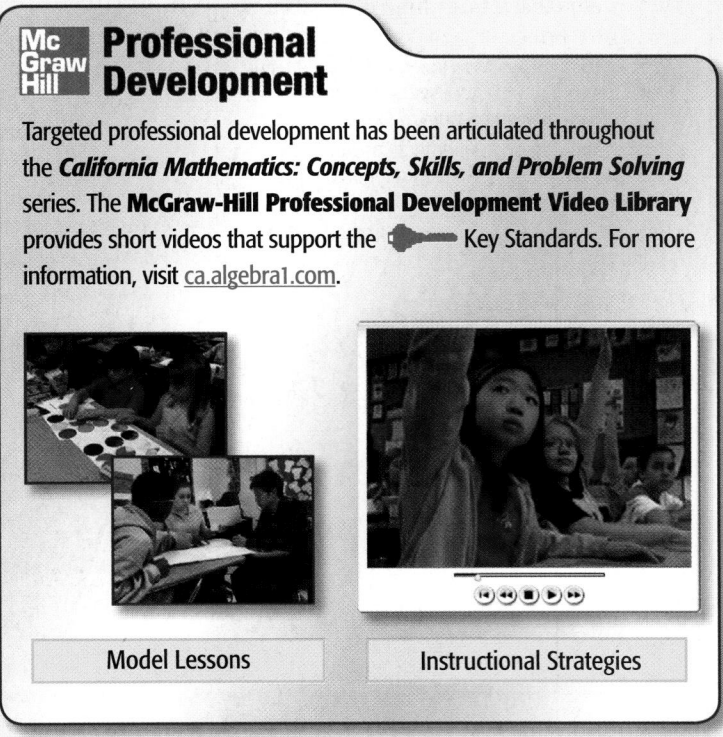

Professional Development

Targeted professional development has been articulated throughout the *California Mathematics: Concepts, Skills, and Problem Solving* series. The **McGraw-Hill Professional Development Video Library** provides short videos that support the ◄━━ Key Standards. For more information, visit <u>ca.algebra1.com</u>.

| Model Lessons | Instructional Strategies |

TeacherWorks™ All-in-One Planner and Resource Center

All of the print materials from the Classroom Resource Masters are available on your TeacherWorks™ CD-ROM.

BL = Below Grade Level   **OL** = On Grade Level   **AL** = Above Grade Level   **ELL** = English Language Learner

Chapter Resource Masters				8-1	8-2	8-3	8-4	8-5	8-6
BL OL		ELL	Lesson Reading Guide	5	12	19	26	34	42
BL OL		ELL	Study Guide and Intervention*	6	13	20	27	35	43
BL OL			Skills Practice*	8	15	22	29	37	45
	OL AL		Practice*	9	16	23	30	38	46
	OL AL		Word Problem Practice*	10	17	24	31	39	47
	OL AL		Enrichment	11	18	25	32	40	48
	OL AL		Calculator and Spreadsheet Activities				33	41	
	OL AL		Chapter Assessments*	49–70					
BL OL AL			5-Minute Check Transparencies	✓	✓	✓	✓	✓	✓
BL OL			Teaching Algebra with Manipulatives		✓	✓	✓	✓	✓

Also available in Spanish.

AssignmentWorks

Differentiated Assignments, Answers, and Solutions

- Print a customized assignment worksheet using the Student Edition exercises along with an answer key or worked-out solutions.
- Use default lesson assignments as outlined in the Differentiated Homework Options in the Teacher Wraparound Edition.
- Includes modified questions from the Student Edition.

Interactive Classroom

This CD-ROM is a customizable Microsoft® PowerPoint® presentation that includes:

- In-Class Examples
- Your Turn Exercises*
- 5-Minute Check Transparencies*
- Links to Online Study Tools
- Concepts in Motion

compatible with response pad technology

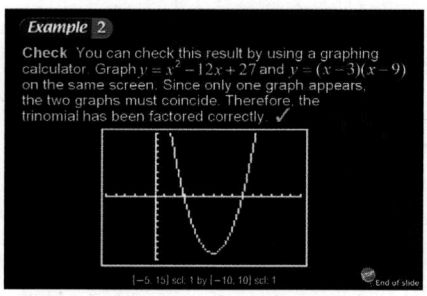

Example 2

Check You can check this result by using a graphing calculator. Graph $y = x^2 - 12x + 27$ and $y = (x - 3)(x - 9)$ on the same screen. Since only one graph appears, the two graphs must coincide. Therefore, the trinomial has been factored correctly. ✓

[−5, 15] scl. 1 by [−10, 10] scl. 1

ExamView® Assessment Suite

 **ExamView** Assessment Suite lets you

- Create, edit, and customize tests and worksheets using QuickTest Wizard
- Create multiple versions of tests and modify them for a desired level of difficulty
- Translate from English to Spanish and vice versa
- Build tests aligned with your state standards
- Track students' progress using the Teacher Management System

Student Resources

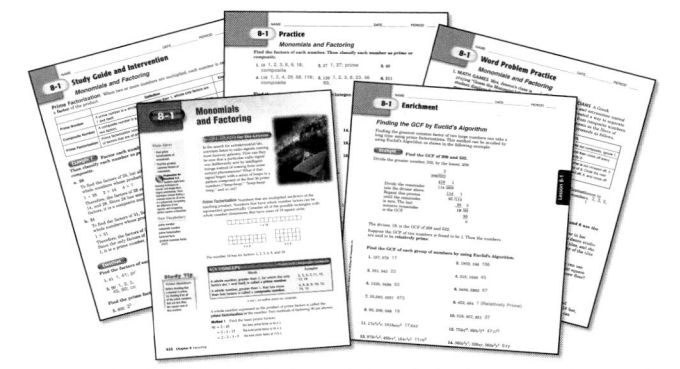

Internet Resources

Math Online ca.algebra1.com

Focus on Mathematical Content

Big Idea for Chapter 8:
Factoring

In Chapter 7, algebraic expressions were multiplied to form a new expression that was the product of the factors. When the product is given and the factors are found, the process is called *factoring*. Factoring is the inverse of multiplying. Algebraic skills are employed in the factoring process, such as looking for a common factor, recognizing the difference in two squares, and factoring trinomials of the form $ax^2 + bx + c$. These same skills can be used to factor polynomial expressions that occur in problem situations.

Why It's Important

For This Chapter
The lessons in this chapter use factoring of monomials and polynomials to solve problem situations that can be modeled by quadratic equations.
- How do you find the GCF of a set of monomials? (Lesson 8-1)
- What is the Zero Product Property and how is it used to solve equations? (Lesson 8-2)
- How do you factor a quadratic expression of the form $x^2 + bx + c$? (Lesson 8-3)
- How do you factor a quadratic expression of the form $ax^2 + bx + c$ where $a \neq 1$? (Lesson 8-4)
- How can the difference of two squares be factored? (Lesson 8-5)
- What pattern is used to determine whether an expression is a perfect square trinomial? (Lesson 8-6)

After This Chapter
- In Chapter 9, solving an equation by factoring is just one of the ways to solve quadratic equations.
- In Chapter 11, students will use factoring to simplify rational expressions and solve rational equations.
- In geometry, students will use factoring to solve problems involving areas and volumes of geometric figures.
- In future courses, students will use factoring as a basis for further studies of polynomial equations and functions.

8-1 Monomials and Factoring

A prime number is a whole number greater than 1 that has only two factors, 1 and itself. The prime factorization of a whole number expresses the number as the product of its prime number factors. Monomials can also be written in factored form.

- To factor a monomial, express it as the product of prime numbers and variables, where no variable has an exponent greater than 1. For example, x^4 in factored form is $x \cdot x \cdot x \cdot x$.

- The greatest common factor (GCF) of two or more monomials can be found by using their prime factorizations. The GCF of two or more monomials is the product of their common factors when each monomial is in factored form.

- If the GCF of two or more monomials is 1, then the two monomials are said to be relatively prime.

8-2 Factoring Using the Distributive Property

Some polynomials can be factored by writing them as the product of a monomial and a polynomial. To factor using the Distributive Property, reverse the process of multiplying a polynomial by a monomial.

- To factor a polynomial, begin by finding the GCF of all its terms. Then rewrite each term as the product of the GCF and its remaining factors. Finally, use the Distributive Property to factor out the GCF.

- Use factoring by grouping for factoring polynomials of 4 or more terms. Group terms that have a common factor in pairs. Factor the GCF out of each pair of factors using the Distributive Property. Each pair of factored terms should now have a common binomial factor. Factor out the common binomial factor using the Distributive Property. Form the second binomial factor from the remaining factors. Sometimes the common binomial factors are additive inverses of each other. In this case, rewrite one of them as the product of -1 and its additive inverse.

- According to the Zero Product Property, if the product of two factors is 0, then one of the factors must be 0. The Zero Product Property can be used to solve equations of the form $ab = 0$ or equations that can be written in this form by factoring. Each factor is set equal to 0 and the resulting equations are solved.

Factoring Trinomials: $x^2 + bx + c$

Two binomials can be multiplied using the FOIL method. By reversing the process, you can factor some quadratic polynomials of the form $x^2 + bx + c$ into two binomials.

- To factor the trinomial, find two integers, m and n, whose sum is b and whose product is c. The factors of the trinomial are the two binomials $(x + m)$ and $(x + n)$, where $b = m + n$ and $c = mn$.

- Determining whether m and n are positive or negative depends on b and c. If b is negative and c is positive, then both m and n are negative. If b is negative and c is negative, then m and n have to have different signs. Remember that the product of a positive and a negative is a negative.

Some quadratic equations written in the form $x^2 + bx + c = 0$ can be solved by using the Zero Product Property. Begin by factoring the trinomial and then setting each factor equal to 0. Solve the resulting equations to find the solutions for the quadratic equation. Solutions should be checked in the original equation.

 Factoring Trinomials: $ax^2 + bx + c$

To factor a trinomial in which the coefficient of x^2 is not 1, first check to see if the terms of the polynomial have a common factor. If they do, factor it out.

- After factoring out the GCF, if x^2 still has a coefficient other than 1, then factor $ax^2 + bx + c$ by listing all of the factors of the product of a and c. You will need two factors, m and n, such that $ac = mn$ and b equals $m + n$. Rewrite the trinomial, replacing bx with $mx + nx$. You now have the polynomial $ax^2 + mx + nx + c$. With four terms, the grouping technique used in Lesson 8-2 can be used to factor the polynomial into two binomial factors.

- Any polynomial that cannot be factored is a prime polynomial.

- Equations of the form $ax^2 + bx + c = 0$ can be solved by using the method above to factor the trinomial and then applying the Zero Product Property.

 Factoring Differences of Squares

The pattern for the product of a sum and difference, $(a + b)(a - b) = a^2 - b^2$, was covered in Lesson 7-7. The binomial $a^2 - b^2$ is known as the difference of squares and can be factored as the product of a sum and a difference.

To factor the difference of squares, find a (the square root of the first term) and b (the square root of the last term). The two binomial factors are the sum of the square roots and the difference of the square roots. In factored form, $a^2 - b^2 = (a + b)(a - b)$.

Other situations may occur when factoring. For example, the terms of the expression may have a common factor. In this case, factor out the GCF before applying any other factoring technique. There are times when a technique may be applied more than one time. Also, there are problems in which several factoring techniques may be applied to the problem.

Many polynomial equations can be solved using the appropriate factoring techniques and/or the Zero Product Property.

 Perfect Squares and Factoring

Lesson 7-7 covered special products such as patterns for the square of a sum, $(a + b)^2 = a^2 + 2ab + b^2$, and the square of a difference, $(a - b)^2 = a^2 - 2ab + b^2$. The products that result from squaring a binomial, $a^2 + 2ab + b^2$ and $a^2 - 2ab + b^2$, are known as perfect square trinomials.

Three conditions must be satisfied for a trinomial to be a perfect square trinomial.

- The first and last terms must be perfect squares.

- The middle term must be twice the product of the square roots of the first and last terms.

- The last term of a perfect square trinomial cannot be negative.

To factor a perfect square trinomial with a positive middle term, use the pattern $a^2 + 2ab + b^2 = (a + b)^2$. To factor a perfect square trinomial with a negative middle term, use the pattern $a^2 - 2ab + b^2 = (a - b)^2$.

The Square Root Property can be used to solve any equation that is in the form $x^2 = n$ or can be written in that form. This property says that for any number n that is greater than 0, if $x^2 = n$, then $x = \pm\sqrt{n}$. The Square Root Property lets you take the square root of each side of the equation as long as both the positive and negative square roots of the number are considered.

CHAPTER 8

Differentiated Instruction

Options for Chapter 8 Lessons

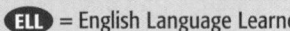 = English Language Learner   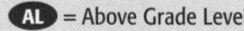 = Above Grade Level   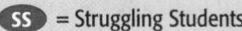 = Struggling Students   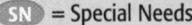 = Special Needs

Using Verbal Skills **ELL**

Use with Lesson 8-1

Factoring integers is a very visual skill, whether it is done by writing out factors in a line or by using a factor tree. Have students describe one of the methods of factoring in their own words, without actually writing out the factors as an example. Alternatively, have students write a description of how to factor, using an example as a guide.

Using Kinesthetic Learning **AL**

Use with Lesson 8-3

As students are learning the rules for factoring trinomials, encourage them to use algebra tiles to confirm their results. Students should soon realize that the greater the values of b and c in the trinomials, the more cumbersome the algebra tiles become, which should reinforce the importance of learning to factor using the method in the text.

Using Interpersonal Skills **SS** **SN**

Use with Lesson 8-5

Consider having students complete the Check for Understanding problems on one day, and then check their own work on the next day, examining their work and answers. Letting their own work sit for a day often allows students to see mistakes or problems in their work that they otherwise might not have noticed. It may also give students more of a chance to ask for help on difficult problems.

Noteables™ Interactive Study Notebook with Foldables™

Noteables™ Interactive Study Notebook with Foldables™ is a study organizer that provides helpful steps for students to follow to organize their notes for Chapter 8.

- Students use Noteables to record notes and to complete their Foldables as you present the material for each lesson.
- Noteables correspond to the Examples in the *Teacher Wraparound Edition* and *Interactive Classroom CD-ROM.*

Intervention

Quick Review Math Handbook*

is Glencoe's mathematical handbook for students and parents.

Hot Words includes a glossary of terms.

Hot Topics consists of two parts:

- explanations of key mathematical concepts
- exercises to check students' understanding.

Lesson	Hot Topics Section	Lesson	Hot Topics Section
8-1	6.2	8-4	3.2

*Also available in Spanish

Teacher To Teacher

Marcia Griffin
J.F. Dobie High School
Houston, TX

USE WITH LESSON 8-3

" I have my students use the 'box method' to factor polynomials. For example, to factor $x^2 + 6x + 8$, they start with a 2 × 2 grid and put the first and last terms into the boxes as shown below. Then they factor x^2 as $x \cdot x$ and put the factors outside the box. The number 8 has two different factor pairs: 1, 8 and 2, 4. They try different factor pairs until they find the one that results in the middle term 6x. "

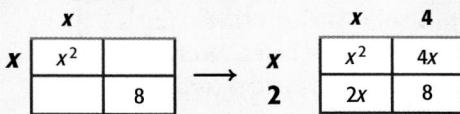

Reading and Writing in Mathematics

STUDY SKILL

Students may find that making study cards is helpful when they are learning new terms, skills, and concepts. Making the cards aids in learning because it requires students to summarize information. Then the cards can be used as students prepare for tests.

The cards shown at the right describe some of the factoring techniques shown in Chapter 8. The name of the factoring technique and an example are on the front of the card and the factored expression is on the back of the card.

Front	Back
Greatest Common Factor $5x^4 + 10x^3 - 20x^2$	$5x^2(x^2 + 2x - 4)$
Difference of Squares $16x^2 - 169$	$(4x - 13)(4x + 13)$

CReating **I**ndependence through **S**tudent-owned **S**trategies

CHAPTER 8 Notes

Focus Students write notes, record concepts, and define terms about factoring for each lesson in this chapter.

Teach Have students make and label their Foldables as illustrated.

Before beginning each lesson, ask students to think of one question that comes to mind as they skim through the lesson. Have them write the questions on the front of the corresponding tabs. As they read and work through the lesson, ask them to record the answers to their questions under the tabs.

When to Use It Students should use their Foldables to take notes, record concepts, define terms, and record other questions about factoring. A version of a completed Foldable is shown on p. 461.

Differentiated Instruction

CRM Student-Built Glossary, pp. 1–2

Students should complete the chart by providing the definition and an example of each term as they progress through Chapter 8. This study tool can also be used to review for the chapter test.

Materials Needed for Chapter 8

- Internet (Lesson 8-1)
- algebra tiles (Explore 8-2, Explore 8-3)
- graphing calculator (Lesson 8-3)
- product mat (Explore 8-2, Explore 8-3)
- straightedge (Lesson 8-5)
- scissors (Lesson 8-5)

CHAPTER 8 Factoring

BIG Ideas

- **Standard 11.0** Students apply basic factoring techniques to second-and simple third-degree polynomials. These techniques include finding a common factor for all terms in a polynomial, recognizing the difference of two squares, and recognizing perfect squares of binomials.

- **Standard 14.0** Students solve a quadratic equation by factoring or completing the square. (Key)

Key Vocabulary

factored form (p. 421)

perfect square trinomials (p. 454)

prime polynomial (p. 443)

● Real-World Link

Dolphins Factoring is used to solve problems involving vertical motion. For example, factoring can be used to determine how long a dolphin that jumps out of the water is in the air.

FOLDABLES Study Organizer **Factoring** Make this Foldable to help you organize your notes on factoring. Begin with a sheet of plain $8\frac{1}{2}$" by 11" paper.

1 **Fold** in thirds and then in half along the width.

2 **Open.** Fold lengthwise, leaving a $\frac{1}{2}$" tab on the right.

3 **Open.** Cut short side along folds to make tabs.

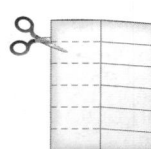

4 **Label** each tab as shown.

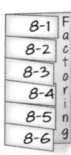

8-1
8-2
8-3
8-4
8-5
8-6
Factoring

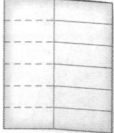

Diagnose Readiness You have two options for checking Prerequisite Skills.

Option 1

Take the Quick Check below. Refer to the Quick Review for help.

Option 2

Math Online Take the Online Readiness Quiz at ca.algebra1.com.

QUICK Check

Rewrite each expression using the Distributive Property. Then simplify.
(Lesson 1-5) **(Used in Lessons 8-2 through 8-6.)**

1. $3(4 - x)$ $12 - 3x$

2. $a(a + 5)$ $a^2 + 5a$

3. $-7(n^2 - 3n + 1)$ $-7n^2 + 21n - 7$

4. $6y(-3y - 5y - 5y^2 + y^3)$ $-48y^2 - 30y^3 + 6y^4$

5. **JOBS** In a typical week, Mr. Jackson averages 4 hours using e-mail, 10 hours of meeting in person, and 20 hours on the telephone. Write an expression that could be used to determine how many hours he will spend on these activities over the next month. $4(4e + 10p + 20t)$

(Used in Lessons 8-3 and 8-4.)
Find each product. (Lesson 7-6)

6. $(x + 4)(x + 7)$ $x^2 + 11x + 28$

7. $(3n - 4)(n + 5)$ $3n^2 + 11n - 20$

8. $(6a - 2b)(9a + b)$ $54a^2 - 12ab - 2b^2$

9. $(-x - 8y)(2x - 12y)$ $-2x^2 - 4xy + 96y^2$

10. **TABLE TENNIS** The dimensions of a homemade table tennis table are represented by a width of $2x + 3$ and a length of $x + 1$. Find an expression for the area of the table tennis table. $2x^2 + 5x + 3$

(Used in Lessons 8-5 and 8-6.)
Find each product. (Lesson 7-7)

11. $(y + 9)^2$ $y^2 + 18y + 81$

12. $(3a - 2)^2$ $9a^2 - 12a + 4$

13. $(3m + 5n)^2$ $9m^2 + 30mn + 25n^2$

14. $(6r - 7s)^2$ $36r^2 - 84rs + 49s^2$

QUICK Review

EXAMPLE 1

Rewrite $n\left(n - 3n^2 + 2 + \frac{4}{n}\right)$ using the Distributive Property. Then simplify.

$n\left(n - 3n^2 + 2 + \frac{4}{n}\right)$ Original expression

$= (n)(n) + (n)(-3n^2) + (n)(2) + (n)\left(\frac{4}{n}\right)$
  Distribute n to each term inside the parentheses.

$= n^2 - 3n^3 + 2n + 4$ Multiply.

$= -3n^3 + n^2 + 2n + 4$ Rewrite in descending order with respect to the exponents.

EXAMPLE 2

Find $(x + 2)(3x - 1)$.

$(x + 2)(3x - 1)$ Original expression

$= (x)(3x) + (x)(-1) + (2)(3x) + (2)(-1)$ FOIL Method

$= 3x^2 - x + 6x - 2$ Multiply.

$= 3x^2 + 5x - 2$ Combine like terms.

EXAMPLE 3

Find $(3 - g)^2$.

$(3 - g)^2 = (3 - g)(3 - g)$ Laws of Exponents

$= 3^2 - 3g - 3g + g^2$ Multiply.

$= 3^2 - 6g + g^2$ Combine like terms.

$= 9 - 6g + g^2$ Simplify.

Chapter 8 Get Ready For Chapter 8 **419**

Diagnostic Assessment

Exercises	California Standards	Intervention
1–5	1.0, 15.1	SE Review Lesson 1-5, pp. 26–31
6–10	10.0	SE Review Lesson 7-6, pp. 398–403
11–14	10.0	SE Review Lesson 7-7, pp. 404–409

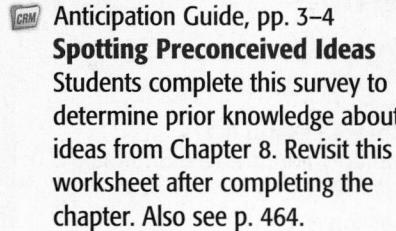

✓ Formative Assessment

CRM Anticipation Guide, pp. 3–4
Spotting Preconceived Ideas
Students complete this survey to determine prior knowledge about ideas from Chapter 8. Revisit this worksheet after completing the chapter. Also see p. 464.

Lesson Activities

• Ticket Out the Door, pp. 424, 452
• Crystal Ball, p. 439
• Name the Math, p. 460
• Yesterday's News, pp. 431, 446

Chapter Checkpoints

SE Mid-Chapter Quiz, p. 440

SE Study Guide and Review, pp. 461–464

SE California Standards Practice, pp. 466–467

CRM Quizzes, pp. 51 and 52

CRM Standardized Test Practice, pp. 68–70

Math Online ca.algebra1.com

• Self-Check Quizzes
• Practice Test
• Standardized Test Practice

✓ Summative Assessment

SE Chapter Practice Test, p. 465

CRM Mid-Chapter Test, p. 53

CRM Vocabulary Test, p. 54

CRM Extended-Response Test, p. 67

CRM Leveled Chapter Tests, pp. 55–66

● ExamView® Assessment Suite

KEY

CRM *Chapter 8 Resource Masters*

SE Student Edition

TWE Teacher Wraparound Edition

● CD-ROM

1 Focus

 Standards Alignment

Before Lesson 8-1
Multiply and divide monomials from ⚷ Standard 7AF2.2

Lesson 8-1
Apply basic factoring techniques to second-and simple third-degree polynomials from ⚷ Standard 11.0

After Lesson 8-1
Factor special polynomials. Solve and graph quadratic equations in the complex number system from ⚷ Standards 2A4.0 and 2A8.0

2 Teach

Scaffolding Questions
Have students read *Get Ready for the Lesson.*
Ask:
- **What is a prime number?** A prime number is any whole number greater than one whose only factors are one and itself.
- **Why might a radio signal from space composed of prime numbers be significant?** Sample answer: A signal composed of only prime numbers would seem to signify that it was sent by intelligent beings.

Main Ideas
- Find prime factorizations of monomials.
- Find the greatest common factors of monomials.

Preparation for Standard 11.0 Students apply basic factoring techniques to second- and simple third-degree polynomials. These techniques include finding a common factor for all terms in a polynomial, recognizing the difference of two squares, and recognizing perfect squares of binomials.

New Vocabulary
prime number
composite number
prime factorization
factored form
greatest common factor (GCF)

Study Tip

Prime Numbers
Before deciding that a number is prime, try dividing it by all of the prime numbers that are less than the square root of that number.

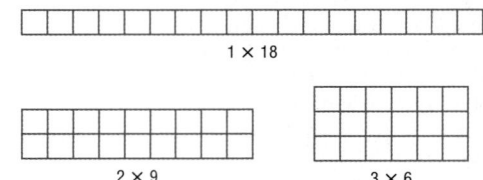 **GET READY for the Lesson**

In the search for extraterrestrial life, scientists listen to radio signals coming from faraway galaxies. How can they be sure that a particular radio signal was deliberately sent by intelligent beings instead of coming from some natural phenomenon? What if that signal began with a series of beeps in a pattern composed of the first 30 prime numbers ("beep-beep," "beep-beep-beep," and so on)?

Prime Factorization Numbers that are multiplied are *factors* of the resulting product. Numbers that have whole number factors can be represented geometrically. Consider all of the possible rectangles with whole number dimensions that have areas of 18 square units.

1×18

2×9 3×6

The number 18 has six factors: 1, 2, 3, 6, 9, and 18.

KEY **CONCEPT**	*Prime and Composite Numbers*
Words	**Examples**
A whole number, greater than 1, for which the only factors are 1 and itself, is called a **prime number**.	2, 3, 5, 7, 11, 13, 17, 19
A whole number, greater than 1, that has more than two factors is called a **composite number**.	4, 6, 8, 9, 10, 12, 14, 15

0 and 1 are neither prime nor composite.

A whole number expressed as the product of prime factors is called the **prime factorization** of the number. Two methods of factoring 90 are shown.

Method 1 Find the least prime factors.

$90 = 2 \cdot 45$	The least prime factor of 90 is 2.
$= 2 \cdot 3 \cdot 15$	The least prime factor of 45 is 3.
$= 2 \cdot 3 \cdot 3 \cdot 5$	The least prime factor of 15 is 3.

Lesson 8-1 Resources

Chapter 8 Resource Masters
Lesson Reading Guide, p. 5 BL OL ELL
Study Guide and Intervention, pp. 6–7 BL OL ELL
Skills Practice, p. 8 BL OL
Practice, p. 9 OL AL
Word Problem Practice, p. 10 OL AL
Enrichment, p. 11 OL AL

Transparencies
5-Minute Check Transparency 8-1
Additional Print Resources
Noteables™ Interactive Study Notebook with Foldables™

Technology
ca.algebra1.com
Interactive Classroom CD-ROM
AssignmentWorks CD-ROM
Graphing Calculator Easy Files

Method 2 Use a factor tree.

90
9 · 10 $90 = 9 \cdot 10$
3 · 3 · 2 · 5 $9 = 3 \cdot 3, 10 = 2 \cdot 5$

All of the factors in the last step are prime. Thus, the prime factorization of 90 is $2 \cdot 3 \cdot 3 \cdot 5$ or $2 \cdot 3^2 \cdot 5$.

Usually the factors are ordered from the least prime factor to the greatest.

Factoring a monomial is similar to factoring a whole number. A monomial is in **factored form** when it is expressed as the product of prime numbers and variables, and no variable has an exponent greater than 1.

Cross-Curricular Project

Math Finding the
Online GCF of
distances will
help you make a scale
model of the solar
system. Visit
ca.algebra1.com to
continue work on
your project.

EXAMPLE Prime Factorization of a Monomial

1 Factor $-12a^2b^3$ completely.

$-12a^2b^3 = -1 \cdot 12a^2b^3$ Express -12 as $-1 \cdot 12$

$= -1 \cdot 2 \cdot 6 \cdot a \cdot a \cdot b \cdot b \cdot b$ $12 = 2 \cdot 6, a^2 = a \cdot a,$ and $b^3 = b \cdot b \cdot b$

$= -1 \cdot 2 \cdot 2 \cdot 3 \cdot a \cdot a \cdot b \cdot b \cdot b$ $6 = 2 \cdot 3$

Thus, $-12a^2b^3$ in factored form is $-1 \cdot 2 \cdot 2 \cdot 3 \cdot a \cdot a \cdot b \cdot b \cdot b$.

CHECK Your Progress

Factor each monomial completely.

1A. $38rs^2t$ $2 \cdot 19 \cdot r \cdot s \cdot s \cdot t$ **1B.** $-66pq^2$ $-1 \cdot 2 \cdot 3 \cdot 11 \cdot p \cdot q \cdot q$

Greatest Common Factor Two or more numbers may have some common prime factors. Consider the prime factorization of 48 and 60.

$48 = ②·②· 2 \cdot 2 ·③$ Factor each number.
$60 = ②·②·③· 5$ Circle the common prime factors.

The common prime factors of 48 and 60 are 2, 2, and 3.

The product of the common prime factors, $2 \cdot 2 \cdot 3$ or 12, is called the greatest common factor of 48 and 60. The **greatest common factor (GCF)** is the greatest number that is a factor of both original numbers. The GCF of two or more monomials can be found in a similar way.

KEY CONCEPT   *Greatest Common Factor (GCF)*

- The GCF of two or more monomials is the product of their common factors when each monomial is written in factored form.
- If two or more integers or monomials have a GCF of 1, then the integers or monomials are said to be *relatively prime*.

Math Online Extra Examples at ca.algebra1.com

Lesson 8-1 Monomials and Factoring **421**

Prime Factorization
Example 1 shows how to determine the prime factorization of a monomial.

 Formative Assessment

Use the Check Your Progress exercises after each example to determine students' understanding of concepts.

 **Common Errors**

Remind students that prime factorization of a constant can have exponents greater than 1, but prime factorization of variable values cannot.

ADDITIONAL EXAMPLE

1 Factor $18x^3y^3$ completely.
$2 \cdot 3 \cdot 3 \cdot x \cdot x \cdot x \cdot y \cdot y \cdot y$

Additional Examples are also in:
- Noteables™ Interactive Study Notebook with Foldables™
- Interactive Classroom PowerPoint® Presentations

Greatest Common Factor
Example 2 shows how to find the GCF of the measurements of a geometric figure. **Example 3** shows how to find the GCF of different sets of monomials.

 Focus on Mathematical Content

Greatest Common Factor To find the GCF of two or more monomials, write the prime factorization of each monomial. The GCF of the monomials will be the product of the GCF of the numerical coefficients and the GCF of the variables. The GCF of the variables is the smaller power of each variable that appears in *both* monomials.

Pre-AP Activity Use after Examples 2 and 3

Ask students to find the greatest common factor of $5x^8(x + 1)^7$ and $9x^3(x - 1)$. x^3

3 Practice

Study Tip

EXAMPLE   Finding GCF

2 **GEOMETRY** The areas of two rectangles are 15 square inches and 16 square inches, respectively. The length and width of both figures are whole numbers. If the rectangles have the same width, what is the greatest possible value for their widths?

Find the GCF of 15 and 16.

$15 = 3 \cdot 5$ Factor each number.

$16 = 2 \cdot 2 \cdot 2 \cdot 2$ There are no common prime factors.

The GCF of 15 and 16 is 1, so 15 and 16 are relatively prime. The width of the rectangles is 1 inch.

✓CHECK Your Progress

2. What is the greatest possible value for the widths if the rectangles described above have areas of 84 square inches and 70 square inches, respectively? 14 in.

EXAMPLE   GCF of a Set of Monomials

3 Find the GCF of $36x^2y$ and $54xy^2z$.

$36x^2y = ②\cdot 2 \cdot ③\cdot ③\cdot ⓧ\cdot x \cdot ⓨ$ Factor each number.

$54xy^2z = ②\cdot ③\cdot ③\cdot 3 \cdot ⓧ\cdot ⓨ\cdot y \cdot z$ Circle the common prime factors.

The GCF of $36x^2y$ and $54xy^2z$ is $2 \cdot 3 \cdot 3 \cdot x \cdot y$ or $18xy$.

✓CHECK Your Progress

Find the GCF of each set of monomials.

3A. $17d^3, 5d^2$ d^2 **3B.** $22p^2q, 32pr^2t$ $2p$

🌐 **Personal Tutor at** ca.algebra1.com

★ indicates multi-step problem

✓ CHECK Your Understanding

Example 1
(p. 421)

Factor each monomial completely. **3.** $-1 \cdot 2 \cdot 2 \cdot 5 \cdot 5 \cdot x \cdot x \cdot x \cdot y \cdot z \cdot z$

1. $4p^2$ $2 \cdot 2 \cdot p \cdot p$ **2.** $39b^3c^2$ **3.** $-100x^3yz^2$
                                          $3 \cdot 13 \cdot b \cdot b \cdot b \cdot c \cdot c$

4. **GARDENING** Corey is planting 120 jalapeno pepper plants in a rectangular arrangement in his garden. In what ways can he arrange them so that he has the same number of plants in each row, at least 4 rows of plants, and at least 6 plants in each row? See margin.

Examples 2, 3
(p. 422)

Find the GCF of each set of monomials.

5. 10, 15 5   **6.** 54, 63 9

7. $18xy, 36y^2$ $18y$ **8.** $25n, 21m$ 1 (relatively prime)

9. $12qr, 8r^2, 16rs$ $4r$ **10.** $42a^2b, 6a^2, 18a^3$ $6a^2$

422 Chapter 8 Factoring

Factor each monomial completely. 16. $-1 \cdot 3 \cdot 3 \cdot 3 \cdot 3 \cdot 3 \cdot n \cdot n \cdot n \cdot m$

11. $66d^4$
$2 \cdot 3 \cdot 11 \cdot d \cdot d \cdot d \cdot d$

12. $85x^2y^2$
$5 \cdot 17 \cdot x \cdot x \cdot y \cdot y$

13. $-49a^3b^2$
$-1 \cdot 7 \cdot 7 \cdot a \cdot a \cdot a \cdot b \cdot b$

14. $50gh$
$2 \cdot 5 \cdot 5 \cdot g \cdot h$

15. $160pq^2$
$2 \cdot 2 \cdot 2 \cdot 2 \cdot 2 \cdot 5 \cdot p \cdot q \cdot q$

16. $-243n^3m$

Exercise Levels
A: 11–27
B: 28–30
C: 31–34

★**17. GEOMETRY** A rectangle has an area of 96 square millimeters and its length and width are both whole numbers. What are the minimum and maximum values for the perimeter of the rectangle? Explain your reasoning. **See margin.**

18. MARCHING BANDS The number of members in two high school marching bands is shown in the table. During the halftime show, the bands plan to march into the stadium from opposite ends using formations with the same number of rows. If the bands match up in the center of the field, what is the maximum number of rows, and how many band members will be in each row? **15 rows; 11 members**

High School	Number of Band Members
Logan	75
Northeast	90

Find the GCF of each set of monomials. 21, 22. **1 (relatively prime)**

19. $27, 72$ **9**

20. $32, 48$ **16**

21. $18, 35$

22. $15a, 28b^2$

23. $24d^2, 30c^2d$ **6d**

24. $20gh, 36g^2h^2$ **4gh**

25. $15r^2s, 35s^2, 70rs$ **5s**

26. $28a^2b^2, 63a^3b^2, 91b^3$ **$7b^2$**

27. $14m^2n^2, 18mn, 2m^2n^3$ **2mn**

28. NUMBER THEORY *Twin primes* are two consecutive odd numbers that are prime. The first pair of twin primes is 3 and 5. List the next five pairs of twin primes. **5, 7; 11, 13; 17, 19; 29, 31; 41, 43**

29. GEOMETRY The area of a triangle is 20 square centimeters. What are possible whole-number dimensions for the base and height of the triangle? **See Ch. 8 Answer Appendix.**

30. RESEARCH Use the Internet or another source to investigate *Mersenne primes*. Describe what they are, and then list three Mersenne primes. **See margin.**

H.O.T. Problems

31. REASONING Determine whether the following statement is *true* or *false*. If false, provide a counterexample. *All prime numbers are odd.* **false; 2**

32b. True; if 6 is a factor of *ab*, then the prime factorization of *ab* must contain 2 • 3. So, 3 must be a factor of either *a* or *b*.

32. CHALLENGE Suppose 6 is a factor of *ab*, where *a* and *b* are natural numbers. Make a valid argument to explain why each assertion is *true* or provide a counterexample to show that an assertion is *false*.

a. 6 must be a factor of *a* or of *b*. **false; counterexample:** $a = 3$, $b = 4$

b. 3 must be a factor of *a* or of *b*.

c. 3 must be a factor of *a* and of *b*. **false; counterexample:** $a = 3$, $b = 1082$

33. OPEN ENDED Name two monomials whose GCF is $5x^2$. Justify your choices. **See Ch. 8 Answer Appendix.**

34. *Writing in Math* Use the information about signals on page 420 to explain how prime numbers are related to the search for extraterrestrial life. Include a list of the first 30 prime numbers and an explanation of how you found them. **See Ch. 8 Answer Appendix.**

Lesson 8-1 Monomials and Factoring **423**

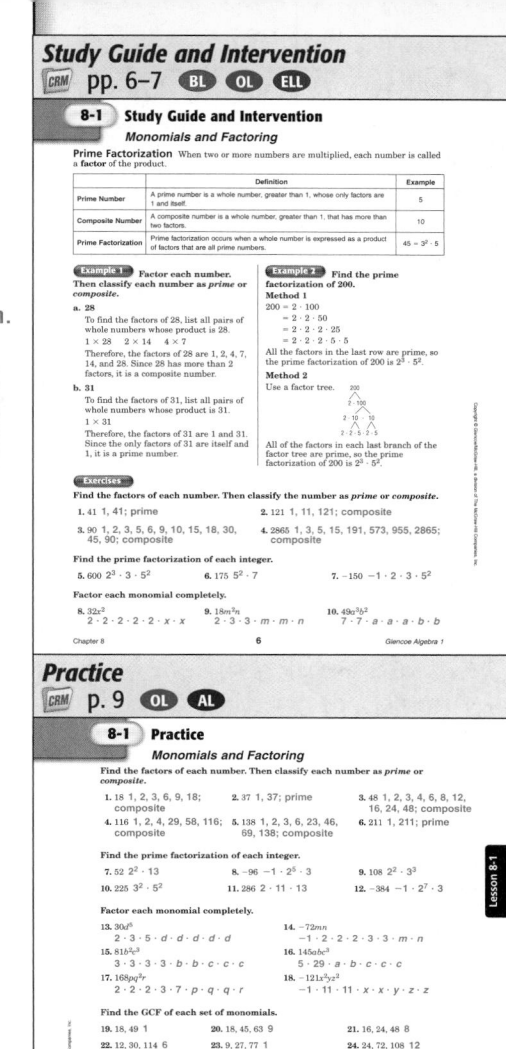

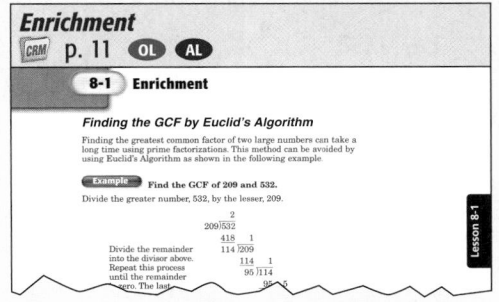

4 Assess

Ticket Out the Door Make several copies each of five different sets of monomials. Give one set to each student. As the students leave the room, ask them to tell you the GCF of their monomials.

FOLDABLES™
Study Organizer
Follow-Up
Remind students to use the flaps in their Foldables to record notes on what they have learned about monomials and factoring.

Additional Answer

43. Sample answer: Let $n =$ the number of video minutes, $10n + 50 \leq 500$; $n \leq 45$; up to 45 min.

Additional Answers (Explore 8-2)

5. yes

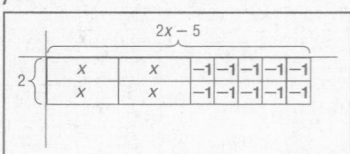

6. no

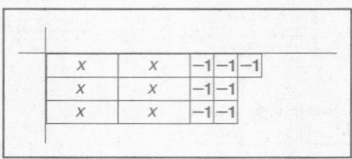

424 Chapter 8 Factoring

STANDARDS PRACTICE 7MR2.3, 6PS3.3

35. If a line passes through A and B, approximately where will the line cross the x-axis? **D**

A between -1 and 0

B between 1 and 2

C between 2.5 and 3.5

D between 3.5 and 4.5

36. REVIEW A shoe store organizes its sale shoes by size. The chart below shows how many pairs of shoes in different styles are on each size rack.

Style	Number of Pairs of Shoes
athletic shoes	15
loafers	8
sandals	22
boots	5

If Bethany chooses a pair without looking, what is the probability that she will choose a pair of boots? **J**

F $\frac{5}{8}$

G $\frac{3}{5}$

H $\frac{4}{25}$

J $\frac{1}{10}$

Spiral Review

Find each product. (Lessons 7-6 and 7-7) **39.** $49p^4 + 56p^2 + 16$

37. $(2x - 1)^2$ $4x^2 - 4x + 1$

38. $(3a + 5)(3a - 5)$ $9a^2 - 25$

39. $(7p^2 + 4)(7p^2 + 4)$

40. $(6r + 7)(2r - 5)$
$12r^2 - 16r - 35$

41. $(10h + k)(2h + 5k)$
$20h^2 + 52hk + 5k^2$

42. $(b + 4)(b^2 + 3b - 18)$
$b^3 + 7b^2 - 6b - 72$

43. VIDEOS Professional closed-captioning services cost $10 per video minute plus a fee of $50. Golden State Digital Services budgeted $500 for closed-captioning for an instructional video. Define a variable. Then write and solve an inequality to find the number of video minutes for which they can have closed-captioning and stay within their budget. (Lesson 6-3) **See margin.**

Find the value of r so that the line that passes through the given points has the given slope. (Lesson 4-1)

44. $(1, 2), (-2, r), m = 3$ -7

45. $(-5, 9), (r, 6), m = -\frac{3}{5}$ 0

46. RETAIL SALES A department store buys clothing at wholesale prices and then marks the clothing up 25% to sell at retail price to customers. If the retail price of a jacket is $79, what was the wholesale price? (Lesson 2-7) **$63.20**

GET READY for the Next Lesson

PREREQUISITE SKILL Use the Distributive Property to rewrite each expression. (Lesson 1-5)

47. $5(2x + 8)$ $10x + 40$

48. $a(3a + 1)$ $3a^2 + a$

49. $2g(3g - 4)$ $6g^2 - 8g$

50. $-4y(3y - 6)$ $-12y^2 + 24y$

51. $7b + 7c$ $7(b + c)$

52. $2x + 3x$ $(2 + 3)x$

424 Chapter 8 Factoring

---

7. yes

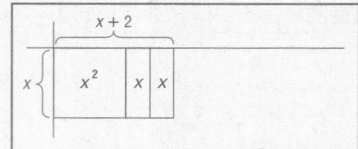

8. no

Algebra Lab
Factoring Using the Distributive Property

 Standard 11.0 **Students apply basic factoring techniques to second- and simple third-degree polynomials.** These techniques include finding a common factor for all terms in a polynomial, recognizing the difference of two squares, and recognizing perfect squares of binomials.

Sometimes you know the product of binomials and are asked to find the factors. This is called factoring. You can use algebra tiles to factor binomials.

ACTIVITY 1   Use algebra tiles to factor $3x + 6$.

Step 1   Model the polynomial $3x + 6$.

Step 2   Arrange the tiles into a rectangle. The total area of the rectangle represents the product, and its length and width represent the factors.

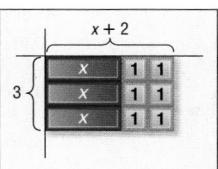

The rectangle has a width of 3 and a length of $x + 2$. So, $3x + 6 = 3(x + 2)$.

ACTIVITY 2   Use algebra tiles to factor $x^2 - 4x$.

Step 1   Model the polynomial $x^2 - 4x$.

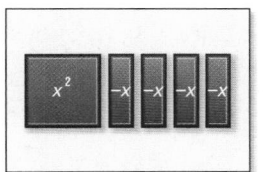

Step 2   Arrange the tiles into a rectangle.

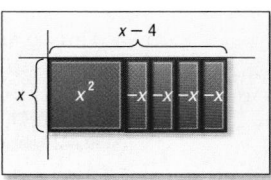

The rectangle has a width of x and a length of $x - 4$. So, $x^2 - 4x = x(x - 4)$.

ANALYZE THE RESULTS

Use algebra tiles to factor each binomial.

1. $2x + 10$ $2(x + 5)$ 2. $6x - 8$ $2(3x - 4)$ 3. $5x^2 + 2x$ $x(5x + 2)$ 4. $9 - 3x$ $3(3 - x)$

Tell whether each binomial can be factored. Justify your answer with a drawing.   5–8. See margin for drawings.

5. $4x - 10$ yes   6. $3x - 7$ no   7. $x^2 + 2x$ yes   8. $x^2 + 4$ no

9. **MAKE A CONJECTURE** Explain how you can use algebra tiles to determine whether a binomial can be factored. Include an example of one binomial that can be factored and one that cannot. See margin.

Explore 8-2   Algebra Lab: Factoring Using the Distributive Property   **425**

Additional Answer

9. Binomials can be factored if they can be represented by a rectangle. Examples: $2x + 2$ can be factored and $2x + 1$ cannot be factored.

From Concrete to Abstract
Write $x^2 + 5x$ on the board. Have students factor the binomial without using tiles. If they answer incorrectly, have them use their tiles to help them find their errors.

1 Focus

Objective
Use algebra tiles to model using the Distributive Property to factor binomials.

Materials
• algebra tiles and product mats

Easy-to-Make Manipulatives
Teaching Algebra with Manipulatives Templates for:
• algebra tiles, pp. 10–11
• product mat, p. 17

2 Teach

Working in Cooperative Groups
Put students in groups of 2 or 3, mixing abilities. Have groups complete Activities 1 and 2 and Exercises 1–4.

• In Exercises 1–4, students should recognize that they must arrange the tiles into a rectangle with a width greater than 1 in order to find the factors of the polynomial.

• Point out that the area of the rectangle represents the product, and the length and width represent the factors of the polynomial.

• In Exercises 5–9, emphasize that if a binomial can only be modeled with a width of 1, it cannot be factored.

Practice Have students complete Exercises 5–9.

3 Assess

 Formative Assessment
Use Exercise 3 to assess whether students can factor a binomial.

1 Focus

Standards Alignment

Before Lesson 8-2
Multiply and divide monomials from ⚫━ Standard 7AF2.2

Lesson 8-2
Apply basic factoring techniques to second-and simple third-degree polynomials from ⚫━ Standard 11.0

After Lesson 8-2
Factor special polynomials. Solve and graph quadratic equations in the complex number system from ⚫━ Standards 2A4.0 and 2A8.0

2 Teach

Scaffolding Questions

Have students read *Get Ready for the Lesson*.

Ask:

- What is the greatest common factor (GCF) of two numbers? The GCF is the greatest number that is a factor of both numbers.
- What is the GCF of 151t and 16t^2? t
- What is the height of the ball when $t = 0$? 0 ft
- What is the height of the ball when $t = 1$? 135 ft

Main Ideas

- Factor polynomials by using the Distributive Property.
- Solve quadratic equations of the form $ax^2 + bx = 0$.

 Standard 11.0 Students apply basic factoring techniques to second- and simple third-degree polynomials. These techniques include finding a common factor for all terms in a polynomial, recognizing the difference of two squares, and recognizing perfect squares of binomials.

New Vocabulary

factoring
factoring by grouping
Zero Products Property
roots

▶ **GET READY for the Lesson**

Brad Penny, pitcher for the Los Angeles Dodgers, has had fastballs clocked at 95 miles per hour or about 139 feet per second. If he threw a ball directly upward with the same velocity, the height h of the ball in feet above the point at which he released it could be modeled by the formula $h = 139t - 16t^2$, where t is the time in seconds. You can use factoring and the Zero Product Property to determine how long the ball would remain in the air before returning to his glove.

Factor by Using the Distributive Property In Chapter 7, you used the Distributive Property to multiply a polynomial by a monomial.

$$2a(6a + 8) = 2a(6a) + 2a(8)$$
$$= 12a^2 + 16a$$

You can reverse this process to express a polynomial as the product of a monomial factor and a polynomial factor.

$$12a^2 + 16a = 2a(6a) + 2a(8)$$
$$= 2a(6a + 8)$$

Thus, a *factored form* of $12a^2 + 16a$ is $2a(6a + 8)$. **Factoring** a polynomial means to find its *completely* factored form.

EXAMPLE Use the Distributive Property

① Use the Distributive Property to factor each polynomial.

a. $12a^2 + 16a$

First, find the GCF of $12a^2$ and $16a$.

$12a^2 =$ ②·②· 3 ·ⓐ· a Factor each monomial.
$16a =$ ②·②· 2 · 2 ·ⓐ   Circle the common prime factors.

GCF: $2 \cdot 2 \cdot a$ or $4a$

Write each term as the product of the GCF and its remaining factors. Then use the Distributive Property to factor out the GCF.

$12a^2 + 16a = 4a(3 \cdot a) + 4a(2 \cdot 2)$ Rewrite each term using the GCF.

$= 4a(3a) + 4a(4)$ Simplify remaining factors.

$= 4a(3a + 4)$ Distributive Property

Thus, the completely factored form of $12a^2 + 16a$ is $4a(3a + 4)$.

Lesson 8-2 Resources

Chapter 8 Resource Masters
Lesson Reading Guide, p. 12 **BL** **OL** **ELL**
Study Guide and Intervention, pp. 13–14 **BL** **OL** **ELL**
Skills Practice, p. 15 **BL** **OL**
Practice, p. 16 **OL** **AL**
Word Problem Practice, p. 17 **OL** **AL**
Enrichment, p. 18 **OL** **AL**
Quiz 1, p. 51

Transparencies
5-Minute Check Transparency 4-1

Additional Print Resources
Noteables™ Interactive Study Notebook with Foldables™
Teaching Algebra With Manipulatives

Technology
ca.algebra1.com
Interactive Classroom CD-ROM
AssignmentWorks CD-ROM
Graphing Calculator Easy Files

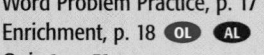

b. $18cd^2 + 12c^2d + 9cd$

$18cd^2 = 2 \cdot ③ \cdot 3 \cdot ⓒ \cdot ⓓ \cdot d$ Factor each monomial.

$12c^2d = 2 \cdot 2 \cdot ③ \cdot ⓒ \cdot c \cdot ⓓ$ Circle the common prime factors.

$9cd = ③ \cdot 3 \cdot ⓒ \cdot ⓓ$

GCF: $3 \cdot c \cdot d$ or $3cd$

$18cd^2 + 12c^2d + 9cd = 3cd(6d) + 3cd(4c) + 3cd(3)$ Rewrite each term using the GCF.

$= 3cd(6d + 4c + 3)$ Distributive Property

✓CHECK Your Progress

1A. $16a + 4b$ $4(4a + b)$ **1B.** $3p^2q - 9pq^2 + 36pq$ $3pq(p - 3q + 12)$

Using the Distributive Property to factor polynomials having four or more terms is called **factoring by grouping** because pairs of terms are grouped together and factored. The Distributive Property is then applied a second time to factor a common binomial factor.

Study Tip

Factoring by Grouping

Sometimes you can group terms in more than one way when factoring a polynomial. For example, the polynomial in Example 2 could have been factored in the following way.

$4ab + 8b + 3a + 6$

$= (4ab + 3a) + (8b + 6)$

$= a(4b + 3) + 2(4b + 3)$

$= (4b + 3)(a + 2)$

Notice that this result is the same as in Example 2.

EXAMPLE   Use Grouping

2 Factor $4ab + 8b + 3a + 6$.

$4ab + 8b + 3a + 6$

$= (4ab + 8b) + (3a + 6)$ Group terms with common factors.

$= 4b(a + 2) + 3(a + 2)$ Factor the GCF from each grouping.

$= (a + 2)(4b + 3)$ Distributive Property

✓CHECK Your Progress   Factor each polynomial.

2A. $6x^2 - 15x - 8x + 20$ **2B.** $rs + 5s - r - 5$ $(r + 5)(s - 1)$

$(3x - 4)(2x - 5)$

Recognizing binomials that are additive inverses is often helpful when factoring by grouping. For example, $7 - y$ and $y - 7$ are additive inverses. By rewriting $7 - y$ as $-1(y - 7)$, factoring by grouping is possible in the following example.

EXAMPLE   Use the Additive Inverse Property

3 Factor $35x - 5xy + 3y - 21$.

$35x - 5xy + 3y - 21 = (35x - 5xy) + (3y - 21)$ Group terms with common factors.

$= 5x(7 - y) + 3(y - 7)$ Factor the GCF from each grouping.

$= 5x(-1)(y - 7) + 3(y - 7)$ $7 - y = -1(y - 7)$

$= -5x(y - 7) + 3(y - 7)$ $5x(-1) = -5x$

$= (y - 7)(-5x + 3)$ Distributive Property

✓CHECK Your Progress   Factor each polynomial.

3A. $c - 2cd + 8d - 4$ **3B.** $3p - 2p^2 - 18p + 27$

$(c - 4)(-2d + 1)$ $(p + 9)(-2p + 3)$

Factor by Using the Distributive Property

Example 1 shows how to use the Distributive Property to factor a polynomial. **Example 2** shows how to use grouping to factor a polynomial. **Example 3** shows how to use the Additive Inverse Property to factor a polynomial.

✓ Formative Assessment

Use the Check Your Progress exercises after each example to determine students' understanding of concepts.

ADDITIONAL EXAMPLES

1 Use the Distributive Property to factor each polynomial.

a. $15x + 25x^2$ $5x(3 + 5x)$

b. $12xy + 24xy^2 - 30x^2y^4$

$6xy(2 + 4y - 5xy^3)$

2 Factor $2xy + 7x - 2y - 7$.

$(x - 1)(2y + 7)$

3 Factor $15a - 3ab + 4b - 20$.

$(-3a + 4)(b - 5)$

Additional Examples are also in:

- Noteables™ Interactive Study Notebook with Foldables™

- Interactive Classroom PowerPoint® Presentations

Focus on Mathematical Content

Greatest Common Factor

Factoring using the Distributive Property requires expressing a polynomial as the product of the greatest common monomial factor of the polynomial's terms and a polynomial factor. To find the polynomial factor, each term of the polynomial is divided by the common monomial factor.

Intervention

Factoring Polynomials   Sometimes students find the monomial that is the GCF of the polynomial but do not know how to get the polynomial factor. One way to find the remaining factor is to divide each term of the polynomial by the GCF. Tell students to check their answers by multiplying their factors using the Distributive Property.

Solve Equations by Factoring

Example 4 shows how to solve two different quadratic equations—one in factored form and one that must be factored.

Focus on Mathematical Content

Zero Product Property Quadratic equations can be solved by using the Zero Product Property: If the product of two factors is zero, then one of the factors is zero. To solve equations using this property, write the equation with the terms in factored form on one side of the equation and zero on the other side. Each factor is then set equal to zero, and the resulting equations are solved to arrive at the solutions.

Study Tip

Zero Product Property
If the product of two factors is equal to a *nonzero* value, then you *cannot* use the Zero Product Property. You must first multiply all the factors, and then put all the terms on one side of the equation, with zero on the other. Then you must factor the new expression and use the Zero Product Property.

CONCEPT SUMMARY — Factoring by Grouping

Words A polynomial can be factored by grouping if *all* of the following situations exist.

- There are four or more terms.
- Terms with common factors can be grouped together.
- The two common binomial factors are identical or are additive inverses of each other.

Symbols $ax + bx + ay + by = x(a + b) + y(a + b)$
$$= (a + b)(x + y)$$

Solve Equations by Factoring Some equations can be solved by factoring. Consider the following products.

$$6(0) = 0 \qquad 0(-3) = 0 \qquad (5 - 5)(0) = 0 \qquad -2(-3 + 3) = 0$$

Notice that in each case, *at least one* of the factors is zero. These examples illustrate the **Zero Product Property**.

KEY CONCEPT — Zero Product Property

Word If the product of two factors is 0, then at least one of the factors must be 0.

Symbols For any real numbers a and b, if $ab = 0$, then either $a = 0$, $b = 0$, or both a and b equal zero.

The solutions of an equation are called the **roots** of the equation.

EXAMPLE Solve an Equation

4 Solve each equation. Check the solutions.

a. $(d - 5)(3d + 4) = 0$

If $(d - 5)(3d + 4) = 0$, then according to the Zero Product Property either $d - 5 = 0$ or $3d + 4 = 0$.

$(d - 5)(3d + 4) = 0$	Original equation
$d - 5 = 0$ or $3d + 4 = 0$	Set each factor equal to zero.
$d = 5 \qquad\qquad 3d = -4$	Solve each equation.
$d = -\frac{4}{3}$	

The roots are 5 and $-\frac{4}{3}$.

CHECK Substitute 5 and $-\frac{4}{3}$ for d in the original equation.

$(d - 5)(3d + 4) = 0$ $\qquad\qquad$ $(d - 5)(3d + 4) = 0$

$(5 - 5)[3(5) + 4] \stackrel{?}{=} 0$ $\qquad$ $\left[\left(-\frac{4}{3}\right) - 5\right]\left[3\left(-\frac{4}{3}\right) + 4\right] \stackrel{?}{=} 0$

$(0)(19) \stackrel{?}{=} 0$ $\qquad\qquad\qquad$ $\left(-\frac{19}{3}\right)(0) \stackrel{?}{=} 0$

$0 = 0$ ✓ $\qquad\qquad\qquad\qquad$ $0 = 0$ ✓

428 Chapter 8 Factoring

Pre-AP Activity — Use after Exercises 9–20

Write the following polynomial on the board: $c^2xy - c^3 - x^2y + cx$

Ask students to factor it by grouping.

$(c^2 - x)(xy - c)$ or $(x - c^2)(c - xy)$

Study Tip

Common Misconception

You may be tempted to try to solve the equation in Example 4b by dividing each side of the equation by x. Remember, however, that x is an *unknown* quantity. If you divide by x, you may actually be dividing by zero, which is undefined.

b. $x^2 = 7x$

Write the equation so that it is of the form $ab = 0$.

$x^2 = 7x$	Original equation
$x^2 - 7x = 0$	Subtract $7x$ from each side.
$x(x - 7) = 0$	Factor using the GCF of x^2 and $-7x$, which is x.
$x = 0$ or $x - 7 = 0$	Zero Product Property
$x = 7$	Solve each equation.

The roots are 0 and 7.   Check by substituting 0 and 7 for x in the original equation.

✓CHECK Your Progress

4A. $3n(n + 2) = 0$ **0, -2**   **4B.** $7d^2 - 35d = 0$ **0, 5**   **4C.** $x^2 = -10x$ **-10, 0**

 Personal Tutor at ca.algebra1.com

✓CHECK Your Understanding

Examples 1–3
(pp. 426–427)

Factor each polynomial.

1. $9x^2 + 36x$ **$9x(x + 4)$**

2. $4r^2 + 8rs + 28r$ **$4r(r + 2s + 7)$**

3. $5y^2 - 15y + 4y - 12$
$(5y + 4)(y - 3)$

4. $5c - 10c^2 + 2d - 4cd$
$(5c + 2d)(-2c + 1)$

Example 4
(pp. 428–429)

Solve each equation. Check the solutions.

5. $h(h + 5) = 0$ **0, -5**

6. $(n - 4)(n + 2) = 0$ **-2, 4**

7. $5m = 3m^2$ **$0, \frac{5}{3}$**

8. PHYSICAL SCIENCE A flare is launched from a life raft. The height h of the flare in feet above the sea is modeled by the formula $h = 100t - 16t^2$, where t is the time in seconds after the flare is launched. Let $h = 0$ and solve $0 = 100t - 16t^2$ for t. How many seconds will it take for the flare to return to the sea? Explain your reasoning. **0, 6.25; 6.25 s; The answer 0 is not reasonable since it represents the time at which the flare is launched.**

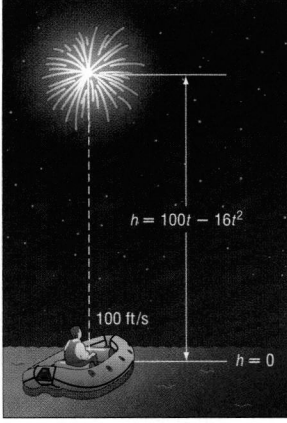

$h = 100t - 16t^2$

100 ft/s

$h = 0$

Exercises

HOMEWORK HELP	
For Exercises	**See Examples**
9–14	1
15–20	2, 3
21–30	4

Factor each polynomial. **13.** $x(15xy^2 + 25y + 1)$ **17.** $(6x - 1)(3x - 5)$

9. $5x + 30y$ **$5(x + 6y)$**

10. $a^5b - a$ **$a(a^4b - 1)$**

11. $14gh - 18h$ **$2h(7g - 9)$**

12. $8bc^2 + 24bc$ **$8bc(c + 3)$**

13. $15x^2y^2 + 25xy + x$

14. $12ax^3 + 20bx^2 + 32cx$ **$4x(3ax^2 + 5bx + 8c)$**

15. $x^2 + 2x + 3x + 6$ **$(x + 3)(x + 2)$**

16. $12y^2 + 9y + 8y + 6$ **$(3y + 2)(4y + 3)$**

17. $18x^2 - 30x - 3x + 5$

18. $2my + 7x + 7m + 2xy$ **$(m + x)(2y + 7)$**

19. $8ax - 6x - 12a + 9$
$(2x - 3)(4a - 3)$

20. $10x^2 - 14xy - 15x + 21y$
$(2x - 3)(5x - 7y)$

Lesson 8-2 Factoring Using the Distributive Property   **429**

DIFFERENTIATED HOMEWORK OPTIONS

Level	Assignment	Two-Day Option	
BL Basic	9–30, 40–42, 44–59	9–29 odd, 45, 46	10–30 even, 40–42, 44, 47–59
OL Core	9–29 odd, 30, 31–35 odd, 36–42, 44–59	9–30, 45, 46	31–42, 44, 47–59
AL Advanced /Pre-AP	31–53 (optional: 54–59)		

---

3 Practice

Formative Assessment

Use Exercises 1–8 to check for understanding.

Use the chart at the bottom of this page to customize assignments for your students.

Odd/Even Assignments

Exercises 9–30 are structured so that students practice the same concepts whether they are assigned odd or even problems.

Differentiated Instruction

Kinesthetic Learners You may wish to allow students to use algebra tiles to solve quadratic equations like Example 4b. They can use the methods from Explore 8-2 to factor the quadratic to solve the equation.

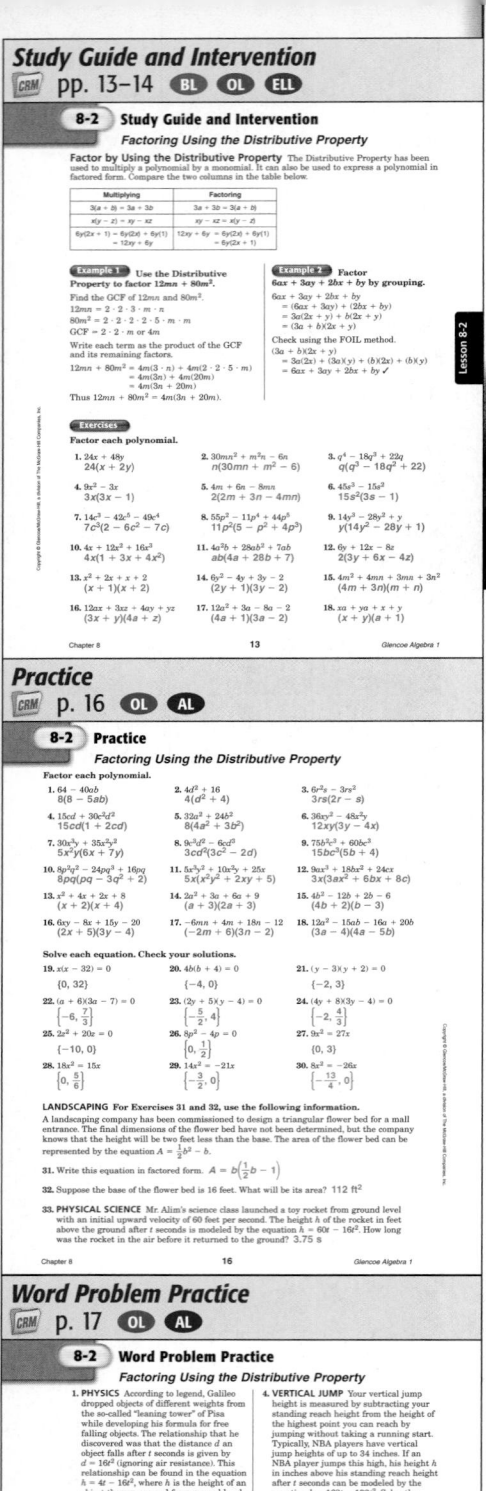
Exercise Levels
A: 9–30
B: 31–39
C: 40–44

Solve each equation. Check the solutions.

21. $x(x - 24) = 0$ **0, 24**

22. $a(a + 16) = 0$ **−16, 0**

23. $(q + 4)(3q - 15) = 0$ **−4, 5**

24. $(3y + 9)(y - 7) = 0$ **−3, 7**

25. $(2b - 3)(3b - 8) = 0$ $\frac{3}{2}, \frac{8}{3}$

26. $(4n + 5)(3n - 7) = 0$ $-\frac{5}{4}, \frac{7}{3}$

27. $3z^2 + 12z = 0$ **−4, 0**

28. $2x^2 = 5x$ $0, \frac{5}{2}$

29. BASEBALL Malik popped a ball straight up with an initial upward velocity of 45 feet per second. The height h, in feet, of the ball above the ground is modeled by the equation $h = 2 + 48t - 16t^2$. How long was the ball in the air if the catcher catches the ball when it is 2 feet above the ground? Is your answer reasonable in the context of this situation? **3 s; yes**

30. MARINE BIOLOGY In a pool at an aquarium, a dolphin jumps out of the water traveling at 20 feet per second. Its height h, in feet, above the water after t seconds is given by the formula $h = 20t - 16t^2$. Solve the equation for $h = 0$ and interpret the solution. **1.25; The dolphin is in the air 1.25 s before returning to the water.**

Factor each polynomial.

31. $12x^2y^2z + 40xy^3z^2$
$4xy^2z(3x + 10yz)$

32. $18a^2bc^2 - 48abc^3$ $6abc^2(3a - 8c)$

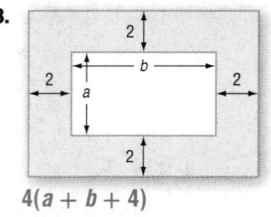

Real-World Career
Marine Biologist
A marine biologist uses math to study and analyze factors that affect organisms living in and near the ocean.

Math Online
For more information, go to ca.algebra1.com.

GEOMETRY Find an expression for the area of a square with the given perimeter.

33. $P = (12x + 20y)$ in.
$(9x^2 + 30xy + 25y^2)$ in^2

34. $P = (36a - 16b)$ cm
$(81a^2 - 72ab + 16b^2)$ cm^2

35. GEOMETRY The expression $\frac{1}{2}n^2 - \frac{3}{2}n$ can be used to find the number of diagonals in a polygon that has n sides. Write the expression in factored form and find the number of diagonals in a decagon (10-sided polygon). **See margin.**

SOFTBALL For Exercises 36 and 37, use the following information.
Alisha is scheduling the games for a softball league. To find the number of games she needs to schedule, she uses the equation $g = \frac{1}{2}n^2 - \frac{1}{2}n$, where g represents the number of games needed for each team to play each other exactly once and n represents the number of teams.

36. Write this equation in factored form. $g = \frac{1}{2}n(n - 1)$

37. How many games are needed for 7 teams to play each other exactly 3 times? **63 games**

GEOMETRY Write an expression in factored form for the area of each shaded region.

38.

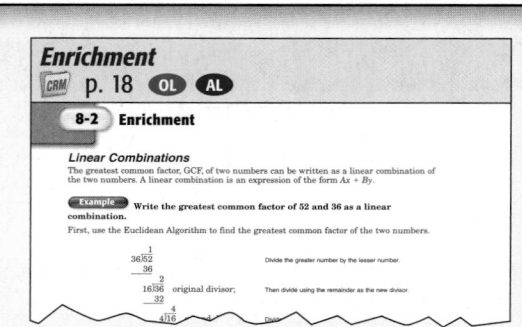

$4(a + b + 4)$

39.

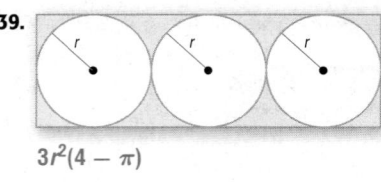

$3r^2(4 - \pi)$

EXTRA PRACTICE
See pages 733, 751.

Math Online
Self-Check Quiz at
ca.algebra1.com.

H.O.T. Problems

40. REASONING Represent $4x^2 + 12x$ as a product of factors in three different ways. Then decide which of the three is the completely factored form. Explain your reasoning. **See margin.**

BL = Below Grade Level
OL = On Grade Level
AL = Above Grade Level
ELL = English Language Learner

Additional pages not shown:
CRM **Lesson Reading Guide**, p. 12 BL OL ELL
CRM **Skills Practice**, p. 15 BL OL

41. Sample answer:
$(x + 3)(x + 2) = 0$; set
each factor equal to
zero and solve each
equation; $x + 3 = 0$,
$x = -3$; $x + 2 = 0$,
$x = -2$. The roots are
-3 and -2.

41. OPEN ENDED Write an equation that can be solved by using the Zero Product Property. Describe how to solve the equation and then find the roots.

42. REASONING Explain why $(x - 2)(x + 4) = 0$ cannot be solved by dividing each side by $x - 2$. **The division would eliminate 2 as a solution.**

43. CHALLENGE Factor $a^{x + y} + a^x b^y - a^y b^x - b^{x + y}$. Describe your steps. **See margin.**

44. *Writing in Math* Use the information about Brad Penny on page 426 to explain how you can determine how long a baseball will remain in the air. Explain how to use factoring and the Zero Product Property to solve the problem. Then interpret each solution in the context of the problem.
  ■ **See margin.**

STANDARDS PRACTICE   11.0, 6PS1.1

45. Which of the following shows $16x^2 - 4x$ factored completely? **B**

  A $4x(x)$

  B $4x(4x - 1)$

  C $x(4x - 1)$

  D $x(x - 4)$

46. REVIEW The frequency table shows the results of a survey in which students were asked to name the colors of their bicycles. Which measure of data describes the most popular color for a bicycle? **H**

Color	Frequency
black	IIII I
blue	IIII IIII IIII IIII
red	IIII III
silver	IIII IIII IIII I
Total	50

  F mean   **H** mode

  G median   **J** range

Spiral Review

Find the GCF of each set of monomials. (Lesson 8-1)

47. $9a, 8ab$ **a**

48. $16h, 28hk^2$ **4h**

49. $3x^2y^2, 9xy, 15x^3y$
  3xy

Find each product. (Lesson 7-7)

50. $(4s^3 + 3)^2$ **$16s^6 + 24s^3 + 9$**

51. $(2p + 5q)(2p - 5q)$ **$4p^2 - 25q^2$**

52. $(3k + 8)(3k + 8)$ **$9k^2 + 48k + 64$**

53. FINANCE Michael uses at most 60% of his annual Flynn Company stock dividend to purchase more shares of Flynn Company stock. If his dividend last year was $885 and Flynn Company stock is selling for $14 per share, what is the greatest number of shares that he can purchase? (Lesson 6-2) **37 shares**

GET READY for the Next Lesson

PREREQUISITE SKILL Find each product. (Lesson 7-6)

54. $(n + 8)(n + 3)$ **$n^2 + 11n + 24$**

55. $(x - 4)(x - 5)$ **$x^2 - 9x + 20$**

56. $(b - 10)(b + 7)$
  $b^2 - 3b - 70$

57. $(3a + 1)(6a - 4)$ **$18a^2 - 6a - 4$**

58. $(5p - 2)(9p - 3)$ **$45p^2 - 33p + 6$**

59. $(2y - 5)(4y + 3)$
  $8y^2 - 14y - 15$

4 Assess

Yesterday's News Have students write how yesterday's concept of finding the GCF of a set of monomials helped them with today's new material.

FOLDABLES *Study Organizer* **Foldables™ Follow-Up**
Remind students to use the second flap in their Foldables to record notes on what they have learned about factoring polynomials using the Distributive Property and solving quadratic equations using the Zero Product Property. Students should include the Concept Summary on p. 421.

✓ Formative Assessment
Check for student understanding of concepts in Lessons 8-1 and 8-2.
  CRM Quiz 1, p. 51

Additional Answers

35. $\frac{1}{2}n(n - 3)$; 35 diagonals

40. Sample answers: $4(x^2 + 3x)$, $x(4x + 12)$ or $4x(x + 3)$; $4x(x + 3)$ $4x$ is the GCF of $4x^2$ and $12x$.

43. $(a^x - b^x)(a^y + b^y)$; Sample answer: Group terms with common factors, $(a^{x + y} + a^x b^y)$ and $(-a^y b^x - b^{x + y})$. Factor the GCF from each grouping to get $a^x(a^y + b^y) - b^x(a^y + b^y)$. Then use the Distributive Property to get $(a^x - b^x)(a^y + b^y)$.

44. Sample answer: Let $h = 0$ in the equation $h = 151t - 16t^2$. To solve $0 = 151t - 16t^2$, factor the right-hand side as $t(151 - 16t)$. Then, since $t(151 - 16t) = 0$, either $t = 0$ or $151 - 16t = 0$. Solving each equation for t, we find that $t = 0$ or $t \approx 0.44$. The solution $t = 0$ represents the point at which the ball was initially thrown into the air. The solution $t \approx 0.44$ represents how long it took after the ball was thrown for it to return to the same height at which it was thrown.

1 Focus

Objective
Use algebra tiles to model factoring trinomials.

Materials
- algebra tiles
- product mat

Easy-to-Make Manipulatives
Teaching Algebra with Manipulatives
Templates for:
- algebra tiles, pp. 10–11
- product mat, p. 17

Teaching Tip
You may want to remind students that the area of the rectangle represents the product, and the length and width of the rectangle represent the factors of the polynomial.

2 Teach

Working in Cooperative Groups
Place students in groups of 2 or 3, mixing abilities. Have groups complete Activities 1–3.

- Ask students to name the shape they must form with the tiles in order to factor a polynomial.
  rectangle

- In Activity 1, remind students to read the width of the tiles along the edge of the rectangle. The x^2-tiles have a width of x and the x-tiles have a width of one.

- For Activity 2, encourage students to try several different arrangements until they can form a rectangle. While the x^2-tile should be in the corner, there is more than one correct way to arrange the tiles into a rectangle.

EXPLORE 8-3

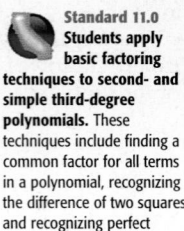

Standard 11.0 Students apply basic factoring techniques to second- and simple third-degree polynomials. These techniques include finding a common factor for all terms in a polynomial, recognizing the difference of two squares, and recognizing perfect squares of binomials.

Algebra Lab
Factoring Trinomials

You can use algebra tiles to factor trinomials. If a polynomial represents the area of a rectangle formed by algebra tiles, then the rectangle's length and width are *factors* of the polynomial.

ACTIVITY 1 Use algebra tiles to factor $x^2 + 6x + 5$.

Step 1 Model $x^2 + 6x + 5$.

Step 2 Place the x^2-tile at the corner of the product mat. Arrange the 1-tiles into a rectangular array. Because 5 is prime, the 5 tiles can be arranged in a rectangle in one way, a 1-by-5 rectangle.

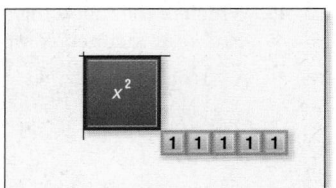

Step 3 Complete the rectangle with the x-tiles. The rectangle has a width of $x + 1$ and a length of $x + 5$. Therefore, $x^2 + 6x + 5 = (x + 1)(x + 5)$.

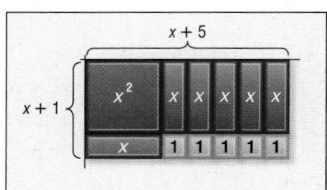

ACTIVITY 2 Use algebra tiles to factor $x^2 + 7x + 6$.

Step 1 Model $x^2 + 7x + 6$.

Step 2 Place the x^2-tile at the corner of the product mat. Arrange the 1-tiles into a rectangular array. Since $6 = 2 \times 3$, try a 2-by-3 rectangle. Try to complete the rectangle. Notice that there are two extra x-tiles.

COncepts in MOtion
Animation ca.algebra1.com

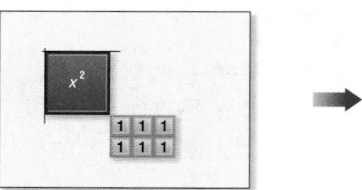
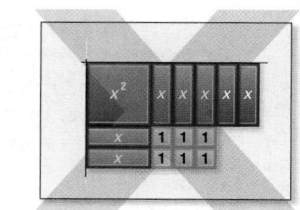

432 Chapter 8 Factoring

Step 3 Arrange the 1-tiles into a 1-by-6 rectangular array. This time you can complete the rectangle with the x-tiles.

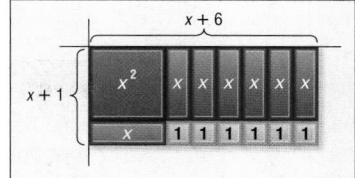

The rectangle has a width of $x + 1$ and a length of $x + 6$. Therefore, $x^2 + 7x + 6 = (x + 1)(x + 6)$.

ACTIVITY 3 Use algebra tiles to factor $x^2 - 2x - 3$.

Step 1 Model the polynomial $x^2 - 2x - 3$.

Step 2 Place the x^2-tile at the corner of the product mat. Arrange the 1-tiles into a 1-by-3 rectangular array as shown.

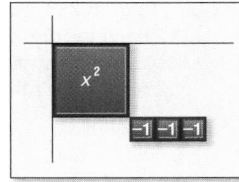

Step 3 Place the x-tile as shown. Recall that you can add zero-pairs without changing the value of the polynomial. In this case, add a zero pair of x-tiles.

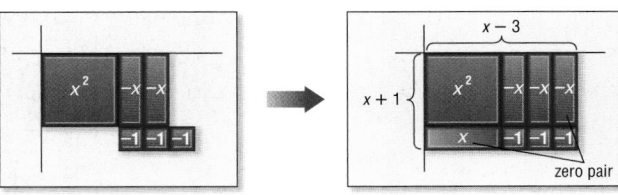

The rectangle has a width of $x + 1$ and a length of $x - 3$. Therefore, $x^2 - 2x - 3 = (x + 1)(x - 3)$.

1. $(x + 3)(x + 1)$
2. $(x + 4)(x + 1)$
3. $(x - 3)(x + 2)$
4. $(x - 2)(x - 1)$
5. $(x + 4)(x + 3)$
6. $(x - 2)(x - 2)$
7. $(x - 2)(x + 1)$
8. $(x - 4)(x - 2)$
9. Sample answer: The sum of the dimensions of the rectangle equals the coefficient of the x-term. Find the factors of the constant that have a sum that is the coefficient of the constant term to help factor the trinomial.

ANALYZE THE RESULTS

Use algebra tiles to factor each trinomial.

1. $x^2 + 4x + 3$
2. $x^2 + 5x + 4$
3. $x^2 - x - 6$
4. $x^2 - 3x + 2$
5. $x^2 + 7x + 12$
6. $x^2 - 4x + 4$
7. $x^2 - x - 2$
8. $x^2 - 6x + 8$

9. Examine the dimensions of the rectangles in each factored model. How does the sum of the dimensions compare to the coefficient of the x-term? Explain how you could use this observation to factor trinomials.

Working in Cooperative Groups continued

- As students work through Activity 3, remind them to pay close attention to the sign of each tile.

- Remind students that adding a zero pair is similar to adding the same number to both sides of an equation. Be sure that students are careful to add one x-tile and one $-x$-tile when they add a zero pair.

Practice Have students complete Exercises 1–9.

3 Assess

Formative Assessment

Use Exercises 7 and 8 to assess whether students can use algebra tiles to factor trinomials.

From Concrete to Abstract After students complete Exercises 1–8, ask them whether they noticed a correlation between the need to use zero pairs to factor the trinomial and the appearance of the resulting factors. Sample answer: When zero pairs are used, the signs of the factors are opposite. When zero pairs are not used, the signs of the factors are the same.

1 Focus

Standards Alignment

Before Lesson 8-3
Multiply and divide monomials
from ⟶ Standard 7AF2.2

Lesson 8-3
Solve a quadratic equation by factoring or completing the square
from ⟶ Standards 11.0 and 14.0

After Lesson 8-3
Factor special polynomials.
Solve and graph quadratic equations in the complex number system from ⟶ Standards 2A4.0 and 2A8.0

2 Teach

Scaffolding Questions Have students read *Get Ready for the Lesson.*
Ask:

• Why do you need to find two numbers whose product is 54 to find the dimensions of the garden? The garden is a rectangle, so the area is equal to the length times the width. Since the garden's area is 54 ft², the length and width must be two numbers whose product is 54.

• What two integers have a product of 54? 1 and 54; 2 and 27; 3 and 18; 6 and 9

(continued on the next page)

Lesson 8-3 Resources

Chapter 8 Resource Masters
Lesson Reading Guide, p. 19 **BL OL ELL**
Study Guide and Intervention, pp. 20–21 **BL OL ELL**
Skills Practice, p. 22 **BL OL**
Practice, p. 23 **OL AL**
Word Problem Practice, p. 24 **OL AL**
Enrichment, p. 25 **OL AL**
Quiz 2, p. 51

Transparencies
5-Minute Check Transparency 8-3
Additional Print Resources
Noteables™ Interactive Study Notebook with Foldables™
Teaching Algebra With Manipulatives

Technology
ca.algebra1.com
Interactive Classroom CD-ROM
AssignmentWorks CD-ROM
Graphing Calculator Easy Files

Factoring Trinomials: $x^2 + bx + c$

Main Ideas

• Factor trinomials of the form $x^2 + bx + c$.
• Solve equations of the form $x^2 + bx + c = 0$.

Standard 11.0 Students apply basic factoring techniques to second- and simple third-degree polynomials. These techniques include finding a common factor for all terms in a polynomial, recognizing the difference of two squares, and recognizing perfect squares of binomials.

Standard 14.0 Students solve a quadratic equation by factoring or completing the square. (Key)

▶ GET READY for the Lesson

Tamika has enough bricks to make a 30-foot border around the rectangular vegetable garden she is planting. The nursery says that the plants will need a space of 54 square feet to grow. What should the dimensions of her garden be?

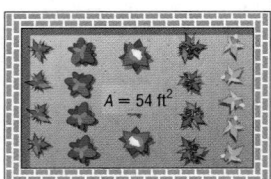
$A = 54$ ft²
$P = 30$ ft

To solve this problem, you need to find two numbers with a product of 54 and a sum of 15, half the perimeter of the garden.

Factor $x^2 + bx + c$ When two numbers are multiplied, each number is a factor of the product. Similarly, when two binomials are multiplied, each binomial is a factor of the product. To factor certain types of trinomials, you will use the pattern for multiplying two binomials. Study the following example.

$$\begin{array}{cccc} & F & O & I & L \\ \end{array}$$
$$(x + 2)(x + 3) = (x \cdot x) + (x \cdot 3) + (x \cdot 2) + (2 \cdot 3) \quad \text{Use the FOIL method.}$$
$$= x^2 + 3x + 2x + 6 \quad \text{Simplify.}$$
$$= x^2 + (3 + 2)x + 6 \quad \text{Distributive Property}$$
$$= x^2 + 5x + 6 \quad \text{Simplify.}$$

Observe the following pattern in this multiplication.

$$(x + 2)(x + 3) = x^2 + (3 + 2)x + (2 \cdot 3)$$
$$(x + m)(x + n) = x^2 + (n + m)x + mn \quad \text{Let } 2 = m \text{ and } 3 = n.$$
$$= x^2 + \underbrace{(m + n)}x + \underbrace{mn} \quad \text{Commutative } (+)$$
$$x^2 + \quad bx \quad + \quad c \quad b = m + n \text{ and } c = mn$$

Notice that the coefficient of the middle term is the sum of m and n and the last term is the product of m and n. This pattern can be used to factor trinomials of the form $x^2 + bx + c$.

KEY CONCEPT   Factoring $x^2 + bx + c$

Words To factor trinomials of the form $x^2 + bx + c$, find two integers, m and n, with a sum equal to b and a product equal to c. Then write $x^2 + bx + c$ as $(x + m)(x + n)$.

Symbols $x^2 + bx + c = (x + m)(x + n)$ when $m + n = b$ and $mn = c$.

Example $x^2 + 5x + 6 = (x + 2)(x + 3)$, since $2 + 3 = 5$ and $2 \cdot 3 = 6$

EXAMPLE *b* and *c* are Positive

1 Factor $x^2 + 6x + 8$.

In this trinomial, $b = 6$ and $c = 8$. You need to find two numbers with a sum of 6 and a product of 8. Make an organized list of the factors of 8, and look for the pair of factors with a sum of 6.

Factors of 8	Sum of Factors
1, 8	9
2, 4	6

The correct factors are 2 and 4.

$x^2 + 6x + 8 = (x + m)(x + n)$ Write the pattern.

$\qquad\qquad = (x + 2)(x + 4)$ $m = 2$ and $n = 4$

CHECK You can check this result by multiplying the two factors.

$$\overset{\text{F}\quad\text{O}\quad\text{I}\quad\text{L}}{(x + 2)(x + 4)} = x^2 + 4x + 2x + 8 \quad\text{FOIL method}$$

$$= x^2 + 6x + 8 \checkmark \quad\text{Simplify.}$$

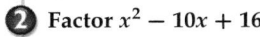 **Your Progress**

Factor each trinomial.

1A. $a^2 + 8a + 15$ $(x + 5)(x + 3)$ **1B.** $9 + 10t + t^2$ $(9 + t)(1 + t)$

When factoring a trinomial where *b* is negative and *c* is positive, use what you know about the product of binomials to narrow the list of possible factors.

EXAMPLE *b* is Negative and *c* is Positive

2 Factor $x^2 - 10x + 16$.

In this trinomial, $b = -10$ and $c = 16$. This means that $m + n$ is negative and mn is positive. So m and n must both be negative. Make a list of the negative factors of 16, and look for the pair with the sum of -10.

Factors of 16	Sum of Factors
$-1, -16$	-17
$-2, -8$	-10
$-4, -4$	-8

The correct factors are -2 and -8.

$x^2 - 10x + 16 = (x + m)(x + n)$ Write the pattern.

$\qquad\qquad = (x - 2)(x - 8)$ $m = -2$ and $n = -8$

CHECK Multiply the two factors to check the result.

$$\overset{\text{F}\quad\text{O}\quad\text{I}\quad\text{L}}{(x - 2)(x - 8)} = x^2 - 8x - 2x + 16 \quad\text{FOIL method}$$

$$= x^2 - 10x + 16 \checkmark \quad\text{Simplify.}$$

Study Tip

Testing Factors
Once you find the correct factors, there is no need to test any other factors. Therefore, it is not necessary to test -4 and -4 in Example 2.

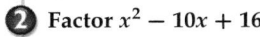 **Your Progress**

Factor each trinomial.

2A. $21 - 22m + m^2$ **2B.** $s^2 - 11s + 28$ $(s - 7)(s - 4)$
$(-21 + m)(-1 + m)$

Lesson 8-3 Factoring Trinomials: $x^2 + bx + c$ **435**

- Which pair has a sum of 15? 6 and 9
- What are the dimensions of the vegetable garden? 6 ft by 9 ft

Factor $x^2 + bx + c$

Examples 1–3 show how to factor trinomials of the form $x^2 + bx + c$, when *b* and *c* are positive, when *b* is negative and *c* is positive, and when *c* is negative.

 Formative Assessment

Use the Check Your Progress exercises after each example to determine students' understanding of concepts.

 **ADDITIONAL EXAMPLES**

1 Factor $x^2 + 7x + 12$.
$(x + 3)(x + 4)$

2 Factor $x^2 - 12x + 27$.
$(x - 3)(x - 9)$

 Focus on Mathematical Content

Factoring Trinomials A trinomial of the form $x^2 + bx + c$ may or may not be factorable into binomial factors. If the trinomial is factorable, then the factors of *c* must be two integers, *m* and *n*, such that $m + n = b$ and $mn = c$.

Intervention

Factoring The concept of factoring trinomials may seem somewhat abstract to some students. Whenever you introduce abstract concepts, it is a good idea to reinforce them with concrete examples. After introducing factoring trinomials, refer students to the lesson-opener problem. Ask students to describe any similarities they notice between finding the dimensions of the garden and factoring a trinomial. Some students may benefit from modeling some problems using algebra tiles. They can then use this method to solve quadratic equations.

Solve Equations by Factoring
Example 4 shows how to solve an equation of the form $x^2 + bx + c = 0$ by factoring. **Example 5** shows how to solve a real-world problem by factoring.

 **Common Errors**

Students often are not careful when rewriting equations so that one side equals zero. Remind them that they must perform the same operation on both sides of the equation and pay attention to the signs in the resulting equation.

Study Tip

Alternate Method

You can use the opposite of FOIL to factor trinomials. For instance, consider Example 3.

$$x^2 + 2x - 15$$

$$(x + \blacksquare)(x + \blacksquare)$$

Try factor pairs of -15 until the sum of the products of the Inner and Outer terms is $2x$.

EXAMPLE *c* is Negative

3 Factor each trinomial.

a. $x^2 + 2x - 15$

Since $b = 2$ and $c = -15$, $m + n$ is positive and mn is negative. So either m or n is negative, but not both. List the factors of -15, where one factor of each pair is negative. Look for the pair of factors with a sum of 2.

Factors of -15	Sum of Factors
1, -15	-14
-1, 15	14
3, -5	-2
-3, 5	2

The correct factors are -3 and 5.

$$x^2 + 2x - 15 = (x + m)(x + n) \quad \text{Write the pattern.}$$
$$= (x - 3)(x + 5) \quad m = -3 \text{ and } n = 5$$

b. $x^2 - 7x - 18$

Since $b = -7$ and $c = -18$, $m + n$ is negative and mn is negative. So either m or n is negative, but not both.

Factors of -18	Sum of Factors
1, -18	-17
-1, 18	17
2, -9	-7

The correct factors are 2 and -9.

$$x^2 - 7x - 18 = (x + m)(x + n) \quad \text{Write the pattern.}$$
$$= (x + 2)(x - 9) \quad m = 2 \text{ and } n = -9$$

✓ CHECK Your Progress Factor each trinomial.

3A. $h^2 + 3h - 40$ $(h + 8)(h - 5)$ **3B.** $r^2 - 2r - 24$ $(r - 6)(r + 4)$

Solve Equations by Factoring Some equations of the form $x^2 + bx + c = 0$ can be solved by factoring and then using the Zero Product Property.

EXAMPLE Solve an Equation by Factoring

4 Solve $x^2 + 5x - 6 = 0$. Check the solutions.

$$x^2 + 5x - 6 = 0 \qquad \text{Original equation}$$
$$(x - 1)(x + 6) = 0 \qquad \text{Factor.}$$
$$x - 1 = 0 \quad \text{or} \quad x + 6 = 0 \qquad \text{Zero Product Property}$$
$$x = 1 \qquad\qquad x = -6 \quad \text{Solve each equation.}$$

The roots are 1 and -6. Check by substituting 1 and -6 for x in the original equation.

✓ CHECK Your Progress

Solve each equation. Check the solutions.

4A. $x^2 + 16x = -28$ $-14, -2$ **4B.** $g^2 + 6g = 27$ $-9, 3$

Pre-AP Activity **Use after Examples 1–4**

Write the trinomials $x^2 + x - 6$ and $x^2 - x - 6$ on the board. Ask students to compare the two trinomials. How are the trinomials related? How are their factors related? The trinomials are the same except for the sign of the middle term. The factors of $x^2 + x - 6$ have the opposite sign of the factors of $x^2 - x - 6$.

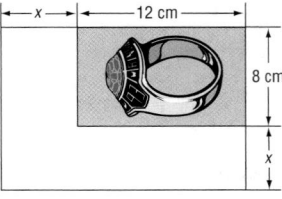

Real-World EXAMPLE Solve a Real-World Problem by Factoring

5 **YEARBOOK DESIGN** A sponsor for the school yearbook has asked that the length and width of a photo in their ad be increased by the same amount in order to double the area of the photo. If the original photo is 12 centimeters wide by 8 centimeters long, what should be the new dimensions of the enlarged photo?

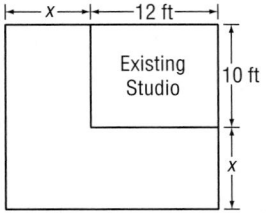

Explore Begin by making a diagram like the one shown above, labeling the appropriate dimensions.

Plan Let x = the amount added to each dimension of the photo.

The new length	times	the new width	equals	twice the old area.
$x + 12$	$\cdot$	$x + 8$	$=$	$2(8)(12)$

Solve

$(x + 12)(x + 8) = 2(8)(12)$ Write the equation.

$x^2 + 20x + 96 = 192$ Multiply.

$x^2 + 20x - 96 = 0$ Rewrite the equation so that one side equals 0.

$(x + 24)(x - 4) = 0$ Factor.

$x + 24 = 0$ or $x - 4 = 0$ Zero Product Property

$x = -24$ $x = 4$ Solve each equation.

Check The solution set is $\{-24, 4\}$. In the context of the situation, only 4 is a valid solution because dimensions cannot be negative. Thus, the new dimensions of the photo should be $4 + 12$ or 16 centimeters, and $4 + 8$ or 12 centimeters.

✓**CHECK Your Progress**

5. GEOMETRY The height of a parallelogram is 18 centimeters less than its base. If the parallelogram has an area of 175 square centimeters, what is its height? **7 cm**

 **Personal Tutor at** ca.algebra1.com

---

★ indicates multi-step problem

✓**CHECK Your Understanding**

Examples 1–3
(pp. 435–436)

Factor each trinomial.

1. $x^2 + 11x + 24$ $(x + 3)(x + 8)$
2. $n^2 - 3n + 2$ $(n - 1)(n - 2)$
3. $w^2 + 13w - 48$ $(w - 3)(w + 16)$
4. $p^2 - 2p - 35$ $(p + 5)(p - 7)$
5. $y^2 + y - 20$ $(y - 4)(y + 5)$
6. $72 + 27a + a^2$ $(a + 3)(a + 24)$

Example 4
(p. 436)

Solve each equation. Check the solutions.

7. $n^2 + 7n + 6 = 0$ $-1, -6$
8. $a^2 + 5a - 36 = 0$ $-9, 4$
9. $y^2 + 9 = 10y$ $1, 9$
10. $d^2 - 3d = 70$ $-7, 10$

Example 5 ★**11. NUMBER THEORY** Find two consecutive integers x and $x + 1$ with a
(p. 437)   product of 156. **−13 and −12 or 12 and 13**

Lesson 8-3 Factoring Trinomials: $x^2 + bx + c$ **437**

ADDITIONAL EXAMPLE

5 **ARCHITECTURE** Marion wants to build a new art studio that has three times the area of her old studio by increasing the length and width of the old studio by the same amount. What are the dimensions of the new studio?

The dimensions of the new studio should be 18 ft by 20 ft.

3 Practice

✓ **Formative Assessment**

Use Exercises 1–11 to check for understanding.

Use the chart at the bottom of this page to customize assignments for your students.

Odd/Even Assignments

Exercises 12–33 are structured so that students practice the same concepts whether they are assigned odd or even problems.

 **Student Misconceptions**

For Exercises 1–6, students may need to be reminded that the order in which they record the factors does not matter. So, $(x + m)(x + n)$ and $(x + n)(x + m)$ are both correct.

	DIFFERENTIATED HOMEWORK OPTIONS		
Level	**Assignment**	**Two-Day Option**	
BL Basic	12–33, 41–43, 48–63	13–33 odd, 49, 50	12–32 even, 41–43, 48, 51–63
OL Core	13–33 odd, 34–35, 37–43, 48–63	12–33, 49, 50	34–40, 41–43, 48, 51–63
AL Advanced/Pre-AP	34–57, (optional: 58–63)		

Lesson 8-3 Factoring Trinomials: $x^2 + bx + c$ **437**

Study Guide and Intervention
CRM pp. 20–21 BL OL ELL

8-3 Study Guide and Intervention

Factoring Trinomials: $x^2 + bx + c$

Factor $x^2 + bx + c$ To factor a trinomial of the form $x^2 + bx + c$, find two integers, m and n, whose sum is equal to b and whose product is equal to c.

Factoring $x^2 + bx + c$ $x^2 + bx + c = (x + m)(x + n)$, where $mn = b$ and $mn = c$.

Example 1 Factor each trinomial.

Example 2 Factor $x^2 + 6x - 16$.

Exercises

Factor each trinomial.

1. $x^2 + 4x + 3$
  $(x + 3)(x + 1)$
2. $m^2 + 12m + 32$
  $(m + 4)(m + 8)$
3. $r^2 - 3r + 2$
  $(r - 2)(r - 1)$
4. $x^2 - x - 6$
  $(x - 3)(x + 2)$
5. $x^2 - 4x - 21$
  $(x - 7)(x + 3)$
6. $x^2 - 22x + 121$
  $(x - 11)(x - 11)$
7. $c^2 - 4c - 12$
  $(c + 2)(c - 6)$
8. $p^2 - 16p + 64$
  $(p - 8)(p - 8)$
9. $9 - 10x + x^2$
  $(9 - x)(1 - x)$
10. $x^2 + 6x + 5$
  $(x + 5)(x + 1)$
11. $a^2 + 8a - 9$
  $(a - 1)(a + 9)$
12. $y^2 - 7y - 8$
  $(y - 8)(y + 1)$
13. $x^2 - 2x - 3$
  $(x - 3)(x + 1)$
14. $y^2 + 14y + 13$
  $(y + 1)(y + 13)$
15. $m^2 + 9m + 20$
  $(m + 4)(m + 5)$
16. $x^2 + 12x + 20$
  $(x + 10)(x + 2)$
17. $a^2 - 14a + 24$
  $(a - 2)(a - 12)$
18. $18 + 11y + y^2$
  $(9 + y)(2 + y)$
19. $x^3 + 2xy + y^2$
  $(x + y)(x + y)$
20. $a^2 - 4ab + 4b^2$
  $(a - 2b)(a - 2b)$
21. $x^2 + 6xy - 7y^2$
  $(x + 7y)(x - y)$

Chapter 8   20   Glencoe Algebra 1

Practice
CRM p. 23 OL AL

8-3 Practice

Factoring Trinomials: $x^2 + bx + c$

Factor each trinomial.

1. $a^2 + 10a + 24$
  $(a + 4)(a + 6)$
2. $h^3 + 12h + 27$
  $(h + 3)(h + 9)$
3. $x^2 + 14x + 33$
  $(x + 11)(x + 3)$
4. $g^2 - 2g - 63$
  $(g + 7)(g - 9)$
5. $w^2 + w - 56$
  $(w + 8)(w - 7)$
6. $y^2 + 4y - 60$
  $(y + 10)(y - 6)$
7. $b^2 + 4b - 32$
  $(b - 4)(b + 8)$
8. $n^2 - 3n - 28$
  $(n - 7)(n + 4)$
9. $c^2 + 4c - 45$
  $(c - 5)(c + 9)$
10. $z^2 - 11z + 30$
  $(z - 6)(z - 5)$
11. $d^2 - 16d + 63$
  $(d - 9)(d - 7)$
12. $x^2 - 11x + 24$
  $(x - 3)(x - 8)$
13. $q^3 - q - 56$
  $(q - 8)(q + 7)$
14. $x^2 - 6x - 55$
  $(x + 5)(x - 11)$
15. $3z^2 + 18r + r^2$
  $(r + 16)(r + 2)$
16. $48 - 16g + g^2$
  $(g - 12)(g - 4)$
17. $j^2 - 9jk - 10k^2$
  $(j - 10k)(j + k)$
18. $m^2 - mv - 56v^2$
  $(m - 8v)(m + 7v)$

Solve each equation. Check your solutions.

19. $x^2 + 17x + 42 = 0$
  $\{-14, -3\}$
20. $p^2 + 5p - 84 = 0$
  $\{-12, 7\}$
21. $k^2 + 3k - 54 = 0$
  $\{-9, 6\}$
22. $b^2 - 12b - 64 = 0$
  $\{-4, 16\}$
23. $n^2 + 4n = 32$
  $\{-8, 4\}$
24. $h^2 - 17h = -60$
  $\{5, 12\}$
25. $c^2 - 26c = 56$
  $\{-2, 28\}$
26. $x^2 - 14x = 72$
  $\{-4, 18\}$
27. $y^2 - 84 = 5y$
  $\{-7, 12\}$
28. $80 + a^2 = 18a$
  $\{8, 10\}$
29. $u^2 = 16u + 36$
  $\{-2, 18\}$
30. $17s + x^2 = -52$
  $\{-13, -4\}$

31. Find all values of k so that the trinomial $x^2 + kx - 35$ can be factored using integers.
  $-34, -2, 2, 34$

CONSTRUCTION For Exercises 32 and 33, use the following information.
A construction company is planning to pour concrete for a driveway. The length of the driveway is 16 feet longer than its width w.

32. Write an expression for the area of the driveway. $w(w + 16)$ ft^2
33. Find the dimensions of the driveway if it has an area of 260 square feet. 10 ft by 26 ft

WEB DESIGN For Exercises 34 and 35, use the following information.
Janeel has a 10-inch by 12-inch photograph. She wants to scan the photograph, then reduce the result by the same amount in each dimension to post on her Web site. Janeel wants the area of the image to be one eighth that of the original photograph.

34. Write an equation to represent the area of the reduced image.
  $(10 - x)(12 - x) = 15$, or $x^2 - 22x + 105 = 0$
35. Find the dimensions of the reduced image. 3 in. by 5 in.

Chapter 8   23   Glencoe Algebra 1

Word Problem Practice
CRM p. 24 OL AL

8-3 Word Problem Practice

Factoring Trinomials: $x^2 + bx + c$

1. **COMPACT DISCS** A standard jewel case for a compact disc has a width 2 cm greater than its length. The area for the front cover is 168 square centimeters. The first two steps to finding the value of x are shown below. Solve the equation and find the length of the case.
  Length $\times$ width $=$ area
  $x(x + 2) = 168$
  $x^2 + 2x - 168 = 0$
  -14 or 12; 12 cm

2. **NUMBER FUN** Fiona and Greg play a number guessing game. Greg gives Fiona this hint about his two secret numbers, "The product of the two consecutive positive integers that I am thinking of is 11 more than their sum." What are Greg's numbers? 4 and 5

3. **BRIDGE ENGINEERING** A car driving over a suspension bridge is supported by a cable hanging between the ends of the bridge. Since its shape is parabolic, it can be modeled by a quadratic equation. The height above the road bed of a bridge's cable h (in inches) measured at distance d (in yards) from the first tower is given by the equation $h = d^2 - 36d + 324$.

  If the driver of a car looks out at a height of 49 inches above the roadbed, at what distance(s) from the tower will the driver's eyes be at the same height as the cable? at 11 and 25 yds from the first tower

4. **PHYSICAL SCIENCE** The boiling point of water depends on altitude. The following equation approximates the number of degrees D below 212°F at which water will boil at altitude h.
  $D^2 + 520D = H$
  In Denver, Colorado, the altitude is approximately 5300 feet above sea level. At approximately what temperature does water boil in Denver?
  $D = 10°$ drop
  The boiling point is about 202°F.

MONUMENTS For Exercises 5 and 6, use the following information.
Susan is designing a pyramidal stone monument for a local park. The design specifications tell her that the height needs to be 9 feet, the width of the base must be 5 feet less than the length, and the volume should be 150 cubic feet. Recall that the volume of a pyramid is given by $V = \frac{1}{3}Bh$, where B is the area of the base and h is the height.

5. Write and solve an equation to find the width of the base of the monument.
  $150 = \frac{1}{3}w(w + 5) \cdot 9$ or
  $3w^2 + 15w - 150 = 0; w = \{5, -10\}$

6. Interpret each answer in terms of the situation. $w = 5$: the width of the pyramid is 5 feet; $w = -10$: negative length doesn't make sense in the situation.

Chapter 8   24   Glencoe Algebra 1

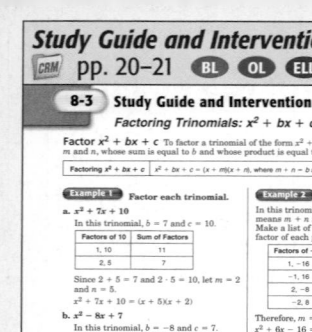

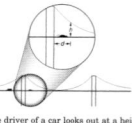

Exercises

HOMEWORK HELP

For Exercises	See Examples
12–23	1–3
24–31	4
32, 33	5

Exercise Levels
A: 12–33
B: 34–40
C: 41–48

Factor each trinomial.

12. $x^2 + 12x + 27$ $(x + 3)(x + 9)$
13. $c^2 + 12c + 35$ $(c + 5)(c + 7)$
14. $y^2 + 13y + 30$ $(y + 10)(y + 3)$
15. $d^2 - 7d + 10$ $(d - 5)(d - 2)$
16. $p^2 - 17p + 72$ $(p - 8)(p - 9)$
17. $g^2 - 19g + 60$ $(g - 4)(g - 15)$
18. $x^2 + 6x - 7$ $(x - 1)(x + 7)$
19. $n^2 + 3n - 54$ $(n - 6)(n + 9)$
20. $y^2 - y - 42$ $(y - 7)(y + 6)$
21. $z^2 - 18z - 40$ $(z + 2)(z - 20)$
22. $-72 + 6w + w^2$ $(w + 12)(w - 6)$
23. $-30 + 13x + x^2$ $(x - 2)(x + 15)$

Solve each equation. Check the solutions.

24. $b^2 + 20b + 36 = 0$ $-18, -2$
25. $y^2 + 4y - 12 = 0$ $-6, 2$
26. $d^2 + 2d - 8 = 0$ $-4, 2$
27. $m^2 - 19m + 48 = 0$ 3, 16
28. $z^2 = 18 - 7z$ 2, -9
29. $h^2 + 15 = -16h$ $-15, -1$
30. $24 + k^2 = 10k$ 4, 6
31. $c^2 - 50 = -23c$ $-25, 2$

★ 32. **GEOMETRY** The triangle has an area of 40 square centimeters. Find the height h of the triangle. 5 cm

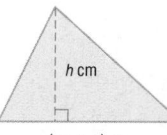

h cm

$(2h + 6)$ cm

★ 33. **SUPREME COURT** When the justices of the Supreme Court assemble each day, each justice shakes hands with each of the other justices. The total number of handshakes h possible for n people is given by $h = \frac{n^2 - n}{2}$. Write and solve an equation to determine the number of justices on the Supreme Court. $36 = \frac{n^2 - n}{2}$; 9 justices

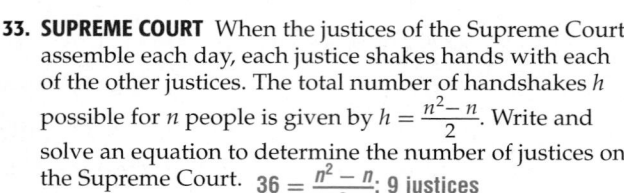

Real-World Link

The "Conference handshake" has been a tradition since the late 19th century. Each day, there is a total of 36 handshakes by the justices.

Source: supremecourtus.gov

RUGBY For Exercises 34 and 35, use the following information.
The length of a Rugby League field is 52 meters longer than its width w.

34. Write an expression for the area of the field. $[w(w + 52)]$ m^2
35. The area of a Rugby League field is 8160 square meters. Find the dimensions of the field. 120 m by 68 m

GEOMETRY Find an expression for the perimeter of a rectangle with the given area.

36. area $= x^2 + 24x - 81$ $4x + 48$
37. area $= x^2 + 13x - 90$ $4x + 26$

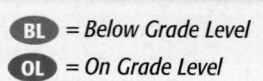

EXTRA PRACTICE
See pages 733, 751.
Math Online
Self-Check Quiz at ca.algebra1.com

SWIMMING For Exercises 38–40, use the following information.
The length of a rectangular swimming pool is 20 feet greater than its width. The area of the pool is 525 square feet. 38. Sample answer: Let w = width; $(w + 20)w = 525$

38. Define a variable and write an equation for the area of the pool.
39. Solve the equation. $-35, 15$
40. Interpret the solutions. Do they both make sense in the context of the problem? Explain. The solution 15 means that the width is 15 feet. The solution -35 does not make sense because length cannot be negative.

H.O.T. Problems

41. **REASONING** Explain why, when factoring $x^2 + 6x + 9$, it is not necessary to check the sum of the factor pairs -1 and -9 or -3 and -3. See margin.

42. **OPEN ENDED** Give an example of an equation that can be solved using the factoring techniques presented in this lesson. Then solve your equation.
  Sample answer: $x^2 - 14x + 40 = 0$; 4, 10

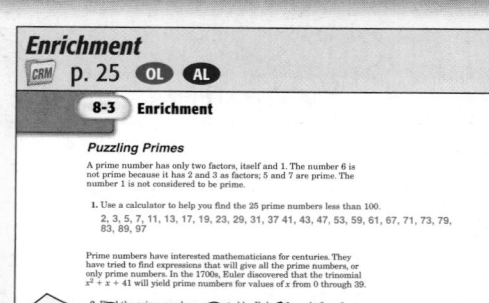

Enrichment
CRM p. 25 OL AL

8-3 Enrichment

Puzzling Primes

A prime number has only two factors, itself and 1. The number 6 is not prime because it has 2 and 3 as factors; 5 and 7 are prime. The number 1 is not considered to be prime.

1. Use a calculator to help you find the 25 prime numbers less than 100.
  2, 3, 5, 7, 11, 13, 17, 19, 23, 29, 31, 37 41, 43, 47, 53, 59, 61, 67, 71, 73, 79, 83, 89, 97

Prime numbers have interested mathematicians for centuries. They have tried to find expressions that will give all the prime numbers, or only prime numbers. In the 1700s, Euler discovered that the trinomial $x^2 + x + 41$ will yield prime numbers for values of x from 0 through 39.

Additional pages not shown:

CRM **Lesson Reading Guide**, p. 19 BL OL ELL
CRM **Skills Practice**, p. 22 BL OL

BL = *Below Grade Level*
OL = *On Grade Level*
AL = *Above Grade Level*
ELL = *English Language Learner*

43. FIND THE ERROR Peter and Aleta are solving $x^2 + 2x = 15$. Who is correct? Explain your reasoning. **Aleta; to use the Zero Product Property, one side of the equation must equal zero.**

Peter
$x^2 + 2x = 15$
$x(x + 2) = 15$
$x = 15$ or $x + 2 = 15$
$x = 13$

Aleta
$x^2 + 2x = 15$
$x^2 + 2x - 15 = 0$
$(x - 3)(x + 5) = 0$
$x - 3 = 0$ or $x + 5 = 0$
$x = 3$ $x = -5$

CHALLENGE Find all values of k so that each trinomial can be factored using integers.

44. $x^2 + kx - 19$ **−18, 18**
45. $x^2 + kx + 14$ **−15, −9, 9, 15**
46. $x^2 - 8x + k, k > 0$ **7, 12, 15, 16**
47. $x^2 - 5x + k, k > 0$ **4, 6**

48. *Writing in Math* Use the information about Tamika's garden on page 434 to explain how factoring can be used to find the dimensions of a garden. Explain how your method is related to the process used to factor trinomials of the form $x^2 + bx + c$. **See margin.**

STANDARDS PRACTICE 11.0, 7MG2.4

49. Which is a factor of $x^2 + 9x + 18$? **C**

A $x + 2$

B $x - 2$

C $x + 3$

D $x - 3$

50. REVIEW An 8-foot by 5-foot section of wall is to be covered by square tiles that measure 4 inches on each side. If the tiles are not cut, how many of them will be needed to cover the wall? **H**

F 30   H 360

G 240   J 1440

 Spiral Review

Solve each equation. Check the solutions. (Lesson 8-2)

51. $(x + 3)(2x - 5) = 0$ $-3, \dfrac{5}{2}$
52. $7b(b - 4) = 0$ **0, 4**
53. $5y^2 = -9y$ $-\dfrac{9}{5}, 0$

Find the GCF of each set of monomials. (Lesson 8-1)

54. $24, 72$ **24**
55. $9pq^5, 21p^3q^3$ **$3pq^3$**
56. $30x^2, 75x^3y^4, 20x^4z$ **$5x^2$**

57. MUSIC Albertina practices the guitar 20 minutes each day. She wants to add 5 minutes to her practice time each day until she is practicing at least 45 minutes daily. How many days will it take her to reach her goal? (Lesson 6-3) **at least 5 days**

GET READY for the Next Lesson

PREREQUISITE SKILL Factor each polynomial. (Lesson 8-2)

58. $3y^2 + 2y + 9y + 6$
59. $3a^2 + 2a + 12a + 8$
60. $4x^2 + 3x + 8x + 6$
61. $2p^2 - 6p + 7p - 21$ $(2p + 7)(p - 3)$
62. $3b^2 + 7b - 12b - 28$ $(b - 4)(3b + 7)$
63. $4g^2 - 2g - 6g + 3$ $(2g - 3)(2g - 1)$

58. $(y + 3)(3y + 2)$ **59.** $(a + 4)(3a + 2)$
60. $(x + 2)(4x + 3)$

 **Exercise Alert!**

Find the Error Remind the students that the Zero Product Property can be used only if the product of two or more factors is 0.

 **Assess**

Crystal Ball Tell students that the next lesson they will study is titled *Factoring Trinomials: $ax^2 + bx + c$*. Ask them to write how they think what they learned today will connect with the next lesson.

Formative Assessment

Check for student understanding of concepts in Lesson 8-3.

[CRM] Quiz 2, p. 51

FOLDABLES Foldables™
Study Organizer Follow-Up

Have students use the flaps for this lesson to record examples of the four kinds of trinomials that can be factored, the Key Concept on p. 428, and examples of solving equations by factoring.

Additional Answers

41. In this trinomial, $b = 6$ and $c = 9$. This means that $m + n$ is positive and mn is positive. Only two positive numbers have both a positive sum and product. Therefore, negative factors of 9 need not be considered.

48. Sample answer: You would use a guess-and-check process, listing the factors of 54, checking to see which pairs added to 15. To factor a trinomial of the form $x^2 + ax + c$, you also use a guess-and-check process, list the factors of c, and check to see which ones add to a.

 Formative Assessment

Use the Mid-Chapter Quiz to assess students' progress in the first half of the chapter.

For problems answered incorrectly, have students review the lessons indicated in parentheses.

 Summative Assessment

 Mid-Chapter Test, p. 53

ExamView  Customize and
Assessment Suite   create multiple
versions of your Mid-Chapter Tests and their answer keys.

FOLDABLES  **Foldables™**
Study Organizer   **Follow-Up**

Before students complete the Mid-Chapter Quiz, encourage them to review their questions, answers, and notes under the lesson tabs on their Foldables.

Additional Answers

3. $2 \cdot 2 \cdot 5 \cdot x \cdot y \cdot y \cdot y$

4. $2 \cdot 3 \cdot 13 \cdot a \cdot a \cdot b \cdot c \cdot c \cdot c$

5. 7 rows of 20 chairs, 10 rows of 14 chairs, 20 rows of 7 chairs, 14 rows of 10 chairs

Additional Answer (Algebra Lab)

1. $3x^2 + 5x + 3x + 5$
$8x^2 - 2x - (-4)x + (-1)$
$12x^2 + (-6)x + 20x + (-10)$

Factor each monomial completely. (Lesson 8-1)

1. $35mn$ $5 \cdot 7 \cdot m \cdot n$ **2.** $27r^2$ $3 \cdot 3 \cdot 3 \cdot r \cdot r$

3. $20xy^3$ **4.** $78a^2bc^3$
3–4. See margin.

5. THEATER Drama students have 140 chairs to place in front of an outdoor stage. In what ways can they arrange the chairs so that there is the same number in each row, at least 6 rows of chairs, and at least 6 chairs in each row? (Lesson 8-1) **See margin.**

Find the GCF of each set of monomials.
(Lesson 8-1)

6. $24ab^2, 21a^3$ $3a$ **7.** $18n, 25p^2$ 1

8. $15q^2r^2, 5r^2s$ $5r^2$ **9.** $42x^2y, 30xy^2$ $6xy$

Factor each polynomial. (Lesson 8-2)

10. $3m + 18n$ $3(m + 6n)$

11. $4xy^2 - xy$ $xy(4y - 1)$

12. $32a^2b + 40b^3 - 8a^2b^2$ $8b(4a^2 + 5b^2 - a^2b)$

13. $6pq + 16p - 15q - 40$ $(2p - 5)(3q + 8)$

14. PHOTOS Olinda is placing matting x inches wide around a photo that is 5 inches long and 3 inches wide. Write an expression in factored form for the area of the matting. (Lesson 8-2) $4x(x + 4)$ in^2

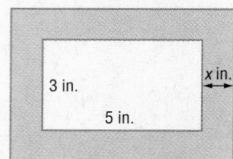

15. FOOTBALL In a football game, Darryl punts the ball downfield. The height h of the football above the ground after t seconds can be modeled by $h = 76.8t - 16t^2$. How long was the football in the air? (Lesson 8-2) **4.8 s**

16. MULTIPLE CHOICE What are the roots of $d^2 - 12d = 0$? (Lesson 8-2) **B**

A 0 and −12   C −12 and 12

B 0 and 12   D 12 and 12

17. GEOMETRY Write an expression in factored form for the area of the shaded region.
(Lesson 8-2) $2a^2 + 30a + 10b + 10c + 100$

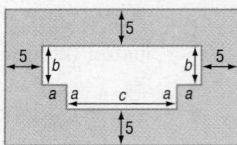

Solve each equation. Check the solutions.
(Lesson 8-2)

18. $(8n + 5)(n - 4) = 0$ $-\frac{5}{8}, 4$

19. $9x^2 - 27x = 0$ $0, 3$

20. $10x^2 = -3x$ $-\frac{3}{10}, 0$

Factor each trinomial. (Lesson 8-3)

21. $n^2 - 2n - 48$ $(n + 6)(n - 8)$

22. $x^2 - 4xy + 3y^2$ $(x - 3y)(x - y)$

23. $a^2 + 5ab + 4b^2$ $(a + b)(a + 4b)$

24. $s^2 - 13st + 36t^2$ $(s - 4t)(s - 9t)$

Solve each equation. Check the solutions.
(Lesson 8-3)

25. $a^2 + 7a + 10 = 0$ $-5, -2$

26. $n^2 + 4n - 21 = 0$ $-7, 3$

27. $x^2 - 2x - 6 = 74$ $-8, 10$

28. $x^2 - x + 56 = 17x$ $4, 14$

29. GEOMETRY The rectangle has an area of 180 square feet. Find the width w of the rectangle. (Lesson 8-3) **10 ft**

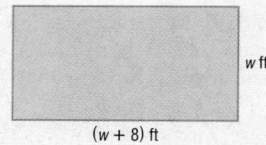

30. MULTIPLE CHOICE Which represents one of the roots of $0 = x^2 + 3x - 18$? (Lesson 8-3) **F**

F −6   H 6

G −3   J $\frac{1}{3}$

Data-Driven Decision Making	Exercises	Lesson	Standard	Resources for Review
Diagnostic Teaching Based on the results of the Chapter 8 Mid-Chapter Quiz, use the following to review concepts that students continue to find challenging.	1–9	8–1	**Preparation for 11.0**	CRM Study Guide and Intervention, pp. 6–7, 13–14, 20–21 Math Online • Extra Examples • Personal Tutor • Concepts in Motion
	10–20	8–2	11.0	
	21–30	8–3	11.0	

Main Ideas

- Factor trinomials of the form $ax^2 + bx + c$.
- Solve equations of the form $ax^2 + bx + c = 0$.

 **Standard 11.0 Students apply basic factoring techniques to second- and simple third-degree polynomials.** These techniques include finding a common factor for all terms in a polynomial, recognizing the difference of two squares, and recognizing perfect squares of binomials.

Standard 14.0 Students solve a quadratic equation by factoring or completing the square. (Key)

New Vocabulary

prime polynomial

 **GET READY for the Lesson**

The factors of $2x^2 + 7x + 6$ are the dimensions of the rectangle formed by the algebra tiles shown below.

The process you use to form the rectangle is the same mental process you can use to factor this trinomial algebraically.

Factor $ax^2 + bx + c$ For trinomials of the form $x^2 + bx + c$, the coefficient of x^2 is 1. To factor trinomials of this form, you find the factors of c with a sum of b. We can modify this approach to factor trinomials for which the leading coefficient is not 1.

ALGEBRA LAB

1. Complete the following table. See margin.

Product of Two Binomials	Use FOIL. $ax^2 + mx + nx + c$	$ax^2 + bx + c$	$m \cdot n$	$a \cdot c$
$(2x + 3)(x + 4)$	$2x^2 + 8x + 3x + 12$	$2x^2 + 11x + 12$	24	24
$(x + 1)(3x + 5)$		$3x^2 + 8x + 5$	15	15
$(2x - 1)(4x + 1)$		$8x^2 - 2x - 1$	-8	-8
$(3x + 5)(4x - 2)$		$12x^2 + 14x - 10$	-120	-120

2. How are m and n related to a and c? $mn = ac$

3. How are m and n related to b? $m + n = b$

You can use the pattern in the Algebra Lab and the method of factoring by grouping to factor trinomials. Consider $6x^2 + 17x + 5$. Find two numbers, m and n, with the product of $6 \cdot 5$ or 30 and the sum of 17. The correct factors are 2 and 15.

$$
\begin{aligned}
6x^2 + 17x + 5 &= 6x^2 + mx + nx + 5 && \text{Write the pattern.} \\
&= 6x^2 + 2x + 15x + 5 && m = 2 \text{ and } n = 15 \\
&= (6x^2 + 2x) + (15x + 5) && \text{Group terms with common factors.} \\
&= 2x(3x + 1) + 5(3x + 1) && \text{Factor the GCF from each grouping.} \\
&= (3x + 1)(2x + 5) && 3x + 1 \text{ is the common factor.}
\end{aligned}
$$

Therefore, $6x^2 + 17x + 5 = (3x + 1)(2x + 5)$.

Lesson 8-4 Factoring Trinomials $ax^2 + bx + c$ **441**

---

1 Focus

Standards Alignment

Before Lesson 8-4
Multiply and divide monomials from ➡ Standard 7AF2.2

Lesson 8-4
Solve a quadratic equation by factoring or completing the square from ➡ Standards 11.0 and 14.0

After Lesson 8-4
Factor special polynomials. Solve and graph quadratic equations in the complex number system from ➡ Standards 2A4.0 and 2A8.0

2 Teach

Scaffolding Questions
Have students read *Get Ready for the Lesson* and examine the Algebra Lab.
Ask:
- How are *mx* and *nx* related to *bx*? $mx + nx = bx$
- How are the trinomials in the table different from those you learned how to factor in Lesson 8-3? The coefficients of the x^2 terms of the trinomials in the table are integers greater than 1, while the coefficients of the x^2 terms of the trinomials in Lesson 8-3 were 1.

Lesson 8-4 Resources

Chapter 8 Resource Masters
Lesson Reading Guide, p. 26 **BL** **OL**
Study Guide and Intervention, pp. 27–28 **BL** **OL**
Skills Practice, p. 29 **BL** **OL**
Practice, p. 30 **OL** **AL**
Word Problem Practice, p. 31 **OL** **AL**
Enrichment, p. 32 **OL** **AL**
Graphing Calculator, p. 33

Transparencies
5-Minute Check Transparency 8-4

Additional Print Resources
Noteables™ Interactive Study Notebook with Foldables™
Teaching Algebra With Manipulatives

Technology
ca.algebra1.com
Interactive Classroom CD-ROM
AssignmentWorks CD-ROM
Graphing Calculator Easy Files

Factor $ax^2 + bx + c$

Example 1 shows how to factor a trinomial of the form $ax^2 + bx + c$.
Example 2 shows how to determine whether a polynomial is prime.

 Formative Assessment

Use the Check Your Progress exercises after each example to determine students' understanding of concepts.

 **Preventing Errors**
Many students forget to include the common factor that they have factored from the trinomial. Remind students to put the common factor in front of the other two factors.

Focus on Mathematical Content

Factoring $ax^2 + bx + c$
Factoring by grouping can be used to factor trinomials where x^2 has a coefficient other than one. To do so, express the trinomial as 4 terms, $ax^2 + mx + nx + c$ where $m + n = b$ and $mn = ac$. Make a table of possible factors for mn and the sum of these factors for b. Replace a, m, n, and c with their values. Group terms with common factors and factor out the GCF from each grouping. Finally, factor using the Distributive Property.

EXAMPLE   Factor $ax^2 + bx + c$

1 Factor each trinomial.

a. $7x^2 + 29x + 4$

In this trinomial, $a = 7$, $b = 29$, and $c = 4$. You need to find two numbers with a sum of 29 and a product of $7 \cdot 4$ or 28. Make an organized list of the factors of 28 and look for the pair of factors with the sum of 29.

Factors of 28	Sum of Factors
1, **28**	29

The correct factors are 1 and 28.

$$
\begin{aligned}
7x^2 + 29x + 4 &= 7x^2 + mx + nx + 4 && \text{Write the pattern.} \\
&= 7x^2 + 1x + 28x + 4 && m = 1 \text{ and } n = 28 \\
&= (7x^2 + 1x) + (28x + 4) && \text{Group terms with common factors.} \\
&= x(7x + 1) + 4(7x + 1) && \text{Factor the GCF from each grouping.} \\
&= (7x + 1)(x + 4) && \text{Distributive Property}
\end{aligned}
$$

b. $10x^2 - 43x + 28$

In this trinomial, $a = 10$, $b = -43$ and $c = 28$. Since b is negative, $m + n$ is negative. Since c is positive, mn is positive. So, both m and n are negative.

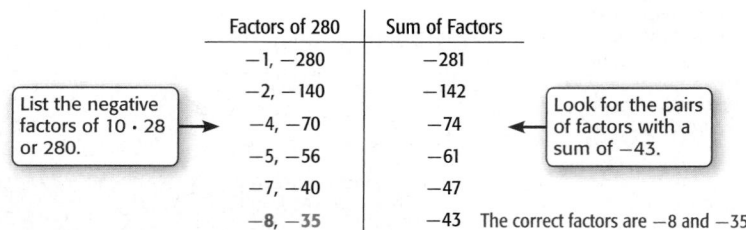

Factors of 280	Sum of Factors
−1, −280	−281
−2, −140	−142
−4, −70	−74
−5, −56	−61
−7, −40	−47
−8, −35	−43

List the negative factors of $10 \cdot 28$ or 280.

Look for the pairs of factors with a sum of −43.

−43 The correct factors are −8 and −35.

$$
\begin{aligned}
10x^2 - 43x + 28 & \\
&= 10x^2 + mx + nx + 28 && \text{Write the pattern.} \\
&= 10x^2 + (-8)x + (-35)x + 28 && m = -8 \text{ and } n = -35 \\
&= (10x^2 - 8x) + (-35x + 28) && \text{Group terms with common factors.} \\
&= 2x(5x - 4) + 7(-5x + 4) && \text{Factor the GCF from each grouping.} \\
&= 2x(5x - 4) + 7(-1)(5x - 4) && -5x + 4 = (-1)(5x - 4) \\
&= 2x(5x - 4) + (-7)(5x - 4) && 7(-1) = -7 \\
&= (5x - 4)(2x - 7) && \text{Distributive Property}
\end{aligned}
$$

c. $3x^2 + 24x + 45$

The GCF of the terms $3x^2$, $24x$, and 45 is 3. Factor this out first.

$3x^2 + 24x + 45 = 3(x^2 + 8x + 15)$ Distributive Property

Now factor $x^2 + 8x + 15$. Since the leading coefficient is 1, find two factors of 15 with a sum of 8. The correct factors are 3 and 5.

So, $x^2 + 8x + 15 = (x + 3)(x + 5)$. Thus, the complete factorization of $3x^2 + 24x + 45$ is $3(x + 3)(x + 5)$.

CHECK Your Progress

1A. $5x^2 + 13x + 6$
$(5x + 3)(x + 2)$

1B. $6x^2 + 22x - 8$
$(3x - 1)(2x + 8)$

1C. $10y^2 - 35y + 30$
$5(2y - 3)(y - 2)$

Study Tip

Finding Factors
Put pairs in an organized list so you do not miss any possible pairs of factors.

Study Tip

Factoring Completely
Always check for a GCF first before trying to factor a trinomial.

Differentiated Instruction

Interpersonal Learners   Place students in groups to factor polynomials such as those in Example 1. Depending on the number of factors and number of students in each group, have each student find one or two factors for mn. By dividing the labor, students should be able to find the factors for mn that sum to $m + n$ quickly. Once they have found the factors, have students complete the factoring as a group.

A polynomial that cannot be written as a product of two polynomials with integral coefficients is called a **prime polynomial**.

EXAMPLE Determine Whether a Polynomial Is Prime

2 Factor $2x^2 + 5x - 2$.

In this trinomial, $a = 2$, $b = 5$, and $c = -2$. Since b is positive, $m + n$ is positive. Since c is negative, mn is negative. So either m or n is negative, but not both. Therefore, make a list of the factors of $2(-2)$ or -4, where one factor in each pair is negative. Look for a pair of factors with a sum of 5.

Factors of -4	Sum of Factors
1, -4	-3
-1, 4	3
-2, 2	0

There are no factors with a sum of 5. Therefore, $2x^2 + 5x - 2$ cannot be factored using integers. Thus, $2x^2 + 5x - 2$ is a prime polynomial.

CHECK Your Progress

2A. Is $4r^2 - r + 7$ prime? yes   **2B.** Is $2x^2 + 3x - 5$ prime? no

Solve Equations by Factoring Some equations of the form $ax^2 + bx + c = 0$ can be solved by factoring and then using the Zero Product Property.

EXAMPLE Solve Equations by Factoring

3 Solve $8a^2 - 9a - 5 = 4 - 3a$. Check the solutions.

$$8a^2 - 9a - 5 = 4 - 3a \qquad \text{Write the equation.}$$
$$8a^2 - 6a - 9 = 0 \qquad \text{Rewrite so that one side equals 0.}$$
$$(4a + 3)(2a - 3) = 0 \qquad \text{Factor the left side.}$$
$$4a + 3 = 0 \quad \text{or} \quad 2a - 3 = 0 \quad \text{Zero Product Property}$$
$$4a = -3 \qquad\qquad 2a = 3 \quad \text{Solve each equation.}$$
$$a = -\frac{3}{4} \qquad\qquad a = \frac{3}{2}$$

The roots are $-\frac{3}{4}$ and $\frac{3}{2}$.

CHECK Check each solution in the original equation.

$$8a^2 - 9a - 5 = 4 - 3a \qquad\qquad 8a^2 - 9a - 5 = 4 - 3a$$
$$8\left(-\frac{3}{4}\right)^2 - 9\left(-\frac{3}{4}\right) - 5 \stackrel{?}{=} 4 - 3\left(-\frac{3}{4}\right) \quad 8\left(\frac{3}{2}\right)^2 - 9\left(\frac{3}{2}\right) - 5 \stackrel{?}{=} 4 - 3\left(\frac{3}{2}\right)$$
$$\frac{9}{2} + \frac{27}{4} - 5 \stackrel{?}{=} 4 + \frac{9}{4} \qquad\qquad 18 - \frac{27}{2} - 5 \stackrel{?}{=} 4 - \frac{9}{2}$$
$$\frac{25}{4} = \frac{25}{4} \quad \checkmark \qquad\qquad -\frac{1}{2} = -\frac{1}{2} \quad \checkmark$$

CHECK Your Progress 3A. $-\frac{4}{3}$, 3

3A. $3x^2 - 5x = 12$ **3B.** $2x^2 - 30x + 88 = 0$ 4, 11

 Math Online Extra Examples at ca.algebra1.com   Lesson 8-4 Factoring Trinomials $ax^2 + bx + c$ **443**

 **Preventing Errors**

Make sure students list all possible factors of mn, including both positive and negative factors, before they decide the polynomial is prime.

ADDITIONAL EXAMPLE

2 Factor $3x^2 + 7x - 5$. prime

Solve Equations by Factoring

Example 3 shows how to solve an equation of the form $ax^2 + bx + c = 0$. **Example 4** shows how to solve a real-world problem by writing an equation of the form $ax^2 + bx + c = 0$ and then solving it.

ADDITIONAL EXAMPLES

3 Solve $18b^2 - 19b - 8 = 3b^2 - 5b$. Check the solutions. $\left\{-\frac{2}{5}, \frac{4}{3}\right\}$

4 **MODEL ROCKETS** Ms. Nguyen's science class built a model rocket for a competition. When they launched their rocket outside the classroom, the rocket cleared the top of a 60-foot high pole and on its descent landed in a nearby tree. If the launch pad was 2 feet above the ground, the initial velocity of the rocket was 64 feet per second, and the rocket landed 30 feet above the ground, how long was the rocket in flight? Use the equation $h = -16t^2 + vt + s$. 3.5 seconds

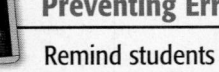 **Preventing Errors**

Remind students that when a polynomial has two factors, there are two solutions. Check each solution by substituting it into the original equation.

✔ **Formative Assessment**

Use Exercises 1–10 to check for understanding.

Use the chart at the bottom of this page to customize assignments for your students.

Odd/Even Assignments

Exercises 11–32 are structured so that students practice the same concepts whether they are assigned odd or even problems.

Additional Answers

7. $-3, -\frac{2}{3}$

8. $\frac{1}{2}, \frac{7}{5}$

9. $-\frac{5}{2}, \frac{4}{3}$

11. $(2x + 5)(x + 1)$

12. $(2p + 3)(3p - 2)$

13. $(5d - 4)(d + 2)$

14. prime

15. $(3g - 2)(3g - 2)$

16. $(2a + 3)(a - 6)$

17. $(x - 4)(2x + 5)$

18. $(5c - 7)(c - 2)$

19. prime

20. $(5n + 2)(2n - 3)$

21. $2(3r + 2)(r - 3)$

22. $5(3x + 2)(2x - 3)$

33. $(12x + 20y)$ in.; The area of the square equals $(3x + 5y)$ $(3x + 5y)$ in^2, so the length of one side is $(3x + 5y)$ in. The perimeter is $4(3x + 5y)$ or $(12x + 20y)$ in.

A model for the vertical motion of a projected object is given by the equation $h = -16t^2 + vt + s$, where h is the height in feet, t is the time in seconds, v is the initial upward velocity in feet per second, and s is the initial height of the object in feet.

🌐 **Real-World EXAMPLE**

Study Tip

Factoring When a Is Negative

When factoring a trinomial of the form $ax^2 + bx + c$ where a is negative, it is helpful to factor out a negative monomial.

④ **PEP RALLY** At a pep rally, small foam footballs are launched by cheerleaders using a sling-shot. How long is a football in the air if a student catches it on its way down 26 feet above the gym floor?

$h = -16t^2 + vt + s$	Vertical motion model
$26 = -16t^2 + 42t + 6$	$h = 26, v = 42, s = 6$
$0 = -16t^2 + 42t - 20$	Subtract 26 from each side.
$0 = -2(8t^2 - 21t + 10)$	Factor out −2.
$0 = 8t^2 - 21t + 10$	Divide each side by −2.
$0 = (8t - 5)(t - 2)$	Factor $8t^2 - 21t + 10$.
$8t - 5 = 0$ or $t - 2 = 0$	Zero Product Property
$8t = 5$ $t = 2$	Solve each equation.
$t = \frac{5}{8}$	

The solutions are $\frac{5}{8}$ second and 2 seconds.

The first time represents how long it takes the football to reach a height of 26 feet on its way up. The later time represents how long it takes the ball to reach a height of 26 feet again on its way down. Thus, the football will be in the air for 2 seconds before the student catches it.

✔ **CHECK Your Progress**

4. Six times the square of a number plus 11 times the number equals 2. What are possible values of x? -2 or $\frac{1}{6}$

🌐 **Personal Tutor at** ca.algebra1.com

★ indicates multi-step problem

✔ **CHECK Your Understanding**

Examples 1–2 (pp. 442–443)

Factor each trinomial, if possible. If the trinomial cannot be factored using integers, write *prime*.

1. $(3a + 2)(a + 2)$
   1. $3a^2 + 8a + 4$
   2. $2t^2 - 11t + 7$ prime
   3. $2p^2 + 14p + 24$ $2(p + 3)(p + 4)$
   4. $2x^2 + 13x + 20$ $(x + 4)(2x + 5)$
   5. $6x^2 + 15x - 9$ $3(2x - 1)(x + 3)$
   6. $4n^2 - 4n - 35$ $(2n + 5)(2n - 7)$

Example 3 (p. 443)

Solve each equation. Check the solutions. 7–9. See margin.

7. $3x^2 + 11x + 6 = 0$
8. $10p^2 - 19p + 7 = 0$
9. $6n^2 + 7n = 20$

Example 4 (p. 444)

★ 10. **CLIFF DIVING** Suppose a diver leaps from the edge of a cliff 80 feet above the ocean with an initial upward velocity of 8 feet per second. How long will it take the diver to enter the water below? **2.5 s**

444 Chapter 8 Factoring

DIFFERENTIATED HOMEWORK OPTIONS

Level	Assignment	Two-Day Option	
BL Basic	11–32, 40, 42–59	11–31 odd, 44, 45	12–32 even, 40, 42, 43, 46–59
OL Core	11–39 odd, 40, 42–59	11–32, 44, 45	33–40, 42, 43, 46–59
AL Advanced/Pre-AP	33–53 (optional: 54–59)		

Exercises

HOMEWORK HELP	
For Exercises	See Examples
11–22	1–2
23–30	3
31–32	4

Exercise Levels
A: 11–32
B: 33–39
C: 40–43

Factor each trinomial, if possible. If the trinomial cannot be factored using integers, write *prime*. 11–22. See margin.

11. $2x^2 + 7x + 5$
12. $6p^2 + 5p - 6$
13. $5d^2 + 6d - 8$
14. $8k^2 - 19k + 9$
15. $9g^2 - 12g + 4$
16. $2a^2 - 9a - 18$
17. $2x^2 - 3x - 20$
18. $5c^2 - 17c + 14$
19. $3p^2 - 25p + 16$
20. $10n^2 - 11n - 6$
21. $6r^2 - 14r - 12$
22. $30x^2 - 25x - 30$

Solve each equation. Check the solutions.

23. $5x^2 + 27x + 10 = 0$
24. $24x^2 - 14x - 3 = 0$
25. $12a^2 - 13a = 35$
26. $6x^2 - 14x = 12$
27. $21x^2 - 6 = 15x$
28. $24x^2 - 46x = 18$
29. $17x^2 - 11x + 2 = 2x^2$
30. $24x^2 - 30x + 8 = -2x$

23. $-5, -\dfrac{2}{5}$
24. $-\dfrac{1}{6}, \dfrac{3}{4}$
25. $-\dfrac{5}{4}, \dfrac{7}{3}$
26. $-\dfrac{2}{7}, 1$
27. $-\dfrac{2}{7}, 1$
28. $-\dfrac{1}{3}, \dfrac{9}{4}$
29. $\dfrac{1}{3}, \dfrac{2}{5}$
30. $\dfrac{1}{2}, \dfrac{2}{3}$

★ **31. ROCK CLIMBING** Damaris is rock climbing at Joshua Tree National Park in the Mojave Desert. She launches a grappling hook from a height of 6 feet with an initial upward velocity of 56 feet per second. The hook just misses the stone ledge that she wants to scale. As it falls, the hook anchors on a ledge 30 feet above the ground. How long was the hook in the air? **3 s**

★ **32. GYMNASTICS** The feet of a gymnast making a vault leave the horse at a height of 8 feet with an initial upward velocity of 8 feet per second. Use the model for vertical motion to find the time t in seconds it takes for the gymnast's feet to reach the mat. (*Hint*: Let $h = 0$, the height of the mat.) **1 s**

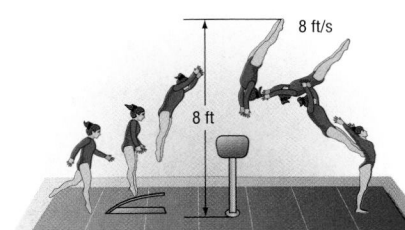

34. $-4, 12$
35. $-\dfrac{7}{3}, \dfrac{5}{2}$
36. $-4, \dfrac{2}{3}$
37. $\dfrac{1}{2}, \dfrac{7}{2}$

★ **33. GEOMETRY** A square has an area of $9x^2 + 30xy + 25y^2$ square inches. What is the perimeter of the square? Explain. **See margin.**

Solve each equation. Check the solutions.

34. $\dfrac{x^2}{12} - \dfrac{2x}{3} - 4 = 0$
35. $t^2 - \dfrac{t}{6} = \dfrac{35}{6}$
36. $(3y + 2)(y + 3) = y + 14$
37. $(4a - 1)(a - 2) = 7a - 5$

GEOMETRY For Exercises 38 and 39, use the following information.
A rectangle 35 square inches in area is formed by cutting off strips of equal width from a rectangular piece of paper.

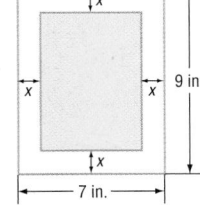

38. Find the width of each strip. **1 in.**
39. Find the dimensions of the new rectangle. **5 in. by 7 in.**

EXTRA PRACTICE
See pages 734, 751.

Math Online
Self-Check Quiz at
ca.algebra1.com

H.O.T. Problems

40. OPEN ENDED Create a trinomial that can be factored using a pair of numbers with a sum of 9 and a product of 14. **Sample answer: $2x^2 + 9x + 7$**

41. CHALLENGE Find all values of k so that $2x^2 + kx + 12$ can be factored as two binomials using integers. **$\pm25, \pm14, \pm11, \pm10$**

Lesson 8-4 Factoring Trinomials $ax^2 + bx + c$ **445**

BL = Below Grade Level
OL = On Grade Level
AL = Above Grade Level
ELL = English Language Learner

Additional pages not shown:
CRM *Lesson Reading Guide*, p. 26 **BL OL ELL**
CRM *Skills Practice*, p. 29 **BL OL**

Study Guide and Intervention
CRM pp. 27–28 **BL OL ELL**

8-4 Study Guide and Intervention
Factoring Trinomials: $ax^2 + bx + c$

Factor $ax^2 + bx + c$ To factor a trinomial of the form $ax^2 + bx + c$, find two integers, m and n whose product is equal to ac and whose sum is equal to b. If there are no integers that satisfy these requirements, the polynomial is called a **prime polynomial**.

Example 1 Factor $2x^2 + 15x + 18$.
In this example, $a = 2$, $b = 15$, and $c = 18$. You need to find two numbers whose sum is 15 and whose product is $2 \cdot 18$ or 36. Make a list of the factors of 36 and look for the pair of factors whose sum is 15.

Factors of 36	Sum of Factors
1, 36	37
2, 18	20
3, 12	15

Use the pattern $ax^2 + mx + nx + c$, with $a = 2$, $m = 3$, $n = 12$, and $c = 18$.
$2x^2 + 15x + 18 = 2x^2 + 3x + 12x + 18$
$= (2x^2 + 3x) + (12x + 18)$
$= x(2x + 3) + 6(2x + 3)$
$= (x + 6)(2x + 3)$
Therefore, $2x^2 + 15x + 18 = (x + 6)(2x + 3)$.

Example 2 Factor $3x^2 - 3x - 18$.
Note that the GCF of the terms $3x^2$, $3x$, and 18 is 3. First factor out this GCF.
$3x^2 - 3x - 18 = 3(x^2 - x - 6)$.
Now factor $x^2 - x - 6$. Since $a = 1$, find the two factors of -6 whose sum is -1.

Factors of 6	Sum of Factors
1, -6	-5
-1, 6	5
-2, 3	1
2, -3	-1

Now use the pattern $(x + m)(x + n)$ with $m = 2$ and $n = -3$.
$x^2 - x - 6 = (x + 2)(x - 3)$
The complete factorization is
$3x^2 - 3x - 18 = 3(x + 2)(x - 3)$.

Exercises
Factor each trinomial, if possible. If the trinomial cannot be factored using integers, write *prime*.

1. $2x^2 - 3x - 2$
$(2x + 1)(x - 2)$
2. $3m^2 - 8m - 3$
$(3m + 1)(m - 3)$
3. $16x^2 - 8r + 1$
$(4r - 1)(4r - 1)$
4. $6x^2 + 5x - 6$
$(2x + 3)(3x - 2)$
5. $3x^2 + 2x - 8$
$(3x - 4)(x + 2)$
6. $18x^2 - 27x - 5$
$(3x - 5)(6x + 1)$
7. $2a^2 + 5a + 3$
$(2a + 3)(a + 1)$
8. $18y^2 + 9y - 5$
$(6y + 5)(3y - 1)$
9. $-4c^2 + 19c - 21$
$(4c - 7)(3 - c)$
10. $8x^2 - 4x - 24$
$(4x - 8)(2x + 3)$
11. $28p^2 + 60p - 25$
$(2p + 5)(14p - 5)$
12. $48x^2 - 22x - 15$
$(6x + 5)(8x - 3)$
13. $3y^2 - 6y - 24$
$3(y + 2)(y - 4)$
14. $4x^2 + 26x - 48$
$2(x + 8)(2x - 3)$
15. $8m^2 - 44m + 48$
$4(2m - 3)(m - 4)$
16. $6x^2 - 7x + 18$
prime
17. $2a^2 - 14a + 18$
$2(a^2 - 7a + 9)$
18. $18 + 11y + 2y^2$
prime

Chapter 8   27   Glencoe Algebra 1

Practice
CRM p. 30 **OL AL**

8-4 Practice
Factoring Trinomials: $ax^2 + bx + c$

Factor each trinomial, if possible. If the trinomial cannot be factored using integers, write *prime*.

1. $2b^2 + 10b + 12$
$2(b + 2)(b + 3)$
2. $3g^2 + 8g + 4$
$(3g + 2)(g + 2)$
3. $4x^2 + 4x - 3$
$(2x + 3)(2x - 1)$
4. $8b^2 - 5b - 10$
prime
5. $6m^2 + 7m - 3$
$(3m - 1)(2m + 3)$
6. $10d^2 + 17d - 20$
$(5d - 4)(2d + 5)$
7. $6x^2 - 17x + 12$
$(3x - 4)(2x - 3)$
8. $8w^2 - 18w + 9$
$(4w - 3)(2w - 3)$
9. $10x^2 - 9x + 6$
prime
10. $15n^2 - n - 28$
$(5n - 7)(3n + 4)$
11. $10x^2 + 21x - 10$
$(2x + 5)(5x - 2)$
12. $9x^2 + 15x + 6$
$3(3x + 2)(x + 1)$
13. $12y^2 - 4y - 5$
$(2y + 1)(6y - 5)$
14. $14k^2 - 9k - 18$
$(2k - 3)(7k + 6)$
15. $8x^2 - 20x - 48$
$4(x + 4)(2x - 3)$
16. $12g^2 + 34g + 24$
$2(3g - 2)(2g + 7)$
17. $18h^2 + 15h - 18$
$3(2h + 3)(3h - 2)$
18. $12p^2 - 22p - 20$
$2(3p + 2)(2p - 5)$

Solve each equation. Check your solutions.

19. $3h^2 + 2h - 16 = 0$
$\left\{-\dfrac{8}{3}, 2\right\}$
20. $15n^2 - n = 2$
$\left\{-\dfrac{1}{3}, \dfrac{2}{5}\right\}$
21. $8g^2 - 10q + 3 = 0$
$\left\{\dfrac{1}{2}, \dfrac{3}{4}\right\}$
22. $6b^2 - 5b = 4$
$\left\{-\dfrac{1}{2}, \dfrac{4}{3}\right\}$
23. $10x^2 - 21c = -4c + 6$
$\left\{-\dfrac{3}{10}, 2\right\}$
24. $10g^2 + 10 = 29g$
$\left\{\dfrac{2}{5}, \dfrac{5}{2}\right\}$
25. $6y^2 = -7y - 2$
$\left\{-\dfrac{2}{3}, -\dfrac{1}{2}\right\}$
26. $9z^2 = -6z + 15$
$\left\{-\dfrac{5}{3}, 1\right\}$
27. $12k^2 + 15k = 16k + 20$
$\left\{-\dfrac{5}{4}, \dfrac{4}{3}\right\}$
28. $12x^2 - 1 = -x$
$\left\{-\dfrac{1}{3}, \dfrac{1}{4}\right\}$
29. $8a^2 - 16a = 6a - 12$
$\left\{\dfrac{3}{4}, 2\right\}$
30. $18a^2 + 10a = -11a + 4$
$\left\{-\dfrac{4}{3}, \dfrac{1}{6}\right\}$

31. DIVING Lauren dove into a swimming pool from a 15-foot-high diving board with an initial upward velocity of 8 feet per second. Find the time t in seconds it took Lauren to enter the water. Use the model for vertical motion given by the equation $h = -16t^2 + vt + s$, where h is height in feet, t is time in seconds, v is the initial upward velocity in feet per second, and s is the initial height in feet. (*Hint*: Let $h = 0$ represent the surface of the pool.) **1.25 s**

32. BASEBALL Brad tossed a baseball in the air from a height of 6 feet with an initial upward velocity of 14 feet per second. Enrique caught the ball on its way down at a point 4 feet above the ground. How long was the ball in the air before Enrique caught it? Use the model of vertical motion from Exercise 31. **1 s**

Chapter 8   30   Glencoe Algebra 1

Word Problem Practice
CRM p. 31 **OL AL**

8-4 Word Problem Practice
Factoring Trinomials: $ax^2 + bx + c$

1. BREAK EVEN Breaking even occurs when the revenues for a business equal the cost. A local children's museum studied their costs (wages, electricity, etc.) and revenues from paid admission. They found that their break-even time is given by the equation $2h^2 - 2h - 24 = 0$, where h is the number of hours the museum is open per day. How many hours must the museum be open per day to reach the point when they break even? **4 hours**

2. CARPENTRY Miko wants to build a toy box for her sister. It is to be 2 feet high, and the width is to be 3 feet less than its length. If it needs to hold a volume of 80 cubic feet, find the length and width of the box. **length = 8 ft; width = 5 ft**

3. FURNITURE The student council wants to purchase a table for the school lobby. The table comes in a variety of dimensions, but for every table, the length is 1 meter greater than twice the width. The student council has budgeted for a table top with an area of 3 square meters.

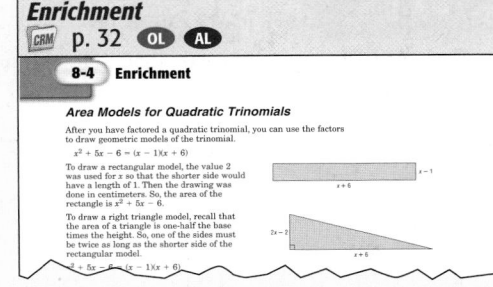

Find the width and length of the table they can purchase. **width = 1 m; length = 3 m**

4. LADDERS A ladder is resting against a wall. The top of the ladder touches the wall at a height of 15 feet, and the length of the ladder is one foot more than twice its distance from the wall. Find the distance from the wall to the bottom of the ladder. (*Hint*: Use the Pythagorean Theorem.) **8 ft**

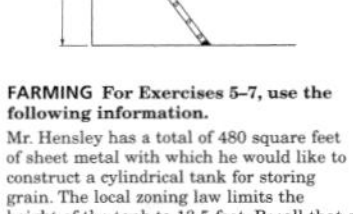

FARMING For Exercises 5–7, use the following information.
Mr. Hensley has a total of 480 square feet of sheet metal with which he would like to construct a cylindrical tank for storing grain. The local zoning law limits the height of the tank to 13.5 feet. Recall that a formula for the surface area of a bottomless cylinder with radius r and height h is $A = \pi r^2 + 2\pi rh$.

5. Write a quadratic equation (set equal to zero) to represent the information. **$0 = \pi r^2 + 27\pi r - 480$**

6. Using 3 as an approximation for π, solve the equation for r. **{5, −32}**

7. What radius should Mr. Hensley use for his tank? **5 ft**

Chapter 8   31   Glencoe Algebra 1

Enrichment
CRM p. 32 **OL AL**

8-4 Enrichment

Area Models for Quadratic Trinomials

After you have factored a quadratic trinomial, you can use the factors to draw geometric models of the trinomial.

$x^2 + 5x - 6 = (x - 1)(x + 6)$

To draw a rectangular model, the value 2 was used for x so that the shorter side would have a length of 1. Then the drawing was done in centimeters. So, the area of the rectangle is $x^2 + 5x - 6$.

To draw a right triangle model, recall that the area of a triangle is one-half the base times the height. So, one of the sides must be twice as long as the shorter side of the rectangular model.

$x^2 + 5x - 6 = (x - 1)(x + 6)$

Lesson 8-4 Factoring Trinomials: $ax^2 + bx + c$ **445**

446 **Chapter 8** Factoring

Real-World Connections
For Exercise 32, tell students that a new vaulting table was approved by the International Gymnastics Federation in 2001, which has led to changes in skills performed. The new table has a height of 125 cm, a width of 95 cm, and a length of 95–105 cm.

 **Exercise Alert!**
Find the Error Tell students to look at the numbers for which Dasan and Luther are finding factors. This clue should immediately tell them which student is correct. Challenge students to find another error in Dasan's work. Students should notice that he factored a 2 out of $2x^2 + 11x + 18$, which is not possible.

 **Assess**

Yesterday's News Have students write how yesterday's lesson on factoring helped them with today's lesson on factoring.

 **Foldables™ Follow-Up**
Remind students to use the flap in their Foldables to record notes on how to factor trinomials of the form $ax^2 + bx + c$.

Additional Answers
42. Luther; when factoring a trinomial of the form $ax^2 + bx + c$, where $a \neq 1$, you must find the factors of ac, not of c.

53. $1(5.5) + 8.09(5.5) = (1 + 8.09)(5.5)$ or $9.09(5.5)$

---

42. FIND THE ERROR Dasan and Luther are factoring $2x^2 + 11x + 18$. Who is correct? Explain your reasoning. **See margin.**

> Dasan
> $2x^2 + 11x + 18 = 2(x^2 + 11x + 18)$
> $= 2(x + 9)(x + 2)$

> Luther
> $2x^2 + 11x + 18$ is prime.

43. *Writing in Math* Explain how to determine which values should be chosen for m and n when factoring a polynomial of the form $ax^2 + bx + c$.
Sample answer: Find two numbers, m and n, that are the factors of ac and that add to b.

STANDARDS PRACTICE 11.0, 7AF4.2

44. Which of the following shows $6x^2 + 24x + 18$ factored completely? **B**

A $(3x + 6)^2$

B $(3x + 3)(2x + 6)$

C $(3x + 2)(2x + 9)$

D $(6x + 3)(x + 6)$

45. REVIEW An oak tree grew 18 inches per year from 1985 to 2006. If the tree was 25 feet tall in 1985, what was the height of the tree in 2001? **G**

F   31.0 ft

G   49.0 ft

H   56.5 ft

J   80.5 ft

Spiral Review

Factor each trinomial, if possible. If the trinomial cannot be factored using integers, write *prime*. (Lesson 8-3)

46. $a^2 - 4a - 21$ $(a + 3)(a - 7)$

47. $t^2 + 2t + 2$ **prime**

48. $d^2 + 15d + 44$ $(d + 4)(d + 11)$

Solve each equation. Check the solutions. (Lesson 8-2)

49. $(y - 4)(5y + 7) = 0$ $-\frac{7}{5}, 4$

50. $(2k + 9)(3k + 2) = 0$ $-\frac{9}{2}, -\frac{2}{3}$

51. $12u = u^2$ **0, 12**

CAMERAS For Exercises 52 and 53, use the graph at the right. (Lessons 2-7 and 7-3)

52. Find the percent of increase in the number of digital cameras sold from 1999 to 2003. **809%**

53. Use the answer from Exercise 52 to verify the statement that digital camera sales increased more than 9 times from 1999 to 2003 is correct.
See margin.

GET READY for the Next Lesson

PREREQUISITE SKILL Find the principal square root of each number. (Lesson 1-8)

54. 49 **7**

55. 36 **6**

56. 100 **10**

57. 121 **11**

58. 169 **13**

59. 225 **15**

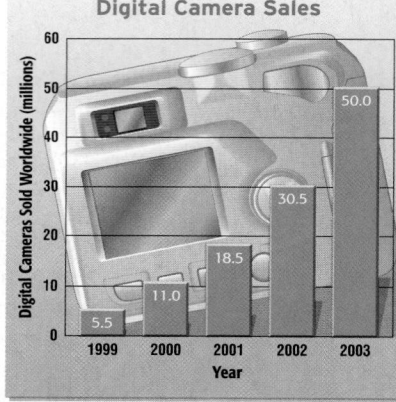
Digital Camera Sales
Source: Digital Photography Review

Pre-AP Activity   Use as an Extension

Have students write a quadratic equation in the form $ax^2 + bx + c = 0$, where a, b, and c are integers, that has the solution $\left\{\frac{1}{2}, 4\right\}$. $2x^2 - 9x + 4 = 0$

Factoring Differences of Squares

Main Ideas

- Factor binomials that are the differences of squares.
- Solve equations involving the differences of squares.

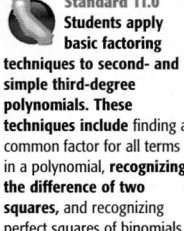 **Standard 11.0** **Students apply basic factoring techniques to second- and simple third-degree polynomials. These techniques include** finding a common factor for all terms in a polynomial, **recognizing the difference of two squares,** and recognizing perfect squares of binomials.

Standard 14.0 Students solve a quadratic equation by factoring or completing the square. (Key)

Study Tip

Look Back
To review the **product of a sum and a difference,** see Lesson 7-7.

COncepts in MOtion
Animation
ca.algebra1.com

GET READY for the Lesson

A basketball player's *hang time* is the length of time he or she is in the air after jumping. Given the maximum height h a player can jump, you can determine his or her hang time t in seconds by solving $4t^2 - h = 0$. If h is a perfect square, this equation can be solved by factoring, using the pattern for the difference of squares.

Factor $a^2 - b^2$ A geometric model can be used to factor the difference of squares.

ALGEBRA LAB

Difference of Squares

Step 1 Use a straightedge to draw two squares similar to those shown below. Choose any measures for a and b.

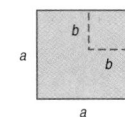

Notice that the area of the large square is a^2, and the area of the small square is b^2.

Step 3 Cut the irregular region into two congruent pieces as shown below.

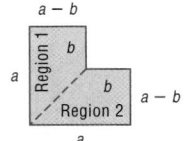

Step 2 Cut the small square from the large square.

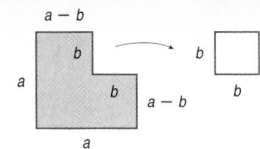

The area of the remaining irregular region is $a^2 - b^2$.

Step 4 Rearrange the two pieces to form a rectangle with length $a + b$ and width $a - b$.

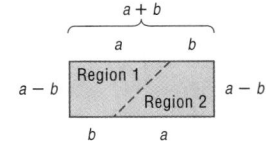

ANALYZE THE RESULTS 1–2. See margin.

1. Write an expression representing the area of the rectangle.
2. Explain why $a^2 - b^2 = (a + b)(a - b)$.

---

1 Focus

Standards Alignment

Before Lesson 8-5
Multiply and divide monomials from Standard 7AF2.2

Lesson 8-5
Solve a quadratic equation by factoring or completing the square from Standards 11.0 and 14.0

After Lesson 8-5
Factor special polynomials. Solve and graph quadratic equations in the complex number system from Standards 2A4.0 and 2A8.0

2 Teach

Scaffolding Questions
Have students read *Get Ready for the Lesson.*
Ask:
- What is a perfect square? A perfect square is a rational number whose square root is a rational number.
  (continued on the next page)

Additional Answers (Algebra Lab)
1. $(a + b)(a - b)$
2. Since $a^2 - b^2$ and $(a + b)(a - b)$ describe the same area, $a^2 - b^2 = (a + b)(a - b)$.

Lesson 8-5 Resources

Chapter 8 Resource Masters
Lesson Reading Guide, p. 34 **BL** **OL** **ELL**
Study Guide and Intervention, pp. 35–36 **BL** **OL** **ELL**
Skills Practice, p. 37 **BL** **OL**
Practice, p. 38 **OL** **AL**
Word Problem Practice, p. 39 **OL** **AL**
Enrichment, p. 40 **OL** **AL**
Spreadsheet, p. 41
Quiz 3, p. 52

Transparencies
5-Minute Check Transparency 8-5
Additional Print Resources
Noteables™ Interactive Study Notebook with Foldables™
Teaching Algebra with Manipulatives
Science and Mathematics Lab Manual, pp. 153–158

Technology
ca.algebra1.com
Interactive Classroom CD-ROM
AssignmentWorks CD-ROM
Graphing Calculator Easy Files

- Is $4t^2$ a perfect square? Yes, the principal square root is $2t$.
- If a basketball player can jump 4 feet, what would be his or her hang time? 1 second

Algebra Lab

Each student or group of students will need a straightedge, grid paper, and scissors to complete the Algebra Lab on p. 441. If students use grid paper, they will be more likely to draw squares with straight sides, which will make the final product appear more like a rectangle. Make sure students label their figures as shown. Explain that the sides of the original square have length of a, and when the b square is cut out, the remaining sides have lengths of $a - b$.

Factor $a^2 - b^2$

Example 1 shows how to factor the differences of squares. **Examples 2–3** show how to apply a factoring technique more than once to factor the polynomial completely.

The Algebra Lab leads to the following rule for finding the difference of two squares.

KEY CONCEPT   Difference of Squares

Symbols	$a^2 - b^2 = (a + b)(a - b)$ or $(a - b)(a + b)$
Examples	$x^2 - 9 = (x + 3)(x - 3)$ or $(x - 3)(x + 3)$

EXAMPLE   Factor the Difference of Squares

1 Factor each binomial.

a. $n^2 - 25$

$n^2 - 25 = n^2 - 5^2$ Write in the form $a^2 - b^2$.

$\qquad = (n + 5)(n - 5)$ Factor the difference of squares.

b. $36x^2 - 49y^2$

$36x^2 - 49y^2 = (6x)^2 - (7y)^2$ $36x^2 = 6x \cdot 6x$ and $49y^2 = 7y \cdot 7y$

$\qquad = (6x + 7y)(6x - 7y)$ Factor the difference of squares.

c. $48a^3 - 12a$

If the terms of a binomial have a common factor, the GCF should be factored out first before trying to apply any other factoring technique.

$48a^3 - 12a = 12a(4a^2 - 1)$ The GCF of $48a^3$ and $-12a$ is $12a$.

$\qquad = 12a[(2a) - 1^2]$ $4a^2 = 2a \cdot 2a$ and $1 = 1 \cdot 1$

$\qquad = 12a(2a + 1)(2a - 1)$ Factor the difference of squares.

✓CHECK Your Progress

1A. $81 - t^2$ $(9 - t)(9 + t)$ **1B.** $64g^2 - h^2$ $(8g - h)(8g + h)$
1C. $9x^3 - 4x$ $x(3x - 2)(3x + 2)$ **1D.** $-4y^3 + 9y$ $-y(2y + 3)(2y - 3)$

Occasionally, the difference of squares pattern needs to be applied more than once to factor a polynomial completely.

EXAMPLE   Apply a Factoring Technique More Than Once

Study Tip

Common Misconception
Remember that the sum of two squares, $x^2 + a^2$, is not factorable. $x^2 + a^2$ is a prime polynomial.

2 Factor $x^4 - 81$.

$x^4 - 81 = [(x^2)^2 - 9^2]$ $x^4 = x^2 \cdot x^2$ and $81 = 9 \cdot 9$

$\qquad = (x^2 + 9)(x^2 - 9)$ Factor the difference of squares.

$\qquad = (x^2 + 9)(x^2 - 3^2)$ $x^2 = x \cdot x$ and $9 = 3 \cdot 3$

$\qquad = (x^2 + 9)(x + 3)(x - 3)$ Factor the difference of squares.

✓CHECK Your Progress

Factor each binomial.
2A. $y^4 - 1$ $(y^2 + 1)(y - 1)(y + 1)$ **2B.** $4a^4 - 4b^4$ $4(a^2 + b^2)(a + b)(a - b)$

 Extra Examples at ca.algebra1.com

Preventing Errors

Students should always check their factoring by multiplying the factors using the FOIL method. The first-degree term should always drop out when the product is a difference of squares.

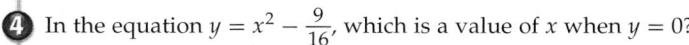

EXAMPLE Apply Several Different Factoring Techniques

3 Factor $5x^3 + 15x^2 - 5x - 15$.

$5x^3 + 15x^2 - 5x - 15$ Original polynomial

$= 5(x^3 + 3x^2 - x - 3)$ Factor out the GCF.

$= 5[(x^3 - x) + (3x^2 - 3)]$ Group terms with common factors.

$= 5[x(x^2 - 1) + 3(x^2 - 1)]$ Factor each grouping.

$= 5(x^2 - 1)(x + 3)$ $x^2 - 1$ is the common factor.

$= 5(x + 1)(x - 1)(x + 3)$ Factor the difference of squares, $x^2 - 1$, into $(x + 1)(x - 1)$.

CHECK Your Progress Factor each polynomial. 3A. $(2x + 1)(x + 5)(x - 5)$

3A. $2x^3 + x^2 - 50x - 25$ **3B.** $r^3 + 6r^2 + 11r + 6$ $(r + 1)(r + 2)(r + 3)$

Solve Equations by Factoring You can apply the Zero Product Property to an equation that is written as the product of factors set equal to 0.

STANDARDS EXAMPLE Solve Equations by Factoring 11.0

4 In the equation $y = x^2 - \dfrac{9}{16}$, which is a value of x when $y = 0$?

A $-\dfrac{9}{4}$ B   0   C $\dfrac{3}{4}$ D $\dfrac{9}{4}$

Read the Item

Factor $x^2 - \dfrac{9}{16}$ as the difference of squares. Then find the values of x.

Solve the Item

$y = x^2 - \dfrac{9}{16}$ Original equation

$0 = x^2 - \dfrac{9}{16}$ Replace y with 0.

$0 = x^2 - \left(\dfrac{3}{4}\right)^2$ $x^2 = x \cdot x$ and $\dfrac{9}{16} = \dfrac{3}{4} \cdot \dfrac{3}{4}$

$0 = \left(x + \dfrac{3}{4}\right)\left(x - \dfrac{3}{4}\right)$ Factor the difference of squares.

$0 = x + \dfrac{3}{4}$ or $0 = x - \dfrac{3}{4}$ Zero Product Property

$-\dfrac{3}{4} = x$ $\dfrac{3}{4} = x$ Solve each equation.

The solutions are $-\dfrac{3}{4}$ and $\dfrac{3}{4}$. The correct answer is C.

CHECK Your Progress

4. Which are the solutions of $18x^3 = 50x$?   H

F $0, \dfrac{5}{3}$ G $-\dfrac{5}{3}, \dfrac{5}{3}$ H $-\dfrac{5}{3}, 0, \dfrac{5}{3}$ J $-\dfrac{5}{3}, 1, \dfrac{5}{3}$

 **Personal Tutor at** ca.algebra1.com

---

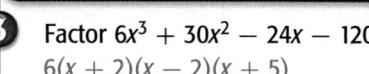
Focus on Mathematical Content

Factoring Differences of Squares
The binomial $a^2 - b^2$ is the difference of two squares, a^2 and b^2. One of the binomial factors, $(a + b)$, is the sum of the principal square roots of a^2 and b^2, and the other binomial factor, $(a - b)$, is the difference of their principal square roots.

Tips for New Teachers   **Preventing Errors**

Students should notice that when the difference of squares factoring technique has been applied once, one of the factors should be prime.

ADDITIONAL EXAMPLE

3 Factor $6x^3 + 30x^2 - 24x - 120$.
$6(x + 2)(x - 2)(x + 5)$

Solve Equations by Factoring

Example 4 shows how to answer a multiple-choice test item on solving equations by factoring. **Example 5** shows how to write and solve an equation that uses the differences of squares.

ADDITIONAL EXAMPLE

4 **STANDARDS EXAMPLE** In the equation $y = q^2 - \dfrac{4}{25}$, which is a value of q when $y = 0$? **D**

A $\dfrac{2}{25}$ C   0

B $\dfrac{4}{25}$ D $-\dfrac{2}{5}$

Intervention

Fractions Students may not be used to thinking of fractions as perfect squares. Remind them that if both the numerator and denominator are perfect squares, then the fraction is a perfect square.

5 **GEOMETRY** A square with side length x is cut from the right triangle shown below.

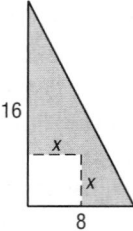

16

x

x

8

What value of x will result in a figure that is $\frac{3}{4}$ of the area of the original triangle? Show how you arrived at your answer.

4; Solve $48 = 64 - x^2$.

3 Practice

 Formative Assessment

Use Exercises 1–10 to check for understanding.

Use the chart at the bottom of this page to customize assignments for your students.

Odd/Even Assignments

Exercises 11–32 are structured so that students practice the same concepts whether they are assigned odd or even problems.

⚠ Exercise Alert!

Find the Error Make sure students can explain what Jessica did wrong. Stress that Jessica's error is a common one. Ask students what they can do to avoid making the same mistake themselves.

Additional Answers

14. $(7h + 4)(7h - 4)$

15. $3(5 + 2p)(5 - 2p)$

16. $2r(11 + 3r)(11 - 3r)$

17. $(12a + 7b)(12a - 7b)$

19. $(n + 2)(n - 2)(n + 5)$

---

5 **GEOMETRY** The area of the shaded part of the square is 72 square inches. Find the dimensions of the square.

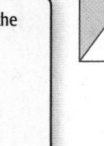

Words	The area of the square less the area of the triangle equals the area of the shaded region.
Variable	Let x = the side length of the square.
Equation	$x^2 - \frac{1}{2}x^2 = 72$

$x^2 - \frac{1}{2}x^2 = 72$ Original equation

$\frac{1}{2}x^2 = 72$ Combine like terms.

$\frac{1}{2}x^2 - 72 = 0$ Subtract 72 from each side.

$x^2 - 144 = 0$ Multiply each side by 2 to remove the fraction.

$(x - 12)(x + 12) = 0$ Factor the difference of squares.

$x - 12 = 0$ or $x + 12 = 0$ Zero Product Property

$x = 12$ $x = -12$ Solve each equation.

Since length cannot be negative, the only reasonable solution is 12. The dimensions of the square are 12 inches by 12 inches. Is this solution reasonable in the context of the original problem?

✓ **CHECK Your Progress**

5. DRIVING The formula $\frac{1}{24}s^2 = d$ approximates a vehicle's speed s in miles per hour given the length d in feet of skid marks on dry concrete. If skid marks on dry concrete are 54 feet long, how fast was the car traveling when the brakes were applied? **36 mph**

★ indicates multi-step problem

✓ **CHECK Your Understanding**

Examples 1–3
(pp. 448–449)

Factor each polynomial, if possible. If the polynomial cannot be factored, write *prime*.

1. $n^2 - 81$ $(n + 9)(n - 9)$

2. $4 - 9a^2$ $(2 + 3a)(2 - 3a)$

3. $2x^5 - 98x^3$ $2x^3(x + 7)(x - 7)$

4. $32x^4 - 2y^4$ $2(4x^2 + y^2)(2x + y)(2x - y)$

5. $4t^2 - 27$ prime

6. $x^3 - 3x^2 - 9x + 27$ $(x + 3)(x - 3)(x - 3)$

Example 4
(p. 449)

Solve each equation by factoring. Check the solutions.

7. $4y^2 = 25$ $-\frac{5}{2}, \frac{5}{2}$

8. $x^2 - \frac{1}{36} = 0$ $-\frac{1}{6}, \frac{1}{6}$

9. $121a = 49a^3$ $-\frac{11}{7}, 0, \frac{11}{7}$

Example 5
(p. 450)

★ **10. GEOMETRY** A corner is cut off a 2-inch by 2-inch square piece of paper as shown. What value of x will result in an area that is $\frac{7}{9}$ the area of the original square? $\frac{4}{3}$ in.

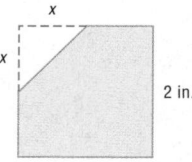

x

x

2 in.

2 in.

450 Chapter 8 Factoring

DIFFERENTIATED **HOMEWORK OPTIONS**			
Level	**Assignment**	**Two-Day Option**	
BL Basic	11–32, 35, 37–52	11–31 odd, 40, 41	12–32 even, 35, 37–39, 42–52
OL Core	11–31 odd, 33–35, 37–52	11–32, 40, 41	33–36, 37–39, 42–52
AL Advanced/Pre-AP	33–48, (optional: 49–52)		

Exercises

HOMEWORK HELP

For Exercises	See Examples
11–22	1–3
23–30	4
31, 32	5

Exercise Levels
A: 11–32
B: 33–34
C: 35–39

Factor each polynomial, if possible. If the polynomial cannot be factored, write *prime*. 14–17, 19. See margin.

11. $x^2 - 49$ $(x + 7)(x - 7)$ **12.** $n^2 - 36$ $(n + 6)(n - 6)$ **13.** $81 + 16k^2$ prime

14. $-16 + 49h^2$ **15.** $75 - 12p^2$ **16.** $-18r^3 + 242r$

17. $144a^2 - 49b^2$ **18.** $9x^2 - 10y^2$ prime **19.** $n^3 + 5n^2 - 4n - 20$

20. $3x^3 + x^2 - 75x - 25$ $(3x + 1)(x - 5)(x + 5)$ **21.** $z^4 - 16$ $(z^2 + 4)(z - 2)(z + 2)$ **22.** $256g^4 - 1$ $(16g^2 + 1)(4g - 1)(4g + 1)$

Solve each equation by factoring. Check the solutions.

23. $25x^2 = 36$ **24.** $9y^2 = 64$ **25.** $12 - 27n^2 = 0$ **26.** $50 - 8a^2 = 0$

27. $w^2 - \frac{4}{49} = 0$ **28.** $\frac{81}{100} - p^2 = 0$ **29.** $36 - \frac{1}{9}r^2 = 0$ **30.** $\frac{1}{4}x^2 - 25 = 0$

23. $-\frac{6}{5}, \frac{6}{5}$

24. $-\frac{8}{3}, \frac{8}{3}$

25. $-\frac{2}{3}, \frac{2}{3}$

26. $-\frac{5}{2}, \frac{5}{2}$

27. $-\frac{2}{7}, \frac{2}{7}$

28. $-\frac{9}{10}, \frac{9}{10}$

29. $-18, 18$

30. $-10, 10$

31. BOATING The basic breaking strength b in pounds for a natural fiber line is determined by the formula $900c^2 = b$, where c is the circumference of the line in inches. What circumference of natural line would have 3600 pounds of breaking strength? **2 in.**

★ **32. GEOMETRY** Find the dimensions of a rectangle with the same area as the shaded region in the drawing. Assume that the dimensions of the rectangle must be represented by binomials with integral coefficients. **Sample answer:** $8(2n + 3)$ cm by $(n - 1)$ cm

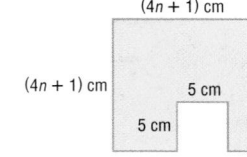

33. AERODYNAMICS The pressure difference P above and below a wing is described by the formula $P = \frac{1}{2}dv_1{}^2 - \frac{1}{2}dv_2{}^2$, where d is the density of the air, v_1 is the velocity of the air passing above, and v_2 is the velocity of the air passing below. Write this formula in factored form.
$$P = \frac{1}{2}d(v_1 + v_2)(v_1 - v_2)$$

EXTRA PRACTICE
See pages 734, 751.

Math Online
Self-Check Quiz at
ca.algebra1.com

34. PACKAGING The width of a box is 9 inches more than its length. The height of the box is 1 inch less than its length. If the box has a volume of 72 cubic inches, what are the dimensions of the box? **3 in. by 12 in. by 2 in.**

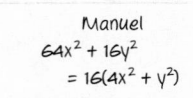

H.O.T. Problems

35. OPEN ENDED Create a binomial that is the difference of two squares. Then factor your binomial. **Sample answer:** $x^2 - 25 = (x + 5)(x - 5)$

36. CHALLENGE Show that $a^2 - b^2 = (a + b)(a - b)$ algebraically. (*Hint:* Rewrite $a^2 - b^2$ as $a^2 - ab + ab - b^2$.) **See Ch. 8 Answer Appendix.**

37. FIND THE ERROR Manuel and Jessica are factoring $64x^2 + 16y^2$. Who is correct? Explain your reasoning. **Manuel;** $4x^2 + y^2$ is not the *difference* of squares.

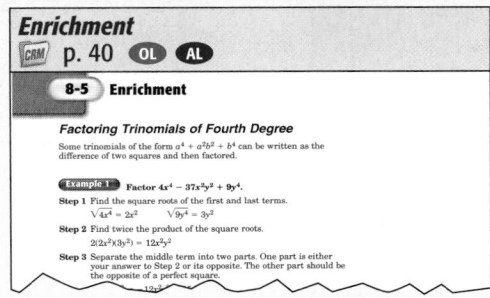

Manuel
$64x^2 + 16y^2$
$= 16(4x^2 + y^2)$

Jessica
$64x^2 + 16y^2$
$= 16(4x^2 + y^2)$
$= 16(2x + y)(2x - y)$

Lesson 8-5 Factoring Differences of Squares **451**

Study Guide and Intervention
CRM pp. 35–36 **BL OL ELL**

8-5 Study Guide and Intervention
Factoring Differences of Squares

Factor $a^2 - b^2$ The binomial expression $a^2 - b^2$ is called the **difference of two squares.** The following pattern shows how to factor the difference of squares.

Difference of Squares $a^2 - b^2 = (a - b)(a + b) = (a + b)(a - b)$.

Example 1 Factor each binomial.
a. $n^2 - 64$
$n^2 - 64$
$= n^2 - 8^2$ Write in the form $a^2 - b^2$.
$= (n + 8)(n - 8)$ Factor.
b. $4m^2 - 81n^2$
$4m^2 - 81n^2$
$= (2m)^2 - (9n)^2$ Write in the form $a^2 - b^2$.
$= (2m - 9n)(2m + 9n)$ Factor.

Example 2 Factor each polynomial.
a. $50a^2 - 72$
$50a^2 - 72$
$= 2(25a^2 - 36)$ Find the GCF.
$= 2[(5a)^2 - 6^2]$ $25a^2 = 5a \cdot 5a$ and $36 = 6 \cdot 6$
$= 2(5a - 6)(5a + 6)$ Factor the difference of squares.
b. $4x^4 + 8x^3 - 4x^2 - 8x$
$4x^4 + 8x^3 - 4x^2 - 8x$
$= 4x(x^3 + 2x^2 - x - 2)$ Find the GCF.
$= 4x[(x^3 + 2x^2) - (x + 2)]$ Group terms.
$= 4x[x^2(x + 2) - 1(x + 2)]$ Find the GCF.
$= 4x[(x^2 - 1)(x + 2)]$ Factor by grouping.
$= 4x[(x - 1)(x + 1)(x + 2)]$ Factor the difference of squares.

Exercises

Factor each polynomial if possible. If the polynomial cannot be factored, write *prime*.

1. $x^2 - 81$ $(x + 9)(x - 9)$ **2.** $m^2 - 100$ $(m + 10)(m - 10)$ **3.** $16n^2 - 25$ $(4n - 5)(4n + 5)$

4. $36x^2 - 100y^2$ $(6x + 10y)(6x - 10y)$ **5.** $49k^2 - 32$ prime **6.** $16a^2 - 9b^2$ $(4a - 3b)(4a + 3b)$

7. $225c^2 - a^2$ $(15c - a)(15c + a)$ **8.** $72p^2 - 50$ $2(6p + 5)(6p - 5)$ **9.** $-2 + 2x^2$ $2(x - 1)(x + 1)$

10. $-81 + a^4$ $(a - 3)(a + 3)(a^2 + 9)$ **11.** $6 - 54c^2$ $6(1 + 3a)(1 - 3a)$ **12.** $8p^2 - 200$ $8(p + 5)(y - 5)$

13. $4x^3 - 100x$ $4x(x + 5)(x - 5)$ **14.** $2y^4 - 32y^2$ $2y^2(y + 4)(y - 4)$ **15.** $8m^3 - 128m$ $8m(m + 4)(m - 4)$

16. $6x^2 - 25$ **17.** $2a^3 - 98ab^2$ $2a(a - 7b)(a + 7b)$ **18.** $18b^2 - 72y^4$ $18y^2(1 - 2yb)(1 + 2y)$

19. $169x^3 - x$ $x(13x + 1)(13x - 1)$ **20.** $3a^4 - 3a^2$ $3a^2(a + 1)(a - 1)$ **21.** $3x^4 + 6x^3 - 3x^2 - 6x$ $3x(x - 1)(x + 1)(x + 2)$

Chapter 8 35 Glencoe Algebra 1

Practice
CRM p. 38 **OL AL**

8-5 Practice
Factoring Differences of Squares

Factor each polynomial, if possible. If the polynomial cannot be factored, write *prime*.

1. $k^2 - 100$ $(k + 10)(k - 10)$ **2.** $81 - r^2$ $(9 + r)(9 - r)$ **3.** $16p^2 - 36$ $(4p + 6)(4p - 6)$

4. $4x^2 + 25$ prime **5.** $144 - 9t^2$ $(12 + 3t)(12 - 3t)$ **6.** $36g^2 - 49h^2$ $(6g + 7h)(6g - 7h)$

7. $121m^2 - 144n^2$ $(11m - 12n)(11m + 12n)$ **8.** $32 - 8y^2$ $8(2 - y)(2 + y)$ **9.** $24a^2 - 54b^2$ $6(2a - 3b)(2a + 3b)$

10. $32t^2 - 18u^2$ $2(4s - 3u)(4s + 3u)$ **11.** $9f^2 - 32$ prime **12.** $36b^3 - 9z$ $9z(2z + 1)(2z - 1)$

13. $45g^3 - 20g$ $5g(3g + 2)(3g - 2)$ **14.** $100b^2 - 36b$ $4b(5b + 3)(5b - 3)$ **15.** $3t^4 - 48t^2$ $3t^2(t + 4)(t - 4)$

Solve each equation by factoring. Check your solutions.

16. $4y^3 = 81$ $\left\{\pm\frac{9}{2}\right\}$ **17.** $64p^2 = 9$ $\left\{\pm\frac{3}{8}\right\}$ **18.** $98b^2 - 50 = 0$ $\left\{\pm\frac{5}{7}\right\}$

19. $32 - 162k^2 = 0$ $\left\{\pm\frac{4}{9}\right\}$ **20.** $a^2 - \frac{64}{121} = 0$ $\left\{\pm\frac{8}{11}\right\}$ **21.** $\frac{16}{49} - r^2 = 0$ $\left\{\pm\frac{4}{7}\right\}$

22. $\frac{1}{36}x^2 - 25 = 0$ $\{\pm 30\}$ **23.** $27h^3 = 48h$ $\left\{\pm\frac{4}{3}, 0\right\}$ **24.** $75g^3 = 147g$ $\left\{\pm\frac{7}{5}, 0\right\}$

25. EROSION A rock breaks loose from a cliff and plunges toward the ground 400 feet below. The distance d that the rock falls in t seconds is given by the equation $d = 16t^2$. How long does it take the rock to hit the ground? **5 s**

26. FORENSICS Mr. Cooper contested a speeding ticket given to him after he applied his brakes and skidded to a halt to avoid hitting another car. In traffic court, he argued that the length of the skid marks on the pavement, 150 feet, proved that he was driving under the posted speed limit of 65 miles per hour. The ticket cited his speed at 70 miles per hour. Use the formula $\frac{1}{24}s^2 = d$, where s is the speed of the car and d is the length of the skid marks, to determine Mr. Cooper's speed when he applied the brakes. Was Mr. Cooper correct in claiming that he was not speeding when he applied the brakes? **60 mi/h; yes**

Chapter 8 38 Glencoe Algebra 1

Word Problem Practice
CRM p. 39 **OL AL**

8-5 Word Problem Practice
Factoring Differences of Squares

1. LOTTERY A state lottery commission analyzes the ticket purchasing patterns of its citizens. The following expression is developed to help officials calculate the likely number of people who will buy tickets for a certain size jackpot.
$$81x^2 - 36b^2$$
Factor the expression completely.
$3(3a + 2b)(3a - 2b)$

4. BALLOONING The function $f(t) = -16t^2 + 576$ represents the height of a freely falling ballast bag that starts from rest on a balloon 576 feet above the ground. After how many seconds t does the ballast bag hit the ground? **after 6 seconds**

2. OPTICS A reflector on the inside of a certain flashlight is a parabola given by the equation $y = x^2 - 25$. Find the points where the reflector meets the lens by finding the values of x when $y = 0$. **5, -5**

DECORATING For Exercises 5 and 6, use the following information.
Marvin wants to purchase a rectangular rug. It has an area of 80 square feet. He cannot remember the length and width, but he remembers that the length was 8 more than some number and the width was 8 less than that same number.

3. ARCHITECTURE The drawing shows a triangular roof truss with a base measuring the same as its height. The area of the truss is 98 square meters.

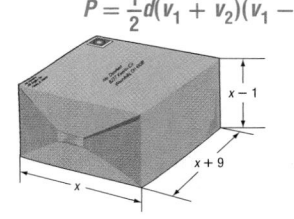

Find the height of the truss. **14 m**

5. Write a quadratic equation using the information given. $x^2 - 64 = 80$ or $x^2 - 144 = 0$

6. What are the length and width of the rug? **20 ft and 4 ft**

Chapter 8 39 Glencoe Algebra 1

BL = Below Grade Level
OL = On Grade Level
AL = Above Grade Level
ELL = English Language Learner

Additional pages not shown:
CRM *Lesson Reading Guide*, p. 34 **BL OL ELL**
CRM *Skills Practice*, p. 37 **BL OL**

Enrichment
CRM p. 40 **OL AL**

8-5 Enrichment

Factoring Trinomials of Fourth Degree

Some trinomials of the form $a^4 + a^2b^2 + b^4$ can be written as the difference of two squares and then factored.

Example 1 Factor $4x^4 - 37x^2y^2 + 9y^4$.

Step 1 Find the square roots of the first and last terms.
$\sqrt{4x^4} = 2x^2$ $\sqrt{9y^4} = 3y^2$

Step 2 Find twice the product of the square roots.
$2(2x^2)(3y^2) = 12x^2y^2$

Step 3 Separate the middle term into two parts. One part is either your answer to Step 2 or its opposite. The other part should be the opposite of a perfect square.

 **Foldables™ Follow-Up**

Remind students to use the flaps in their Foldables to record notes on what they have learned about factoring the differences of squares. They should include the Key Concept on page 442.

 4 Assess

Ticket Out the Door Have students write the factors of $18x^2 - 50$.

$2(3x + 5)(3x - 5)$

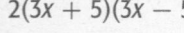 **Formative Assessment**

Check for student understanding of concepts in Lessons 8-4 and 8-5.

 Quiz 3, p. 52.

Additional Answer

39. Sample answer: A maximum height would be 1 foot. To find the hang time of a student athlete who attains a maximum height of 1 foot, solve the equation $4t^2 - 1 = 0$. You can factor the left side using the difference of squares pattern since $4t^2$ is the square of $2t$ and 1 is the square of 1. Thus, the equation becomes $(2t + 1)(2t - 1) = 0$. Using the Zero Product Property, each factor can be set equal to zero, resulting in two solutions, $t = -\frac{1}{2}$ and $t = \frac{1}{2}$. Since time cannot be negative, the hang time is $\frac{1}{2}$ second.

---

38. REASONING The following statements appear to prove that 2 is equal to 1. Find the flaw in this "proof."

Suppose a and b are real numbers such that $a = b$, $a \neq 0$, $b \neq 0$.

(1)	$a = b$	Given.
(2)	$a^2 = ab$	Multiply each side by a.
(3)	$a^2 - b^2 = ab - b^2$	Subtract b^2 from each side.
(4)	$(a - b)(a + b) = b(a - b)$	Factor.
(5)	$a + b = b$	Divide each side by $a - b$.
(6)	$a + a = a$	Substitution Property; $a = b$
(7)	$2a = a$	Combine like terms.
(8)	$2 = 1$	Divide each side by a.

The flaw is in line 5. Since $a = b$, $a - b = 0$. Therefore, dividing by $a - b$ is dividing by zero, which is undefined.

39. *Writing in Math* Use the information about basketball on page 447 to explain how to determine a basketball player's hang time. Include a maximum height that is a perfect square and that would be considered a reasonable distance for a student athlete to jump. Describe how to find the hang time for this height. **See margin.**

STANDARDS PRACTICE 14.0, 7AF1.1

40. What are the solutions to the quadratic equation $25b^2 - 1 = 0$? **D**

A $0, \frac{1}{5}$

B $-\frac{1}{5}, 0$

C $\frac{1}{5}, 1$

D $-\frac{1}{5}, \frac{1}{5}$

41. REVIEW Carla's Candle Shop sells 3 small candles for a total of $5.94. Which expression can be used to find the total cost c of x candles? **J**

F $\frac{5.94}{x}$

G $5.94x$

H $\frac{x}{1.98}$

J $1.98x$

Spiral Review

Factor each trinomial, if possible. If the trinomial cannot be factored using integers, write *prime*. (Lesson 8-4)

42. $2n^2 + 5n + 7$ **prime**   **43.** $6x^2 - 11x + 4$ $(2x - 1)(3x - 4)$ **44.** $21p^2 + 29p - 10$ $(3p + 5)(7p - 2)$

Solve each equation. Check the solutions. (Lesson 8-3)

45. $y^2 + 18y + 32 = 0$ $-16, -2$ **46.** $k^2 - 8k = -15$ 3, 5   **47.** $b^2 - 8 = 2b$ $-2, 4$

★ **48. STATISTICS** Amy's scores on the first three of four 100-point biology tests were 88, 90, and 91. To get a B+ in the class, her average must be between 88 and 92, inclusive, on all tests. What score must she receive on the fourth test to get a B+ in biology? (Lesson 5-4) **between 83 and 99, inclusive**

GET READY for the Next Lesson

PREREQUISITE SKILL Find each product. (Lesson 7-7)

49. $(x + 1)(x + 1)$ **50.** $(x + 8)^2$ **51.** $(3x - 4)(3x - 4)$ **52.** $(5x - 2)^2$
    $x^2 + 2x + 1$ $x^2 + 16x + 64$ $9x^2 - 24x + 16$ $25x^2 - 20x + 4$

452 Chapter 8 Factoring

Pre-AP Activity Use as an Extension

Have students solve the equation $x^3 - 4x = 12 - 3x^2$ by factoring. Ask them to check their solutions.
$\{-3, -2, 2\}$

Standard 25.1 Students use properties of numbers to construct simple, valid arguments (direct and indirect) for, or formulate counterexamples to, claimed assertions.

Proofs

When you solve an equation by factoring, you are using a deductive argument. Each step can be justified by an algebraic property.

Solve $4x^2 - 324 = 0$.

$4x^2 - 324 = 0$	Original equation
$(2x)^2 - 18^2 = 0$	$4x^2 = (2x)^2$ and $324 = 18^2$
$(2x + 18)(2x - 18) = 0$	Factor the difference of squares.
$2x + 18 = 0$ or $2x - 18 = 0$	Zero Product Property
$x = -9 \qquad x = 9$	Solve each equation.

Notice that the column on the left is a step-by-step process that leads to a solution. The column on the right contains the reasons for each statement. A *two-column proof* is a deductive argument that contains statements and reasons.

Two-Column Proof

Given: a, x, and y are real numbers such that $a \neq 0$, $x \neq 0$, and $y \neq 0$.
Prove: $ax^4 - ay^4 = a(x^2 + y^2)(x + y)(x - y)$

> There is a reason for each statement.

> The first statement contains the given information.

> The last statement is what you want to prove.

Statements	Reasons
1. a, x, and y are real numbers such that $a \neq 0$, $x \neq 0$, and $y \neq 0$.	**1.** Given
2. $ax^4 - ay^4 = a(x^4 - y^4)$	**2.** The GCF of ax^4 and ay^4 is a.
3. $ax^4 - ay^4 = a[(x^2)^2 - (y^2)^2]$	**3.** $x^4 = (x^2)^2$ and $y^4 = (y^2)^2$
4. $ax^4 - ay^4 = a(x^2 + y^2)(x^2 - y^2)$	**4.** Factor the difference of squares.
5. $ax^4 - ay^4 = a(x^2 + y^2)(x + y)(x - y)$	**5.** Factor the difference of squares.

Reading to Learn 1–2. See Ch. 8 Answer Appendix.

1. Solve $\frac{1}{16}t^2 - 100 = 0$ by using a two-column proof.

2. Write a two-column proof using the following information. (*Hint:* Group terms with common factors.)

   Given: c and d are real numbers such that $c \neq 0$ and $d \neq 0$.
   Prove: $c^3 - cd^2 - c^2d + d^3 = (c + d)(c - d)(c - d)$

3. Explain how the process used to write two-column proofs can be useful in solving Find the Error exercises, such as Exercise 37 on page 451. **Sample answer: By examining each step of a calculation and its reason, you can determine where the error was made.**

Additional Answer

1. (1) explains how to factor a perfect square trinomial; (2) summarizes methods used to factor polynomials; (3) explains how to solve equations involving perfect squares using the Square Root Property

1 Focus

Before using this page, ask students to name some common mathematical symbols. As student make suggestions, write the symbols on the board. Some examples might be

$+$ the addition sign
$-$ the minus sign
$=$ the equal sign.

2 Teach

Interpreting Concepts Write a mathematical sentence on the board similar to the one on this page. Have students interpret the sentence and list the concepts that they need to know in order to interpret the sentence.

Point out that a similar technique can be used when answering an essay question:

Step 1: Ask, "What does the question say?"

Step 2: Make a brief list of the information that will answer the question.

Step 3: Use this list to write the essay.

Learning New Concepts Explain to students that they can get an idea of the important concepts in a new lesson by looking over the lesson before reading it. Point out that headings, bold words, and examples illustrate these concepts.

You may want to assign Exercises 1–4 as homework.

ELL While math symbols are universal, English Language Learners may benefit from working in small groups when translating the symbols into concepts. Have group members discuss the concepts in their native language and then translate the concepts into English.

3 Assess

Ask students to discuss what they have learned about reading and interpreting mathematical concepts.

8-6 Perfect Squares and Factoring

1 Focus

 Standards Alignment

Before Lesson 8-6
Multiply and divide monomials
from 🔑 Standard 7AF2.2

Lesson 8-6
Solve a quadratic equation by
factoring or completing the square
from 🔑 Standards 11.0 and 14.0

After Lesson 8-6
Factor special polynomials.
Solve and graph quadratic
equations in the complex number
system from 🔑 Standards 2A4.0
and 2A8.0

2 Teach

Scaffolding Questions
Have students read *Get Ready for the Lesson.*
Ask:
• What does the expression $8 + 2x$ represent? The expression represents the side length of the entire square pavilion.
• What does 144 represent? 144 is the area of the entire square pavilion.
(continued on the next page)

Main Ideas
• Factor perfect square trinomials.
• Solve equations involving perfect squares.

 Standard 11.0 Students apply basic factoring techniques to second- and simple third-degree polynomials. These techniques include finding a common factor for all terms in a polynomial, recognizing the difference of two squares, and **recognizing perfect squares of binomials.**

Standard 14.0 Students solve a quadratic equation by factoring or completing the square. (Key)

New Vocabulary
perfect square trinomials

▶ GET READY for the Lesson

The senior class has decided to build an outdoor pavilion. It will have an 8-foot by 8-foot portrayal of the school's mascot in the center. The class is selling bricks with students' names on them to finance the project. If they sell enough bricks to cover 80 square feet and want to arrange the bricks around the art, how wide should the border of bricks be?

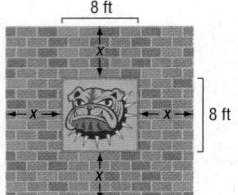

To solve this problem, you need to solve the equation $(8 + 2x)^2 = 144$.

Factor Perfect Square Trinomials Numbers like 16, 49, and 144 are perfect squares, since each can be expressed as the square of an integer.

$$16 = 4 \cdot 4 \text{ or } 4^2 \qquad 49 = 7 \cdot 7 \text{ or } 7^2 \qquad 144 = 12 \cdot 12 \text{ or } 12^2$$

Products of the form $(a + b)^2$ and $(a - b)^2$, such as $(8 + 2x)^2$, are also perfect squares. Recall that these are special products that follow specific patterns.

$$(a + b)^2 = (a + b)(a + b) \qquad\qquad (a - b)^2 = (a - b)(a - b)$$
$$= a^2 + ab + ab + b^2 \qquad\qquad = a^2 - ab - ab + b^2$$
$$= a^2 + 2ab + b^2 \qquad\qquad = a^2 - 2ab + b^2$$

These patterns can help you factor **perfect square trinomials**, which are trinomials that are the squares of binomials.

Squaring a Binomial	Factoring a Perfect Square
$(x + 7)^2 = x^2 + 2(x)(7) + 7^2$ $= x^2 + 14x + 49$	$x^2 + 14x + 49 = x^2 + 2(x)(7) + 7^2$ $= (x + 7)^2$
$(3x - 4)^2 = (3x)^2 - 2(3x)(4) + 4^2$ $= 9x^2 - 24x + 16$	$9x^2 - 24x + 16 = (3x)^2 - 2(3x)(4) + 4^2$ $= (3x - 4)^2$

For a trinomial to be factorable as a perfect square, three conditions must be satisfied as illustrated in the example below.

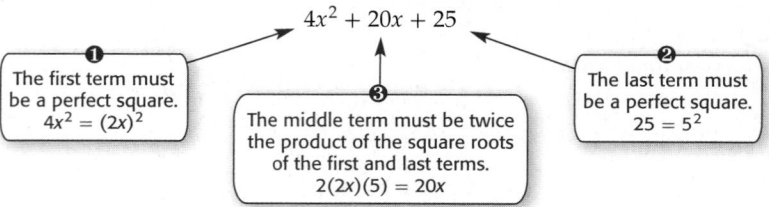

$$4x^2 + 20x + 25$$

❶ The first term must be a perfect square. $4x^2 = (2x)^2$

❸ The middle term must be twice the product of the square roots of the first and last terms. $2(2x)(5) = 20x$

❷ The last term must be a perfect square. $25 = 5^2$

Lesson 8-6 Resources

Chapter 8 Resource Masters
Lesson Reading Guide, p. 42 **BL** **OL** **ELL**
Study Guide and Intervention, pp. 43–44
BL **OL** **ELL**
Skills Practice, p. 45 **BL** **OL**
Practice, p. 46 **OL** **AL**
Word Problem Practice, p. 47 **OL** **AL**
Enrichment, p. 48 **OL** **AL**
Quiz 4, p. 52

Transparencies
5-Minute Check Transparency 8-6

Additional Print Resources
Noteables™ Interactive Study Notebook with Foldables™
Teaching Algebra with Manipulatives

Technology
ca.algebra1.com
Interactive Classroom CD-ROM
AssignmentWorks CD-ROM
Graphing Calculator Easy Files

Words   If a trinomial can be written in the form $a^2 + 2ab + b^2$ or $a^2 - 2ab + b^2$, then it can be factored as $(a + b)^2$ or as $(a - b)^2$, respectively.

Symbols $a^2 + 2ab + b^2 = (a + b)^2$ and $a^2 - 2ab + b^2 = (a - b)^2$

EXAMPLE   Factor Perfect Square Trinomials

1 Determine whether each trinomial is a perfect square trinomial. If so, factor it.

a. $16x^2 + 32x + 64$

❶ Is the first term a perfect square?   Yes, $16x^2 = (4x)^2$.

❷ Is the last term a perfect square?   Yes, $64 = 8^2$.

❸ Is the middle term equal to $2(4x)(8)$?   No, $32x \neq 2(4x)(8)$.

$16x^2 + 32x + 64$ is not a perfect square trinomial.

b. $9y^2 - 12y + 4$

❶ Is the first term a perfect square?   Yes, $9y^2 = (3y)^2$.

❷ Is the last term a perfect square?   Yes, $4 = 2^2$.

❸ Is the middle term equal to $2(3y)(2)$?   Yes, $12y = 2(3y)(2)$.

$9y^2 - 12y + 4$ is a perfect square trinomial.

$9y^2 - 12y + 4 = (3y)^2 - 2(3y)(2) + 2^2$ Write as $a^2 - 2ab + b^2$.

$ = (3y - 2)^2$ Factor using the pattern.

✓CHECK Your Progress

1A. $n^2 - 24n + 144$ yes; $(n - 12)^2$ **1B.** $x^2 + 9x + 81$ no

You have learned various techniques for factoring polynomials. The Concept Summary can help you decide when to use a specific technique.

CONCEPT SUMMARY   *Factoring Polynomials*

Number of Terms	Factoring Technique		Example
2 or more	greatest common factor		$3x^2 + 6x^2 - 15x = 3x(x^2 + 2x - 5)$
2	difference of squares	$a^2 - b^2 = (a + b)(a - b)$	$4x^2 - 25 = (2x + 5)(2x - 5)$
3	perfect square trinomial	$a^2 + 2ab + b^2 = (a + b)^2$ $a^2 - 2ab + b^2 = (a - b)^2$	$x^2 + 6x + 9 = (x + 3)^2$ $4x^2 - 4x + 1 = (2x - 1)^2$
	$x^2 + bx + c$	$x^2 + bx + c = (x + m)(x + n)$ when $m + n = b$ and $mn = c$.	$x^2 - 9x + 20 = (x - 5)(x - 4)$
	$ax^2 + bx + c$	$ax^2 + bx + c = ax^2 + mx + nx + c$ when $m + n = b$ and $mn = ac$. Then use factoring by grouping.	$6x^2 - x - 2 = 6x^2 + 3x - 4x - 2$ $= 3x(2x + 1) - 2(2x + 1)$ $= (2x + 1)(3x - 2)$
4 or more	factoring by grouping	$ax + bx + ay + by$ $= x(a + b) + y(a + b)$ $= (a + b)(x + y)$	$3xy - 6y + 5x - 10$ $= (3xy - 6y) + (5x - 10)$ $= 3y(x - 2) + 5(x - 2)$ $= (x - 2)(3y + 5)$

Tips for New Teachers   **Assessment Tip**

During the last lesson of a chapter, it is often good to review some of the major concepts of the chapter to assess whether students have mastered the concepts. The concept summary table on factoring polynomials provides a perfect opportunity for review. Briefly review each factoring technique with students. After your review, you might consider giving students a quiz on the different techniques to assess student mastery.

• **How do you know the area of the pavilion is 144 square feet?** The square mascot area has an area of 8^2 or 64 ft^2 because its side length is 8 ft. The problem states that the bricks will cover 80 ft^2, so the area of the entire structure is $64 + 80$ or 144 ft^2.

• **What feature of the pavilion tells you that 144 must be a perfect square?** The building is square, so the area must be the square of the side length. Since the area is 144, $8 + 2x = 12$, and $x = 2$.

Factor Perfect Square Trinomials

Example 1 shows how to determine whether a trinomial is a perfect square trinomial and, if it is, how to factor it. **Example 2** shows how to use various factoring methods to factor a polynomial completely.

ADDITIONAL EXAMPLE

1 Determine whether each trinomial is a perfect square trinomial. If so, factor it.

a. $25x^2 - 30x + 9$ yes; $(5x - 3)^2$

b. $49y^2 + 42y + 36$ not a perfect square trinomial

Additional Examples are also in:

• Noteables™ Interactive Study Notebook with Foldables™

• Interactive Classroom PowerPoint® Presentations

 Preventing Errors

Students should be reminded to look closely at the operation sign in front of the second term of the trinomial. This sign signifies whether the factors are in the form $(a + b)^2$ or $(a - b)^2$.

Common Errors

Students often fail to factor polynomials completely. Point out that $4x^2 - 36$ is a difference of squares and can be factored as $(2x - 6)(2x + 6)$, but remind students that a polynomial is not considered completely factored if the terms of any of its factors have a GCF greater than 1.

ADDITIONAL EXAMPLE

 Factor each polynomial.

a. $6x^2 - 96$ $6(x + 4)(x - 4)$

b. $16y^2 + 8y - 15$
$(4y + 5)(4y - 3)$

Focus on Mathematical Content

Factor Perfect Square Trinomials
Once a trinomial has been determined to be a perfect square trinomial, it can be factored into two identical binomials or expressed as a binomial squared. The binomial factors are the sum or difference, depending on sign of the middle term of the trinomial, of the principal square roots of the first term and last term of the trinomial.

Solve Equations with Perfect Squares

Example 3 shows how to solve equations with repeated factors.
Examples 4–5 show how to solve equations using the Square Root Property.

ADDITIONAL EXAMPLE

 Solve $4x^2 + 36x + 81 = 0$.
$\left\{-\dfrac{9}{2}\right\}$

Study Tip

Factoring Methods

When there is a GCF other than 1, it is usually easier to factor it out first. Then, check the appropriate factoring methods in the order shown in the table.

EXAMPLE Factor Completely

2 Factor each polynomial.

a. $4x^2 - 36$

First check for a GCF. Then, since the polynomial has two terms, check for the difference of squares.

$$\begin{aligned}4x^2 - 36 &= 4(x^2 - 9) & &\text{4 is the GCF.}\\ &= 4(x^2 - 3^2) & &x^2 = x \cdot x \text{ and } 9 = 3 \cdot 3\\ &= 4(x + 3)(x - 3) & &\text{Factor the difference of squares.}\end{aligned}$$

b. $25x^2 + 5x - 6$

This is not a perfect square trinomial. It is of the form $ax^2 + bx + c$. Are there two numbers m and n with a product of $25(-6)$ or -150 and a sum of 5? Yes, the product of 15 and -10 is -150 and the sum is 5.

$$\begin{aligned}25x^2 + 5x - 6 &= 25x^2 + mx + nx - 6 & &\text{Write the pattern.}\\ &= 25x^2 + 15x - 10x - 6 & &m = 15 \text{ and } n = -10\\ &= (25x^2 + 15x) + (-10x - 6) & &\text{Group terms with common factors.}\\ &= 5x(5x + 3) - 2(5x + 3) & &\text{Factor out the GCF from each grouping.}\\ &= (5x + 3)(5x - 2) & &5x + 3 \text{ is the common factor.}\end{aligned}$$

 **CHECK Your Progress**

2A. $2x^2 - 32$ $2(x + 4)(x - 4)$ **2B.** $9t^2 - 3t - 20$ $(3t + 4)(3t - 5)$

Online Personal Tutor at ca.algebra1.com

Solve Equations with Perfect Squares When solving equations involving repeated factors, it is only necessary to set one of the repeated factors equal to zero.

EXAMPLE Solve Equations with Repeated Factors

3 Solve $x^2 - x + \dfrac{1}{4} = 0$.

$$\begin{aligned}x^2 - x + \frac{1}{4} &= 0 & &\text{Original equation}\\ x^2 - 2(x)\left(\frac{1}{2}\right) + \left(\frac{1}{2}\right)^2 &= 0 & &\text{Recognize } x^2 - x + \tfrac{1}{4} \text{ as a perfect square trinomial.}\\ \left(x - \frac{1}{2}\right)^2 &= 0 & &\text{Factor the perfect square trinomial.}\\ x - \frac{1}{2} &= 0 & &\text{Set repeated factor equal to zero.}\\ x &= \frac{1}{2} & &\text{Solve for } x.\end{aligned}$$

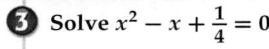 **CHECK Your Progress**

Solve each equation. Check the solutions.
3A. $a^2 + 12a + 36 = 0$ -6 **3B.** $y^2 - \dfrac{4}{3}y + \dfrac{4}{9} = 0$ $\dfrac{2}{3}$

456 Chapter 8 Factoring

Student Misconceptions

Students have been taught that second-degree equations will have two solutions, but are confused when an equation involving a perfect square trinomial has only one solution. Explain that perfect square trinomials have a repeated factor, so that both solutions are the same number. Thus, only one solution is listed.

You have solved equations like $x^2 - 36 = 0$ by factoring. You can also use the definition of a square root to solve this equation.

$$x^2 - 36 = 0 \qquad \text{Original equation}$$
$$x^2 = 36 \qquad \text{Add 36 to each side.}$$
$$x = \pm\sqrt{36} \qquad \text{Take the square root of each side.}$$

Remember that there are two square roots of 36, namely 6 and -6. Therefore, the solution set is $\{-6, 6\}$. You can express this as $\{\pm 6\}$.

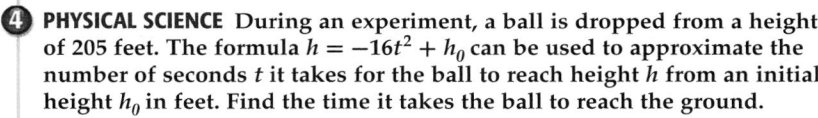

KEY CONCEPT   *Square Root Property*

Symbols For any number $n > 0$, if $x^2 = n$, then $x = \pm\sqrt{n}$.

Example $x^2 = 9$
$$x = \pm\sqrt{9} \text{ or } \pm 3$$

EXAMPLE

4 **PHYSICAL SCIENCE** During an experiment, a ball is dropped from a height of 205 feet. The formula $h = -16t^2 + h_0$ can be used to approximate the number of seconds t it takes for the ball to reach height h from an initial height h_0 in feet. Find the time it takes the ball to reach the ground.

$$h = -16t^2 + h_0 \qquad \text{Original formula}$$
$$0 = -16t^2 + 205 \qquad \text{Replace } h \text{ with 0 and } h_0 \text{ with 205.}$$
$$-205 = -16t^2 \qquad \text{Subtract 205 from each side.}$$
$$12.8125 = t^2 \qquad \text{Divide each side by } -16.$$
$$\pm 3.6 \approx t \qquad \text{Take the square root of each side.}$$

Since a negative number does not make sense in this situation, the solution is 3.6. This means that it takes about 3.6 seconds for the ball to reach the ground.

✓CHECK Your Progress

4. Find the time it takes a ball to reach the ground if it is dropped from a bridge that is half as high as the one described above. **2.5 s**

EXAMPLE   Use the Square Root Property to Solve Equations

5 Solve each equation. Check the solutions.

a. $(a + 4)^2 = 49$

$$(a + 4)^2 = 49 \qquad \text{Original equation}$$
$$a + 4 = \pm\sqrt{49} \qquad \text{Square Root Property}$$
$$a + 4 = \pm 7 \qquad 49 = 7 \cdot 7$$
$$a = -4 \pm 7 \qquad \text{Subtract 4 from each side.}$$
$$a = -4 + 7 \quad \text{or} \quad a = -4 - 7 \qquad \text{Separate into two equations.}$$
$$= 3 \qquad\qquad = -11 \qquad \text{Simplify.}$$

The roots are -11 and 3.   Check in the original equation.

(continued on the next page)

Preventing Errors

Preventing Errors

Remind students that any of the factoring methods they have studied thus far can be used in the exercises.

3 Practice

Formative Assessment

Use Exercises 1–11 to check for understanding.

Use the chart at the bottom of this page to customize assignments for your students.

Odd/Even Assignments

Exercises 12–37 are structured so that students practice the same concepts whether they are assigned odd or even problems.

Foldables™
Follow-Up

Remind students to use the flap for this lesson in their Foldables to record the Concept Summary on page 449 and examples of factoring perfect square trinomials.

Real-World Connections

For Exercise 37, you may wish to tell students that a fourteen-year-old girl, whose stage name was "Zazel," was the first recorded person to be shot from a cannon. This occurred in England, circa 1877. Since then, dozens have been propelled from cannons at speeds up to 90 mph and as far as 201 feet at a height of 100 feet.

Additional Answer

43. $8x^2 - 22x + 14$ in^2 if $x > \frac{7}{4}$,

$8x^2 - 34x + 35$ in^2 if $x < \frac{7}{4}$

---

b. $(x - 3)^2 = 5$

$\quad (x - 3)^2 = 5$ Original equation

$\quad\quad x - 3 = \pm\sqrt{5}$ Square Root Property

$\quad\quad\quad x = 3 \pm \sqrt{5}$ Add 3 to each side.

Since 5 is not a perfect square, the roots are $3 \pm \sqrt{5}$. Using a calculator, the roots are $3 + \sqrt{5}$ or about 5.24 and $3 - \sqrt{5}$ or about 0.76.

COncepts in MOtion
Interactive Lab
ca.algebra1.com

CHECK Your Progress

5A. $z^2 + 2z + 1 = 16$ $-5, 3$ **5B.** $(y - 8)^2 = 7$ $8 \pm \sqrt{7}$

★ indicates multi-step problem

CHECK Your Understanding

Example 1
(p. 455)

Determine whether each trinomial is a perfect square trinomial. If so, factor it.

1. $y^2 + 8y + 16$ yes; $(y + 4)^2$ **2.** $9x^2 - 30x + 10$ no

Example 2
(p. 456)

Factor each polynomial, if possible. If the polynomial cannot be factored, write *prime*.

3. $2x^2 + 18$ $2(x^2 + 9)$ **4.** $c^2 - 5c + 6$ $(c - 3)(c - 2)$

5. $8x^2 - 18x - 35$ $(2x - 7)(4x + 5)$ **6.** $9g^2 + 12g - 4$ prime

Examples 3, 5
(pp. 456–458)

Solve each equation. Check the solutions.

7. $4y^2 + 24y + 36 = 0$ -3 **8.** $3n^2 = 48$ ± 4

9. $a^2 - 6a + 9 = 16$ $-1, 7$ **10.** $(m - 5)^2 = 13$ $5 \pm \sqrt{13}$

Example 4
(p. 457)

11. HISTORY Galileo showed that objects of different weights fall at the same velocity by dropping two objects of different weights from the top of the Leaning Tower of Pisa. A model for the height h in feet of an object dropped from an initial height h_0 feet is $h = -16t^2 + h_0$, where t is the time in seconds after the object is dropped. Use this model to determine approximately how long it took for objects to hit the ground if Galileo dropped them from a height of 180 feet.   about 3.35 s

Exercises

HOMEWORK HELP	
For Exercises	**See Examples**
12–15	1
16–23	2
24–33	3, 5
34–37	4

Exercise Levels
A: 12–37
B: 38–43
C: 44–50

Determine whether each trinomial is a perfect square trinomial. If so, factor it.

12. $4y^2 - 44y + 121$ yes; $(2y - 11)^2$ **13.** $2c^2 + 10c + 25$ no

14. $9n^2 + 49 + 42n$ yes; $(3n + 7)^2$ **15.** $25a^2 - 120ab + 144b^2$ yes; $(5a - 12b)^2$

Factor each polynomial, if possible. If the polynomial cannot be factored, write *prime*.

16. $4k^2 - 100$ $4(k + 5)(k - 5)$ **17.** $4a^2 - 36b^2$ $4(a - 3b)(a + 3b)$

18. $x^2 + 6x - 9$ prime   **19.** $50g^2 + 40g + 8$ $2(5g + 2)^2$

20. $9t^3 + 66t^2 - 48t$ $3t(3t - 2)(t + 8)$ **21.** $20n^2 + 34n + 6$ $2(5n + 1)(2n + 3)$

22. $5y^2 - 90$ $5(y^2 - 18)$ **23.** $18y^2 - 48y + 32$ $2(3y - 4)^2$

DIFFERENTIATED HOMEWORK OPTIONS

Level	Assignment	Two-Day Option	
BL Basic	12–37, 44–46, 50–62	13–37 odd, 51, 52	12–36 even, 44–46, 50, 53–62
OL Core	13–41 odd, 42–46, 50–62	12–37, 51, 52	38–46, 50, 53–61
AL Advanced/Pre-AP	38–62		

Solve each equation. Check the solutions.

24. $3x^2 + 24x + 48 = 0$ $\;-4$
25. $7r^2 = 70r - 175$ $\;5$
26. $49a^2 + 16 = 56a$ $\;\frac{4}{7}$
27. $18y^2 + 24y + 8 = 0$ $\;-\frac{2}{3}$
28. $y^2 - \frac{2}{3}y + \frac{1}{9} = 0$ $\;\frac{1}{3}$
29. $a^2 + \frac{4}{5}a + \frac{4}{25} = 0$ $\;-\frac{2}{5}$
30. $x^2 + 10x + 25 = 81$ $\;-14, 4$
31. $(w + 3)^2 = 2$ $\;-3 \pm \sqrt{2}$
32. $p^2 + 2p + 1 = 6$ $\;-1 \pm \sqrt{6}$
33. $x^2 - 12x + 36 = 11$ $\;6 \pm \sqrt{11}$

34. FORESTRY The number of board feet B that a log will yield can be estimated by using the formula $B = \frac{L}{16}(D^2 - 8D + 16)$, where D is the diameter in inches and L is the log length in feet. For logs that are 16 feet long, what diameter will yield approximately 256 board feet? **20**

FREE-FALL RIDE For Exercises 35 and 36, use the following information.
The height h in feet of a car above the exit ramp of an amusement park's free-fall ride can be modeled by $h = -16t^2 + s$, where t is the time in seconds after the car drops and s is the starting height of the car in feet.

35. How high above the car's exit ramp should the ride's designer start the drop in order for riders to experience free fall for at least 3 seconds? **144 ft**

36. Approximately how long will riders be in free fall if their starting height is 160 feet above the exit ramp? **3.16 s**

Real-World Link
Some amusement park free-fall rides can seat 4 passengers across per coach and reach speeds of up to 62 miles per hour.
Source: pgathrills.com

★ **37. HUMAN CANNONBALL** A circus acrobat is shot out of a cannon with an initial upward velocity of 64 feet per second. If the acrobat leaves the cannon 6 feet above the ground, will he reach a height of 70 feet? If so, how long will it take him to reach that height? Use the model for vertical motion. **yes; 2 s**

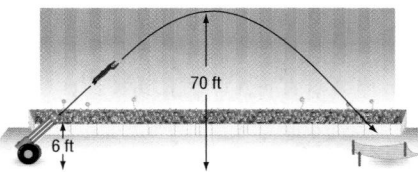
70 ft
6 ft

Factor each polynomial, if possible. If the polynomial cannot be factored, write *prime*. **38.** $(a^2 + 2)(4a + 3b^2)$

38. $4a^3 + 3a^2b^2 + 8a + 6b^2$
39. $5a^2 + 7a + 6b^2 - 4b$ **prime**
40. $x^2y^2 - y^2 - z^2 + x^2z^2$
$(y^2 + z^2)(x + 1)(x - 1)$
41. $4m^4n + 6m^3n - 16m^2n^2 - 24mn^2$
$2mn(m^2 - 4n)(2m + 3)$

★ **42. GEOMETRY** The volume of a rectangular prism is $x^3y - 63y^2 + 7x^2 - 9xy^3$ cubic meters. Find the dimensions of the prism if they can be represented by binomials with integral coefficients. $(x - 3y)$ m, $(x + 3y)$ m, $(xy + 7)$ m

EXTRA PRACTICE
See pages 734, 751.
Mathonline
Self-Check Quiz at
ca.algebra1.com

43. GEOMETRY If the area of the square shown is $16x^2 - 56x + 49$ square inches, what is the area of the rectangle in terms of x? **See margin.**

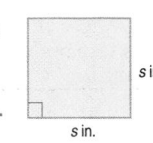
s in.
s in.

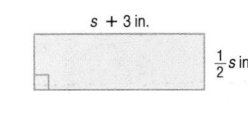
$s + 3$ in.
$\frac{1}{2}s$ in.

H.O.T. Problems

44. REASONING Determine whether the following statement is *sometimes*, *always*, or *never* true. Explain your reasoning. **never;** $(a - b)^2 = a^2 - 2ab + b^2$
$$a^2 - 2ab - b^2 = (a - b)^2, b \neq 0$$

Lesson 8-6 Perfect Squares and Factoring **459**

BL = Below Grade Level
OL = On Grade Level
AL = Above Grade Level
ELL = English Language Learner

Additional pages not shown:

CRM *Lesson Reading Guide*, p. 42 **BL** **OL** **ELL**

CRM *Skills Practice*, p. 45 **BL** **OL**

Enrichment
CRM p. 48 **OL** **AL**

8-6 Enrichment

Squaring Numbers: A Shortcut

A shortcut helps you to square a positive two-digit number ending in 5. The method is developed using the idea that a two-digit number may be expressed as $10t + u$. Suppose $u = 5$.

$(10t + 5)^2 = (10t + 5)(10t + 5)$
$= 100t^2 + 50t + 50t + 25$
$= 100t^2 + 100t + 25$

$(10t + 5)^2 = 100t(t + 1) + 25$

In words, this formula says that the square of a two-digit number ending in 5 has $t(t + 1)$ in the hundreds place. Then 2 is the tens digit and 5 is the units digit.

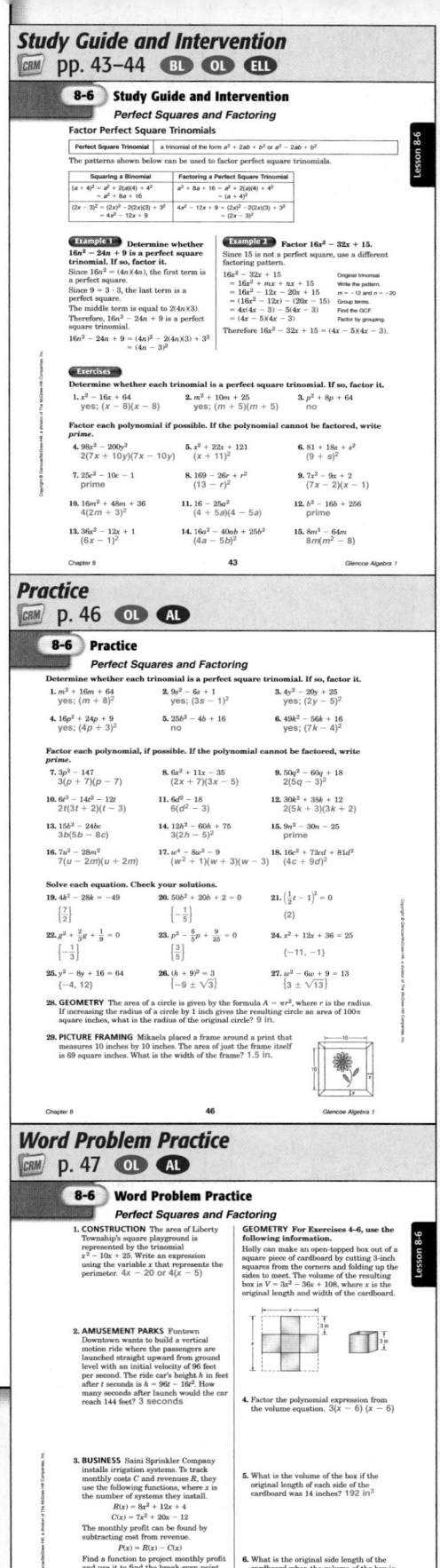

Lesson 8-6 Perfect Squares and Factoring **459**

Name the Math Have each student tell a partner or write how to determine if a trinomial is a perfect square trinomial.

Formative Assessment

Check for student understanding of concepts in Lesson 8-6.

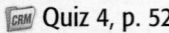 Quiz 4, p. 52

Foldables™
Follow-Up

Remind students to use the flaps in their Foldables to record notes on what they have learned about perfect squares and factoring.

Additional Answers

45. Sample answer: $x^3 + 5x^2 - 4x - 20$; group terms with common factors and factor out the GCF from each grouping to get $(x^2 - 4)(x + 5)$. Then factor the perfect square trinomial to get $(x - 2)(x + 2)(x + 5)$.

50. Sample answer: The length of each side of the pavilion is $8 + x + x$ or $8 + 2x$ feet. Thus, the area of the pavilion is $(8 + 2x)^2$ square feet. This area includes the 80 square feet of bricks and the 82 or 64-square foot piece of art, for a total area of 144 square feet. These two representations of the area of the pavilion must be equal, so we can write the equation $(8 + 2x)^2 = 144$.   Original equation

$8 + 2x = \pm 12$ Square Root Property

$8 + 2x = 12$ or $8 + 2x = -12$
Separate into two equations.

$2x = 4$ $2x = -20$

Solve each equation.

$x = 2$ $x = -10$

Since length cannot be negative, the border should be 2 feet wide.

---

45. OPEN ENDED Create a polynomial that requires at least two different factoring techniques to factor it completely. Then factor the polynomial completely, describing the techniques that were used. See margin.

46. $4x^2 + 10x + 4$ because it is the only expression that is not a perfect square trinomial.

46. Which One Doesn't Belong? Identify the trinomial that does not belong with the other three. Explain your reasoning.

| $4x^2 - 36x + 81$ | $25x^2 + 10x + 1$ | $4x^2 + 10x + 4$ | $9x^2 - 24x + 16$ |

CHALLENGE Determine all values of k that make each of the following a perfect square trinomial.

47. $4x^2 + kx + 1$ 4, −4   **48.** $x^2 - 18x + k$ 81   **49.** $x^2 + 20x + k$ 100

50. *Writing in Math* Use the information about the project on page 454 to explain how factoring can be used to design a pavilion. Explain how the equation $(8 + 2x)^2 = 144$ models the given situation, solve this equation, and interpret its solutions. See margin.

STANDARDS PRACTICE 11.0, 6PS3.4

51. What are the solutions for the equation $3(5x - 1)^2 = 27$? C

A $-\frac{9}{5}$ and 2

B -2 and $\frac{9}{5}$

C $-\frac{2}{5}$ and $\frac{4}{5}$

D $-\frac{1}{5}$ and $\frac{3}{5}$

52. REVIEW Marta has a bag of 8 marbles. There are 3 red marbles, 2 blue marbles, 2 white marbles, and 1 black marble. If she picks one marble without looking, what is the probability that it is either black or white? H

F $\frac{1}{8}$ H $\frac{3}{8}$

G $\frac{1}{4}$ J $\frac{5}{8}$

Spiral Review

Solve each equation. Check the solutions. (Lessons 8-4 and 8-5)

53. $9x^2 - 16 = 0$ $\pm\frac{4}{3}$ **54.** $49m^2 = 81$ $\pm\frac{9}{7}$ **55.** $8k^2 + 22k - 6 = 0$ $-3, \frac{1}{4}$ **56.** $12w^2 + 23x = -5$ $-\frac{5}{3}, -\frac{1}{4}$

Solve each inequality. Check the solution. (Lesson 6-2)

57. $\{r \mid r > -55\}$
57. $\frac{r}{5} > -11$ **58.** $8 > \frac{2}{3}n$ $\{n \mid n < 12\}$ **59.** $76 < 4t$ $\{t \mid t > 19\}$ **60.** $-14c \le 84$ $\{c \mid c \ge -6\}$

★ **61. BUSINESS** Jake's Garage charges $180 for a two-hour repair job and $375 for a five-hour repair job. Write a linear equation that Jake can use to bill customers for repair jobs of any length of time. (Lesson 4-3) $y = 65x + 50$

62. MODEL TRAINS One of the most popular sizes of model trains is called the HO. Every dimension of the HO model measures $\frac{1}{87}$ times that of a real engine. The HO model of a modern diesel locomotive is about 8 inches long. About how many feet long is the real locomotive? (Lesson 3-6) 58

460 Chapter 8 Factoring

Pre-AP Activity   Use as an Extension

Write the following polynomial on the board for students to factor completely:

$(m - n)m^2 - 2m(m - n) + (m - n)$

$(m - n)(m - 1)(m - 1)$

STUDY TO GO Download Vocabulary Review from ca.algebra1.com

CHAPTER 8 Study Guide and Review

FOLDABLES Study Organizer

GET READY to Study

Be sure the following Key Concepts are noted in your Foldable.

8-1	F
8-2	a c
8-3	t o
8-4	r i
8-5	n
8-6	g

Key Concepts

Monomials and Factoring (Lesson 8-1)

- The greatest common factor (GCF) of two or more monomials is the product of their common prime factors.

Factoring Using the Distributive Property (Lesson 8-2)

- Using the Distributive Property to factor polynomials with four or more terms is called factoring by grouping.

$$ax + bx + ay + by = x(a + b) + y(a + b)$$
$$= (a + b)(x + y)$$

- Factoring can be used to solve some equations. According to the Zero Product Property, for any real numbers a and b, if $ab = 0$, then either $a = 0$, $b = 0$, or both a and b equal zero.

Factoring Trinomials and Differences of Squares (Lessons 8-3, 8-4, and 8-5)

- To factor $x^2 + bx + c$, find m and n with a sum of b and a product of c. Then write $x^2 + bx + c$ as $(x + m)(x + n)$.

- To factor $ax^2 + bx + c$, find m and n with a product of ac and a sum of b. Then write as $ax^2 + mx + nx + c$ and factor by grouping.
$$a^2 - b^2 = (a + b)(a - b) \text{ or } (a - b)(a + b)$$

Perfect Squares and Factoring (Lesson 8-6)

- $a^2 + 2ab + b^2 = (a + b)^2$ and
$a^2 - 2ab + b^2 = (a - b)^2$

- For a trinomial to be a perfect square, the first and last terms must be perfect squares, and the middle term must be twice the product of the square roots of the first and last terms.

- For any number $n > 0$, if $x^2 = n$, then $x = \pm\sqrt{n}$.

 Vocabulary Review at ca.algebra1.com

Key Vocabulary

composite number (p. 420)
factored form (p. 421)
factoring (p. 426)
factoring by grouping (p. 427)
greatest common factor (p. 422)
perfect square trinomials (p. 454)
prime factorization (p. 421)
prime number (p. 420)
prime polynomial (p. 443)
roots (p. 428)

Vocabulary Check

State whether each sentence is *true* or *false*. If *false*, replace the underlined word, phrase, expression, or number to make a true sentence.

1. The number 27 is an example of a <u>prime</u> number. **false; composite**

2. <u>2x</u> is the greatest common factor of $12x^2$ and $14xy$. **true**

3. <u>66</u> is an example of a perfect square.

4. 61 is a <u>factor</u> of 183. **true**

5. The prime factorization of 48 is <u>$3 \cdot 4^2$</u>.

6. $x^2 - 25$ is an example of a <u>perfect square trinomial</u>. **false; difference of squares**

7. The number 35 is an example of a <u>composite number</u>. **true**

8. <u>$x^2 - 3x - 70$</u> is an example of a prime polynomial.

9. Expressions with four or more unlike terms can sometimes be <u>factored by grouping</u>. **true**

10. <u>$(b - 7)(b + 7)$</u> is the factorization of a difference of squares. **true**

3. false; sample answer: 64
5. false; $2^4 \cdot 3$
8. false; sample answer: $x^2 + 2x + 2$

 Summative Assessment

[CRM] Vocabulary Test, p. 54

FOLDABLES Study Organizer

Dinah Zike's Foldables™

Have students look through the chapter to make sure they have included questions, notes, and examples in their Foldables for each lesson of Chapter 8.

Suggest that students keep their Foldables handy while completing the Study Guide and Review pages. Point out that their Foldables can serve as a review tool for studying for the chapter test.

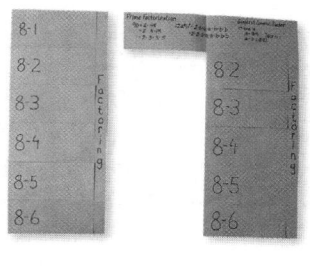

✓ Formative Assessment

Key Vocabulary The page reference after each word denotes where that term was first introduced. If students have difficulty answering questions 1–10, remind them that they can use these page references to refresh their memories about the vocabulary terms.

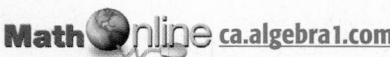 **ca.algebra1.com**

Vocabulary PuzzleMaker improves students' mathematics vocabulary using four puzzle formats—crossword, scramble, word search using a word list, and word search using clues. Students can work online or from a printed worksheet.

CHAPTER 8 Study Guide and Review

Lesson-by-Lesson Review

Intervention If the given examples are not sufficient to review the topics covered by the questions, remind students that the page references tell them where to review that topic in their textbooks.

Two-Day Option Have students complete the Lesson-by-Lesson Review on pages 462–464. Then you can use ExamView® Assessment Suite to customize another review worksheet that practices all the objectives of this chapter or only the objectives with which your students need more help.

For more information on ExamView® Assessment Suite, see p. 418C.

Differentiated Instruction
Super DVD: MindJogger Videoquizzes Use this DVD as an alternative format of review for the test. For more information on this game show format, see p. 418D.

Additional Answers

11. $2^2 \cdot 7 \cdot n \cdot n \cdot n$

12. $-1 \cdot 3 \cdot 11 \cdot a \cdot a \cdot b$

13. $2 \cdot 3 \cdot 5^2 \cdot s \cdot t$

14. $-1 \cdot 2 \cdot 3^3 \cdot 7 \cdot p \cdot q \cdot q \cdot r \cdot r$

22. $13(x + 2y)$

23. $(a - 4c)(a + b)$

Lesson-by-Lesson Review

8–1 **Monomials and Factoring** (pp. 420–424)

Factor each monomial completely.

11. $28n^3$ **12.** $-33a^2b$

13. $150st$ **14.** $-378pq^2r^2$

11–14. See margin.

Find the GCF of each set of monomials.

15. $35, 30$ **5**   **16.** $12, 18, 40$ **2**

17. $12ab, 4a^2b^2$ **4ab**   **18.** $16mrt, 30m^2r$ **2mr**

19. $20n^2, 25np^5$ **5n**

20. $60x^2y^2, 15xyz, 35xz^3$ **5x**

21. HOME IMPROVEMENT A landscape architect is designing a stone path to cover an area 36 inches by 120 inches. What is the maximum size square stone that can be used so that none of the stones have to be cut? **12-in. square**

Example 1 Factor $68cd^2$ completely.

$68cd^2 = 4 \cdot 17 \cdot c \cdot d \cdot d$ $68 = 4 \cdot 17, d^2 = d \cdot d$

$\qquad = 2 \cdot 2 \cdot 17 \cdot c \cdot d \cdot d$ $4 = 2 \cdot 2$

Thus, $68cd^2$ in factored form is $2 \cdot 2 \cdot 17 \cdot c \cdot d \cdot d$.

Example 2 Find the GCF of $15x^2y$ and $45xy^2$.

$15x^2y = ③ \cdot ⑤ \cdot ⓧ \cdot x \cdot ⓨ$ Factor each number.

$45xy^2 = ③ \cdot 3 \cdot ⑤ \cdot ⓧ \cdot ⓨ \cdot y$ Circle the common prime factors.

The GCF is $3 \cdot 5 \cdot x \cdot y$ or $15xy$.

8–2 **Factoring Using the Distributive Property** (pp. 426–431)

Factor each polynomial. **22–23. See margin.**

22. $13x + 26y$ **23.** $a^2 - 4ac + ab - 4bc$

24. $24a^2b^2 - 18ab$ **25.** $26ab + 18ac + 32a^2$

   6ab(4ab − 3)   **2a(13b + 9c + 16a)**

26. $4rs + 12ps + 2mr + 6mp$ **2(r + 3p)(2s + m)**

27. $24am - 9an + 40bm - 15bn$

   (8m − 3n)(3a + 5b)

Solve each equation. Check the solutions.

28. $x(2x - 5) = 0$ **0, $\frac{5}{2}$**

29. $4x^2 = -7x$ **0, $-\frac{7}{4}$**

30. $(3n + 8)(2n - 6) = 0$ **$-\frac{8}{3}$, 3**

31. EXERCISE A gymnast jumps on a trampoline traveling at 12 feet per second. Her height h in feet above the trampoline after t seconds is given by the formula $h = 12t - 16t^2$. How long is the gymnast in the air before returning to the trampoline? **0.75 s**

Example 3 Factor $2x^2 - 3xz - 2xy + 3yz$.

$2x^2 - 3xz - 2xy + 3yz$

$= (2x^2 - 3xz) + (-2xy + 3yz)$

$= x(2x - 3z) - y(2x - 3z)$

$= (x - y)(2x - 3z)$

Example 4 Solve $x^2 = 5x$. Check the solutions.

Write the equation so that it is of the form $ab = 0$.

$x^2 = 5x$ Original equation

$x^2 - 5x = 0$ Subtract 5x from each side.

$x(x - 5) = 0$ Factor using the GCF, x.

$x = 0$ or $x - 5 = 0$ Zero Product Property

$\qquad\qquad x = 5$ Solve the equation.

The roots are 0 and 5. Check by substituting 0 and 5 for x in the original equation.

8-3 **Factoring Trinomials: $x^2 + bx + c$** (pp. 434–439)

Factor each trinomial. 32–35. See margin.
32. $y^2 + 7y + 12$ **33.** $x^2 - 9x - 36$
34. $b^2 + 5b - 6$ **35.** $18 - 9r + r^2$

Solve each equation. Check the solutions.
36. $y^2 + 13y + 40 = 0$ $-5, -8$
37. $x^2 - 5x - 66 = 0$ $-6, 11$

38. SOCCER In order for a town to host an international soccer game, its field's length must be 110–120 yards, and its width must be 70–80 yards. Green Meadows soccer field is 30 yards longer than it is wide. Write an expression for the area of the rectangular field. If the area of the field is 8800 square yards, will Green Meadows be able to host an international game? Explain.
$[w(w + 30)]$ yd^2; Yes; the field's length is 110 yd and the width is 80 yd.

Example 5 Factor $x^2 - 9x + 20$.

$b = -9$ and $c = 20$, so $m + n$ is negative and mn is positive. Therefore, m and n must both be negative. List the negative factors of 20, and look for the pair of factors with a sum of -9.

Factors of 20	Sum of Factors
$-1, -20$	-21
$-2, -10$	-12
$-4, -5$	-9

The correct factors are -4 and -5.

$x^2 - 9x + 20 = (x + m)(x + n)$ Write the pattern.

$\qquad = (x - 4)(x - 5)$ $m = -4$ and $n = -5$

8-4 **Factoring Trinomials: $ax^2 + bx + c$** (pp. 441–446)

Factor each trinomial, if possible. If the trinomial cannot be factored using integers, write *prime*. 39–40. See margin.
39. $2a^2 - 9a + 3$ **40.** $2m^2 + 13m - 24$
41. $12b^2 + 17b + 6$ **42.** $3n^2 - 6n - 45$
   $(4b + 3)(3b + 2)$ $3(n - 5)(n + 3)$

Solve each equation. Check the solutions.
43. $2r^2 - 3r - 20 = 0$ **44.** $40x^2 + 2x = 24$
43–44. See margin.

45. BASEBALL Victor hit a baseball into the air that modeled the equation $h = -16t^2 + 36t + 1$, where h is the height in feet and t is the time in seconds. How long was the ball in the air if Casey caught the ball 9 feet above the ground on its way down? **2 s**

Example 6 Factor $12x^2 + 22x - 14$.

$12x^2 + 22x - 14 = 2(6x^2 + 11x - 7)$ Factor.

So, $a = 6$, $b = 11$, and $c = -7$. Since b is positive, $m + n$ is positive. Since c is negative, mn is negative. So either m or n is negative. List the factors of $6(-7)$ or -42, where one factor in each pair is negative. The correct factors are -3 and 14.

$6x^2 + 11x - 7 = 6x^2 + mx + nx - 7$

$\qquad = 6x^2 - 3x + 14x - 7$

$\qquad = (6x^2 - 3x) + (14x - 7)$

$\qquad = 3x(2x - 1) + 7(2x - 1)$

$\qquad = (2x - 1)(3x + 7)$

Thus, the complete factorization of $12x^2 + 22x - 14$ is $2(2x - 1)(3x + 7)$.

Additional Answers

32. $(y + 3)(y + 4)$

33. $(x - 12)(x + 3)$

34. $(b + 6)(b - 1)$

35. $(r - 3)(r - 6)$

39. prime

40. $(2m - 3)(m + 8)$

43. $4, -\dfrac{5}{2}$

44. $\dfrac{3}{4}, -\dfrac{4}{5}$

Problem Solving Review

For additional practice in problem solving for Chapter 8, see the Mixed Problem Solving Appendix, p. 751 in the Student Handbook section.

Anticipation Guide

Have students complete the Chapter 8 Anticipation Guide and discuss how their responses have changed now that they have completed Chapter 8.

Anticipation Guide, p. 3

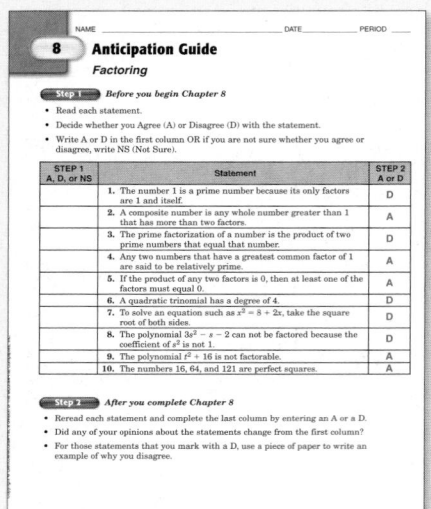

Additional Answers

49. $\left(\frac{1}{2}n - \frac{3}{4}r\right)\left(\frac{1}{2}n + \frac{3}{4}r\right)$

50. $-4, 4$

51. $-\frac{5}{3}, \frac{5}{3}$

52. $-\frac{9}{4}, \frac{9}{4}$

53. $-\frac{5}{7}, \frac{5}{7}$

55. $(a + 9)^2$

56. $(3k - 2)^2$

8-5 **Factoring Differences of Squares** (pp. 447–452)

Factor each polynomial, if possible. If the polynomial cannot be factored, write *prime*. **47.** $2y(y - 8)(y + 8)$

46. $64 - 4s^2$
  $4(4 - s)(4 + s)$
47. $2y^3 - 128y$

48. $9b^2 - 20$
  prime
49. $\frac{1}{4}n^2 - \frac{9}{16}r^2$
  See margin.

Solve each equation by factoring. Check the solutions. **50–53. See margin.**

50. $b^2 - 16 = 0$
51. $25 - 9y^2 = 0$
52. $16a^2 = 81$
53. $\frac{25}{49} - r^2 = 0$

54. EROSION A boulder breaks loose from the face of a mountain and falls toward the water 576 feet below. The distance d that the boulder falls in t seconds is given by the equation $d = 16t^2$. How long does it take the boulder to hit the water? **6 s**

Example 7 Solve $y^2 + 9 = 90$ by factoring.

$$y^2 + 9 = 90 \quad \text{Original equation}$$
$$y^2 - 81 = 0 \quad \text{Subtract 90 from each side.}$$
$$y^2 - (9)^2 = 0 \quad y^2 = y \cdot y \text{ and } 81 = 9 \cdot 9$$
$$(y + 9)(y - 9) = 0 \quad \text{Factor the difference of squares.}$$

$y + 9 = 0$ or $y - 9 = 0$ Zero Product Property

$\quad y = 9 \qquad\qquad y = -9$ Solve each equation.

The roots are -9 and 9.

8-6 **Perfect Squares and Factoring** (pp. 454–460)

Factor each polynomial, if possible. If the polynomial cannot be factored, write *prime*. **55–56. See margin.**

55. $a^2 + 18a + 81$
56. $9k^2 - 12k + 4$
57. $4 - 28r + 49r^2$
  $(2 - 7r)^2$
58. $32n^2 - 80n + 50$
  $2(4n - 5)^2$

Solve each equation. Check the solutions.

59. $6b^3 - 24b^2 + 24b = 0$
60. $144b^2 = 36$
61. $49m^2 - 126m + 81 = 0$
62. $(c - 9)^2 = 144$
  $-3, 21$

63. PICTURE FRAMING A picture that measures 7 inches by 7 inches is being framed. The area of the frame is 32 square inches. What is the width of the frame? **1 in.**

59. 0, 2   **60.** $-\frac{1}{2}, \frac{1}{2}$ **61.** $\frac{9}{7}$

Example 8 Solve $(x - 4)^2 = 121$.

$$(x - 4)^2 = 121 \quad \text{Original equation}$$
$$x - 4 = \pm\sqrt{121} \quad \text{Square Root Property}$$
$$x - 4 = \pm 11 \quad 121 = 11 \cdot 11$$
$$x = 4 \pm 11 \quad \text{Add 4 to each side.}$$

$x = 4 + 11$ or $x = 4 - 11$ Separate into two
$\quad = 15 \qquad\qquad = -7$ equations.

The roots are -7 and 15.

Additional Answers (Practice Test)

23. $-\frac{2}{3}, \frac{3}{4}$
24. $-3, 3$
25. $-4, 0$
26. 5
27. $-4, 13$

28. $-6, 0, 11$
29. $-\frac{1}{2}, 5$
30. $\frac{2}{3}, 3$

Factor each monomial completely.

1. $9g^2h$ $3 \cdot 3 \cdot g \cdot g \cdot h$ **2.** $-40ab^3c$
2. $-1 \cdot 2 \cdot 2 \cdot 2 \cdot 5 \cdot a \cdot b \cdot b \cdot b \cdot c$

Find the GCF of each set of monomials.

3. $16c^2, 4cd^2$ **4c**   **4.** $12r, 35st$ **1**
5. $10xyz, 15x^2y$ **5xy**   **6.** $18a^2b^2, 28a^3b^2$ **2a²b²**

Factor each polynomial, if possible. If the
polynomial cannot be factored using integers,
write *prime*. **7–12. See margin.**

7. $x^2 + 14x + 24$ **8.** $28m^2 + 18m$
9. $a^2 - 11ab + 18b^2$ **10.** $2h^2 - 3h - 18$
11. $6x^3 + 15x^2 - 9x$ **12.** $15a^2b + 5a^2 - 10a$

13. MULTIPLE CHOICE What are the roots of
$x^2 - 3x - 4 = 0$? **C**

A -4 and -1

B -4 and 1

C 4 and -1

D 4 and 1

14. GEOMETRY When the length and width of
the rectangle are increased by the same
amount, the area is increased by 26 square
inches. What are the dimensions of the new
rectangle? **6 in. by 9 in.**

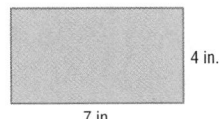

4 in.

7 in.

Factor each polynomial, if possible. If the
polynomial cannot be factored using integers,
write *prime*.

15. $a^2 - 4$ $(a + 2)(a - 2)$
16. $t^2 - 16t + 64$ $(t - 8)^2$
17. $64p^2 - 63p + 16$ **prime**
18. $36m^2 + 60mn + 25n^2$ $(6m + 5n)^2$
19. $x^3 - 4x^2 - 9x + 36$ $(x - 4)(x - 3)(x + 3)$
20. $4my - 20m + 3py - 15p$ $(y - 5)(4m + 3p)$

21. ART An artist is designing
square tiles like the one
shown at the right. The
area of the shaded part of
each tile is 98 square
centimeters. Find the
dimensions of the tile. **14 cm by 14 cm**

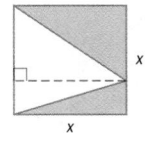

22. CONSTRUCTION A
sidewalk will be built
along the inside
edges of all four sides
of the rectangular
lawn described in the table. The remaining
lawn will have an area of 425 square feet.
How wide will the walk be? **3.5 ft**

Dimensions of Lawn	
length	32 ft
width	24 ft

23–30. See margin.
Solve each equation. Check the solutions.

23. $(4x - 3)(3x + 2) = 0$
24. $4x^2 = 36$
25. $18s^2 + 72s = 0$
26. $t^2 + 25 = 10t$
27. $a^2 - 9a - 52 = 0$
28. $x^3 - 5x^2 - 66x = 0$
29. $2x^2 = 9x + 5$
30. $3b^2 + 6 = 11b$

31. GEOMETRY The parallelogram has an area of
52 square centimeters. Find the height h of
the parallelogram. **4 cm**

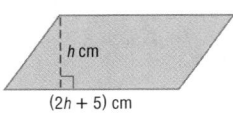

h cm

$(2h + 5)$ cm

32. MULTIPLE CHOICE Which represents one of
the roots of $0 = 2x^2 + 9x - 5$? **F**

F -5 H $\frac{5}{2}$

G $-\frac{1}{2}$ J 5

 **Summative Assessment**

CRM **Chapter 8 Resource Masters**

Leveled Chapter 8 Tests			
Form	Type	Level	Pages
1	MC	BL	55–56
2A	MC	OL	57–58
2B	MC	OL	59–60
2C	FR	OL	61–62
2D	FR	OL	63–64
3	FR	AL	65–66

MC = multiple-choice questions
FR = free-response questions

BL = below grade level
OL = on grade level
AL = above grade level

- Vocabulary Test, p. 54
- Extended-Response Test, p. 67

ExamView
Assessment Suite
Customize and
create multiple
versions of your chapter test and
answer keys. All of the questions from
the leveled chapter tests in the *Chapter
8 Resource Masters* are also available
on ExamView Assessment Suite with the
California Standard that each item
assesses.

Additional Answers

7. $(x + 12)(x + 2)$
8. $2m(14m + 9)$
9. $(a - 2b)(a - 9b)$
10. prime
11. $3x(x + 3)(2x - 1)$
12. $5a(3ab + a - 2)$

Data-Driven Decision Making	Exercises	Lesson	Standard	Resources for Review
Diagnostic Teaching Based on the results of the Chapter 8 Practice Test, use the following to review concepts that students continue to find challenging.	17, 18, 29, 30, 32	8–4	11.0	**CRM** Study Guide and Intervention pp. 27–28, 35–36, 43–44 **Math Online** • Extra Examples • Personal Tutor • Concepts in Motion
	15, 24	8–5	14.0	
	27–28, 31	8–6	14.0	

Formative Assessment

You can use these two pages to benchmark student progress. The California Standards are listed with each question.

 Chapter 8 Resource Masters
• Standardized Test Practice, pp. 68–70

 Create practice worksheets or tests that align to the California Standards, as well as TIMSS and NAEP tests.

 Read each question. Then fill in the correct answer on the answer document provided by your teacher or on a sheet of paper.

1 Jacob's solution to an equation is shown below.

Given: $x^2 + 5x + 4 = 0$
Step 1: $(x + 1)(x + 4) = 0$
Step 2: $x + 1 = 0$ or $x + 4 = 0$
Step 3: $x = -1$ or $x = -4$

Which property of real numbers did Jacob use in Step 2? **C**

A commutative property of multiplication

B multiplication property of equality

C zero product property of multiplication

D distributive property of multiplication over addition

2 What is the solution for this equation? **G**
$$|4x - 2| = 14$$
F $x = -4$ or $x = 3$

G $x = -3$ or $x = 4$

H $x = -1$ or $x = 3$

J $x = -1$ or $x = 4$

3 Which of the following shows $16x^2 + 24x + 9$ factored completely? **A**

A $(4x + 3)^2$

B $(4x + 9)(4x + 1)$

C $(16x + 9)(x + 1)$

D $16x^2 + 24x + 9$

TEST-TAKING TIP

Question 3 When solving a problem involving simplifying a polynomial, you can check your answer by using the Distributive Property to find the product represented by each answer choice.

---

466 Chapter 8 Factoring

---

4 Determine the number of solutions for the following system of equations. **J**
$$x - 3y = 5$$
$$2x - 6y = 10$$

F zero

G one

H two

J infinitely many

5 Marlo went on a shopping trip for back to school supplies. She recorded the price of each item in the table below. She bought 6 notebooks, 12 pencils, 8 pens, 1 backpack, 2 binders and 1 calendar. According to the chart below, which equation best represents the total amount she spent? **C**

Item	Cost
Notebooks	2 for $4.50
Pencils	4 for $1.25
Pens	2 for $1.00
Backpack	2 for $35.00
Binders	1 for $2.50
Calendars	3 for $21.00

A Cost = $6(4.50) + 12(1.25) + 8(1.00) + 1(35.00) + 2(2.50) + 1(21.00)$

B Cost = $2(4.50) + 4(1.25) + 2(1.00) + 2(35.00) + 1(2.50) + 3(21.00)$

C Cost = $3(4.50) + 3(1.25) + 4(1.00) + \frac{1}{2}(35.00) + 2(2.50) + \frac{1}{3}(21.00)$

D Cost = $\frac{1}{3}(4.50) + \frac{1}{3}(1.25) + \frac{1}{4}(1.00) + 2(35.00) + \frac{1}{2}(2.50) + 3(21.00)$

6 The slope of the line below is $\frac{3}{4}$. What is the value of b? **9**

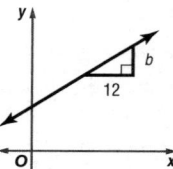

More California
Standards Practice
For practice by standard,
see pages CA1–CA43.

CHAPTER
8
California
Standards Practice

7 The area of a rectangle is $24a^6b^{13}$ square units. If the width of the rectangle is given, what is the length of the rectangle? ($a \neq 0, b \neq 0$) **G**

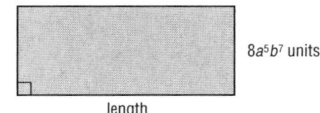

$8a^5b^7$ units

length

F $3a^{11}b^{20}$ units

G $3ab^6$ units

H $16a^{11}b^{20}$ units

J $32ab^6$ units

8 Which of the following is an equation of the line that passes through the point $(8, -1)$ and is parallel to the line graphed below? **B**

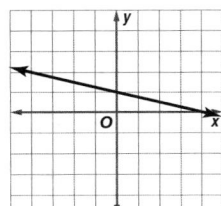

A $y = -\dfrac{1}{4}x$

B $y = -\dfrac{1}{4}x + 1$

C $y = -\dfrac{1}{4}x + 3$

D $y = -\dfrac{1}{4}x + 5$

9 Tiffany bought a new DVD that cost $24.99 and two new CDs that cost $14.99 each. If the sales tax was 6.75%, what was the total dollar amount Tiffany spent? **H**

F $54.97

G $56.34

H $58.68

J $60.35

10 A chef baked twice as many loaves of bread on Tuesday as he did on Monday and 12 more loaves on Wednesday as he did on Tuesday. If the chef baked 24 loaves of bread on Monday, how many loaves did the chef bake over the three days? **132**

Pre-AP/Anchor Problem

Record your answer on a sheet of paper. Show your work.

11 Madison is building a fenced, rectangular dog pen. The width of the pen will be 3 yards less than the length. The total area enclosed is 28 square yards.

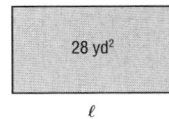

28 yd²

ℓ

a. Using ℓ to represent the length of the pen, write an equation showing the area of the pen in terms of its length. $\ell(\ell - 3) = 28$

b. What is the length of the pen? **7 yards**

c. How many yards of fencing will Madison need to enclose the pen completely? **22 yards**

TEST-TAKING TIP

Question 8 When a question involves a geometric object and no figure is shown, it is often helpful to draw one. A diagram can help students see relationships among the pieces of information given.

Item Analysis

Questions 3 and 10 are griddable questions. In griddable questions, students arrive at an answer and then record it in a special grid, coloring in the appropriate bubble under each digit of the answer.

Answer Sheet Practice

Have students simulate taking a standardized test by recording their answers on practice recording sheets.

CRM Student Recording Sheet, p. 49

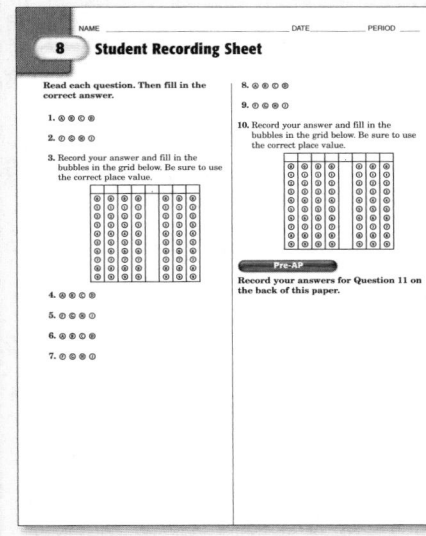

NEED EXTRA HELP?

If You Missed Question...	1	2	3	4	5	6	7	8	9	10	11
Go to Lesson...	8-3	6-6	4-1	8-6	2-1	5-4	7-2	4-7	2-7	1-2	8-4
For Help with Standard...	25.1	3.0	7AF3.3	11.0	6AF1.2	9.0	10.0	8.0	5.0	7AF1.2	11.0

Homework Option

Get Ready for Chapter 9   Assign students the exercises on p. 469 as homework to assess whether they possess the prerequisite skills needed for the next chapter.

Page 423, Lesson 8-1

29. base 1 cm, height 40 cm; base 2 cm, height 20 cm; base 4 cm, height 10 cm; base 5 cm, height 8 cm; base 8 cm, height 5 cm; base 10 cm, height 4 cm; base 20 cm, height 2 cm; base 40 cm, height 1 cm

33. Sample answer: $5x^2$ and $10x^3$; $5x^2 = 5 \cdot x \cdot x$ and $10x^3 = 2 \cdot 5 \cdot x \cdot x \cdot x$. The GCF is $5 \cdot x \cdot x$ or $5x^2$.

34. Sample answer: Scientists listening to radio signals would suspect that a modulated signal beginning with prime numbers would indicate a message from an extraterrestrial. The first 30 prime numbers are 2, 3, 5, 7, 11, 13, 17, 19, 23, 29, 31, 37, 41, 43, 47, 53, 59, 61, 67, 71, 79, 83, 89, 97, 101, 103, 107, 109, and 113. See students' explanations.

Page 451, Lesson 8-5

36. Use factoring by grouping.
$$a^2 - b^2 = a^2 - ab + ab - b^2$$
$$= (a^2 - ab)(ab - b^2)$$
$$= a(a - b) + b(a - b)$$
$$= (a - b)(a + b)$$

Page 453, Reading Math

1.

Statements	Reasons
1. $\frac{1}{16}t^2 - 100 = 0$	**1.** Given
2. $\left(\frac{1}{4}t\right)^2 - 10^2 = 0$	**2.** $\frac{1}{16}t^2 = \left(\frac{1}{4}t\right)^2$ and $100 = 10^2$
3. $\left(\frac{1}{4}t + 10\right)\left(\frac{1}{4}t - 10\right) = 0$	**3.** Factor the difference of squares.
4. $\frac{1}{4}t + 10 = 0$ or $\frac{1}{4}t - = 10 = 0$	**4.** Zero Product Property
5. $t = -40 \qquad t = 40$	**5.** Solve each equation.

2. Given: c and d are real numbers such that $c \neq 0$ and $d \neq 0$.
Prove: $c^3 - cd^2 - c^2d + d^3 = (c + d)(c - d)(c - d)$

Statements	Reasons
1. c and d are real numbers such that $c \neq 0$ and $d \neq 0$.	**1.** Given
2. $c^3 - cd^2 - c^2d + d^3 = (c^3 - cd^2) - (c^2d - d^3)$	**2.** Group terms with common factors.
3. $c^3 - cd^2 - c^2d + d^3 = c(c^2 - d^2) - d(c^2 - d^2)$	**3.** Factor each grouping.
4. $c^3 - cd^2 - c^2d + d^3 = (c^2 - d^2)(c - d)$	**4.** $c^2 - d^2$ is the common factor.
5. $c^3 - cd^2 - c^2d + d^3 = (c + d)(c - d)(c - d)$	**5.** Factor the difference of squares, $c^2 - d^2$, into $(c + d)(c - d)$.

CHAPTER 9

Chapter Overview

Quadratic and Exponential Functions

Standards-Based Lesson Plan		Pacing Your Lessons	
LESSONS AND OBJECTIVES	California Standards	40-50 Minute Periods	90-Minute Periods
Explore 9-1 **Graphing Calculator Lab: Exploring Graphs of Quadratic Functions** (p. 470) **9-1** **Graphing Quadratic Functions** (pp. 471–477) • Graph quadratic functions. • Find the equation of the axis of symmetry and the coordinates of the vertex of a parabola. **Extend 9-1** **Graphing Calculator Lab: The Family of Quadratic Functions** (pp. 478–479)	1A21.0	3	2
9-2 **Solving Quadratic Equations by Graphing** (pp. 480–485) • Solve quadratic equations by graphing. • Estimate solutions of quadratic equations by graphing.	1A21.0 1A22.0	2	1
9-3 **Solving Quadratic Equations by Completing the Square** (pp. 486–491) • Solve quadratic equations by finding the square root. • Solve quadratic equations by completing the square.	1A14.0	2	1
9-4 **Solving Quadratic Equations by Using the Quadratic Formula** (pp. 493–499) • Solve quadratic equations by using the Quadratic Formula. • Use the discriminant to determine the number of solutions for a quadratic equation. **Extend 9-4** **Algebra Lab: Applying Quadratic Equations** (pp. 500–501)	1A19.0 1A20.0 1A22.0	2	1
9-5 **Exponential Functions** (pp. 502–508) • Graph exponential functions. • Identify data that displays exponential behavior.	2A12.0	2	1
Explore 9-6 **Algebra Lab: Investigating Exponential Functions** (p. 509) • Use paper stacking to investigate an exponential function. **9-6** **Growth and Decay** (pp. 510–514) • Solve problems involving exponential growth. • Solve problems involving exponential decay. **Extend 9-6** **Graphing Calculator Lab: Curve Fitting** (pp. 515–516)	2A12.0	3	1.5
REVIEW		1	0.5
ASSESSMENT		1	0.5
The complete **Assessment Planner** for Chapter 9 is provided on page 469.	**TOTAL**	16	8.5

* Begin Chapter 10 in the second half of the period.

Professional Development

California Standards Vertical Alignment

Before Chapter 9

Related Topics from Grade 7

- Graph functions of the form $y = nx^2$ and $y = nx^3$ and use in solving problems ◆— Standard 7AF3.1
- Use order of operations to evaluate algebraic expressions ◆— Standard 7AF1.2

Chapter 9

Topics from Algebra I

- Solve a quadratic equation by factoring or completing the square
- Graph quadratic functions and know that their roots are the x-intercepts
- Determine whether the graph of a quadratic function will intersect the x-axis in zero, one, or two points
- Apply quadratic equations to physical problems

See individual lessons for the specific Standards covered.

After Chapter 9

Preparation for Algebra II

- Solve and graph quadratic equations and quadratic equations in the complex number system ◆— Standard 2A8.0
- Use the definition of logarithms to translate between logarithms in any base ◆— Standard 2A13.0

Back-Mapping

California Algebra 1 was conceived and developed with the final result in mind, student success in Algebra I and beyond. The authors, using the California Mathematics Standards as their guide, developed this brand-new series by "back-mapping" from the desired result of student success in Algebra I and beyond. McGraw-Hill's *California Geometry, California Algebra 2,* and *California Algebra Readiness* were developed utilizing the same philosophy.

What the Research Says...

According to Ellington (2003), students' operational and problem-solving skills improve when calculators are an integral part of testing and instruction.

- In Lessons 9-1A and 9-1B, graphing calculators are used to explore properties of quadratic functions.
- In Lesson 9-6B, graphing calculators are used in data analysis to do curve fitting.
- Graphing calculators are used for problem-solving in Lessons 9-2, 9-4, and 9-5.

[Source: Ellington, A.J. (2003). "A Meta-Analysis of the Effects of calculators on Students' Achievement and Attitude Levels in Precollege Mathematics Classes," *Journal for Research in Mathematics Education*, 34(5), pp. 433–463.]

Professional Development

Targeted professional development has been articulated throughout the *California Mathematics: Concepts, Skills, and Problem Solving* series. The **McGraw-Hill Professional Development Video Library** provides short videos that support the ◆— Key Standards. For more information, visit ca.algebra1.com.

Model Lessons	Instructional Strategies

CHAPTER 9

Technology Solutions

Teacher Resources

AssignmentWorks

Differentiated Assignments, Answers, and Solutions

- Print a customized assignment worksheet using the Student Edition exercises along with an answer key or worked-out solutions.
- Use default lesson assignments as outlined in the Differentiated Homework Options in the Teacher Wraparound Edition.
- Includes modified questions from the Student Edition.

Interactive Classroom

This CD-ROM is a customizable Microsoft® PowerPoint® presentation that includes:

- In-Class Examples
- Your Turn Exercises*
- 5-Minute Check Transparencies*
- Links to Online Study Tools
- Concepts in Motion

compatible with response pad technology

ExamView®Assessment Suite

ExamView Assessment Suite lets you

- Create, edit, and customize tests and worksheets using QuickTest Wizard
- Create multiple versions of tests and modify them for a desired level of difficulty
- Translate from English to Spanish and vice versa
- Build tests aligned with your state standards
- Track students' progress using the Teacher Management System

Student Resources

StudentWorks™ Plus

Textbook, Audio, Workbooks, and more

This CD-ROM is a valuable resource for students to access content online and use online resources to continue learning Chapter 9 concepts. Includes:

• Complete Student Editions in both English and Spanish
• English audio integrated throughout the text
• Links to Concepts in Motion, Personal Tutor, and other online resources
• Access to all student worksheets
• Daily Assignments and Grade Log

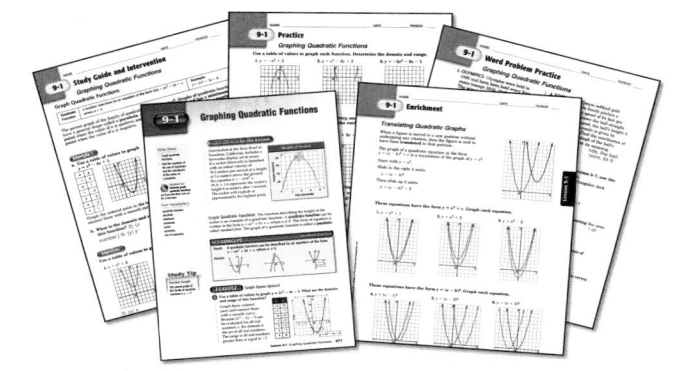

Super DVD

The Super DVD contains two Glencoe multimedia products.

MindJogger Plus   An alternative review of concepts in which students work as teams in a game show format to gain points for correct answers.

What's Math Got to Do With It? Real Life Math Videos
Engaging video that shows students how math is used in everyday situations

Unit 3 theme: Polynomials and Nonlinear Functions

Internet Resources

Math Online ca.algebra1.com

TEACHER	PARENT	STUDENT	
			Online Study Tools
	•	•	Online Student Edition
•	•	•	Multilingual Glossary
			Lesson Resources
	•	•	BrainPOP®
•	•	•	Concepts in Motion
•	•	•	Extra Examples
	•	•	Other Calculator Keystrokes
•			Problem of the Week Cards
	•	•	Real-World Careers
	•	•	Self-Check Quizzes
			Chapter Resources
	•	•	Chapter Readiness
	•	•	Chapter Test
	•	•	Standardized Test Practice
	•	•	Vocabulary Review/Chapter Review Activities
			Unit Resources
•		•	Cross-Curricular Internet Project
			Other Resources
•			Dinah Zike's Foldables
	•	•	Hotmath Homework Help
•			Key Concepts
•	•	•	Meet the Authors
	•	•	Personal Tutor
•			Project CRISS℠
	•	•	Scavenger Hunts and Answer Sheets
•			Vocabulary PuzzleMakers

Focus on Mathematical Content

Big Idea for Chapter 9:
Quadratic and Exponential Functions

In some situations, quadratic functions can be used to model non-linear problems. Depending on the situation, quadratic equations may be solved in different ways. For example, a problem involving physical motion may be solved by graphing, allowing the situation to be visualized. However, when solutions cannot be determined from a graph, other methods, such as completing the square and using the Quadratic Formula, may be appropriate. There are also situations that may be modeled by functions that are neither linear nor quadratic. Exponential functions may be used to describe changes in population growth, to solve compound interest problems, and to model other situations that display exponential behavior.

Why It's Important

For This Chapter
The lessons in this chapter introduce students to quadratic and exponential functions.
• What is a parabola? (Lesson 9-1)
• How many roots does a quadratic equation have and how do you find them? (Lesson 9-2)
• How do you complete the square for a quadratic expression of the form $x^2 + bx$? (Lesson 9-3)
• According to the Quadratic Formula, what are the solutions of a quadratic equation in the form $ax^2 + bx + c = 0$? (Lesson 9-4)
• How can you determine whether a set of data displays exponential behavior? (Lesson 9-5)
• What is the difference between exponential growth and exponential decay? (Lesson 9-6)

After This Chapter
• In future studies of math, students can use the Quadratic Formula to solve any second-degree polynomial equation.
• In many fields, including science and finance, exponential functions can be applied to solve problems involving growth and decay.

9-1 Graphing Quadratic Functions

The standard form of a quadratic function is $y = ax^2 + bx + c$, where $a \neq 0$. The graph of a quadratic function is a symmetrical curve called a *parabola*. If a is positive, the parabola opens upward and the vertex is the minimum of the function. If a is negative, the parabola opens downward and the vertex is the maximum of the function.

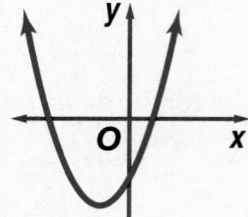 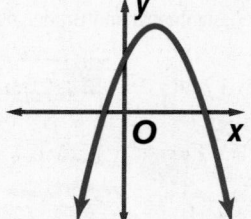

If the graph of a parabola is folded in half, the two sides match exactly. The line that divides a parabola in half is called the *axis of symmetry,* and the *vertex* is the only point on the parabola that is on the axis of symmetry. The equation for the axis of symmetry for the graph of $y = ax^2 + bx + c$ is $x = -\dfrac{b}{2a}$. You can find the x-coordinate of the vertex by knowing the axis of symmetry. However, to find the y-coordinate, you must substitute the value of x into the quadratic equation.

9-2 Solving Quadratic Equations by Graphing

The solutions of a quadratic equation are called *roots.* The roots can be found by graphing the related quadratic function and finding the x-intercepts of the parabola. Quadratic equations always have two roots. The roots can be two real roots, a double real root, or two roots that are not real numbers.

A quadratic equation has:

• two real roots when the parabola crosses the x-axis at two distinct points,

• a double real root when the vertex of the parabola is on the x-axis, or

• no real roots when the parabola does not intersect the x-axis.

• Sometimes the roots are not integers and must be estimated from the graph.

9-3 Solving Quadratic Equations by Completing the Square

If the quadratic expression on one side of the equation in the form $ax^2 + bx + c = n$ is a perfect square, the equation can be solved by taking the square root of each side. However, since few quadratic expressions are perfect squares, a method called *completing the square* may be used.

To solve an equation of the form $x^2 + bx + c = 0$ by completing the square, isolate the x^2 and bx terms on one side of the equation. Find half of b and square it. Then add this amount to each side of the equation. Solve by factoring and taking the square root of each side. If the coefficient of x^2 is not 1, divide each term by the coefficient before completing the square.

9-4 Solving Quadratic Equations by Graphing

A quadratic equation in the standard form $ax^2 + bx + c = 0$, where $a \neq 0$, can be solved using the Quadratic Formula. The coefficients a and b and the constant c are substituted into the formula $x = \dfrac{-b \pm \sqrt{b^2 - 4ac}}{2a}$. Then the expression is simplified to determine the solutions.

The expression under the radical sign, $b^2 - 4ac$, is called the *discriminant*. The value of the discriminant can be used to determine the number of real roots for a quadratic equation.

- A positive discriminant indicates two real roots.

- A negative discriminant indicates that there are no real roots.

- If the discriminant is 0, there is one real root.

9-5 Exponential Functions

Exponential functions are neither linear nor quadratic. An exponential function has a variable as an exponent and can be described by an equation of the form $y = ax$, where $a > 0$ and $a \neq 1$. Graphs of exponential functions have distinctive shapes.

- When a is greater than 1, y-values change little for small values of x, but increase quickly as the values of x become greater. The graph rises faster and faster as you move from left to right.

- When $0 < a < 1$, y values decrease as x increases. The graph falls more slowly as the x values increase.

- Two ways to identify exponential functions are to look at the graph and to look for a pattern in the data. If domain values at regular intervals have corresponding range values that have a common factor, the behavior is exponential.

9-6 Growth and Decay

Many real-world problems can be solved using methods for modeling exponential growth and decay. Compound interest is an application of exponential growth. Depreciation is an application of exponential decay.

- Exponential growth can be modeled using the general equation $y = C(1 + r)^t$. The initial amount C increases by the same percent over a given period of time. In the general equation, y represents the final amount, C represents the initial amount, r represents the rate of change expressed as a decimal, and t represents time.

- Exponential decay is a variation of exponential growth. Instead of increasing, the original amount decreases by the same percent over a given period of time. The general equation for exponential decay is $y = C(1 - r)^t$.

Options for Chapter 9 Lessons

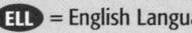 = English Language Learner	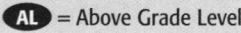 = Above Grade Level	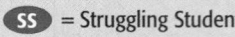 = Struggling Students	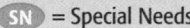 = Special Needs

Using Interpersonal Skills AL

Use with Lesson 9-1

Place students in small groups. Since there are several tasks involved in graphing quadratic functions, have the group members decide which of the tasks they should complete in order to graph a given function. For example, one member can be responsible for finding the equation for the axis of symmetry, another can substitute values in order to determine points on the graph, and a third member can graph the points and draw the curve of the parabola.

Using Verbal Skills SS SN

Use with Lesson 9-4

Have students come up with a riddle, poem, rap, or other mnemonic device to help them remember how to use the Quadratic Formula, and how to interpret the discriminant. Ask students to share their mnemonic devices with the class.

Connecting Mathematics to Music ELL

Use with Lesson 9-5

Ask students who are familiar with music to examine the different types of notes (whole, half, quarter, etc.) to determine whether the length of the notes exhibits exponential behavior. Have them create posters displaying the different notes, their length, and an exponential expression for determining each note's length.

Noteables™ Interactive Study Notebook with Foldables™

Noteables™ Interactive Study Notebook with Foldables™ is a study organizer that provides helpful steps for students to follow to organize their notes for Chapter 9.

- Students use Noteables to record notes and to complete their Foldables as you present the material for each lesson.
- Noteables correspond to the Examples in the *Teacher Wraparound Edition* and *Interactive Classroom CD-ROM.*

Intervention

Quick Review Math Handbook*

is Glencoe's mathematical handbook for students and parents.

Hot Words includes a glossary of terms.

Hot Topics consists of two parts:

• explanations of key mathematical concepts

• exercises to check students' understanding.

Lesson	Hot Topics Section	Lesson	Hot Topics Section
9-1	6.8	9-4	6.3
9-3	6.3	9-5	6.3

*Also available in Spanish

Teacher to Teacher

Linda Hayek
Ralston Public Schools
Omaha, NE

USE BEFORE LESSON 9-4

❝ I like for my students to discuss all the different ways that a quadratic equation can be solved before presenting the Concept Summary on p. 489. We conduct a class discussion, listing the possibilities when each type might be used. Then we write a summary on our Foldables. ❞

Reading and Writing in Mathematics

Project CRISS℠

STUDY SKILL

Power notes can help students organize and outline a lesson or chapter. Students often benefit from making power notes as a cooperative activity. In the outline at the right, Power 1 is the main idea, Power 2 provides details about the main idea, Power 3 provides details about Power 2, and so on.

You may have students copy the power notes at the right and complete them using the information in Chapter 9. Point out that more than one detail can be placed under each power.

1. Solving Quadratic Equations
  2. Graph the Equation
    3. zero roots; if it doesn't intersect the *x*-axis
    3. one root; if it touches the *x*-axis at one point
    3. two roots; if it intersects the *x*-axis at two points
  2. Complete the Square
    3. Find $\frac{1}{2}$ of the coefficient of *x*.
    3. Square the result from above.
    3. Add the new result to each side of the original equation.
    3. Solve
  2. Use the Quadratic Formula
    3. Rewrite the equation in standard form.
    3. Substitute values into the formula.
    3. Simplify.

CReating **I**ndependence through **S**tudent-owned **S**trategies

FOLDABLES™
Study Organizer

Dinah Zike's Foldables™

Focus As students work through the lessons in this chapter, they write notes and show examples about quadratic and exponential functions.

Teach Have students make and label their Foldables as illustrated.

Suggest that students use their Foldables to take notes, define terms, record concepts, and write examples. Ask students to note the order in which the concepts are presented in this chapter. Have them write about why the concepts were presented in that sequence. If they have difficulty recognizing the logic in this sequence, have them outline the key concepts in their own order and justify their reasoning in writing.

When to Use It As students read and study the chapter, have them fill their journals with notes, graphs, and examples of quadratic and exponential functions. *A version of a completed Foldable is shown on p. 517.*

Materials Needed for Chapter 9

- data collection device (Explore 9-1)
- motion sensor (Explore 9-1)
- graphing calculator (Extend 9-1, Lessons 9-1, 9-2, 9-4, 9-5, Extend 9-6)
- algebra tiles (Lesson 9-3)
- scissors (Explore 9-6)
- Internet (Lesson 9-6)

CHAPTER 9

Quadratic and Exponential Functions

BIG Ideas

- **Standard 14.0** Students solve a quadratic equation by factoring or completing the square. (Key)
- **Standard 21.0** Students graph quadratic functions and know that their roots are the *x*-intercepts.
- **Standard 23.0** Students apply quadratic equations to physical problems, such as the motion of an object under the force of gravity. (Key)

Key Vocabulary

completing the square (p. 487)
exponential function (p. 502)
parabola (p. 471)
Quadratic Formula (p. 493)

● **Real-World Link**
Dinosaurs Exponential decay is one type of exponential function. Carbon dating uses exponential decay to determine the age of fossils and dinosaurs.

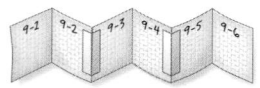
FOLDABLES™
Study Organizer

Quadratic and Exponential Functions Make this Foldable to help you organize your notes. Begin with three sheets of grid paper.

① **Fold** each sheet in half along the width.

② **Unfold** each sheet and tape to form one long piece.

③ **Label** each page with the lesson number as shown. Refold to form a booklet.

9-1 9-2 9-3 9-4 9-5 9-6

Differentiated Instruction

CRM Student-Built Glossary, pp. 1–2

Students should complete the chart by providing a definition and an example of each term as they progress through Chapter 9. This study tool can also be used to review for the chapter test.

Additional Answer

7.
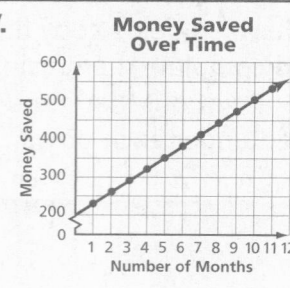
Money Saved Over Time

GET READY for Chapter 9

Diagnose Readiness You have two options for checking Prerequisite Skills.

Option 1

Take the Quick Check below. Refer to the Quick Review for help.

Option 2

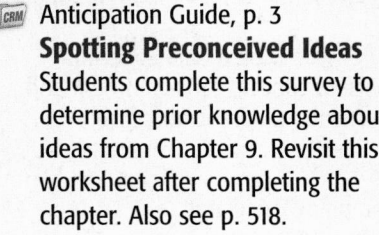 Take the Online Readiness Quiz at **ca.algebra1.com**.

QUICK Check

Use a table of values to graph each equation. (Lesson 3-3) **(Used in Lesson 9-1.)**

1. $y = x + 5$
2. $y = 2x - 3$
3. $y = 0.5x + 1$
4. $y = -3x - 2$
5. $2x - 3y = 12$
6. $5y = 10 + 2x$

1–6. Ch. 9 Answer Appendix.

7. **SAVINGS** Suppose you have already saved $200 toward the cost of a car. You plan to save $35 each month for the next several months. Graph the equation for the total amount T you will have in m months. $T = 200 + 35m$; see margin for graph.

Determine whether each trinomial is a perfect square trinomial. If so factor it. (Lesson 8-6) **(Used in Lesson 9-3.)**

8. $t^2 + 12t + 36$
   yes; $(t + 6)^2$
9. $a^2 - 14a + 49$
   yes; $(a - 7)^2$
10. $m^2 - 18m + 81$
    $(m - 9)^2$
11. $y^2 + 8y + 12$
    no
12. $9b^2 - 6b + 1$
    yes; $(3b - 1)^2$
13. $6x^2 + 4x + 1$
    no
14. $4p^2 + 12p + 9$
    yes; $(2p + 3)^2$
15. $16s^2 - 24s + 9$
    yes; $(4s - 3)^2$

Find the next three terms of each arithmetic sequence. (Lesson 3-4) **(Used in Lessons 9-5 and 9-6.)**

16. 5, 9, 13, 17, …
    21, 25, 29
17. 12, 5, −2, −9, …
    −16, −23, −30
18. −4, −1, 2, 5, …
    8, 11, 14
19. 24, 32, 40, 48, …
    56, 64, 72

20. **GEOMETRY** Write a formula that can be used to find the number of sides of a pattern containing n triangles.

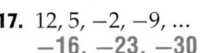

3 sides   5 sides   7 sides

$3 + 2(n - 1)$ or $2n + 1$

QUICK Review

EXAMPLE 1

Use a table of values to graph $y = 2x - 2$.

x	y = 2x − 2	y
−1	2(−1) − 2	−4
0	2(0) − 2	−2
1	2(1) − 2	0
2	2(2) − 2	2

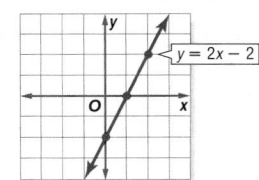

EXAMPLE 2

Determine whether $x^2 - 22x + 121$ is a perfect square trinomial. If so, factor it.

1. Is the first term a perfect square? yes
2. Is the last term a perfect square? yes
3. Is the middle term equal to $2(1x)(11)$? yes

$x^2 - 22x + 121$ is a perfect square trinomial.

$x^2 - 22x + 121 = (x - 11)^2$

EXAMPLE 3

Find the next three terms of the arithmetic sequence −104, −4, 96, 196, … .

Find the common difference by subtracting successive terms.

$-4 - (-104) = 100$

The common difference is 100.

Add to find the next three terms.

$196 + 100 = 296, 296 + 100 = 396,$
$396 + 100 = 496$

The next three terms are 296, 396, 496.

Diagnostic Assessment

Exercises	California Standards	Intervention
1–7	1A6.0, 1A7.0	SE Review Lesson 3-3, pp. 155–161
8–15	1A11.0, 1A14.0	SE Review Lesson 8-6, pp. 454–460
16–20	1A1.0	SE Review Lesson 3-4, pp. 165–170

ASSESSMENT PLANNER

CHAPTER 9

✓ Formative Assessment

CRM Anticipation Guide, p. 3
Spotting Preconceived Ideas
Students complete this survey to determine prior knowledge about ideas from Chapter 9. Revisit this worksheet after completing the chapter. Also see p. 518.

TWE **Lesson Activities**
- Ticket Out the Door, pp. 477, 499, 514
- Crystal Ball, p. 508
- Name the Math, p. 491
- Yesterday's News, p. 485

Chapter Checkpoints

SE Mid-Chapter Quiz, p. 492

SE Study Guide and Review, pp. 517–520

SE California Standards Practice, pp. 522–523

CRM Quizzes, pp. 51 and 52

CRM Standardized Test Practice, pp. 68–70

Math Online **ca.algebra1.com**

- Self-Check Quizzes
- Practice Test
- Standardized Test Practice

✓ Summative Assessment

SE Chapter Practice Test, p. 521

CRM Mid-Chapter Test, p. 53

CRM Vocabulary Test, p. 54

CRM Extended-Response Test, p. 67

CRM Leveled Chapter Tests, pp. 55–66

💿 ExamView® Assessment Suite

KEY

CRM *Chapter 9 Resource Masters*

SE Student Edition

TWE Teacher Wraparound Edition

💿 CD-ROM

1 Focus

Objective Use a data collection device to conduct an experiment and investigate quadratic functions.

Materials
- graphing calculator
- data collection device and compatible motion detector
- ball

Teaching Tip During this activity, one person will operate the data collection device and the other will toss the ball. To keep the data as accurate as possible, it is important that students synchronize their activities.

2 Teach

Working in Cooperative Groups
Put students in groups of 2 or 3, mixing abilities. Have groups complete the Activity and Analyze the Results 1–4.

- Make sure students know how to use the TRACE feature of the calculator for Analyze the Results 4.

- Students should recognize that the graphs of these experiments are not linear and should look like graphs of quadratic functions.

Practice Have students complete Exercises 5 and 6.

3 Assess

Formative Assessment
Use Exercise 2 to assess whether students can explain why their graphs are not linear.

From Concrete to Abstract
Ask: What do all the graphs in this lab have in common? Sample answer: They all have a U shape.

Exploring Graphs of Quadratic Functions

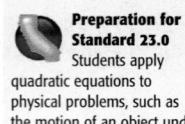

Preparation for Standard 23.0 Students apply quadratic equations to physical problems, such as the motion of an object under the force of gravity. (Key)

Not all functions are linear. The graphs of nonlinear functions have different shapes. One type of nonlinear function is a *quadratic function*. The graph of a quadratic function is a *parabola*. You use a data collection device to conduct an experiment and investigate quadratic functions.

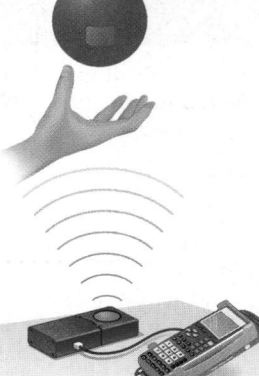

▶ SET UP the Lab

- Set up the data collection device to collect data every 0.2 second for 4 seconds.
- Connect the motion sensor to your data collection device. Position the motion detector on the floor pointed upward.

ACTIVITY

Step 1 Have one group member hold a ball about 3 feet above the motion detector. Another group member will operate the data collection device.

Step 2 When the person operating the data collection device says "go," he or she should press the start button to begin data collection. At the same time, the ball should be tossed straight upward.

Step 3 Try to catch the ball at about the same height at which it was tossed. Stop collecting data when the ball is caught.

ANALYZE THE RESULTS 1, 4–6. See students' work.

1. The domain contains values represented by the independent variable, time. The range contains values represented by the dependent variable, distance. Use the graphing calculator to graph the data.

2. Write a sentence that describes the shape of the graph. Is the graph linear? Explain.

3. Describe the position of the point on the graph that represents the starting position of the ball. **The starting position is the *y*-intercept.**

4. Use the TRACE feature of the calculator to find the maximum height of the ball. At what time was the maximum height achieved?

5. Repeat the experiment and toss the ball higher. Compare and contrast the new graph and the first graph.

6. Conduct an experiment in which the motion detector is held at a height of 4 feet and pointed downward at a dropped ball. How does the graph for this experiment compare to the other graphs?

2. Sample answer: It's a parabola. The graph is not linear because it is not a line.

Extending the Concept Introduce the quadratic function $y + x^2$. Show students how to enter it in the Y= LIST. Encourage them to investigate the graph using the TRACE function of their calculators. Have them compare the graph to the graphs of their data in the lab.

9-1 Graphing Quadratic Functions

Main Ideas

- Graph quadratic functions.
- Find the equation of the axis of symmetry and the coordinates of the vertex of a parabola.

Standard 21.0 Students graph quadratic functions and know that their roots are the *x*-intercepts.

New Vocabulary

quadratic function
parabola
minimum
maximum
vertex
symmetry
axis of symmetry

GET READY for the Lesson

Americafest at the Rose Bowl in Pasadena, California, includes a fireworks display set to music. If a rocket (firework) is launched with an initial velocity of 39.2 meters per second at a height of 1.6 meters above the ground, the equation $h = -4.9t^2 + 39.2t + 1.6$ represents the rocket's height *h* in meters after *t* seconds. The rocket will explode at approximately the highest point.

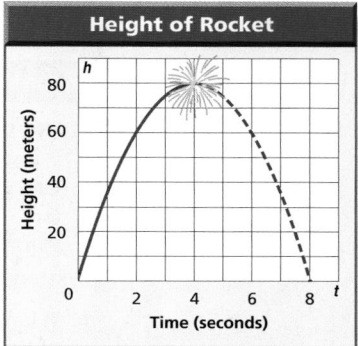

Height of Rocket

Graph Quadratic Functions The function describing the height of the rocket is an example of a quadratic function. A **quadratic function** can be written in the form $y = ax^2 + bx + c$, where $a \neq 0$. This form of equation is called *standard form*. The graph of a quadratic function is called a **parabola**.

KEY CONCEPT — *Quadratic Function*

Words   A quadratic function can be described by an equation of the form $y = ax^2 + bx + c$, where $a \neq 0$.

Models

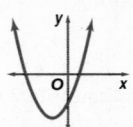 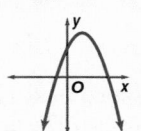 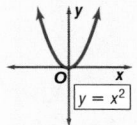

$y = x^2$

Study Tip

Parent Graph
The parent graph of the family of quadratic functions is $y = x^2$.

EXAMPLE   Graph Opens Upward

1 Use a table of values to graph $y = 2x^2 - 4x - 5$. What are the domain and range of this function?

Graph these ordered pairs and connect them with a smooth curve. Because $2x^2 - 4x - 5$ can be evaluated for all real numbers *x*, the domain is the set of all real numbers. The range is all real numbers greater than or equal to −7.

x	y
−2	11
−1	1
0	−5
1	−7
2	−5
3	1
4	11

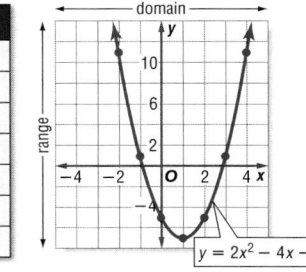

$y = 2x^2 - 4x - 5$

Lesson 9-1 Graphing Quadratic Functions   **471**

---

1 Focus

Standards Alignment

Before Lesson 9-1
Graph functions of the form $y = nx^2$ and $y = nx^3$ and use in solving problems from Standard 7AF3.1

Lesson 9-1
Graph quadratic functions and know that their roots are the *x*-intercepts from Standard 21.0

After Lesson 9-1
Solve and graph quadratic equations and quadratic equations in the complex number system from ◆ Standard 2A8.0

2 Teach

Scaffolding Questions
Have students read *Get Ready for the Lesson.*
Ask:
- Which is more important to the music planners: the height of the firework when it explodes, or the time at which it explodes? The time is more important if the planners want to coordinate the explosions with the music.
- Why must the planners still know the height? The firework explodes at approximately its highest point. When the highest point is found, the value of *t* at this point is the time at which the firework will explode.

Lesson 9-1 Resources

Chapter 9 Resource Masters
Lesson Reading Guide, p. 5 **BL** **OL** **ELL**
Study Guide and Intervention, pp. 6–7 **BL** **OL** **ELL**
Skills Practice, p. 8 **BL** **OL**
Practice, p. 9 **OL** **AL**
Word Problem Practice, p. 10 **OL** **AL**
Enrichment, p. 11 **OL** **AL**

Transparencies
5-Minute Check Transparency 9-1

Additional Print Resources
Noteables™ Interactive Study Notebook with Foldables™
Teaching Algebra with Manipulatives
Science and Mathematics Lab Manual, pp. 61–64

Technology
ca.algebra1.com
Interactive Classroom CD-ROM
AssignmentWorks CD-ROM
Graphing Calculator Easy Files

Graph Quadratic Equations

Example 1 shows how to graph a quadratic function when the parabola opens upward. **Example 2** shows how to graph a quadratic function when the parabola opens downward.

 Formative Assessment

Use the Check Your Progress exercises after each example to determine students' understanding of concepts.

ADDITIONAL EXAMPLES

1

a. Use a table of values to graph $y = x^2 - x - 2$.

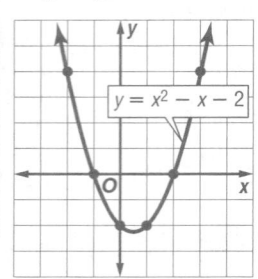

x	y
-2	4
-1	0
0	-2
1	-2
2	0
3	4

b. What are the domain and range of this function?

domain: all real numbers; range: $\{y \mid y \geq -2\frac{1}{4}\}$

2 **ARCHERY** The equation $y = -x^2 + 6x + 4$ represents the height, y, of an arrow x seconds after it is shot into the air.

a. Use a table of values to graph $y = -x^2 + 6x + 4$.

See bottom margin for graph.

x	y
-1	-3
0	4
1	9
2	12
3	13
4	12
5	9
6	4
7	-3

b. What are the mathematical domain and range of this function? domain: all real numbers; range: $\{y \mid y \leq 13\}$

(continued on the next page)

CHECK Your Progress

1. Use a table of values to graph $y = x^2 + 3$. What are the domain and range of this function? **See Ch. 9 Answer Appendix.**

Consider the standard form $y = ax^2 + bx + c$. Notice that the value of a in Example 1 is positive and the curve opens upward. The graph of any quadratic function in which a is positive opens upward. The lowest point, or **minimum**, of this graph is located at $(1, -7)$.

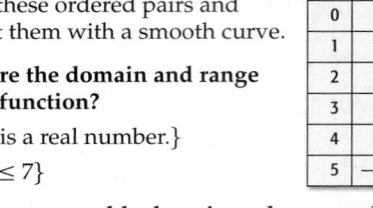 **Graph Opens Downward**

2 **FLYING DISKS** The equation $y = -x^2 + 4x + 3$ represents the height y of a flying disk x seconds after it is tossed.

a. Use a table of values to graph $y = -x^2 + 4x + 3$.

Graph these ordered pairs and connect them with a smooth curve.

x	y
-1	-2
0	3
1	6
2	7
3	6
4	3
5	-2

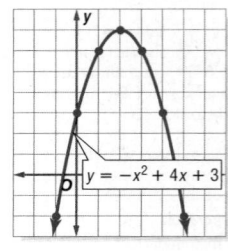

b. What are the domain and range of this function?

D: $\{x \mid x$ is a real number.$\}$

R: $\{y \mid y \leq 7\}$

c. Describe reasonable domain and range values for this situation.

The flying disk is in the air for about 4.6 seconds, so a reasonable domain is $\{x \mid 0 \leq x \leq 4.6\}$. The height of the flying disk ranges from 0 to 7 feet, so a reasonable range is $\{y \mid 0 \leq y \leq 7\}$.

CHECK Your Progress

2. Use a table of values to graph $y = -2x^2 + x + 1$. What are the domain and range of this function? **See Ch. 9 Answer Appendix.**

Reading Math

Vertex The plural of vertex is *vertices*. In math, vertex has several meanings. For example, there are the vertex of an angle, the vertices of a polygon, and the vertex of a parabola.

Notice that the value of a in Example 2 is negative and the curve opens downward. The graph of any quadratic function in which a is negative opens downward. The highest point, or **maximum**, of the graph is located at $(2, 3)$. The maximum or minimum point of a parabola is called the **vertex**.

Symmetry and Vertices Parabolas possess a geometric property called **symmetry**. Symmetrical figures are those in which each half of the figure matches the other exactly.

The line that divides a parabola into two halves is called the **axis of symmetry**. Each point on the parabola that is on one side of the axis of symmetry has a corresponding point on the parabola on the other side of the axis. The vertex is the only point on the parabola that is on the axis of symmetry. Notice the relationship between the values a and b and the equation of the axis of symmetry.

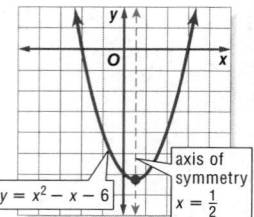

axis of symmetry

$y = x^2 - x - 6$ $x = \frac{1}{2}$

472 Chapter 9 Quadratic and Exponential Functions

Tips for New Teachers

Preventing Errors

Tell students that their sketches of parabolas do not have to be perfect. However, students should not "connect the dots" with straight lines. The important thing is for the curve to pass through the graphed ordered pairs.

Answer for Additional Example 2a

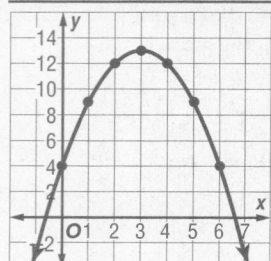

Words The equation of the axis of symmetry for the graph of $y = ax^2 + bx + c$, where $a \neq 0$, is $x = -\dfrac{b}{2a}$.

Model

$x = -\dfrac{b}{2a}$

EXAMPLE Vertex and Axis of Symmetry

3 Consider the graph of $y = -3x^2 - 6x + 4$.

a. Write the equation of the axis of symmetry.

In $y = -3x^2 - 6x + 4$, $a = -3$ and $b = -6$.

$x = -\dfrac{b}{2a}$ Equation for the axis of symmetry of a parabola

$x = -\dfrac{-6}{2(-3)}$ or -1 $a = -3$ and $b = -6$

The equation of the axis of symmetry is $x = -1$.

b. Find the coordinates of the vertex.

Since the equation of the axis of symmetry is $x = -1$ and the vertex lies on the axis, the x-coordinate for the vertex is -1.

$y = -3x^2 - 6x + 4$ Original equation

$y = -3(-1)^2 - 6(-1) + 4$ $x = -1$

$y = -3 + 6 + 4$ Simplify.

$y = 7$ Add.

The vertex is at $(-1, 7)$.

c. Identify the vertex as a maximum or minimum.

Since the coefficient of the x^2 term is negative, the parabola opens downward and the vertex is a maximum point.

d. Graph the function.

You can use the symmetry of the parabola to help you draw its graph. On a coordinate plane, graph the vertex and the axis of symmetry. Choose a value for x other than -1. For example, choose 1 and find the y-coordinate that satisfies the equation.

$y = -3x^2 - 6x + 4$ Original equation

$y = -3(1)^2 - 6(1) + 4$ Let $x = 1$.

$y = -5$ Simplify.

Graph $(1, -5)$. Since the graph is symmetrical about its axis of symmetry $x = -1$, you can find another point on the other side of the axis of symmetry. The point at $(1, -5)$ is 2 units to the right of the axis. Go 2 units to the left of the axis and plot the point $(-3, -5)$. Repeat this for several other points. Then sketch the parabola.

$y = -3x^2 - 6x + 4$

$x = -1$

$(-1, 7)$ $(-3, -5)$ $(1, -5)$

Lesson 9-1 Graphing Quadratic Functions   **473**

Study Tip

Coordinates of Vertex

Notice that you can find the x-coordinate by knowing the axis of symmetry. However, to find the y-coordinate, you must substitute the value of x into the quadratic equation.

ADDITIONAL EXAMPLE

2 **c.** Describe reasonable domain and range values for this situation. The arrow is in the air for about 6.6 seconds, so a reasonable domain is $\{x \mid 0 \leq x \leq 6.6\}$. A reasonable range is $\{y \mid 0 \leq y \leq 13\}$.

Additional Examples are also in:
- Noteables™ Interactive Study Notebook with Foldables™
- Interactive Classroom PowerPoint® Presentations

Symmetry and Vertices

Example 3 shows how to find an equation for the axis of symmetry and the coordinates of the vertex of a parabola. **Example 4** shows how to match an equation with its corresponding graph.

ADDITIONAL EXAMPLE

3 Consider the graph of $y = -2x^2 - 8x - 2$.

a. Write the equation of the axis of symmetry. $x = -2$

b. Find the coordinates of the vertex. The coordinates of the vertex are $(-2, 6)$.

c. Identify the vertex as a maximum or minimum. Since the coefficient of the x^2 term is negative, the parabola opens downward and the vertex is a maximum point.

d. Graph the function.

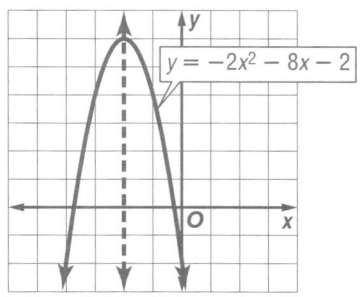

$y = -2x^2 - 8x - 2$

Focus on Mathematical Content

Vertex The maximum or minimum point of a parabola is called the *vertex*. When a quadratic function is written in standard form, $y = ax^2 + bx + c$, and a is positive, the parabola opens upward, and the vertex is a minimum. When a is negative, the parabola opens downward, and the vertex is a maximum.

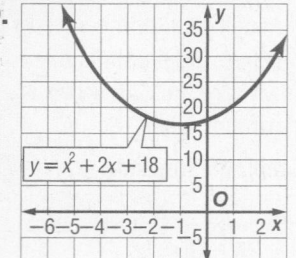

Consider the graph of $y = x^2 + 2x + 18$.

3A. Write the equation of the axis of symmetry. $x = -1$

3B. Find the coordinates of the vertex. $(-1, 17)$

3C. Identify the vertex as a maximum or minimum. **minimum**

3D. Graph the function. **See margin.**

 STANDARDS EXAMPLE Match Equations and Graphs 21.0

4 Which is the graph of $y + 1 = (x + 1)^2$?

A 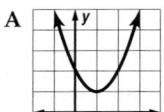 **B** 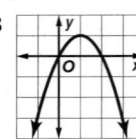 **C** 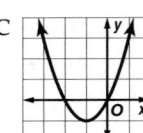 **D**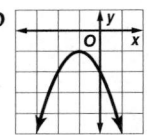

Read the Item

You are given a quadratic function, and you are asked to choose its graph.

Solve the Item

Step 1 First write the equation in standard form.

$$y + 1 = (x + 1)^2 \qquad \text{Original equation}$$
$$y + 1 = x^2 + 2x + 1 \qquad (x + 1)^2 = x^2 + 2x + 1$$
$$y + 1 - 1 = x^2 + 2x + 1 - 1 \qquad \text{Subtract 1 from each side.}$$
$$y = x^2 + 2x \qquad \text{Simplify.}$$

Step 2 Then find the axis of symmetry of the graph of $y = x^2 + 2x$.

$$x = -\frac{b}{2a} \qquad \text{Equation for the axis of symmetry}$$
$$x = -\frac{2}{2(1)} \text{ or } -1 \qquad a = 1 \text{ and } b = 2$$

The axis of symmetry is $x = -1$. Look at the graphs. Since only choices C and D have $x = -1$ as their axis of symmetry, you can eliminate choices A and B. Since the coefficient of the x^2 term is positive, the graph opens upward. Eliminate choice D. The answer is C.

CHECK Your Progress

4. Which is the equation of the graph? **H**

   F $y - 1 = (x + 2)^2$

   G $y - 1 = (x - 2)^2$

   H $y + 2 = (x - 1)^2$

   J $y - 2 = (x + 1)^2$

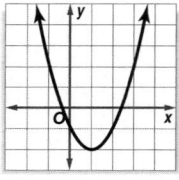

Online Personal Tutor at ca.algebra1.com

★ indicates multi-step problem

✓ CHECK Your Understanding

Examples 1, 2
(pp. 471–472)

Use a table of values to graph each function. **1–4. See margin.**

1. $y = x^2 - 5$

2. $y = x^2 + 2$

3. $y = -x^2 + 4x + 5$

4. $y = x^2 + x - 1$

Example 3
(pp. 473–474)

Write the equation of the axis of symmetry, and find the coordinates of the vertex of the graph of each function. Identify the vertex as a maximum or minimum. Then graph the function. **5–8. See Ch. 9 Answer Appendix for graphs.**

5. $y = x^2 + 4x - 9$

6. $y = -x^2 + 5x + 6$

7. $y = -(x - 2)^2 + 1$

8. $y = (x + 3)^2 - 4$

Example 4
(p. 474)

21.0

5. $x = -2$;
   $(-2, -13)$; min

6. $x = 2.5$;
   $(2.5, 12.25)$; max

7. $x = 2$; $(2, 1)$;
   max

8. $x = -3$; $(-3, 4)$;
   min

9. **STANDARDS PRACTICE** Which is the graph of $y = -\frac{1}{2}x^2 + 1$? **B**

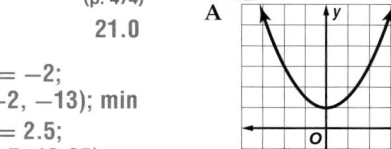
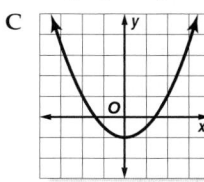

Exercises

HOMEWORK HELP	
For Exercises	**See Examples**
10–15	1, 2
16–29	3

Use a table of values to graph each function. **10–15. See Ch. 9 Answer Appendix.**

10. $y = x^2 - 3$

11. $y = -x^2 + 7$

12. $y = x^2 - 2x - 8$

13. $y = x^2 - 4x + 3$

14. $y = -3x^2 - 6x + 4$

15. $y = -3x^2 + 6x + 1$

Exercise Levels
A: 10–29
B: 30–41
C: 42–46

Write the equation of the axis of symmetry, and find the coordinates of the vertex of the graph of each function. Identify the vertex as a maximum or minimum. Then graph the function. **16–23. See Ch. 9 Answer Appendix for graphs.**

16. $y = 4x^2$ $x = 0$; $(0, 0)$; min

17. $y = -2x^2$ $x = 0$; $(0, 0)$; max

18. $y = x^2 + 2$ $x = 0$; $(0, 2)$; min

19. $y = -x^2 + 5$ $x = 0$; $(0, 5)$; max

20. $y = -x^2 + 2x + 3$ $x = 1$; $(1, 4)$; max

21. $y = -x^2 - 6x + 15$ $x = -3$; $(-3, 24)$; max

22. $y = 3x^2 - 6x + 4$ $x = 1$; $(1, 1)$; min

23. $y = 9 - 8x + 2x^2$ $x = 2$; $(2, 1)$; min

24. What is the equation of the axis of symmetry of the graph of $y = -3x^2 + 2x - 5$? $x = \frac{1}{3}$

25. $x = \frac{5}{8}$

25. Find the equation of the axis of symmetry of the graph of $y = 4x^2 - 5x + 16$.

Lesson 9-1 Graphing Quadratic Functions **475**

✓ Formative Assessment

Use Exercises 1–9 to check for understanding.

Use the chart at the bottom of this page to customize assignments for your students.

Odd/Even Assignments

Exercises 10–29 and 47–48 are structured so that students practice the same concepts whether they are assigned odd or even problems.

Additional Answers

1.
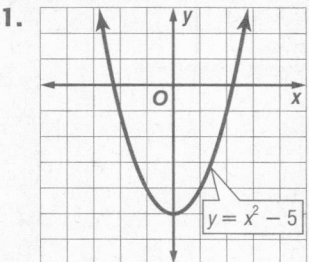

2.
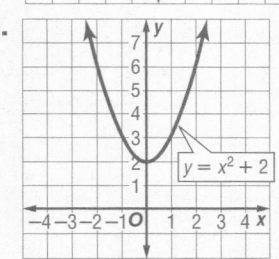

3.
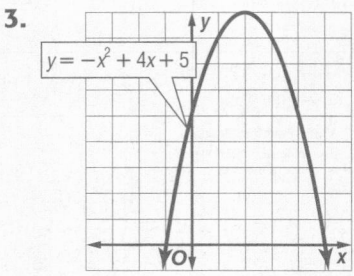

4.
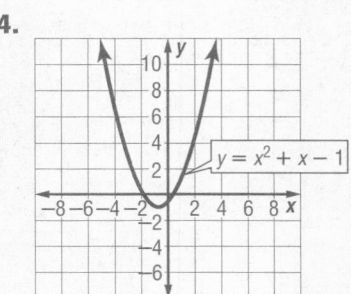

DIFFERENTIATED HOMEWORK OPTIONS			
Level	**Assignment**	**Two-Day Option**	
BL Basic	10–29, 42–48, 50–65	11–29 odd, 51, 52	10–28 even, 42–48, 50, 53–65
OL Core	11–33 odd, 34–48, 50–65	10–29 odd, 51, 52	30–48, 50, 53–65
AL Advanced /Pre-AP	30–62 (optional: 63–65)		

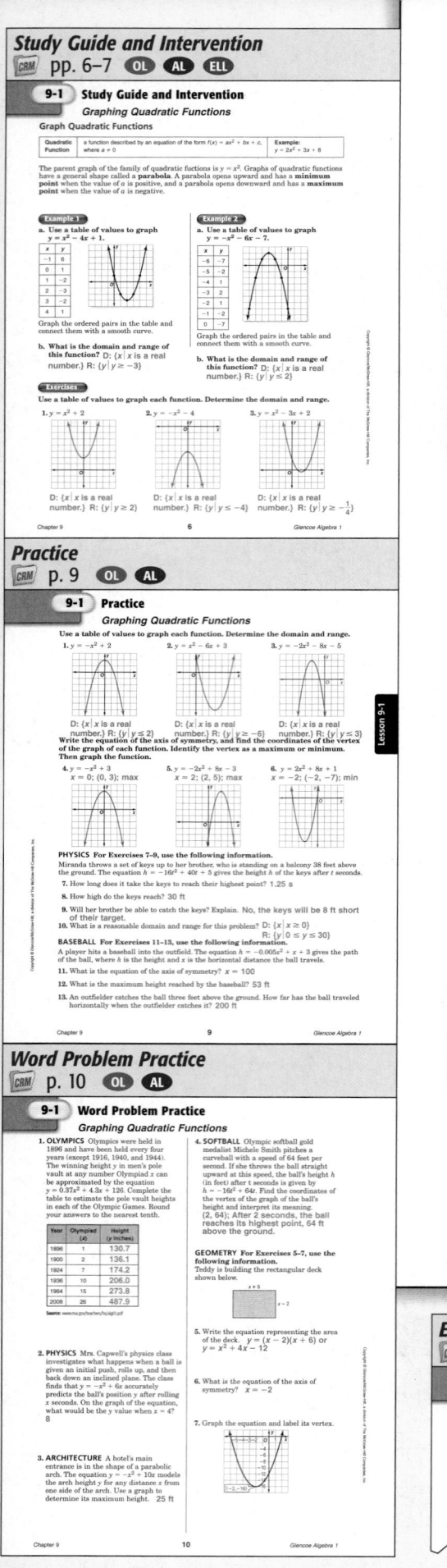

ENTERTAINMENT For Exercises 26 and 27, use the following information.

A carnival game involves striking a lever that forces a weight up a tube. If the weight reaches 20 feet to ring the bell, the contestant wins a prize. The equation $h = -16t^2 + 32t + 3$ gives the height of the weight if the initial velocity is 32 feet per second.

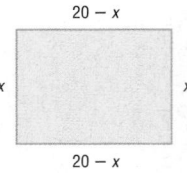
← winner

★ **26.** Find the maximum height of the weight. **19 ft**

27. Will a prize be won? Explain. **No, the height needs to be 20 ft to win a prize.**

PETS For Exercises 28 and 29, use the following information.

Miriam has 40 meters of fencing to build a pen for her dog.

★ **28.** Use the diagram to write an equation for the area A of the pen. Describe a reasonable domain and range for this situation. **See Ch. 9 Answer Appendix.**

★ **29.** What value of x will result in the greatest area? What is the greatest possible area of the pen? **10 m; 100 m²**

$20 - x$

x x

$20 - x$

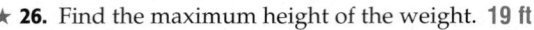

Real-World Link

The Gateway Arch is part of a tribute to Thomas Jefferson, the Louisiana Purchase, and the pioneers who settled the West. Each year about 2.5 million people visit the arch.

Source: *World Book Encyclopedia*

Write the equation of the axis of symmetry, and find the coordinates of the vertex of the graph of each function. Identify the vertex as a maximum or minimum. Then graph the function. **30–33. See Ch. 9 Answer Appendix for graphs.**

30. $y = -2(x - 4)^2 - 3$

31. $y + 2 = x^2 - 10x + 25$

32. $y - 5 = \frac{1}{3}(x + 2)^2$

33. $y + 1 = \frac{1}{3}(x + 1)^2$

34. The vertex of a parabola is at $(-4, -3)$. If one x-intercept is -11, what is the other x-intercept? **3**

35. What is the equation of the axis of symmetry of a parabola if its x-intercepts are -6 and 4? $x = -1$

30. $x = 4$; $(4, -3)$; max

31. $x = 5$; $(5, -2)$; min

32. $x = -2$; $(-2, 5)$; min

33. $x = -1$; $(-1, -1)$; min

ARCHITECTURE For Exercises 36–38, use the following information.

The shape of the Gateway Arch in St. Louis, Missouri, is a *catenary* curve. It resembles a parabola with the equation $h = -0.00635x^2 + 4.0005x - 0.07875$, where h is the height in feet and x is the distance from one base in feet.

36. What is the equation of the axis of symmetry? $x = 315$

37. What is the distance from one end of the arch to the other? **630 ft**

38. What is the maximum height of the arch? **630 ft**

FOOTBALL For Exercises 39–41, use the following information.

A football is kicked from ground level at an initial velocity of 90 feet per second. The equation $h = -16t^2 + 90t$ gives the height h of the football after t seconds.

EXTRA PRACTICE
See pages 735, 752.

Math Online
Self-Check Quiz at ca.algebra1.com

39. What is the height of the ball after one second? **74 ft**

40. When is the ball 126 feet high? **3 s or 2.625 s**

41. When is the height of the ball zero feet? Describe the events these represent. $t = 0$ and 5.625 s; The height of the ball is zero feet before it is kicked and again when the ball lands on the ground.

H.O.T. Problems

42. OPEN ENDED Sketch a parabola that models a real-life situation and describe what the vertex represents. Determine reasonable domain and range values for this type of situation. **See Ch. 9 Answer Appendix.**

43. REASONING Sketch the parent graph of the function $y = 3x^2 - 5x - 2$. **See Ch. 9 Answer Appendix.**

476 Chapter 9 Quadratic and Exponential Functions

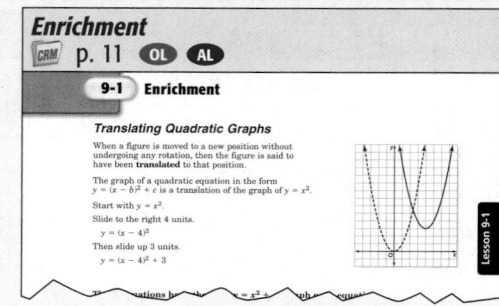

Enrichment
CRM p. 11 **OL** **AL**

9-1 **Enrichment**

Translating Quadratic Graphs

When a figure is moved to a new position without undergoing any rotation, then the figure is said to have been **translated** to that position.

The graph of a quadratic equation in the form $y = (x - h)^2 + c$ is a translation of the graph of $y = x^2$.

Start with $y = x^2$.
Slide to the right 4 units.
$y = (x - 4)^2$
Then slide up 3 units.
$y = (x - 4)^2 + 3$

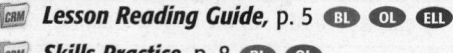

BL = Below Grade Level
OL = On Grade Level
AL = Above Grade Level
ELL = English Language Learner

Additional pages not shown:

CRM *Lesson Reading Guide*, p. 5 **BL** **OL** **ELL**

CRM *Skills Practice*, p. 8 **BL** **OL**

47. domain $x \leq -3$ and $x \geq 3$; range $y \geq 0$

REASONING Let $f(x) = x^2 - 9$.

44. What is the domain of $f(x)$? all real numbers

45. What is the range of $f(x)$? $\{y \mid y \geq -9\}$

46. For what values of x is $f(x)$ negative? $\{x \mid -3 < x < 3\}$

47. When x is a real number, what are the domain and range of $f(x) = \sqrt{x^2 - 9}$?

48. REASONING Determine the range of $f(x) = (x - 5)^2 - 6$. $\{y \mid y \geq -6\}$

49. CHALLENGE Write and graph a quadratic equation whose graph has the axis of symmetry $x = -\frac{3}{8}$. Summarize the steps that you took to determine the equation. See margin.

50. *Writing in Math* Use the information about a rocket's path on page 471 to explain how a fireworks display can be coordinated with recorded music. Include an explanation of how to determine when the rocket will explode and how to find the height of the rocket when it explodes. See margin.

STANDARDS PRACTICE 6NS1.4

51. In the graph of the function $y = x^2 - 3$, which describes the shift in the vertex of the parabola if, in the function, -3 is changed to 1? B

A 2 units up

B 4 units up

C 2 units down

D 4 units down

52. REVIEW The costs of two packs of Brand A gum and two packs of Brand B gum are shown in the table. What percent of the cost of Brand B gum does James save by buying two packs of Brand A gum? G

Gum	Cost of Two Packs
Brand A	\$1.98
Brand B	\$2.50

F 11.6% H 26.3%

G 20.8% J 79.2%

Spiral Review

Factor each polynomial, if possible. (Lessons 8-5 and 8-6)

53. $x^2 + 6x - 9$ prime

54. $a^2 + 22a + 121$ $(a + 11)^2$

55. $4m^2 - 4m + 1$ $(2m - 1)^2$

56. $4q^2 - 9$ $(2q - 3)(2q + 3)$

57. $2a^2 - 25$ prime

58. $1 - 16g^2$ $(1 - 4g)(1 + 4g)$

Find each sum or difference. (Lesson 7-5)

59. $(13x + 9y) + 11y$ $13x + 20y$

60. $(8 - 2c^2) + (1 + c^2)$ $9 - c^2$

61. $(7p^2 - p - 7) - (p^2 + 11)$ $6p^2 - p - 18$

62. RECREATION At a recreation facility, 3 members and 3 nonmembers pay a total of \$180 to take an aerobics class. A group of 5 members and 3 nonmembers pay \$210 to take the same class. How much does it cost each to take an aerobics class? (Lesson 5-3) \$15 for members, \$45 for nonmembers

GET READY for the Next Lesson

PREREQUISITE SKILL Find the x-intercept of the graph of each equation. (Lesson 3-3)

63. $3x + 4y = 24$ 8

64. $2x - 5y = 14$ 7

65. $-2x - 4y = 7$ -3.5

Tips for New Teachers — Student Misconceptions

Point out that although the equations in Exercises 30–33 are not in the standard form $y = ax^2 + bx + c$, they still have a degree of 2, so they are quadratic. Furthermore, when the expressions in parentheses are multiplied, the equations take on more traditional forms.

4 Assess

Ticket Out the Door Make several copies each of five graphs of parabolas. Give one graph to each student. As the students leave the room, ask them to tell you the coordinates of the parabolas' vertices and to identify them as maximums or minimums.

FOLDABLES Study Organizer — Foldables™ Follow-Up

At the end of this lesson, remind students to take notes and show examples on the page in their Foldables labeled 9-1.

49. Sample answer: $y = 4x^2 + 3x + 5$; write the equation for the axis of symmetry of a parabola, $x = -\frac{b}{2a}$. From the equation, $b = 3$ and $2a = 8$, so $a = 4$. Substitute these values for a and b into the equation $y = ax^2 + bx + c$.

50. Sample answer: In order to coordinate a firework with recorded music, you must know when and how high it will explode. The rocket will explode when the rocket reaches the vertex or when $t = -\frac{39.2}{2(-4.9)}$, which is 4 seconds. The height of the rocket when it explodes is the height when $t = 4$. Therefore, $h = -4.9(4^2) + 39.2(4) + 1.6$ or 80 meters

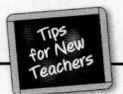

EXTEND 9-1

Graphing Calculator Lab
The Family of Quadratic Functions

1 Focus

Objective Use the graphing calculator to graph families of quadratic graphs.

Materials
• graphing calculator

Teaching Tip Remind students that the $\boxed{x^2}$ key squares a quantity but does not enter x^2 into the equation. To enter $3x^2$, press 3 $\boxed{\text{X,T,}\theta,n}$ $\boxed{x^2}$.

2 Teach

Working in Cooperative Groups
Put students in groups of 2 or 3, mixing abilities. Have groups complete Activities 1 and 2 and Exercises 1–4.

• Make sure students know how to set the standard viewing window for graphs and how to change the appearance of the viewing window.

• To help students remember how the value of a in $y = ax^2$ affects the shape of the graph, suggest that students sketch some of the parabolas and their equations on grid paper.

• Have students use the TRACE feature to help them identify the different parabolas on the screen. After pressing $\boxed{\text{TRACE}}$, students can use the arrow keys to move the cursor. The up and down arrows switch the cursor between graphs. The left and right arrows move the cursor along the individual graphs. The graph on which the cursor lies is identified in the top left-hand corner of the screen.

Practice Have students complete Exercises 5–12.

Standard 21.0 Students graph quadratic functions and know that their roots are the x-intercepts.

The parent function of the family of quadratic functions is $y = x^2$.

ACTIVITY 1

COncepts in MOtion
Animation ca.algebra1.com

Graph each group of equations on the same screen. Use the standard viewing window. Compare and contrast the graphs.

KEYSTROKES: *Review graphing equations on pages* 162 *and* 163.

a. $y = x^2, y = 2x^2, y = 4x^2$

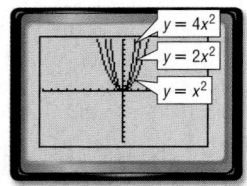

Each graph opens upward and has its vertex at the origin. The graphs of $y = 2x^2$ and $y = 4x^2$ are narrower than the graph of $y = x^2$.

b. $y = x^2, y = 0.5x^2, y = 0.2x^2$

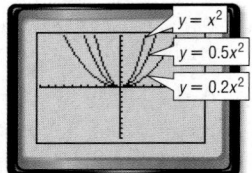

Each graph opens upward and has its vertex at the origin. The graphs of $y = 0.5x^2$ and $y = 0.2x^2$ are wider than the graph of $y = x^2$.

1A. How does the value of a in $y = ax^2$ affect the shape of the graph?
It makes the graph narrower or wider.

c. $y = x^2, y = x^2 + 3, y = x^2 - 2,$
$y = x^2 - 4$

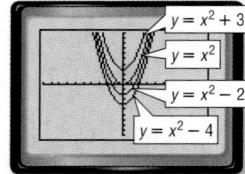

Each graph opens upward and has the same shape as $y = x^2$. However, each parabola has a different vertex, located along the y-axis.

d. $y = x^2, y = (x - 3)^2, y = (x + 2)^2,$
$y = (x + 4)^2$

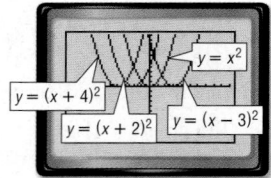

Each graph opens upward and has the same shape as $y = x^2$. However, each parabola has a different vertex located along the x-axis.

1B. How does the value of the constant affect the position of the graph?
It moves the graph up and down.
1C. How is the location of the vertex related to the equation of the graph?

1C. The vertex moves right or left depending on the value in the parentheses.

 Other Calculator Keystrokes at ca.algebra1.com

Additional Answer

1.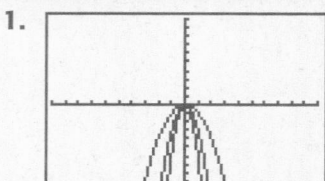

All of the graphs open downward from the origin. $y = -3x^2$ is narrower than $y = -x^2$, and $y = -6x^2$ is the narrowest.

Suppose you graph the same equation using different windows. How will the appearance of the graph change?

ACTIVITY 2

Graph $y = x^2 - 7$ in each viewing window. What conclusions can you draw about the appearance of a graph in the window used?

a. standard viewing window

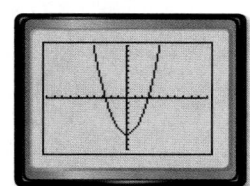

b. [−10, 10] scl: 1 by [−200, 200] scl: 50

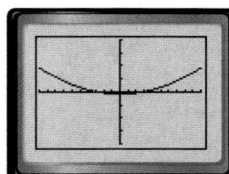

c. [−50, 50] scl: 5 by [−10, 10] scl: 1

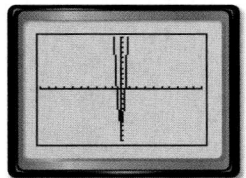

d. [−0.5, 0.5] scl: 0.1 by [−10, 10] scl: 1

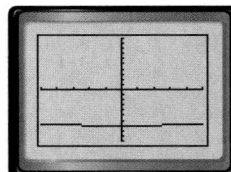

Without knowing the window, graph **b** might be of the family $y = ax^2$, where $0 < a < 1$. Graph **c** looks like a member of $y = ax^2 - 7$, where $a > 1$. Graph **d** looks more like a line. However, all are graphs of the same equation.

EXERCISES

Graph each family of equations on the same screen. Compare and contrast the graphs. 1–4. See margin.

1. $y = -x^2$
   $y = -3x^2$
   $y = -6x^2$

2. $y = -x^2$
   $y = -0.6x^2$
   $y = -0.4x^2$

3. $y = -x^2$
   $y = -(x + 5)^2$
   $y = -(x - 4)^2$

4. $y = -x^2$
   $y = -x^2 + 7$
   $y = -x^2 - 5$

Use the graphs on page 478 and Exercises 1–4 above to predict the appearance of the graph of each equation. Then draw the graph. 5–8. See Ch. 9 Answer Appendix.

5. $y = -0.1x^2$

6. $y = (x + 1)^2$

7. $y = 4x^2$

8. $y = x^2 - 6$

Describe how each change in $y = x^2$ would affect the graph of $y = x^2$. Be sure to consider all values of *a, h,* and *k*. 9–12. See margin.

9. $y = ax^2$

10. $y = (x + h)^2$

11. $y = x^2 + k$

12. $y = (x + h)^2 + k$

Extend 9–1 Graphing Calculator Lab: The Family of Quadratic Functions **479**

10. The graph has the same shape as $y = x^2$, but is shifted *h* units (left if $h > 0$, right if $h < 0$).

11. The graph has the same shape as $y = x^2$, but is shifted *k* units (up if $k > 0$, down if $k < 0$).

12. The graph has the same shape as $y = x^2$, but is shifted *h* units left or right and *k* units up or down as prescribed in Exercises 10 and 11.

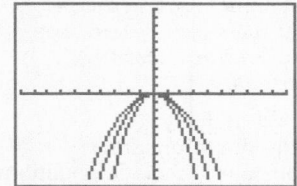

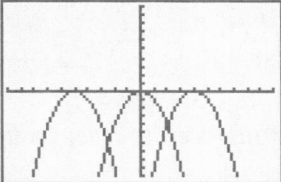
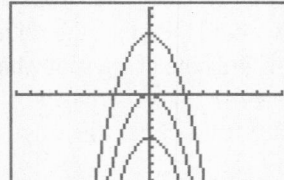

9-2 Solving Quadratic Equations by Graphing

1 Focus

Standards Alignment

Before Lesson 9-2
Graph functions of the form $y = nx^2$ and $y = nx^3$ and use in solving problems from Standard 7AF3

Lesson 9-2
Graph quadratic functions and know that their roots are the x- intercepts and determine whether the graph of a quadratic function will intersect the x-axis in zero, one, or two points from Standards 22.0 and 21.0

After Lesson 9-2
Solve and graph quadratic equations and quadratic equations in the complex number system from ⚷ Standard 2A8.0

2 Teach

Scaffolding Questions
Have students read *Get Ready for the Lesson.*
Ask:
- If one of the x-intercepts represents where the ball hits the ground, what represents the ground? the x-axis
- Suppose the green is uphill from the tee. How would this affect the value of the y-coordinate of the spot where the ball lands? The y-coordinate would be positive if the shot was uphill.

Lesson 9-2 Resources

Main Idea
- Solve quadratic equations by graphing.
- Estimate solutions of quadratic equations by graphing.

Standard 21.0 Students graph quadratic functions and know that their roots are the x-intercepts.

Standard 22.0 Students use the quadratic formula or factoring techniques or both to determine whether the graph of a quadratic function will intersect the x-axis in zero, one, or two points.

New Vocabulary
quadratic equation
roots
zeros
double root

Concepts in Motion
Animation ca.algebra1.com

Study Tip
x-intercepts
The x-intercepts of a graph are also called the *horizontal intercepts.*

 GET READY for the Lesson

A golf ball follows a path much like a parabola. Because of this property, quadratic functions can be used to simulate parts of a computer golf game. One of the x-intercepts of the quadratic function represents the location where the ball will hit the ground.

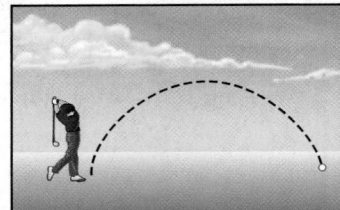

Solve by Graphing A **quadratic equation** is an equation that can be written in the form $ax^2 + bx + c = 0$, where $a \neq 0$. The value of the related quadratic function is 0.

Quadratic Equation	Related Quadratic Function
$x^2 - 2x - 3 = 0$	$f(x) = x^2 - 2x - 3$

The solutions of a quadratic equation are called the **roots** of the equation. The roots of a quadratic equation can be found by finding the x-intercepts or **zeros** of the related quadratic function.

EXAMPLE Two Roots

1 Solve $x^2 + 6x - 7 = 0$ by graphing.

Graph the related function $f(x) = x^2 + 6x - 7$. The equation of the axis of symmetry is $x = -\dfrac{6}{2(1)}$ or $x = -3$. When x equals -3, $f(x)$ equals $(-3)^2 + 6(-3) - 7$ or -16. So, the coordinates of the vertex are $(-3, -16)$. Make a table of values to find other points to sketch the graph.

x	$f(x)$
-8	9
-6	-7
-4	-15
-3	-16
-2	-15
0	-7
2	9

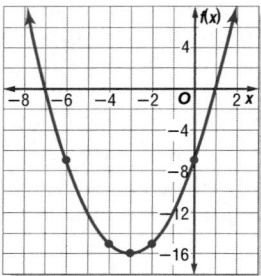

To solve $x^2 + 6x - 7 = 0$, you need to know where the value of $f(x)$ is 0. This occurs at the x-intercepts. The x-intercepts of the parabola appear to be -7 and 1.

CHECK Solve by factoring.

$$x^2 + 6x - 7 = 0 \quad \text{Original equation}$$

$$(x + 7)(x - 1) = 0 \quad \text{Factor.}$$

$$x + 7 = 0 \quad \text{or} \quad x - 1 = 0 \quad \text{Zero Product Property}$$

$$x = -7 \checkmark \qquad\qquad x = 1 \checkmark \quad \text{The solutions are } -7 \text{ and } 1.$$

 Your Progress

1. Solve $-c^2 + 5c - 4 = 0$ by graphing.

1, 4; See Ch. 9 Answer Appendix for graph.

Quadratic equations always have two roots. However, these roots are not always two distinct numbers. Sometimes the two roots are the same number, called a **double root.** In other cases the roots are not real numbers.

EXAMPLE A Double Root

② Solve $b^2 + 4b = -4$ by graphing.

First rewrite the equation so one side is equal to zero.

$$b^2 + 4b = -4 \quad \text{Original equation}$$

$$b^2 + 4b + 4 = 0 \quad \text{Add 4 to each side.}$$

Graph the related function $f(b) = b^2 + 4b + 4$.

Notice that the vertex of the parabola is the b-intercept. Thus, one solution is -2. What is the other solution?

Try solving the equation by factoring.

$$b^2 + 4b + 4 = 0 \quad \text{Original equation}$$

$$(b + 2)(b + 2) = 0 \quad \text{Factor.}$$

$$b + 2 = 0 \quad \text{or} \quad b + 2 = 0 \quad \text{Zero Product Property}$$

$$b = -2 \qquad\qquad b = -2 \quad \text{The solution is } -2.$$

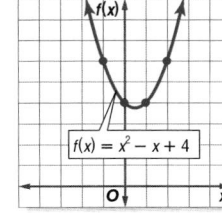

 Your Progress

2. Solve $0 = x^2 - 6x + 9$ by graphing. 3; See Ch. 9 Answer Appendix for graph.

EXAMPLE No Real Roots

Study Tip

Empty Set
The symbol ∅, indicating an empty set, is often used to represent no real solutions.

③ Solve $x^2 - x + 4 = 0$ by graphing.

Graph the related function $f(x) = x^2 - x + 4$.

The graph has no x-intercept. Thus, there are no real number solutions for this equation.

x	f(x)
−1	6
0	4
1	4
2	6

 Your Progress

3. Solve $-t^2 - 3t = 5$ by graphing. ∅; See Ch. 9 Answer Appendix for graph.

 Extra Examples at ca.algebra1.com

Lesson 9-2 Solving Quadratic Equations by Graphing **481**

Solve By Graphing

Example 1 shows how to use graphing to find the two roots of a quadratic equation. **Example 2** shows how to use graphing to find the double root of a quadratic equation. **Example 3** shows how to use a graph to identify a quadratic equation that has no real number solutions.

 Formative Assessment

Use the Check Your Progress exercises after each example to determine students' understanding of concepts.

ADDITIONAL EXAMPLES

① Solve $x^2 - 3x - 10 = 0$ by graphing. $\{-2, 5\}$

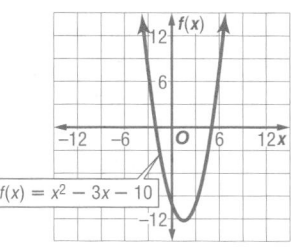

② Solve $x^2 + 8x = -16$ by graphing. $\{-4\}$

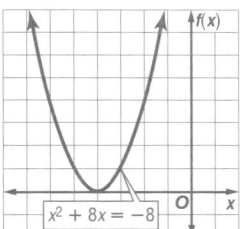

③ Solve $x^2 + 2x + 3 = 0$ by graphing. ∅ [empty set, or no real roots]

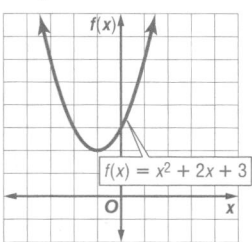

Additional Examples are also in:
- Noteables™ Interactive Study Notebook with Foldables™
- Interactive Classroom PowerPoint® Presentations

Differentiated Instruction

Logical Learners Students may assume that the vertex of a parabola lies on coordinates that are integers. Point out that in Example 3, the y-value for the vertex of the function is greater than 3 and somewhat less than 4.

Tips for New Teachers

Solving with Graphs and Tables

A graphing calculator is a powerful tool for solving quadratic equations by graphing or using tables. You may wish to discuss these techniques with students.

Estimate Solutions

Example 4 shows how to find roots of a quadratic equation by factoring.
Example 5 shows how to use graphing to estimate rational roots of a quadratic equation when integral roots cannot be found. **Example 6** shows how to estimate a solution to a real-world problem involving quadratic equations.

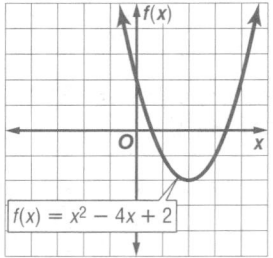
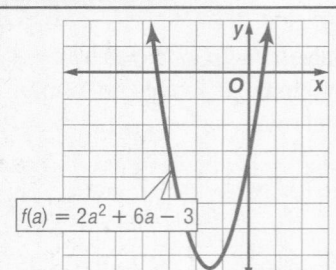
Factoring can be used to determine whether the graph of a quadratic function intersects the x-axis in zero, one, or two points.

EXAMPLE Factoring

4 Use factoring to determine how many times the graph of $f(x) = x^2 + x - 12$ intersects the x-axis. Identify each root.

The graph intersects the x-axis when $f(x) = 0$.

$x^2 + x - 12 = 0$	Original equation
$(x - 3)(x + 4) = 0$	Factor.

Since the trinomial factors into two distinct factors, the graph of the function intersects the x-axis 2 times. The roots are $x = 3$ and $x = -4$.

✓CHECK Your Progress

4. Use factoring to determine how many times the graph of $f(x) = x^2 - 10x + 25$ intersects the x-axis. Identify each root. **1; 5**

Estimate Solutions In Examples 1 and 2, the roots of the equation were integers. Usually the roots of a quadratic equation are not integers. In these cases, use estimation to approximate the roots of the equation.

EXAMPLE Rational Roots

5 Solve $n^2 + 6n + 7 = 0$ by graphing. If integral roots cannot be found, estimate the roots by stating the consecutive integers between which the roots lie.

Graph the related function $f(n) = n^2 + 6n + 7$.

n	$f(n)$
−6	7
−5	2
−4	−1
−3	−2
−2	−1
−1	2
0	7

Notice that the value of the function changes from negative to positive between the n values of −5 and −4 and between −2 and −1.

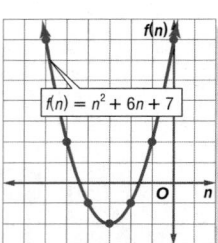

$f(n) = n^2 + 6n + 7$

The n-intercepts are between −5 and −4 and between −2 and −1. So, one root is between −5 and −4, and the other root is between −2 and −1.

✓CHECK Your Progress

5. Solve $2a^2 + 6a - 3 = 0$ by graphing. If integral roots cannot be found, estimate the roots by stating the consecutive integers between which the roots lie. **−4 < a < −3, 0 < a < 1; See margin for graph.**

 **Personal Tutor at** ca.algebra1.com

482 Chapter 9 Quadratic and Exponential Functions

Focus on Mathematical Content

No Real Roots Creating a table of values before graphing a function helps to reveal whether a function has no real roots. If all y-values of a function are positive, first decreasing then increasing, or if all are negative, first increasing then decreasing, the graph of the function does not cross the x-axis, and there are no real roots.

Double Root When there are two identical factors for a quadratic function, there is only one root, called a *double root*. If either the greatest or least y-value in the range of the function is 0, then the vertex is on the x-axis and the solution is a double root.

Real-World EXAMPLE

6 **SOCCER** If a goalie kicks a soccer ball with an upward velocity of 65 feet per second and his foot meets the ball 3 feet off the ground, the function $y = -16t^2 + 65t + 3$ represents the height of the ball y in feet after t seconds. Approximately how long is the ball in the air?

You need to find the solution of the equation $0 = -16t^2 + 65t + 3$. Use a graphing calculator to graph the related function $y = -16t^2 + 65t + 3$. The x-intercept is about 4. Therefore, the ball is in the air about 4 seconds.

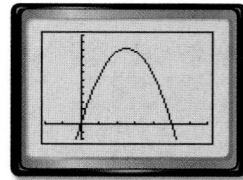

[−2, 7] scl: 1 by [−20, 80] scl: 10

Real-World Link

The game of soccer, called "football" in countries other than North America, began in 1857 in Britain. It is played on every continent of the world.

Source:
worldsoccer.about.com

✓CHECK Your Progress

6. NUMBER THEORY Use a quadratic equation to find two numbers whose sum is 5 and whose product is −24.   **−3, 8**

★ indicates multi-step problem

✓CHECK Your Understanding

Examples 1–3
(pp. 480–481)

Solve each equation by graphing. **1–3. See margin.**

1. $x^2 - 7x + 6 = 0$ **2.** $-a^2 - 10a = 25$ **3.** $c^2 + 3 = 0$

Example 4
(p. 482)

Use factoring to determine how many times the graph of each function intersects the x-axis. Identify each root.

4. $f(x) = x^2 + 2x - 24$ **2; −6, 4**   **5.** $f(x) = x^2 + 14x + 49$ **1; −7**

Example 5
(p. 482)

Solve each equation by graphing. If integral roots cannot be found, estimate the roots by stating the consecutive integers between which the roots lie.

6. $-t^2 - 5t + 1 = 0$ **7.** $0 = x^2 - 16$ **8.** $w^2 - 3w = 5$
6–8. See margin.

Example 6
(p. 483)

9. NUMBER THEORY Two numbers have a sum of 4 and a product of −12. Use a quadratic equation to determine the two numbers.   **−2, 6**

Exercises

HOMEWORK HELP	
For Exercises	See Examples
10–17	1–3
18–21	4
22–30	5
31, 32	6

Exercise Levels
A: 10–32
B: 33–40
C: 41–44

Solve each equation by graphing. **10–15. See margin.**

10. $c^2 - 5c - 24 = 0$ **11.** $5n^2 + 2n + 6 = 0$ **12.** $0 = x^2 + 6x + 9$
13. $-b^2 + 4b = 4$ **14.** $x^2 + 2x + 5 = 0$ **15.** $-2r^2 - 6r = 0$

16. The roots of a quadratic equation are −2 and −6. The minimum point of the graph of its related function is at (−4, −2). Sketch the graph of the function and compare the graph to the graph of the parent function $y = x^2$.

17. The roots of a quadratic equation are −6 and 0. The maximum point of the graph of its related function is at (−3, 4). Sketch the graph of the function and compare the graph to the graph of the parent function $y = x^2$.
16–17. See Ch. 9 Answer Appendix.

Use factoring to determine how many times the graph of each function intersects the x-axis. Identify each root.

18. $g(x) = x^2 - 8x + 16$ **1; 4**   **19.** $h(x) = x^2 + 12x + 32$ **2; −4, −8**
20. $f(x) = x^2 + 3x + 4$ **0; no real roots** **21.** $g(x) = x^2 + 3x + 4$ **0; no real roots**

Lesson 9-2 Solving Quadratic Equations by Graphing   **483**

ADDITIONAL EXAMPLE

6 **MODEL ROCKETS** Shelly built a model rocket for her science project. The equation $y = -16t^2 + 250t$ models the flight of the rocket launched from ground level at a velocity of 250 feet per second, where y is the height of the rocket in feet after t seconds. For how many seconds was Shelly's rocket in the air?
between 15 and 16 seconds

3 Practice

✓ Formative Assessment

Use Exercises 1–7 to check for understanding.

Use the chart at the bottom of this page to customize your assignments for students.

Odd/Even Assignments

Exercises 8–26 are structured so that students practice the same concepts whether they are assigned odd or even problems.

Additional Answers

See Chapter 9 Answer Appendix for graphs.

1. 1, 6
2. −5
3. ∅
6. $-6 < t < -5, 0 < t < 1$
7. −4, 4
8. $-2 < w < -1, 4 < w < 5$
10. −3, 8
11. ∅
12. −3
13. 2
14. ∅
15. −3, 0

DIFFERENTIATED HOMEWORK OPTIONS

Level	Assignment	Two-Day Option	
BL Basic	10–32, 41, 44–60	11–31 odd, 45, 46	10–32 even, 41, 44, 47–60
OL Core	11–31 odd, 33–41, 44–60	10–32, 45, 46	33–41, 44, 47–60
AL Advanced /Pre-AP	33–56 (optional: 57–60)		

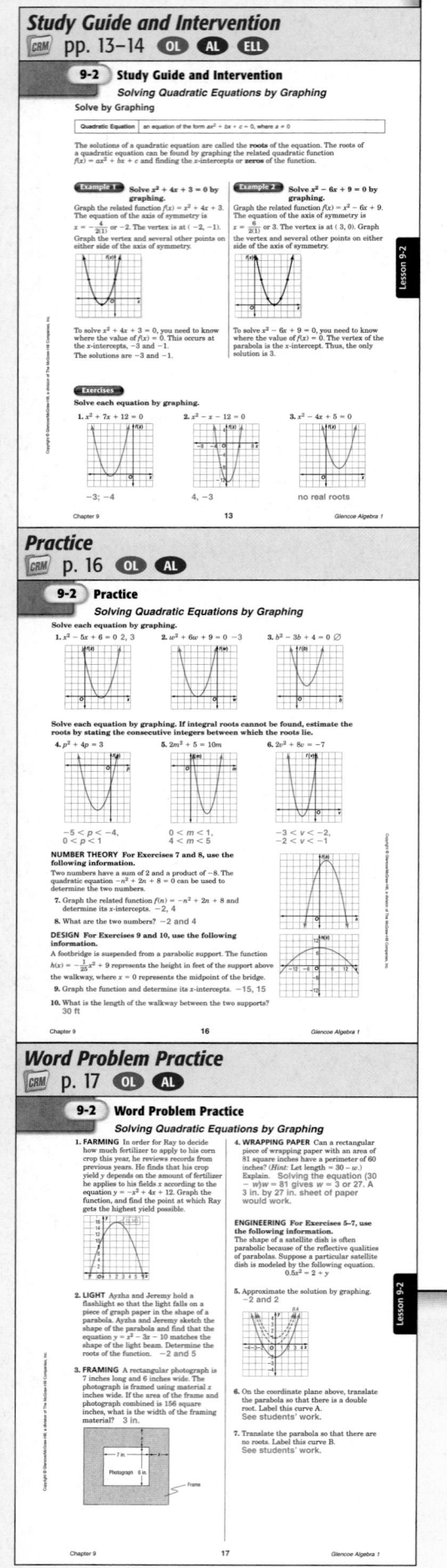

Solve each equation by graphing. If integral roots cannot be found, estimate the roots by stating the consecutive integers between which the roots lie.

22. $a^2 - 12 = 0$ **23.** $-n^2 + 7 = 0$ **24.** $2c^2 + 20c + 32 = 0$

25. $3s^2 + 9s - 12 = 0$ **26.** $0 = x^2 + 6x + 6$ **27.** $0 = -y^2 + 4y - 1$

28. $-a^2 + 8a = -4$ **29.** $x^2 + 6x = -7$ **30.** $m^2 - 10m = -21$

22–30. See Ch. 9 Answer Appendix.

31. NUMBER THEORY Use a quadratic equation to find two numbers whose sum is 9 and whose product is 20. **4, 5**

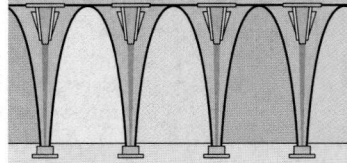
32. COMPUTER GAMES In a computer football game, the function $-0.005d^2 + 0.22d = h$ simulates the path of a football at the kickoff. In this equation, h is the height of the ball and d is the horizontal distance in yards. What is the horizontal distance the ball will travel before it hits the ground? **44 yd**

33. HIKING While hiking in the San Bernardino Mountains, Monya and Kishi stop for lunch on a ledge 1000 feet above a valley. Kishi decides to climb to another ledge 20 feet above Monya. Monya throws an apple up to Kishi, but Kishi misses it. The equation $h = -16t^2 + 30t + 1000$ represents the height in feet above the valley of the apple t seconds after it was thrown. How long did it take for the apple to reach the ground? **about 9 s**

THEATER For Exercises 34–37, use the following information.

The drama club is building a backdrop using arches whose shape can be represented by the function $f(x) = -x^2 + 2x + 8$, where x is the length in feet. The area under each arch is to be covered with fabric.

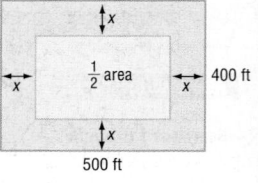

34. Graph the quadratic function and determine its x-intercepts. **See margin.**

35. What is the length of the segment along the floor of each arch? **6 ft**

36. What is the height of the arch? **9 ft**

37. The formula $A = \frac{2}{3}bh$ can be used to estimate the area A under a parabola. In this formula, b represents the length of the base, and h represents the height. If there are five arches, calculate the total amount of fabric that is needed. **about 180 ft²**

39. $(500 - 2x) \cdot (400 - 2x) = 100,000$ or $4x^2 - 1800x + 100,000 = 0$; about 65 ft

WORK For Exercises 38–40, use the following information.

Kirk and Montega mow the soccer playing fields. They must mow an area 500 feet long and 400 feet wide. They agree that each will mow half the area. Kirk will mow around the edge in a path of equal width until half the area is left.

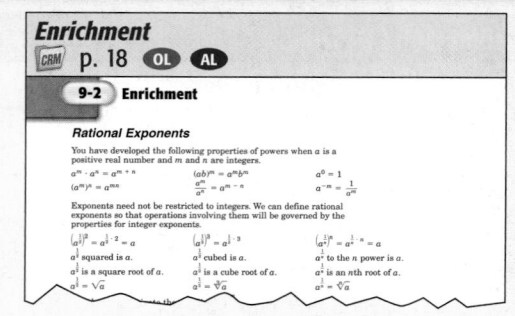

38. What is the area each person will mow? **100,000 ft²**

39. Write a quadratic equation that could be used to find the width x that Kirk should mow. What width should Kirk mow?

40. The mower can mow a path 5 feet wide. To the nearest whole number, how many times should Kirk go around the field? **13 times**

H.O.T. Problems

42. −3, 0, 1; These are the x-intercepts of the graph.

41. OPEN ENDED Draw a graph to show a counterexample to the following statement. Explain. *All quadratic equations have two different solutions.*
See Ch. 9 Answer Appendix.

42. CHALLENGE Describe the zeros of $f(x) = \dfrac{x^3 + 2x^2 - 3x}{x + 5}$. Explain your reasoning.

43. CHALLENGE The graph shown is a *quadratic inequality*. Similar to a linear inequality, the quadratic equation is a boundary between two half-planes. Analyze the graph and determine whether the inequality is *always, sometimes,* or *never* greater than 2. Explain. **See margin.**

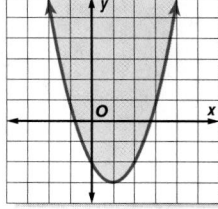

44. *Writing in Math* Use the information about computer games on page 480 to explain how quadratic equations can be used in computer simulations. Describe what the roots of a simulation equation for a computer golf game represent. **See margin.**

STANDARDS PRACTICE 21.0, 6AF1.1

45. The graph of the equation $y = x^2 + 10x + 21$ is shown. For what value or values of x is $y = 0$? **D**

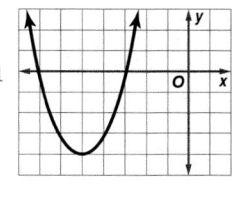

A $x = -4$
B $x = -5$
C $x = 7$ and $x = 3$
D $x = -7$ and $x = -3$

46. REVIEW Q-Mart has 1200 blue towels in stock. If they sell half of their towels every three months and do not receive any more shipments of towels, how many towels will they have left after a year? **G**

F 60
G 75
H 150
J 300

Spiral Review

Write the equation of the axis of symmetry, and find the coordinates of the vertex of the graph of each equation. Identify the vertex as a maximum or minimum. Then graph the function. (Lesson 9-1) **47–49. See Ch. 9 Answer Appendix.**

47. $y = x^2 + 6x + 9$

48. $y = -x^2 + 4x - 3$

49. $y = 0.5x^2 - 6x + 5$

Solve each equation. Check your solutions. (Lesson 8-6)

50. $m^2 - 24m = -144$ {12}

51. $7r^2 = 70r - 175$ {5}

52. $4d^2 + 9 = -12d$ $\left\{-\dfrac{3}{2}\right\}$

Simplify. Assume that no denominator is equal to zero. (Lesson 7-2)

53. $\dfrac{10m^4}{30m} \cdot \dfrac{m^3}{3}$

54. $\dfrac{22a^2b^5c^7}{-11abc^2}$ $-2ab^4c^5$

55. $\dfrac{-9m^3n^5}{27m^{-2}n^5y^{-4}} \cdot \dfrac{m^5y^4}{3}$

★ **56. SHIPPING** An empty book crate weighs 30 pounds. The weight of a book is 1.5 pounds. For shipping, the crate must weigh at least 55 pounds and no more than 60 pounds. What is the acceptable number of books that can be packed in the crate? (Lesson 6-4) **17 to 20 books**

GET READY for the Next Lesson

PREREQUISITE SKILL Determine whether each trinomial is a perfect square trinomial. If so, factor it. (Lesson 8-6)

57. $a^2 + 14 + 49$
yes; $(a + 7)^2$

58. $m^2 - 10m + 25$
yes; $(m - 5)^2$

59. $t^2 + 16t - 64$ **no**

60. $4y^2 + 12y + 9$
yes; $(2y + 3)^2$

Lesson 9-2 Solving Quadratic Equations by Graphing **485**

Study Tip

Look Back
To review **linear inequalities**, see Lesson 6-6.

4 Assess

Yesterday's News Ask students to write two ways in which learning to graph quadratic functions in the previous lesson helped them to solve quadratic equations in this lesson.

Formative Assessment

Check for student understanding of concepts in Lessons 9-1 and 9-2.

CRM Quiz 1, p. 51

Additional Answers

34.
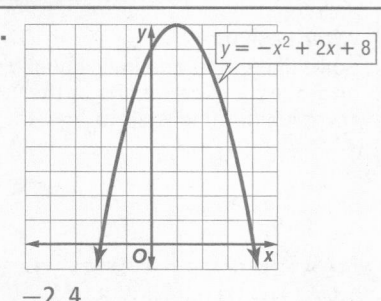
$-2, 4$

43. Always; the shaded region of the graph includes y-values greater than 2.

44. Sample answer: Since quadratic functions can be used to model a golf ball after it is hit, solving the related quadratic equation will determine where the ball hits the ground. In the golf problem, one intercept represents the ball's original location and the other intercept represents where the ball hits the ground.

Pre-AP Activity Use after Example 5

Tell students that in a computer golf game, the function $y = -0.002x^2 + 0.22x$ models the path of a golf ball, where y is the height of the ball and x is the horizontal distance in yards. The green lies uphill from the tee, 90 yards away, atop a hill that has a steady incline of 1 yard per 10 yards of distance. Ask, "Will the ball reach the green without hitting the ground first? Explain your answer." No. On level ground, this ball would travel over 90 yards, but on the uphill slope it will hit the ground after approximately 70 yards.

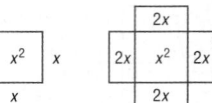 **9-3**

Solving Quadratic Equations by Completing the Square

 Standards Alignment

Before Lesson 9-3
Apply basic factoring techniques to second- and simple third-degree polynomials from Standard 1A11.0

Lesson 9-3
Solve a quadratic equation by completing the square from Standard 14.0

After Lesson 9-3
Solve and graph quadratic equations and quadratic equations in the complex number system from
 Standard 2A8.0

Scaffolding Questions
Have students read *Get Ready for the Lesson*.
Ask:
• Look at the completed square. What is the side length of the square? Remember, each of the smaller squares is made up of 4 unit squares.
side length $= x + 4$
• What is the area of the square?
$(x + 4)^2$ or $x^2 + 8x + 16$ units^2
(continued on the next page)

Main Ideas

• Solve quadratic equations by finding the square root.
• Solve quadratic equations by completing the square.

 Standard 14.0
Students solve a quadratic equation by factoring or **completing the square.** (Key)

New Vocabulary

completing the square

GET READY for the Lesson

Al-Khwarizmi, born in Baghdad in 780, is considered to be one of the foremost mathematicians of all time. He wrote algebra in sentences instead of using equations, and he explained the work with geometri sketches. Al-Khwarizmi would have described $x^2 + 8x = 35$ as "A sq and 8 roots are equal to 35 units." He would solve the problem using following sketch.

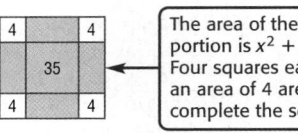

The area of the shaded portion is $x^2 + 8x$ or 35. Four squares each with an area of 4 are used to complete the square.

The important insight is that the square has a side length of $x + 4$ therefore, $x + 4 = \sqrt{35 + (4 + 4 + 4 + 4)}$. To solve problems this w today, you might use algebra tiles or a method called *completing the s*

Find the Square Root Some equations can be solved by taking the square root of each side.

EXAMPLE Irrational Roots

① Solve $x^2 - 10x + 25 = 7$ by taking the square root of each side. Round to the nearest tenth if necessary.

$x^2 - 10x + 25 = 7$	Original equation
$(x - 5)^2 = 7$	$x^2 - 10x + 25$ is a perfect square trinomial.
$\sqrt{(x - 5)^2} = \sqrt{7}$	Take the square root of each side.
$|x - 5| = \sqrt{7}$	Simplify.
$x - 5 = \pm\sqrt{7}$	Definition of absolute value
$x - 5 + 5 = \pm\sqrt{7} + 5$	Add 5 to each side.
$x = 5 \pm \sqrt{7}$	Simplify.

Use a calculator to evaluate each value of x.

$x = 5 + \sqrt{7}$	or $x = 5 - \sqrt{7}$	Write each solution.
≈ 7.6	≈ 2.4	Simplify.

The solution set is $\{2.4, 7.6\}$.

CHECK Your Progress

1. Solve $m^2 + 18m + 81 = 90$ by taking the square root of each side. Round to the nearest tenth if necessary. **−18.5, 0.5**

Chapter 9 Resource Masters
Lesson Reading Guide, p. 19 **BL** **OL** **ELL**
Study Guide and Intervention, pp. 20–21
BL **OL** **ELL**
Skills Practice, p. 22 **BL** **OL**
Practice, p. 23 **OL** **AL**
Word Problem Practice, p. 24 **OL** **AL**
Enrichment, p. 25 **OL** **AL**
Quiz 2, p. 51

Transparencies
5-Minute Check Transparency 9-3
Additional Print Resources
Noteables™ Interactive Study Notebook with Foldables™
Teaching Math With Manipulatives

Technology
ca.algebra1.com
Interactive Classroom CD-ROM
AssignmentWorks CD-ROM
Graphing Calculator Easy Files

Complete the Square In Example 1, the quadratic expression on one side of the equation was a perfect square. However, few quadratic expressions are perfect squares. To make any quadratic expression a perfect square, a method called **completing the square** may be used.

Consider the pattern for squaring a binomial such as $x + 6$.

$$(x + 6)^2 = x^2 + 2(6)(x) + 6^2$$
$$= x^2 + 12x + 36$$
$$\downarrow \qquad \uparrow$$
$$\left(\frac{12}{2}\right)^2 \rightarrow 6^2 \quad \text{Notice that one half of 12 is 6 and } 6^2 \text{ is 36.}$$

KEY CONCEPT — Completing the Square

To complete the square for a quadratic expression of the form $x^2 + bx$, you can follow the steps below.

Step 1 Find $\frac{1}{2}$ of b, the coefficient of x.

Step 2 Square the result of Step 1.

Step 3 Add the result of Step 2 to $x^2 + bx$, the original expression.

EXAMPLE Complete the Square

2 Find the value of c that makes $x^2 + 6x + c$ a perfect square.

Method 1 Use algebra tiles.

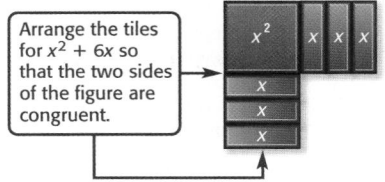

Arrange the tiles for $x^2 + 6x$ so that the two sides of the figure are congruent.

To make the figure a square, add 9 positive 1-tiles.

$x^2 + 6x + 9$ is a perfect square.

Method 2 Complete the square.

Step 1 Find $\frac{1}{2}$ of 6. $\frac{6}{2} = 3$

Step 2 Square the result of Step 1. $3^2 = 9$

Step 3 Add the result of Step 2 to $x^2 + 6x$. $x^2 + 6x + 9$

Thus, $c = 9$. Notice that $x^2 + 6x + 9 = (x + 3)^2$.

CHECK Your Progress

2. Find the value of c that makes $r^2 + 8r + c$ a perfect square. **16**

You can use the technique of completing the square to solve quadratic equations.

- Graphically, 16 unit squares were added to the original figure to complete the square. How would you change the original equation to represent this addition?
$x^2 + 8x + 16 = 35 + 16$

Find the Square Root

Example 1 shows how to solve a quadratic equation by taking the square root of each side of an equation.

 Formative Assessment

Use the Check Your Progress exercises after each example to determine students' understanding of concepts.

Tips for New Teachers   **Preventing Errors**

Tell students that when taking the square root of a number, there are two square roots, one positive and one negative. Explain that this is why the plus or minus sign is placed in front of the square root of 7 in Example 1 when the absolute value signs are removed. Without the plus or minus sign, there would be only one solution.

Complete the Square

Example 2 shows how to make any quadratic expression a perfect square by completing the square. **Example 3** shows how to solve a quadratic equation by completing the square. **Example 4** shows how to solve a quadratic equation in which a does not equal one.

3 Solve $x^2 - 18x + 5 = -12$ by completing the square. {1, 17}

4 **CANOEING** Suppose the rate of flow of an 80-foot-wide river is given by the equation $r = -0.01x^2 + 0.8x$, where r is the rate in miles per hour and x is the distance from the shore in feet. Joacquim does not want to paddle his canoe against a current that is faster than 5 miles per hour. At what distance from the river bank must he paddle in order to avoid a current of 5 miles per hour? about 7 ft from either bank **Note:** The solutions of the equation are about 7 ft and about 73 ft. Since the river is 80 ft wide, $80 - 73 = 7$.

Differentiated Instruction
Kinesthetic Learners Some students may benefit from using algebra tiles to complete the square when solving quadratic equations like the one in Example 3. Have students use an equation mat. Remind them to add or remove the same number of tiles to each side of the mat.

EXAMPLE Solve an Equation by Completing the Square

3 Solve $a^2 - 14a + 3 = -10$ by completing the square.

Isolate the a^2 and a terms. Then complete the square and solve.

$a^2 - 14a + 3 = -10$	Original equation
$a^2 - 14a + 3 - 3 = -10 - 3$	Subtract 3 from each side.
$a^2 - 14a = -13$	Simplify.
$a^2 - 14a + 49 = -13 + 49$	Since $\left(\frac{-14}{2}\right)^2 = 49$, add 49 to each side.
$(a - 7)^2 = 36$	Factor $a^2 - 14a + 49$.
$a - 7 = \pm 6$	Take the square root of each side.
$a = 7 \pm 6$	Add 7 to each side.
$a = 7 + 6$ or $a = 7 - 6$	Separate the solutions.
$= 13 \qquad = 1$	Simplify.

The solution set is {1, 13}.

CHECK Your Progress

3. Solve $x^2 - 8x = 4$ by completing the square. Round to the nearest tenth if necessary. **−0.5, 8.5**

To solve a quadratic equation in which the leading coefficient is not 1, first divide each term by the coefficient. Then complete the square.

Real-World EXAMPLE Solve a Quadratic Equation in Which $a \neq 1$

4 **ENTERTAINMENT** The path of debris from fireworks when the wind is about 15 miles per hour can be modeled by the quadratic function $h = -0.04x^2 + 2x + 8$, where h is the height and x is the horizontal distance in feet. How far away from the launch site will the debris land?

Explore You know the function that relates the horizontal and vertical distances. You want to know how far away the debris will land.

Plan The debris will hit the ground when $h = 0$. Complete the square to solve $-0.04x^2 + 2x + 8 = 0$.

Solve

$-0.04x^2 + 2x + 8 = 0$	Equation for where debris will land
$\dfrac{-0.04x^2 + 2x + 8}{-0.04} = \dfrac{0}{-0.04}$	Divide each side by −0.04.
$x^2 - 50x - 200 = 0$	Simplify.
$x^2 - 50x - 200 + 200 = 0 + 200$	Add 200 to each side.
$x^2 - 50x = 200$	Simplify.
$x^2 - 50x + 625 = 200 + 625$	Since $\left(\frac{50}{2}\right)^2 = 625$, add 625 to each side.
$x^2 - 50x + 625 = 825$	Simplify.
$(x - 25)^2 = 825$	Factor $x^2 - 50x + 625$.
$x - 25 = \pm\sqrt{825}$	Take the square root of each side.
$x = 25 \pm \sqrt{825}$	Add 25 to each side.

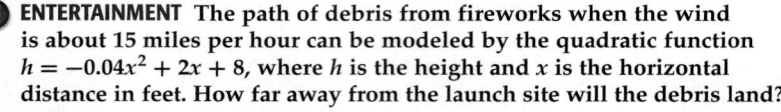

Real-World Link
One of the exploded fireworks for the Lake Toya Festival in Japan on July 15, 1988, broke a world record. The diameter of the burst was 3937 feet.

Source: *The Guinness Book of Records*

Pre-AP Activity Use as an Extension

Have students solve $\frac{1}{3}x^2 - \frac{7}{6}x + \frac{1}{2} = 0$ by completing the square. Ask them how this strategy compares to factoring and graphing. $x = \frac{1}{2}$, 3; the equation can be solved more easily by factoring. Graphing may not produce an exact answer if fractions are converted to decimals.

Use a calculator to evaluate each value of x.

$x = 25 + \sqrt{825}$ or $x = 25 - \sqrt{825}$ Separate the solutions.

≈ 53.7 ≈ -3.7 Evaluate.

Check Since you are looking for a distance, the negative number is not reasonable. The debris will land about 53.7 feet from the launch site.

 **CHECK Your Progress**

4. Solve $3n^2 - 18n = 30$ by completing the square. Round to the nearest tenth if necessary. **−1.4, 7.4**

Online **Personal Tutor at** ca.algebra1.com

★ indicates multi-step problem

CHECK Your Understanding

Example 1 (p. 486)
Solve each equation by taking the square root of each side. Round to the nearest tenth if necessary.

1. $b^2 - 6b + 9 = 25$ **−2, 8**
2. $m^2 + 14m + 49 = 20$ **−11.5, −2.5**

Example 2 (p. 487)
Find the value of c that makes each trinomial a perfect square.

3. $a^2 - 12a + c$ **36**
4. $t^2 + 5t + c$ $\frac{25}{4}$

Example 3 (p. 488)
Solve each equation by completing the square. Round to the nearest tenth if necessary. **7. −15, 1**

5. $c^2 - 6c = 7$ **−1, 7**
6. $x^2 + 7x = -12$ **−4, −3**
7. $v^2 + 14v - 9 = 6$
8. $r^2 - 4r = 2$ **−0.4, 4.4**
9. $4a^2 + 9a - 1 = 0$ **−2.4, 0.1**
10. $7 = 2p^2 - 5p + 8$ **0.2, 2.3**

Example 4 ★ (pp. 488–489)
11. GEOMETRY The area of a square can be doubled by increasing the length by 6 inches and the width by 4 inches. What is the length of the side of the square? **12 in.**

Exercises

HOMEWORK HELP	
For Exercises	See Examples
12–15	1
16–19	2
20–27	3
28–33	4

Exercise Levels
A: 12–33
B: 34–42
C: 43–47

23. −27, 7
28. −1.4, 3.4

Solve each equation by taking the square root of each side. Round to the nearest tenth if necessary.

12. $b^2 - 4b + 4 = 16$ **−2, 6**
13. $t^2 + 2t + 1 = 25$ **−6, 4**
14. $g^2 - 8g + 16 = 2$ **2.6, 5.4**
15. $w^2 + 16w + 64 = 18$ **−12.2, −3.8**

Find the value of c that makes each trinomial a perfect square.

16. $s^2 - 16s + c$ **64**
17. $y^2 - 10y + c$ **25**
18. $p^2 - 7p + c$ $\frac{49}{4}$
19. $c + 11k + k^2$ $\frac{121}{4}$

Solve each equation by completing the square. Round to the nearest tenth if necessary.

20. $s^2 - 4s - 12 = 0$ **−2, 6**
21. $d^2 + 3d - 10 = 0$ **−5, 2**
22. $y^2 - 19y + 4 = 70$ **−3, 22**
23. $d^2 + 20d + 11 = 200$
24. $a^2 - 5a = -4$ **1, 4**
25. $p^2 - 4p = 21$ **−3, 7**
26. $x^2 + 4x + 3 = 0$ **−3, −1**
27. $d^2 - 8d + 7 = 0$ **1, 7**
28. $5s^2 - 10s = 23$
29. $9r^2 + 49 = 42r$ **2.3**
30. $4h^2 + 25 = 20h$ **2.5**
31. $9w^2 - 12w - 1 = 0$ **−0.1, 1.4**

Irrational Solutions
Completing the square to solve a quadratic equation does not mean that the solutions will be integers. If the equation already has a constant term, it is likely that after completing the square, the constant will not be a perfect square, and the solutions will be irrational.

Tips for New Teachers

 **Student Misconceptions**
Tell students not to throw out negative solutions to real-world problems. Remind them that they must first examine the problem to see if the solution fits the situation.

3 Practice

 Formative Assessment
Use Exercises 1–11 to check for understanding.

Odd/Even Assignments
Exercises 12–33 are structured so that students practice the same concepts whether they are assigned odd or even problems.

Tips for New Teachers

 **Preventing Errors**
For Exercises 20–31, remind students that the amount that they add to one side of the equation to complete the square must also be added to the other side of the equation.

DIFFERENTIATED HOMEWORK OPTIONS

Level	Assignment	Two-Day Option	
BL Basic	12–33, 43, 44, 46–65	13–33 odd, 48, 49	12–32 even, 43, 44, 46, 47, 50–65
OL Core	13–41 odd, 42–44, 46–65	12–33, 48, 49	34–44, 46, 47, 50–65
AL Advanced /Pre-AP	34–61 (optional: 62–65)		

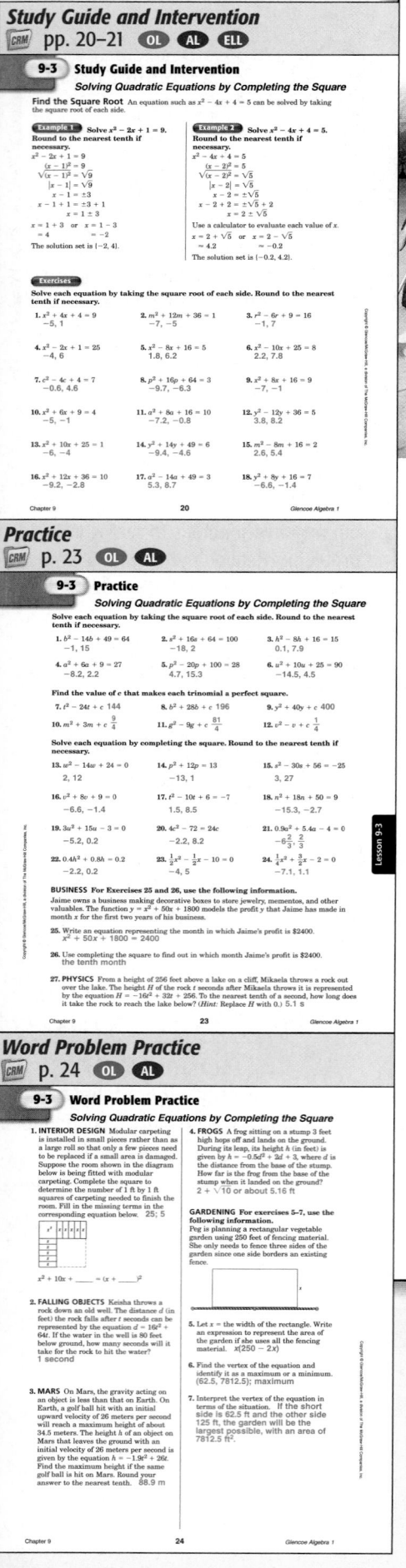

Study Guide and Intervention
CRM pp. 20–21 OL AL ELL

Practice
CRM p. 23 OL AL

Word Problem Practice
CRM p. 24 OL AL

★ **32. PARK PLANNING** A rectangular garden of wild flowers is 9 meters long by 6 meters wide. A pathway of constant width goes around the garden. If the area of the path equals the area of the garden, what is the width of the path? **1.5 m**

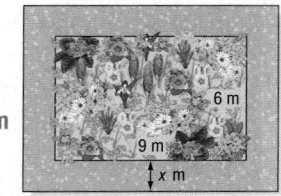

6 m
9 m
x m

33. NUTRITION The consumption of bread and cereal in the United States is increasing and can be modeled by the function $y = 0.059x^2 - 7.423x + 362.1$, where y represents the consumption of bread and cereal in pounds and x represents the number of years since 1900. If this trend continues, in what future year will the average American consume 300 pounds of bread and cereal? **about 2017**

Solve each equation by completing the square. Round to the nearest tenth if necessary.

34. $0.3t^2 + 0.1t = 0.2$ **−1, 0.7**

35. $0.4v^2 + 2.5 = 2v$ **2.5**

36. $\frac{1}{2}d^2 - \frac{5}{4}d - 3 = 0$ **$-\frac{3}{2}$, 4**

37. $\frac{1}{3}f^2 - \frac{7}{6}f + \frac{1}{2} = 0$ **$\frac{1}{2}$, 3**

38. Find all values of c that make $x^2 + cx + 81$ a perfect square. **−18, 18**

39. Find all values of c that make $x^2 + cx + 144$ a perfect square. **−24, 24**

Solve each equation for x in terms of c by completing the square.

40. $x^2 + 4x + c = 0$ **$-2 \pm \sqrt{4 - c}$**

41. $x^2 - 6x + c = 0$ **$3 \pm \sqrt{9 - c}$**

★ **42. PHOTOGRAPHY** Emilio is placing a photograph behind a 12-inch-by-12-inch piece of matting. The photograph is to be positioned so that the matting is twice as wide at the top and bottom as it is at the sides. If the area of the photograph is to be 54 square inches, what are the dimensions? **9 in. by 6 in.**

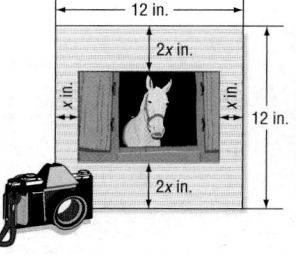

12 in.
2x in.
x in.
x in.
12 in.
2x in.

Real-World Career
Photographer
Photographers must consider lighting, lens setting, and composition to create the best photograph.

Math Online
For more information, go to ca.algebra1.com.

EXTRA PRACTICE
See pages 735, 752.

Math Online
Self-Check Quiz at ca.algebra1.com

H.O.T. Problems

43. OPEN ENDED Make a square using one or more of each of the following types of tiles. **See margin.**
- x^2-tile
- x-tile
- 1-tile

Describe the area of your square using an algebraic expression.

44. REASONING Compare and contrast the following strategies for solving $x^2 - 5x - 7 = 0$: completing the square, graphing the related function, and factoring.

44. Sample answer: Completing the square gives an exact solution. Graphing $f(x) = x^2 - 5x - 7$ does not give an exact solution. Since $x^2 - 5x - 7$ cannot be factored, this strategy cannot be used in this case.

45. CHALLENGE Without graphing, describe the solution of $x^2 + 4x + 12 = 0$. Explain your reasoning. Then describe the graph of the related function. **See margin.**

46. Which One Doesn't Belong? Identify the expression that does not belong with the other three. Explain your reasoning. **See margin.**

$$n^2 - n + \frac{1}{4} \qquad n^2 + n + \frac{1}{4} \qquad n^2 - \frac{2}{3}n + \frac{1}{9} \qquad n^2 + \frac{1}{3}n + \frac{1}{9}$$

490 Chapter 9 Quadratic and Exponential Functions

Enrichment
CRM p. 25 OL AL

9-3 Enrichment

Parabolas Through Three Given Points

BL = Below Grade Level
OL = On Grade Level
AL = Above Grade Level
ELL = English Language Learner

Additional pages not shown:
CRM **Lesson Reading Guide**, p. 19 BL OL ELL
CRM **Skills Practice**, p. 22 BL OL

47. *Writing in Math* Use the information about Al-Khwarizmi on page 486 to explain how ancient mathematicians used squares to solve algebraic equations. Include an explanation of Al-Khwarizmi's drawings for $x^2 + 8x = 35$ and a step-by-step algebraic solution with justification for each step of the equation. **See Ch. 9 Answer Appendix.**

 **STANDARDS PRACTICE** 4.0, 7AF1.2

48. What are the solutions to the quadratic equation $p^2 - 14p = 32$? **C**

　A 16

　B $-3, 14$

　C $-2, 16$

　D $-4, 7$

49. REVIEW If $a = -5$ and $b = 6$, then $3a - 2ab = $ **J**

　F -75

　G -55

　H 30

　J 45

Spiral Review

Solve each equation by graphing. (Lesson 9-2) **50–52. See margin.**

50. $x^2 + 7x + 12 = 0$

51. $x^2 - 16 = 0$

52. $x^2 - 2x + 6 = 0$

PARKS For Exercises 53 and 54, use the following information. (Lesson 9-1)
A city is building a dog park that is rectangular in shape and measures 280 feet around three of the four sides as shown in the diagram.

 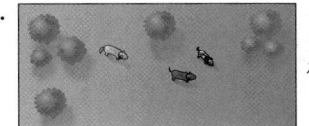

53. If the width of the park in feet is x, write an equation that models the area A of the park. **$A = (280 - 2x)x$ or $A = 280x - 2x^2$**

54. Analyze the graph of the related function by finding the coordinates of the vertex and describing what this point represents. **The vertex is at (70, 9800). This means that the width of the park with the greatest area is 70 feet and the area is 9800 square feet.**

Find the GCF for each set of monomials. (Lesson 8-1)

55. $14a^2b^3, 20a^3b^2c, 35ab^3c^2$ **ab^2**

56. $32m^2n^3, 8m^2n, 56m^3n^2$ **$8m^2n$**

Write an inequality for each graph. (Lesson 6-4)

57.
　　-6 -5 -4 -3 -2 -1　0　1　2　3　4　5　6
　　$-3 < x < 1$

58.
　　-6 -5 -4 -3 -2 -1　0　1　2　3　4　5　6
　　$x \le -2$ or $x > 1$

Use substitution to solve each system of equations. If the system does not have exactly one solution, state whether it has no solution or infinitely many solutions. (Lesson 5-2)

59. $y = 2x$　**(3, 6)**
　　$x + y = 9$

60. $x = y + 3$　**(4, 1)**
　　$2x - 3y = 5$

61. $x - 2y = 3$　**(7, 2)**
　　$3x + y = 23$

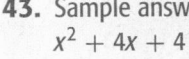 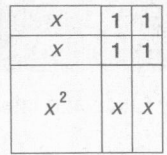 for the Next Lesson

PREREQUISITE SKILL Evaluate $\sqrt{b^2 - 4ac}$ for each set of values. Round to the nearest tenth if necessary. (Lesson 1-2)

62. $a = 1, b = -2, c = -15$ **8**

63. $a = 2, b = 7, c = 3$ **5**

64. $a = 1, b = 5, c = -2$ **5.7**

65. $a = -2, b = 7, c = 5$ **9.4**

Lesson 9-3 Solving Quadratic Equations by Completing the Square　**491**

4 Assess

Name the Math Ask students what mathematical procedures they would use to solve a quadratic equation by completing the squares.

Formative Assessment

Check for student understanding of concepts in Lesson 9-3.

CRM Quiz 2, p. 51

Additional Answers

50.
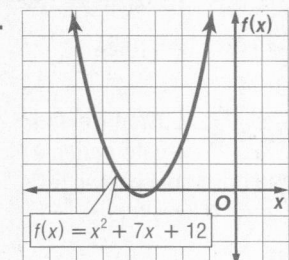
$f(x) = x^2 + 7x + 12$
$-4, -3$

51.
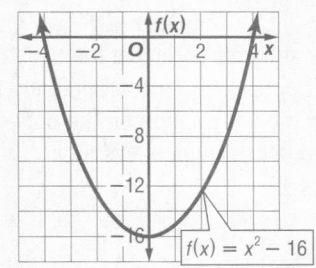
$f(x) = x^2 - 16$
$-4, 4$

52.
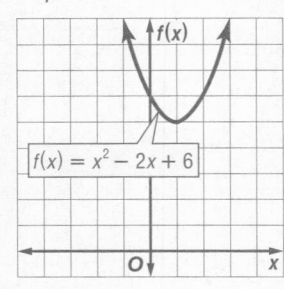
$f(x) = x^2 - 2x + 6$
$\varnothing$

43. Sample answer:
　$x^2 + 4x + 4$

	x	1	1
x		1	1
x		1	1
x^2		x	x

46. $n^2 + \frac{1}{3}n + \frac{1}{9}$; It is the only trinomial that is not a perfect square.

45. There are no real solutions since completing the square results in $(x + 2)^2 = -8$ and the square of a number cannot be negative.

Formative Assessment

Use the Mid-Chapter Quiz to assess students' progress in the first half of the chapter.

For problems answered incorrectly, have students review the lessons indicated in parentheses.

 Summative Assessment

CRM Mid-Chapter Test, p. 53

ExamView®
Assessment Suite

Customize and create multiple versions of your Mid-Chapter Tests and their answer keys.

FOLDABLES
Study Organizer

Foldables™ Follow-Up

Before students complete the Mid-Chapter Quiz, encourage them to review the information on the pages labeled 9-1 through 9-3 of their Foldables.

Additional Answers

1.

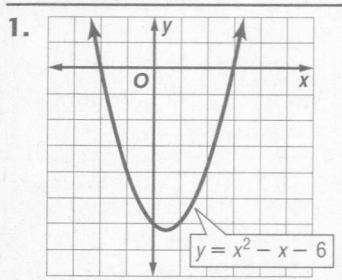

$$y = x^2 - x - 6$$

$x = 0.5$; $(0.5, -6.25)$; minimum

For Exercises 2–3, 5–7, see Ch. 9 Answer Appendix.

Write the equation of the axis of symmetry, and find the coordinates of the vertex of the graph of each function. Identify the vertex as a maximum or minimum. Then graph the function. (Lesson 9-1) **1–3. See margin.**

1. $y = x^2 - x - 6$

2. $y = 2x^2 + 3$

3. $y = -3x^2 - 6x + 5$

4. MULTIPLE CHOICE Which graph shows a function $y = x^2 + b$ when $b > 1$? (Lesson 9-1) **B**

A
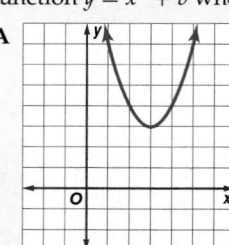

B
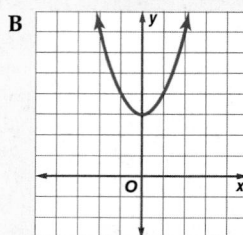

C
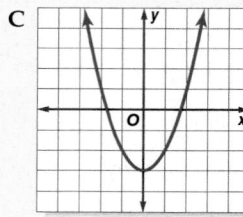

D
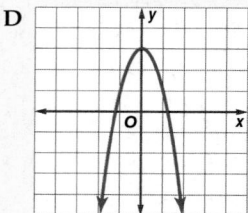

Solve each equation by graphing. If integral roots cannot be found, estimate the roots by stating the consecutive integers between which the roots lie. (Lesson 9-2) **5–7. See margin.**

5. $x^2 + 6x + 10 = 0$

6. $x^2 - 2x - 1 = 0$

7. $x^2 - 5x - 6 = 0$

8. SOFTBALL In a softball game, Lola hit the ball straight up with an initial upward velocity of 47 feet per second. The height h of the softball in feet above ground after t seconds can be modeled by the equation $h = -16t^2 + 47t + 3$. How long was the softball in the air before it hit the ground? (Lesson 9-2) **3 s**

Solve each equation by completing the square. Round to the nearest tenth if necessary. (Lesson 9-3)

9. $s^2 + 8s = -15$ **$-5, -3$**

10. $a^2 - 10a = -24$ **4, 6**

11. $y^2 - 14y + 49 = 5$ **4.8, 9.2**

12. $2b^2 - b - 7 = 14$ **$-3, 3.5$**

13. ROCKETS A model rocket is launched from the ground with an initial upward velocity of 475 feet per second. About how many seconds will it take to reach the ground? Use the formula $h = -16t^2 + 175t$, where h is the height of the rocket and t is the time in seconds. Round to the nearest tenth if necessary. (Lesson 9-3) **10.9 s**

14. GEOMETRY The length and width of the rectangle are increased by the same amount so that the new area is 154 square centimeters. Find the dimensions of the new rectangle. (Lesson 9-3) **11 cm by 14 cm**

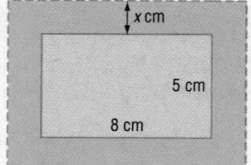

492 Chapter 9 Quadratic and Exponential Functions

Data-Driven Decision Making	Exercises	Lesson	Standard	Resources for Review
Diagnostic Teaching Based on the results of the Chapter 9 Mid-Chapter Quiz, use the following to review concepts that students continue to find challenging.	1–4	9–1	21.0	CRM Study Guide and Intervention pp. 6–7, 13–14, 20–21 Math Online • Extra Examples • Personal Tutor • Concepts in Motion
	5–8	9–2	21.0	
	9–14	9–3	14.0	

Solving Quadratic Equations by Using the Quadratic Formula

Main Ideas

- Solve quadratic equations by using the Quadratic Formula.
- Use the discriminant to determine the number of solutions for a quadratic equation.

 Standard 19.0 Students know the quadratic formula and are familiar with its proof by completing the square. (Key)

Standard 20.0 Students use the quadratic formula to find the roots of a second-degree polynomial and to solve quadratic equations. (Key)

Standard 22.0 Students use the quadratic formula or factoring techniques or both to determine whether the graph of a quadratic function will intersect the *x*-axis in zero, one, or two points.

New Vocabulary

Quadratic Formula
discriminant

Study Tip

Quadratic Formula
The Quadratic Formula is proved in Lesson 10–1.

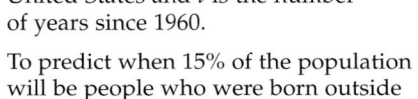 **GET READY for the Lesson**

In the past few decades, there has been a dramatic increase in the percent of people living in the United States who were born in other countries. This trend can be modeled by the quadratic function $P = 0.006t^2 - 0.080t + 5.281$, where P is the percent born outside the United States and t is the number of years since 1960.

Percent Born Outside the U.S.

$P = 0.006t^2 - 0.080t + 5.281$

Years Since 1960

To predict when 15% of the population will be people who were born outside of the U.S., you can solve the equation $15 = 0.006t^2 - 0.080t + 5.281$. This equation would be impossible or difficult to solve using factoring, graphing, or completing the square.

Quadratic Formula You can solve the standard form of the quadratic equation $ax^2 + bx + c = 0$ for x. The result is the **Quadratic Formula**.

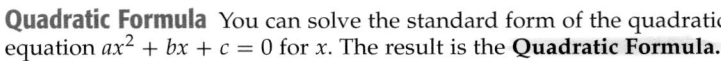

KEY CONCEPT   *The Quadratic Formula*

The solutions of a quadratic equation in the form $ax^2 + bx + c = 0$, where $a \neq 0$, are given by the Quadratic Formula.

$$x = \frac{-b \pm \sqrt{b^2 - 4ac}}{2a}$$

You can solve quadratic equations by factoring, graphing, completing the square, or using the Quadratic Formula.

EXAMPLE   Solve Quadratic Equations

 Solve each equation. Round to the nearest tenth if necessary.

a. $x^2 - 2x - 24 = 0$

    Method 1   Factoring

    $x^2 - 2x - 24 = 0$ Original equation

    $(x + 4)(x - 6) = 0$ Factor $x^2 - 2x - 24$.

    $x + 4 = 0$ or $x - 6 = 0$ Zero Product Property

       $x = -4$ $x = 6$ Solve for *x*.

(continued on the next page)

1 Focus

Standards Alignment

Before Lesson 9-4
Use the correct order of operations to evaluate algebraic expressions from Standard 7AF1.2

Lesson 9-4
Know the quadratic formula. Use the quadratic formula to find the roots of a second-degree polynomial and to solve quadratic equations from Standards 19.0, 20.0, and 22.0

After Lesson 9-4
Solve and graph quadratic equations and quadratic equations in the complex number system from Standard 2A8.0

2 Teach

Scaffolding Questions Have students read *Get Ready for the Lesson*. **Ask:**

- Since this population trend is represented by a quadratic equation, what does it assume about the percent of people who were born in other countries in the past? *It was higher in the past, then bottomed out and has since been rising.*

(continued on the next page)

Lesson 9-4 Resources

- Why would the equation be difficult to solve using factoring or completing the square? The fractional values of the coefficients would make using the methods very difficult, if not impossible.

Quadratic Formula

Example 1 shows how to use the Quadratic Formula to solve a quadratic equation with integral roots. **Example 2** shows how to use the Quadratic Formula to solve a real-world problem.

ADDITIONAL EXAMPLE

① Solve each equation. Round to the nearest tenth if necessary.
 a. $x^2 - 2x - 35 = 0$
 $\{-5, 7\}$
 b. $15x^2 - 8x = 4$
 $\{-0.3, 0.8\}$

Additional Examples are also in:
- Noteables™ Interactive Study Notebook with Foldables™
- Interactive Classroom PowerPoint® Presentations

 **Preventing Errors**

Some students may notice that the trinomial in Example 1 can be factored. Explain that an equation that could be factored was used to demonstrate that the Quadratic Formula produces the correct solutions. Tell students that if they see an easier way (such as factoring) to solve a quadratic equation, they should use the easier method.

Method 2 Quadratic Formula

For this equation, $a = 1$, $b = -2$, and $c = -24$.

$x = \dfrac{-b \pm \sqrt{b^2 - 4ac}}{2a}$ Quadratic Formula

$= \dfrac{-(-2) \pm \sqrt{(-2)^2 - 4(1)(-24)}}{2(1)}$ $a = 1, b = -2$, and $c = -24$

$= \dfrac{2 \pm \sqrt{4 + 96}}{2}$ Multiply.

$= \dfrac{2 \pm \sqrt{100}}{2}$ or $\dfrac{2 \pm 10}{2}$ Add and simplify.

$x = \dfrac{2 - 10}{2}$ or $x = \dfrac{2 + 10}{2}$ Separate the solutions.

$= -4$ $= 6$ Simplify.

The solution set is $\{-4, 6\}$.

b. $24x^2 - 14x = 6$

Step 1 Rewrite the equation in standard form.
$24x^2 - 14x = 6$ Original equation
$24x^2 - 14x - 6 = 0$ Subtract 6 from each side.

Step 2 Apply the Quadratic Formula.

$x = \dfrac{-b \pm \sqrt{b^2 - 4ac}}{2a}$ Quadratic Formula

$= \dfrac{-(-14) \pm \sqrt{(-14)^2 - 4(24)(-6)}}{2(24)}$ $a = 24, b = -14$, and $c = -6$

$= \dfrac{14 \pm \sqrt{196 + 576}}{48}$ Multiply.

$= \dfrac{14 \pm \sqrt{772}}{48}$ Add.

$x = \dfrac{14 - \sqrt{772}}{48}$ or $x = \dfrac{14 + \sqrt{772}}{48}$ Separate the solutions.

≈ -0.3 ≈ 0.9 Simplify.

You can use a graphing calculator to check the solutions. Use the CALC menu to determine the zeros of the related quadratic function.

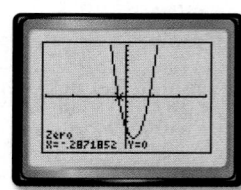 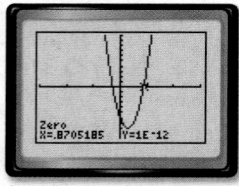

$[-3, 3]$ scl: 1 by $[-10, 10]$ scl: 1 $[-3, 3]$ scl: 1 by $[-10, 10]$ scl: 1

To the nearest tenth, the solution set is $\{-0.3, 0.9\}$.

✓ **CHECK Your Progress**

1A. $x^2 + 3x - 18 = 0$ **−6, 3**   **1B.** $4x^2 + 2x = 17$ **−2.3, 1.8**

Online Personal Tutor at ca.algebra1.com

Study Tip

The Quadratic Formula

You may want to simplify this equation by dividing each side by 2 before applying the Quadratic Formula. However, the Quadratic Formula can help you find the solution of *any* quadratic equation.

Focus on Mathematical Content

The Quadratic Formula Even though the Quadratic Formula may not be the easiest way to solve some quadratic equations, it always works. The derivation of the formula is the solution of the equation $ax^2 + bx + c = 0$ by completing the square. The deviation is shown in Lesson 10-1 when students learn about simplifying radical expressions.

The table summarizes the five methods for solving quadratic equations.

Method	Can Be Used	Comments	Lesson(s)
factoring	sometimes	Use if constant term is 0 or factors are easily determined.	8-2 to 8-6
using a table	sometimes	Not always exact; use only when an approximate solution is sufficient.	9-2
graphing	always	Not always exact; use only when an approximate solution is sufficient.	9-2
completing the square	always	Useful for equations of the form $x^2 + bx + c = 0$, where b is an even number.	9-3
Quadratic Formula	always	Other methods may be easier to use in some cases, but this method always gives accurate solutions.	9-4

CONCEPT SUMMARY — Solving Quadratic Equations

Real-World Link

Astronauts have found walking on the Moon to be very different from walking on Earth because the gravitational pull of the Moon is only 1.6 meters per second squared. The gravitational pull on Earth is 9.8 meters per second squared.

Source: *World Book Encyclopedia*

Real-World EXAMPLE Use the Quadratic Formula to Solve a Problem

2 **SPACE TRAVEL** The height H of an object t seconds after it is propelled upward with an initial velocity v is represented by $H = -\frac{1}{2}gt^2 + vt + h$, where g is the gravitational pull and h is the initial height. Suppose an astronaut on the Moon throws a baseball upward with an initial velocity of 10 meters per second, letting go of the ball 2 meters above the ground. Use the information at the left to find how much longer the ball will stay in the air than a similarly thrown baseball on Earth.

In order to find when the ball hits the ground, you must find when $H = 0$. Write two equations to represent the situation on the Moon and on Earth.

Baseball Thrown on the Moon

$$H = -\frac{1}{2}gt^2 + vt + h$$
$$0 = -\frac{1}{2}(1.6)t^2 + 10t + 2$$
$$0 = -0.8t^2 + 10t + 2$$

Baseball Thrown on Earth

$$H = -\frac{1}{2}gt^2 + vt + h$$
$$0 = -\frac{1}{2}(9.8)t^2 + 10t + 2$$
$$0 = -4.9t^2 + 10t + 2$$

To find accurate solutions, use the Quadratic Formula.

$$t = \frac{-b \pm \sqrt{b^2 - 4ac}}{2a}$$
$$= \frac{-10 \pm \sqrt{10^2 - 4(-0.8)(2)}}{2(-0.8)}$$
$$= \frac{-10 \pm \sqrt{106.4}}{-1.6}$$
$$t \approx 12.7 \quad \text{or} \quad t \approx -0.2$$

$$t = \frac{-b \pm \sqrt{b^2 - 4ac}}{2a}$$
$$= \frac{-10 \pm \sqrt{10^2 - 4(-4.9)(2)}}{2(-4.9)}$$
$$= \frac{-10 \pm \sqrt{139.2}}{-9.8}$$
$$t \approx 2.2 \quad \text{or} \quad t \approx -0.2$$

Since a negative time is not reasonable, use the positive solutions. The ball will stay in the air about $12.7 - 2.2$ or 10.5 seconds longer on the Moon.

CHECK Your Progress

2. GEOMETRY The perimeter of a rectangle is 60 inches. Find the dimensions of the rectangle if its area is 221 square inches.

13 in. by 17 in.

Lesson 9-4 Solving Quadratic Equations by Using the Quadratic Formula **495**

Intervention

Using the Quadratic Formula
Tell students that it is best to simplify the Quadratic Formula one step at a time. For example, students should first simplify under the radical sign, then find the square root, then simplify the numerator and denominator, and finally perform the division. Skipping steps may introduce errors.

Solving Quadratic Equations
While the chart on this page offers suggestions for when to use each quadratic method, do not hold students to using all methods. Some students do not yet have the mathematical maturity to analyze each equation and determine the best method to use to save time.

ADDITIONAL EXAMPLE

2 **SPACE TRAVEL** Two possible future destinations for astronauts are the planet Mars and Europa, a moon of the planet Jupiter. The gravitational pull on Mars is about 3.7 meters per second squared; on Europa, it is 1.3 meters per second squared. Using the information and equation from Example 3, find how much longer baseballs thrown on Mars and Europa will stay above the ground than baseballs thrown on Earth. The ball thrown on Mars will stay aloft about 3.4 seconds longer than the ball thrown on Earth. The ball thrown on Europa will stay aloft 13.4 seconds longer than the ball thrown on Earth.

Lesson 9-4 Solving Quadratic Equations by Using the Quadratic Formula **495**

The Discriminant

Example 3 shows how to use the discriminant to determine the number of real roots for a quadratic equation.

Tips for New Teachers

Preventing Errors

Remind students to be careful to include any negative signs when finding the discriminant. One missed negative sign can turn the discriminant from positive to negative and yield an incorrect result.

The Discriminant In the Quadratic Formula, the expression under the radical sign, $b^2 - 4ac$, is called the **discriminant**. The value of the discriminant can be used to determine the number of real roots for a quadratic equation.

KEY CONCEPT
Using the Discriminant

Discriminant	negative	zero	positive
Example	$2x^2 + x + 3 = 0$ $$x = \frac{-1 \pm \sqrt{1^2 - 4(2)(3)}}{2(2)}$$ $$= \frac{-1 \pm \sqrt{-23}}{4}$$ There are no real roots since no real number can be the square root of a negative number.	$x^2 + 6x + 9 = 0$ $$x = \frac{-6 \pm \sqrt{6^2 - 4(1)(9)}}{2(1)}$$ $$= \frac{-6 \pm \sqrt{0}}{2}$$ $$= \frac{-6}{2} \text{ or } -3$$ There is a double root, -3.	$x^2 - 5x + 2 = 0$ $$x = \frac{-(-5) \pm \sqrt{(-5)^2 - 4(1)(2)}}{2(1)}$$ $$= \frac{5 \pm \sqrt{17}}{2}$$ There are two roots, $\frac{5 + \sqrt{17}}{2}$ and $\frac{5 - \sqrt{17}}{2}$.
Graph of Related Function	The graph does not cross the *x*-axis.	The graph touches the *x*-axis in one place.	The graph crosses the *x*-axis twice.
Number of Real Roots	0	1	2

EXAMPLE   Use the Discriminant

3 State the value of the discriminant for each equation. Then determine the number of real roots of the equation.

a. $2x^2 + 10x + 11 = 0$

$b^2 - 4ac = 10^2 - 4(2)(11)$ $a = 2, b = 10,$ and $c = 11$

$= 12$ Simplify.

Since the discriminant is positive, the equation has two real roots.

b. $3m^2 + 4m = -2$

Step 1   Rewrite the equation in standard form.

$3m^2 + 4m = -2$ Original equation

$3m^2 + 4m + 2 = -2 + 2$ Add 2 to each side.

$3m^2 + 4m + 2 = 0$ Simplify.

Step 2   Find the discriminant.

$b^2 - 4ac = 4^2 - 4(3)(2)$ $a = 3, b = 4,$ and $c = 2$

$= -8$ Simplify.

Since the discriminant is negative, the equation has no real roots.

3A. $4n^2 - 20n + 25 = 0$ **3B.** $5x^2 - 3x + 8 = 0$ **3C.** $2x^2 + 11x + 15 = 0$

−151; no real roots   1; two real roots

★ indicates multi-step problem

CHECK Your Understanding

Example 1
(pp. 493–494)

Solve each equation by using the Quadratic Formula. Round to the nearest tenth if necessary.

1. $x^2 + 7x + 6 = 0$ −6, −1
2. $t^2 + 11t = 12$ −12, 1
3. $r^2 + 10r + 12 = 0$ −8.6, −1.4
4. $3v^2 + 5v + 11 = 0$ ∅

Example 2 ★
(p. 495)

5. MANUFACTURING A pan is to be formed by cutting 2-centimeter-by-2-centimeter squares from each corner of a square piece of sheet metal and then folding the sides. If the volume of the pan is to be 441 square centimeters, what should the dimensions of the original piece of sheet metal be?
about 18.8 cm by 18.8 cm

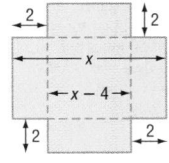

Example 3
(p. 496)

State the value of the discriminant for each equation. Then determine the number of real roots of the equation.

6. $m^2 + 5m - 6 = 0$
49; 2 real roots
7. $s^2 + 8s + 16 = 0$
0; 1 real root
8. $2z^2 + z = -50$
−399; no real roots

Exercises

HOMEWORK HELP	
For Exercises	**See Examples**
9–20	1, 2
21, 22	3
23–28	4

Solve each equation by using the Quadratic Formula. Round to the nearest tenth if necessary.

9. $v^2 + 12v + 20 = 0$
10. $3t^2 - 7t - 20 = 0$
11. $5y^2 - y - 4 = 0$
12. $x^2 - 25 = 0$ −5, 5
13. $r^2 + 25 = 0$ ∅
14. $2x^2 + 98 = 28x$ 7
15. $4s^2 + 100 = 40s$ 5
16. $2r^2 + r - 14 = 0$
17. $2n^2 - 7n - 3 = 0$
18. $5v^2 - 7v = 1$
−0.1, 1.5
19. $11z^2 - z = 3$
−0.5, 0.6
20. $2w^2 = -(7w + 3)$
−3, −0.5

Exercise Levels
A: 9–28
B: 29–39
C: 40–44

9. −10, −2
10. −1.7, 4
11. −0.8, 1
16. −2.9, 2.4
17. −0.4, 3.9
23. 25; 2 real roots
24. 5; 2 real roots
25. 0; 1 real root

21. GEOMETRY What are the dimensions of rectangle *ABCD*? **5 cm by 16 cm**

Rectangle *ABCD*	
perimeter	42 cm
area	80 cm²

22. PHYSICAL SCIENCE A projectile is shot vertically up in the air from ground level. Its distance s, in feet, after t seconds is given by $s = 96t - 16t^2$. Find the values of t when s is 96 feet. **about 1.3 s and 4.7 s**

State the value of the discriminant for each equation. Then determine the number of real roots of the equation.

23. $x^2 + 3x - 4 = 0$
24. $y^2 + 3y + 1 = 0$
25. $4p^2 + 10p = -6.25$
26. $1.5m^2 + m = -3.5$
−20; no real roots
27. $2r^2 = \frac{1}{2}r - \frac{2}{3}$
$-\frac{61}{12}$, no real roots
28. $\frac{4}{3}n^2 + 4n = -3$
0; 1 real root

Solve each equation by using the Quadratic Formula. Round to the nearest tenth if necessary.

29. $1.34d^2 - 1.1d = -1.02$ ∅
30. $-2x^2 + 0.7x = -0.3$ −0.3, 0.6
31. $2y^2 - \frac{5}{4}y = \frac{1}{2}$ −0.3, 0.9
32. $w^2 + \frac{2}{25} = \frac{3}{5}w$ 0.2, 0.4

Lesson 9-4 Solving Quadratic Equations by Using the Quadratic Formula   **497**

3 Practice

Formative Assessment

Use Exercises 1–8 to check for understanding.

Use the chart at the bottom of this page to customize assignments for your students.

Odd/Even Assignments

Exercises 9–28 are structured so that students practice the same concepts whether they are assigned odd or even problems.

⚠ Exercise Alert!

Use a Calculator Exercises 9–20, 29–32 and 39 ask students either to round their answers or to give approximations. You may wish to have students use a calculator for these exercises.

DIFFERENTIATED HOMEWORK OPTIONS

Level	Assignment	Two-Day Option	
BL Basic	9–28, 40–65	9–27 odd, 45, 46	10–28 even, 40–44, 47–65
OL Core	9–35 odd, 37–65	9–28, 45, 46	29–44, 47–65
AL Advanced /Pre-AP	29–62 (optional: 63–65)		

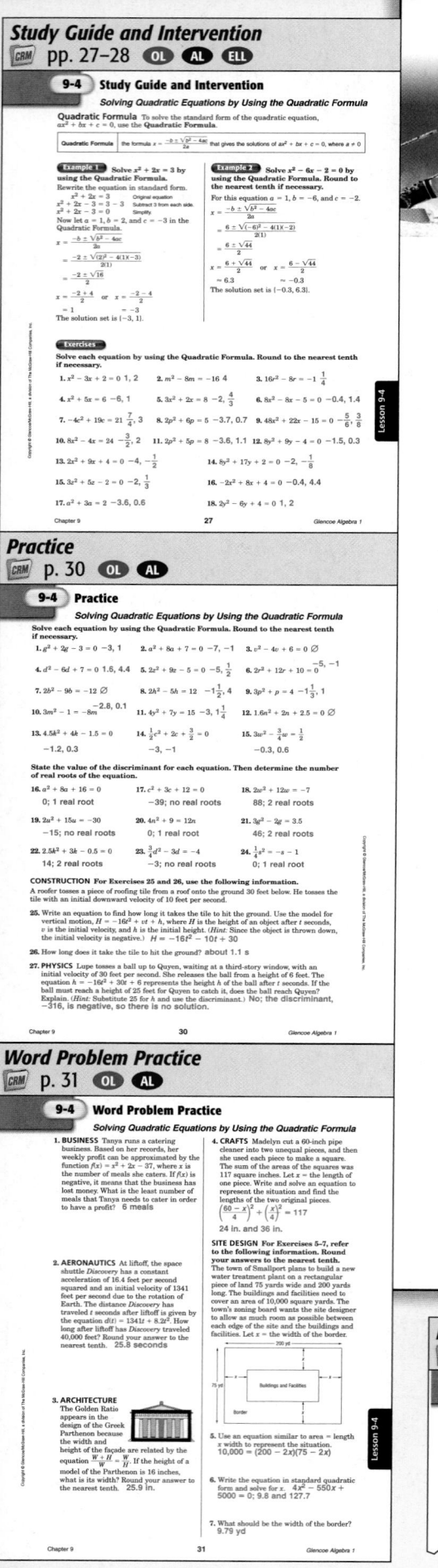

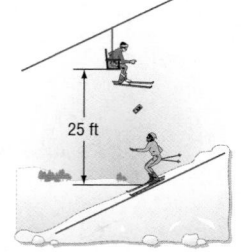

Real-World Link

Downhill skiing is the most popular type of snow skiing. Skilled skiers can obtain speeds of about 60 miles per hour as they race down mountain slopes.

Source: *World Book Encyclopedia*

Without graphing, determine the *x*-intercepts of the graph of each function.

33. $f(x) = 4x^2 - 9x + 4$
about 0.6 and 1.6

34. $f(x) = 13x^2 - 16x - 4$
about −0.2 and 1.4

Without graphing, determine the number of *x*-intercepts of the graph of each function.

35. $f(x) = 7x^2 - 3x - 1$ 2

36. $f(x) = x^2 + 4x + 7$ 0

RECREATION For Exercises 37 and 38, use the following information.

As Darius is skiing down a ski slope, Jorge is on the chairlift on the same slope. The chair lift has stopped. Darius stops directly below Jorge and attempts to toss a disposable camera up to him. If the camera is thrown with an initial velocity of 35 feet per second, the equation for the height of the camera is $h = -16t^2 + 35t + 5$, where *h* represents the height in feet and *t* represents the time in seconds.

★ **37.** If the chairlift is 25 feet above the ground, will Jorge have 0, 1, or 2 chances to catch the camera? **0**

38. If Jorge is unable to catch the camera, when will it hit the ground? **about 2.3 s**

EXTRA PRACTICE
See pages 736, 752.

Math Online
Self-Check Quiz at
ca.algebra1.com

39. AMUSEMENT PARKS The Demon Drop ride at Cedar Point takes riders to the top of a tower and drops them 60 feet at speeds reaching 80 feet per second. A function that models this ride is $h = -16t^2 + 64t - 60$, where *h* is the height in feet and *t* is the time in seconds. About how many seconds does it take for riders to drop from 60 feet to 0 feet? **about 2.5 s**

H.O.T. Problems

40. Let $a = 3$, $b = -2$, and $c = -4$. Substituting into the Quadratic Formula yields $\dfrac{2 \pm \sqrt{52}}{6}$. The roots of the function are $\dfrac{2 + \sqrt{52}}{6}$ and $\dfrac{2 - \sqrt{52}}{6}$.

41. Juanita; you must first write the equation in the form $ax^2 + bx + c = 0$ to determine the values of *a*, *b*, and *c*. Therefore, the value of *c* is −2, not 2.

40. REASONING Use the Quadratic Formula to show that $f(x) = 3x^2 - 2x - 4$ has two real roots.

41. FIND THE ERROR Lakeisha and Juanita are determining the number of solutions of $5y^2 - 3y = 2$. Who is correct? Explain your reasoning.

Lakeisha
$5y^2 - 3y = 2$
$b^2 - 4ac = (-3)^2 - 4(5)(2)$
$= -31$
Since the discriminant is negative, there are no real solutions.

Juanita
$5y^2 - 3y = 2$
$5y^2 - 3y - 2 = 0$
$b^2 - 4ac = (-3)^2 - 4(5)(-2)$
$= 49$
Since the discriminant is positive, there are two real roots.

42. OPEN ENDED Write a quadratic equation with no real solutions. Explain how you know there are no solutions. **Sample answer:** $x^2 - x + 5 = 0$; the discriminant is −19, so the equation has no real solutions.

43. REASONING Use factoring techniques to determine the number of real roots of the function $f(x) = x^2 - 8x + 16$. Compare this method to using the discriminant. **See Ch. 9 Answer Appendix.**

44. *Writing in Math* Describe three different ways to solve $x^2 - 2x - 15 = 0$. Which method do you prefer and why? **See Ch. 9 Answer Appendix.**

498 Chapter 9 Quadratic and Exponential Functions

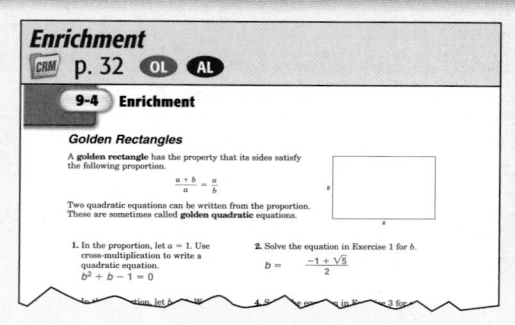
BL = Below Grade Level
OL = On Grade Level
AL = Above Grade Level
ELL = English Language Learner

Additional pages not shown:

45. Which statement *best* describes why there is no real solution to the quadratic equation $y = x^2 - 6x + 13$? **C**

  A The value of $(-6)^2 - 4 \cdot 1 \cdot 13$ is a perfect square.

  B The value of $(-6)^2 - 4 \cdot 1 \cdot 13$ is equal to zero.

  C The value of $(-6)^2 - 4 \cdot 1 \cdot 13$ is negative.

  D The value of $(-6)^2 - 4 \cdot 1 \cdot 13$ is positive.

46. REVIEW In the system of equations $6x - 3y = 12$ and $2x + 5y = 9$, which expression can be correctly substituted for y in the equation $2x + 5y = 9$? **H**

  F $12 + 2x$

  G $12 - 2x$

  H $-4 + 2x$

  J $4 - 2x$

⚠ **Exercise Alert!**
Find the Error Challenge students not only to find which student was incorrect, but also to explain what incorrect procedure led to the mistake.

4 Assess

Ticket Out the Door Make several copies each of five quadratic equations. Give one equation to each student. As students leave the room, ask them to tell you the discriminants of the equations and the number of real roots.

Additional Answers

50.

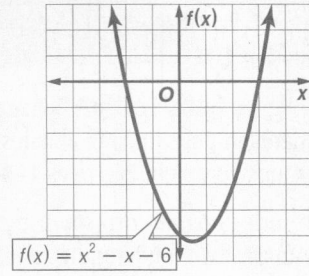

$-2, 3$

51.

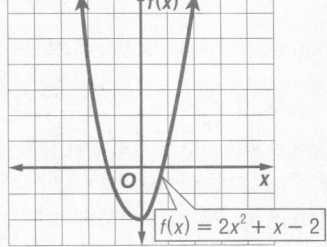

$-2 < x < -1, 0 < x < 1$

52.

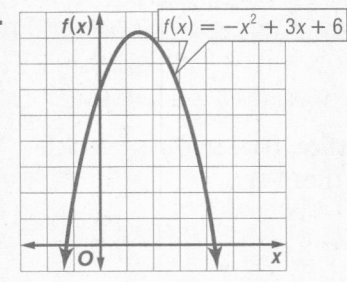

$-2 < x < -1, 4 < x < 5$

Spiral Review

Solve each equation by completing the square. Round to the nearest tenth if necessary. (Lesson 9-3)

47. $x^2 - 8x = -7$ **1, 7**

48. $a^2 + 2a + 5 = 20$ **−5, 3**

49. $n^2 - 12n = 5$
  −0.4, 12.4

Solve each equation by graphing. If integral roots cannot be found, estimate the roots by stating the consecutive integers between which the roots lie. (Lesson 9-2)

50. $x^2 - x = 6$
50–52. See margin.

51. $2x^2 + x = 2$

52. $-x^2 + 3x + 6 = 0$

53. GEOMETRY The triangle has an area of 96 square centimeters. Find the base b of the triangle. (Lesson 8-3) **12 cm**

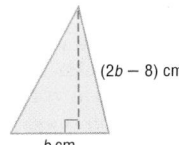

$(2b - 8)$ cm

b cm

Factor each polynomial. (Lesson 8-2)

54. $24r + 6s$ **$6(4r + s)$**

55. $15xy^3 + y^4$ **$y^3(15x + y)$**

56. $2ax + 6xc + ba + 3bc$
  $(2x + b)(a + 3c)$

Solve each inequality. Then check your solution. (Lesson 6-3)

57. $2m + 7 > 17$ $\{m \mid m > 5\}$

58. $-2 - 3x \geq 2$ $\left\{x \mid x \leq -1\frac{1}{3}\right\}$

59. $-20 \geq 8 + 7k$
  $\{k \mid k \leq -4\}$

Write an equation of the line that passes through each point with the given slope. (Lesson 4-4)

60. $(2, 13)$, $m = 4$ $y = 4x + 5$

61. $(-2, -7)$, $m = 0$ $y = -7$

62. $(-4, 6)$, $m = \frac{3}{2}$
  $y = \frac{3}{2}x + 12$

GET READY for the Next Lesson

PREREQUISITE SKILL Evaluate $c(a^x)$ for each of the given values. (Lesson 1-1)

63. $a = 2, c = 1, x = 4$ **16**

64. $a = 7, c = 3, x = 2$ **147**

65. $a = 5, c = 2, x = 3$ **250**

Pre-AP Activity Use after the Exercises

Since students are much more likely to retain a concept that they have researched and explained, ask them to research the derivation of the Quadratic Formula and to write short paragraphs showing and explaining the derivation.

Applying Quadratic Equations

1 Focus

Materials for Each Group
• calculator

Teaching Tip
Remind students to look at the units in the question in order to determine whether to use 9.8 meters per second squared or 32 feet per second squared for the acceleration due to gravity.

2 Teach

Working in Cooperative Groups
Put students in pairs, mixing abilities. Have groups complete Exercises 1–5.

• Make sure students correctly use parentheses when typing the simplified quadratic formula solution into the calculator.

Ask:
• When does the velocity equal zero? When an object is dropped and not thrown.
• When is the velocity positive? When the object is projected upward.
• When is the velocity negative? When the object is projected downward.
• How does changing h affect the trajectory of an object? A change in h represents a change in height, a shift upward if h is positive and a shift downward if h is negative.

Practice Have students complete Exercises 1–4.

 Standard 23.0 Students apply quadratic equations to physical problems, such as the motion of an object under the force of gravity. (Key)

Many of the real-world problems you solved in Chapters 8 and 9 were physical problems involving the path of an object that is influenced by gravity. These paths, called **trajectories**, can be modeled by a quadratic function. The formula relating the height of the object $H(t)$ and time t is shown below.

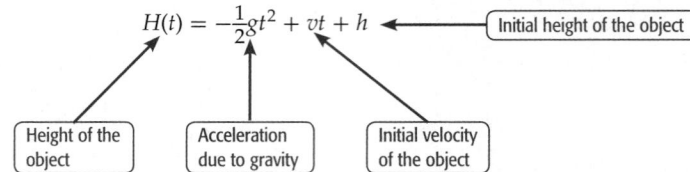

$$H(t) = -\frac{1}{2}gt^2 + vt + h$$

Initial height of the object

Height of the object

Acceleration due to gravity

Initial velocity of the object

The acceleration due to gravity is 9.8 meters per second, per second; we express this by saying 9.8 meters per second squared. Similarly, it is 32 feet per second squared.

EXAMPLE 1

Juan kicks a football at a velocity of 25 meters per second. If the ball makes contact with his foot 0.5 meter off the ground, how long will the ball stay in the air?

We want to find the time t when $H(t)$ is 0. First substitute the known values into the motion formula. Since the known measures are written in terms of meters and meters per second, use 9.8 meters per second squared for the acceleration due to gravity.

$H(t) = -\frac{1}{2}gt^2 + vt + h$ Motion Formula

$0 = -\frac{1}{2}(9.8)t^2 + 25t + 0.5$ $H(t) = 0, g = 9.8, v = 25, h = 0.5$

$0 = -4.9t^2 + 25t + 0.5$ Simplify.

Use the Quadratic Formula to solve for t.

$t = \dfrac{-b \pm \sqrt{b^2 - 4ac}}{2a}$ Quadratic Formula

$= \dfrac{-25 \pm \sqrt{25^2 - 4(-4.9)(0.5)}}{2(-4.9)}$ $a = -4.9, b = 25, c = 0.5$

$= \dfrac{-25 \pm \sqrt{634.8}}{-9.8}$ Simplify.

$t \approx -0.02$ or $t \approx 5.12$ Use a calculator.

Since time cannot be a negative value, discard the negative solution. The football will be in the air about 5 seconds.

500 Chapter 9 Quadratic and Exponential Functions

If an object were projected downward, the initial velocity of the object is negative.

EXAMPLE 2

Katharine is on a bridge 12 feet above a pond. She throws a handful of fish food straight down with a velocity of 8 feet per second. In how many seconds will it reach the surface of the water?

Since the units given are in feet, use $g = 32$ ft/s². Katharine throws the food down, so the initial velocity is negative. When the food hits the water, $H(t)$ will be 0 feet.

$H(t) = -\frac{1}{2}gt^2 + vt + h$ Motion Formula

$0 = -\frac{1}{2}(32)t^2 - 8t + 12$ $H(t) = 0, g = 32, v = -8, h = 12$

$0 = -16t^2 - 8t + 12$ Simplify.

$0 = -4t^2 - 2t + 3$ Divide each side by 4.

Use the Quadratic Formula to solve for t.

$t = \dfrac{-b \pm \sqrt{b^2 - 4ac}}{2a}$ Quadratic Formula

$= \dfrac{2 \pm \sqrt{(-2)^2 - 4(-4)(3)}}{2(-4)}$ $a = -4, b = -2, c = 3$

$= \dfrac{2 \pm \sqrt{52}}{-8}$ Simplify.

$t \approx -1.15$ or $t \approx 0.65$ Use a calculator.

Discard the negative solution. The fish food will hit the water in 0.65 second.

EXERCISES

1. Darren swings at a golf ball on the ground with a velocity of 10 feet per second. How long was the ball in the air? **about 0.625 s**

2. Amalia hits a volleyball at a velocity of 15 meters per second. If the ball was hit from a height of 1.8 meters, determine the time it takes for the ball to land on the floor. Assume that the ball is not hit by another player. **about 3.2 s**

3. Michael is repairing the roof on a shed. He accidentally dropped a box of nails from a height of 14 feet. How long did it take for the box to land on the ground? Since the box was dropped and not thrown, $v = 0$. **about 0.94 s**

4. Carmen threw a penny into a fountain. She threw it from a height of 1.2 meters and at a velocity of 6 meters per second. How long did it take for the penny to hit the surface of the water? **about 0.17 s**

Extend 9–4 Algebra Lab: Applying Quadratic Equations   **501**

 Assess

☑ **Formative Assessment**

Use Exercise 4 to assess whether students can apply the quadratic equation to physical problems where the motion of an object is under the force of gravity.

From Concrete to Abstract What other real-world problems can be modeled by parabolas? Sample answer: designing arched doorways, landscaping patterns.

Extending the Concept
Ask: What factors other than gravity may affect the trajectory of an object? Sample answer: wind, pressure.

9-5 Exponential Functions

1 Focus

 Standards Alignment

Before Lesson 9-5
Graph functions of the form $y = nx^2$ and $y = nx^3$ and use in solving problems from Standard 7AF3.1

Lesson 9-5
Use the laws of fractional exponents in problems involving exponential growth and decay from Standard 2A12.0

After Lesson 9-5
Use the definition of logarithms to translate between logarithms in any base from Standard 2A13.0

2 Teach

Scaffolding Questions Have students read *Get Ready for the Lesson.* **Ask:**

• What happens to the number of pliers in each level? It doubles.
• How many pliers would there be in a ninth level? In a tenth level? 512 in a ninth level; 1024 in a tenth
• Suppose Mr. Warther carved pliers for powers of 3. By how much would the number of pliers increase at each level? by three times
• How many pliers would be on the eighth level if each level were a power of three? 6561 pliers

Lesson 9-5 Resources

Chapter 9 Resource Masters
Lesson Reading Guide, p. 33 BL OL ELL
Study Guide and Intervention, pp. 34–35 BL OL ELL
Skills Practice, p. 36 BL OL
Practice, p. 37 OL AL
Word Problem Practice, p. 38 OL AL
Enrichment, p. 39 OL AL
Spreadsheet, p. 40
Quiz 3, p. 52

Main Ideas

• Graph exponential functions.
• Identify data that displays exponential behavior.

 Preparation for Algebra II Standard 12.0
Students know the laws of fractional exponents, understand exponential functions, and use these functions in problems involving exponential growth and decay. (Key)

New Vocabulary

exponential function

Transparencies
5-Minute Check Transparency 9-5
Additional Print Resources
Noteables™ Interactive Study Notebook with Foldables™
Teaching Algebra with Manipulatives

▶ **GET READY for the Lesson**

Earnest "Mooney" Warther was a whittler and a carver. For one of his most unusual carvings, Mooney carved a large pair of pliers in a tree.

From this original carving, he carved another pair of pliers in each handle of the original. Then he carved another pair of pliers in each of those handles. He continued this pattern to create the original pliers and 8 more layers of pliers. Even more amazing is the fact that all of the pliers work.

Graph Exponential Functions The number of pliers on each level is given in the table below.

Level	Number of Pliers	Power of 2
Original	1	2^0
First	$1(2) = 2$	2^1
Second	$2(2) = 4$	2^2
Third	$2(2)(2) = 8$	2^3
Fourth	$2(2)(2)(2) = 16$	2^4
Fifth	$2(2)(2)(2)(2) = 32$	2^5
Sixth	$2(2)(2)(2)(2)(2) = 64$	2^6
Seventh	$2(2)(2)(2)(2)(2)(2) = 128$	2^7
Eighth	$2(2)(2)(2)(2)(2)(2)(2) = 256$	2^8

Study the last column above. Notice that the exponent matches the level. So we can write an equation to describe y, the number of pliers for any given level x as $y = 2^x$. This function is neither linear nor quadratic. It is in the class of functions called **exponential functions** in which the variable is the exponent.

KEY CONCEPT *Exponential Function*

An exponential function is a function that can be described by an equation of the form $y = a^x$, where $a > 0$ and $a \neq 1$.

As with other functions, you can use ordered pairs to graph an exponential function.

502 Chapter 9 Quadratic and Exponential Functions

Technology
ca.algebra1.com
Interactive Classroom CD-ROM
AssignmentWorks CD-ROM
Graphing Calculator Easy Files

Graph an Exponential Function with $a > 1$

1 **a.** Graph $y = 4^x$. State the y-intercept.

x	4^x	y
−2	4^{-2}	$\frac{1}{16}$
−1	4^{-1}	$\frac{1}{4}$
0	4^0	1
1	4^1	4
2	4^2	16
3	4^3	64

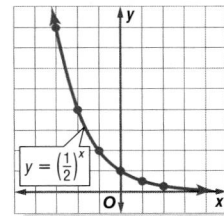

Graph the ordered pairs and connect the points with a smooth curve. The y-intercept is 1.

b. Use the graph to determine the approximate value of $4^{1.8}$.

The graph represents all real values of x and their corresponding values of y for $y = 4^x$. So, the value of y is about 12 when $x = 1.8$. Use a calculator to confirm this value. $4^{1.8} \approx 12.12573253$

✓CHECK Your Progress

1A. Graph $y = 7^x$. State the y-intercept. **1; See margin for graph.**
1B. Use the graph to determine the approximate value of $y = 7^{0.1}$ to the nearest tenth. Use a calculator to confirm the value. **1.2**

The graphs of functions of the form $y = a^x$, where $a > 1$, all have the same shape as the graph in Example 1, rising faster and faster as you move from left to right.

Graph Exponential Functions with $0 < a < 1$

2 **a.** Graph $y = \left(\frac{1}{2}\right)^x$. State the y-intercept.

x	$\left(\frac{1}{2}\right)^x$	y
−3	$\left(\frac{1}{2}\right)^{-3}$	8
−2	$\left(\frac{1}{2}\right)^{-2}$	4
−1	$\left(\frac{1}{2}\right)^{-1}$	2
0	$\left(\frac{1}{2}\right)^0$	1
1	$\left(\frac{1}{2}\right)^1$	$\frac{1}{2}$
2	$\left(\frac{1}{2}\right)^2$	$\frac{1}{4}$

The y-intercept is 1. *Notice that the y-values decrease less rapidly as x increases.*

b. Use the graph to determine the approximate value of $\left(\frac{1}{2}\right)^{-2.5}$.

The value of y is about $5\frac{1}{2}$ when $x = -2.5$. Use a calculator to confirm this value. $\left(\frac{1}{2}\right)^{-2.5} \approx 5.656854249$

Study Tip

Exponential Graphs

Notice that the y-values change little for small values of x, but they increase quickly as the values of x become greater.

Graph Exponential Functions

Example 1 shows how to graph an exponential function when a is greater than 1. **Example 2** shows how to graph an exponential function when a is greater than 0 and less than 1. **Example 3** shows how to use exponential functions to solve a real-world problem.

✓ Formative Assessment

Use the Check Your Progress exercises after each example to determine students' understanding of concepts.

ADDITIONAL EXAMPLES

1 **a.** Graph $y = 3^x$. State the y-intercept. **1**

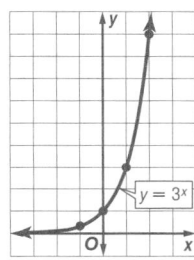

b. Use the graph to determine the approximate value of $3^{1.5}$. **about 5**

2 **a.** Graph $y = \left(\frac{1}{4}\right)^x$. State the y-intercept. **1**

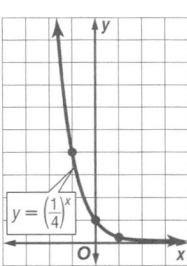

b. Use the graph to determine the approximate value of $\left(\frac{1}{4}\right)^{-1.5}$. **8**

Additional Examples are also in:
• Noteables™ Interactive Study Notebook with Foldables™
• Interactive Classroom PowerPoint® Presentations

Additional Answer

1A.

y-axis graph with $y = 7^x$ labeled.

Student Misconceptions

Make sure students understand that the graphs of exponential functions never actually touch the x-axis. It is acceptable for hand-drawn graphs to show the graph just above and about parallel to the x-axis as long as students understand that the graph gets infinitely closer to the axis without touching it.

2A. Graph $y = \left(\frac{1}{3}\right)^x + 2$. State the y-intercept. **3; See margin for graph.**

2B. Use the graph to determine the approximate value of $y = \left(\frac{1}{3}\right)^{-1.5} + 2$ to the nearest tenth. Use a calculator to confirm the value. **7.2**

ALGEBRA LAB

Transformations of Exponential Functions

The graphs of $y = 2^x$, $y = 3 \cdot 2^x$, and $y = 0.5 \cdot 2^x$ are shown at the right. Notice that the y-intercept of $y = 2^x$ is 1, the y-intercept of $y = 3 \cdot 2^x$ is 3, and the y-intercept of $y = 0.5 \cdot 2^x$ is 0.5. The graph of $y = 3 \cdot 2^x$ is steeper than the graph of $y = 2^x$. The graph of $y = 0.5 \cdot 2^x$ is not as steep as the graph of $y = 2^x$.

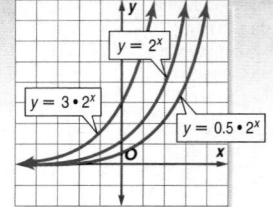

THINK AND DISCUSS

Graph each set of equations on the same plane. Compare and contrast the graphs. **1–4. See Ch. 9 Answer Appendix.**

1.	**2.**	**3.**	**4.**
$y = 2^x$	$y = 2^x$	$y = 2^x$	$y = 3 \cdot 2^x$
$y = 2^x + 3$	$y = 2^{x+5}$	$y = 3^x$	$y = 3(2^x - 1)$
$y = 2^x - 4$	$y = 2^{x-4}$	$y = 5^x$	$y = 3(2^x + 1)$

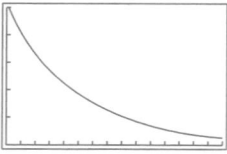

Real-World Link

The first successful photographs of motion were made in 1877. Today, the motion picture industry is big business, with the highest-grossing movie making \$1,835,300,000.

Source: imdb.com

Real-World EXAMPLE — Use Exponential Functions to Solve Problems

3 **MOTION PICTURES** Movie ticket sales decrease each weekend after an opening. The function $E = 49.9 \cdot 0.692^w$ models the earnings of a popular movie. In this equation, E represents earnings in millions of dollars and w represents the weekend number.

a. Make a table. What values of E and w are meaningful in the context of the problem?

Only values where $E \leq 49.9$ and $w > 0$ are meaningful in the context of the problem.

w	E
0	49.9
1	34.5308
2	23.8953136
3	16.535557
4	11.44260545
5	7.91828297

b. How much did the movie make on the first weekend?

$E = 49.9 \cdot 0.692^w$ Original equation

$ = 49.9 \cdot 0.692^1$ $w = 1$

$ = 34.5308$ Use a calculator.

On the first weekend, the movie grossed about \$34.53 million.

504 Chapter 9 Quadratic and Exponential Functions

Intervention

Identifying Exponential Functions The LIST and STAT PLOT features of a graphing calculator can be used to graph data and determine whether functions are exponential. Enter the x-values into L1 and the corresponding y-values into L2. Turn on STAT PLOT and view the plotted points. After adjusting the window to fit the data, it should be possible to determine whether the data exhibits exponential behavior.

c. How much did it make on the fifth weekend?

$E = 49.9 \cdot 0.692^w$ Original equation

$\quad = 49.9 \cdot 0.692^5$ $w = 5$

$\quad \approx 7.918282973$ Use a calculator.

On the fifth weekend, the movie grossed about $7.92 million.

✓CHECK Your Progress

3. BIOLOGY A certain bacteria doubles every 20 minutes. How many will there be after 2 hours? **64**

nline Personal Tutor at ca.algebra1.com

Personal Tutor at ca.algebra1.com

Identify Exponential Behavior How do you know if a set of data is exponential? One method is to observe the shape of the graph. Another way is to use the problem-solving strategy *look for a pattern*.

EXAMPLE   Identify Exponential Behavior

4 Determine whether the set of data at the right displays exponential behavior. Explain why or why not.

x	0	10	20	30	40	50
y	80	40	20	10	5	2.5

Method 1   Look for a Pattern

The domain values are at regular intervals of 10. Look for a common factor among the range values.

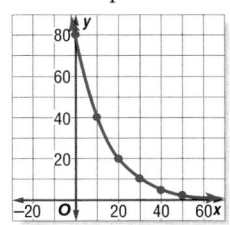

80   40   20   10   5   2.5

$\times \frac{1}{2}$ $\times \frac{1}{2}$ $\times \frac{1}{2}$ $\times \frac{1}{2}$ $\times \frac{1}{2}$

Since the domain values are at regular intervals and the range values differ by a common factor, the data are probably exponential. Its equation may involve $\left(\frac{1}{2}\right)^x$.

Method 2   Graph the Data

The graph shows a rapidly decreasing value of y as x increases. This is a characteristic of exponential behavior.

✓CHECK Your Progress

4. Determine whether the set of data displays exponential behavior. Explain why or why not.

x	0	10	20	30	40	50
y	15	21	27	33	39	45

4. The domain values are at regular intervals of 10. The range values have a common difference 6. The data do not display exponential behavior, but rather linear behavior.

★ indicates multi-step problem

✓CHECK Your Understanding

Examples 1, 2   Graph each function. State the y-intercept. Then use the graph to determine
(pp. 503–504)   the approximate value of the given expression. Use a calculator to confirm the value. **1–3. See margin.**

1. $y = 3^x; 3^{1.2}$ **2.** $y = \left(\frac{1}{4}\right)^x; \left(\frac{1}{4}\right)^{1.7}$ **3.** $y = 9^x; 9^{0.8}$

Graph each function. State the y-intercept. **4–5. See margin.**

4. $y = 2 \cdot 3^x$ **5.** $y = 4(5^x - 10)$

Lesson 9-5 Exponential Functions   **505**

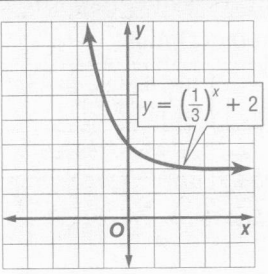

Odd/Even Assignments

Exercises 9–26 are structured so that students practice the same concepts whether they are assigned odd or even problems.

 Exercise Alert!

Find the Error If students have trouble with Exercise 43, suggest that they multiply $\frac{1}{3} \times \frac{1}{3}$ and then $\frac{1}{3} \times \frac{1}{3} \times \frac{1}{3}$. Does the product increase or decrease as the exponent increases?

Additional Answers

6a. D: $\{d \mid d \geq 0\}$, the number of days is greater than or equal to 0; R: $\{y \mid y \geq 100\}$, the number of fruit flies is greater than or equal to 100.

7. Yes; the domain values are at regular intervals and the range values have a common factor 6.

8. No; the domain values are at regular intervals and the range values have a common difference 4.

9–18. See Chapter 9 Answer Appendix for graphs.

9. 1; 5.9
10. 1; 2.0
11. 1; 20
12. 1; 0.4
13. 1; 1.7
14. 1; 5.3
15. 5
16. 3
17. −6
18. 5
20. y-int is 300; There are 300 bacteria at 9:00 A.M. D: $\{t \mid t \geq 0\}$; R: $\{p \mid p \geq 300\}$.
22. See Chapter 9 Answer Appendix for graph; 12; $12 million in sales in 1995.

6. BIOLOGY The function $f(t) = 100 \cdot 1.05^t$ models the growth of a fruit fly population, where $f(t)$ is the number of flies and t is time in days.

Example 3 (pp. 504–505)

a. What values for the domain and range are reasonable in the context of this situation? Explain. **See margin.**

b. After two weeks, approximately how many flies are in this population? **about 198 fruit flies**

Example 4 (p. 505)

Determine whether the data in each table display exponential behavior. Explain why or why not. **7–8. See margin.**

7.

x	0	1	2	3	4	5
y	1	6	36	216	1296	7776

8.

x	4	6	8	10	12	14
y	5	9	13	17	21	25

Exercises

HOMEWORK HELP

For Exercises	See Examples
9–18	1, 2
19–22	3
23–26	4

Exercise Levels
A: 9–26
B: 28–40
C: 41–47

23. No; the domain values are at regular intervals and the range values have a common difference 3.

24. Yes; the domain values are at regular intervals and the range values have a common factor 0.5.

25. Yes; the domain values are at regular intervals and the range values have a common factor 0.75.

26. No; the domain values are at regular intervals, but the range values do not have a positive common factor.

Graph each function. State the y-intercept. Then use the graph to determine the approximate value of the given expression. Use a calculator to confirm the value. **9–14. See margin.**

9. $y = 5^x$; $5^{1.1}$
10. $y = 10^x$; $10^{0.3}$
11. $y = \left(\frac{1}{10}\right)^x$; $\left(\frac{1}{10}\right)^{-1.3}$
12. $y = \left(\frac{1}{5}\right)^x$; $\left(\frac{1}{5}\right)^{0.5}$
13. $y = 6^x$; $6^{0.3}$
14. $y = 8^x$; $8^{0.8}$

Graph each function. State the y-intercept. **15–18. See margin.**

15. $y = 5(2^x)$
16. $y = 3(5^x)$
17. $y = 3^x - 7$
18. $y = 2^x + 4$

BIOLOGY For Exercises 19 and 20, use the following information.
A population of bacteria in a culture increases according to the model $p = 300 \cdot 2.7^{0.02t}$, where t is the number of hours and $t = 0$ corresponds to 9:00 A.M.

19. Use this model to estimate the number of bacteria at 11 A.M. **about 312**

★ **20.** Graph the function and name the y-intercept. Describe what the y-intercept represents and describe a reasonable domain and range for this situation. **See margin.**

BUSINESS For Exercises 21 and 22, use the following information.
The amount of money spent at West Outlet Mall in Midtown continues to increase. The total $T(x)$ in millions of dollars can be estimated by the function $T(x) = 12(1.12)^x$, where x is the number of years after it opened in 1995.

★ **21.** According to the function, find the amount of sales for the mall in the years 2005, 2006, and 2007.

★ **22.** Graph the function and name the y-intercept. What does the y-intercept represent in this problem? **See Ch. 9 Answer Appendix.**

21. about $37.27 million; about $41.74 million; about $46.75 million

Determine whether the data in each table display exponential behavior. Explain why or why not.

23.

x	−2	−1	0	1
y	−5	−2	1	4

24.

x	0	1	2	3
y	1	0.5	0.25	0.125

25.

x	10	20	30	40
y	16	12	9	6.75

26.

x	−1	0	1	2
y	−0.5	1.0	−2.0	4.0

27–29. See Ch. 9 Answer Appendix for graphs.
Graph each function. State the y-intercept.
27. $y = 2(3^x) - 1$ 1
28. $y = 2(3^x + 1)$ 4
29. $y = 3(2^x - 5)$ −12

506 Chapter 9 Quadratic and Exponential Functions

DIFFERENTIATED HOMEWORK OPTIONS

Level	Assignment	Two-Day Option	
BL Basic	9–26, 41–43, 47–66	9–25 odd, 48, 49	10–26 even, 41–43, 47, 50–66
OL Core	9–35 odd, 36–43, 47–66	9–26, 48, 49	27–43, 47, 50–66
AL Advanced /Pre-AP	27–62 (optional: 63–66)		

Identify each function as *linear*, *quadratic*, or *exponential*.

30. $y = 4^x + 3$ **exponential** **31.** $y = 2x(x - 1)$ **quadratic** **32.** $5x + y = 8$ **linear**

33.

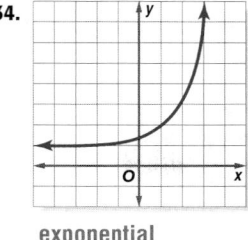

quadratic

34.

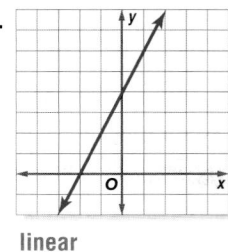

exponential

35.

linear

TOURNAMENTS For Exercises 36–38, use the following information.
In a quiz bowl competition, three schools compete, and the winner advances to the next round. Therefore, after each round, only $\frac{1}{3}$ of the schools remain in the competition for the next round. Suppose 729 schools start the competition.

36. Write an exponential function to describe the number of schools remaining after x rounds.

36. $y = 729\left(\frac{1}{3}\right)^x$

37. How many schools are left after 3 rounds? **27 schools**

38. How many rounds will it take to declare a champion? **6 rounds**

ANALYZE TABLES For Exercises 39 and 40, use the following information.
A runner is training for a marathon, running a total of 20 miles per week on a regular basis. She plans to increase the distance $D(x)$ in miles according to the function $D(x) = 20(1.1)^x$, where x represents the number of weeks of training.

39. Copy and complete the table showing the number of miles she plans to run.

40. The runner's goal is to work up to 50 miles per week. What is the first week that the total will be 50 miles or more? **10th week**

Week	Distance (miles)
1	22
2	24.2
3	26.62
4	29.282

H.O.T. Problems

41. REASONING Determine whether the graph of $y = a^x$, where $a > 0$ and $a \neq 1$, *sometimes*, *always*, or *never* has an x-intercept. Explain your reasoning.
Never; the graph will never intersect the x-axis.

42. OPEN ENDED Choose an exponential function that represents a real-world situation and graph the function. Analyze the graph.
See Ch. 9 Answer Appendix.

43. FIND THE ERROR Amalia and Hannah are graphing $y = \left(\frac{1}{3}\right)^x$. Who is correct? Explain your reasoning.

Hannah;
the graph
of $y = \left(\frac{1}{3}\right)^x$
decreases as
x increases.

Amalia
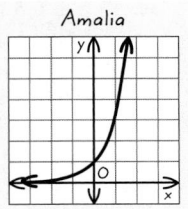

Hannah
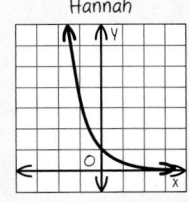

44. a reflection over the *y*-axis

45. a translation 2 units up

46. a translation 4 units down

CHALLENGE Describe the graph of each equation as a transformation of the graph of $y = 5^x$.

44. $y = \left(\frac{1}{5}\right)^x$

45. $y = 5^x + 2$

46. $y = 5^x - 4$

Lesson 9-5 Exponential Functions **507**

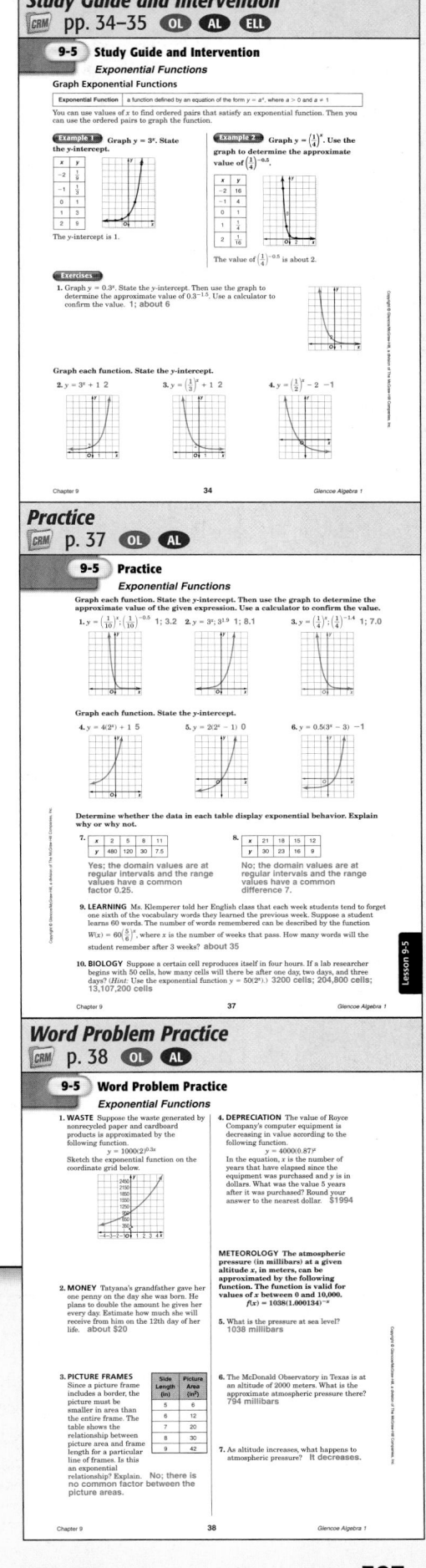

Crystal Ball Ask students to write how they think exponential functions will connect with the next lesson which involves growth and decay situations.

 **Formative Assessment**

Check for student understanding of concepts in Lessons 9-4 and 9-5.

[CRM] **Quiz 3, p. 52**

FOLDABLES **Foldables™**
Study Organizer **Follow-Up**

At the end of this lesson, remind students to write notes and show examples on the page in their Foldables for this lesson.

Additional Answer

47. Sample answer: If the number of items on each level of a piece of art is a given number times the number of items on the previous level, an exponential function can be used to describe the situation. For the carving of the pliers, $y = 2^x$. For this situation, x is an integer between 0 and 8 inclusive. The values of y are 1, 2, 4, 8, 16, 32, 64, 128, and 256.

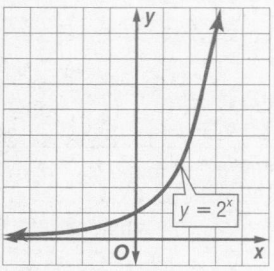

47. *Writing in Math* Use the information about the carving on page 502 to explain how exponential functions can be used in art. Include the exponential function representing the pliers, an explanation of which x and y values are meaningful, and the graph of this function. **See margin.**

STANDARDS PRACTICE 6NS1.3

48. Compare the graphs of $y = 2^x$ and $y = 6^x$. **A**

  A The graph of $y = 6^x$ increases at a faster rate than the graph of $y = 2^x$.

  B The graph of $y = 2^x$ increases at a faster rate than the graph of $y = 6^x$.

  C The graph of $y = 6^x$ is the graph of $y = 2^x$ translated 4 units up.

  D The graph of $y = 6^x$ is the graph of $y = 2^x$ translated 3 units up.

49. REVIEW $\triangle KLM$ is similar to $\triangle HIJ$. Which scale factor is used to transform $\triangle KLM$ to $\triangle HIJ$? **H**

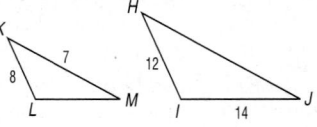

  F $\frac{1}{2}$ **H** $1\frac{1}{2}$

  G 1   **J** 2

Spiral Review

Solve each equation by using the Quadratic Formula. Round to the nearest tenth if necessary. (Lesson 9-4)

50. $x^2 - 9x - 36 = 0$ **−3, 12**   **51.** $2t^2 + 3t - 1 = 0$ **−1.8, 0.3**   **52.** $5y^2 + 3 = y$ **∅**

Solve each equation by completing the square. Round to the nearest tenth if necessary. (Lesson 9-3)

53. $x^2 - 7x = -10$ **2, 5**   **54.** $a^2 - 12a = 3$ **−0.2, 12.2**   **55.** $t^2 + 6t + 3 = 0$
                                                  −5.4, −0.6

Factor each trinomial, if possible. If the trinomial cannot be factored using integers, write *prime*. (Lesson 8-3)

56. $m^2 - 14m + 40$ **57.** $t^2 - 2t + 35$ **prime**   **58.** $z^2 - 5z - 24$
   $(m - 4)(m - 10)$ $(z - 8)(z + 3)$

Solve each inequality. (Lesson 6-1)

59. $x + 7 > 2$ $\{x \mid x > -5\}$ **60.** $10 \geq x + 8$ $\{x \mid x \leq 2\}$ **61.** $y - 7 < -12$
                                                          $\{y \mid y < -5\}$

62. NUMBER THEORY Three times one number equals twice a second number. Twice the first number is 3 more than the second number. Find the numbers. (Lesson 5-4) **6, 9**

GET READY for the Next Lesson

PREREQUISITE SKILL Evaluate $p(1 + r)^t$ for each of the given values. (Lesson 1-1)

63. $p = 5, r = \frac{1}{2}, t = 2$ **11.25**   **64.** $p = 300, r = \frac{1}{4}, t = 3$ **585.9375**

65. $p = 100, r = 0.2, t = 2$ **144**   **66.** $p = 6, r = 0.5, t = 3$ **20.25**

508 Chapter 9 Quadratic and Exponential Functions

Pre-AP Activity Use as an Extension

Give students this scenario: a wise man asked his ruler to provide rice for his people. Rather than receiving a daily supply of rice, the wise man asked the ruler to give him 2 grains of rice for the first square on a chess board, 4 grains for the second, 8 for the third, 16 for the fourth, and so on, doubling the amount of rice with each square of the board.

Ask:

- "How many grains of rice will the wise man receive for the sixty-fourth square on the chessboard?" about 1.84×10^{19} grains

- "If one pound of rice has approximately 24,000 grains, how many tons of rice will the wise man receive on the last day?" (*Hint*: 1 ton = 2000 pounds) about 3.84×10^{11} tons

Algebra Lab
Investigating Exponential Functions

Preparation for
Algebra II
Standard 12.0
Students know the laws of
fractional exponents,
understand exponential
functions, and use these
functions in problems
involving exponential growth
and decay. (Key)

ACTIVITY

Step 1 Cut a sheet of notebook paper in half.

Step 2 Stack the two halves, one on top of the other.

Step 3 Make a table like the one at the right and record the number of sheets of paper you have in the stack after one cut.

Number of Cuts	Number of Sheets
0	1
1	2
2	4

Step 4 Cut the two stacked sheets in half, placing the resulting pieces in a single stack. Record the number of sheets of paper in the new stack after 2 cuts.

Step 5 Continue cutting the stack in half, each time putting the resulting piles in a single stack and recording the number of sheets in the stack. Stop when the resulting stack is too thick to cut.

ANALYZE THE RESULTS

1. Write a list of ordered pairs (x, y), where x is the number of cuts and y is the number of sheets in the stack. Notice that the list starts with the ordered pair $(0, 1)$, which represents the single sheet of paper before any cuts were made. **(0, 1), (1, 2), (2, 4), (3, 8), (4, 16), …**

2. Continue the list beyond the point where you stopped cutting, until you reach the ordered pair for 7 cuts. Explain how you calculated the last y values for your list after you had stopped cutting.

3. Plot the ordered pairs in your list on a coordinate grid. Be sure to choose a scale for the y-axis so that you can plot all of the points.

4. Write a function that expresses y as a function of x. $y = 2^x$

5. Evaluate the function you wrote in Exercise 4 for $x = 8$ and $x = 9$. Does it give the correct number of sheets in the stack after 8 and 9 cuts?

6. Notebook paper usually stacks about 500 sheets to the inch. How thick would your stack of paper be if you had been able to make 9 cuts?

7. Suppose each cut takes about 5 seconds. If you had been able to keep cutting, you would have made 36 cuts in three minutes. At 500 sheets to the inch, make a conjecture as to how thick you think the stack would be after 36 cuts.

8. Calculate the thickness of your stack after 36 cuts. Write your answer in miles. **2169 mi**

9. Use the results of the Activity to complete a table like the one at the right for 0 to 7 cuts. Then write a function to describe the area y after x cuts.

Number of Cuts	Area of Sheet
0	1
1	0.5
2	
…	

Answers (margin):

2. (5, 32), (6, 64), (7, 128); The y-value is found by raising 2 to the number of cuts.

3. See Ch. 9 Answer Appendix.

5. 256, 512; yes

6. about 1 in.

7. Sample answer: 1 million ft

9. $y = \left(\dfrac{1}{2}\right)^x$; See Ch. 9 Answer Appendix for table.

1 Focus

Objective Use paper stacking to investigate an exponential function.

Materials
• scissors

Teaching Tip You may wish to do the Activity as a demonstration while students complete the table on the board.

2 Teach

Working in Cooperative Groups Place students in groups of 2 or 3, mixing abilities. Have groups complete the Activity and Exercises 1–4.

• Students may recognize that the y-value is doubled for each successive cut. Guide them to see that this can be written in the form 2^x.
• After students have plotted the ordered pairs in their lists, show them how to connect the points with a smooth curve rather than connecting each pair of points with a straight line.

Practice Have students complete Exercises 5–8.

3 Assess

 Formative Assessment

Use Exercise 4 to assess whether students can write the function that models the activity.

From Concrete to Abstract
Ask: Which function increases more rapidly: $y = 2x$ or $y = 2^x$? Sample answer: $y = 2^x$ grows faster than $y = 2x$. If $x = 1000$, $y = 2^{1000}$ is clearly much larger than $y = 2 \cdot 1000 = 2000$.

1 Focus

Standards Alignment

Before Lesson 9-6
Graph functions of the form $y = nx^2$ and $y = nx^3$ and use in solving problems from Standard 7AF3.1

Lesson 9-6
Use the laws of fractional exponents in problems involving exponential growth and decay from Standard 2A12.0

After Lesson 9-6
Use the definition of logarithms to translate between logarithms in any base from Standard 2A13.0

2 Teach

Scaffolding Questions Have students read *Get Ready for the Lesson*. **Ask:**

- Looking at the graph, how do you know it is not linear? The *y*-value increases by the factor 1.137 each month. Since the values increase by a common factor, the function is exponential.

- Use the graph to predict the total number of blogs in millions in November 2005. About 54 million

Lesson 9-6 Resources

Main Ideas

- Solve problems involving exponential growth.
- Solve problems involving exponential decay.

 Preparation for Algebra II Standard 12.0
Students know the laws of fractional exponents, understand exponential functions, and use these functions in problems involving exponential growth and decay. (Key)

New Vocabulary

exponential growth
compound interest
exponential decay

▶ GET READY for the Lesson

The number of Weblogs or "blogs" increased at a monthly rate of about 13.7% between November 2003 and July 2005. Let *y* represent the total number of blogs in millions, and let *t* represent the number of months since November 2003. Then the average number per month can be modeled by $y = 1.1(1 + 0.137)^t$ or $y = 1.1(1.137)^t$.

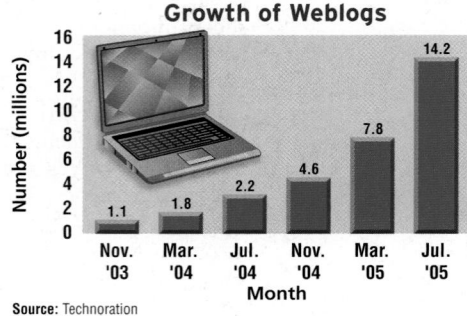

Growth of Weblogs

Month	Number (millions)
Nov. '03	1.1
Mar. '04	1.8
Jul. '04	2.2
Nov. '04	4.6
Mar. '05	7.8
Jul. '05	14.2

Source: Technoration

Exponential Growth The equation for the number of blogs is in the form $y = C(1 + r)^t$. This is the general equation for **exponential growth** in which the initial amount *C* increases by the same percent over a given period of time.

> **KEY CONCEPT** *General Equation for Exponential Growth*
>
> The general equation for exponential growth is $y = C(1 + r)^t$ where *y* represents the final amount, *C* represents the initial amount, *r* represents the rate of change expressed as a decimal, and *t* represents time.

● Real-World EXAMPLE Exponential Growth

① **SPORTS** In 1971, there were 294,105 females in high school sports. Since then, the number has increased an average of 8.5% per year.

  a. Write an equation to represent the number of females participating in high school sports since 1971.

$$y = C(1 + r)^t \qquad \text{General equation for exponential growth}$$
$$= 294,105(1 + 0.085)^t \qquad C = 294,105 \text{ and } r = 8.5\% \text{ or } 0.085$$
$$= 294,105(1.085)^t \qquad \text{Simplify.}$$

  An equation to represent the number of females participating in high school sports is $y = 294,105(1.085)^t$, where *y* is the number of female athletes and *t* is the number of years since 1971.

Chapter 9 Resource Masters

Lesson Reading Guide, p. 41 **BL** **OL** **ELL**
Study Guide and Intervention, pp. 42–43 **BL** **OL** **ELL**
Skills Practice, p. 44 **BL** **OL**
Practice, p. 45 **OL** **AL**
Word Problem Practice, p. 46 **OL** **AL**
Enrichment, p. 47 **OL** **AL**
Quiz 4, p. 52

Transparencies
5-Minute Check Transparency 9-6
Additional Print Resources
Noteables™ Interactive Study Notebook with Foldables™
Teaching Algebra with Manipulatives

Technology
ca.algebra1.com
Interactive Classroom CD-ROM
AssignmentWorks CD-ROM
Graphing Calculator Easy Files

b. According to the equation, how many females participated in high school sports in 2005?

$y = 294{,}105(1.085)^t$ Equation for females participating in sports

$\quad = 294{,}105(1.085)^{34}$ $t = 2005 - 1971$ or 34

$\quad \approx 4{,}711{,}004$ Use a calculator.

In 2005, about 4,711,004 females participated.

 **Your Progress**   **1A.** $C = 18.9(1.19)^t$

TECHNOLOGY Computer use has risen 19% annually since 1980.

  1A. If 18.9 million computers were in use in 1980, write an equation for the number of computers in use for t years after 1980.

  1B. Predict the number of computers in 2015. **about 8329.24 million computers**

 Personal Tutor at ca.algebra1.com

One special application of exponential growth is **compound interest.** The equation for compound interest is $A = P\left(1 + \frac{r}{n}\right)^{nt}$, where A is the current amount of the investment, P is the principal (initial amount of the investment), r represents the annual rate of interest expressed as a decimal, n represents the number of times the interest is compounded each year, and t represents the number of years that the money is invested.

Real-World EXAMPLE   **Compound Interest**

2 **COLLEGE** Maria's parents invested $14,000 at 6% per year compounded monthly. How much money will there be in 10 years?

$A = P\left(1 + \frac{r}{n}\right)^{nt}$ Compound interest equation

$\quad = 14{,}000\left(1 + \frac{0.06}{12}\right)^{12(10)}$ $P = 14{,}000$, $r = 6\%$ or 0.06, $n = 12$, and $t = 10$

$\quad = 14{,}000(1.005)^{120}$ Simplify.

$\quad \approx 25{,}471.55$ Use a calculator.

There will be about $25,471.55.

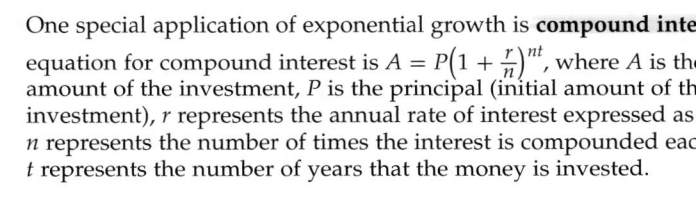 **Your Progress**

2. MONEY Determine the amount of an investment if $300 is invested at an interest rate of 3.5% compounded monthly for 22 years.

about $647.20

Real-World Link

According to the College Board, the 2004–2005 average costs for college were $14,640 for students attending 4-year public colleges and $30,295 for students at 4-year private colleges.

Source: *World Book Encyclopedia*

Exponential Decay A variation of the growth equation can be used as the general equation for exponential decay. In **exponential decay,** the original amount decreases by the same percent over a period of time.

KEY CONCEPT   *General Equation for Exponential Decay*

The general equation for exponential decay is $y = C(1 - r)^t$, where y represents the final amount, C represents the initial amount, r represents the rate of decay expressed as a decimal, and t represents time.

Math Online Extra Examples at ca.algebra1.com

Lesson 9-6 Growth and Decay   **511**

Focus on Mathematical Content

Compound Interest In contrast to simple interest, compound interest is applied to the original principal and any previously earned interest. There are four ways to increase the amount in a compound-interest account: the investor can increase the initial principal, increase the annual interest rate, increase the number of compoundings per year, or increase the time that the money is in the account.

Exponential Growth

Example 1 shows how to solve a real-world problem involving exponential growth. **Example 2** shows how to solve a real-world problem involving compound interest.

 Formative Assessment

Use the Check Your Progress exercises after each example to determine students' understanding of concepts.

ADDITIONAL EXAMPLES

1 **POPULATION** In 2005 the town of Flat Creek had a population of about 280,000 and a growth rate of 0.85% per year.

  a. Write an equation to represent the population of Flat Creek since 2005.
$y = 280{,}000\ (1.0085)^t$

  b. According to the equation, what will be the population of Flat Creek in the year 2015? about 304,731

2 **COLLEGE** When Jing May was born, her grandparents invested $1000 in a fixed rate savings account at a rate of 7% compounded annually. The money will go to Jing May when she turns 18 to help with her college expenses. What amount of money will Jing May receive from the investment? She will receive about $3380.

Additional Examples are also in:

• Noteables™ Interactive Study Notebook with Foldables™

• Interactive Classroom PowerPoint® Presentations

Exponential Decay

Example 3 shows how to solve a real-world problem involving exponential decay.

ADDITIONAL EXAMPLE

3 **CHARITY** During an economic recession, a charitable organization found that its donations dropped by 1.1% per year. Before the recession, its donations were $390,000.

a. Write an equation to represent the charity's donations since the beginning of the recession.
$A = 390,000(0.989)^t$

b. Estimate the amount of the donations 5 years after the start of the recession.
about $369,017

Student Misconceptions

Tips for New Teachers

Remind students that in growth and decay equations, the amount inside the parentheses will be greater than for growth and less than for decay.

3 Practice

Formative Assessment

Use Exercises 1–4 to check for understanding.

Use the chart at the bottom of this page to customize assignments for your students.

Odd/Even Assignments

Exercises 6–13 are structured so that students practice the same concepts whether they are assigned odd or even problems.

Real-World Connections

For Exercise 12, tell students that although industry experts believe music cassettes will not be around much longer in the West, Turkey sells 88 million cassettes a year, and India sells 80 million. In fact, cassette sales account for 50% of music sales in these countries.

Real-World EXAMPLE Exponential Decay

3 **SWIMMING** A fully inflated raft loses 6.6% of its air every day. The raft originally contains 4500 cubic inches of air.

a. Write an equation to represent the loss of air.

$y = C(1 - r)^t$ General equation for exponential decay

$\quad = 4500(1 - 0.066)^t$ $C = 4500$ and $r = 6.6\%$ or 0.066

$\quad = 4500(0.934)^t$ Simplify.

An equation to represent the loss of air is $y = 4500(0.934)^t$, where y represents the amount of air in the raft in cubic inches and t represents the number of days.

b. Estimate the amount of air that will be lost after 7 days.

$y = 4500(0.934)^t$ Equation for air loss

$\quad = 4500(0.934)^7$ $t = 7$

$\quad \approx 2790$ Use a calculator.

The amount of air lost after 7 days will be about 2790 cubic inches.

CHECK Your Progress   3A. $y = 776,677(1 - 0.01)^t$

POPULATION During the past several years, the population of San Francisco County, California, has been decreasing at an average rate of about 1% per year. In 2000, its population was 776,677.

3A. Write an equation to represent the population since 2000.

3B. If the trend continues, predict the population in 2010. **about 702,413**

★ indicates multi-step problem

CHECK Your Understanding

Example 1
(pp. 510–511)

ANALYZE GRAPHS For Exercises 1 and 2, use the graph at the right and the following information.
The median house price in the United States increased an average of 8.9% each year between 2002 and 2004. Assume this pattern continues.

1. Write an equation for the median house price for t years after 2004.

2. Predict the median house price in 2009. **about $338,479**

1. $I = 221,000(1.089)^t$

SOLD

Median House Price	
2002	$187,600
2003	$195,000
2004	$221,000

Source: RealEstateJournal.com

Example 2
(p. 511)

3. **INVESTMENTS** Determine the amount of an investment if $400 is invested at an interest rate of 7.25% compounded quarterly for 7 years. **about $661.44**

Example 3
(p. 512)

★ **4.** **POPULATION** In 1995, the population of West Virginia reached 1,821,000, its highest in the 20th century. During the rest of the 20th century, its population decreased 0.2% each year. If this trend continues, predict the population of West Virginia in 2010. **about 1,767,128 people**

512 Chapter 9 Quadratic and Exponential Functions

DIFFERENTIATED HOMEWORK OPTIONS

Level	Assignment	Two-Day Option	
BL Basic	6–12, 16–27	7–11 odd, 19, 20	6–12 even, 16–18, 21–27
OL Core	7–11 odd, 13–27	6–12, 19, 20	13–18, 21–27
AL Advanced /Pre-AP	13–27		

Exercises

HOMEWORK HELP

For Exercises	See Examples
5–8	1
9, 10	2
11, 12	3

Exercise Levels
A: 5–12
B: 13–16
C: 17–18

WEIGHT TRAINING For Exercises 5 and 6, use the following information.
In 1997, there were 43.2 million people who used free weights.

5. Assuming the use of free weights increases 6% annually, write an equation for the number of people using free weights t years from 1997. $W = 43.2(1.06)^t$

6. Predict the number of people using free weights in 2007.
about 77.36 million people

★ 7. **POPULATION** The population of Mexico has been increasing 1.7% annually. If the population was 100,350,000 in 2000, predict the population in 2012.
about 122,848,204 people

★ 8. **ANALYZE GRAPHS** The increase in the number of visitors to the Grand Canyon National Park is similar to an exponential function. If the average visitation has increased 5.63% annually since 1920, predict the number of visitors to the park in 2020.
about 17,125,650 visitors

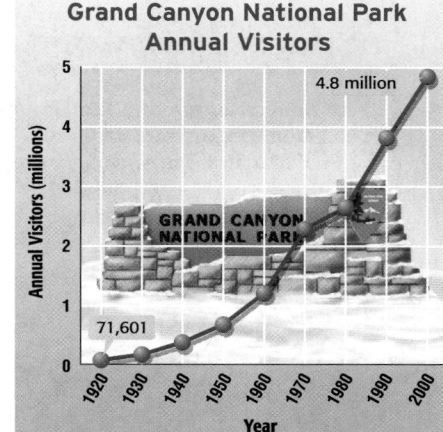

Grand Canyon National Park Annual Visitors
4.8 million
71,601
Annual Visitors (millions)
Year: 1920 1930 1940 1950 1960 1970 1980 1990 2000
Source: Grand Canyon National Park

9. **INVESTMENTS** Determine the amount of an investment if $500 is invested at an interest rate of 5.75% compounded monthly for 25 years.
about $2097.86

10. **INVESTMENTS** Determine the amount of an investment if $250 is invested at an interest rate of 7.3% compounded quarterly for 40 years. about $4514.89

★ 11. **POPULATION** The country of Latvia has been experiencing a 1.1% annual decrease in population. In 2005, its population was 2,290,237. If the trend continues, predict Latvia's population in 2015. about 2,050,422

★ 12. **MUSIC** In 1994, the sales of music cassettes reached its peak at $2,976,400,000. Since then, cassette sales have been declining. If the annual percent of decrease in sales is 18.6%, predict the sales of cassettes in the year 2009.
about $135,849,289

13. about 128 g
14. about 76.36 g

ARCHAEOLOGY For Exercises 13–15, use the following information.
The *half-life* of a radioactive element is defined as the time that it takes for one-half a quantity of the element to decay. Radioactive Carbon-14 is found in all living organisms and has a half-life of 5730 years. Archaeologists use this information to estimate the age of fossils. Consider a living organism with an original Carbon-14 content of 256 grams. The number of grams remaining in the fossil of the organism after t years would be $256(0.5)^{\frac{t}{5730}}$.

13. If the organism died 5730 years ago, what is the amount of Carbon-14 today?

14. If an organism died 10,000 years ago, what is the amount of Carbon-14 today?

15. If the fossil has 32 grams of Carbon-14 remaining, how long ago did it live? (*Hint:* Make a table.) about 17,190 years ago

EXTRA PRACTICE
See pages 736, 752.

Math Online
Self-Check Quiz at
algebra1.com

BL = Below Grade Level
OL = On Grade Level
AL = Above Grade Level
ELL = English Language Learner

Additional pages not shown:
CRM **Lesson Reading Guide**, p. 41 BL OL ELL
CRM **Skills Practice**, p. 44 BL OL

Enrichment
CRM p. 47 OL AL

9-6 Enrichment

Growth and Decay
Sierpinski Triangle is an example of a fractal that changes exponentially. Start with an equilateral triangle and find the midpoints of each side. Then connect the midpoints to form a smaller triangle. Remove this smaller triangle from the larger one.

Repeat the process to create the next triangle in the sequence. Find the midpoints of the sides of the three remaining triangles and connect them to form smaller triangles to be removed.

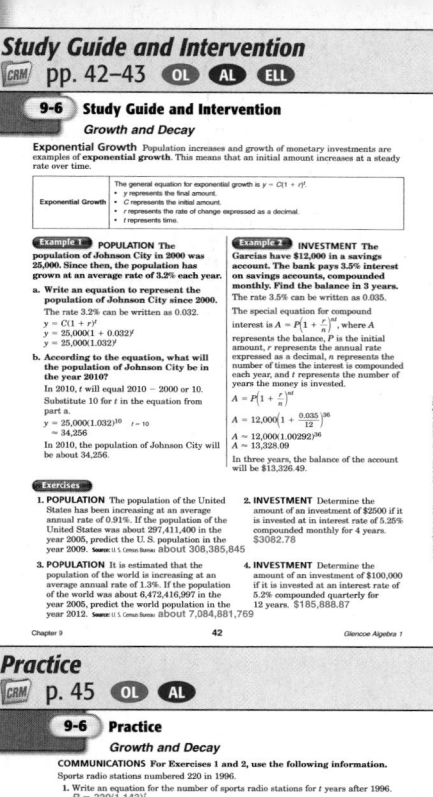

Exercise Alert!
Exercises 16 requires students to use the Internet or other resources.

4 Assess

Ticket Out the Door Make several copies each of five equations for exponential growth or decay. Give one equation to each student. As students leave the room, ask them to tell you whether their equations are for growth or decay.

 Formative Assessment
Check for student understanding of concepts in Lesson 9-6.

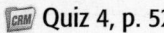 Quiz 4, p. 52

Additional Answers

17. Sample answer: Determine the amount of the investment if $500 is invested at an interest rate of 7% compounded quarterly for 6 years.

21.
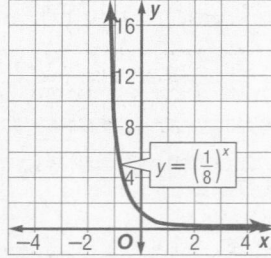

22.
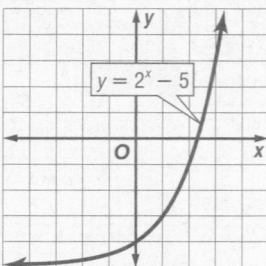

23.
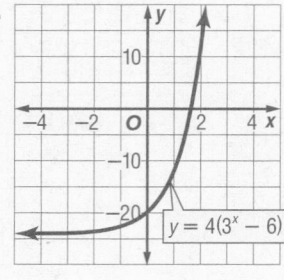

---

16. RESEARCH Find the enrollment of your school district each year for the last decade. Find the rate of change from one year to the next. Then, determine the average annual rate of change for those years. Use this information to estimate the enrollment for your school district in ten years. **See students' work.**

H.O.T. Problems.......

17. OPEN ENDED Create a compound interest problem that could be solved by the equation $A = 500\left(1 + \frac{0.07}{4}\right)^{4(6)}$. **See margin.**

18. *Writing in Math* Use the information about Weblogs on page 510 to explain how exponential growth can be used to predict future blogs. Include an explanation of the equation $y = 1.1(1 + 0.137)^t$ and an estimate of the number of blogs in January 2010. **See Ch. 9 Answer Appendix.**

STANDARDS PRACTICE 7MG3.3

19. Lorena is investing a $5000 inheritance from her aunt in a certificate of deposit that matures in 4 years. The interest rate is 6.25% compounded quarterly. What is the balance of the account after 4 years? **D**

A $5078.13

B $5319.90

C $5321.82

D $6407.73

20. REVIEW Diego is building a 10-foot ramp for loading heavy equipment into the back of a semi-truck. If the floor of the truck is 3.5 feet off the ground, about how far from the truck should the ramp be? **F**

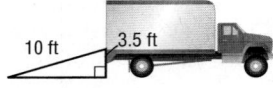

F   9 ft   H   10.6 ft

G   10 ft   J   11 ft

Spiral Review

Graph each function. State the *y*-intercept. (Lesson 9-5) **21–23. See margin for graphs.**

21. $y = \left(\frac{1}{8}\right)^x$ **1**

22. $y = 2^x - 5$ **−4**

23. $y = 4(3^x - 6)$ **−20**

Solve each equation by using the Quadratic Formula. Round to the nearest tenth if necessary. (Lesson 9-4)

24. $m^2 - 9m - 10 = 0$ **−1, 10**

25. $2t^2 - 4t = 3$ **−0.6, 2.6**

26. $7x^2 + 3x + 1 = 0$ **∅**

27. SKIING A course for cross-country skiing is regulated so that the slope of any hill cannot be greater than 0.33. A hill rises 60 meters over a horizontal distance of 250 meters. Does the hill meet the requirements? Explain. (Lesson 4-1) **Yes; slope $= \frac{60}{250} = 0.24 < 0.33$.**

Cross-Curricular Project

Algebra and Science

Out of This World It is time to complete your project. Use the information and data you have gathered about the solar system to prepare a brochure, poster, or Web page. Be sure to include the three graphs, tables, diagrams, or calculations in the presentation.

Math Online **Cross-Curricular Project at** ca.algebra1.com

Pre-AP Activity   Use after the Exercises

Ask students to write their own exponential growth or decay problems, using data from periodicals or the Internet. Have students share their problems with the class when they are complete.

Graphing Calculator Lab
Curve Fitting

COncepts in MOtion
Interactive Lab ca.algebra1.com

Preparation for Probability and Statistics Standard 4.0 Students are familiar with the standard distributions (normal, binomial, and exponential) and can use them to solve for events in problems in which the distribution belongs to those families. (Key)

If there is a constant increase or decrease in data values, there is a linear trend. If the values are increasing or decreasing more and more rapidly, there may be a quadratic or exponential trend.

Linear Trend

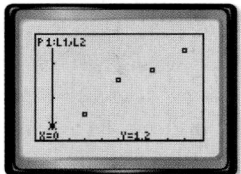

Quadratic Trend

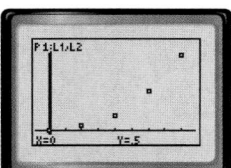

Exponential Trend

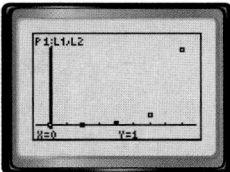

1 Focus

Objective Use a graphing calculator to find an appropriate regression equation for a set of data.

Materials
• graphing calculator

Teaching Tip Remind students that before entering data for a new problem into a list, they need to press STAT 4 ENTER to clear any previously entered data from particular lists. Clear previously entered equations from the Y=LIST by highlighting each equation and pressing the CLEAR key.

ACTIVITY 1

FARMING A study is conducted in which groups of 25 corn plants are given a different amount of fertilizer and the gain in height after a certain time is recorded. The table below shows the results.

Fertilizer (mg)	0	20	40	60	80
Gain in Height (in.)	6.48	7.35	8.73	9.00	8.13

Step 1 Make a scatter plot.

• Enter the fertilizer in L1 and the height in L2.

KEYSTROKES: *Review entering a list on page 234.*

• Use STAT PLOT to graph the scatter plot.

KEYSTROKES: *Review statistical plots on page 234. Use ZOOM 9 to graph.*

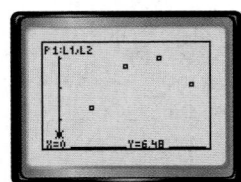

[−8, 88] scl: 5 by [6.0516, 9.4284] scl: 1

The graph appears to be a quadratic regression.

Step 2 Find the regression equation.

• Select DiagnosticOn from the CATALOG.

• Select QuadReg on the STAT CALC menu.

KEYSTROKES: STAT ▶ 5 ENTER

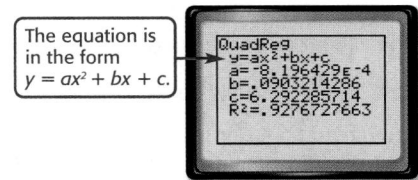

The equation is in the form $y = ax^2 + bx + c$.

The equation is about
$y = -0.0008x^2 + 0.1x + 6.3$.

R^2 is the **coefficient of determination**. The closer R^2 is to 1, the better the model. To choose a quadratic or exponential model, fit both and use the one with the R^2 value closer to 1.

2 Teach

Working in Cooperative Groups
Put students in groups of 2 or 3, mixing abilities. Have groups complete the Activity and Exercises 1–4.

• In Step 1 of the Activity, make sure students clear previous lists before entering the data. Students should enter the amount of fertilizer in L1 and the height gain in L2.

• In Step 2 of the Activity, point out that the a-value, −8.196429E−4, is in scientific notation. This value corresponds to -8.196429×10^{-4}, or −0.0008196429.

• For Step 3 of the Activity, tell students that they must copy the quadratic regression exactly to the Y=LIST in order to get the proper graph.

• In Step 4, point out that to calculate the maximum for the function, press 2nd [CALC] 4. Remind students to set the left and right bounds far enough from the vertex to calculate the correct maximum.

Practice Have students complete Exercises 5–9.

Other Calculator Keystrokes at ca.algebra1.com

Extend 9-6 Graphing Calculator Lab: Curve Fitting **515**

In Step 4 of the Activity, the quadratic regression predicted that 55 milligrams produces the maximum height gain, while the data suggested that 60 milligrams would produce the greatest gain. Ask students to explain the difference. Sample answer: The quadratic regression equation is a best fit to data points that do not fall on an actual graphed function. There will be differences between actual data points and points that fall on the regression function.

From Concrete to Abstract
Ask:

How do you determine whether to use a linear, quadratic, or exponential regression equation for your data? Sample answer: Make a scatter plot of your data points. If it looks close to a straight line, use a linear regression equation. If the data points follow a curve, fit a quadratic regression equation and an exponential regression equation to your points. The model with the coefficient of determination closest to 1 is the model to use.

Additional Answers

1. exponential; 0.9969724389

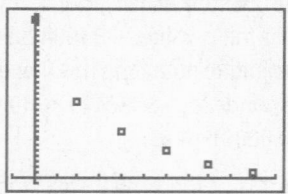

2. linear; 0.389164209

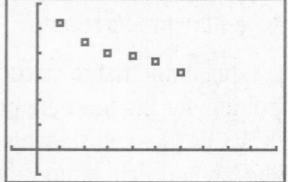

Step 3 Graph the regression equation.
• Copy the equation to the Y= list and graph.

KEYSTROKES: Y= VARS 5 ▶ ▶ 1 ZOOM 9

[−8, 88] scl: 5 by [6.0516, 9.4284] scl: 1

Step 4 Predict using the equation.
• Find the amount of fertilizer that produces the maximum gain in height.

KEYSTROKES: 2nd [CALC] 4

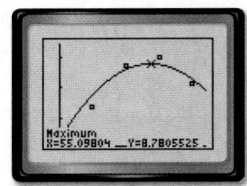

[−8, 88] scl: 5 by [6.0516, 9.4284] scl: 1

According to the graph, on average about 55 milligrams of the fertilizer produces the maximum gain.

EXERCISES

Plot each set of data points. Determine whether to use a *linear, quadratic,* or *exponential* regression equation. State the coefficient of determination.

1. x	y
0.0	2.98
0.2	1.46
0.4	0.90
0.6	0.51
0.8	0.25
1.0	0.13

2. x	y
1	25.9
2	22.2
3	20.0
4	19.3
5	18.2
6	15.9

3. x	y
10	35
20	50
30	70
40	88
50	101
60	120

4. x	y
1	3.67
3	5.33
5	6.33
7	5.67
9	4.33
11	2.67

1–4. See margin.   **6.** $y = 0.326x^2 − 1299.082x + 1,295,315.229$; $r^2 = 0.995298$

TECHNOLOGY DVD players were introduced in 1997. For Exercises 5–8, use the table at the right.

5. Make a scatter plot of the data. **See margin.**

6. Find an appropriate regression equation, and state the coefficient of determination.

7. Use the regression equation to predict the number of DVD players that will sell in 2008. **59.1 million**

8. Do you believe your equation would be accurate for a year beyond the range of the data, such as 2020? Explain. **See margin.**

Year	DVD Players Sold (millions)
1997	0.32
1998	1.09
1999	4.02
2000	8.50
2001	12.71
2002	17.09
2003	21.99

Source: Consumer Electronics Association

516 Chapter 9 Quadratic and Exponential Functions

---

3. linear; 0.9974802029

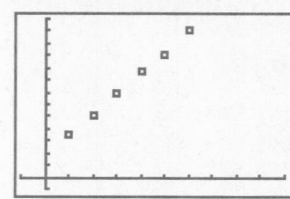

4. quadratic; 0.97716799

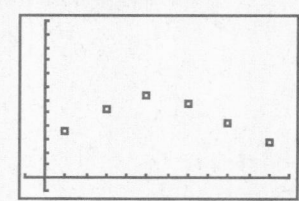

5.

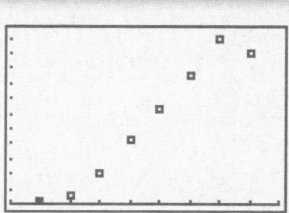

8. Sample answer: Yes; the price will start to increase using the quadratic model.

CHAPTER 9 Study Guide and Review

FOLDABLES Study Organizer

GET READY to Study

Be sure the following Key Concepts are noted in your Foldable.

Key Concepts

Graphing Quadratic Functions (Lesson 9-1)

- A quadratic function can be described by an equation of the form $y = ax^2 + bx + c$, where $a \neq 0$.

- The axis of symmetry for the graph of $y = ax^2 + bx + c$, where $a \neq 0$, is $x = -\dfrac{b}{2a}$.

Solving Quadratic Equations (Lessons 9-2, 9-3, and 9-4)

- The solutions of a quadratic equation are called the roots of the equation. They are the x-intercepts or zeros of the related quadratic function.

- Quadratic equations can be solved by completing the square. To complete the square for $x^2 + bx$, find $\frac{1}{2}$ of b, square this result, and then add the final result to $x^2 + bx$.

- The solutions of a quadratic equation can be found by using the Quadratic Formula $x = \dfrac{-b \pm \sqrt{b^2 - 4ac}}{2a}$.

Exponential Functions (Lessons 9-5 and 9-6)

- An exponential function can be described by an equation of the form $y = a^x$, where $a > 0$ and $a \neq 1$.

- The general equation for exponential growth is $y = C(1 + r)^t$ and the general equation for exponential decay is $y = C(1 - r)^t$, where y = the final amount, C = the initial amount, r = the rate of change, and t = the time.

Math Online Vocabulary Review at ca.algebra1.com

Key Vocabulary

axis of symmetry (p. 472)
completing the square (p. 487)
compound interest (p. 511)
discriminant (p. 496)
exponential function (p. 502)
general equation for exponential decay (p. 511)
general equation for exponential growth (p. 510)
maximum (p. 472)
minimum (p. 472)
parabola (p. 471)
quadratic equation (p. 480)
Quadratic Formula (p. 493)
quadratic function (p. 471)
roots (p. 480)
symmetry (p. 472)
vertex (p. 472)
zeros (p. 480)

Vocabulary Check

State whether each sentence is *true* or *false*. If *false*, replace the underlined word or phrase to make a true sentence.

1. The graph of a quadratic function is a <u>parabola</u>. **true**

2. The solutions of a quadratic equation are called <u>roots</u>. **true**

3. The <u>zeros</u> of a quadratic function can be found by using the equation $x = -\dfrac{b}{2a}$. **false; axis of symmetry**

4. The <u>vertex</u> is the maximum or minimum point of a parabola. **true**

5. The <u>exponential decay</u> equation is $y = C(1 + r)^t$. **false; exponential growth**

6. An example of a <u>quadratic function</u> is $y = 8^x$. **false; exponential function**

7. <u>Symmetry</u> is a geometric property possessed by parabolas. **true**

8. The graph of a quadratic function has a <u>minimum</u> if the coefficient of the x^2 term is negative. **false; maximum**

9. The expression $b^2 - 4ac$ is called the <u>discriminant</u>. **true**

10. A quadratic equation whose graph has two x-intercepts has <u>no</u> real roots. **false; two**

 Summative Assessment

CRM Vocabulary Test, p. 54

FOLDABLES Study Organizer

Dinah Zike's Foldables™

Have students review the chapter to make sure they have included information for every lesson page in their Foldables. Now is a good time to ask if students have any questions about the concepts that they recorded.

Suggest that students keep their Foldables handy while completing the Study Guide and Review pages. Point out that their Foldables can serve as quick review tools for studying for the chapter test.

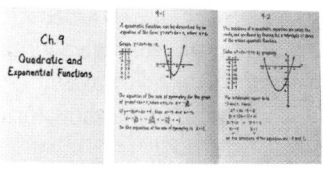

 Formative Assessment

Key Vocabulary The page reference after each word denotes where that term was first introduced. If students have difficulty answering questions 1–10, remind them that they can use these page references to refresh their memories about the vocabulary terms.

Math Online ca.algebra1.com

Vocabulary PuzzleMaker improves students' mathematics vocabulary using four puzzle formats—crossword, scramble, word search using a word list, and word search using clues. Students can work online or from a printed worksheet.

Lesson-by-Lesson Review

Intervention If the given examples are not sufficient to review the topics covered by the questions, remind students that the page references tell them where to review that topic in their textbooks.

Two-Day Option Have students complete the Lesson-by-Lesson Review on pp. 518–520. Then you can use ExamView® Assessment Suite to customize another review worksheet that practices all the objectives of this chapter or only the objectives on which your students need more help.

For more information on ExamView® Assessment Suite, see p. 468C.

Differentiated Instruction
Super DVD: MindJogger Videoquizzes
Use this DVD as an alternative format of review for the test. For more information on this game show format, see p. 468D.

Additional Answers

11. $x = -1$; $(-1, -1)$; min

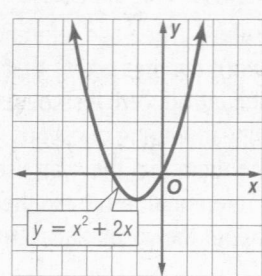

12. $x = 0$; $(0, 4)$; max

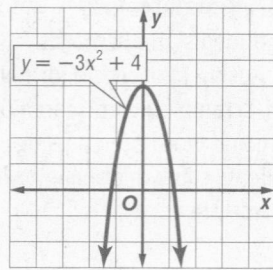

Lesson-by-Lesson Review

9-1 **Graphing Quadratic Functions** (pp. 471–477)

Write the equation of the axis of symmetry, and find the coordinates of the vertex of the graph of each function. Identify the vertex as a maximum or minimum. Then graph the function.

11. $y = x^2 + 2x$ **12.** $y = -3x^2 + 4$

13. $y = x^2 - 3x - 4$ **14.** $y = 3x^2 + 6x - 17$

15. $y = -2x^2 + 1$ **16.** $y = -x^2 - 3x$

11–16. See margin.

PHYSICAL SCIENCE For Exercises 17–20, use the following information.
A model rocket is launched with a velocity of 64 feet per second. The equation $h = -16t^2 + 64t$ gives the height of the rocket t seconds after it is launched.

17. Write the equation of the axis of symmetry and find the coordinates of the vertex. $x = 2$; $(2, 64)$

18. Graph the function. **See margin.**

19. What is the maximum height that the rocket reaches? **64 ft**

20. How many seconds is the rocket in the air? **4 s**

Example 1 Consider the graph of $y = x^2 - 8x + 12$.

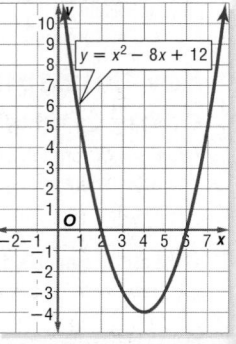

a. Write the equation of the axis of symmetry.

$x = -\dfrac{b}{2a}$

$x = -\dfrac{-8}{2(1)}$

$x = 4$

The equation of the axis of symmetry is $x = 4$.

b. Find the coordinates of the vertex.

The x-coordinate for vertex is 4.

$y = x^2 - 8x + 12$	Original equation
$= (4)^2 - 8(4) + 12$	$x = 4$
$= 16 - 32 + 12$	Simplify.
$= -4$	Simplify.

The coordinates of the vertex are $(4, -4)$.

9-2 **Solving Quadratic Equations by Graphing** (pp. 480–485)

Solve each equation by graphing. If integral roots cannot be found, estimate the roots by stating the consecutive integers between which the roots lie.

21. $x^2 - x - 12 = 0$ **22.** $-x^2 + 6x - 9 = 0$

23. $x^2 + 4x - 3 = 0$ **24.** $2x^2 - 5x + 4 = 0$

25. $x^2 - 10x = -21$ **26.** $6x^2 - 13x = 15$

25–26. See Ch. 9 Answer Appendix.

27. **NUMBER THEORY** Use a quadratic equation to find two numbers whose sum is 5 and whose product is -24. **-3 and 8**

Example 2 Solve $x^2 - 3x - 4 = 0$ by graphing.
Graph the related function $f(x) = x^2 - 3x - 4$.

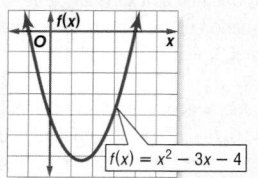

The x-intercepts are -1 and 4. Therefore, the solutions are -1 and 4.

518 Chapter 9 Quadratic and Exponential Functions

13. $x = 1\frac{1}{2}$; $\left(1\frac{1}{2}, -6\frac{1}{4}\right)$; min

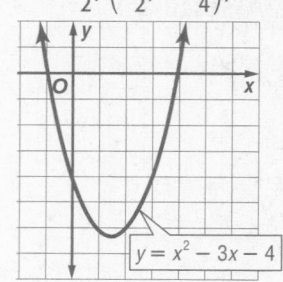

14. $x = -1$; $(-1, -20)$; min

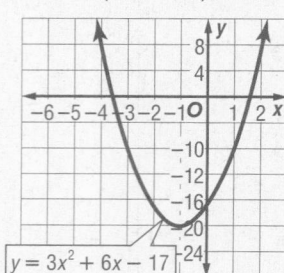

Mixed Problem Solving
For mixed problem-solving practice,
see page 752.

CHAPTER
9 **Study Guide and Review**

9-3 **Solving Quadratic Equations by Completing the Square** (pp. 486–491)

Solve each equation by taking the square root of each side. Round to the nearest tenth if necessary.

28. $a^2 + 6a + 9 = 4$ **−5, −1**

29. $n^2 - 2n + 1 = 25$ **−4, 6**

Solve each equation by completing the square. Round to the nearest tenth if necessary.

30. $-3x^2 + 4 = 0$ **−1.2, 1.2**

31. $x^2 - 16x + 32 = 0$ **2.3, 13.7**

32. $m^2 - 7m = 5$ **−0.7, 7.7**

33. GEOMETRY The area of a square can be tripled by increasing the length by 6 centimeters and the width by 3 centimeters. What is the length of the side of the square? **6 cm**

Example 3 Solve $y^2 + 6y + 2 = 0$ by completing the square. Round to the nearest tenth if necessary.

Step 1 Isolate the y^2 and y terms.

$y^2 + 6y + 2 = 0$ Original equation

$y^2 + 6y = -2$ Subtract 2 from each side.

Step 2 Complete the square and solve.

$y^2 + 6y + 9 = -2 + 9$ $\left(\frac{6}{2}\right)^2 = 9$; add 9 to each side.

$(y + 3)^2 = 7$ Factor $y^2 + 6y + 9$.

$y + 3 = \pm\sqrt{7}$ Take the square root of each side.

$y = -3 \pm \sqrt{7}$ Subtract 3 from each side.

The solutions are about −5.6 and −0.4.

9-4 **Solving Quadratic Equations by Using the Quadratic Formula** (pp. 493–499)

Solve each equation by using the Quadratic Formula. Round to the nearest tenth if necessary.

34. $x^2 - 8x = 20$ **−2, 10**

35. $r^2 + 10r + 9 = 0$ **−9, −1**

36. $4p^2 + 4p = 15$ **−2.5, 1.5**

37. $2y^2 + 3 = -8y$ **−3.6, −0.4**

38. $2d^2 + 8d + 3 = 3$ **−4, 0**

39. $21a^2 + 5a - 7 = 0$ **−0.7, 0.5**

40. ENTERTAINMENT A stunt person attached to a safety harness drops from a height of 210 feet. A function that models the drop is $h = -16t^2 + 210$, where h is the height in feet and t is the time in seconds. About how many seconds does it take to drop from 210 feet to 30 feet? **about 3.4 s**

Example 4 Solve $2x^2 + 7x - 15 = 0$ by using the Quadratic Formula.

For this equation, $a = 2$, $b = 7$, and $c = -15$.

$x = \dfrac{-b \pm \sqrt{b^2 - 4ac}}{2a}$ Quadratic Formula

$= \dfrac{-7 \pm \sqrt{7^2 - 4(2)(-15)}}{2(2)}$ $a = 2, b = 7,$ and $c = -15$

$= \dfrac{-7 \pm \sqrt{169}}{4}$ Simplify.

$= \dfrac{-7 + 13}{4}$ or $\dfrac{-7 - 13}{4}$ Separate the solutions.

$x = 1.5$ or $x = -5$ Simplify.

The solutions are −5 and 1.5.

Additional Answers

15. $x = 0$; (0, 1); max

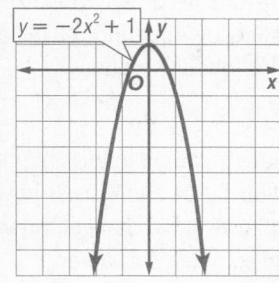

16. $x = -1\frac{1}{2}$; $\left(-1\frac{1}{2}, 2\frac{1}{4}\right)$; max

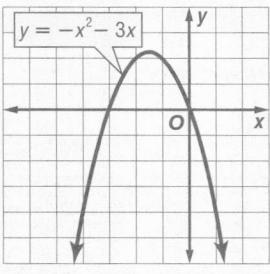

18.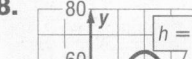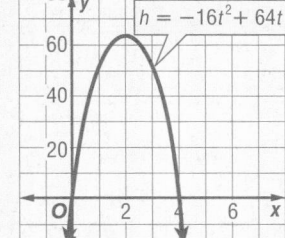

21.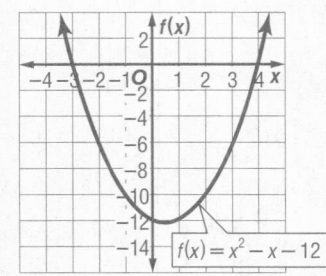

−3, 4

22.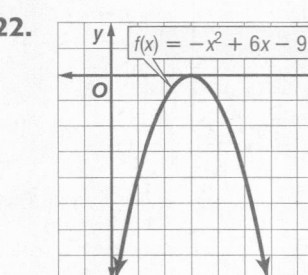

3

23.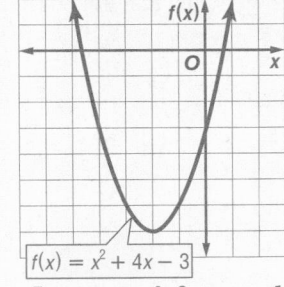

$-5 < x < -4, 0 < x < 1$

24.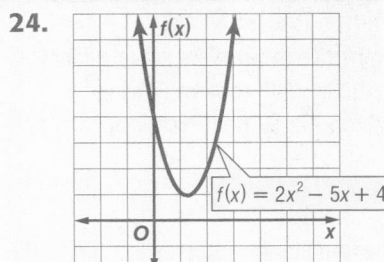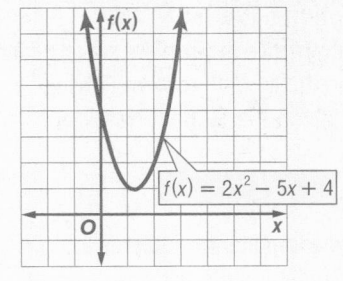

∅

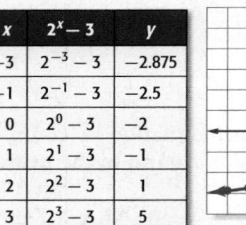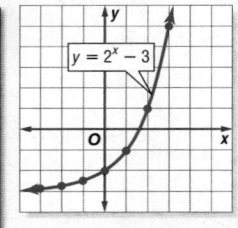

Problem Solving Review

For additional practice in problem solving for Chapter 9, see the Mixed Problem Solving Appendix, p. 752 in the Student Handbook section.

Anticipation Guide

Have students complete the Chapter 9 Anticipation Guide and discuss how their responses have changed now that they have completed Chapter 9.

 Anticipation Guide, p. 3

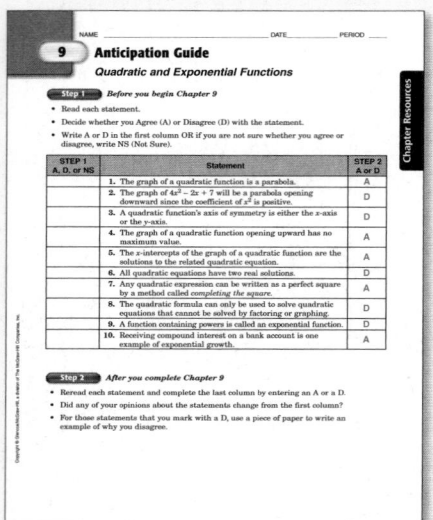

Additional Answers

41.

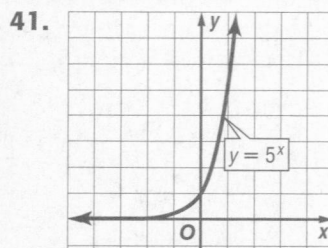

1: 3.1

42.

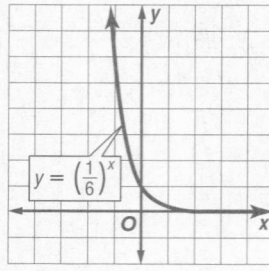

1; 0.7

9–5 **Exponential Functions** (pp. 502–508)

Graph each function. State the y-intercept. Then use the graph to determine the approximate value of the given expression. Use a calculator to confirm the value. 41–42. See margin.

41. $y = 5^x$; $5^{0.7}$
42. $y = \left(\frac{1}{6}\right)^x$; $\left(\frac{1}{6}\right)^{0.2}$

Graph each function. State the y-intercept. 43–44. See margin.

43. $y = 3^x + 6$
44. $y = 3^{x+2}$

45. BIOLOGY The population of bacteria in a Petri dish increases according to the model $p = 550 \cdot 2.7^{0.008t}$, where t is the number of hours and $t = 0$ corresponds to 1:00 P.M. Use this model to estimate the number of bacteria in the dish at 5 P.M. **about 568**

Example 5 Graph $y = 2^x - 3$. State the y-intercept.

x	$2^x - 3$	y
−3	$2^{-3} - 3$	−2.875
−1	$2^{-1} - 3$	−2.5
0	$2^0 - 3$	−2
1	$2^1 - 3$	−1
2	$2^2 - 3$	1
3	$2^3 - 3$	5

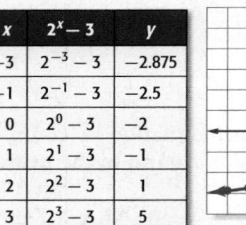

Graph the ordered pairs and connect the points with a smooth curve. The y-intercept is −2.

9–6 **Growth and Decay** (pp. 510–514)

Determine the final amount for each investment.

	Principal	Annual Interest Rate	Time (yr)	Type of Compounding
46.	$2000	3%	8	quarterly
47.	$5500	2.25%	15	monthly
48.	$15,000	2.5%	25	monthly
49.	$500	1.75%	40	daily

RESTAURANTS For Exercises 50 and 51, use the following information.
The total restaurant sales in the United States increased at an annual rate of about 5.2% between 1996 and 2004. In 1996, the total sales were $310 billion.

50. Write an equation for the average sales per year for t years after 1996.

51. Predict the total restaurant sales in 2008. **about $570 billion**

Example 6 Find the final amount of an investment if $1500 is invested at an interest rate of 2.5% compounded quarterly for 10 years.

$A = p\left(1 + \frac{r}{n}\right)^{nt}$ Compound interest equation

$= 1500\left(1 + \frac{0.025}{4}\right)^{4(10)}$ $P = 1500, r = 2.5\%$ or 0.025, $n = 4$, and $t = 10$

≈ 1924.54 Simplify.

The final amount in the account is about $1924.54.

46. $2540.22
47. $7705.48
48. $28,005.48
49. $1006.86
50. $y = 310(1.052)^t$

Problem Solving Review

For additional practice in problem solving for Chapter 9, see the Mixed Problem Solving Appendix, p. 752 in the Student Handbook section.

Anticipation Guide

Have students complete the Chapter 9 Anticipation Guide and discuss how their responses have changed now that they have completed Chapter 9.

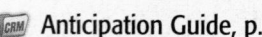 Anticipation Guide, p. 3

Write the equation of the axis of symmetry, and find the coordinates of the vertex of the graph of each function. Identify the vertex as a maximum or minimum. Then graph the function. **1–4. See margin.**

1. $y = x^2 - 4x + 13$ **2.** $y = -3x^2 - 6x + 4$
3. $y = 2x^2 + 3$ **4.** $y = -1(x - 2)^2 + 1$

Solve each equation by graphing. If integral roots cannot be found, estimate the roots by stating the consecutive integers between which the roots lie.

5. $x^2 - 2x + 2 = 0$ $\varnothing$
6. $x^2 + 6x = -7$ $-5 < x < -4; -2 < x < -1$
7. $x^2 + 24x + 144 = 0$ -12
8. $2x^2 - 8x = 42$ $-3, 7$
   5–8. See Ch. 9 Answer Appendix for graphs.

9. MULTIPLE CHOICE Which function is graphed below? **D**

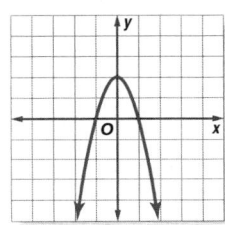

 A $y = 2x^2 - 2$

 B $y = 2x^2 + 2$

 C $y = -2x^2 - 2$

 D $y = -2x^2 + 2$

Solve each equation. Round to the nearest tenth if necessary. **10–17. See margin.**

10. $x^2 + 7x + 6 = 0$ **11.** $2x^2 - 5x - 12 = 0$
12. $6n^2 + 7n = 20$ **13.** $3k^2 + 2k = 5$
14. $y^2 - \frac{3}{5}y + \frac{2}{25} = 0$ **15.** $-3x^2 + 5 = 14x$
16. $z^2 - 13z = 32$ **17.** $7m^2 = m + 5$

18. MULTIPLE CHOICE Which equation best represents the parabola graphed below if it is shifted 3 units to the right? **H**

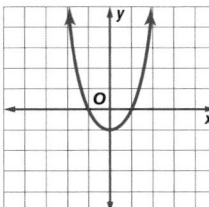

 F $y = x^2 - 1$

 G $y = x^2 + 2$

 H $y = x^2 - 6x + 8$

 J $y = x^2 + 6x + 8$

19–22. See Ch. 9 Answer Appendix for graphs.
Graph each function. State the y-intercept.

19. $y = \left(\frac{1}{2}\right)^x$ **1**   **20.** $y = 4 \cdot 2^x$ **4**

21. $y = 0.5(4^x)$ **0.5**   **22.** $y = 5^x - 4$ **−3**

23. Graph $y = \left(\frac{1}{3}\right)^x - 3$ and state the y-intercept. Then use the graph to determine the approximate value of $y = \left(\frac{1}{3}\right)^{3.5} - 3$. Use a calculator to confirm the value.
−2, −3.0; See Ch. 9 Answer Appendix for graph.

24. CARS Ley needs to replace her car. If she leases a car, she will pay $410 a month for 2 years and then has the option to buy the car for $14,458. The current price of the car is $17,369. If the car depreciates at 16% per year, how will the depreciated price compare with the buy-out price of the lease?
$2002 less than the buyout price

25. FINANCE Find the total amount of the investment shown in the table if interest is compounded quarterly. **about $2721.03**

Principal	$1500
Length of Investment	10 yr
Annual Interest Rate	6%

✓ **Summative Assessment**

CRM **Chapter 9 Resource Masters**

Leveled Chapter 9 Tests			
Form	**Type**	**Level**	**Pages**
1	MC	BL	55–56
2A	MC	OL	57–58
2B	MC	OL	59–60
2C	FR	OL	61–62
2D	FR	OL	63–64
3	FR	AL	65–66

MC = multiple-choice questions
FR = free-response questions
BL = below grade level
OL = on grade level
AL = above grade level

• Vocabulary Test, p. 54
• Extended-Response Test, p. 67

ExamView®
Assessment Suite

Customize and create multiple versions of your chapter tests and their answer keys. All of the questions from the leveled chapter tests in the *Chapter 9 Resource Masters* are also available on ExamView Assessment Suite with the California Standard that each item assesses.

Additional Answers

1–4. See Chapter 9 Answer Appendix for graphs.

1. $x = 2$; $(2, 9)$; min
2. $x = -1$; $(-1, 7)$; max
3. $x = 0$; $(0, 3)$; min
4. $x = 2$; $(2, 1)$; max

Data-Driven Decision Making	Exercises	Lesson	Standard	Resources for Review
Diagnostic Teaching Based on the results of the Chapter 9 Practice Test, use the following to review concepts that students continue to find challenging.	10–17	9–4	20.0	CRM Study Guide and Intervention pp. 27-28, 34–35, 42–43
	19–23	9–5	**Preparation for Algebra II 12.0**	Math Online • Extra Examples
	24–25	9–6	**Preparation for Algebra II 12.0**	• Personal Tutor • Concepts in Motion

CHAPTER
9
California
Standards Practice

CHAPTER
9
California Standards Practice
Cumulative, Chapters 1–9

 Formative Assessment

You can use these two pages to benchmark student progress. The California Standards are listed with each question.

 Chapter 9 Resource Masters
• Standardized Test Practice, pp. 68–70

Assessment Suite

Create practice worksheets or tests that align to the California Standards, as well as TIMSS and NAEP tests.

 Read each question. Then fill in the correct answer on the answer document provided by your teacher or on a sheet of paper.

1 Trevor is solving this equation by completing the square.

$$rx^2 + sx + t = 0 \text{ (where } r \geq 0)$$

Step 1: $rx^2 + sx = -t$

Step 2: $x^2 + \frac{s}{r}x = -\frac{t}{r}$

Step 3: ?

Which should be Step 3 in the solution? **D**

A $x^2 = -\frac{s}{r} - \frac{s}{r}x$

B $x^2 + \frac{s}{r}x + \frac{s}{2r} = -\frac{t}{r} + \frac{s}{2r}$

C $x + \frac{s}{r} = -\frac{t}{rx}$

D $x^2 + \frac{s}{r}x + \left(\frac{s}{2r}\right)^2 = -\frac{t}{r} + \left(\frac{s}{2r}\right)^2$

2 How many times does the graph of $y = 3x^2 - 3x + 4$ intersect the x-axis? **F**

F none   **H** two

G one   **J** three

3 An object that is projected straight downward with initial velocity v feet per second travels a distance $s = vt + 16t^2$, where t = time in seconds. Rafael is in a hot air balloon 204 feet above the ground and throws a penny straight down with an initial velocity of 20 feet per second. In how many seconds will the penny reach the ground? **A**

A 3   **C** 5

B 4   **D** 6

TEST-TAKING TIP

Question 3 Always write down your calculations on scrap paper or in the test booklet, even if you think you can do the calculations in your head. Writing down your calculations will help you avoid making simple mistakes.

---

4 Which is a factor of $x^2 + x - 20$? **G**

F $x - 5$

G $x + 5$

H $x - 6$

J $x + 6$

5 Find the product of $(3m - 4)(m + 5)$. **A**

A $3m^2 + 11m - 20$

B $3m^2 + 11m + 20$

C $3m^2 + 19m - 20$

D $3m^2 + 19m + 20$

6 What is the solution to this system of equations? **G**

$$4x + 7y = 9$$
$$-x - 5y = -12$$

F $(-3, -3)$

G $(-3, 3)$

H $(3, -3)$

J $(3, 3)$

7 What is the slope of the line graphed below? **C**

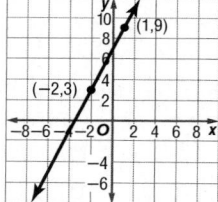

A -6

B -2

C 2

D 6

 California Standards Practice at ca.algebra1.com

More California Standards Practice
For practice by standard, see pages CA1–CA43.

CHAPTER 9 California Standards Practice

8 When is this statement true? **H**

> The multiplicative inverse of a number is less than the original number.

F This statement is never true.

G This statement is always true.

H This statement is true for numbers greater than 1.

J This statement is true for numbers less than −1.

9 The length of a rectangle is three more than twice the width. If the perimeter of the rectangle is 15, what is the length of the rectangle? **6**

10 Jennie hit a baseball straight up in the air. The height h, in feet, of the ball above the ground is modeled by the equation $h = -16t^2 + 64t$. How long is the ball above ground? **C**

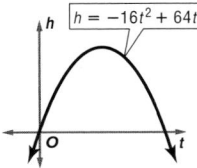
$h = -16t^2 + 64t$

A 1 second

B 2 seconds

C 4 seconds

D 16 seconds

11 Which inequality is shown on the graph below? **F**

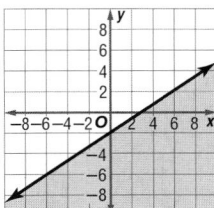

F $y \leq \frac{2}{3}x - 2$

G $y < \frac{2}{3}x - 2$

H $y \geq \frac{2}{3}x - 2$

J $y > \frac{2}{3}x - 2$

Pre-AP/Anchor Problem

Record your answers on a sheet of paper. Show your work.

12 Annika Sorenstam hit a golf ball and its path through the air is modeled by the equation $h = -16t^2 + 80t + 1$, where h is the height in feet of the golf ball and t is the time in seconds.

a. Approximately how long was the ball in the air? **5.01 seconds**

b. How high was the ball at its highest point? **101.0 feet**

TEST-TAKING TIP

Question 7 One advantage of this multiple-choice question is that a correct answer is among the choices. When this is the case, it is sometimes possible to work backward by taking the answers and testing each of them in the original problem.

Item Analysis
Question 9 is a griddable question. In griddable questions, students arrive at an answer and then record it in a special grid, coloring in the appropriate bubble under each digit of the answer.

Answer Sheet Practice
Have students simulate taking a standardized test by recording their answers on practice recording sheets.

CRM **Student Recording Sheet, p. 49**

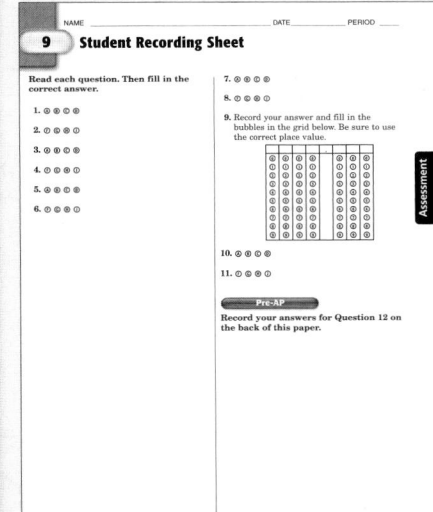

NEED EXTRA HELP?

If You Missed Question...	1	2	3	4	5	6	7	8	9	10	11	12
Go to Lesson...	9–3	9–2	9–4	8–3	7–6	5–4	4–1	1–4	5–2	9–4	6–6	9–2
For Help with Standard...	9.0	22.0	23.0	11.0	10.0	8.0	7AF3.3	25.1	9.0	23.0	6.0	23.0

Homework Option

Get Ready for Chapter 10 Assign students the exercises on p. 519 as homework to assess whether they possess the prerequisite skills needed for the next chapter.

Page 469, Get Ready for Chapter 9

1.

x	y
−6	−1
−4	1
−2	3
0	5
2	7

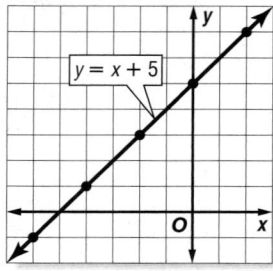
$y = x + 5$

2.

x	y
0	−3
1	−1
2	1
3	3

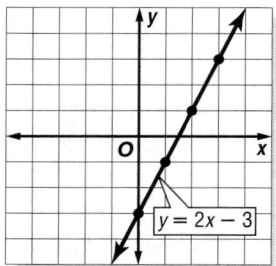
$y = 2x − 3$

3.

x	y
−4	−1
−2	0
0	1
2	2
4	3

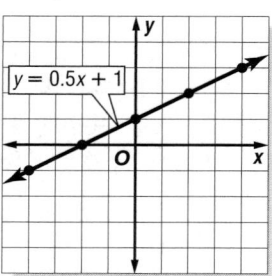
$y = 0.5x + 1$

4.

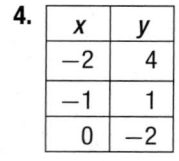

x	y
−2	4
−1	1
0	−2

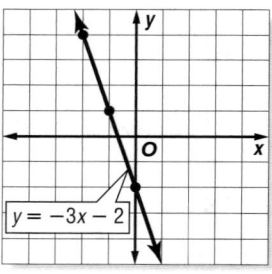
$y = −3x − 2$

5.

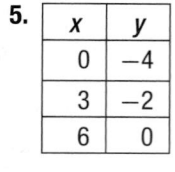

x	y
0	−4
3	−2
6	0

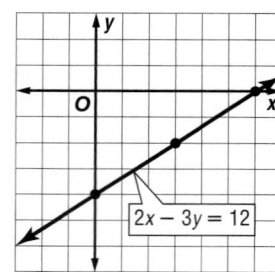
$2x − 3y = 12$

6.

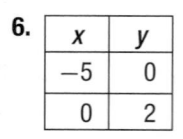

x	y
−5	0
0	2

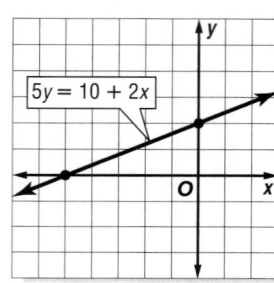
$5y = 10 + 2x$

Page 472, Lesson 9-1 (Check Your Progress)

1.

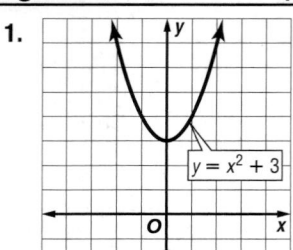
$y = x^2 + 3$

D: {x | x is a real number};
R: {y | y ≥ 3}

2.

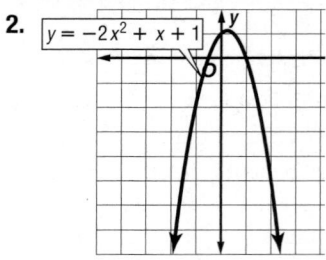
$y = −2x^2 + x + 1$

D: {x | x is a real number};
R: $\left\{ y \mid y \geq 1\frac{1}{8} \right\}$

Pages 475-476, Lesson 9-1

5.

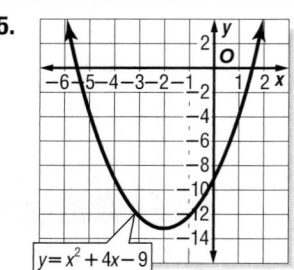
$y = x^2 + 4x − 9$

6.

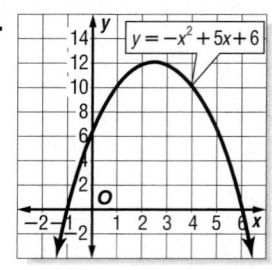
$y = −x^2 + 5x + 6$

7.

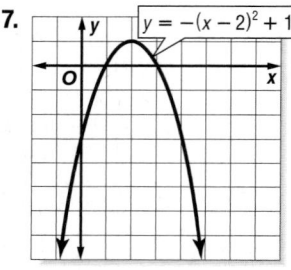
$y = −(x − 2)^2 + 1$

8.

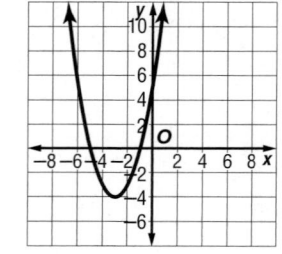

10.

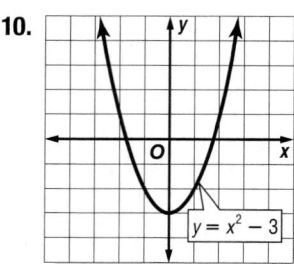
$y = x^2 − 3$

11.

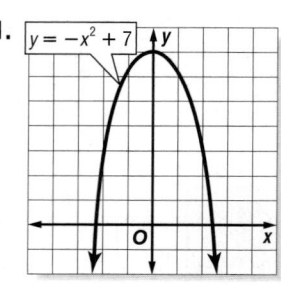
$y = −x^2 + 7$

12.

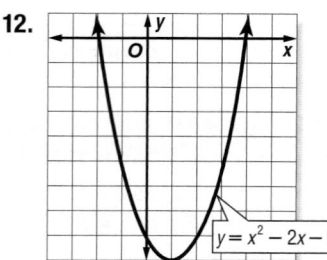
$y = x^2 − 2x − 8$

13.

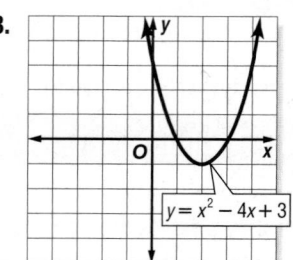
$y = x^2 − 4x + 3$

14.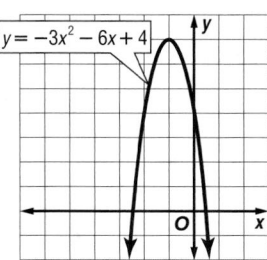
$y = -3x^2 - 6x + 4$

15.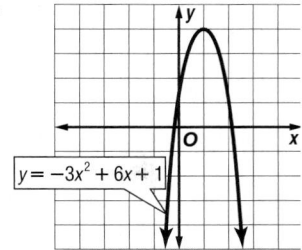
$y = -3x^2 + 6x + 1$

16.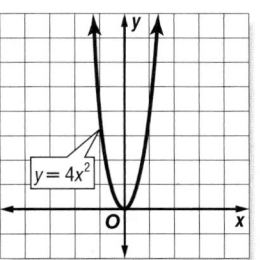
$y = 4x^2$

17.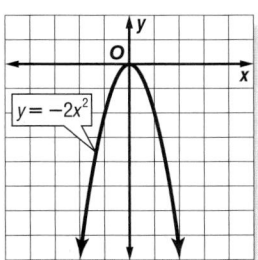
$y = -2x^2$

18.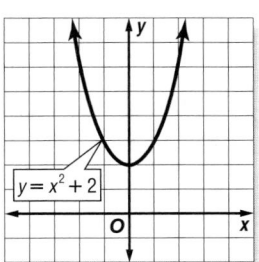
$y = x^2 + 2$

19.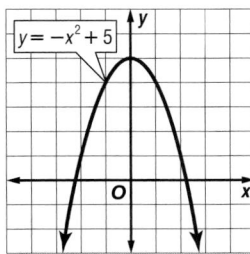
$y = -x^2 + 5$

20.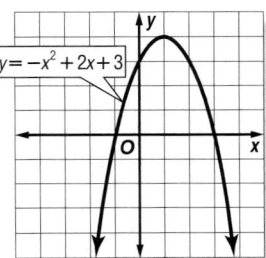
$y = -x^2 + 2x + 3$

21.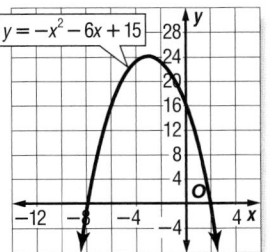
$y = -x^2 - 6x + 15$

22.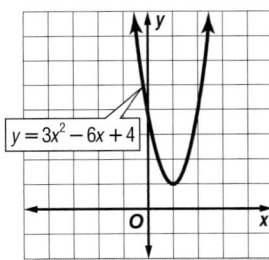
$y = 3x^2 - 6x + 4$

23.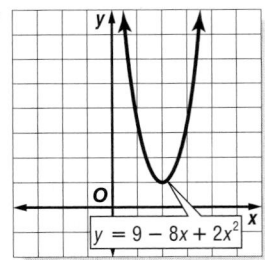
$y = 9 - 8x + 2x^2$

28. $A = x(20 - x)$ or $A = -x^2 + 20x$; A reasonable domain is $\{x \mid 0 < x < 20\}$ because if x is less than or equal to 0 or greater than or equal to 20, the area has a value of zero or it has a negative value. A reasonable range is $\{y \mid 0 < y < 100\}$, because these are the values when x is between 0 and 20.

30.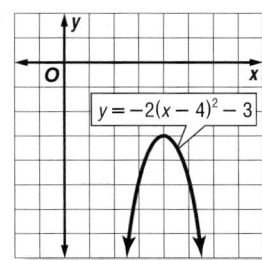
$y = -2(x - 4)^2 - 3$

31.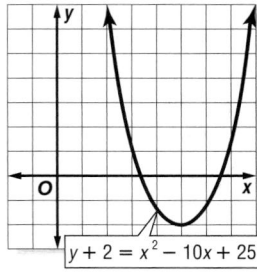
$y + 2 = x^2 - 10x + 25$

32.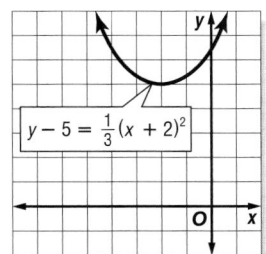
$y - 5 = \frac{1}{3}(x + 2)^2$

33.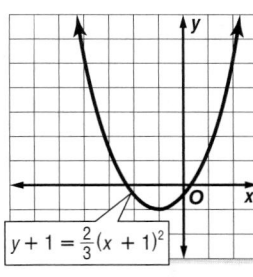
$y + 1 = \frac{2}{3}(x + 1)^2$

42. Sample answer:

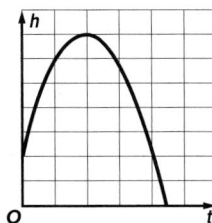

The vertex represents the height of a ball after it is tossed up in the air. Reasonable domain and range values are real numbers greater than or equal to 0.

43.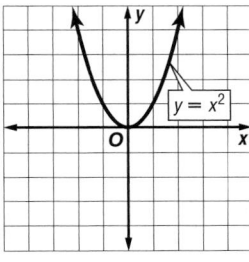
$y = x^2$

Page 479, Extend 9-1

5. The graph will have a vertex at the origin, open downward, and be wider than $y = -x^2$.

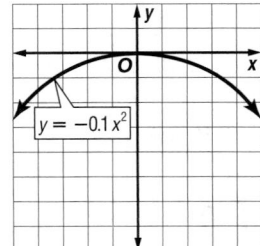
$y = -0.1x^2$

6. The graph will open upward and have the same shape as $y = x^2$, but the vertex will be at $(-1, 0)$.

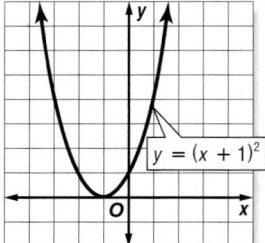

$y = (x + 1)^2$

7. The graph will open upward, have a vertex at the origin, and be narrower than $y = x^2$.

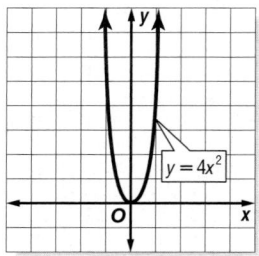

$y = 4x^2$

8. The graph will open upward and have the same shape as $y = x^2$, but its vertex will be at $(0, -6)$.

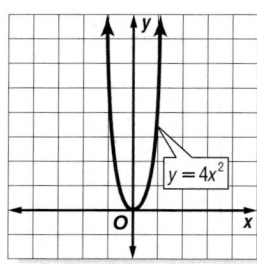

$y = 4x^2$

Page 481, Lesson 9-2 (Check Your Progress)

1.
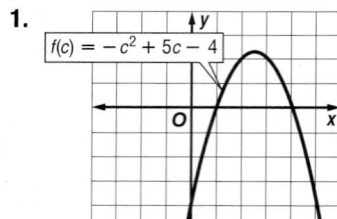

$f(c) = -c^2 + 5c - 4$

2.
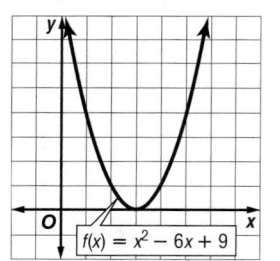

$f(x) = x^2 - 6x + 9$

3.
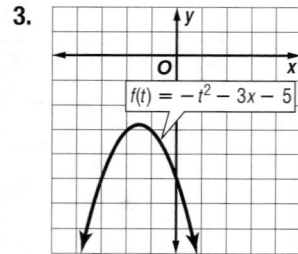

$f(t) = -t^2 - 3x - 5$

Pages 483–485, Lesson 9-2

1.
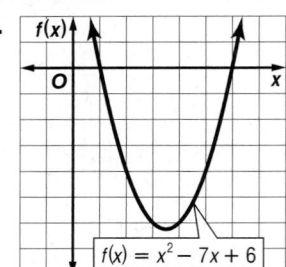

$f(x) = x^2 - 7x + 6$

2.
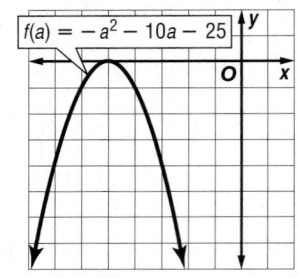

$f(a) = -a^2 - 10a - 25$

3.
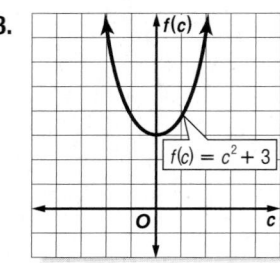

$f(c) = c^2 + 3$

4.
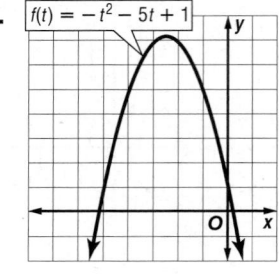

$f(t) = -t^2 - 5t + 1$

7.
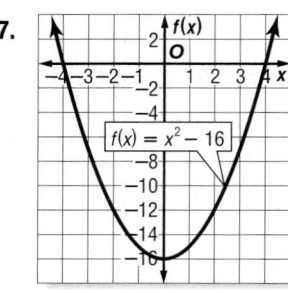

$f(x) = x^2 - 16$

8.
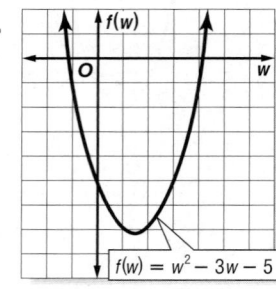

$f(w) = w^2 - 3w - 5$

10.
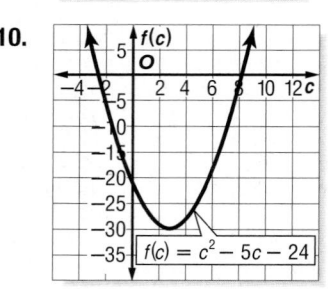

$f(c) = c^2 - 5c - 24$

11.
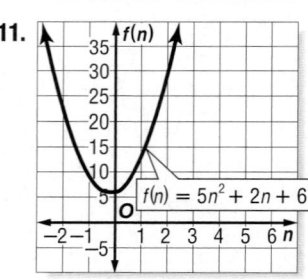

$f(n) = 5n^2 + 2n + 6$

12.
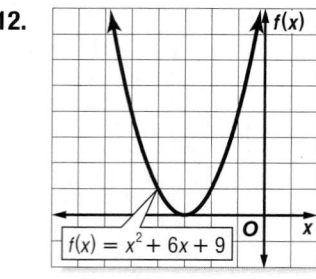

$f(x) = x^2 + 6x + 9$

13.
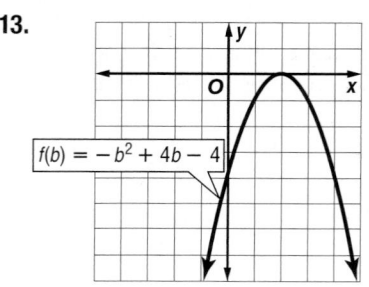

$f(b) = -b^2 + 4b - 4$

14.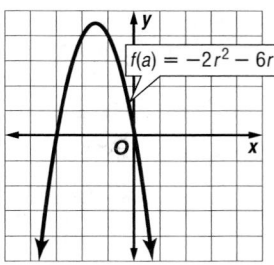

$f(x) = x^2 + 2x + 5$

15.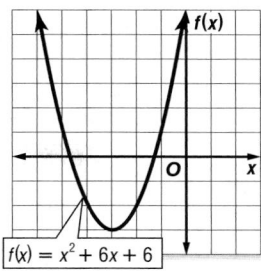

$f(a) = -2r^2 - 6r$

The graph is wider than the graph of $y = x^2$. Also, the vertex is 4 units left and 2 units down from the vertex of the graph of $y = x^2$.

16.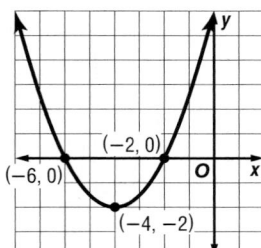

$(-2, 0)$
$(-6, 0)$
$(-4, -2)$

17.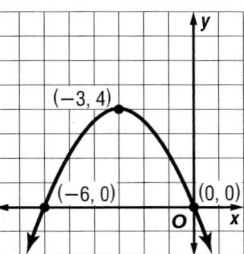

$(-3, 4)$
$(-6, 0)$ $(0, 0)$

The graph is wider than the graph of $y = x^2$ and opens downward rather than upward. Also, the vertex is 3 units left and 4 units up from the vertex of the graph of $y = x^2$.

22.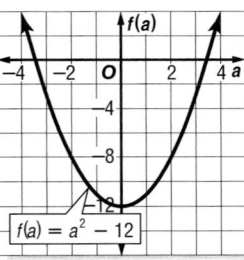

$f(a) = a^2 - 12$

$-4 < a < -3, 3 < a < 4$

23.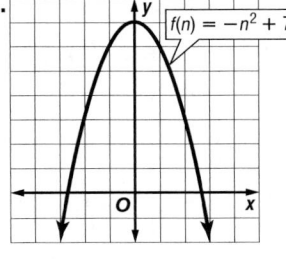

$f(n) = -n^2 + 7$

$-3 < n < -2, 2 < n < 3$

24.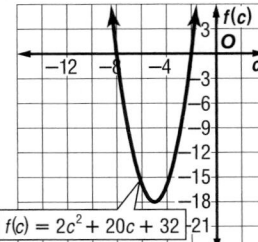

$f(c) = 2c^2 + 20c + 32$

$-8, -2$

25.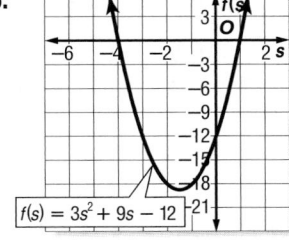

$f(s) = 3s^2 + 9s - 12$

$-4, 1$

26.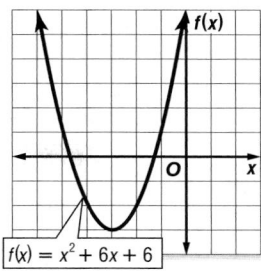

$f(x) = x^2 + 6x + 6$

$-5 < x < -4, -2 < x < -1$

27.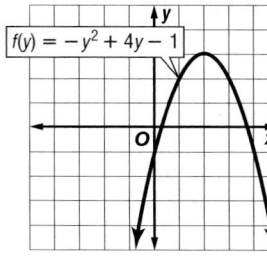

$f(y) = -y^2 + 4y - 1$

$0 < y < 1, 3 < y < 4$

28.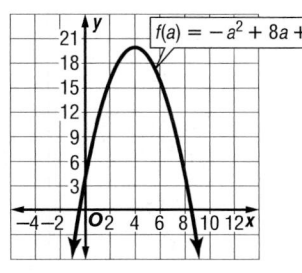

$f(a) = -a^2 + 8a + 4$

$-1 < a < 0, 8 < a < 9$

29.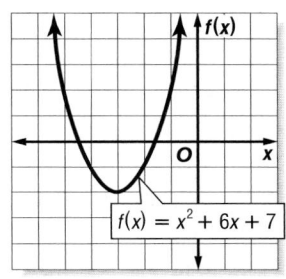

$f(x) = x^2 + 6x + 7$

$-5 < x < -4, -2 < x < -1$

30.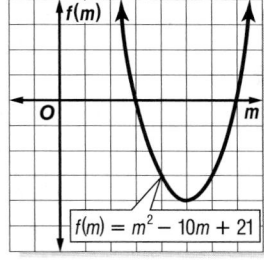

$f(m) = m^2 - 10m + 21$

$3, 7$

41. Sample answer:

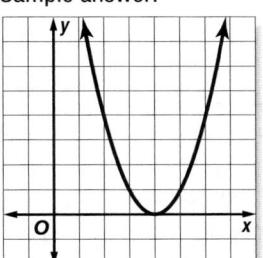

The only solution to the equation with the graph shown is 4.

47.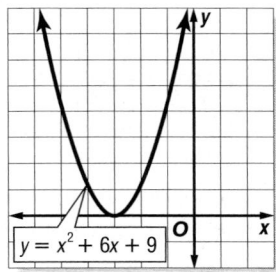

$y = x^2 + 6x + 9$

$x = -3; (-3, 0); \text{min}$

48.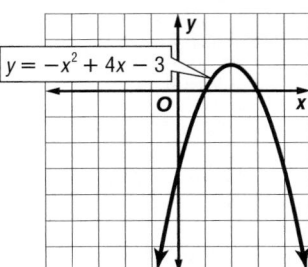

$y = -x^2 + 4x - 3$

$x = 2; (2, 1); \text{max}$

49.

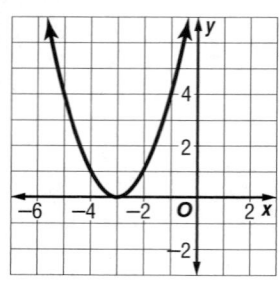
$y = 0.5x^2 - 6x + 5$

$x = 6; (6, -13);$ min

Page 485, Lesson 9-2

47.

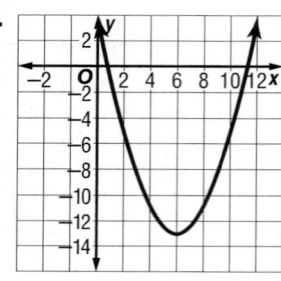

$x = -3; (-3, 0);$ min

48.

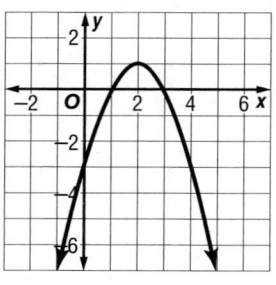

$x = 2; (2, 1);$ max

49.

$x = 6; (6, -13);$ min

Page 491, Lesson 9-3

47. Sample answer: Al-Khwarizmi used squares to geometrically represent quadratic equations. He represented x^2 by a square whose sides were each x units long. To this square, he added 4 rectangles with length x units long and width $\frac{8}{4}$ or 2 units long. This area represents 35. To make this a square, four 4×4 squares must be added. To solve $x^2 + 8x = 35$ by completing the square, use the following steps.

$x^2 + 8x = 35$	Original equation.
$x^2 + 8x + 16 = 35 + 16$	Since $\left(\frac{8}{2}\right)^2 = 16$, add 16 to each side.
$(x + 4)^2 = 51$	Factor $x^2 + 8x + 16$.
$x + 4 = \pm\sqrt{51}$	Take the square root of each side.
$x + 4 - 4 = \pm\sqrt{51} - 4$	Subtract 4 from each side.
$x = -4 \pm\sqrt{51}$	Simplify.

$x = -4 - \sqrt{51}$ or $x = -4 + \sqrt{51}$	Simplify.
$x \approx -11.14$	$x \approx 3.14$

The solutions are -11.14 and 3.14.

Page 492, Mid-Chapter Quiz

2.

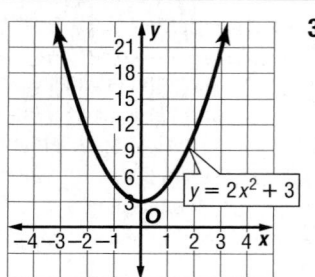
$y = 2x^2 + 3$

$x = 0; (0, 3);$ minimum

3.

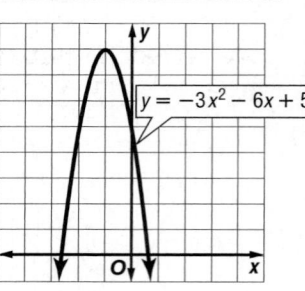
$y = -3x^2 - 6x + 5$

$x = -1; (-1, 8);$ maximum

5.

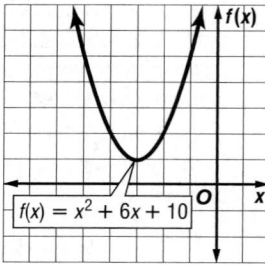
$f(x) = x^2 + 6x + 10$

$\varnothing$

6.

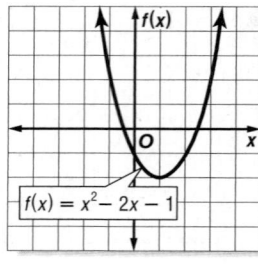
$f(x) = x^2 - 2x - 1$

$-1 < x < 0, 2 < x < 3$

7.

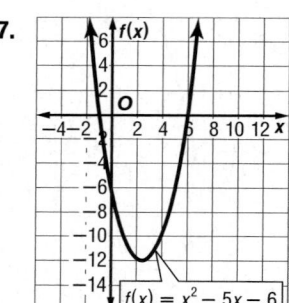
$f(x) = x^2 - 5x - 6$

$-1, 6$

Page 498, Lesson 9-4

43. The function can be factored to $f(x) = (x - 4)^2$, so there is one real root at (4, 0). Using the discriminant to determine the number of roots involves more computation and potential for error.

44. Sample answer: (1) Factor $x^2 - 2x - 15$ as $(x + 3)(x - 5)$. Then according to the Zero Product Property, either $x + 3 = 0$ or $x - 5 = 0$. Solving these equations, $x = -3$ or $x = 5$. (2) Rewrite the equation as $x^2 - 2x = 15$. Then add 1 to each side of the equation to complete the square on the left side. Then $(x - 1)^2 = 16$. Taking the square root of each side, $x - 1 = \pm 4$. Therefore, $x = 1 \pm 4$ and $x = -3$ or $x = 5$. (3) Use the Quadratic Formula. Therefore,
$$x = \frac{2 \pm \sqrt{2^2 - 4(1)(-15)}}{2(1)} \text{ or } x = \frac{2 \pm \sqrt{64}}{2}. \text{ Simplifying the}$$
expression, $x = -3$ or $x = 5$. See students' preferences.

Page 504, Lesson 9-5 (Graphing Calculator Lab)

1. The graphs are the same shape. The graph of $y = 2^x + 3$ is the graph of $y = 2^x$ translated 3 units up. The graph of $y = 2^x - 4$ is the graph of $y = 2^x$ translated 4 units down.

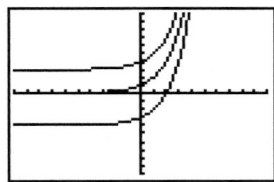

[−10, 10] scl: 1 by [−10, 10] scl: 1

2. The graphs are the same shape. The graph of $y = 2^{x+5}$ is the graph of $y = 2^x$ translated 5 units to the left. The graph of $y = 2^{x-4}$ is the graph of $y = 2^x$ translated 4 units to the right.

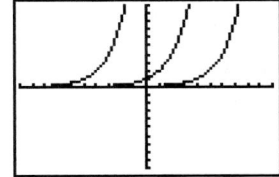

[−10, 10] scl: 1 by [−10, 10] scl: 1

3. All of the graphs cross the y-axis at 1. The graph of $y = 3^x$ is steeper than the graph of $y = 2^x$, and the graph of $y = 5^x$ is steeper yet.

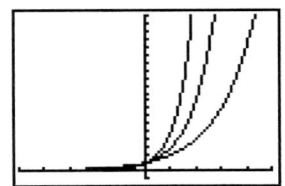

[−5, 5] scl: 1 by [−1, 20] scl: 1

4. The graphs are the same shape. The graph of $y = 3(2^x - 1)$ is the graph of $y = 3(2^x)$ translated 3 units down. The graph of $y = 3(2^x + 1)$ is the graph of $y = 3(2^x)$ translated 3 units up.

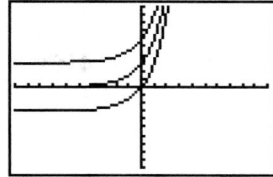

[−10, 10] scl: 1 by [−10, 10] scl: 1

Pages 505–507, Lesson 9-5

1.

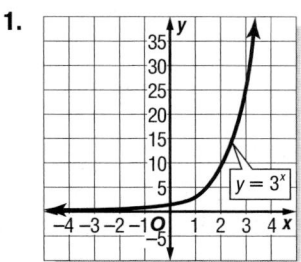

2.

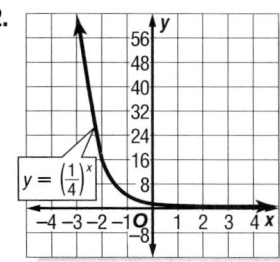

3.

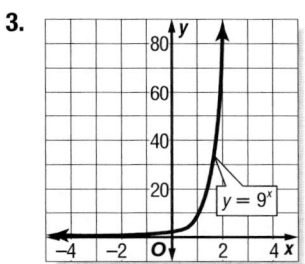

4.

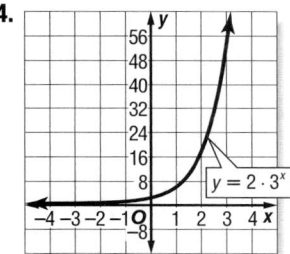

5.

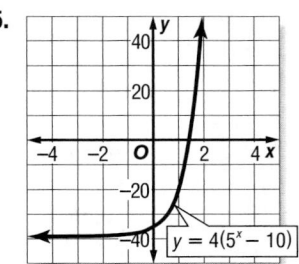

9.

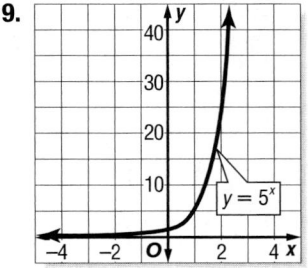

10.

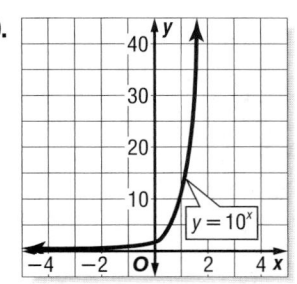

11.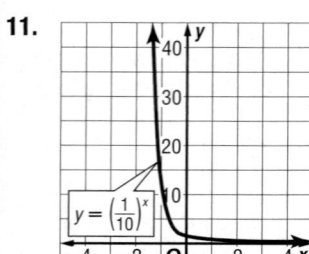

12.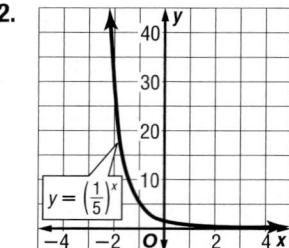

13.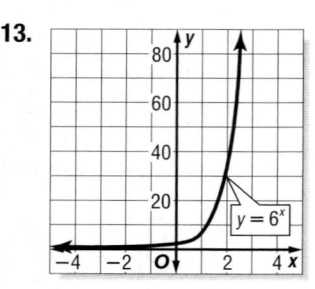

14.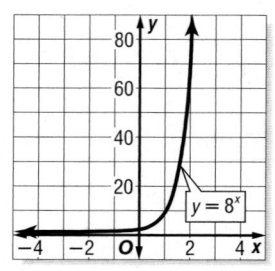

15.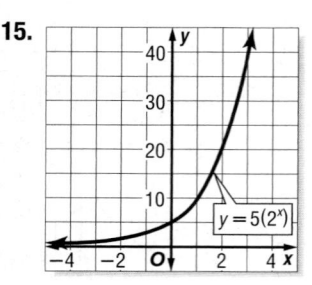

16.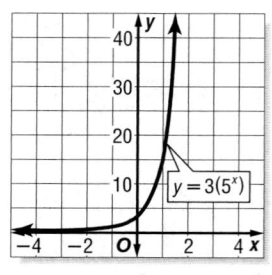

17.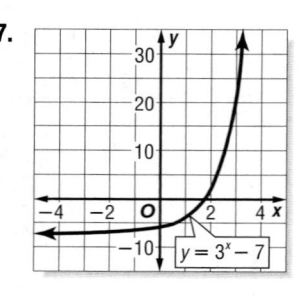

18.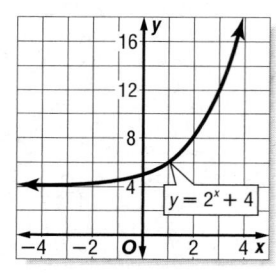

22.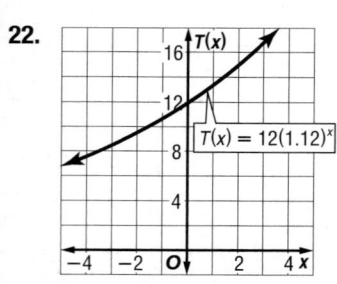

27.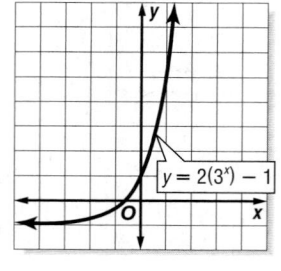

28.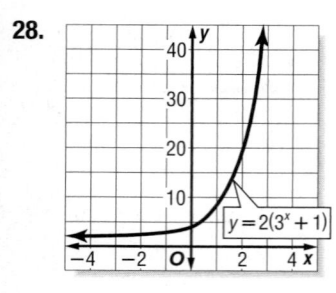

29.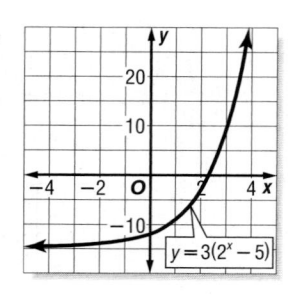

42. Sample answer: The number of teams competing in a basketball tournament can be represented by $y = 2^x$, where the number of teams competing is y and the number of rounds is x.

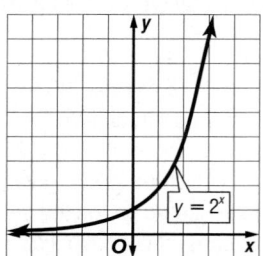

The y-intercept of the graph is 1. The graph increases quickly for $x > 0$.

Page 509, Explore 9-6

3.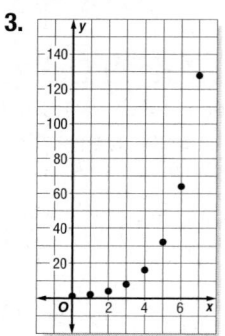

9.

Number of Cuts	Area of Sheet
0	1
1	0.5
2	0.25
3	0.125
4	0.0625
5	0.03125
6	0.015625
7	0.0078125

Page 514, Lesson 9-6

18. Sample answer: If the number of blogs is growing by the same percent each month, an exponential equation can be used to model blogs and predict future blogs. The equation states that the new value equals the amount in November 2003 or 1.1 times the sum of 1 plus 13.7% raised to the power that is equal to the number of months since November 2003. According to the equation, there will be about 14,712 million blogs in January 2010.

Page 518, Study Guide and Review

25.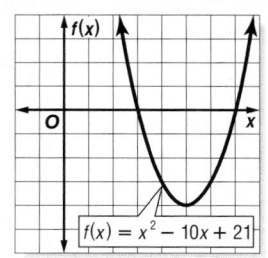
$f(x) = x^2 - 10x + 21$

26.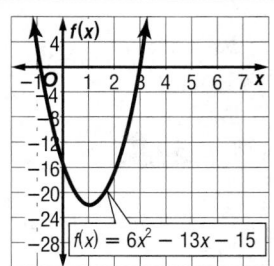
$f(x) = 6x^2 - 13x - 15$

Page 521, Practice Test

1.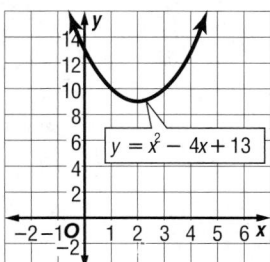
$y = x^2 - 4x + 13$

2.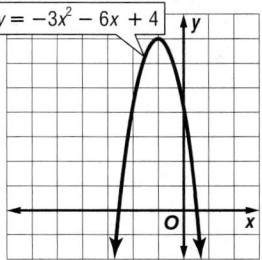
$y = -3x^2 - 6x + 4$

3.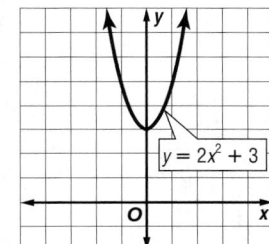
$y = 2x^2 + 3$

4.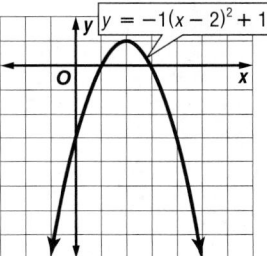
$y = -1(x - 2)^2 + 1$

5.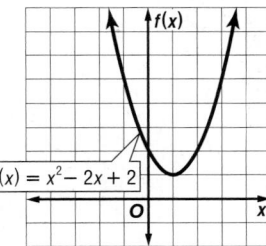
$f(x) = x^2 - 2x + 2$

6.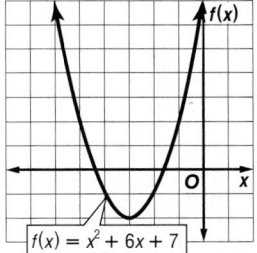
$f(x) = x^2 + 6x + 7$

7.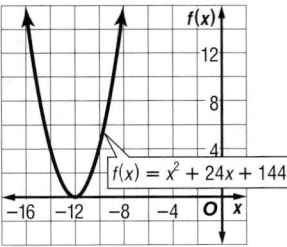
$f(x) = x^2 + 24x + 144$

8.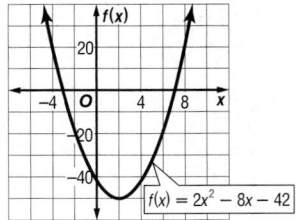
$f(x) = 2x^2 - 8x - 42$

10. $-6, -1$

11. $-1\frac{1}{2}, 4$

12. $-2\frac{1}{2}, 1\frac{1}{3}$

13. $-1\frac{2}{3}, 1$

14. $\frac{1}{5}, \frac{2}{5}$

15. $-5, \frac{1}{3}$

16. $-2.1, 15.1$

17. $-0.8, 0.9$

19.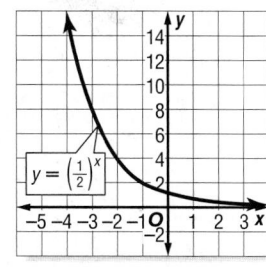
$y = \left(\frac{1}{2}\right)^x$

20.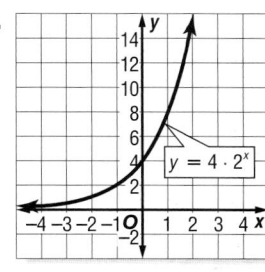
$y = 4 \cdot 2^x$

21.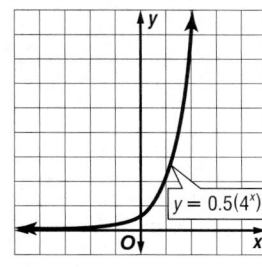
$y = 0.5(4^x)$

22.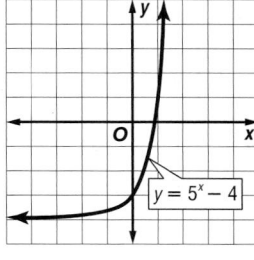
$y = 5^x - 4$

23.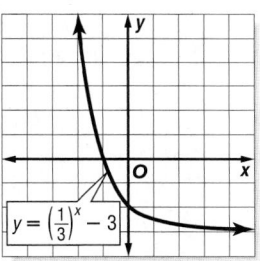
$y = \left(\frac{1}{3}\right)^x - 3$

Introduction

In this unit, students are introduced to additional nonlinear functions such as radical and rational functions. They learn to simplify radical and rational expressions and learn to solve radical and rational equations.

Students investigate the Pythagorean Theorem, the Distance Formula, and similar triangles, and learn to apply this knowledge to solving real-world problems. This unit concludes with students examining sampling techniques and using probability to predict outcomes.

Assessment Options

Unit 4 Test Pages 71–72 of the *Chapter 12 Resource Masters* may be used as a test or review for Unit 4. This assessment contains both multiple-choice and short answer items.

 **ExamView®** Assessment Suite   Create additional customized Unit Tests and review worksheets for differentiated instruction.

UNIT 4
Advanced Expressions and Data Analysis

Focus
Use a variety of representations, tools, and technology to model mathematical situations to solve meaningful problems.

CHAPTER 10
Radical Expressions and Triangles

BIG Idea Use algebraic skills to simplify radical expressions and solve equations in problem situations.

CHAPTER 11 **Rational Expressions and Equations**

BIG Idea Use algebraic skills to simplify rational expressions and solve equations.

CHAPTER 12
Statistics and Probability

BIG Idea Use graphical and numerical techniques to study patterns and analyze data.

BIG Idea Use probability models to describe everyday situations involving chance.

524 Unit 4

Real-Life Math Videos *Real-Life Math Videos* engage students by showing them how math is used in everyday situations. Use Video 4 with this unit.

Cross-Curricular Project

Algebra and Physical Science

Building the Best Roller Coaster Each year, amusement park owners compete to earn part of the billions of dollars Americans spend at amusement parks. Often, the parks draw customers with new, taller, and faster roller coasters. In this project, you will examine how radical and rational functions are related to buying and building a new roller coaster and analyze data involving U.S. amusement parks.

Math Online **Log on to** ca.algebra1.com **to begin.**

Cross-Curricular Project

Algebra and Physical Science

Building the Best Roller Coaster This Cross-Curricular Project is an online project in which students do research on the Internet, gather data, and make presentations using word processing, graphing, page-making, or presentation software. In each chapter, students advance to the next step in their project. At the end of Chapter 12, the project culminates with a presentation of their findings.

Math Online
ca.algebra1.com Log on for teaching suggestions and sample answers for this project.

Team Teaching You can use this Cross-Curricular Project with your students' physical science or physics teacher to make the connection from mathematics to the health topics your students are studying.

Chapter Overview

Radical Expressions and Triangles

Standards-Based Lesson Plan		Pacing Your Lessons	
LESSONS AND OBJECTIVES	California Standards	40-50 Minute Periods	90-Minute Periods
10-1 Simplifying Radical Expressions (pp. 528–534) • Simplify radical expressions using the Product Property of Square Roots. • Simplify radical expressions using the Quotient Property of Square Roots. **Extend 10-1 Graphing Calculator Lab: Fractional Exponents** (p. 535) • Use a calculator to explore the meaning of fractional exponents.	2.0 19.0	1	0.5
10-2 Operations with Radical Expressions (pp. 536–540) • Add and subtract radical expressions. • Multiply radical expressions.	1.0 2.0	1	0.5
10-3 Radical Equations (pp. 541–546) • Solve radical equations. • Solve radical equations with extraneous solutions. **Extend 10-3 Graphing Calculator Lab: Graphs of Radical Equations** (p. 547) • Use a graphing calculator to explore graphs of radical equations.	2.0	1	1
10-4 The Pythagorean Theorem (pp. 549–554) • Solve problems by using the Pythagorean Theorem. • Determine whether a triangle is a right triangle.	G15.0	1	0.5
10-5 The Distance Formula (pp. 555–559) • Find the distance between two points on the coordinate plane. • Find a point that is a given distance from a second point on a plane.	G17.0	1	0.5
10-6 Similar Triangles (pp. 560–565) • Determine whether two triangles are similar. • Find the unknown measures of sides of two similar triangles.	G5.0	1	0.5
REVIEW		1	0.5
ASSESSMENT		1	0.5*
TOTAL		8	4.5

*The complete **Assessment Planner** for Chapter 10 is provided on p. 527.*

* Begin Chapter 11 in the second half of the period.

Professional Development

California Standards Vertical Alignment

Before Chapter 10

Related Topics from Grade 7

- Multiply and divide monomials Standard 7AF2.2
- Know and understand the Pythagorean Theorem
  ⊶ Standard 7MG3.3
- Understand and use coordinate graphs Standard 7MG3.2
- Compute the perimeter, surface area and the volume of a three-dimensional object Standard 7MG2.3

Chapter 10

Topics from Algebra 1

- Use the arithmetic properties of real numbers
- Understand and use such properties as taking a root. Understand and use the rules of exponents

See individual lessons for the specific Standards covered.

After Chapter 10

Preparation for Algebra 2 and Geometry

- Know the laws of fractional exponents and understand exponential functions ⊶ Standard 2A12.0
- Prove the Pythagorean theorem ⊶ Standard G14.0
- Determine how changes in dimensions affect the perimeter, area, and volume of common geometric figures and solids Standard G11.0

Back-Mapping

California Algebra 1 was conceived and developed with the final result in mind, student success in Algebra I and beyond. The authors, using the California Mathematics Standards as their guide, developed this brand-new series by "back-mapping" from the desired result of student success in Algebra I and beyond. McGraw-Hill's *California Geometry, California Algebra 2,* and *California Algebra Readiness* were developed utilizing the same philosophy.

What the Research Says...

Trafton (1984) states that each lesson should present a sufficient number and range of examples prior to independent practice.

- Numerous detailed examples are provided throughout Chapter 10 to give students models for working with radicals and geometry.
- The additional examples provided in the Teacher Wraparound Edition can be used to help students prepare for their own problem-solving practice.

[Source: Trafton, P.R. (1984). "Toward More Effective, Efficient Instruction in Mathematics." *Elementary School Journal,*" 84, Issue 5, pp. 514–528.]

Mc Graw Hill Professional Development

Targeted professional development has been articulated throughout the *California Mathematics: Concepts, Skills, and Problem Solving* series. The **McGraw-Hill Professional Development Video Library** provides short videos that support the ⊶ Key Standards. For more information, visit ca.algebra1.com.

| Model Lessons | Instructional Strategies |

CHAPTER 10

Technology Solutions

Teacher Resources

TeacherWorks™ All-in-One Planner and Resource Center

All of the print materials from the Classroom Resource Masters are available on your TeacherWorks™ CD-ROM.

BL = Below Grade Level   **OL** = On Grade Level   **AL** = Above Grade Level   **ELL** = English Language Learner

Chapter Resource Masters	10-1	10-2	10-3	10-4	10-5	10-6
BL OL ELL Lesson Reading Guide	5	12	19	27	35	42
BL OL ELL Study Guide and Intervention*	6	13	20	28	36	43
BL OL Skills Practice*	8	15	22	30	38	45
OL AL Practice*	9	16	23	31	39	46
OL AL Word Problem Practice*	10	17	24	32	40	47
OL AL Enrichment	11	18	25	33	41	48
OL AL Calculator and Spreadsheet Activities				26	34	
OL AL Chapter Assessments*	49–70					
BL OL AL 5-Minute Check Transparencies	✓	✓	✓	✓	✓	✓
BL OL Teaching Algebra with Manipulatives		✓		✓		✓

Also available in Spanish.

AssignmentWorks

Differentiated Assignments, Answers, and Solutions

- Print a customized assignment worksheet using the Student Edition exercises along with an answer key or worked-out solutions.
- Use default lesson assignments as outlined in the Differentiated Homework Options in the Teacher Wraparound Edition.
- Includes modified questions from the Student Edition.

Interactive Classroom

This CD-ROM is a customizable Microsoft® PowerPoint® presentation that includes:

- In-Class Examples
- Your Turn Exercises*
- 5-Minute Check Transparencies*
- Links to Online Study Tools
- Concepts in Motion

compatible with response pad technology

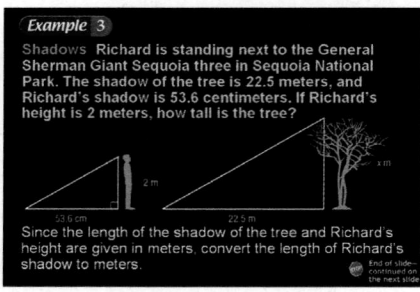

ExamView® Assessment Suite

 lets you

- Create, edit, and customize tests and worksheets using QuickTest Wizard
- Create multiple versions of tests and modify them for a desired level of difficulty
- Translate from English to Spanish and vice versa
- Build tests aligned with your state standards
- Track students' progress using the Teacher Management System

Student Resources

StudentWorks™ Plus

Textbook, Audio, Workbooks, and more

This CD-ROM is a valuable resource for students to access content online and use online resources to continue learning Chapter 10 concepts. Includes:

- Complete Student Editions in both English and Spanish
- English audio integrated throughout the text
- Links to Concepts in Motion, Personal Tutor, and other online resources
- Access to all student worksheets
- Daily Assignments and Grade Log

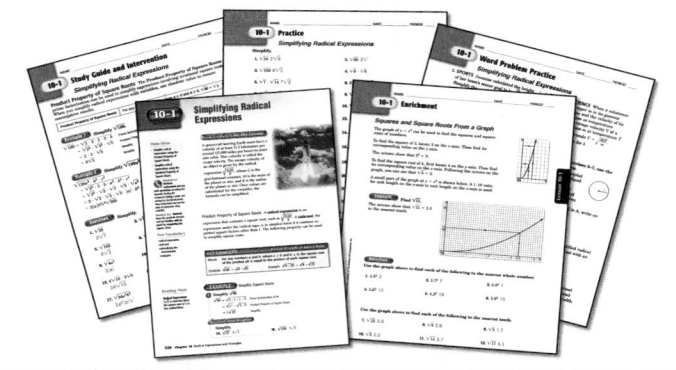

Super DVD

The Super DVD contains two Glencoe multimedia products.

MindJogger Plus   An alternative review of concepts in which students work as teams in a game show format to gain points for correct answers.

What's Math Got to Do With It? Real Life Math Videos Engaging video that shows students how math is used in everyday situations

Internet Resources

Math Online **ca.algebra1.com**

TEACHER	PARENT	STUDENT	Online Study Tools
	●	●	Online Student Edition
●	●	●	Multilingual Glossary
			Lesson Resources
	●	●	BrainPOP®
●	●	●	Concepts in Motion
●	●	●	Extra Examples
	●	●	Other Calculator Keystrokes
●			Problem of the Week Cards
	●	●	Real-World Careers
	●	●	Self-Check Quizzes
			Chapter Resources
	●	●	Chapter Readiness
	●	●	Chapter Test
	●	●	Standardized Test Practice
	●	●	Vocabulary Review/Chapter Review Activities
			Unit Resources
●		●	Cross-Curricular Internet Project
			Other Resources
●			Dinah Zike's Foldables
	●	●	Hotmath Homework Help
●			Key Concepts
●	●	●	Meet the Authors
	●	●	Personal Tutor
●			Project CRISS℠
	●	●	Scavenger Hunts and Answer Sheets
●			Vocabulary PuzzleMakers

Focus on Mathematical Content

Big Idea for Chapter 10:
Radical Expressions and Triangles

Simplifying radical expressions is more than finding a principal square root of a perfect square. Algebraic skills are needed to evaluate expressions and equations containing variables with odd exponents. The concept of similar triangles carries over into deeper studies of triangles in later mathematics courses.

Why It's Important

For This Chapter
The lessons in this chapter use algebraic skills to simplify radical expressions and solve equations in problem situations. Students apply concepts of similarity to determine similar triangles.

- How do you know an expression is a radical expression?
  (Lesson 10-1)

- What must be true of radicands before you can add or subtract them? (Lesson 10-2)

- What is the first step in solving radical equations?
  (Lesson 10-3)

- How does knowing how to simplify radical expressions help you find the length of the sides of right triangles?
  (Lesson 10-4)

- How can right triangles help you find the distance between two points on a coordinate plane? (Lesson 10-5)

- What do you know about the sides of similar triangles?
  (Lesson 10-6)

After This Chapter

- In Algebra 2, knowing how to simplify radicands can help you solve radical equations and inequalities.

- In geometry and trigonometry, knowing how to apply the Pythagorean Theorem and distance formula can help you find many unknown lengths.

10-1 Simplifying Radical Expressions

When an expression contains a square root, it is called a radical expression. When the radicand, the expression under the square root sign, contains no perfect square factors other than 1, it is said to be in simplest form. There are properties of square roots you can use to simplify radical expressions.

- Use the Product Property of Square Roots.

$$\sqrt{18} = \sqrt{2 \cdot 3 \cdot 3} = \sqrt{2} \cdot \sqrt{3^2} = 3\sqrt{2}$$

For any numbers greater than or equal to 0, the square root of their product is equal to the product of each number's square root. Notice how prime factorization plays a role in simplifying radical expressions.

- Use the Quotient Property of Square Roots.

$$\sqrt{\frac{25}{4}} = \frac{\sqrt{25}}{\sqrt{4}} = \frac{5}{2}$$

For any number greater than or equal to 0 divided by a number greater than 0, the square root of their quotient is equal to the quotient of each number's square root. Principal square roots are never negative, so absolute value symbols must be used to signify that some results are not negative,

for example, $\sqrt{x^2} = |x|$. Having no radical expression in the denominator of a fraction is another criteria for a radical expression to be in simplest form. Since squaring and taking a square root are inverse functions, you multiply the numerator and the denominator by the same radical expression so that the radical in the denominator contains a perfect square. Remember that the numerator must be multiplied by the same amount so that the whole fraction is being multiplied by a value of 1. For example,

$$\frac{\sqrt{3}}{\sqrt{5}} = \frac{\sqrt{3}}{\sqrt{5}} \cdot \frac{\sqrt{5}}{\sqrt{5}} = \frac{\sqrt{15}}{5}$$

This process is called *rationalizing the denominator*.

If the denominator is an expression containing a radical, multiply by its conjugate. For example, if the denominator is in the form $a + \sqrt{b}$, multiply both the numerator and the denominator by $a - \sqrt{b}$.

10-2 Operations with Radical Expressions

Use the process of combining like terms to simplify expressions in which radicals are added or subtracted. For terms to be combined, their radicands must be the same. As in combining monomials with variables (Lesson 1-5), only the coefficients of the radicands are combined. Be sure to simplify all radicals first. Multiplying two radical expressions that each have two terms is similar to multiplying binomials.

10-3 Radical Equations

Equations that contain radicals with variables in the radicand are called *radical equations*. To solve radical equations, the radical must first be isolated on one side of the equation. Then both sides are squared. This will eliminate the radical. Squaring each side sometimes produces *extraneous solutions*, results that are not solutions of the original equation. Be sure to substitute all solutions back into the original equation to check their validity.

10-4 The Pythagorean Theorem

In a right triangle, the longest side, or *hypotenuse*, is the side opposite the right angle. The other two sides are called the *legs* of the triangle.

The Pythagorean Theorem states that in a right triangle, the square of the length of the hypotenuse equals the sum of the squares of the other legs, that is, $c^2 = a^2 + b^2$, where c is the measure of the hypotenuse and a and b are the measures of the legs. This formula can be used to find the length of any missing side of a right triangle if two sides are known. Any three whole numbers that satisfy this equation are known as a *Pythagorean triple*. These triples represent side lengths that always form right triangles. It follows that if three numbers do not satisfy the Pythagorean Theorem, then a triangle of those lengths will not be a right triangle.

10-5 The Distance Formula

If the Pythagorean Theorem is solved for c, $c = \sqrt{a^2 + b^2}$, the result is a form of the Distance Formula in which a is expressed as the difference of the x-coordinates of the endpoints of the hypotenuse and b is expressed as the difference of the y-coordinates.

$$d = \sqrt{(x_2 - x_1)^2 + (y_2 - y_1)^2}$$

This formula can be used to find the distance d between any two points on a coordinate plane. You can also use the Distance Formula to find one missing coordinate of an endpoint if you know the other coordinate, both coordinates of the other endpoint, and the distance between the two points.

10-6 Similar Triangles

Similar triangles are triangles that have the same shape, but are not necessarily the same size. All corresponding angles will have equal measures, and all corresponding sides will be proportional. If the sides have a 1 to 1 ratio of proportionality, then the similar triangles are the same size.

When determining whether triangles are similar, check to see if the corresponding angles have the same measure. If all angle measures cannot be determined, then check the corresponding sides to see if they are proportional.

Proportions can be used to find the lengths of missing sides of similar triangles. You must know the lengths of at least one pair of corresponding sides and the length of the side that corresponds to the missing side's length. Set up the proportion and solve for the missing length.

CHAPTER 10
Differentiated Instruction

Options for Chapter 10 Lessons

ELL = English Language Learner   **AL** = Above Grade Level   **SS** = Struggling Students   **SN** = Special Needs

Using Visual Learning **AL**

Use with Lesson 10-2

Have students write all the perfect squares from 1 to 100 on an index card using a colored pen or pencil. Then have them rework Example 3 on p. 527. After they multiply the binomials, have students use their colored pen or pencil to circle the terms inside radicals that have perfect square factors. Using the same color, have students write the factorization in the line below each radical expression that can be factored.

Using Verbal Skills **ELL** **SS** **SN**

Use with Lesson 10-3

Have students write a short paragraph in their own words explaining why checking solutions is important when solving radical equations. Students should include an example of a radical equation that has an extraneous solution.

Using Interpersonal Skills **SS**

Use with Lesson 10-5

Place students in pairs. Have each person in the pair drop a penny on a coordinate grid, and record the coordinates of the point closest to where the center of the penny landed. Then have the students work together to find the distance between the two points, using the Distance Formula.

Noteables™ Interactive Study Notebook with Foldables™

Noteables™ Interactive Study Notebook with Foldables™ is a study organizer that provides helpful steps for students to follow to organize their notes for Chapter 10.

- Students use Noteables to record notes and to complete their Foldables as you present the material for each lesson.
- Noteables correspond to the Examples in the *Teacher Wraparound Edition* and *Interactive Classroom CD-ROM.*

Intervention

Quick Review Math Handbook*

is Glencoe's mathematical handbook for students and parents.

Hot Words includes a glossary of terms.

Hot Topics consists of two parts:

- explanations of key mathematical concepts
- exercises to check students' understanding.

Lesson	Hot Topics Section	Lesson	Hot Topics Section
10-1	3.2	10-4	7.9
10-2	3.2	10-6	8.6

*Also available in Spanish

Teacher To Teacher

Judy Buchholtz
Dublin Scioto High School
Dublin, OH

USE WITH LESSON 10-1

" To make algebra more meaningful to my students, I bring in the school police officer to discuss the formula used in Exercises 41–43. "

Reading and Writing in Mathematics

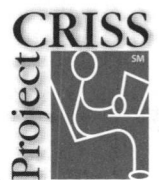

CRISS _{SM}
Project

STUDY SKILL

To help students organize their notes, encourage them to create frames. The math frame at the right describes the Distance Formula, which students study in Lesson 10-5. Creating frames helps students understand topics by explaining them in their own words. Frames can also be used by students to quickly review information in a lesson or chapter.

Term/ Concept	Definition (in your own words)	Formula	Original Question with Answer
The Distance Formula	A formula to find the distance between any two points on a coordinate plane.	The distance between two points with coordinates (x_1, y_1) and (x_2, y_2) is $d = \sqrt{(x_2 - x_1)^2 + (y_2 - y_1)^2}$.	Find the distance between $(-7, 7)$ and $(2, -5)$. $d = \sqrt{[2 - (-7)]^2 + (-5 - 7)^2}$ $= \sqrt{81 + 144}$ $= 15$

CReating **I**ndependence through **S**tudent-owned **S**trategies

CHAPTER 10 Notes

 **Dinah Zike's Foldables™**

Focus As students read and study this chapter, they show examples and write notes about radical expressions and triangles on their study cards.

Teach Have students make and label their Foldables as illustrated.

Students should use the appropriate pocket as they cover each lesson in this chapter.

When to Use It At the end of each lesson, ask students to use the study cards to take notes, write and solve equations, solve real-world problems, or record and define vocabulary words and concepts.

A version of a completed Foldable is shown on p. 567.

Differentiated Instruction

Student-Built Glossary, pp. 1–2

Students complete the chart by providing a definition for each term and an example as they progress through Chapter 10. This study tool can be used to review for the chapter test.

Materials Needed for Chapter 10

- calculator (Lessons 10-1, 10-2, 10-4, 10-5)
- graphing calculator (Lessons 10-1, 10-3, Extend 10-3)
- grid paper (Extend 10-3, Lesson 10-5)
- Internet (Lesson 10-4)
- tape measure (Lesson 10-6)

CHAPTER 10 Radical Expressions and Triangles

 **BIG Idea**

- **Standard 2.0** Students understand and use such operations as taking the opposite, finding the reciprocal, taking a root, and raising to a fractional power. They understand and use the rules of exponents. (Key, CAHSEE)

Key Vocabulary

Distance Formula (p. 555)

Pythagorean triple (p. 550)

radical equation (p. 541)

radical expression (p. 528)

Real-World Link

PENDULUMS The Foucault Pendulum at the California Academy of Sciences in San Francisco consists of a 240-pound brass ball suspended on a 30-foot cable. It appears that the pendulum moves, but it is actually stationary. As Earth rotates, the floor under the pendulum moves. The period of the pendulum can be found using radical equations.

 **Study Organizer**

Radical Expressions and Triangles Make this Foldable to help you organize your notes. Begin with one $8\frac{1}{2}"$ by 11" paper.

1 Fold in half matching the short sides.

2 Unfold and fold the long side up 2 inches to form a pocket.

3 Staple or glue the outer edges to complete the pocket.

4 Label each side as shown. Use index cards to record examples.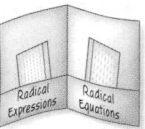

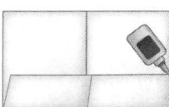

526 Chapter 10 Radical Expressions and Triangles

GET READY for Chapter 10

Diagnose Readiness You have two options for checking Prerequisite Skills.

Option 1

Take the Quick Check below. Refer to the Quick Review for help.

Option 2

 Take the Online Readiness Quiz at ca.algebra1.com.

QUICK Check

(For use in Lesson 10-1.)
Find each square root. If necessary, round to the nearest hundredth. (Lesson 1-8)

1. $\sqrt{25}$ **5**
2. $\sqrt{80}$ **8.94**
3. $\sqrt{56}$ **7.48**

4. **PAINTING** Todd is painting a square mural with an area of 81 square feet. What is the length of the side of the mural? **9 feet**

(Used in Lesson 10-2.)
Simplify each expression. (Lesson 1-6)

5. $(10c - 5d) + (6c + 5d)$ **16c**

6. $3a + 7b - 2a$ **a + 7b**

7. $(21m + 15n) - (9n - 4m)$ **25m + 6n**

8. $14x - 6y + 2y$ **14x − 4y**

(Used in Lesson 10-3)
Solve each equation. (Lesson 8-3)

9. $x^2 + 10x + 24 = 0$ **{−6, −4}**
10. $2x^2 + x + 1 = 2$ **$\left\{\frac{1}{2}, -1\right\}$**

11. **GEOMETRY** The triangle has an area of 120 square centimeters. Find h. **8 cm**

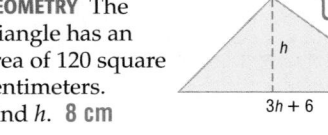

(Used in Lesson 10-6)
Use cross products to determine whether each pair of ratios forms a proportion. Write *yes* or *no*. (Lesson 2-6)

12. $\frac{2}{3}, \frac{8}{12}$ **yes**
13. $\frac{4}{5}, \frac{16}{25}$ **no**
14. $\frac{8}{10}, \frac{12}{16}$ **no**

15. **MODELS** A collector's model train is scaled so that 1 inch on the model equals 3.5 feet on the actual train. If the model is 3.25 inches tall, how tall is the actual train? **11.375 feet**

QUICK Review

EXAMPLE 1

Find the square root of $\sqrt{82}$. If necessary, round to the nearest hundredth.

$\sqrt{82} = 9.05538513814\ldots$ Use a calculator.
To the nearest hundredth, $\sqrt{82} \approx 9.06$.

EXAMPLE 2

Simplify $6m + 3 + 2k - 17b - 100 - 16k + 8b + m$.

$6m + 3 + 2k - 17b - 100 - 16k + 8b + m$

$= (6m + m) + (2k - 16k) + (8b - 17b) + (3 - 100)$

$= 7m - 14k - 9b - 97$ Simplify.

EXAMPLE 3

Solve $3x^2 + 4x - 4 = 0$.

$3x^2 + 4x - 4 = 0$ Original equation
$(3x - 2)(x + 2) = 0$ Factor.
$(3x - 2) = 0$ or $(x + 2) = 0$ Zero Product Property
$x = \frac{2}{3}$ or $x = -2$ Solve each equation.

EXAMPLE 4

Use cross products to determine whether $\frac{5}{8}$ and $\frac{60}{96}$ form a proportion. Write *yes* or *no*.

$\frac{5}{8} \overset{?}{=} \frac{60}{96}$ Write the equation.

$5(96) \overset{?}{=} 8(60)$ Find the cross products.

$480 = 480$ Simplify. They form a proportion.

Chapter 10 Get Ready For Chapter 10 **527**

ASSESSMENT PLANNER

CHAPTER **10**

✓ Formative Assessment

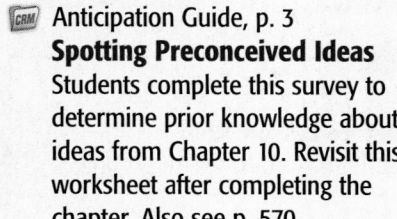 Anticipation Guide, p. 3
Spotting Preconceived Ideas
Students complete this survey to determine prior knowledge about ideas from Chapter 10. Revisit this worksheet after completing the chapter. Also see p. 570

TWE Lesson Activities
- Ticket Out the Door, pp. 534, 559
- Crystal Ball, pp. 540, 552
- Name the Math, p. 565
- Yesterday's News, pp. 546

Chapter Checkpoints

SE Mid-Chapter Quiz, p. 548

SE Study Guide and Review, pp. 567–570

SE California Standards Practice, pp. 572–573

CRM Quizzes, pp. 51 and 52

CRM Standardized Test Practice, pp. 68–70

Math **nline** ca.algebra1.com
- Self-Check Quizzes
- Practice Test
- Standardized Test Practice

✓ Summative Assessment

SE Chapter Practice Test, p. 571

CRM Mid-Chapter Test, p. 53

CRM Vocabulary Test, p. 54

CRM Extended-Response Test, p. 67

CRM Leveled Chapter Tests, pp. 55–66

⊙ ExamView® Assessment Suite

KEY

CRM *Chapter 10 Resource Masters*

SE Student Edition

TWE Teacher Wraparound Edition

⊙ CD-ROM

✓ Diagnostic Assessment

Exercises	California Standards	Intervention
1–4	1.0, 2.0	**SE** Review Lesson 1-8, pp. 46–52
5–8	25.0	**SE** Review Lesson 1-6, pp. 33–37
9–11	11.0	**SE** Review Lesson 8-3, pp. 434–439
12–15	15.0	**SE** Review Lesson 2-6, pp. 105–110

Chapter 10 Get Ready for Chapter 10 **527**

1 Focus

Standards Alignment

Before Lesson 10-1
Multiply and divide monomials
from Standard 7AF2.2

Lesson 10-1
Understand and use the rules of exponents. from ► Standard 2.0
Know the quadratic formula and its proof by completing the square from ► Standard 19.0

After Lesson 10-1
Know the laws of fractional exponents and understand exponential functions from ► Standard 2A12.0

2 Teach

Scaffolding Questions Have students read *Get Ready for the Lesson.*
Ask:

• In the formula for escape velocity, what does the radical sign mean? The radical sign means that you must find the square root of the value under the radical sign.

• Based on what you know about the order of operations, how do you think you should simplify the radical expression in the escape velocity formula? You should simplify the expression under the radical sign before finding the square root.

Lesson 10-1 Resources

10-1 # Simplifying Radical Expressions

Main Ideas

• Simplify radical expressions using the Product Property of Square Roots.

• Simplify radical expressions using the Quotient Property of Square Roots.

 Standard 2.0 Students understand and use such operations as taking the opposite, finding the reciprocal, **taking a root,** and raising to a fractional power. They understand and use the rules of exponents. (Key, CAHSEE)

Standard 19.0 Students know the quadratic formula and **are familiar with its proof by completing the square.** (Key)

New Vocabulary

radical expression
radicand
rationalizing the denominator
conjugate

GET READY for the Lesson

A spacecraft leaving Earth must have a velocity of at least 11.2 kilometers per second (25,000 miles per hour) to enter into orbit. This velocity is called the *escape velocity.* The escape velocity of an object is given by the radical expression $\sqrt{\frac{2GM}{R}}$, where G is the gravitational constant, M is the mass of the planet or star, and R is the radius of the planet or star. Once values are substituted for the variables, the formula can be simplified.

Product Property of Square Roots A **radical expression** is an expression that contains a square root, such as $\sqrt{\frac{2GM}{R}}$. A **radicand**, the expression under the radical sign, is in simplest form if it contains no perfect square factors other than 1. The following property can be used to simplify square roots.

KEY CONCEPT *Product Property of Square Roots*

Words For any numbers a and b, where $a \geq 0$ and $b \geq 0$, the square root of the product ab is equal to the product of each square root.

Symbols $\sqrt{ab} = \sqrt{a} \cdot \sqrt{b}$ **Example** $\sqrt{4 \cdot 25} = \sqrt{4} \cdot \sqrt{25}$

Reading Math

Radical Expressions
$2\sqrt{3}$ is read *two times the square root of 3* or *two radical three.*

EXAMPLE Simplify Square Roots

① Simplify $\sqrt{90}$.

$\sqrt{90} = \sqrt{2 \cdot 3 \cdot 3 \cdot 5}$ Prime factorization of 90

$= \sqrt{3^2} \cdot \sqrt{2 \cdot 5}$ Product Property of Square Roots

$= 3\sqrt{10}$ Simplify.

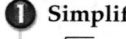 **CHECK Your Progress**

Simplify.
1A. $\sqrt{27}$ $3\sqrt{3}$ **1B.** $\sqrt{150}$ $5\sqrt{6}$

528 Chapter 10 Radical Expressions and Triangles

Chapter 10 Resource Masters
Lesson Reading Guide, p. 5 BL OL ELL
Study Guide and Intervention, pp. 6–7
BL OL ELL
Skills Practice, p. 8 BL OL
Practice, p. 9 OL AL
Word Problem Practice, p. 10 OL AL
Enrichment, p. 11 OL AL

Transparencies
5-Minute Check Transparency 10-1
Additional Print Resources
Noteables™ Interactive Study Notebook with Foldables™

Technology
ca.algebra1.com
Interactive Classroom CD-ROM
AssignmentWorks CD-ROM
Graphing Calculator Easy Files

Study Tip

Alternative Method

To find $\sqrt{3} \cdot \sqrt{15}$, you could multiply first and then use the prime factorization.

$$\sqrt{3} \cdot \sqrt{15} = \sqrt{45}$$
$$= \sqrt{3^2} \cdot \sqrt{5}$$
$$= 3\sqrt{5}$$

EXAMPLE Multiply Square Roots

2 Simplify $\sqrt{3} \cdot \sqrt{15}$.

$$\sqrt{3} \cdot \sqrt{15} = \sqrt{3} \cdot \sqrt{3} \cdot \sqrt{5} \qquad \text{Product Property of Square Roots}$$
$$= \sqrt{3^2} \cdot \sqrt{5} \text{ or } 3\sqrt{5} \qquad \text{Product Property; then simplify.}$$

CHECK Your Progress Simplify.

2A. $\sqrt{5} \cdot \sqrt{10}$ $5\sqrt{2}$ **2B.** $\sqrt{6} \cdot \sqrt{8}$ $4\sqrt{3}$

When finding the principal square root of an expression containing variables, be sure that the result is not negative. Consider the expression $\sqrt{x^2}$. It may seem that $\sqrt{x^2} = x$. Let's look at $x = -2$.

$$\sqrt{x^2} \stackrel{?}{=} x$$
$$\sqrt{(-2)^2} \stackrel{?}{=} -2 \qquad \text{Replace } x \text{ with } -2.$$
$$\sqrt{4} \stackrel{?}{=} -2 \qquad (-2)^2 = 4$$
$$2 \neq -2 \qquad \sqrt{4} = 2$$

For radical expressions where the exponent of the variable inside the radical is even and the resulting simplified exponent is odd, you must use absolute value to ensure nonnegative results.

$$\sqrt{x^2} = |x| \qquad \sqrt{x^4} = x^2 \qquad \sqrt{x^6} = |x^3|$$

EXAMPLE Simplify a Square Root with Variables

3 Simplify $\sqrt{40x^4y^5z^3}$.

$$\sqrt{40x^4y^5z^3} = \sqrt{2^3 \cdot 5 \cdot x^4 \cdot y^5 \cdot z^3} \qquad \text{Prime factorization}$$
$$= \sqrt{2^2} \cdot \sqrt{2} \cdot \sqrt{5} \cdot \sqrt{x^4} \cdot \sqrt{y^4} \cdot \sqrt{y} \cdot \sqrt{z^2} \cdot \sqrt{z} \qquad \text{Product Property}$$
$$= 2 \cdot \sqrt{2} \cdot \sqrt{5} \cdot x^2 \cdot y^2 \cdot \sqrt{y} \cdot |z| \cdot \sqrt{z} \qquad \text{Simplify.}$$
$$= 2x^2y^2|z|\sqrt{10yz} \qquad \text{The absolute value of } z \text{ ensures a nonnegative result.}$$

CHECK Your Progress Simplify.

3A. $\sqrt{32r^2s^4t^5}, t \geq 0$ $4|r|s^2t^2\sqrt{2t}$ **3B.** $\sqrt{56xy^{10}z^5}, x \geq 0, z \geq 0$ $2|y^5|z^2\sqrt{14xz}$

Quotient Property of Square Roots You can divide square roots and simplify radical expressions by using the Quotient Property of Square Roots.

KEY CONCEPT   *Quotient Property of Square Roots*

Words   For any numbers a and b, where $a \geq 0$ and $b > 0$, the square root of the quotient $\dfrac{a}{b}$ is equal to the quotient of each square root.

Symbols $\sqrt{\dfrac{a}{b}} = \dfrac{\sqrt{a}}{\sqrt{b}}$ **Example** $\sqrt{\dfrac{49}{4}} = \dfrac{\sqrt{49}}{\sqrt{4}}$

  Extra Examples at ca.algebra1.com   Lesson 10-1 Simplifying Radical Expressions   **529**

Intervention

Common Misconceptions   In order to simplify square roots with the Product Property of Square Roots, students need to be able to find the prime factorization of the radicand. Take a few minutes to review finding prime factorizations so that students can focus on learning the new concept rather than trying to recall earlier material.

Product Property of Square Roots

Example 1 shows how to simplify a radical expression in which the radicand is not a perfect square, using the Product Property of Square Roots. **Example 2** shows how the Product Property can be used to multiply square roots. **Example 3** shows how to find the principal square root of an expression containing variables.

 Formative Assessment

Use the Check Your Progress exercises after each example to determine students' understanding of concepts.

ADDITIONAL EXAMPLES

1 Simplify $\sqrt{52}$. $2\sqrt{13}$
2 Simplify $\sqrt{2} \cdot \sqrt{24}$. $4\sqrt{3}$
3 Simplify $\sqrt{45a^4b^5c^6}$. $3a^2b^2|c^3|\sqrt{5b}$

Additional Examples are also in:

- Noteables™ Interactive Study Notebook with Foldables™
- Interactive Classroom PowerPoint® Presentations

Focus on Mathematical Content

Product Property of Square Roots The Product Property can be used to simplify radical expressions. For all nonnegative numbers, the product of each square root equals the square root of the products.

Tips for New Teachers   **Preventing Errors**

For Example 1, point out that since 10 is the product of two different prime numbers, 2 and 5, that cannot be factored further, $\sqrt{10}$ cannot be simplified further.

The derivation of the Quadratic Formula is an algebraic proof. Algebraic proof is further developed in Geometry.

Quotient Property of Square Roots

Example 4 shows how to rationalize the denominator of a radical expression to eliminate radicals from the denominator of a fraction. **Example 5** shows how to use conjugates to rationalize the two-term denominator of a radical expression to eliminate radicals from the denominator of a fraction.

You can use the Quotient Property of Square Roots to derive the Quadratic Formula by solving the quadratic equation $ax^2 + bx + c = 0$.

$ax^2 + bx + c = 0$	Original equation.
$x^2 + \dfrac{b}{a}x + \dfrac{c}{a} = 0$	Divide each side by a, $a \neq 0$.
$x^2 + \dfrac{b}{a}x = -\dfrac{c}{a}$	Subtract $\dfrac{c}{a}$ from each side.
$x^2 + \dfrac{b}{a}x + \dfrac{b^2}{4a^2} = -\dfrac{c}{a} + \dfrac{b^2}{4a^2}$	Complete the square; $\left(\dfrac{b}{2a}\right)^2 = \dfrac{b^2}{4a^2}$.
$\left(x + \dfrac{b}{2a}\right)^2 = \dfrac{-4ac + b^2}{4a^2}$	Factor $x^2 + \dfrac{b}{a}x + \dfrac{b^2}{4a^2}$.
$\left\lvert x + \dfrac{b}{2a}\right\rvert = \sqrt{\dfrac{b^2 - 4ac}{4a^2}}$	Take the square root of each side.
$x + \dfrac{b}{2a} = \pm\sqrt{\dfrac{b^2 - 4ac}{4a^2}}$	Remove the absolute value symbols and insert $\pm$.
$x + \dfrac{b}{2a} = \pm\dfrac{\sqrt{b^2 - 4ac}}{\sqrt{4a^2}}$	Quotient Property of Square Roots
$x + \dfrac{b}{2a} = \pm\dfrac{\sqrt{b^2 - 4ac}}{2a}$	$\sqrt{4a^2} = 2a$
$x = \dfrac{-b \pm \sqrt{b^2 - 4ac}}{2a}$	Subtract $\dfrac{b}{2a}$ from each side.

If no prime factors with an exponent greater than 1 appear under the radical sign and if no radicals are left in the denominator, then a fraction containing radicals is in simplest form. **Rationalizing the denominator** of a radical expression is a method used to eliminate radicals from a denominator.

EXAMPLE   Rationalizing the Denominator

4 Simplify.

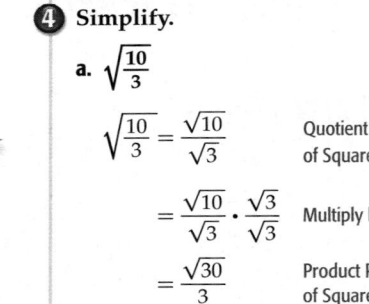

a. $\sqrt{\dfrac{10}{3}}$

$\sqrt{\dfrac{10}{3}} = \dfrac{\sqrt{10}}{\sqrt{3}}$ Quotient Property of Square Roots

$= \dfrac{\sqrt{10}}{\sqrt{3}} \cdot \dfrac{\sqrt{3}}{\sqrt{3}}$ Multiply by $\dfrac{\sqrt{3}}{\sqrt{3}}$.

$= \dfrac{\sqrt{30}}{3}$ Product Property of Square Roots

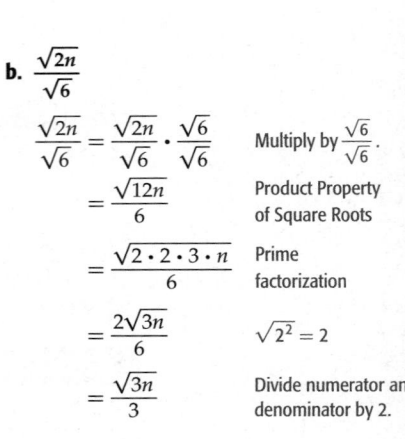

b. $\dfrac{\sqrt{2n}}{\sqrt{6}}$

$\dfrac{\sqrt{2n}}{\sqrt{6}} = \dfrac{\sqrt{2n}}{\sqrt{6}} \cdot \dfrac{\sqrt{6}}{\sqrt{6}}$ Multiply by $\dfrac{\sqrt{6}}{\sqrt{6}}$.

$= \dfrac{\sqrt{12n}}{6}$ Product Property of Square Roots

$= \dfrac{\sqrt{2 \cdot 2 \cdot 3 \cdot n}}{6}$ Prime factorization

$= \dfrac{2\sqrt{3n}}{6}$ $\sqrt{2^2} = 2$

$= \dfrac{\sqrt{3n}}{3}$ Divide numerator and denominator by 2.

✓CHECK Your Progress

4A. $\dfrac{\sqrt{14}}{\sqrt{5}}$ $\dfrac{\sqrt{70}}{5}$

4B. $\dfrac{\sqrt{6y}}{\sqrt{12}}$ $\dfrac{\sqrt{2y}}{2}$

Differentiated Instruction

Logical Learners   Have students use the same method that is shown for the derivation of the Quadratic Formula to solve actual quadratic equations. Have students turn back to Lesson 9-4 and solve an example problem using this method.

Binomials of the form $p\sqrt{q} + r\sqrt{s}$ and $p\sqrt{q} - r\sqrt{s}$ are called **conjugates**. For example, $3 + \sqrt{2}$ and $3 - \sqrt{2}$ are conjugates. Conjugates are useful when simplifying radical expressions because if p, q, r, and s are rational numbers, the product of the two conjugates is a rational number. Use the pattern for the difference of squares $(a - b)(a + b) = a^2 - b^2$ to find their product.

$$\left(3 + \sqrt{2}\right)\left(3 - \sqrt{2}\right) = 3^2 - \left(\sqrt{2}\right)^2 \quad a = 3, b = \sqrt{2}$$
$$= 9 - 2 \text{ or } 7 \quad \left(\sqrt{2}\right)^2 = \sqrt{2} \cdot \sqrt{2} \text{ or } 2$$

EXAMPLE Use Conjugates to Rationalize a Denominator

5 Simplify $\dfrac{2}{6 - \sqrt{3}}$.

$$\frac{2}{6 - \sqrt{3}} = \frac{2}{6 - \sqrt{3}} \cdot \frac{6 + \sqrt{3}}{6 + \sqrt{3}} \quad \frac{6 + \sqrt{3}}{6 + \sqrt{3}} = 1; \text{ The conjugate of } 6 - \sqrt{3} \text{ is } 6 + \sqrt{3}.$$

$$= \frac{2\left(6 + \sqrt{3}\right)}{6^2 - \left(\sqrt{3}\right)^2} \quad (a - b)(a + b) = a^2 - b^2$$

$$= \frac{12 + 2\sqrt{3}}{36 - 3} \quad \left(\sqrt{3}\right)^2 = 3$$

$$= \frac{12 + 2\sqrt{3}}{33} \quad \text{Simplify.}$$

CHECK Your Progress Simplify.

5A. $\dfrac{3}{2 + \sqrt{2}}$ $\dfrac{6 - 3\sqrt{2}}{2}$ **5B.** $\dfrac{7}{3 - \sqrt{7}}$ $\dfrac{21 + 7\sqrt{7}}{2}$

Online Personal Tutor at ca.algebra1.com

Cross-Curricular Project

Math Online The speed of a roller coaster can be determined by evaluating a radical expression. Visit ca.algebra1.com to continue work on your project.

When simplifying radical expressions, check the following conditions to determine if the expression is in simplest form.

CONCEPT SUMMARY   *Simplest Radical Form*

A radical expression is in simplest form when the following three conditions have been met.

1. No radicands have perfect square factors other than 1.

2. No radicands contain fractions.

3. No radicals appear in the denominator of a fraction.

★ indicates multi-step problem

CHECK Your Understanding

Examples 1, 2
(pp. 528–529)

Simplify.

1. $\sqrt{20}$ $2\sqrt{5}$ **2.** $\sqrt{52}$ $2\sqrt{13}$ **3.** $2\sqrt{32}$ $8\sqrt{2}$

4. $\sqrt{2} \cdot \sqrt{8}$ 4 **5.** $\sqrt{3} \cdot \sqrt{18}$ $3\sqrt{6}$ **6.** $3\sqrt{10} \cdot 4\sqrt{10}$ 120

7. GEOMETRY A square has sides measuring $2\sqrt{7}$ feet each. Determine the area of the square. 28 ft^2

Lesson 10-1 Simplifying Radical Expressions   **531**

ADDITIONAL EXAMPLE

5 Simplify $\dfrac{3}{5 - \sqrt{2}}$. $\dfrac{15 + 3\sqrt{2}}{23}$

3 **Practice**

Formative Assessment

Use Exercises 1–16 to check for understanding.

Use the chart at the bottom of this page to customize assignments for your students.

DIFFERENTIATED HOMEWORK OPTIONS

Level	Assignment	Two-Day Option	
BL Basic	17–40, 53–55, 57–59, 66–82	17–39 odd, 58, 59	18–40 even, 53–55, 57, 66–82
OL Core	17–39 odd, 41–55, 57–59, 66–82	17–40, 58, 59	41–55, 57, 66–82
AL Advanced /Pre-AP	41–76, (optional: 77–82)		

Odd/Even Assignments
Exercises 17–40 are structured so that students practice the same concepts whether they are assigned odd or even problems.

 Exercise Alert!
Use a Calculator Exercises 43 and 49 require students to use a calculator to find the decimal approximation for a radical.

 For Exercises 17–40, if a variable with an odd power is under the radical, assume that the value of the variable is nonnegative.

Real-World Connections
For Exercises 51 and 52, tell students the windchill factor is the colder-than-measured temperature that a person feels because of the wind. There is also a heat index. The heat index takes the day's temperature and humidity into account and calculates what the temperature would be if the air were not humid.

Examples 3, 4
(pp. 529–530)

Simplify. 10. $2|m|np^2\sqrt{22mp}$

8. $\sqrt{54a^2b^2}$ $3|ab|\sqrt{6}$

9. $\sqrt{60x^5y^6}$ $2x^2|y^3|\sqrt{15x}$

10. $\sqrt{88m^3n^2p^5}$

11. $\dfrac{4}{\sqrt{6}}$ $\dfrac{2\sqrt{6}}{3}$

12. $\sqrt{\dfrac{3}{10}}$ $\dfrac{\sqrt{30}}{10}$

13. $\sqrt{\dfrac{7}{2}} \cdot \sqrt{\dfrac{5}{3}}$ $\dfrac{\sqrt{210}}{6}$

14. **PHYSICS** The period of a pendulum is the time required for it to make one complete swing back and forth. The formula of the period P of a pendulum is $P = 2\pi\sqrt{\dfrac{\ell}{32}}$, where ℓ is the length of the pendulum in feet. If a pendulum in a clock tower is 8 feet long, find the period. Use 3.14 for π. **3.14 s**

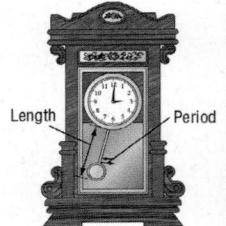
Length   Period

Example 5
(p. 531)

Simplify.
15. $\dfrac{8}{3-\sqrt{2}}$ $\dfrac{8(3+\sqrt{2})}{7}$

16. $\dfrac{2\sqrt{5}}{-4+\sqrt{8}}$ $\dfrac{-2\sqrt{5}-\sqrt{10}}{2}$

Exercises

HOMEWORK HELP	
For Exercises	See Examples
17–20	1
21–24	2
25–28	3
29–34	4
35–40	5

Simplify. 28. $6xy^2z^2\sqrt{2xz}$

37. $2\sqrt{7}-2\sqrt{2}$

17. $\sqrt{18}$ $3\sqrt{2}$

18. $\sqrt{24}$ $2\sqrt{6}$

19. $\sqrt{80}$ $4\sqrt{5}$

20. $\sqrt{75}$ $5\sqrt{3}$

21. $\sqrt{5} \cdot \sqrt{6}$ $\sqrt{30}$

22. $\sqrt{3} \cdot \sqrt{8}$ $2\sqrt{6}$

23. $7\sqrt{30} \cdot 2\sqrt{6}$ $84\sqrt{5}$

24. $2\sqrt{3} \cdot 5\sqrt{27}$ 90

25. $\sqrt{40a^4}$ $2a^2\sqrt{10}$

26. $\sqrt{50m^3n^5}$ $5mn^2\sqrt{2mn}$

27. $\sqrt{147x^6y^7}$ $7|x^3y^3|\sqrt{3y}$

28. $\sqrt{72x^3y^4z^5}$

29. $\sqrt{\dfrac{2}{7}} \cdot \sqrt{\dfrac{7}{3}}$ $\dfrac{\sqrt{6}}{3}$

30. $\sqrt{\dfrac{3}{5}} \cdot \sqrt{\dfrac{6}{4}}$ $\dfrac{3\sqrt{10}}{10}$

31. $\sqrt{\dfrac{t}{8}}$ $\dfrac{\sqrt{2t}}{4}$

32. $\sqrt{\dfrac{27}{p^2}}$ $\dfrac{3\sqrt{3}}{|p|}$

33. $\sqrt{\dfrac{5c^5}{4d^5}}$ $\dfrac{c^2\sqrt{5cd}}{2d^3}$

34. $\dfrac{\sqrt{9x^5y}}{\sqrt{12x^2y^6}}$ $\dfrac{x\sqrt{3xy}}{2y^3}$

35. $\dfrac{18}{6-\sqrt{2}}$ $\dfrac{54+9\sqrt{2}}{17}$

36. $\dfrac{3\sqrt{3}}{-2+\sqrt{6}}$ $\dfrac{6\sqrt{3}+9\sqrt{2}}{2}$

37. $\dfrac{10}{\sqrt{7}+\sqrt{2}}$

38. $\dfrac{2}{\sqrt{3}+\sqrt{6}}$ $\dfrac{2\sqrt{3}-2\sqrt{6}}{-3}$

39. $\dfrac{4}{4-3\sqrt{3}}$ $\dfrac{16+12\sqrt{3}}{-11}$

40. $\dfrac{3\sqrt{7}}{5\sqrt{3}+3\sqrt{5}}$

40. $\dfrac{5\sqrt{21}-3\sqrt{35}}{10}$

INVESTIGATION For Exercises 41–43, use the following information.
Police officers can use the formula $s = \sqrt{30fd}$ to determine the speed s that a car was traveling in miles per hour by measuring the distance d in feet of its skid marks. In this formula, f is the coefficient of friction for the type and condition of the road. 41. $3\sqrt{2d}$ 42. $2\sqrt{6d}$

41. Write a simplified formula for the speed if $f = 0.6$ for a wet asphalt road.

42. What is a simplified formula for the speed if $f = 0.8$ for a dry asphalt road?

★ 43. An officer measures skid marks that are 110 feet long. Determine the speed of the car for both wet road conditions and for dry road conditions. Write in both simplified radical form and as a decimal approximation.
$6\sqrt{55} \approx 44$ mph, $4\sqrt{165} \approx 51$ mph

★ 44. **GEOMETRY** A rectangle has a width of $3\sqrt{5}$ centimeters and a length of $4\sqrt{10}$ centimeters. Find the area of the rectangle. Write as a simplified radical expression. $60\sqrt{2}$ cm^2

Exercise Levels
A: 17–40
B: 41–52
C: 53–57

★ **45. GEOMETRY** The formula for the area A of a square with side length s is $A = s^2$. Solve this equation for s, and find the side length of a square having an area of 72 square inches. Write as a simplified radical expression. $s = \sqrt{A}$; $6\sqrt{2}$ in.

PHYSICS For Exercises 46 and 47, use the following information.
The formula for the kinetic energy of a moving object is $E = \frac{1}{2}mv^2$, where E is the kinetic energy in joules, m is the mass in kilograms, and v is the velocity in meters per second.

46. Solve the equation for v. $V = \sqrt{\dfrac{2E}{m}}$

★ **47.** Find the velocity of an object whose mass is 0.6 kilogram and whose kinetic energy is 54 joules. Write as a simplified radical expression.
$6\sqrt{5}$ m/s

48. GEOMETRY A rectangle has a length of $\sqrt{\dfrac{a}{8}}$ meters and a width of $\sqrt{\dfrac{a}{2}}$ meters. What is the area of the rectangle? $\frac{a}{4}$ m^2

★ **49. SPACE EXPLORATION** Refer to the application at the beginning of the lesson. Find the escape velocity for the Moon in kilometers per second if $G = \dfrac{6.7 \times 10^{-20} \text{ km}}{s^2 \text{ kg}}$, $M = 7.4 \times 10^{22}$ kg, and $R = 1.7 \times 10^3$ km. Use a calculator and write your answer as a decimal approximation. How does this compare to the escape velocity for Earth?
2.4 km/s; The Moon has a much lower escape velocity than Earth.

★ **50. GEOMETRY** Hero's Formula can be used to calculate the area A of a triangle given the three side lengths a, b, and c. Determine the area of a triangle if the side lengths of a triangle are 13, 10, and 7 feet. $20\sqrt{3}$ ft^2

$$A = \sqrt{s(s - a)(s - b)(s - c)}, \text{ where } s = \frac{1}{2}(a + b + c)$$

51. QUADRATIC FORMULA Determine the next step in the derivation of the Quadratic Formula.

Step 1 $x^2 + \dfrac{b}{a}x + \dfrac{c}{a} = 0$ $\quad x^2 + \dfrac{b}{a}x + \dfrac{b^2}{4a^2} = -\dfrac{c}{a} + \dfrac{b^2}{4a^2}$

Step 2 $x^2 + \dfrac{b}{a}x = -\dfrac{c}{a}$

52. QUADRATIC FORMULA Four steps in the derivation of the Quadratic Formula are shown below. Determine the correct order of the steps.
4, 3, 1, 2

1 $\quad x + \dfrac{b}{2a} = \pm\sqrt{\dfrac{b^2 - 4ac}{4a^2}}$	**2** $\quad x + \dfrac{b}{2a} = \pm\dfrac{\sqrt{b^2 - 4ac}}{2a}$
3 $\quad \left\lvert x + \dfrac{b}{2a} \right\rvert = \sqrt{\dfrac{b^2 - 4ac}{4a^2}}$	**4** $\quad x^2 + \dfrac{b}{a}x = -\dfrac{c}{a}$

EXTRA PRACTICE
See pages 737, 753.

Math online
Self-Check Quiz at
ca.algebra1.com

H.O.T. Problems

53. REASONING Kary takes any number, subtracts 4, multiplies by 4, takes the square root, and takes the reciprocal to get $\frac{1}{2}$. What number did she start with? Write a formula to describe the process. 5; $\dfrac{1}{\sqrt{4(x-4)}} = \dfrac{1}{2}$

54. OPEN ENDED Give an example of a binomial in the form $a\sqrt{b} + c\sqrt{d}$ and its conjugate. Then find their product.
Sample answer: $2\sqrt{2} + 3\sqrt{3}$ and $2\sqrt{2} - 3\sqrt{3}$; -19

Lesson 10-1 Simplifying Radical Expressions **533**

BL = Below Grade Level
OL = On Grade Level
AL = Above Grade Level
ELL = English Language Learner

Additional pages not shown:
Lesson Reading Guide, p. 5 **BL OL ELL**
Skills Practice, p. 8 **BL OL**

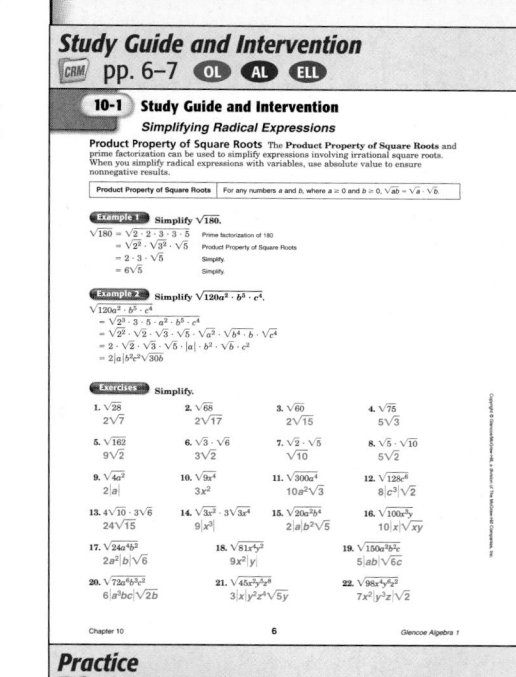

Study Guide and Intervention
CRM pp. 6–7 **OL AL ELL**

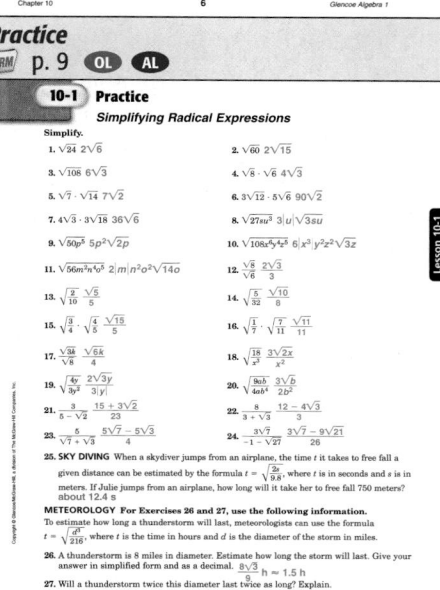

Practice
CRM p. 9 **OL AL**

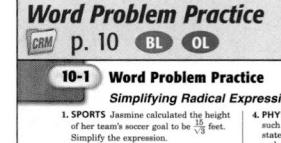

Word Problem Practice
CRM p. 10 **BL OL**

Enrichment
CRM p. 11 **OL AL**

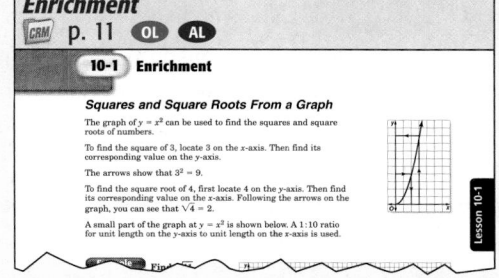

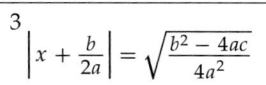

Ticket Out the Door Ask students to write radical expressions in which they need to use a conjugate to rationalize the denominators. Have students simplify the expressions.

Foldables™ Follow-Up

Remind students to record notes on what they have learned about simplifying radical expressions. Have them write their notes in their Foldables on the card labeled *Radical Expressions*.

Additional Answers

55. No; to solve the equation, take the square root of each side remembering that $a^2 = b^2$ implies $a = \pm b$. Thus, $3x - 2 = 2x + 6$ yields $x = 8$; but $3x - 2 = -(2x + 6)$ yields $x = -\frac{4}{5}$.

57. A lot of formulas and calculations that are used in space exploration contain radical expressions. To determine the escape velocity of a planet, you would need to know its mass and the radius. It would be very important to know the escape velocity of a planet before you landed on it so you would know if you had enough fuel and velocity to launch from it to get back into space.

---

55. **FIND THE ERROR** Ben is solving $(3x - 2)^2 = (2x + 6)^2$. He found that $x = -4$. Is this solution correct? Explain. **See margin.**

56. **CHALLENGE** Solve the equation $\left| y^3 \right| = \frac{1}{3\sqrt{3}}$ for y. $\pm\frac{\sqrt{3}}{3}$

57. *Writing in Math* Use the information about space exploration on page 580 to explain how radical expressions can be used in space exploration. Include an explanation of how you could determine the escape velocity of a planet and why you would need this information before you landed on it.
See margin.

STANDARDS PRACTICE 7MG2.1, 2.0

58. **REVIEW** If the cube has a surface area of $96a^2$, what is its volume? **C**

Formula for surface area of a cube = $6s^2$

A $32a^3$
B $48a^3$
C $64a^3$
D $96a^3$

59. The perimeter P of a square can be found using the formula $\frac{1}{4}P = \sqrt{A}$, where A is the area of the square. What is the perimeter of a square with an area of 81 square centimeters? **J**

F 108 cm   H 54 cm
G 72 cm   J 36 cm

Spiral Review

Find the next three terms in each geometric sequence. (Lesson 9-7) **62. 24, 12, 6**

60. 2, 6, 18, 54 **162, 486, 1458**
61. 1, −2, 4, −8 **16, −32, 64**
62. 384, 192, 96, 48

63. $\frac{1}{9}, \frac{2}{3}, 4, 24$ **144, 864, 5184**
64. $3, \frac{3}{4}, \frac{3}{16}, \frac{3}{64}$ $\frac{3}{256}, \frac{3}{1024}, \frac{3}{4096}$
65. 50, 10, 2, 0.4 **0.08, 0.016, 0.0032**

★ 66. **BIOLOGY** A certain type of bacteria, if left alone, doubles its number every 2 hours. If there are 1000 bacteria at a certain point in time, how many bacteria will there be 24 hours later? (Lesson 9-6) **4,096,000**

67. **PHYSICS** According to Newton's Law of Cooling, the difference between the temperature of an object and its surroundings decreases exponentially in time. Suppose a cup of coffee is 95°C and it is in a room that is 20°C. The cooling of the coffee can be modeled by the equation $y = 75(0.875)^t$, where y is the temperature difference and t is the time in minutes. Find the temperature of the coffee after 15 minutes. (Lesson 9-6) **84.9°C**

Factor each trinomial, if possible. If the trinomial cannot be factored using integers, write *prime*. (Lesson 8-4)

68. $6x^2 + 7x - 5$ **$(3x + 5)(2x - 1)$**
69. $35x^2 - 43x + 12$ **$(5x - 4)(7x - 3)$**
70. $5x^2 + 3x + 31$ **prime**

▶ **GET READY for the Next Lesson**

PREREQUISITE SKILL Find each product. (Lesson 7-6)

71. $(x - 3)(x + 2)$ $x^2 - x - 6$
72. $(a + 2)(a + 5)$ $a^2 + 7a + 10$
73. $(2t + 1)(t - 6)$ $2t^2 - 11t - 6$
74. $(4x - 3)(x + 1)$ $4x^2 + x - 3$
75. $(5x + 3y)(3x - y)$ $15x^2 + 4xy - 3y^2$
76. $(3a - 2b)(4a + 7b)$ $12a^2 + 13ab - 14b^2$

534 **Chapter 10** Radical Expressions and Triangles

Pre-AP Activity   Use as an Extension

Remind students that to undo squaring a number, they take the square root. Write $4^2 = 16$ and $\sqrt{16} = 4$ on the board. Challenge students to determine whether a square root can be written with an exponent. In future algebra classes, students will learn that square roots can be expressed as a number with the exponent $\frac{1}{2}$, and that $16^{\frac{1}{2}} = 4$.

Graphing Calculator Lab
Fractional Exponents

 Standard 2.0 Students understand and use such operations as taking the opposite, finding the reciprocal, taking a root, and **raising to a fractional power. They understand and use the rules of exponents.** (Key, CAHSEE)

You have studied the properties of exponents that are whole numbers. You can use a calculator to explore the meaning of fractional exponents.

ACTIVITY

Step 1 Evaluate $9^{\frac{1}{2}}$ and $\sqrt{9}$.

KEYSTROKES: 9 [∧] [( ] 1 [÷] 2 [ )] [ENTER] 3

KEYSTROKES: [2nd] [√] 9 [ENTER] 3

Record the results in a table like the one at the right.

Step 2 Use calculator to evaluate each expression. Record each result in your table. To find a root other than a square root, choose the $\sqrt[x]{}$ function from the [MATH] menu.

Expression	Value	Expression	Value
$9^{\frac{1}{2}}$	3	$\sqrt{9}$	3
$16^{\frac{1}{2}}$	4	$\sqrt{16}$	4
$8^{\frac{1}{3}}$	2	$\sqrt[3]{8}$	2
$27^{\frac{1}{3}}$	3	$\sqrt[3]{27}$	3
$8^{\frac{2}{3}}$	4	$\sqrt[3]{8^2}$	4
$16^{\frac{3}{4}}$	8	$\sqrt[4]{8^3}$	8

1A. Study the table. What do you observe about the value of an expression of the form $a^{\frac{1}{n}}$? **It is equal to $\sqrt[n]{a}$.**

1B. What do you observe about the value of an expression of the form $a^{\frac{m}{n}}$? **It is equal to $\sqrt[n]{a^m}$.**

ANALYZE THE RESULTS

1. Recall the Power of a Power Property. For any number a and all integers m and n, $(a^m)^n = a^{m \cdot n}$. Assume that fractional exponents behave as whole number exponents and find the value of $\left(b^{\frac{1}{2}}\right)^2$.

$$\left(b^{\frac{1}{2}}\right)^2 = b^{\frac{1}{2} \cdot 2} \quad \text{Power of a Power Property}$$
$$= b^1 \text{ or } b \quad \text{Simplify.}$$

Thus, $b^{\frac{1}{2}}$ is a number whose square equals b. So it makes sense to define $b^{\frac{1}{2}} = \sqrt{b}$. Use a similar process to define $b^{\frac{1}{n}}$. **See margin.**

2. Define $b^{\frac{m}{n}}$. Justify your answer. **See margin.**

Write each expression as a power of x.

3. $\dfrac{\sqrt{x}}{(\sqrt[4]{x})(x)}$ $x^{-\frac{3}{4}}$

4. $\dfrac{(x)(\sqrt[3]{x})}{(\sqrt{x})(\sqrt[5]{x})}$ $x^{\frac{19}{30}}$

Write each root as an expression using a fractional exponent. Then evaluate the expression.

5. $\sqrt{49}$ $49^{\frac{1}{2}}$; 7

6. $\sqrt[4]{81}$ $81^{\frac{1}{4}}$; 3

7. $\sqrt{4^3}$ $4^{\frac{3}{2}}$; 8

8. $\sqrt[3]{125^2}$ $125^{\frac{2}{3}}$; 25

 **Other Calculator Keystrokes at** ca.algebra1.com **Extend 10–1** Graphing Calculator Lab **535**

Additional Answers

1. $\left(b^{\frac{1}{n}}\right)^n = b^{\frac{1}{n} \cdot n}$ Power of a Power Property
$= b^1$ or b Simplify.
Therefore $b^{\frac{1}{n}} = \sqrt[n]{b}$.

2. $b^{\frac{m}{n}} = \sqrt[n]{b^m}$;
$\left(b^{\frac{1}{n}}\right)^m = \left(\sqrt[n]{b}\right)^m$ Definition of $b^{\frac{1}{n}}$
$= b^1$ or b Simplify.
Therefore $b^{\frac{1}{n}} = \sqrt[n]{b}$.

From Concrete to Abstract For Exercise 2, students should be able to show $b^{\frac{m}{n}} = \sqrt[n]{b^m}$. Point out that $b^{\frac{m}{n}} = \sqrt[n]{b^m} = (\sqrt[n]{b})^m$. Demonstrate for students that it is easier to evaluate $\sqrt[n]{b}$ first and then raise $\sqrt[n]{b}$ to the mth power.

---

1 Focus

Objective: Use a graphing calculator to explore the meaning of fractional exponents.

Materials
• graphing calculator

Teaching Tip Show students the keystrokes needed to evaluate $9^{\frac{1}{2}}$ and $\sqrt{9}$ on the calculator. Point out that the calculator also has a key for cube roots. To find roots other than square roots and cube roots, tell students to choose the $\sqrt[x]{}$ function from the MATH menu.

2 Teach

Working in Cooperative Groups
Put students in groups of 2 or 3, mixing abilities. Have groups complete the Activity and Exercises 1 and 2.

• Make sure students use parentheses under the radical sign when needed. For example, to calculate $\sqrt[4]{8^3}$, have students enter 4, select 5·$\sqrt[x]{}$ from the MATH menus, and then enter [( ] 8 [∧] 3 [ )]. Point out that the 4 is entered before hitting [MATH].

• For Exercise 2, you may wish to review the property $(a^m)^n = a^{mn}$.

Practice Have students complete Exercises 3–6.

3 Assess

 **Formative Assessment**

Use Exercises 5 and 6 to assess whether students can correctly write the roots using a fractional exponent.

Operations with Radical Expressions

1 Focus

Standards Alignment

Before Lesson 10-2
Multiply and divide monomials
from Standard 7AF2.2

Lesson 10-2
Identify and use the arithmetic properties of irrational and real numbers. Understand and use such operations as taking a root. Understand and use the rules of exponents from Standards 1.0 and 2.0

After Lesson 10-2
Know the laws of fractional exponents and understand exponential functions from 🔑 Standard 2A12.0

2 Teach

Scaffolding Questions
Have students read *Get Ready for the Lesson*.
Ask:
• What is an assumption that the formula makes? Sample answer: There are no obstructions that would block a person from seeing the entire distance.
• Assuming that nothing blocks the view, how much farther can a person atop the Sears Tower see than a person atop the Empire State Building? about 3.3 miles farther

(continued on the next page)

Lesson 10-2 Resources

Main Ideas

• Add and subtract radical expressions.
• Multiply radical expressions.

Standard 1.0 Students identify and use the arithmetic properties of subsets of integers and rational, **irrational, and real numbers,** including closure properties for the four basic arithmetic operations where applicable.

Standard 2.0 Students understand and use such operations as taking the opposite, finding the reciprocal, **taking a root,** and raising to a fractional power. **They understand and use the rules of exponents.** (Key, CAHSEE)

▶ **GET READY for the Lesson**

The formula $d = \sqrt{\frac{3h}{2}}$ represents the distance d in miles that a person h feet high can see. To determine how much farther a person can see from atop the Sears Tower than from atop the Empire State Building, we can substitute the heights of both buildings into the equation.

World's Tall Structures

| 984 feet Eiffel Tower Paris | 1,002 feet JP Morgan Chase Houston | 1,250 feet Empire State Building New York | 1,450 feet Sears Tower Chicago | 1,667 feet Taipei 101 Taipei |

Add and Subtract Radical Expressions Radical expressions in which the radicands are alike can be added or subtracted in the same way that like monomials are added or subtracted.

Monomials	**Radical Expressions**
$2x + 7x = (2 + 7)x$	$2\sqrt{11} + 7\sqrt{11} = (2 + 7)\sqrt{11}$
$\quad = 9x$	$\quad = 9\sqrt{11}$
$15y - 3y = (15 - 3)y$	$15\sqrt{2} - 3\sqrt{2} = (15 - 3)\sqrt{2}$
$\quad = 12y$	$\quad = 12\sqrt{2}$

EXAMPLE Expressions with Like Radicands

1 Simplify each expression.

a. $4\sqrt{3} + 6\sqrt{3} - 5\sqrt{3}$
$4\sqrt{3} + 6\sqrt{3} - 5\sqrt{3} = (4 + 6 - 5)\sqrt{3}$ Distributive Property
$\quad\quad\quad\quad\quad = 5\sqrt{3}$ Simplify.

b. $12\sqrt{5} + 3\sqrt{7} + 6\sqrt{7} - 8\sqrt{5}$
$12\sqrt{5} + 3\sqrt{7} + 6\sqrt{7} - 8\sqrt{5} = 12\sqrt{5} - 8\sqrt{5} + 3\sqrt{7} + 6\sqrt{7}$
$\quad\quad\quad\quad\quad = (12 - 8)\sqrt{5} + (3 + 6)\sqrt{7}$ Distributive Property
$\quad\quad\quad\quad\quad = 4\sqrt{5} + 9\sqrt{7}$ Simplify.

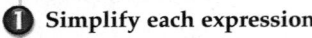**CHECK Your Progress**

1A. $3\sqrt{2} - 5\sqrt{2} + \sqrt{2}$ $-\sqrt{2}$
1B. $15\sqrt{11} - 14\sqrt{13} + 6\sqrt{13} - 11\sqrt{11}$ $4\sqrt{11} - 8\sqrt{13}$

536 Chapter 10 Radical Expressions and Triangles

 **Extra Examples at** ca.algebra1.com

Chapter 10 Resource Masters

Lesson Reading Guide, p. 12 **BL OL ELL**
Study Guide and Intervention, pp. 13–14
BL OL ELL
Skills Practice, p. 15 **BL OL**
Practice, p. 16 **OL AL**
Word Problem Practice, p. 17 **OL AL**
Enrichment, p. 18 **OL AL**
Quiz 1, p. 51

Transparencies
5-Minute Check Transparency 10-2
Additional Print Resources
Noteables™ Interactive Study Notebook with Foldables™
Teaching Algebra with manipulatives

Technology
ca.algebra1.com
Interactive Classroom CD-ROM
AssignmentWorks CD-ROM
Graphing Calculator Easy Files

In Example 1b, $4\sqrt{5} + 9\sqrt{7}$ cannot be simplified further because the radicands are different. There are no common factors, and each radicand is in simplest form. If the radicals in an expression are not in simplest form, simplify them first.

EXAMPLE Expressions with Unlike Radicands

2 Simplify $2\sqrt{20} + 3\sqrt{45} + \sqrt{180}$.

$$2\sqrt{20} + 3\sqrt{45} + \sqrt{180} = 2\sqrt{2^2 \cdot 5} + 3\sqrt{3^2 \cdot 5} + \sqrt{6^2 \cdot 5}$$
$$= 2\left(\sqrt{2^2} \cdot \sqrt{5}\right) + 3\left(\sqrt{3^2} \cdot \sqrt{5}\right) + \sqrt{6^2} \cdot \sqrt{5}$$
$$= 2\left(2\sqrt{5}\right) + 3\left(3\sqrt{5}\right) + 6\sqrt{5}$$
$$= 4\sqrt{5} + 9\sqrt{5} + 6\sqrt{5}$$
$$= 19\sqrt{5}$$

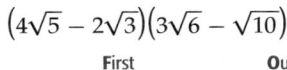 **Your Progress**

Simplify.
2A. $4\sqrt{54} + 2\sqrt{24} - \sqrt{150}$ $11\sqrt{6}$ **2B.** $4\sqrt{12} - 6\sqrt{48} + 5\sqrt{24}$ $-16\sqrt{3} + 10\sqrt{6}$

Multiply Radical Expressions Multiplying two radical expressions with different radicands is similar to multiplying binomials.

EXAMPLE Multiply Radical Expressions

3 GEOMETRY Find the area of the rectangle in simplest form.

To find the area of the rectangle, multiply the measures of the length and width.

$4\sqrt{5} - 2\sqrt{3}$

$3\sqrt{6} - \sqrt{10}$

$$\left(4\sqrt{5} - 2\sqrt{3}\right)\left(3\sqrt{6} - \sqrt{10}\right)$$

Study Tip

Look Back
To review the **FOIL method**, see Lesson 7-6.

First terms	Outer terms	Inner terms	Last terms

$$= \left(4\sqrt{5}\right)\left(3\sqrt{6}\right) + \left(4\sqrt{5}\right)\left(-\sqrt{10}\right) + \left(-2\sqrt{3}\right)\left(3\sqrt{6}\right) + \left(-2\sqrt{3}\right)\left(-\sqrt{10}\right)$$
$$= 12\sqrt{30} - 4\sqrt{50} - 6\sqrt{18} + 2\sqrt{30} \qquad \text{Multiply.}$$
$$= 12\sqrt{30} - 4\sqrt{5^2 \cdot 2} - 6\sqrt{3^2 \cdot 2} + 2\sqrt{30} \qquad \text{Prime factorization}$$
$$= 12\sqrt{30} - 20\sqrt{2} - 18\sqrt{2} + 2\sqrt{30} \qquad \text{Simplify.}$$
$$= 14\sqrt{30} - 38\sqrt{2} \qquad \text{Combine like terms.}$$

 **Your Progress**

Find each product.
3A. $\left(5\sqrt{5} - 4\sqrt{3}\right)\left(6\sqrt{10} - 2\sqrt{6}\right)$ $174\sqrt{2} - 34\sqrt{30}$
3B. $\left(6\sqrt{7} + 3\sqrt{2}\right)\left(4\sqrt{10} - 5\sqrt{6}\right)$ $24\sqrt{70} - 30\sqrt{42} + 24\sqrt{5} - 30\sqrt{3}$

Online **Personal Tutor at** ca.algebra1.com

• Mount Everest, the tallest mountain in the world, is about 12,000 feet above the plateau out of which it rises. How far would a climber be able to see from the peak of Mount Everest? about 134 miles

Add and Subtract Radical Expressions

Example 1 shows how to use the Distributive Property to add or subtract like radicands in a radical expression. **Example 2** shows how to simplify the radicals in a radical expression with unlike radicands.

✓ **Formative Assessment**

Use the Check Your Progress exercises after each example to determine students' understanding of concepts.

ADDITIONAL EXAMPLES

1 Simplify each expression.
   a. $6\sqrt{5} + 2\sqrt{5} - 5\sqrt{5}$ $3\sqrt{5}$
   b. $7\sqrt{2} + 8\sqrt{11} - 4\sqrt{11} - 6\sqrt{2}$ $\sqrt{2} + 4\sqrt{11}$

2 Simplify $6\sqrt{27} + 8\sqrt{12} + 2\sqrt{75}$. $44\sqrt{3}$

Additional Examples are also in:
• Noteables™ Interactive Study Notebook with Foldables™
• Interactive Classroom PowerPoint® Presentations

ADDITIONAL EXAMPLE

3 GEOMETRY Find the area of a rectangle in simplest form with a width of $4\sqrt{6} - 2\sqrt{10}$ and a length of $5\sqrt{3} + 7\sqrt{5}$. $18\sqrt{30} - 10\sqrt{2}$

Multiply Radical Expressions
Example 3 shows how to multiply two radical expressions with different radicands.

Focus on Mathematical Content

Operations with Radical Expressions Radical expressions can be added or subtracted only if the radicands are the same. Radical expressions can be multiplied whether the radicands are the same or different.

Tips for New Teachers

Preventing Errors

Have students use their calculators to verify that their answers to Additional Example 2 are correct.

3 Practice

 Formative Assessment

Use Exercises 1–10 to check for understanding.

Use the chart at the bottom of this page to customize assignments for your students.

Odd/Even Assignments

Exercises 11–33 are structured so that students practice the same concepts whether they are assigned odd or even problems.

⚠ Exercise Alert!

Use a Calculator Students will need calculators for Exercises 38–41.

Real-World Connections

For Exercises 38 and 39, tell students the tallest structure in a forest is often a fire tower. Fire towers enable firefighters to scan large areas for potential trouble. The towers are usually 80 to 100 feet above the ground on which they are built. Ask students to tell how knowing how far a person can see from a fire tower could help determine how far apart to set the towers.

Additional Answer

39. Approximately 853 feet; solve

$$\sqrt{\frac{3(1250)}{2}} - \sqrt{\frac{3h}{2}} = 7.53;$$

may guess and test, graphical, or analytical methods.

You can use a calculator to verify that a simplified radical expression is equivalent to the original expression. Consider Example 3. First, find a decimal approximation for the original expression.

KEYSTROKES: (4 2nd [√] 5) − 2 2nd [√] 3)) (3 2nd [√] 6) − 2nd [√] 10)) ENTER
22.94104268

Next, find a decimal approximation for the simplified expression.

KEYSTROKES: 14 2nd [√] 30) − 38 2nd [√] 2) ENTER
22.94104268

Since the approximations are equal, the expressions are equivalent.

★ indicates multi-step problem

✓ CHECK Your Understanding

Examples 1, 2 (pp. 536–537)

Simplify.

1. $4\sqrt{3} + 7\sqrt{3}$ $11\sqrt{3}$
2. $2\sqrt{6} - 7\sqrt{6}$ $-5\sqrt{6}$
3. $5\sqrt{5} - 3\sqrt{20}$ $-\sqrt{5}$
4. $2\sqrt{3} + \sqrt{12}$ $4\sqrt{3}$
5. $3\sqrt{5} + 5\sqrt{6} + 3\sqrt{20}$ $9\sqrt{5} + 5\sqrt{6}$
6. $8\sqrt{3} + \sqrt{3} + \sqrt{9}$ $9\sqrt{3} + 3$

Example 3 (p. 537)

Find each product.

7. $\sqrt{2}(\sqrt{8} + 4\sqrt{3})$ $4 + 4\sqrt{6}$
8. $(4 + \sqrt{5})(3 + \sqrt{5})$ $17 + 7\sqrt{5}$

★ 9. **GEOMETRY** Find the perimeter and the area of the square. $P = 16 + 12\sqrt{6}$ ft; $A = 70 + 24\sqrt{6}$ ft²

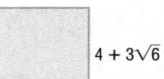
$4 + 3\sqrt{6}$ ft

10. **ELECTRICITY** The voltage V required for a circuit is given by $V = \sqrt{PR}$, where P is the power in watts and R is the resistance in ohms. How many more volts are needed to light a 100-watt bulb than a 75-watt bulb if the resistance for both is 110 ohms? $10\sqrt{110} - 5\sqrt{330} \approx 14.05$ volts

Exercises

HOMEWORK HELP	
For Exercises	**See Examples**
11–18	1
19–22	2
23–33	3

Exercise Levels
A: 11–33
B: 34–43
C: 44–48

Simplify.

11. $8\sqrt{5} + 3\sqrt{5}$ $11\sqrt{5}$
12. $3\sqrt{6} + 10\sqrt{6}$ $13\sqrt{6}$
13. $2\sqrt{15} - 6\sqrt{15} - 3\sqrt{15}$ $-7\sqrt{15}$
14. $5\sqrt{19} + 6\sqrt{19} - 11\sqrt{19}$ 0
15. $16\sqrt{x} + 2\sqrt{x}$ $18\sqrt{x}$
16. $3\sqrt{5b} - 4\sqrt{5b} + 11\sqrt{5b}$ $10\sqrt{5b}$
17. $8\sqrt{3} - 2\sqrt{2} + 3\sqrt{2} + 5\sqrt{3}$ $13\sqrt{3} + \sqrt{2}$
18. $4\sqrt{6} + \sqrt{17} - 6\sqrt{2} + 4\sqrt{17}$ $4\sqrt{6} - 6\sqrt{2} + 5\sqrt{17}$
19. $\sqrt{18} + \sqrt{12} + \sqrt{8}$ $5\sqrt{2} + 2\sqrt{3}$
20. $\sqrt{6} + 2\sqrt{3} + \sqrt{12}$ $\sqrt{6} + 4\sqrt{3}$
21. $3\sqrt{7} - 2\sqrt{28}$ $-\sqrt{7}$
22. $2\sqrt{50} - 3\sqrt{32}$ $-2\sqrt{2}$

Find each product.

23. $\sqrt{6}(\sqrt{3} + 5\sqrt{2})$ $3\sqrt{2} + 10\sqrt{3}$
24. $\sqrt{5}(2\sqrt{10} + 3\sqrt{2})$ $10\sqrt{2} + 3\sqrt{10}$
25. $(3 + \sqrt{5})(3 - \sqrt{5})$ 4
26. $(7 - \sqrt{10})^2$ $59 - 14\sqrt{10}$
27. $(\sqrt{6} + \sqrt{8})(\sqrt{24} + \sqrt{2})$ $10\sqrt{3} + 16$
28. $(\sqrt{5} - \sqrt{2})(\sqrt{14} + \sqrt{35})$ $3\sqrt{7}$
29. $(2\sqrt{10} + 3\sqrt{15})(3\sqrt{3} - 2\sqrt{2})$ $19\sqrt{5}$
30. $(5\sqrt{2} + 3\sqrt{5})(2\sqrt{10} - 3)$ $15\sqrt{2} + 11\sqrt{5}$

538   Chapter 10 Radical Expressions and Triangles

DIFFERENTIATED HOMEWORK OPTIONS

Level	Assignment	Two-Day Option	
BL Basic	11–33, 45, 46, 48–70	11–33 odd, 49, 50	12–32 even, 45, 46, 48, 51–70
OL Core	11–37 odd, 38–43, 45–70	11–33, 49, 50	34–37 odd, 45, 46, 48, 51–70
AL Advanced /Pre-AP	34–64, (optional: 65–70)		

★ **31. GEOMETRY** Find the perimeter and area of a rectangle with a length of $8\sqrt{7} + 4\sqrt{5}$ inches and a width of $2\sqrt{7} - 3\sqrt{5}$ inches.
$20\sqrt{7} + 2\sqrt{5}$ in; $52 - 16\sqrt{35}$ in^2

32. GEOMETRY The perimeter of a rectangle is $2\sqrt{3} + 4\sqrt{11} + 6$ centimeters, and its length is $2\sqrt{11} + 1$ centimeters. Find the width. $\sqrt{3} + 2$ cm

33. GEOMETRY The area A of a rhombus can be found using the formula $A = \frac{1}{2}d_1d_2$, where d_1 and d_2 are the lengths of the diagonals of the rhombus. What is the area of the rhombus at the right? $15\sqrt{6}$ cm^2

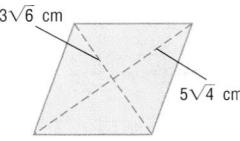

3√6 cm

5√4 cm

Simplify.

34. $\sqrt{2} + \sqrt{\frac{1}{2}}$ $\frac{3\sqrt{2}}{2}$

35. $\sqrt{10} - \sqrt{\frac{2}{5}}$ $\frac{4\sqrt{10}}{5}$

36. $3\sqrt{3} - \sqrt{45} + 3\sqrt{\frac{1}{3}}$ $4\sqrt{3} - 3\sqrt{5}$

37. $6\sqrt{\frac{7}{4}} + 3\sqrt{28} - 10\sqrt{\frac{1}{7}}$ $\frac{53\sqrt{7}}{7}$

DISTANCE For Exercises 38 and 39, refer to the application at the beginning of the lesson.

38. How much farther can a person see from atop the Sears Tower than from atop the Empire State Building? Write as a simplified radical expression and as a decimal approximation. $5\sqrt{87} - 25\sqrt{3} \approx 3.34$ mi

39. A person atop the Empire State Building can see approximately 7.53 miles farther than a person atop the TransAmerica Building in San Francisco. Explain how you could find the height of the TransAmerica Building. **See margin.**

ENGINEERING For Exercises 40 and 41, use the following information.
The equation $r = \sqrt{\frac{F}{5\pi}}$ relates the radius r of a drainpipe, in inches, to the flow rate F of water passing through it, in gallons per minute.

★ **40.** Find the radius of a pipe that can carry 500 gallons of water per minute. Write as a simplified radical expression, and use a calculator to find the decimal approximation. Round to the nearest whole number.

41. An engineer determines that a drainpipe must be able to carry 1000 gallons of water per minute and instructs the builder to use an 8-inch radius pipe. Can the builder use two 4-inch radius pipes instead? Justify your answer.

MOTION For Exercises 42 and 43, use the following information.
The velocity of an object dropped from a certain height can be found using the formula $v = \sqrt{2gd}$, where v is the velocity in feet per second, g is the acceleration due to gravity, and d is the distance the object drops, in feet.

42. Find the speed of an object that has fallen 25 feet and the speed of an object that has fallen 100 feet. Use 32 feet per second squared for g. Write as a simplified radical expression. **40 ft/s; 80 ft/s**

43. When you increased the distance by 4 times, what happened to the velocity? Explain. **The velocity doubled because $\sqrt{4} = 2$.**

H.O.T. Problems

44. CHALLENGE Determine whether the following statement is *true* or *false*. Provide an example or counterexample to support your answer.
$$x + y > \sqrt{x^2 + y^2} \text{ when } x > 0 \text{ and } y > 0$$
True; substituting 1 for x and 1 for y leaves $2 > \sqrt{2}$, which is true.

Lesson 10-2 Operations with Radical Expressions **539**

Real-World Link

The Sears Tower was the tallest building in the world from 1974 to 1996. You can see four states from its roof: Michigan, Indiana, Illinois, and Wisconsin.

Source: the-skydeck.com

40. $10\sqrt{\frac{1}{\pi}} \approx 6$ in.

41. No, each pipe would need to carry 500 gallons per minute, so the pipes would need at least a 6-inch radius.

EXTRA PRACTICE
See pages 737, 753.

Math Online
Self-Check Quiz at
ca.algebra1.com

Additional pages not shown:

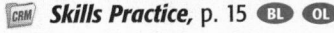

CRM *Lesson Reading Guide*, p. 12 **BL** **OL** **ELL**

CRM *Skills Practice*, p. 15 **BL** **OL**

Enrichment
CRM p. 18 **OL** **AL**

10-2 **Enrichment**

The Wheel of Theodorus

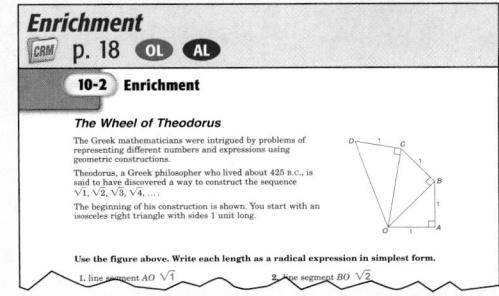

The Greek mathematicians were intrigued by problems of representing different numbers and expressions using geometric constructions.

Theodorus, a Greek philosopher who lived about 425 B.C., is said to have discovered a way to construct the sequence $\sqrt{1}, \sqrt{2}, \sqrt{3}, \sqrt{4}, \ldots$

The beginning of his construction is shown. You start with an isosceles right triangle with sides 1 unit long.

Use the figure above. Write each length as a radical expression in simplest form.

1. line segment AO $\sqrt{1}$ 2. line segment BO $\sqrt{2}$

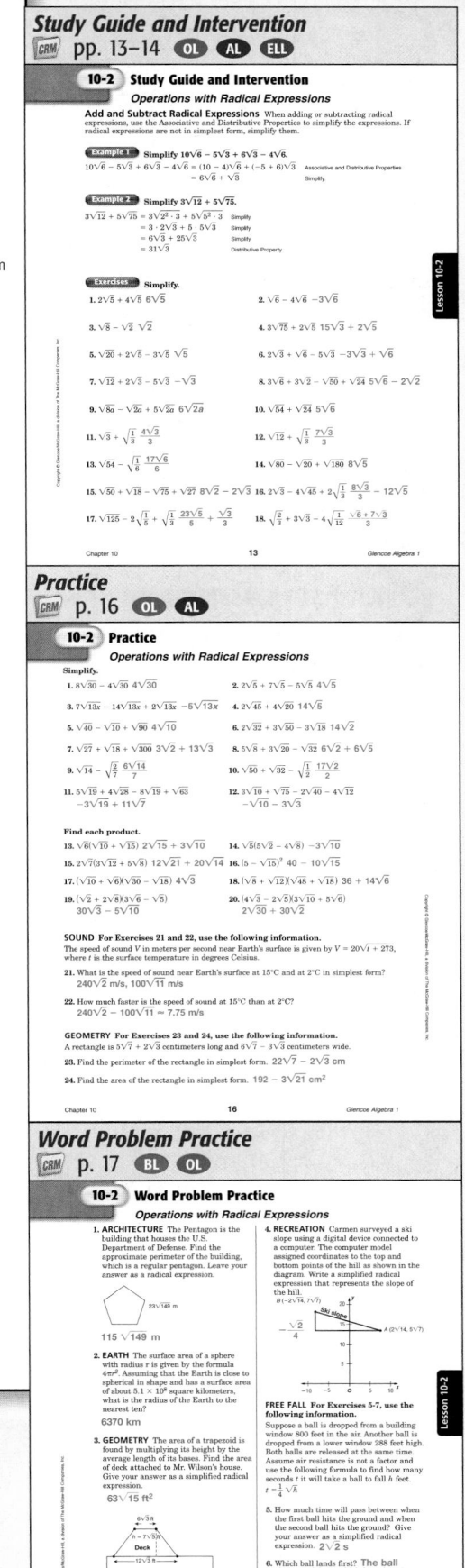

10-2 **Study Guide and Intervention**
Operations with Radical Expressions

Add and Subtract Radical Expressions When adding or subtracting radical expressions, use the Associative and Distributive Properties to simplify the expressions. If radical expressions are not in simplest form, simplify them.

Example 1 Simplify $10\sqrt{6} - 5\sqrt{3} + 6\sqrt{3} - 4\sqrt{6}$.
$10\sqrt{6} - 5\sqrt{3} + 6\sqrt{3} - 4\sqrt{6} = (10 - 4)\sqrt{6} + (-5 + 6)\sqrt{3}$ Associative and Distributive Properties
$= 6\sqrt{6} + \sqrt{3}$ Simplify.

Example 2 Simplify $3\sqrt{12} + 5\sqrt{75}$.
$3\sqrt{12} + 5\sqrt{75} = 3\sqrt{2^2 \cdot 3} + 5\sqrt{5^2 \cdot 3}$ Simplify.
$= 3 \cdot 2\sqrt{3} + 5 \cdot 5\sqrt{3}$ Simplify.
$= 6\sqrt{3} + 25\sqrt{3}$ Simplify.
$= 31\sqrt{3}$ Distributive Property

Exercises Simplify.

1. $2\sqrt{5} + 4\sqrt{5}$ $6\sqrt{5}$
2. $\sqrt{6} - 4\sqrt{6}$ $-3\sqrt{6}$
3. $\sqrt{8} - \sqrt{2}$ $\sqrt{2}$
4. $3\sqrt{75} + 2\sqrt{5}$ $15\sqrt{3} + 2\sqrt{5}$
5. $\sqrt{20} + 2\sqrt{5} - 3\sqrt{5}$ $\sqrt{5}$
6. $2\sqrt{3} + \sqrt{6} - 5\sqrt{3}$ $-3\sqrt{3} + \sqrt{6}$
7. $\sqrt{12} + 2\sqrt{3} - 5\sqrt{3}$ $-\sqrt{3}$
8. $3\sqrt{6} + 3\sqrt{2} - \sqrt{50} + \sqrt{24}$ $5\sqrt{6} - 2\sqrt{2}$
9. $\sqrt{8a} - \sqrt{2a} + 5\sqrt{2a}$ $6\sqrt{2a}$
10. $\sqrt{54} + \sqrt{24}$ $5\sqrt{6}$
11. $\sqrt{3} + \sqrt{\frac{1}{3}}$ $\frac{4\sqrt{3}}{3}$
12. $\sqrt{12} + \sqrt{\frac{1}{3}}$ $\frac{7\sqrt{3}}{3}$
13. $\sqrt{54} - \sqrt{\frac{1}{6}}$ $\frac{17\sqrt{6}}{6}$
14. $\sqrt{80} - \sqrt{20} + \sqrt{180}$ $8\sqrt{5}$
15. $\sqrt{50} + \sqrt{18} - \sqrt{75} + \sqrt{27}$ $8\sqrt{2} - 2\sqrt{3}$
16. $2\sqrt{3} - 4\sqrt{45} + 2\sqrt{\frac{1}{3}}$ $\frac{8\sqrt{3}}{3} - 12\sqrt{5}$
17. $\sqrt{125} - 2\sqrt{\frac{1}{5}} + \sqrt{\frac{1}{3}}$ $\frac{23\sqrt{5}}{5} + \frac{\sqrt{3}}{3}$
18. $\sqrt{\frac{2}{3}} + 3\sqrt{3} - 4\sqrt{\frac{1}{12}}$ $\frac{\sqrt{6} + 7\sqrt{3}}{3}$

Chapter 10   13   Glencoe Algebra 1

10-2 **Practice**
Operations with Radical Expressions

Simplify.

1. $8\sqrt{30} - 4\sqrt{30}$ $4\sqrt{30}$
2. $2\sqrt{5} + 7\sqrt{5} - 5\sqrt{5}$ $4\sqrt{5}$
3. $7\sqrt{13x} - 14\sqrt{13x} + 2\sqrt{13x}$ $-5\sqrt{13x}$
4. $2\sqrt{45} + 4\sqrt{20}$ $14\sqrt{5}$
5. $\sqrt{40} - \sqrt{10} + \sqrt{90}$ $4\sqrt{10}$
6. $2\sqrt{32} + 3\sqrt{50} - 3\sqrt{18}$ $14\sqrt{2}$
7. $\sqrt{27} + \sqrt{18} + \sqrt{300}$ $3\sqrt{2} + 13\sqrt{3}$
8. $5\sqrt{8} + 3\sqrt{20} - \sqrt{32}$ $6\sqrt{2} + 6\sqrt{5}$
9. $\sqrt{14} - \sqrt{\frac{2}{7}}$ $\frac{6\sqrt{14}}{7}$
10. $\sqrt{50} + \sqrt{32} - \sqrt{\frac{1}{2}}$ $\frac{17\sqrt{2}}{2}$
11. $5\sqrt{19} + 4\sqrt{28} - 8\sqrt{19} + \sqrt{63} - 3\sqrt{19} + 11\sqrt{7}$
12. $3\sqrt{10} + \sqrt{75} - 2\sqrt{40} - 4\sqrt{12} - \sqrt{10} - 3\sqrt{3}$

Find each product.

13. $\sqrt{6}(\sqrt{10} + \sqrt{15})$ $2\sqrt{15} + 3\sqrt{10}$
14. $\sqrt{5}(5\sqrt{2} - 4\sqrt{8})$ $-3\sqrt{10}$
15. $2\sqrt{7}(3\sqrt{12} + 5\sqrt{8})$ $12\sqrt{21} + 20\sqrt{14}$
16. $(5 - \sqrt{15})^2$ $40 - 10\sqrt{15}$
17. $(\sqrt{10} + \sqrt{6})(\sqrt{10} - \sqrt{18})$ $4\sqrt{3}$
18. $(\sqrt{8} + \sqrt{12})(\sqrt{48} + \sqrt{18})$ $36 + 14\sqrt{6}$
19. $(\sqrt{2} + 2\sqrt{8})(3\sqrt{6} - \sqrt{5})$ $30\sqrt{3} - 5\sqrt{10}$
20. $(4\sqrt{3} - 2\sqrt{5})(3\sqrt{10} + 5\sqrt{6})$ $2\sqrt{30} + 30\sqrt{2}$

SOUND For Exercises 21 and 22, use the following information.
The speed of sound V in meters per second near Earth's surface is given by $V = 20\sqrt{t + 273}$, where t is the surface temperature in degrees Celsius.

21. What is the speed of sound near Earth's surface at 15°C and at 2°C in simplest form?
$240\sqrt{2}$ m/s, $100\sqrt{11}$ m/s

22. How much faster is the speed of sound at 15°C than at 2°C?
$240\sqrt{2} - 100\sqrt{11} \approx 7.75$ m/s

GEOMETRY For Exercises 23 and 24, use the following information.
A rectangle is $5\sqrt{7} + 2\sqrt{3}$ centimeters long and $6\sqrt{7} - 3\sqrt{3}$ centimeters wide.

23. Find the perimeter of the rectangle in simplest form. $22\sqrt{7} - 2\sqrt{3}$ cm
24. Find the area of the rectangle in simplest form. $192 - 3\sqrt{21}$ cm^2

Chapter 10   16   Glencoe Algebra 1

10-2 **Word Problem Practice**
Operations with Radical Expressions

1. **ARCHITECTURE** The Pentagon is the building that houses the U.S. Department of Defense. Find the approximate perimeter of the building, which is a regular pentagon. Leave your answer as a radical expression.
$115\sqrt{149}$ m

2. **EARTH** The surface area of a sphere with radius r is given by the formula $4\pi r^2$. Assuming that the Earth is close to spherical in shape and has a surface area of about 5.1×10^8 square kilometers, what is the radius of the Earth to the nearest ten?
6370 km

3. **GEOMETRY** The area of a trapezoid is found by multiplying its height by the average length of its bases. Find the area of deck attached to Mr. Wilson's house. Give your answer as a simplified radical expression.
$63\sqrt{15}$ ft^2

4. **RECREATION** Carmen surveyed a ski slope using a digital device connected to a computer. The computer model assigned coordinates to the top and bottom points of the hill as shown in the diagram. Write a simplified radical expression that represents the slope of the hill.
$-\frac{\sqrt{2}}{4}$

FREE FALL For Exercises 5–7, use the following information.
Suppose a ball is dropped from a building window 800 feet in the air. Another ball is dropped from a lower window 288 feet high. Both balls are released at the same time. Assume air resistance is not a factor and use the following formula to find how many seconds t it will take a ball to fall h feet.
$t = \frac{1}{4}\sqrt{h}$

5. How much time will pass between when the first ball hits the ground and when the second ball hits the ground? Give your answer as a simplified radical expression. $2\sqrt{2}$ s

6. Which ball lands first? The ball dropped from 288 feet lands first.

7. Find a decimal approximation of the answer for Exercise 5. Round your answer to the nearest tenth. about 2.8 s

Chapter 10   17   Glencoe Algebra 1

For Exercises 51–56, if a variable with an odd power is under the radical, assume that the value of the variable is nonnegative.

4 Assess

Crystal Ball Tell students that the next lesson they will study is titled *Radical Equations*. Ask them to write how they think what they learned today about adding, subtracting, and multiplying radical expressions will connect with the next lesson they will study.

✔ Formative Assessment

Check for student understanding of concepts in Lessons 10-1 and 10-2.

[CRM] Quiz 1, p. 51

Additional Answers

45. Sample Answer: Let $x = 2$ and $y = 3$.
$(\sqrt{2} + \sqrt{3})^2 = 2 + 2\sqrt{6} + 3$ or $5 + 2\sqrt{6}$

48. The distance a person can see is related to the height of the person using $d = \sqrt{\frac{3h}{2}}$. You can find how far each lifeguard can see from the height of the lifeguard tower. Each tower should have some overlap to cover the entire beach area. On early ships, a lookout position (Crow's nest) was situated high on the foremast. Sailors could see farther from this position than from the ship's deck.

---

47. Sample answer:
$a = 1$,
$b = 1$: $\left(\sqrt{1 + 1}\right)^2$
$= \left(\sqrt{1}\right)^2 + \left(\sqrt{1}\right)^2$
$2 = 1 + 1$ or 2

45. OPEN ENDED Choose values for x and y. Then find $\left(\sqrt{x} + \sqrt{y}\right)^2$. See margin.

46. Which One Doesn't Belong? Three of these expressions are equivalent. Which one is not? $29\sqrt{2} - 12\sqrt{6}$

$$6\sqrt{6} - 24\sqrt{2} + 6\sqrt{6} - 5\sqrt{2} \qquad 12\sqrt{6} - 29\sqrt{2}$$
$$29\sqrt{2} - 12\sqrt{6} \qquad 3\sqrt{24} - 6\sqrt{32} + 2\sqrt{54} - \sqrt{50}$$

47. CHALLENGE Under what conditions is $\left(\sqrt{a + b}\right)^2 = \left(\sqrt{a}\right)^2 + \left(\sqrt{b}\right)^2$ true?

48. *Writing in Math* Use the information about the world's tall structures on page 536 to explain how you can use radicals to determine how far a person can see. Include an explanation of how this information could help determine how far apart lifeguard towers should be on a beach.
See margin.

STANDARDS PRACTICE 2.0, 7NS2.3

49. $\sqrt{3}(4 + \sqrt{12})^2 = $ **D**

A $4\sqrt{3} + 6$

B $28\sqrt{3}$

C $28 + 16\sqrt{3}$

D $48 + 28\sqrt{3}$

50. REVIEW Which expression is equivalent to $3^8 \cdot 3^2 \cdot 3^4$? **F**

F 3^{14} **H** 27^{14}

G 3^{64} **J** 27^{64}

Spiral Review

Simplify. (Lesson 10-1)

51. $\sqrt{40}$ $2\sqrt{10}$

52. $\sqrt{128}$ $8\sqrt{2}$

53. $-\sqrt{196x^2y^3}$ $-14|x|y\sqrt{y}$

54. $\dfrac{\sqrt{50}}{\sqrt{8}}$ $\dfrac{5}{2}$

55. $\sqrt{\dfrac{225c^4d}{18c^2}}$ $\dfrac{5|c|\sqrt{2d}}{2}$

56. $\sqrt{\dfrac{63a}{128a^3b^2}}$ $\dfrac{3\sqrt{14}}{16a|b|}$

Find the nth term of each geometric sequence. (Lesson 9-7)

57. $a_1 = 4, n = 6, r = 4$ **4096**

58. $a_1 = -7, n = 4, r = 9$ **−5103**

59. $a_1 = 2, n = 8, r = -0.8$ **−0.4194304**

Solve each equation by factoring. Check your solutions. (Lesson 8-5)

60. $81 = 49y^2$ $\left\{\pm\dfrac{9}{7}\right\}$

61. $q^2 - \dfrac{36}{121} = 0$ $\left\{\pm\dfrac{6}{11}\right\}$

62. $48n^3 - 75n = 0$ $\left\{-\dfrac{5}{4}, 0, \dfrac{5}{4}\right\}$

63. $5x^3 - 80x = 240 - 15x^2$ {−4, −3, 4}

★ **64. RUNNING** Tyler runs 17 miles each Saturday. It takes him about 2 hours to run this distance. At this rate, how far could he run in 3 hours and 30 minutes? (Lesson 2-6) **29.75 mi**

GET READY for the Next Lesson

PREREQUISITE SKILL Find each product. (Lesson 7-7)

65. $(x - 2)^2$ $x^2 - 4x + 4$

66. $(x + 5)^2$ $x^2 + 10x + 25$

67. $(x + 6)^2$
$x^2 + 12x + 36$

68. $(3x - 1)^2$ $9x^2 - 6x + 1$

69. $(2x - 3)^2$ $4x^2 - 12x + 9$

70. $(4x + 7)^2$
$16x^2 + 56x + 49$

Pre-AP Activity Use after the Exercises

Write $\sqrt{6} + \sqrt{3} = \sqrt{9} = 3$ and $\sqrt{40} = \sqrt{36} + \sqrt{4} = 8$ on the board. Ask students to explain the errors. You cannot add different radicals, and you cannot write the square root of a sum as the sum of the square roots.

Main Ideas

- Solve radical equations.
- Solve radical equations with extraneous solutions.

 Standard 2.0 Students understand and use such operations as taking the opposite, finding the reciprocal, **taking a root,** and raising to a fractional power. **They understand and use the rules of exponents.** (Key, CAHSEE)

New Vocabulary

radical equation

extraneous solution

GET READY for the Lesson

Skydivers fall 1050 to 1480 feet every 5 seconds, reaching speeds of 120 to 150 miles per hour at *terminal velocity.* It is the highest speed they can reach and occurs when the air resistance equals the force of gravity. With no air resistance, the time t in seconds that it takes an object to fall h feet can be determined by the equation $t = \frac{\sqrt{h}}{4}$. How would you find the value of h if you are given the value of t?

Radical Equations Equations like $t = \frac{\sqrt{h}}{4}$ that contain radicals with variables in the radicand are called **radical equations**. To solve these equations, first isolate the radical on one side of the equation. Then square each side of the equation to eliminate the radical.

 Real-World EXAMPLE **Variable in Radical**

1 FREE-FALL HEIGHT Two objects are dropped simultaneously. The first object reaches the ground in 2.5 seconds, and the second object reaches the ground 1.5 seconds later. From what heights were the two objects dropped?

First Object		Second Object	
$t = \frac{\sqrt{h}}{4}$	Original equation	$t = \frac{\sqrt{h}}{4}$	Original equation
$2.5 = \frac{\sqrt{h}}{4}$	Replace t with 2.5.	$4 = \frac{\sqrt{h}}{4}$	Replace t with 4.
$10 = \sqrt{h}$	Multiply each side by 4.	$16 = \sqrt{h}$	Multiply each side by 4.
$10^2 = \left(\sqrt{h}\right)^2$	Square each side.	$16^2 = \left(\sqrt{h}\right)^2$	Square each side.
$100 = h$	Simplify.	$256 = h$	Simplify.

Check the results by substituting 100 and 256 for h in the original equation.

(continued on the next page)

 Extra Examples at ca.algebra1.com

---

1 Focus

Standards Alignment

Before Lesson 10-3 Multiply and divide monomials from Standard 7AF2.2

Lesson 10-3 Understand and use the rules of exponents from ➤ Standard 2.0

After Lesson 10-3 Know the laws of fractional exponents and understand exponential functions from ➤ Standard 2A12.0

2 Teach

Scaffolding Questions Have students read *Get Ready for the Lesson.* **Ask:**

- Is $\frac{\sqrt{h}}{4}$ in simplest form? Explain. Yes; there is no radical in the denominator.

- How would you solve $t = \frac{x}{4}$ for x? Multiply each side by 4.

- How could you remove the radical sign from $4t = \sqrt{h}$? Square each side of the equation.

Lesson 10-3 Resources

Chapter 10 Resource Masters

Lesson Reading Guide, p. 19 **BL** **OL** **ELL**
Study Guide and Intervention, pp. 20–21 **BL** **OL** **ELL**
Skills Practice, p. 22 **BL** **OL**
Practice, p. 23 **OL** **AL**
Word Problem Practice, p. 24 **OL** **AL**
Enrichment, p. 25 **OL** **AL**
Graphing Calculator, p. 26 **OL** **AL**
Quiz 2, p. 51

Transparencies
5-Minute Check Transparency 10-3
Additional Print Resources
Noteables™ Interactive Study Notebook with Foldables™

Technology
ca.algebra1.com
Interactive Classroom CD-ROM
AssignmentWorks CD-ROM
Graphing Calculator Easy Files

Radical Equations

Example 1 shows how to solve a real–world problem by writing an equation with a variable in the radicand.

Example 2 shows how to solve a radical equation with a radical expression by isolating the radical expression.

 Formative Assessment

Use the Check Your Progress exercises after each example to determine students' understanding of concepts.

ADDITIONAL EXAMPLES

① **FREE-FALL HEIGHT** An object is dropped from an unknown height and reaches the ground in 5 seconds. Use the equation $t = \frac{\sqrt{h}}{4}$ to find the height from which the object was dropped.
400 ft

② Solve $\sqrt{x - 3} + 8 = 15.$ 52

Additional Examples are also in:
- Noteables™ Interactive Study Notebook with Foldables™
- Interactive Classroom PowerPoint® Presentations

Extraneous Solutions

Example 3 shows how to determine extraneous solutions when solving a radical equation with a variable on each side of the equal sign.

ADDITIONAL EXAMPLE

③ Solve $\sqrt{2 - y} = y.$ 1

 Solving with Radicals

Remind students that they must isolate the radical part of the expression before squaring each side

CHECK $t = \frac{\sqrt{h}}{4}$	Original equation	CHECK $t = \frac{\sqrt{h}}{4}$	Original equation
$\stackrel{?}{=} \frac{\sqrt{100}}{4}$	$h = 100$	$\stackrel{?}{=} \frac{\sqrt{256}}{4}$	$h = 256$
$\stackrel{?}{=} \frac{10}{4}$	$\sqrt{100} = 10$	$\stackrel{?}{=} \frac{16}{4}$	$\sqrt{256} = 16$
$= 2.5 \checkmark$	Simplify.	$= 4 \checkmark$	Simplify.

The first object was dropped from 100 feet.

The second object was dropped from 256 feet.

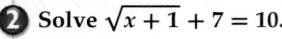 **Your Progress**

1. **DIVING** At the swim meet, Brandon dived off two platforms at different heights. On the first dive, it took him 0.78 second to reach the water. On the next dive, it took Brandon 1.43 seconds to reach the water. How much higher is the second platform than the first? **22.98 ft**

EXAMPLE Radical Equation with an Expression

② Solve $\sqrt{x + 1} + 7 = 10.$

$\sqrt{x + 1} + 7 = 10$	Original equation
$\sqrt{x + 1} = 3$	Subtract 7 from each side to isolate the radical expression.
$\left(\sqrt{x + 1}\right)^2 = 3^2$	Square each side.
$x + 1 = 9$	$\left(\sqrt{x + 1}\right)^2 = x + 1$
$x = 8$	Subtract 1 from each side. Check this result.

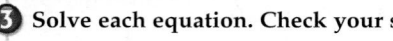 **Your Progress**

Solve each equation. Check your solution.
2A. $\sqrt{x - 3} - 2 = 4$ **39** **2B.** $4 + \sqrt{x + 1} = 14$ **99**

Extraneous Solutions Squaring each side of an equation sometimes produces extraneous solutions. An **extraneous solution** is a solution derived from an equation that is not a solution of the original equation. Therefore, you must check all solutions in the original equation when you solve radical equations.

EXAMPLE Variable on Each Side

③ Solve each equation. Check your solution.

a. $\sqrt{x + 2} = x - 4.$

Review Vocabulary

Zero Product Property
For all numbers a and b, if $ab = 0$, then $a = 0$, $b = 0$, or both a and b equal 0. (Lesson 9-2)

$\sqrt{x + 2} = x - 4$	Original equation
$\left(\sqrt{x + 2}\right)^2 = (x - 4)^2$	Square each side.
$x + 2 = x^2 - 8x + 16$	Simplify.
$0 = x^2 - 9x + 14$	Subtract x and 2 from each side.
$0 = (x - 7)(x - 2)$	Factor.
$x - 7 = 0$ or $x - 2 = 0$	Zero Product Property
$x = 7$ $x = 2$	Solve.

Additional Answers (Graphing Calculator Lab)

1.
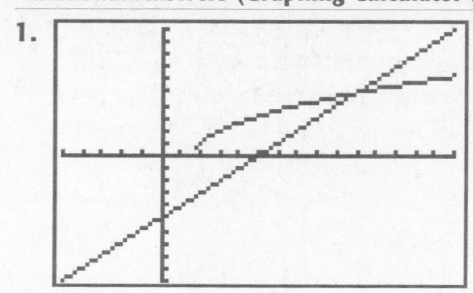

3. $x = 10$; the solution is the same as the solution from the graph. However, when solving algebraically, you have to check that $x = 3$ is an extraneous solution.

CHECK

$$\sqrt{x+2} = x - 4 \qquad\qquad\qquad \sqrt{x+2} = x - 4$$

$\sqrt{7+2} \overset{?}{=} 7 - 4 \quad x = 7 \qquad\qquad \sqrt{2+2} \overset{?}{=} 2 - 4 \quad x = 2$

$\qquad \sqrt{9} \overset{?}{=} 3 \qquad$ Simplify. $\qquad\qquad \sqrt{4} \overset{?}{=} -2 \qquad$ Simplify.

$\qquad\quad 3 = 3 \checkmark \quad$ True $\qquad\qquad\qquad\quad 2 \neq -2 \; X \quad$ False

Since 2 does not satisfy the original equation, 7 is the only solution.

b. $x - 4 = \sqrt{x - 3} + 5.$

$\qquad\qquad x - 4 = \sqrt{x - 3} + 5 \qquad$ Original equation

$\qquad x - 4 - 5 = \sqrt{x - 3} + 5 - 5 \qquad$ Subtract 5 from each side.

$\qquad\qquad x - 9 = \sqrt{x - 3} \qquad$ Simplify.

$\qquad (x - 9)^2 = (\sqrt{x - 3})^2 \qquad$ Square each side.

$x^2 - 18x + 81 = x - 3 \qquad$ Simplify.

$x^2 - 19x + 84 = 0 \qquad$ Subtract x from each side and add 3 to each side.

$(x - 12)(x - 7) = 0 \qquad$ Factor.

$x - 12 = 0 \quad$ or $\quad x - 7 = 0 \qquad$ Zero Product Property

$\qquad x = 12 \qquad\qquad x = 7 \qquad$ Solve.

CHECK

$$x - 4 = \sqrt{x - 3} + 5 \qquad\qquad x - 4 = \sqrt{x - 3} + 5$$

$12 - 4 \overset{?}{=} \sqrt{12 - 3} + 5 \quad x = 12 \qquad 7 - 4 \overset{?}{=} \sqrt{7 - 3} + 5 \quad x = 7$

$\qquad 8 \overset{?}{=} \sqrt{9} + 5 \qquad$ Simplify. $\qquad\qquad 3 \overset{?}{=} \sqrt{4} + 5 \qquad$ Simplify.

$\qquad 8 = 8 \qquad\qquad$ True $\qquad\qquad\qquad 3 \neq 7 \qquad\qquad$ False

Since 7 does not satisfy the original equation, the only solution is 12.

 **Your Progress**

Solve each equation. Check your solution.

3A. $\sqrt{x + 5} = x + 3$ −1 **3B.** $x - 3 = \sqrt{x - 1}$ 5

 Personal Tutor at ca.algebra1.com

★ indicates multi-step problem

 Your Understanding

Example 1
(pp. 541–542)

Solve each equation. Check your solution.

1. $\sqrt{x} = 5$ 25 **2.** $\sqrt{2b} = -8$ no solution **3.** $\sqrt{7x} = 7$ 7

4. GEOMETRY The surface area of a basketball is x square inches. What is the radius of the basketball if the formula for the surface area of a sphere is $SA = 4\pi r^2$? $\frac{1}{2}\sqrt{\frac{x}{\pi}}$

Examples 2, 3
(pp. 542–543)

Solve each equation. Check your solution.

5. $\sqrt{8s} + 1 = 5$ 2 **6.** $\sqrt{7x + 18} = 9$ 9 **7.** $\sqrt{5x + 1} + 2 = 6$ 3

8. $\sqrt{3x - 5} = x - 5$ 10 **9.** $4 + \sqrt{x - 2} = x$ 6 **10.** $\sqrt{2x + 3} = x$ 3

Math Online Extra Examples at ca.algebra1.com

Lesson 10-3 Radical Equations **543**

Focus on Mathematical Content

Solutions to Radical Equations
Most quadratic equations have two solutions. When solving radical equations, it is possible to introduce a second solution when squaring both sides of an equation. It is always important to check all solutions in the *original* equation, since one or more of the solutions could be extraneous.

Graphing Calculator Lab
Each student or group of students will need a graphing calculator. Point out that an alternative to graphing each side of the equation separately is to graph the single equation as it is. Subtract $x - 5$ from both sides of the equation and then enter the equation as $Y_1 = \sqrt{3x - 5} - x + 5$. Press 2nd CALC 2 to calculate the zero point of the graph. The zero point is the solution, which for this equation is 10.

3 Practice

Formative Assessment

Use Exercises 1–10 to check for understanding.

Use the chart at the bottom of the next page to customize assignments for your students.

Exercises

HOMEWORK HELP

For Exercises	See Examples
11–15, 29–30	1
16–22	2
23–28	3

Exercise Levels
A: 11–28
B: 29–62
C: 63–67

 Real-World Link

Piloted by A. Scott Crossfield on November 20, 1953, the Douglas D-558-2 Skyrocket became the first aircraft to fly faster than Mach 2, twice the speed of sound.

Source: National Air and Space Museum

43. $r = \sqrt{\dfrac{A}{\pi}}$

Solve each equation. Check your solution. 18. no solution

11. $\sqrt{-3a} = 6$ −12
12. $\sqrt{a} = 10$ 100
13. $\sqrt{-k} = 4$ −16
14. $5\sqrt{2} = \sqrt{x}$ 50
15. $3\sqrt{7} = \sqrt{-y}$ −63
16. $3\sqrt{4a} - 2 = 10$ 4
17. $3 + 5\sqrt{n} = 18$ 9
18. $\sqrt{x + 3} = -5$
19. $\sqrt{x - 5} = 2\sqrt{6}$ 29
20. $\sqrt{3x + 12} = 3\sqrt{3}$ 5
21. $\sqrt{2c - 4} = 8$ 34
22. $\sqrt{4b + 1} - 3 = 0$ 2
23. $x = \sqrt{6 - x}$ 2
24. $x = \sqrt{x + 20}$ 5
25. $\sqrt{5x - 6} = x$ 2, 3
26. $\sqrt{28 - 3x} = x$ 4
27. $\sqrt{x + 1} = x - 1$ 3
28. $\sqrt{1 - 2b} = 1 + b$ 0

AVIATION For Exercises 29 and 30, use the following information.
The formula $L = \sqrt{kP}$ represents the relationship between a plane's length L and the pounds P its wings can lift, where k is a constant of proportionality calculated for a plane.

29. The length of the Douglas D-558-II, called the Skyrocket, was approximately 42 feet, and its constant of proportionality was $k = 0.1669$. Calculate the maximum takeoff weight of the Skyrocket. **10,569 lb**

30. A Boeing 747 is 232 feet long and has a takeoff weight of 870,000 pounds. Determine the value of k for this plane. **0.0619**

31. The square root of the sum of a number and 7 is 8. Find the number. **57**
32. The square root of the quotient of a number and 6 is 9. Find the number. **486**

Solve each equation. Check your solution.
33. $\sqrt{3r - 5} + 7 = 3$ **no solution**
34. $\sqrt{x^2 + 9x + 14} = x + 4$ 2
35. $5\sqrt{\dfrac{4t}{3}} - 2 = 0$ $\dfrac{3}{25}$
36. $\sqrt{\dfrac{4x}{5}} - 9 = 3$ 180
37. $4 + \sqrt{m - 2} = m$ 6
38. $\sqrt{3d - 8} = d - 2$ 3, 4
39. $x + \sqrt{6 - x} = 4$ 2
40. $\sqrt{6 - 3x} = x + 16$ −10
41. $\sqrt{2r^2 - 121} = r$ 11
42. $\sqrt{5p^2 - 7} = 2p$ $\sqrt{7}$

GEOMETRY For Exercises 43–46, use the figure.
The area A of a circle is equal to πr^2, where r is the radius of the circle.

43. Write an equation for r in terms of A.
44. The area of the larger circle is 96π square meters. Find the radius. $4\sqrt{6}$ m
45. The area of the smaller circle is 48π square meters. Find the radius. $4\sqrt{3}$ m
46. If the area of a circle is doubled, what is the change in the radius? It increases by a factor of $\sqrt{2}$.

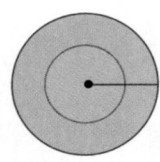

OCEANS For Exercises 47–49, use the following information.
Tsunamis, or large waves, are generated by undersea earthquakes. The speed of the tsunami in meters per second is $s = 3.1\sqrt{d}$, where d is the depth of the ocean in meters. 48. 5994 m

47. Find the speed of the tsunami if the depth of the water is 10 meters. **9.8 m/s**
48. Find the depth of the water if a tsunami's speed is 240 meters per second.
★ 49. A tsunami may begin as a 2-foot high wave traveling 500 miles per hour. It can approach a coastline as a 50-foot wave. How much speed does the wave lose if it travels from a depth of 10,000 meters to a depth of 20 meters? **approximately 296 m/s**

544 Chapter 10 Radical Expressions and Triangles

DIFFERENTIATED HOMEWORK OPTIONS

Level	Assignment	Two-Day Option	
BL Basic	11–30, 63–65, 67–89	11–29 odd, 68, 69	12–30 even, 63–65, 67, 70–89
OL Core	11–41 odd, 43, 65, 67–89	11–30, 68, 69	31–65, 67, 70–89
AL Advanced /Pre-AP	31–83, (optional: 84–89)		

50. State whether the following equation is *sometimes*, *always*, or *never* true.

$$\sqrt{(x-5)^2} = x - 5 \quad \text{sometimes, } x \geq 5$$

PHYSICAL SCIENCE For Exercises 51–53, use the following information.

The formula $P = 2\pi\sqrt{\dfrac{\ell}{32}}$ gives the period of a pendulum of length ℓ feet. The period P is the number of seconds it takes for the pendulum to swing back and forth once.

51. Suppose we want a pendulum to complete three periods in 2 seconds. How long should the pendulum be? **0.36 ft**

★ **52.** Two clocks have pendulums of different lengths. The first clock requires 1 second for its pendulum to complete one period. The second clock requires 2 seconds for its pendulum to complete one period. How much longer is one pendulum than the other? **2.43 ft**

★ **53.** Repeat Exercise 52 if the pendulum periods are t and $2t$ seconds. $\dfrac{24t^2}{\pi^2}$

Real-World Link

The Foucault Pendulum appears to change its path during the day, but it moves in a straight line. The path under the pendulum changes because Earth is rotating beneath it.

Source: California Academy of Sciences

BROADCASTING For Exercises 54–56, use the following information.

Sports broadcasts often include sound collection from the field of play. The temperature affects the speed of sound near Earth's surface. The speed V when the surface temperature t degrees Celsius can be found using the equation $V = 20\sqrt{t + 273}$.

54. Find the temperature at a baseball game if the speed of sound is 346 meters per second. **about 26.3°C**

55. The speed of sound at Earth's surface is often given as 340 meters per second, but that is only accurate at a certain temperature. On what temperature is this figure based? **16°C**

56. For what speeds is the surface temperature below 0°C? $V < 330.45$ m/s

Solve each radical equation. Round to the nearest hundredth.

57. $3 + \sqrt{2x} = 7$ **8**

58. $\sqrt{3x - 8} = 5$ **11**

59. $\sqrt{x + 6} - 4 = x$ **−2**

60. $\sqrt{4x + 5} = x - 7$ **15.08**

61. $x + \sqrt{7 - x} = 4$ **1.70**

62. $\sqrt{3x - 9} = 2x + 6$ **no solution**

H.O.T. Problems

63. REASONING Explain why it is necessary to check for extraneous solutions in radical equations. **The solution may not satisfy the original equation.**

64. OPEN ENDED Give an example of a radical equation. Then solve the equation for the variable. **Sample answer:** $\sqrt{x + 1} = 8$; 63

65. FIND THE ERROR Alex and Victor are solving $-\sqrt{x - 5} = -2$. Who is correct? Explain your reasoning. **Alex; the square of $-\sqrt{x-5}$ is $x - 5$.**

Alex	Victor
$-\sqrt{x-5} = -2$	$-\sqrt{x-5} = -2$
$(-\sqrt{x-5})^2 = (-2)^2$	$-(\sqrt{x-5})^2 = (-2)^2$
$x - 5 = 4$	$-(x - 5) = 4$
$x = 9$	$-x + 5 = 4$
	$x = 1$

66. CHALLENGE Solve $\sqrt{h + 9} - \sqrt{h} = \sqrt{3}$. **3**

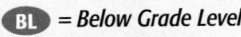

BL = Below Grade Level

OL = On Grade Level

AL = Above Grade Level

ELL = English Language Learner

Additional pages not shown:

📄 **Lesson Reading Guide,** p. 19 **BL** **OL** **ELL**

📄 **Skills Practice,** p. 22 **BL** **OL**

4 Assess

Yesterday's News Have students tell how knowing how to solve quadratic equations has helped them with today's lesson.

Check for student understanding of concepts in Lesson 10–3.

 Formative Assessment

Check for student understanding of concepts in Lesson 10-3.

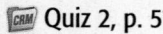 Quiz 2, p. 51

Additional Answer

67. You can determine the time it takes an object to fall from a given height using a radical equation. It would take a skydiver approximately 42 seconds to fall 10,000 feet. Using the equation, it would take 25 seconds. The time is different in the two calculations because air resistance slows the skydiver.

---

67. *Writing in Math* Use the information about skydiving on page 541 to explain how radical equations can be used to find free-fall times. Include the time it would take a skydiver to fall 10,000 feet if he falls 1200 feet every 5 seconds and also the time it would take using the equation $t = \frac{\sqrt{h}}{4}$, with an explanation of why the two methods find different times. **See margin.**

STANDARDS PRACTICE 2.0, 7MG2.4

68. What is the solution for this equation? **B**

$$\sqrt{x + 3} - 2 = 7$$

A 22
B 78
C 36
D 15

69. REVIEW Mr. and Mrs. Hataro are putting fresh sod onto their yard. The yard is 30 feet wide and 24 feet long, and the sod comes in pieces that are 12 inches wide and 24 inches long. If they decide to cover the entire yard in sod, about how many pieces of sod will they need? **H**

F 2.5   H 360
G 30   J 720

Spiral Review

Simplify. (Lessons 10-2 and 10-1) **72.** $-4\sqrt{2}$

70. $5\sqrt{6} + 12\sqrt{6}$ $17\sqrt{6}$
71. $\sqrt{12} + 6\sqrt{27}$ $20\sqrt{3}$
72. $\sqrt{18} + 5\sqrt{2} - 3\sqrt{32}$

73. $\sqrt{192}$ $8\sqrt{3}$
74. $\sqrt{6} \cdot \sqrt{10}$ $2\sqrt{15}$
75. $\frac{21}{\sqrt{10} + \sqrt{3}}$ $3(\sqrt{10} - \sqrt{3})$

Find each product. (Lesson 7-6)

76. $(r + 3)(r - 4)$ $r^2 - r - 12$
77. $(3z + 7)(2z + 10)$
  $6z^2 + 44z + 70$
78. $(2p + 5)(3p^2 - 4p + 9)$
  $6p^3 + 7p^2 - 2p + 45$

79. PHYSICAL SCIENCE A European-made hot tub is advertised to have a temperature of 35°C to 40°C, inclusive. What is the temperature range for the hot tub in degrees Fahrenheit? Use $F = \frac{9}{5}C + 32$. (Lesson 6-4) **95° ≤ F ≤ 104°**

Write each equation in standard form. (Lesson 4-5)

80. $y = 2x + \frac{3}{7}$ $14x - 7y = -3$
81. $y - 3 = -2(x - 6)$
  $2x + y = 15$
82. $y + 2 = 7.5(x - 3)$
  $15x - 2y = 49$

83. MUSIC The table shows the number of country music radio stations in the United States. What was the percent of change in the number of stations from 2002 to 2004? (Lesson 2-7)
3.9% decrease

Year	Number of Stations
2002	2131
2004	2047

Source: M Street Corporation

GET READY for the Next Lesson

PREREQUISITE SKILL Evaluate $\sqrt{a^2 + b^2}$ for each value of a and b. (Lesson 1-2)

84. $a = 3, b = 4$ **5**
85. $a = 24, b = 7$ **25**
86. $a = 5, b = 12$ **13**
87. $a = 6, b = 8$ **10**
88. $a = 1, b = 1$ $\sqrt{2}$
89. $a = 8, b = 12$ $4\sqrt{13}$

---

546 Chapter 10 Radical Expressions and Triangles

Pre-AP Activity   Use as an Extension.

Explain that the *geometric mean* of two positive numbers is the positive square root of their product. Ask students to find a pair of consecutive positive even integers whose geometric mean is $4\sqrt{5}$. Since $4\sqrt{5} = \sqrt{x(x + 2)}$, $x = 8$ or -10. Since the two numbers are positive, x must equal only 8 and, therefore, $x + 2 = 10$. The two numbers are 8 and 10.

Graphing Calculator Lab
Graphs of Radical Equations

Standard 17.0 Students determine the domain of independent variables and the range of dependent variables defined by a graph, a set of ordered pairs, **or a symbolic expression.**

In order for a square root to be a real number, the radicand cannot be negative. When graphing a radical equation, determine when the radicand would be negative and exclude those values from the domain.

ACTIVITY 1

Graph $y = \sqrt{x}$.

Enter the equation in the Y= list.

KEYSTROKES: Y= 2nd [√] X,T,θ,n Graph

1A. Examine the graph. What is the domain of the function $y = \sqrt{x}$? $\{x \mid x \geq 0\}$

1B. What is the range of $y = \sqrt{x}$? $\{y \mid y \geq 0\}$

COncepts in MOtion
Interactive Lab ca.algebra1.com

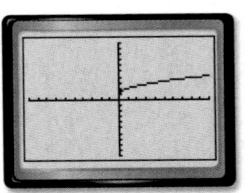

[−10, 10] scl: 1 by [−10, 10] scl: 1

ACTIVITY 2

Graph $y = \sqrt{x + 4}$.

Enter the equation in the Y= list.

KEYSTROKES: Y= 2nd [√] X,T,θ,n + 4) Graph

2A. What are the domain and range of $y = \sqrt{x + 4}$? $\{x \mid x \geq -4\}$, $\{y \mid y \geq 0\}$

2B. How does the graph of $y = \sqrt{x + 4}$ compare to the graph of the parent function $y = \sqrt{x}$? It is translated 4 units to the left.

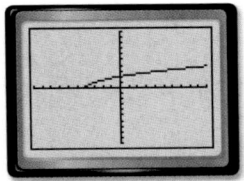

[−10, 10] scl: 1 by [−10, 10] scl: 1

ANALYZE THE RESULTS 1–13. See Ch. 10 Answer Appendix.

Graph each equation and sketch the graph on your paper. State the domain of the graph. Then describe how the graph differs from the parent function $y = \sqrt{x}$.

1. $y = \sqrt{x} + 1$
2. $y = \sqrt{x} - 3$
3. $y = \sqrt{x + 2}$

4. $y = \sqrt{x - 5}$
5. $y = \sqrt{-x}$
6. $y = \sqrt{3x}$

7. $y = -\sqrt{x}$
8. $y = \sqrt{1 - x} + 6$
9. $y = \sqrt{2x + 5} - 4$

10. $y = \sqrt{|x| + 2}$
11. $y = \sqrt{|x| - 3}$

12. Is the graph of $x = y^2$ a function? Explain your reasoning.

13. Does the equation $x^2 + y^2 = 1$ determine y as a function of x? Explain.

14. Write a function whose graph is the graph of $y = \sqrt{x}$ shifted 3 units up. $y = \sqrt{x} + 3$

Other Calculator Keystrokes at ca.algebra1.com

Extend 10-3 Graphing Calculator Lab   **547**

---

1 Focus

Objective Use a TI-83/84 Plus graphing calculator to investigate the graphs of radicand equations.

Materials for Each Student
• graphing calculator
• grid paper

Teaching Tip Before starting this lab, familiarize students with the **ZoomFit** option on their calculators. The **ZoomFit** option in the **ZOOM** menu lets the calculator automatically zoom the viewing window to fit the graph. Suggest that students use this option with the activities in this lab to get a better view of the shape of the graph of a radical equation.

2 Teach

Working in Cooperative Groups
Put students in groups of 2 or 3, mixing abilities. Then have groups complete Activities 1 and 2 and Exercises 1–3.

• Have students use the 1 · value operation from the CALCULATE menu to find the value of the function at different x-values. Press 2nd CALC 1 and then enter an x-value. Students should see that as the cursor moves along the curve, the value of the function is the square root of the radicand of the function.

Practice Have students complete Exercises 4–11.

---

3 Assess

 Formative Assessment

Use Exercise 12 to assess whether students comprehend how the equation for the graph of a parent function differs from the equation for a graph of the parent function shifted a specific number of units in a specific direction.

From Concrete to Abstract Ask students to use words like shift up, shift down, shift left, and shift right to describe how to use the graph of $y = \sqrt{x}$, to obtain the graphs of $y = \sqrt{x + 1}$, $y = \sqrt{x - 1}$, $y = \sqrt{x} + 1$, and $y = \sqrt{x} - 1$. Shift left 1; shift right 1; shift up 1; shift down 1.

Formative Assessment

Use the Mid-Chapter Quiz to assess students' progress in the first half of the chapter.

For problems answered incorrectly, have students review the lessons indicated in parentheses.

Summative Assessment

CRM Mid-Chapter Test, p. 53

ExamView®
Assessment Suite

Customize and create multiple versions of your Mid-Chapter Tests and their answer keys.

FOLDABLES™
Study Organizer
Foldables™ Follow-Up
Before students complete the Mid-Chapter Quiz, encourage them to review the information for Lessons 10-1 through 10-3 in their Foldables.

CHAPTER 10 Mid-Chapter Quiz
Lessons 10–1 through 10–3

Simplify. (Lesson 10-1)

1. $\sqrt{48}$ $4\sqrt{3}$

2. $\sqrt{3} \cdot \sqrt{6}$ $3\sqrt{2}$

3. $\dfrac{3}{2+\sqrt{10}}$ $\dfrac{-2+\sqrt{10}}{2}$

4. **MULTIPLE CHOICE** If $x = 81b^2$ and $b > 0$, then $\sqrt{x} =$ (Lesson 10-1) **B**

   A $-9b$.

   B $9b$.

   C $3b\sqrt{27}$.

   D $27b\sqrt{3}$.

FENCE For Exercises 5–7, use the following information.
Hailey wants to put up a fence. She has a square backyard with an area of 160 square feet. The formula for the area A of a square with side length s is $A = s^2$. (Lesson 10-1)

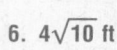
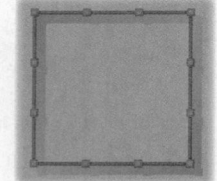

6. $4\sqrt{10}$ ft

5. Solve the equation for s. $s = \sqrt{A}$

6. What is the side length of Hailey's backyard?

7. What is the perimeter of Hailey's backyard?
   $4(4\sqrt{10})$ or $16\sqrt{10}$

8. **GEOMETRY** A rectangle has a length of $\sqrt{\dfrac{a}{8}}$ meters and a width of $\sqrt{\dfrac{a}{2}}$ meters. What is the area of the rectangle? $\dfrac{a}{4}$ m²

Simplify. (Lesson 10-2)

9. $6\sqrt{5} + 3\sqrt{11} + 5\sqrt{5}$ $11\sqrt{5} + 3\sqrt{11}$

10. $2\sqrt{3} + 9\sqrt{12}$ $20\sqrt{3}$

11. $(3 - \sqrt{6})^2$ $15 - 6\sqrt{6}$

12. **GEOMETRY** Find the area of a square with a side measure of $2 + \sqrt{7}$ centimeters. (Lesson 10-2)
    $11 + 4\sqrt{7}$ or 21.6 cm²

548 Chapter 10 Radical Expressions and Triangles

---

13. $80\sqrt{17}$ m/s, $60\sqrt{31}$ m/s

SOUND For Exercises 13 and 14, use the following information.
The speed of sound V in meters per second near Earth's surface is given by $V = 20\sqrt{t + 273}$, where t is the surface temperature in degrees Celsius. (Lesson 10-2)

13. What is the speed of sound near Earth's surface at $-1°C$ and at $6°C$ in simplest form?

14. How much faster is the speed of sound at $6°C$ than at $-1°C$? $60\sqrt{31} - 80\sqrt{17}$ **4.22 m/s**

Solve each equation. Check your solution.
(Lesson 10-3)

15. $\sqrt{15 - x} = 4$ -1

16. $\sqrt{3x^2 - 32} = x$ 4

17. $\sqrt{2x - 1} = 2x - 7$ 5

18. **MULTIPLE CHOICE** The surface area S of a cone can be found by using $S = \pi r\sqrt{r^2 + h^2}$, where r is the radius of the base and h is the height of the cone. Find the height of the cone. (Lesson 10-3) **H**

    F 2.70 in.

    G 11.03 in.

    H 12.84 in.

    J 13.30 in.

19. **PHYSICS** When an object is dropped from the top of a 250-foot tall building, the object will be h feet above the ground after t seconds, where $\dfrac{\sqrt{250 - h}}{4} = t$. How far above the ground will the object be after 1 second?
    (Lesson 10-3) **234 ft**

20. **SKYDIVING** The approximate time t in seconds that it takes an object to fall a distance of d feet is given by $t = \sqrt{\dfrac{d}{16}}$. Suppose a parachutist falls 13 seconds before the parachute opens. How far does the parachutist fall during this time period?
    (Lesson 10-3) **2704 ft**

Data-Driven Decision Making	Exercises	Lesson	◆ Standard	Resources for Review
Diagnostic Teaching Based on the results of the Chapter 10 Mid-Chapter Quiz, use the following to review concepts that students continue to find challenging.	1–8	10–1	2.0	CRM Study Guide and Intervention pp. 6–7, 13–14, 20–21 **Math Online** • Extra Examples • Personal Tutor • Concepts in Motion
	9–14	10–2	2.0	
	15–20	10–3	2.0	

Main Ideas

- Solve problems by using the Pythagorean Theorem.
- Determine whether a triangle is a right triangle.

 Preparation for Geometry Standard 15.0
Students use the Pythagorean theorem to determine distance and find missing lengths of sides of right triangles.

New Vocabulary

hypotenuse
legs
Pythagorean triple
converse

Study Tip

Triangles
Sides of a triangle are represented by lowercase letters a, b, and c.

▶ GET READY for the Lesson

The *Cyclone* roller coaster at New York's Coney Island is one of the most copied roller coasters in the world. Since it was built in 1927, seven copies of the coaster have been built. The first drop is 85 feet tall, and it descends at a 60° angle. The top speed is 60 miles per hour. You can use the Pythagorean Theorem to estimate the length of the first hill.

The Pythagorean Theorem In a right triangle, the side opposite the right angle is the **hypotenuse**. This side is always the longest side of a right triangle. The other two sides are the **legs**. To find the length of any side of a right triangle when the lengths of the other two are known, use a formula named for the Greek mathematician Pythagoras.

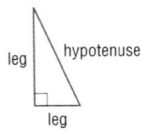

KEY CONCEPT   *The Pythagorean Theorem*

Words   If a and b are the lengths of the legs of a right triangle and c is the length of the hypotenuse, then the square of the length of the hypotenuse is equal to the sum of the squares of the lengths of the legs.

Symbols $c^2 = a^2 + b^2$

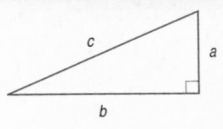

EXAMPLE   Find the Length of the Hypotenuse

1 Find the length of the hypotenuse of a right triangle if $a = 8$ and $b = 15$.

$c^2 = a^2 + b^2$ Pythagorean Theorem
$c^2 = 8^2 + 15^2$ $a = 8$ and $b = 15$
$c^2 = 289$ Simplify.
$c = \pm\sqrt{289}$ Take the square root of each side.
$c = \pm 17$ Disregard −17. Why?

The length of the hypotenuse is 17 units.

 CHECK Your Progress   1A. $\sqrt{218} \approx 14.76$ 1B. $\sqrt{136} \approx 11.66$

Find the length of the hypotenuse of each right triangle. If necessary, round to the nearest hundredth.
   1A. $a = 7, b = 13, c = ?$ **1B.** $a = 10, b = 6, c = ?$

Lesson 10-4 The Pythagorean Theorem   **549**

---

1 Focus

Standards Alignment

Before Lesson 10-4
Know and understand the Pythagorean Theorem from ☞ Standard 7MG3.3

Lesson 10-4
Use the Pythagorean theorem to determine distance and find missing lengths of sides of right triangles from Standard G15.0

After Lesson 10-4
Prove the Pythagorean theorem from ☞ Standard G14.0

2 Teach

Scaffolding Questions Have students read *Get Ready for the Lesson.*
Ask:
- What shape is being used to estimate the length of the hill? a right triangle
- Is the height of the hill a leg or the hypotenuse of the right triangle? leg
- Is the length of the hill a leg or the hypotenuse? hypotenuse
- What information is useful in finding the length of the hill? What is extraneous? The height of the hill and the angle of the drop are more useful than the maximum speed.

Lesson 10-4 Resources

Chapter 10 Resource Masters
Lesson Reading Guide, p. 27 `BL` `OL` `ELL`
Study Guide and Intervention, pp. 28–29 `BL` `OL` `ELL`
Skills Practice, p. 30 `BL` `OL`
Practice, p. 31 `OL` `AL`
Word Problem Practice, p. 32 `OL` `AL`
Enrichment, p. 33 `OL` `AL`
Spreadsheet, p. 34

Transparencies
5-Minute Check Transparency 10-4
Additional Print Resources
Noteables™ Interactive Study Notebook with Foldables™
Teaching Algebra with Manipulatives

Technology
ca.algebra1.com
Interactive Classroom CD-ROM
AssignmentWorks CD-ROM
Graphing Calculator Easy Files

The Pythagorean Theorem

Example 1 shows how to use the Pythagorean Theorem to find the length of the hypotenuse of a right triangle given the lengths of the legs.
Example 2 shows how to use the Pythagorean Theorem to find the length of one leg of a right triangle given the hypotenuse and length of the other leg.
Example 3 shows how to use common Pythagorean triples to find the height of a right triangle in order to find the area of the triangle.

 Formative Assessment

Use the Check Your Progress exercises after each example to determine students' understanding of concepts.

ADDITIONAL EXAMPLES

1 Find the length of the hypotenuse of a right triangle if $a = 18$ and $b = 24$. **30 units**

2 Find the length of the missing side. If necessary, round to the nearest hundredth. **13.23 units**

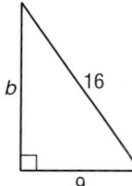

3 **STANDARDS EXAMPLE** What is the area of triangle *XYZ*? **C**

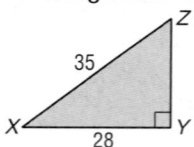

A 94 units^2 **C** 294 units^2

B 128 units^2 **D** 588 units^2

Additional Examples are also in:

• Noteables™ Interactive Study Notebook with Foldables™

• Interactive Classroom PowerPoint® Presentations

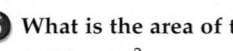 **EXAMPLE** Find the Length of a Side

2 Find the length of the missing side. If necessary, round to the nearest hundredth.

$c^2 = a^2 + b^2$ — Pythagorean Theorem
$25^2 = a^2 + 10^2$ — $b = 10$ and $c = 25$
$625 = a^2 + 100$ — Evaluate squares.
$525 = a^2$ — Subtract 100 from each side.
$\pm\sqrt{525} = a$ — Use a calculator to evaluate $\sqrt{525}$.
$22.91 \approx a$ — Use the positive value.

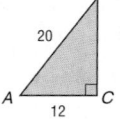

✓ CHECK Your Progress

2A. $a = 6, c = 14, b = ?$ **12.65** **2B.** $b = 11, c = 21, a = ?$ **17.89**

A group of three whole numbers that satisfy the Pythagorean Theorem is called a **Pythagorean triple**. Examples include (3, 4, 5) and (5, 12, 13). Multiples of Pythagorean triples also satisfy the Pythagorean Theorem, so (6, 8, 10) and (10, 24, 26) are also Pythagorean triples.

STANDARDS EXAMPLE **Pythagorean Triples 15.0**

3 What is the area of triangle *ABC*?

A 96 units^2 **C** 120 units^2

B 160 units^2 **D** 196 units^2

Read the Item

The area of a triangle is $A = \frac{1}{2}bh$. In a right triangle, the legs are the base and height. Use the given measures to find the height.

Solve the Item

Step 1 Check to see if the measurements are a multiple of a common Pythagorean triple. The hypotenuse is 4 · 5 units, and the leg is 4 · 3 units. This triangle is a multiple of a (3, 4, 5) triangle.

$4 \cdot 3 = 12$ $4 \cdot 4 = 16$ $4 \cdot 5 = 20$ The height is 16 units.

Step 2 Find the area of the triangle.

$A = \frac{1}{2}bh$ — Area of a triangle
$A = \frac{1}{2} \cdot 12 \cdot 16$ — $b = 12$ and $h = 16$
$A = 96$ — Choice A is correct.

✓ CHECK Your Progress

3. A square shopping center has a diagonal walkway from one corner to another. If the walkway is about 70 meters long, what is the approximate length of each side of the center? **H**

F 8 meters **G** 35 meters **H** 50 meters **J** 100 meters

 **Personal Tutor at** ca.algebra1.com

---

Test-Taking Tip

Memorize common Pythagorean triples and check for multiples such as (6, 8, 10). This will save you time on the test. Some other common triples are (8, 15, 17) and (7, 24, 25).

Tips for New Teachers

Preventing Errors

Caution students that Example 3 is a two-step problem. First, they must find the missing side length, and then they must calculate the area of the triangle. Stress that it is important to read each answer choice carefully before selecting the correct answer. In Example 3, choices A and D look similar, and one could mistakenly choose D, 196, instead of the correct answer A, 96.

Right Triangles If you exchange the hypothesis and conclusion of an if-then statement, the result is the **converse** of the statement. The following theorem, the converse of the Pythagorean Theorem, can be used to determine whether a triangle is a right triangle.

Study Tip

Converses

Converses of theorems are not necessarily true. But the converse of the Pythagorean Theorem is true.

KEY CONCEPT *Converse of the Pythagorean Theorem*

If a and b are measures of the shorter sides of a triangle, c is the measure of the longest side, and $c^2 = a^2 + b^2$, then the triangle is a right triangle. If $c^2 \neq a^2 + b^2$, then the triangle is not a right triangle.

EXAMPLE Check for Right Triangles

4 **Determine whether the following side measures form right triangles.**

a. 20, 21, 29

Since the measure of the longest side is 29, let $c = 29$, $a = 20$, and $b = 21$. Then determine whether $c^2 = a^2 + b^2$.

$c^2 = a^2 + b^2$	Pythagorean Theorem
$29^2 \stackrel{?}{=} 20^2 + 21^2$	$a = 20$, $b = 21$, and $c = 29$
$841 \stackrel{?}{=} 400 + 441$	Multiply.
$841 = 841$	Add.

Since $c^2 = a^2 + b^2$, the triangle is a right triangle.

b. 8, 10, 12

Since the measure of the longest side is 12, let $c = 12$, $a = 8$, and $b = 10$. Then determine whether $c^2 = a^2 + b^2$.

$c^2 = a^2 + b^2$	Pythagorean Theorem
$12^2 \stackrel{?}{=} 8^2 + 10^2$	$a = 8$, $b = 10$, and $c = 12$
$144 \stackrel{?}{=} 64 + 100$	Multiply.
$144 \neq 164$	Add.

Since $c^2 \neq a^2 + b^2$, the triangle is not a right triangle.

CHECK Your Progress

4A. 9, 12, 16 no

4B. 18, 24, 30 yes

★ indicates multi-step problem

CHECK Your Understanding

Examples 1, 2 (pp. 549–550)

If c is the measure of the hypotenuse of a right triangle, find each missing measure. If necessary, round to the nearest hundredth.

1. $a = 10, b = 24, c = ?$ 26

2. $a = 11, c = 61, b = ?$ 60

3. $b = 13, c = \sqrt{233}, a = ?$ 8

4. $a = 7, b = 4, c = ?$ $\sqrt{65} \approx 8.06$

Math Online **Extra Examples at** ca.algebra1.com

Focus on Mathematical Content

Pythagorean Theorem The Pythagorean Theorem can be used to find the length of a side of a right triangle when the lengths of two sides are known. To find a side, rewrite the formula for the Pythagorean Theorem in terms of that side, for example, to find the hypotenuse solve for c: $c = \sqrt{a^2 + b^2}$.

Right Triangles

Example 4 shows how to use the converse of the Pythagorean Theorem to find whether a triangle is a right triangle.

ADDITIONAL EXAMPLE

4 Determine whether the following side measures form right triangles.

a. 7, 12, 15 not a right triangle

b. 27, 36, 45 right triangle

Tips for New Teachers

Preventing Errors Point out to students that with Pythagorean triples, the greatest value is always the measure of the hypotenuse, and the two lesser values are the measures of the two legs.

3 Practice

Formative Assessment

Use Exercises 1–9 to check for understanding.

Use the chart at the bottom of the next page to customize assignments for your students.

Pre-AP Activity Use as an Extension.

Tell students that when x equals any odd number, x, $\frac{1}{2}(x^2 - 1)$, and $\frac{1}{2}(x^2 + 1)$ will give them numbers that are Pythagorean triples. Ask students to use the expressions to find a set of Pythagorean triples not given in this lesson. Have students verify that their results are actually Pythagorean triples. Sample answer: $x = 11$, 60, 61; $61^2 = 60^2 + 11^2$, $3721 = 3600 + 121$, $3721 = 3721$

Odd/Even Assignments
Exercises 10–35 are structured so that students practice the same concepts whether they are assigned odd or even problems.

 Exercise Alert!
Use the Internet Exercise 41 requires students to search the Internet for measurements of a roller coaster located in an amusement park near them.

Find the length of each missing side. If necessary, round to the nearest hundredth.

5.
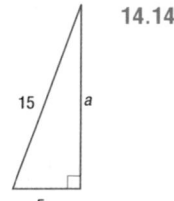
18.44
c
12
14

6.
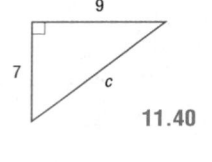
a
41
9
40

Example 3
(p. 550)
15.0

★ **7.** 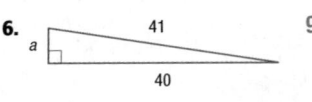 **STANDARDS PRACTICE** In right triangle XYZ, the length of $\overline{YZ}$ is 6, and the length of the hypotenuse is 8. Find the area of the triangle. **A**

A $6\sqrt{7}$ units^2 **B** 30 units^2 **C** 40 units^2 **D** 48 units^2

Example 4
(p. 551)

Determine whether the following side measures form right triangles. Justify your answer.

8. 4, 6, 9 no; $4^2 + 6^2 \neq 9^2$ **9.** 10, 24, 26 yes; $10^2 + 24^2 = 26^2$

Exercises

HOMEWORK HELP	
For Exercises	**See Examples**
10–27	1, 2
28–29	3
30–35	4

Exercise Levels
A: 10–35
B: 36–47
C: 48–51

If c is the measure of the hypotenuse of a right triangle, find each missing measure. If necessary, round to the nearest hundredth.

10. $a = 16, b = 63, c = ?$ **65**   **11.** $a = 16, c = 34, b = ?$ **30**

12. $b = 3, a = \sqrt{112}, c = ?$ **11**   **13.** $a = \sqrt{15}, b = \sqrt{10}, c = ?$ **5**

14. $c = 14, a = 9, b = ?$ $\sqrt{115} \approx 10.72$ **15.** $a = 6, b = 3, c = ?$ $\sqrt{45} \approx 6.71$

16. $b = \sqrt{77}, c = 12, a = ?$ $\sqrt{67} \approx 8.19$ **17.** $a = 4, b = \sqrt{11}, c = ?$ $\sqrt{27} \approx 5.20$

18. $a = \sqrt{225}, b = \sqrt{28}, c = ?$ **19.** $a = \sqrt{31}, c = \sqrt{155}, b = ?$ $\sqrt{124} \approx 11.14$

20. $a = 8x, b = 15x, c = ?$ **17x**   **21.** $b = 3x, c = 7x, a = ?$ $\sqrt{40x} \approx 6.32x$

18. $\sqrt{253} \approx 15.91$

Find the length of each missing side. If necessary, round to the nearest hundredth.

22.
14.14
15
a
5

23.
9
7
c
11.40

24.
28
53
c
45

25.
14
5
13.08
b

26.
175
180
a
42.13

27.
99
b
20
101

30. yes; $30^2 + 40^2 = 50^2$
31. no; $6^2 + 12^2 \neq 18^2$
32. no; $24^2 + 30^2 \neq 36^2$
33. yes; $45^2 + 60^2 = 75^2$
34. yes; $15^2 + (\sqrt{31})^2 = 16^2$
35. yes; $4^2 + 7^2 = (\sqrt{65})^2$

GEOMETRY For Exercises 28 and 29, refer to the triangle.

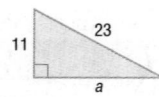
11
23
a

28. What is the length of side a? **20.20**

29. Find the area of the triangle. **111.1 units^2**

Determine whether the following side measures form right triangles. Justify your answer.

30. 30, 40, 50   **31.** 6, 12, 18   **32.** 24, 30, 36

33. 45, 60, 75   **34.** 15, $\sqrt{31}$, 16   **35.** 4, 7, $\sqrt{65}$

552 Chapter 10 Radical Expressions and Triangles

DIFFERENTIATED HOMEWORK OPTIONS			
Level	**Assignment**	**Two-Day Option**	
BL Basic	10–35, 48, 50–64	11–35 odd, 51, 52	10–34 even, 48, 50, 54–68
OL Core	11–37 odd, 38–48, 50–64	10–35, 51, 52	36, 48, 50, 53–64
AL Advanced /Pre-AP	36–61, (optional: 62–64)		

Find the length of the hypotenuse. Round to the nearest hundredth.

36.
13.45 units

37.
14.56

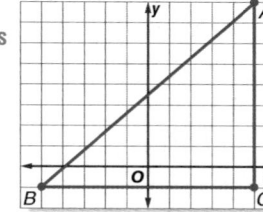

Real-World Link
Fastest, Tallest, Largest
Drop: *Kingda Ka,*
Jackson, New Jersey;
128 mph, 456 ft, and
418 ft, respectively

Longest: *Millennium
Force,* Sandusky, Ohio;
6,595 ft

Source:
ultimaterollercoaster.com

40. The roller
coaster makes a
total horizontal
advance of 404
feet, reaches a
vertical height of
208 feet, and
travels a total track
length of 628.4
feet.

ROLLER COASTERS For Exercises 38–40, use the following information.
Suppose a roller coaster climbs 208 feet higher
than its starting point making a horizontal
advance of 360 feet. When it comes down, it
makes a horizontal advance of 44 feet.

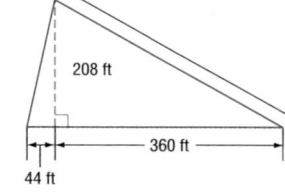

38. How far will it travel to get to the top of
the ride? 415.8 ft

39. How far will it travel on the downhill track? 212.6 ft

40. Compare the total horizontal advance,
vertical height, and total track length.

41. RESEARCH Use the Internet or other reference to find the measurements of
your favorite roller coaster or a roller coaster that is in an amusement park
close to you. Draw a model of the first drop. Include the height of the hill,
length of the vertical drop, and steepness of the hill. See students' work.

42. SAILING A sailboat's mast and boom form a right
angle. The sail itself, called a *mainsail*, is in the shape
of a right triangle. If the edge of the mainsail that is
attached to the mast is 100 feet long and the edge of
the mainsail that is attached to the boom is 60 feet
long, what is the length of the longest edge of the
mainsail? 116.6 ft

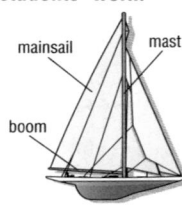

Solve each problem. If necessary, round to the nearest hundredth.

★ **43.** Find the length of a diagonal of a square if its area is 162 square feet. 18 ft

★ **44.** A right triangle has one leg that is 5 centimeters longer than the other leg.
The hypotenuse is 25 centimeters long. Find the length of each leg of the
triangle. 15 cm, 20 cm

45. Find the length of the diagonal of a cube if each side of the cube is
4 inches long. $4\sqrt{3}$ in. or about 6.93 in.

46. The ratio of the length of the hypotenuse to the length of the *shorter* leg in a
right triangle is 8:5. The hypotenuse measures 144 meters. Find the length
of the *longer* leg. 112.41 m

EXTRA PRACTICE
See pages 738, 753.

Math Online
Self-Check Quiz at
ca.algebra1.com

47. ROOFING A garage roof is 30 feet long and hangs an additional 2 feet over
the walls. How many square feet of shingles are needed for the entire roof?
900

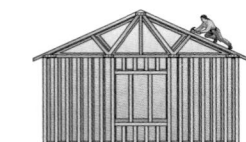
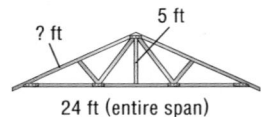

Lesson 10-4 The Pythagorean Theorem **553**

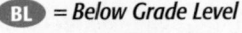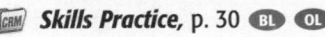
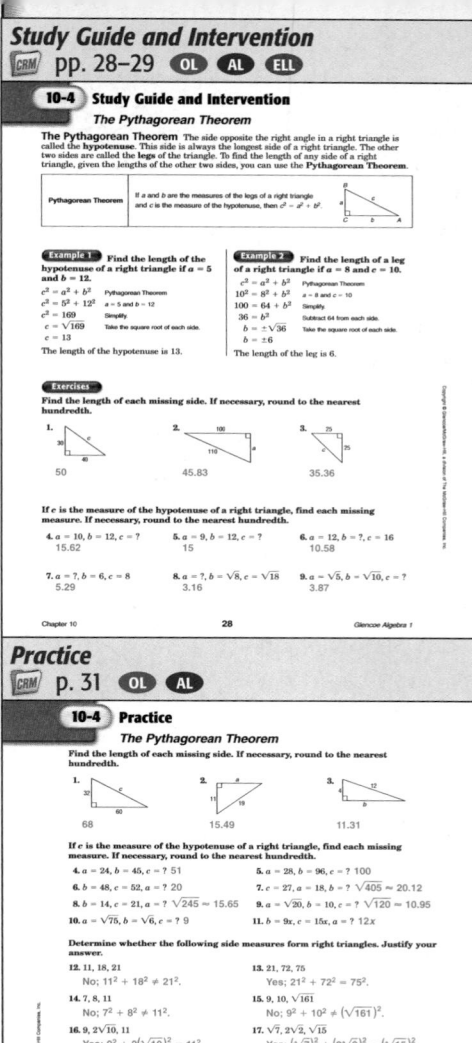
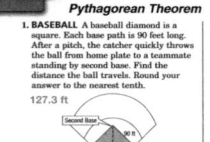

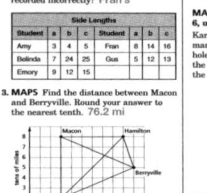
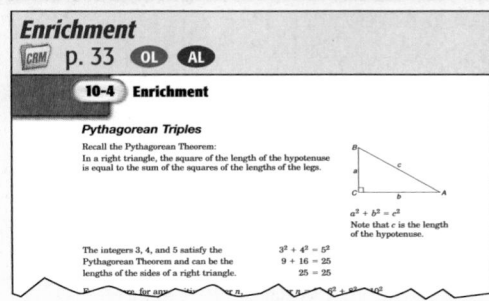
Lesson 10-4 The Pythagorean Theorem **553**

4 Assess

Crystal Ball Have students write how they think today's lesson will connect to tomorrow's lesson, titled *The Distance Formula.*

FOLDABLES Study Organizer **Foldables™ Follow-Up**
Remind students to record notes and examples on the Pythagorean Theorem in their Foldables. Suggest that students include a diagram like that in the *Key Concept* box on p. 549.

Additional Answers

48. See bottom margin.

49. The area of the largest semicircle is $\frac{\pi c^2}{4} = \frac{\pi}{4}c^2$. The sum of the other two areas is $\frac{\pi}{4}(a^2 + b^2)$. Using the Pythagorean Theorem, $c^2 = a^2 + b^2$, we can show that the sum of the two small areas is equal to the area of the largest semicircle.

50. The Pythagorean Theorem can be used to design roller coasters by using the height and the horizontal distance to determine the length of the hill. The higher a roller coaster is, the faster it will go. The steeper a roller coaster is, the faster it will go.

H.O.T. Problems

48. OPEN ENDED Draw and label a right triangle with legs and hypotenuse with rational lengths. Draw a second triangle with legs of irrational lengths and a hypotenuse of rational length. **See margin.**

49. See margin.

49. CHALLENGE Compare the area of the largest semicircle to the areas of the two smaller semicircles at the right.

50. *Writing in Math* Use the information on page 549 to explain how the Pythagorean Theorem can be used in designing roller coasters. How are the height, speed, and steepness of a roller coaster related? **See margin.**

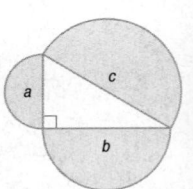

STANDARDS PRACTICE 2.0, 7MG3.3

51. If the perimeter of square 1 is 160 units and the perimeter of square 2 is 120 units, what is the perimeter of square 3? **B**

A 100 units

B 200 units

C 250 units

D 450 units

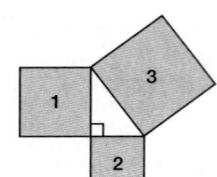

52. REVIEW Sara says that if x is any nonnegative real number, then for any positive integer n, $\sqrt[n]{x^n} = x$. Which values could she use to show that she might be right? **H**

F $x = -4$ and $n = 2$

G $x = 5$ and $n = -3$

H $x = 2$ and $n = 15$

J $x = -3$ and $n = 6$

Spiral Review

Solve each equation. Check your solution. (Lesson 10-3)

53. $\sqrt{y} = 12$ **144**   **54.** $3\sqrt{s} = 126$ **1764**   **55.** $4\sqrt{2v + 1} - 3 = 17$ **12**

Simplify. (Lesson 10-2)

56. $\sqrt{72}$ **$6\sqrt{2}$**   **57.** $7\sqrt{z} - 10\sqrt{z}$ **$-3\sqrt{z}$**   **58.** $\sqrt{\frac{3}{7}} + \sqrt{21}$ **$\frac{8\sqrt{21}}{7}$**

59. AVIATION Flying with the wind, a plane travels 300 miles in 40 minutes. Flying against the wind, it travels 300 miles in 45 minutes. Find its air speed. (Lesson 5-4) **425 mph**

Write an equation in function notation for each relation. (Lesson 3-5)

60. 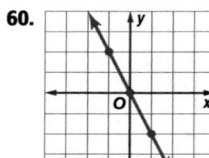 $f(x) = -2x$

61. 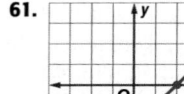 $f(x) = x - 2$

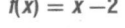
GET READY for the Next Lesson

PREREQUISITE SKILL Simplify each expression. (Lesson 10-1) **63. 10**

62. $\sqrt{(6-3)^2 + (8-4)^2}$ **5**   **63.** $\sqrt{(10-4)^2 + (13-5)^2}$ **64.** $\sqrt{(5-3)^2 + (2-9)^2}$ **$\sqrt{53}$**

554 Chapter 10 Radical Expressions and Triangles

Additional Answer

48. Sample answer:

3

5

$\sqrt{5}$

5

4

$\sqrt{20}$

10-5

The Distance Formula

Main Ideas

- Find the distance between two points on the coordinate plane.
- Find a point that is a given distance from a second point on a plane.

 Preparation for Geometry Standard 17.0
Students prove theorems by using coordinate geometry, including the midpoint of a line segment, the distance formula, and various forms of equations of lines and circles. (Key)

New Vocabulary

Distance Formula

► GET READY for the Lesson

A certain helicopter can fly 450 miles before it needs to refuel. Suppose a person needs to be flown from a hospital in Washington, North Carolina, to one in Huntington, West Virginia. Each side of a square is 50 miles. If Asheville, North Carolina, is at the origin, Huntington is at (0, 196), and Washington is at (310, 0), can the helicopter make the trip one way without refueling?

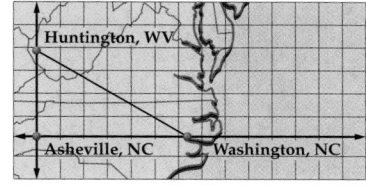

The Distance Formula You can find the distance between any two points in the coordinate plane using the **Distance Formula**, which is based on the Pythagorean Theorem.

KEY CONCEPT *The Distance Formula*

Words The distance d between any two points with coordinates (x_1, y_1) and (x_2, y_2) is given by $d = \sqrt{(x_2 - x_1)^2 + (y_2 - y_1)^2}$.

Model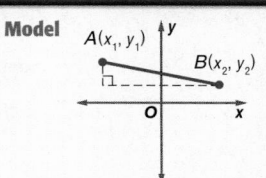

EXAMPLE Distance Between Two Points

1 Find the distance between the points at (2, 3) and (−4, 6).

$$d = \sqrt{(x_2 - x_1)^2 + (y_2 - y_1)^2}$$ Distance Formula

$$= \sqrt{(-4 - 2)^2 + (6 - 3)^2}$$ $(x_1, y_1) = (2, 3)$ and $(x_2, y_2) = (-4, 6)$

$$= \sqrt{(-6)^2 + 3^2}$$ Simplify.

$$= \sqrt{45}$$ Evaluate squares and simplify.

$$= 3\sqrt{5}$$ or about 6.71 units

✓CHECK Your Progress 1. $2\sqrt{13}$ or about 7.21 units
1. Find the distance between the points at (4, −1) and (−2, −5).

 Math Online Extra Examples at ca.algebra1.com

Lesson 10-5 The Distance Formula **555**

Standards Alignment

Before Lesson 10-5
Understand and use coordinate graphs from Standard 7MG3.2

Lesson 10-5
Prove theorems by using coordinate geometry from Standard G17.0

After Lesson 10-5
Prove the Pythagorean theorem from ◄— Standard G14.0

2 Teach

Scaffolding Questions Have students read *Get Ready for the Lesson.* **Ask:**

- What must you know in order to use the Pythagorean Theorem to determine the distance between the two points? You must know the lengths of the two legs in order to find the hypotenuse.
- How do you find the vertical distance from Oklahoma to Dallas? difference in the *y*-coordinates of *O* and *D*
- How do you find the horizontal distance from Oklahoma to Little Rock? the difference in the *x*-coordinates of *O* and *L*

Lesson 10-5 Resources

Chapter 10 Resource Masters

Lesson Reading Guide, p. 35 (BL) (OL) (ELL)
Study Guide and Intervention, pp. 36–37 (BL) (OL) (ELL)
Skills Practice, p. 38 (BL) (OL)
Practice, p. 39 (OL) (AL)
Word Problem Practice, p. 40 (OL) (AL)
Enrichment, p. 4 (OL) (AL)
Quiz 3, p. 52

Transparencies

5-Minute Check Transparency 10-5

Additional Print Resources

Noteables™ Interactive Study Notebook with Foldables™
Science and Mathematics Lab Manual, pp. 159–164

Technology

ca.algebra1.com
Interactive Classroom CD-ROM
AssignmentWorks CD-ROM
Graphing Calculator Easy Files

The Distance Formula

Example 1 shows how to use the Distance Formula to find the distance between two points on a coordinate plane.

Example 2 shows how to use the Distance Formula to solve a real-world problem.

ADDITIONAL EXAMPLES

1 Find the distance between the points at $(1, 2)$ and $(-3, 0)$. $2\sqrt{5} \approx 4.47$ units

2 **BIATHLON** Julianne is sighting in her rifle for an upcoming biathlon competition. Her first shot is 2 inches to the right and 7 inches below the bull's-eye. What is the distance between the bull's-eye and where her first shot hit the target? $\sqrt{53} \approx 7.28$ inches

Additional Examples are also in:
- Noteables™ Interactive Study Notebook with Foldables™
- Interactive Classroom PowerPoint® Presentations

 **Student Misconceptions** Point out to students that it does not matter which of the two points are designated (x_1, y_1) and (x_2, y_2).

Find Coordinates

Example 3 shows how to use the Distance Formula to find a missing coordinate when you know the coordinates of a point, one coordinate of another point, and the distance between the two points.

ADDITIONAL EXAMPLE

3 Find the value of a if the distance between the points at $(2, -1)$ and $(a, -4)$ is 5 units. -2 or 6

Real-World Link

There are four major tournaments that make up the "grand slam" of golf: Masters, U.S. Open, British Open, and PGA Championship. At age 24, Tiger Woods became the youngest player to win the four major events (called a career grand slam).

Source: PGA

Real-World EXAMPLE

2 **GOLF** Tracy's golf ball is 20 feet short and 8 feet to the right of the cup. On her first putt, the ball lands 2 feet to the left and 3 feet beyond the cup. If the ball went in a straight line, how far did it go?

Model the situation. If the cup is at $(0, 0)$, then the location of the ball is $(8, -20)$. The location after the first putt is $(-2, 3)$.

$$d = \sqrt{(x_2 - x_1)^2 + (y_2 - y_1)^2}$$ Distance Formula

$$= \sqrt{(-2 - 8)^2 + [3 - (-20)]^2}$$ $(x_1, y_1) = (8, -20)$, $(x_2, y_2) = (-2, 3)$

$$= \sqrt{(-10)^2 + 23^2}$$ Simplify.

$$= \sqrt{629} \text{ or about } 25$$

The ball traveled about 25 feet on her first putt.

✓ CHECK Your Progress

2. Shelly hit the golf ball 12 feet past the hole and 3 feet to the left. Her first putt traveled to 2 feet beyond the cup and 1 foot to the right. How far did the ball travel on her first putt? $2\sqrt{29}$ **or about 10.77 ft**

Find Coordinates Suppose you know the coordinates of a point, one coordinate of another point, and the distance between the two points. You can use the Distance Formula to find the missing coordinate.

EXAMPLE Find a Missing Coordinate

3 Find the possible values of a if the distance between the points at $(7, 5)$ and $(a, -3)$ is 10 units.

$$d = \sqrt{(x_2 - x_1)^2 + (y_2 - y_1)^2}$$ Distance Formula

$$10 = \sqrt{(a - 7)^2 + (-3 - 5)^2}$$ Let $x_2 = a, x_1 = 7, y_2 = -3, y_1 = 5,$ and $d = 10$.

$$10 = \sqrt{(a - 7)^2 + (-8)^2}$$ Simplify.

$$10 = \sqrt{a^2 - 14a + 49 + 64}$$ Evaluate squares.

$$10 = \sqrt{a^2 - 14a + 113}$$ Simplify.

$$100 = a^2 - 14a + 113$$ Square each side.

$$0 = a^2 - 14a + 13$$ Subtract 100 from each side.

$$0 = (a - 1)(a - 13)$$ Factor.

$a - 1 = 0$ or $a - 13 = 0$ Zero Product Property

$a = 1$ $\qquad\qquad a = 13$ The value of a is 1 or 13.

✓ CHECK Your Progress

3. Find the value of a if the distance between the points at $(3, a)$ and $(-4, 5)$ is $\sqrt{58}$ units. **2 or 8**

 **Personal Tutor at** ca.algebra1.com

---

Focus on Mathematical Content

Distance Formula You can use the Distance Formula, $d = \sqrt{(x_2 - x_1)^2 + (y^2 - y_1)^2}$, to find the distance between any two points, (x_1, y_1) and (x_2, y_2), in the coordinate plane. Since the differences are squared, the order in which the points are chosen does not matter.

★ indicates multi-step problem

✓ CHECK Your Understanding

Example 1
(p. 555)

Find the distance between each pair of points with the given coordinates. Express in simplest radical form and as decimal approximations rounded to the nearest hundredth, if necessary.

1. $(5, -1), (11, 7)$ **10**
2. $(3, 7), (-2, -5)$ **13**
3. $(2, 2), (5, -1)$ **$3\sqrt{2}$ or 4.24**
4. $(-3, -5), (-6, -4)$ **$\sqrt{10}$ or 3.16**

Example 2 ★
(p. 556)

5. GEOMETRY An isosceles triangle has two sides of equal length. Determine whether $\triangle ABC$ with vertices $A(-3, 4)$, $B(5, 2)$, and $C(-1, -5)$ is isosceles.

5. yes;
$AB = \sqrt{68}$,
$BC = \sqrt{85}$,
$AC = \sqrt{85}$

★ **FOOTBALL** For Exercises 6 and 7, use the information at the right.

6. A quarterback can throw the football to one of the two receivers. Find the distance from the quarterback to each receiver. **25.5 yd, 25 yd**

7. What is the distance between the two receivers? **20.6 yd**

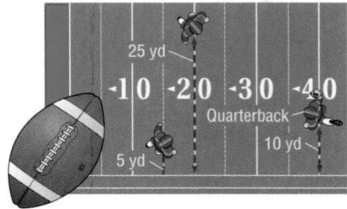

Example 3
(p. 556)

Find the possible values of a if the points with the given coordinates are the indicated distance apart.

8. $(3, -1), (a, 7); d = 10$ **9 or −3**
9. $(10, a), (1, -6); d = \sqrt{145}$ **2 or −14**

Exercises

HOMEWORK HELP	
For Exercises	See Examples
10–17	1
18–23	2
24–29	3

Find the distance between each pair of points whose coordinates are given. Express in simplest radical form and as decimal approximations rounded to the nearest hundredth, if necessary.

10. $(12, 3), (-8, 3)$ **20**
11. $(0, 0), (5, 12)$ **13**
12. $(6, 8), (3, 4)$ **5**
13. $(-4, 2), (4, 17)$ **17**
14. $(-3, 8), (5, 4)$ **$4\sqrt{5}$ or 8.94**
15. $(9, -2), (3, -6)$ **$2\sqrt{13}$ or 7.21**
16. $(-8, -4), (-3, -8)$ **$\sqrt{41}$ or 6.40**
17. $(2, 7), (10, -4)$ **$\sqrt{185}$ or 13.60**

Exercise Levels
A: 10–29
B: 30–39
C: 40–44

★ **18. FREQUENT FLYERS** To determine the mileage between cities for their frequent flyer programs, some airlines superimpose a coordinate grid over the United States. The units of this grid are approximately equal to 0.316 mile. So, a distance of 3 units on the grid equals an actual distance of 3(0.316) or 0.948 mile. Suppose the locations of two airports are at (132, 428) and (254, 105). Find the actual distance between these airports to the nearest mile. **109 mi**

★ **COLLEGE** For Exercises 19 and 20, use the map of a college campus.

19. 0.53 mi

20. Yes; it will take her 10.6 minutes to walk between the two buildings.

19. Kelly has her first class in Rhodes Hall and her second class in Fulton Lab. How far does she have to walk between her first and second classes?

20. She has 12 minutes between the end of her first class and the start of her second class. If she walks an average of 3 miles per hour, will she make it to her second class on time?

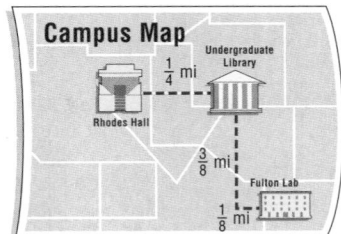

Lesson 10-5 The Distance Formula **557**

3 Practice

✓ Formative Assessment

Use Exercises 1–9 to check for understanding.

Use the chart at the bottom of this page to customize assignments for your students.

Odd/Even Assignments

Exercises 10–29 are structured so that students practice the same concepts whether they are assigned odd or even problems.

DIFFERENTIATED HOMEWORK OPTIONS

Level	Assignment	Two-Day Option	
BL Basic	10–29, 40–42, 44–61	11–29 odd, 45, 46	10–28 even, 40–42, 44, 47–61
OL Core	11–29 odd, 30–33, 35–39 odd, 40–42, 44–61	10–29, 45, 46	30–42, 44, 47–61
AL Advanced /Pre-AP	30–57, (optional: 58–61)		

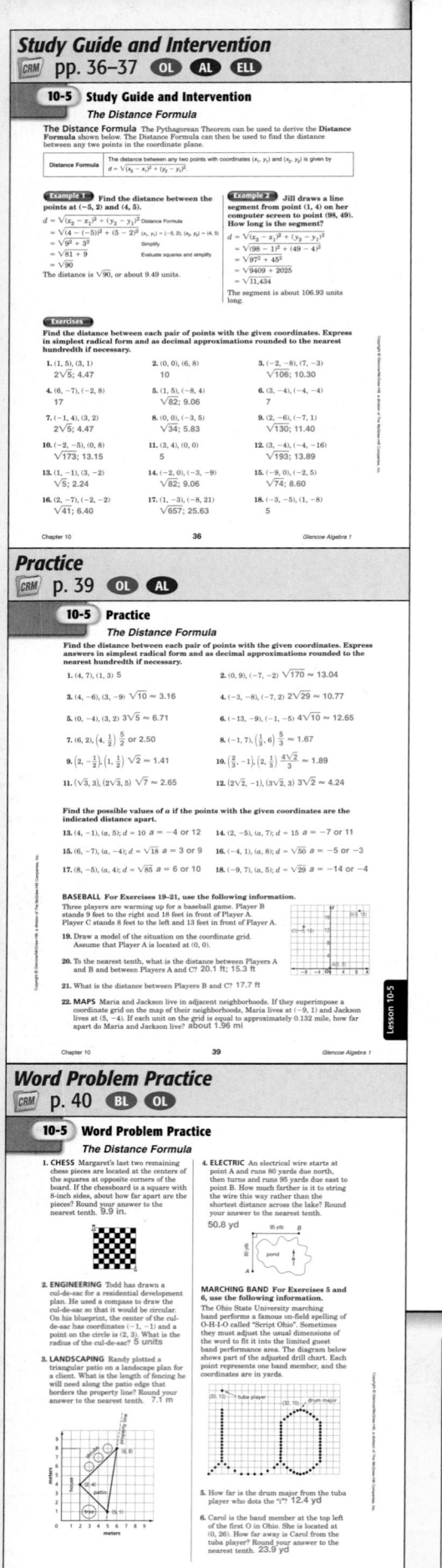
21. Duluth, (44, 116); St. Cloud, (−46, 39); Eau Claire, (71, −8); Rochester (27, −58)

22. Minneapolis-St. Cloud, 53 mi; St. Paul-Rochester, 64 mi; Minneapolis-Eau Claire, 79 mi; Duluth-St. Cloud, 118 mi

23. all cities except Duluth

GEOGRAPHY For Exercises 21–23, use the map at the right that shows part of Minnesota and Wisconsin.

A coordinate grid has been superimposed on the map with the origin at St. Paul. The grid lines are 20 miles apart. Minneapolis is at $(−7, 3)$.

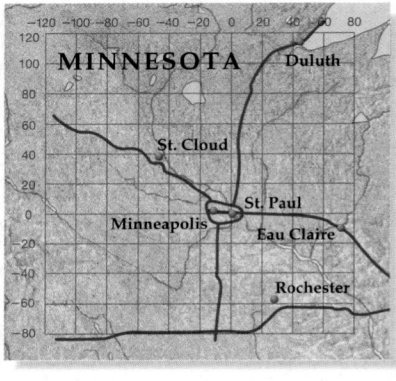

21. Estimate the coordinates for Duluth, St. Cloud, Eau Claire, and Rochester.

22. Find the distance between the following pairs of cities: Minneapolis and St. Cloud, St. Paul and Rochester, Minneapolis and Eau Claire, and Duluth and St. Cloud.

23. A radio station in St. Paul has a range of 75 miles. Which cities shown can receive the broadcast?

Find the possible values of a if the points with the given coordinates are the indicated distance apart.

★ 24. $(4, 7), (a, 3); d = 5$ **1 or 7**
25. $(−4, a), (4, 2); d = 17$ **17 or −13**
26. $(5, a), (6, 1); d = \sqrt{10}$ **−2 or 4**
27. $(a, 5), (−7, 3); d = \sqrt{29}$ **−2 or −12**
28. $(6, −3), (−3, a); d = \sqrt{130}$ **−10 or 4**
29. $(20, 5), (a, 9); d = \sqrt{340}$ **2 or 38**

★ 30. **GEOMETRY** Triangle ABC has vertices $A(7, −4)$, $B(−1, 2)$, and $C(5, −6)$. Determine whether the triangle has three, two, or no sides that are equal in length. **two; $AB = BC = 10$**

★ 31. **GEOMETRY** If the diagonals of a trapezoid have the same length, then the trapezoid is isosceles. Is trapezoid $ABCD$ with vertices $A(−2, 2)$, $B(10, 6)$, $C(9, 8)$, and $D(0, 5)$ isosceles? Explain. **$\sqrt{157} \neq \sqrt{101}$; The trapezoid is not isosceles.**

★ 32. **GEOMETRY** Triangle LMN has vertices $L(−4, −3)$, $M(2, 5)$, and $N(−13, 10)$. If the distance from point $P(x, −2)$ to L equals the distance from P to M, what is the value of x? **3**

★ 33. **GEOMETRY** Plot the points $Q(1, 7)$, $R(3, 1)$, $S(9, 3)$, and $T(7, d)$. Find the value of d so that each side of $QRST$ has the same length. **9**

37. $\dfrac{\sqrt{74}}{7}$ or 1.23

EXTRA **PRACTICE**
See page 738, 753.
Math Online
Self-Check Quiz at ca.algebra1.com

H.O.T. Problems

Find the distance between each pair of points with the given coordinates. Express in simplest radical form and as decimal approximations rounded to the nearest hundredth, if necessary.

34. $(4, 2), \left(6, −\frac{2}{3}\right)$ **$\frac{10}{3}$ or 3.33**
35. $\left(5, \frac{1}{4}\right), (3, 4)$ **$\frac{17}{4}$ or 4.25**
36. $\left(\frac{4}{5}, −1\right), \left(2, −\frac{1}{2}\right)$ **$\frac{13}{10}$ or 1.30**
37. $\left(3, \frac{3}{7}\right), \left(4, −\frac{2}{7}\right)$
38. $(4\sqrt{5}, 7), (6\sqrt{5}, 1)$ **$2\sqrt{14}$ or 7.48**
39. $(5\sqrt{2}, 8), (7\sqrt{2}, 10)$ **$2\sqrt{3}$ or 3.46**

40. **OPEN ENDED** Plot two ordered pairs and find the distance between their graphs. Does it matter which ordered pair is first when using the Distance Formula? Explain. **See margin.**

41. **REASONING** Explain why the value calculated under the radical sign in the Distance Formula will never be negative. **See margin.**

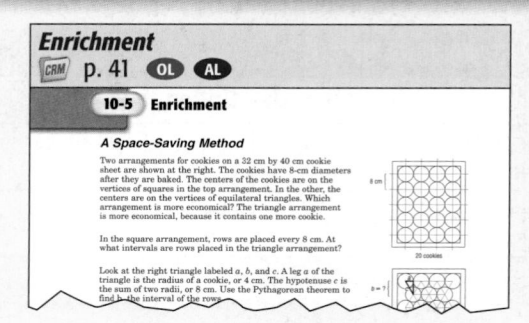

42. REASONING Explain why there are two values for *a* in Example 3. Draw a diagram to support your answer. **See margin.**

43. CHALLENGE Plot $A(-4, 4)$, $B(-7, -3)$, and $C(4, 0)$, and connect them to form triangle *ABC*. Demonstrate two different ways to determine whether *ABC* is a right triangle. **See Ch. 10 Answer Appendix.**

44. *Writing in Math* Use the information on page 555 to explain how the Distance Formula can be used to find the distance between two cities. Explain how the Distance Formula is derived from the Pythagorean Theorem, and why the helicopter can or cannot make the trip without refueling. **See Ch. 10 Answer Appendix.**

STANDARDS PRACTICE 5.0, 7MG1.2

45. Find the perimeter of a square *ABCD* if two of the vertices are $A(3, 7)$ and $B(-3, 4)$. **B**

 A 12 units

 B $12\sqrt{5}$ units

 C $9\sqrt{5}$ units

 D 45 units

46. REVIEW Helen is making a scale model of her room. She uses a $\frac{1}{16}$ scale, and the dimensions of her model are $w = 9$ inches and $\ell = 12$ inches. What are the actual dimensions of her room? **H**

 F $w = 3$ ft and $\ell = 4$ ft

 G $w = 6\frac{3}{4}$ ft and $\ell = 9$ ft

 H $w = 12$ ft and $\ell = 16$ ft

 J $w = 144$ ft and $\ell = 192$ ft

Spiral Review

If *c* is the measure of the hypotenuse of a right triangle, find each missing measure. If necessary, round to the nearest hundredth. (Lesson 10-4)

47. $a = 7, b = 24, c = ?$ **25**   **48.** $b = 30, c = 34, a = ?$ **16**   **49.** $a = \sqrt{7}, c = \sqrt{16}, b = ?$ **3**

Solve each equation. Check your solution. (Lesson 10-3)

50. $\sqrt{p-2} + 8 = p$ **11**   **51.** $\sqrt{r+5} = r - 1$ **4**   **52.** $\sqrt{5t^2 + 29} = 2t + 3$ **{2, 10}**

Solve each inequality. Then check your solution and graph it on a number line. (Lesson 6-1) **53–56. See Ch. 10 Answer Appendix.**

53. $8 \le m - 1$ **54.** $3 > 10 + k$ **55.** $3x \le 2x - 3$ **56.** $s + \frac{1}{6} \le \frac{2}{3}$

57. TRAVEL Two trains leave the station at the same time going in opposite directions. The first train travels south at a speed of 60 miles per hour, and the second train travels north at a speed of 75 miles per hour. How many hours will it take for the trains to be 675 miles apart? (Lesson 2-9) **5 hours**

GET READY for the Next Lesson

PREREQUISITE SKILL Solve each proportion. (Lesson 2-6)

58. $\frac{x}{4} = \frac{3}{2}$ **6**   **59.** $\frac{20}{x} = \frac{-5}{2}$ **−8**   **60.** $\frac{6}{9} = \frac{8}{x}$ **12**   **61.** $\frac{2}{3} = \frac{6}{x+4}$ **5**

Real-World Connections
For Exercises 21–23, provide students with a map of your city with a coordinate grid superimposed on it, making sure at least one of the landmarks on the map has whole number coordinates. Have students use the Distance Formula to find the distance between two landmarks on the map.

4 Assess

Ticket Out the Door On a coordinate grid, have students draw line segments that are neither vertical nor horizontal and have endpoints whose coordinates are whole numbers. Have students use the Distance Formula to find the lengths of their line segments.

✓ Formative Assessment
Check for student understanding of concepts in Lessons 10-4 and 10-5.
CRM Quiz 3, p. 52

Additional Answers

40. See students' graph; the distance from *A* to *B* equals the distance from *B* to *A*. Using the Distance Formula, the solution is the same no matter which ordered pair is used first.

41. The values that are subtracted are squared before being added and the square of a negative number is always positive. The sum of two positive numbers is positive, so the distance will never be negative.

42. See students' diagrams; there are exactly two points that lie on the line $y = -3$ that are 10 units from the point (7, 5).

Explain that a circle is the set of points in a coordinate plane, each of which is the same distance from a given point. Write $(x - h)^2 + (y - k)^2 = r^2$ on the board. Tell students that in the equation, (h, k) is the center point, (x, y) represents any point on the circle, and *r* is the length of the radius of the circle. Ask students to compare the equation for a circle to the Distance Formula. Sample answer: The equation of a circle appears to have been derived from the Distance Formula. $(x - h)^2 + (y - k)^2 = r^2$ can be rewritten as $r = \sqrt{(x-h)^2 + (y-k)^2}$, which looks a lot like $d = \sqrt{(x_1 - x_2)^2 + (y_1 - y_2)^2}$.

 10-6 **Similar Triangles**

1 Focus

Standards Alignment

Before Lesson 10-6
Compute the perimeter, surface area and the volume of a three-dimensional object from Standard 7MG2.3

Lesson 10-6
Prove that triangles are congruent or similar from Standard G5.0

After Lesson 10-6
Determine how changes in dimensions affect the area and volume of common geometric figures from Standard G11.0

2 Teach

Scaffolding Questions Have students read *Get Ready for the Lesson.*
Ask:
- If you photograph two people from the same distance, one of whom is twice the height of the other, what are their heights in the photograph? One image will be twice the height of the other.
- How would you describe this idea using ratios? The ratio of the heights of the people is the same as the ratio of the heights of the images.
- What is an equation that states that two ratios are equal? a proportion

Lesson 10-6 Resources

Chapter 10 Resource Masters
Lesson Reading Guide, p. 42 **BL** **OL** **ELL**
Study Guide and Intervention, pp. 43–44 **BL** **OL** **ELL**
Skills Practice, p. 45 **BL** **OL**
Practice, p. 46 **OL** **AL**
Word Problem Practice, p. 47 **OL** **AL**
Enrichment, p. 48 **OL** **AL**
Quiz 4, p. 52

Main Ideas
- Determine whether two triangles are similar.
- Find the unknown measures of sides of two similar triangles.

Preparation for Geometry Standard 5.0
Students prove that triangles are congruent or similar, and they are able to use the concept of corresponding parts of congruent triangles.

New Vocabulary
similar triangles

 **COncepts in MOtion**
Animation **ca.algebra1.com**

GET READY for the Lesson

The image of an object being photographed is projected by the camera lens onto the film. The height of the image on the film can be related to the height of the object using similar triangles.

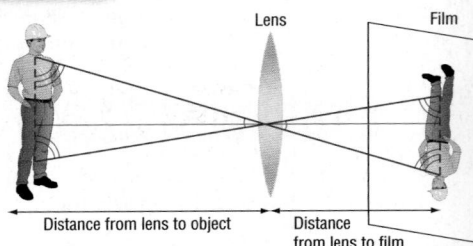

Similar Triangles **Similar triangles** have the same shape, but not necessarily the same size. There are two main tests for similarity.
- If the angles of one triangle and the corresponding angles of a second triangle have equal measures, then the triangles are similar.
- If the measures of the sides of two triangles form equal ratios, or are *proportional*, then the triangles are similar.

The triangles below are similar. The vertices of similar triangles are written in order to show the corresponding parts. So, $\triangle ABC \sim \triangle DEF$. The symbol $\sim$ is read *is similar to.*

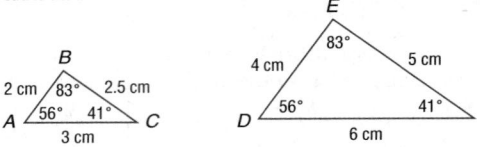

corresponding angles	corresponding sides
$\angle A$ and $\angle D$	$\overline{AB}$ and $\overline{DE} \rightarrow \frac{AB}{DE} = \frac{2}{4} = \frac{1}{2}$
$\angle B$ and $\angle E$	$\overline{BC}$ and $\overline{EF} \rightarrow \frac{BC}{EF} = \frac{2.5}{5} = \frac{1}{2}$
$\angle C$ and $\angle F$	$\overline{AC}$ and $\overline{DF} \rightarrow \frac{AC}{DF} = \frac{3}{6} = \frac{1}{2}$

KEY CONCEPT   Similar Triangles

Words If two triangles are similar, then the measures of their corresponding sides are proportional, and the measures of their corresponding angles are equal.

Symbols If $\triangle ABC \sim \triangle DEF$, then $\frac{AB}{DE} = \frac{BC}{EF} = \frac{AC}{DF}$.

Model

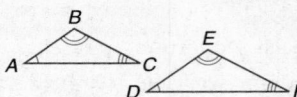

560 **Chapter 10** Radical Expressions and Triangles

Transparencies
5-Minute Check Transparency 10-6
Additional Print Resources
Noteables™ Interactive Study Notebook with Foldables™
Teaching Algebra with Manipulatives

Technology
ca.algebra1.com
Interactive Classroom CD-ROM
AssignmentWorks CD-ROM
Graphing Calculator Easy Files

EXAMPLE   Determine Whether Two Triangles Are Similar

1 **Determine whether the pair of triangles is similar. Justify your answer.**

Remember that the sum of the measures of the angles in a triangle is 180°.

The measure of ∠P is 180° − (51° + 51°) or 78°.

In △MNO, ∠N and ∠O have the same measure.

Let x = the measure of ∠N and ∠O.

$x + x + 78° = 180°$
$2x = 102°$
$x = 51°$

So ∠N = 51° and ∠O = 51°. Since the corresponding angles have equal measures, △MNO ~ △PQR.

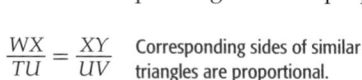 **Your Progress**

1. Determine whether ∠ABC with $m\angle A = 68$ and $m\angle B = m\angle C$ is similar to △DEF with $m\angle E = m\angle F = 56$. Justify your answer.

They are similar; the corresponding angles have equal measures.

Find Unknown Measures Proportions can be used to find missing measures of the sides of similar triangles, when some of the measurements are known.

EXAMPLE   Find Missing Measures

2 **Find the missing measures for each pair of similar triangles.**

a. Since the corresponding angles have equal measures, △TUV ~ △WXY. The lengths of the corresponding sides are proportional.

$\dfrac{WX}{TU} = \dfrac{XY}{UV}$ Corresponding sides of similar triangles are proportional.

$\dfrac{a}{3} = \dfrac{16}{4}$ $WX = a, XY = 16, TU = 3, UV = 4$

$4a = 48$ Find the cross products.

$a = 12$ Divide each side by 4.

$\dfrac{WY}{TV} = \dfrac{XY}{UV}$ Corresponding sides of similar triangles are proportional.

$\dfrac{b}{6} = \dfrac{16}{4}$ $WY = b, XY = 16, TV = 6, UV = 4$

$4b = 96$ Find the cross products.

$b = 24$ Divide each side by 4.

The missing measures are 12 and 24.

Study Tip

Corresponding Vertices

Always use the corresponding order of the vertices to write proportions for similar triangles.

 Math Online Extra Examples at ca.algebra1.com

Lesson 10-6 Similar Triangles   **561**

Concepts in MOtion

BrainPOP®
ca.algebra1.com

Similar Triangles

Example 1 shows how to use proportions to determine whether two triangles are similar.

✓ Formative Assessment

Use the Check Your Progress exercises after each example to determine students' understanding of concepts.

ADDITIONAL EXAMPLES

1 Determine whether the pair of triangles is similar. Justify your answer.

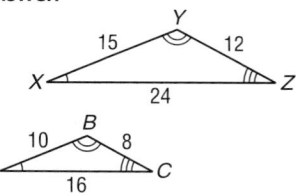

The corresponding sides of the triangles are proportional, so the triangles are similar.

2 Find the missing measures if each pair of triangles below is similar.

a.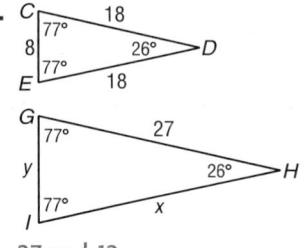

27 and 12

b.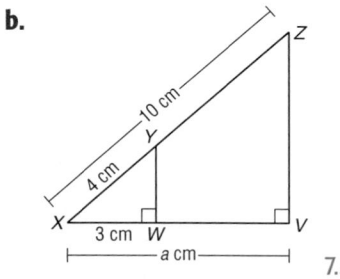

7.5

Additional Examples are also in:

• Noteables™ Interactive Study Notebook with Foldables™

• Interactive Classroom PowerPoint® Presentations

Reading Math

Tips for New Teachers   In drawings of triangles, arcs are often used to show angles that have equal measures. Angles with one arc have measure that are equal to each other, angles with two arcs have measure that are equal to each other, and so on.

Preventing Errors

Tips for New Teachers   Tell students to look closely at all the angles and sides of the two triangles for clues about whether the triangles are similar. In Example 1, the same angles are not marked on both triangles, but there is sufficient information to determine that the angles are congruent.

Find Unknown Measures

Example 2 shows how to use proportions to find the missing measures of the sides of similar triangles when some of the measurements are known.

Example 3 shows how to use similar triangles to solve a real-world problem.

ADDITIONAL EXAMPLE

3 SHADOWS Richard is standing next to the General Sherman Giant Sequoia tree in Sequoia National Park. The shadow of the tree is 22.5 meters, and Richard's shadow is 53.6 centimeters. If Richard's height is 2 meters, about how tall is the tree? **84 m**

Focus on Mathematical Content

Similar Triangles Similar triangles have the same shape, but not necessarily the same size. The corresponding sides of similar triangles are proportional, and the corresponding angles are equal in measure.

b. $\triangle ABE \sim \triangle ACD$

$\dfrac{BE}{CD} = \dfrac{AE}{AD}$ Corresponding sides of similar triangles are proportional.

$\dfrac{10}{x} = \dfrac{6}{9}$ $BE = 10, CD = x, AE = 6, AD = 9$

$90 = 6x$ Find the cross products.

$15 = x$ Divide each side by 6.

$15^2 + 9^2 = y^2$ Pythagorean Theorem

$\sqrt{306}$ or $17.49 = y$ Simplify.

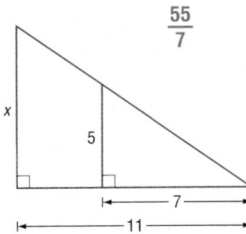

CHECK Your Progress

2A. $a = \dfrac{35}{3}$; $b = \dfrac{49}{9}$; $50°$

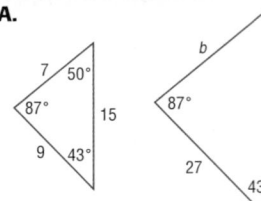

2B. $\dfrac{55}{7}$

Online Personal Tutor at ca.algebra1.com

Real-World Link

The monument has a shape of an Egyptian *obelisk*. A pyramid made of solid aluminum caps the top of the monument.
Source: nps.gov

Real-World EXAMPLE

3 SHADOWS Jenelle is standing near the Washington Monument in Washington, D.C. The shadow of the monument is 151.5 feet, and Jenelle's shadow is 1.5 feet. If Jenelle is 5.5 feet tall, how tall is the monument?

The shadows form similar triangles. Write a proportion that compares the heights of the objects and the lengths of their shadows.

Let $x =$ the height of the monument.

Jenelle's shadow → $\dfrac{1.5}{151.5} = \dfrac{5.5}{x}$ ← Jenelle's height
monument's shadow →   ← monument's height

$1.5x = 833.25$ Cross products

$x = 555.5$ Divide each side by 1.5.

The height of the monument is about 555.5 feet.

CHECK Your Progress

3. Jody is trying to follow the directions that explain how to pitch a triangular tent. The directions include a scale drawing where 1 inch = 4.5 feet. In the drawing, the tent is $1\frac{3}{4}$ inches tall. How tall should the actual tent be? **7.875 ft**

562 Chapter 10 Radical Expressions and Triangles

Differentiated Instruction

Naturalist Learners Have students use the method in Example 3 to find the heights of trees that are native to your area. Make sure students record the locations and types of trees along with the heights. Students will need tape measures and should take measurements on a sunny day.

562 Chapter 10 Radical Expressions and Triangles

✓CHECK Your Understanding

Example 1
(p. 561)

Determine whether each pair of triangles is similar. Justify your answer.

1. 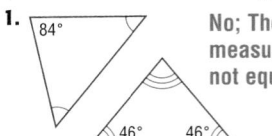 No; The angle measures are not equal.

2. 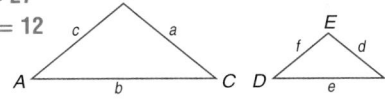 Yes; the angle measures are equal.

Example 2
(pp. 561–562)

For each set of measures given, find the measures of the missing sides if $\triangle ABC \sim \triangle DEF$.

3. $c = 15, d = 7, e = 9, f = 5$ $a = 21, b = 27$

4. $a = 18, c = 9, e = 10, f = 6$ $b = 15, d = 12$

5. $a = 5, d = 7, f = 6, e = 5$

6. $a = 17, b = 15, c = 10, f = 6$

5. $b = \dfrac{25}{7}$, $c = \dfrac{30}{7}$

6. $d = 10.2$, $e = 9$

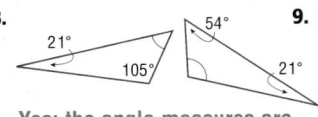

Example 3
(p. 562)

7. SHADOWS A 25-foot flagpole casts a shadow that is 10 feet long and the nearby building casts a shadow that is 26 feet long. How tall is the building? **65 ft**

Exercises

Determine whether each pair of triangles is similar. Justify your answer.

HOMEWORK HELP	
For Exercises	**See Examples**
8–13	1
14–21	2
22–24	3

Exercise Levels
A: 8–24
B: 25–27
C: 28–34

9. No; the angle measures are not equal.

10. No; the angle measures are not equal.

11. Yes; the angle measures are equal.

8. Yes; the angle measures are equal.

9. No; the angle measures are not equal.

10.

11.

12. No; the angle measures are not equal.

13. Yes; the angle measures are equal.

For each set of measures given, find the measures of the missing sides if $\triangle KLM \sim \triangle NOP$. **14–21. See margin.**

14. $k = 9, n = 6, o = 8, p = 4$

15. $k = 24, \ell = 30, m = 15, n = 16$

16. $m = 11, p = 6, n = 5, o = 4$

17. $k = 16, \ell = 13, m = 12, o = 7$

18. $n = 6, p = 2.5, \ell = 4, m = 1.25$

19. $p = 5, k = 10.5, \ell = 15, m = 7.5$

20. $n = 2.1, \ell = 4.5, p = 3.2, o = 3.4$

21. $m = 5, k = 12.6, o = 8.1, p = 2.5$

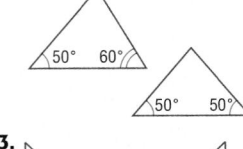

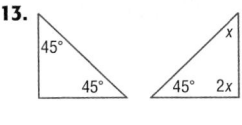

22. PHOTOGRAPHY Refer to the diagram of a camera at the beginning of the lesson. Suppose the image of a man who is 2 meters tall is 1.5 centimeters tall on film. If the film is 3 centimeters from the lens of the camera, how far is the man from the camera? **4 m**

Lesson 10-6 Similar Triangles   **563**

3 Practice

✓ **Formative Assessment**

Use Exercises 1–7 to check for understanding.

Use the chart at the bottom of the next page to customize assignments for your students.

Odd/Even Assignments

Exercises 8–24 are structured so that students practice the same concepts whether they are assigned odd or even problems.

Additional Answers

14. $\ell = 12, m = 6$

15. $o = 20, p = 10$

16. $k = \dfrac{55}{6}, \ell = \dfrac{22}{3}$

17. $n = \dfrac{112}{13}, p = \dfrac{84}{13}$

18. $k = 3, o = 8$

19. $n = 7, o = 10$

20. $k = 2.78, m = 4.24$

21. $\ell = 16.2, n = 6.3$

DIFFERENTIATED HOMEWORK OPTIONS

Level	Assignment	Two-Day Option	
BL Basic	8–24, 28–46	9–23 odd, 35, 36	8–24 even, 28–34, 37–46
OL Core	9–23 odd, 25–46	8–24, 35, 36	25–34, 37–46
AL Advanced /Pre-AP	25–46		

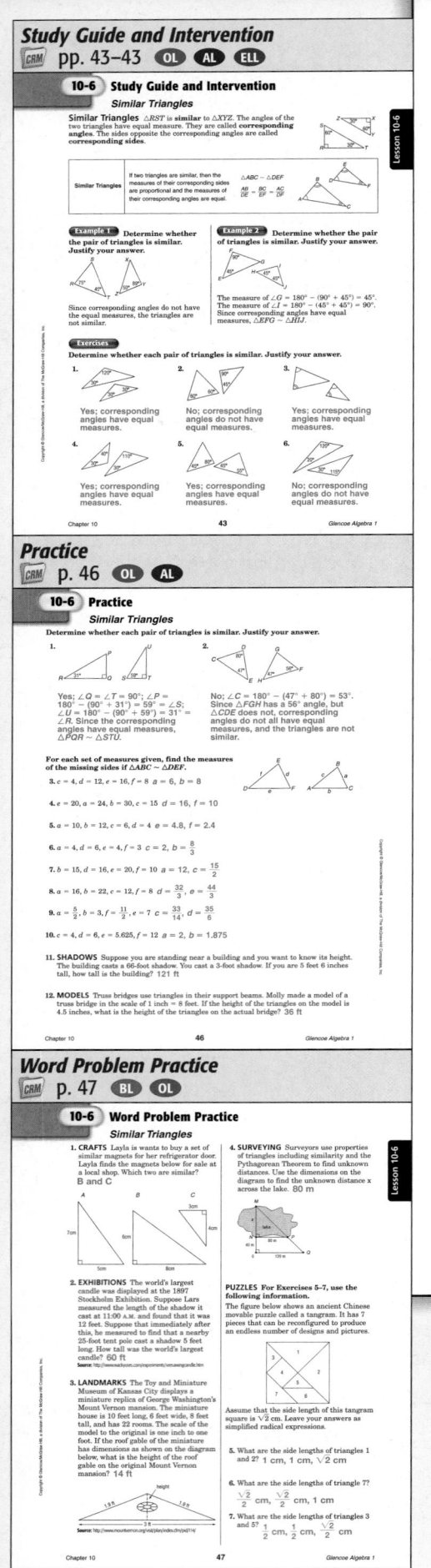

Study Guide and Intervention
CRM pp. 43–43 OL AL ELL

10-6 Study Guide and Intervention
Similar Triangles

Practice
CRM p. 46 OL AL

10-6 Practice
Similar Triangles

Word Problem Practice
CRM p. 47 BL OL

10-6 Word Problem Practice
Similar Triangles

23. TOYS Diecast model cars use a scale of 1 inch : 2 feet of the real vehicle. The original vehicle has a window shaped like a right triangle. If the height of the window on the actual vehicle is 2.5 feet, what will the height of the window be on the model? **1.25 in**

★ **24. GOLF** Jessica is playing miniature golf on a hole like the one shown at the right. She wants to putt her ball U so that it will bank at T and travel into the hole at R. Use similar triangles to find where Jessica's ball should strike the wall.
20 in from S

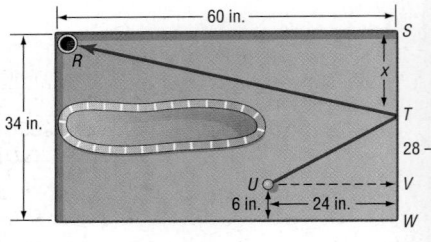

25. CRAFTS Melinda is working on a quilt pattern containing isosceles triangles whose sides measure 2 inches, 2 inches, and 2.5 inches. She has several square pieces of material that measure 4 inches on each side. From each square piece, how many triangles with the required dimensions can she cut? **8**

MIRRORS For Exercises 26 and 27, use the diagram and the following information.
Viho wanted to measure the height of a nearby building. He placed a mirror on the pavement at point P, 80 feet from the base of the building. He then backed away until he saw an image of the top of the building in the mirror.

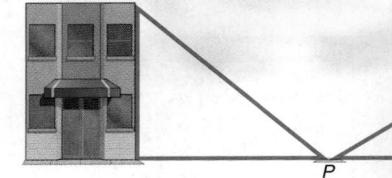

26. If Viho is 6 feet tall and he is standing 9 feet from the mirror, how tall is the building? **about 53 ft**

27. What assumptions did you make in solving the problem?

27. Viho's eyes are 6 feet off the ground, Viho and the building each create right angles with the ground, and the two angles with the ground at P have equal measure.

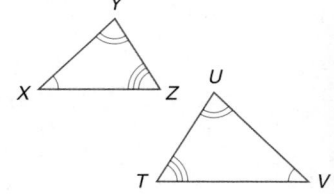

EXTRA PRACTICE
See page 738, 753.
Math Online
Self-Check Quiz at
ca.algebra1.com

H.O.T. Problems

28. OPEN ENDED Draw and label a triangle ABC. Then draw and label a similar triangle MNO so that the area of $\triangle MNO$ is four times the area of $\triangle ABC$. Explain your strategy. **See Ch. 10 Answer Appendix.**

29. REASONING Determine whether the following statement is *sometimes*, *always*, or *never* true. Explain your reasoning.
If the measures of the sides of a triangle are multiplied by 3, then the measures of the angles of the enlarged triangle will have the same measures as the angles of the original triangle.

29. The angles will always be the same because the sides are proportional with a scale factor of three which means the triangles are similar and the angles are congruent.

30. FIND THE ERROR Russell and Consuela are comparing the similar triangles below to determine their corresponding parts. Who is correct? Explain your reasoning. **See margin.**

Russell	Consuela
$m\angle X = m\angle T$	$m\angle X = m\angle V$
$m\angle Y = m\angle U$	$m\angle Y = m\angle U$
$m\angle Z = m\angle V$	$m\angle Z = m\angle T$
$\triangle XYZ, \triangle TUV$	$\triangle XYZ, \triangle VUT$

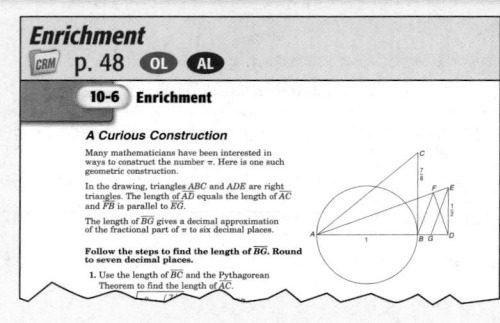

Enrichment
CRM p. 48 OL AL

10-6 Enrichment

A Curious Construction

Many mathematicians have been interested in ways to construct the number π. Here is one such geometric construction.

In the drawing, triangles ABC and ADE are right triangles. The length of AD equals the length of AC and FB is parallel to EG.

The length of BG gives a decimal approximation of the fractional part of π to six decimal places.

Follow the steps to find the length of BG. Round to seven decimal places.

1. Use the length of BC and the Pythagorean Theorem to find the length of AC.

BL = Below Grade Level
OL = On Grade Level
AL = Above Grade Level
ELL = English Language Learner

Additional pages not shown:
CRM *Lesson Reading Guide*, p. 42 BL OL ELL
CRM *Skills Practice*, p. 45 BL OL

564 **Chapter 10** Radical Expressions and Triangles

CRITICAL THINKING For Exercises 31–33, use the following information.
The radius of one circle is twice the radius of another.

31. Are the circles similar? Explain your reasoning. **See margin.**

32. What is the ratio of their circumferences? Explain your reasoning. **See margin.**

33. What is the ratio of their areas? Explain your reasoning. **See margin.**

34. *Writing in Math* Use the information about photography on page 560 to explain how similar triangles are related to photography. Include an explanation of the effect of moving a camera with a zoom lens closer to the object being photographed and a description of what you could do to fit the entire image of a large object on the picture. **See Ch. 10 Answer Appendix.**

STANDARDS PRACTICE 7MG2.1

35. Which is a true statement about the figure? **D**

A $\triangle ABC \sim \triangle ADC$

B $\triangle ABC \sim \triangle ACD$

C $\triangle ABC \sim \triangle CAD$

D none of the above

36. REVIEW Kareem needs to know the length and width of his room but does not have a tape measure. He knows that the room is square and that it has an area of 121 square feet. What should Kareem do to find the dimensions of his room? **J**

F Divide the area by the number of sides.

G Multiply the area by 2.

H Square the area.

J Take the square root of the area.

Spiral Review

Find the distance between each pair of points whose coordinates are given. Express answers in simplest radical form and as decimal approximations rounded to the nearest hundredth, if necessary. (Lesson 10-5)

37. $(1, 8), (-2, 4)$ **5**

38. $(4, 7), (3, 12)$ $\sqrt{26}$ or **5.1**

39. $\left(1, 5\sqrt{6}\right), \left(6, 7\sqrt{6}\right)$ **7**

The lengths of three sides of a triangle are given. Determine whether each triangle is a right triangle. (Lesson 10-4)

40. $25, 60, 65$ **yes**

41. $20, 25, 35$ **no**

42. $49, 168, 175$ **yes**

Use elimination to solve each system of equations. (Lesson 5-3)

43. $2x + y = 4$ **(3, −2)**
$x - y = 5$

44. $3x - 2y = -13$ **(−5, −1)**
$2x - 5y = -5$

45. $\frac{1}{3}x + \frac{1}{2}y = 8$
$\frac{1}{2}x - \frac{1}{4}y = 0$ **(6, 12)**

★ **46. AVIATION** An airplane passing over Sacramento at an elevation of 37,000 feet begins its descent to land at Reno, 140 miles away. If the elevation of Reno is 4500 feet, what should the approximate slope of descent be? (*Hint*: 1 mi = 5280 ft) (Lesson 4-1) **−232 ft/mi or about −0.044**

Pre-AP Activity Use after the Exercises.

Tell students that if two triangles are similar, the ratio of their areas is equal to the square of the ratio of their corresponding sides. Write the following rule on the board: 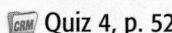. Tell students that A_1 is the area of the first triangle, A_2 is the area of the second triangle, s_1 is the side of the first triangle, and s_2 is the corresponding side of the second triangle. Ask students to use this proportion to find the ratio of the area of two triangles whose sides are in the ratio of 2:3.

Real-World Connections
For Exercise 23, tell students that many people collect model train sets. Model trains built to the HO scale have a ratio of 1:87. This means a 75-foot-long locomotive is $10\frac{1}{2}$ inches long. The rails of the track are 16.5 mm apart. Have students tell about the different scales of model trains they might own.

⚠ **Exercise Alert!**
Find the Error Remind students to pay close attention to the arcs that denote which angles are congruent.

4 Assess

Name the Math Have students write the proportions that can be formed by knowing that $\triangle PQR \sim \triangle RST$.

✓ **Formative Assessment**
Check for student understanding of concepts in Lessons 10-6.

[CRM] Quiz 4, p. 52

FOLDABLES **Foldables™**
Study Organizer **Follow-Up**
Remind students to use their Foldables to record notes on what they have learned about similar triangles.

Additional Answers

30. Consuela; the arcs indicate which angles correspond. The vertices of the triangles are written in order to show the corresponding parts.

31. Yes; all circles are similar because they have the same shape.

32. 2:1; Let the first circle have radius r and the larger circle have radius $2r$. The circumference of the first is $2\pi r$ and the other is $2\pi(2r) = 4\pi r$.

33. 4:1; The area of the first is πr^2 and the area of the other is $\pi(2r)^2 = 4\pi r^2$.

READING MATH

1 Focus

Ask:
Can you think of some words that have the same spelling but different meanings?

Student examples may include:

bat: a mammal that flies at night; a wooden stick used for hitting a ball
snap: a fastener used to hold clothing together; to break suddenly with a sharp sound

2 Teach

Connecting to Vocabulary Tell students that there are many words that have the same spelling but different meanings, depending on the context, or framework, in which the word is used. For example, in everyday usage, the word *power* can mean the right or capacity to do something. In mathematical terminology, a *power* can denote the amount of times a number is multiplied by itself.

Divide the class into small groups. Give each group several of the words listed in this activity. Ask the groups to use their textbooks, dictionaries, or the Internet to find the definitions.

3 Assess

Ask students to summarize what they have learned about the language of mathematics.

Additional Answers

1a. Sample answer: A circumstance that brings about a result; any of two or more quantities that form a product when multiplied together; the quantities bring about a result, a product.

The Language of Mathematics

 Reinforcement of Standard 7MR2.5 Use a variety of methods, such as words, numbers, symbols, charts, graphs, tables, diagrams, and models, to explain mathematical reasoning.

The language of mathematics is a specific one, but it borrows from everyday language, scientific language, and world languages. To find a word's correct meaning, you will need to be aware of some confusing aspects of language.

Confusing Aspect	Words
Some words are used in English and in mathematics, but have distinct meanings.	factor, **leg**, prime, power, **rationalize**
Some words are used in English and in mathematics, but the mathematical meaning is more precise.	difference, even, **similar**, slope
Some words are used in science and in mathematics, but the meanings are different.	divide, **radical**, solution, variable
Some words are only used in mathematics.	decimal, **hypotenuse**, integer, quotient
Some words have more than one mathematical meaning.	base, **degree**, range, round, square
Sometimes several words come from the same root word.	polygon and polynomial, **radical** and **radicand**
Some mathematical words sound like English words.	**sum** and some, whole and hole, base and bass

Words in boldface are in this chapter.

Reading to Learn 1–3. See margin.

1. How do the mathematical meanings of the following words compare to the everyday meanings?

   a. factor

   b. leg

   c. rationalize

2. State two mathematical definitions for each word. Give an example for each definition.

   a. degree

   b. range

   c. round

3. Each word below is shown with its root word and the root word's meaning. Find three additional words that come from the same root.

   a. domain, from the root word *domus,* which means house

   b. radical, from the root word *radix,* which means root

   c. similar, from the root word *similis,* which means like

566 Chapter 10 Radical Expressions and Triangles

1b. Sample answer: The legs of an animal support the animal; one of the two shorter sides of a right triangle; the legs of a triangle support the hypotenuse.

1c. Sample answer: To devise rational explanations for one's acts without being aware that these are not the real motives; to remove the radical signs from an expression without changing its value; to justify an action without changing its intent.

2a. Sample answer: Rank as determined by the sum of a term's exponents; the degree of x^2y^2 is 4. $\frac{1}{360}$ of a circle; a semicircle measures 180.

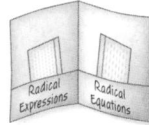

FOLDABLES™
Study Organizer

GET READY to Study

Be sure the following Key Concepts are noted in your Foldable.

Key Concepts

Simplifying Radical Expressions
(Lesson 10-1)
- A radical expression is in simplest form when
- no radicands have perfect square factors other than 1,
- no radicands contain fractions,
- and no radicands appear in the denominator of a fraction.

Operations with Radical Expressions and Equations *(Lessons 10-2 and 10-3)*
- Radical expressions with like radicands can be added or subtracted.
- Use the FOIL Method to multiply radicand expressions.
- Solve radical equations by isolating the radical on one side of the equation. Square each side of the equation to eliminate the radical.

Pythagorean Theorem and Distance Formula *(Lessons 10-4 and 10-5)*
- If a and b are the measures of the legs of a right triangle and c is the measure of the hypotenuse, then $c^2 = a^2 + b^2$.
- If a and b are measures of the shorter sides of a triangle, c is the measure of the longest side, and $c^2 = a^2 + b^2$, then the triangle is a right triangle.
- The distance d between any two points with coordinates (x_1, y_1) and (x_2, y_2) is given by $d = \sqrt{(x_2 - x_1)^2 + (y_2 - y_1)^2}$.

Similar Triangles *(Lesson 10-6)*
- Similar Triangles have congruent corresponding angles and proportional corresponding sides. If $\triangle ABC \sim \triangle DEF$, then $\frac{AB}{DE} = \frac{BC}{EF} = \frac{AC}{DF}$.

 Vocabulary Review at ca.algebra1.com

Key Vocabulary

conjugate *(p. 531)*
converse *(p. 551)*
Distance Formula *(p. 555)*
extraneous solution *(p. 542)*
hypotenuse *(p. 549)*
leg *(p. 549)*
Pythagorean triple *(p. 550)*
radical equation *(p. 541)*
radical expression *(p. 528)*
radicand *(p. 528)*
rationalizing the denominator *(p. 530)*
similar triangles *(p. 560)*

4. false, $3x + 19 = x^2 + 6x + 9$

Vocabulary Check

State whether each sentence is *true* or *false*. If *false*, replace the underlined word or number to make a true sentence. 2. true

1. The binomials $-3 + \sqrt{7}$ and $3 - \sqrt{7}$ are conjugates. **false, $-3 - \sqrt{7}$**

2. In the expression $-4\sqrt{5}$, the radicand is $\underline{5}$.

3. The <u>longest</u> side of a right triangle is the hypotenuse. **true**

4. After the first step in solving $\sqrt{3x + 19} = x + 3$, you would have $\underline{3x + 19 = x^2 + 9}$.

5. The two sides that form the right angle in a right triangle are called the <u>legs</u> of the triangle. **true**

6. If $x > 0$ and $y > 0$, then the expression $\frac{2x\sqrt{3x}}{\sqrt{6y}}$ is in simplest radical form. **false, $\frac{x\sqrt{2xy}}{y}$**

7. A triangle with sides having measures of <u>25, 20, and 15</u> is a right triangle. **true**

8. Two triangles are <u>similar</u> if the corresponding angles are congruent. **true**

Additional Answers

2b. Sample answer: The difference between the greatest and least values in a set of data; the range of 2, 3, 6 is $6 - 2$ or 4. The set of all y-values in a function; the range of $\{(2, 6), (1, 3)\}$ is $\{6, 3\}$.

2c, 3a–3c. See Chapter 10 Answer Appendix.

 Summative Assessment

 Vocabulary Test, p. 54

FOLDABLES™
Study Organizer

Dinah Zike's Foldables™

Have students look through the chapter to make sure they have included examples in their Foldables for each lesson of the chapter.

Suggest that students keep their Foldables handy while completing the Study Guide and Review pages. Point out that their Foldables can serve as a quick review tool for studying for the chapter test.

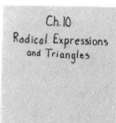
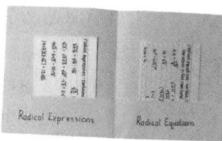

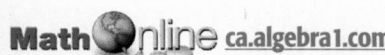 **Formative Assessment**

Key Vocabulary The page references after each word denotes where that term was first introduced. If students have difficulty answering questions 1–8, remind them that they can use these page references to refresh their memories about the vocabulary terms.

Math Online ca.algebra1.com

Vocabulary PuzzleMaker improves students' mathematics vocabulary using four puzzle formats—crossword, scramble, word search using a word list, and word search using clues. Students can work online or from a printed worksheet.

Lesson-by-Lesson Review

Intervention If the given examples are not sufficient to review the topics covered by the questions, remind students that the page references tell them where to review that topic in their textbooks.

Two-Day Option Have students complete the Lesson-by-Lesson Review on pp. 568–570. Then you can use ExamView® Assessment Suite to customize another review worksheet that practices all the objectives of this chapter or only the objectives on which your students need more help.

For more information on ExamView® Assessment Suite, see p. 516C.

Differentiated Instruction
Super DVD: MindJogger Videoquizzes

Use this DVD as an alternative format of review for the test. For more information on this game show format, see p. 516D.

For Exercises 9-14, if a variable with an odd power is under the radical, assume that the value of the variable is nonnegative.

Additional Answers

13. $\dfrac{3\sqrt{35} - 5\sqrt{21}}{-15}$

22. $18\sqrt{10} + 30 + 6\sqrt{2} + 2\sqrt{5}$

Lesson-by-Lesson Review

10-1 Simplifying Radical Expressions (pp. 528–534) 10. $2|a|b^2\sqrt{11b}$

Simplify. **13. See margin.**

9. $\sqrt{\dfrac{60}{y^2}}$ $\dfrac{2\sqrt{15}}{|y|}$

10. $\sqrt{44a^2b^5}$

11. $\left(3 - 2\sqrt{12}\right)^2$ $57 - 24\sqrt{3}$

12. $\dfrac{9}{3 + \sqrt{2}}$ $\dfrac{27 - 9\sqrt{2}}{7}$

13. $\dfrac{2\sqrt{7}}{3\sqrt{5} + 5\sqrt{3}}$

14. $\dfrac{\sqrt{3a^3b^4}}{\sqrt{8ab^{10}}}$ $\dfrac{a\sqrt{6}}{4|b^3|}$

15. **METEOROLOGY** To estimate how long a thunderstorm will last, meteorologists use the formula $t = \sqrt{\dfrac{d^3}{216}}$, where t is time in hours and d is the diameter of the storm in miles. A storm is 10 miles in diameter. How long will it last? **about 2 h**

Example 1 Simplify $\dfrac{3}{5 - \sqrt{2}}$.

$\dfrac{3}{5 - \sqrt{2}}$

$= \dfrac{3}{5 - \sqrt{2}} \cdot \dfrac{5 + \sqrt{2}}{5 + \sqrt{2}}$ Rationalize the denominator.

$= \dfrac{3(5) + 3\sqrt{2}}{5^2 - \left(\sqrt{2}\right)^2}$ $(a - b)(a + b) = a^2 - b^2$

$= \dfrac{15 + 3\sqrt{2}}{25 - 2}$ $\left(\sqrt{2}\right)^2 = 2$

$= \dfrac{15 + 3\sqrt{2}}{23}$ Simplify.

10-2 Operations with Radical Expressions (pp. 536–540)

Simplify each expression.

16. $2\sqrt{3} + 8\sqrt{5} - 3\sqrt{5} + 3\sqrt{3}$ $5\sqrt{3} + 5\sqrt{5}$

17. $2\sqrt{6} - \sqrt{48}$ $2\sqrt{6} - 4\sqrt{3}$

18. $4\sqrt{7k} - 7\sqrt{7k} + 2\sqrt{7k}$ $-\sqrt{7k}$

19. $\sqrt{8} + \sqrt{\dfrac{1}{8}}$ $\dfrac{9\sqrt{2}}{4}$

Find each product.

20. $\sqrt{2}\left(3 + 3\sqrt{3}\right)$ $3\sqrt{2} + 3\sqrt{6}$

21. $\left(\sqrt{3} - \sqrt{2}\right)\left(2\sqrt{2} + \sqrt{3}\right)$ $\sqrt{6} - 1$

22. $\left(6\sqrt{5} + 2\right)\left(3\sqrt{2} + \sqrt{5}\right)$ **See margin.**

23. **MOTION** The velocity of a dropped object can be found using $v = \sqrt{2gd}$, where v is the velocity in feet per second, g is the acceleration due to gravity, and d is the distance in feet the object drops. Find the speed of a penny when it hits the ground, after being dropped off the Eiffel Tower. Use 32 feet per second squared for g and 984 feet for the height of the Eiffel Tower. **250.95 ft/s**

Example 2 $\sqrt{6} - \sqrt{54} + 3\sqrt{12} + 5\sqrt{3}$.

$\sqrt{6} - \sqrt{54} + 3\sqrt{12} + 5\sqrt{3}$

$= \sqrt{6} - \sqrt{3^2 \cdot 6} + 3\sqrt{2^2 \cdot 3} + 5\sqrt{3}$

$= \sqrt{6} - \left(\sqrt{3^2} \cdot \sqrt{6}\right) + 3\left(\sqrt{2^2} \cdot \sqrt{3}\right) + 5\sqrt{3}$

$= \sqrt{6} - 3\sqrt{6} + 3\left(2\sqrt{3}\right) + 5\sqrt{3}$

$= \sqrt{6} - 3\sqrt{6} + 6\sqrt{3} + 5\sqrt{3}$

$= -2\sqrt{6} + 11\sqrt{3}$

Example 3 Find $\left(2\sqrt{3} - \sqrt{5}\right)\left(\sqrt{10} + 4\sqrt{6}\right)$.

$\left(2\sqrt{3} - \sqrt{5}\right)\left(\sqrt{10} + 4\sqrt{6}\right)$

$= \left(2\sqrt{3}\right)\left(\sqrt{10}\right) + \left(2\sqrt{3}\right)\left(4\sqrt{6}\right)$
$\quad + \left(-\sqrt{5}\right)\left(\sqrt{10}\right) + \left(-\sqrt{5}\right)\left(4\sqrt{6}\right)$

$= 2\sqrt{30} + 8\sqrt{18} - \sqrt{50} - 4\sqrt{30}$

$= 2\sqrt{30} + 8\sqrt{3^2 \cdot 2} - \sqrt{5^2 \cdot 2} - 4\sqrt{30}$

$= -2\sqrt{30} + 19\sqrt{2}$

Mixed Problem Solving
For mixed problem-solving practice,
see page 753.

CHAPTER
10 Study Guide
and Review

10-3 **Radical Equations** (pp. 541–546)

Solve each equation. Check your
solution. **24. no solution**

24. $10 + 2\sqrt{b} = 0$ **25.** $\sqrt{a + 4} = 6$ **32**

26. $\sqrt{7x - 1} = 5$ $\frac{26}{7}$ **27.** $\sqrt{\frac{4a}{3}} - 2 = 0$ **3**

28. $\sqrt{x + 4} = x - 8$ **29.** $\sqrt{3x - 14} + x = 6$ **5**
12

30. FREE FALL Assuming no air resistance,
the time t in seconds that it takes an
object to fall h feet can be determined
by $t = \frac{\sqrt{h}}{4}$. If a skydiver jumps from
an airplane and free falls for 8 seconds
before opening the parachute, how
many feet does the skydiver fall? **1024 ft**

Example 4 Solve $\sqrt{5 - 4x} - 6 = 7$.

$\sqrt{5 - 4x} - 6 = 7$	Original equation
$\sqrt{5 - 4x} = 13$	Add 6 to each side.
$5 - 4x = 169$	Square each side.
$-4x = 164$	Subtract 5 from each side.
$x = -41$	Divide each side by −4.

10-4 **The Pythagorean Theorem** (pp. 549–554)

If c is the measure of the hypotenuse of a
right triangle, find each missing measure.
If necessary, round answers to the nearest
hundredth.

31. $a = 30, b = 16, c = ?$ **34**

32. $b = 4, c = 56, a = ?$ $4\sqrt{195} \approx 55.86$

33. $a = 6, b = 10, c = ?$ $2\sqrt{34} \approx 11.66$

34. $a = 10, c = 15, b = ?$ $5\sqrt{5} \approx 11.18$

35. $a = 18, c = 30, b = ?$ **24**

36. $a = 1.2, b = 1.6, c = ?$ **2**

Determine whether the following side
measures form right triangles.

37. $9, 16, 20$ **no**   **38.** $20, 21, 29$ **yes**

39. $9, 40, 41$ **yes**   **40.** $18, \sqrt{24}, 30$ **no**

41. MOVING The door of Julio's apartment
measures 7 feet high and 3 feet wide.
Julio would like to buy a square table
that is 7 feet on a side. If the table
cannot go through the door sideways,
will it fit diagonally? Explain. **yes**

Example 5 Find the length of the
missing side.

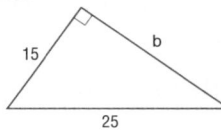

$c^2 = a^2 + b^2$	Pythagorean Theorem
$25^2 = 15^2 + b^2$	$c = 25$ and $a = 15$
$625 = 225 + b^2$	Evaluate squares.
$400 = b^2$	Subtract 225 from each side.
$20 = b$	Take the square root of each side.

Example 6 Determine whether the side
measures, 6, 10, and 12, form a right
triangle.

$c^2 = a^2 + b^2$	Pythagorean Theorem
$12^2 \stackrel{?}{=} 6^2 + 10^2$	$a = 6, b = 10,$ and $c = 12$
$144 \stackrel{?}{=} 36 + 100$	Multiply.
$144 \neq 136$	Add. These side measures do *not* form a right triangle.

Problem Solving Review

For additional practice in problem solving for Chapter 10, see the Mixed Problem Solving Appendix, p. 753 in the Student Handbook section.

Anticipation Guide

Have students complete the Chapter 10 Anticipation Guide and discuss how their responses have changed now that they have completed Chapter 10.

[CRM] Anticipation Guide, p. 3

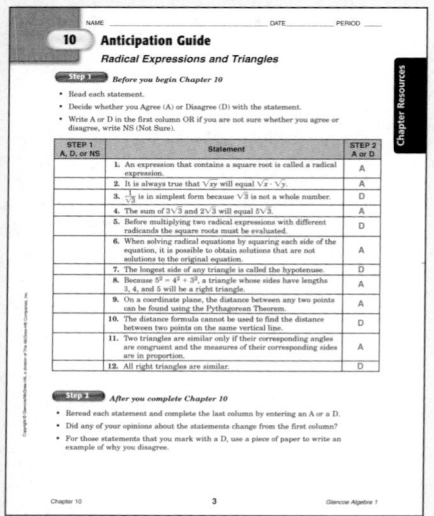

Additional Answers

49. $d = \dfrac{45}{8}, e = \dfrac{27}{4}$

50. $d = 9.6, e = 7.2$

51. $b = \dfrac{44}{3}, d = 6$

52. $a = 17.5, e = 8$

10-5 The Distance Formula (pp. 555–559)

Find the distance between each pair of points with the given coordinates. Express in simplest radical form and as decimal approximations rounded to the nearest hundredth if necessary.

42. $(9, -2), (1, 13)$ **17** **43.** $(4, 2), (7, 9)$ $\sqrt{58}$ or 7.62

44. $(4, 8), (-7, 12)$ $\sqrt{137}$ or 11.70 **45.** $(-2, 6), (5, 11)$ $\sqrt{74}$ or 8.60

Find the value of a if the points with the given coordinates are the indicated distance apart.

46. $(-3, 2), (1, a); d = 5$ **5 or −1**

47. $(5, -2), (a, -3); d = \sqrt{170}$ **18 or −8**

48. SAILING A boat leaves the harbor and sails 5 miles east and 3 miles north to an island. The next day, they travel to a fishing spot 10 miles south and 4 miles west of the harbor. How far is it from the fishing spot to the island? **15.8 mi**

Example 7 Find the distance between the points with coordinates $(-5, 1)$ and $(1, 5)$.

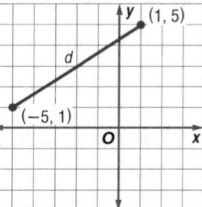

Use the Distance Formula.

$$d = \sqrt{(x_2 - x_1)^2 + (y_2 - y_1)^2}$$
$$= \sqrt{(1 - (-5))^2 + (5 - 1)^2}$$
$$= \sqrt{6^2 + 4^2} \quad \text{Simplify.}$$
$$= \sqrt{36 + 16} \quad \text{Evaluate squares.}$$
$$= \sqrt{52} \text{ or about 7.21 units} \quad \text{Simplify.}$$

10-6 Similar Triangles (pp. 560–565)

For each set of measures given, find the measures of the remaining sides if $\triangle ABC \sim \triangle DEF$. **49–52. See margin.**

49. $c = 16, b = 12, a = 10, f = 9$

50. $a = 8, c = 10, b = 6, f = 12$

51. $c = 12, f = 9, a = 8, e = 11$

52. $b = 20, d = 7, f = 6, c = 15$

53. HOUSES Josh plans to make a model of his house in the scale 1 inch = 6 feet. If the height to the top of the roof on the house is 24 feet, what will the height of the model be? **4 in.**

Example 8 Find the measure of side a if the two triangles are similar.

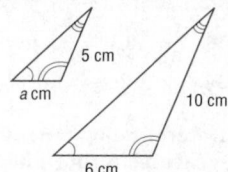

$\dfrac{10}{5} = \dfrac{6}{a}$ Corresponding sides of similar triangles are proportional.

$10a = 30$ Find the cross products.

$a = 3$ Divide each side by 10.

Simplify.
1. $2\sqrt{27} - 4\sqrt{3}$ **1.** $2\sqrt{3}$

2. $\sqrt{6} + \sqrt{\frac{2}{3}}$ **3.** $4\sqrt{6} + 6\sqrt{2}$ $\frac{4\sqrt{6}}{3}$

3. $\sqrt{6}(4 + \sqrt{12})$

4. $\sqrt{\frac{10}{3}} \cdot \sqrt{\frac{4}{30}}$ $\frac{2}{3}$

5. $(1 - \sqrt{3})(3 + \sqrt{2})$ **6.** $\sqrt{112x^4y^6}$ $4x^2|y^3|\sqrt{7}$
$3 + \sqrt{2} - 3\sqrt{3} - \sqrt{6}$

Solve each equation. Check your solution.

7. $\sqrt{10x} = 20$ **40**   **8.** $\sqrt{4s} + 1 = 11$ **25**

9. $\sqrt{4x + 1} = 5$ **6**   **10.** $x = \sqrt{-6x - 8}$ **no solution**

11. $x = \sqrt{5x + 14}$ **7**   **12.** $\sqrt{4x - 3} = 6 - x$ **3**

If c is the measure of the hypotenuse of a right triangle, find each missing measure. If necessary, round to the nearest hundredth.

13. $a = 8, b = 10, c = ?$ $\sqrt{164} \approx 12.81$

14. $a = 6\sqrt{2}, c = 12, b = ?$ $\sqrt{72} \approx 8.49$

15. DISC GOLF The sport of disc golf is similar to golf except that the players throw a disc into a basket instead of hitting a ball into a cup. Bob's first disc lands 10 feet short and 12 feet to the left of the basket. On his next throw, the disc lands 5 feet to the right and 2 feet beyond the basket. Assuming that the disc traveled in a straight line, how far did the disc travel on the second throw?
$\sqrt{433}$ or about 21 ft

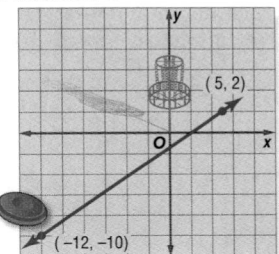

16. SPORTS A hiker leaves her camp in the morning. How far is she from camp after walking 9 miles due west and then 12 miles due north?   **15 mi**

Find the distance between each pair of points with the given coordinates. Express in simplest radical form and as decimal approximations rounded to the nearest hundredth, if necessary.

17. $(4, 7), (4, -2)$ **9**
18. $(-1, 1), (1, -5)$ $2\sqrt{10} \approx 6.32$
19. $(-9, 2), (21, 7)$ $5\sqrt{37} \approx 30.41$

For each set of measures given, find the measures of the missing sides if $\triangle ABC \sim \triangle JKH$.

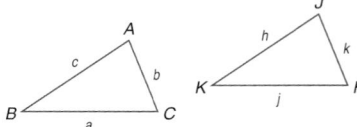

20. $c = 20, h = 15, k = 16, j = 12$ $a = 16, b = \frac{64}{3}$
21. $c = 12, b = 13, a = 6, h = 10$ $j = 5, k = \frac{65}{6}$
22. $k = 5, c = 6.5, b = 7.5, a = 4.5$ $h = 4.\overline{3}, j = 3$
23. $h = 1\frac{1}{2}, c = 4\frac{1}{2}, k = 2\frac{1}{4}, a = 3$ $b = 6\frac{3}{4}, j = 1$

24. MULTIPLE CHOICE Find the area of the rectangle.   **C**

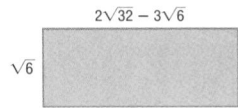
$2\sqrt{32} - 3\sqrt{6}$
$\sqrt{6}$

A $2\sqrt{32} - 18$ units^2

B $16\sqrt{2} - 4\sqrt{6}$ units^2

C $16\sqrt{3} - 18$ units^2

D $32\sqrt{3} - 18$ units^2

25. SHADOWS Suppose you are standing near the flag pole in front of your school and you want to know its height. The flag pole casts a 22-foot shadow. You cast a 3-foot shadow. If you are 5 feet tall, how tall is the flag pole?
about 36.7 ft

Data-Driven Decision Making	**Exercises**	**Lesson**	**Standard**	**Resources for Review**
Diagnostic Teaching Based on the results of the Chapter 10 Practice Test, use the following to review concepts that students continue to find challenging.	13–14	10–4	**Preparation for Geometry 15.0**	CRM Study Guide and Intervention pp. 27–28, 35–36, 42–43
	15–19	10–5	**Preparation for Geometry 17.0**	Math Online • Extra Examples
	10–6	10–6	**Preparation for Geometry 5.0**	• Personal Tutor • Concepts in Motion

CHAPTER 10

California Standards Practice

TEST-TAKING TIP

Question 9 When a figure is not provided for a question about a geometric object, it is usually helpful to draw one. By looking at a drawing for this question, answer choices F and G can be eliminated.

Formative Assessment

You can use these two pages to benchmark student progress. The California Standards are listed with each question.

Chapter 10 Resource Masters
- Standardized Test Practice, pp. 68–70

ExamView Assessment Suite Create practice worksheets or tests that align to the California Standards, as well as TIMSS and NAEP tests.

Item Analysis

Question 3 is a griddable question. In griddable questions, students arrive at an answer and then record it in a special grid, coloring in the appropriate bubble under each digit of the answer.

CHAPTER 10

California Standards Practice

Cumulative, Chapters 1–10

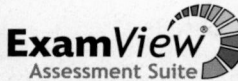

Read each question. Then fill in the correct answer on the answer document provided by your teacher or on a sheet of paper.

1 Four steps to derive the quadratic formula are shown below.

I	$x^2 + \frac{bx}{a} + \left(\frac{b}{2a}\right)^2 = \frac{-c}{a} + \left(\frac{b}{2a}\right)^2$
II	$x + \frac{b}{2a} = \sqrt{\frac{b^2 - 4ac}{4a^2}}$
III	$\left(x + \frac{b}{2a}\right)^2 = \frac{b^2 - 4ac}{4a^2}$
IV	$x^2 + \frac{bx}{a} = \frac{-c}{a}$

What is the correct order for these steps? C

A III, I, IV, II
B III, II, IV, I
C IV, I, III, II
D IV, II, I, III

2 The perimeter p of a square may be found by using the formula $\left(\frac{1}{4}\right)p = \sqrt{a}$, where a is the area of the square. What is the perimeter of the square with an area of 64 square feet? H

F 2
G 12
H 32
J 64

3 Simplify $\frac{\sqrt{16} + 2}{2\sqrt{36}}$. 0.5

4 $(2n + 6)^2 =$ D

A $n^2 + 12n + 36$
B $n^2 + 24n + 36$
C $4n^2 + 12n + 36$
D $4n^2 + 24n + 36$

5 Which *best* explains why there is no real solution to the quadratic equation $3x^2 + 4x + 5 = 0$? H

F The value of $4^2 - 4(-3)(5)$ is positive.
G The value of $4^2 - 4(-3)(5)$ is equal to zero.
H The value of $4^2 - 4(-3)(5)$ is negative.
J The value of $4^2 - 4(-3)(5)$ is not a perfect square.

6 What are the solutions for the quadratic equation $x^2 - 2x = 24$? B

A −4, −6
B −4, 6
C 4, −6
D 4, 6

7 What quantity should be added to both sides of this equation to complete the square? H

$$x^2 - 6x = 7$$

F 3
G −3
H 9
J −9

TEST-TAKING TIP

Question 3 Be sure to follow the order of operations when evaluating expressions of any kind. Recall that the fraction bar acts as a grouping symbol.

Math Online California Standards Practice at ca.algebra1.com

More California
Standards Practice
For practice by standard,
see pages CA1–CA43.

CHAPTER
10 California
Standards Practice

8 The graph of the linear equation $y = \frac{1}{2}x + 3$ is shown below.

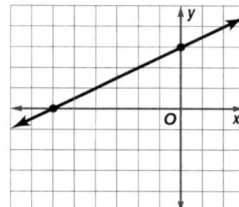

Which point is not in the solution set of $y > \frac{1}{2}x + 3$? **D**

A $(1, 5)$

B $(-6, 1)$

C $(-3, 4)$

D $(-2, 1)$

9 Which equation represents the line that passes through the points $(2, 1)$ and $(4, -3)$? **G**

F $y = -2x - 5$

G $y = -2x + 5$

H $y = 2x - 5$

J $y = 2x + 5$

10 The equation of line ℓ is $3x - 5y = 5$, and the equation of line m is $5x - 3y = 3$. Which statement about the two lines is true? **D**

A Lines ℓ and m are perpendicular.

B Lines ℓ and m are parallel.

C Lines ℓ and m have the same x-intercept.

D Lines ℓ and m have the same y-intercept.

11 Which is always a correct conclusion about the quantities in the function $y = 2x$? **H**

F The value of y will always be positive.

G The value of y will always be greater than the value of x.

H The value of y is always twice x.

J As the value of x increases, the value of y decreases.

12 What is the value of c in feet in the right triangle below? **15**

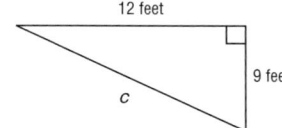

12 feet

9 feet

c

Pre-AP/Anchor Problem

Record your answer on a sheet of paper. Show your work.

13 Haley hikes 3 miles north, 7 miles east, and then 6 miles north again.

a. Draw a diagram showing the direction and distance of each segment of Haley's hike. Label Haley's starting point, her ending point, and the distance, in miles, of each segment of her hike. **See margin.**

b. To the nearest tenth of a mile, how far (in a straight line) is Haley from her starting point? **11.4 mi**

c. How did your diagram help you to find Haley's distance from her starting point?

d. Describe the direction and distance of Haley's return trip back to her starting position if she used the same trail. **south 6 miles, west 7 miles, south 3 more miles**

13c. See students' work.

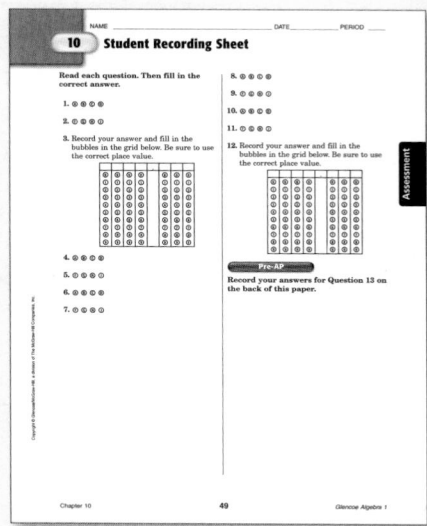

Additional Answers

13a.

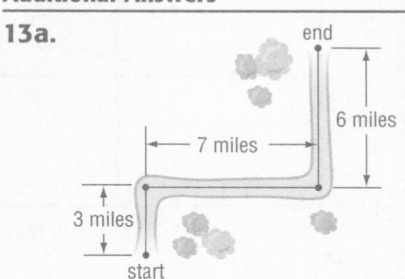

NEED EXTRA HELP?													
If You Missed Question...	1	2	3	4	5	6	7	8	9	10	11	12	13
Go to Lesson...	10-1	10-3	10-1	7-7	9-4	8-3	9-3	6-6	4-4	4-7	3-3	10-4	10-4
For Help with Standard...	19.0	2.0	2.0	10.0	20.0	14.0	14.0	6.0	7.0	8.0	25.3	7MG3.3	7MG3.3

Chapter 10 California Standards Practice **573**

Homework Option

Get Ready for Chapter 11 Assign students the exercises on p. 575 as homework to assess whether they possess the prerequisite skills needed for the next chapter.

1. $\{x \mid x \geq 0\}$; shifted up 1

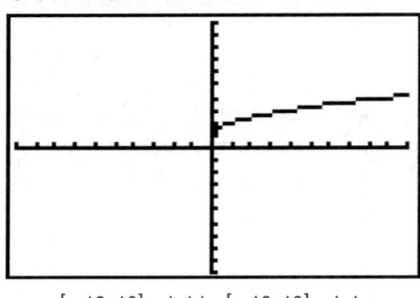

[−10, 10] scl: 1 by [−10, 10] scl: 1

2. $\{x \mid x \geq 0\}$; shifted down 3

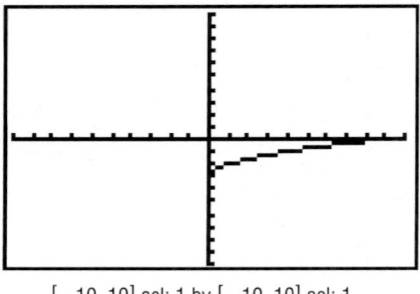

[−10, 10] scl: 1 by [−10, 10] scl: 1

3. $\{x \mid x \geq 2\}$; shifted left 2

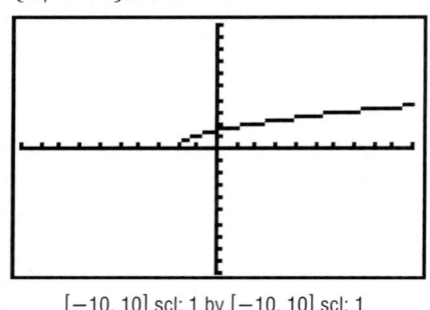

[−10, 10] scl: 1 by [−10, 10] scl: 1

4. $\{x \mid x \geq 5\}$; shifted right 5

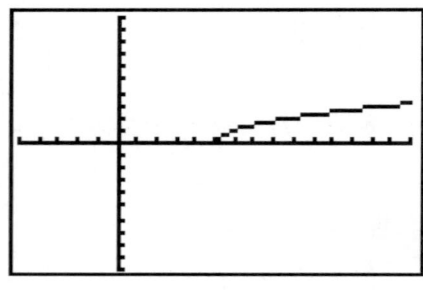

[−5, 15] scl: 1 by [−10, 10] scl: 1

5. $\{x \mid x \leq 0\}$; reflected across *y*-axis

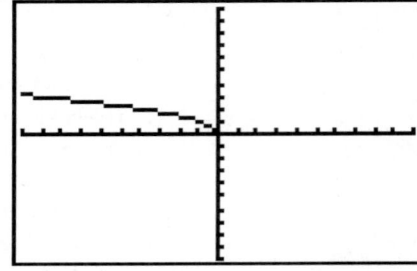

[−10, 10] scl: 1 by [−10, 10] scl: 1

6. $\{x \mid x \geq 0\}$; expanded

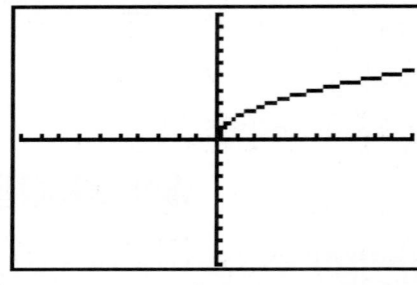

[−10, 10] scl: 1 by [−10, 10] scl: 1

7. $\{x \mid x \geq 0\}$; reflected across *x*-axis

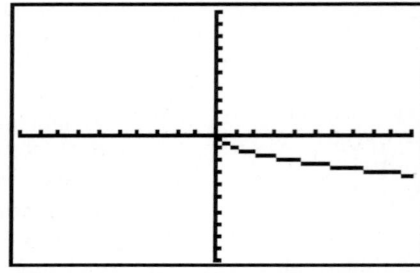

[−10, 10] scl: 1 by [−10, 10] scl: 1

8. $\{x \mid x \leq 1\}$; reflected across *y*-axis, shifted right 1, up 6

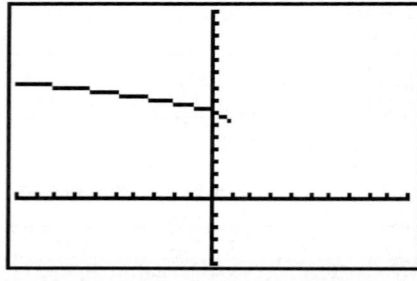

[−10, 10] scl: 1 by [−5, 15] scl: 1

Chapter 10 Answer Appendix

9. $\{x \mid x \geq -2.5\}$; shifted left 2.5, down 4

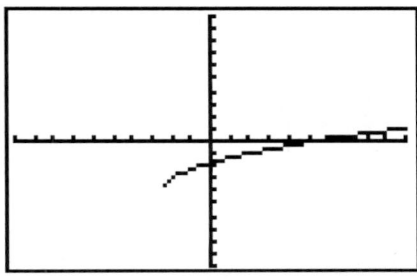

[−10, 10] scl: 1 by [−10, 10] scl: 1

10. The domain is all real numbers. The graph is symmetrical about the *y*-axis with the right side similar to the parent graph.

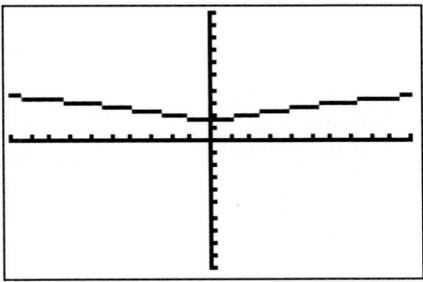

11. $\{x \mid x \geq 3 \text{ or } x \leq -3\}$; The graph is symmetrical about the *y*-axis with the right side similar to the parent graph shifted 3 units to the right.

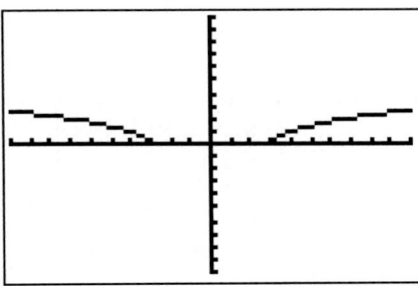

12. No; you must consider the graph of $y = \sqrt{x}$ and the graph of $y = -\sqrt{x}$. This graph fails the vertical line test. For every value of $x > 0$, there are two values for *y*.

13. No; the equation $y = \pm\sqrt{1 - x^2}$ is not a function since there are both positive and negative values for *y* for each value of *x*.

Page 559, Lesson 10-5

43. Compare the slopes of the two potential legs to determine whether the slopes are negative reciprocals of each other. You can also compute the lengths of the three sides and determine whether the square of the longest side length is equal to the sum of the squares of the other two side lengths. Neither test holds true in this case because the triangle is not a right triangle.

44. You can determine the distance between the two cities by forming a right triangle connecting the three cities and use the Pythagorean Theorem to find the length of the hypotenuse. When you find the length of the hypotenuse using the Pythagorean Theorem, you have actually found the distance between the two cities thus giving you the Distance Formula. The helicopter could transport the injured person because it can travel 450 miles before refueling and the distance between Washington and Huntington is about 367 miles.

53. $\{m \mid m \geq 9\}$

54. $\{k \mid k < -7\}$

55. $\{x \mid x \leq -3\}$

56. $\left\{s \mid s \leq \dfrac{1}{2}\right\}$

Pages 564–565, Lesson 10-6

28. $\triangle MNO$ has a base that is twice the base and twice the height of $\triangle ABC$. The triangles are similar because their corresponding angles are congruent. The area of $\triangle MNO$ is four times the area of $\triangle ABC$.

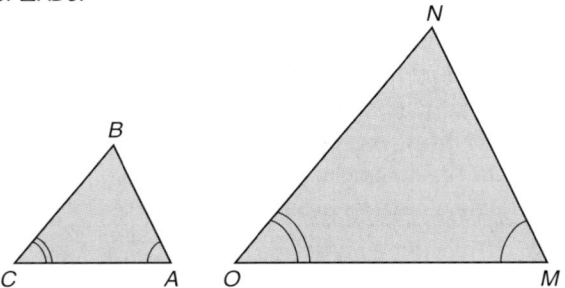

34. The size of an object on the film can be related to its actual size using similar triangles. Moving the lens closer to the object (and farther from the film) makes the object appear larger. Taking a picture of a building; you would need to be a great distance away to fit the entire building into the picture.

Page 566, Reading Math

2c. Sample answer: Circular or spherical; circles are round. To abbreviate a number by replacing its ending digits with zeros; 235,611 rounded to the nearest hundred is 235,600.

3a. Sample answer: dome, domestic, domicile

3b. Sample answer: eradicate, radicand, radius

3c. Sample answer: similie, similarity, similitude

Rational Expressions and Equations

Standards-Based Lesson Plan	Pacing Your Lessons		
LESSONS AND OBJECTIVES	California Standards	40-50 Minute Periods	90-Minute Periods
Explore 11-1 **Graphing Calculator Lab: Investigating Inverse Variation** **11-1** **Inverse Variation** (pp. 577–582) • Graph inverse variations. • Solve problems involving inverse variation.	13.0	1	1
11-2 **Rational Expressions** (pp. 583–588) • Identify values excluded from the domain of a rational expression. • Simplify rational expressions. **Extend 11-2** **Graphing Calculator Lab: Rational Expressions**	10.0 11.0 12.0	1	0.5
11-3 **Multiply Rational Expressions** (pp. 590–594) • Multiply rational expressions. • Use dimensional analysis with multiplication.	10.0, 11.0 13.0, 25.2	1	0.5
11-4 **Dividing Rational Expressions** (pp. 595–599) • Divide rational expressions. • Use dimensional analysis with division.	10.0 11.0 13.0	1	0.5
11-5 **Dividing Polynomials** (pp. 601–606) • Divide a polynomial by a monomial. • Divide a polynomial by a binomial.	10.0 11.0	1	0.5
11-6 **Rational Expressions with Like Denominators** (pp. 608–613) • Add rational expressions with like denominators. • Subtract rational expressions with like denominators.	10.0, 11.0 13.0, 25.2	1	0.5
11-7 **Rational Expressions with Unlike Denominators** (pp. 614–619) • Add rational expressions with unlike denominators. • Subtract rational expressions with unlike denominators.	10.0, 11.0 13.0, 24.3, 25.1	1	0.5
11-8 **Mixed Expressions and Complex Fractions** (pp. 620–625) • Simplify mixed expressions. • Simplify complex fractions.	12.0 13.0	1	0.5
11-9 **Rational Equations and Functions** (pp. 626–632) • Solve rational equations. • Eliminate extraneous solutions.	12.0, 13.0 15.0, 24.3, 25.1	1	0.5
REVIEW		1	0.5
ASSESSMENT		1	0.5*
TOTAL		11	6

*The complete **Assessment Planner** for Chapter 11 is provided on p. 567*

* *Begin Chapter 12 in the second half of the period.*

Professional Development

California Standards Vertical Alignment

Before Chapter 11

Related Topics from Grade 7

- Solve multi-step problems involving rate, average speed, distance, and time ← Standard 7AF4.2
- Differentiate between rational and irrational numbers Standard 7NS1.4
- Multiply, divide, and simplify rational numbers by using exponent rules ← Standard 7NS2.3
- Multiply and divide monomials Standard 7AF2.2
- Add and subtract fractions by using factoring to find the common denominators ← Standard 7NS2.2
- Solve two-step linear equations and inequalities in one variable ← Standard 7AF4.1

Chapter 11

Related Topics from Algebra I

- Solve multi-step problems with polynomials
  ← Standard 1A10.0
- Simplify fractions with polynomials in the numerator and denominator ← Standard 1A12.0
- Solve both computationally and conceptually challenging problems by using operations with rational expressions
  ← Standard 1A13.0

See individual lessons for the specific Standards covered.

After Chapter 11

Preparation for Algebra II

- Simplify complicated rational expressions
  ← Standard 2A7.0
- Adept at operations on polynomials ← Standard 2A3.0
- Determine the truth of a specific algebraic statement involving rational, radical and logarithmic expressions
  ← Standard 2A15.0

Back-Mapping

California Algebra 1 was conceived and developed with the final result in mind, student success in Algebra I and beyond. The authors, using the California Mathematics Standards as their guide, developed this brand-new series by "back-mapping" from the desired result of student success in Algebra I and beyond. McGraw-Hill's *California Geometry, California Algebra 2,* and *California Algebra Readiness* were developed utilizing the same philosophy.

What the Research Says...

Collis (1976) describes the use of the reciprocal strategy as involving a relatively complex system. Students often mistakenly apply the simpler inverse strategy when the reciprocal strategy is essential.

- Students frequently make the error of multiplying only one term in a rational equation by the LCD (the inverse strategy). They may need to be reminded that every term must be multiplied by the LCD in order to solve it.

[Source: Collis, K.F. (1976). "Mathematical Thinking in Children," in Ved P. Varma and Phillip Williams (Eds.) *Piaget, Psychology and Education*, Itasca, IL, F.E. Peacock, pp. 144-154.]

Mc Graw Hill Professional Development

Targeted professional development has been articulated throughout the *California Mathematics: Concepts, Skills, and Problem Solving* series. The **McGraw-Hill Professional Development Video Library** provides short videos that support the ← Key Standards. For more information, visit ca.algebra1.com.

| Model Lessons | Instructional Strategies |

CHAPTER 11

Technology Solutions

Teacher Resources

TeacherWorks™ All-in-One Planner and Resource Center

All of the print materials from the Classroom Resource Masters are available on your TeacherWorks™ CD-ROM.

BL = Below Grade Level   **OL** = On Grade Level   **AL** = Above Grade Level   **ELL** = English Language Learner

Chapter Resource Masters					11-1	11-2	11-3	11-4	11-5	11-6	11-7	11-8	11-9
BL	OL		ELL	Lesson Reading Guide	5	12	19	26	34	41	48	55	62
BL	OL		ELL	Study Guide and Intervention*	6	13	20	27	35	42	49	56	63
BL	OL			Skills Practice*	8	15	22	29	37	44	51	58	65
	OL	AL		Practice*	9	16	23	30	38	45	52	59	66
	OL	AL		Word Problem Practice*	10	17	24	31	39	46	53	60	67
	OL	AL		Enrichment	11	18	25	32	40	47	54	61	68
	OL	AL		Calculator and Spreadsheet Activities					33				69
	OL	AL		Chapter Assessments*	71–92								
BL	OL	AL		5-Minute Check Transparencies	✓	✓	✓	✓	✓	✓	✓	✓	✓
BL	OL			Teaching Algebra with Manipulatives					✓				✓

Also available in Spanish.

AssignmentWorks

Differentiated Assignments, Answers, and Solutions

- Print a customized assignment worksheet using the Student Edition exercises along with an answer key or worked-out solutions.
- Use default lesson assignments as outlined in the Differentiated Homework Options in the Teacher Wraparound Edition.
- Includes modified questions from the Student Edition.

Interactive Classroom

This CD-ROM is a customizable Microsoft® PowerPoint® presentation that includes:

- In-Class Examples
- Your Turn Exercises*
- 5-Minute Check Transparencies*
- Links to Online Study Tools
- Concepts in Motion

compatible with response pad technology

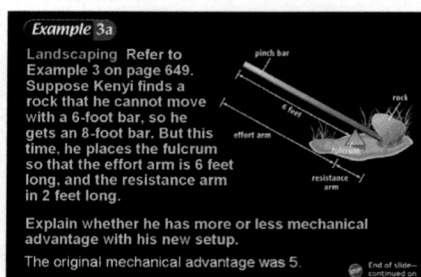

ExamView®Assessment Suite

 lets you

- Create, edit, and customize tests and worksheets using QuickTest Wizard
- Create multiple versions of tests and modify them for a desired level of difficulty
- Translate from English to Spanish and vice versa
- Build tests aligned with your state standards
- Track students' progress using the Teacher Management System

Student Resources

StudentWorks™ Plus

Textbook, Audio, Workbooks, and more

This CD-ROM is a valuable resource for students to access content online and use online resources to continue learning Chapter 11 concepts. Includes:

- Complete Student Editions in both English and Spanish
- English audio integrated throughout the text
- Links to Concepts in Motion, Personal Tutor, and other online resources
- Access to all student worksheets
- Daily Assignments and Grade Log

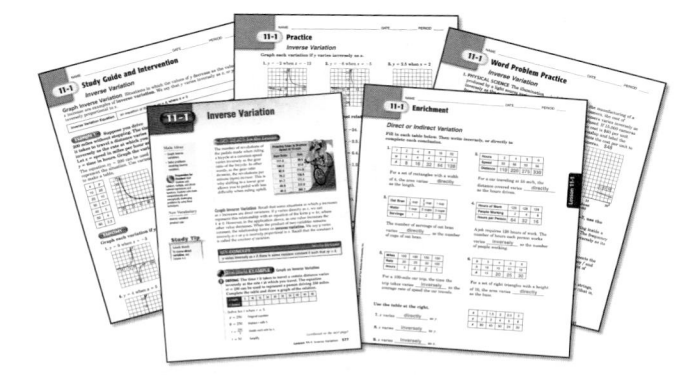

Super DVD

The Super DVD contains two Glencoe multimedia products.

MindJogger Plus An alternative review of concepts in which students work as teams in a game show format to gain points for correct answers.

What's Math Got to Do With It? Real Life Math Videos Engaging video that shows students how math is used in everyday situations

Internet Resources

Math Online **ca.algebra1.com**

TEACHER	PARENT	STUDENT	
			Online Study Tools
	•	•	Online Student Edition
•	•	•	Multilingual Glossary
			Lesson Resources
	•	•	BrainPOP®
•	•	•	Concepts in Motion
•	•	•	Extra Examples
	•	•	Other Calculator Keystrokes
•			Problem of the Week Cards
	•	•	Real-World Careers
	•	•	Self-Check Quizzes
			Chapter Resources
	•	•	Chapter Readiness
	•	•	Chapter Test
	•	•	Standardized Test Practice
	•	•	Vocabulary Review/Chapter Review Activities
			Unit Resources
•		•	Cross-Curricular Internet Project
			Other Resources
•			Dinah Zike's Foldables™
	•	•	Hotmath Homework Help
•			Key Concepts
•	•	•	Meet the Authors
	•	•	Personal Tutor
•			Project CRISS℠
	•	•	Scavenger Hunts and Answer Sheets
•			Vocabulary PuzzleMakers

Focus on Mathematical Content

Big Idea for Chapter 11:
Rational Expressions and Equations

Basic arithmetic operations are extended to rational expressions. The idea of excluded values of a rational expression carries over into the graphing of a rational function.

Why It's Important

For This Chapter
The lessons in this chapter use algebraic skills to simplify rational expressions and solve equations in problem situations.
- What is the difference between direct and inverse variation? (Lesson 11-1)
- When might a rational expression have excluded values? (Lesson 11-2)
- Once you have multiplied rational expressions, how do you simplify the product? (Lesson 11-3)
- How is dividing rational expressions connected to multiplying rational expressions? (Lessons 11-4 and 11-5)
- How is dividing polynomials similar to the long division process used in arithmetic? (Lesson 11-5)
- How is adding and subtracting rational expressions with like denominators similar to adding and subtracting rational numbers? (Lesson 11-6)
- How can you find the least common denominator of two rational expressions? (Lesson 11-7)
- How do you simplify an algebraic complex fraction? (Lesson 11-8)
- When can you use cross products to solve rational equations? (Lesson 11-9)

After This Chapter
In Chapter 12, the concept of simplifying rational expressions/ equations is applied to finding permutations and combinations.

In Algebra II and beyond, simplifying rational expressions and understanding excluded values can help you graph rational functions.

11-1 Inverse Variation

Situations in which y increases as x increases are known as direct variations (Lesson 4-2). Situations where y decreases as x increases, or vice versa, are known as inverse variations. Inverse variations can be represented by equations of the form $xy = k$, where $k \neq 0$. If you solve for k and make a table of values for x and y, you can draw a graph of the relation.

The *product rule* of inverse variations states that if (x_1, y_1) and (x_2, y_2) are solutions of an inverse variation, then $x_1y_1 = x_2y_2$ because both x_1y_1 and x_2y_2 equal k. The equation $x_1y_1 = x_2y_2$ can be used to solve for missing values of x and y.

11-2 Rational Expressions

Algebraic fractions that have polynomials for numerators and denominators are called rational expressions. All properties that apply to rational numbers also apply to rational expressions, including the fact that the denominator cannot equal zero. You must be sure to identify values for variables in the denominator that may produce a value of zero in the denominator, as these values must be excluded from the domain of the expression. To determine these excluded values, apply the Zero Product Property (Lesson 1-4) to the factors of the denominator.

The numerator and denominator of a simplified rational expression will have no common factors other than 1.

- To simplify rational expressions in which both the numerator and denominator are monomials, divide each by the GCF.

- To simplify rational expressions in which both the numerator and denominator are polynomials, first factor each polynomial and then divide each by the common factors.

11-3 Multiplying Rational Expressions

The process of multiplying rational expressions is similar to that of multiplying rational numbers. Simply multiply the numerators, then multiply the denominators. If the rational expressions can be factored, do so before multiplying. If there are common factors, simplify, then multiply.

When you multiply fractions or rational expressions that involve units of measure, you can divide by the common units in the same way that you divide by common variables. This process allows you to convert between units of measure. It is a process known as *dimensional analysis* (Lesson 2-8).

Dividing Rational Expressions

To divide rational expressions, multiply by the reciprocal of the divisor, just as you would do when dividing rational numbers. If the rational expressions can be factored, do so before multiplying. If there are common factors, simplify, then multiply. Follow the rules for multiplying rational expressions (Lesson 11-3).

When you divide fractions or rational expressions that involve units of measure, you can use *dimensional analysis* (Lesson 2-8).

 Dividing Polynomials

To divide a polynomial by a monomial, simply divide each term of the polynomial by the monomial.

To divide a polynomial by a binomial, first try to factor the polynomial to see if there is perhaps a common binomial factor. If factoring is not possible, use a division process similar to the one used for dividing whole numbers. If the polynomial has a missing term for a particular power, write the term as the power with a coefficient of 0 to hold its place. Then divide.

Using $(a^3 - 4a) \div (a - 2)$ as an example,

$$\frac{a^3 - 4a}{a - 2} = \frac{a(\cancel{a - 2})(a + 2)}{\cancel{a - 2}} = a^2 + 2a \text{ or}$$

$$a - 2 \overline{\smash{\big)}\ a^3 + 0a^2 - 4a} \quad \uparrow^{a^2 + 2a}$$
$$(-)\ \frac{a^3 - 2a^2}{2a^2 - 4a}$$
$$(-)\frac{2a^2 - 4a}{0}$$

 Rational Expressions with Like Denominators

When adding/subtracting rational expressions with like denominators, add/subtract the numerators and write the sum/difference over the common denominator. When subtracting rational expressions, be sure to subtract each term of the numerator, not just the first one. You can think of the subtraction in terms of adding the additive inverse of the expression. For example, subtracting $(x - 7)$ is the same as adding $-x + 7$.

If the denominators are polynomials, they must be exactly alike in all ways. Some denominators do not appear to be

alike, but can be manipulated so that they are. For example, when the denominators are additive inverses of each other, such as $x - 5$ and $5 - x$, you can rewrite $5 - x$ as $-(x - 5)$. Then rewrite one of the expressions so that each has the same denominator.

 Rational Expressions with Unlike Denominators

When adding/subtracting rational expressions with unlike denominators, a common denominator must first be found. Use the following steps to add/subtract rational expressions with unlike denominators.

Step 1 Identify the LCD by finding the prime factorization of the denominators. Use each factor the greatest number of times it appears in either of the factorizations.

Step 2 Rewrite each rational expression as an equivalent expression with the LCD as the denominator.

Step 3 Add/subtract.

Step 4 Simplify whenever possible.

 Mixed Expressions and Complex Fractions

A mixed number contains the sum of a whole number and a fraction. Similarly, a mixed expression contains the sum of a monomial and a rational expression. To simplify mixed expressions, change them into a single rational expression by rewriting the monomial as a rational expression with the same denominator as the given expression.

A complex fraction is a fraction with additional fractions in the numerator, denominator, or both. You can rewrite a complex fraction as a division sentence. Divide the numerator of the fraction by the denominator and then write the quotient as a simple fraction.

 Rational Equations and Functions

Rational equations are equations that contain rational expressions. If both sides of a rational equation are single fractions, cross products can be used to solve the equation. Or, you can multiply each side of the equation by the LCD of the fractions to eliminate the fractions, and then solve the resulting equation.

When solving a rational equation, more than one solution may result. Always check all solutions in the original equation to determine which actually work and which are *extraneous solutions*.

CHAPTER 11
Differentiated Instruction

Options for Chapter 11 Lessons

ELL = English Language Learner	**AL** = Above Grade Level	**SS** = Struggling Students	**SN** = Special Needs

Using Interpersonal Skills **AL**

Use with Lesson 11-2

Place students in pairs to work through Example 4 on p. 577. Have one student factor the numerator and the other student factor the denominator. Then, ask them to compare their factors to identify the GCF in order to simplify the expression.

Using Visual Learning **SS** **SN**

Use with Lesson 11-4

Have students write division problems involving rational expressions on note cards, pieces of scrap paper, or any other item that they can manipulate. Then have students physically "flip" the fractions to multiply by the reciprocal. The act of "flipping" the fractions will help cement the concept in students' minds.

Using Interpersonal Skills **ELL**

Use with Lesson 11-5

Ask students to write a journal entry about what they learned in this lesson. Tell them to include the aspects of the lesson that they liked, and that they did not like. They should also explain which concepts they feel like they mastered, and which ones they are still not comfortable with. Have students share their journal entries with you privately.

Noteables™ Interactive Study Notebook with Foldables™

Noteables™ Interactive Study Notebook with Foldables™ is a study organizer that provides helpful steps for students to follow to organize their notes for Chapter 11.

- Students use Noteables to record notes and to complete their Foldables as you present the material for each lesson.
- Noteables correspond to the Examples in the *Teacher Wraparound Edition* and *Interactive Classroom CD-ROM.*

Intervention

Quick Review Math Handbook*

is Glencoe's mathematical handbook for students and parents.

Hot Words includes a glossary of terms.

Hot Topics consists of two parts:

- explanations of key mathematical concepts
- exercises to check students' understanding.

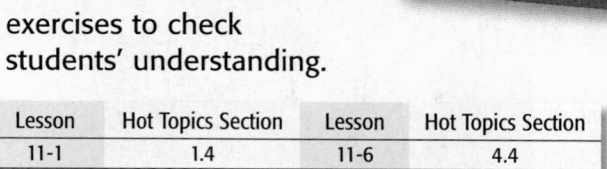

Lesson	Hot Topics Section	Lesson	Hot Topics Section
11-1	1.4	11-6	4.4
11-2	8.2	11-8	6.4

*Also available in Spanish

Teacher To Teacher

Diane Stilwell
South M.S.,
Morgantown, WV

USE WITH LESSON 11-3

❝ I remind my students that only common factors, not common terms, can be cancelled when simplifying rational expressions. I use Exercise 36 to determine whether my students understand the difference between the factors and the terms of a polynomial. ❞

Reading and Writing in Mathematics

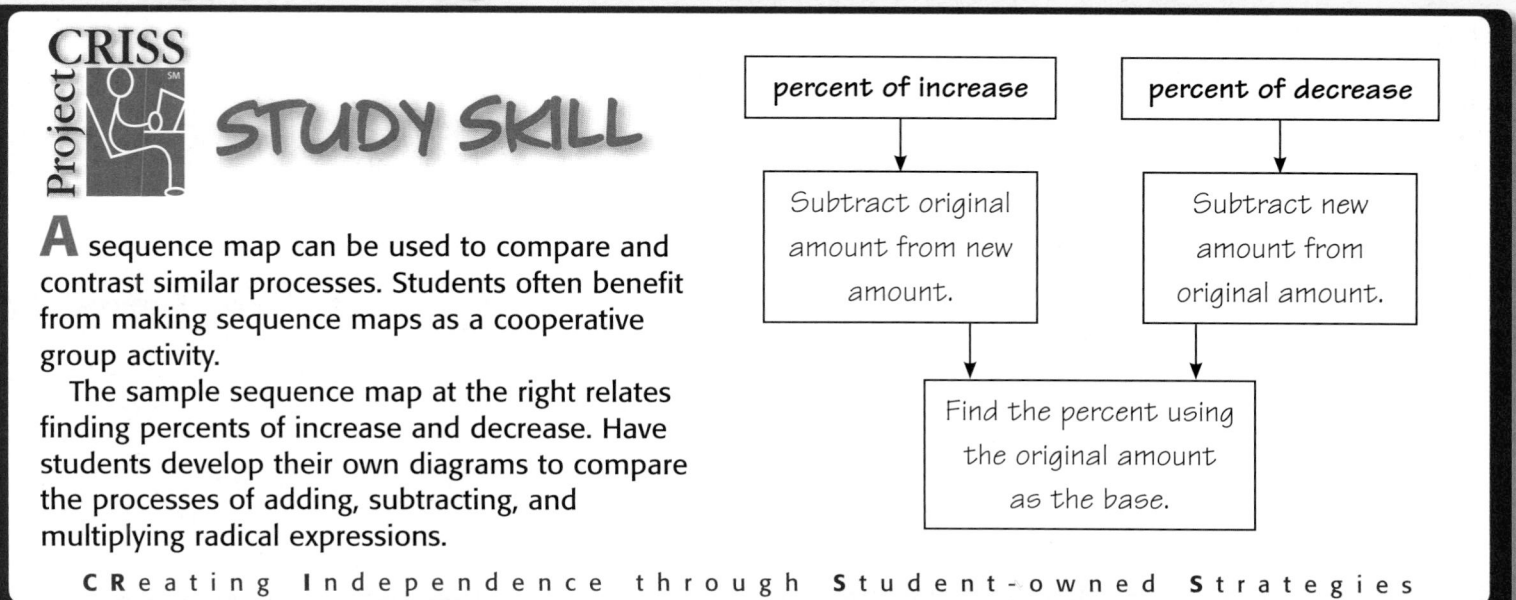

Project CRISS℠

STUDY SKILL

A sequence map can be used to compare and contrast similar processes. Students often benefit from making sequence maps as a cooperative group activity.

The sample sequence map at the right relates finding percents of increase and decrease. Have students develop their own diagrams to compare the processes of adding, subtracting, and multiplying radical expressions.

percent of increase → Subtract original amount from new amount. →

percent of decrease → Subtract new amount from original amount. →

Find the percent using the original amount as the base.

CReating **I**ndependence **t**hrough **S**tudent-owned **S**trategies

FOLDABLES Study Organizer

Dinah Zike's Foldables™

Focus Students write notes about rational expressions and equations for each lesson in this chapter.

Teach Have students make and label their Foldables as illustrated.

Ask students to write explanations for the operations with rational expressions or for solving rational equations. Encourage students to present the information in such a way that someone who did not understand rational expressions and equations would understand them after reading what was written.

When to Use It Students should use the appropriate tab for their explanations, notes, and examples as they cover each lesson in this chapter.

A version of a completed Foldable is shown on p. 625.

Differentiated Instruction

[CRM] **Student-Built Glossary, pp. 1–2**

Students should complete the chart by providing a definition and an example of each term as they progress through Chapter 11. This study tool can also be used to review for the chapter test.

Additional Answers
(Get Ready for Chapter 11)

12. $3c^2d(1 - 2d)$

13. $3m(2n + 5)$

14. $(x + 3)(x + 8)$

15. $(x - 5)(x + 9)$

16. $(2x + 7)(x - 3)$

17. $3(x - 3)(x - 1)$

CHAPTER 11 Rational Expressions and Equations

 **BIG Ideas**

- **Standard 12.0** Students simplify fractions with polynomials in the numerator and denominator by factoring both and reducing them to the lowest terms. (Key)

- **Standard 13.0** Students add, subtract, multiply, and divide rational expressions and functions. Students solve both computationally and conceptually challenging problems by using these techniques. (Key)

Key Vocabulary
extraneous solutions (p. 629)
rational expression (p. 583)

🌐 Real-World Link
Marching Band The uniform manager for the Cal Band at University of California, Berkeley can use rational expressions to determine the number of uniforms that can be repaired in a certain time given the number of tailors available and the time needed to repair each uniform.

FOLDABLES Study Organizer

Rational Expressions and Equations Make this Foldable to help you organize information about rational expressions and equations. Begin with a sheet of $8\frac{1}{2}$" by 11" paper.

1 **Fold** in half lengthwise.

2 **Fold** the top to the bottom.

 **3** **Open.** Cut along the second fold to make two tabs.

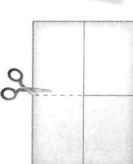

4 **Label** each tab as shown.

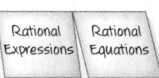

Rational Expressions | Rational Equations

574 **Chapter 11** Rational Expressions and Equations

Materials Needed for Chapter 11

- syringe, gas pressure sensor, data collection device (Explore 11-1)
- graphing calculator (Explore 11-1, Lessons 11-2, 11-5)
- grid paper (Lessons 11-1)
- paper clips (Lesson 11-1)
- drinking straws (Lesson 11-1)
- cardboard cutouts (Lesson 11-1)
- Internet (Lesson 11-3)
- algebra tiles (Lesson 11-5)
- product mat (Lesson 11-5)
- index cards (Lesson 11-5)

GET READY for Chapter 11

Diagnose Readiness You have two options for checking Prerequisite Skills.

Option 1

Take the Quick Check below. Refer to the Quick Review for help.

Option 2

Math Online Take the Online Readiness Quiz at **ca.algebra1.com**.

QUICK Check

(Used in Lesson 11-1)
Solve each proportion. (Lesson 2-6)

1. $\frac{y}{9} = -\frac{7}{16}$ $-\frac{63}{16}$

2. $\frac{4}{x} = \frac{2}{10}$ 20

3. $\frac{3}{15} = \frac{1}{n}$ 5

4. $\frac{x}{8} = \frac{0.21}{2}$ 0.84

5. $\frac{1.1}{0.6} = \frac{8.47}{n}$ 4.62

6. $\frac{9}{8} = \frac{y}{6}$ 6.75

7. $\frac{2.7}{3.6} = \frac{8.1}{a}$ 10.8

8. $\frac{0.19}{2} = \frac{x}{24}$ 2.28

(Used in Lesson 11-2)
Find the greatest common factor for each pair of monomials. (Lesson 8-1)

9. 30, 42 6

10. $60r^2, 45r^3$ $15r^2$

11. **GAMES** There are 64 girls and 80 boys who attend an after-school program. For a game, the boys are going to split into groups and the girls are going to split into groups. The number of people in each group has to be the same. How large can the groups be? 16

(Used in Lessons 11-3 through 11-8)
Factor each polynomial. (Lessons 8-1 through 8-4)

12. $3c^2d - 6c^2d^2$

13. $6mn + 15m$

14. $x^2 + 11x + 24$

15. $x^2 + 4x - 45$

16. $2x^2 + x - 21$

17. $3x^2 - 12x + 9$

12–17. See margin.

18. **AREA** The area of a rectangle can be represented by the expression $x^2 + 7x + 12$. What expressions represent the sides of the rectangle? $(x + 3), (x + 4)$

QUICK Review

EXAMPLE 1

Solve the proportion $\frac{4}{z} = \frac{13}{5}$.

$\frac{4}{z} = \frac{13}{5}$ Original equation

$4 \cdot 5 = 13 \cdot z$ Cross multiply.

$20 = 13z$ Simplify.

$\frac{20}{13} = \frac{13z}{13}$ Divide each side by 13.

$\frac{20}{13} = z$ Simplify.

EXAMPLE 2

Find the greatest common factor of 12 and 18.

3, 2, 2   Factors of 12
3, 3, 2   Factors of 18

$3 \cdot 2$ The product of the common factors

The greatest common factor of 12 and 18 is 6.

EXAMPLE 3

Factor $12x^2y^3 - 3xy$.

3, 2, 2, x, x, y, y, y   Factors of $12x^2y^3$
$-1, 3, x, y$ Factors of $-3xy$

$3 \cdot x \cdot y$ The product of the common factors

Factor out the common factors from each term of the expression.

$3xy(4xy^2) - 3xy(1)$ Rewrite the terms using the GCF.

$= 3xy(4xy^2 - 1)$ Distributive Property

Diagnostic Assessment

Exercises	California Standards	Intervention
1–8	5.0, 15.0	SE Review Lesson 2-6, pp. 105–110
9–10	6NS2.4	SE Review Lesson 8-1, pp. 420–424
11–18	11.0	SE Review Lesson 8-2 through 8-4, pp. 426–446

ASSESSMENT PLANNER

CHAPTER 11

✓ Formative Assessment

CRM Anticipation Guide, p. 3
Spotting Preconceived Ideas
Students complete this survey to determine prior knowledge about ideas from Chapter 11. Revisit this worksheet after completing the chapter. Also see p. 628.

TWE Lesson Activities

- Ticket Out the Door, p. 613
- Crystal Ball, pp. 587, 594
- Name the Math, pp. 582, 606, 625, 632
- Yesterday's News, pp. 599, 619

Chapter Checkpoints

SE Mid-Chapter Quiz, p. 607

SE Study Guide and Review, pp. 633–636

SE California Standards Practice, pp. 638–639

CRM Quizzes, pp. 73 and 74

CRM Standardized Test Practice, pp. 90–92

Math Online **algebra1.com**

- Self-Check Quizzes
- Practice Test
- Standardized Test Practice

✓ Summative Assessment

SE Chapter Practice Test, p. 637

CRM Mid-Chapter Test, p. 75

CRM Vocabulary Test, p. 76

CRM Extended-Response Test, p. 89

CRM Leveled Chapter Tests, pp. 77–88

💿 ExamView® Assessment Suite

KEY

CRM *Chapter 11 Resource Masters*

SE Student Edition

TWE Teacher Wraparound Edition

💿 CD-ROM

1 Focus

Objective Collect data to investigate the relationship between volume and pressure.

Materials for Each Group
• syringe
• gas pressure sensor
• data collection device
• graphing calculator

Teaching Tip Before performing the experiment, ask students to think about what they expect to happen. As they push the syringe in, do they expect it to get harder or easier to push?

2 Teach

Working in Cooperative Groups
Put students in groups of 4 or 5, mixing abilities to complete the activity.
Ask:
• Does the volume of air in the syringe change as you press the plunger? Explain. Yes; the volume decreases.

• Does the air pressure in the syringe change as you press the plunger? Explain. Yes; the pressure increases.

• Does the volume of air in the syringe change as you pull the plunger? Explain. Yes; the volume increases.

• Does the air pressure in the syringe change as you pull the plunger? Explain. Yes; the pressure decreases.

Practice Have students complete Exercises 1–5.

3 Assess

Formative Assessment

Use Exercise 5 to assess whether students can determine if there is a relationship between the pressure and volume of gas.

Graphing Calculator Lab
Investigating Inverse Variation

You can use a data collection device to investigate the relationship between volume and pressure.

Preparation for Standard 13.0 Students add, subtract, multiply, and divide rational expressions and functions. Students solve both computationally and conceptually challenging problems by using these techniques.

▶ SET UP the Lab

• Connect a syringe to the gas pressure sensor. Then connect the data collection device to both the sensor and the calculator as shown.
• Start the data collection program and select the sensor.

⋯ ACTIVITY

Step 1 Open the valve between the atmosphere and the syringe. Set the inside ring of the syringe to 20 mL and close the valve. This ensures that the amount of air inside the syringe will be constant throughout the experiment.

Step 2 Press the plunger of the syringe down to the 5 mL mark. Wait for the pressure gauge to stop changing, then take the data reading. Enter 5 as the volume on the calculator. The pressure will be measured in atmospheres (atm).

Step 3 Repeat step 2, pressing the plunger down to 7.5 mL, 10.0 mL, 12.5 mL, 15.0 mL, 17.5 mL, and 20.0 mL. Record the volume as you take each data reading.

Step 4 After taking the last data reading, use STAT PLOT to create a line graph of the data.

ANALYZE THE RESULTS

1. No, the pressure increases as the volume decreases.

4. Sample answer: The products are close to constant.

1. Does the pressure vary directly as the volume? Explain.
2. As the volume changes from 10 to 20 mL, what happens to the pressure? **Sample answer: The pressure decreases by about half.**
3. Predict what the pressure of the gas in the syringe would be if the volume was increased to 40 mL. **Sample answer: 0.48**
4. Add a column to the data table to find the product of the volume and the pressure for each data reading. What pattern do you observe?
5. **MAKE A CONJECTURE** The relationship between the pressure and volume of a gas is called Boyle's Law. Write an equation relating the volume v in milliliters and pressure p in atmospheres in your experiment.
   Sample answer: $pv = 18$

576 Chapter 11 Rational Expressions and Equations

From Concrete to Abstract
Explain that Boyle's Law states that, at constant temperature, the volume of a given mass of gas is inversely proportional to the pressure upon the gas, or $V = k\frac{1}{P}$, where $V =$ volume, $p =$ pressure, and $k =$ a constant. Ask students to explain whether the results of the experiment follow the pattern of Boyle's Law.

Inverse Variation

Main Ideas

- Graph inverse variations.
- Solve problems involving inverse variation.

 Preparation for Standard 13.0 Students add, subtract, multiply, and divide rational expressions and functions. Students solve both computationally and conceptually challenging problems by using these techniques.

New Vocabulary

inverse variation
product rule

Study Tip

Look Back
To review **direct variation**, see Lesson 4-2.

GET READY for the Lesson

The number of revolutions of the pedals made when riding a bicycle at a constant speed varies inversely as the gear ratio of the bicycle. In other words, as the gear ratio *decreases*, the revolutions per minute (rpm) *increase*. This is why shifting to a lower gear allows you to pedal with less difficulty when riding uphill.

Pedaling Rates to Maintain Speed of 10 mph	
Gear Ratio	**Rate**
117.8	89.6
108.0	97.8
92.6	114.0
76.2	138.6
61.7	171.2
49.8	212.0
40.5	260.7

Graph Inverse Variation Recall that some situations in which y increases as x increases are *direct variations*. If y varies directly as x, we can represent this relationship with an equation of the form $y = kx$, where $k \neq 0$. However, in the application above, as one value increases the other value decreases. When the product of two variables remains constant, the relationship forms an **inverse variation**. We say y *varies inversely as x* or y *is inversely proportional to x*. Recall that the constant k is called the *constant of variation*.

KEY CONCEPT
Inverse Variation

y varies inversely as x if there is some nonzero constant k such that $xy = k$.

Real-World EXAMPLE — Graph an Inverse Variation

 DRIVING The time t it takes to travel a certain distance varies inversely as the rate r at which you travel. The equation $rt = 250$ can be used to represent a person driving 250 miles. Complete the table and draw a graph of the relation.

r (mph)	5	10	15	20	25	30	35	40	45	50
t (hours)										

Solve for t when $r = 5$.

$rt = 250$	Original equation
$5t = 250$	Replace r with 5.
$t = \dfrac{250}{5}$	Divide each side by 5.
$t = 50$	Simplify.

(continued on the next page)

  Standards Alignment

Before Lesson 11-1
Solve multi-step problems involving rate, average speed, distance, and time from Standard 7AF4.2

Lesson 11-1
Solve both computationally and conceptually challenging problems by using operations with rational expressions from Standard 1A13.0

After Lesson 11-1
Simplify complicated rational expressions from Standard 2A7.0

2 Teach

Scaffolding Questions
Have students read *Get Ready for the Lesson*.
Ask:
- Which gear ratio would you want to use for pedaling on a level surface? The 117.8 gear ratio requires the slowest pedaling rate, meaning you have to pedal less to maintain your speed.
- Which gear ratio would you want to use for pedaling up a steep hill? Explain. 40.5 ratio; this requires a much faster pedaling rate to maintain your speed.

(continued on the next page)

Lesson 11-1 Resources

Chapter 11 Resource Masters
Lesson Reading Guide, p. 5 **BL** **OL** **ELL**
Study Guide and Intervention, pp. 6–7 **BL** **OL** **ELL**
Skills Practice, p. 8 **BL** **OL**
Practice, p. 9 **OL** **AL**
Word Problem Practice, p. 10 **OL** **AL**
Enrichment, p. 11 **OL** **AL**

Transparencies
5-Minute Check Transparency 11-1
Additional Print Resources
Noteables™ Interactive Study Notebook with Foldables™

Technology
ca.algebra1.com
Interactive Classroom CD-ROM
AssignmentWorks CD-ROM
Graphing Calculator Easy Files

- What can you say about the product of each gear ratio and the pedaling rate required to maintain a speed of 10 miles per hour? The product of the gear ratio and the rate is about 10,600 for each gear ratio given in the chart.

Graph Inverse Variation

Example 1 shows how to complete a table of values and a graph for a real-world relation that varies inversely. **Example 2** shows how to graph an inverse variation in which there are negative values of x.

 Formative Assessment

Use the Check Your Progress exercises after each example to determine students' understanding of concepts.

ADDITIONAL EXAMPLES

1 **MANUFACTURING** The owner of Superfast Computer Company has calculated that the time t in hours that it takes to build a particular model of computer varies inversely with the number of people p working on the computer. The equation $pt = 12$ can be used to represent the people building a computer. Complete the table and draw a graph of the relation.

p	2	4	6	8	10	12
t	6	3	2	1.5	1.2	1

2 Graph an inverse variation in which y varies inversely as x, and $y = 1$ when $x = 4$.

Solve for t using the other values of r. Complete the table.

r (mph)	5	10	15	20	25	30	35	40	45	50
t (hours)	50	25	16.67	12.5	10	8.33	7.14	6.25	5.56	5

Next, graph the ordered pairs.

Because rate cannot be negative, it is only reasonable to use positive values for r.

The graph of an inverse variation is not a straight line like the graph of a direct variation. As the rate r increases, the time t that it takes to travel the same distance decreases.

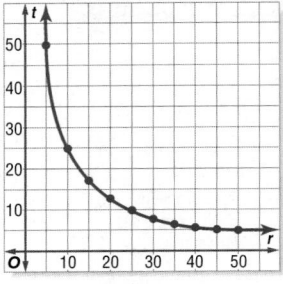

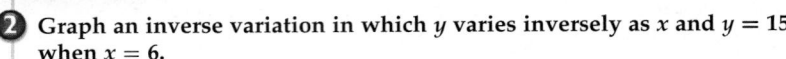 **Your Progress**

1. Graph $64 = xy$ using a table. **See margin.**

Graphs of inverse variations can also be drawn using negative values of x.

EXAMPLE Graph an Inverse Variation

2 Graph an inverse variation in which y varies inversely as x and $y = 15$ when $x = 6$.

Solve for k.

$xy = k$ Inverse variation equation

$(6)(15) = k$ $x = 6, y = 15$

$90 = k$ The constant of variation is 90.

Choose values for x and y with a product of 90.

x	−9	−6	−3	−45	0	2	3	6	9
y	−10	−15	−30	−2	undefined	45	30	15	10

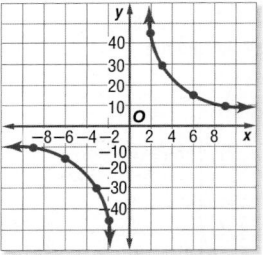

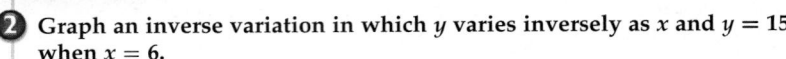 **Your Progress**

2. Graph an inverse variation equation in which y varies inversely as x when $y = 12$ and when $x = 4$. **See margin.**

Use Inverse Variation If (x_1, y_1) and (x_2, y_2) are solutions of an inverse variation, then $x_1 y_1 = k$ and $x_2 y_2 = k$.

$$x_1 y_1 = k \text{ and } x_2 y_2 = k$$

$$x_1 y_1 = x_2 y_2 \quad \text{Substitute } x_2 y_2 \text{ for } k.$$

Study Tip

Proportions
Notice that the proportion for inverse variations is different from the proportion for direct variation, $\frac{x_1}{x_2} = \frac{y_1}{y_2}$.

The equation $x_1 y_1 = x_2 y_2$ is called the **product rule** for inverse variations. You can use this equation to form a proportion.

$$x_1 y_1 = x_2 y_2 \quad \text{Product rule for inverse variations}$$

$$\frac{x_1 y_1}{x_2 y_1} = \frac{x_2 y_2}{x_2 y_1} \quad \text{Divide each side by } x_2 y_1.$$

$$\frac{x_1}{x_2} = \frac{y_2}{y_1} \quad \text{Simplify.}$$

578 **Chapter 11** Rational Expressions and Equations

Additional Answer

1.

x	1	2	4	8	16	32	64
y	64	32	16	8	4	2	1

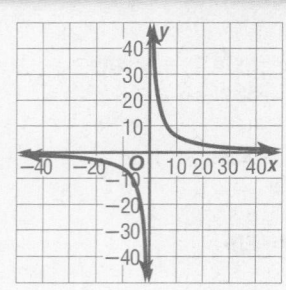

EXAMPLE Solve for *x* or *y*

3 If *y* varies inversely as *x* and *y* = 4 when *x* = 7, find *x* when *y* = 14.

Let $x_1 = 7$, $y_1 = 4$, and $y_2 = 14$. Solve for x_2.

Method 1 Use the product rule.

$$x_1y_1 = x_2y_2 \quad \text{Product rule for inverse variations}$$

$$7 \cdot 4 = x_2 \cdot 14 \quad x_1 = 7, y_1 = 4, \text{ and } y_2 = 14$$

$$\frac{28}{14} = x_2 \quad \text{Divide each side by 14.}$$

$$x_2 = 2 \quad \text{Simplify.}$$

Method 2 Use a proportion.

$$\frac{x_1}{x_2} = \frac{y_2}{y_1} \quad \text{Proportion for inverse variations}$$

$$\frac{7}{x_2} = \frac{14}{4} \quad x_1 = 7, y_1 = 4, \text{ and } y_2 = 14$$

$$28 = 14x_2 \quad \text{Cross multiply.}$$

$$x_2 = 2 \quad \text{Divide each side by 14.}$$

 CHECK Your Progress

3. If *y* varies inversely as *x* and *y* = 4 when *x* = −8, find *y* when *x* = −4.
y = 8

 Real-World EXAMPLE Use Inverse Variation

4 **PHYSICAL SCIENCE** When two people are balanced on a seesaw, their distances from the center of the seesaw are inversely proportional to their weights. If a 118-pound person sits 1.8 meters from the center of the seesaw, how far should a 125-pound person sit from the center to balance the seesaw?

Let $w_1 = 118$, $d_1 = 1.8$, and $w_2 = 125$. Solve for d_2.

$$w_1d_1 = w_2d_2 \quad \text{Product rule for inverse variations}$$

$$118 \cdot 1.8 = 125 \cdot d_2 \quad \text{Substitution}$$

$$\frac{212.4}{125} = d_2 \quad \text{Divide each side by 125.}$$

$$d_2 \approx 1.7 \quad \text{Simplify.}$$

To balance the seesaw, the second person should sit about 1.7 meters from the center.

 CHECK Your Progress

4. **EARTH SCIENCE** As the temperature increases, the level of water in a river decreases. When the temperature was 90° Fahrenheit, the water level was 11 feet. If the temperature was 110° Fahrenheit, what was the level of water in the river? **9 ft**

Online Personal Tutor at ca.algebra1.com

Lesson 11-1 Inverse Variation **579**

Study Tip

Levers
A lever is a bar with a pivot point called the *fulcrum*. For a lever to balance, the lesser weight must be positioned farther from the fulcrum.

Tips for New Teachers

Preventing Errors

Ask students why negative values are included for the inverse variation in Example 2 but not for Example 1. Negative rate and time values are not realistic in Example 1.

Additional Answer

2.

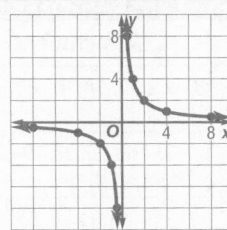

Use Inverse Variation

Example 3 shows how to use the product rule for inverse variations to find a value for *x* or *y*. **Example 4** shows how to use the product rule for inverse variations in a real-world situation.

 Focus on Mathematical Content

Inverse Variation When the product of two quantities remains constant, the quantities form an inverse variation. As one quantity increases, the other decreases. The nonzero product of the two quantities, *xy*, is called the constant of variation, *k*.

ADDITIONAL EXAMPLES

3 If *y* varies inversely as *x* and *y* = 5 when *x* = 12, find *x* when *y* = 15. **4**

4 **PHYSICAL SCIENCE** Suppose two people are sitting on a seesaw. How far should a 105-pound person sit from the center of the seesaw to balance a 63-pound person sitting 3.5 feet from the center? about 2.1 ft

Additional Examples are also in:

- Noteables™ Interactive Study Notebook with Foldables™
- Interactive Classroom PowerPoint® Presentations

 **Tips for New Teachers**

Preventing Errors

For Example 4, encourage students to estimate that a reasonable answer must be less than 1.8 meters since the 125-pound person must sit closer to the center of the seesaw in order to balance it.

Formative Assessment

Use Exercises 1–7 to check for understanding.

Use the chart at the bottom of this page to customize assignments for your students.

Odd/Even Assignments

Exercises 8-23 are structured so that students practice the same concepts whether they are assigned odd or even problems.

Real-World Connections

For Exercise 33, have students make their own simple mobiles using a drinking straw, paper clips, and cardboard cut-out objects.

Additional Answers

1.

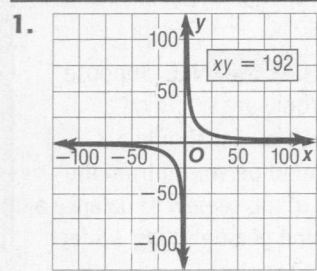

2.

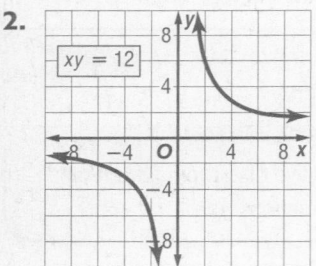

24. Yes; the family would save about 37 minutes if they were to travel at 65 miles an hour.

34. inverse variation $y = -\dfrac{18}{x}$

35. neither

36. inverse variation $y = \dfrac{21}{x}$

★ indicates multi-step problem

✓ CHECK Your Understanding

Examples 1, 2
(pp. 577–578)

Graph each variation if y varies inversely as x. 1–2. See margin.

1. $y = 24$ when $x = 8$
2. $y = -6$ when $x = -2$

Example 3
(p. 579)

Write an inverse variation equation that relates x and y. Assume that y varies inversely as x. Then solve.

3. If $y = 2.7$ when $x = 8.1$, find x when $y = 5.4$. **$xy = 21.87$; 4.05**
4. If $x = \frac{1}{2}$ when $y = 16$, find x when $y = 32$. **$xy = 8$; $\frac{1}{4}$**
5. If $y = 12$ when $x = 6$, find y when $x = 8$. **$xy = 72$; 9**
6. If $y = -8$ when $x = -3$, find y when $x = 6$. **$xy = 24$; 4**

Example 4
(p. 579)

7. **MUSIC** When under equal tension, the frequency of a vibrating string from a piano varies inversely with the string length. If a string that is 420 millimeters in length vibrates at a frequency of 523 cycles a second, at what frequency will a 707-millimeter string vibrate? **approximately 311 cycles per second**

Exercises

HOMEWORK HELP	
For Exercises	See Examples
8–13	1, 2
14, 15	4
16–23	3

Exercise Levels
A: 8–23
B: 24–36
C: 37–41

Graph each variation if y varies inversely as x. 8–13. See Ch. 11 Answer Appendix.

8. $y = 24$ when $x = -8$
9. $y = 3$ when $x = 4$
10. $y = 5$ when $x = 15$
11. $y = -4$ when $x = -12$
12. $y = 9$ when $x = 8$
13. $y = 2.4$ when $x = 8.1$

14. **MUSIC** The pitch of a musical note varies inversely as its wavelength. If the tone has a pitch of 440 vibrations per second and a wavelength of 2.4 feet, find the pitch of a tone that has a wavelength of 1.6 feet.
660 vibrations per second

15. **COMMUNITY SERVICE** Students at Roosevelt High School are collecting canned goods for a local food pantry. They plan to distribute flyers to homes in the community asking for donations. Last year, 12 students were able to distribute 1000 flyers in nine hours. How long would it take if 15 students hand out 1000 flyers this year? **7.2 h**

Write an inverse variation equation that relates x and y. Assume that y varies inversely as x. Then solve.

16. If $y = 8.5$ when $x = -1$, find x when $y = -1$. **$xy = -8.5$; 8.5**
17. If $y = 8$ when $x = 1.55$, find x when $y = -0.62$. **$xy = 12.4$; -20**
18. If $y = 6.4$ when $x = 4.4$, find x when $y = 3.2$. **$xy = 28.16$; 8.8**
19. If $y = 1.6$ when $x = 0.5$, find x when $y = 3.2$. **$xy = 0.8$; 0.25**
20. If $y = 12$ when $x = 5$, find y when $x = 3$. **$xy = 60$; 20**
21. If $y = 7$ when $x = -2$, find y when $x = 7$. **$xy = -14$; -2**
22. If $y = 4$ when $x = 4$, find y when $x = 7$. **$xy = 16$; $\frac{16}{7}$**
23. If $y = -6$ when $x = -2$, find y when $x = 5$. **$xy = 12$; $\frac{12}{5}$**

★ 24. **TRAVEL** The Zalinski family can drive the 220 miles to their cabin in 4 hours at 55 miles per hour. Son Jeff claims that they could save half an hour if they drove 65 miles per hour, the speed limit. Is Jeff's claim true? Explain.
See margin.

580 Chapter 11 Rational Expressions and Equations

DIFFERENTIATED HOMEWORK OPTIONS

Level	Assignment	Two-Day Option	
BL Basic	8–23, 37, 38, 41–60	9–23 odd, 42, 43	8–22 even, 37, 38, 41, 44–60
OL Core	9–23 odd, 25, 27, 29–33, 35, 37, 38, 41–60	8–23, 42, 43	24–38, 41, 44–60
AL Advanced /Pre-AP	24–54 (optional: 55–60)		

Write an inverse variation equation that relates x and y. Assume that y varies inversely as x. Then solve.

25. Find the value of y when $x = 7$ if $y = -7$ when $x = \frac{2}{3}$. $xy = -\frac{14}{3}; -\frac{2}{3}$

26. Find the value of y when $x = 32$ if $y = -16$ when $x = \frac{1}{2}$. $xy = -8; -\frac{1}{4}$

27. If $x = 6.1$ when $y = 4.4$, find x when $y = 3.2$. $xy = 26.84; 8.3875$

28. If $x = 0.5$ when $y = 2.5$, find x when $y = 20$. $xy = 1.25; 0.0625$

CHEMISTRY For Exercises 29–31, use the following information.
Boyle's Law states that the volume of a gas V varies inversely with applied pressure P.

29. Write an equation to show this relationship. $PV = k$ or $P_1V_1 = P_2V_2$

30. Pressure on 60 cubic meters of a gas is raised from 1 atmosphere to 3 atmospheres. What new volume does the gas occupy? 20 m^3

31. A helium-filled balloon has a volume of 22 cubic meters at sea level where the air pressure is 1 atmosphere. The balloon is released and rises to a point where the air pressure is 0.8 atmosphere. What is the volume of the balloon at this height? 27.5 m^3

Real-World Link
American sculptor Alexander Calder was the first artist to use mobiles as an art form.
Source: infoplease.com

★**32. GEOMETRY** A rectangle is 36 inches wide and 20 inches long. How wide is a rectangle of equal area if its length is 90 inches? 8 in.

33. ART Anna is designing a mobile to suspend from a gallery ceiling. A chain is attached eight inches from the end of a bar that is 20 inches long. On the shorter end of the bar is a sculpture weighing 36 kilograms. She plans to place another piece of artwork on the other end of the bar. How much should the second piece of art weigh if she wants the bar to be balanced? 24 kg

Determine whether the data in each table represent an inverse variation or a direct variation. Explain. 34–36. See margin.

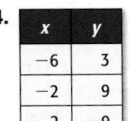
EXTRA PRACTICE
See pages 739, 754.
Math Online
Self-Check Quiz at
ca.algebra1.com

34.

x	y
-6	3
-2	9
2	-9

35.

x	y
5	2.5
8	6
11	11.5

36.

x	y
-3	-7
-2	-10.5
4	5.25

H.O.T. Problems

37. OPEN ENDED Give a real-world situation or phenomena that can be modeled by an indirect variation equation. Use the correct terminology to describe your example and explain why this situation is an indirect variation.
See Ch. 11 Answer Appendix.

38. REASONING Determine which situation is an example of inverse variation. Justify your answer.
a. Emily spends $2 each day for snacks on her way home from school. The total amount she spends each week depends on the number of days school was in session.
b. A business donates $200 to buy prizes for a school event. The number of prizes that can be purchased depends upon the price of each prize.
b; As the price increases, the number purchased decreases.

CHALLENGE For Exercises 39 and 40, assume that y varies inversely as x.

39. If the value of x is doubled, what happens to the value of y? It is half.

40. If the value of y is tripled, what happens to the value of x? It is one third.

BL = Below Grade Level
OL = On Grade Level
AL = Above Grade Level
ELL = English Language Learner

Additional pages not shown:
CRM **Lesson Reading Guide**, p. 5 **BL OL ELL**
CRM **Skills Practice**, p. 8 **BL OL**

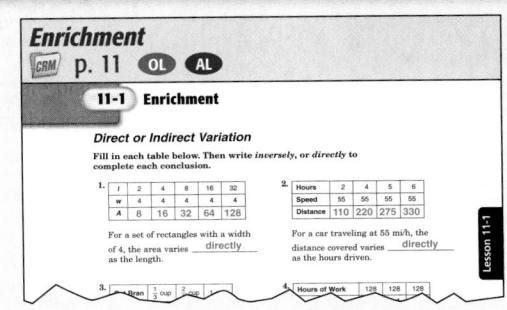
Enrichment
CRM p. 11 **OL AL**

11-1 Enrichment

Direct or Indirect Variation
Fill in each table below. Then write *inversely*, or *directly* to complete each conclusion.

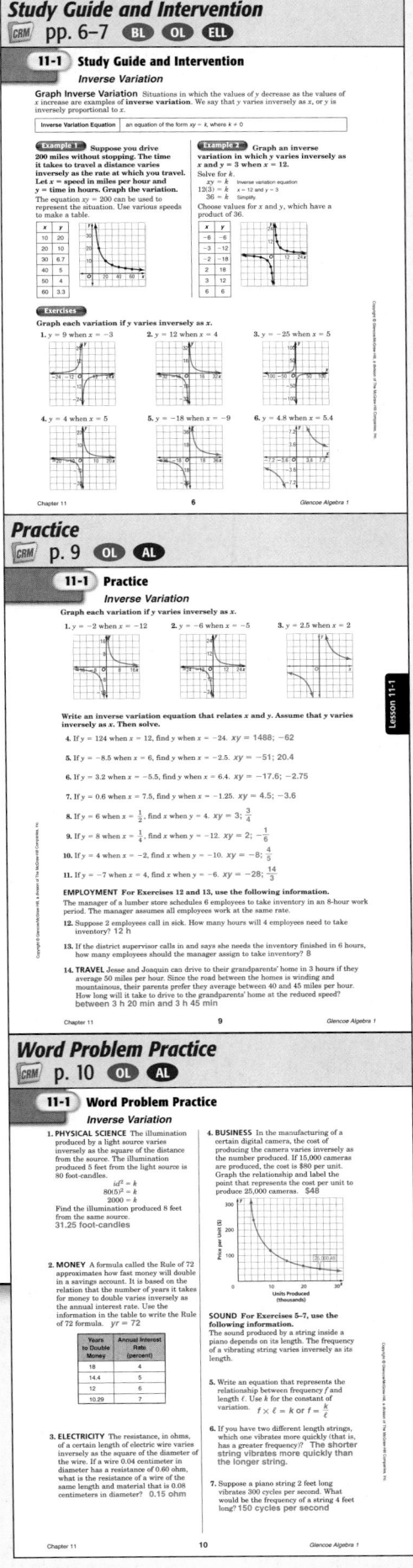

Study Guide and Intervention
CRM pp. 6–7 **BL OL ELL**

11-1 Study Guide and Intervention
Inverse Variation

Practice
CRM p. 9 **OL AL**

11-1 Practice
Inverse Variation

Word Problem Practice
CRM p. 10 **OL AL**

11-1 Word Problem Practice
Inverse Variation

Name the Math Prepare two paper bags containing slips of paper: one containing a value for x on each slip, the other a value for y on each slip. Have each student select both an x-value and a y-value and graph an inverse variation in which y varies inversely as x.

FOLDABLES **Foldables™**
Study Organizer **Follow-Up**
Remind students to use their Foldables to record notes on what they have learned about inverse variation. Have them write their notes under the tab labeled *Rational Equations*.

Additional Answers

41. When the gear ratio is lower, the pedaling revolutions increase to keep a constant speed. Lower gears at a constant rate will cause a decrease in speed, while higher gears at a constant rate will cause an increase in speed.

50.
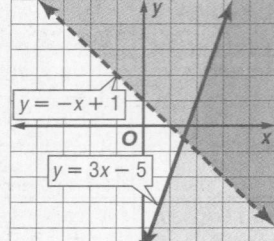

51.
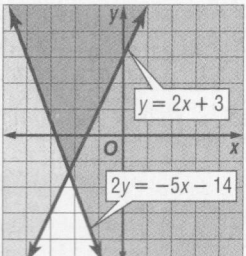

52.
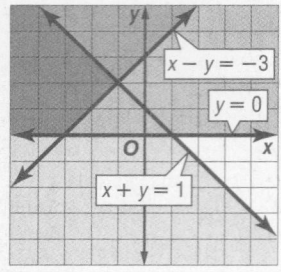

41. *Writing in Math* Use the data provided on page 577 to explain how the gears on a bicycle are related to inverse variation. Include an explanation of why the gear ratio affects the pedaling speed of the rider. **See margin.**

STANDARDS PRACTICE 7AF1.1

42. Which function *best* describes the graph? **A**

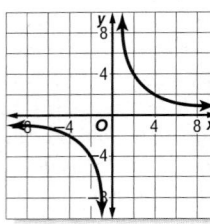

A $xy = 8$ C $x + y = 8$
B $xy = -8$ D $y = x + 8$

43. REVIEW A submarine is currently 200 feet below sea level. If the submarine begins to descend at a rate of 35 feet per minute, which equation could be used to determine t the time in minutes it will take the submarine to reach a depth of 2750 feet below sea level? **J**

F $2750 = 200 + (-35)t$
G $-2750 = (-200 + 35)t$
H $2750 = (200 + 35)t$
J $-2750 = -200 + (-35)t$

Spiral Review

For each set of measures given, find the measures of the missing sides if $\triangle ABC \sim \triangle DEF$. (Lesson 10-6)

44. $a = 3, b = 10, c = 9, d = 12$
$e = 40, f = 36$

45. $b = 8, c = 4, d = 21, e = 28$
$a = 6, f = 14$

Find the possible values of a if the points with the given coordinates are the indicated distance apart. (Lesson 10-5)

46. $(3, 2), (a, 9); d = \sqrt{113}$
$a = -5$ or 11

47. $(a, 6), (13, -6); d = 13$
$a = 8$ or 18

48. $(-7, 1), (2, a); d = \sqrt{82}$
$a = 2$ or 0

★**49. MUSIC** Two musical notes played at the same time produce harmony. The closest harmony is produced by frequencies with the greatest GCF. A, C, and C sharp have frequencies of 220, 264, and 275, respectively. Which pair of these notes produce the closest harmony? (Lesson 8-1) **A and C sharp**

Solve each system of inequalities by graphing. (Lesson 6-8) **50–52. See margin.**

50. $y \leq 3x - 5$
$y > -x + 1$

51. $y \geq 2x + 3$
$2y \geq -5x - 14$

52. $x + y \leq 1$
$x - y \leq -3$
$y \geq 0$

Solve each equation. (Lesson 2-5)

53. $7(2y - 7) = 5(4y + 1)$ **−9**

54. $w(w + 2) = 2w(w - 3) + 16$ **4**

GET READY for the Next Lesson

PREREQUISITE SKILL Find the greatest common factor for each set of monomials. (Lesson 8-1)

55. 36, 15, 45 **3**

56. 48, 60, 84 **12**

57. 210, 330, 150 **30**

58. $17a, 34a^2$ **17a**

59. $12xy^2, 18x^2y^3$ **6xy²**

60. $12pr^2, 40p^4$ **4p**

582 **Chapter 11** Rational Expressions and Equations

Pre-AP Activity **Use as an Extension.**

Write $k = 4$ on the board. Ask students to write and graph a direct variation equation and an inverse variation equation that uses 4 as the constant of variation. Sample answer: $y = 4x; xy = 4$

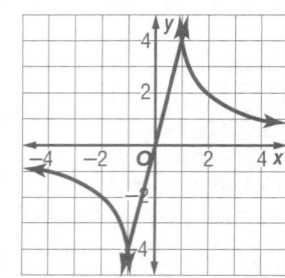

Rational Expressions

Main Ideas

- Identify values excluded from the domain of a rational expression.
- Simplify rational expressions.

 Standard 12.0 Students simplify fractions with polynomials in the numerator and denominator by factoring both and reducing them to the lowest terms. (Key)

New Vocabulary

rational expression
excluded values

GET READY for the Lesson

The intensity I of an image on a movie screen is inversely proportional to the square of the distance d between the projector and the screen. Recall from Lesson 11-1 that this can be represented by the equation $I = \dfrac{k}{d^2}$, where k is a constant.

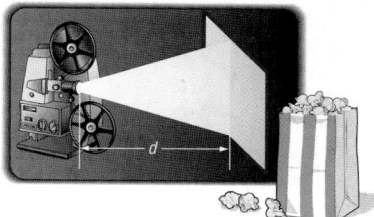

EXCLUDED VALUES OF RATIONAL EXPRESSIONS The expression $\dfrac{k}{d^2}$ is an example of a **rational expression**. A **rational expression** is an algebraic fraction whose numerator and denominator are polynomials.

Because a rational expression involves division, the denominator may not equal zero. Any values of a variable that result in a denominator of zero must be excluded from the domain of that variable. These are called **excluded values** of the rational expression.

EXAMPLE Excluded Values

1 State the excluded value for each rational expression.

a. $\dfrac{5m + 3}{m - 6}$

Exclude the values for which $m - 6 = 0$, because the denominator cannot equal 0.

$m - 6 = 0 \rightarrow m = 6$ Therefore, m cannot equal 6.

b. $\dfrac{x^2 - 5}{x^2 - 5x + 6}$

Exclude the values for which $x^2 - 5x + 6 = 0$.

$$x^2 - 5x + 6 = 0$$
$$(x - 2)(x - 3) = 0 \quad \text{Factor.}$$

$x - 2 = 0 \quad \text{or} \quad x - 3 = 0 \quad$ Zero Product Property
$x = 2 \qquad\qquad x = 3 \qquad$ Therefore, x cannot equal 2 or 3.

Study Tip

Look Back
You can review the Zero Product Property in Lesson 8-2.

CHECK Your Progress State the excluded values.

1A. $\dfrac{16x + 5}{3x}$ 0

1B. $\dfrac{2x + 1}{3x^2 + 14x - 5}$ $\dfrac{1}{3}, -5$

1 Focus

Standards Alignment

Before Lesson 11-2
Differentiate between rational and irrational numbers from Standard 7NS1.4

Lesson 11-2
Simplify fractions with polynomials in the numerator and denominator from Standard 1A12.0

After Lesson 11-2
Adept at operations on polynomials from Standard 2A3.0

2 Teach

Scaffolding Questions
Have students read *Get Ready for the Lesson.*
Ask:
- How does the equation in this example differ from the inverse variations studied in Lesson 11-1? There is a squared term, and the variables are on different sides of the equation.
- As the projector is moved away from the screen, what happens to the image? The image will become larger but also dimmer.

(continued on the next page)

Lesson 11-2 Resources

Chapter 11 Resource Masters
Lesson Reading Guide, p. 12 **BL** **OL** **ELL**
Study Guide and Intervention, pp. 13, 14 **BL** **OL** **ELL**
Skills Practice, p. 15 **BL** **OL**
Practice, p. 16 **OL** **AL**
Word Problem Practice, p. 17 **OL** **AL**
Enrichment, p. 18 **OL** **AL**

Transparencies
5-Minute Check Transparency 11-2
Additional Print Resources
Noteables™ Interactive Study Notebook with Foldables™

Technology
ca.algebra1.com
Interactive Classroom CD-ROM
AssignmentWorks CD-ROM
Graphing Calculator Easy Files

- What values of d for the given equation should be excluded for the example given? $d \neq 0$, and d cannot be a negative number.

Excluded Values of Rational Expressions

Example 1 shows how to determine the excluded values for rational expressions. **Example 2** shows how to use rational expressions to solve real-world problems.

 Formative Assessment

Use the Check Your Progress exercises after each example to determine students' understanding of concepts.

Cross-Curricular Project

 Math Online You can use a rational expression to determine how an amusement park can finance a new roller coaster. Visit ca.algebra1.com.

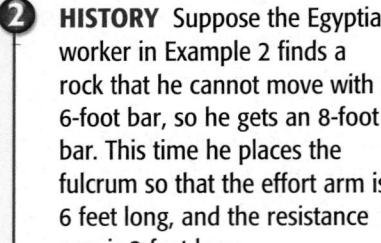

 EXAMPLE Use Rational Expressions

2 HISTORY The ancient Egyptians probably used levers to help them maneuver the giant blocks they used to build the pyramids. The diagram shows how the devices may have worked using a 10-foot lever.

a. The mechanical advantage of a lever is $\dfrac{L_E}{L_R}$, where L_E is the length of the effort arm and L_R is the length of the resistance arm. Calculate the mechanical advantage of the lever the Egyptian worker is using.

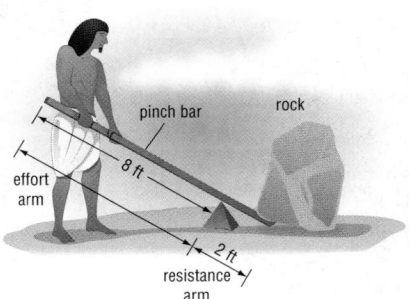

pinch bar   rock
effort arm   8 ft
resistance arm   2 ft

Let b represent the length of the bar and e represent the length of the effort arm. Then $b - e$ is the length of the resistance arm.

Use the expression for mechanical advantage to write an expression for the mechanical advantage in this situation.

$$\frac{L_E}{L_R} = \frac{e}{b - e} \qquad L_E = e, L_R = b - e$$

$$= \frac{8}{10 - 8} \qquad e = 8, b = 10$$

$$= 4 \qquad \text{Simplify.}$$

The mechanical advantage is 4.

b. The force placed on the rock is the product of the mechanical advantage and the force applied to the end of the lever. If the Egyptian worker can apply a force of 180 pounds, what is the greatest weight he can lift with the lever?

Since the mechanical advantage is 4, the Egyptian worker can lift $4 \cdot 180$ or 720 pounds with this lever.

CHECK Your Progress

2. Kelli is going to lift a 535-pound rock using a 7-foot lever. If she places the fulcrum 2 feet from the rock, how much force will she have to use to lift the rock? **214 lb**

Simplify Rational Expressions Simplifying rational expressions is similar to simplifying fractions with numbers. To simplify a rational expression, you must eliminate any common factors in the numerator and denominator. To do this, use their greatest common factor (GCF). Remember that $\frac{ab}{ac} = \frac{a}{a} \cdot \frac{b}{c}$ and $\frac{a}{a} = 1$. So, $\frac{ab}{ac} = 1 \cdot \frac{b}{c}$ or $\frac{b}{c}$.

When a rational expression is in simplest form, the numerator and denominator have no common factors other than 1 or -1.

584 Chapter 11 Rational Expressions and Equations

Intervention

Excluded Values Students may assume that excluded values are determined from the simplified expression. This may or may not be true. Stress that excluded values must *always* be determined from the original denominator.

3 Which expression is equivalent to $\dfrac{(-3x^2)(4x^5)}{9x^6}$?

A $\dfrac{4}{3}x$ B $\dfrac{4}{3x}$ C $\dfrac{-4}{3x}$ D $\dfrac{-4}{3}x$

Test-Taking Tip

Eliminate possibilities
Sometimes you can eliminate some of the answer choices before solving the problem. For example, since there is only one negative factor in the expression in Example 3, the simplified expression must be negative. You can eliminate choices A and B.

Read the Item

The expression $\dfrac{(-3x^2)(4x^5)}{9x^6}$ represents the product of two monomials and the division of that product by another monomial.

Solve the Item

Step 1 Find the product in the numerator. $(-3x^2)(4x^5) = -12x^7$

Step 2 Find the GCF of the numerator and denominator. $\dfrac{(3x^6)(-4x)}{(3x^6)(3)}$

Step 3 Simplify. The correct answer is D. $\dfrac{(3x^6)(-4x)}{(3x^6)(3)}$ or $\dfrac{-4x}{3}$

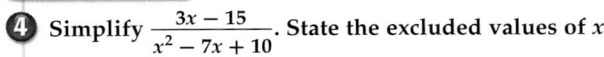

Your Progress

3. Which expression is equivalent to $\dfrac{16c^2b^4}{8c^3b}$?   **F**

F $\dfrac{2b^3}{c}$ G $\dfrac{b^3}{2c}$ H $\dfrac{1}{2b^3c}$ J $2b^3c$

Online Personal Tutor at ca.algebra1.com

You can use the same procedure to simplify a rational expression in which the numerator and denominator are polynomials. Determine the excluded values using the *original* expression rather than the simplified expression.

EXAMPLE   Excluded Values

4 Simplify $\dfrac{3x - 15}{x^2 - 7x + 10}$. State the excluded values of x.

$$\dfrac{3x - 15}{x^2 - 7x + 10} = \dfrac{3(x - 5)}{(x - 2)(x - 5)} \quad \text{Factor.}$$

$$= \dfrac{3(\overset{1}{x - 5})}{(x - 2)(\underset{1}{x - 5})} \quad \text{Divide the numerator and denominator by the GCF, } x - 5.$$

$$= \dfrac{3}{x - 2} \quad \text{Simplify.}$$

Exclude the values for which $x^2 - 7x + 10$ equals 0.

$x^2 - 7x + 10 = 0$ The denominator cannot equal zero.

$(x - 5)(x - 2) = 0$ Factor.

$x = 5$ or $x = 2$ Zero Product Property   Therefore, $x \neq 5$ and $x \neq 2$.

Your Progress

Simplify each expression. State the excluded values.

4A. $\dfrac{12x + 36}{x^2 - x - 12}$ 4 and −3; $\dfrac{12}{x - 4}$ **4B.** $\dfrac{x^2 - 2x - 35}{x^2 - 9x + 14}$ 2 and 7; $\dfrac{x + 5}{x - 2}$

Simplify Rational Expressions

Example 3 shows how to simplify a rational expression using the greatest common factor of the numerator and the denominator. **Example 4** shows the importance of finding the excluded values of a rational expression using the original expression rather than the simplified expression.

ADDITIONAL EXAMPLES

3 **STANDARDS EXAMPLE** Which expression is equivalent to $\dfrac{32x^5y^2}{4xy^7}$?   C

A $\dfrac{8x^5}{y^5}$ C $\dfrac{8x^4}{y^5}$

B $\dfrac{8x^6}{y^9}$ D $\dfrac{24x^4}{y^5}$

4 Simplify $\dfrac{4x + 16}{x^2 - 5x - 36}$. State the excluded values of x.

$\dfrac{4}{x - 9}$; −4 and 9

Additional Examples are also in:

• Noteables™ Interactive Study Notebook with Foldables™

• Interactive Classroom PowerPoint® Presentations

Focus on Mathematical Content

Simplifying Rational Expressions
A rational expression is simplified when the numerator and denominator of the expression have no factor in common. Identifying excluded values should be the first step in the simplification process since *all* restrictions found in a problem should be included in the answer.

Preventing Errors

Tips for New Teachers
Refer students to Chapter 8 if they need to review how to factor polynomials.

Pre-AP Activity   Use as an Extension.

Write the expression $\dfrac{7}{x - 9} + 5$ on the board. Ask students to explain how adding 5 to the rational term $\dfrac{7}{x - 9}$ affects the excluded values in the expression. The excluded value is 9 whether or not 5 is added to $\dfrac{7}{x - 9}$.

3 Practice

 Formative Assessment

Use Exercises 1–11 to check for understanding.

Use the chart at the bottom of this page to customize assignments for your students.

Odd/Even Assignments
Exercises 12–39 are structured so that students practice the same concepts whether they are assigned odd or even problems.

Real-World Connections
For Exercises 20 and 21, remind students that there are differences in cooking time as you change elevation. Potatoes, for example, take longer to cook at timberline than at sea level. Ask students who have lived at or traveled to different elevations to share their experiences with cooking in those areas.

⚠ Exercise Alert!
Graphing Calculator
Exercise 47 refers to two equations that are graphed on a graphing calculator. You may wish to have students see the graphs of these two equations by having them graph the equations on their own graphing calculators.

Additional Answers

4. $\frac{4}{5xy}$; 0, 0

5. $x - 7$; -7

6. $\frac{1}{x + 4}$; -4

7. $\frac{3}{x - 4}$; 4, 3

8. $\frac{a + 6}{a + 4}$; -4, 2

9. $\frac{x + 3}{x - 4}$; $\frac{7}{2}$, 4

10. Let g represent the number of guppies; $\frac{4}{4 + g}$.

★ indicates multi-step problem

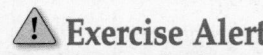 **CHECK Your Understanding**

Example 1
(p. 583)

State the excluded values for each rational expression.

1. $\frac{4a}{3 + a}$ -3

2. $\frac{x^2 - 9}{2x + 6}$ -3

3. $\frac{n + 5}{n^2 + n - 20}$ -5, 4

Examples 3, 4
(pp. 584–585)

Simplify each expression. State the excluded values of the variables.

4. $\frac{56x^2y}{70x^3y^2}$

5. $\frac{x^2 - 49}{x + 7}$

6. $\frac{x + 4}{x^2 + 8x + 16}$

7. $\frac{3x - 9}{x^2 - 7x + 12}$

8. $\frac{a^2 + 4a - 12}{a^2 + 2a - 8}$

9. $\frac{2x^2 - x - 21}{2x^2 - 15x + 28}$

4–9. See margin.

Example 2
(p. 584)

AQUARIUMS For Exercises 10 and 11, use the following information.
Jenna has guppies in her aquarium. One week later, she adds four neon fish.

10. Define a variable. Then write an expression that represents the fraction of neon fish in the aquarium. **See margin.**

11. Suppose that two months later the guppy population doubles. Jenna still has four neons, and she buys 5 different tropical fish. Write an expression that shows the fraction of neons in the aquarium after the other fish have been added. $\frac{4}{9 + 2g}$

Exercises

HOMEWORK HELP	
For Exercises	See Examples
12–17	1
18–21	2
22–39	3, 4

Exercise Levels
A: 12–39
B: 40–44
C: 45–48

State the excluded values for each rational expression.

12. $\frac{m + 3}{m - 2}$ 2

13. $\frac{3b}{b + 5}$ -5

14. $\frac{3n + 18}{n^2 - 36}$ -6, 6

15. $\frac{2x - 10}{x^2 - 25}$ -5, 5

16. $\frac{n^2 - 36}{n^2 + n - 30}$ -6, 5

17. $\frac{25 - x^2}{x^2 + 12x + 35}$ -5, -7

PHYSICAL SCIENCE For Exercises 18 and 19, use the following information.
To pry the lid off a crate, a crowbar that is 18.2 inches long is used as a lever. It is placed so that 1.5 inches of its length extends inward from the edge of the crate.

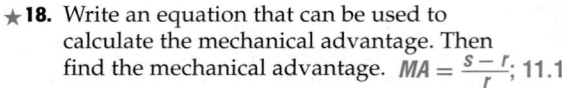

★18. Write an equation that can be used to calculate the mechanical advantage. Then find the mechanical advantage. $MA = \frac{s - r}{r}$; 11.13

19. If a force of 16 pounds is applied to the end of the crowbar, what is the force placed on the lid? **178.13 lb**

COOKING For Exercises 20 and 21, use the following information.
The formula $t = \frac{40(25 + 1.85a)}{50 - 1.85a}$ relates the time t in minutes that it takes to cook an average-size potato in an oven that is at an altitude of a thousands of feet.

20. What is the value of a for an altitude of 4500 feet? **4.5**

21. Calculate the time it takes to cook a potato at an altitude of 3500 feet and at 7000 feet. How do your cooking times compare at these two altitudes?
The difference is 12 minutes.

586 Chapter 11 Rational Expressions and Equations

DIFFERENTIATED HOMEWORK OPTIONS

Level	Assignment	Two-Day Option	
BL Basic	12–39, 45, 46, 48–67	13–39 odd, 49, 50	12–38 even, 45, 46, 48, 51–67
OL Core	13–39 odd, 40–46, 48–67	12–39, 49, 50	40–46, 48, 51–67
AL Advanced /Pre-AP	40–67 (optional: 62–67)		

Simplify each expression. State the excluded values of the variables.

22. $\dfrac{35yz^2}{14y^2z}$ $\dfrac{5z}{2y}$; 0, 0

23. $\dfrac{14a^3b^2}{42ab^3}$ $\dfrac{a^2}{3b}$; 0, 0

24. $\dfrac{64qr^2s}{16q^2rs}$ $\dfrac{4r}{q}$; 0, 0, 0

25. $\dfrac{9x^2yz}{24xyz^2}$ $\dfrac{3x}{8z}$; 0, 0, 0

26. $\dfrac{7a^3b^2}{21a^2b + 49ab^3}$

27. $\dfrac{3m^2n^3}{36mn^3 - 12m^2n^2}$

26–39. See margin.

28. $\dfrac{x^2 + x - 20}{x + 5}$

29. $\dfrac{z^2 + 10z + 16}{z + 2}$

30. $\dfrac{4x + 8}{x^2 + 6x + 8}$

31. $\dfrac{2y - 4}{y^2 + 3y - 10}$

32. $\dfrac{m^2 - 36}{m^2 - 5m - 6}$

33. $\dfrac{a^2 - 9}{a^2 + 6a - 27}$

34. $\dfrac{x^2 + x - 2}{x^2 - 3x + 2}$

35. $\dfrac{b^2 + 2b - 8}{b^2 - 20b + 64}$

36. $\dfrac{x^2 - x - 20}{x^3 + 10x^2 + 24x}$

37. $\dfrac{n^2 - 8n + 12}{n^3 - 12n^2 + 36n}$

38. $\dfrac{4x^2 - 6x - 4}{2x^2 - 8x + 8}$

39. $\dfrac{3m^2 + 9m + 6}{4m^2 + 12m + 8}$

FIELD TRIPS For Exercises 40–43, use the following information.

Mrs. Hoffman's art class is taking a trip to the museum. A bus that can seat up to 56 people costs $450 for the day, and group rate tickets at the museum cost $4 each.

40. If there are no more than 56 students going on the field trip, write an expression for the total cost for n students to go to the museum. **450 + 4n**

Real-World Career
Farmer
Farmers use mathematics to optimize usage of space, crop output, and profits while running their farms.

41. Write a rational expression that could be used to calculate the cost of the trip per student. $\dfrac{450 + 4n}{n}$

42. How many students must attend in order to keep the cost under $15 per student? **41 or more**

43. How would you change the expression for cost per student if the school were to cover the cost of two adult chaperones? $\dfrac{450 + 4(n + 2)}{n}$

Math Online
For more information, go to ca.algebra1.com.

44. **AGRICULTURE** Some farmers use an irrigation system that ★ waters a circular region in a field. Suppose a square field with sides of length $2x$ is irrigated from the center of the square. The irrigation system can reach a radius of x. What percent of the field is irrigated to the nearest whole percent? **79%**

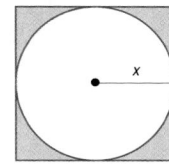

H.O.T. Problems

EXTRA PRACTICE
See pages 739, 754.
Math Online
Self-Check Quiz at
ca.algebra1.com

45. **OPEN ENDED** Write a rational expression involving one variable for which the excluded values are −4 and −7. Explain how you found the expression.
See margin.

46. **REASONING** Explain why −2 may not be the only excluded value of a rational expression that simplifies to $\dfrac{x - 3}{x + 2}$. **See margin.**

47. **CHALLENGE** Two students graphed the following equations on their calculators.

$$y = \dfrac{x^2 - 16}{x - 4} \qquad y = x + 4$$

They were surprised to see that the graphs appeared to be identical. Explain how the graphs are different. **Sample answer: The first graph has a hole at $x = 4$ because it is an excluded value of the equation.**

48. *Writing in Math* Use the information on page 583 to explain how rational expressions can be used in a movie theater. Include a description of how you determine the excluded values of the rational expression that is given.
See margin.

Lesson 11-2 Rational Expressions **587**

48. Sample answer: Use the rational expression for light intensity to help determine the brightness of the picture on the screen for the distance between the projector and the screen. Find the solutions for the expression in the denominator.

Crystal Ball Tell students that the next lesson they will study is titled *Multiplying Rational Expressions*. Ask them to write how they think what they have learned today will connect with the next lesson.

Additional Answers

26. $\dfrac{a^2b}{3a + 7b^2}$; $a \neq -\dfrac{7}{3}b^2$, 0, 0

27. $\dfrac{mn}{12n - 4m}$; $m \neq 3n$, 0, 0

28. $x - 4$; −5

29. $z + 8$; −2

30. $\dfrac{4}{x + 4}$; −4, −2

31. $\dfrac{2}{y + 5}$; −5, 2

32. $\dfrac{m + 6}{m + 1}$; −1, 6

33. $\dfrac{a + 3}{a + 9}$; −9, 3

34. $\dfrac{x + 2}{x - 2}$; 2, 1

35. $\dfrac{(b + 4)(b - 2)}{(b - 4)(b - 16)}$; 4, 16

36. $\dfrac{x - 5}{x(x + 6)}$; −4, −6, 0

37. $\dfrac{n - 2}{n(n - 6)}$; 0, 6

38. $\dfrac{2x + 1}{x - 2}$; 2

39. $\dfrac{3}{4}$; −2, −1

45. Sample answer: $\dfrac{1}{(x + 4)(x + 7)}$; since the excluded values are −4 and −7 the denominator of the rational expression must contain the factors $(x + 4)$ and $(x + 7)$.

46. Sample answer: You need to determine excluded values before simplifying. One of more factors may have been cancelled in the denominator.

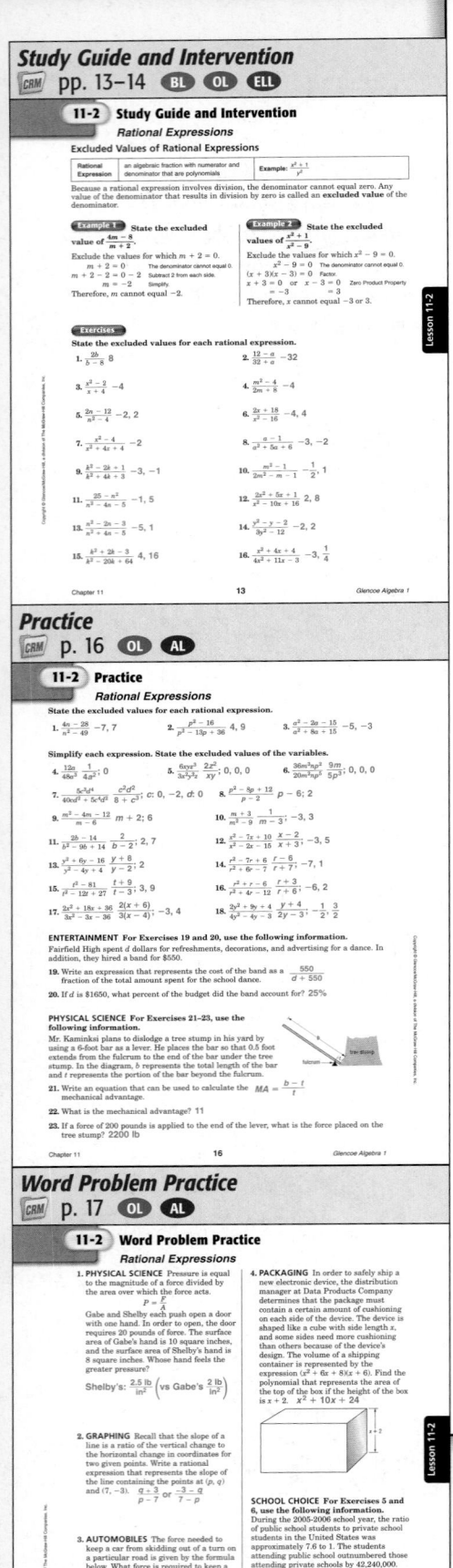

STANDARDS PRACTICE 13.0, 7MG2.3

49. The area of each wall in LaTisha's room is $x^2 + 3x + 2$ square feet. A gallon of paint will cover an area of $x^2 - 2x - 3$ square feet. Which expression gives the number of gallons of paint that LaTisha will need to buy to paint her room? **B**

A $\dfrac{4x}{x-3}$

B $\dfrac{x+2}{x-3}$

C $\dfrac{4x+4}{x-3}$

D $\dfrac{4x+8}{x-3}$

50. REVIEW What is the volume of the triangular prism shown below? **H**

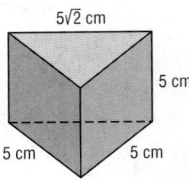

F 12.5 cm^3

G $25\sqrt{2}$ cm^3

H 62.5 cm^3

J $125\sqrt{2}$ cm^3

Spiral Review

Write an inverse variation equation that relates x and y. Assume that y varies inversely as x. Then solve. (Lesson 11-1)

51. If $y = 6$ when $x = 10$, find y when $x = -12$. *xy = 60; −5*

52. If $y = 16$ when $x = \frac{1}{2}$, find x when $y = 32$. **52.** $xy = 8; \frac{1}{4}$

53. If $y = -9$ when $x = 6$, find x when $y = 3$. *xy = −54; −18*

54. If $y = -2.5$ when $x = 3$, find y when $x = -8$. *xy = −7.5; 0.9375*

For each set of measures given, find the measures of the missing sides if $\triangle KLM \sim \triangle NOP$. (Lesson 10-6)

55. $k = 5, \ell = 3, m = 2, n = 10$ *o = 6, p = 4*

56. $\ell = 9, m = 3, n = 12, p = 4.5$
k = 8, o = 13.5

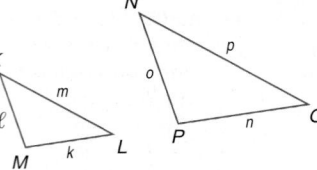

Solve each equation. Check your solution(s). (Lesson 10-3)

57. $\sqrt{a+3} = 2$ 1

58. $\sqrt{2z+2} = z - 3$ 7

59. $\sqrt{13-4p} - p = 8$ −3

60. $\sqrt{3r^2+61} = 2r + 1$ 6

61. GROCERIES The Ricardos drink about 5 gallons of milk every 2.5 weeks. At this rate, how much money will they spend on milk in a year if it costs $3.58 a gallon? (Lesson 2-6) **$372.32**

▶ GET READY for the Next Lesson

PREREQUISITE SKILL Complete. **64. 15,300**

62. 84 in. = ___ ft 7

63. 4.5 m = ___ cm 450

64. 4 h 15 min = ___ s

65. 18 mi = ___ ft 95,040

66. 3 days = ___ h 72

67. 220 mL = ___ L
0.22

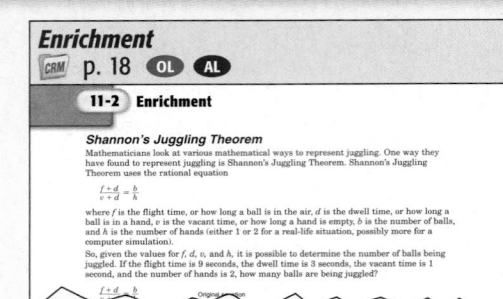

Enrichment
CRM p. 18 OL AL

11-2 Enrichment

Shannon's Juggling Theorem
Mathematicians look at various mathematical ways to represent juggling. One way they have found to represent juggling is Shannon's Juggling Theorem. Shannon's Juggling Theorem uses the rational equation

$\dfrac{f+d}{v+d} = \dfrac{b}{h}$

where f is the flight time, or how long a ball is in the air, d is the dwell time, or how long a ball is in a hand, v is the vacant time, or how long a hand is empty, b is the number of balls, and h is the number of hands (either 1 or 2 for a real-life situation, possibly more for a computer simulation).

So, given the values for f, d, v, and h, it is possible to determine the number of balls being juggled. If the flight time is 9 seconds, the dwell time is 3 seconds, the vacant time is 1 second, and the number of hands is 2, how many balls are being juggled?

$\dfrac{f+d}{h}$

BL = Below Grade Level

OL = On Grade Level

AL = Above Grade Level

ELL = English Language Learner

Additional pages not shown:

CRM **Lesson Reading Guide**, p. 12 BL OL ELL

CRM **Skills Practice**, p. 15 BL OL

Graphing Calculator Lab

Rational Expressions

Standard 12.0 Students simplify fractions with polynomials in the numerator and denominator by factoring both and reducing them to the lowest terms. (Key)

When simplifying rational expressions, you can use a graphing calculator to support your answer. If the graphs of the original expression and the simplified expression coincide, they are equivalent.

ACTIVITY

Simplify .

Step 1 Factor the numerator and denominator.

 When $x = -5$, $x + 5 = 0$. Therefore, x cannot equal -5 because you cannot divide by zero.

Step 2 Graph the original expression.

- Set the calculator to **Dot** mode.

- Enter $\dfrac{x^2 + 5x}{x^2 + 10x + 25}$ as **Y1** and graph.

KEYSTROKES: MODE ▼ ▼ ▼ ▼ ▶

ENTER Y= (X,T,θ,n x^2

+ 5 X,T,θ,n) ÷ (X,T,θ,n

x^2 + 10 X,T,θ,n + 25)

ZOOM 6

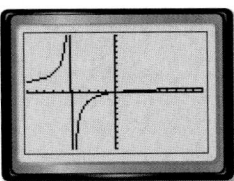

[−10, 10] scl: 1 by [−10, 10] scl: 1

Step 3 Graph the simplified expression.

- Enter $\dfrac{x}{(x + 5)}$ as **Y2** and graph.

KEYSTROKES: Y= ▼ X,T,θ,n ÷

(X,T,θ,n +

5) GRAPH

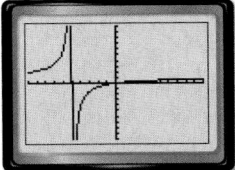

[−10, 10] scl: 1 by [−10, 10] scl: 1

Since the graphs overlap, the two expressions are equivalent.

EXERCISES   1. $\dfrac{3}{x + 5}$; −5, −2

Simplify each expression. Then verify your answer graphically. Name the excluded values. 1–3. See Ch. 11 Answer Appendix for graphs.

1. $\dfrac{3x + 6}{x^2 + 7x + 10}$

2. $\dfrac{2x + 8}{x^2 + 6x + 8}$ $\dfrac{2}{x + 2}$; −2, −4

3. $\dfrac{5x^2 + 10x + 5}{3x^2 + 6x + 3}$ $\dfrac{5}{3}$; −1

4. Simplify $\dfrac{2x - 9}{4x^2 - 18x}$ 4a. **Sample answer: Examine the values and verify that they are identical.** and answer each question using the **TABLE** menu.

   a. How can you use the **TABLE** function to verify that the original expression and the simplified expression are equivalent?

   b. How does the **TABLE** function show you that an x-value is excluded? **It displays "ERROR".**

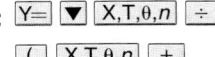

1 Focus

Objective Simplify rational expressions and verify solutions with technology.

Materials for Each Student
- graphing calculator

Teaching Tip Be sure students understand that when they enter two functions that should produce identical graphs, it is impossible to tell from the screen whether there are two graphs or one. To make sure there are two graphs and that they overlap, have students press TRACE. Tell students to use the up and down arrow keys to switch between the two graphs. Each time they press the keys, the equation in the upper left-hand corner of the screen should change.

2 Teach

Working in Cooperative Groups
Put students in groups of 2 or 3, mixing abilities. Have groups complete the activity and Exercises 1–3.

- Make sure students enter the equations exactly as shown in the keystrokes. If students fail to put the numerator and denominator in parentheses, the resulting graph may be incorrect.

Practice
Have students complete Exercise 4.

3 Assess

✓ Formative Assessment

Ask students when they would use a graphing calculator to confirm the simplification of a rational expression.
Sample answer: when the simplification is very complicated

From Concrete to Abstract
Ask: Will the graphs of the original expression and the simplified expression always be the same? Graph $\dfrac{x^2 - 64}{x - 8}$ and its simplified version, $x + 8$. Explain how the graphs are different.
When there are excluded values for the original rational expression and not for the simplified expression, the graphs might be slightly different; the first graph has a hole at $x = 8$ because it is an excluded value of the equation.

11-3 Lesson Notes

11-3 Multiplying Rational Expressions

1 Focus

Standards Alignment

Before Lesson 11-3
Multiply, divide, and simplify rational numbers by using exponent rules from Standard 7NS2.3

Lesson 11-3
Solve both computationally and conceptually challenging problems by using operations with rational expressions from Standard 1A13.0

After Lesson 11-3
Simplify complicated rational expressions from Standard 2A7.0

2 Teach

Scaffolding Questions
Have students read *Get Ready for the Lesson.*
Ask:
• In what way are the units in these expressions similar to variables? The common units in the numerator and denominator can be factored out.
• How do you know that you ended up with the correct units at the end of the simplification? The final unit left is dollars, which is the correct unit for cost.

Lesson 11-3 Resources

Main Ideas
• Multiply rational expressions.
• Use dimensional analysis with multiplication.

Standard 13.0
Students add, subtract, **multiply**, and divide **rational expressions** and functions. Students solve both computationally and conceptually challenging problems by using these techniques. (Key)

Study Tip

Rational Expressions
From this point on, you may assume that no denominator of a rational expression in this text has a value of zero.

11-3 Multiplying Rational Expressions

> **GET READY for the Lesson**
>
> There are 25 lights around a patio. Each light is 40 watts, and the cost of electricity is 15 cents per kilowatt-hour. You can use the expression below to calculate the cost of using the lights for h hours.
>
> $$25 \text{ lights} \cdot \frac{40 \text{ watts}}{\text{light}} \cdot \frac{1 \text{ kilowatt}}{1000 \text{ watts}} \cdot \frac{15 \text{ cents}}{1 \text{ kilowatt} \cdot \text{hour}} \cdot \frac{1 \text{ dollar}}{100 \text{ cents}} \cdot h \text{ hours}$$

MULTIPLY RATIONAL EXPRESSIONS The multiplication expression above is similar to the multiplication of rational expressions. Recall that to multiply fractions, you multiply numerators and multiply denominators. You can use the same method to multiply rational expressions.

EXAMPLE Expressions Involving Monomials

1 Find $\dfrac{5ab^3}{8c^2} \cdot \dfrac{16c^3}{15a^2b}$.

Method 1 Divide by the greatest common factor after multiplying.

$$\frac{5ab^3}{8c^2} \cdot \frac{16c^3}{15a^2b} = \frac{80ab^3c^3}{120a^2bc^2} \qquad \begin{array}{l}\leftarrow \text{Multiply the numerators.} \\ \leftarrow \text{Multiply the denominators.}\end{array}$$

$$= \frac{\overset{1}{40abc^2}(2b^2c)}{\underset{1}{40abc^2}(3a)} \qquad \text{The GCF is } 40abc^2.$$

$$= \frac{2b^2c}{3a} \qquad \text{Simplify.}$$

Method 2 Divide by the common factors before multiplying.

$$\frac{5ab^3}{8c^2} \cdot \frac{16c^3}{15a^2b} = \frac{\overset{1}{\cancel{5}}\overset{b^2}{a\cancel{b^3}}}{\underset{1}{\cancel{8}}\underset{1}{c^2}} \cdot \frac{\overset{2}{\cancel{16}}\overset{c}{\cancel{c^3}}}{\underset{3}{\cancel{15}}\underset{a}{a^2}\underset{1}{\cancel{b}}} \qquad \text{Divide by common factors 5, 8, } a, b, \text{ and } c^2.$$

$$= \frac{2b^2c}{3a} \qquad \text{Multiply.}$$

 CHECK Your Progress Find each product.

1A. $\dfrac{5c^3d}{c^4d} \cdot \dfrac{f^2d^3c}{10cf^4} \cdot \dfrac{d^3}{2cf^2}$

1B. $\dfrac{16g^2h^3}{8gh^2} \cdot \dfrac{3g^2h}{32hj^2} \cdot \dfrac{3g^3h}{16j^2}$

 **Extra Examples at** ca.algebra1.com

---

Sometimes you must factor a quadratic expression before you can simplify a product of rational expressions.

EXAMPLE Expressions Involving Polynomials

2 Find $\dfrac{x - 5}{x} \cdot \dfrac{x^2}{x^2 - 2x - 15}$.

$$\dfrac{x - 5}{x} \cdot \dfrac{x^2}{x^2 - 2x - 15} = \dfrac{x - 5}{x} \cdot \dfrac{x^2}{(x - 5)(x + 3)}$$ Factor the denominator.

$$= \dfrac{\overset{x}{\cancel{x^2}}(\cancel{x - 5})}{\underset{1}{\cancel{x}}(\cancel{x - 5})(x + 3)}$$ The GCF is $x(x - 5)$.

$$= \dfrac{x}{x + 3}$$ Simplify.

CHECK Your Progress Find each product.

2A. $\dfrac{x + 3}{x} \cdot \dfrac{5}{x^2 + 7x + 12}$ $\dfrac{5}{x^2 + 4x}$ **2B.** $\dfrac{y^2 - 3y - 4}{y + 5} \cdot \dfrac{y + 5}{y^2 - 4y}$ $\dfrac{y + 1}{y}$

DIMENSIONAL ANALYSIS When you multiply fractions that involve units of measure, you can divide by the units in the same way that you divide by variables. Recall that this process is called *dimensional analysis.*

Real-World Link ....
American sprinter Thomas Burke won the 100-meter dash at the first modern Olympics in Athens, Greece, in 1896 in 12.0 seconds.

Source: olympics.org

Real-World EXAMPLE Dimensional Analysis

3 **OLYMPICS** In the 2004 Summer Olympics in Athens, Greece, Justin Gatlin of the United States won the gold medal for the 100-meter sprint. His winning time was 9.85 seconds. What was his speed in kilometers per hour? Round to the nearest hundredth.

$$\dfrac{100\text{ m}}{9.85\text{ s}} \cdot \dfrac{1\text{ k}}{1000\text{ m}} \cdot \dfrac{60\text{ s}}{1\text{ min}} \cdot \dfrac{60\text{ min}}{1\text{ h}} = \dfrac{100\text{ \cancel{m}}}{9.85\text{ \cancel{s}}} \cdot \dfrac{1\text{ k}}{1000\text{ \cancel{m}}} \cdot \dfrac{60\text{ \cancel{s}}}{1\text{ \cancel{min}}} \cdot \dfrac{60\text{ \cancel{min}}}{1\text{ h}}$$

$$= \dfrac{\overset{1}{100} \cdot 1 \cdot 60 \cdot 60 \cdot \text{k}}{9.85 \cdot \underset{10}{1000} \cdot 1 \cdot 1\text{ h}}$$ Simplify.

$$= \dfrac{60 \cdot 60\text{ k}}{9.85 \cdot 10\text{ h}}$$ Multiply.

$$= \dfrac{3600\text{ k}}{98.5\text{ h}}$$ Multiply.

$$= \dfrac{36.54\text{ k}}{1\text{ h}}$$ Divide numerator and denominator by 98.5.

His speed was 36.54 kilometers per hour.

CHECK Your Progress

3. **SPEED** Todd is driving to his grandparents' house at 65 miles per hour. How fast is he going in feet per second? $95\frac{1}{3}$ ft/s

Online **Personal Tutor at** ca.algebra1.com

Lesson 11-3 Multiplying Rational Expressions **591**

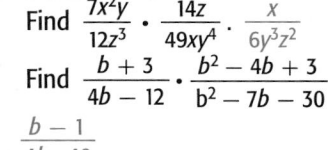

Formative Assessment

Use Exercises 1–8 to check for understanding.

Use the chart at the bottom of this page to customize assignments for your students.

Odd/Even Assignments

Exercises 9–24 are structured so that students practice the same concepts whether they are assigned odd or even problems.

⚠ Exercise Alert!

Internet Exercise 25 requires students to use the Internet to research exchange rates for the U.S. dollar against foreign currency.

Find the Error Remind students that only common *factors* can be eliminated from the numerator and denominator. Use this exercise to determine whether your students understand the difference between factors and the terms of a polynominal.

Additional Answers

21. $\dfrac{b+1}{(b+3)(b-3)}$

31. 5 tracks $\cdot \dfrac{2 \text{ miles}}{1 \text{ track}} \cdot$

$\dfrac{5280 \text{ feet}}{1 \text{ mile}} \cdot \dfrac{1 \text{ car}}{75 \text{ feet}}$

37. Sample answer: When the negative sign in front of the first expression is distributed, the numerator is $-x - 6$; Distributive Property.

38. Sample answer: Multiply rational expressions to perform dimensional analysis. The cost of using a 60 watt bulb is given by the expression: 24 lights $\cdot$

h hours $\cdot \dfrac{60 \text{ watts}}{\text{light}} \cdot \dfrac{1 \text{ kilowatt}}{1000 \text{ watts}} \cdot$

$\dfrac{15 \text{ cents}}{1 \text{ kilowatt} \cdot \text{hour}} \cdot \dfrac{1 \text{ dollar}}{100 \text{ cents}}.$

★ indicates multi-step problem

✓ CHECK Your Understanding

Find each product.

Example 1 (p. 590)

1. $\dfrac{64y^2}{5y} \cdot \dfrac{5y}{8y}$ $8y$

2. $\dfrac{15s^2t^3}{12st} \cdot \dfrac{16st^2}{10s^3t^3}$ $\dfrac{2t}{s}$

Example 2 (p. 591)

3. $\dfrac{m+4}{3m} \cdot \dfrac{4m^2}{(m+4)(m+5)}$ $\dfrac{4m}{3(m+5)}$

4. $\dfrac{x^2-4}{2} \cdot \dfrac{4}{x-2}$ $2(x+2)$

5. $\dfrac{n^2-16}{n+4} \cdot \dfrac{n+2}{n^2+-8n+16}$ $\dfrac{n+2}{n-4}$

6. $\dfrac{x-5}{x^2-7x+10} \cdot \dfrac{x^2+x-6}{5}$ $\dfrac{x+3}{5}$

Example 3 (p. 591)

7. Find $\dfrac{24 \text{ feet}}{1 \text{ second}} \cdot \dfrac{60 \text{ seconds}}{1 \text{ minute}} \cdot \dfrac{60 \text{ minutes}}{1 \text{ hour}} \cdot \dfrac{1 \text{ mile}}{5280 \text{ feet}}.$ 16.36 mph

8. SPACE The Moon is about 240,000 miles from Earth. How many days would it take a spacecraft to reach the Moon if it travels at an average speed of 100 miles per minute? $1\frac{2}{3}$ days

Exercises

Find each product.

HOMEWORK HELP	
For Exercises	See Examples
9–12	1
13–22	2
23, 24	3

Exercise Levels:
A: 9–24   B: 25–33
C: 34–38

9. $\dfrac{8}{x^2} \cdot \dfrac{x^4}{4x}$ $2x$

10. $\dfrac{10r^3}{6n^3} \cdot \dfrac{42n^2}{35r^3}$ $\dfrac{2}{n}$

11. $\dfrac{10y^3z^2}{6wx^3} \cdot \dfrac{12w^2x^2}{25y^2z^4}$ $\dfrac{4wy}{5xz^2}$

12. $\dfrac{3a^2b}{2gh} \cdot \dfrac{24g^2h}{15ab^2}$ $\dfrac{12ag}{5b}$

13. $\dfrac{(x-8)}{(x+8)(x-3)} \cdot \dfrac{(x+4)(x-3)}{(x-8)}$

14. $\dfrac{(n-1)(n+1)}{(n+1)} \cdot \dfrac{(n-4)}{(n-1)(n+4)}$ $\dfrac{n-4}{n+4}$

15. $\dfrac{(z+4)(z+6)}{(z-6)(z+1)} \cdot \dfrac{(z+1)(z-5)}{(z+3)(z+4)}$

16. $\dfrac{(x-1)(x+7)}{(x-7)(x-4)} \cdot \dfrac{(x-4)(x+10)}{(x+1)(x+10)}$

13. $\dfrac{x+4}{x+8}$ **15.** $\dfrac{(z+6)(z-5)}{(z-6)(z+3)}$ **16.** $\dfrac{(x-1)(x+7)}{(x-7)(x+1)}$

17. $\dfrac{x^2-25}{9} \cdot \dfrac{x+5}{x-5}$ $\dfrac{(x+5)^2}{9}$

18. $\dfrac{y^2-4}{y^2-1} \cdot \dfrac{y+1}{y+2}$ $\dfrac{y-2}{y-1}$

19. $\dfrac{x+3}{x+4} \cdot \dfrac{x}{x^2+7x+12}$ $\dfrac{x}{(x+4)^2}$

20. $\dfrac{n}{n^2+8n+15} \cdot \dfrac{2n+10}{n^2}$ $\dfrac{2}{n(n+3)}$

21. $\dfrac{b^2+12b+11}{b^2-9} \cdot \dfrac{b+9}{b^2+20b+99}$ See margin.

22. $\dfrac{a^2-a-6}{a^2-16} \cdot \dfrac{a^2+7a+12}{a^2+4a+4}$ $\dfrac{(a-3)(a+3)}{(a-4)(a+2)}$

23. DECORATING Alani's bedroom is 12 feet wide and 14 feet long. What will it cost to carpet her room if the carpet costs $18 per square yard? Is this a reasonable answer? $336 if carpet is sold in sq. ft. It is not reasonable to assume that carpet is sold only in square feet. If the carpet is sold in sq. yd. the price will be $360.

24. EXCHANGE RATES While traveling in Canada, Johanna bought some gifts to bring home. She bought 2 T-shirts that cost a total of $21.95 (Canadian). If the exchange rate at the time was 1 U.S. dollar for 1.21 Canadian dollars, how much did Johanna spend in U.S. dollars?   about $18.14

25. RESEARCH Use the Internet or other sources to research exchange rates for the U.S. dollar against a foreign currency of your choosing over the last six months. What has been the average rate of exchange? What has been the overall trend of the exchange rate? What current events have affected the change in rates?   See students' work.

592 Chapter 11 Rational Expressions and Equations

DIFFERENTIATED HOMEWORK OPTIONS

Level	Assignment	Two-Day Option	
BL Basic	9–24, 34, 36–60	9–23 odd, 39, 40	10–24 even, 34, 36–38, 41–67
OL Core	9–23 odd, 25, 27, 29–34, 36–60	9–24, 39, 40	25–34, 36–38, 41–60
AL Advanced /Pre-AP	25–60 (optional: 55–60)		

Find each product.

26. $\dfrac{2.54 \text{ centimeters}}{1 \text{ inch}} \cdot \dfrac{12 \text{ inches}}{1 \text{ foot}} \cdot \dfrac{3 \text{ feet}}{1 \text{ yard}}$ **91.44 cm/yd**

27. $\dfrac{60 \text{ kilometers}}{1 \text{ hour}} \cdot \dfrac{1000 \text{ meters}}{1 \text{ kilometer}} \cdot \dfrac{1 \text{ hour}}{60 \text{ minutes}} \cdot \dfrac{1 \text{ minute}}{60 \text{ seconds}}$ **16.67 m/s**

28. $\dfrac{32 \text{ feet}}{1 \text{ second}} \cdot \dfrac{60 \text{ seconds}}{1 \text{ minute}} \cdot \dfrac{60 \text{ minutes}}{1 \text{ hour}} \cdot \dfrac{1 \text{ mile}}{5280 \text{ feet}}$ **about 21.8 mi/h**

29. $10 \text{ feet} \cdot 18 \text{ feet} \cdot 3 \text{ feet} \cdot \dfrac{1 \text{ yard}^3}{27 \text{ feet}^3}$ **20 yd^3**

30. **CITY MAINTENANCE** Street sweepers can clean 3 miles of streets per hour. A city owns 2 street sweepers, and each sweeper can be used for three hours before it comes in for an hour to refuel. During an 18 hour shift, how many miles of street can be cleaned?   **84 mi**

TRAINS For Exercises 31–33, use the following information.

Trying to get into a train yard one evening, all of the trains are backed up for 2 miles along a system of tracks. Assume that each car occupies an average of 75 feet of space on a track and that the train yard has 5 tracks.

31. Write and solve an expression that could be used to determine the number of train cars involved in the backup. **See margin.**

32. How many train cars are involved in the backup? **704 cars**

33. Suppose that there are 8 attendants doing safety checks on each car, and it takes each vehicle an average of 45 seconds for each check. Approximately how many hours will it take for all the vehicles in the backup to exit? **1.1 h**

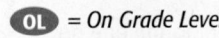
EXTRA PRACTICE
See pages 739, 754.
Math online
Self-Check Quiz at
ca.algebra1.com

H.O.T. Problems..........

35. c and e; sample answer: the expressions each have a GCF that can be used to simplify the expressions.

36. Amiri; sample answer: Amiri correctly divided by the GCF.

34. **OPEN ENDED** Write two rational expressions with a product of $\dfrac{2}{x}$. $\dfrac{2}{1} \cdot \dfrac{1}{x}$

35. **CHALLENGE** Identify the expressions that are equivalent to $\dfrac{x}{y}$. Explain why the expressions are equivalent.

   a. $\dfrac{x+3}{y+3}$ **b.** $\dfrac{3-x}{3-y}$ **c.** $\dfrac{3x}{3y}$ **d.** $\dfrac{x^3}{y^3}$ **e.** $\dfrac{n^3 x}{n^3 y}$

36. **FIND THE ERROR** Amiri and Hoshi multiplied $\dfrac{x-3}{x+3}$ and $\dfrac{4x}{x^2-4x+3}$. Who is correct? Explain your reasoning.

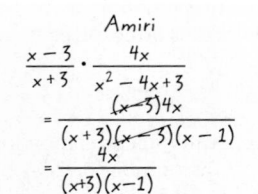

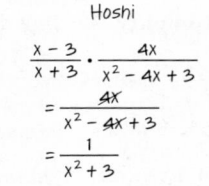

37. **CHALLENGE** Explain why $-\dfrac{x+6}{x-5}$ is not equivalent to $\dfrac{-x+6}{x-5}$. What property of mathematics was used to reach this conclusion? **See margin.**

38. *Writing in Math* Use the information provided on page 590 to explain how multiplying rational expressions can determine the cost of electricity. Include an expression that you could use to determine the cost of using 60-watt light bulbs instead of 40-watt bulbs. **See margin.**

BL = Below Grade Level
OL = On Grade Level
AL = Above Grade Level
ELL = English Language Learner

Additional pages not shown:
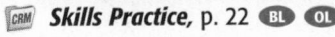
CRM *Lesson Reading Guide*, p. 19 **BL** **OL** **ELL**
CRM *Skills Practice*, p. 22 **BL** **OL**

Enrichment
CRM p. 25 **OL** **AL**

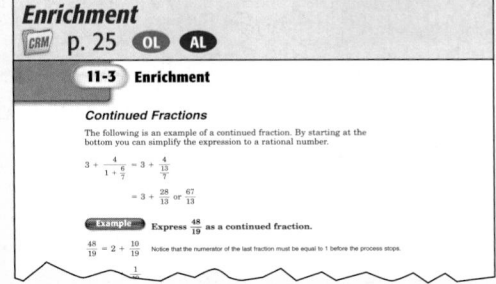

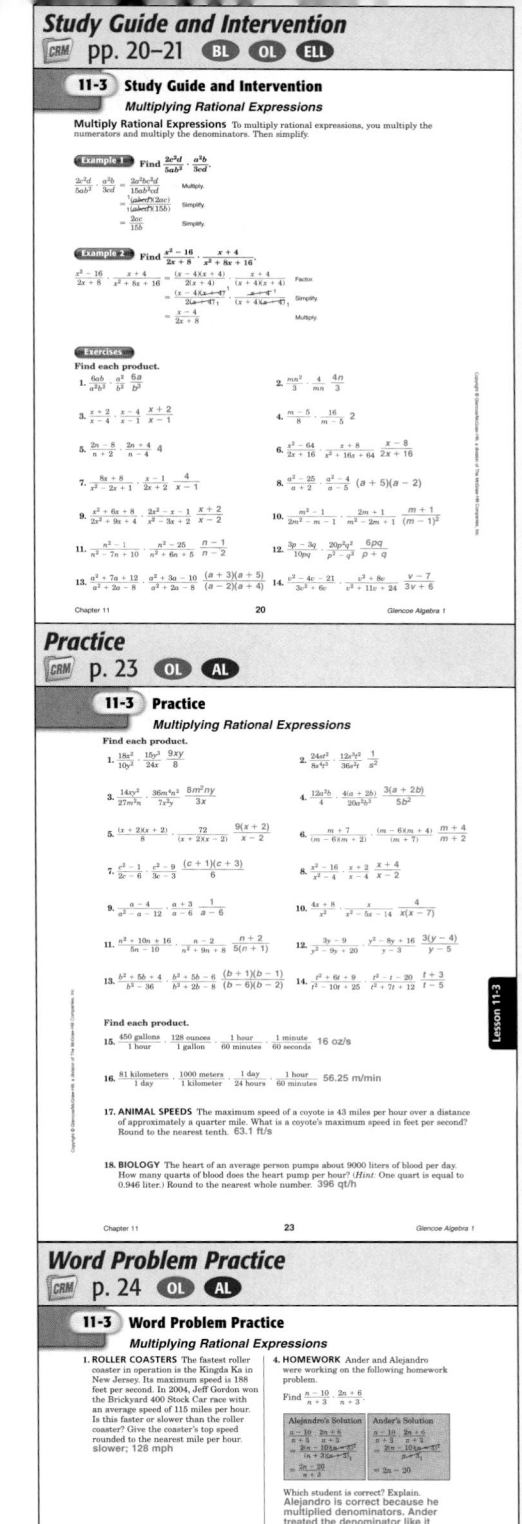

Crystal Ball Tell students that the next lesson they will study is titled *Dividing Rational Expressions*. Ask them to write how they think what they have learned about multiplying rational expressions will connect with the next lesson.

✓ Formative Assessment

Check for student understanding of concepts in Lessons 11-1 through 11-3.

📄 Quiz 1, p. 73.

---

39. In order to stay in a low-Earth orbit, an object must reach a speed of about 17,500 miles per hour. How fast is this in meters per second?
(1609.34 meters ≈ 1 mile) **B**

A 10.9 m/s

B 7823.18 m/s

C 469,390.8 m/s

D 2.8×10^7 m/s

40. REVIEW Stanley used toothpicks to make the shapes below. If x is a shape's order in the pattern (for the first shape $x = 1$, for the second shape $x = 2$, and so on), which expression can be used to find the number of toothpicks needed to make any shape in the pattern? **H**

F $3x - 3$

G $4x$

H $3x + 1$

J $4x + 3$

Spiral Review

State the excluded values for each rational expression. (Lesson 11-2)

41. $\dfrac{s + 6}{s^2 - 36}$ **−6, 6**

42. $\dfrac{a^2 - 25}{a^2 + 3a - 10}$ **−5, 2**

43. $\dfrac{x + 3}{x^2 + 6x + 9}$ **−3**

Write an inverse variation equation that relates x and y. Assume that y varies inversely as x. Then solve. (Lesson 11-1)

44. If $y = 9$ when $x = 8$, find x when $y = 6$.
$xy = 72; 12$

45. If $y = 2.4$ when $x = 8.1$, find y when $x = 3.6$.
$xy = 19.44; 5.4$

46. If $y = 24$ when $x = -8$, find y when $x = 4$.
$xy = -192; -48$

47. If $y = 6.4$ when $x = 4.4$, find x when $y = 3.2$.
$xy = 28.16; 8.8$

Solve each inequality. Then check your solution. (Lesson 6-2)

48. $\dfrac{g}{8} < \dfrac{7}{2}$ $\{g \mid g < 28\}$

49. $3.5r \geq 7.35$ $\{r \mid r \geq 2.1\}$

50. $\dfrac{9k}{4} > \dfrac{3}{5}$ $\left\{ k \mid k > \dfrac{4}{15} \right\}$

Simplify. Assume that no denominator is equal to zero. (Lesson 7-2)

51. $\dfrac{-7^{12}}{7^9}$ -7^3 or -343

52. $\dfrac{20p^6}{8p^8}$ $\dfrac{5}{2p^2}$

53. $\dfrac{24a^3b^4c^7}{6a^6c^2}$ $\dfrac{4b^4c^5}{a^3}$

★**54. FINANCE** The total amount of money Antonio earns mowing lawns and doing yard work varies directly with the number of days he works. At one point, he earned $340 in 4 days. At this rate, how long will it take him to earn $935? (Lesson 4-2) **11 days**

▶ GET READY for the Next Lesson

Factor each polynomial (Lessons 8-3 and 8-4)

55. $x^2 - 3x - 40$ $(x + 5)(x - 8)$
56. $n^2 - 64$ $(n + 8)(n - 8)$
57. $x^2 - 12x + 36$ $(x - 6)^2$

58. $a^2 + 2a - 35$ $(a + 7)(a - 5)$
59. $2x^2 - 5x - 3$
$(2x + 1)(x - 3)$
60. $3x^3 - 24x^2 + 36x$
$3x(x - 2)(x - 6)$

Pre-AP Activity Use as an Extension.

Write $\dfrac{3}{x + 4}$ on the board. Ask students to write rational expressions that are equivalent to the one on the board. Have students tell how the excluded values change from the original expression to the equivalent expressions. Sample answer: $\dfrac{3x - 12}{x^2 - 16}$; the excluded value in $\dfrac{3}{x + 4}$ is $x = -4$; the excluded value in $\dfrac{3x - 12}{x^2 - 16}$ is $x = -4$ and 4.

 **11-4**

Dividing Rational Expressions

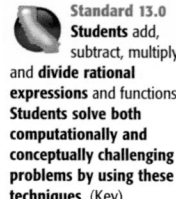
GET READY for the Lesson

Most soft drinks come in aluminum cans. Although more cans are used today than in the 1970s, the demand for new aluminum has declined. This is due in large part to the great number of cans that are recycled. In recent years, approximately 63.9 billion cans were recycled annually. This represents $\frac{5}{8}$ of all cans produced.

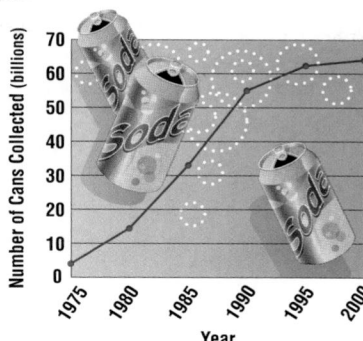

DIVIDE RATIONAL EXPRESSIONS Recall that to divide fractions, you multiply by the reciprocal of the divisor. You can use this same method to divide rational expressions.

EXAMPLE Divide by Fractions

1 Find each quotient.

a. $\frac{5x^2}{7} \div \frac{10x^3}{21}$

$\frac{5x^2}{7} \div \frac{10x^3}{21} = \frac{5x^2}{7} \cdot \frac{21}{10x^3}$ Multiply by $\frac{21}{10x^3}$, the reciprocal of $\frac{10x^3}{21}$.

$= \frac{\overset{1}{5x^2}}{\underset{1}{7}} \cdot \frac{\overset{3}{21}}{\underset{2x}{10x^3}}$ Divide by common factors 5, 7, and x^2.

$= \frac{3}{2x}$ Simplify.

b. $\frac{n+1}{n+3} \div \frac{2n+2}{n+4}$

$\frac{n+1}{n+3} \div \frac{2n+2}{n+4} = \frac{n+1}{n+3} \cdot \frac{n+4}{2n+2}$ Multiply by $\frac{n+4}{2n+2}$, the reciprocal of $\frac{2n+2}{n+4}$.

$= \frac{n+1}{n+3} \cdot \frac{n+4}{2(n+1)}$ Factor $2n + 2$.

$= \frac{\overset{1}{n+1}}{n+3} \cdot \frac{n+4}{2(\underset{1}{n+1})}$ The GCF is $n + 1$.

$= \frac{n+4}{2(n+3)}$ or $\frac{n+4}{2n+6}$ Simplify.

 Math Online Extra Examples at ca.algebra1.com

Lesson 11-4 Dividing Rational Expressions **595**

Divide Rational Expressions

Example 1 shows how to divide rational expressions involving monomials. **Example 2** shows how to use factoring to divide rational expressions involving polynomials.

Dimensional Analysis

Example 3 shows how to use dimensional analysis in a real-world situation to divide rational expressions involving units of measure.

 **CHECK Your Progress** Find each quotient.

1A. $\dfrac{15y^2}{4x} \div \dfrac{5y}{8x^3}$ $6yx^2$

1B. $\dfrac{27c^3d^2}{11d} \div \dfrac{2c^3}{9d^3e}$ $\dfrac{243}{22}d^4e$

1C. $\dfrac{b + 4}{3b + 2} \div \dfrac{3b + 12}{b + 1}$ $\dfrac{b + 1}{9b + 6}$

1D. $\dfrac{6b - 12}{3b + 15} \div \dfrac{12b + 18}{b + 5}$ $\dfrac{b - 2}{6b + 9}$

Sometimes you must factor a quadratic expression before you can simplify the quotient of rational expressions.

EXAMPLE   Expression Involving Polynomials

2 Find $\dfrac{m^2 + 3m + 2}{4} \div \dfrac{m + 2}{m + 1}$.

$\dfrac{m^2 + 3m + 2}{4} \div \dfrac{m + 2}{m + 1} = \dfrac{m^2 + 3m + 2}{4} \cdot \dfrac{m + 1}{m + 2}$ Multiply by the reciprocal, $\dfrac{m + 1}{m + 2}$.

$\phantom{\dfrac{m^2 + 3m + 2}{4} \div \dfrac{m + 2}{m + 1}} = \dfrac{(m + 1)(m + 2)}{4} \cdot \dfrac{m + 1}{m + 2}$ Factor $m^2 + 3m + 2$.

$\phantom{\dfrac{m^2 + 3m + 2}{4} \div \dfrac{m + 2}{m + 1}} = \dfrac{(m + 1)(\overset{1}{\cancel{m + 2}})}{4} \cdot \dfrac{m + 1}{\underset{1}{\cancel{m + 2}}}$ The GCF is $m + 2$.

$\phantom{\dfrac{m^2 + 3m + 2}{4} \div \dfrac{m + 2}{m + 1}} = \dfrac{(m + 1)^2}{4}$ Simplify.

 **CHECK Your Progress** Find each quotient.

2A. $\dfrac{p^2 - 4}{5p} \div \dfrac{p - 2}{p + q}$ **2A.** $\dfrac{p^2 + 2p + 2q + pq}{5p}$

2B. $\dfrac{q^2 + 3q + 2}{12} \div \dfrac{q + 1}{q^2 + 4}$ **2B.** $\dfrac{q^3 + 2q^2 + 4q + 8}{12}$

DIMENSIONAL ANALYSIS You can divide rational expressions that involve units of measure by using dimensional analysis.

Real-World EXAMPLE

3 **SPACE** In April, 2001, NASA launched the *Mars Odyssey* spacecraft. It took 200 days for the spacecraft to travel 466,000,000 miles from Earth to Mars. What was the average speed of the spacecraft in miles per hour? Round to the nearest mile per hour.

$rt = d$ rate · time = distance

$r \cdot 200 \text{ days} = 466,000,000 \text{ mi}$ $t = 200$ days, $d = 466,000,000$

$r = \dfrac{466,000,000 \text{ mi}}{200 \text{ days}}$ Divide each side by 200 days.

$ = \dfrac{466,000,000 \text{ miles}}{200 \text{ days}} \cdot \dfrac{1 \text{ day}}{24 \text{ hours}}$ Convert days to hours.

$ = \dfrac{466,000,000 \text{ miles}}{4800 \text{ hours}}$ or about $\dfrac{97,083 \text{ miles}}{1 \text{ hour}}$

Thus, the spacecraft traveled at a rate of about 97,083 miles per hour.

 Real-World Link

The first successful Mars probe was the Mariner 4, which arrived at Mars on July 14, 1965.

Source: NASA

3. On July 7, 2003, the rover *Opportunity* was launched. It landed on Mars on January 25, 2004. Assuming that *Opportunity* traveled the same distance as the *Mars Odyssey Spacecraft,* how fast did *Opportunity* travel? Round to the nearest mile per hour. **96,122.11 mph**

online **Personal Tutor at** ca.algebra1.com

★ indicates multi-step problem

CHECK Your Understanding

Find each quotient.

Example 1
(p. 595)

1. $\dfrac{10n^3}{7} \div \dfrac{5n^2}{21}$ **6n**

2. $\dfrac{2a}{3} \div \dfrac{a^7}{b^3}$ $\dfrac{2b^3}{3a^6}$

3. $\dfrac{3m + 15}{m + 4} \div \dfrac{m + 5}{6m + 24}$ **18**

4. $\dfrac{3n^2 + 18n + 24}{n^2 - 12n + 36}$

5. $\dfrac{3n^2 - 12}{n - 6} \div \dfrac{(n - 6)(n - 2)}{n + 4}$

6. $\dfrac{2(x + 2)(x + 3)}{(x + 1)(x + 9)}$

Example 2
(p. 596)

5. $\dfrac{k + 3}{k^2 + 4k + 4} \div \dfrac{2k + 6}{k + 2}$ $\dfrac{1}{2(k + 2)}$

6. $\dfrac{2x + 4}{x^2 + 11x + 18} \div \dfrac{x + 1}{x^2 + 5x + 6}$

Example 3
(p. 596)

7. Express 85 kilometers per hour in meters per second. **23.61 m/s**

8. Express 32 pounds per square foot as pounds per square inch. $\dfrac{2}{9}$ lb/in^2

★9. **COOKING** Latisha was making candy using a two-quart pan. As she stirred the mixture, she noticed that the pan was about $\dfrac{2}{3}$ full. If each piece of candy has a volume of about $\dfrac{3}{4}$ ounce, approximately how many pieces of candy will Latisha make? (*Hint*: There are 32 ounces in a quart.) **about 57 pieces**

Exercises

Find each quotient.

16. $\dfrac{(x - 1)(x + 1)}{2}$

18. $\dfrac{3(a + 4)}{2(a - 3)}$

20–21. See margin.

HOMEWORK HELP	
For Exercises	See Examples
10–15	1
16–21	2
28, 29	3

Exercise Levels
A: 10–21, 28–29
B: 22–27, 30–35
C: 36–39

10. $\dfrac{a^2}{b^2} \div \dfrac{a}{b^3}$ **ab**

11. $\dfrac{n^4}{p^2} \div \dfrac{n^2}{p^3}$ n^2p

12. $\dfrac{10m^2}{7n^2} \div \dfrac{25m^4}{14n^3}$ $\dfrac{4n}{5m^2}$

13. $\dfrac{a^4bc^3}{g^2h^3} \div \dfrac{ab^2c^2}{g^3h^3}$ $\dfrac{a^3cg}{b}$

14. $\dfrac{3x + 12}{4x - 18} \div \dfrac{2x + 8}{x + 4}$ $\dfrac{3(x + 4)}{4(2x - 9)}$

15. $\dfrac{4a - 8}{2a - 6} \div \dfrac{2a - 4}{a - 4}$ $\dfrac{a - 4}{a - 3}$

16. $\dfrac{x^2 + 2x + 1}{2} \div \dfrac{x + 1}{x - 1}$

17. $\dfrac{n^2 + 3n + 2}{4} \div \dfrac{n + 1}{n + 2}$ $\dfrac{(n + 2)^2}{4}$

18. $\dfrac{a^2 + 8a + 16}{a^2 - 6a + 9} \div \dfrac{2a + 8}{3a - 9}$

19. $\dfrac{b + 2}{b^2 + 4b + 4} \div \dfrac{2b + 4}{b + 4}$ $\dfrac{b + 4}{2(b + 2)^2}$

20. $\dfrac{x^2 + x - 2}{x^2 + 5x + 6} \div \dfrac{x^2 + 2x - 3}{x^2 + 7x + 12}$

21. $\dfrac{x^2 + 2x - 15}{x^2 - x - 30} \div \dfrac{x^2 - 3x - 18}{x^2 - 2x - 24}$

22. What is the quotient when $\dfrac{2x + 6}{x + 5}$ is divided by $\dfrac{2}{x + 5}$? $x + 3$

23. Find the quotient when $\dfrac{m - 8}{m + 7}$ is divided by $m^2 - 7m - 8$. $\dfrac{1}{(m + 7)(m + 1)}$

Complete.

24. 24 yd^3 = _____ ft^3 **648**

25. 0.35 m^3 = _____ cm^3 **350,000**

26. 330 ft/s = _____ mi/h **225**

27. 1730 plants/km^2 = _____ plants/m^2 **0.00173**

Lesson 11-4 Dividing Rational Expressions **597**

Focus on Mathematical Content

Dividing Rational Expressions
As with rational numbers, dividing rational expressions involves multiplying by the reciprocal of the divisor. To divide rational expressions, multiply by the reciprocal of the divisor.

3 Practice

Formative Assessment

Use Exercises 1–9 to check for understanding.

Use the chart at the bottom of this page to customize assignments for your students.

Odd/Even Assignments
Exercises 10–21 and 28–29 are structured so that students practice the same concepts whether they are assigned odd or even problems.

Real-World Connections
For Exercises 32 and 33, tell students that tires are normally identified by 3 numbers, such as 215/65/15. The first number is the width of the tire in millimeters (215 mm). The second number is the ratio of height to width. (The height is 65% of the width). The third number is the diameter of the wheel in inches (15 inches).

Additional Answers

20. $\dfrac{x + 4}{x + 3}$

21. $\dfrac{(x - 3)(x + 4)}{(x - 6)(x + 3)}$

DIFFERENTIATED HOMEWORK OPTIONS

Level	Assignment	Two-Day Option	
BL Basic	10–21, 28, 29, 36, 37, 39–54	11–21 odd, 29, 40, 41	10–22 even, 36, 37, 39, 42–54
OL Core	11–21 odd, 22–27, 29–37, 40–54	10–21, 28, 29, 40, 41	22–27, 30–37, 39, 42–54
AL Advanced /Pre-AP	24–54 (optional: 50–54)		

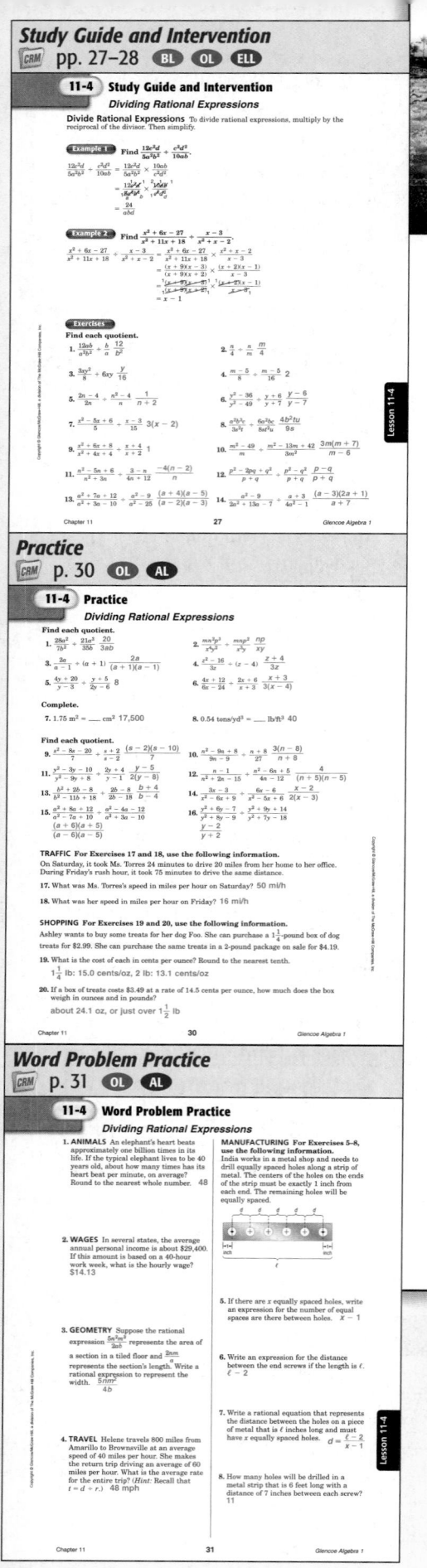

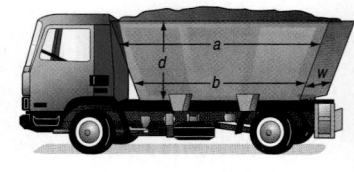

28. TRIATHLONS Sadie is training for an upcoming triathlon and plans to run the full length of the running section today. Jorge offered to ride his bicycle to help her maintain her pace. If Sadie wants to finish her run in about 4 hours and 28 minutes, how fast should Jorge ride in miles per hour? **about 5.87 mph**

29. VOLUNTEERING Tyrell is passing out orange drink from a 3.5-gallon cooler. If each cup of orange drink is 4.25 ounces, about how many cups can he hand out? (*Hint:* There are 128 ounces in a gallon.) **about 105.4 cups**

Real-World Link

The Ironman Championship Triathlon held in Hawaii consists of a 2.4-mile swim, a 112-mile bicycle ride, and a 26.2-mile run.

Source: www.infoplease.com

LANDSCAPING For Exercises 30 and 31, use the following information.

A landscaping supervisor needs to determine how many truckloads of dirt must be removed from a site before a brick patio can be completed. The truck bed has the shape shown at the right.

30. Write an equation involving units that represents the volume of the truck bed in cubic yards. Use the formula $V = \dfrac{d(a + b)}{2} \cdot w$ with $a = 10$ feet, $b = 17$ feet, $w = 4$ feet, and $d = 3.5$ feet. **See margin.**

31. The supervisor found that there are 45 cubic yards of dirt that must be removed from the site. Write an equation involving units that represents the number of truckloads that will be required to remove all of the dirt. How many trips will they have to take to remove all the dirt? **See margin.**

TRUCKS For Exercises 32 and 33, use the following information.

The speedometer of John's truck uses the revolutions of his tires to calculate the speed of the truck.

★**32.** How many times per minute do the tires revolve when the truck is traveling at 55 miles per hour? **about 711 rpm**

★**33.** Suppose John buys tires with a diameter of 30 inches. When the speedometer reads 55 miles per hour, the tires would still revolve at the same rate as before. However, with the new tires, the truck travels a different distance in each revolution. Calculate the actual speed when the speedometer reads 55 miles per hour. **63.5 mph**

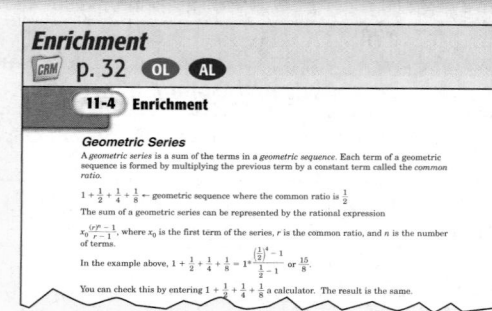

34. $\left(x - \dfrac{1}{2}\right)\left(x - \dfrac{3}{4}\right)$ (**x**)

SCULPTURE For Exercises 34 and 35, use the following information.

A sculptor had a block of marble in the shape of a cube with sides x feet long. A piece that was $\frac{1}{2}$-foot thick was chiseled from the bottom of the block. Later, the sculptor removed a piece $\frac{3}{4}$-foot wide from the side of the marble block.

34. Write a rational expression that represents the volume of the block of marble.

35. If the remaining marble was cut into pieces weighing 85 pounds each, write an expression that represents the weight of the original block of marble. **See margin.**

EXTRA PRACTICE
See pages 740, 754.

Math Online
Self-Check Quiz at ca.algebra1.com

H.O.T. Problems

36. OPEN ENDED Give an example of a real-world situation that could be modeled by the quotient of two rational expressions. Provide an example of this quotient. **See margin.**

37. REASONING Tell whether the following statement is *always, sometimes,* or *never* true. Explain your reasoning. *For a real number x, there is a reciprocal y.* **See margin.**

598 Chapter 11 Rational Expressions and Equations

38. CHALLENGE Which expression is *not* equivalent to the reciprocal of $\dfrac{x^2 - 4y^2}{x + 2y}$? Justify your answer. **d; Sample answer:** $\dfrac{1}{x} - \dfrac{1}{2y} = \dfrac{2y - x}{2xy}$

a. $\dfrac{1}{\dfrac{x^2 - 4y^2}{x + 2y}}$ b. $\dfrac{-1}{2y - x}$ c. $\dfrac{1}{x - 2y}$ d. $\dfrac{1}{x} - \dfrac{1}{2y}$

39. *Writing in Math* Use the information about soft drinks and aluminum on page 595 to explain how you can determine the number of aluminum soft drink cans made each year. Include a rational expression that will give the amount of new aluminum needed to produce x aluminum cans today when $\dfrac{5}{8}$ of the cans are recycled and 33 cans are produced from a pound of aluminum. **See margin.**

STANDARDS PRACTICE   10.0, 7MG2.3

40. Which expression could be used to represent the width of the rectangle? **C**

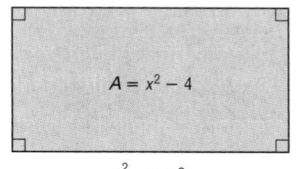

$A = x^2 - 4$

$\dfrac{x^2 - x - 2}{x + 1}$

A $x - 2$ C $x + 2$

B $(x + 2)(x - 2)^2$ D $(x + 2)(x - 2)$

41. REVIEW What is the surface area of the regular square pyramid? **F**

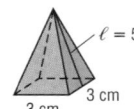

$\ell = 5$ cm
3 cm   3 cm

F   39 cm^2 H   83 cm^2

G   65 cm^2 J   117 cm^2

Spiral Review

Find each product. (Lesson 11-3)

42. $\dfrac{x - 5}{x^2 - 7x + 10} \cdot \dfrac{x - 2}{1}$ **1**

43. $\dfrac{x^2 + 3x - 10}{x^2 + 8x + 15} \cdot \dfrac{x^2 + 5x + 6}{x^2 + 4x + 4}$ $\dfrac{x - 2}{x + 2}$

44. $\dfrac{x + 4}{4y} \cdot \dfrac{16y}{x^2 + 7x + 12}$ $\dfrac{4}{x + 3}$

Simplify each expression. (Lesson 11-2)

45. $\dfrac{c - 6}{c^2 - 12c + 36}$ $\dfrac{1}{c - 6}$

46. $\dfrac{25 - x^2}{x^2 + x - 30}$ $\dfrac{x + 5}{x + 6}$

47. $\dfrac{a + 3}{a^2 + 4a + 3}$ $\dfrac{1}{a + 1}$

48. $\dfrac{n^2 - 16}{n^2 - 8n + 16}$ $\dfrac{n + 4}{n - 4}$

49. MANUFACTURING Global Sporting Equipment sells tennis racket covers for $2.35 each. It costs the company $0.68 in materials and labor for each cover and $1300 each month for equipment and building rental. Write an equation that gives the net profit the company makes, if x is the number of racket covers they can make in a month. (Lesson 4-4) $y = 1.67x - 1300$

GET READY for the Next Lesson

PREREQUISITE SKILL Simplify. (Lesson 7-2)

50. $\dfrac{6x^2}{x^4}$ $\dfrac{6}{x^2}$

51. $\dfrac{5m^4}{25m}$ $\dfrac{m^3}{5}$

52. $\dfrac{b^6c^3}{b^3c^6}$ $\dfrac{b^3}{c^3}$

53. $\dfrac{12x^3y^2}{28x^4y}$ $\dfrac{3y}{7x}$

54. $\dfrac{7x^4z^2}{z^3}$ $\dfrac{7x^4}{z}$

Pre-AP Activity   Use as an Extension.

Write $\dfrac{5 - x}{x - 5} \div \dfrac{1}{(x + 5)}$ on the board. Ask students to explain why $\dfrac{5 - x}{x - 5} \div \dfrac{1}{(x + 5)}$ is equal to $-x - 5$ and why x cannot equal 5 or -5.

$\dfrac{5 - x}{x - 5} \div \dfrac{1}{(x + 5)} = \dfrac{-1(x - 5)}{x - 5} \cdot \dfrac{(x + 5)}{1} = -1(x + 5) = -x - 5$

READING MATH

1 Focus

Have students describe what they think of when they see a fraction. Some may think of fractions, no matter the value of the numerator or denominator, as numbers that are less than one. Others may think of fractions as division problems. Discuss with students what the different parts of a fraction mean.

2 Teach

Rules for Decoding The concept that a single denominator divides each term of the numerator will be very important to students when dividing polynomials. Give students additional problems of this type so they can practice rewriting (decoding) them as separate fractions. Have the class as a whole work through Reading to Learn 1–6. Allow time for students to complete Reading to Learn 7–12.

3 Assess

Ask students to summarize what they have learned about writing and simplifying rational expressions.

ELL English Language Learners may benefit from writing key concepts from this activity in their native languages and then in English.

Standard 12.0 Students simplify fractions with polynomials in the numerator and denominator by factoring both and reducing them to the lowest terms. (Key)

Rational Expressions

Several concepts need to be applied when reading rational expressions.

A fraction bar acts as a grouping symbol, where the entire numerator is divided by the entire denominator.

EXAMPLE

 Read the expression $\frac{6x + 4}{10}$.

It is <u>correct</u> to read the expression as *the quantity six x plus four divided by ten*.

It is <u>incorrect</u> to read the expression as *six x divided by ten plus four, or six x plus four divided by ten*.

If a fraction consists of two or more terms divided by a one-term denominator, the denominator divides each term.

EXAMPLE

 Simplify $\frac{6x + 4}{10}$.

It is <u>correct</u> to write $\frac{6x + 4}{10} = \frac{6x}{10} + \frac{4}{10}$.

$$= \frac{3x}{5} + \frac{2}{5} \quad \text{or} \quad \frac{3x + 2}{5}$$

It is also <u>correct</u> to write $\frac{6x + 4}{10} = \frac{2(3x + 2)}{2 \cdot 5}$.

$$= \frac{2(3x + 2)}{2 \cdot 5} \quad \text{or} \quad \frac{3x + 2}{5}$$

It is <u>incorrect</u> to write $\frac{6x + 4}{10} = \frac{\overset{3x}{6x} + 4}{\underset{5}{10}} = \frac{3x + 4}{5}$.

Reading to Learn

Write the verbal translation of each rational expression. 1–6. See margin.

1. $\frac{m + 2}{4}$

2. $\frac{3x}{x - 1}$

3. $\frac{a + 2}{a^2 + 8}$

4. $\frac{x^2 - 25}{x + 5}$

5. $\frac{x^2 - 3x + 18}{x - 2}$

6. $\frac{x^2 + 2x - 35}{x^2 - x - 20}$

Simplify each expression.

7. $\frac{3x + 6}{9} \quad \frac{x + 2}{3}$

8. $\frac{2n - 12}{8} \quad \frac{n - 3}{2}$

9. $\frac{5x^2 - 25x}{10x} \quad \frac{x - 5}{2}$

10. $\frac{x + 3}{x^2 + 7x + 12} \quad \frac{1}{x + 4}$

11. $\frac{x + y}{x^2 + 2xy + y^2} \quad \frac{1}{x + y}$

12. $\frac{x^2 - 16}{x^2 - 8x + 16} \quad \frac{x + 4}{x - 4}$

600 Chapter 11 Rational Expressions and Equations

Additional Answers

1. Sample answer: the quantity *m* plus two, divided by 4

2. Sample answer: 3*x* divided by the quantity *x* minus 1

3. Sample answer: the quantity *a* plus 2 divided by the quantity *a* squared plus 8

4. Sample answer: the quantity *x* squared minus 25 divided by the quantity *x* plus 5

5. Sample answer: the quantity *x* squared minus 3*x* plus 18 divided by the quantity *x* minus 2

6. Sample answer: the quantity *x* squared plus 2*x* minus 35 divided by the quantity *x* squared minus *x* minus 20

Main Ideas

- Divide a polynomial by a monomial.
- Divide a polynomial by a binomial.

Standard 10.0 Students add, subtract, multiply, **and divide monomials and polynomials. Students solve multistep problems, including word problems, by using these techniques.** (Key, CAHSEE)

▶ GET READY for the Lesson

Suppose a partial bolt of fabric is used to make marching band flags. The original bolt was 36 yards long, and $7\frac{1}{2}$ yards of the fabric were used to make a banner for the band. Each flag requires $1\frac{1}{2}$ yards of fabric. The expression $\dfrac{36 \text{ yards} - 7\frac{1}{2} \text{ yards}}{1\frac{1}{2} \text{ yards}}$ can be used to represent the number of flags that can be made using the bolt of fabric.

1 **Focus**

Standards Alignment

Before Lesson 11-5
Multiply and divide monomials from   Standard 7AF2.2

Lesson 11-5
Solve multi-step problems with polynomials from   Standard 1A10.0

After Lesson 11-5
Adept at operations on polynomials from   Standard 2A3.0

Divide Polynomials By Monomials To divide a polynomial by a monomial, divide each term of the polynomial by the monomial.

EXAMPLE Divide Polynomials by Monomials

1 **a.** Find $(3r^2 - 15r) \div 3r$.

$(3r^2 - 15r) \div 3r = \dfrac{3r^2 - 15r}{3r}$ Write as a rational expression.

$= \dfrac{3r^2}{3r} - \dfrac{15r}{3r}$ Divide each term by 3r.

$= \dfrac{3\overset{r}{r^2}}{3\underset{1}{r}} - \dfrac{15\overset{5}{r}}{3\underset{1}{r}}$ Simplify each term.

$= r - 5$ Simplify.

b. Find $(n^2 + 10n + 12) \div 5n$.

$(n^2 + 10n + 12) \div 5n = \dfrac{n^2 + 10n + 12}{5n}$ Write as a rational expression.

$= \dfrac{n^2}{5n} + \dfrac{10n}{5n} + \dfrac{12}{5n}$ Divide each term by 5n.

$= \dfrac{n^2}{5\underset{5}{n}} + \dfrac{10\overset{2}{n}}{5\underset{1}{n}} + \dfrac{12}{5n}$ Simplify each term.

$= \dfrac{n}{5} + 2 + \dfrac{12}{5n}$ Simplify.

✓ CHECK Your Progress Find each quotient.

1A. $(3q^3 - 6q) \div 3q$ $q^2 - 2$

1B. $(4t^5 - 5t^2 - 12) \div 2t^2$ $2t^3 - \dfrac{5}{2} - \dfrac{6}{t^2}$

Study Tip

Alternative Method
You could also solve Example 1a as
$\dfrac{3r^2 - 15r}{3r} = \dfrac{3r(r-5)}{3r}$ or $r - 5$.

2 **Teach**

Scaffolding Questions
Have students read *Get Ready for the Lesson.*
Ask:
- How might you read the expression given? the quantity 36 yards minus seven and one-half yards, divided by one and one-half yards
- How can the fraction be written so that the denominator divides each term? $\dfrac{36 \text{ yards}}{1\frac{1}{2} \text{ yards}} - \dfrac{7\frac{1}{2} \text{ yards}}{1\frac{1}{2} \text{ yards}}$
- Use a calculator to find the number of flags that can be made using the bolt of fabric. 19 flags

Lesson 11-5 Resources

Chapter 11 Resource Masters
Lesson Reading Guide, p. 34 BL OL ELL
Study Guide and Intervention, pp. 35–36
BL OL ELL
Skills Practice, p. 37 BL OL
Practice, p. 38 OL AL
Word Problem Practice, p. 39 OL AL
Enrichment, p. 40 OL AL
Quiz 2, p. 73

Transparencies
5-Minute Check Transparency 11-5
Additional Print Resources
Noteables™ Interactive Study Notebook with Foldables™

Technology
ca.algebra1.com
Interactive Classroom CD-ROM
AssignmentWorks CD-ROM
Graphing Calculator Easy Files

Lesson 11-5 Dividing Polynomials **601**

Divide Polynomials by Monomials

Example 1 shows how to divide a polynomial by a monomial by dividing each term of the polynomial by the monomial.

 Formative Assessment

Use the Check Your Progress exercises after each example to determine students' understanding of concepts.

Algebra Lab

Each student or group of students will need algebra tiles and a product mat. Point out to students that the divisor in this example is found along the horizontal axis of the mat, and the quotient is found along the vertical axis. Suggest that students arrange their problems in this way as they use algebra tiles in this activity.

 **Preventing Errors**

As an alternative to dividing each term of the polynomial by the monomial, students can factor and then eliminate the GCF.

Remind students that only factors can be divided, not the terms.

Divide Polynomials by Binomials You can use algebra tiles to model some quotients of polynomials.

 **ALGEBRA LAB**

Dividing Polynomials

Use algebra tiles to find $(x^2 + 3x + 2) \div (x + 1)$.

Step 1 Model the polynomial $x^2 + 3x + 2$.

Step 2 Place the x^2 tile at the corner of the product mat. Place one of the 1 tiles as shown to make a length of $x + 1$ because $x = 1$ is the divisor.

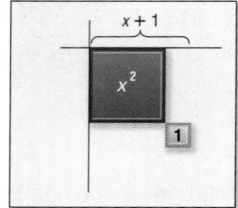

Step 3 Use the remaining tiles to make a rectangular array. Make sure the length of the rectangle, $x + 1$, does not change.

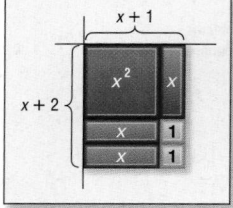

The width of the array, $x + 2$, is the quotient. This is because the dividend now fills the entire rectangular area.

MODEL AND ANALYZE
Use algebra tiles to find each quotient.

1. $(x^2 + 3x - 4) \div (x - 1)$ $(x + 4)$
2. $(x^2 - 5x + 6) \div (x - 2)$ $(x - 3)$
3. $(x^2 - 16) \div (x + 4)$ $(x - 4)$
4. $(2x^2 - 4x - 6) \div (x - 3)$ $(2x + 2)$
5. Describe what happens when you try to model $(3x^2 - 4x + 3) \div (x + 2)$. What do you think the result means? You cannot do it. There is a remainder.

EXAMPLE Divide a Polynomial by a Binomial

2 Find $(s^2 + 6s - 7) \div (s + 7)$.

$(s^2 + 6s - 7) \div (s + 7) = \dfrac{s^2 + 6s - 7}{(s + 7)}$ Write as a rational expression.

$= \dfrac{(s + 7)(s - 1)}{(s + 7)}$ Factor the numerator.

$= \dfrac{(\overset{1}{\cancel{s + 7}})(s - 1)}{\underset{1}{\cancel{(s + 7)}}}$ Divide by the GCF.

$= s - 1$ Simplify.

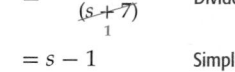 **Your Progress** Find each quotient.

2A. $(b^2 - 2b - 15) \div (3 + b)$ $b - 5$ **2B.** $(x^2 + 3x - 28) \div (x + 7)$ $(x - 4)$

If you cannot factor and divide by a common factor, you can use a long division process similar to the one you use to divide numbers.

EXAMPLE   Long Division

3 Find $(x^2 + 3x - 24) \div (x - 4)$.

Step 1 Divide the first term of the dividend, x^2, by the first term of the divisor, x.

$$
\begin{array}{r}
x \phantom{{}+ 3x - 24} \\
x - 4 \overline{\smash{)}\, x^2 + 3x - 24} \\
\underline{(-)\ x^2 - 4x} \\
7x
\end{array}
$$

$x^2 \div x = x$

Multiply x and $x - 4$.

Subtract.

Step 2 Divide the first term of the partial dividend, $7x - 24$, by the first term of the divisor, x.

$$
\begin{array}{r}
x + 7 \phantom{{}- 24} \\
x - 4 \overline{\smash{)}\, x^2 + 3x - 24} \\
\underline{(-)\ x^2 - 4x} \\
7x - 24 \\
\underline{(-)\ 7x - 28} \\
4
\end{array}
$$

$7x \div x = 7$

Subtract and bring down the -24.

Multiply 7 and $x - 4$.

Subtract.

So, $(x^2 + 3x - 24) \div (x - 4)$ is $x + 7$ with a remainder of 4. This answer can be written as $x + 7 + \dfrac{4}{x - 4}$.

 **CHECK Your Progress**   Find each quotient.

3A. $(y^2 + 3y + 12) \div (y + 3)$ **3B.** $(3x^2 + 9x - 15) \div (x + 5)$

3A. $y + \dfrac{12}{y + 3}$

3B. $3x - 6 + \dfrac{15}{x + 5}$

Some dividends have missing terms. These are terms that have zero as their coefficient. In this situation, you must rewrite the dividend, including the missing term with a coefficient of zero.

EXAMPLE   Polynomial with Missing Terms

4 Find $(a^3 + 8a - 24) \div (a - 2)$.

$$
\begin{array}{r}
a^2 + 2a + 12 \\
a - 2 \overline{\smash{)}\, a^3 + 0a^2 + 8a - 24} \\
\underline{(-)\ a^3 - 2a^2} \\
2a^2 + 8a \\
\underline{(-)\ 2a^2 - 4a} \\
12a - 24 \\
\underline{(-)\ 12a - 24} \\
0
\end{array}
$$

Insert an a^2 term that has a coefficient of 0.

Multiply a^2 and $a - 2$.

Subtract and bring down $8a$.

Multiply $2a$ and $a - 2$.

Subtract and bring down 24.

Multiply 12 and $a - 2$.

Subtract.

Therefore, $(a^3 + 8a - 24) \div (a - 2) = a^2 + 2a + 12$.

4A. $c^3 + 6 - \dfrac{22}{c + 2}$

4B. $3x^2 - 7x + 5 - \dfrac{11}{2x + 10}$

CHECK Your Progress   Find each quotient.

4A. $(c^4 + 2c^3 + 6c - 10) \div (c + 2)$ **4B.** $(6x^3 + 16x^2 - 60x + 39) \div (2x + 10)$

Online Personal Tutor at ca.algebra1.com

Lesson 11-5 Dividing Polynomials   **603**

Study Tip

Factors

In Example 3, since there is a nonzero remainder, $x - 4$ is not a factor of $x^2 + 3x - 24$.

COncepts in MOtion

Animation
ca.algebra1.com

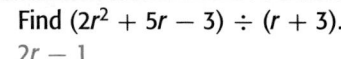

Focus on Mathematical Content

Long Division Long division can be used to divide a polynomial by a binomial whether or not the polynomial can be factored. If the polynomial is missing a term, use 0 for the coefficient of the missing term, then divide by the binomial. This is possible because a term with a zero coefficient has a value of zero, so it does not affect the quotient. It is simply a placeholder.

Divide Polynomials by Binomials

Example 2 shows how to divide a polynomial by a binomial by factoring the dividend. **Example 3** shows how to use long division to divide a polynomial by a binomial when the polynomial cannot be factored. **Example 4** shows how to rename a polynomial with a missing term, in order to divide the polynomial by a binomial.

ADDITIONAL EXAMPLES

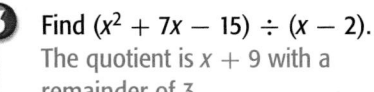 **2** Find $(2r^2 + 5r - 3) \div (r + 3)$.
$2r - 1$

3 Find $(x^2 + 7x - 15) \div (x - 2)$.
The quotient is $x + 9$ with a remainder of 3.

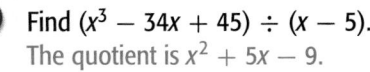 **4** Find $(x^3 - 34x + 45) \div (x - 5)$.
The quotient is $x^2 + 5x - 9$.

Tips for New Teachers

Preventing Errors

Remind students to pay close attention to the signs of the binomials as they perform long division. Since each binomial is subtracted, the sign of the second term in the binomial changes.

3 Practice

Formative Assessment

Use Exercises 1–11 to check for understanding.

Use the chart at the bottom of this page to customize assignments for your students.

Odd/Even Assignments

Exercises 12–29 are structured so that students practice the same concepts whether they are assigned odd or even problems.

Additional Answers

24. $3p + 2 - \dfrac{1}{p + 6}$

25. $3x^2 + 2x - 3 - \dfrac{1}{x + 2}$

26. $3x^2 + \dfrac{6}{2x - 3}$

27. $3g^2 + 2g + 3 - \dfrac{2}{3g - 2}$

28. $3n^2 - 2n + 3 + \dfrac{3}{2n + 3}$

32.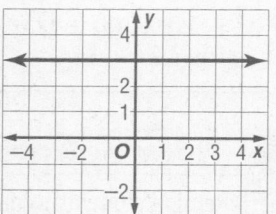

34. $x - 1 + \dfrac{1}{x + 1}$; yes

40. No, there will always be a difference of 15 minutes between the two times, and so the ratio can never be equal to one.

48. $3 + \dfrac{7}{x - 1}$

49. See Ch. 11 Answer Appendix.

50. The graph of the quotient ignoring the remainder is an asymptote of the graph of the function.

51. As x approaches 1 from the left y approaches negative infinity, and as x approaches y from the right y approaches positive infinity.

54. $\dfrac{212 - 0.9\left(\dfrac{x}{500}\right)}{212 - 0.9\left(\dfrac{x}{1000}\right)}$

✓ CHECK Your Understanding

Find each quotient. 7. $b + 2 - \dfrac{3}{2b - 1}$

Example 1 (p. 601)
1. $(5q^2 + q) \div q$ $5q + 1$
2. $(4z^3 + 1) \div 2z$ $2z^2 + \dfrac{1}{2z}$
3. $(4x^3 + 2x^2 - 5) \div 2x$ $2x^2 + x - \dfrac{5}{2x}$
4. $\dfrac{14a^2b^2 + 35ab^2 + 2a^2}{7a^2b^2}$ $2 + \dfrac{5}{a} + \dfrac{2}{7b^2}$

Example 2 (p. 602)
5. $(n^2 + 7n + 12) \div (n + 3)$ $n + 4$
6. $(r^2 + 12r + 36) \div (r + 9)$ $r + 3 + \dfrac{9}{r + 9}$

Example 3 (p. 603)
7. $(2b^2 + 3b - 5) \div (2b - 1)$
8. $(x^2 + x + 12) \div (x - 3)$ $x + 4$

Example 4 (p. 603)
9. $\dfrac{4m^3 + 5m - 21}{2m - 3}$ $2m^2 + 3m + 7$
10. $\dfrac{2n^4 + 2n^2 - 4}{n^2 - 1}$ $2n^2 + 4$

11. **ENVIRONMENT** The equation $C = \dfrac{120{,}000p}{1 - p}$ models the cost C in dollars for a manufacturer to reduce pollutants by p percent. How much will the company have to pay to remove 75% of the pollutants it emits? **$360,000**

Exercises

Find each quotient. 24–28. See margin.

HOMEWORK HELP	
For Exercises	See Examples
12–17	1
18–21	2
22–25	3
26–29	4

Exercise Levels:
A: 12–29
B: 30–54
C: 55–60

16. $3s - \dfrac{5}{t} + \dfrac{8t}{s^2}$

22. $z - 9 + \dfrac{33}{z + 7}$

12. $(9m^2 + 5m) \div 6m$ $\dfrac{3}{2}m + \dfrac{5}{6}$
13. $(8k^2 - 6) \div 2k$ $4k - \dfrac{3}{k}$
14. $(x^2 + 9x - 7) \div 3x$ $\dfrac{x}{3} + 3 - \dfrac{7}{3x}$
15. $(a^2 + 7a - 28) \div 7a$ $\dfrac{a}{7} + 1 - \dfrac{4}{a}$
16. $\dfrac{9s^3t^2 - 15s^2t + 24t^3}{3s^2t^2}$
17. $\dfrac{12a^3b + 16ab^3 - 8ab}{4ab}$ $3a^2 + 4b^2 - 2$
18. $(x^2 + 9x + 20) \div (x + 5)$ $x + 4$
19. $(x^2 + 6x - 16) \div (x - 2)$ $x + 8$
20. $(n^2 - 2n - 35) \div (n + 5)$ $n - 7$
21. $(s^2 + 11s + 18) \div (s + 9)$ $s + 2$
22. $(z^2 - 2z - 30) \div (z + 7)$
23. $(a^2 + 4a - 22) \div (a - 3)$ $a + 7 - \dfrac{1}{a - 3}$
24. $(3p^2 + 20p + 11) \div (p + 6)$
25. $(3x^3 + 8x^2 + x - 7) \div (x + 2)$
26. $(6x^3 - 9x^2 + 6) \div (2x - 3)$
27. $(9g^3 + 5g - 8) \div (3g - 2)$

28. Determine the quotient when $6n^3 + 5n^2 + 12$ is divided by $2n + 3$.
29. What is the quotient when $4t^3 + 17t^2 - 1$ is divided by $4t + 1$? $t^2 + 4t - 1$

GEOMETRY For Exercises 30–34, refer to the diagrams at the right. 31. $7^2 \div 8$ 33. $x^2 \div (x + 1) = x - 1 + \dfrac{1}{x + 1}$

30. The first picture models $6^2 \div 7$. Notice that the square is divided into seven equal parts. What are the quotient and the remainder? $5\dfrac{1}{7}$

31. What division problem does the second picture model?

★32. Draw diagrams for $3^2 \div 4$ and $2^2 \div 3$. **See margin.**

33. Do you observe a pattern in the previous exercises? Express this pattern algebraically.

★34. Use long division to find $x^2 \div (x + 1)$. Does this result match your expression from the previous exercise?
See margin.

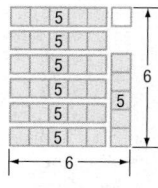

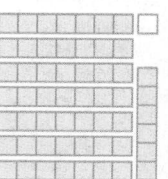

DIFFERENTIATED HOMEWORK OPTIONS

Level	Assignment	Two-Day Option	
BL Basic	12–29, 55, 56, 60–71	13–29 odd, 61, 62	12–28 even, 55, 56, 60, 63–71
OL Core	13–51 odd, 52–56, 60–71	12–29, 61, 62	30–56, 60, 63–71
AL Advanced /Pre-AP	30–71 (optional: 68–71)		

Use long division to find the expression that represents the missing side.

35.

$A = x^2 - 3x - 18$? $x + 3$

$x - 6$

36.

$A = 4x^2 + 16x + 16$ $2x + 4$ $2x + 4$

?

ROAD TRIP For Exercises 37–40, use the following information.
The Ski Club is taking two vans to Colorado. The first van has been on the road for 20 minutes, and the second van has been on the road for 35 minutes.

★ **37.** Write an expression for the amount of time that each van has spent on the road after an additional t minutes. $t + 20; t + 35$

38. $\dfrac{t + 20}{t + 35}$;
$1 - \dfrac{15}{t + 35}$

38. Write a ratio for the first van's time on the road to the second van's time on the road. Then use long division to rewrite this ratio as an expression.

★ **39.** Use the expression you wrote to find the ratio of the first van's time on the road to the second van's time on the road after 15 minutes, 60 minutes, 200 minutes, and 500 minutes. $0.7; 0.84; 0.946; 0.97$

40. As t increases, the ratio of the vans' times approaches 1. If t continues to increase, will this ratio ever be equal to 1? **See margin.**

43. $3x^2 - 12 + \dfrac{16}{x} + 5$

45. $-x^4 - 4x^2 + 2x$

Find each quotient. 41. $9d + 3$

41. $(21d^2 - 29d - 12) \div \left(\dfrac{7}{3}d - 4\right)$

42. $(x^2 - 4x + 4) \div (x + 3)$ $x - 7 + \dfrac{25}{x + 3}$

43. $(3x^3 + 15x^2 - 12x) - 44 \div (x + 5)$

44. $\left(\dfrac{3}{2}x^2 - 8x - 32\right) \div (3x + 8)$ $\dfrac{1}{2}x - 4$

45. $\left(-5x^5 - \dfrac{5}{2}x^4 - 20x^3 + 5x\right) \div \left(5x + \dfrac{5}{2}\right)$

46. $(14y^5 + 21y^4 - 6y^3 - 9y^2 + 32y + 48) \div (2y + 3)$ $7y^4 - 3y^2 + 16$

★ **47. GEOMETRY** The volume of a prism with a triangular base is $10w^3 + 23w^2 + 5w - 2$. The height of the prism is $2w + 1$, and the height of the triangle is $5w - 1$. What is the measure of the base of the triangle? $\left(Hint: V = \dfrac{1}{2}Bh\right)$ $2w + 4$

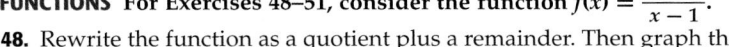

$5w - 1$

$2w + 1$

48–51. See margin.

FUNCTIONS For Exercises 48–51, consider the function $f(x) = \dfrac{3x + 4}{x - 1}$.

48. Rewrite the function as a quotient plus a remainder. Then graph the quotient, ignoring the remainder.

49. Graph the original function using a graphing calculator.

50. How are the graphs of the function and quotient related?

51. What happens to the graph near the excluded value of x?

Real-World Link

Since water boils at a lower temperature in high altitudes, more water is lost through evaporation when cooking. To counteract this, add about 20% more water to the recipe.

Source: crisco.com

BOILING POINT For Exercises 52–54, use the following information.
The temperature at which water boils decreases by approximately 0.9°F for every 500 feet you are above sea level. The boiling point of water at sea level is 212°F.

52. Write an equation that gives the temperature at which water boils for x every foot you are above sea level. $T = 212° - \left(\dfrac{0.9}{500}\right)x$

53. Mount Whitney, the tallest point in California, is 14,494 feet above sea level. At approximately what temperature does water boil on Mount Whitney? $185.9°F$

54. Write an expression for the quotient of the boiling point of water at any height x and the boiling point of water at half that height. **See margin.**

EXTRA PRACTICE
See pages 740, 754.

Math online
Self-Check Quiz at
ca.algebra1.com

BL = Below Grade Level
OL = On Grade Level
AL = Above Grade Level
ELL = English Language Learner

Additional pages not shown:

CRM Lesson Reading Guide, p. 34 **BL** **OL** **ELL**

CRM Skills Practice, p. 37 **BL** **OL**

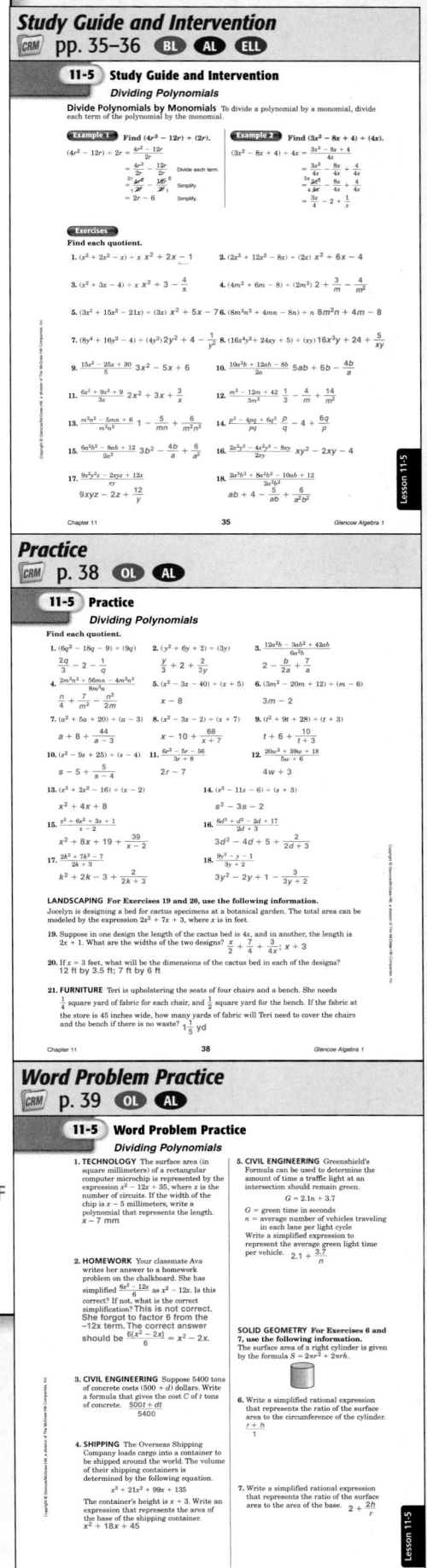

Practice
CRM p. 38 **OL** **AL**

11-5 Practice
Dividing Polynomials

Word Problem Practice
CRM p. 39 **OL** **AL**

11-5 Word Problem Practice
Dividing Polynomials

Enrichment
CRM p. 40 **OL** **AL**

11-5 Enrichment

Synthetic Division

Assess

Name the Math On an index card, have students divide $x^2 + 9x - 2$ by $x + 1$. Beside each step, have students write one or two sentences explaining and justifying their methods.

✓ **Formative Assessment**

Check for student understanding of concepts in Lessons 11-4 and 11-5.

CRM **Quiz 2, p. 73.**

Additional Answers

60. Sample answer: Division can be used to find the number of pieces of fabric available when you divide a large piece of fabric into smaller pieces. When you simplify the right side of the equation, the numerator is $a - b$ and the denominator is c. This is the same as the expression on the left.

68. $4m^3 + 6n^2 - n$

69. $4x^2 + 13xy + 2y^2$

70. $-2a^3 - 2a^2b + b^2 - 3b^3$

71. $2g^3 - 4g^2 - 2h$

Additional Answers (p. 607)

2.

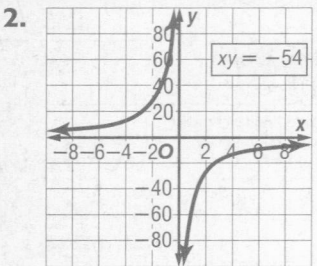

16. $\dfrac{2x}{a + 9}$

17. $\dfrac{4}{5(n + 5)}$

18. $\dfrac{1}{(3x + 1)(x - 1)}$

H.O.T. Problems

55. OPEN ENDED Write a third-degree polynomial that has a missing term. Rewrite the polynomial so that it can be divided by $x + 5$ using long division. Sample answer: $x^3 + 2x^2 + 8$; $x^3 + 2x^2 + 0x + 8$

56. Which One Doesn't Belong? Select the divisor of $2x^2 - 9x + 9$ that does not belong with the other three. Explain your reasoning.

| $x + 3$ | $x - 2$ | $2x - 3$ | $2x + 3$ |

$2x - 3$; This is the only divisor that gives a remainder of 0.

CHALLENGE Find the value of k in each situation.

57. k is an integer and $x + k$ is a factor of $x^2 + 7x + 12$. **3, 4**

58. When $x^2 + 7x + k$ is divided by $x + 2$, there is a remainder of 2. **12**

59. $x + 7$ is a factor of $x^2 - 2x - k$. **63**

60. *Writing in Math* Use the information about sewing on page 601 to describe how division can be used in sewing. Include a convincing argument to show that $\dfrac{a - b}{c} = \dfrac{a}{c} - \dfrac{b}{c}$. **See margin.**

STANDARDS PRACTICE 10.0, 7MG3.3

61. Which expression represents the length of the rectangle? **D**

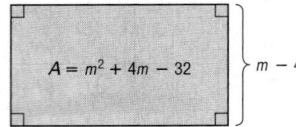

$A = m^2 + 4m - 32$ } $m - 4$

A $m + 7$ **C** $m - 7$
B $m - 8$ **D** $m + 8$

62. REVIEW Paul and Lupe are building a shelter for their dog. The length of the shelter is 4.5 feet and the width is 2.5 feet. If each corner is a right angle, what is the length of each diagonal? **H**

F 26.5 feet   **H** 5.15 feet
G 20.25 feet   **J** 3.25 feet

Spiral Review

Find each quotient. (Lesson 11-4)

63. $\dfrac{x^2 + 5x + 6}{x^2 - x - 12} \div \dfrac{x + 2}{x^2 + x - 20}$ $x + 5$

64. $\dfrac{m^2 + m - 6}{m^2 + 8m + 15} \div \dfrac{m^2 - m - 2}{m^2 + 9m + 20}$ $\dfrac{m + 4}{m + 1}$

Find each product. (Lesson 11-3)

65. $\dfrac{b^2 + 19b + 84}{b - 3} \cdot \dfrac{b^2 - 9}{b^2 + 15b + 36}$ $b + 7$

66. $\dfrac{z^2 + 16z + 39}{z^2 + 9z + 18} \cdot \dfrac{z + 5}{z^2 + 18z + 65}$ $\dfrac{1}{z + 6}$

67. BUSINESS Jorge Martinez has budgeted $150 to have business cards printed. A card printer charges $11 to set up each job and an additional $6 per box of 100 cards printed. What is the greatest number of cards Mr. Martinez can have printed? (Lesson 6-3) **2300 cards**

GET READY for the Next Lesson

PREREQUISITE SKILL Find each sum. (Lesson 7-4) **68–71. See margin.**

68. $(6n^2 - 6n + 10m^3) + (5n - 6m^3)$ **69.** $(3x^2 + 4xy - 2y^2) + (x^2 + 9xy + 4y^2)$

70. $(a^3 - b^3) + (-3a^3 - 2a^2b + b^2 - 2b^3)$ **71.** $(2g^3 + 6h) + (-4g^2 - 8h)$

Pre-AP Activity Use as an Extension.

Ask half the class to find the value of $(2x^2 - 13x + 15) \div (2x - 3)$ for $x = 12$ by first substituting, then simplifying. Ask the other half of the class to divide first, then substitute. Have the students discuss which of the two methods made it easier to evaluate the expression. For both methods, the resulting value is 7.

Graph each variation if y varies inversely as x. (Lesson 11-1) **1–2. See margin.**

1. $y = 28$ when $x = 7$

2. $y = -6$ when $x = 9$

3. If y varies inversely as x and $y = 3$ when $x = 6$, find x when $y = -14$. $\frac{-9}{7} = x$

4. If y varies inversely as x and $y = -6$ when $x = 9$, find y when $x = 6$. $-9 = y$

5. DESIGN The height of a rectangular tank varies inversely with the area of the base. If the tank has a height of 2 feet when the area of the base is 9 square feet, how tall will the tank be if the area of the base is 6 square feet? (Lesson 11-1) **3 ft**

State the excluded value(s). (Lesson 11-2)

6. $\frac{16x + 5}{3x}$ 0

7. $\frac{12y + 4}{3y + 6}$ −2

8. $\frac{x^2 + 1}{x^2 - 1}$ 1 and −1

9. $\frac{15x}{3x^2 - x - 2}$ 1 and $-\frac{2}{3}$

Simplify each expression. (Lesson 11-2) **12.** $\frac{b+1}{b-9}$

10. $\frac{28a^2}{49ab}$ $\frac{4a}{7b}$

11. $\frac{y + 3y^2}{3y + 1}$ y

12. $\frac{b^2 - 3b - 4}{b^2 - 13b + 36}$

13. $\frac{3n^2 + 5n - 2}{3n^2 - 13n + 4}$ $\frac{n+2}{n-4}$

14. LANDSCAPING Kenyi is helping his parents landscape their yard and needs to move some large rocks. He plans to use a 6-foot bar as a lever. He positions the fulcrum 1 foot from the end of the bar touching the rock. If the rock weighs 200 pounds, how much force does he need to apply to the bar to lift the rock? (Lesson 11-2) **40 pounds**

Find each product. (Lesson 11-3) **16–18. See margin.**

15. $\frac{3m^2}{2m} \cdot \frac{18m^2}{9m}$ $3m^2$

16. $\frac{5a + 10}{10x^2} \cdot \frac{4x^3}{a^2 + 11a + 18}$

17. $\frac{4n + 8}{n^2 - 25} \cdot \frac{n - 5}{5n + 10}$

18. $\frac{x + 1}{3x^2 - 5x - 2} \cdot \frac{x - 2}{x^2 - 1}$

19. $\frac{x^2 - x - 6}{x^2 - 9} \cdot \frac{x^2 + 7x + 12}{x^2 + 4x + 4}$ $\frac{x+4}{x+2}$

20. $\frac{a^2 + 7a + 10}{a + 1} \cdot \frac{3a + 3}{a + 2}$ $3a + 15$

21. TOYS If a remote control car is advertised to travel at a speed of 44 feet per second, how fast can the car travel in miles per hour? (Lesson 11-3) **30 mph**

22. MULTIPLE CHOICE Which expression *best* represents the length of the rectangle? (Lesson 11-4) **C**

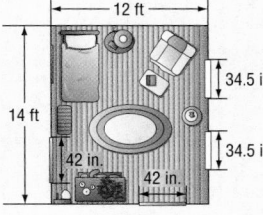

$A = x^2 - 9$ $\frac{x^2 - x - 12}{x - 4}$

A $x + 4$

B $x + 3$

C $x - 3$

D $x - 4$

Find each quotient. (Lessons 11-4 and 11-5)

23. $\frac{a}{a + 3} \div \frac{a + 11}{a + 3}$ $\frac{a}{a + 11}$

24. $\frac{4z + 8}{z + 3} \div (z + 2)$ $\frac{4}{z + 3}$

25. $\frac{b^2 - 9}{4b} \div (b - 3)$ $\frac{b + 3}{4b}$

26. $\frac{m^2 - 16}{5m} \div (m + 4)$ $\frac{m - 4}{5m}$

27. $\frac{(2x - 1)(x - 2)}{(x - 2)(x - 3)} \div \frac{(2x - 1)(x + 5)}{(x - 3)(x - 1)}$ $\frac{x - 1}{x + 5}$

28. $(9xy^2 - 15xy + 3) \div 3xy$ $3y - 5 + \frac{1}{xy}$

29. $(2x^2 - 7x - 16) \div (2x + 3)$ $x - 5 - \frac{1}{2x + 3}$

30. $\frac{y^2 - 19y + 9}{y - 4}$ $y - 15 - \frac{51}{y - 4}$

31. DECORATING Anoki wants to put a decorative border 3 feet above the floor around his bedroom walls. If the border comes in 5-yard rolls, how many rolls of border should Anoki buy? (Lesson 11-5) **3 rolls**

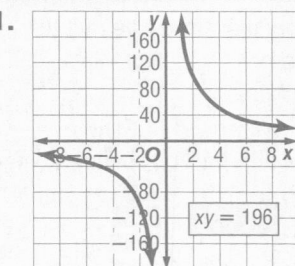

12 ft
34.5 in.
14 ft
34.5 in.
42 in.   42 in.

Mid-Chapter Quiz

Formative Assessment

Use the Mid-Chapter Quiz to assess students' progress in the first half of the chapter.

For problems answered incorrectly, have students review the lessons indicated in parentheses.

Summative Assessment

[CRM] Mid-Chapter Test, p. 75

[CRM] Customize and create multiple versions of your Mid-Chapter Tests and their answer keys.

FOLDABLES **Foldables™**
Study Organizer **Follow-Up**

Before students complete the Mid-Chapter Quiz, encourage them to review the information under the labeled tabs for Lessons 11-1 through 11-5 in their Foldables.

Additional Answers

1.

$xy = 196$

Data-Driven Decision Making	Exercises	Lesson	Standard	Resources for Review
Diagnostic Teaching Based on the results of the Chapter 11 Mid-Chapter Quiz, use the following to review concepts that students continue to find challenging.	1–5	11–1	13.0	[CRM] Study Guide and Intervention pp. 6–7, 13–14, 20–21, 27–28, 35–36 **Math Online** • Extra Examples • Personal Tutor • Concepts in Motion
	6–14	11–2	12.0	
	15–21	11–3	13.0	
	22–30	11–4	13.0	
	23–31	11–5	10.0	

11-6 Lesson Notes

11-6 Rational Expressions with Like Denominators

1 Focus

Standards Alignment

Before Lesson 11-6
Add and subtract fractions from ☞ Standard 7NS2.2

Lesson 11-6
Solve both computationally and conceptually challenging problems by using operations with rational expressions from ☞ Standard 1A13.0

After Lesson 11-6
Simplify complicated rational expressions from ☞ Standard 2A7.0

2 Teach

Scaffolding Questions
Have students read *Get Ready for the Lesson*.
Ask:
- What conditions must be met to add fractions? They must have like denominators.
- Do you really need to change percents into fractions before adding them? Explain. No; percents are fractions of 100, so they can be added without converting them to fraction form.

(continued on the next page)

Lesson 11-6 Resources

Chapter 11 Resource Masters
Lesson Reading Guide, p. 41 (BL) (OL) (ELL)
Study Guide and Intervention, pp. 42–43 (BL) (OL) (ELL)
Skills Practice, p. 44 (BL) (OL)
Practice, p. 45 (OL) (AL)
Word Problem Practice, p. 46 (OL) (AL)
Enrichment, p. 47 (OL) (AL)

Transparencies
5-Minute Check Transparency 11-6

Additional Print Resources
Noteables™ Interactive Study Notebook with Foldables™

Technology
ca.algebra1.com
Interactive Classroom CD-ROM
AssignmentWorks CD-ROM
Graphing Calculator Easy Files

Main Ideas
- Add rational expressions with like denominators.
- Subtract rational expressions with like denominators.

 Standard 13.0 Students add, **subtract**, multiply, and divide **rational expressions** and functions. Students solve both computationally and conceptually challenging problems by using these techniques. (Key)

▶ GET READY for the Lesson

The graph at the right shows the results of a survey that asked families how often they eat takeout. To determine what fraction of those surveyed eat takeout more than once a week, you can use addition. Remember that percents can be written as fractions with denominators of 100.

How Many Times a Week Families Eat Takeout

- 8% Daily
- 30% 2–3 times a week
- 40% less often
- 22% once a week

Source: *Reader's Digest*

2–3 times a week	plus	daily	equals	more than once a week.
$\frac{30}{100}$	$+$	$\frac{8}{100}$	$=$	$\frac{38}{100}$

Thus, $\frac{38}{100}$ or 38% eat takeout more than once a week.

Add Rational Expressions Recall that to add fractions with like denominators, you add the numerators and then write the sum over the common denominator. You can add rational expressions with like denominators in the same way. Answers should always be expressed in simplest form.

EXAMPLE — Numbers in Denominator

1 Find $\frac{3n}{12} + \frac{7n}{12}$.

$\frac{3n}{12} + \frac{7n}{12} = \frac{3n + 7n}{12}$ The common denominator is 12.

$= \frac{10n}{12}$ Add the numerators.

$= \frac{\overset{5}{10n}}{\underset{6}{12}}$ or $\frac{5n}{6}$ Divide by the common factor, 2, and simplify.

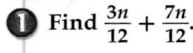 **Your Progress**   Find each sum.

1A. $\frac{8x}{6} + \frac{5x}{6}$ $\frac{13x}{6}$ **1B.** $\frac{4x}{5dy} + \frac{7}{5dy}$ $\frac{4x + 7}{5dy}$

Sometimes the denominators of rational expressions are binomials. As long as each rational expression has exactly the same binomial as its denominator, the process of addition is the same.

608 Chapter 11 Rational Expressions and Equations

EXAMPLE · Binomials in Denominator

2 Find $\dfrac{2x}{x+1} + \dfrac{2}{x+1}$.

$\dfrac{2x}{x+1} + \dfrac{2}{x+1} = \dfrac{2x+2}{x+1}$ The common denominator is $x + 1$.

$= \dfrac{2(x+1)}{x+1}$ Factor the numerator.

$= \dfrac{2(\overset{1}{x+1})}{\underset{1}{x+1}}$ Divide by the common factor, $x + 1$.

$= \dfrac{2}{1}$ or 2   Simplify.

✓CHECK Your Progress   Find each sum.

2A. $\dfrac{3y}{3+y} + \dfrac{y^2}{3+y}$ y **2B.** $\dfrac{15x}{33x+9} + \dfrac{3}{33x+9}$ $\dfrac{5x+1}{11x+3}$

EXAMPLE · Find a Perimeter

3 **GEOMETRY** Find an expression for the perimeter of parallelogram $PQRS$.

Remember that opposite sides of a parallelogram have the same length.

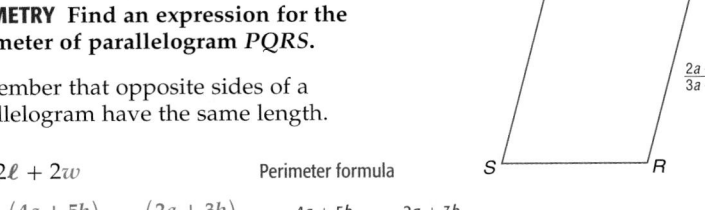

$P = 2\ell + 2w$ Perimeter formula

$= 2\left(\dfrac{4a+5b}{3a+7b}\right) + 2\left(\dfrac{2a+3b}{3a+7b}\right)$ $\ell = \dfrac{4a+5b}{3a+7b}, \; w = \dfrac{2a+3b}{3a+7b}$

$= \dfrac{2(4a+5b) + 2(2a+3b)}{3a+7b}$ The common denominator is $3a + 7b$.

$= \dfrac{8a+10b+4a+6b}{3a+7b}$ Distributive Property

$= \dfrac{12a+16b}{3a+7b}$ Combine like terms.

$= \dfrac{4(3a+4b)}{3a+7b}$ Factor.

The perimeter can be represented by the expression $\dfrac{4(3a+4b)}{3a+7b}$.

✓CHECK Your Progress

Find an expression for the perimeter of each figure.

3A. (triangle with sides $\frac{2t+1}{t+2}$, $\frac{2t+1}{t+2}$, and base $\frac{2t}{t+2}$) $\dfrac{6t+2}{t+2}$

3B. (trapezoid with top $\frac{8h-14}{h+1}$, legs $\frac{5h+1}{h+1}$ and $\frac{5h+1}{h+1}$, bottom $\frac{7h}{h+1}$) $\dfrac{25h-12}{h+1}$

nline **Personal Tutor at** ca.algebra1.com

Study Tip

Common Misconceptions
You may be tempted to divide out common factors like the $3a$ in the final step of Example 3. But remember that every term of the numerator and the denominator must be multiplied or divided by a number for the fraction to remain equivalent.

• How do you simplify $\dfrac{38}{100}$? Divide the numerator and denominator by the common factor 2 to get $\dfrac{19}{50}$.

Add Rational Expressions

Example 1 shows how to add rational expressions with the same number in the denominator. **Example 2** shows how to add rational expressions with the same binomial in the denominator. **Example 3** shows how to add rational expressions to find the perimeter of a rectangle.

✓ Formative Assessment

Use the Check Your Progress exercises after each example to determine students' understanding of concepts.

ADDITIONAL EXAMPLES

1 Find $\dfrac{4b}{15} + \dfrac{16b}{15}$. $\dfrac{4D}{3}$

2 Find $\dfrac{6c}{c+2} + \dfrac{12}{c+2}$.   6

3 **GEOMETRY** Find the perimeter of the rectangle $WXYZ$.

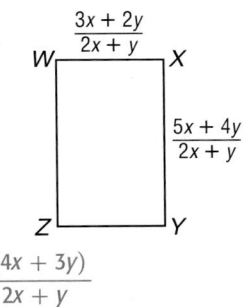

$\dfrac{4(4x+3y)}{2x+y}$

Additional Examples are also in:
• Noteables™ Interactive Study Notebook with Foldables™
• Interactive Classroom PowerPoint® Presentations

Adding Rational Expressions Whether the denominators of rational expressions are numbers, monomials, or binomials, the denominators must be the same in order to add two or more rational expressions. If the denominators are the same, the numerator of the sum is found by adding the numerators of the addends. The denominator of the sum is the same as the like denominators of the addends. Sums should be simplified.

Subtract Rational Expressions

Example 4 shows how to subtract rational expressions with like denominators by adding the additive inverse of the expression being subtracted. **Example 5** shows how to rewrite a denominator as its additive inverse in order to have like denominators so that the rational expressions can be added.

Focus on Mathematical Content

Subtracting Rational Expressions
Whether the denominators of rational expressions are numbers, monomials, or binomials, the denominators must be the same in order to subtract the rational expressions. If the denominators are the same, add the inverse of the numerator of the rational expression to the numerator from which it is being subtracted, use the like denominator, and then simplify.

 **Preventing Errors**

Alert students to the fact that they must rewrite the numerator as well as the denominator when rewriting inverse denominators. In Example 5, the numerator changes from positive to negative.

Subtract Rational Expressions To subtract rational expressions with like denominators, subtract the numerators and write the difference over the common denominator. Recall that to subtract an expression, you add its additive inverse. As with addition, answers should always be expressed in simplest form.

EXAMPLE   Subtract Rational Expressions

 a. Find $\dfrac{3x+4}{x-2} - \dfrac{x-1}{x-2}$.

$\dfrac{3x+4}{x-2} - \dfrac{x-1}{x-2} = \dfrac{(3x+4)-(x-1)}{x-2}$ The common denominator is $x-2$.

$\qquad\qquad = \dfrac{(3x+4)+[-(x-1)]}{x-2}$ The additive inverse of $(x-1)$ is $-(x-1)$.

$\qquad\qquad = \dfrac{3x+4-x+1}{x-2}$ Distributive Property

$\qquad\qquad = \dfrac{2x+5}{x-2}$ Simplify.

b. Find $\dfrac{3m-5}{m+4} - \dfrac{4m+2}{m+4}$.

$\dfrac{3m-5}{m+4} - \dfrac{4m+2}{m+4} = \dfrac{(3m-5)-(4m+2)}{m+4}$ The common denominator is $m+4$.

$\qquad\qquad = \dfrac{(3m-5)+[-(4m+2)]}{m+4}$ The additive inverse of $(4m+2)$ is $-(4m+2)$.

$\qquad\qquad = \dfrac{3m-5-4m-2}{m+4}$ Distributive Property

$\qquad\qquad = \dfrac{-m-7}{m+4}$ Simplify.

> **Study Tip**
>
> **Common Misconception**
> Adding the additive inverse will help you avoid the following error in the numerator.
> $(3x+4) - (x-1) = 3x+4-x-1.$

✔ CHECK **Your Progress**   Find each difference.

4A. $\dfrac{2h+4}{h+1} - \dfrac{5+h}{h+1} \quad \dfrac{h-1}{h+1}$

4B. $\dfrac{17h+4}{15h-5} - \dfrac{2h-6}{15h-5} \quad \dfrac{3h+2}{3h-1}$

Sometimes you must express a denominator as its additive inverse to have like denominators.

EXAMPLE   Inverse Denominators

 Find $\dfrac{2m}{m-9} + \dfrac{4m}{9-m}$.

$\dfrac{2m}{m-9} + \dfrac{4m}{9-m} = \dfrac{2m}{m-9} + \dfrac{4m}{-(m-9)}$ Rewrite $9-m$ as $-(m-9)$.

$\qquad\qquad = \dfrac{2m}{m-9} - \dfrac{4m}{m-9}$ Rewrite so the denominators are the same.

$\qquad\qquad = \dfrac{2m-4m}{m-9}$ The common denominator is $m-9$.

$\qquad\qquad = \dfrac{-2m}{m-9}$ Subtract.

✔ CHECK **Your Progress**   Find each sum.

5A. $\dfrac{3n}{n-4} + \dfrac{6n}{4-n} - \dfrac{3n}{n-4}$

5B. $\dfrac{t^2}{t-3} + \dfrac{3}{3-t} \quad \dfrac{t^2-3}{t-3}$

Math nline **Extra Examples at** ca.algebra1.com

Intervention

Additive Inverses Tell students to pay close attention to signs any time that they are dealing with additive inverses. It is easy to forget to change a sign when finding the additive inverse of an expression. Have students use the Distributive Property to help them change the signs correctly.

★ indicates multi-step problem

✓ CHECK Your Understanding

Find each sum.

Example 1
(p. 608)

1. $\frac{a+2}{4} + \frac{a-2}{4}$ $\frac{a}{2}$

2. $\frac{12z}{7} + \frac{-5z}{7}$ z

Example 2
(p. 609)

3. $\frac{2-n}{n-1} + \frac{1}{n-1}$ $\frac{3-n}{n-1}$

4. $\frac{4t-1}{1-4t} + \frac{2t+3}{1-4t}$ $\frac{6t+2}{1-4t}$

Example 3
(p. 609)

5. Find an expression for the perimeter of the figure.
$\frac{8x-6}{5}$

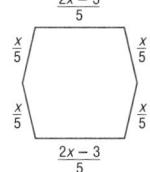

Find each difference.

Example 4
(p. 610)

6. $\frac{5a}{12} - \frac{7a}{12}$ $-\frac{a}{6}$

7. $\frac{7}{n-3} - \frac{4}{n-3}$ $\frac{3}{n-3}$

Example 5
(p. 610)

8. $\frac{3m}{m-2} - \frac{6}{2-m}$ $\frac{3m+6}{m-2}$

9. $\frac{x^2}{x-y} - \frac{y^2}{y-x}$ $\frac{x^2+y^2}{x-y}$

3 Practice

✓ Formative Assessment

Use Exercises 1–9 to check for understanding.

Use the chart at the bottom of this page to customize assignments for your students.

Odd/Even Assignments

Exercises 10–25 are structured so that students practice the same concepts whether they are assigned odd or even problems.

Exercises

Find each sum.

HOMEWORK	HELP
For Exercises	**See Examples**
10, 11	1
12–17	2
18, 19	3
20–23	4
24, 25	5

10. $\frac{m}{3} + \frac{2m}{3}$ m

11. $\frac{x+3}{5} + \frac{x+2}{5}$ $\frac{2x+5}{5}$

12. $\frac{2y}{y+3} + \frac{6}{y+3}$ 2

13. $\frac{3r}{r+5} + \frac{15}{r+5}$ 3

14. $\frac{k-5}{k-1} + \frac{4}{k-1}$ 1

15. $\frac{n-2}{n+3} + \frac{-1}{n+3}$ $\frac{n-3}{n+3}$

16. What is the sum of $\frac{12x-7}{3x-2}$ and $\frac{9x-5}{2-3x}$? 1

17. Find the sum of $\frac{11x-5}{2x+5}$ and $\frac{11x+12}{2x+5}$. $\frac{22x+7}{2x+5}$

Exercise Levels
A: 10–25
B: 26–37
C: 38–41

GEOMETRY For Exercises 18 and 19, use the following information.
Each figure has a perimeter of x units.

a.
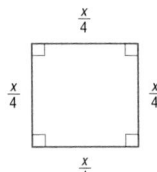

b.
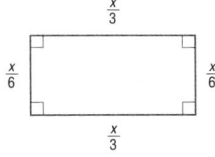

c.
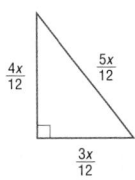

18. Find the ratio of the area of each figure to its perimeter. $\frac{x}{16}, \frac{x}{18}, \frac{x}{24}$

19. Which figure has the greatest ratio?   square

Find each difference.

25. $\frac{10y}{y-3}$

20. $\frac{5x}{7} - \frac{3x}{7}$ $\frac{2x}{7}$

21. $\frac{x+4}{5} - \frac{x+2}{5}$ $\frac{2}{5}$

22. $\frac{5}{3x-5} - \frac{3x}{3x-5}$ -1

23. $\frac{8}{3t-4} - \frac{6t}{3t-4}$ -2

24. $\frac{2x}{x-2} - \frac{2x}{2-x}$ $\frac{4x}{x-2}$

25. $\frac{5y}{y-3} - \frac{5y}{3-y}$

DIFFERENTIATED HOMEWORK OPTIONS

Level	Assignment	Two-Day Option	
BL Basic	10–25, 38, 39, 41–45	11–25 odd, 42, 43	10–24 even, 38, 39, 41, 44–51
OL Core	11–25 odd, 26–28, 29–33 odd, 35–39, 41–51	10–25, 42, 43	26–39, 41, 44–51
AL Advanced /Pre-AP	26–51 (optional: 48–51)		

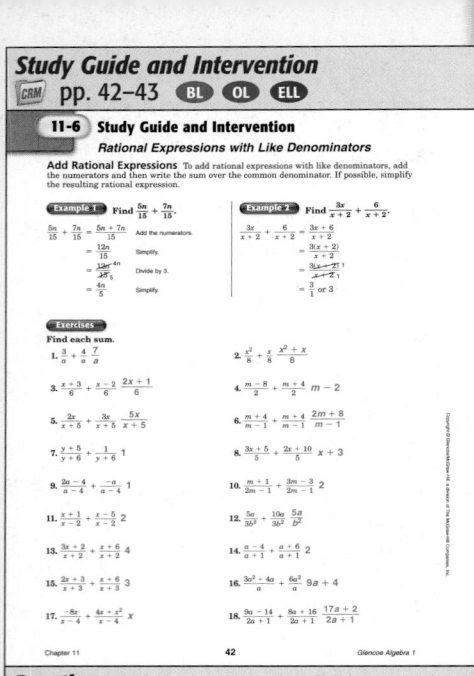

11-6 Study Guide and Intervention

Rational Expressions with Like Denominators

Add Rational Expressions To add rational expressions with like denominators, add the numerators and then write the sum over the common denominator. If possible, simplify the resulting rational expression.

Example 1 Find $\frac{5n}{15} + \frac{7n}{15}$.

$\frac{5n}{15} + \frac{7n}{15} = \frac{5n + 7n}{15}$ Add the numerators.

$= \frac{12n}{15}$ Simplify.

$= \frac{12n}{15} \cdot \frac{4n}{5}$ Divide by 3.

$= \frac{4n}{5}$ Simplify.

Example 2 Find $\frac{3x}{x+2} + \frac{6}{x+2}$.

$\frac{3x}{x+2} + \frac{6}{x+2} = \frac{3x + 6}{x+2}$

$= \frac{3(x + 2)}{x+2}$

$= \frac{3(x + 2)}{x+2}$

$= \frac{3}{1}$ or 3

Exercises

Find each sum.

1. $\frac{3}{a} + \frac{4}{a}$ $\frac{7}{a}$

2. $\frac{x^2}{8} + \frac{x}{8}$ $\frac{x^2 + x}{8}$

3. $\frac{x+3}{6} + \frac{x-2}{6}$ $\frac{2x+1}{6}$

4. $\frac{m-8}{2} + \frac{m+4}{2}$ $m - 2$

5. $\frac{2x}{x+5} + \frac{3x}{x+5}$ $\frac{5x}{x+5}$

6. $\frac{m+4}{m-1} + \frac{m+4}{m-1}$ $\frac{2m+8}{m-1}$

7. $\frac{y+5}{y+6} + \frac{1}{y+6}$

8. $\frac{8x+5}{5} + \frac{2x+10}{5}$ $x + 3$

9. $\frac{3a-4}{a-4} + \frac{-a}{a-4}$

10. $\frac{m+1}{2m-1} + \frac{3m-3}{2m-1}$

11. $\frac{x+1}{x-2} + \frac{x+5}{x-2}$ 2

12. $\frac{5a}{3b^2} + \frac{10a}{3b^2}$ $\frac{5a}{b^2}$

13. $\frac{3x+2}{x+2} + \frac{x+6}{x+2}$ 2

14. $\frac{n-4}{a+1} + \frac{a+6}{a+1}$ 2

15. $\frac{3x+3}{x+3} + \frac{x+6}{x+3}$ 3

16. $\frac{3b^2 - 4a}{3b^2} + \frac{6a^2}{3b^2}$ $9a + 4$

17. $\frac{-8x}{x-4} + \frac{4x+x^2}{x-4}$ x

18. $\frac{2a-14}{2a+1} + \frac{6a+16}{2a+1}$ $\frac{17a+2}{2a+1}$

Chapter 11   42   Glencoe Algebra 1

11-6 Practice

Rational Expressions with Like Denominators

Find each sum.

1. $\frac{n}{8} + \frac{3n}{8}$ $\frac{n}{2}$

2. $\frac{7u}{16} + \frac{5u}{16}$ $\frac{3u}{4}$

3. $\frac{w+9}{9} + \frac{w+4}{9}$ $\frac{2w+13}{9}$

4. $\frac{s-8}{4} + \frac{s-4}{4}$ $\frac{s-6}{2}$

5. $\frac{4c}{c+1} + \frac{4}{c+1}$ 4

6. $\frac{a+6}{4} + \frac{-8}{4}$ $\frac{a}{1}$

7. $\frac{x-5}{x+2} + \frac{-2}{x+2}$ $\frac{x-7}{x+2}$

8. $\frac{r+5}{r-5} + \frac{2r-1}{r-5}$ $\frac{3r+4}{r-5}$

9. $\frac{4p+14}{p+4} + \frac{2p+10}{p+4}$ 6

10. $\frac{2y+1}{3y-2} + \frac{4y-5}{3y-2}$

11. $\frac{5a+2}{2a-2} + \frac{2}{2a-2}$ $\frac{7a-2}{2a-2}$

12. $\frac{6t-5}{3t+1} + \frac{4t+3}{3t+1}$ $\frac{10t-2}{3t+1}$

Find each difference.

13. $\frac{3y}{8} - \frac{y}{8}$ $\frac{y}{4}$

14. $\frac{9n}{5} - \frac{4n}{5}$ n

15. $\frac{r+2}{3} - \frac{r+5}{3}$ -1

16. $\frac{s-6}{2} - \frac{s-7}{2}$ $\frac{1}{2}$

17. $\frac{s+14}{4} - \frac{s-14}{4}$ $\frac{28}{4}$

18. $\frac{6}{c-1} - \frac{-2}{c-1}$ $\frac{1}{c-1}$

19. $\frac{7}{d+6} - \frac{6}{d+6}$ $\frac{1}{d+6}$

20. $\frac{2y}{2y-3} - \frac{9}{3-2y}$

21. $\frac{4p}{5-p} - \frac{8p}{5-p}$ $\frac{p}{p-5}$

22. $\frac{2y}{y-2} - \frac{7y}{y-2}$ $\frac{9y}{2-y}$

23. $\frac{6a-4}{2a+2} - \frac{4a-6}{2a+2}$ 1

24. $\frac{30x}{6x-1} - \frac{30x+5}{6x-1}$

25. **GEOMETRY** Find an expression for the perimeter of rectangle ABCD. Use the formula $P = 2\ell + 2w$. $\frac{4(4a + 3b)}{2a + b}$

26. **MUSIC** Kerrie is burning an 80-minute CD-R containing her favorite dance songs. Suppose she has burned 41 minutes of songs and has five more songs in the queue that total x minutes. When she is done, write an expression for the fraction of the CD that has been filled with music. $\frac{41 + x}{80}$

Chapter 11   45   Glencoe Algebra 1

11-6 Word Problem Practice

Rational Expressions with Like Denominators

1. **TEXAS** Of the 254 counties in Texas, 4 are larger than 6000 square miles. Another 21 counties are smaller than 300 square miles. What fraction of the counties are 300 to 6000 square miles in size? $\frac{229}{254}$

2. **TRAVEL** Trevor is driving across the country with his friend Max after their college graduation. Between Newport and Springfield, progress is slow because of a bumpy road; they drive for three hours and cover 130 miles. Once they pass Springfield, they speed up on the smooth highway and arrive in Middleton three hours later, 200 miles from Springfield. Recall the relationship rate $= \frac{\text{distance}}{\text{time}}$. What was Trevor and Max's average speed from Newport to Middleton?   55 mph

3. **CHOOSING A COSTUME** The color guard at Wayne High School performs in competitions. The guard captain wants to design a 14-inch diameter prop disc to help them choose from their costume colors: black, orange, green, and gold. She designs the disc so that the circular sections have the central angle measurements as shown in the diagram below.

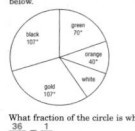

black 107°, green 70°, orange 40°, gold 107°, white

What fraction of the circle is white? $\frac{36}{360}$ or $\frac{1}{10}$

4. **INSURANCE** For a hospital stay, Paul's health insurance plan requires him to pay $\frac{2}{5}$ the cost of the first day in the hospital and $\frac{1}{5}$ the cost of the second and third days. If Paul's hospital stay is 3 days and cost him $420, what was the full daily cost? $525

5. **MAGAZINE DRIVE For Exercises 5 and 6, refer to the following information.** Ninth graders Victor, Barbara, and Robyn are participating in a magazine drive to raise money for special programs at their school. One of the incentives for selling magazine subscriptions is that for each subscription sold, the student gets one raffle ticket for a drawing to win a prize. Victor, Barbara, and Robyn sell 43, 18, and x magazine subscriptions, respectively.

5. In the grand prize drawing, all ninth graders put their tickets together for one drawing to see who will win a new stereo. The ninth grade sold a total of 4372 subscriptions. Write an expression representing the probability that one of these three students will win a new stereo. $\frac{61 + x}{4372}$

6. Robyn won the grand prize! The second prize drawing is for a gift card at a local music store. The winner of the grand prize is not eligible for the second prize. Write an expression representing the probability that Victor or Barbara will win the second prize. $\frac{61}{4372 - x}$

Chapter 11   46   Glencoe Algebra 1

11-6 Enrichment

Sum and Difference of Any Two Like Powers

The sum of any two like powers can be written $a^n + b^n$, where n is a positive integer. The difference of like powers is $a^n - b^n$. Under what conditions are these expressions exactly divisible by $(a + b)$ and $(a - b)$? The answer depends on whether n is an odd or even number.

Use long division to find the following quotients. (*Hint:* Write $a^3 + b^3$ as $a^3 + 0a^2 + 0a + b^3$.) Is the numerator exactly divisible by the denominator? Write yes or no.

1. $\frac{a^3 + b^3}{a + b}$ yes

2. $\frac{a^3 + b^3}{a - b}$ no

3. $\frac{a^3 - b^3}{a + b}$ no

4. $\frac{a^3 - b^3}{a - b}$ yes

★ 26. **POPULATION** The population of Cupertino, California, is 610 greater than the population of San Clemente, California. Write an expression for the fraction of the Cupertino population that is under 19 years old if the population of San Clemente is n. $\frac{14361}{n + 610}$

Cupertino Population	
Age	**Number of People**
Under 5 years	3060
5 to 9 years	4156
10 to 14 years	4089
15 to 19 years	3056

Source: U.S. Census Bureau

27. **CONSERVATION** The freshman class chose to plant spruce and pine trees at a wildlife sanctuary for a service project. Some students can plant 140 trees on Saturday, and others can plant 20 trees after school on Monday and again on Tuesday. Write an expression for the fraction of the trees that could be planted on these days if n represents the number of spruce trees and there are twice as many pine trees. $\frac{60}{n}$

28. **SCHOOL** Most schools create daily attendance reports to keep track of their students. The school office manager knows that, of the 960 students, 45 are absent due to illness, 10 are excused for appointments, and both the wrestling team and the choir are at competitions. Though she doesn't know exactly how many people attended the competitions, she does know that there are twice as many people in the choir as there are on the wrestling team. Write an expression that gives the percentage of students who are absent. $\frac{55 + 3s}{960}$

Find each sum or difference.

29. $\frac{4}{7m - 2} + \frac{7m}{2 - 7m}$ $\frac{4 - 7m}{7m - 2}$

30. $\frac{b - 15}{2b + 12} - \frac{-3b + 8}{2b + 12}$ $\frac{4b - 23}{2b + 12}$

31. $\frac{a + 5}{6} - \frac{a + 3}{6}$ $\frac{1}{3}$

32. $\frac{10a - 12}{2a - 6} - \frac{6a}{6 - 2a}$ $\frac{8a - 6}{a - 3}$

33. $\frac{2}{x + 7} - \frac{-5}{x + 7}$ $\frac{7}{x + 7}$

34. $\frac{15x}{5x + 1} + \frac{-3}{-1 - 5x}$ 3

Real-World Link

Due to its popularity, the Grand Canyon is one of the most threatened natural areas in the United States.

Source: *The Wildlife Foundation*

★ 35. **GEOMETRIC DESIGN** The Jerome Student Center has a square room that is 25 feet wide and 25 feet long. The walls are 10 feet high, and each wall is painted white with a red diagonal stripe as shown. What fraction of the walls are painted red? $\frac{1}{5}$

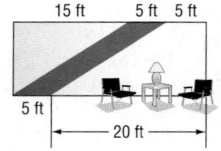

15 ft   5 ft   5 ft   5 ft   20 ft

HIKING For Exercises 36 and 37, use the following information.

A tour guide recommends that hikers carry a gallon of water on hikes to the bottom of the Grand Canyon. Water weighs 62.4 pounds per cubic foot, and one cubic foot of water contains 7.48 gallons.

EXTRA PRACTICE
See pages 740, 754.

Math Online
Self-Check Quiz at ca.algebra1.com

36. Tanika plans to carry two 1-quart bottles and four 1-pint bottles for her hike. Write a rational expression for this amount of water written as a fraction of a cubic foot. $\frac{1}{7.48}$ ft^3

37. How much does this amount of water weigh?   8.3 lb

H.O.T. Problems

38. **OPEN ENDED** Describe a real-life situation that could be expressed by adding two rational expressions that are fractions. Explain what the denominator and numerator represent in both expressions.   See margin.

612   Chapter 11 Rational Expressions and Equations

Additional pages not shown:

CRM **Lesson Reading Guide**, p. 41 BL OL ELL

CRM **Skills Practice**, p. 44 BL OL

BL = *Below Grade Level*

OL = *On Grade Level*

AL = *Above Grade Level*

ELL = *English Language Learner*

39. FIND THE ERROR Russell and Ginger are finding the difference of $\frac{7x + 2}{4x - 3}$ and $\frac{x - 8}{3 - 4x}$. Who is correct? Explain your reasoning. **See margin.**

Russell

$$\frac{7x+2}{4x-3} - \frac{x-8}{3-4x} = \frac{7x+2}{4x-3} + \frac{x-8}{4x-3}$$
$$= \frac{7x+x+2-8}{4x-3}$$
$$= \frac{8x-6}{4x-3}$$
$$= \frac{2(4x-3)}{4x-3}$$
$$= 2$$

Ginger

$$\frac{7x+2}{4x-3} - \frac{x-8}{3-4x} = \frac{-2-7x}{3-4x} + \frac{x-8}{3-4x}$$
$$= \frac{-2-8-7x+x}{3-4x}$$
$$= \frac{-6-8x}{3-4x}$$
$$= \frac{-2(3-4x)}{3-4x}$$
$$= -2$$

40. CHALLENGE Which of the following rational expressions is *not* equivalent to the others? **C**

a. $\dfrac{3}{2 - x}$ b. $\dfrac{-3}{x - 2}$ c. $-\dfrac{3}{2 - x}$ d. $-\dfrac{3}{x - 2}$

41. *Writing in Math* Use the chart on page 608 to explain how rational expressions can be used to interpret graphics. Include an explanation of how the numbers in the graphic relate to rational expressions and a description of how to add rational expressions with denominators that are additive inverses. **See margin.**

STANDARDS PRACTICE 10.0, 7NS1.7

42. Which is an expression for the perimeter of the pentagon? **A**

A $\dfrac{16r}{s + 3r}$

B $\dfrac{16r}{2s + 6r}$

C $\dfrac{32}{s + 3r}$

D $\dfrac{32}{4s + 12r}$

$\frac{5r}{2s+6r}$ $\frac{5r}{2s+6r}$

$\frac{9r}{2s+6r}$ $\frac{9r}{2s+6r}$

$\frac{4r}{2s+6r}$

43. REVIEW Shelby sells cosmetics door-to-door. She makes $5 an hour and 17% commission on the total dollar value on whatever she sells. To the nearest dollar, how much money will she make if she sells $300 dollars worth of product and works 30 hours? **F**

F $201   H $255

G $226   J $283

Spiral Review

Find each quotient. (Lessons 11-4 and 11-5)

44. $\dfrac{x^3 - 7x + 6}{x - 2}$ $x^2 + 2x - 3$

45. $\dfrac{56x^3 + 32x^2 - 63x - 36}{7x + 4}$ $8x^2 - 9$

46. $\dfrac{b^2 - 9}{4b} \div (b - 3)$ $\dfrac{b + 3}{4b}$

47. $\dfrac{x}{x + 2} \div \dfrac{x^2}{x^2 + 5x + 6}$ $\dfrac{x + 3}{x}$

GET READY for the Next Lesson

PREREQUISITE SKILL Find the least common multiple for each set of numbers.

48. $4, 9, 12$ **36**

49. $45, 10, 6$ **90**

50. $16, 20, 25$ **400**

51. $36, 48, 60$ **720**

Exercise Alert!

Find the Error Some students may think the error is in the first line of the solution. Ginger writes the inverse of the first rational expression instead of the expression being subtracted, as is done in Example 5. Point out to students that it is mathematically correct to write the inverse of either expression. Tell students that it is important to pay close attention to signs when factoring an expression with negative numbers.

4 Assess

Ticket Out the Door Ask students to choose two letters from A through F. On the board write the letters A through F. Under each letter write a different rational expression, three with the same denominator and three with denominators that are the additive inverse denominator of the first three. Ask students to first add the rational expressions that are under their two letters. Then have student subtract the rational expressions.

Additional Answers

39. Russell; sample answer: Ginger factored incorrectly in the next-to-last step of her work.

41. Sample answer: Since any rational number can be expressed as a fraction, values on graphics can be written as rational expressions for clarification. The numbers in the graphic are percents which can be written as rational expressions with a denominator of 100. To add rational expressions with inverse denominators, factor -1 out of either denominator so that it is like the other.

Pre-AP Activity Use as an Extension.

Ask students to find $\dfrac{3x - 4}{x^2 - 5x + 4} - \dfrac{x - 4}{x^2 + 5x - 4}$

$-\dfrac{x - 4}{-x^2 + 5x - 4}$. $\dfrac{2}{x - 1}$

38. Survey data can be represented with rational expressions that are fractions; $\dfrac{a}{d} + \dfrac{3a - 12}{d}$; the numerator is the number of people who gave a certain response to a survey and the denominator is the number of people that took the survey.

11-7 Rational Expressions with Unlike Denominators

1 Focus

Standards Alignment

Before Lesson 11-7
Add and subtract fractions from ⭕━ Standard 7NS2.2

Lesson 11-7
Solve both computationally and conceptually challenging problems by using operations with rational expressions from ⭕━ Standard 1A13.0

After Lesson 11-7
Simplify complicated rational expressions from ⭕━ Standard 2A7.0

2 Teach

Scaffolding Questions
Have students read *Get Ready for the Lesson.*

Ask:
• In what year will the senator face his or her first reelection? The second reelection? The senator will face reelection in 2010 and 2016.
• What years are the next three presidential elections after 2004? 2008, 2012, 2016
• Based on this information, when will the senator's reelection fall in the same year as a presidential election? 2016

Lesson 11-7 Resources

Main Ideas
• Add rational expressions with unlike denominators.
• Subtract rational expressions with unlike denominators.

Standard 13.0 Students add, subtract, multiply, and divide **rational expressions** and functions. **Students solve both computationally and conceptually challenging problems by using these techniques.** (Key)

New Vocabulary
least common multiple (LCM)
least common denominator (LCD)

GET READY for the Lesson

The President of the United States is elected every four years, and senators are elected every six years. A certain senator is elected in 2004, the same year as a presidential election, and is reelected in subsequent elections. In what year is the senator's reelection the same year as a presidential election?

Add Rational Expressions The least number of years that will pass until the next election for both a specific senator and the President is the least common multiple of 4 and 6. The **least common multiple (LCM)** is the least number that is a multiple of two or more numbers. You can also find the LCM of a set of polynomials.

 EXAMPLE LCMs of Polynomials

1 **a.** Find the LCM of $15m^2b^3$ and $18mb^2$.

Find the prime factors of each coefficient and variable expression.
$15m^2b^3 = 3 \cdot 5 \cdot m \cdot m \cdot b \cdot b \cdot b$ $18mb^2 = 2 \cdot 3 \cdot 3 \cdot m \cdot b \cdot b$

Use each prime factor the greatest number of times it appears in any of the factorizations.
$15m^2b^3 = 3 \cdot 5 \cdot m \cdot m \cdot b \cdot b \cdot b$ $18mb^2 = 2 \cdot 3 \cdot 3 \cdot m \cdot b \cdot b$
$LCM = 2 \cdot 3 \cdot 3 \cdot 5 \cdot m \cdot m \cdot b \cdot b \cdot b$ or $90m^2b^3$

b. Find the LCM of $x^2 + 8x + 15$ and $x^2 + x - 6$.

Express each polynomial in factored form.
$x^2 + 8x + 15 = (x + 3)(x + 5)$ $x^2 + x - 6 = (x - 2)(x + 3)$

Use each factor the greatest number of times it appears.
$LCM = (x + 3)(x + 5)(x - 2)$

CHECK Your Progress

Find the LCM of each pair of polynomials. **1B.** $(x + 2)(x - 4)(x - 7)$
1A. $28m^2n$ and $12m^2n^3p$ $84m^2n^3p$ **1B.** $x^2 - 2x - 8$ and $x^2 - 5x - 14$

614 Chapter 11 Rational Expressions and Equations

Transparencies
5-Minute Check Transparency 11-7
Additional Print Resources
Noteables™ Interactive Study Notebook with Foldables™

Technology
ca.algebra1.com
Interactive Classroom CD-ROM
AssignmentWorks CD-ROM
Graphing Calculator Easy Files

To add fractions with unlike denominators, you need to rename the fractions using the least common multiple (LCM) of the denominators, known as the **least common denominator (LCD)**. You can add rational expressions with unlike denominators in the same way.

KEY CONCEPT   *Add Rational Expressions*

Use the following steps to add rational expressions with unlike denominators.

Step 1   Find the LCD.

Step 2   Change each rational expression into an equivalent expression with the LCD as the denominator.

Step 3   Add rational expressions with like denominators.

Step 4   Simplify if necessary.

Study Tip

Checking Answers

You can check to see that you have simplified rational expressions involving variables by substituting a few values. If the results are different for the original expression and the simplified expression, check for an error in arithmetic.

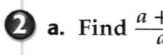 **EXAMPLE**   **Polynomial Denominators**

2   **a.** Find $\dfrac{a+1}{a} + \dfrac{a-3}{3a}$.

Factor each denominator and find the LCD.

$$a = a$$
$$3a = 3 \cdot a \qquad LCD = 3a$$

Since the denominator of $\dfrac{a-3}{3a}$ is already $3a$, only $\dfrac{a+1}{a}$ needs to be renamed.

$$\dfrac{a+1}{a} + \dfrac{a-3}{3a} = \dfrac{3(a+1)}{3(a)} + \dfrac{a-3}{3a} \qquad \text{Multiply } \dfrac{a+1}{a} \text{ by } \dfrac{3}{3}.$$

$$= \dfrac{3a+3}{3a} + \dfrac{a-3}{3a} \qquad \text{Distributive Property}$$

$$= \dfrac{3a+3+a-3}{3a} \qquad \text{Add the numerators.}$$

$$= \dfrac{\overset{1}{4a}}{\underset{1}{3a}} \text{ or } \dfrac{4}{3} \qquad \text{Divide by the common factor, } a, \text{ and simplify.}$$

b. Find $\dfrac{y-2}{y^2+4y+4} + \dfrac{y-2}{y+2}$.

$$\dfrac{y-2}{y^2+4y+4} + \dfrac{y-2}{y+2} = \dfrac{y-2}{(y+2)^2} + \dfrac{y-2}{y+2} \qquad \text{Factor the denominators.}$$

$$= \dfrac{y-2}{(y+2)^2} + \dfrac{y-2}{y+2} \cdot \dfrac{y+2}{y+2} \qquad \text{The LCD is } (y+2)^2.$$

$$= \dfrac{y-2}{(y+2)^2} + \dfrac{y^2-4}{(y+2)^2} \qquad (y-2)(y+2) = y^2-4$$

$$= \dfrac{y-2+y^2-4}{(y+2)^2} \qquad \text{Add the numerators.}$$

$$= \dfrac{y^2+y-6}{(y+2)^2} \text{ or } \dfrac{(y-2)(y+3)}{(y+2)^2} \qquad \text{Simplify.}$$

Add Rational Expressions

Example 1 shows how to find the least common multiple of two or more polynomials. **Example 2** shows how to add rational expressions with unlike denominators by using the least common multiple of the denominators to rename the denominators.

 Formative Assessment

Use the Check Your Progress exercises after each example to determine students' understanding of concepts.

ADDITIONAL EXAMPLES

1   Find the LCM of each pair of polynomials.

   a. $12b^4c^5$ and $32bc^2$ 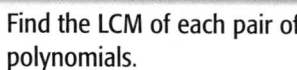 $96b^4c^5$

   b. $x^2 - 3x - 28$ and $x^2 - 8x + 7$
     $(x+4)(x-7)(x-1)$

2   Find each sum.

   a. $\dfrac{z+2}{5z} + \dfrac{z-6}{z}$ $\dfrac{2(3z-14)}{5z}$

   b. $\dfrac{x+7}{x^2-6x+9} + \dfrac{x+3}{x-3}$

     $\dfrac{(x+2)(x-1)}{(x-3)^2}$

Additional Examples are also in:

- Noteables™ Interactive Study Notebook with Foldables™

- Interactive Classroom PowerPoint® Presentations

 **Preventing Errors**

Point out that it is possible for two polynomials to have no common multiple other than their product and multiples of their product.

Focus on Mathematical Content

Adding Rational Expressions To add rational expressions with unlike denominators, find the LCD of the denominators. Once the expressions are changed into equivalent expressions with the LCD as the denominators, add just as with rational expressions with like denominators.

Subtract Rational Expressions

Examples 3 shows how use a common denominator to rename rational expressions with polynomials in their denominators.

Preventing Errors

Remind students that they must multiply the numerator by the expression by which they multiplied the denominator.

Focus on Mathematical Content

Subtracting Rational Expressions
To subtract rational expressions with unlike denominators, find the LCD of the denominators. Once the expressions are changed into equivalent expressions with the LCD as the denominators, subtract.

CHECK Your Progress

Find each sum.

2A. $\dfrac{4d^2}{d} + \dfrac{d + 2}{d^2}$ $\dfrac{4d^3 + d + 2}{d^2}$

2B. $\dfrac{b + 3}{b} + \dfrac{b - 5}{b + 1}$ $\dfrac{2b^2 - b + 3}{b^2 + b}$

Subtract Rational Expressions As with addition, to subtract rational expressions with unlike denominators, you must first rename the expressions using a common denominator.

EXAMPLE   Polynomials in Denominators

3 Find each difference.

a. $\dfrac{4}{3a - 6} - \dfrac{a}{a + 2}$

$\dfrac{4}{3a - 6} - \dfrac{a}{a + 2} = \dfrac{4}{3(a - 2)} - \dfrac{a}{a + 2}$ Factor.

$= \dfrac{4(a + 2)}{3(a - 2)(a + 2)} - \dfrac{3a(a - 2)}{3(a - 2)(a + 2)}$ The LCD is $3(a - 2)(a + 2)$.

$= \dfrac{4(a + 2) - 3a(a - 2)}{3(a - 2)(a + 2)}$ Subtract the numerators.

$= \dfrac{4a + 8 - 3a^2 + 6a}{3(a - 2)(a + 2)}$ Multiply.

$= \dfrac{-3a^2 + 10a + 8}{3(a - 2)(a + 2)}$ Add like terms.

b. $\dfrac{h - 2}{h^2 + 4h + 4} - \dfrac{h - 4}{h^2 - 4}$

$\dfrac{h - 2}{(h + 2)^2} - \dfrac{h - 4}{(h + 2)(h - 2)} = \dfrac{(h - 2)}{(h + 2)^2} \cdot \dfrac{(h - 2)}{(h - 2)} - \dfrac{(h - 4)}{(h + 2)(h - 2)} \cdot \dfrac{(h + 2)}{(h + 2)}$

$= \dfrac{(h - 2)(h - 2)}{(h + 2)^2(h - 2)} - \dfrac{(h - 4)(h + 2)}{(h + 2)^2(h - 2)}$ The LCD is $(h + 2)^2(h - 2)$.

$= \dfrac{h^2 - 4h + 4}{(h + 2)^2(h - 2)} - \dfrac{h^2 - 2h - 8}{(h + 2)^2(h - 2)}$ Multiply.

$= \dfrac{(h^2 - 4h + 4) - (h^2 - 2h - 8)}{(h + 2)^2(h - 2)}$ Subtract.

$= \dfrac{h^2 - h^2 - 4h + 2h + 4 + 8}{(h + 2)^2(h - 2)}$ Combine like terms.

$= \dfrac{-2h + 12}{(h - 2)(h + 2)^2}$ Simplify.

CHECK Your Progress

Find each sum.

3A. $\dfrac{5}{2\ell + 2} + \dfrac{\ell}{\ell + 5}$ $\dfrac{2\ell^2 + 7\ell + 25}{2\ell^2 + 12\ell + 10}$

3B. $\dfrac{k - 3}{k^2 + k - 12} + \dfrac{k}{k^2 - 9}$ $\dfrac{2k^2 + 4k - 9}{k^3 - 9k + 4k^2 - 36}$

3C. $\dfrac{x}{x - 3} - \dfrac{3}{x + 2}$ $\dfrac{x^2 - x + 9}{x^2 - x - 6}$

3D. $\dfrac{m}{m^2 - 2m - 8} - \dfrac{m + 3}{m - 4}$ $\dfrac{-m^2 - 4m - 6}{m^2 - 2m - 2}$

 **Personal Tutor at** <u>ca.algebra1.com</u>

Differentiated Instruction

Visual/Spatial Learners   Have students solve Example 3b by writing each fraction in a different color. Once the two fractions have the same denominator, have students switch to a third color and combine the numerators. Using different colors may help students visualize how each fraction is changed while helping students to differentiate one fraction from another.

CHECK Your Understanding

Example 1
(p. 614)

Find the LCM for each pair of expressions.

1. $5a^2, 7a$ $35a^2$

2. $2x - 4, 3x - 6$ $6(x - 2)$

3. $n^2 + 3n - 4, (n - 1)^2$
$(n + 4)(n - 1)^2$

★ **4. MUSIC** A music director wants to form a group of students to sing and dance at community events. Sometimes the music is 2-part, 3-part, or 4-part harmony, and she would like to have the same number of voices on each part. What is the least number of students that would allow for an even distribution on all these parts? **12**

Example 2
(p. 615)

Find each sum.

5. $\dfrac{6}{5x} + \dfrac{7}{10x^2}$ $\dfrac{12x + 7}{10x^2}$

6. $\dfrac{3z}{6w^2} + \dfrac{z}{4w}$ $\dfrac{6z + 3zw}{12w^2}$

7. $\dfrac{2y}{y^2 - 25} + \dfrac{y + 5}{y - 5}$ $\dfrac{y^2 + 12y + 25}{(y - 5)(y + 5)}$

8. $\dfrac{a + 2}{a^2 + 4a + 3} + \dfrac{6}{a + 3}$ $\dfrac{7a + 8}{(a + 3)(a + 1)}$

Example 3
(p. 616)

Find each difference.

9. $\dfrac{a}{a - 4} - \dfrac{4}{a + 4}$ $\dfrac{a^2 + 16}{a^2 - 16}$

10. $\dfrac{b + 8}{b^2 - 16} - \dfrac{1}{b - 4}$ $\dfrac{4}{(b - 4)(b + 4)}$

11. $\dfrac{2y}{y^2 + 7y + 12} - \dfrac{y + 2}{y + 4}$ $\dfrac{-y^2 - 3y - 6}{y^2 + 7y + 12}$

12. $\dfrac{x}{x - 2} - \dfrac{3}{x^2 + 3x - 10}$ $\dfrac{x^2 + 5x - 3}{(x - 2)(x + 5)}$

Exercises

HOMEWORK HELP	
For Exercises	**See Examples**
13–18	1
19–30	2
31–39	3

Exercise Levels
A: 13–39
B: 40–50
C: 51–53

36. $\dfrac{-3a + 6}{a(a - 6)}$

37. $\dfrac{-n^2 - 5n - 3}{(n - 5)(n + 5)}$

38. $\dfrac{3a + 5}{-3(a - 2)}$

39. $\dfrac{k^2 - 2k - 2}{(2k + 1)(k + 2)}$

Find the LCM for each pair of expressions. **15.** $(x - 4)(x + 2)$

13. a^2b, ab^3 a^2b^3

14. $7xy, 21x^2y$ $21x^2y$

15. $x - 4, x + 2$

16. $2n - 5, n + 2$
$(2n - 5)(n + 2)$

17. $x^2 + 5x - 14, (x - 2)^2$
$(x + 7)(x - 2)^2$

18. $p^2 - 5p - 6, p + 1$
$(p + 1)(p - 6)$

Find each sum. **22–30. See margin.**

19. $\dfrac{3}{x^2} + \dfrac{5}{x}$ $\dfrac{3 + 5x}{x^2}$

20. $\dfrac{2}{a^3} + \dfrac{7}{a^2}$ $\dfrac{2 + 7a}{a^3}$

21. $\dfrac{7}{6a^2} + \dfrac{5}{3a}$ $\dfrac{7 + 10a}{6a^2}$

22. $\dfrac{3}{7m} + \dfrac{4}{5m^2}$

23. $\dfrac{3}{x + 5} + \dfrac{4}{x - 4}$

24. $\dfrac{n}{n + 4} + \dfrac{3}{n - 3}$

25. $\dfrac{7a}{a + 5} + \dfrac{a}{a - 2}$

26. $\dfrac{6x}{x - 3} + \dfrac{x}{x + 1}$

27. $\dfrac{-3}{5 - a} + \dfrac{5}{a^2 - 25}$

28. $\dfrac{18}{y^2 - 9} + \dfrac{-7}{3 - y}$

29. $\dfrac{x}{x^2 + 2x + 1} + \dfrac{1}{x + 1}$

30. $\dfrac{2x + 1}{(x - 1)^2} + \dfrac{x - 2}{x^2 + 3x - 4}$

Find each difference. **33.** $\dfrac{-2x}{x - 1}$ **34.** $\dfrac{2m^2 - m - 9}{(m + 2)(2m + 5)}$ **35.** $\dfrac{2 + 3x}{(x - 5)}$

31. $\dfrac{7}{3x} - \dfrac{3}{6x^2}$ $\dfrac{14x - 3}{6x^2}$

32. $\dfrac{5a}{7x} - \dfrac{3a}{21x^2}$ $\dfrac{5ax - a}{7x^2}$

33. $\dfrac{x^2 - 1}{x + 1} - \dfrac{x^2 + 1}{x - 1}$

34. $\dfrac{m - 1}{m + 1} - \dfrac{4}{2m + 5}$

35. $\dfrac{2x}{x^2 - 5x} - \dfrac{-3x}{x - 5}$

36. $\dfrac{-3}{a - 6} - \dfrac{-6}{a^2 - 6a}$

37. $\dfrac{n}{5 - n} - \dfrac{3}{n^2 - 25}$

38. $\dfrac{3a + 2}{6 - 3a} - \dfrac{a + 2}{a^2 - 4}$

39. $\dfrac{k}{2k + 1} - \dfrac{2}{k + 2}$

Lesson 11-7 Rational Expressions with Unlike Denominators **617**

3 Practice

 Formative Assessment

Use Exercises 1–12 to check for understanding.

Use the chart at the bottom of this page to customize assignments for your students.

Odd/Even Assignments
Exercises 13–39 are structured so that students practice the same concepts whether they are assigned odd or even problems.

Additional Answers

22. $\dfrac{15m + 28}{35m^2}$

23. $\dfrac{7x + 8}{(x + 5)(x - 4)}$

24. $\dfrac{n^2 + 12}{(n + 4)(n - 3)}$

25. $\dfrac{8a^2 - 9a}{(a + 5)(a - 2)}$

26. $\dfrac{7x^2 + 3x}{(x - 3)(x + 1)}$

27. $\dfrac{3a + 20}{(a - 5)(a + 5)}$

28. $\dfrac{7y + 39}{(y + 3)(y - 3)}$

29. $\dfrac{2x + 1}{(x + 1)^2}$

30. $\dfrac{3x^2 + 6x + 6}{(x + 4)(x - 1)^2}$

DIFFERENTIATED HOMEWORK OPTIONS

Level	Assignment	Two-Day Option	
BL Basic	13–39, 51–53, 55–72	13–39 odd, 56, 57	14–38 even, 51–53, 55, 58–72
OL Core	13–39 odd, 40–43, 45, 47, 49, 51–53, 55–72	13–39, 56, 57	40–53, 55, 58–72
AL Advanced /Pre-AP	40–70 (optional: 65–72)		

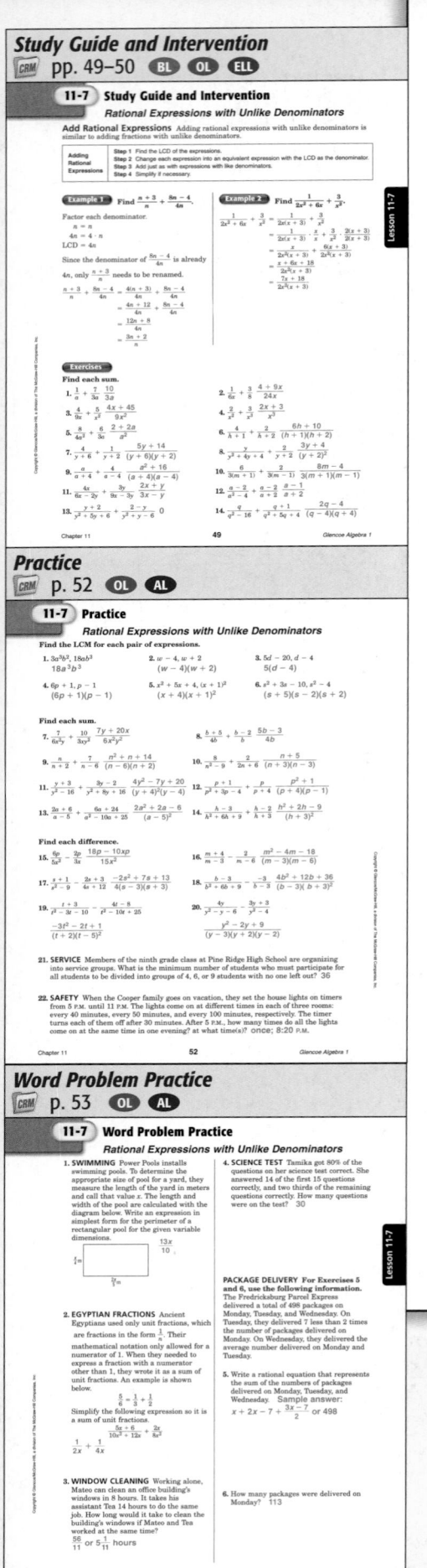

Practice
CRM p. 52 OL AL

Word Problem Practice
CRM p. 53 OL AL

★ **40. PET CARE** Kendra takes care of pets while their owners are out of town. One week she has three dogs that all eat the same kind of dog food. The first dog eats a bag of food every 12 days, the second dog eats a bag every 15 days, and the third dog eats a bag every 16 days. How many bags of food should Kendra buy for one week? **2 bags**

★ **41. CHARITY** Maya, Makalla, and Monya can walk one mile in 12, 15, and 20 minutes respectively. They plan to participate in a walk-a-thon to raise money for a local charity. Sponsors have agreed to pay $2.50 for each mile that is walked. What is the total number of miles the girls will walk in one hour? How much money will they raise? **12 miles; $30**

★ **42. COMPUTERS** Computer owners need to follow a regular maintenance schedule to keep their computers running effectively and efficiently. The table shows several items that should be performed on a regular basis. If Jamie got his computer 53 weeks ago and he has been appropriately maintaining it, how many weeks will it be until he has to perform all of the items on the same week? **19 weeks**

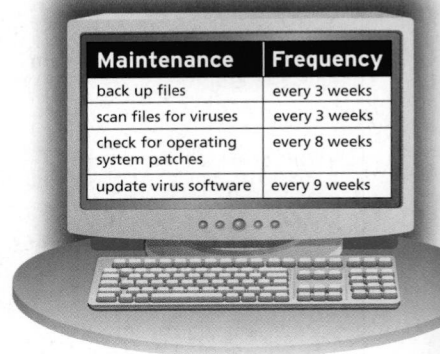

Maintenance	Frequency
back up files	every 3 weeks
scan files for viruses	every 3 weeks
check for operating system patches	every 8 weeks
update virus software	every 9 weeks

47. $\dfrac{a^3 - a^2b + a^2 + ab}{(a + b)(a - b)^2}$

49. $\dfrac{9x + 6}{(x + 1)(x + 2)^2}$

50. $\dfrac{15x^2 - 11x - 7}{9x^3 + 51x^2 - 80x - 28}$

Find each sum or difference.

43. $\dfrac{4}{15x^2} - \dfrac{5}{3x}$ $\dfrac{4 - 25x}{15x^2}$

44. $\dfrac{x^2}{4x^2 - 9} + \dfrac{x}{(2x + 3)^2}$ $\dfrac{2x^3 + 5x^2 - 3x}{(2x - 3)(2x + 3)^2}$

45. $\dfrac{11x}{3y^2} - \dfrac{7x}{6y}$ $\dfrac{22x - 7xy}{6y^2}$

46. $\dfrac{k}{k + 5} - \dfrac{3}{k - 3}$ $\dfrac{k^2 - 6k - 15}{(k + 5)(k - 3)}$

47. $\dfrac{a^2}{a^2 - b^2} + \dfrac{a}{(a - b)^2}$

48. $\dfrac{x^2 + 4x - 5}{x^2 - 2x - 3} - \dfrac{2}{x + 1}$ $\dfrac{x + 1}{x - 3}$

49. $\dfrac{3x}{x^2 + 3x + 2} - \dfrac{3x - 6}{x^2 + 4x + 4}$

50. $\dfrac{5x}{3x^2 + 19x - 14} - \dfrac{1}{9x^2 - 12x + 4}$

EXTRA PRACTICE
See pages 741, 754.

Math Online
Self-Check Quiz at
ca.algebra1.com

H.O.T. Problems

51. REASONING Describe how to find the LCD of two rational expressions with unlike denominators.

52. OPEN ENDED Write two rational expressions in which the LCD is twice the denominator of one of the expressions. **See margin.**

53. REASONING Explain how to rename rational expressions using their LCD.

54. CHALLENGE Janelle says that a shortcut for adding fractions with unlike denominators is to add the cross products for the numerator and write the denominator as the product of the denominators. For example, $\dfrac{2}{7} + \dfrac{5}{8} = \dfrac{2 \cdot 8 + 5 \cdot 7}{7 \cdot 8} = \dfrac{51}{56}$. Explain why the method will always work or provide a counterexample to show that it does not always work. **See margin.**

55. *Writing in Math* Use the information about elections on page 614 to explain how rational expressions can be used to describe elections. Include an explanation of how to determine the least common multiple of two or more rational expressions. **See margin.**

51. Sample answer: To find the LCD, determine the least common multiple of all the factors of the denominators.

53. Sample answer: Multiply both the numerator and denominator by factors necessary to form the LCD.

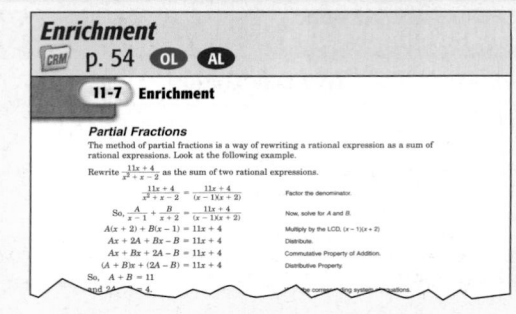

BL = Below Grade Level

OL = On Grade Level

AL = Above Grade Level

ELL = English Language Learner

Additional pages not shown:

CRM **Lesson Reading Guide,** p. 48 BL OL ELL

CRM **Skills Practice,** p. 51 BL OL

56. $\dfrac{x}{7x-3} + \dfrac{x+2}{15x+30} = $ B

A $\dfrac{22x-3}{210x-90}$

B $\dfrac{22x-3}{105x-45}$

C $\dfrac{41x-6}{210x-90}$

D $\dfrac{41x-6}{105x-45}$

57. REVIEW A rectangle with length x and width $2x$ is inside a rectangle with length 12 and width 8. Which expression represents the area of the shaded region in terms of x? J

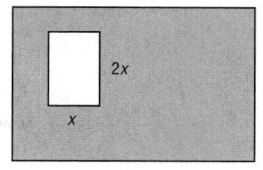

F $96-x$ H $96-x^2$

G $96-2x$ J $96-2x^2$

Spiral Review

Find each sum. (Lesson 11-6)

58. $\dfrac{3m}{2m+1} + \dfrac{3}{2m+1}$ $\dfrac{3m+3}{2m+1}$

59. $\dfrac{4x}{2x+3} + \dfrac{5}{2x+3}$ $\dfrac{4x+5}{2x+3}$

60. $\dfrac{2y}{y-3} + \dfrac{5}{3-y}$ $\dfrac{2y-5}{y-3}$

Find each quotient. (Lesson 11-5)

61. $\dfrac{b^2+8b-20}{b-2}$ $b+10$

62. $\dfrac{t^3-19t+9}{t-4}$ $t^2+4t-3-\dfrac{3}{t-4}$

63. $\dfrac{4m^2+8m-19}{2m+7}$ $2m-3+\dfrac{2}{2m+7}$

Determine the best method to solve each system of equations. Then solve the system. (Lesson 5-5)

64. $2x+3y=9$ $(-3, 5)$
$-x+5y=28$

65. $y=\dfrac{1}{4}x$ $(24, 6)$
$-x+3y=-6$

★**66. CURRENCY** The table shows the exchange rate for the American dollar to the British pound over the course of 30 days. Create a graph to display this data. Determine whether the graph shows a positive or negative correlation and draw a line of fit. (Lesson 5-7) **Positive correlation; see Ch. 11 Answer Appendix.**

Day	5	10	15	20	25	30
British Pound to 1 American Dollar	0.5532	0.5621	0.5715	0.5832	0.5681	0.5721

GET READY for the Next Lesson

PREREQUISITE SKILL Find each quotient. (Lesson 11-4)

67. $\dfrac{x}{2} \div \dfrac{3x}{5}$ $\dfrac{5}{6}$

68. $\dfrac{a^2}{5b} \div \dfrac{4a}{10b^2}$ $\dfrac{ab}{2}$

69. $\dfrac{x+7}{x} \div \dfrac{x+7}{x+3}$ $\dfrac{x+3}{x}$

70. $\dfrac{3n}{2n+5} \div \dfrac{12n^2}{2n+5}$ $\dfrac{1}{4n}$

71. $\dfrac{3x}{x+2} \div (x-1)$ $\dfrac{3x}{(x+2)(x-1)}$

72. $\dfrac{x^2+7x+12}{x+6} \div (x+3)$ $\dfrac{x+4}{x+6}$

Yesterday's News Have students write how yesterday's lesson on adding and subtracting rational expressions with like denominators helped them with today's new material.

FOLDABLES Study Organizer **Foldables™ Follow-Up**
Remind students to use their Foldables to record notes on what they have learned in this lesson. Students should include the steps given in the Key Concept on p. 607.

✓ **Formative Assessment**
Check for student understanding of concepts in Lessons 11-6 and 11-7

CRM Quiz 3, p. 74.

Additional Answers

52. Sample answer: A field of 15 acres is divided into x lots, and a neighboring field of the same acreage is divided into $2x$ lots; $\dfrac{15}{x}$, $\dfrac{15}{2x}$.

54. Sample answer: This method will always work;
$\dfrac{a}{x} + \dfrac{b}{y} = \dfrac{a}{x} \cdot \dfrac{y}{y} + \dfrac{b}{y} \cdot \dfrac{x}{x}$
$= \dfrac{ay}{xy} + \dfrac{bx}{yx} = \dfrac{ay+bx}{xy}$.

55. Sample answer: You can use rational expressions and their least common denominators to determine when elections will coincide. Use each factor of the denominators the greatest number of times it appears.

Pre-AP Activity Use as an Extension.

Have students solve the following problems: $\dfrac{x-4}{(x-2)^2} - \dfrac{x-5}{x^2+x-6}$ and $\dfrac{x-4}{(2-x)^2} - \dfrac{x-5}{x^2+x-6}$.

Have students point out the similarities and differences between the two problems. Direct students to notice that, when they are written as trinomials, the denominators $(x-2)^2$ and $(2-x)^2$ are actually the same denominators. Both problems equal $\dfrac{6x-22}{(x-2)^2(x+3)}$.

11-8 Mixed Expressions and Complex Fractions

① Focus

Standards Alignment

Before Lesson 11-8
Add and subtract fractions from Standard 7NS2.2

Lesson 11-8
Simplify fractions with polynomials in the numerator and denominator Solve both computationally and conceptually challenging problems by using operations with rational expressions from Standards 1A12.0 and 1A13.0

After Lesson 11-8
Simplify complicated rational expressions from Standard 2A7.0

② Teach

Scaffolding Questions
Have students read *Get Ready for the Lesson*.
Ask:
• Why can't you find the number of cookies that Katelyn can make by just simplifying the given expression? The units are different. The amount of dough is given in pounds, and the amount of dough per cookie is given in ounces.

(continued on the next page)

Main Ideas
• Simplify mixed expressions.
• Simplify complex fractions.

Standard 12.0 Students simplify fractions with polynomials in the numerator and denominator by factoring both and reducing them to the lowest terms. (Key)

Standard 13.0 Students add, subtract, multiply, and divide rational expressions and functions. Students solve both computationally and conceptually challenging problems by using these techniques. (Key)

New Vocabulary
• mixed expression
• complex fraction

▶ GET READY for the Lesson

Katelyn bought $2\frac{1}{2}$ pounds of chocolate chip cookie dough. If the average cookie requires $1\frac{1}{2}$ ounces of dough, the number of cookies that Katelyn can bake can be found by simplifying the expression $\dfrac{2\frac{1}{2} \text{ pounds}}{1\frac{1}{2} \text{ ounces}}$.

Simplify Mixed Expressions Recall that a number like $2\frac{1}{2}$ is a mixed number because it is the sum of an integer, 2, and a fraction, $\frac{1}{2}$. An expression like $3 + \dfrac{x+2}{x-3}$ is called a **mixed expression** because it contains the sum of a monomial, 3, and a rational expression, $\dfrac{x+2}{x+3}$. Changing mixed expressions to rational expressions is similar to changing mixed numbers to improper fractions.

EXAMPLE Mixed Expression to Rational Expression

① Simplify $3 + \dfrac{6}{x+3}$.

$$3 + \frac{6}{x+3} = \frac{3(x+3)}{x+3} + \frac{6}{x+3} \qquad \text{The LCD is } x+3.$$

$$= \frac{3(x+3)+6}{x+3} \qquad \text{Add the numerators.}$$

$$= \frac{3x+9+6}{x+3} \text{ or } \frac{3x+15}{x+3} \qquad \text{Distributive Property}$$

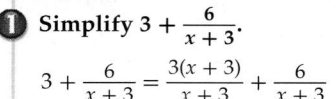 **Simplify each expression.**

1A. $\dfrac{6y}{4y+8} + 5y \qquad \dfrac{10y^2 + 23y}{2y+4}$

1B. $15 - \dfrac{17x+5}{5x+10} \qquad \dfrac{58x+145}{5x+10}$

620 Chapter 11 Rational Expressions and Equations

Lesson 11-8 Resources

Chapter 11 Resource Masters
Lesson Reading Guide, p. 55 **BL OL ELL**
Study Guide and Intervention, pp. 56–57
BL OL ELL
Skills Practice, p. 58 **BL OL**
Practice, p. 59 **OL AL**
Word Problem Practice, p. 60 **OL AL**
Enrichment, p. 61 **OL AL**

Transparencies
5-Minute Check Transparency 11-8

Additional Print Resources
Noteables™ Interactive Study Notebook with Foldables™

Technology
ca.algebra1.com
Interactive Classroom CD-ROM
AssignmentWorks CD-ROM
Graphing Calculator Easy Files

620 Chapter 11 Rational Expressions and Equations

Simplify Complex Fractions If a fraction has one or more fractions in the numerator or denominator, it is called a **complex fraction**. You simplify an algebraic complex fraction in the same way that you simplify a numerical complex fraction.

numerical complex fraction

$$\frac{\frac{8}{3}}{\frac{7}{5}} = \frac{8}{3} \div \frac{7}{5}$$

$$= \frac{8}{3} \cdot \frac{5}{7}$$

$$= \frac{40}{21}$$

algebraic complex fraction

$$\frac{\frac{a}{b}}{\frac{c}{d}} = \frac{a}{b} \div \frac{c}{d}$$

$$= \frac{a}{b} \cdot \frac{d}{c}$$

$$= \frac{ad}{bc}$$

KEY CONCEPT   *Simplifying a Complex Fraction*

Any complex fraction $\dfrac{\frac{a}{b}}{\frac{c}{d}}$, where $b \neq 0$, $c \neq 0$, and $d \neq 0$, can be expressed as $\dfrac{ad}{bc}$.

Real-World EXAMPLE   Complex Fraction Involving Numbers

2 **BAKING** Refer to the application at the beginning of the lesson. How many cookies can Katelyn make with $2\frac{1}{2}$ pounds of dough?

To find the total number of cookies, divide the amount of cookie dough by the amount of dough needed for each cookie.

$$\frac{2\frac{1}{2} \text{ pounds}}{1\frac{1}{2} \text{ ounces}} = \frac{2\frac{1}{2} \cancel{\text{ pounds}}}{1\frac{1}{2} \text{ ounces}} \cdot \frac{16 \cancel{\text{ ounces}}}{1 \cancel{\text{ pound}}} \qquad \text{Convert pounds to ounces.}$$
Divide by common units.

$$= 16 \cdot \frac{2\frac{1}{2}}{1\frac{1}{2}} \qquad \text{Simplify.}$$

$$= \frac{\frac{16}{1} \cdot \frac{5}{2}}{\frac{3}{2}} \qquad \text{Express each term as an improper fraction.}$$

$$= \frac{\frac{80}{2}}{\frac{3}{2}} \qquad \text{Multiply in the numerator.}$$

$$= \frac{80 \cdot 2}{2 \cdot 3} \qquad \frac{\frac{a}{b}}{\frac{c}{d}} = \frac{ad}{bc}$$

$$= \frac{160}{6} \text{ or } 26\frac{2}{3} \qquad \text{Simplify.}$$

> **Study Tip**
>
> **Order of Operations**
>
> Recall that when applying the order of operations, simplify the numerator and denominator of a complex fraction before proceeding with division.

CHECK Your Progress

2. The Centralville High School Cooking Club has $12\frac{1}{2}$ pounds of flour with which to make tortillas. If there are $3\frac{3}{4}$ cups of flour in a pound and it takes about $\frac{1}{3}$ cup of flour per tortilla, how many tortillas can they make?

about 140

Online Personal Tutor at ca.algebra1.com

Lesson 11-8 Mixed Expressions and Complex Fractions   **621**

- What method could you use to find out how many cookies Katelyn can make? You could use dimensional analysis to convert pounds to ounces.
- How many ounces equal one pound? 16 ounces = 1 pound

Simplify Mixed Expressions
Example 1 shows how to change a mixed expression to a rational expression.

 Formative Assessment

Use the Check Your Progress exercises after each example to determine students' understanding of concepts.

ADDITIONAL EXAMPLE

1 Simplify $3 + \dfrac{7}{x-2} \cdot \dfrac{3x+1}{x-2}$

Additional Examples are also in:
- Noteables™ Interactive Study Notebook with Foldables™
- Interactive Classroom PowerPoint® Presentations

Simplify Complex Fractions
Example 2 shows how to simplify a complex fraction involving fractions.
Example 3 shows how to simplify a complex fraction involving monomials.
Example 4 shows how to simplify a complex fraction involving polynomials.

ADDITIONAL EXAMPLE

 BAKING Refer to the application at the beginning of this lesson. If Katelyn used 2 pounds of dough, how many cookies would she be able to make? 21 cookies

Focus on Mathematical Content

Complex Fractions You can simplify an algebraic complex fraction in the same way that you simplify a numerical complex fraction. Multiply the numerator by the reciprocal of the denominator.

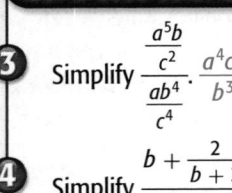
Tips for New Teachers

Preventing Errors

When simplifying complex fractions, there are many steps in which errors can occur, even for those students who clearly understand the concept. Encourage students to write out each step of the simplifying process.

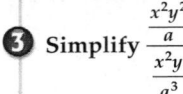 **Complex Fraction Involving Monomials**

3 Simplify $\dfrac{\frac{x^2y^2}{a}}{\frac{x^2y}{a^3}}$.

$$\dfrac{\frac{x^2y^2}{a}}{\frac{x^2y}{a^3}} = \frac{x^2y^2}{a} \div \frac{x^2y}{a^3} \qquad \text{Rewrite as a division sentence.}$$

$$= \frac{x^2y^2}{a} \cdot \frac{a^3}{x^2y} \qquad \text{Rewrite as multiplication by the reciprocal.}$$

$$= \frac{\overset{1}{x^2}\overset{y}{y^2}}{\underset{1}{a}} \cdot \frac{\overset{a^2}{a^3}}{\underset{1}{\underset{1}{x^2}}y} \qquad \text{Divide by common factors } x^2, y, \text{ and } a.$$

$$= a^2y \qquad \text{Simplify.}$$

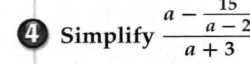 **Simplify each expression.**

3A. $\dfrac{\frac{g^3h}{b}}{\frac{gh^3i}{b^2}} \quad \dfrac{g^2b}{h^2i}$

3B. $\dfrac{\frac{-24m^3n^5}{p^2q}}{\frac{16pm^2}{n^4q}} \quad \dfrac{-3mn^9}{2p^3}$

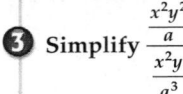 **Complex Fraction Involving Polynomials**

4 Simplify $\dfrac{a - \frac{15}{a-2}}{a+3}$.

The numerator contains a mixed expression. Rewrite it as a rational expression first.

$$\dfrac{a - \frac{15}{a-2}}{a+3} = \dfrac{\frac{a(a-2)}{a-2} - \frac{15}{a-2}}{a+3} \qquad \text{The LCD of the fractions in the numerator is } a-2.$$

$$= \dfrac{\frac{a^2 - 2a - 15}{a-2}}{a+3} \qquad \text{Simplify the numerator.}$$

$$= \dfrac{\frac{(a+3)(a-5)}{a-2}}{a+3} \qquad \text{Factor.}$$

$$= \dfrac{(a+3)(a-5)}{a-2} \div (a+3) \qquad \text{Rewrite as a division sentence.}$$

$$= \dfrac{(a+3)(a-5)}{a-2} \cdot \dfrac{1}{a+3} \qquad \text{Multiply by the reciprocal of } a+3.$$

$$= \dfrac{(\overset{1}{a+3})(a-5)}{a-2} \cdot \dfrac{1}{\underset{1}{a+3}} \qquad \text{Divide by the GCF, } a+3.$$

$$= \dfrac{a-5}{a-2} \qquad \text{Simplify.}$$

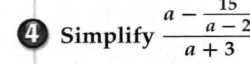 **Simplify each expression.**

4A. $\dfrac{\frac{b}{b+3} + 2}{b^2 - 2b - 8} \quad \dfrac{3}{(b+3)(b-4)}$

4B. $\dfrac{1 + \frac{2c^2 - 6c - 10}{c+7}}{2c+1} \quad \dfrac{c-3}{c+7}$

 Extra Examples at ca.algebra1.com

★ indicates multi-step problem

Example 1 (p. 620)

Write each mixed expression as a rational expression.

1. $3 + \frac{4}{x}$ $\frac{3x + 4}{x}$

2. $7 + \frac{5}{6y}$ $\frac{42y + 5}{6y}$

3. $\frac{a - 1}{3a} + 2a$ $\frac{6a^2 + a - 1}{3a}$

Example 2 (p. 622)

4. **ENTERTAINMENT** The student talent committee is arranging the performances for their holiday pageant. The first-act performances and their lengths are shown in the table. What is the average length of each performance? $7\frac{29}{100}$ min

Holiday Pageant Line-Up

Performance	Length (min)
A	7
B	$4\frac{1}{2}$
C	$6\frac{1}{2}$
D	$8\frac{1}{4}$
E	$10\frac{1}{5}$

Examples 3, 4 (p. 620)

Simplify each expression.

5. $\dfrac{3\frac{1}{2}}{4\frac{3}{4}}$ $\frac{14}{19}$

6. $\dfrac{\frac{x^3}{y^2}}{\frac{y^3}{x}}$ $\frac{x^4}{y^5}$

7. $\dfrac{\frac{x - y}{a + b}}{\frac{x^2 - y^2}{a^2 - b^2}}$ $\frac{a - b}{x + y}$

Exercises

HOMEWORK HELP	
For Exercises	See Examples
8–19	1
20, 21	2
22–25	3
26–33	4

Exercise Levels
A: 8–33
B: 34–37
C: 38–41

Write each mixed expression as a rational expression.

8. $8 + \frac{3}{n}$ $\frac{8n + 3}{n}$

9. $4 + \frac{5}{a}$ $\frac{4a + 5}{a}$

10. $2x + \frac{x}{y}$ $\frac{2xy + x}{y}$

11. $6z + \frac{2z}{w}$ $\frac{6wz + 2z}{w}$

12. $2m - \frac{4 + m}{m}$

13. $3a - \frac{a + 1}{2a}$

14. $b^2 + \frac{a - b}{a + b}$

15. $r^2 + \frac{r - 4}{r + 3}$

16. $5n^2 + \frac{n + 3}{n^2 - 9}$

17. $3s^2 - \frac{s + 1}{s^2 - 1}$ $\frac{3s^3 - 3s^2 - 1}{s - 1}$

18. $(x - 5) + \frac{x + 2}{x - 3}$ $\frac{x^2 - 7x + 17}{x - 3}$

19. $(p + 4) + \frac{p + 1}{p - 4}$ $\frac{p^2 + p - 15}{p - 4}$

12. $\frac{2m^2 - m - 4}{m}$

13. $\frac{6a^2 - a - 1}{2a}$

14. $\frac{b^3 + ab^2 + a - b}{a + b}$

15. $\frac{r^3 + 3r^2 + r - 4}{r + 3}$

16. $\frac{5n^3 - 15n^2 + 1}{n - 3}$

20. **PARTIES** The student council is planning a party for the school volunteers. There are five 66-ounce unopened bottles of soda left from a recent dance. When poured over ice, $5\frac{1}{2}$ ounces of soda fills a cup. How many servings of soda can they get from the bottles they have? **60**

★21. **SCIENCE** When air is pumped into a bicycle tire, the pressure P required varies inversely as the volume of the air V and is given by the equation $P = \frac{k}{V}$. If the pressure is 30 lb/in² when the volume is $1\frac{2}{3}$ cubic feet, find the pressure when the volume is $\frac{3}{4}$ cubic feet. $66\frac{2}{3}$ lb/in²

Simplify each expression.

22. $\dfrac{5\frac{3}{4}}{7\frac{2}{3}}$ $\frac{3}{4}$

23. $\dfrac{8\frac{2}{7}}{4\frac{4}{5}}$ $\frac{145}{84}$

24. $\dfrac{\frac{a}{b^3}}{\frac{a^2}{b}}$ $\frac{1}{ab^2}$

3 Practice

✓ **Formative Assessment**

Use Exercises 1–7 to check for understanding.

Use the chart at the bottom of this page to customize assignments for your students.

Odd/Even Assignments

Exercises 8–33 are structured so that students practice the same concepts whether they are assigned odd or even problems.

Real-World Connections

For Exercises 34 and 35, remind students that sirens are used to provide early warning of a variety of situations such as tornadoes, fires, and medical emergencies. Ask students to tell about the use of sirens in places where they have lived.

DIFFERENTIATED HOMEWORK OPTIONS

Level	Assignment	Two-Day Option	
BL Basic	8–33, 38, 40–58	9–33 odd, 42, 43	8–32 even, 38, 40, 41, 44–58
OL Core	9–33 odd, 34–38, 40–58	8–33, 42, 43	34–39, 40, 41, 44–58
AL Advanced /Pre-AP	34–58 (optional: 53–58)		

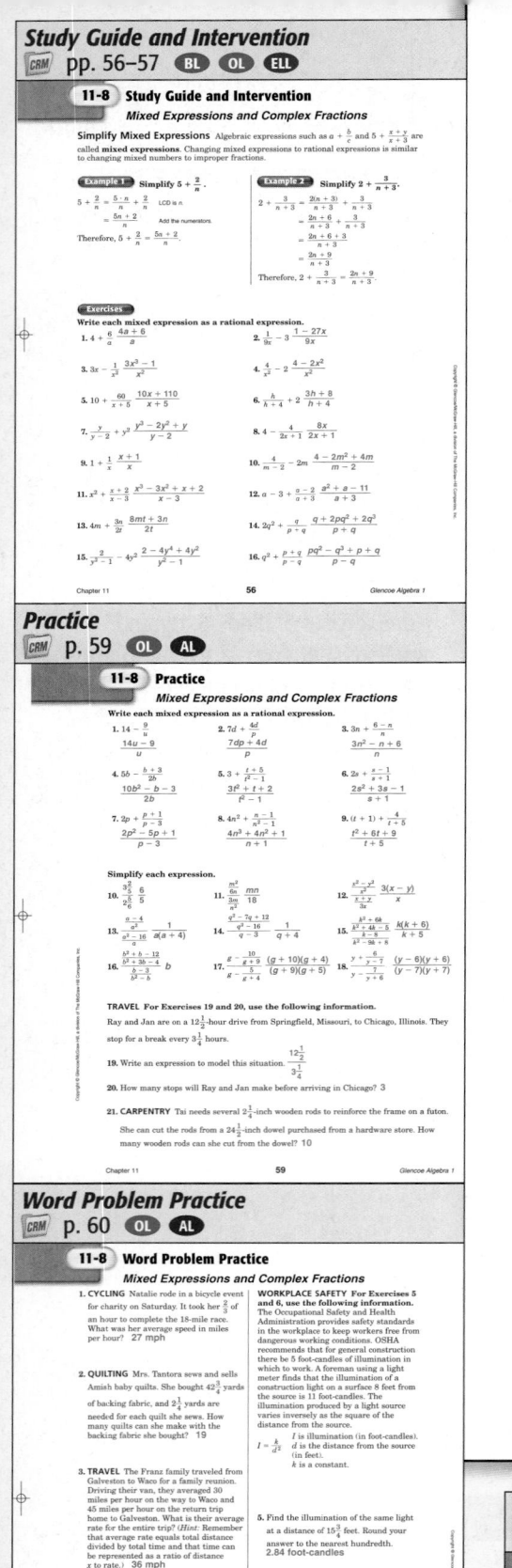

Simplify each expression.

25. $\dfrac{\frac{n^3}{m^2}}{\frac{n^2}{m^2}}$ n

26. $\dfrac{\frac{x+4}{y-2}}{\frac{x^2}{y^2}}$ $\dfrac{y^2(x+4)}{x^2(y-2)}$

27. $\dfrac{\frac{s^3}{t^2}}{\frac{s+t}{s-t}}$ $\dfrac{s^3(s-t)}{t^2(s+t)}$

28. $\dfrac{\frac{y^2-1}{y^2+3y-4}}{y+1}$ $\dfrac{1}{y+4}$

29. $\dfrac{\frac{a^2-2q-3}{a^2-1}}{a-3}$ $\dfrac{1}{a-1}$

30. $\dfrac{\frac{n^2+2n}{n^2+9n+18}}{\frac{n^2-5n}{n^2+n-30}}$ $\dfrac{n+2}{n+3}$

32. $\dfrac{(x+3)(x-1)}{(x-2)(x+4)}$

31. $\dfrac{\frac{x^2+4x-21}{x^2-9x+18}}{\frac{x^2+3x-28}{x^2-10x+24}}$ 1

32. $\dfrac{x-\frac{15}{x-2}}{x-\frac{20}{x-1}}$

33. $\dfrac{(n+5)(n-2)}{(n+12)(n-9)}$

33. $\dfrac{n+\frac{35}{n+12}}{n-\frac{63}{n-2}}$

SIRENS For Exercises 34 and 35, use the following information.

As an ambulance approaches, the siren sounds different than if it were sitting still. If the ambulance is moving toward you at v miles per hour and blowing its siren at a frequency of f, then you hear the siren as if it were blowing at a frequency of h. This can be defined by the equation $h = \dfrac{f}{1-\frac{v}{s}}$, where s is the speed of sound, approximately 760 miles per hour.

34. Simplify the complex fraction in the formula. $\dfrac{fs}{s-v}$

35. Suppose a siren blows at 45 cycles per minute and is moving toward you at 65 miles per hour. Find the frequency of the siren as you hear it.
49.21 cycles/min

36. **POPULATION** According to a recent census, Union City, New Jersey, was the most densely populated city in the U.S., and Anchorage City, Alaska, was one of the least. The population of Union City was 67,088, and the population of Anchorage City was 260,283. The land area of Union City is about 1.3 square miles, and the land area of Anchorage City is about 1,697.3 square miles. How many more people were there per square mile in Union City than in Anchorage City?   **51,453 people per square mile**

37. What is the product of $\dfrac{2b^2}{5c}$ and the quotient of $\dfrac{4b^3}{2c}$ and $\dfrac{7b^3}{8c^2}$? $\dfrac{32b^2}{35}$

EXTRA PRACTICE
See pages 741, 754.
Math Online
Self-Check Quiz at
ca.algebra1.com

H.O.T. Problems

38. **OPEN ENDED** Think of a real-world complex fraction and explain how you would simplify it.   **See margin.**

39. **CHALLENGE** Which expressions are equivalent to 0?   **a and c**

a. $\dfrac{a}{1-\frac{3}{a}} + \dfrac{a}{\frac{3}{a}-1}$

b. $\dfrac{a-\frac{1}{3}}{b} - \dfrac{a+\frac{1}{3}}{b}$

c. $\dfrac{\frac{1}{2}+2a}{b-1} + \dfrac{2a+\frac{1}{2}}{1-b}$

40. Bolton; Lian omitted the factor $2x+1$ and replaced it with an additional $x+1$.

40. **FIND THE ERROR** Bolton and Lian found the LCD of $\dfrac{4}{2x+1} - \dfrac{5}{x+1} + \dfrac{2}{x-1}$. Who is correct? Explain your reasoning.

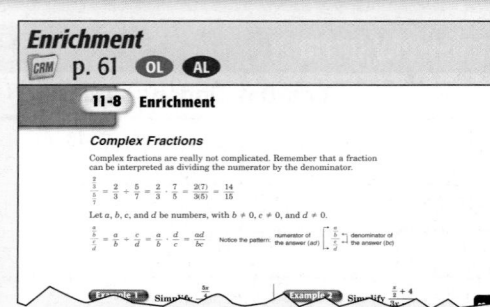

Bolton
$\dfrac{4}{2x+1} - \dfrac{5}{x+1} + \dfrac{2}{x-1}$
LCD: $(2x+1)(x+1)(x-1)$

Lian
$\dfrac{4}{2x+1} - \dfrac{5}{x+1} + \dfrac{2}{x-1}$
LCD: $2(x+1)(x-1)$

BL = Below Grade Level
OL = On Grade Level
AL = Above Grade Level
ELL = English Language Learner

Additional pages not shown:
CRM *Lesson Reading Guide*, p. 55 **BL** **OL** **ELL**
CRM *Skills Practice*, p. 58 **BL** **OL**

41. *Writing in Math* Refer to the information on page 620. Explain how complex fractions are used in baking. Include an explanation of the process used to simplify a complex fraction. **See margin.**

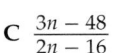 **STANDARDS PRACTICE** 13.0, 7AF4.2

42. The perimeter of hexagon $ABCDEF$ is 12. Which expression can be used to represent the measure of $\overline{BC}$? **C**

A $\dfrac{6n-96}{n-8}$

B $\dfrac{9n-96}{n-8}$

C $\dfrac{3n-48}{2n-16}$

D $\dfrac{9n-96}{4n-32}$

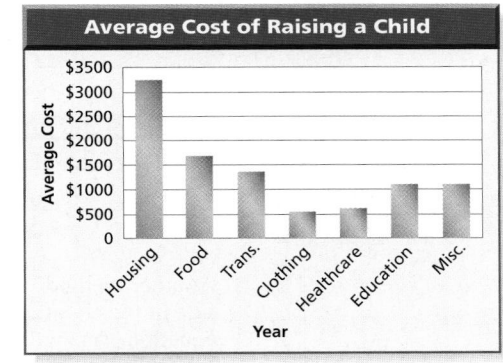

43. REVIEW Ms. Roberts is draining her cylindrical above-ground pool. The pool has a radius of 12 feet and a height of 4 feet. If water is pumped out at a constant rate of 5.5 gallons per minute, about how long will it take to drain the pool? (1 ft³ = 7.5 gal) **J**

F 43.9 min H 35.2 h

G 3.8 h J 41.1 h

Spiral Review

Find each sum. (Lesson 11-7)

44. $\dfrac{12x}{4y^2}+\dfrac{8}{6y}$ **44.** $\dfrac{9x+4y}{3y^2}$

45. $\dfrac{a}{a-b}+\dfrac{b}{2b+3a}$ **45.** $\dfrac{3a^2+3ab-b^2}{(a-b)(2b+3a)}$

46. $\dfrac{a+3}{3a^2-10a-8}+\dfrac{2a}{a^2-8a+16}$ **46.** $\dfrac{7a^2+3a-12}{(3a+2)(a-4)^2}$

Find each difference. (Lesson 11-6)

47. $\dfrac{7}{x^2}-\dfrac{3}{x^2}$ $\dfrac{4}{x^2}$

48. $\dfrac{x}{(x-3)^2}-\dfrac{3}{(x-3)^2}$ $\dfrac{1}{x-3}$

49. $\dfrac{2}{t^2-t-2}-\dfrac{t}{t^2-t-2}$ $-\dfrac{1}{t+1}$

FAMILIES For Exercises 50–52, refer to the graph. (Lesson 7-1)

50. Write each number in the graph using scientific notation. **See margin.**

51. How many times as great is the amount spent on food as the amount spent on clothing? Express your answer in scientific notation. **3.2 × 10⁰**

52. What percent of the total amount is spent on housing? **33.3%**

Average Cost of Raising a Child

Source: University of Minnesota

GET READY for the Next Lesson

PREREQUISITE SKILL Solve each equation. (Lessons 2-2, 2-3, and 2-4)

53. $-12=\dfrac{x}{4}$ **−48**

54. $1.8=g-0.6$ **2.4**

55. $\dfrac{3}{4}n-3=9$ **16**

56. $7x^2=28$ **−2, 2**

57. $3.2=\dfrac{-8+n}{-7}$ **−14.4**

58. $\dfrac{-3n-(-4)}{-6}=-9$ **$-\dfrac{50}{3}$**

Lesson 11-8 Mixed Expressions and Complex Fractions **625**

⚠ **Exercise Alert!**

Find the Error Ask students to explain the mistake Lian made. Ask students how many of them have made similar mistakes. Discuss ways students might avoid errors in factoring.

4 Assess

Name the Math Have students tell what mathematical procedures they used to simplify the expression in Exercise 30. Then have students substitute 4 for n in the original expression and in their simplified expressions. Students should see that when $n=4$, the value of both expressions is $\dfrac{6}{7}$.

Additional Answers

38. Sample answer: scuba diver figuring out how long the air in his tank will last; $\dfrac{75\frac{3}{4} \text{ cubic feet}}{17\frac{1}{2} \text{ liter/minute}}$

41. Sample answer: Most measurements used in baking are fractions or mixed numbers, which are examples of rational expressions. Divide the expression in the numerator of a complex fraction by the expression in the denominator.

50. 3.2×10^3; 1.6×10^3; 1.4×10^3; 5.0×10^2; 7.5×10^2; 1.1×10; 1.1×10^3; 1.1×10^3

Pre-AP Activity Use as an Extension.

Write $1+\dfrac{1}{1+\dfrac{1}{1+\dfrac{1}{x}}}$ on the board. Ask students to write this mixed expression as a rational expression.

$\dfrac{3x+2}{2x+1}$

11-9 Rational Equations and Functions

1 Focus

 Standards Alignment

Before Lesson 11-9
Solve two-step linear equations and inequalities in one variable from Standard 7AF4.1

Lesson 11-9
Solve both computationally and conceptually challenging problems by using operations with rational expressions
Solve rate, work and percent mixture problems from Standards 1A13.0 and 1A15.0

Before Lesson 11-9
Determine the truth of a specific algebraic statement involving rational, radical and logarithmic expressions from Standard 2A15.0

2 Teach

Scaffolding Questions

Have students read *Get Ready for the Lesson*.
Ask:
• Why is it important to know where trains are? Sample answer: So that the trains do not run into each other.

(continued on the next page)

Lesson 11-9 Resources

Main Ideas

• Solve rational equations.
• Eliminate extraneous solutions.

 Standard 13.0 Students add, subtract, multiply, and **divide rational expressions** and functions. **Students solve both computationally and conceptually challenging problems by using these techniques.** (Key)

Standard 15.0 Students apply algebraic techniques to solve rate problems, work problems, and percent mixture problems. (Key, CAHSEE)

New Vocabulary

rational equations
work problems
rate problems
extraneous solutions

Study Tip

Proportions
If the rational equation is a proportion, you can cross multiply to solve.

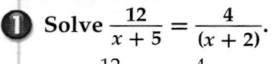 **for the Lesson**

The Washington, D.C., Metrorail is one of the safest subway systems in the world, serving a population of more than 3.5 million. It is vital that a rail system of this size maintain a consistent schedule. Rational equations can be used to determine the exact positions of trains at any given time.

Washington Metropolitan Area Transit Authority	
Train	**Distance**
● Red Line	19.4 mi
● Orange Line	24.14 mi
● Blue Line	19.95 mi
● Green Line	20.59 mi
● Yellow Line	9.46 mi

Solve Rational Equations **Rational equations** are equations that contain rational expressions. You can use cross products to solve rational equations, but *only* when both sides of the equation are single fractions.

EXAMPLE Use Cross Products

1 Solve $\dfrac{12}{x+5} = \dfrac{4}{(x+2)}$.

$\dfrac{12}{x+5} = \dfrac{4}{(x+2)}$ Original equation

$12(x+2) = 4(x+5)$ Cross multiply.

$12x + 24 = 4x + 20$ Distributive Property

$8x = -4$ Add $-4x$ and -24 to each side.

$x = -\dfrac{4}{8}$ or $-\dfrac{1}{2}$ Divide each side by 8.

CHECK Your Progress

Solve each equation.

1A. $\dfrac{7}{y-3} = \dfrac{3}{y+1}$ -4

1B. $\dfrac{13}{f+10} = \dfrac{2}{7f}$ 4.45

Another method you can use to solve rational equations is to multiply each side of the equation by the LCD of all of the fractions on both sides of the equation. This will eliminate all of the fractions. This method works for any rational equation.

EXAMPLE Use the LCD

2 Solve $\dfrac{n-2}{n} - \dfrac{n-3}{n-6} = \dfrac{1}{n}$.

$\dfrac{n-2}{n} - \dfrac{n-3}{n-6} = \dfrac{1}{n}$ Original equation

---

Technology

$$n(n-6)\left(\frac{n-2}{n} - \frac{n-3}{n-6}\right) = n(n-6)\left(\frac{1}{n}\right)$$ The LCD is $n(n-6)$.

$$\left(\frac{\overset{1}{n}(n-6)}{1} \cdot \frac{n-2}{\underset{1}{n}}\right) - \left(\frac{n(\overset{1}{n-6})}{1} \cdot \frac{n-3}{\underset{1}{n-6}}\right) = \frac{\overset{1}{n}(n-6)}{1} \cdot \frac{1}{\underset{1}{n}}$$ Distributive Property

$$(n-6)(n-2) - n(n-3) = n - 6$$ Simplify.

$$(n^2 - 8n + 12) - (n^2 - 3n) = n - 6$$ Multiply.

$$n^2 - 8n + 12 - n^2 + 3n = n - 6$$ Subtract.

$$-5n + 12 = n - 6$$ Simplify.

$$-6n = -18$$ Subtract.

$$n = 3$$ Divide.

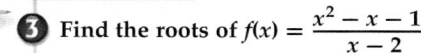 **CHECK Your Progress** Solve each equation.

2A. $\dfrac{2b-5}{b-2} - 2 = \dfrac{3}{b+2}$ 1   **2B.** $1 + \dfrac{1}{c+2} = \dfrac{28}{c^2 + 2c}$ 4, −7

Recall that to find the roots of a quadratic function, find the values of x when $y = 0$. The roots of a rational function are found similarly.

EXAMPLE **Rational Functions**

3 Find the roots of $f(x) = \dfrac{x^2 - x - 12}{x - 2}$.

$f(x) = \dfrac{x^2 - x - 12}{x - 2}$ Original function

$0 = \dfrac{x^2 - x - 12}{x - 2}$ $f(x) = 0$

$0 = \dfrac{(x-4)(x+3)}{x - 2}$ Factor.

When $x = 4$ and -3, the numerator becomes zero, so $f(x) = 0$. Therefore, the roots of the function are 4 and −3.

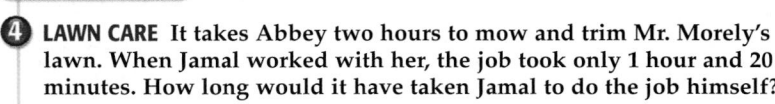 **CHECK Your Progress** Find the roots of each function.

3A. $f(x) = \dfrac{x^2 + 3x - 18}{x - 3}$ −6   **3B.** $f(x) = \dfrac{x^2 + 6x + 8}{x^2 + x - 2}$ −4

Rational equations can be used to solve **work problems**.

EXAMPLE **Work Problem**

4 **LAWN CARE** It takes Abbey two hours to mow and trim Mr. Morely's lawn. When Jamal worked with her, the job took only 1 hour and 20 minutes. How long would it have taken Jamal to do the job himself?

Explore Since it takes Abbey two hours to do the yard, she can finish $\frac{1}{2}$ the job in one hour. Thus, her rate of work is $\frac{1}{2}$ of the job per hour. The amount of work Jamal can do in one hour can be represented by $\frac{1}{t}$. To determine how long it takes Jamal to do the job alone, use the formula Abbey's portion of the job + Jamal's portion of the job = 1 completed yard.   *(continued on the next page)*

Study Tip

Look Back
To review **solving quadratic equations by factoring**, see Lessons 9-3 through 9-6.

- If you're given the positions of two moving trains, is that sufficient information to determine whether they will collide in the future? No, you need to know their position, direction of travel, and speed.

Solve Rational Equations

Example 1 shows how to use cross-products to solve rational expressions when both sides of the equation are single fractions. **Example 2** shows how to solve rational equations by multiplying each side of the equation by the LCD to eliminate fractions. **Example 3** shows how to use rational equations to solve real-world work problems. **Example 4** shows how to use rational equations to solve real-world rate problems.

 Formative Assessment

Use the Check Your Progress exercises after each example to determine students' understanding of concepts.

ADDITIONAL EXAMPLE

1 Solve $\dfrac{8}{x+3} = \dfrac{2}{x-6}$. 9

2 Solve each equation.

a. $\dfrac{5}{x+1} - \dfrac{1}{x} = \dfrac{2}{x^2 + x}$ $\frac{3}{4}$

b. $a + \dfrac{a^2 - 5}{a^2 - 1} = \dfrac{a^2 + a + 2}{a + 1}$ 3

3 Find the roots of $f(x) = \dfrac{x^2 + 6x - 16}{x + 4}$. 2, −8

4 **TV INSTALLATION** On Saturdays, Lee helps her father install satellite TV systems. The jobs normally take Lee's father about $2\frac{1}{2}$ hours. But when Lee helps, the jobs only take them $1\frac{1}{2}$ hours. If Lee were installing a satellite system herself, how long would the job take? $3\frac{3}{4}$ hours

---

Additional Examples are also in:

- Noteables™ Interactive Study Notebook with Foldables™
- Interactive Classroom PowerPoint® Presentations

Tips for New Teachers

Preventing Errors

Suggest students make a mental note on the values for the variable that make the denominator equal to zero.

Suggest that students check their solutions by substituting them back into the original equation.

⑤ TRANSPORTATION Refer to the application at the beginning of the lesson. Suppose two Red Line trains leave their stations at opposite ends of the line at exactly 2:00 P.M. One train travels between the two stations in 48 minutes and the other train takes 54 minutes. At what time do the two trains pass each other? *The trains pass each other at about 25 minutes after they left their stations, at 2:25 P.M.*

Plan The time that both of them worked was $1\frac{1}{3}$ hours. Each rate multiplied by this time results in the amount of work done by each person.

Solve

Abbey's portion	plus	Jamal's portion	equals	1 job.
$\frac{1}{2}\left(\frac{4}{3}\right)$	$+$	$\frac{1}{t}\left(\frac{4}{3}\right)$	$=$	1

$$\frac{4}{6} + \frac{4}{3t} = 1 \qquad \text{Multiply.}$$

$$6t\left(\frac{4}{6} + \frac{4}{3t}\right) = 6t \cdot 1 \qquad \text{The LCD is } 6t.$$

$$\overset{1}{6t}\left(\frac{4}{\underset{1}{6}}\right) + \overset{2}{6t}\left(\frac{4}{\underset{1}{3t}}\right) = 6t \qquad \text{Distributive Property}$$

$$4t + 8 = 6t \qquad \text{Simplify.}$$

$$8 = 2t \qquad \text{Add } -4t \text{ to each side.}$$

$$4 = t \qquad \text{Divide each side by 2.}$$

Check The time that it would take Jamal to do the yard by himself is 4 hours. This seems reasonable because the combined efforts of the two took longer than half of Abbey's usual time.

✓CHECK Your Progress

4. Lupe can paint a 60 square foot wall in 40 minutes. Working with her friend Steve, the two of them can paint the wall in 25 minutes. How long would it take Steve to do the job himself? $\frac{10}{9}$ h

◉nline Personal Tutor at ca.algebra1.com

Rational equations can also be used to solve **rate problems**.

EXAMPLE Rate Problem

⑤ TRANSPORTATION Refer to the application at the beginning of the lesson. The Yellow Line runs between Huntington and Mt. Vernon Square. Suppose one train leaves Mt. Vernon Square at noon and arrives at Huntington 24 minutes later, and a second train leaves Huntington at noon and arrives at Mt. Vernon Square 28 minutes later. At what time do the two trains pass each other?

Determine the rates of both trains. The total distance is 9.46 miles.

Train 1 $\dfrac{9.46 \text{ mi}}{24 \text{ min}}$ **Train 2** $\dfrac{9.46 \text{ mi}}{28 \text{ min}}$

Next, since both trains left at the same time, the time both have traveled when they pass will be the same. And since they started at opposite ends of the route, the sum of their distances is equal to the total route, 9.46 miles.

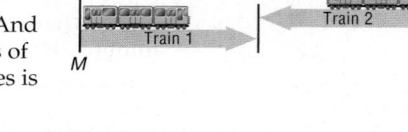

	r	t	d
Train 1	$\frac{9.46 \text{ mi}}{24 \text{ min}}$	t min	$\frac{9.46t}{24}$ mi
Train 2	$\frac{9.46 \text{ mi}}{28 \text{ min}}$	t min	$\frac{9.46t}{28}$ mi

$$\frac{9.46t}{24} + \frac{9.46t}{28} = 9.46 \qquad \text{The sum of the distances is 9.46.}$$

$$168\left(\frac{9.46t}{24} + \frac{9.46t}{28}\right) = 168 \cdot 9.46 \qquad \text{The LCD is 168.}$$

$$\frac{\overset{7}{168}}{1} \cdot \frac{9.46t}{\underset{1}{24}} + \frac{\overset{6}{168}}{1} \cdot \frac{9.46t}{\underset{1}{28}} = 1589.28 \qquad \text{Distributive Property}$$

$$66.22t + 56.76t = 1589.28 \qquad \text{Simplify.}$$

$$122.98t = 1589.28 \qquad \text{Add.}$$

$$t = 12.92 \qquad \text{Divide each side by 122.98.}$$

The trains passed at about 12.92 or about 13 minutes after leaving their stations. This would be 12:13 P.M.

CHECK Your Progress

5. Debbie leaves the house walking at a rate of 3 miles per hour. After 10 minutes, her mother realizes that Debbie has forgotten her homework and leaves the house riding a bicycle at a rate of 10 miles per hour. How many minutes after Debbie initially left the house will her mother catch up to her? $14\frac{2}{7}$ min

Extraneous Solutions Multiplying each side of an equation by the LCD of two rational expressions can yield results that are not solutions to the original equation. Recall that such solutions are called **extraneous solutions**. Rational equations can have both valid solutions and extraneous solutions.

Vocabulary Link

Extraneous
Everyday Use:
irrelevant, unimportant

Extraneous solution
Math Use: a result that is not a solution of the original equation

EXAMPLE Extraneous Solutions

6 Solve $\dfrac{3x}{x-1} + \dfrac{6x-9}{x-1} = 6$.

$$\frac{3x}{x-1} + \frac{6x-9}{x-1} = 6 \qquad \text{Original equation}$$

$$(x-1)\left(\frac{3x}{x-1} + \frac{6x-9}{x-1}\right) = (x-1)6 \qquad \text{The LCD is } x-1.$$

$$(x\overset{1}{-}1)\left(\frac{3x}{x\underset{1}{-}1}\right) + (x\overset{1}{-}1)\left(\frac{6x-9}{x\underset{1}{-}1}\right) = (x-1)6 \qquad \text{Distributive Property}$$

$$3x + 6x - 9 = 6x - 6 \qquad \text{Simplify.}$$

$$9x - 9 = 6x - 6 \qquad \text{Add like terms.}$$

$$3x = 3 \qquad \text{Add 9 to each side.}$$

$$x = 1 \qquad \text{Divide each side by 3.}$$

Notice that 1 is an excluded value for x. If we substitute 1 for x in the original equation, we get undefined expressions. Since $x = 1$ is an extraneous solution, this equation has no solution.

COncepts in MOtion

Interactive Lab
ca.algebra1.com

CHECK Your Progress Solve each equation.

6A. $\dfrac{3x}{x-4} - \dfrac{4x+4}{x-4} = -1$ **6B.** $\dfrac{n^2-3n}{n^2-4} - \dfrac{10}{n^2-4} = 2$

no solution   −1, extraneous solution −2

Lesson 11-9 Rational Equations and Functions **629**

Extraneous Solutions

Example 6 shows how to determine which solutions are extraneous solutions when both sides of a rational equation are multiplied by the LCD of the rational expressions that make up the equation.

ADDITIONAL EXAMPLE

6 Solve $\dfrac{x^2}{x-2} = \dfrac{4}{x-2} - 2$.
no solutions

Student Misconceptions

Make sure students understand that the equation in Example 6 does have a solution; however, that solution is undefined. Therefore, we say it has no solutions.

Focus on Mathematical Content

Extraneous Roots It is always important to check the solution to an equation in the *original* equation, but it is especially important when each side of an equation has been multiplied by a variable. If your solution is an approximation, it is sometimes difficult to determine whether a discrepancy is due to rounding or if it is an incorrect solution.

Formative Assessment

Use Exercises 1–8 to check for understanding.

Use the chart at the bottom of this page to customize assignments for your students.

Odd/Even Assignments

Exercises 9–32 are structured so that students practice the same concepts whether they are assigned odd or even problems.

Real-World Connections

For Exercise 28, discuss with students whether it is always possible to reduce the time required for a job to be completed by adding workers.

Additional Answers

16. 0

17. $\frac{1}{2}$

18. −3

19. −4; extraneous 1

20. no real solution

21. extraneous −2 and 0; no solution

22. extraneous 5; no solution

35a. line

35b. $f(x) = \frac{(x+5)(x-6)}{x-6} = x + 5$

35c. −5

36a. parabola

36b. $f(x) = \frac{x(x+2)(x-1)}{x+2} = x(x-1)$

36c. 0, 1

37a. parabola

37b. $f(x) = x^2 + 6x + 12$

37c. no real roots

Examples 1, 2, 6
(pp. 626–627, 629)

Solve each equation. State any extraneous solutions.

1. $\frac{2}{x} = \frac{3}{x+1}$ 2

2. $\frac{3x}{5} + \frac{3}{2} = \frac{7x}{10}$ 15

3. $\frac{x+2}{x-2} - \frac{2}{x+2} = -\frac{7}{3}$ −1, $\frac{2}{5}$

4. $\frac{n^2 - n - 6}{n^2 - n} - \frac{n-5}{n-1} = \frac{n-3}{n^2-n}$ extraneous 1; no solution

Example 3
(p. 627)

Find the roots of each function.

5. $f(x) = \frac{x^2 - 8x + 15}{x^2 + 5x - 6}$ 3, 5

6. $f(x) = \frac{x^2 - x - 6}{x^2 + 8x + 12}$ 3

Example 4
(pp. 627–628)

7. BASEBALL Omar has 32 hits in 128 times at bat. He wants his batting average to be .300. His current average is $\frac{32}{128}$ or .250. How many at bats does Omar need to reach his goal if he gets a hit in each of his next b at bats? **10**

Example 5
(pp. 628–629)

8. LANDSCAPING Kumar is filling a 3.5-gallon bucket to water plants at a faucet that flows at a rate of 1.75 gallons a minute. If he were to add a hose that flows at a rate of 1.45 gallons per minute, how many minutes would it take him to fill the bucket? Round to the nearest tenth of a minute. **1.1 min**

Exercises

HOMEWORK HELP	
For Exercises	See Examples
9–12	1
13–18	2
19–22	6
23–26	3
27, 28	4
29–32	5

Exercise Levels
A: 9–32
B: 33–37
C: 38–42

Solve each equation. State any extraneous solutions. 16–22. See margin.

9. $\frac{4}{a} = \frac{3}{a-2}$ 8

10. $\frac{3}{x} = \frac{1}{x-2}$ 3

11. $\frac{x-3}{x} = \frac{x-3}{x-6}$ 3

12. $\frac{x}{x+1} = \frac{x-6}{x-1}$ −$\frac{3}{2}$

13. $\frac{2n}{3} + \frac{1}{2} = \frac{2n-3}{6}$ −3

14. $\frac{5}{4} + \frac{3y}{2} = \frac{7y}{6}$ −$\frac{15}{4}$

15. $\frac{a-1}{a+1} - \frac{2a}{a-1} = -1$ 0

16. $\frac{m-1}{m+1} - \frac{2m}{m-1} = -1$

17. $\frac{4x}{2x+3} - \frac{2x}{2x-3} = 1$

18. $\frac{a}{3a+6} - \frac{a}{5a+10} = \frac{2}{5}$

19. $\frac{2n}{n-1} + \frac{n-5}{n^2-1} = 1$

20. $\frac{5}{5-p} - \frac{p^2}{p-5} = -8$

21. $\frac{x^2 - x - 6}{x+2} + \frac{x^3 + x^2}{x} = 3$

22. $\frac{x - \frac{6}{5}}{x} - \frac{x - 10\frac{1}{5}}{x-5} = \frac{x+21}{x^2-5x}$

Find the roots of each function.

23. $f(x) = \frac{x^2 - x - 12}{x^2 + 2x - 35}$ −3, 4

24. $f(x) = \frac{x^2 + 3x - 4}{x^2 + 9x + 20}$ 1

25. $f(x) = \frac{x^3 + x^2 - 6x}{x-1}$ 0, −3, 2

26. $f(x) = \frac{x^3 - 4x^2 - 12x}{x+2}$ 0, 6

27. CAR WASH Ian and Nadya can each wash a car and clean its interior in about 2 hours, but Raul needs 3 hours to do the work. If the three work together, how long will it take to clean seven cars? **5 h and 15 min**

28. JOBS Ron works as a dishwasher and can wash 500 plates in two hours and 15 minutes. Occasionally, the busser, Chris, helps. Together they can finish 500 plates in 77 minutes. About how long would it take Chris to finish all of the plates by himself? **approx. 2 h and 58 min**

630 Chapter 11 Rational Expressions and Equations

DIFFERENTIATED HOMEWORK OPTIONS

Level	Assignment	Two-Day Option	
BL Basic	9–32, 40, 41, 43–52	9–31 odd, 44, 45	10–32 even, 40, 41, 43, 46–52
OL Core	9–31 odd, 33–41, 43–52	9–32, 44, 45	33–41, 43, 46–52
AL Advanced /Pre-AP	33–52		

SWIMMING POOLS For Exercises 29 and 30, use the following information.

The pool in Kara's backyard is cleaned and ready to be filled for the summer. It measures 15 feet long and 10 feet wide with an average depth of 4 feet.

29. If Kara's hose runs at a rate of 5 gallons per minute, how long will it take to fill the pool? **900 min or 15 h**

30. Kara's neighbor's hose runs at a rate of 9 gallons per minute. How long will it take to fill the pool using both hoses? **321.4 min or about 5.4 h**

BOATING For Exercises 31 and 32, use the following information.

Jim and Mateo live across a lake from each other at a distance of about 3 miles. Jim can row his boat to Mateo's house in 1 hour and 20 minutes. Mateo can drive his power boat the same distance in a half hour.

Real-World Link
Started in 1851, the America's Cup is the oldest and most prestigious race in yachting. This race of just two boats involves 3 laps of an 18.55-nautical-mile course.

Source: americascup.com

★ **31.** If they leave their houses at the same time and head for each other, how long will it be before they meet? **about 22 min**

★ **32.** How far from the nearest shore will they be when they meet? **about 0.82 mi**

33. QUIZZES Each week, Mandy's algebra teacher gives a 10-point quiz. After 5 weeks, Mandy has earned a total of 36 points for an average of 7.2 points per quiz. She would like to raise her average to 9 points. On how many quizzes must she score 10 points in order to reach her goal? **9**

34. PAINTING Morgan can paint a standard-sized house in about 5 days. For his latest assignment, Morgan is going to hire two assistants. At what rate must these assistants work for Morgan to meet a deadline of two days?

3 houses in 20 days or 1 house in $6\frac{2}{3}$ days

35–37.
See margin.

GRAPHING CALCULATOR For Exercises 35–37, use a graphing calculator.

For each rational function, a) describe the shape of the graph, b) use factoring to simplify the function, and c) determine the roots of the function.

35. $f(x) = \dfrac{x^2 - x - 30}{x - 6}$ **36.** $f(x) = \dfrac{x^3 + x^2 - 2x}{x + 2}$ **37.** $f(x) = \dfrac{x^3 + 6x^2 + 12x}{x}$

AIRPLANES For Exercises 38 and 39, use the following information.

Headwinds push against a plane and reduce its total speed, while tailwinds push on a plane and increase its total speed. Let w = the speed of the wind, r = the speed set by the pilot, and s = the total speed.

38. Write an equation for the total speed with a headwind and an equation for the total speed with a tailwind. $s = r - w; s = r + w$

EXTRA PRACTICE
See pages 741, 754.

Math Online
Self-Check Quiz at
ca.algebra1.com

★ **39.** Use the rate formula to write an equation for the distance traveled by a plane with a headwind and another equation for the distance traveled by a plane with a tailwind. Then solve each equation for time instead of distance.

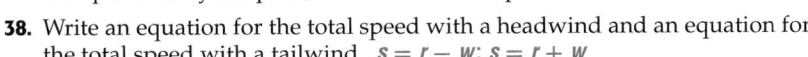

$d = t(r - w), \ d = t(r + w); \ t = \dfrac{d}{r - w}, \ t = \dfrac{d}{r + w}$

H.O.T. Problems

40. OPEN ENDED Write an expression that models a real-world situation where work is being done. **See students' work.**

41. REASONING Find a counterexample for the following statement.
The solution of a rational equation can never be zero. **Sample answer:** $\dfrac{x}{4} = 0$

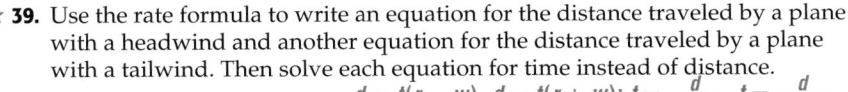

42. CHALLENGE Solve $\dfrac{\dfrac{x+3}{x-2} \cdot \dfrac{x^2+x-2}{x+5}}{x-1} + 2 = 0.$ $-\dfrac{14}{3}$

Lesson 11-9 Rational Equations and Functions **631**

 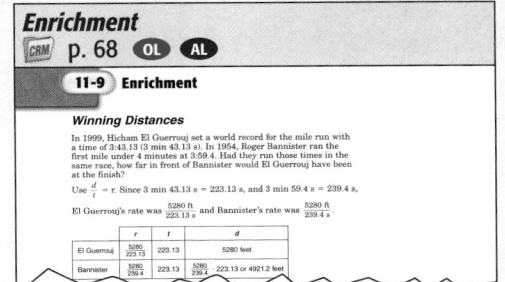

4 Assess

Name the Math Have each student create a rate problem and then solve it, showing the work for each step.

 Formative Assessment

Check for student understanding of concepts in Lessons 11–8 and 11–9.

CRM Quiz 4, p. 74.

Additional Answer

43. Sample answer: Rational equations are used in solving rate problems, so they can be used to determine traveling times, speeds, and distances related to subways. Since both trains leave at the same time, their traveling time is the same. The sum of the distances of both trains is equal to the total distance between the two stations. So, add the two expressions to represent the distance each train travels and solve for time.

43. *Writing in Math* Refer to the information on page 626. How are rational equations important in the operation of a subway system? Include in your answer an explanation of how rational equations can be used to approximate the time that trains will pass each other if they leave distant stations and head toward each other. **See margin.**

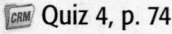 **STANDARDS PRACTICE** 13.0, 6PS1.2

44. A group of band students went to a restaurant after the football game. They agreed to split the bill equally. When the bill arrived, three people discovered that they had forgotten their wallets. The others in the group agreed to make up the difference by paying an extra $2.70 each. If the total bill was $117, how many band students went to dinner? **A**

A 13   C 10

B 11   D 9

45. **REVIEW** Lorenzo's math test scores are shown below.

85%, 92%, 95%

If he earns a 92% on the next test, then **J**

F the median would decrease.

G the mean would decrease.

H the median would increase.

J the mean would increase.

 **Spiral Review**

Simplify each expression. (Lesson 11-8)

46. $\dfrac{\dfrac{x^2 + 8x + 15}{x^2 + x - 6}}{\dfrac{x^2 + 2x - 15}{x^2 - 2x - 3}}$ $\dfrac{x+1}{x-2}$

47. $\dfrac{\dfrac{a^2 - 6a + 5}{a^2 + 13a + 42}}{\dfrac{a^2 - 4a + 3}{a^2 + 3a - 18}}$ $\dfrac{a-5}{a+7}$

48. $\dfrac{x + 2 + \dfrac{2}{x+5}}{x + 6 + \dfrac{6}{x+1}}$ $\dfrac{x+1}{x+5}$

Find each difference. (Lesson 11-7)

49. $\dfrac{3}{2m-3} - \dfrac{m}{6-4m}$ $\dfrac{6+m}{2(2m-3)}$

50. $\dfrac{y}{y^2 - 2y + 1} - \dfrac{1}{y-1}$ $\dfrac{1}{y^2 - 2y + 1}$

51. $\dfrac{a+2}{a^2 - 9} - \dfrac{2a}{6a^2 - 17a - 3}$ $\dfrac{4a^2 + 7a + 2}{(6a+1)(a-3)(a+3)}$

52. **CHEMISTRY** One solution is 50% glycol, and another is 30% glycol. How much of each solution should be mixed to make a 100 gallon solution that is 45% glycol? (Lesson 2-9) **75 gal of 50%, 25 gal of 30%**

Cross-Curricular Project

Math and Science

Building the Best Roller Coaster It is time to complete your project. Use the information and data you have gathered about the building and financing of a roller coaster to prepare a portfolio or Web page. Be sure to include graphs and/or tables in the presentation.

Math Online **Cross-Curricular Project at** ca.algebra1.com

Chapter 11 Rational Expressions and Equations

Pre-AP Activity **Use as an Extension.**

Solve $\dfrac{a}{x} = \dfrac{2}{3}$ for x in terms of a. $x = \dfrac{3a}{2}$

CHAPTER
11
Study Guide and Review

FOLDABLES™
Study Organizer

GET READY to Study

Be sure the following Key Concepts are noted in your Foldable.

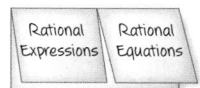
Rational Expressions | Rational Equations

Key Concepts

Inverse Variation (Lesson 11-1)
- You can use $\frac{x_1}{x_2} = \frac{y_1}{y_2}$ to solve problems involving inverse variation.

Rational Expressions (Lessons 11-2 to 11-4)
- Excluded values are values of a variable that result in a denominator of zero.
- Multiplying rational expressions is similar to multiplying rational numbers.
- Divide rational expressions by multiplying by the reciprocal of the divisor.

Dividing Polynomials (Lesson 11-5)
- To divide a polynomial by a monomial, divide each term of the polynomial by the monomial.

Rational Expressions (Lessons 11-6 and 11-7)
- Add (or subtract) rational expressions with like denominators by adding (or subtracting) the numerators and writing the sum (or difference) over the denominator.
- Rewrite rational expressions with unlike denominators using the least common denominator (LCD). Then add or subtract.

Complex Fractions (Lesson 11-8)
- Simplify complex fractions by writing them as division problems.

Solving Rational Equations (Lesson 11-9)
- Use cross product rule to solve rational equations with a single fraction on each side of the equals sign.

Math Online Vocabulary Review at ca.algebra1.com

Key Vocabulary

complex fraction (p. 621)
excluded values (p. 583)
extraneous solution (p. 629)
inverse variation (p. 577)
least common denominator (p. 615)
least common multiple (p. 614)
mixed expression (p. 620)
product rule (p. 578)
rate problem (p. 628)
rational equation (p. 626)
rational expression (p. 583)

Vocabulary Check

State whether each sentence is *true* or *false*. If *false*, replace the underlined word or number to make a true sentence.

1. A <u>mixed</u> expression is a fraction whose numerator and denominator are polynomials. **false; rational**

2. The complex fraction $\frac{\frac{4}{5}}{\frac{2}{3}}$ can be simplified as $\frac{6}{5}$. **true**

3. The equation $\frac{x}{x-1} + \frac{2x-3}{x-1}$ has an extraneous <u>1</u>. **true**

4. The mixed expressions $6 - \frac{a-2}{a+3}$ can be rewritten as $\frac{5a+16}{a+3}$.

5. The least common multiple for $(x^2 - 144)$ and $(x + 12)$ is $\underline{(x + 12)}$. **false; $x^2 - 144$**

6. The equation $x_1y_1 = x_2y_2$ is called the <u>product rule</u> for inverse variations. **true**

7. The excluded values for $\frac{4x}{x^2-x-12}$ are <u>−3 and 4</u>. **true**

8. When the product of two values remains constant, the relationship forms an <u>inverse variation</u>. **true**

4. false; $\frac{5a+20}{a+3}$

Summative Assessment

CRM Vocabulary Test, p. 76

FOLDABLES™
Study Organizer

Dinah Zike's Foldables™

Have students look through the chapter to make sure they have included examples in their Foldables for each lesson of the chapter.

Suggest that students keep their Foldables handy while completing the Study Guide and Review pages. Point out that their Foldables can serve as a quick review tool for studying for the chapter test.

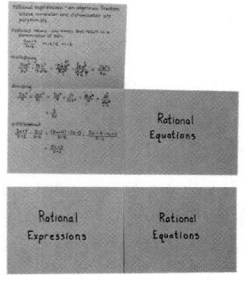

Formative Assessment

Key Vocabulary The page references after each word denote where that term was first introduced. If students have difficulty answering questions 1–8, remind them that they can use these page references to refresh their memories about the vocabulary terms.

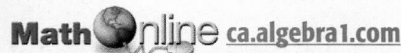
Math Online ca.algebra1.com

Vocabulary PuzzleMaker improves students' mathematics vocabulary using four puzzle formats—crossword, scramble, word search using a word list, and word search using clues. Students can work online or from a printed worksheet.

Lesson-by-Lesson Review

Intervention If the given examples are not sufficient to review the topics covered by the questions, remind students that the page references tell them where to review that topic in their textbooks.

Two-Day Option Have students complete the Lesson-by-Lesson Review on pp. 634–636. Then you can use ExamView® Assessment Suite to customize another review worksheet that practices all the objectives of this chapter or only the objectives on which your students need more help.

For more information on ExamView® Assessment Suite, see p. 574C.

Differentiated Instruction
Super DVD: MindJogger Videoquizzes
Use this DVD as an alternative format of review for the test. For more information on this game show format, see page 574D.

Additional Answers

14. $\dfrac{a-5}{a-2}$

15. $\dfrac{x+3}{x(x-6)}$

16. $\dfrac{a-5}{a-2}$

17. $\dfrac{x}{x+2}$

Lesson-by-Lesson Review

11-1 **Inverse Variation** (pp. 577–582)

Write an inverse variation equation that relates x and y. Assume that y varies inversely as x. Then solve.

9. If $y = 28$ when $x = 42$, find y when $x = 56$. **$xy = 1176;\ 21$**

10. If $y = 35$ when $x = 175$, find x when $y = 75$. **$xy = 6125;\ 81.67$**

11. PHYSICS If a 135-pound person sits 5 feet from the center of a seesaw and a 108-pound person is on the other end, how far from the center should the 108-pound person sit to balance?
6.25 ft or 6 feet 3 inches

Example 1 If y varies inversely as x and $y = 24$ when $x = 30$, find x when $y = 10$.

Let $x_1 = 30$, $y_1 = 24$, and $y_2 = 10$. Solve for x_2. Use a proportion.

$\dfrac{x_1}{x_2} = \dfrac{y_2}{y_1}$ Proportion for inverse variations

$\dfrac{30}{x_2} = \dfrac{10}{24}$ $x_1 = 30$, $y_1 = 24$, and $y_2 = 10$

$720 = 10x$ Cross multiply.

$72 = x_2$ Divide each side by 10.

Thus, $x = 72$ when $y = 10$.

11-2 **Operations with Radical Expressions** (pp. 583–588)

Simplify each expression. **14–17. See margin.**

12. $\dfrac{3x^2y}{12xy^3z} \cdot \dfrac{x}{4y^2z}$ **13.** $\dfrac{n^2 - 3n}{n - 3}$ **n**

14. $\dfrac{a^2 - 25}{a^2 + 3a - 10}$ **15.** $\dfrac{x^2 + 10x + 21}{x^3 + x^2 - 42x}$

16. $\dfrac{b^2 - 5b + 6}{b^2 - 13b + 36}$ **17.** $\dfrac{3x^3}{3x^3 + 6x^2}$

Example 2 Simplify $\dfrac{x+4}{x^2 + 12x + 32}$.

$\dfrac{x+4}{x^2 + 12x + 32} = \dfrac{\overset{1}{\cancel{x+4}}}{(\cancel{x+4})(x+8)}$ Factor.

$= \dfrac{1}{x+8}$ Simplify.

11-3 **Multiplying Rational Expressions** (pp. 590–594)

Find each product.

18. $\dfrac{7b^2}{9} \cdot \dfrac{6a^2}{b}$ **$\dfrac{14a^2b}{3}$**

19. $\dfrac{5x^2y}{8ab} \cdot \dfrac{12a^2b}{25x}$ **$\dfrac{3axy}{10}$**

20. $(3x + 30) \cdot \dfrac{10}{x^2 - 100}$ $\dfrac{30}{x - 10}$

21. $\dfrac{3a - 6}{a^2 - 9} \cdot \dfrac{a + 3}{a^2 - 2a}$ $\dfrac{3}{a^2 - 3a}$

22. $\dfrac{b^2 + 19b + 84}{b - 3} \cdot \dfrac{b^2 - 9}{b^2 + 15b + 36}$ **$b + 7$**

Example 3 Find $\dfrac{6m^2n^4}{12} \cdot \dfrac{3m^3n^2}{mn}$.

$\dfrac{6m^2n^4}{12} \cdot \dfrac{3m^3n^2}{mn}$

$= \dfrac{2mn^3}{4} \cdot \dfrac{m^2n}{1}$ Divide by GCF $3mn$.

$= \dfrac{2m^3n^4}{4}$ or $\dfrac{m^3n^4}{2}$ Multiply.

634 Chapter 11 Rational Expressions and Equations

Mixed Problem Solving
For mixed problem-solving practice,
see page 754.

CHAPTER 11

Study Guide and Review

11-4 Dividing Rational Expressions (pp. 595–599)

Find each quotient. 24. $\dfrac{y(y-4)}{3}$

23. $\dfrac{p^3}{2q} \div \dfrac{p^3}{4q}$ $2p$ **24.** $\dfrac{y^2}{y+4} \div \dfrac{3y}{y^2-16}$

25. $\dfrac{3x-12}{y+4} \div (y^2-6y+8)$ $\dfrac{3}{(x+4)(x-2)}$

26. $\dfrac{2m^2+7m-15}{m+5} \div \dfrac{9m^2-4}{3m+2}$ $\dfrac{2m-3}{3m-2}$

27. PIZZA On average, Americans eat 18 acres of pizza a day. If an average slice of pizza is about 5 square inches, how many pieces of pizza is this? (*Hint*: 43,560 square feet per acre)

22,581,504 slices per day

Example 4 Find $\dfrac{y^2-16}{y^2-64} \div \dfrac{y+4}{y-8}$.

$\dfrac{y^2-16}{y^2-64} \div \dfrac{y+4}{y-8}$

$= \dfrac{y^2-16}{y^2-64} \cdot \dfrac{y-8}{y+4}$ Multiply by the reciprocal of $\dfrac{y+4}{y-8}$.

$= \dfrac{(y-4)(y+4)}{(y-8)(y+8)} \cdot \dfrac{y-8}{y+4}$ Factor.

$= \dfrac{(y-4)\overset{1}{(y+4)}}{(y-8)(y+8)} \cdot \dfrac{\overset{1}{y-8}}{\overset{1}{y+4}}$ Simplify.

$= \dfrac{y-4}{y+8}$

11-5 Dividing Polynomials (pp. 601–606)

Find each quotient. 28–30. See margin.
28. $(4a^2b^2c^2 - 8a^3b^2c + 6abc^2) \div 2ab^2$

29. $(x^3 + 7x^2 + 10x - 6) \div (x + 3)$

30. $(48b^2 + 8b + 7) \div (12b - 1)$

31. $(4t^2 + 17t - 1) \div (4t + 1)$ $t + 4 - \dfrac{5}{4t+1}$

32. GEOMETRY The volume of a prism with a triangular base is $x^3 + 6.5x^2 + 8.5x - 6$. If the height of the prism is $2x - 1$, what is the area of the triangular base?
$\dfrac{1}{2}x^2 + \dfrac{7}{2}x + 6$

Example 5 Find $(x^3 - 2x^2 - 22x + 21) \div (x - 3)$.

$$
\begin{array}{r}
x^2 + x - 19 \\
x - 3 \overline{\smash{\big)}\, x^3 - 2x^2 - 22x + 21} \\
\underline{x^3 - 3x^2} \qquad\qquad \\
x^2 - 22x \qquad\; \\
\underline{x^2 - 3x} \qquad\;\; \\
-19x + 21 \\
\underline{-19x + 57} \\
-36
\end{array}
$$

Multiply x^2 and $x - 3$.
Subtract.
Multiply x and $x - 3$.
Subtract.
Multiply -19 and $x - 3$.
Subtract.

The quotient is $x^3 + x - 19 - \dfrac{36}{x-3}$.

11-6 Rational Expressions with Like Denominators (pp. 608–613)

Find each sum or difference.

33. $\dfrac{m+4}{5} + \dfrac{m-1}{5}$ **34.** $\dfrac{-5}{2n-5} + \dfrac{2n}{2n-5}$ 1
See margin.

35. $\dfrac{a^2}{a-b} + \dfrac{-b^2}{a-b}$ **36.** $\dfrac{7a}{b^2} - \dfrac{5a}{b^2}$ $\dfrac{2a}{b^2}$
$a + b$

37. $\dfrac{2x}{x-3} - \dfrac{6}{x-3}$ 2 **38.** $\dfrac{m^2}{m-n} - \dfrac{2mn-n^2}{m-n}$
$m - n$

Example 6 Find $\dfrac{n^2 + 10n}{n + 5} + \dfrac{25}{n + 5}$.

$\dfrac{n^2 + 10n}{n + 5} + \dfrac{25}{n + 5}$

$= \dfrac{n^2 + 10n + 25}{n + 5}$ Add the numerators.

$= \dfrac{(n+5)(n+5)}{(n+5)}$ Factor.

$= n + 5$ Simplify.

Additional Answers

28. $2ac^2 - 4a^2c + \dfrac{3c^2}{b}$

29. $x^2 + 2x - 2$

30. $4b + 1 + \dfrac{8}{12b-1}$

33. $\dfrac{2m+3}{5}$

Problem Solving Review

For additional practice in problem solving for Chapter 11, see the Mixed Problem Solving Appendix, page 754 in the Student Handbook section.

Anticipation Guide

Have students complete the Chapter 11 Anticipation Guide and discuss how their responses have changed now that they have completed Chapter 11.

📄 Anticipation Guide, p. 3

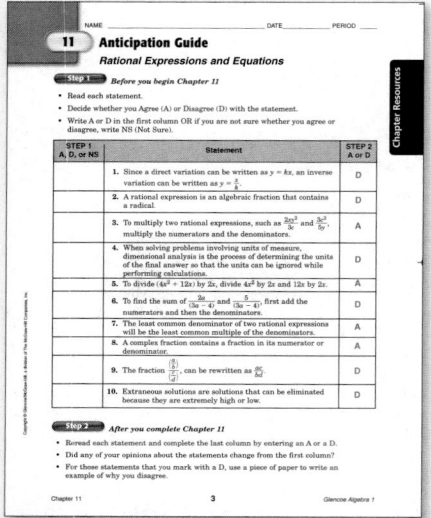

11-7 Rational Expressions with Unlike Denominators (pp. 614–619)

Find each sum or difference.
39–42. See margin.

39. $\dfrac{2c}{3d^2} + \dfrac{3}{2cd}$

40. $\dfrac{r^2 + 21r}{r^2 - 9} + \dfrac{3r}{r + 3}$

41. $\dfrac{7}{3a} - \dfrac{3}{6a^2}$

42. $\dfrac{2x}{2x + 8} - \dfrac{4}{5x + 20}$

Example 7 Find $\dfrac{3}{y + 1} - \dfrac{y}{y + 3}$.

$\dfrac{3}{y + 1} - \dfrac{y}{y + 3}$

$= \dfrac{y + 3}{y + 3} \cdot \dfrac{3}{y + 1} - \dfrac{y}{y + 3} \cdot \dfrac{y + 1}{y + 1}$

$= \dfrac{3y + 9}{(y + 3)(y + 1)} - \dfrac{y^2 + y}{(y + 3)(y + 1)}$

$= \dfrac{-y^2 + 2y + 9}{(y + 3)(y + 1)}$

11-8 Mixed Expressions and Complex Fractions (pp. 620–625)

Write each mixed expression as a rational expression. 43–46. See margin.

43. $4 + \dfrac{x}{x - 2}$

44. $2 - \dfrac{x + 2}{x^2 - 4}$

Simplify each expression.

45. $\dfrac{x + \dfrac{35}{x + 2}}{x + \dfrac{42}{x + 13}}$

46. $\dfrac{y + 9 - \dfrac{6}{y + 4}}{y + 4 + \dfrac{2}{y + 1}}$

Example 8 Simplify $\dfrac{\dfrac{a^2 b^4}{c}}{\dfrac{a^3 b}{c^2}}$.

$\dfrac{\dfrac{a^2 b^4}{c}}{\dfrac{a^3 b}{c^2}} = \dfrac{a^2 b^4}{c} \div \dfrac{a^3 b}{c^2}$ Rewrite as a division sentence.

$= \dfrac{a^2 b^4}{c} \cdot \dfrac{c^2}{a^3 b}$ Multiply by the reciprocal.

$= \dfrac{b^3 c}{a}$ Simplify.

11-9 Rational Equations and Functions (pp. 626–632)

Solve each equation. State any extraneous solutions.

47. $\dfrac{4x}{3} + \dfrac{7}{2} = \dfrac{7x}{12} - 14$ -5

48. $\dfrac{11}{2x} - \dfrac{2}{3x} = \dfrac{1}{6}$ 29

49. $\dfrac{3}{x^2 + 3x} + \dfrac{x + 2}{x + 3} = \dfrac{1}{x}$ -1; extraneous 0

50. $\dfrac{1}{n + 4} - \dfrac{1}{n - 1} = \dfrac{2}{n^2 + 3n - 4}$ no solution

51. JOBS Normally, it takes Jeffery 1 hour 45 minutes to mow and trim an average lawn. When Lupe worked with him, an average lawn only took an hour. How long would it take Lupe to mow and trim an average yard on her own? **1 hr and 40 minutes**

Example 9 Solve $\dfrac{5n}{6} + \dfrac{1}{n - 2} = \dfrac{n + 1}{3(n - 2)}$.

$\dfrac{5n}{6} + \dfrac{1}{n - 2} = \dfrac{n + 1}{3(n - 2)}$

$6(n - 2)\left(\dfrac{5n}{6} + \dfrac{1}{n - 2}\right) = 6(n - 2)\dfrac{n + 1}{3(n - 2)}$

$\dfrac{6(n - 2)(5n)}{6} + \dfrac{6(n - 2)}{n - 2} = \dfrac{6(n - 2)(n + 1)}{3(n - 2)}$

$(n - 2)(5n) + 6 = 2(n + 1)$ Simplify.

$5n^2 - 12n + 4 = 0$ Simplify.

$(5n - 2)(n - 2) = 0$ Factor.

$n = \dfrac{2}{5}$ or $n = 2$

When you check the value 2, you get a zero in the denominator. So, 2 is an extraneous solution.

Additional Answers

39. $\dfrac{4c^2 + 9c}{6cd^2}$

40. $\dfrac{4r}{r - 3}$

41. $\dfrac{14a - 3}{6a^2}$

42. $\dfrac{5x - 4}{5x + 20}$

43. $\dfrac{5x - 8}{x - 2}$

44. $\dfrac{2x - 5}{x - 2}$

45. $\dfrac{x^2 + 8x - 65}{x^2 + 8x + 12}$

46. $\dfrac{y^2 + 11y + 10}{y^2 + 6y + 8}$

Additional Answers (p. 637)

1. $x^3 - \dfrac{7}{4}x + x - \dfrac{3}{16}$

2. $x^2 + \dfrac{1}{4}x + \dfrac{3}{2} + \dfrac{2\frac{13}{16}}{x - 2}$

6. $-\dfrac{1}{3}, \dfrac{5}{2}$

7. $\dfrac{1}{2x - 1}; \dfrac{1}{2}, -3$

8. $\dfrac{2c + 3}{c - 7}; -\dfrac{3}{2}, 7$

9. $\dfrac{x - 1}{x + 1}$

18. $\dfrac{y^2 - 16y - 28}{7(y + 2)(y - 2)}$

WINTER For Exercises 1 and 2 use the following information.

An ice sculptor has a cube of ice. The length of each side of the cube is x inches. To begin a sculpture, he removes $\frac{3}{4}$ of an inch from the top. Then he removes $\frac{1}{2}$ inch from the width and length of the block. **1–2. See margin.**

1. Write an expression that represents the current volume of the block.

2. The sculptor scraps his idea and decides to divide the block into $x - 2$ blocks. What is the volume of the smaller blocks?

Solve each variation. Assume that y varies inversely as x. **3.** $xy = 840;\ 10$ **4.** $xy = 88;\ 5.5$

3. If $y = 21$ when $x = 40$, find y when $x = 84$.

4. If $y = 22$ when $x = 4$, find x when $y = 16$.

5. **MULTIPLE CHOICE** Willie can type a 200 word essay in 6 hours. Myra can type the same essay in $4\frac{1}{2}$ hours. If they work together, how long will it take them to type the essay? **B**

  A $2\frac{3}{5}$ hr   C $1\frac{4}{7}$ hr

  B $2\frac{4}{7}$ hr   D $1\frac{3}{5}$ hr

Simplify each rational expression. State the excluded values of the variables. **6–9. See margin.**

6. $\dfrac{5 - 2m}{6m - 15}$ 7. $\dfrac{3 + x}{2x^2 + 5x - 3}$

8. $\dfrac{4c^2 + 12c + 9}{2c^2 - 11c - 21}$ 9. $\dfrac{x + 4 + \dfrac{5}{x - 2}}{x + 6 + \dfrac{15}{x - 2}}$

10. $\dfrac{1 - \dfrac{9}{t}}{1 - \dfrac{81}{t^2}}\ \dfrac{t}{t + 9}$ 11. $\dfrac{\dfrac{5}{6} + \dfrac{u}{t}}{\dfrac{2u}{t} - 3}\ \dfrac{6u + 5t}{12u - 18t}$

Perform the indicated operations.

12. $\dfrac{2x}{x - 7} - \dfrac{14}{x - 7}\ \ 2$

13. $\dfrac{n + 3}{2n - 8} \cdot \dfrac{6n - 24}{2n + 1} \div (z - 3)\ \ \dfrac{3n + 9}{2n + 1}$

14. $(10m^2 + 9m - 36) \div (2m - 3)\ \ 5m + 12$

15. $\dfrac{x^2 + 4x - 32}{x + 5} \cdot \dfrac{x - 3}{x^2 - 7x + 12}\ \ \dfrac{x + 8}{x + 5}$

16. $\dfrac{4x^2 + 11x + 6}{x^2 - x - 6} \div \dfrac{x^2 + 8x + 16}{x^2 + x - 12}\ \ \dfrac{4x + 3}{x + 4}$

17. $(10z^4 + 5z^3 - z^2) \div 5z^3\ \ 2z + 1 - \dfrac{1}{5z}$

18. $\dfrac{y}{7y + 14} + \dfrac{6}{-3y + 6}$ See margin.

19. $\dfrac{x + 5}{x + 2} + 6\ \ \dfrac{7x + 17}{x + 2}$

Solve each equation. **21.** -14

20. $\dfrac{2}{3t} + \dfrac{1}{2} = \dfrac{3}{4t}\ \ \dfrac{1}{6}$ 21. $\dfrac{2c}{c - 4} - 2 = \dfrac{4}{c + 5}$

22. **FINANCE** Barrington High School is raising money to build a house for Habitat for Humanity by doing lawn work for friends and neighbors. Scott can rake a lawn and bag the leaves in 5 hours, while Kalyn can do it in 3 hours. If Scott and Kalyn work together, how long will it take them to rake a lawn and bag the leaves? $1\frac{7}{8}$ h

23. **MULTIPLE CHOICE** Which expression can be used to represent the area of the triangle? **G**

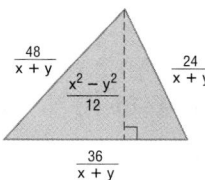

  F $2(x - y)$ H $4(x - y)$

  G $\dfrac{3}{2}(x - y)$ J $\dfrac{108}{x + y}$

 **Summative Assessment**

CRM *Chapter 11 Resource Masters*

Leveled Chapter 11 Tests			
Form	Type	Level	Pages
1	MC	BL	77–78
2A	MC	OL	79–80
2B	MC	OL	81–82
2C	FR	OL	83–84
2D	FR	OL	85–86
3	FR	AL	87–88

MC = multiple-choice questions
FR = free-response questions
BL = below grade level
OL = on grade level
AL = above grade level

• Vocabulary Test, p. 76
• Extended-Response Test, p. 89

ExamView Assessment Suite   Customize and create multiple versions of your chapter tests and their answer keys. All of the questions from the leveled chapter tests in the *Chapter 11 Resource Masters* are also available on the ExamView® Assessment Suite with the California Standard that each item assesses.

Data-Driven Decision Making	Exercises	Lesson	Standard	Resources for Review
Diagnostic Teaching Based on the results of the Chapter 11 Practice Test, use the following to review concepts that students continue to find challenging.	12	11–6	13.0	**CRM** Study Guide and Intervention pp. 42–43, 49–50, 56–57, 63–64 **Math Online** • Extra Examples • Personal Tutor • Concepts in Motion
	18	11–7	13.0	
	19	11–8	13.0	
	20–22	11–9	13.0	

Item Analysis

Questions 3 and 11 are griddable questions on a standardized test. In a griddable question, students arrive at an answer then record it in a special grid, coloring in the appropriate bubble under each digit of the answer.

 Formative Assessment

You can use these two pages to benchmark student progress. The California Standards are listed with each question.

 Chapter 11 Resource Masters
- Standardized Test Practice, pp. 90–92

 Create practice worksheets or tests that align to the California Standards, as well as TIMSS and NAEP tests.

 Read each question. Then fill in the correct answer on the answer document provided by your teacher or on a sheet of paper.

1 What is $\dfrac{x^2 - 6xy + 9y^2}{4xy - 12y^2}$ reduced to lowest terms? **B**

A $\dfrac{x - 3y}{4}$

B $\dfrac{x - 3y}{4y}$

C $\dfrac{x + 3y}{4}$

D $\dfrac{x + 3y}{4y}$

2 $\dfrac{9w^2 + 18w}{5w + 15} \cdot \dfrac{w^2 - 9}{w^3 + 4w^2 + 4w} = $ **J**

F $\dfrac{9(w + 2)}{5(w - 3)}$

G $\dfrac{9(w - 2)}{5(w + 3)}$

H $\dfrac{9(w + 3)}{5(w + 2)}$

J $\dfrac{9(w - 3)}{5(w + 2)}$

3 The height of a triangle is 6 inches greater than twice its base. The area of the triangle is 180 square inches. What is the base of the triangle in inches? **12**

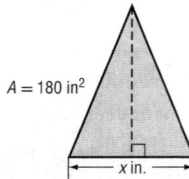

$A = 180 \text{ in}^2$

x in.

4 $2\sqrt{16x^8} = $ **C**

A $4x^4$

B $4x^8$

C $8x^4$

D $8x^8$

5 The graph of the equation $y = x^2 - x - 6$ is shown below.

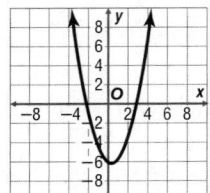

For what value or values of x is $y = 0$? **H**

F $x = -2$ only

G $x = -3$ only

H $x = -2$ and $x = 3$

J $x = 2$ and $x = -3$

6 Simplify $\dfrac{12x^2 + 28x + 8}{9x^2 - 1}$ to lowest terms. **B**

A $\dfrac{4(x + 2)(3x + 1)}{(3x - 1)(3x + 1)}$

B $\dfrac{4(x + 2)}{3x - 1}$

C $\dfrac{2x + 4}{3(x - 1)}$

D $\dfrac{4(x + 2)}{3x + 1}$

TEST-TAKING TIP

Question 6 When solving problems involving fractions or rational expressions, be sure to choose the expression in simplest form.

 Math Online California Standards Practice at ca.algebra1.com

More California
Standards Practice
For practice by standard,
see pages CA1–CA43.

CHAPTER
11
California Standards Practice

7 What is the solution set of the quadratic equation $6x^2 + 4x + 3 = 0$? **J**

F $\{-1, -3\}$

G $\left\{\dfrac{-2 - \sqrt{14}}{6}, \dfrac{-2 + \sqrt{14}}{6}\right\}$

H $\left\{-1 - \sqrt{14}, -1 + \sqrt{14}\right\}$

J no real solution

8 Which is a factor of $x^2 - 9x + 20$? **B**

A $x + 4$

B $x - 4$

C $x - 10$

D $x + 10$

9 Which equation represents a line that is parallel to the line shown on the graph below? **F**

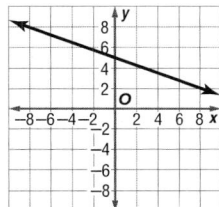

F $y = -\dfrac{3}{8}x + 1$

G $y = \dfrac{8}{3}x + 2$

H $y = \dfrac{3}{8}x + 3$

J $y = \dfrac{8}{3}x + 4$

10 What is the solution to this system of equations? **B**

$$y = 5x - 2$$
$$y = 3x$$

A $(1, -3)$

B $(1, 3)$

C $(5, 15)$

D $(-5, 15)$

11 John can word process 15 pages in 50 minutes. Libby can word process 15 pages in 75 minutes. Together, how many minutes will it take John and Libby to word process 15 pages? **30**

Pre-AP/Anchor Problem

Record your answers on a sheet of paper. Show your work. a. $\dfrac{6}{x - c} = \dfrac{9}{x + c}$

12 A steamboat runs sightseeing tours on the Ohio River. The boat can travel 6 kilometers upstream in the same amount of time that it takes the boat to travel 9 kilometers downstream.

a. Suppose the boat travels x kilometers per hour in still water and the rate of the current is c kilometers per hour. Write an equation for the situation.

b. If the boat travels at a rate of 1.5 kilometers per hour in still water, what is the rate of the current? **0.3 kph**

TEST-TAKING TIP

Question 9 Estimation can be used to find an answer, eliminate answer choices, and to check an answer.

Answer Sheet Practice
Have students simulate taking a standardized test by recording their answers on practice recording sheets.

CRM Student Recording Sheet, p. 71

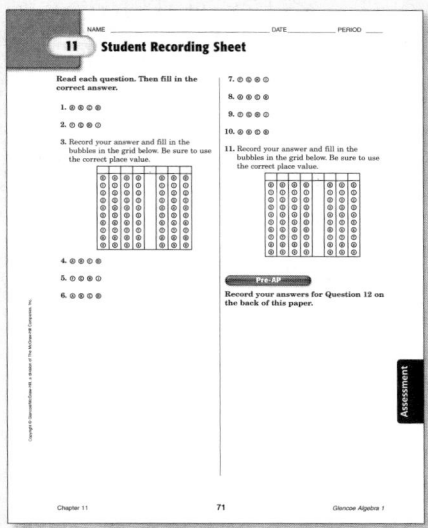

NEED EXTRA HELP?												
If You Missed Question...	1	2	3	4	5	6	7	8	9	10	11	12
Go to Lesson...	11-2	11-3	9-4	10-2	9-2	11-2	9-4	8-3	4-7	5-2	11-9	11-9
For Help with Standard...	12.0	13.0	23.0	7AF2.2	21.0	12.0	20.0	11.0	8.0	9.0	15.0	15.0

Chapter 11 California Standards Practice **639**

Homework Option

Get Ready for Chapter 12 Assign students the exercises on p. 641 as homework to assess whether they possess the prerequisite skills needed for the next chapter.

Pages 580–581, Lesson 11-1

8.
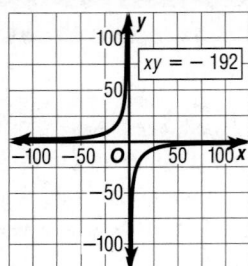

9.
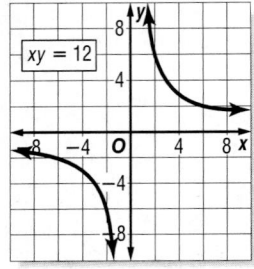

10.
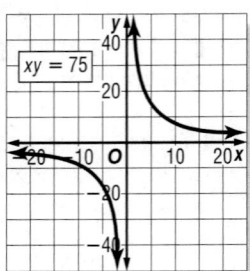

11.
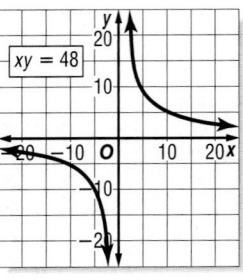

12.
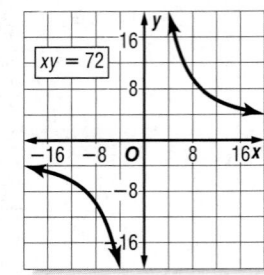

13.
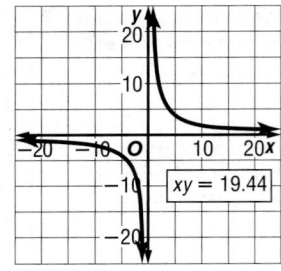

37. Sample answer: Though it has been replaced by Einstein's theory of relativity, Newton's law of Gravitational Force is an example of an indirect variation which models real world situations. The gravitational force exerted on two objects is inversely proportional to the square of the distances between the two objects. The force exerted on the two objects, times the square of the distance between the two objects, is equal to the gravitational constant times the masses of the two objects.

Page 588, Extend 11-2

1.
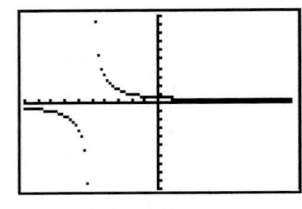
[−10, 10] scl: 1 by [−10, 10] scl: 1

2.
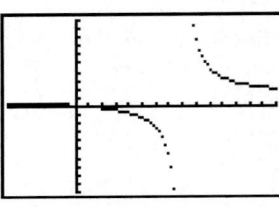
[−5, 15] scl: 1 by [−10, 10] scl: 1

3.
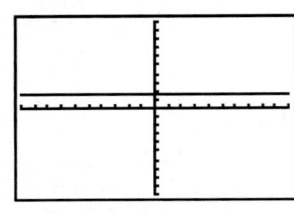
[−10, 10] scl: 1 by [−10, 10] scl: 1

Page 604, Lesson 11-5

49.
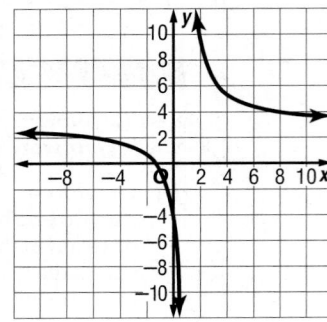

Page 618, Lesson 11-7

66. **American Dollar to British Pound Over Time**
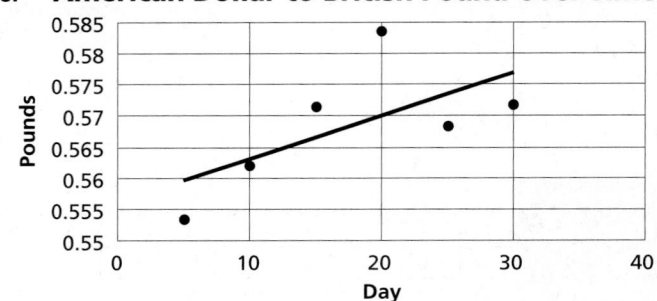

NOTES

Standards-Based Lesson Plan		**Pacing Your Lessons**	
LESSONS AND OBJECTIVES	**California Standards**	**40-50 Minute Periods**	**90-Minute Periods**
12-1 Sampling and Bias (pp. 642–648) • Identify various sampling techniques. • Recognize a biased sample.	6SDAP2.2 6SDAP2.4	1	0.5
12-2 Counting Outcomes (pp. 650–654) • Count outcomes using a tree diagram. • Count outcomes using the Fundamental Counting Principle.	2A18.0	1	0.5
12-3 Permutations and Combinations (pp. 655–662) • Determine probabilities using permutations. • Determine probabilities using combinations.	PS1.0	1	0.5
12-4 Probability of Compound Events (pp. 663–670) • Find the probability of two independent events or dependent events. • Find the probability of two mutually exclusive or inclusive events.	PS1.0	1	0.5
12-5 Probability Distributions (pp. 672–676) • Use random variables to compute probability. • Use probability distributions to solve real-world problems.	PS3.0 PS8.0	1	0.5
12-6 Probability Simulations (pp. 677–683) • Use theoretical and experimental probability to represent and solve problems involving uncertainty. • Perform probability simulations to model real-world situations involving uncertainty.	6SDAP3.0 6SDAP3.2	1	0.5
REVIEW		1	0.5
ASSESSMENT		1	1
TOTAL		8	4.5

*The complete **Assessment Planner** for Chapter 12 is provided on p 641.*

Professional Development

Before Chapter 12

Related Topics from Grade 6

- Analyze data displays ◀━━ Standard 6SDAP2.3

- Represent all possible outcomes for compound events in an organized way ◀━━ Standard 6SDAP3.1

- Represent probabilities as ratios, proportions and decimals ◀━━ Standard 6SDAP3.3

Chapter 12

Preparation for Probability and Statistics

- Find probabilities of particular events in finite sample spaces ◀━━

- Use *discrete random variables* to solve for the probabilities of outcomes, ◀━━

- Organize and describe distributions of data by using a number of different methods ◀━━

See individual lessons for the specific Standards covered.

After Chapter 12

Preparation for Algebra 2 and Advanced Placement Probability and Statistics

- Use fundamental counting principles to compute combinations and permutations ◀━━ Standard 2A18.0

- Students use combinations and permutations to compute probabilities ◀━━ Standard 2A19.0

- Solve for probabilities in finite sample spaces ◀━━ Standard 2APS2.0

Back-Mapping

California Algebra 1 was conceived and developed with the final result in mind, student success in Algebra I and beyond. The authors, using the California Mathematics Standards as their guide, developed this brand-new series by "back-mapping" from the desired result of student success in Algebra I and beyond. McGraw-Hill's *California Geometry, California Algebra 2,* and *California Algebra Readiness* were developed utilizing the same philosophy.

What the Research Says...

Hembree and Marsh (1993) found that developing skill with diagrams gave the most pronounced effects on problem solving performance (at all grades).

- Tree diagrams are used in Lessons 12-2 and 12-3 to enumerate choices.

- Probabilities for compound events are illustrated with Venn diagrams in Lesson 12-4.

- Histograms are used to represent probability distributions in Lesson 12-5.

[Source: Hembree, R. and Marsh, H. (1993). "Problem Solving in Early Childhood: Building Foundations," in R.J. Jensen (Ed.) *Research Ideas for the Classroom: Early Childhood Mathematics.* New York: Macmillan, pp. 151–170.]

Professional Development

Targeted professional development has been articulated throughout the *California Mathematics: Concepts, Skills, and Problem Solving* series. The **McGraw-Hill Professional Development Video Library** provides short videos that support the ◀━━ Key Standards. For more information, visit ca.algebra1.com.

Model Lessons	Instructional Strategies

CHAPTER 12

Technology Solutions

Teacher Resources

Chapter Resource Masters				12-1	12-2	12-3	12-4	12-5	12-6
BL **OL**		**ELL**	Lesson Reading Guide	5	12	19	26	34	42
BL **OL**		**ELL**	Study Guide and Intervention*	6	13	20	27	35	43
BL **OL**			Skills Practice*	8	15	22	29	37	45
	OL	**AL**	Practice*	9	16	23	30	38	46
	OL	**AL**	Word Problem Practice*	10	17	24	31	39	47
	OL	**AL**	Enrichment	11	18	25	32	40	48
	OL	**AL**	Calculator and Spreadsheet Activities				33	41	
	OL	**AL**	Chapter Assessments*	49–70					
BL **OL**	**AL**		5-Minute Check Transparencies	✓	✓	✓	✓	✓	✓
BL **OL**			Teaching Algebra with Manipulatives			✓	✓		✓

Also available in Spanish.

AssignmentWorks

Differentiated Assignments, Answers, and Solutions

- Print a customized assignment worksheet using the Student Edition exercises along with an answer key or worked-out solutions.
- Use default lesson assignments as outlined in the Differentiated Homework Options in the Teacher Wraparound Edition.
- Includes modified questions from the Student Edition.

Interactive Classroom

This CD-ROM is a customizable Microsoft® PowerPoint® presentation that includes:

- In-Class Examples
- Your Turn Exercises*
- 5-Minute Check Transparencies*
- Links to Online Study Tools
- Concepts in Motion

compatible with response pad technology

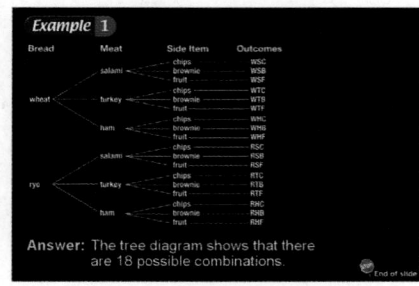

ExamView®Assessment Suite

ExamView® Assessment Suite lets you

- Create, edit, and customize tests and worksheets using QuickTest Wizard
- Create multiple versions of tests and modify them for a desired level of difficulty
- Translate from English to Spanish and vice versa
- Build tests aligned with your state standards
- Track students' progress using the Teacher Management System

Student Resources

Textbook, Audio, Workbooks, and more

This CD-ROM is a valuable resource for students to access content online and use online resources to continue learning Chapter 12 concepts. Includes:

- Complete Student Editions in both English and Spanish
- English audio integrated throughout the text
- Links to Concepts in Motion, Personal Tutor, and other online resources
- Access to all student worksheets
- Daily Assignments and Grade Log

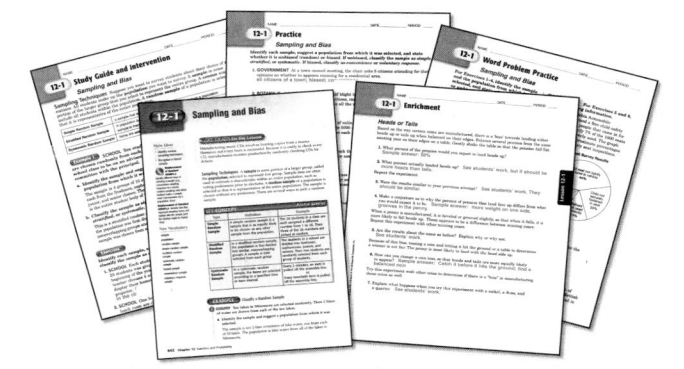

Super DVD

The Super DVD contains two Glencoe multimedia products.

MindJogger Plus   An alternative review of concepts in which students work as teams in a game show format to gain points for correct answers.

What's Math Got to Do With It? Real Life Math Videos Engaging video that shows students how math is used in everyday situations

Internet Resources

Math Online ca.algebra1.com

TEACHER	PARENT	STUDENT	Online Study Tools
	●	●	Online Student Edition
●	●	●	Multilingual Glossary
			Lesson Resources
	●	●	BrainPOP®
●	●	●	Concepts in Motion
●	●	●	Extra Examples
	●	●	Other Calculator Keystrokes
●			Problem of the Week Cards
	●	●	Real-World Careers
	●	●	Self-Check Quizzes
			Chapter Resources
	●	●	Chapter Readiness
	●	●	Chapter Test
	●	●	Standardized Test Practice
	●	●	Vocabulary Review/Chapter Review Activities
			Unit Resources
●		●	Cross-Curricular Internet Project
			Other Resources
●			Dinah Zike's Foldables
	●	●	Hotmath Homework Help
●			Key Concepts
●	●	●	Meet the Authors
	●	●	Personal Tutor
●			Project CRISS℠
	●	●	Scavenger Hunts and Answer Sheets
●			Vocabulary PuzzleMakers

Focus on Mathematical Content

Big Idea for Chapter 12:
Statistics and Probability

The study of statistics and probability gives students the graphical and numerical techniques they need to analyze data. These include counting techniques, the use of histograms and tables to study patterns, and probability models. These techniques allow students to make predictions about real-world situations that involve chance and make sound decisions based on an analysis of data presented in polls and surveys.

Why It's Important

For This Chapter
The lessons in this chapter use statistical techniques and probability models to analyze data and describe everyday situations.
- What are the different ways to take a random sample? How can you tell whether a sample is biased or not? (Lesson 12-1)
- What methods can be used to count the number of outcomes in a sample space? (Lesson 12-2)
- What are the differences between permutations and combinations, and why is this important? (Lesson 12-3)
- How do you determine the probability of compound events? (Lesson 12-4)
- What does a probability distribution reveal about a real-world situation? What types of displays can be used to show the probability distribution? (Lesson 12-5)
- What techniques can be used to simulate real-world events that involve probability? (Lesson 12-6)

After This Chapter
- In Algebra 2, students will use probability models in binomial experiments and apply statistical techniques to sampling and testing hypotheses.
- In advanced mathematics, counting techniques are used in combinatorics, and data analysis tools can be used to determine frequency distributions and normal distributions.

12-1 Sampling and Bias

A sample is a small portion of a larger group called a population. Samples are taken to represent a group because they are smaller and easier to survey. They often are used to find characteristics or preferences of a population. There are various sampling techniques which can be biased or unbiased.

A random sample is a sample that is chosen without preference. Random samples can be classified as simple, stratified, or systematic.

- A simple random sample picks members from the population at random.
- A stratified random sample first divides the population into groups, and then picks members at random. For example, an algebra teacher who picks one student at random from each of three classes is using a stratified random sample.
- A systematic random sample picks members by following a certain pattern, such as picking every sixth person who enters a store or checking parts on a conveyor belt every ten minutes.

Samples are biased if they favor one or more parts of a population.

- One type of biased sample is a convenience sample, in which members are picked because they are convenient for the person taking the sample.
- Another type of biased sample is a voluntary response sample in which members of the sample participated only because they wanted to be included in the sample.

12-2 Counting Outcomes

There are several methods for counting the number of outcomes in a given number of events. For example, given the choice of three types of metals for a class ring, five types of stones, and four types of insignias, you can use a counting method to determine the number of possible outcomes for choosing a class ring.

- A tree diagram is helpful when counting outcomes. In a tree diagram, the first column lists all of the outcomes for one choice. The second column lists all of the outcomes for the first and second choice, and so on until the last column, which lists all of the possible outcomes for all of the choices. The last column is the sample space. Each item or collection of items in the sample space is an event.

- Another counting method that can be used is the Fundamental Counting Principle. When using this method, multiply the number of choices for each event by the number of choices for each of the other events. For example, given a choice of 6 different sandwiches, 5 different drinks, and 4 different side dishes, there are $6 \times 5 \times 4$ or 120 different choices.

- The number of possible arrangements or orders for a set of events can be determined by using factorials. A factorial is the product of a number and all of the positive integers between that number and zero, and is written as $n!$. If 5 books are arranged on a shelf, the possible arrangements are $5!$ or $5 \times 4 \times 3 \times 2 \times 1$ or 120 possible arrangements.

 ## Permutations and Combinations

A permutation is an arrangement or listing in which the order or placement of the arrangement is important. A combination is an arrangement or listing in which order or placement is not important.

- An example of a permutation is the selection of a class president, vice-president, and secretary from among three students. Each order in which the students are chosen is unique, so order is important. Tree Diagrams can be used to show permutations. You can also find the number of permutations by using the formula $\frac{n!}{(n-r)!}$, where n is the number of items to choose from and r is the number of items to be chosen. The symbol for permutations is $_nP_r$.

- An example of a combination is the selection of two pizza toppings from a list of 8 toppings. The order in which the toppings are chosen is not important. The formula for finding the number of combinations is $\frac{n!}{(n-r)!r!}$, where n is the number of items to choose from, and r is the number of items to be chosen. The symbol for combinations is $_nC_r$.

 ## Probability of Compound Events

A simple event is a single event while a compound event consists of two or more simple events.

- If two events occur separately and the outcome of one does not affect the outcome of the other, the events are *independent*. To find the probability of independent events, multiply the probability of the first event by the probability of the second event: $P(A) \cdot P(B)$.

- If the outcome of one event affects the outcome of another, the events are *dependent*. To find the probability of the two dependent events, multiply the first event by the probability of the second event following the first event: $P(A) \cdot P(B$ following $A)$.

- *Mutually exclusive* events are events that cannot occur at the same time. An example is choosing both a red card and a black card from a deck of cards at the same time. To find the probability of mutually exclusive events, find the sum of the probabilities of two events: $P(A) + P(B)$.

- *Inclusive events* can occur at the same time. For example, you can draw a red card and a queen at the same time. To find the probability of inclusive events, find the sum of the probabilities of the two events decreased by the probability of both events occurring: $P(A) + P(B) - P(A \text{ and } B)$.

 ## Probability Distributions

A random variable is a variable with a value that is the numerical outcome of a random event. A probability distribution shows all of the possible values of the random variable X. For example, a survey of 100 people shows whether they own 0, 1, 2, or 3 televisions. The random variable X in this example is the number of televisions. A probability distribution based on the survey will show the probability that a person chosen at random owns 0 televisions, 1 television, 2 televisions, or 3. The probabilities for each value of X will add up to 1. Probability distributions can be shown in tables or histograms.

 ## Probability Simulations

Probabilities can be theoretical or experimental. Theoretical probability is determined mathematically and describes what should happen. Experimental probability describes what happens based on repeated experiments. A simulation is a method used to find experimental probability. It uses objects, such as dice, coins, and spinners, to simulate an event. For example, a spinner could be used to determine the experimental probability that a person randomly chooses a blue cube out of 3 blue cubes and 7 green cubes. Given few trials, the differences between experimental and theoretical probability may be great, but as the number of trials increases, the differences between the two decreases.

Options for Chapter 12 Lessons

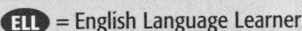 = English Language Learner 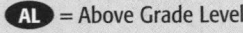 = Above Grade Level 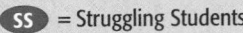 = Struggling Students **SN** = Special Needs

Using Logic **AL**

Use with Lesson 12-2

Before you introduce the Fundamental Counting Principle, ask students to study Example 1 on p. 650 and make a conjecture about any relationship between the number of possible jerseys, pants, and shoes and the number of outcomes. Guide students to see that the number of outcomes is the product of the number of choices.

Using Visual Learning **SS** **SN** **ELL**

Use with Lesson 12-3

Have students write the digits 1, 2, 4, 5, 6, 7, and 9 on index cards. Have them rearrange the cards in different ways to help them visualize how the permutation formula relates to the cards. Compare their results with the calculations in Example 3 on p. 657.

Using Kinesthetic Learning **AL**

Use after Lesson 12-6

Allow students to design their own experiments to find experimental probability, such as finding the probability of tossing a wad of paper in a wastebasket, the probability of a student being able to do more than 10 jumping jacks in 10 seconds, and so on.

Noteables™ Interactive Study Notebook with Foldables™

Noteables™ Interactive Study Notebook with Foldables™ is a study organizer that provides helpful steps for students to follow to organize their notes for Chapter 12.

- Students use Noteables to record notes and to complete their Foldables as you present the material for each lesson.
- Noteables correspond to the Examples in the *Teacher Wraparound Edition* and *Interactive Classroom CD-ROM.*

Intervention

Quick Review Math Handbook*

is Glencoe's mathematical handbook for students and parents.

Hot Words includes a glossary of terms.

Hot Topics consists of two parts:

- explanations of key mathematical concepts
- exercises to check students' understanding.

Lesson	Hot Topics Section	Lesson	Hot Topics Section
12-1	2.6, 4.1	12-4	2.9, 4.6
12-2	4.5, 4.6	12-5	2.1, 4.6
12-3	2.3, 2.4, 4.5	12-6	4.6

*Also available in Spanish

Teacher To Teacher

Ruth Casey
Mathematics Chairperson
Glencoe author
Anderson County High School
Lawrenceburg, KY

USE WITH LESSON 12-6

❝ I like to do an activity similar to the one done in Exercises 7–10. I have my students toss an inflated globe around the room. Students record whether the person catching the ball does so with his or her right thumb on land or on water. ❞

Reading and Writing in Mathematics

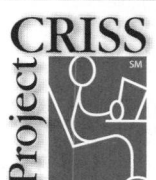

Project CRISS℠

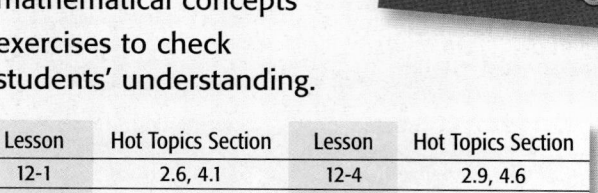
STUDY SKILL

Most students begin Chapter 12 having some background in the topics presented there. Using a **K**now-**W**ant to Learn-**L**earned (KWL) chart will help them build on their prior knowledge.

Before beginning this chapter, draw a KWL chart like the one on the right on an overhead transparency. Name some topics covered in the chapter, such as the probability of compound events. Have students tell what they already know about the topics as you record their ideas. Next,

have them list what they would like to know about the topics. Then, after the chapter has been completed, have students complete the last column, describing what they learned.

Compound Events		
Know	**What to Learn**	**Learned**
The probability of two independent events A and B occurring is the product of the probability of A and the probability of B.	What is the probability of two events that cannot occur at the same time?	

CReating **I**ndependence through **S**tudent-owned **S**trategies

Focus Students write notes about statistics, counting outcomes, and probability for each lesson in this chapter.

Teach Have students make and label their Foldables as illustrated.

Begin with the central theme of Statistics and Probability and have students record key words and phrases under the four tabs.

When to Use It Students should use their Foldables to take notes, define terms, record concepts, and write examples as they cover each lesson in this chapter.

A version of a completed Foldable is shown on p. 684.

Differentiated Instruction

[CRM] Student-Built Glossary, pp. 1–2 Students should complete the chart by providing a definition and an example of each term as they progress through Chapter 12. This study tool can also be used to review the chapter test.

CHAPTER 12

Statistics and Probability

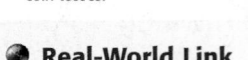
BIG Ideas

- **Probability and Statistics Standard 1.0** Students know the definition of the notion of *independent events* and can use the rules for addition, multiplication, and complementation to solve for probabilities of particular events in finite sample spaces.

- **Probability and Statistics Standard 3.0** Students demonstrate an understanding of the notion of *discrete random variables* by using them to solve for the probabilities of outcomes, such as the probability of the occurrence of five heads in 14 coin tosses.

● Real-World Link

U.S. Senate The United States Senate forms committees to focus on different issues. These committees are made up of senators from various states and political parties. You can use probability to find how many ways these committees can be formed.

FOLDABLES™
Study Organizer

Statistics and Probability Make this Foldable to help you organize what you learn about statistics and probability. Begin with a sheet of $8\frac{1}{2}$" × 11" paper.

1 **Fold** in half lengthwise.

2 **Fold** the top to the bottom twice.

3 **Open.** Cut along the second fold to make four tabs.

4 **Label** as shown.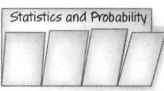

Statistics and Probability

Materials Needed for Chapter 12

- calculator (Lessons 12-3, 12-6)
- six-sided die (Lesson 12-6)

GET READY for Chapter 12

Diagnose Readiness You have two options for checking Prerequisite Skills.

Option 1

Take the Quick Check below. Refer to the Quick Review for help.

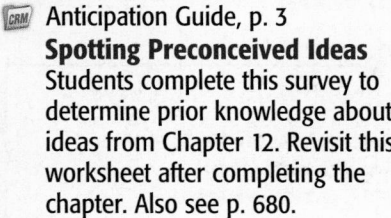

Option 2

Math Online Take the Online Readiness Quiz at ca.algebra1.com.

QUICK Check

(Used in Lessons 12-2 and 12-5.)
Determine the probability of each event if you randomly select a cube from a bag containing 6 red cubes, 4 yellow cubes, 3 blue cubes, and 1 green cube.
(Prerequisite Skill)

1. $P(\text{red})$ $\frac{3}{7}$ 2. $P(\text{blue})$ $\frac{3}{14}$ 3. $P(\text{not red})$ $\frac{4}{7}$

4. **GAMES** Paul is going to roll a game cube with 3 sides painted red, two painted blue, and 1 painted green. What is the probability that a red side will land face up? $\frac{1}{2}$

(Used in Lesson 12-2.)
Find each product. (Prerequisite Skill)

5. $\frac{4}{5} \cdot \frac{3}{4}$ $\frac{3}{5}$ 6. $\frac{5}{12} \cdot \frac{6}{11}$ $\frac{5}{22}$

7. $\frac{7}{20} \cdot \frac{4}{19}$ $\frac{7}{95}$ 8. $\frac{4}{32} \cdot \frac{7}{32}$ $\frac{7}{256}$

9. $\frac{13}{52} \cdot \frac{4}{52}$ $\frac{1}{52}$ 10. $\frac{56}{100} \cdot \frac{24}{100}$ $\frac{84}{625}$

(Used in Lesson 12-5.)
Write each fraction as a percent. Round to the nearest tenth. (Prerequisite Skill)

11. $\frac{7}{8}$ **87.5%**   12. $\frac{33}{80}$ **41.3%**

13. $\frac{107}{125}$ **85.6%**   14. $\frac{625}{1024}$ **61%**

15. **CONCERTS** At a local concert, 585 of 2000 people were under the age of 18. What percentage of the audience were under 18? Round to the nearest tenth. **29.3%**

QUICK Review

EXAMPLE 1

Determine the probability of selecting a green cube if you randomly select a cube from a bag containing 6 red cubes, 4 yellow cubes, and 1 green cube.
There is 1 green cube and a total of 11 cubes in the bag.

$$\frac{1}{11} = \frac{\text{number of green cubes}}{\text{total number of cubes}}$$

The probability of selecting a green cube is $\frac{1}{11}$.

EXAMPLE 2

Find $\frac{5}{4} \cdot \frac{2}{3}$.

$\frac{5}{4} \cdot \frac{2}{3} = \frac{5 \cdot 2}{4 \cdot 3}$ Multiply both the numerators and the denominators.

$= \frac{10}{12}$ or $\frac{5}{6}$ Simplify.

EXAMPLE 3

Write the fraction $\frac{14}{17}$ as a decimal. Round to the nearest tenth.

$\frac{14}{17} = 0.823$ Simplify and round.

0.823×100 Multiply the decimal by 100.

$= 82.3$ Simplify.

$\frac{14}{17}$ written as a percent is 82.3%.

Chapter 12 Get Ready For Chapter 12   **641**

Formative Assessment

CRM **Anticipation Guide, p. 3**
Spotting Preconceived Ideas
Students complete this survey to determine prior knowledge about ideas from Chapter 12. Revisit this worksheet after completing the chapter. Also see p. 680.

TWE **Lesson Activities**
- Ticket Out the Door, pp. 648, 670
- Crystal Ball, p. 676
- Name the Math, p. 654
- Yesterday's News, pp. 662, 683

Chapter Checkpoints

SE Mid-Chapter Quiz, p. 671

SE Study Guide and Review, pp. 684–688

SE California Standards Practice, pp. 690–691

CRM Quizzes, pp. 51 and 52

CRM Standardized Test Practice, pp. 68–70

Math Online ca.algebra1.com
- Self-Check Quizzes
- Practice Test
- Standardized Test Practice

Summative Assessment

SE Chapter Practice Test, p. 689

CRM Mid-Chapter Test, p. 53

CRM Vocabulary Test, p. 54

CRM Extended-Response Test, p. 67

CRM Leveled Chapter Tests, pp. 55–66

ExamView® Assessment Suite

Key

CRM *Chapter 12 Resource Masters*

SE Student Edition

TWE Teacher Wraparound Edition

CD-ROM

Diagnostic Assessment

Exercises	California Standards	Intervention
1–4	PS1.0	SE Prerequisite Skill, pp. 709–710 *Prerequisite Skills Workbook*, pp. 99–100
5–10	7NS1.2	SE Prerequisite Skill, pp. 698–699 *Prerequisite Skills Workbook*, pp. 47–48
11–15	7NS1.3	*Prerequisite Skills Workbook*, pp. 71–72

1 Focus

Standards Alignment

Before Lesson 12-1
Analyze data displays from
Standard 6SDAP2.3

Lesson 12-1
Identify different ways of selecting a sample. Identify data that represent sampling errors and bias from Standards 6SDAP2.2 and 6SDAP2.4

After Lesson 12-1
Determine the mean and the standard deviation of a normally distributed random variables from Standard PS5.0

2 Teach

Scaffolding Questions
Have students read *Get Ready for the Lesson.*
Ask:
• Suppose the manufacturer produces 100 CDs an hour and takes a sample every hour. How many CDs would be sampled in an 8-hour day? 8 CDs

• How might the manufacturer pick CDs at random? Sample answer: The manufacturer might pick the fiftieth CD produced every hour.

Lesson 12-1 Resources

Chapter 12 Resource Masters
Lesson Reading Guide, p. 5 **BL** **OL** **ELL**
Study Guide and Intervention, pp. 6–7
BL **OL** **ELL**
Skills Practice, p. 8 **BL** **OL**
Practice, p. 9 **OL** **AL**
Word Problem Practice, p. 10 **OL** **AL**
Enrichment, p. 11 **OL** **AL**

Main Ideas
• Identify various sampling techniques.
• Recognize a biased sample.

Reinforcement of Standard 6SDAP2.2
Identify different ways of selecting a sample (e.g., convenience sampling, responses to a survey, random sampling) and which method makes a sample more representative for a population. (Key)

Reinforcement of Standard 6SDAP2.4 Identify data that represent sampling errors and explain why the sample (and the display) might be biased. (Key)

New Vocabulary
sample
population
random sample
simple random sample
stratified random sample
systematic random sample
biased sample
convenience sample
voluntary response sample

 GET READY for the Lesson

Manufacturing music CDs involves burning copies from a master. However, not every burn is successful. Because it is costly to check every CD, manufacturers monitor production by randomly checking CDs for defects.

Sampling Techniques A **sample** is some portion of a larger group, called the **population,** selected to represent that group. Sample data are often used to estimate a characteristic within an entire population, such as voting preferences prior to elections. A **random sample** of a population is selected so that it is representative of the entire population. The sample is chosen without any preference. There are several ways to pick a random sample.

KEY CONCEPT		Random Samples
Type	**Definition**	**Example**
Simple Random Sample	A simple random sample is a sample that is as equally likely to be chosen as any other sample from the population.	The 26 students in a class are each assigned a different number from 1 to 26. Then three of the 26 numbers are picked at random.
Stratified Random Sample	In a stratified random sample, the population is first divided into similar, nonoverlapping groups. A sample is then selected from each group.	The students in a school are divided into freshmen, sophomores, juniors, and seniors. Then two students are randomly selected from each group of students.
Systematic Random Sample	In a systematic random sample, the items are selected according to a specified time or item interval.	Every 2 minutes, an item is pulled off the assembly line. or Every twentieth item is pulled off the assembly line.

EXAMPLE Classify a Random Sample

1 **ECOLOGY** Ten lakes in Minnesota are selected randomly. Then 2 liters of water are drawn from each of the ten lakes.

  a. Identify the sample and suggest a population from which it was selected.

  The sample is ten 2-liter containers of lake water, one from each of 10 lakes. The population is lake water from all of the lakes in Minnesota.

642 Chapter 12 Statistics and Probability

Transparencies
5-Minute Check Transparency 12-1
Additional Print Resources
Noteables™ Interactive Study Notebook with Foldables™

Technology
ca.algebra1.com
Interactive Classroom CD-ROM
AssignmentWorks CD-ROM
Graphing Calculator Easy Files

b. Classify the sample as *simple, stratified,* or *systematic.*

This is a simple random sample. Each of the ten lakes was equally likely to have been chosen from the list.

✓ CHECK **Your Progress**

1A. The sample is approximately 19 cooks chosen from the 190 cooks that make up the population.

BARBECUE Refer to the information at the left. The cooks lined up randomly within their category, and every tenth cook in each category was selected.

1A. Identify the sample and a population from which it was selected.

1B. Classify the sample as *simple, stratified,* or *systematic.* stratified

⦿nline **Personal Tutor at** ca.algebra1.com

Biased Sample Random samples are unbiased. In a **biased sample,** one or more parts of a population are favored over others.

EXAMPLE Identify Sample as Biased or Unbiased

2 Identify each sample as *biased* or *unbiased.* Explain your reasoning.

a. MANUFACTURING Every 1000th bolt is pulled from the production line and measured for length.

The sample is chosen using a specified interval. This is an unbiased sample because it is a systematic random sample.

b. MUSIC Every tenth customer in line for a certain rock band's concert tickets is asked about his or her favorite rock band.

The sample is a biased sample because customers in line for concert tickets are more likely to name the band giving the concert as a favorite.

✓ CHECK **Your Progress**

2. POLITICS A journalist visited a senior center and chose 10 individuals randomly to poll about various political topics.

Real-World Link

Each year, Meridian, Texas, hosts The National Championship Barbecue Cook-Off. In 2003, there were 190 cooks in the competition, and they competed in one of three categories: brisket, chicken, or pork spare ribs.

Source: bbq.htcomp.net

2. The sample is biased because the people at the senior center only represent one age category of respondents.

Two popular forms of samples that are often biased include convenience samples and voluntary response samples.

KEY CONCEPT		*Biased Samples*
Type	**Definition**	**Example**
Convenience Sample	A convenience sample includes members of a population who are easily accessed.	To check spoilage, a produce worker selects 10 apples from the top of the bin. The 10 apples are unlikely to represent all of the apples in the bin.
Voluntary Response Sample	A voluntary response sample involves only those who want to participate in the sampling.	A radio call-in show records that 75% of its 40 callers voiced negative opinions about a local football team. Those 40 callers are unlikely to represent the entire local population. Volunteer callers are more likely to have strong opinions and are typically more negative than the entire population.

 Extra Examples at ca.algebra1.com

Lesson 12-1 Sampling and Bias **643**

Sampling Techniques
Example 1 shows how to identify and classify a random sample in a real-world situation.

ADDITIONAL EXAMPLE

1 RETAIL Each day, a department store chain selects one male and one female shopper randomly from each of its 57 stores and asks them survey questions about their shopping habits.

a. Identify the sample and suggest a population from which it was selected.
Sample: 57 male and 57 female shoppers. Population: shoppers in the chain's stores

b. Classify the sample as *simple, stratified,* or *systematic.*
stratified random sample

Additional Examples are also in:
• Noteables™ Interactive Study Notebook with Foldables™
• Interactive Classroom PowerPoint® Presentations

Biased Sample
Example 2 shows how to tell whether a sample is biased or unbiased.

ADDITIONAL EXAMPLE

2 Identify each sample as *biased* or *unbiased.* Explain your reasoning.

a. STUDENT COUNCIL The student council surveys the students in one classroom to decide the theme for the spring dance. Biased; It includes only the students in one classroom.

b. SCHOOL The Parent Association surveys the parents of every fifth student to decide whether to hold a fund-raiser. Unbiased; The parents are picked using a systematic method.

Focus on Mathematical Content

Samples and Populations By taking a sample of a population, you can estimate the characteristics of the population and make predictions based on the characteristics. A sample is a portion of a group, and the population is the group from which the sample is taken.

 Formative Assessment

Use the Check Your Progress exercises after each example to determine students' understanding of concepts.

Example 3 shows how to identify and classify a biased sample. **Example 4** shows how to identify a sample, suggest a population, and identify and classify the sample according to whether it is biased or unbiased.

ADDITIONAL EXAMPLES

3 **COMMUNITY** The maintenance chairperson of a neighborhood association has been asked by the association to survey the residents of the neighborhood to find out when to hold a neighborhood clean-up day. The chairperson decides to ask her immediate neighbors and the neighbors in the houses directly across the street from her house.

a. Identify the sample, and suggest a population from which it was selected. Sample: chairperson's immediate neighbors and the neighbors across the street; population: residents of the neighborhood

b. Classify the sample as a *convenience sample* or a *voluntary response sample*. This is a convenience sample because the chairperson asked only her closest neighbors.

ADDITIONAL EXAMPLE

4 **SCHOOL** The high school Parent Association sent a letter to the parents of all graduating seniors asking them to return the enclosed ballot if they had a preference on where the graduation party was to be held.

a. Identify the sample. Sample: a group of parents of the graduating seniors

(continued on the next page)

3A. The samples are the first and last 20 cards received. The population is all of the students in the school who responded to the question.

Study Tip

Random Sample
A sample is *random* if every member of the population has an equal probability of being chosen for the sample.

4A. The sample is those people on the committee's mailing list.

4B. The population consists of all the residents of the city.

EXAMPLE Identify and Classify a Biased Sample

3 **BUSINESS** The travel account records from 4 of the 20 departments in a corporation are to be reviewed. The accountant states that the first 4 departments to voluntarily submit their records will be reviewed.

a. **Identify the sample and a population from which it was selected.**

The sample is the travel account records from 4 departments in the corporation. The population is the travel account records from all 20 departments in the corporation.

b. **Classify the sample as *convenience* or *voluntary response*.**

Since the departments voluntarily submit their records, this is a voluntary response sample.

CHECK Your Progress

POLL A principal asks the students in her school to write down the name of a favorite teacher on an index card. She then tabulates the results from the first 20 and the last 20 cards received.

3A. Identify the sample and a population from which it was selected.

3B. Classify the sample as *convenience* or *voluntary response*. **convenience**

EXAMPLE Identify the Sample

4 **NEWS REPORTING** Rafael needs to determine whether students in his school believe that an arts center should be added to the school. He polls 15 of his friends who sing in the chorale. Twelve of them think the school needs an arts center, so Rafael reports that 80% of the students surveyed support the project.

a. **Identify the sample.**

The sample is a group of students from the chorale.

b. **Suggest a population from which the sample was selected.**

The population for the survey is all of the students in the school.

c. **State whether the sample is *unbiased* (random) or *biased*. If unbiased, classify it as *simple*, *stratified*, or *systematic*. If biased, classify it as *convenience* or *voluntary response*.**

The sample was from the chorale. So the reported support is not likely to be representative of the student body. The sample is biased. Since Rafael polled only his friends, it is a convenience sample.

CHECK Your Progress

ELECTIONS To estimate the leading candidate, a candidate's committee randomly sends a survey to the people on their mailing list. The returns indicate that their candidate is leading by a margin of 58% to 42%.

4A. Identify the sample.

4B. Suggest a population from which the sample was selected.

4C. State whether the sample is *unbiased* (random) or *biased*. If unbiased, classify it as *simple*, *stratified*, or *systematic*. If biased, classify it as *convenience* or *voluntary response*. **biased; convenience**

644 Chapter 12 Statistics and Probability

Differentiated Instruction

Visual/Spatial Learners Place students in small groups. Give each group a different number of colored beads to serve as a population. Have the groups model the different types of random samples with the beads. For example, for stratified random samples, students would first divide the beads into groups by color and then take random beads from each group. Have students describe how they would take a systematic random sample.

★ indicates multi-step problem

✔ CHECK Your Understanding

Examples 1–4
(pp. 642–644)

Identify each sample, suggest a population from which it was selected, and state whether it is *unbiased* (random) or *biased*. If unbiased, classify the sample as *simple*, *stratified*, or *systematic*. If biased, classify as *convenience* or *voluntary response*.

1. a group of readers of a newspaper; all readers of the newspaper; biased; voluntary response

2. work from 4 students; work from all students in the 1st period math class; biased; voluntary response

1. **NEWSPAPERS** The local newspaper asks readers to write letters stating their preferred candidates for mayor.

2. **SCHOOL** A teacher needs a sample of work from four students in her first-period math class to display at the school open house. She selects the work of the first four students who raise their hands.

3. **BUSINESS** A hardware store wants to assess the strength of nails it sells. Store personnel select 25 boxes at random from among all of the boxes on the shelves. From each of the 25 boxes, they select one nail at random and subject it to a strength test.
   25 nails; all nails on the store shelves; unbiased; stratified

4. **SCHOOL** A class advisor hears complaints about an incorrect spelling of the school name on pencils sold at the school store. The advisor goes to the store and asks Namid to gather a sample of pencils and look for spelling errors. Namid grabs the closest box of pencils and counts out 12 pencils from the top of the box. She checks the pencils, returns them to the box, and reports the results to the advisor.
   12 pencils; all pencils in the school store; biased; convenience

Exercises

HOMEWORK HELP	
For Exercises	See Examples
5–18	1-4

Exercise Levels
A: 5–18
B: 19–26
C: 27–31

7. people who are home between 9 A.M. and 4 P.M.; all people in the neighborhood; biased; convenience

9. 10 scooters; all scooters manufactured on a particular production line during one day; biased; convenience

Identify each sample, suggest a population from which it was selected, and state whether it is *unbiased* (random) or *biased*. If unbiased, classify the sample as *simple*, *stratified*, or *systematic*. If biased, classify as *convenience* or *voluntary response*.

5. **SCHOOL** Pieces of paper with the names of three sophomores are drawn from a hat containing identical pieces of paper with all sophomores' names.
   3 sophomores; all sophomores in the school; unbiased; simple

6. **FOOD** Twenty shoppers outside a fast-food restaurant are asked to name their preferred cola between two choices.
   20 shoppers; all shoppers; biased; convenience

7. **RECYCLING** An interviewer goes from house to house on weekdays between 9 A.M. and 4 P.M. to determine how many people recycle.

8. **POPULATION** Ten people from each of the 58 counties in California are chosen at random and asked their opinion on a state issue.
   580 people from California; all people in California; unbiased; stratified

9. **SCOOTERS** A scooter manufacturer is concerned about quality control. The manufacturer checks the first five scooters off the line in the morning and the last five off the line in the afternoon for defects.

10. **SCHOOL** To determine who will speak for her class at the school board meeting, Ms. Finchie used the numbers appearing next to her students' names in her grade book. She writes each of the numbers on an identical piece of paper and shuffles the pieces of papers in a box. Without seeing the contents of the box, one student draws 3 pieces of paper from the box. The students with these numbers will speak for the class.
    3 students; all of the students in Ms. Finchie's class; unbiased; simple

Lesson 12-1 Sampling and Bias **645**

ADDITIONAL EXAMPLES

④
b. Suggest a population from which the sample was selected. Population: all the parents of the graduating seniors

c. State whether the sample is *unbiased* (random) or *biased*. If unbiased, classify it as *simple*, *stratified*, or *systematic*. If biased, classify it as *convenience* or *voluntary response*. biased; voluntary response

③ Practice

✔ Formative Assessment

Use Exercises 1–4 to check for understanding.

Use the chart at the bottom of this page to customize assignments for your students.

Odd/Even Assignments
Exercises 5–18 are structured so that students practice the same concepts whether they are assigned odd or even problems.

DIFFERENTIATED HOMEWORK OPTIONS

Level	Assignment	Two-Day Option	
BL Basic	5–18, 27–29, 31–52	5–17 odd, 32, 33	6–18 even, 27–29, 31, 34–52
OL Core	5–17 odd, 19–29, 31–52	5–18, 32, 33	19–29, 34–52
AL Advanced /Pre-AP	19–46 (optional: 47–52)		

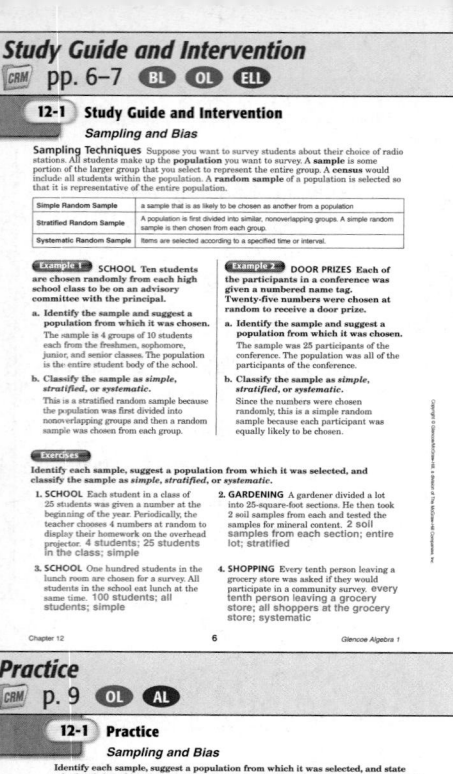

Identify each sample, suggest a population from which it was selected, and state whether it is *unbiased* (random) or *biased*. If unbiased, classify the sample as *simple*, *stratified*, or *systematic*. If biased, classify as *convenience* or *voluntary response*.

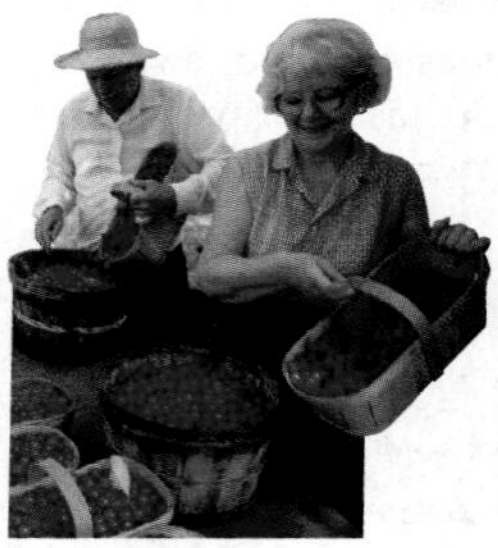

Real-World Link

In 2002, Washington led the nation in cherry production by growing 194 million pounds of cherries.

Source: USDA

11. **FARMING** An 8-ounce jar was filled with corn from a storage silo by dipping the jar into the pile of corn. The corn in the jar was then analyzed for moisture content.
    an 8-oz jar of corn; all corn in the storage silo; biased; convenience
12. **COURTS** The gender makeup of district court judges in the United States is to be estimated from a sample. All judges are grouped geographically by federal reserve districts. Within each of the 11 federal reserve districts, all judges' names are assigned a distinct random number. In each district, the numbers are then listed in order. A number between 1 and 20 inclusive is selected at random, and the judge with that number is selected. Then every 20th name after the first selected number is also included in the sample. a group of U.S. district court judges; all U.S. district court judges; unbiased; stratified
13. **TELEVISION** A television station asks its viewers to share their opinions about a proposed golf course to be built just outside the city limits. Viewers can call one of two 800 numbers. One number represents a "yes" vote, and the other number represents a "no" vote. a group of people who watch a television station; all people who watch the television station; biased; voluntary response
14. **GOVERNMENT** To discuss leadership issues shared by all United States Senators, the President asks four of his closest colleagues in the Senate to meet with him.
    4 U.S. Senators; all U.S. Senators; biased; convenience
15. **FOOD** To sample the quality of the Bing cherries throughout the produce department, the produce manager picks up a handful of cherries from the edge of one case and checks to see if these cherries are spoiled. a handful of Bing cherries; all Bing cherries in the produce department; biased; convenience
16. **MANUFACTURING** During the manufacture of high-definition televisions, units are checked for defects. Within the first 10 minutes of a work shift, a television is randomly chosen from the line of completed sets. For the rest of the shift, every 15th television on the line is checked for defects.
17. **BUSINESS** To get reaction about a benefits package, a company uses a computer program to randomly pick one person from each of its departments.
    a group of employees; all employees of the company; unbiased; stratified
18. **MOVIES** A magazine is trying to determine the most popular actor of the year. It asks its readers to mail the name of their favorite actor to their office.
    a group of readers of a magazine; all readers of the magazine; biased; voluntary response

COLLEGE **For Exercises 19 and 20, use the following information.**

The graph at the right reveals that 56% of survey respondents did not have a formal financial plan for a child's college tuition.

19. Write a statement to describe what you do know about the sample.
20. What additional information would you like to have about the sample to determine whether the sample is biased?

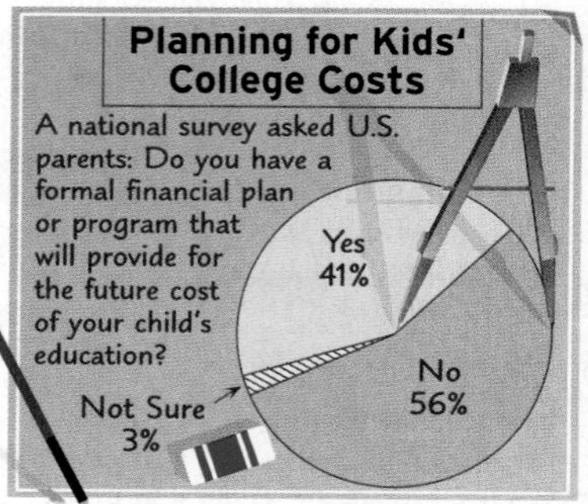

Source: Yankelovich Partners for Microsoft Corp.

16. a group of high-definition television sets; all high-definition television sets manufactured on one line during one shift; unbiased; systematic

19. We know that the results are from a national survey conducted by Yankelovich Partners for Microsoft Corporation.

20. Additional information needed includes how the survey was conducted, how the survey respondents were selected, and the number of respondents.

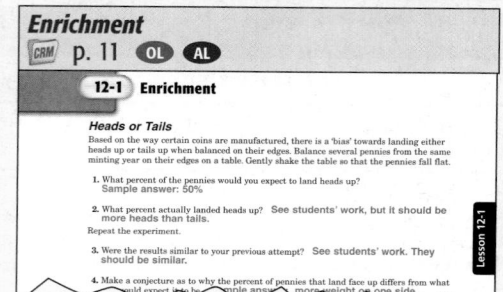

Study Guide and Intervention

CRM pp. 6–7 BL OL ELL

12-1 Study Guide and Intervention

Sampling and Bias

Sampling Techniques Suppose you want to survey students about their choice of radio stations. All students make up the **population** you want to survey. A **sample** is some portion of the larger group that you select to represent the entire group. A **census** would include all students within the population. A **random sample** of a population is selected so that it is representative of the entire population.

Simple Random Sample	a sample that is as likely to be chosen as another from a population
Stratified Random Sample	A population is first divided into similar, nonoverlapping groups. A simple random sample is then chosen from each group.
Systematic Random Sample	Items are selected according to a specified time or interval.

Example 1 SCHOOL **Ten students are chosen randomly from each high school class to be on an advisory committee with the principal.**

a. **Identify the sample and suggest a population from which it was chosen.**
The sample is 4 groups of 10 students each from the freshmen, sophomore, junior, and senior classes. The population is the entire student body of the school.

b. **Classify the sample as *simple*, *stratified*, or *systematic*.**
This is a stratified random sample because the population was first divided into nonoverlapping groups and then a random sample was chosen from each group.

Example 2 DOOR PRIZES **Each of the participants in a conference was given a numbered name tag. Twenty-five numbers were chosen at random to receive a door prize.**

a. **Identify the sample and suggest a population from which it was chosen.**
The sample was 25 participants of the conference. The population was all of the participants of the conference.

b. **Classify the sample as *simple*, *stratified*, or *systematic*.**
Since the numbers were chosen randomly, this is a simple random sample because each participant was equally likely to be chosen.

Exercises

Identify each sample, suggest a population from which it was selected, and classify the sample as *simple*, *stratified*, or *systematic*.

1. SCHOOL Each student in a class of 25 students was given a number at the beginning of the year. Periodically, the teacher chooses 4 numbers at random to display their homework on the overhead projector. 4 students; 25 students in the class; simple
2. GARDENING A gardener divided a lot into 25-square-foot sections. He then took 2 soil samples from each and tested the samples for mineral content. 2 soil samples from each section; entire lot; stratified
3. SCHOOL One hundred students in the lunch room are chosen for a survey. All students in the school eat lunch at the same time. 100 students; all students; simple
4. SHOPPING Every tenth person leaving a grocery store was asked if they would participate in a community survey. every tenth person leaving a grocery store; all shoppers at the grocery store; systematic

Chapter 12 6 *Glencoe Algebra 1*

Practice

CRM p. 9 OL AL

12-1 Practice

Sampling and Bias

Identify each sample, suggest a population from which it was selected, and state whether it is *unbiased* (random) or *biased*. If unbiased, classify the sample as *simple*, *stratified*, or *systematic*. If biased, classify as *convenience* or *voluntary response*.

1. GOVERNMENT At a town council meeting, the chair asks 5 citizens attending for their opinions on whether to approve rezoning for a residential area. 5 citizens of a town; all citizens of a town; biased; convenience
2. BOTANY To determine the extent of leaf blight in the maple trees at a nature preserve, a botanist divides the reserve into 10 sections, randomly selects a 200-foot by 200-foot square in the section, and then examines all the maple trees in the section. the maple trees in a square area of each of 10 sections at a nature preserve; all the maple trees at the nature preserve; unbiased; stratified
3. FINANCES To determine the popularity of online banking in the United States, a polling company sends a mail-in survey to 5000 adults to see if they bank online, and if they do, how many times they bank online each month. 5000 U.S. adults; all U.S. adults; biased; voluntary response
4. SHOES A shoe manufacturer wants to check the quality of its shoes. Every twenty minutes, 20 pairs of shoes are pulled off the assembly line for a thorough quality inspection. 20 pairs of shoes every 20 minutes on an assembly line; all the pairs of shoes coming down an assembly line; unbiased; systematic
5. BUSINESS To learn which benefits employees at a large company think are most important, the management has a computer select 50 employees at random. The employees are then interviewed by the Human Relations department. 50 employees of a company; all employees of a company; unbiased; simple
6. BUSINESS An insurance company checks every hundredth claim payment to ensure that claims have been processed correctly. every hundredth claim payment at an insurance company; all claim payments at an insurance company; unbiased; systematic
7. ENVIRONMENT Suppose you want to know if a manufacturing plant is discharging contaminants into a local river. Describe an unbiased way in which you could check the river water for contaminants. Sample answer: At a different time each day, take a 10-ounce sample of water from given locations just upstream and just downstream from where the plant discharges its wastes. Compare the samples for contaminants to see if any are entering the river from the discharge.
8. SCHOOL Suppose you want to know the issues most important to teachers at your school. Describe an unbiased way in which you could conduct your survey. Sample answer: Obtain a list of all teachers at the school. Assign each teacher a number, and then randomly select 10 numbers. Interview each of the teachers assigned one of the selected numbers.

Lesson 12-1

Chapter 12 9 *Glencoe Algebra 1*

Word Problem Practice

CRM p. 10 OL AL

12-1 Word Problem Practice

Sampling and Bias

For Exercises 1–4, identify the sample and the population from which it was selected, and state whether it is *biased* or *unbiased*. If unbiased, classify the sample as *simple*, *stratified*, or *systematic*. If biased, classify as *convenience* or *voluntary response*.

1. SCHOOL Ms. Yeong chooses four students to pass out snacks each day. To choose the students, she writes the names of each of her 18 students on small pieces of paper, and places them in a cup. She mixes up the names and pulls out four to be the snack helpers. sample: 4 helpers; population: the 18 students in the class unbiased, simple random sample
2. ELECTIONS In Summerville, residents vote for mayor at one of the eight precinct voting places near where they live. To acquire early election results for the evening news, a reporter stands outside one of the city's eight voting stations and asks as many people as possible for whom they voted. sample: the voters the reporter interviews; population: all voters biased, convenience sample
3. DISEASE A European country's health department uses nets to trap birds near a local wildlife refuge. The bird is tested for the presence of the avian flu virus. sample: birds captured; population: birds in the region biased, convenience sample
4. SOIL To check for the presence of harmful chemicals in the ground at a new construction site, geotechnical engineers divide the site into 12 rectangular areas and remove a pint of soil from each area for testing. sample: 12 pt of soil; population: all of the soil on the site; unbiased, stratified random sample

CHILD SAFETY For Exercises 5 and 6, use the following information.

The British Columbia Automobile Association performed a free child safety seat inspection for people that came in for the safety check. Only 7% of the 1000 seats inspected were properly used. The graph below shows the approximate percentages of results for the safety seat inspections.

Child Safety Seat Survey Results

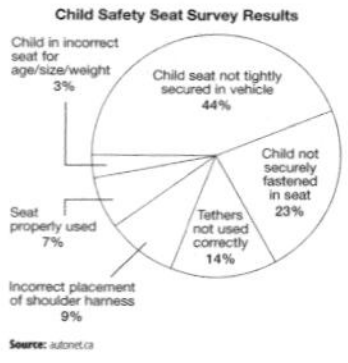

Source: autonet.ca

5. Write a statement to describe the sampling technique. The sample is biased because it was based on voluntary response.
6. Is it appropriate to say that 25% of children in child safety seats in British Columbia are not securely fastened in their seat? Explain. No. This was not a random sample, so the data cannot be generalized to the population. We do not know how the seats are being used in vehicles that were not brought in.

Chapter 12 10 *Glencoe Algebra 1*

Enrichment

CRM p. 11 OL AL

12-1 Enrichment

Heads or Tails

Based on the way certain coins are manufactured, there is a 'bias' towards landing either heads up or tails up when balanced on their edges. Balance several pennies from the same minting year on their edges on a table. Gently shake the table so that the pennies fall flat.

1. What percent of the pennies would you expect to land heads up? Sample answer: 50%
2. What percent actually landed heads up? See students' work, but it should be more heads than tails.

Repeat the experiment.

3. Were the results similar to your previous attempt? See students' work. They should be similar.
4. Make a conjecture as to why the percent of pennies that land face up differs from what ... [illegible] ... more weight on one side

Lesson 12-1

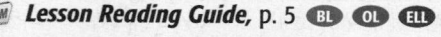

BL = *Below Grade Level*

OL = *On Grade Level*

AL = *Above Grade Level*

ELL = *English Language Learner*

Additional pages not shown:

CRM ***Lesson Reading Guide,*** p. 5 BL OL ELL

CRM ***Skills Practice,*** p. 8 BL OL

DESIGN A SURVEY For Exercises 21–23, describe an unbiased way to conduct each survey.

21. SCHOOL Suppose you want to sample the opinion of the students in your school about a new dress code.

22. ELECTIONS Suppose you are running for mayor of your city and want to know if you are likely to be elected.

23. PICK A TOPIC Write a question you would like to conduct a survey to answer. Then describe an unbiased way to conduct your survey. **See students' work.**

24. FAMILY Study the graph at the right. Describe the information that is revealed in the graph. What information is there about the type or size of the sample? **See margin.**

Topics at Family Dinners

How the Day Was 73%
Family-Related News 65%
Plans For Tomorrow 49%
Current Events 46%

Source: National Pork Producers Council

25. FARMING Suppose you are a farmer and want to know if your tomato crop is ready to harvest. Describe an unbiased way to determine whether the crop is ready to harvest. **See margin.**

26. MANUFACTURING Suppose you want to know whether the infant car seats manufactured by your company meet the government standards for safety. Describe an unbiased way to determine whether the seats meet the standards. **Sample answer: Every hour, pull one infant seat from the end of the assembly line for testing.**

EXTRA PRACTICE
See pages 742, 755.
Math Online
Self-Check Quiz at
ca.algebra1.com

H.O.T. Problems......

27. REASONING Describe how the following three types of sampling techniques are similar and how they are different. **See margin.**
- simple random sample
- stratified random sample
- systematic random sample

28. REASONING Explain the difference between a convenience sample and a voluntary response sample.

29. OPEN ENDED Give a real-world example of a biased sample.

30. CHALLENGE The following is a proposal for surveying a stratified random sample of the student body.

Divide the student body according to those who are on the basketball team, those who are in the band, and those who are in the drama club. Then take a simple random sample from each of the three groups. Conduct the survey using this sample.

Study the proposal. Describe its strengths and weaknesses. Is the sample a stratified random sample? Explain. **See margin.**

31. *Writing in Math* Refer to the information on page 642 to explain why sampling is important in manufacturing. Describe two different ways, one biased and one unbiased, to pick which CDs to check. **See margin.**

Sidebar left answers:

21. Sample answer: Get a copy of the school's list of students and call every 10th person on the list.

22. Sample answer: Get a copy of the list of registered voters in the city and call every 100th person.

28. A convenience sample is a biased sample that is determined based on the ease with which it is possible to gather the sample. A voluntary sample is a biased sample composed of voluntary responses.

29. Sample answer: Ask the members of the school's football team to name their favorite sport.

Bottom answers:

represented in the survey. Other students may be involved in two or three of these activities. These students will be more likely to be chosen for the survey.

31. Usually it is impossible for a company to test every item coming off its production lines. Therefore, testing a sample of these items is helpful in determining quality control. Sample Answers: A biased way to pick the CDs to be checked is to take the first 5 CDs coming off the production line in the morning. An unbiased way to pick the CDs to be checked is to take every 25th CD off the production line.

Additional Answers

24. The graph shows four phrases with a percent associated with each phrase. We can assume that the percents indicate that the percent of respondents who said the indicated topic was discussed during family dinners. Based on the sum of the percents, respondents must have been able to choose or state more than one topic. We do not know how many respondents there were, whether the respondents selected topics from a list of choices or stated their own topics, whether there were any restrictions that may have existed about the topics, and the time period of the family dinners considered in this survey (a night, a week, a month, or more).

25. Sample answer: Randomly pick 5 rows from each field of tomatoes and then pick a tomato every 50 ft along each row.

27. All three are unbiased samples. However, the methods for selecting each type of sample are different. In a simple random sample, a sample is as likely to be chosen as any other from the population. In a stratified random sample, the population is first divided into similar, nonoverlapping groups. Then a simple random sample is selected from each group. In a systematic random sample, the items are selected according to a specified time or item interval.

30. It is a good idea to divide the school population into groups and to take a simple random sample from each group. The problem that prevents this from being a legitimate stratified random sample is the way the three groups are formed. The three groups probably do not represent all students. The students who do not participate in any of these three activities will not be

Real-World Connections For Exercise 27, suggest that students describe similarities and differences in the types of random samples by using an example that relates to their own interests, such as music or sports. After students describe topics of interest, they can describe each type of random sample, and then show how the samples are similar and different.

 Assess

Ticket out the Door Write an example of each of the types of random and biased samples and give one to each student. As students leave the room, ask them to tell whether the sample is *biased* or *unbiased* and then classify it.

 **Foldables™ Follow-Up**

Remind students to record the concepts they have learned in this lesson in their Foldables. Suggest that they give an example of each type of random and biased sample similar to the examples in the Key Concept boxes on pp. 642 and 643.

---

32. To predict the candidate who will win the seat in city council, which method would give the newspaper the *most* accurate result? **B**

   A Ask every fifth person that passes a reporter in the mall.

   B Use a list of registered voters and call every 20th person.

   C Publish a survey and ask readers to reply.

   D Ask reporters at the newspaper.

33. REVIEW Which equation *best* represents the relationship between x and y? **H**

x	y
−1	8
0	5
1	2
2	−1
3	−4
4	−7

   F $y = 8 - 3x$

   G $y = 5x - 3$

   H $y = -3x + 5$

   J $y = 3x + 5$

Spiral Review

Solve each equation. (Lesson 11-9)

34. $\dfrac{10}{3y} - \dfrac{5}{2y} = \dfrac{1}{4}$ $3\dfrac{1}{3}$

35. $\dfrac{3}{r+4} - \dfrac{1}{r} = \dfrac{1}{r}$ 8

36. $\dfrac{1}{4m} + \dfrac{2m}{m-3} = 2$ $\dfrac{3}{25}$

Simplify. (Lesson 11-8)

37. $\dfrac{2 + \frac{5}{x}}{\frac{x}{3} + \frac{5}{6}}$ $\dfrac{6}{x}$

38. $\dfrac{a + \frac{35}{a+12}}{a+7}$ $\dfrac{a+5}{a+12}$

39. $\dfrac{t^2 - 4}{\frac{t^2 + 5t + 6}{t-2}}$ $\dfrac{(t-2)^2}{t+3}$

★**40. GEOMETRY** The sides of a triangle have measures of $4\sqrt{24}$ centimeters, $5\sqrt{6}$ centimeters, and $3\sqrt{54}$ centimeters. What is the perimeter of the triangle? Write in simplest form. (Lesson 10-2) **$22\sqrt{6}$ cm**

Solve each equation by using the Quadratic Formula. Approximate any irrational roots to the nearest tenth. (Lesson 9-4)

41. $x^2 - 6x - 40 = 0$ **−4, 10**

42. $6b^2 + 15 = -19b$ $-1\dfrac{2}{3}, -1\dfrac{1}{2}$

43. $2d^2 = 9d + 3$ **−0.3, 4.8**

Find each product. (Lesson 7-6)

44. $(y + 5)(y + 7)$ $y^2 + 12y + 35$

45. $(c - 3)(c - 7)$ $c^2 - 10c + 21$

46. $(x + 4)(x - 8)$ $x^2 - 4x - 32$

GET READY for the Next Lesson

PREREQUISITE SKILL Find each product.

47. $3 \cdot 2 \cdot 1$ **6**

48. $11 \cdot 10 \cdot 9$ **990**

49. $6 \cdot 5 \cdot 4 \cdot 3 \cdot 2 \cdot 1$ **720**

50. $8 \cdot 7 \cdot 6 \cdot 5$ **1680**

51. $19 \cdot 18 \cdot 17$ **5814**

52. $30 \cdot 29 \cdot 28 \cdot 27$ **657,720**

Pre-AP Activity   Use as an Extension

Pass out examples of opinion polls taken from news magazines and newspapers. Have students identify the sample and the population for the poll. Then have students describe how the people conducting the poll could make sure the sample was not biased.

READING MATH

Survey Questions

 Reinforcement of Standard 6SDAP2.5 Identify claims based on statistical data and, in simple cases, evaluate the validity of the claims. (Key, CAHSEE)

Even though taking a random sample eliminates bias or favoritism in the choice of a sample, questions may be worded to influence people's thoughts in a desired direction. Two different surveys on Internet sales tax had different results.

Question 1
Should there be sales tax on purchases made on the Internet?

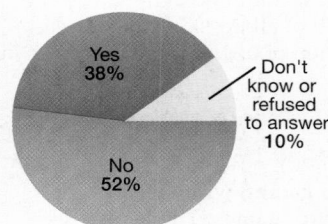

Question 2
Do you think people should or should not be required to pay the same sales tax for purchases made over the Internet as those bought at a local store?

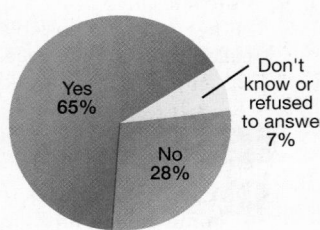

Notice the difference in Questions 1 and 2. Question 2 includes more information. Pointing out that customers pay sales tax for items bought at a local store may give the people answering the survey a reason to answer "yes." Asking the question in that way probably led people to answer the way they did.

Because they are random samples, the results of both of these surveys are accurate. However, the results could be used in a misleading way by someone with an interest in the issue. For example, an Internet retailer would prefer to state the results of Question 1. Be sure to think about survey questions carefully so the results can be interpreted correctly.

Reading to Learn

For Exercises 1–2, tell whether each question is likely to bias the results. Explain your reasoning. 1–2. See margin.

1. On a survey on environmental issues:
   a. "Due to diminishing resources, should a law be made to require recycling?"
   b. "Should the government require citizens to participate in recycling efforts?"

2. On a survey on education:
   a. "Should schools fund extracurricular sports programs?"
   b. "The budget of the River Valley School District is short of funds. Should taxes be raised in order for the district to fund extracurricular sports programs?"

3. Suppose you want to determine whether to serve hamburgers or pizza at the class party.
   a. Write a survey question that would likely produce biased results.
   b. Write a survey question that would likely produce unbiased results.
   See Ch. 12 Answer Appendix.

Reading Math Survey Questions **649**

Additional Answers
Reading to Learn 1–2

1a. This question will bias people toward answering "yes" because it gives them a reason to think that recycling will help alleviate a shortage in resources.

1b. This question will bias people toward answering "no" because most citizens are against the government making laws that require certain behaviors.

2a. This question is not biased. It does not influence a person to answer one way or the other.

2b. This question will bias people toward answering "no" because most people do not want taxes to be raised.

READING MATH

1 Focus

Ask:
Have you ever asked your parents for permission to do something and tried to influence the way in which they answered?

Ask volunteers to describe some of the methods they use to influence their parents' answers.

2 Teach

Biased Questions Have the class discuss why the two questions about sales tax on Internet purchases elicited different responses. Point out that Question 2 tells respondents that the sales tax would have to be paid if purchases were made in a local store. Explain that respondents are more likely to feel that a sales tax on Internet purchases should be required if they realize they pay a sales tax when they buy the same item at a store.

Have the class as a whole work on Reading to Learn 1–3. Ask volunteers to explain why a question is likely or unlikely to bias the results.

ELL English Language Learners may benefit from working in small groups. Have one member of the group translate the questions into his or her native language. Have the other members of the group discuss the questions in their native language and then give the answers in English.

3 Assess

Ask students to summarize what they have learned about asking biased survey questions.

Reading Math Survey Questions **649**

12-2 Counting Outcomes

1 Focus

Standards Alignment

Before Lesson 12-2
Represent all possible outcomes for compound events in an organized way from ⟶ Standard 6SDAP3.1

Lesson 12-2
Use fundamental counting principles to compute combinations and permutations from ⟶ Standard 2A18.0

After Lesson 12-2
Use combinations and permutations to compute probabilities from ⟶ Standard 2A19.0

2 Teach

Scaffolding Questions
Have students read *Get Ready for the Lesson.*
Ask:
- How many different ways can the team end up with a 3–0 record?
  one way
- Why are there three different ways the team could end up with a 2–1 record? They could win, win, lose; win, lose, win; or lose, win, win.
- College football teams can now play overtime to break a tie score. How many different ways could the team's record be determined in three games if ties were possible outcomes? 27

Lesson 12-2 Resources

Main Ideas
- Count outcomes using a tree diagram.
- Count outcomes using the Fundamental Counting Principle.

Preparation for Algebra II Standard 18.0
Students use fundamental counting principles to compute combinations and permutations. (Key)

New Vocabulary
tree diagram
sample space
event
Fundamental Counting Principle
factorial

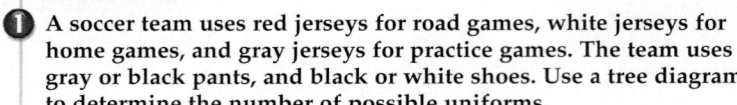

GET READY for the Lesson

The Atlantic Coast Conference (ACC) football championship is decided by the number of conference wins. If there is a tie, the team with more nonconference wins is champion. If Florida State plays 3 nonconference games, a tree diagram can be used to show the different records they could have for those games.

Tree Diagrams One method used for counting the number of possible outcomes is to draw a **tree diagram.** The last column of a tree diagram shows all of the possible outcomes. The list of all possible outcomes is called the **sample space**, while any collection of one or more outcomes in the sample space is called an **event.**

EXAMPLE Tree Diagram

① A soccer team uses red jerseys for road games, white jerseys for home games, and gray jerseys for practice games. The team uses gray or black pants, and black or white shoes. Use a tree diagram to determine the number of possible uniforms.

Jersey	Pants	Shoes	Outcomes
Red	Gray	Black	RGB
		White	RGW
	Black	Black	RBB
		White	RBW
White	Gray	Black	WGB
		White	WGW
	Black	Black	WBB
		White	WBW
Gray	Gray	Black	GGB
		White	GGW
	Black	Black	GBB
		White	GBW

The tree diagram shows that there are 12 possible uniforms.

CHECK Your Progress

1. At the cafeteria, you have several options for a sandwich. You can choose either white (W) or wheat (E) bread. You can choose turkey (T), ham (H), or roast beef (R). You can choose mustard (M) or mayonnaise (A). Use a tree diagram to determine the number of possibilities for your sandwich. **12; See Ch. 12 Answer Appendix for diagram.**

650 Chapter 12 Statistics and Probability

Chapter 12 Resource Masters
Lesson Reading Guide, p. 12 **BL** **OL** **ELL**
Study Guide and Intervention, pp. 13–14
BL **OL** **ELL**
Skills Practice, p. 15 **BL** **OL**
Practice, p. 16 **OL** **AL**
Word Problem Practice, p. 17 **OL** **AL**
Enrichment, p. 18 **OL** **AL**
Quiz 1, p. 51

Transparencies
5-Minute Check Transparency 12-2
Additional Print Resources
Noteables™ Interactive Study Notebook with Foldables™

Technology
ca.algebra1.com
Interactive Classroom CD-ROM
AssignmentWorks CD-ROM
Graphing Calculator Easy Files

The Fundamental Counting Principle The number of possible uniforms in Example 1 can also be found by multiplying the number of choices for each item. If the team can choose from 3 different colored jerseys, 2 different colored pants, and 2 different colored pairs of shoes, there are 3 · 2 · 2, or 12, possible uniforms. This example illustrates the **Fundamental Counting Principle**.

Study Tip

Fundamental Counting Principle
This rule for counting outcomes can be extended to any number of events.

KEY CONCEPT   *Fundamental Counting Principle*

If an event *M* can occur in *m* ways and is followed by an event *N* that can occur in *n* ways, then the event *M* followed by event *N* can occur in *m* · *n* ways.

EXAMPLE   Fundamental Counting Principle

2 The Uptown Deli offers a lunch special in which you can choose from 10 different sandwiches, 12 different side dishes, and 7 different beverages. How many different lunch specials can you order?

Multiply to find the number of lunch specials.

sandwich choices		side dish choices		beverage choices		number of specials
10	·	12	·	7	=	840

CHECK Your Progress

2. When ordering a certain car, there are 7 colors for the exterior, 8 colors for the interior, and 4 choices of interior fabric. How many different possibilities are there for color and fabric when ordering this car?
7 · 8 · 4 or 224 possibilities

EXAMPLE   Counting Arrangements

3 Mackenzie is setting up a display of the ten most popular video games from the previous week. If she places the games side-by-side on a shelf, in how many different ways can she arrange them?

Multiply the number of choices for each position.

• Mackenzie has ten games from which to choose for the first position.

• After choosing a game for the first position, there are nine games left from which to choose for the second position.

• There are now eight choices for the third position.

• This process continues until all positions have been filled.

The number of arrangements is

$n = 10 \cdot 9 \cdot 8 \cdot 7 \cdot 6 \cdot 5 \cdot 4 \cdot 3 \cdot 2 \cdot 1$ or 3,628,800.

There are 3,628,800 different ways to arrange the video games.

CHECK Your Progress

3. Student Council has a president, vice-president, treasurer, secretary, and two representatives from each of the four grades. For the school assembly they were all required to sit in a row up on the stage. In how many different ways can they arrange themselves? 12! or 479,001,600

 Extra Examples at ca.algebra1.com

Lesson 12-2 Counting Outcomes   **651**

Tree Diagrams
Example 1 shows how to use a tree diagram to count possible outcomes.

 Formative Assessment

Use the Check Your Progress exercises after each example to determine students' understanding of concepts.

ADDITIONAL EXAMPLE

1 At football games, a student concession stand sells sandwiches on either wheat or rye bread. The sandwiches come with salami, turkey, or ham, and either chips, a brownie, or fruit. Use a tree diagram to determine the number of possible sandwich combinations. 18 possible combinations

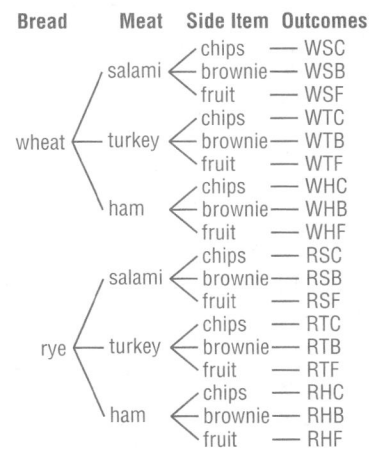

Additional Examples also in:

• Noteables™ Interactive Study Notebook with Foldables™

• Interactive Classroom PowerPoint® Presentations

The Fundamental Counting Principle

Example 2 shows how to use the Fundamental Counting Principle to count possible outcomes. **Example 3** shows how to count arrangements. **Example 4** shows how to count the number of ways a group of items can be arranged. **Example 5** shows how to use factorials to solve a real-world problem.

Focus on Mathematical Content

Fundamental Counting Principle You can use the Fundamental Counting Principle to count the number of possible outcomes in a sample space. The Fundamental Counting Principle states that if an event can happen *m* number of ways, and is followed by another event that can happen in *n* ways, then the number of ways in which both can happen is *mn*.

2 The Best Deal computer company sells custom-made personal computers. Customers have a choice of 11 different hard drives, 6 different keyboards, 4 different mice, and 4 different monitors. How many different computers can a customer order? 11 · 6 · 4 · 4 = 1056 different custom computers

3 There are 8 students in the Algebra Club at Central High School. The students want to stand in a line for their yearbook picture. In how many different ways can the 8 students stand for their picture? 8 · 7 · 6 · 5 · 4 · 3 · 2 · 1 = 40,320 ways they could stand

4 Find the value of each expression.

a. 9! = 9 · 8 · 7 · 6 · 5 · 4 · 3 · 2 · 1 = 362,880

b. 12! = 12 · 11 · 10 · 9 · 8 · 7 · 6 · 5 · 4 · 3 · 2 · 1 = 479,001,600

5 **OUTDOORS** Jill and Miranda are going to a national park for their vacation. Near the campground where they are staying, there are 8 hiking trails.

a. How many different ways can they hike all the trails if they hike each trail only once? 40,320 ways

b. If they only have time to hike 5 of the trails, in how many ways can they do this? 6720 ways

Preventing Errors

Explain to students that in Part b of Example 5, even though Zach and Kurt only ride 8 of the roller coasters, there are still 12 to choose from when they ride the first one, 11 for the second one, 10 for the third one, and so on.

Study Tip

Technology
You can use a TI 83/84 Plus graphing calculator to find 10! by pushing 10 [MATH], scroll to PRB, 4 [ENTER].

The expression $n = 10 \cdot 9 \cdot 8 \cdot 7 \cdot 6 \cdot 5 \cdot 4 \cdot 3 \cdot 2 \cdot 1$ used in Example 3 can be written as 10! using a **factorial**.

KEY CONCEPT	*Fundamental Counting Principle*

Words The expression $n!$, read n factorial, where n is greater than zero, is the product of all positive integers beginning with n and counting backward to 1.

Symbols $n! = n \cdot (n - 1) \cdot (n - 2) \cdot \ldots \cdot 3 \cdot 2 \cdot 1$

Example $5! = 5 \cdot 4 \cdot 3 \cdot 2 \cdot 1$ or 120

By definition, $0! = 1$.

EXAMPLE Factorial

4 Find the value of each expression.

a. **6!**

$6! = 6 \cdot 5 \cdot 4 \cdot 3 \cdot 2 \cdot 1$
$= 720$

b. **10!**

$10! = 10 \cdot 9 \cdot 8 \cdot 7 \cdot 6 \cdot 5 \cdot 4 \cdot 3 \cdot 2 \cdot 1$
$= 3,628,800$

✓ **CHECK Your Progress**

4A. 5! **120**

4B. 8! **40,320**

Real-World Link
In 2005, there were 658 roller coasters in the United States.

Type	Number
Wood	121
Steel	537
Inverted	45
Stand Up	9
Suspended	9
Bobsled	4

Source: Roller Coaster Database

EXAMPLE Use Factorials to Solve a Problem

5 **ROLLER COASTERS** Zach and Kurt are going to an amusement park. They cannot decide in which order to ride the 12 roller coasters in the park.

a. In how many different orders can they ride all of the roller coasters if they ride each once?

Use a factorial.

$12! = 12 \cdot 11 \cdot 10 \cdot 9 \cdot 8 \cdot 7 \cdot 6 \cdot 5 \cdot 4 \cdot 3 \cdot 2 \cdot 1$ Definition of factorial
$= 479,001,600$ Simplify.

b. If they only have time to ride 8 of the roller coasters, how many ways can they do this?

Use the Fundamental Counting Principle to count the sample space.

$s = 12 \cdot 11 \cdot 10 \cdot 9 \cdot 8 \cdot 7 \cdot 6 \cdot 5$ Fundamental Counting Principle
$= 19,958,400$ Simplify.

✓ **CHECK Your Progress**

José needs to speak with six college representatives.

5A. In how many different orders can he speak to these people if he only speaks to each person once? **720**

5B. He decides that he will not have time to talk to two of the people. In how many ways can he speak to the others? **360**

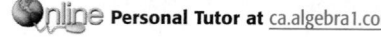
Personal Tutor at ca.algebra1.com

Differentiated Instruction

Visual/Spatial Learners Have student use construction paper to model sandwich ingredients, such as different types of bread, meat, and vegetables. Have students first calculate how many different sandwiches they could make. Have them make the sandwiches to confirm their calculations.

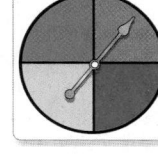
Examples 1–3
(pp. 650–651)

For Exercises 1–3, suppose the spinner at the right is spun three times. **1. See Ch. 12 Answer Appendix.**

1. Draw a tree diagram to show the sample space.
2. How many outcomes involve both green and blue? **18**
3. How many outcomes are possible? **64**

Example 4
(p. 652)

4. Find the value of 8!. **40,320**

Example 5
(p. 652)

5. **SCHOOL** In a science class, each student must choose a lab project from a list of 15, write a paper on one of 6 topics, and give a presentation about one of 8 subjects. How many ways can students choose to do their assignments? **720**

Exercises

HOMEWORK HELP	
For Exercises	**See Examples**
6, 7, 16	1
8–10	2, 3
11–14	4
15, 17–20	5

Exercise Levels
A: 6–20
C: 21–23

Draw a tree diagram to show the sample space for each event. Determine the number of possible outcomes. **6–7. See Ch. 12 Answer Appendix for diagrams.**

6. earning an A, B, or C in English, math, and science classes **27**
7. buying a computer with a choice of a CD-ROM, a CD recorder, or a DVD drive, one of 2 monitors, and either a printer or a scanner **12**

For Exercises 8–10, determine the possible number of outcomes.

8. Three dice, one red, one white, and one blue are rolled. How many outcomes are possible? **216**
9. How many outfits are possible if you choose one each of 5 shirts, 3 pairs of pants, 3 pairs of shoes, and 4 jackets? **180**
10. **TRAVEL** Suppose four different airlines fly from Seattle to Denver. Those same four airlines and two others fly from Denver to St. Louis. In how many ways can a traveler use these airlines to book a flight from Seattle to St. Louis? **24**

Find the value of each expression.

13. 39,916,800
14. 6,227,020,800

11. 4! **24**	**12.** 7! **5,040**	**13.** 11!	**14.** 13!

COMMUNICATIONS For Exercises 15 and 16, use the following information.
A new 3-digit area code is needed to accommodate new telephone numbers.

15. If the first digit must be odd, the second digit must be a 0 or a 1, and the third digit can be anything, how many area codes are possible? **100**
16. Draw a tree diagram to show the different area codes using 4 or 5 for the first digit, 0 or 1 for the second digit, and 7, 8, or 9 for the third digit. **See Ch. 12 Answer Appendix.**

SOCCER For Exercises 17–19, use the following information.
The Columbus Crew is playing FC Dallas in a best three out of five championship soccer series.

17. What are the possible outcomes of the series? **See Ch. 12 Answer Appendix.**
18. How many outcomes require only four games be played to determine the champion? **6**
19. How many ways can FC Dallas win the championship? **10**

 EXTRA PRACTICE
See page 742, 755.
Math Online
Self-Check Quiz at
ca.algebra1.com

20. **GAMES** William has been dealt seven different cards in a game he is playing. How many different ways are there for him to play his cards if he is required to play one card at a time? **5040**

3 Practice

 Formative Assessment

Use Exercises 1–5 to check for understanding.

Use the chart on this page to customize assignments for your students.

Odd/Even Assignments
Exercises 6–20 are structured so that students practice the same concepts whether they are assigned odd or even problems.

Real-World Connections
For Exercise 23, have students demonstrate the number of possible outcomes for the school team or a favorite sports team, depending on how many home games the respective teams will play. Have students research their favorite teams and then present their calculations to the class.

4 Assess

Name the Math Have students describe how to use a tree diagram or the Fundamental Counting Principle to find the possible combinations of classes they could take if they have a choice of 2 science classes, 2 math classes, 3 English classes, and 6 electives.

Formative Assessment

Check for student understanding of concepts in Lessons 12-1 and 12-2.

CRM Quiz 1, p. 51

DIFFERENTIATED HOMEWORK OPTIONS			
Level	**Assignment**	**Two-Day Option**	
BL Basic	6–21, 23–39	7–19 odd, 24, 25	6–20 even, 21, 23, 26–39
OL Core	7–19 odd, 21, 23–39	6–20, 24, 25	21, 23, 26–39
AL Advanced /Pre-AP	21–33, (optional: 34–39)		

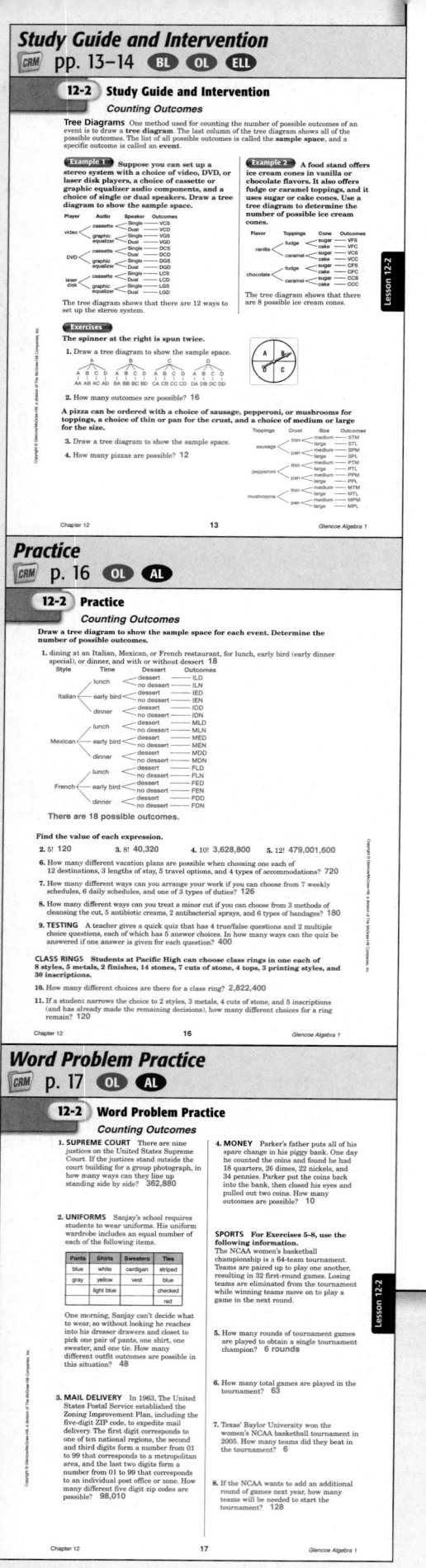

12-2 Study Guide and Intervention
Counting Outcomes

Tree Diagrams One method used for counting the number of possible outcomes of an event is to draw a **tree diagram**. The last column of the tree diagram shows all of the possible outcomes. The list of all possible outcomes is called the **sample space**, and a specific outcome is called an **event**.

Example 1 Suppose you can set up a stereo system with a choice of video, DVD, or laser disk players, a choice of cassette or graphic equalizer audio components, and a choice of single or dual speakers. Draw a tree diagram to show the sample space.

The tree diagram shows that there are 12 ways to set up the stereo system.

Example 2 A food stand offers ice cream cones in vanilla or chocolate flavors. It also offers fudge or caramel toppings, and it uses sugar or cake cones. Use a tree diagram to determine the number of possible ice cream cones.

The tree diagram shows that there are 8 possible ice cream cones.

Exercises

The spinner at the right is spun twice.

1. Draw a tree diagram to show the sample space.

2. How many outcomes are possible? **16**

A pizza can be ordered with a choice of sausage, pepperoni, or mushrooms for toppings, a choice of thin or pan for the crust, and a choice of medium or large for the size.

3. Draw a tree diagram to show the sample space.

4. How many pizzas are possible? **12**

Chapter 12   13   Glencoe Algebra 1

Practice
CRM p. 16 OL AL

12-2 Practice
Counting Outcomes

Draw a tree diagram to show the sample space for each event. Determine the number of possible outcomes.

1. dining at an Italian, Mexican, or French restaurant, for lunch, early bird (early dinner special), or dinner, with or without dessert **18**

There are 18 possible outcomes.

Find the value of each expression.

2. 5! **120**
3. 8! **40,320**
4. 10! **3,628,800**
5. 12! **479,001,600**

6. How many different vacation plans are possible when choosing one each of 12 destinations, 3 lengths of stay, 5 travel options, and 4 types of accommodations? **720**

7. How many different ways can you arrange your work if you can choose from 7 weekly schedules, 6 daily schedules, and one of 3 types of duties? **126**

8. How many different ways can you treat a minor cut if you can choose from 3 methods of cleansing the cut, 5 antibiotic creams, 2 antibacterial sprays, and 6 types of bandages? **180**

9. TESTING A teacher gives a quick quiz that has 4 true/false questions and 2 multiple choice questions, each of which has 5 answer choices. In how many ways can the quiz be answered if one answer is given for each question? **400**

CLASS RINGS Students at Pacific High can choose class rings in one each of 8 styles, 5 metals, 2 finishes, 14 stones, 7 cuts of stone, 4 tops, 3 printing styles, and 30 inscriptions.

10. How many different choices are there for a class ring? **2,822,400**

11. If a student narrows the choice to 2 styles, 3 metals, 4 cuts of stone, and 5 inscriptions (and has already made the remaining decisions), how many different choices for a ring remain? **120**

Chapter 12   16   Glencoe Algebra 1

Word Problem Practice
CRM p. 17 OL AL

12-2 Word Problem Practice
Counting Outcomes

1. SUPREME COURT There are nine justices on the United States Supreme Court. If the justices stand outside the court building for a group photograph, in how many ways can they line up standing side by side? **362,880**

2. UNIFORMS Sanjay's school requires students to wear uniforms. His uniform wardrobe includes an equal number of each of the following items.

Pants	Shirts	Sweaters	Ties
blue	white	cardigan	striped
gray	yellow	vest	blue
	light blue		checked
			red

One morning, Sanjay can't decide what to wear, so without looking he reaches into his dresser drawers and closet to pick one pair of pants, one shirt, one sweater, and one tie. How many different outfit outcomes are possible in this situation? **48**

3. MAIL DELIVERY In 1963, The United States Postal Service established the Zoning Improvement Plan, including the five-digit ZIP code, to expedite mail delivery. The first digit corresponds to one of ten national regions, the second and third digits form a number from 01 to 99 that corresponds to a metropolitan area, and the last two digits form a number from 01 to 99 that corresponds to an individual post office or zone. How many different five digit zip codes are possible? **98,010**

4. MONEY Parker's father puts all of his spare change in his piggy bank. One day he counted the coins and found he had 18 quarters, 26 dimes, 22 nickels, and 34 pennies. Parker put the coins back into the bank, then closed his eyes and pulled out two coins. How many outcomes are possible? **10**

SPORTS For Exercises 5–8, use the following information.
The NCAA women's basketball championship is a 64-team tournament. Teams are paired up to play one another, resulting in 32 first-round games. Losing teams are eliminated from the tournament while winning teams move on to play a game in the next round.

5. How many rounds of tournament games are played to obtain a single tournament champion? **6 rounds**

6. How many total games are played in the tournament? **63**

7. Texas' Baylor University won the women's NCAA basketball tournament in 2005. How many times did they beat in the tournament? **6**

8. If the NCAA wants to add an additional round of games next year, how many teams will be needed to start the tournament? **128**

Chapter 12   17   Glencoe Algebra 1

H.O.T. Problems

23. Sample answer: You can make a chart showing all possible outcomes to help determine a football team's record. You can use a tree diagram or calculations to show 16 possible outcomes.

21. **OPEN ENDED** Give a real-world example of an event that has 7 · 6 or 42 outcomes. **Sample answer: choosing 2 books in order from 7 books on a shelf**

22. **CHALLENGE** To get to and from school, Tucker can walk, ride his bike, or get a ride with a friend. Suppose that one week he walked 60% of the time, rode his bike 20% of the time, and rode with his friend 20% of the time, not necessarily in that order. How many outcomes represent this situation? Assume that he returns home the same way that he went to school. **20**

23. *Writing in Math* Refer to the information on page 650 to explain how possible win/loss records can be determined in football. Demonstrate how to find the number of possible outcomes for a team's four home games.

STANDARDIZED TEST PRACTICE

24. A car manufacturer offers a sports car in 4 different models with 6 different option packages. Each model is available in 12 different colors. How many different possibilities are available for this car? **D**

   A 48   B 54   C 76   D 288

25. **REVIEW** Ko collects soup can labels to raise money for his school. He receives $4 for every 75 labels that he collects. If Ko wants to raise $96, how many labels does he need? **G**

   F 7200   G 1800   H 900   J 24

Spiral Review

PRINTING For Exercises 26–28, use the following information.
To determine the quality of calendars printed at a local shop, the last 10 calendars printed each day are examined. (Lesson 12-1)

26. Identify the sample. **10 calendars**

27. Suggest a population from which it was selected. **all calendars printed in a day**

28. State whether it is *unbiased* (random) or *biased*. If unbiased, classify the sample as *simple*, *stratified*, or *systematic*. If biased, classify as *convenience* or *voluntary response*. **biased; convenience**

Solve each equation. (Lesson 11-9)

29. $\dfrac{-4}{a+1} + \dfrac{3}{a} = 1$ **−3, 1**

30. $\dfrac{3}{x} + \dfrac{4x}{x-3} = 4$ **$3\frac{3}{5}$**

31. $\dfrac{d+3}{d+5} + \dfrac{2}{d-9} = \dfrac{5}{2d+10}$ **1, 5.5**

Find each sum. (Lesson 11-7)

32. $\dfrac{2x+1}{3x-1} + \dfrac{x+4}{x-2}$ **$\dfrac{5x^2+8x-6}{(3x-1)(x-2)}$**

33. $\dfrac{4n}{2n+6} + \dfrac{3}{n+3}$ **$\dfrac{2n+3}{n+3}$**

GET READY for the Next Lesson

PREREQUISITE SKILL Colored marbles are placed in a bag and selected at random. There are 12 yellow, 15 red, 11 green, 16 blue, and 14 black marbles in the bag. Find each probability.

34. $P(\text{green})$ **$\dfrac{11}{68}$**

35. $P(\text{black})$ **$\dfrac{7}{34}$**

36. $P(\text{yellow or blue})$ **$\dfrac{7}{17}$**

37. $P(\text{green or red})$ **$\dfrac{13}{34}$**

38. $P(\text{purple})$ **0**

39. $P(\text{yellow or red or green})$ **$\dfrac{19}{34}$**

654 Chapter 12 Statistics and Probability

Enrichment
CRM p. 18 OL AL

12-2 Enrichment

Pascal's Triangle

Pascal's Triangle is a pattern of numbers used at many levels of mathematics. It is named for Blaise Pascal, a seventeenth-century French mathematician who discovered several applications of the pattern. However, records of the triangle have been traced as far back as twelfth-century China and Persia. In the year 1303, the Chinese mathematician Zhu-Shijié wrote *The Precious Mirror of the Four Elements*, in which he described how the triangle could be used to solve polynomial equations. The figure at the right is adapted from the original Chinese manuscript. In the figure, some circles are empty while others contain Chinese symbols.

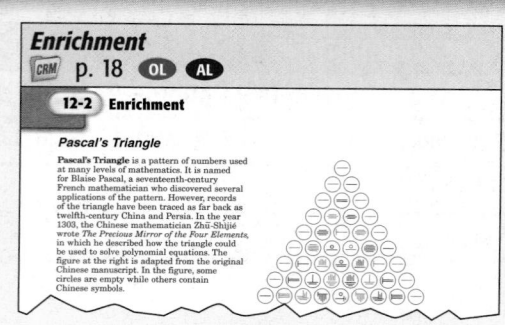

BL = Below Grade Level
OL = On Grade Level
AL = Above Grade Level
ELL = English Language Learner

Additional pages not shown:

CRM *Lesson Reading Guide*, p. 12 BL OL ELL

CRM *Skills Practice*, p. 15 BL OL

Main Ideas

- Determine probabilities uing permutations.
- Determine probabilities using combinations.

 Preparation for Probability and Statistics

Standard 1.0 Students know the definition of the notion of *independent events* and can use the rules for addition, multiplication, and complementation to solve for probabilities of particular events in finite sample spaces. (Key)

New Vocabulary

permutation

combination

Study Tip

Common Misconception

When arranging two objects *A* and *B* using a permutation, the arrangement *AB* is different from the arrangement *BA*.

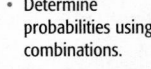 **GET READY** for the Lesson

The United States Senate forms various committees by selecting senators from both political parties. The Senate Health, Education, Labor, and Pensions Committee of the 109th Congress was made up of 10 Republican senators and 9 Democratic senators. How many different ways could the committee have been selected? Assume that the members of the committee were selected in no particular order. This is an example of a combination.

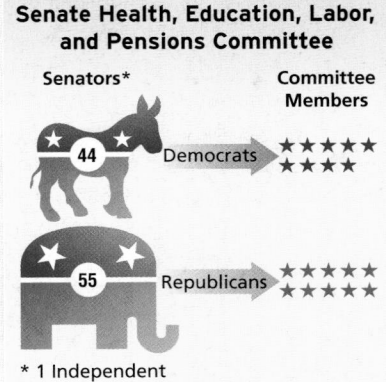

Senate Health, Education, Labor, and Pensions Committee

Senators*   Committee Members

44   Democrats   ★★★★★ ★★★★

55   Republicans   ★★★★★ ★★★★★

* 1 Independent

Permutations An arrangement or listing in which order or placement is important is called a **permutation**.

EXAMPLE Tree Diagram Permutation

1 **EMPLOYMENT** The manager of a coffee shop needs to hire two employees, one to work at the counter and one to work at the drive-through window. Katie, Bob, and Alicia all applied for the jobs. How many possible ways can the manager place them?

Use a tree diagram to show the possible arrangements.

Counter	Drive-Through	Outcomes
Katie (K)	Bob	KB
	Alicia	KA
Bob (B)	Katie	BK
	Alicia	BA
Alicia (A)	Katie	AK
	Bob	AB

There are 6 different ways for the 3 applicants to hold the 2 positions.

✓ CHECK Your Progress

1. **MUSIC** At Rock City Music Store, customers can purchase CDs, cassettes, and downloads. They can choose from rock, jazz, hip-hop, and gospel. How many possible ways are there for a customer to buy music? **12 ways; See Ch.12 Answer Appendix for tree diagram.**

Lesson 12-3 Permutations and Combinations **655**

 Standards Alignment

Before Lesson 12-3
Represent all possible outcomes for compound events in an organized list from ⚷ Standard 6SDAP3.1

Lesson 12-3
Find probabilities of particular events in finite sample spaces from ⚷ Standard PS1.0

After Lesson 12-3
Use fundamental counting principles to compute combinations and permutations. Use combinations and permutations to compute probabilities from ⚷ Standards 2A18.0 and 2A19.0

2 **Teach**

Scaffolding Questions
Have students read *Get Ready for the Lesson.*

Ask:

- Senators Kennedy, Jeffords, and Frist are three members of the committee. Does the order in which they were selected matter? Explain. No; no matter how the three senators were selected, all three are still on the committee.

(continued on the next page)

Lesson 12-3 Resources

Chapter 12 Resource Masters
Lesson Reading Guide, p. 19 **BL** **OL** **ELL**
Study Guide and Intervention, pp. 20–21
BL **OL** **ELL**
Skills Practice, p. 22 **BL** **OL**
Practice, p. 23 **OL** **AL**
Word Problem Practice, p. 24 **OL** **AL**
Enrichment, p. 25 **OL** **AL**
Quiz 2, p. 51

Transparencies
5-Minute Check Transparency 12-3
Additional Print Resources
Noteables™ Interactive Study Notebook with Foldables™

Technology
ca.algebra1.com
Interactive Classroom CD-ROM
AssignmentWorks CD-ROM
Graphing Calculator Easy Files

- Suppose there were more Democrats in the Senate than Republicans. Would the number of ways in which the committee members could be selected be affected? Explain. No; there would still be 19 members, which does not change the ways in which they could be selected.

Permutations

Example 1 shows how to use a tree diagram to find a permutation.
Example 2 shows how to use a permutation to find the probability of an event occurring.

 Formative Assessment

Use the Check Your Progress exercises after each example to determine students' understanding of concepts.

In Example 1, the positions are in a specific order, so each arrangement is unique. The symbol $_3P_2$ denotes the number of permutations when arranging 3 applicants in 2 positions. You can also use the Fundamental Counting Principle to determine the number of permutations.

$$\begin{array}{ccc} & \text{ways to choose} & \text{ways to choose} \\ & \text{first employee} & \text{second employee} \\ _3P_2 = & 3 & \cdot \quad 2 \end{array}$$

$$= 3 \cdot 2 \cdot \frac{1}{1} \qquad \frac{1}{1} = 1$$

$$= \frac{3 \cdot 2 \cdot 1}{2 \cdot 1} \qquad \text{Multiply.}$$

$$= \frac{3!}{2!} \qquad 3 \cdot 2 \cdot 1 = 3!, 2 \cdot 1 = 2!$$

In general, $_nP_r$ is used to denote the number of permutations of n objects taken r at a time.

KEY CONCEPT   *Permutation*

Word   The number of permutations of n objects taken r at a time is the quotient of $n!$ and $(n - r)!$.

Symbols $_nP_r = \dfrac{n!}{(n - r)!}$

EXAMPLE   Permutation and Probability

2 A word processing program requires a user to enter a 7-digit registration code made up of the digits 1, 2, 4, 5, 6, 7, and 9. Each number has to be used, and no number can be used more than once.

a. How many different registration codes are possible?

Since the order of the numbers in the code is important, this situation is a permutation of 7 digits taken 7 at a time.

$_nP_r = \dfrac{n!}{(n - r)!}$ Definition of permutation

$_7P_7 = \dfrac{7!}{(7 - 7)!}$ $n = 7, r = 7.$

$_7P_7 = \dfrac{7 \cdot 6 \cdot 5 \cdot 4 \cdot 3 \cdot 2 \cdot 1}{1}$ or 5040   Since $0! = 1$, 5040 codes are possible.

b. What is the probability that the first three digits of the code are even?

Use the Fundamental Counting Principle to determine the number of ways for the first three digits to be even.

- There are three even digits and four odd digits.
- The number of choices for the first three digits, if they are even, is $3 \cdot 2 \cdot 1$.
- The number of choices for the remaining odd digits is $4 \cdot 3 \cdot 2 \cdot 1$.
- The number of favorable outcomes is $3 \cdot 2 \cdot 1 \cdot 4 \cdot 3 \cdot 2 \cdot 1$ or 144.

Focus on Mathematical Content

Permutations A permutation is an arrangement or listing in which order is important. For example, if the arrangement of DVDs on a shelf is alphabetical, then the order in which they are arranged is important and this situation is a permutation. Permutations are expressed as $_nP_r$, where n is the number of items to choose from and r is the number of items to be chosen. To find the number of permutations, use the formula $_nP_r = \dfrac{n!}{(n - r)!}$.

$$P(\text{first 3 digits even}) = \frac{144}{5040} \quad \leftarrow \text{number of favorable outcomes}$$
$$\leftarrow \text{number of possible outcomes}$$

$$= \frac{1}{35} \qquad \text{Simplify.}$$

The probability that the first three digits are even is $\frac{1}{35}$ or about 3%.

✓ CHECK Your Progress

BICYCLES A combination bike lock requires a three-digit code made up of the digits 0, 1, 2, 3, 4, 5, 6, 7, 8, and 9. No number can be used more than once.

2A. How many different combinations are possible? **720**

2B. What is the probability that all of the digits are odd numbers? $\frac{1}{12}$

Combinations An arrangement or listing in which order is not important is called a **combination**. For example, if you are choosing 2 salad ingredients from a list of 10, the order in which you choose the ingredients does not matter.

KEY CONCEPT   *Combination*

Words   The number of combinations of n objects taken r at a time is the quotient of $n!$ and $(n - r)!r!$.

Symbols $_nC_r = \dfrac{n!}{(n - r)!r!}$

EXAMPLE   Combinations and Probability

Study Tip

Common Misconception

Not all everyday uses of the word *combination* are descriptions of mathematical combinations. For example, the combination to a lock is described by a permutation.

3 **SCHOOL** A group of 7 seniors, 5 juniors, and 4 sophomores have volunteered to be peer tutors. Mr. DeLuca needs to choose 12 students out of the group.

a. How many ways can the 12 students be chosen?

The order in which the students are chosen does not matter, so we must find the number of combinations of 16 students taken 12 at a time.

$$_nC_r = \frac{n!}{(n - r)!r!} \qquad \text{Definition of combination}$$

$$_{16}C_{12} = \frac{16!}{(16 - 12)!12!} \qquad n = 16, r = 12$$

$$= \frac{16!}{4!12!} \qquad 16 - 12 = 4$$

$$= \frac{16 \cdot 15 \cdot 14 \cdot 13 \cdot \overset{1}{12!}}{4! \cdot \underset{1}{12!}} \qquad \text{Divided by the GCF, 12!.}$$

$$= \frac{43,680}{24} \text{ or } 1820 \qquad \text{Simplify.}$$

There are 1820 ways to choose 12 students out of 16.

(continued on the next page)

 Math Online Extra Examples at ca.algebra1.com

Point out that in Example 2, the numbers 0, 3, and 8 are not possible choices for the code.

Combinations

Example 3 shows how to use combinations to solve a real-world problem.

ADDITIONAL EXAMPLE

3 **MONEY** Diane has a bag full of coins. There are 10 pennies, 6 nickels, 4 dimes, and 2 quarters in the bag.

a. How many ways can Diane pull four coins out of the bag? **7315**

b. What is the probability that she will pull two pennies and two nickels out of the bag? $\frac{135}{1463}$ or about 9%

 **Tips for New Teachers**   **Reading**

Combinations of n objects taken r at a time can also be written as $C(n, r)$.

Focus on Mathematical Content

Combinations A combination is an arrangement or listing in which order is not important. For example, when choosing the decorations for a school party, the order in which the decorations are chosen does not matter, so this situation is a combination. Combinations are expressed as $_nC_r$, where n is the number of items to choose from and r is the number of items to be chosen. To find the number of combinations, use the formula $_nC_r = \dfrac{n!}{(n-r)!r!}$.

Intervention

Common Misconceptions After students learn how to calculate combinations in Example 3, discuss the difference between combinations and permutations. In Example 3, the order in which the students are chosen does not matter because the positions for which they are being chosen are the same. All 12 students are going to be peer tutors with the same duties. However, if the teacher were choosing 12 out of 16 students to be president, vice president, secretary, treasurer, and so forth, of the student council, then the order in which they are chosen would matter.

Preventing Errors

Caution students that many word problems are multi-part even though they are not presented in parts. Help students to see that they cannot determine the probability until they first know the number of ways in which the teacher can choose 12 students. To calculate this number, tell students that they do not need to know that there are 7 seniors, 5 juniors, and 4 sophomores in the group. All they need to know is that 12 students are to be chosen out of a group of 16.

![Tips for New Teachers]

Teaching Techniques

The details in Example 3 may be confusing for some students. Consider representing the problem information on an overhead transparency. Assign three different colors to represent seniors, juniors, and sophomores and draw groups of colored dots to represent the 16 students. For the second part of the problem, show students how to focus on one group of students at a time by examining only one color of dot.

3 Practice

✓ Formative Assessment

Use Exercises 1–11 to check for understanding.

Use the chart at the bottom of the next page to customize assignments for your students.

---

b. If the students are chosen randomly, what is the probability that 4 seniors, 4 juniors, and 4 sophomores will be selected?

To find the probability, there are three questions to consider.

- How many ways can 4 seniors be chosen from 7?
- How many ways can 4 juniors be chosen from 5?
- How many ways can 4 sophomores be chosen from 4?

Using the Fundamental Counting Principle, the number of combinations with 4 students from each grade is the product of the three combinations.

$$\text{ways to choose 4 seniors out of 7} \quad \text{ways to choose 4 juniors out of 5} \quad \text{ways to choose 4 sophomores out of 4}$$
$$(_7C_4) \qquad \cdot \qquad (_5C_4) \qquad \cdot \qquad (_4C_4)$$

$(_7C_4)(_5C_4)(_4C_4) = \dfrac{7!}{(7-4)!4!} \cdot \dfrac{5!}{(5-4)!4!} \cdot \dfrac{4!}{(4-4)!4!}$ Definition of combination

$\qquad\qquad = \dfrac{7!}{3!4!} \cdot \dfrac{5!}{1!4!} \cdot \dfrac{4!}{0!4!}$ Simplify.

$\qquad\qquad = \dfrac{7 \cdot 6 \cdot 5}{3!} \cdot \dfrac{5}{1}$ Divide by the GCF, 4!.

$\qquad\qquad = 175$ Simplify.

Finally, there are 175 ways to choose this particular combination out of 1820 possible combinations.

$P(\text{4 seniors, 4 juniors, 4 sophomores}) = \dfrac{175}{1820}$ ← number of favorable outcomes / ← number of possible outcomes

$\qquad\qquad\qquad\qquad\qquad = \dfrac{5}{52}$ Simplify.

The probability that Mr. DeLuca will randomly select 4 seniors, 4 juniors, and 4 sophomores is $\dfrac{5}{52}$ or about 10%.

✓CHECK Your Progress

PARADE A group of 7 Army veterans, 5 Air Force veterans, 6 Navy veterans, and 4 Marine veterans have volunteered to march in the Memorial Day Parade.

3A. In how many ways can 12 veterans be chosen to march? **646,646**

3B. If the 12 veterans are chosen randomly, what is the probability that 3 veterans from each branch of the military will be selected? $\dfrac{14,000}{323,323}$

⦿nline **Personal Tutor at** ca.algebra1.com

✓CHECK Your Understanding

Example 1, 3
(pp. 655, 657)

Determine whether each situation involves a *permutation* or *combination*. Explain your reasoning. **1. Combination; order is not important.**

1. choosing 6 books from a selection of 12 for summer reading
2. choosing digits for a personal identification number
   Permutation; order is important.

Example 2
(pp. 656–657)

Evaluate each expression.

3. $_8P_5$ **6720**

4. $(_{10}P_5)(_3P_2)$ **181,440**

For Exercises 5–7, use the following information.
The digits 0 through 9 are written on index cards. Three of the cards are randomly selected to form a three-digit code.

5. Permutation; order is important.

5. Does this situation represent a permutation or a combination? Explain.
6. How many different codes are possible? **720**
7. What is the probability that all three digits will be odd? $\frac{1}{12}$

Example 3
(pp. 657–658)

8. A diner offers a choice of two side items from the list with each entrée. How many ways can two items be selected? **28**

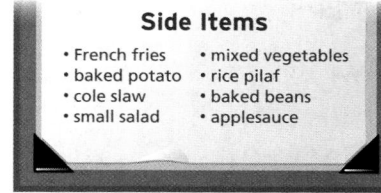

Side Items
• French fries   • mixed vegetables
• baked potato   • rice pilaf
• cole slaw   • baked beans
• small salad   • applesauce

9. PROBABILITY 15 marbles out of 20 must be randomly selected. There are 7 red marbles, 8 purple marbles, and 5 green marbles from which to choose. What is the probability that 5 of each color is selected? $\frac{49}{646}$

Evaluate each expression.

10. $_7C_5$ **21**

11. $(_6C_2)(_4C_3)$ **60**

Exercises

HOMEWORK HELP

For Exercises	See Examples
12–19, 32, 36, 38, 43	1, 3
20–31, 33–35, 37, 39–40, 44–45	2, 3

Exercise Levels
A: 12–45
B: 46–50
C: 51–56

16. Permutation; order is important.
18. Combination; order is not important.
32. Combination; order is not important.

Determine whether each situation involves a *permutation* or *combination*. Explain your reasoning.

12. team captains for the soccer team Combination; order is not important.
13. three mannequins in a display window Permutation; order is important.
14. a hand of 10 cards from a selection of 52 Combination; order is not important.
15. the batting order of the New York Yankees Permutation; order is important.
16. first-place and runner-up winners for the table tennis tournament
17. a selection of 5 DVDs from a group of eight Combination; order is not important.
18. selection of 2 candy bars from six equally-sized bars
19. the selection of 2 trombones, 3 clarinets, and 2 trumpets for a jazz combo
Combination; order is not important.

Evaluate each expression.

20. $_{12}P_3$ **1320**   **21.** $_4P_1$ **4**   **22.** $_6C_6$ **1**   **23.** $_7C_3$ **35**
24. $_{15}C_3$ **455**   **25.** $_{20}C_8$ **125,970**   **26.** $_{15}P_3$ **2730**   **27.** $_{16}P_5$ **524,160**
28. $(_7P_7)(_7P_1)$ **35,280**   **29.** $(_{20}P_2)(_{16}P_4)$ **16,598,400**   **30.** $(_3C_2)(_7C_4)$ **105**   **31.** $(_8C_5)(_5P_5)$ **6720**

SCHOOL For Exercises 32–35, use the following information.
Mrs. Moyer's class has to choose 4 out of 12 people for an activity committee.

32. Does the selection involve a permutation or a combination? Explain.
33. How many different groups of students could be selected? **495**
34. Suppose the students are selected for the positions of chairperson, activities planner, activity leader, and treasurer. How many different groups of students could be selected? **11,880**
35. What is the probability that any one of the students is chosen to be the chairperson? $\frac{1}{12}$

Odd/Even Assignments
Exercises 12–40 and 43–45 are structured so that students practice the same concepts whether they are assigned odd or even problems.

DIFFERENTIATED HOMEWORK OPTIONS

Level	Assignment	Two-Day Option	
BL Basic	12–45, 52–54, 57–76	13–45 odd, 58, 59	12–44 even, 52–54, 57, 60–76
OL Core	13–45 odd, 46–54, 57–76	12–45, 58, 59	46–54, 57, 60–76
AL Advanced /Pre-AP	46–70, (optional: 71–76)		

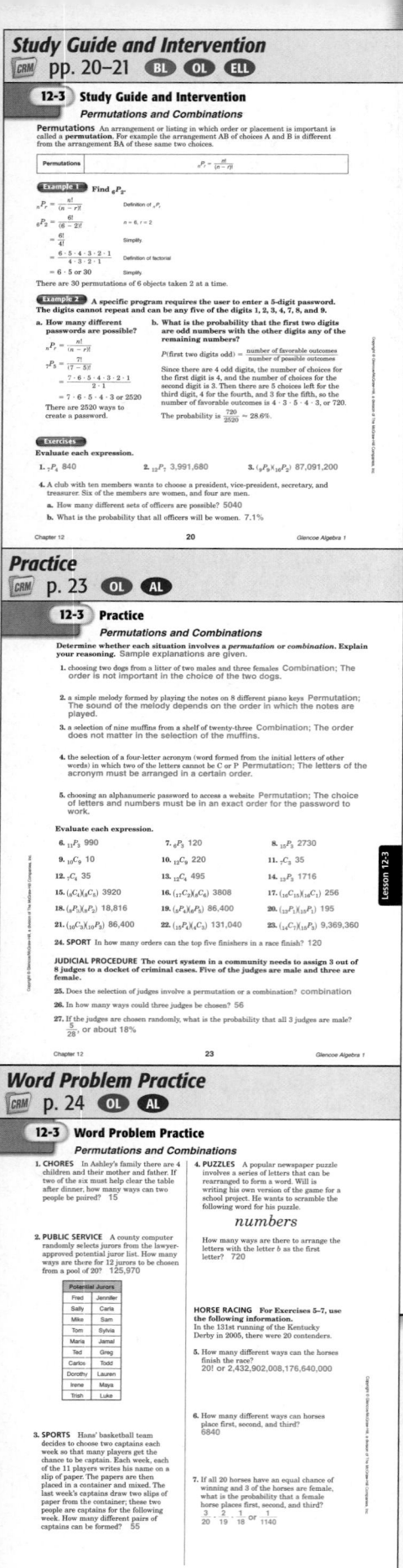

Study Guide and Intervention
CRM pp. 20–21 BL OL ELL

12-3 Study Guide and Intervention
Permutations and Combinations

Permutations An arrangement or listing in which order or placement is important is called a **permutation**. For example the arrangement AB of choices A and B is different from the arrangement BA of these same two choices.

Permutations	$_nP_r = \dfrac{n!}{(n-r)!}$

Example 1 Find $_6P_2$.

$_nP_r = \dfrac{n!}{(n-r)!}$ Definition of $_nP_r$

$_6P_2 = \dfrac{6!}{(6-2)!}$ $n = 6, r = 2$

$= \dfrac{6!}{4!}$ Simplify.

$= \dfrac{6 \cdot 5 \cdot 4 \cdot 3 \cdot 2 \cdot 1}{4 \cdot 3 \cdot 2 \cdot 1}$ Definition of factorial

$= 6 \cdot 5$ or 30 Simplify.

There are 30 permutations of 6 objects taken 2 at a time.

Example 2 A specific program requires the user to enter a 5-digit password. The five digits cannot repeat and can be any five of the digits 1, 2, 3, 4, 7, 8, and 9.

a. How many different passwords are possible?

$_nP_r = \dfrac{n!}{(n-r)!}$

$_7P_5 = \dfrac{7!}{(7-5)!}$

$= \dfrac{7 \cdot 6 \cdot 5 \cdot 4 \cdot 3 \cdot 2 \cdot 1}{2 \cdot 1}$

$= 7 \cdot 6 \cdot 5 \cdot 4 \cdot 3$ or 2520

There are 2520 ways to create a password.

b. What is the probability that the first two digits are odd numbers with the other digits any of the remaining numbers?

$P(\text{first two digits odd}) = \dfrac{\text{number of favorable outcomes}}{\text{number of possible outcomes}}$

Since there are 4 odd digits, the number of choices for the first digit is 4, and the number of choices for the second digit is 3. Then there are 5 choices left for the third digit, 4 for the fourth, and 3 for the fifth, so the number of favorable outcomes is $4 \cdot 3 \cdot 5 \cdot 4 \cdot 3$, or 720.

The probability is $\dfrac{720}{2520} \approx 28.6\%$.

Exercises

Evaluate each expression.

1. $_7P_4$ 840   2. $_{12}P_7$ 3,991,680   3. $(_8P_3)(_{10}P_2)$ 87,091,200

4. A club with ten members wants to choose a president, vice-president, secretary, and treasurer. Six of the members are women, and four are men.

a. How many different sets of officers are possible? 5040

b. What is the probability that all officers will be women. 7.1%

Chapter 12   20   Glencoe Algebra 1

Practice
CRM p. 23 OL AL

12-3 Practice
Permutations and Combinations

Determine whether each situation involves a *permutation* or *combination*. Explain your reasoning. Sample explanations are given.

1. choosing two dogs from a litter of two males and three females Combination; The order is not important in the choice of the two dogs.

2. a simple melody formed by playing the notes on 8 different piano keys Permutation; The sound of the melody depends on the order in which the notes are played.

3. a selection of nine muffins from a shelf of twenty-three Combination; The order does not matter in the selection of the muffins.

4. the selection of a four-letter acronym (word formed from the initial letters of other words) in which two of the letters cannot be C or P Permutation; The letters of the acronym must be arranged in a certain order.

5. choosing an alphanumeric password to access a website Permutation; The choice of letters and numbers must be in an exact order for the password to work.

Evaluate each expression.

6. $_{11}P_3$ 990   7. $_6P_3$ 120   8. $_{15}P_2$ 2730

9. $_{10}C_9$ 10   10. $_{12}C_9$ 220   11. $_7C_3$ 35

12. $_7C_4$ 35   13. $_{12}C_4$ 495   14. $_{13}P_3$ 1716

15. $(_8C_1)(_8C_5)$ 3920   16. $(_{17}C_2)(_9C_6)$ 3808   17. $(_{30}C_{15})(_{16}C_1)$ 256

18. $(_8P_5)(_9P_2)$ 18,816   19. $(_9P_4)(_8P_5)$ 86,400   20. $(_{22}P_7)(_{15}P_1)$ 195

21. $(_{10}C_9)(_{10}P_3)$ 86,400   22. $(_{10}P_4)(_4C_3)$ 131,040   23. $(_{14}C_7)(_{15}P_3)$ 9,369,360

24. **SPORT** In how many orders can the top five finishers in a race finish? 120

JUDICIAL PROCEDURE The court system in a community needs to assign 3 out of 8 judges to a docket of criminal cases. Five of the judges are male and three are female.

25. Does the selection of judges involve a permutation or a combination? combination

26. In how many ways could three judges be chosen? 56

27. If the judges are chosen randomly, what is the probability that all 3 judges are male? $\frac{5}{28}$, or about 18%

Chapter 12   23   Glencoe Algebra 1

Word Problem Practice
CRM p. 24 OL AL

12-3 Word Problem Practice
Permutations and Combinations

1. **CHORES** In Ashley's family there are 4 children and their mother and father. If two of the six must help clear the table after dinner, how many ways can two people be paired? 15

2. **PUBLIC SERVICE** A county computer randomly selects jurors from the lawyer-approved potential juror list. How many ways are there for 12 jurors to be chosen from a pool of 20? 125,970

Potential Jurors	
Fred	Jennifer
Sally	Carla
Mike	Sam
Tom	Sylvia
Maria	Jamal
Ted	Greg
Carlos	Todd
Dorothy	Lauren
Irene	Maya
Trish	Luke

3. **SPORTS** Hans' basketball team decides to choose two captains each week so that many players get the chance to be captain. Each week, each of the 11 players writes his name on a slip of paper. The papers are then placed in a container and mixed. The last week's captains draw two slips of paper from the container; these two people are captains for the following week. How many different pairs of captains can be formed? 55

4. **PUZZLES** A popular newspaper puzzle involves a series of letters that can be rearranged to form a word. Will is writing his own version of the game for a school project. He wants to scramble the following word in his puzzle.

numbers

How many ways are there to arrange the letters with the letter *b* as the first letter? 720

HORSE RACING For Exercises 5–7, use the following information.
In the 131st running of the Kentucky Derby in 2005, there were 20 contenders.

5. How many different ways can the horses finish the race? 20! or 2,432,902,008,176,640,000

6. How many different ways can horses place first, second, and third? 6840

7. If all 20 horses have an equal chance of winning and 3 of the horses are female, what is the probability that a female horse places first, second, and third? $\frac{3}{20} \cdot \frac{2}{19} \cdot \frac{1}{18}$ or $\frac{1}{1140}$

Chapter 12   24   Glencoe Algebra 1

SOFTBALL For Exercises 36 and 37, use the following information.
The manager of a softball team needs to prepare a batting lineup using her nine starting players.

36. Is this situation a permutation or a combination? **permutation**

37. How many different lineups can she make? **362,880**

Real-World Link
The game of softball was developed in 1888 as an indoor sport for practicing baseball during the winter months.

Source: encyclopedia.com

GAMES For Exercises 38–40, use the following information.
For a certain game, each player rolls five dice at the same time.

38. Do the outcomes of rolling the five dice represent a permutation or a combination? Explain. **Combination; order is not important.**

39. How many outcomes are possible? **7776**

40. What is the probability that all five dice show the same number on a single roll? $\dfrac{1}{1296}$

BUSINESS For Exercises 41 and 42, use the following information.
There are six positions available in the research department of a software company. Of the applicants, 15 are men and 10 are women.

41. In how many ways could 4 men and 2 women be chosen if each were equally qualified? **61,425**

42. What is the probability that five women would be selected if the positions were randomly filled? $\dfrac{27}{1265}$

DINING For Exercises 43–45, use the following information.
For lunch in the school cafeteria, you can select one item from each category to get the daily combo.

Entree	Side Dish	Beverage
Burger	Soup	Lemonade
Deli Sandwich	Salad	Iced Tea
Taco	French Fries	Soft Drink
Pizza		

43. Find the number of possible meal combinations. **36**

44. If a side dish is chosen at random, what is the probability that a student will choose soup? $\frac{1}{3}$ **or about 33%**

45. What is the probability that a student will randomly choose a sandwich and soup? $\frac{1}{12}$ **or about 8%**

SWIMMING For Exercises 46–48, use the following information.
A swimming coach plans to pick four swimmers out of a group of 6 to form the 400-meter freestyle relay team.

46. How many different teams can he form? **15**

47. The swimmers have been chosen for the relay team. The coach must now decide in which order the four swimmers should swim. He timed the swimmers in each possible order and chose the best time. How many relays did the four swimmers have to swim so that the coach could collect all the data necessary? **24**

48. If Tomás is chosen to be on the team, what is the probability that he will swim in the third leg? $\frac{1}{4}$ **= 25%**

Cross-Curricular Project

Math Online You can use permutations and combinations to analyze data on U.S. amusement parks.
Visit ca.algebra1.com

Enrichment
CRM p. 25 OL AL

12-3 Enrichment

A Great Pizza Deal

A television commercial advertised a pizza deal in which customers could choose two pizzas each with up to five toppings chosen from a set of eleven toppings. On the commercial, a boy claims that there are 1024^2 or 1,048,576 ways for the customer to choose the two pizzas. Is this a valid claim?

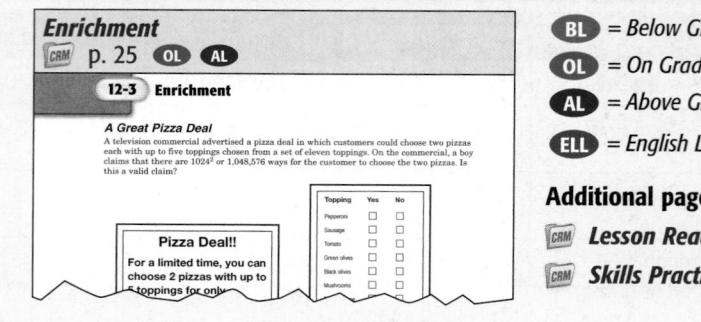

Topping	Yes	No
Pepperoni	☐	☐
Sausage	☐	☐
Tomato	☐	☐
Green olives	☐	☐
Black olives	☐	☐
Mushrooms	☐	☐

Pizza Deal!!
For a limited time, you can choose 2 pizzas with up to 5 toppings for only

BL = Below Grade Level
OL = On Grade Level
AL = Above Grade Level
ELL = English Language Learner

Additional pages not shown:
CRM Lesson Reading Guide, p. 19 BL OL ELL
CRM Skills Practice, p. 22 BL OL

49. BASKETBALL The coach had to select 5 out of 12 players on his basketball team to start the game. How many different groups of players could be selected to start the game? **792**

SPORTS For Exercises 50 and 51, use the following information.
Central High School is competing against West High School at a track meet. Each team entered four girls to run the 1600-meter event. The top three finishers are awarded medals.

50. If there are only the runners from Central and West in this race, how many different ways can the runners place first, second, and third? **336**

51. If all eight runners have an equal chance of placing, what is the probability that the first and second place finishers are from West and the third place finisher is from Central? $\frac{1}{7} \approx 14\%$

EXTRA PRACTICE
See pages 742, 755.
Math Online
Self-Check Quiz at
ca.algebra1.com

H.O.T. Problems.......

52. OPEN ENDED Describe the difference between a permutation and a combination. Then give an example of each. **See margin.**

53. Which One Doesn't Belong? Determine which situation does not belong. Explain your reasoning.

The five starters on a basketball team.	Choosing 10 colored marbles out of a bag.
Choosing 4 horses from 6 to run in the race.	Determining class rank in a senior class of 100 students.

Determining class rank in a senior class of 100 students.

54. Alisa; both are correct in that the situation is a combination, but Alisa's method correctly computes the combination. Eric's calculations find the number of permutations.

54. FIND THE ERROR Eric and Alisa are taking a trip to Washington, D.C., to visit the Lincoln Memorial, the Jefferson Memorial, the Washington Monument, the White House, the Capitol Building, the Supreme Court, and the Pentagon. Both are finding the number of ways they can choose to visit 5 of these 7 sites. Who is correct? Explain your reasoning.

Eric
$$_7C_5 = \frac{7!}{2!}$$
$$= 2520$$

Alisa
$$_7C_5 = \frac{7!}{2!5!}$$
$$= 21$$

CHALLENGE For Exercises 55 and 56, use the following information.
Larisa is trying to solve a word puzzle. She needs to arrange the letters H, P, S, T, A, E, O into a two-word arrangement.

55. How many different arrangements of the letters can she make? **5040**

56. If each arrangement has an equal chance of occurring, what is the probability that she will form the words "tap shoe" on her first try? $\frac{1}{5040}$

57. *Writing in Math* Refer to the information on page 655 to explain how combinations can be used to form Senate committees. Discuss why the formation of a Senate committee is a combination and not a permutation. Explain how this would change if the selection of the committee was based on seniority. **See margin.**

⚠ **Exercise Alert!**
Find the Error First students must determine whether Eric and Alisa need to find the number of permutations or combinations. Since the order in which the bus visits the sites does not matter, they need to find the number of combinations. Next, students must examine whether Eric or Alisa used the correct procedure to find the number of combinations.

Additional Answers

52. Sample answer: Order is important in a permutation but not in a combination. Permutation: the finishing order of a race. Combination: toppings on a pizza.

57. Sample answer: Combinations can be used to how many different ways a committee can be formed by various members. Without seniority, order of selection is not important. Order is important when seniority is involved, so you need to find the number of permutations.

662 Chapter 12 Statistics and Probability

Real-World Connections For Exercise 57, some students might enjoy researching the various Senate committees and using the information they find to determine the number of combinations for forming the committee. They can use the same information to determine the number of permutations if the selection of committee members is based on seniority.

Pacing

Because permutations and combinations are frequently confused, consider discussing many examples of each. For each example, show how to find the permutation or combination.

4 Assess

Yesterday's News Have students explain how yesterday's concepts on counting outcomes helped to prepare them for today's lesson on the concepts of permutations and combinations.

 Formative Assessment

Check for student understanding of concepts in Lesson 12-3.

 Quiz 2, p. 51

 **Foldables™ Follow-Up**

Encourage students to use several examples when describing permutations and combinations in their Foldables. For one example of each, suggest that they show a step-by-step method for calculating the permutation or combination.

---

58. Julie remembered that the 4 digits of her locker combination were 4, 9, 15, and 22, but not their order. What is the maximum number of attempts Julie could have to make before her locker opens? **C**

A 4

B 16

C 24

D 256

59. **REVIEW** Jimmy has $23 in a jar at home, and he is saving to buy a $175 video game system. If he can save $15 a week, which equation could be used to determine w, the number of weeks it will take Jimmy to buy the video game system? **H**

F $23 = 175 + 15w$

G $23 = 15(w + 175)$

H $175 = 15w + 23$

J $175 = 23w + 15$

Spiral Review

60. The Sanchez family acts as a host family for a foreign exchange student during each school year. It is equally likely that they will host a girl or a boy. In how many different ways can they host boys and girls over the next four years? (Lesson 12-2) **16**

61. **MANUFACTURING** Every 15 minutes, a CD player is taken off the assembly line and tested. State whether this sample is *unbiased* (random) or *biased*. If unbiased, classify the sample as *simple*, *stratified*, or *systematic*. If biased, classify as *convenience* or *voluntary response*. (Lesson 12-1) **unbiased; systematic**

Simplify each expression. (Lesson 11-2)

62. $\dfrac{x+3}{x^2+6x+9} \quad \dfrac{1}{x+3}$

63. $\dfrac{x^2-49}{x^2-2x-35} \quad \dfrac{x+7}{x+5}$

64. $\dfrac{n^2-n-20}{n^2+9n+20} \quad \dfrac{n-5}{n+5}$

Find the distance between each pair of points with the given coordinates. Express answers in simplest radical form and as decimal approximations rounded to the nearest hundredth if necessary. (Lesson 10-5)

65. $(12, 20), (16, 34)$
$2\sqrt{53}; 14.56$

66. $(-18, 7), (2, 15)$
$4\sqrt{29}; 21.54$

67. $(-2, 5), \left(-\dfrac{1}{2}, 3\right) \; 2\dfrac{1}{2}; 2.5$

Solve each equation by using the Quadratic Formula. Approximate irrational roots to the nearest hundredth. (Lesson 9-4)

68. $m^2 + 4m + 2 = 0$
$-2 \pm \sqrt{2}; -0.59, -3.41$

69. $2s^2 + s - 15 = 0 \; \dfrac{5}{2}, -3$

70. $2n^2 - n = 4$
$\dfrac{1 \pm \sqrt{33}}{4}; 1.69, -1.19$

GET READY for the Next Lesson

PREREQUISITE SKILL Find each sum or difference. (Pages 694–695)

71. $\dfrac{8}{52} + \dfrac{4}{52} \quad \dfrac{3}{13}$

72. $\dfrac{7}{32} + \dfrac{5}{8} \quad \dfrac{27}{32}$

73. $\dfrac{5}{15} + \dfrac{6}{15} - \dfrac{2}{15} \quad \dfrac{3}{5}$

74. $\dfrac{15}{24} + \dfrac{11}{24} - \dfrac{3}{4} \quad \dfrac{1}{3}$

75. $\dfrac{2}{3} + \dfrac{15}{36} - \dfrac{1}{4} \quad \dfrac{5}{6}$

76. $\dfrac{16}{25} + \dfrac{3}{10} - \dfrac{1}{4} \quad \dfrac{69}{100}$

Pre-AP Activity Use as an Extension

Ask students whether they would expect the number of combinations of n items taken r at a time to be less or more than the number of permutations of n items taken r at a time. Have them explain their reasoning by using real-life examples. The number of combinations would be less than the number of permutations. Sample answer: If you listen to jazz recording A and jazz recording B in no particular order, this is a combination, and AB and BA are the same. If the order in which you listen to the recordings is important, then listening to the recordings in the order AB is different from listening to the recordings in the order BA. The number of combinations is therefore less than the number of permutations.

Main Ideas

- Find the probability of two independent events or dependent events.
- Find the probability of two mutually exclusive or inclusive events.

 Probability and Statistics Standard 1.0
Students know the definition of the notion of *independent events* and can use the rules for addition, multiplication, and complementation to solve for probabilities of particular events in finite sample spaces. (Key)

New Vocabulary

simple event
compound event
independent events
dependent events
complements
mutually exclusive

GET READY for the Lesson

The weather forecast for Saturday calls for rain in Chicago and Los Angeles. By using the probabilities for both cities, we can find other probabilities. What is the probability that it will rain in both cities? only in Chicago? Chicago or Los Angeles?

Saturday Forecast: Rain Likely

Chicago 40%

Los Angeles 80%

Independent and Dependent Events A single event, like rain in Los Angeles, is called a **simple event**. Suppose you wanted to determine the probability that it will rain in both Chicago and Los Angeles. This is an example of a **compound event**, which is made up of two or more simple events. The weather in Chicago does not affect the weather in Los Angeles. These two events are called **independent events** because the outcome of one event does not affect the outcome of the other.

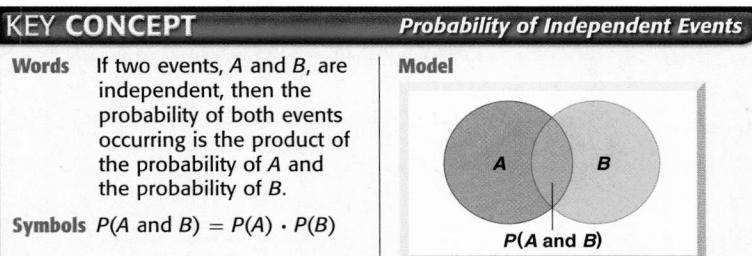

KEY **CONCEPT**		*Probability of Independent Events*
Words	If two events, A and B, are independent, then the probability of both events occurring is the product of the probability of A and the probability of B.	**Model**
Symbols	$P(A \text{ and } B) = P(A) \cdot P(B)$	$P(A \text{ and } B)$

EXAMPLE Independent Events

❶ Refer to the application above. Find the probability that it will rain in Chicago and Los Angeles.

P(Chicago and Los Angeles)

$= P$(Chicago) $\cdot P$(Los Angeles)   Probability of independent events

$=$ 0.4 $\cdot$ 0.8   40% = 0.4 and 80% = 0.8

$= 0.32$ Multiply.

The probability that it will rain in Chicago and Los Angeles is 32%.

CHECK Your Progress

1. Find the probability of rain in Chicago and no rain in Los Angeles.
0.08 or 8 %

1 Focus

Standards Alignment

Before Lesson 12-4
Understand when to add and multiply probabilities from Standard 6SDAP3.1

Lesson 12-4
Find probabilities of particular events in finite sample spaces from Standard PS1.0

After Lesson 12-4
Know the definition of conditional probability and use it to solve for probabilities in finite sample spaces from Standard 2APS2.0

2 Teach

Scaffolding Questions

Have students read *Get Ready for the Lesson.*

Ask:

- Suppose it does not rain in Chicago. Does this affect whether it will rain in Los Angeles? no
- What does the word *independent* mean? free or unrelated
- Could the word *independent* be used to describe Chicago's weather as related to Los Angeles's weather? Explain. Yes. Because the weather in Chicago does not affect the weather in Los Angeles; these events are independent of each other.

(continued on the next page)

Lesson 12-4 Resources

Chapter 12 Resource Masters
Lesson Reading Guide, p. 26 **BL** **OL** **ELL**
Study Guide and Intervention, pp. 27–28 **BL** **OL** **ELL**
Skills Practice, p. 29 **BL** **OL**
Practice, p. 30 **OL** **AL**
Word Problem Practice, p. 31 **OL** **AL**
Enrichment, p. 32 **OL** **AL**
Graphing Calculator, p. 33

Transparencies
5-Minute Check Transparency 12-4
Additional Print Resources
Noteables™ Interactive Study Notebook with Foldables™

Technology
ca.algebra1.com
Interactive Classroom CD-ROM
AssignmentWorks CD-ROM
Graphing Calculator Easy Files

- **Is there anything that does affect the weather on a given day of the year? Explain.** The season affects the weather. For example, the probability of having snow in July is very low because the weather in July is too warm.

Independent and Dependent Events

Example 1 shows how to find the probability of two independent events occurring. **Example 2** shows how to find the probability of dependent events occurring.

✓ Formative Assessment

Use the Check Your Progress exercises after each example to determine students' understanding of concepts.

When the outcome of one event affects the outcome of another event, the events are **dependent events.** For example, drawing a marble from a bag, not returning it, then drawing a second marble are dependent events because the probability of drawing the second marble depends on what marble was drawn first.

Study Tip

More Than Two Dependent Events

Notice that the formula for the probability of dependent events can be applied to more than two events.

> **KEY CONCEPT**   *Probability of Dependent Events*
>
> **Words**   If two events, A and B, are dependent, then the probability of both events occurring is the product of the probability of A and the probability of B after A occurs.
>
> **Symbols** $P(A \text{ and } B) = P(A) \cdot P(B \text{ following } A)$

EXAMPLE   Dependent Events

2 A bag contains 8 red marbles, 12 blue marbles, 9 yellow marbles, and 11 green marbles. Three marbles are randomly drawn from the bag one at a time and not replaced. Find each probability if the marbles are drawn in the order indicated.

a. P(red, blue, green)

The selection of the first marble affects the selection of the next marble since there is one less marble from which to choose. So, the events are dependent.

First marble: $P(\text{red}) = \dfrac{8}{40}$ or $\dfrac{1}{5}$ ← number of red marbles
                                              ← total number of marbles

Second marble: $P(\text{blue}) = \dfrac{12}{39}$ or $\dfrac{4}{13}$ ← number of blue marbles
                                              ← number of marbles remaining

Third marble: $P(\text{green}) = \dfrac{11}{38}$ ← number of green marbles
                                              ← number of marbles remaining

$P(\text{red, blue, green}) = P(\text{red}) \cdot P(\text{blue}) \cdot P(\text{green})$

$\qquad\qquad = \dfrac{1}{5} \cdot \dfrac{4}{13} \cdot \dfrac{11}{38}$ Substitution

$\qquad\qquad = \dfrac{44}{2470}$ or $\dfrac{22}{1235}$ Multiply.

b. P(yellow, yellow, *not* green)

Notice that after selecting a yellow marble, not only is there one fewer marble from which to choose, there is also one fewer yellow marble. Also, since the marble that is not green is selected after the first two marbles, there are $29 - 2$ or 27 marbles that are not green.

$P(\text{yellow, yellow, } not \text{ green}) = P(\text{yellow}) \cdot P(\text{yellow}) \cdot P(\text{not green})$

$\qquad\qquad\qquad = \dfrac{9}{40} \cdot \dfrac{8}{39} \cdot \dfrac{27}{38}$

$\qquad\qquad\qquad = \dfrac{1944}{59,280}$ or $\dfrac{81}{2470}$

✓ CHECK Your Progress

2A. P(red, green, green) $\dfrac{11}{741}$ **2B.** P(red, blue, *not* yellow) $\dfrac{58}{1235}$

Online Personal Tutor at ca.algebra1.com

Differentiated Instruction

Spatial/Visual Learners   Bring a packet of raw sunflower seeds or other fast-sprouting seeds to class. Ensure that you have slightly more seeds than students. Explain that each student will take a seed and plant it either on school grounds or in a small plant pot. As students take a seed from the packet, lead them to understand that the number of seeds from which they can choose is a dependent event for all but the first student.

In part b of Example 2, the events for drawing a marble that is green and for drawing a marble that is *not* green are called **complements.** Consider the probabilities for drawing the third marble.

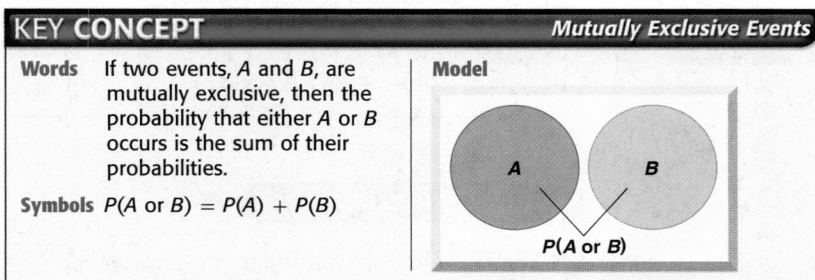

$$\frac{11}{38} + \frac{27}{38} = 1$$

This is always true for any two complementary events.

Mutually Exclusive and Inclusive Events Events that cannot occur at the same time are called **mutually exclusive.** Suppose you want to find the probability of rolling a 2 *or* a 4 on a die. Since a die cannot show both a 2 and a 4 at the same time, the events are mutually exclusive.

KEY CONCEPT   Mutually Exclusive Events

Words If two events, A and B, are mutually exclusive, then the probability that either A or B occurs is the sum of their probabilities.

Symbols $P(A \text{ or } B) = P(A) + P(B)$

Model

$P(A \text{ or } B)$

EXAMPLE   Mutually Exclusive Events

3 During a magic trick, a magician randomly draws one card from a standard deck of cards. What is the probability that the card drawn is a heart or a diamond?

Since a card cannot be both a heart and a diamond, the events are mutually exclusive.

$P(\text{heart}) = \frac{13}{52} \text{ or } \frac{1}{4}$ ← number of hearts
                                        ← total number of cards

$P(\text{diamond}) = \frac{13}{52} \text{ or } \frac{1}{4}$ ← number of diamonds
                                           ← total number of cards

$P(\text{heart or diamond}) = P(\text{heart}) + P(\text{diamond})$ Definition of mutually exclusive events

$= \frac{1}{4} + \frac{1}{4}$ Substitution

$= \frac{2}{4} \text{ or } \frac{1}{2}$ Add.

The probability of drawing a heart or a diamond is $\frac{1}{2}$.

CHECK Your Progress
3. What is the probability that the card drawn is an ace or a face card? $\frac{4}{13}$

Mutually Exclusive and Inclusive Events

Example 3 shows how to find the probability that either one or the other of two mutually exclusive events will occur. **Example 4** shows how to find the probability that either one or the other of two inclusive events will occur.

ADDITIONAL EXAMPLE

3 Alfred is going to the Lakeshore Animal Shelter to choose a new pet. Today, the shelter has 8 dogs, 7 cats, and 5 rabbits available for adoption. If Alfred randomly picks an animal to adopt, what is the probability that the animal will be a cat or a dog? $\frac{3}{4}$

Tips for New Teachers   Preventing Errors

For Example 3, explain to students that there are four suits or types of cards in a standard card deck: spades, hearts, diamonds, and clubs. There are 13 cards in each suit, for a total of 52 cards. The cards in each suit are: ace, 2, 3, 4, 5, 6, 7, 8, 9, 10, jack, queen, and king.

Focus on Mathematical Content

Mutually Exclusive Events Events that cannot occur at the same time are mutually exclusive. For example, if you randomly draw either a blue marble or a yellow marble from a bag of marbles, these events are mutually exclusive since you cannot draw a blue marble and a yellow marble at the same time. Find the probability of mutually exclusive events by finding the sum of the probabilities of each event. If the probability of drawing a blue marble from the bag is $\frac{3}{8}$ and the probability of drawing a yellow marble is $\frac{1}{4}$, the probability of drawing either a blue marble or a yellow marble is $\frac{3}{8} + \frac{1}{4} = \frac{5}{8}$.

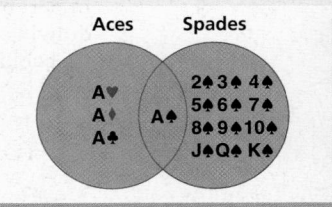

ADDITIONAL EXAMPLE

4 **PETS** A dog has just given birth to a litter of 9 puppies. There are 3 brown females, 2 brown males, 1 mixed-color female, and 3 mixed-color males. If you choose a puppy at random from the litter, what is the probability that the puppy will be male or mixed-color? **D**

A $\frac{2}{9}$ **C** $\frac{5}{9}$

B $\frac{1}{3}$ **D** $\frac{2}{3}$

Intervention

Common Misconceptions If students are having trouble understanding why they must subtract the probability of both A and B occurring when finding the probability of inclusive events, Additional Example 4 should help clarify the issue. If you add the probability of picking a puppy that is male $\left(\frac{5}{9}\right)$ to the probability of picking a puppy that is mixed-color $\left(\frac{4}{9}\right)$, the sum is $\frac{9}{9}$, or 100%. This is obviously incorrect because not all of the puppies are male, nor are they all mixed-color. However, when you subtract the probability of picking a puppy that is both male and mixed-color $\left(\frac{3}{9}\right)$, you get the correct probability of $\left(\frac{2}{3}\right)$.

Suppose you want to find the probability of randomly selecting an ace or a spade from a standard deck of cards. Since it is possible to draw a card that is both an ace and a spade, these events are not mutually exclusive. They are called **inclusive** events. The following formula allows you to find the probability of inclusive events.

KEY CONCEPT — Mutually Inclusive Events

Words	If two events, A and B, are inclusive, then the probability that either A or B occurs is the sum of their probabilities decreased by the probability of both occurring.
Symbols	$P(A \text{ or } B) = P(A) + P(B) - P(A \text{ and } B)$

Model

$P(A \text{ or } B)$

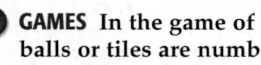

STANDARDS EXAMPLE   PS1.0

4 **GAMES** In the game of bingo, balls or tiles are numbered 1 through 75. These numbers correspond to columns on a bingo card, as shown in the table. A number is selected at random. What is the probability that it is a multiple of 4 or is in the O column?

B	I	N	G	O
1–15	16–30	31–45	46–60	61–75

A $\frac{1}{5}$ **B** $\frac{2}{5}$ **C** $\frac{1}{2}$ **D** $\frac{4}{5}$

Since the numbers 64, 68, and 72 are multiples of 4 and they are also in the O column, these events are inclusive.

$P(\text{multiple of 4 or O column})$

    $P(\text{multiple of 4}) + P(\text{O column}) - P(\text{multiple of 4 and O column})$

$= \frac{18}{75} + \frac{15}{75} - \frac{3}{75}$ Substitution

$= \frac{18 + 15 - 3}{75}$ LCD is 75.

$= \frac{30}{75}$ or $\frac{2}{5}$ Simplify.

The correct choice is B.

✓CHECK Your Progress

4. Refer to the table above. What is the probability that a number selected is even or is in the N column? **H**

F $\frac{1}{5}$ **G** $\frac{2}{5}$ **H** $\frac{1}{2}$ **J** $\frac{4}{5}$

COncepts in MOtion
BrainPOP®
ca.algebra1.com

★ indicates multi-step problem

Example 1
(p. 663)

BUSINESS For Exercises 1–3, use the following information.
Mr. Salyer is a buyer for an electronics store. He received a shipment of 5 hair dryers in which one is defective. He randomly chose 3 of the hair dryers to test.

1. Determine whether choosing the hair dryers are independent or dependent events. **independent**
2. What is the probability that he selected the defective dryer? $\frac{3}{5}$
3. Suppose the defective dryer is one of the three that Mr. Salyer tested. What is the probability that the last one tested was the defective one? $\frac{1}{3}$

Examples 1, 2
(pp. 663–664)

4. $\frac{10}{147}$

A bin contains colored chips as shown in the table. Find each probability.

Color	Number
Blue	8
Red	5
Green	6
Yellow	2

4. drawing a red chip, replacing it, then drawing a green chip
5. choosing green, then blue, then red, replacing each chip after it is drawn $\frac{80}{3087}$
6. selecting two yellow chips without replacement $\frac{1}{210}$
7. choosing green, then blue, then red without replacing each chip $\frac{4}{133}$

Examples 3, 4
(pp. 665–666)

A student is selected at random from a group of 12 male and 12 female students. There are 3 male students and 3 female students from each of the 9th, 10th, 11th, and 12th grades. Find each probability.

8. P(9th or 12th grader) $\frac{1}{2}$
9. P(male or female) 1
10. P(10th grader or female) $\frac{5}{8}$
11. P(male or not 11th grader) $\frac{7}{8}$

Example 4
(p. 666)
PS1.0

12. 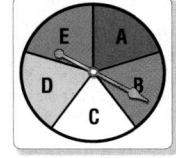 **STANDARDS PRACTICE** At the basketball game, 50% of the fans cheered for the home team. In the same crowd, 20% of the fans were waving banners. What is the probability that a fan cheered for the home team and waved a banner? **B**

A $\frac{1}{20}$ B $\frac{1}{10}$ C $\frac{1}{5}$ D $\frac{2}{5}$

Exercises

HOMEWORK HELP	
For Exercises	See Examples
13–19, 31–32	1
20–27	2
28–30	3
33–34	4

Exercise Levels
A: 13–39
B: 35–42
C: 43–50

A die is rolled and a spinner like the one at the right is spun. Find each probability.

13. P(3 and D) $\frac{1}{30}$
14. P(an odd number and a vowel) $\frac{1}{5}$
15. P(a prime number and A) $\frac{1}{10}$
16. P(2 and A, B, or C) $\frac{1}{10}$

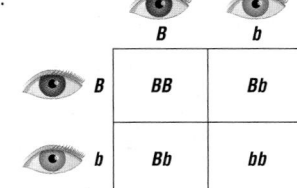

BIOLOGY For Exercises 17–19, use the diagram and following information.
Each person carries two types of genes for eye color. The gene for brown eyes (B) is dominant over the gene for blue eyes (b). That is, if a person has one gene for brown eyes and the other for blue, that person will have brown eyes. The Punnett square at the right shows the genes for two parents.

	B	b
B	BB	Bb
b	Bb	bb

17. What is the probability that any child will have blue eyes? $\frac{1}{4}$
18. What is the probability that the couple's two children both have brown eyes? $\frac{9}{16}$
19. Find the probability that the first or the second child has blue eyes. $\frac{7}{16}$

✓ **Formative Assessment**

Use Exercises 1–12 to check for understanding.

Use the chart at the bottom of this page to customize assignments for your students.

Odd/Even Assignments
Exercises 13–34 are structured so that students practice the same concepts whether they are assigned odd or even problems.

Tips for New Teachers **Preventing Errors**
Students are often confused about whether compound events are dependent, independent, mutually exclusive, or inclusive. You might want to preview Exercises 13–23 with the class before they begin the exercises. Ask students to identify the type of compound event in each exercise. If students consistently fail to identify the type of event, suggest that they review each of the examples in the lesson.

DIFFERENTIATED HOMEWORK OPTIONS

Level	Assignment	Two-Day Option	
BL Basic	13–34, 43–45, 50–71	13–33 odd, 51, 52	14–34 even, 43–45, 50, 53–71
OL Core	13–33 odd, 35–45, 50–71	13–34, 51, 52	35–45, 50, 53–71
AL Advanced /Pre-AP	35–63, (optional: 64–71)		

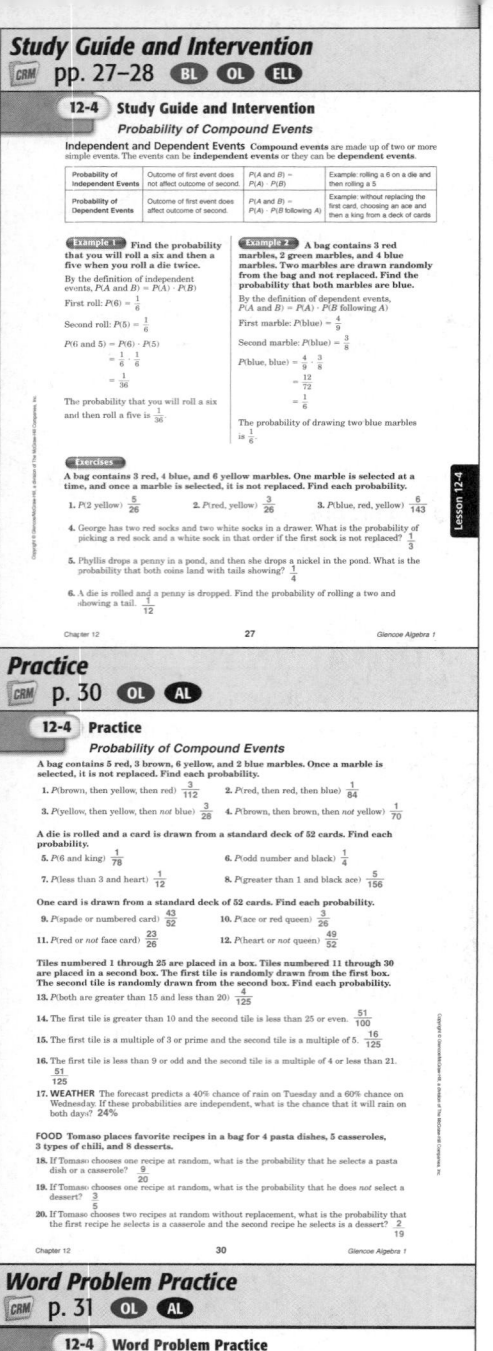

SAFETY For Exercises 20–23, use the following information.
A carbon monoxide detector system uses two sensors, A and B. If carbon monoxide is present, there is a 96% chance that sensor A will detect it, a 92% chance that sensor B will detect it, and a 90% chance that both sensors will detect it.

20. Draw a Venn diagram that illustrates this situation. **See margin.**

21. 98% or 0.98

21. If carbon monoxide is present, what is the probability that it will be detected?

22. 2% or 0.02

22. What is the probability that carbon monoxide would go undetected?

23. Do sensors A and B operate independently of each other? Explain.
No; $P(A \text{ and } B) \neq P(A) \cdot P(B)$.

A bag contains 2 red, 6 blue, 7 yellow, and 3 orange marbles. Once a marble is selected, it is not replaced. Find each probability.

24. $P(2 \text{ orange})$ $\frac{1}{51}$ 25. $P(\text{blue, then red})$ $\frac{2}{51}$

26. $\frac{7}{272}$

26. $P(2 \text{ yellows in a row then orange})$ 27. $P(\text{blue, then yellow, then red})$ $\frac{7}{408}$

ECONOMICS For Exercises 28–30, use the table below that compares the total number of hourly workers who earned the minimum wage of $5.15 with those making less than minimum wage.

Number of Hourly Workers (thousands), 2005			
Age (years)	Total	At $5.15	Below $5.15
16–24	16,174	272	750
25+	57,765	249	733

Source: U.S. Bureau of Labor Statistics

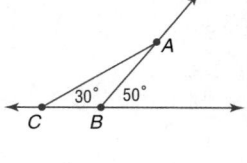

28. If an hourly worker was chosen at random, what is the probability that he or she earned minimum wage? less than minimum wage? $\approx 0.007; \approx 0.02$

29. What is the probability that a randomly-chosen hourly worker earned less than or equal to minimum wage? ≈ 0.03

30. If you randomly chose an hourly worker from each age group, which would you expect to have earned no more than minimum wage? Explain.
A worker in the 16–24 age group; the probability is less.

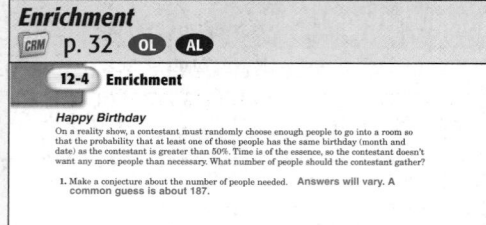

Real-World Link
The first federal minimum wage was set in 1938 at $0.25 per hour. That was the equivalent of $3.22 in 2005.

Source: U.S. Department of Labor

Raffle tickets numbered 1 through 30 are placed in a box. Tickets for a second raffle numbered 21 to 48 are placed in another box. One ticket is randomly drawn from each box. Find each probability. 33. $\frac{23}{42}$

31. Both tickets are even. $\frac{1}{4}$

32. Both tickets are greater than 20 and less than 30. $\frac{27}{280}$

33. The first ticket is greater than 10, and the second ticket is less than 40 or odd.

34. The first ticket is greater than 12 or prime, and the second ticket is a multiple of 6 or a multiple of 4. $\frac{69}{280}$

GEOMETRY For Exercises 35–37, use the figure and the following information.
Two of the six angles in the figure are chosen at random.

★35. What is the probability of choosing an angle inside $\angle ABC$ or an obtuse angle? $\frac{5}{6}$

★36. What is the probability of selecting a straight angle or a right angle? 0

★37. Find the probability of picking a 20° angle or a 130° angle. $\frac{1}{3}$

BL = Below Grade Level
OL = On Grade Level
AL = Above Grade Level
ELL = English Language Learner

Additional pages not shown:
CRM *Lesson Reading Guide*, p. 26 BL OL ELL
CRM *Skills Practice*, p. 29 BL OL

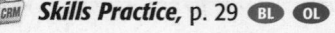

38. RESEARCH Use the Internet or other reference to investigate various blood types. Use this information to determine the probability of a child having blood type O if the father has blood type A(Ai) and the mother has blood type B(Bi). $\frac{1}{4}$

A dart is thrown at a dartboard like the one at the right. If the dart can land anywhere on the board, find the probability that it lands in each of the following.

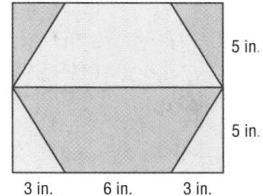

5 in.

5 in.

3 in.   6 in.   3 in.

EXTRA PRACTICE
See page 743, 755.

Math Online
Self-Check Quiz at
ca.algebra1.com

★ **39.** a triangle or a yellow region $\frac{5}{8}$

★ **40.** a trapezoid or a blue region $\frac{7}{8}$

★ **41.** a blue triangle or a yellow triangle $\frac{1}{4}$

★ **42.** a square or a hexagon $\frac{3}{4}$

H.O.T. Problems

43. OPEN ENDED Explain how dependent events are different from independent events. Give specific examples in your explanation.

43. Sample answer: In a dependent event, an object is selected and not replaced. In an independent event, an object is selected and replaced.

44. FIND THE ERROR On the school debate team, 6 of the 14 girls are seniors, and 9 of the 20 boys are seniors. Chloe and Amber are both seniors on the team. Each girl calculated the probability that either a girl or a senior would randomly be selected to argue a position at a state debate. Who is correct? Explain your reasoning.

44. Chloe; sample answer: Since it is possible for the person chosen to be a girl and a senior, the events are inclusive. So, add the probability that a girl is chosen, $\frac{14}{34}$, and the probability that a senior is chosen, $\frac{15}{34}$, then subtract the probability that a senior girl is chosen, $\frac{6}{34}$.

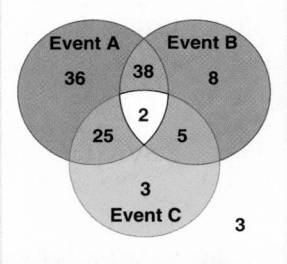

Chloe
P(girl or senior)
$= \frac{14}{34} + \frac{15}{34} - \frac{6}{34}$
$= \frac{23}{34}$

Amber
P(girl or senior)
$= \frac{6}{34} + \frac{15}{34} - \frac{14}{34}$
$= \frac{7}{34}$

45. REASONING Find a counterexample for the following statement.

If two events are independent, then the probability of both events occurring is less than 1. **Sample answer: The probability of rolling a number less than or equal to six on a number cube and tossing heads or tails on a coin.**

CHALLENGE For Exercises 46–49, use the following information.
A sample of high school students were asked if they
A) drive a car to school,
B) are involved in after-school activities, or
C) have a part-time job.
The results are shown in the Venn diagram.

46. How many students were surveyed? **120**

47. How many students said that they drive a car to school? **101**

48. If a student is chosen at random, what is the probability that he or she does all three? $\frac{1}{60}$

Event A   Event B

36   38   8

2

25   5

3

Event C   3

49. What is the probability that a randomly chosen student drives a car to school or is involved in after-school activities or has a part-time job? $\frac{39}{40}$

50. *Writing in Math* Refer to the information on page 663 to explain how probabilities are used by meteorologists. Illustrate how compound probabilities can be used to predict the weather. **Sample answer: Meteorologists use probabilities to forecast the weather. You can use compound probabilities to forecast the weather over an extended period of time.**

Lesson 12-4 Probability of Compound Events   **669**

Additional Answer

20.

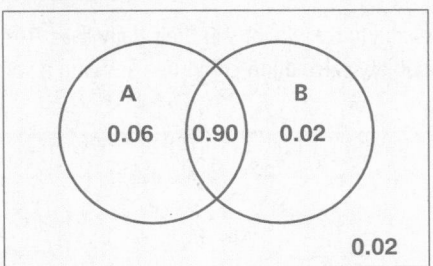

A   B

0.06   0.90   0.02

0.02

Ticket out the Door Write probability examples on slips of paper, using each type of compound event. Give each student one of the examples. As students walk out the door, have them tell whether their events are independent, dependent, mutually exclusive, or inclusive, and have them give the probability of the events.

STANDARDS PRACTICE 6PS3.5, 7AF1.1

51. A bag contains 8 red marbles, 5 blue marbles, 4 green marbles, and 7 yellow marbles. Five marbles are randomly drawn from the bag one at a time and not replaced. What is the probability that the first three marbles drawn are red? **C**

   A $\frac{1}{27}$ C $\frac{7}{253}$

   B $\frac{28}{1771}$ D $\frac{7}{288}$

52. **REVIEW** The sum of a number x and -12 is 64. Which equation shows this relationship? **F**

   F $x - 12 = 64$

   G $x + 12 = 64$

   H $12x = 64$

   J $64x = -12$

Spiral Review

CIVICS For Exercises 53 and 54, use the following information.
Stratford City Council wants to form a 3-person parks committee. Five people have applied to be on the committee. (Lesson 12-2)

53. How many committees are possible? **10**

54. What is the probability of any one person being selected if each has an equal chance? $\frac{3}{5}$

55. **BUSINESS** A real estate developer built a strip mall with seven different-sized stores. Ten businesses have shown interest in renting space in the mall. The developer must decide which business would be best suited for each store. How many different arrangements are possible? (Lesson 12-1)
   604,800

Find each quotient. Assume that no denominator has a value of 0. (Lesson 11-4)

56. $\frac{s}{s+7} \div \frac{s-5}{s+7}$ $\frac{s}{s-5}$

57. $\frac{2m^2 + 7m - 15}{m+2} \div \frac{2m-3}{m^2 + 5m + 6}$
   $(m+5)(m+3)$

Simplify. (Lesson 10-1)

58. $\sqrt{45}$ $3\sqrt{5}$

59. $\sqrt{128}$ $8\sqrt{2}$

60. $\sqrt{40b^4}$ $2b^2\sqrt{10}$

61. $\sqrt{120a^3b}$ $2|a|\sqrt{30ab}$

62. $3\sqrt{7} \cdot 6\sqrt{2}$ $18\sqrt{14}$

63. $\sqrt{3}(\sqrt{3} + \sqrt{6})$ $3 + 3\sqrt{2}$

GET READY for the Next Lesson

PREREQUISITE SKILL Express each fraction as a decimal. Round to the nearest thousandth. (pp. 700–701)

64. $\frac{9}{24}$ 0.375

65. $\frac{2}{15}$ 0.133

66. $\frac{63}{128}$ 0.492

67. $\frac{5}{52}$ 0.096

68. $\frac{8}{36}$ 0.222

69. $\frac{11}{38}$ 0.289

70. $\frac{81}{2470}$ 0.033

71. $\frac{18}{1235}$ 0.015

670 **Chapter 12** Statistics and Probability

Pre-AP Activity   Use after the Exercises

Have students write an example of how they could use probability calculations in their daily lives. The example should include both a description of how the probability calculation could be used and a sample calculation with sample data.

Identify each sample, suggest a population from which it was selected, and state whether it is *unbiased* (random) or *biased*. If unbiased, classify the sample as *simple*, *stratified*, or *systematic*. If biased, classify as *convenience* or *voluntary response*. (Lesson 12-1) **1–2. See margin.**

1. Every other household in a neighborhood is surveyed to determine how to improve the neighborhood park.

2. Every other household in a neighborhood is surveyed to determine the favorite candidate for the state's governor.

Find the number of outcomes for each event. (Lesson 12-2)

3. A die is rolled, and two coins are tossed. **24**

4. A certain model of mountain bike comes in 5 sizes, 4 colors, with regular or off-road tires, and with a choice of 1 of 5 accessories. **200**

5. **MULTIPLE CHOICE** There are seven teams in a league, but only four teams qualify for the post-season tournament. How many ways can the four spaces on the tournament bracket be filled by the teams in the league? (Lesson 12-2) **C**

   A 210
   B 420
   C 840
   D 5040

Find each value. (Lesson 12-3)

6. $_{13}C_8$ **1287**
7. $_9P_6$ **60,480**
8. $(_5C_2)(_7C_4)$ **350**
9. $(_{10}P_5)(_{13}P_8)$ **1,569,209,242,000**

10. **SCHOOL** The students in Ms. Kish's homeroom had to choose 4 out of the 7 people who were nominated to serve on the Student Council. How many different groups of students could be selected? **35**

11. **FLOWERS** A vase holds 5 carnations, 6 roses, and 3 lilies. Eliza picks four at random to give to her grandmother. What is the probability of selecting two roses and two lilies? (Lesson 12-3) $\frac{45}{1001}$

12. **MULTIPLE CHOICE** In a standard 52-card deck, what is the probability of randomly drawing an ace or a club? (Lesson 12-4) **G**

   F $\frac{1}{13}$

   G $\frac{4}{13}$

   H $\frac{1}{4}$

   J $\frac{17}{52}$

A ten-sided die, numbered 1 through 10, is rolled. Find each probability. (Lesson 12-4)

13. P(odd or greater than 4) $\frac{4}{5}$
14. P(less than 3 or greater than 7) $\frac{1}{2}$

15. **ACTIVITIES** There are 650 students in a high school. The Venn diagram shows the number of students involved in the band and at least one sport. What is the probability a student is randomly selected who participates in one of these extracurricular activities? (Lesson 12-4) $\frac{142}{325}$ or about 44%

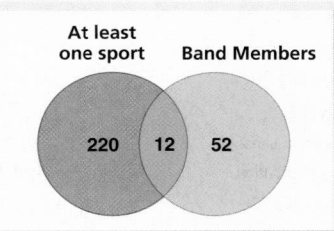

At least one sport | Band Members
220 | 12 | 52

16. **MULTIPLE CHOICE** A teacher took a survey of his class of 28 students about their favorite foods. Thirteen students chose pizza, 7 chose ice cream, 5 chose steak, and 3 chose chicken. If the teacher randomly selects one person's favorite food for a party, what is the probability that he chooses ice cream or steak? (Lesson 12-4) **B**

   A $\frac{2}{7}$ C $\frac{4}{7}$

   B $\frac{3}{7}$ D $\frac{5}{7}$

Chapter 12 Mid-Chapter Quiz   **671**

 Formative Assessment

Use the Mid-Chapter Quiz to assess students' progress in the first half of the chapter.

For problems answered incorrectly, have students review the lessons indicated in parentheses.

 Summative Assessment

[SE] Chapter Practice Test, p. 689

ExamView  Customize and create multiple versions of your Mid-Chapter Tests and their answer keys.

FOLDABLES Study Organizer **Foldables™ Follow-Up**

Before students complete the Mid-Chapter Quiz, encourage them to use their Foldables to review concepts on identifying samples, counting outcomes, using permutations and combinations, and finding probabilities of compound events.

Additional Answers

1. Half of the households in a neighborhood; all households in the neighborhood; unbiased; systematic

2. Half of the households in a neighborhood; voters in the state; biased; convenience

Data-Driven Decision Making	Exercises	Lesson	Standard	Resources for Review
Diagnostic Teaching Based on the results of the Chapter 12 Mid-Chapter Quiz, use the following to review concepts that students continue to find challenging.	1–2	12–1	6SDAP2.2	[CRM] Study Guide and Intervention, pp. 6–7, 13–14, 20–21, 27-28
	3–5	12–2	Preparation for Algebra II 18.0	Math Online
	6–11	12–3	Preparation for Probability and Statistics 1.0	• Extra Examples • Personal Tutor
	12–16	12–4	Preparation for Probability and Statistics 1.0	• Concepts in Motion

12-5 Probability Distributions

1 Focus

Standards Alignment

Before Lesson 12-5
Represent probabilities as ratios, proportions and decimals from  Standard 6SDAP3.3

Lesson 12-5
Use *discrete random variables* to solve for the probabilities of outcomes, from 🔑 Standard PS3.0
Organize and describe distributions of data by using a number of different methods from 🔑 Standard PS8.0

After Lesson 12-5
Use standard distributions to solve for events in problems in which the distribution belongs to those families from 🔑 Standard PS4.0

2 Teach

Scaffolding Questions
Have students read *Get Ready for the Lesson*.
Ask:
• How many customers were surveyed?
100 customers
• How many pets in all do the pet owners surveyed own? 193 pets
(continued on the next page)

Main Ideas
• Use random variables to compute probability.
• Use probability distributions to solve real-world problems.

 Probability and Statistics Standard 3.0
Students demonstrate an understanding of the notion of *discrete random variables* by using them to solve for the probabilities of outcomes, such as the probability of the occurrence of five heads in 14 coin tosses. (Key)

Probability and Statistics Standard 8.0 Students organize and describe distributions of data by using a number of different methods, including **frequency tables, histograms,** standard line and bar graphs, stem-and-leaf displays, scatterplots, and box-and-whisker plots. (Key)

New Vocabulary
random variable
discrete random variable
probability distribution
probability histogram

Reading Math
Notation The notation $P(X = 2)$ means the same as $P(2$ pets$)$, the probability of a customer having 2 pets.

▶ GET READY for the Lesson

The owner of a pet store asked customers how many pets they owned. The results of this survey are shown in the table.

Number of Pets	Number of Customers
0	3
1	37
2	33
3	18
4	9

Random Variables and Probability A **random variable** is a variable with a value that is the numerical outcome of a random event. A **discrete random variable** has a finite number of possible outcomes. In the situation above, we can let the random variable X represent the number of pets owned. Thus, X can equal 0, 1, 2, 3, or 4.

EXAMPLE Random Variable

❶ Refer to the application above.

a. Find the probability that a randomly chosen customer has 2 pets.

There is only one outcome in which there are 2 pets owned, and there are 100 survey results.

$$P(X = 2) = \frac{2 \text{ pets owned}}{\text{customers surveyed}}$$
$$= \frac{33}{100}$$

The probability is $\frac{33}{100}$ or 33%.

b. Find the probability that a randomly chosen customer has at least 3 pets.

There are $18 + 9$ or 27 customers who own at least 3 pets.

$$P(X \geq 3) = \frac{27}{100}$$

The probability is $\frac{27}{100}$ or 27%.

✓ CHECK Your Progress

GRADES On an algebra test, there are 7 students with As, 9 students with Bs, 11 students with Cs, 3 students with Ds, and 2 students with Fs. 1A. $\frac{11}{32}$ or 34%

1A. Find the probability that a randomly chosen student has a C.

1B. Find the probability that a randomly chosen student has at least a B. $\frac{1}{2}$ or 50%

Lesson 12-5 Resources

Transparencies
5-Minute Check Transparency 12-5
Additional Print Resources
Noteables™ Interactive Study Notebook with Foldables™

Technology
ca.algebra1.com
Interactive Classroom CD-ROM
AssignmentWorks CD-ROM
Graphing Calculator Easy Files

Probability Distributions The probability of every possible value of the random variable X is called a **probability distribution**.

KEY **CONCEPT**	Properties of Probability Distributions

1. The probability of each value of X is greater than or equal to 0 and less than or equal to 1.

2. The sum of the probabilities of all values of X is 1.

The probability distribution for a random variable can be given in a table or in a **probability histogram**. A probability distribution table and a probability histogram for the application at the beginning of the lesson are shown below.

Probability Distribution Table	
X = Number of Pets	$P(X)$
0	0.03
1	0.37
2	0.33
3	0.18
4	0.09

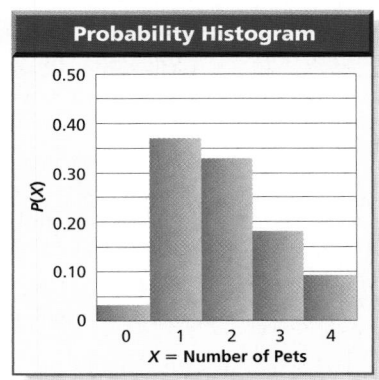

Probability Histogram

Real-World Link

In 1900, there were 8000 registered cars in the United States. By 2002, there were over 136 million. This is an increase of more than 1,699,900.

Source: *The World Almanac*

EXAMPLE Probability Distribution

2 **CARS** The table shows the probability distribution of the number of vehicles per household for the Oakland, California, area.

a. Show that the distribution is valid.

Check to see that each property holds.

1. For each value of X, the probability is greater than or equal to 0 and less than or equal to 1.

2. $0.12 + 0.44 + 0.30 + 0.14 = 1$, so the probabilities add up to 1.

Vehicles per Household Oakland, CA	
X = Number of Vehicles	Probability
0	0.12
1	0.44
2	0.30
3+	0.14

Source: U.S. Census Bureau

b. What is the probability that a household has fewer than 2 vehicles?

Recall that the probability of a compound event is the sum of the probabilities of each individual event.

The probability of a household having fewer than 2 vehicles is the sum of the probability of 0 vehicles and the probability of 1 vehicle.

$P(X < 2) = P(X = 0) + P(X = 1)$ Sum of individual probabilities

$= 0.12 + 0.44$ or 0.56 $P(X = 0) = 0.12, P(X = 1) = 0.44$

(continued on the next page)

Tips for New Teachers

Modeling

Give volunteers sets of data to put into probability distribution tables and histograms on the board. Have students model how to determine whether the given data fits the properties of probability distributions.

Probability Distributions

Example 2 shows how to determine whether a probability distribution for a real-world situation is valid, and how to use a probability table and histogram to represent the probability distribution.

• Use a table similar to the one shown on this page to survey the students in your classroom to find out how many pets each student owns. What is the greatest number of pets owned by a student in your class? Are there any students who have no pets? Answers depend on student responses.

Random Variables and Probability

Example 1 shows how to use random variables to find probabilities.

✓ Formative Assessment

Use the Check Your Progress exercises after each example to determine students' understanding of concepts.

ADDITIONAL EXAMPLE

1 Use the data from the application at the beginning of the lesson to solve the following problems.

a. Find the probability that a randomly chosen customer has at most 2 pets.

$P(X \le 2) = \dfrac{73}{100}$ or 73%

b. Find the probability that a randomly chosen customer has 2 or 3 pets.

$P(2 \le X \le 3) = \dfrac{51}{100}$ or 51%

ADDITIONAL EXAMPLE

2 **POPULATION** The table shows the probability distribution of students in each grade at Sunnybrook High School.

X = Grade	$P(X)$
9	0.29
10	0.26
11	0.25
12	0.2

a. Show that the distribution is valid. For each value of X, the probability is greater than or equal to 0 and less than or equal to 1. Also, $0.29 + 0.26 + 0.25 + 0.2 = 1$, so the probabilities add up to 1. *(continued on the next page)*

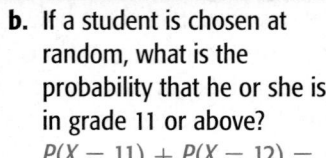
b. If a student is chosen at random, what is the probability that he or she is in grade 11 or above?

$P(X = 11) + P(X = 12) = 0.45$

c. Make a probability histogram of the data.

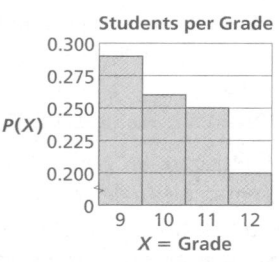

Students per Grade

Additional Examples are also in:

- Noteables™ Interactive Study Notebook with Foldables™
- Interactive Classroom PowerPoint® Presentations

---

3 Practice

 Formative Assessment

Use Exercises 1–6 to check for understanding.

Use the chart at the bottom of this page to customize assignments for your students.

Odd/Even Assignments

Exercises 7–17 are structured so that students practice the same concepts whether they are assigned odd or even problems.

---

c. Make a probability histogram of the data.

Draw and label the vertical and horizontal axes. Remember to use equal intervals on each axis. Include a title.

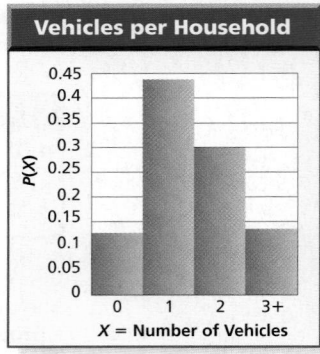

Vehicles per Household

CHECK Your Progress

The table shows the probability distribution of adults who have played golf by age range.

2A. 0.13 + 0.18 + 0.21 + 0.19 + 0.12 + 0.17 = 1

2A. Show that the distribution is valid.

2B. What is the probability that an adult golfer is 35 years or older? **0.69**

2C. Make a probability histogram of the data. **See Ch. 12 Answer Appendix.**

Golfers by Age	
X = Age	Probability
18–24	0.13
25–34	0.18
35–44	0.21
45–54	0.19
55–64	0.12
65+	0.17

online **Personal Tutor at** ca.algebra1.com

CHECK Your Understanding

Example 1 (p. 672)

For Exercises 1–3, use the table that shows the possible sums when rolling two dice and the number of ways each sum can be found.

Sum of Two Dice	2	3	4	5	6	7	8	9	10	11	12
Ways to Achieve Sum	1	2	3	4	5	6	5	4	3	2	1

2. $P(X = 4) = \frac{1}{12}$,

$P(X = 5) = \frac{1}{9}$,

$P(X = 6) = \frac{5}{36}$

1. Draw a table to show the sample space of all possible outcomes. **See Ch.12 Answer Appendix.**

2. Find the probabilities for $X = 4$, $X = 5$, and $X = 6$.

3. What is the probability that the sum of two dice is greater than 6 on three separate rolls? $\frac{343}{1728}$

Example 2 (pp. 673–674)

GRADES For Exercises 4–6, use the table that shows a class's grade distribution, where A = 4.0, B = 3.0, C = 2.0, D = 1.0, and F = 0.

X = Grade	0	1.0	2.0	3.0	4.0
Probability	0.05	0.10	0.40	0.40	0.05

4. 0.05 + 0.1 + 0.40 + 0.40 + 0.05 = 1

4. Show that the probability distribution is valid.

5. What is the probability that a student passes the course? **0.95**

6. What is the probability that a student chosen at random from the class receives a grade of B or better? **0.45**

674 Chapter 12 Statistics and Probability

DIFFERENTIATED HOMEWORK OPTIONS

Level	Assignment	Two-Day Option	
BL Basic	7–17, 20, 22–39	7–17 odd, 23, 24	8–16 even, 20, 22, 25–39
OL Core	7–17 odd, 18–20, 22–39	7–17, 23, 24	18–20, 22, 25–39
AL Advanced /Pre-AP	18–33, (optional: 34–39)		

Exercises

HOMEWORK

For Exercises	See Examples
7–8, 11,	1
9–10, 12–14, 16–17	2

Exercise Levels
A: 7–17
B: 18–19
C: 20–22

For Exercises 7–10, the spinner shown is spun three times.

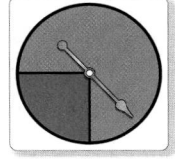

7. Write the sample space with all possible outcomes.

8. Find the probability distribution X, where X represents the number of times the spinner lands on blue for $X = 0$, $X = 1$, $X = 2$, and $X = 3$. **7–9. See Ch. 12 Answer Appendix.**

9. Make a probability histogram.

10. Do all possible outcomes have an equal chance of occurring? Explain. **No; it is more probable to spin blue than red.**

SALES For Exercises 11–14, use the following information.
A music store manager takes an inventory of the top 10 CDs sold each week. After several weeks, the manager has enough information to estimate sales and make a probability distribution table.

Number of Top 10 CDs Sold Each Week	0–100	101–200	201–300	301–400	401–500
Probability	0.10	0.15	0.40	0.25	0.10

11. Let $X =$ number of CDs; $X = 100, 200, 300, 400, 500$.

12. $0.10 + 0.15 + 0.40 + 0.25 + 0.10 = 1$

16. See Ch. 12 Answer Appendix.

11. Define a random variable and list its values.

12. Show that this is a valid probability distribution.

13. In a given week, what is the probability that fewer than 400 CDs sell? **0.90**

14. In a given week, what is the probability that more than 200 CDs sell? **0.75**

EDUCATION For Exercises 15–17, use the table, which shows the education level of persons aged 25 and older in the United States.

$X =$ Level of Education	Probability
Some High School	0.154
High School Graduate	0.320
Some College	0.172
Associate's Degree	0.082
Bachelor's Degree	0.179
Advanced Degree	0.093

15. If a person was randomly selected, what is the probability that he or she completed at most some college? **0.646**

16. Make a probability histogram of the data.

17. Explain how you can find the probability that a randomly selected person has earned at least a bachelor's degree.

17. Sample answer: Add the values for the bars representing bachelor's and advanced degrees.

18. No; 0.221 + 0.136 + 0.126 + 0.065 + 0.043 = 0.591. The sum of the probabilities does not equal 1.

SPORTS For Exercises 18 and 19, use the graph that shows the sports most watched by women on TV.

18. Determine whether this is a valid probability distribution. Justify your answer.

19. Based on the graph, in a group of 45 women how many would you expect to say they watch figure skating? **3**

Top 5 Sports Watched by Women

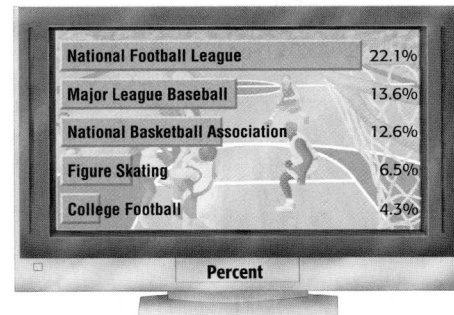

- National Football League — 22.1%
- Major League Baseball — 13.6%
- National Basketball Association — 12.6%
- Figure Skating — 6.5%
- College Football — 4.3%

Percent

Source: ESPN Sports Poll

EXTRA PRACTICE
See pages 743, 755.

Math Online
Self-Check Quiz at
ca.algebra1.com

H.O.T. Problems

20. OPEN ENDED Describe real-life data that could be displayed in a probability histogram. **Sample answer: the number of possible correct answers on a 5-question multiple choice quiz, and the probability of each**

Lesson 12-5 Probability Distributions **675**

BL = Below Grade Level

OL = On Grade Level

AL = Above Grade Level

ELL = English Language Learner

Additional pages not shown:

CRM *Lesson Reading Guide,* p. 34 **BL** **OL** **ELL**

CRM *Skills Practice,* p. 37 **BL** **OL**

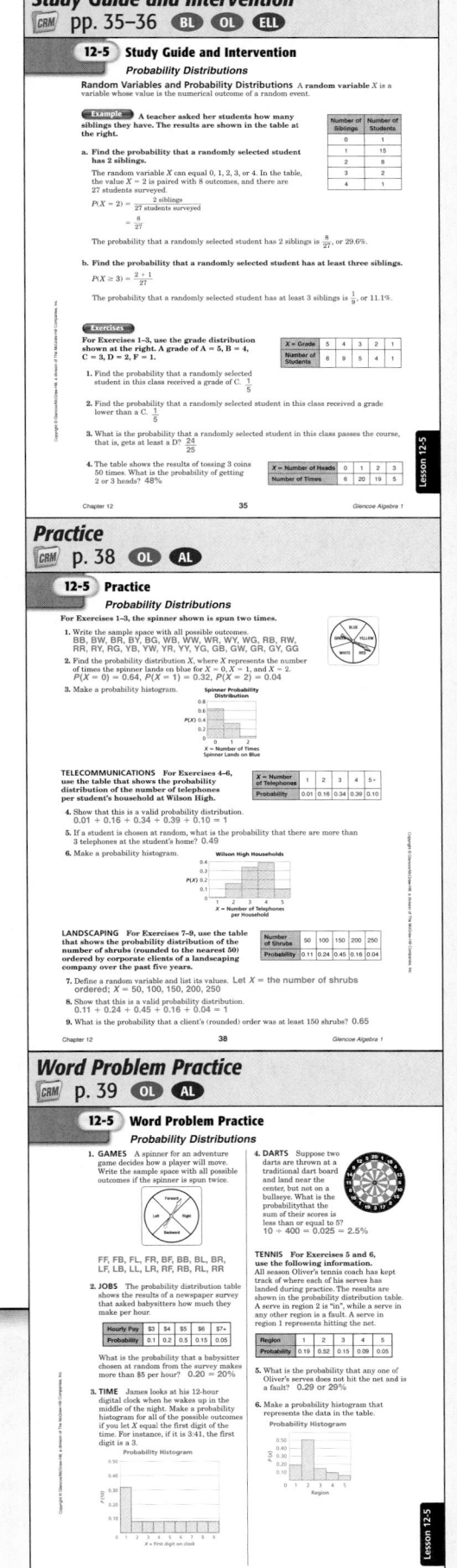

Study Guide and Intervention
CRM pp. 35–36 **BL** **OL** **ELL**

12-5 Study Guide and Intervention
Probability Distributions

Random Variables and Probability Distributions A random variable X is a variable whose value is the numerical outcome of a random event.

Practice
CRM p. 38 **OL** **AL**

12-5 Practice
Probability Distributions

Word Problem Practice
CRM p. 39 **OL** **AL**

12-5 Word Problem Practice
Probability Distributions

Enrichment
CRM p. 40 **OL** **AL**

12-5 Enrichment

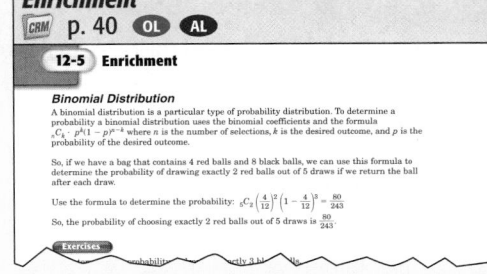

Binomial Distribution

A binomial distribution is a particular type of probability distribution. To determine a probability a binomial distribution uses the binomial coefficients and the formula ${}_nC_k \cdot p^k (1-p)^{n-k}$ where n is the number of selections, k is the desired outcome, and p is the probability of the desired outcome.

So, if we have a bag that contains 4 red balls and 8 black balls, we can use this formula to determine the probability of drawing exactly 2 red balls out of 5 draws if we return the ball after each draw.

Use the formula to determine the probability: ${}_5C_2 \left(\frac{4}{12}\right)^2 \left(1 - \frac{4}{12}\right)^3 = \frac{80}{243}$

So, the probability of choosing exactly 2 red balls out of 5 draws is $\frac{80}{243}$.

Crystal Ball Have students write how they think today's lesson on probability distributions will connect with the next lesson on theoretical and experimental probability.

 Formative Assessment

Check for student understanding of concepts in Lessons 12-4 and 12-5.

 Quiz 3, p. 52

Additional Answer

22. Sample answer: A pet store owner could use probability distributions to plan sales and special events. The owner could determine the probability of each outcome of an event and list them in a table. The owner could then look at the probability of a customer owning more than one pet and create special discounts for larger purchases.

21a. $P(X = 1) = \frac{1}{2}$,
$P(X = 2) = \frac{1}{4}$,
$P(X = 3) = \frac{1}{8}$,
$P(X = 4) = \frac{1}{16}$

21. CHALLENGE Suppose a married couple keeps having children until they have a girl. Let the random variable X represent the number of children in their family. Assume that the probability of having a boy or a girl is each $\frac{1}{2}$.

a. Calculate the probability distribution for $X = 1, 2, 3,$ and 4.

b. Find the probability that the couple will have more than 4 children. $\frac{1}{16}$

22. *Writing in Math* Refer to the information on page 672 to explain how a pet store owner could use a probability distribution. How could the owner create a probability distribution and use it to establish a frequent buyer program? **See margin.**

STANDARDS PRACTICE 7NS1.7

23. The table shows the probability distribution for the number of heads when four coins are tossed. What is the probability that no more than two heads show on a random toss? **C**

X = Number of Heads	Probability P(X)
0	0.0625
1	0.25
2	0.375
3	0.25
4	0.0625

A 0.3125

B 0.375

C 0.6875

D 0.875

24. **REVIEW** Mr. Perez works 40 hours a week at The Used Car Emporium. He earns $7 an hour and 10% commission on every car he sells. If his hourly wage is increased to $7.50 and his commission to 13%, how much money would he earn in a week if he sold $20,000 worth of cars? **J**

F $1700   H $2300

G $2200   J $2900

Spiral Review

A card is drawn from a standard deck of 52 cards. Find each probability. (Lesson 12-4)

25. P(ace or 10) $\frac{2}{13}$

26. P(3 or diamond) $\frac{4}{13}$

27. P(odd number or spade) $\frac{25}{52}$

Evaluate. (Lesson 12-3)

28. $_{10}C_7$ **120**

29. $_{12}C_5$ **792**

30. $(_6P_3)(_5P_3)$ **7200**

SAVINGS For Exercises 31–32, use the following information.
Selena is investing her $900 tax refund in a certificate of deposit that matures in 4 years. The interest rate is 4.25% compounded quarterly. (Lesson 9-6)

31. Determine the balance in the account after 4 years. **$1065.82**

32. Her friend Monique invests the same amount of money at the same interest rate, but her bank compounds interest monthly. Determine how much she will have after 4 years. **$1066.45**

33. Which type of compounding appears more profitable? Explain.
Sample answer: Monthly; the interest earned is higher than quarterly.

GET READY for the Next Lesson

PREREQUISITE SKILL Write each fraction as a percent rounded to the nearest whole number. (pages 702–703)

34. $\frac{16}{80}$ **20%**   35. $\frac{20}{52}$ **38%**   36. $\frac{30}{114}$ **26%**   37. $\frac{57}{120}$ **48%**   38. $\frac{72}{340}$ **21%**   39. $\frac{54}{162}$ **33%**

Pre-AP Activity   Use as an Extension

Have students conduct a survey of their classmates on a topic of interest and create a probability distribution table or histogram. Have them write and answer two probability questions about the data. Avoid sensitive topics such as age, weight, height, or shoe size. Suggest topics such as the number of books students have read this semester, the number of trees in their yards, or the number of languages they expect to speak by the time they graduate from college. Check that probability distribution tables and histograms match the data from the survey and that the questions are relevant to the data and are answered correctly.

Main Ideas

- Use theoretical and experimental probability to represent and solve problems involving uncertainty.
- Perform probability simulations to model real-world situations involving uncertainty.

Reinforcement of Standard 6SDAP3.0 Students determine theoretical and experimental probabilities and use these to make predictions about events.

Reinforcement of Standard 6SDAP3.2 Use data to estimate the probability of future events (e.g., batting averages or number of accidents per mile driven).

New Vocabulary

theoretical probability
experimental probability
relative frequency
empirical study
simulation

GET READY for the Lesson

Researchers at a pharmaceutical company expect a new drug to work successfully in 70% of patients. To test the drug's effectiveness, the company performs three clinical studies of 100 volunteers who use the drug for six months. The results of the studies are shown in the table.

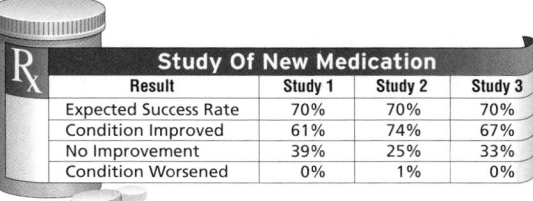

Study Of New Medication			
Result	Study 1	Study 2	Study 3
Expected Success Rate	70%	70%	70%
Condition Improved	61%	74%	67%
No Improvement	39%	25%	33%
Condition Worsened	0%	1%	0%

Theoretical and Experimental Probability The probability we have used to describe events in previous lessons is theoretical probability. **Theoretical probabilities** are determined mathematically and describe what should happen. In the situation above, the expected success rate of 70% is a theoretical probability.

A second type of probability is **experimental probability,** which is determined using data from tests or experiments. Experimental probability is the ratio of the number of times an outcome occurred to the total number of events or trials. This ratio is also known as the **relative frequency.**

$$\text{experimental probability} = \frac{\text{frequency of an outcome}}{\text{total number of trials}}$$

EXAMPLE Experimental Probability

1 **MEDICAL RESEARCH** Refer to the application at the beginning of the lesson. What is the experimental probability that the drug was successful for a patient in Study 1?

$$\text{experimental probability} = \frac{61}{100} \quad \begin{array}{l} \leftarrow \text{frequency of successes} \\ \leftarrow \text{total number of patients} \end{array}$$

The experimental probability of Study 1 is $\frac{61}{100}$ or 61%.

CHECK Your Progress

1. Trevor says he is able to make at least 63% of free throws he takes. To prove this, he decides to take 50 free throws, of which he made 33. Did his experimental probability support his assertion? $\frac{33}{50}$ or 66%; Yes, it supports his assertion.

Lesson 12-6 Probability Simulations **677**

---

1 Focus

Standards Alignment

Before Lesson 12-6
Represent probabilities as ratios, proportions and decimals from Standard 6SDAP3.3

Lesson 12-6
Determine theoretical and experimental probabilities and use these to make predictions about events from Standards 6SDAP3.0 and 6SDAP3.2

After Lesson 12-6
Organize and describe distributions of data by using a number of different methods from Standard PS3.0

2 Teach

Scaffolding Questions
Have students read *Get Ready for the Lesson.*
Ask:
- If researchers think the probability of success of their new drug will be 70%, how many patients out of 100 should see an improvement in their condition? 70 patients

(continued on the next page)

Lesson 12-6 Resources

Chapter 12 Resource Masters
Lesson Reading Guide, p. 42 **BL** **OL** **ELL**
Study Guide and Intervention, pp. 43–44 **BL** **OL** **ELL**
Skills Practice, p. 45 **BL** **OL**
Practice, p. 46 **OL** **AL**
Word Problem Practice, p. 47 **OL** **AL**
Enrichment, p. 48 **OL** **AL**
Quiz 4, p. 52

Transparencies
5-Minute Check Transparency 12-6
Additional Print Resources
Noteables™ Interactive Study Notebook with Foldables™

Technology
ca.algebra1.com
Interactive Classroom CD-ROM
AssignmentWorks CD-ROM
Graphing Calculator Easy Files

- How did the expected success rate compare to the number of people who actually saw their condition improve in the three studies? Fewer than 70 improved in the first study, more than 70 improved in the second study, and fewer than 70 improved in the third study.

Theoretical and Experimental Probability

Example 1 shows how to find the experimental probability of data using one study. **Example 2** shows how to find the experimental probability of an empirical study.

 Formative Assessment

Use the Check Your Progress exercises after each example to determine students' understanding of concepts.

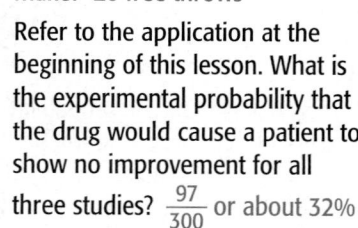

Algebra Lab Give each student or pair of students a single die. Once students have collected their data, have them create a probability distribution table to record the number of times each number comes up. After the activity is complete, suggest that students repeat the die tosses 100 times for experimental results that will more closely resemble the theoretical probability.

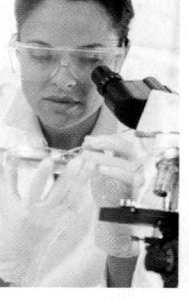

Real-World Career

Medical Scientist
Many medical scientists conduct research to advance knowledge of living organisms, including viruses and bacteria.

Math Online
For more information, go to ca.algebra1.com.

Reading Math

Law of Large Numbers The *Law of Large Numbers* states that as the number of trials increases, the experimental probability gets closer to the theoretical probability.

6. Sample answer: The more times an experiment is performed, the experimental probability is closer to the theoretical probability.

It is often useful to perform an experiment repeatedly, collect and combine the data, and analyze the results. This is known as an **empirical study**.

 EXAMPLE Empirical Study

2 Refer to the application at the beginning of the lesson. What is the experimental probability of success for all three studies?

The number of successful outcomes of the three studies was $61 + 74 + 67$ or 202 out of the 300 total patients.

$$\text{experimental probability} = \frac{202}{300} \text{ or } \frac{101}{150}$$

The experimental probability of the three studies was $\frac{101}{150}$ or about 67%.

 **Your Progress**

2. Refer to Check Your Progress 1. Trevor decided to shoot 50 free throws two more times. He makes 29 of the first 50 free throws and 34 of the second 50. What is the experimental probability of all three tests? $\frac{96}{150}$ or $\frac{16}{25}$ or 64%

Performing Simulations A **simulation** allows you to find an experimental probability by using objects to act out an event that would be difficult or impractical to perform.

Algebra Lab

Simulations

COLLECT THE DATA

- Roll a die 20 times. Record the value on the die after each roll.
- Determine the experimental probability distribution for *X*, the value on the die.
- Combine your results with the rest of the class to find the experimental probability distribution for *X* given the new number of trials. *(20 · the number of students in your class)*

ANALYZE THE DATA

1. Find the theoretical probability of rolling a 2. $\frac{1}{6}$
2. Find the theoretical probability of rolling a 1 or a 6. $\frac{1}{3}$
3. Find the theoretical probability of rolling a value less than 4. $\frac{1}{2}$
4. Compare the experimental and theoretical probabilities. Which pair of probabilities was closer to each other: your individual probabilities or your class's probabilities? **See margin.**
5. Suppose each person rolls the die 50 times. Explain how this would affect the experimental probabilities for the class. **See margin.**
6. What can you conclude about the relationship between the number of experiments in a simulation and the experimental probability?

You can conduct simulations of the outcomes for many problems by using one or more objects such as dice, coins, marbles, or spinners. The objects you choose should have the same number of outcomes as the number of possible outcomes of the problem, and all outcomes should be equally likely.

EXAMPLE Simulation

3 In one season, Malcolm made 75% of the field goals he attempted.

a. What could be used to simulate his kicking a field goal? Explain.

You could use a spinner like the one at the right, where 75% of the spinner represents making a field goal.

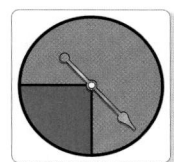

b. Describe a way to simulate his next 8 attempts.

Spin the spinner once to simulate a kick. Record the result, then repeat this 7 more times.

✓CHECK Your Progress

In a trivia game, Becky answered an average of two out of three questions correctly.

3A. What could be used to simulate her correctly answering a question? Explain.

3B. Describe a way to simulate the next 12 questions.

3A. Sample answer: You could use a six-sided die, where rolling a one through four represents a correct answer.

3B. Sample answer: Roll the die to simulate a question. Record the result, then repeat this 11 more times.

EXAMPLE Theoretical and Experimental Probability

4 **DOGS** Ali raises purebred dogs. One of her dogs had a litter of four puppies. What is the most likely mix of male and female puppies? Assume that $P(\text{male}) = P(\text{female}) = \frac{1}{2}$.

a. What objects can be used to simulate the possible outcomes of the puppies?

Each puppy can be male or female, so there are $2 \cdot 2 \cdot 2 \cdot 2$ or 16 possible outcomes for the litter. Use a simulation that also has 2 outcomes for each of 4 events. One possible simulation would be to toss four coins, one for each puppy, with heads representing female and tails representing male.

b. Find the theoretical probability that there are two female and two male puppies.

There are 16 possible outcomes, and the number of combinations that have two female and two male puppies is $_4C_2$ or 6. So the theoretical probability is $\frac{6}{16}$ or $\frac{3}{8}$.

c. The results of a simulation Ali performed are shown in the table at the right. What is the experimental probability that there are three male puppies?

Ali performed 50 trials and 12 of those resulted in three males. So, the experimental probability is $\frac{12}{50}$ or 24%.

Outcomes	Frequency
4 female, 0 male	3
3 female, 1 male	13
2 female, 2 male	18
1 female, 3 male	12
0 female, 4 male	4

(continued on the next page)

Performing Simulations

Example 3 shows how to simulate a situation. **Example 4** shows how to conduct a simulation of a situation and then determine and compare the theoretical and experimental probability of the situation.

ADDITIONAL EXAMPLES

3 In the last 30 days, Bobbie's older brother has given her a ride to school 5 times.

a. What could be used to simulate whether Bobbie's brother will give her a ride to school? Bobbie got a ride to school on $\frac{5}{30}$ or $\frac{1}{6}$ of the days. You could use one side of a die to represent a ride to school.

b. Describe a way to simulate whether Bobbie's brother will give her a ride to school in the next 20 school days. Let one side of the die equal a ride to school. Toss the die 20 times and record each result.

4 **DOGS** Use the data in Example 4 to answer the following questions.

a. What is an alternative to using 4 coins that could model the possible combinations of the puppies? Sample answer: spinner with 16 equal divisions

b. Find the theoretical probability that there will be 4 female puppies in the litter. $\frac{1}{16}$

c. Find the experimental probability that there will be 4 female puppies in the litter. $\frac{3}{50}$ or 6%.

d. How does the theoretical probability compare with the experimental probability? The theoretical probability is a little more than 6% and the experimental probability is 6%, so they are very close.

Additional Answers

4. Sample answer: The class's probability since there are more trials.

5. Sample answer: The class's probability should be closer to the theoretical probability.

Use Exercises 1–10 to check for understanding.

Use the chart at the bottom of the next page to customize assignments for your students.

4A. Sample answer: Use 10 marbles, 1 red marble (10%) representing the defects and 9 yellow marbles (90%) representing the good automobiles, placed in a bag. Then draw out 1 marble at random, record the result, and replace it. Repeat this nine more times representing 10 automobiles.

4D. They are relatively close. As the number of trials increased it would get closer to the theoretical probability.

d. How does the experimental probability compare to the theoretical probability of a litter with three males?

Theoretical probability:

$$P(3 \text{ males}) = \frac{_4C_3}{16} \qquad \frac{\text{combinations with 3 male puppies}}{\text{possible outcomes}}$$

$$= \frac{4}{16} \text{ or } 25\% \qquad \text{Simplify.}$$

The experimental probability, 24%, is very close to the theoretical probability.

✓ **CHECK Your Progress**

QUALITY CONTROL Brandon inspects automobile frames as they come through on the assembly line. On average, he finds a weld defect in one out of ten of the frames each day. He sends these back to correct the defect.

4A. What objects can be used to model the possible outcomes of the automobiles per hour?

4B. What is the theoretical probability that there is one automobile found with defects in a certain hour? $\frac{1}{10}$

4C. The results of a simulation Brandon performed are shown in the table at the right. What is the experimental probability that there will be one defect found in a certain hour? $\frac{3}{20}$ or 15%

Defects	Frequency
0	14
1	3
2	2
3	1

4D. How does the experimental probability compare to the theoretical probability of one defect found in a certain hour?

🌐 **Personal Tutor at** ca.algebra1.com

★ indicates multi-step problem

✓ **CHECK Your Understanding**

Example 1
(p. 677)

GAMES Games at the fair require the majority of people who play to lose in order for game owners to make a profit. Therefore, new games need to be tested to make sure they have sufficient difficulty. The results of three test groups are listed in the table. The owners would like a maximum of 33% of players to win the game. There were 50 participants in each test group.

★ **1.** What is the experimental probability that the participant was a winner in the second group? $\frac{3}{10}$ or 30%

Result	Group 1	Group 2	Group 3
Winners	13	15	19
Losers	37	35	31

Example 2
(p. 678)

★ **2.** What is the experimental probability of winning for all three groups? $\frac{47}{150}$ or 31%

3. A baseball player has a batting average of .300. That is, he gets a hit 30% of the time he is at bat. What could be used to simulate the player taking a turn at bat? **Sample answer: a spinner with 3 red sections of 10 equal sections, a spin on a red section simulates a hit**

For Exercises 4–6, roll a die 25 times and record your results.

Example 3
(p. 679)

4. Based on your results, what is the probability of rolling a 3? **See students' work.**

5. Based on your results, what is the probability of rolling a 5 or an odd number? **See students' work.**

6. Compare your results to the theoretical probabilities. **See students' work.**

680 Chapter 12 Statistics and Probability

Pre-AP Activity **Use as an Extension**

Have students work in groups of three or four to design an experiment that has 8 possible outcomes. Have them brainstorm ways to simulate the outcome and then select a method and build the simulator. Students should create a probability distribution table and compare the theoretical and experimental probabilities of the situation. Have students present their results to the class.

Example 4
(p. 679)

ASTRONOMY For Exercises 7–10, use the following information.
Enrique is writing a report about meteorites and wants to determine the probability that a meteor reaching Earth's surface hits land. He knows that 70% of Earth's surface is covered by water. He places 7 blue marbles and 3 brown marbles in a bag to represent hitting water $\left(\frac{7}{10}\right)$ and hitting land $\left(\frac{3}{10}\right)$. He draws a marble from the bag, records the color, and then replaces the marble. Enrique drew 56 blue and 19 brown marbles.

7. Did Enrique choose an appropriate simulation? Explain.
8. What is the theoretical probability that a meteorite reaching Earth's surface hits land? **30%**
9. Based on his results, what is the probability that a meteorite hits land?
10. Using the experimental probability, how many of the next 500 meteorites that strike Earth would you expect to hit land? **125**

7. Yes; 70% of the marbles in the bag represent water and 30% represent land.
9. 0.25 or 25%

Odd/Even Assignments
Exercises 11–29 are structured so that students practice the same concepts whether they are assigned odd or even problems.

⚠ **Exercise Alert!**
Calculator You may wish to have students use a calculator to determine probabilities in Exercises 8–10.

Additional Answer
11. $P(\text{Preschool}) = 0.060$
$P(\text{Kindergarten}) = 0.058$
$P(\text{Elementary}) = 0.480$
$P(\text{High School}) = 0.256$
$P(\text{College}) = 0.146$

Exercises

HOMEWORK HELP	
For Exercises	**See Examples**
11–13	1, 2
14–17	3
18–29	4

Exercise Levels
A: 11–29
B: 30–32
C: 33–35

GOVERNMENT For Exercises 11–13, use the following information.
The Lewiston School Board sent surveys to randomly selected households to determine needs for the school district. The results of the survey are shown.

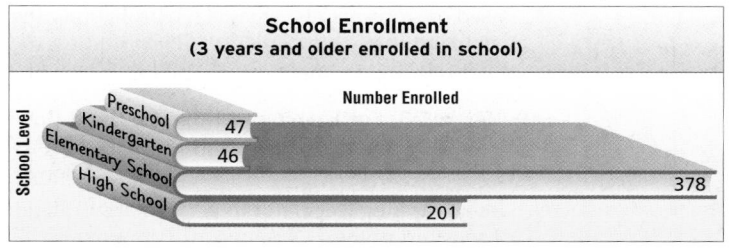

School Enrollment
(3 years and older enrolled in school)

★**11.** Find the experimental probability distribution for the number of people enrolled at each level. **See margin.**
★**12.** Based on the survey, what is the probability that a student chosen at random is in elementary school or high school? **≈ 0.74 or 74%**
13. Suppose the school district is expecting school enrollment to increase by 1800 over the next 5 years due to new homes in the area. Of the new enrollment, how many will most likely be in kindergarten? **123**

14. What could you use to simulate guessing on 15 true-false questions?
15. There are 12 cans of cola, 8 cans of diet cola, and 4 cans of root beer in a cooler. What could be used for a simulation to determine the probability of randomly picking any one type of soft drink?

For Exercises 16 and 17, use the following information.
A mall randomly gives each shopper one of 12 different gifts during a sale.

16. What could be used to perform a simulation of this situation? Explain.
17. How could you use this simulation to model the next 100 gifts handed out?
Sample answer: Toss a coin and roll a number cube 100 times each.

For Exercises 18 and 19, toss 3 coins, one at a time, 25 times and record your results. Find each probability based on your results.

18. What is the probability that any two coins will show heads? **See students' work.**
19. What is the probability that the first and third coins show tails? **See students' work.**

14. Sample answer: a coin tossed 15 times
15. Sample answer: a spinner divided into 3 sections where $\frac{1}{2}$ represents cola, $\frac{1}{3}$ represents diet cola, and $\frac{1}{6}$ represents root beer
16. Sample answer: a coin and a number cube since there are 12 possible outcomes

Lesson 12-6 Probability Simulations **681**

DIFFERENTIATED HOMEWORK OPTIONS			
Level	**Assignment**	**Two-Day Option**	
BL Basic	11–29, 33, 35–46	11–29 odd, 36, 37	12–28 even, 33, 35, 38–46
OL Core	11–29 odd, 30–33, 35–46	11–29, 36, 37	30–33, 35, 38–46
AL Advanced /Pre-AP	30–46		

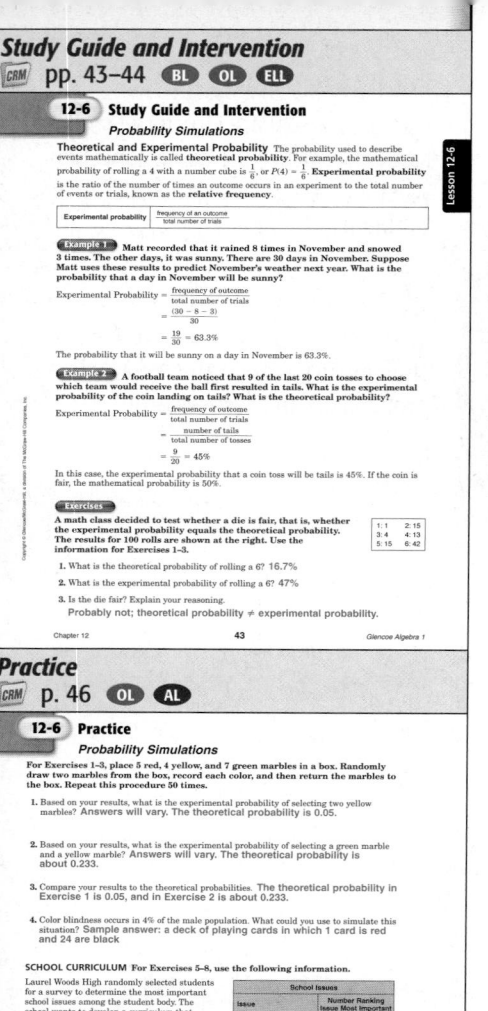

Study Guide and Intervention

CRM pp. 43–44 BL OL ELL

12-6 Study Guide and Intervention

Probability Simulations

Theoretical and Experimental Probability The probability used to describe events mathematically is called **theoretical probability**. For example, the mathematical probability of rolling a 4 with a number cube is $\frac{1}{6}$, or $P(4) = \frac{1}{6}$. **Experimental probability** is the ratio of the number of times an outcome occurs in an experiment to the total number of events or trials, known as the **relative frequency**.

Experimental probability	$\frac{\text{frequency of an outcome}}{\text{total number of trials}}$

Example 1 **Matt recorded that it rained 8 times in November and snowed 3 times. The other days, it was sunny. There are 30 days in November. Suppose Matt uses these results to predict November's weather next year. What is the probability that a day in November will be sunny?**

$$\text{Experimental Probability} = \frac{\text{frequency of outcome}}{\text{total number of trials}} = \frac{(30 - 8 - 3)}{30} = \frac{19}{30} = 63.3\%$$

The probability that it will be sunny on a day in November is 63.3%.

Example 2 **A football team noticed that 9 of the last 20 coin tosses to choose which team would receive the ball first resulted in tails. What is the experimental probability of the coin landing on tails? What is the theoretical probability?**

$$\text{Experimental Probability} = \frac{\text{frequency of outcome}}{\text{total number of trials}} = \frac{\text{number of tails}}{\text{total number of tosses}} = \frac{9}{20} = 45\%$$

In this case, the experimental probability that a coin toss will be tails is 45%. If the coin is fair, the mathematical probability is 50%.

Exercises

A math class decided to test whether a die is fair, that is, whether the experimental probability equals the theoretical probability. The results for 100 rolls are shown at the right. Use the information for Exercises 1–3.

1: 1	2: 15
3: 4	4: 13
5: 15	6: 42

1. What is the theoretical probability of rolling a 6? 16.7%
2. What is the experimental probability of rolling a 6? 47%
3. Is the die fair? Explain your reasoning.
   Probably not; theoretical probability ≠ experimental probability.

Lesson 12-6

Chapter 12 43 Glencoe Algebra 1

Practice

CRM p. 46 OL AL

12-6 Practice

Probability Simulations

For Exercises 1–3, place 5 red, 4 yellow, and 7 green marbles in a box. Randomly draw two marbles from the box, record each color, and then return the marbles to the box. Repeat this procedure 50 times.

1. Based on your results, what is the experimental probability of selecting two yellow marbles? Answers will vary. The theoretical probability is 0.05.
2. Based on your results, what is the experimental probability of selecting a green marble and a yellow marble? Answers will vary. The theoretical probability is about 0.233.
3. Compare your results to the theoretical probabilities. The theoretical probability in Exercise 1 is 0.05, and in Exercise 2 is about 0.233.
4. Color blindness occurs in 4% of the male population. What could you use to simulate this situation? Sample answer: a deck of playing cards in which 1 card is red and 24 are black

SCHOOL CURRICULUM **For Exercises 5–8, use the following information.**

Laurel Woods High randomly selected students for a survey to determine the most important school issues among the student body. The school wants to develop a curriculum that addresses these issues. The survey results are shown in the table.

School Issues

Issue	Number Ranking Issue Most Important
Grades	37
School Standards	17
Popularity	84
Dating	76
Violence	68
Drugs, including tobacco	29

5. Find the experimental probability distribution of the importance of each issue.
   $P(\text{Grades}) \approx 0.119$, $P(\text{School Standards}) \approx 0.055$, $P(\text{Popularity}) \approx 0.270$, $P(\text{Dating}) \approx 0.244$, $P(\text{Violence}) \approx 0.219$, $P(\text{Drugs}) \approx 0.093$
6. Based on the survey, what is the experimental probability that a student chosen at random thinks the most important issue is grades or school standards? about 0.174
7. The enrollment in the 9th and 10th grades at Laurel Woods High is 168. If their opinions are reflective of those of the school as a whole, how many of them would you expect to have chosen popularity as the most important issue? about 45
8. Suppose the school develops a curriculum incorporating the top three issues. What is the probability that a student selected at random will think the curriculum addresses the most important issue at school? about 0.733

Chapter 12 46 Glencoe Algebra 1

Word Problem Practice

CRM p. 47 OL AL

12-6 Word Problem Practice

Probability Simulations

1. GAMES Suppose you spin the spinner below 20 times. You get 6 red, 4 blue, 5 yellow, and 5 green. What is the theoretical probability of spinning red? What is the experimental probability of spinning red? 25%; 30%

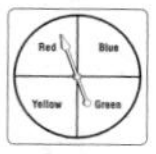

2. EARTHQUAKES Geologists conclude that there is a 62% probability of a magnitude 6.7 or greater quake striking the San Francisco Bay region before 2032. Does this represent *empirical probability, theoretical probability,* or *experimental probability?* empirical
3. TOYS There is a toy on the market that is sold as a mother dog with her puppies. Each mother dog comes with 2, 3, or 4 puppies. The number of puppies in the package remains a surprise until the toy is purchased and opened. Suppose the toy company has stated that one half of the toy packages contain 2 puppies, one third of the packages contain 3 puppies, and one sixth of the packages contain 4 puppies. Describe what could be used to perform a simulation for determining the probability of randomly receiving a certain number of puppies. Sample answer: A number cube could be used to simulate the random event of receiving 2, 3, or 4 puppies. Let #1-3 represent receiving 2 puppies; let #4 and 5 represent receiving 3 puppies; let #6 represent receiving 4 puppies.
4. AUTOMOBILES A consumer group surveyed its members and found that many of them had flats or blowouts with a certain brand of tire. Out of a total of 20,224 tires purchased, 984 developed problems within the first 1000 miles. Lea has just had one of these tires installed on her car. What is the probability that her tire will have a flat or blowout in the first 1000 miles? about 4.9%

POLYGRAPH TESTING **For Exercises 5 and 6, use the following information.**
A former FBI detective has developed a voice stress analysis device to determine whether or not a person is telling the truth. He claims that the device is accurate 95% of the time. Additionally, a traditional polygraph machine has a reported accuracy rate of 80%.

5. Suppose four criminal suspects are given the voice stress analysis. According to the reported empirical probability, what is the probability that the device can correctly analyze the accuracy of all four suspects' statements? Round your answer to the nearest tenth of a percent. 81.5%
6. If a randomly chosen person is given both the voice stress analysis and the traditional polygraph to validate his or her statements, what is the probability that both devices are able to correctly determine the accuracy of the person's statements? 76%

Lesson 12-6

Chapter 12 47 Glencoe Algebra 1

For Exercises 20–22, roll two dice 50 times and record the sums.

20. Based on your results, what is the probability that the sum is 8?
21. Based on your results, what is the probability that the sum is 7, or the sum is greater than 5? See students' work.
22. If you roll the dice 25 more times, which sum would you expect to see about 10% of the time? 5 or 9

20. See students' work.

Real-World Link

Labrador retrievers are the most popular breed of dog in the United States.

Source: American Kennel Club

RESTAURANTS **For Exercises 23–25, use the following information.**
A family restaurant gives away a free toy with each child's meal. There are eight different toys that are randomly given. There is an equally likely chance of getting each toy each time. 23. Sample answer: 4 coins

23. What objects could be used to perform a simulation of this situation?
24. Conduct a simulation until you have one of each toy. Record your results.
25. Based on your results, how many meals must be purchased so that you get all 8 toys?

24–25. See students' work.

ANIMALS **For Exercises 26–29, use the following information.**
Refer to Example 4 on page 679. Suppose Ali's dog has a litter of 5 puppies.

26. List the possible outcomes of the genders of the puppies. See Ch.12 Answer Appendix.
27. Perform a simulation and list your results in a table. See students' work.
28. Based on your results, what is the probability that there are 3 females and two males in the litter? See students' work.
29. What is the experimental probability that the litter has at least three males? See students' work.

ENTERTAINMENT **For Exercises 30–32, use the following information.**
A CD changer contains 5 CDs with 14 songs each. When "Random" is selected, each CD is equally likely to be chosen as each song. 30–32. See students' work.

30. Use a graphing calculator to perform a simulation of randomly playing 20 songs from the 5 CDs. Record your answer.
    KEYSTROKES: [MATH] [◄] 5 1 [,] 70 [,] 20 [)] [ENTER]
31. Do the experimental probabilities for your simulation support the statement that each CD is equally likely to be chosen? Explain.
32. Based on your results, what is the probability that the first three songs played are on the third disc?

EXTRA PRACTICE
See page 743, 755.

Math Online
Self-Check Quiz at ca.algebra1.com

H.O.T. Problems

33. **OPEN ENDED** Describe a real-life situation that could be represented by a simulation. What objects would you use for this experiment?
34. **CHALLENGE** The captain of a football team believes that the coin the referee uses for the opening coin toss gives an advantage to one team. The referee has players toss the coin 50 times each and record their results. Based on the results, do you think the coin is fair? Explain your reasoning.

Player	1	2	3	4	5	6
Heads	38	31	29	27	26	30
Tails	12	19	21	23	24	20

35. ***Writing in Math*** Refer to the information on page 677 to explain how simulations can be used in health care. Include an explanation of experimental probability and why more trials are better than fewer trials when considering experimental probability. See Ch.12 Answer Appendix.

33. Sample answer: a survey of 100 people voting in a two-person election where 50% of the people favor each candidate; 100 coin tosses
34. No; there were 181 heads out of the 300 tosses. The experimental probability of heads is about 60%.

682 Chapter 12 Statistics and Probability

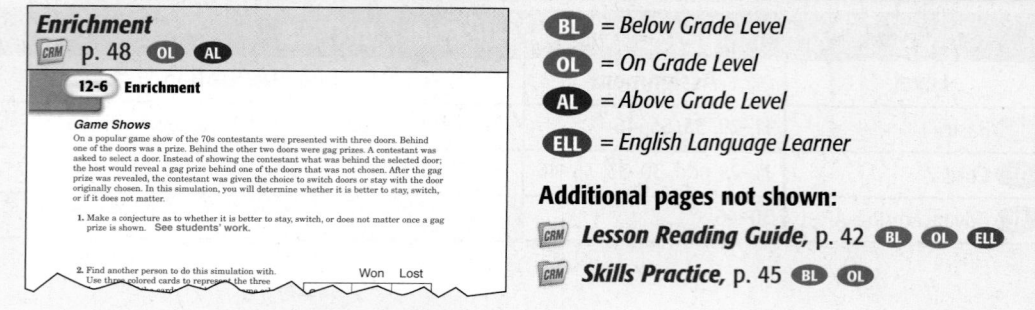

Enrichment

CRM p. 48 OL AL

12-6 Enrichment

Game Shows

On a popular game show of the 70s contestants were presented with three doors. Behind one of the doors was a prize. Behind the other two doors were gag prizes. A contestant was asked to select a door. Instead of showing the contestant what was behind the selected door; the host would reveal a gag prize behind one of the doors that was not chosen. After the gag prize was revealed, the contestant was given the choice to switch doors or stay with the door originally chosen. In this simulation, you will determine whether it is better to stay, switch, or if it does not matter.

1. Make a conjecture as to whether it is better to stay, switch, or does not matter once a gag prize is shown. See students' work.
2. Find another person to do this simulation with. Use three colored cards to represent the three

Won Lost

BL = *Below Grade Level*
OL = *On Grade Level*
AL = *Above Grade Level*
ELL = *English Language Learner*

Additional pages not shown:

CRM ***Lesson Reading Guide,*** p. 42 BL OL ELL
CRM ***Skills Practice,*** p. 45 BL OL

682 Chapter 12 Statistics and Probability

36. Ramón tossed two coins and rolled a die. What is the probability that he tossed two tails and rolled a 3? **D**

A $\frac{1}{4}$ C $\frac{5}{12}$

B $\frac{1}{6}$ D $\frac{1}{24}$

37. REVIEW Miranda bought a DVD boxed set for $\frac{1}{3}$ off the original price and another 10% off the sale price. If the original cost of the DVD set was $44.99, what price did Miranda pay? **J**

F $29.99   H $27.79

G $28.34   J $26.99

Spiral Review

For Exercises 38–40, use the probability distribution for the random variable X, the number of computers per household. (Lesson 12-5)

Computers per Household	
X = Number of Computers	$P(X)$
0	0.579
1	0.276
2	0.107
3+	0.038

Source: U.S. Dept. of Commerce

38. Show that the probability distribution is valid.
$0.579 + 0.276 + 0.107 + 0.038 = 1$

39. If a household is chosen at random, what is the probability that it has at least 2 computers? **0.145**

40. Determine the probability of randomly selecting a household with no more than one computer. **0.855**

For Exercises 41–43, use the following information.
A jar contains 18 nickels, 25 dimes, and 12 quarters. Three coins are randomly selected one at a time. Find each probability. (Lesson 12-4)

41. picking three dimes, replacing each after it is drawn $\frac{125}{1331}$

42. a nickel, then a quarter, then a dime without replacing the coins $\frac{20}{583}$

43. 2 dimes and a quarter, without replacing the coins, if order does not matter $\frac{80}{1749}$

Determine whether the following side measures would form a right triangle. (Lesson 10-4)

44. 5, 7, 9 **no**   **45.** $3\sqrt{34}$, 9, 15 **yes**   **46.** 36, 86.4, 93.6 **yes**

Cross-Curricular Project

Algebra and Physical Science

Building the Best Roller Coaster It is time to complete your project. Use the information and data you have gathered about the building and financing of a roller coaster to prepare a portfolio or Web page. Be sure to include graphs, tables, and/or calculations in the presentation.

 Math Online Cross-Curricular Project at ca.algebra1.com

Graphing Calculator Exercises 30–32 and 33–35 require students to perform simulations with a graphing calculator.

Real-World Connections For Exercises 30–32 and 33–35, explain to students that simulations are used to analyze risks in a wide range of industries, including government, education, environment, financial planning, health care, pharmaceuticals, telecommunications, and utilities. Have students research the use of simulations in one of these industries and share their research with the class.

4 Assess

Yesterday's News Have students describe how yesterday's lesson on probability distributions helped them with today's lesson on probability simulations.

FOLDABLES Study Organizer
Foldables™ Follow-Up
Remind students to add what they have learned about probability simulations and the differences between theoretical and experimental probability to their Foldables. Since this is the last lesson in the chapter, suggest that students review their Foldables. They should look for and correct any gaps in concepts.

✓ **Formative Assessment**
Check for student understanding of concepts in Lesson 12-6.

CRM Quiz 4, p. 52

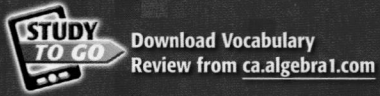

Dinah Zike's Foldables™

Have students look through the chapter to make sure they have included examples in their Foldables to illustrate outcomes, permutations, combinations, and compound events. Suggest that students keep their Foldables handy while completing the Study Guide and Review pages. Point out that their Foldables can serve as a quick review tool for studying for the chapter test.

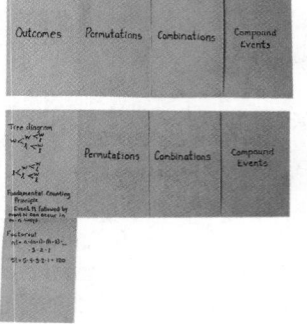

 Formative Assessment

Key Vocabulary The page reference after each word denotes where that term was first introduced. If students have difficulty answering questions 1–8, remind them that they can use these page references to refresh their memories about the vocabulary terms.

 ca.algebra1.com

Vocabulary PuzzleMaker
improves students' mathematics vocabulary using four puzzle formats—crossword, scramble, word search using a word list, and word search using clues. Students can work online or from a printed worksheet.

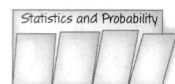

Be sure the following Key Concepts are noted in your Foldable.

Key Concepts

Sampling and Bias (Lesson 12-1)
- Simple random sample, stratified random sample, and systematic random sample are types of unbiased, or random, samples.
- Convenience sample and voluntary response sample are types of biased samples.

Counting Outcomes, Permutations, and Combinations (Lessons 12-2 and 12-3)
- If an event M can occur m ways and is followed by an event N that can occur n ways, the event M followed by event N can occur $m \cdot n$ ways.
- In a permutation, the order of objects is important. $_nP_r = \dfrac{n!}{(n-r)!}$
- In a combination, the order of objects is not important. $_nC_r = \dfrac{n!}{(n-r)!r!}$

Probability of Compound Events (Lesson 12-4)
- For independent events, use $P(A \text{ and } B) = P(A) \cdot P(B)$.
- For dependent events, use $P(A \text{ and } B) = P(A) \cdot P(B \text{ following } A)$.
- For mutually exclusive events, use $P(A \text{ or } B) = P(A) + P(B)$.
- For inclusive events, use $P(A \text{ or } B) = P(A) + P(B) - P(A \text{ and } B)$.

Probability Distributions and Simulations (Lessons 12-5 and 12-6)
- For each value of X, $0 \leq P(X) \leq 1$. The sum of the probabilities of each value of X is 1.
- Theoretical probability describes expected outcomes, while experimental probability describes tested outcomes.
- Simulations are used to perform experiments that would be difficult or impossible to perform in real life.

 Summative Assessment

 Vocabulary Test, p. 54

Key Vocabulary

biased sample (p. 643)	inclusive (p. 666)
combination (p. 657)	independent events (p. 663)
complements (p. 665)	population (p. 642)
compound event (p. 663)	random sample (p. 642)
convenience sample (p. 643)	sample (p. 642)
dependent events (p. 664)	simple random sample (p. 642)
discrete random variable (p. 672)	stratified random sample (p. 642)
empirical study (p. 678)	systematic random sample (p. 642)
event (p. 650)	voluntary response sample (p. 643)
experimental probability (p. 677)	
factorial (p. 652)	

Vocabulary Check

Choose the word or term that best completes each sentence.

1. The arrangement in which order is important is called a (combination, <u>permutation</u>).

2. The notation 10! refers to a (prime factor, <u>factorial</u>).

3. Rolling one die and then another die are (dependent, <u>independent</u>) events.

4. The sum of probabilities of complements equals (0, <u>1</u>).

5. Randomly drawing a coin from a bag and then drawing another coin are dependent events if the coins (are, <u>are not</u>) replaced.

6. Events that cannot occur at the same time are (<u>mutually exclusive</u>, inclusive).

7. The sum of the probabilities in a probability distribution equals (0, <u>1</u>).

8. (<u>Theoretical</u>, Experimental) probabilities are precise and predictable.

 Math Online Vocabulary Review at ca.algebra1.com

Lesson-by-Lesson Review

12-1 Sampling and Bias (pp. 642–648)

Identify the sample, suggest a population from which it was selected, and state whether the sample is *unbiased* (random) or *biased*. If unbiased, classify the sample as *simple*, *stratified*, or *systematic*. If biased, classify as *convenience* or *voluntary response*. 9–10. See margin.

9. **SCIENCE** A laboratory technician needs a sample of results of chemical reactions. She selects test tubes from the first 8 experiments performed on Tuesday.

10. **CANDY BARS** To ensure that all of the chocolate bars are the appropriate weight, every 50th bar on the conveyor belt in the candy factory is removed and weighed.

Example 1 GOVERNMENT To determine whether voters support a new trade agreement, 5 people from the list of registered voters in each state and in the District of Columbia are selected at random. Identify the sample, suggest a population from which it was selected, and state whether the sample is *unbiased* (random) or *biased*. If unbiased, classify the sample as *simple*, *stratified*, or *systematic*. If biased, classify as *convenience* or *voluntary response*.

Since $5 \times 51 = 255$, the sample is 255 registered voters in the United States.

The sample is unbiased. It is an example of a stratified random sample.

12-2 Counting Outcomes (pp. 650–654)

Determine the number of outcomes for each event.

11. **MOVIES** Samantha wants to watch 3 videos one rainy afternoon. She has a choice of 3 comedies, 4 dramas, and 3 musicals. **720**

12. **BOOKS** Marquis buys 4 books, one from each category. He can choose from 12 mystery, 8 science fiction, 10 classics, and 5 biographies. **4800**

13. **SOCCER** The Jackson Jackals and the Westfield Tigers are going to play a best three-out-of-five games soccer tournament. **20**

Example 2 When Jerri packs her lunch, she can choose to make a turkey (T) or roast beef (R) sandwich on French (F) or sourdough bread (S). She also can pack an apple (A) or an orange (O). Draw a tree diagram to show the number of different ways Jerri can select these items.

Meat	Bread	Fruit	Possible Lunches
T	F	A	TFA
		O	TFO
	S	A	TSA
		O	TSO
R	F	A	RFA
		O	RFO
	S	A	RSA
		O	RSO

There are 8 different ways for Jerri to select these items.

Lesson-by-Lesson Review
Intervention If the given examples are not sufficient to review the topics covered by the questions, remind students that the page references tell them where to review that topic in their textbooks.

Two-Day Option Have students complete the Lesson-by-Lesson Review on pp. 685–688. Then you can use ExamView® Assessment Suite to customize another review worksheet that practices all the objectives of this chapter or only the objectives on which your students need more help.

For more information on ExamView® Assessment Suite, see p. 640C.

Differentiated Instruction
Super DVD: MindJogger Videoquizzes Use this DVD as an alternative format of review for the test. For more information on this game show format, see p. 640D.

Additional Answers

9. 8 test tubes with results of chemical reactions; the results of all chemical reactions performed; biased; convenience

10. a group of chocolate bars; all chocolate bars made at the candy factory; unbiased; systematic

Additional Answers

22. $\dfrac{605}{16{,}206}$

23. $\dfrac{1595}{32{,}412}$

12-3 **Permutations and Combinations** (pp. 653–662)

Evaluate each expression.

14. $_4P_2$ **12**

15. $_8C_3$ **56**

16. $_4C_4$ **1**

17. $(_7C_1)(_6C_3)$ **140**

18. $(_7P_3)(_7P_2)$ **8820**

19. $(_3C_2)(_4P_1)$ **12**

CLASS PHOTO For Exercises 20 and 21, use the following information.

The French teacher at East High School wants to arrange the 7 students who joined the French club for a yearbook photo.

20. Does this situation involve a permutation or a combination? **permutation**

21. How many different ways can the 7 students be arranged? **5040**

Example 3 Find $_{12}C_8$.

$$_{12}C_8 = \frac{12!}{(12-8)!8!}$$

$$= \frac{12!}{4!8!}$$

$$= \frac{12 \cdot 11 \cdot 10 \cdot 9}{4!}$$

$$= 495$$

Example 4 Find $_9P_4$.

$$_9P_4 = \frac{9!}{(9-4)!}$$

$$= \frac{9!}{5!}$$

$$= \frac{9 \cdot 8 \cdot 7 \cdot 6 \cdot 5 \cdot 4 \cdot 3 \cdot 2 \cdot 1}{5 \cdot 4 \cdot 3 \cdot 2 \cdot 1}$$

$$= 3024$$

12-4 **Probability of Compound Events** (pp. 663–670)

A bag of colored paper clips contains 30 red clips, 22 blue clips, and 22 green clips. Find each probability if three clips are drawn randomly from the bag and are not replaced. **22–23. See margin.**

22. P(blue, red, green)   **23.** P(red, red, blue)

One card is randomly drawn from a standard deck of 52 cards. Find each probability.

24. P(heart or red) $\dfrac{1}{2}$ **25.** P(10 or spade) $\dfrac{4}{13}$

26. BASEBALL Travis Hafner of the Cleveland Indians has a batting average of .391, which means he has gotten a hit 39.1% of the time. Victor Martinez bats directly after Hafner and has a batting average of .375. What are the chances that both men will get hits their first time up to bat? **14.7%**

Example 5 A box contains 8 red chips, 6 blue chips, and 12 white chips. Three chips are randomly drawn from the box and not replaced. Find P(red, white, blue).

First chip: $P(\text{red}) = \dfrac{8}{26}$ $\dfrac{\text{red chips}}{\text{total chips}}$

Second chip: $P(\text{white}) = \dfrac{12}{25}$ $\dfrac{\text{white chips}}{\text{chips remaining}}$

Third chip: $P(\text{blue}) = \dfrac{6}{24}$ $\dfrac{\text{blue chips}}{\text{chips remaining}}$

$P(\text{red, white, blue})$

$= P(\text{red}) \cdot P(\text{white}) \cdot P(\text{blue})$

$= \dfrac{8}{26} \cdot \dfrac{12}{25} \cdot \dfrac{6}{24}$

$= \dfrac{576}{15600}$ or $\dfrac{12}{325}$

Mixed Problem Solving
For mixed problem-solving practice,
see page 755.

CHAPTER
12 Study Guide
and Review

12-5 **Probability Distributions** (pp. 672–676)

ACTIVITIES The table shows the probability distribution for the number of extracurricular activities in which students at Boardwalk High School participate.

27. Show that the probability distribution is valid.

28. If a student is chosen at random, what is the probability that the student participates in 1 to 3 activities?

29. Make a probability histogram of the data. **See margin.**

Extracurricular Activities	
X = Number of Activities	Probability
0	0.04
1	0.12
2	0.37
3	0.30
4+	0.17

27. $0.04 + 0.12 + 0.37 + 0.30 + 0.17 = 1$
28. 0.79 or 79%

Example 6 A local cable provider asked its subscribers how many television sets they had in their homes. The results of their survey are shown in the probability distribution.

Televisions per Household	
X = Number of Televisions	Probability
1	0.18
2	0.36
3	0.34
4	0.08
5+	0.04

a. **Show that the probability distribution is valid.**

For each value of X, the probability is greater than or equal to 0 and less than or equal to 1. $0.18 + 0.36 + 0.34 + 0.08 + 0.04 = 1$, so the sum of the probabilities is 1.

b. **If a household is selected at random, what is the probability that it has fewer than 4 televisions?**

$P(X < 4)$
$\quad = P(X = 1) + P(X = 2) + P(X = 3)$
$\quad = 0.18 + 0.36 + 0.34$
$\quad = 0.88$

The probability that a randomly selected household has fewer than 4 televisions is 88%.

Additional Answer

29. **Extracurricular Activities**

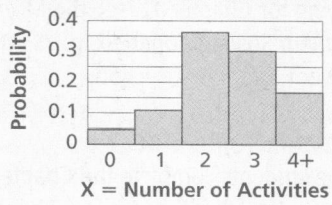

CHAPTER 12 — Study Guide and Review

Problem Solving Review
For additional practice in problem solving for Chapter 12, see the Mixed Problem Solving Appendix, p. 755 in the Student Handbook section.

Anticipation Guide
Have students complete the Chapter 12 Anticipation Guide and discuss how their responses have changed now that they have completed Chapter 12.

CRM Anticipation Guide, pp. 3–4

Additional Answer
31. Sample answer: There are 6 possible outcomes. So, you could use a die.

CHAPTER 12 — Study Guide and Review

12-6 **Probability Simulations** (pp. 677–683)

BIOLOGY While studying flower colors in biology class, students are given the Punnett square below. The Punnett square shows that red parent plant flowers (Rr) produce red flowers (RR and Rr) and pink flowers (rr).

	R	r
R	RR	Rr
r	Rr	rr

30. If 5 flowers are produced, find the theoretical probability that there will be 4 red flowers and 1 pink flower. **39.6%**

31. Describe items that the students could use to simulate the colors of 5 flowers. **See margin.**

32. The results of a simulation of flowers are shown in the table. What is the experimental probability that there will be 3 red flowers and 2 pink flowers? **28.8%**

Outcomes	Frequency
5 red, 0 pink	15
4 red, 1 pink	30
3 red, 2 pink	23
2 red, 3 pink	7
1 red, 4 pink	4
0 red, 5 pink	1

Example 7 A group of 3 coins are tossed.

a. Find the theoretical probability that there will be 2 heads and 1 tail.

Each coin toss can be heads or tails, so there are $2 \cdot 2 \cdot 2$ or 8 possible outcomes. There are 3 possible combinations of 2 heads and one tail, HHT, HTH, or TTH. So, the theoretical probability is $\frac{3}{8}$.

b. The results of a simulation in which three coins are tossed ten times are shown in the table. What is the experimental probability that there will be 2 heads and 1 tail?

Outcomes	Frequency
3 heads, 0 tails	1
2 heads, 1 tail	4
1 head, 2 tails	3
0 heads, 3 tails	2

Of the 10 trials, 4 resulted in 2 heads and 1 tail, so the experimental probability is $\frac{4}{10}$ or 40%.

c. Compare the theoretical probability of 2 heads and 1 tail and the experimental probability of 2 heads and 1 tail.

The theoretical probability is $\frac{3}{8}$ or 37.5%, while the experimental probability is $\frac{4}{10}$ or 40%. The probabilities are close.

Problem Solving Review
For additional practice in problem solving for Chapter 12, see the Mixed Problem Solving Appendix, p. 755 in the Student Handbook section.

Anticipation Guide
Have students complete the Chapter 12

Anticipation Guide and discuss how their responses have changed now that they have completed Chapter 12.

 Anticipation Guide, pp. 3–4

Identify the sample, suggest a population from which it was selected, and state whether it is *unbiased* (random) or *biased*. If unbiased, classify the sample as *simple*, *stratified*, or *systematic*. If biased, classify as *convenience* or *voluntary response*. **1–2. See margin.**

1. **DOGS** A veterinarian needs a sample of dogs in her kennel to be tested for fleas. She selects the first five dogs who run from the pen.

2. **LIBRARIES** A librarian wants to sample book titles checked out on Wednesday. He randomly chooses a book checked out each hour that the library is open.

There are two roads from Ashville to Bakersville, four roads from Bakersville to Clifton, and two roads from Clifton to Derry.

3. Draw a tree diagram showing the possible routes from Ashville to Derry.

4. How many different routes are there from Ashville to Derry? **16**

3. See Ch. 12 Answer Appendix.

Determine whether each situation involves a *permutation* or a *combination*. Then determine the number of possible arrangements.

5. Six students in a class meet in a room that has nine chairs. **combination; 84**

6. the top four finishers in a race with ten participants **permutation; 5040**

7. A class has 15 girls and 19 boys. A committee is formed with two girls and two boys, each with a distinct responsibility. **permutation; 71,820**

A bag contains 4 red, 6 blue, 4 yellow, and 2 green marbles. Once a marble is selected, it is not replaced. Find each probability.

8. P(blue, green) $\frac{1}{20}$

9. P(yellow, yellow) $\frac{1}{20}$

10. P(red, blue, yellow) $\frac{1}{35}$

11. P(blue, red, not green) $\frac{3}{35}$

The spinner is spun, and a die is rolled. Find each probability.

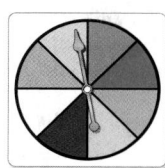

12. P(yellow, 4) $\frac{1}{48}$

13. P(red, even) $\frac{1}{16}$

14. P(purple or white, not prime) $\frac{1}{8}$

15. P(green, even or less than 5) $\frac{5}{48}$

A magician randomly selects a card from a standard deck of 52 cards. Without replacing it, the magician has a member of the audience randomly select a card. Find each probability.

16. P(club, heart) $\frac{13}{204}$

17. P(jack or queen) $\frac{2}{13}$

18. P(black 7, diamond) $\frac{1}{102}$

19. P(queen or red, jack of spades) $\frac{7}{663}$

20. P(black 10, ace or heart) $\frac{8}{663}$

The table shows the number of ways the coins can land heads up when four coins are tossed at the same time. Find each probability.

Four Coins Tossed	
Number of Heads	Possible Outcomes
0	1
1	4
2	6
3	4
4	1

21. P(no heads) **6.25%**

22. P(at least two heads)

23. P(two tails) **37.5%**

22. 68.75%

24. **MULTIPLE CHOICE** Two numbers a and b can be arranged in two different orders: a, b and b, a. In how many ways can three numbers be arranged? **D**

A 3   B 4   C 5   D 6

25. **MULTIPLE CHOICE** If a coin is tossed three times, what is the probability that the results will be heads exactly one time? **H**

F $\frac{2}{3}$ H $\frac{3}{8}$

G $\frac{1}{5}$ J $\frac{1}{8}$

CHAPTER 12 Practice Test

✓ Summative Assessment

CRM Chapter 12 Resource Masters

Leveled Chapter 12 Tests			
Form	Type	Level	Pages
1	MC	BL	55–56
2A	MC	OL	57–58
2B	MC	OL	59–60
2C	FR	OL	61–62
2D	FR	OL	63–64
3	FR	AL	65–66

MC = multiple-choice questions
FR = free-response questions
BL = below grade level
OL = on grade level
AL = above grade level

- Vocabulary Test, p. 54
- Extended-Response Test, p. 67

ExamView Assessment Suite   Customize and create multiple versions of your chapter tests and their answer keys. All of the questions from the leveled chapter tests in the *Chapter 12 Resource Masters* are also available on ExamView Assessment Suite with the California Standard that each item assesses.

Additional Answers

1. a set of dogs; dogs in the kennel; biased convenience sample

2. the set of all books in the library; books checked out on Wednesday; unbiased systematic sample

Data-Driven Decision Making	Exercises	Lesson	📊 Standard	Resources for Review
Diagnostic Teaching Based on the results of the Chapter 12 Practice Test, use the following to review concepts that students continue to find challenging.	21–23	12–5	**Probability and Statistics 3.0**	CRM Study Guide and Intervention, pp. 35–36, 42–43 **Math Online** • Extra Examples • Personal Tutor • Concepts in Motion
	25	12–6	**Reinforcement of 6SDAP3.2**	

CHAPTER

12

California
Standards Practice

Item Analysis

Questions 3 and 7 are griddable questions on a standardized test. In a griddable question, students arrive at an answer then record it in a special grid, coloring in the appropriate bubble under each digit of the answer.

 Formative Assessment

You can use these two pages to benchmark student progress. The California Standards objectives are listed with each question.

 Chapter 12 Resource Masters
• Standardized Test Practice, pp. 68–70

 Create practice worksheets or tests that align to the California Standards, as well as TIMSS and NAEP tests.

Read each question. Then fill in the correct answer on the answer document provided by your teacher or on a sheet of paper.

1 The table shows the results of a survey given to 600 customers at a music store.

Music Survey

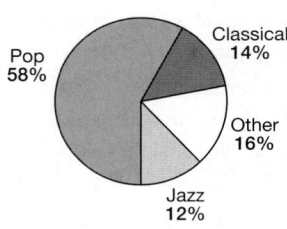

Pop 58%
Classical 14%
Other 16%
Jazz 12%

According to the circle graph shown above— **B**

A more than half of the customers' favorite music is classical or jazz.

B more customers' chose pop music as their favorite than all other types of music.

C more customers' favorite music is something other than either jazz or classical.

D the number of customers whose favorite music is pop is more than five times the number of customers whose favorite music is jazz.

2 Which fraction equals the product $\left(\dfrac{x+6}{5x+4}\right)\left(\dfrac{4x-5}{x-6}\right)$? **J**

F $\dfrac{4x-5}{5x+4}$

G $\dfrac{5x+4}{4x-5}$

H $\dfrac{x^2-36}{20x^2-9x-20}$

J $\dfrac{4x^2+19x-30}{5x^2-26x-24}$

690 **Chapter 12** Statistics and Probability

---

3 Ms. Milo's classroom is square, with sides that are 20 feet long. What is the approximate distance in feet from one corner of the room to the other corner diagonally? **28**

4 Miguel rolled a six-sided die 60 times. The results are shown in the table below.

Side	Number of Times Landed
1	12
2	10
3	8
4	15
5	7
6	8

Which number has the same experimental probability as theoretical probability? **G**

F 1
G 2
H 3
J 4

5 What is the solution set of the quadratic equation $4x^2 - 2x - 3 = 0$? **C**

A $\left\{-\dfrac{1}{4}, \dfrac{1}{4}\right\}$

B $\left\{1 + \sqrt{13}, 1 - \sqrt{13}\right\}$

C $\left\{\dfrac{1+\sqrt{13}}{4}, \dfrac{1-\sqrt{13}}{4}\right\}$

D no real solution

TEST-TAKING TIP

Question 5 Review common mathematical formulas such as the Quadratic Formula before taking standardized tests.

 Math **online** California Standards Practice at ca.algebra1.com

More California
Standards Practice
For practice by standard,
see pages CA1–CA43.

CHAPTER
12 California
Standards Practice

6 At Marvin's Pizza Place, 30% of the customers order pepperoni pizza. Also, 65% of the customers order a Cola to drink. What is the probability that a customer selected at random orders a pepperoni pizza and a cola? **J**

F $\dfrac{95}{100}$

G $\dfrac{1}{3}$

H $\dfrac{35}{100}$

J $\dfrac{39}{200}$

7 The box below shows the prices of running shoes on sale at RunnersSource.

$99, $72, $54, $58, $107, $81, $69, $108, $99

What is the median price in dollars? **81**

8 If a and b are related so that $a + b > a - b$, which statement must be true about a and b? **G**

F a is greater than b.

G a is a negative number and b is a positive number.

H b is a negative number and a is a positive number..

J a and b are negative numbers.

9 Which expression below illustrates the Commutative Property? **C**

A $(x + y) + 2 = x + (y + 2)$

B $-3(a + b) = -3a + -3b$

C $(qr)s = (rq)s$

D $2 + 0 = 2$

10 Lauren sold T-shirts for 10 days in a row for her band fund-raiser. In those 10 days, she sold 120 T-shirts for an average of 12 T-shirts per day. For how many days must she sell 20 T-shirts to bring her average to 18 T-shirts per day? **H**

F 10   H 30

G 20   J 40

11 $(9x^2 - 6x + 4) - (x^2 + 5x - 4) =$ **C**

A $8x^2 - x + 8$

B $8x^2 - x - 8$

C $8x^2 - 11x + 8$

D $8x^2 - 11x - 8$

Pre-AP/Anchor Problem

Record your answers on a sheet of paper. Show your work.

12 At WackyWorld Pizza, the Random Special is a random selection of two different toppings on a large cheese pizza. The available toppings are pepperoni, sausage, onion, mushrooms, and green peppers.

a. How many different Random Specials are possible? Show how you found your answer. **See below.**

b. If you order the Random Special, what is the probability that it will have mushrooms? **2/5**

c. If you order the Random Special, what is the probability that it will have neither onion nor green peppers? **3/10**

12a. 10 Random Specials are possible. You can list all of the combinations, using letters for each topping. PS PO PM PG SO SM SG OM OG MG. There are 10 possible combinations.

Answer Sheet Practice
Have students simulate taking a standardized test by recording their answers on practice recording sheets.

CRM Student Recording Sheet, p. 49

TEST-TAKING TIP

Question 10 Always read every answer choice, particularly when questions contain the word **NOT**.

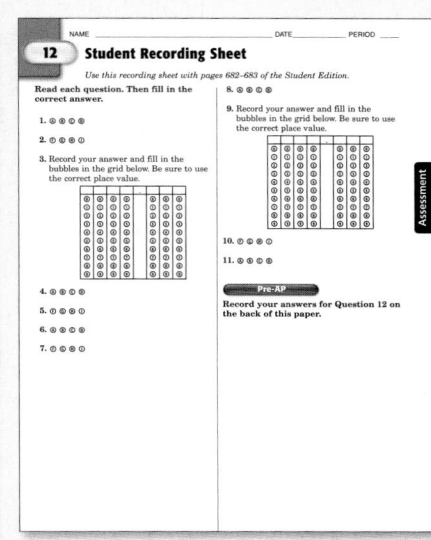

NEED EXTRA HELP?

If You Missed Question...	1	2	3	4	5	6	7	8	9	10	11	12
Go to Lesson or Page...	12-6	11-3	10-4	12-6	9-4	12-4	711	6-1	1-2	11-9	7-4	12-3
For Help with Standard...	6PS2.5	13.0	7MG3.3	6PS3.5	20.0	6PS3.5	6PS1.1	25.2	25.1	15.0	10.0	PS1.0

Page 649, Reading Math

3a. Sample answer: Since we had hamburgers at the last party, would you prefer pizza for the next party?

3b. Sample answer: Would you prefer hamburgers or pizza for the class party?

Page 650, Lesson 12-2 (Check Your Progress)

1.
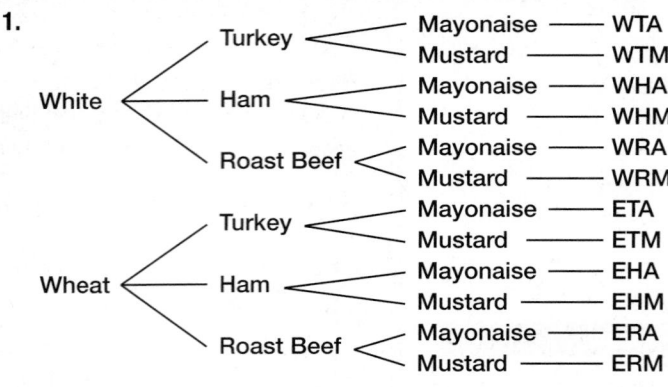

Page 653, Lesson 12-2

1.
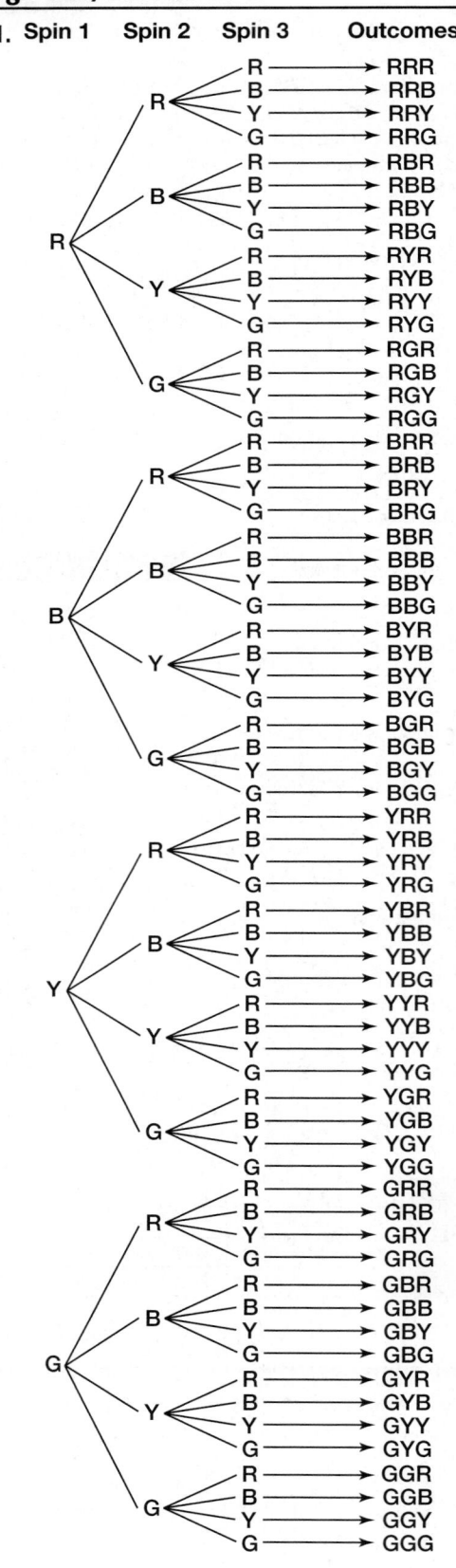

6. 27;

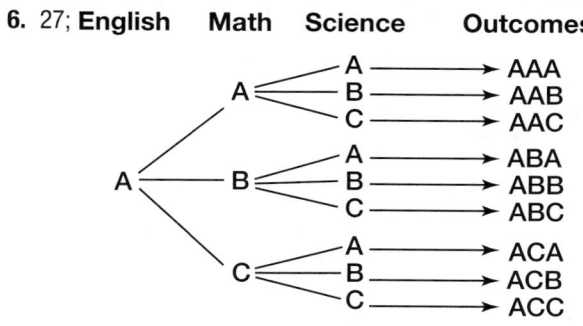

7. 12;

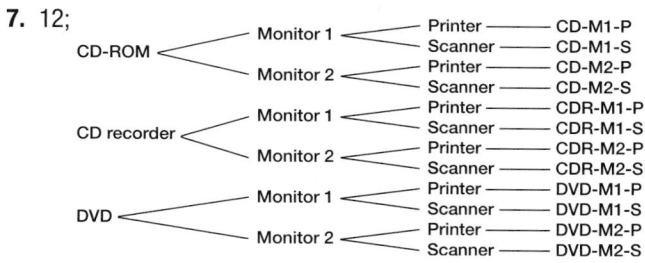

16.

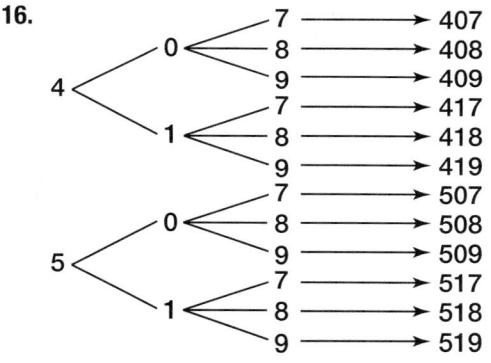

17. Columbus in three games : C-C-C; Columbus in four games: C-C-D-C, C-D-C-C, D-C-C-C; Columbus in 5 games: C-C-D-D-C, C-D-C-D-C, C-D-D-C-C, D-C-C-D-C, D-C-D-C-C, D-D-C-C-C

Dallas in three games: D-D-D; Dallas in four games: C-D-D-D, D-C-D-D, D-D-C-D; Dallas in five games: C-C-D-D-D, C-D-C-D-D, C-D-D-C-D, D-C-C-D-D, D-C-D-C-D, D-D-C-C-D

1.

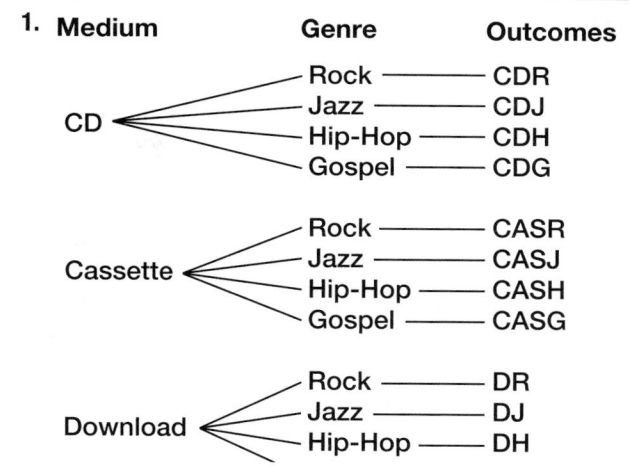

2C.

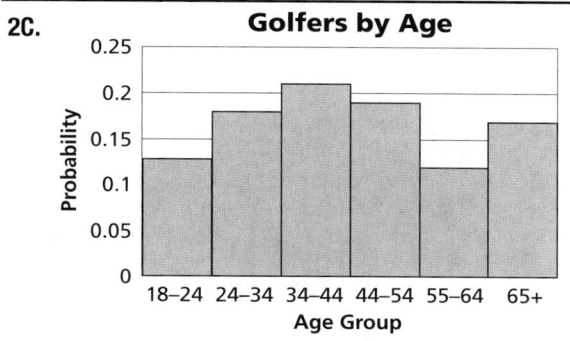

1.

	1	2	3	4	5	6
1	2	3	4	5	6	7
2	3	4	5	6	7	8
3	4	5	6	7	8	9
4	5	6	7	8	9	10
5	6	7	8	9	10	11
6	7	8	9	10	11	12

Page 675, Lesson 12-5

7. RRR, RRB, RBR, RBB, BRR, BRB, BBR, BBB

8. $P(X = 0) = \frac{1}{64}$, $P(X = 1) = \frac{3}{64}$, $P(X = 2) = \frac{9}{64}$,

$P(X = 3) = \frac{27}{64}$

9.

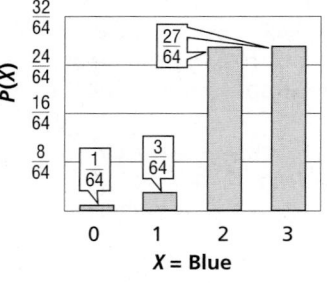

16.

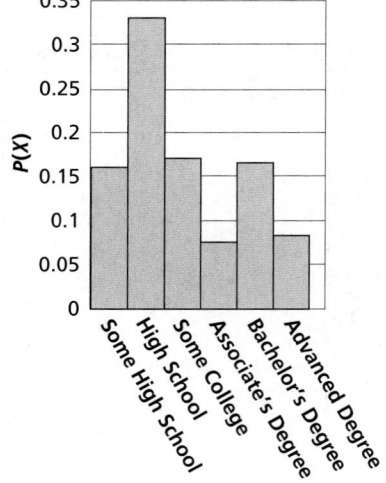

Page 682, Lesson 12-6

26. MMMMM, MMMMF, MMMFM, MMMFF, MMFMM, MMFMF, MMFFM, MMFFF, MFMMM, MFMMF, MFMFM, MFMFF, MFFMM, MFFMF, MFFFM, MFFFF, FMMMM, FMMMF, FMMFM, FMMFF, FMFMM, FMFMF, FMFFM, FMFFF, FFMMM, FFMMF, FFMFM, FFMFF, FFFMM, FFFMF, FFFFM, FFFFF

35. Sample answer: Probability can be used to determine the likelihood that a medication or treatment will be successful. Experimental probability is determining probability based on trials or studies. To have the experimental more closely resemble the theoretical probability the researchers should perform more trials.

Page 689, Chapter 12 Practice Test

3.

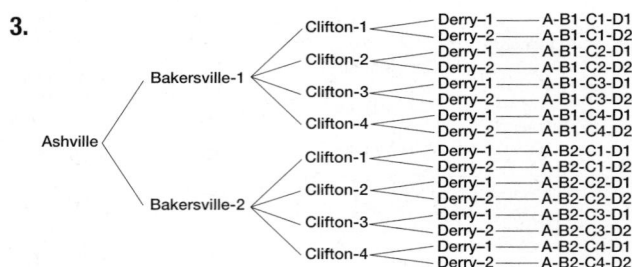

Additional Standard Review

Mastering the California Mathematics Standards

This consumable workbook includes multiple assessment tools to determine how well your students have mastered the Algebra I standards.

Diagnose Use the Diagnostic Test to pinpoint which California Standards need reinforcement.

Prescribe Use the results from the Diagnostic Test to assign practice pages for each student. The student workbook includes a recording chart so that students monitor their own progress in mastering each Standard. The Teacher Edition also includes a class recording chart to monitor all of your students' progress.

Practice There are two ways in which students can practice multiple-choice questions that relate to the Algebra I standards. One practice set is organized by standard and has at least one page of questions per standard. The other practice set is organized by the sequence in which the topics are taught in this textbook.

A *Standards Assessment* is modeled after the CST blueprint for Algebra I and includes multiple-choice questions to assess student progress in mastering the standards.

Periodic Assessment The workbook also includes four Periodic Assessments that help you monitor your students progress in mastering the California Standards. These tests can be used to pinpoint those Standards that need more instruction.

The Teacher Edition includes answers for ease in grading as well as additional diagnostic tools.

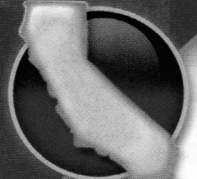

Standards Review

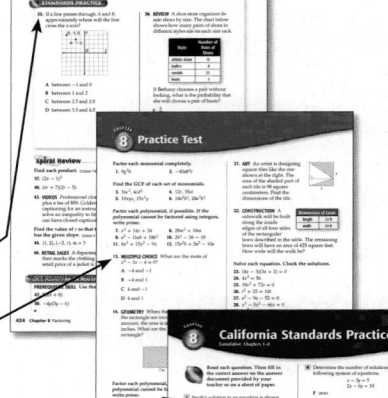

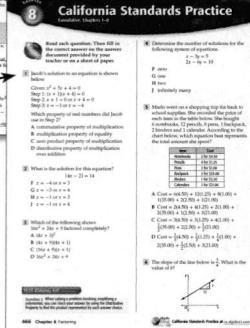

Throughout the year, you may be required to take several tests, and you may have some questions about them. Here are some answers to help you get ready.

How Should I Study?

The good news is that you've been studying all along — a little bit every day. Here are some of the ways your textbook has been preparing you.

- **Every Day** Each lesson had practice questions that cover the California Standards.
- **Every Week** The Mid-Chapter Quizzes and Practice Tests had several multiple-choice practice questions.
- **Every Month** The California Standards Practice pages at the end of each chapter had even more questions similar to those on the tests.

Are There Other Ways to Review?

Absolutely! The following pages contain even more practice for each California standard.

Tips for SUCCESS

Prepare
- Go to bed early the night before the test. You will think more clearly after a good night's rest.
- Become familiar with common formulas and when they should be used.
- Think positively.

During the Test
- Read each problem carefully. Underline key words and think about different ways to solve the problem.
- Watch for key words like NOT. Also look for order words like *least, greatest, first,* and *last.*
- Answer questions you are sure about first. If you do not know the answer to a question, skip it and go back to that question later.
- Check your answer to make sure it is reasonable.
- Make sure that the number of the question on the answer sheet matches the number of the question on which you are working in your test booklet.

Whatever you do...
- Don't try to do it all in your head. If no figure is provided, draw one.
- Don't rush. Try to work at a steady pace.
- Don't give up. Some problems may seem hard to you, but you may be able to figure out what to do if you read each question carefully or try another strategy.

 The questions from the *Mastering the California Standards* workbook are also available in an electronic format on the ExamView Assessment Suite. These standard-based questions can easily be incorporated into your tests or used separately for Standards practice.

The Teacher Management System allows you to automatically grade tests and track students' progress using multiple reporting features.

CA1

Multiple-Choice Questions

Many tests have multiple-choice questions. You are asked to choose the best answer from four or five possible answers.

To record a multiple-choice answer, you will be asked to shade in a bubble that is a circle or an oval. Always make sure that your shading is dark enough and completely covers the bubble.

The answer to a multiple-choice question is usually not immediately obvious from the choices, but you may be able to eliminate some of the possibilities by using your knowledge of mathematics.

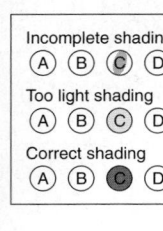

Incomplete shading
Ⓐ Ⓑ Ⓒ Ⓓ

Too light shading
Ⓐ Ⓑ Ⓒ Ⓓ

Correct shading
Ⓐ Ⓑ ● Ⓓ

STANDARDS EXAMPLE

1 A storm signal flag is used to warn small craft of wind speeds that are greater than 38 miles per hour. The length of the square flag is always three times the length of the side of the black square. If y is the area of the black square and x is the length of the side of the flag, which equation describes the relationship between x and y?

A $y = \frac{1}{3}x^2$

B $y = \frac{1}{9}x^2$

C $y = x^2 - 1$

D $y = 3x$

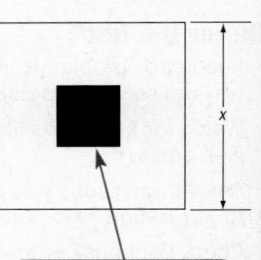

If x is 3 times the length of this side, then this side length is $\frac{1}{3}x$.

STRATEGY

Elimination You can eliminate any obvious wrong answers.

For the area of a square, $A = s^2$.
So, $A = x \cdot x$ or x^2.

The area of the black square is part of the area of the flag, which is x^2. Eliminate choice D because it does not include x^2.

$A = \left(\frac{1}{3}x\right)^2$ or $\frac{1}{9}x^2$ square units

So, $y = \frac{1}{9}x^2$. This is choice B.

Use some random numbers to check your choice.

Multiples of 3 make calculations easier.

Length of Flag (x)	Length of Black Square	Area of Black Square	Area $= \frac{1}{9}x^2$
12	4	16	$16 \stackrel{?}{=} \frac{1}{9}(12^2)$ ✓
27	9	81	$81 \stackrel{?}{=} \frac{1}{9}(27^2)$ ✓
60	20	400	$400 \stackrel{?}{=} \frac{1}{9}(60^2)$ ✓

Many multiple-choice questions are actually two- or three-step problems. If you do not read the question carefully, you may select a choice that is an intermediate step instead of the correct final answer.

STANDARDS EXAMPLE

2 **Barrington can skateboard down a hill five times as fast as he can walk up the hill. If it takes 9 minutes to walk up the hill and skateboard back down, how many minutes does it take him to walk up the hill?**

  F 1.5 min   **G** 4.5 min   **H** 7.2 min   **J** 7.5 min

STRATEGY

Reread the Problem
Read the problem carefully to find what the question is asking.

Before involving any algebra, let's think about the problem using random numbers. Skating is five times as fast as walking, so walking time equals 5 times the skate time. Use a table to find a pattern.

Use the pattern to find a general expression for walk time given any skate time.

Skate Time	Skate Time $\times$ 5 = Walk Time
6 min	$6 \cdot 5 = 30$ min
3 min	$3 \cdot 5 = 15$ min
2 min	$2 \cdot 5 = 10$ min
x min	$x \cdot 5 = 5x$ min

The problem states that the walk time and the skate time total 9 minutes.

Use the expression to write an equation for the problem.

$x + 5x = 9$ skate time + walk time = 9 minutes

   $6x = 9$ Add like terms.

    $x = 1.5$ Divide each side by 6.

Looking at the choices, you might think that choice F is the correct answer. But what does x represent, and what is the problem asking?

The problem asks for the time it takes to walk up the hill, but the value of x is the time it takes to skateboard. So, the actual answer is found using $5x$ or $5(1.5)$, which is 7.5 minutes. The correct choice is J.

STANDARDS EXAMPLE

3 **The Band Boosters are making ice cream to sell at an open house. Each batch of ice cream calls for 5 cups of milk. They plan to make 20 batches. How many gallons of milk do they need?**

  A 800   **B** 100   **C** 25   **D** 6.25

STRATEGY

Units of Measure
Make certain your answer reflects the correct unit of measure.

The Band Boosters need 5×20 or 100 cups of milk. However, choice B is not the correct answer. The question asks for *gallons* of milk.

4 cups = 1 quart and 4 quarts = 1 gallon, so 1 gallon = 4×4 or 16 cups.

$100 \text{ cups} \times \dfrac{1 \text{ gallon}}{16 \text{ cups}} = 6.25$ gallons, which is choice D.

Multiple-Choice Questions   **CA3**

Practice by Standard

Standard 1.0: Students identify and use arithmetic properties of subsets of integers and rational, irrational, and real numbers, including closure properties for the four basic arithmetic operations where applicable.

DIRECTIONS Choose the best answer.

QUICK Practice

1 Which illustrates the Transitive Property of Equality? **B**

  A If $a = b$, then $b = a$.

  B If $a = b$ and $b = c$, then $a = c$.

  C $a = a$

  D If $a = b$ and $b = c$, then $a = 0$.

QUICK Review

STRATEGY Eliminate the choices that are incorrect. Then choose from the remaining choices.

The Transitive Property of Equality states that if one quantity equals a second quantity and the second quantity equals a third quantity, then the first quantity equals the third quantity.

For more help with properties, see page 22.

Practice on Your Own

Standard 1.0

2 Which set of numbers is closed under addition? **H**

  F $\{0, 1, 2, 3, 4\}$

  G $\{0, 2, 4, 6, 8\}$

  H $\{0, 2, 4, 6, \ldots\}$

  J $\{1, 3, 5, 7, \ldots\}$

3 What property is illustrated below?
$3(0) = 0$ **C**

  A Additive Identity

  B Multiplicative Identity

  C Multiplicative Property of Zero

  D Zero Product Property

4 What property is illustrated below?
$4(x + 10) = 4x + 4 \cdot 10$ **G**

  F Commutative Property of Addition

  G Distributive Property

  H Substitution

  J Transitive Property of Equality

5 Which statement illustrates the Commutative Property of Addition? **C**

  A $(3 + 2) + 7 = 3 + (2 + 7)$

  B $(3 + 2) \cdot 7 = 3 \cdot 7 + 2 \cdot 7$

  C $(3 + 2) + 7 = (2 + 3) + 7$

  D $(3 \cdot 2) \cdot 7 = (2 \cdot 3) \cdot 7$

6 The following set of numbers is closed under which operation(s)? **J**
$\{1, 2, 3, 4, 5, 6, \ldots\}$

  F addition

  G subtraction

  H multiplication

  J addition and multiplication

7 Which statement illustrates the Symmetric Property of Equality? **B**

  A If $x = y$ and $y = 2$, then $x = 2$.

  B If $x = 2$, then $2 = x$.

  C $3 + x = x + 3$

  D If $x = 2$, then $3x = 6$.

Practice by Standard

Standard 1.1: Students use properties of numbers to demonstrate whether assertions are true or false.

DIRECTIONS Choose the best answer.

QUICK Practice

1 Which number disproves the statement below? **C**

$n^2 + 1$ is a prime number for all numbers n.

A $n = 1$ **C** $n = 3$

B $n = 2$ **D** $n = 4$

QUICK Review

READING HINT A prime number is a number that can be written only as the product of itself and 1.

This question can be answered by replacing the n with the choices and determining which results in a number that is not prime.

For more help with counterexamples, see page 41.

Practice on Your Own

Standard 1.1

2 Which of the following statements is *true*? **F**

F $3(x + 2) = 3x + 6$

G $3(x + 2) = 3x + 2$

H $3(x + 2) = 3x + 5$

J $3(x + 2) = x + 6$

3 Which statement is a valid conclusion from the statement below if the two numbers are 3 and 5? **D**

If one number is even and another number is odd, then the product of the two numbers is even.

A The product of the two numbers is even.

B The product of the two numbers is odd.

C The sum of the two numbers is even.

D No valid conclusion

4 Which statement below represents the Commutative Property of Addition? **H**

F $(a + b) + c = a + (b + c)$

G $ab = ba$

H $a + b = b + a$

J $a = a$

5 Which numbers disprove the statement below? **A**

If $a > b$, then $a + b > 0$.

A $a = -1$ and $b = -3$

B $a = 10$ and $b = -1$

C $a = 4$ and $b = 0$

D $a = 10$ and $b = 5$

6 Which of the following statements is *true*? **F**

F If $x = y$ and $y = 3$, then $x = 3$.

G If $x = y$ and $y = 3$, then $x = 6$.

H If $x = y$, then $x = 0$.

J If $x = 3$ and $y = 1$, then $x = y$.

Practice by Standard

Standard 2.0: Students understand and use such operations as taking the opposite, finding the reciprocal, taking a root, and raising to a fractional power. They understand and use rules of exponents.

DIRECTIONS Choose the best answer.

QUICK Practice	QUICK Review
1 $\sqrt{25} + \sqrt[3]{27} =$ **B** **A** $\sqrt{8}$ **B** 8 **C** $\sqrt{52}$ **D** 52	**STRATEGY** Try to determine if the first number is a perfect square and if the second number is a perfect cube. First, simplify the roots, and then combine the results. For more help with operations with roots, see page 536.
2 Which expression is equivalent to $x^5 x^4$? **G** **F** x^1 **G** x^9 **H** x^{10} **J** x^{20}	**READING HINT** To multiply like bases, add the exponents. Look for the choice that uses the sum of the exponents to find the product of the bases. For more help with exponents, see page 358.
3 The perimeter P of a square may be found using the formula $P = 4\sqrt{A}$, where A is the area of the square. What is the perimeter of a square with an area of 81 square inches? **C** **A** 324 inches **B** 81 inches **C** 36 inches **D** 4 inches	**STRATEGY** Draw the square for this problem. Substitute 81 for A, simplify the square root of 81, and multiply the result by 4. For more help with simplifying roots, see page 528.
4 If $x = -10$, then $-x =$ **F** **F** 10 **G** -10 **H** $\frac{1}{10}$ **J** $-\frac{1}{10}$	**READING HINT** Read the negative sign as *opposite*. If $x = -10$, then $-x$ is the opposite of -10. For more help with opposites, see page 697.

Practice on Your Own

5 What is the reciprocal of $\frac{\pi r^2}{3}$? **A**

  A $\frac{3}{\pi r^2}$

  B 3

  C $\frac{3\pi}{r^2}$

  D $3\pi r^2$

6 Which expression is equivalent to $x^3 x^{11}$? **H**

  F $2x^{14}$

  G x^{33}

  H x^{14}

  J x^8

7 $(8)^{\frac{2}{3}} =$ **A**

  A 4

  B 12

  C 16

  D 64

8 The length of a side s of a square may be found using the formula $s = \sqrt{A}$, where A is the area of the square. What is the length of a side of a square with an area of 100 square inches? **J**

  F 100 inches

  G 75 inches

  H 50 inches

  J 10 inches

9 If $x = 13$, then $-x =$ **B**

  A 13

  B -13

  C $\frac{1}{13}$

  D $-\frac{1}{13}$

10 $\sqrt{36} + \sqrt[3]{64} =$ **H**

  F $\sqrt{99}$

  G $\sqrt{10}$

  H 10

  J 14

11 What is the reciprocal of $\frac{xy}{z}$? **C**

  A $\frac{zx}{y}$

  B z

  C $\frac{z}{xy}$

  D xyz

12 Which expression is equivalent to $(x^5)^3$? **F**

  F x^{15}

  G x^8

  H x^2

  J $3x^5$

13 Which expression is equivalent to $\frac{x^{12}}{x^3}$? **B**

  A x^4

  B x^9

  C x^{15}

  D 4

14 $(16)^{\frac{3}{4}} =$ **F**

  F 8

  G 10

  H 12

  J 16

California Standards Review

Practice by Standard: Standard 2.0   **CA7**

Practice by Standard: Standard 2.0   **CA7**

Practice by Standard

Standard 3.0: Students solve equations and inequalities involving absolute values.

DIRECTIONS Choose the best answer.

QUICK Practice

1 If x is an integer, which of the following is the solution set to $4|x| = 16$? **B**

A $\{-4\}$

B $\{-4, 4\}$

C $\{-4, 0, 4\}$

D $\{4\}$

QUICK Review

READING HINT Remember that absolute value equations often have two answers.

Divide each side by 4 before solving for x.

For more help with absolute value equations, see page 322.

Practice on Your Own

Standard 3.0

2 What is the solution to this equation? **G**
$$|2x + 5| = 17$$
F $x = -22$ or $x = 12$

G $x = -11$ or $x = 6$

H $x = 6$

J $x = 11$ or $x = -6$

3 What is the solution to the inequality $4 - |x + 2| \leq 3$? **B**

A $-3 \leq x \leq -1$

B $x \leq -3$ or $x \geq -1$

C $-14 \leq x \leq 10$

D $x \leq -14$ or $x \geq 10$

4 What is the solution to this equation? **G**
$$|3x + 3| = 24$$
F $x = -27$ or $x = 21$

G $x = -9$ or $x = 7$

H $x = -7$ or $x = 9$

J $x = 7$

5 If x is an integer, which of the following is the solution set to $|x - 5| < 3$? **C**

A $\{2\}$

B $\{2, 3, 4, 5, 6, 7, 8\}$

C $\{3, 4, 5, 6, 7\}$

D $\{8\}$

6 Assume y is an integer and solve for y. **J**
$$|y + 6| = 12$$
F $y = 18$

G $y = 6$

H $y = -6$ or $y = 18$

J $y = -18$ or $y = 6$

7 What is the solution to this equation? **D**
$$|x + 7| = -4$$
A $x = -11$

B $x = -11$ or $x = -3$

C $x = -4$ or $x = 4$

D No solution

Practice by Standard

Standard 4.0: Students simplify expressions before solving linear equations and inequalities in one variable, such as $3(2x - 5) + 4(x - 2) = 12$.

DIRECTIONS Choose the best answer.

QUICK Practice | QUICK Review

1 Which equation is equivalent to $3(3 - 2x) = 5 - 4(2 - 3x)$? **D**

A $-6x = 12$

B $x = 12$

C $4x = -2$

D $18x = 12$

> **STRATEGY** Use the Distributive Property to eliminate any grouping symbols.

Simplify the expression, and then pick the choice that is correct.

For more help with solving equations, see page 98.

---

2 Which of the following is equivalent to $8 - 2x > 5(x - 4)$? **G**

F $x > 4$

G $x < 4$

H $x < -4$

J $x > -4$

> **READING HINT** Remember that when dividing by a negative number, the inequality symbol must be reversed.

Be careful when choosing between answer choices that are similar. Check the direction of the inequality symbol and the sign of the number.

For more help with inequalities, see page 308.

---

3 Which of the following is equivalent to $\frac{4}{x} = \frac{2}{x - 1}$? **A**

A $4(x - 1) = 2x$

B $2(x - 1) = 4x$

C $4x - 1 = 2x$

D $2x - 1 = 4x$

> **READING HINT** To solve proportions, cross multiply.

Cross multiply, and then pick the choice that matches your work.

For more help with proportions, see page 105.

---

4 Which of the following is equivalent to $2 - x > 2(x - 3)$? **H**

F $x > 3$

G $2 - x < 2x - 3$

H $2 - x > 2x - 6$

J $2 - x < 2x - 6$

> **STRATEGY** First, remove any grouping symbols.

Do not reverse the inequality sign unless multiplying or dividing by a negative number.

For more help with inequalities, see page 308.

Practice by Standard: Standard 4.0 **CA9**

Practice on Your Own

5 Which equation is equivalent to
$4(6 - 2x) - 2(3 - 2x) = -2x$? **D**

A $-4x + 30 = -2x$

B $-4x - 18 = -2x$

C $4x + 18 = -2x$

D $-4x + 18 = -2x$

6 Which of the following is equivalent to
$\frac{3}{x} = \frac{2}{x-6}$? **F**

F $3x - 18 = 2x$

G $3x - 6 = 2x$

H $2x - 12 = 3x$

J $2x - 6 = 3x$

7 Which of the following is equivalent to
$5 - 3x \leq 4(x - 4)$? **D**

A $x \leq 3$

B $x \geq -3$

C $x \leq -3$

D $x \geq 3$

8 Which equation is equivalent to
$6(2 - x) = 3 - 3(4 - 2x)$? **G**

F $12 - 6x = 3 - 12 - 6x$

G $12 - 6x = 3 - 12 + 6x$

H $12 - 6x = 3 - 12 - 2x$

J $12 - x = 3 - 12 + 6x$

9 Which of the following is equivalent to
$2 + 5x \leq -3(x + 2)$? **D**

A $2 + 5x \leq -3x + 2$

B $2 + 5x \leq -3x - 2$

C $2 + 5x \leq -3x + 6$

D $2 + 5x \leq -3x - 6$

10 Which of the following is equivalent to
$\frac{12}{x} = \frac{2}{x-5}$? **G**

F $x = -6$

G $x = 6$

H $x = 12$

J $x = 60$

11 Which equation is equivalent to
$4(3 - 2x) = 5 - 2(3 - x)$? **C**

A $12 - 2x = 5 - 6 + x$

B $12 - 8x = 5 - 6 - x$

C $12 - 8x = 5 - 6 + 2x$

D $12 - 2x = 5 - 6 + 2x$

12 Which of the following is equivalent to
$3 - x > 2(x - 3)$? **F**

F $3 - x > 2x - 6$

G $3 - x > 2x - 3$

H $3 - x < 2x - 6$

J $3 - x < 2x - 3$

13 Which equation is equivalent to
$2(5 - 3x) - (2 - 4x) = -3x$? **A**

A $-2x + 8 = -3x$

B $-2x + 10 = -3x$

C $-10x + 8 = -3x$

D $-10x + 12 = -3x$

14 Which of the following is equivalent to
$\frac{4}{3x} = \frac{2}{x-1}$? **J**

F $4x - 1 = 2(3x)$

G $2(x - 1) = 4(3x)$

H $2x - 1 = 2(3x)$

J $4x - 4 = 2(3x)$

Practice by Standard

Standard 5.0: Students solve multistep problems, including word problems, involving linear equations and linear inequalities in one variable and provide justification for each step.

DIRECTIONS Choose the best answer.

QUICK Practice

QUICK Review

1 The cost c in dollars of renting the pool for a pool party for h hours is given by the equation $c = 50 + 10h$.

If the total cost was $100, for how many hours was the pool rented? **D**

A 50 hours

B 20 hours

C 10 hours

D 5 hours

> **STRATEGY** Replace h with the choices to see which is correct.

Replace c with 100 and solve for h to determine the number of hours that the pool was rented.

For more help with writing and solving equations, see page 70.

---

2 Solve: $2(x + 3) = 3x + 4$

   Step 1: $2x + 3 = 3x + 4$
   Step 2: $-x + 3 = 4$
   Step 3: $-x = 1$
   Step 4: $x = -1$

Which is the first incorrect step in the solution shown above? **F**

F Step 1

G Step 2

H Step 3

J Step 4

> **STRATEGY** Solve the equation, and then compare your solution to the one shown to look for the error.

When solving equations, the first step is to remove the grouping symbols by using the Distributive Property.

For more help with solving equations, see page 98.

---

3 A 10-foot-long board is cut into two pieces. The first piece is 2 feet longer than the second piece. What is the length of the longer piece of board? **C**

A 4 feet

B 5 feet

C 6 feet

D 10 feet

> **STRATEGY** Draw a picture of the board, and label the pieces.

Let x represent the shorter piece, and let $x + 2$ represent the longer piece.

For more help with writing and solving equations, see page 70.

Practice on Your Own

Standard 5.0

4 Solve for x. **H**

$3(2x - 4) - 5x > 14$

F $x > 2$

G $x > -26$

H $x > 26$

J $x < 26$

5 Nelly solved $3(2x + 6) = 6$ using the following steps.

Step 1: $3(2x + 6) = 6$

Step 2: $6x + 18 = 6$

Step 3: $6x = -12$

Step 4: $x = -2$

To get from Step 1 to Step 2, she — **A**

A used the Distributive Property.

B subtracted 18 from each side.

C divided each side by 6.

D divided each side by 3.

6 The cost c of Tim's monthly cell phone bill if he talked for m minutes is given by the equation $c = 25 + 0.10m$.

If the total bill was $35, for how many minutes did Tim talk? **J**

F 10 minutes

G 25 minutes

H 50 minutes

J 100 minutes

7 Solve for x. **B**

$3(x + 2) = 2x - 4$

A $x = 10$

B $x = -10$

C $x = -6$

D $x = 6$

8 Solve: $3(2x + 4) = 2x + 8$

Step 1: $6x + 12 = 2x + 8$

Step 2: $4x + 12 = 8$

Step 3: $4x = 20$

Step 4: $x = 5$

Which is the first incorrect step in the solution shown above? **H**

F Step 1

G Step 2

H Step 3

J Step 4

9 A 100-foot wire is cut into three pieces. The second piece is three times as long as the first piece. The third piece is twice as long as the second piece. What is the length of the longest piece of wire? **C**

A 10 feet

B 30 feet

C 60 feet

D 100 feet

10 Solve for x. **J**

$4(2x + 2) - 7x > 12$

F $x < -4$

G $x < 4$

H $x > -4$

J $x > 4$

11 Todd solved $4(x + 5) = 8$ using the following steps.

Step 1: $4(x + 5) = 8$

Step 2: $4x + 20 = 8$

Step 3: $4x = -12$

Step 4: $x = -3$

To get from Step 3 to Step 4, he — **C**

A used the Distributive Property.

B subtracted 20 from each side.

C divided each side by 4.

D divided each side by −3.

CA12 California Standards Review

Practice by Standard

Standard 6.0: Students graph a linear equation and compute the x- and y-intercepts (e.g., graph $2x + 6y = 4$). They are also able to sketch the region defined by linear inequality (e.g., they sketch the region defined by $2x + 6y < 4$).

DIRECTIONS Choose the best answer.

QUICK Practice | QUICK Review

1 What is the y-intercept of the graph of $3x + 2y = 6$? **B**

  A $(0, 2)$

  B $(0, 3)$

  C $(2, 0)$

  D $(3, 0)$

> **READING HINT** The y-intercept is where the graph of the equation crosses the y-axis.
>
> To find the y-intercept, let $x = 0$ and solve for y.
>
> For more help with finding the y-intercept, see page 154.

---

2 Which inequality is shown on the graph below? **G**

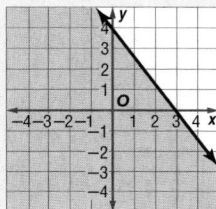

  F $y < -\frac{4}{3}x + 4$

  G $y \leq -\frac{4}{3}x + 4$

  H $y \geq -\frac{4}{3}x + 4$

  J $y > -\frac{4}{3}x + 4$

> **STRATEGY** Use a test point in the shaded region, such as $(0, 0)$, to determine which choices make sense.
>
> Since the line is a solid line, the inequality must be either $\geq$ or $\leq$.
>
> For more help with graphing inequalities, see page 334.

---

3 What is the x-intercept of the graph of $x + 4y = -8$? **C**

  A $(-2, 0)$

  B $(0, -8)$

  C $(-8, 0)$

  D $(0, -2)$

> **READING HINT** The x-intercept is where the graph of the equation crosses the x-axis.
>
> To find the x-intercept, let $y = 0$ and solve for x.
>
> For more help with finding the x-intercept, see page 154.

Practice on Your Own

4 What is an equation of the line shown in the graph below? **F**

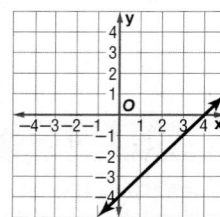

F $4x - 4y = 16$

G $4x + 4y = 16$

H $4x - y = 16$

J $x - 4y = 16$

5 What are the coordinates of the x-intercept of the line $4x + 5y = 20$? **D**

A $(0, 4)$

B $(0, 5)$

C $(4, 0)$

D $(5, 0)$

6 Which inequality is shown on the graph below? **H**

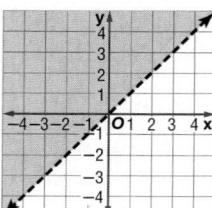

F $y \geq x$

G $y \leq x$

H $y > x$

J $y < x$

7 Which of the following is the graph of $y = \frac{1}{3}x + 1$? **A**

A

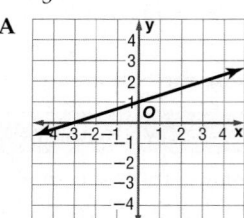

B

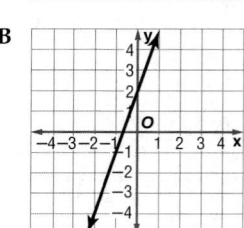

C

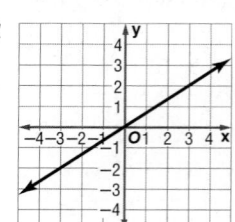

D

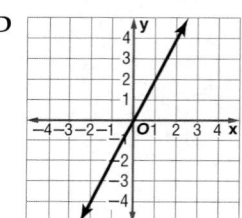

8 What is the y-intercept of the line $3x - 5y = 15$? **F**

F $(0 - 3)$

G $(0, 5)$

H $(3, 0)$

J $(5, 0)$

Practice by Standard

Standard 7.0: Students verify that a point lies on a line, given an equation of the line. Students are able to derive linear equations by using the point-slope formula.

DIRECTIONS Choose the best answer.

QUICK Practice | QUICK Review

1 What is the equation of the line that has a slope of 3 and passes through the point $(2, -4)$? **D**

  A $y = 3x - 4$

  B $y = 3x + 2$

  C $y = x - 6$

  D $y = 3x - 10$

> **STRATEGY** Replace x and y in the equations with the x- and y-values of the given point to eliminate choices that do not work.
>
> Use the point-slope form to find the equation of the line.
>
> For more help with writing equations of lines, see page 213.

2 The data in the table show the cost of playing laser tag by the hour, including a deposit on the equipment.

Hours	Cost ($)
3	16
5	20
8	26

If hours h were graphed on a horizontal axis and cost c were graphed on a vertical axis, what would be the equation of a line that fits the data? **H**

  F $h = 10 + 2c$

  G $c = h + 13$

  H $c = 10 + 2h$

  J $c = h$

> **STRATEGY** Graph the ordered pairs on a coordinate plane to determine the shape of the line.
>
> Replace h and c in the equations with values from the table to eliminate the equations that do not work.
>
> For more help with writing equations of lines, see page 213.

3 Which point lies on the line defined by $2x + 5y = 15$? **D**

  A $(2, 0)$

  B $(2, 5)$

  C $(5, 0)$

  D $(5, 1)$

> **STRATEGY** Graph the equation on a coordinate plane to determine which point lies on the line.
>
> Replace x and y in the equation with the ordered pairs to determine which ordered pair lies on the line.
>
> For more help with equations of lines, see page 213.

Practice by Standard: Standard 7.0 **CA15**

Practice on Your Own

4 Which of the following points lies on the line defined by $y = 2x$? **J**

F $(2, 1)$

G $(2, 0)$

H $(0, 2)$

J $(3, 6)$

5 What is the equation of the line that has a slope of -2 and passes through the point $(-2, 5)$? **C**

A $y = -2x$

B $y = -2x + 5$

C $y = -2x + 1$

D $y = -2x - 2$

6 The data in the table show the amount Sue will earn baby-sitting by the hour.

Hours	Amount ($)
2	14
5	35
7	49

If hours h were graphed on a horizontal axis and amount a were graphed on a vertical axis, what would be the equation of a line that fits the data? **F**

F $a = 7h$

G $a = 7h + 14$

H $a = h + 14$

J $a = h$

7 Which point lies on the line defined by $3x - y = 10$? **B**

A $(0, 10)$

B $(1, -7)$

C $(-2, -4)$

D $(3, 10)$

8 What is the equation of the line that has a slope of -2 and passes through the point $(0, 5)$? **G**

F $y = -2x - 5$

G $y = -2x + 5$

H $y = 2x + 5$

J $y = 5x - 2$

9 Which of the following points lies on the line defined by $y = -3x$? **B**

A $(-2, -6)$

B $(-2, 6)$

C $(0, -3)$

D $(1, 3)$

10 Which point lies on the line defined by $2x - 3y = 12$? **J**

F $(0, -3)$

G $(0, 2)$

H $(-3, 2)$

J $(9, 2)$

11 The data in the table show the amount Elias will earn mowing lawns by the hour, including a flat fee for pulling weeds.

Hours	Amount ($)
2	15
5	30
7	40

If hours h were graphed on a horizontal axis and amount a were graphed on a vertical axis, what would be the equation of a line that fits the data? **A**

A $a = 5h + 5$

B $a = 5h$

C $a = h + 13$

D $a = h$

Practice by Standard

Standard 8.0: Students understand the concepts of parallel lines and perpendicular lines and how those slopes are related. Students are able to find the equation of a line perpendicular to a given line that passes through a given point.

DIRECTIONS Choose the best answer.

QUICK Practice

1 What is the slope of a line parallel to the line $y = -\frac{2}{3}x + 5$? **A**

A $-\frac{2}{3}$ C $\frac{3}{2}$

B $\frac{2}{3}$ D 5

QUICK Review

READING HINT Parallel lines have the same slope.

The slope of the line is the coefficient of the x-term.

For more help with slope and parallel lines, see page 236.

Practice on Your Own

Standard 8.0

2 Which of the following statements describes perpendicular lines? **H**

F Same slopes but different y-intercepts

G Same slopes and same y-intercepts

H Opposite reciprocal slopes

J Opposite slopes

3 What is the slope of a line parallel to the line below? **D**

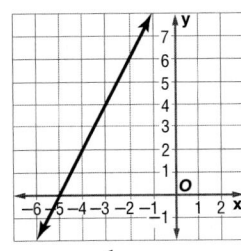

A -2 C $\frac{1}{2}$

B $-\frac{1}{2}$ D 2

4 Which of the following could be the equation of a line parallel to the line $y = -2x + 3$? **G**

F $y = 2x + 5$

G $y = -2x + 1$

H $y = \frac{1}{2}x + 3$

J $y = -\frac{1}{2}x + 1$

5 The equation of a line m is $3x + 5y = 15$, and the equation of a line n is $5x - 3y = 0$. Which statement about the two lines is true? **B**

A Lines m and n are parallel.

B Lines m and n are perpendicular.

C Lines m and n have the same y-intercept.

D Lines m and n are the same line.

Practice by Standard

Standard 9.0: Students solve a system of two linear equations in two variables algebraically and are able to interpret the answer graphically. Students are able to solve a system of two linear inequalities in two variables and to sketch the solution sets.

DIRECTIONS Choose the best answer.

QUICK Practice

1 $\begin{cases} 3x + 2y = 6 \\ 2x - y = 4 \end{cases}$

What is the solution to the system of equations shown above? **C**

A $(0, -4)$

B $(0, 2)$

C $(2, 0)$

D $(4, -3)$

2 Which graph represents the system of equations shown below? **H**

$\begin{cases} y = 2x + 1 \\ y = 2x + 2 \end{cases}$

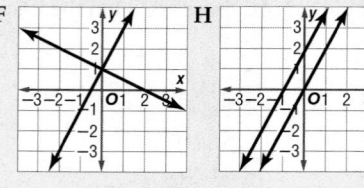
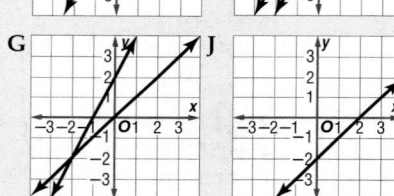

3 $\begin{cases} x + 3y = 14 \\ 4x + 2y = -4 \end{cases}$

What is the solution to this system of equations shown above? **A**

A $(-4, 6)$ **C** $(2, 8)$

B $\left(-4, \dfrac{16}{7}\right)$ **D** $\left(2, \dfrac{5}{7}\right)$

QUICK Review

STRATEGY Replace x and y in both equations with the choices given to determine which ordered pair is a solution to both equations.

Use elimination to solve this system of equations.

For more help with solving systems of equations, see page 272.

STRATEGY Since the slopes of the two lines are the same and the y-intercepts are different, the two lines are parallel.

Choose the option that has two parallel lines.

For more help with graphing systems of equations, see page 253.

STRATEGY Since the x-term in the first equation does not have a coefficient, use substitution to solve the system of equations.

Use substitution to solve this system of equations.

For more help with solving systems of equations, see page 260.

Practice on Your Own

4 $\begin{cases} 4x - 3y = 9 \\ -5x - y = 22 \end{cases}$

What is the solution to this system of equations shown above? **H**

F $(-1, -5)$

G $(-2, -6)$

H $(-3, -7)$

J $(-7, -13)$

5 $\begin{cases} y = 2x + 1 \\ y = 3x + 4 \end{cases}$

What is the solution to the system of equations shown above? **A**

A $(-3, -5)$

B $(0, -1)$

C $(0, 4)$

D $(1, 3)$

6 $\begin{cases} -2x + 4y = 5 \\ 2x - 3y = -2 \end{cases}$

What is the solution to the system of equations shown above? **J**

F $\left(-\dfrac{5}{2}, 0\right)$

G $(-1, 0)$

H $(0, 2)$

J $\left(\dfrac{7}{2}, 3\right)$

7 $\begin{cases} y = 4x - 6 \\ y = 4x + 5 \end{cases}$

What is the solution to the system of equations shown above? **D**

A $(0, -6)$

B $(0, 5)$

C infinitely many solutions

D no solution

8 $\begin{cases} -x + 3y = 4 \\ 2x - 5y = -2 \end{cases}$

What is the solution to the system of equations shown above? **J**

F $(-1, 1)$

G $(-1, 0)$

H $(-4, 0)$

J $(14, 6)$

9 Which graph represents the system of equations shown below? **D**

$\begin{cases} y = 3x + 2 \\ y = -\dfrac{1}{3}x \end{cases}$

A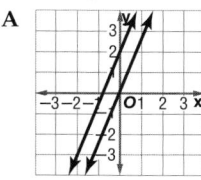

C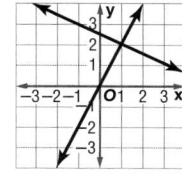

B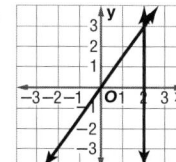

D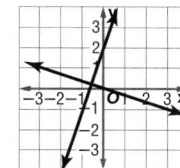

10 $\begin{cases} x + 3y = 8 \\ -x - 2y = -5 \end{cases}$

What is the solution to the system of equations shown above? **F**

F $(-1, 3)$

G $(1, 2)$

H $(2, 2)$

J $(8, 0)$

Practice by Standard

Standard 10.0: Students add, subtract, multiply, and divide monomials and polynomials. Students solve multistep problems, including word problems, by using these techniques.

DIRECTIONS Choose the best answer.

QUICK Practice

1 $\dfrac{2x^4}{6x^8} =$ **B**

  A $3x^4$

  B $\dfrac{1}{3x^4}$

  C $\dfrac{3}{x^2}$

  D $\dfrac{1}{3x^2}$

2 $\left(6x^2 + 3x + 2\right) - \left(2x^2 - 4x + 1\right) =$ **G**

  F $4x^2 - x + 3$

  G $4x^2 + 7x + 1$

  H $4x^2 + 7x + 3$

  J $8x^2 - x + 3$

3

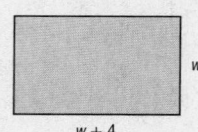

$w + 4$

The length of the rectangle above is 4 units longer than the width. Which expression could be used to represent the area of the rectangle? **D**

  A $w^2 + 4$

  B $w^2 + w$

  C $w^2 + 4w + 4$

  D $w^2 + 4w$

QUICK Review

STRATEGY Eliminate any choices that do not make sense.

To divide monomials, subtract the exponents.

For more help with dividing monomials, see page 366.

READING HINT To subtract polynomials, distribute the negative sign through the second polynomial.

The polynomials can be written into column form before subtracting.
$$\begin{array}{r} 6x^2 + 3x + 2 \\ -(2x^2 - 4x + 1) \end{array}$$

For more help with subtracting polynomials, see page 384.

READING HINT Recall that the area of a rectangle is the length times the width.

To multiply a polynomial by a monomial, use the Distributive Property.

For more help with multiplying polynomials, see page 398.

Practice on Your Own

4 Simplify. **G**

$$\frac{6x^3 + 9x^2 + 3x}{3x}$$

F $2x^2 + 3x$

G $2x^2 + 3x + 1$

H $2x^2 + 6x$

J $3x^2 + 6x + 1$

5 Simplify. **C**

$$(2x^2 + x + 3) + (x^2 + 5x - 2)$$

A $x^2 - 4x + 1$

B $x^2 - 4x + 5$

C $3x^2 + 6x + 1$

D $3x^2 + 6x + 5$

6

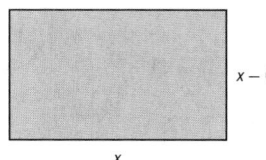

The length of the rectangle above is 6 units shorter than the width. Which expression could be used to represent the area of the rectangle? **H**

F $2x - 6$

G $x^2 + 6$

H $x^2 - 6x$

J $x^2 - 6$

7 Simplify. **D**

$$2(x^2 + 3x + 2) - 4(x^2 - 4x + 1)$$

A $-2x^2 + 14x - 16$

B $-2x^2 - 18x - 8$

C $-2x^2 + 14x$

D $-2x^2 + 22x$

8

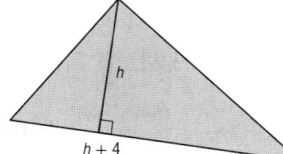

The base of the triangle is 4 units longer than the height. Which expression could be used to represent the area of the triangle? **J**

F $h^2 + 4$

G $h^2 + 4h$

H $\frac{1}{2}h^2 + 2$

J $\frac{1}{2}h^2 + 2h$

9

Which expression could be used to represent the perimeter of the rectangle? **D**

A $x^2 - x$

B $x^2 - 2x$

C $2x^2 - x$

D $4x^2 - 2x$

10 Simplify. **G**

$$\frac{10x^3 + 15x^2 - 5x}{5x}$$

F $2x^2 + 3x$

G $2x^2 + 3x - 1$

H $2x^2 + 10x + 1$

J $5x^2 + 10x + 1$

Practice by Standard

Standard 11.0: Students apply basic factoring techniques to second- and simple third-degree polynomials. These techniques include finding a common factor for all terms in a polynomial, recognizing the difference of two squares, and recognizing perfect squares of binomials.

DIRECTIONS Choose the best answer.

QUICK Practice

1 What is the factored form of $2x^2 - 2xy - 12y^2$? **A**

A $2(x + 2y)(x - 3y)$

B $(2x + 2y)(x - 3y)$

C $(2x + 4y)(x - 3y)$

D $(x + 2y)(x - 3y)$

QUICK Review

STRATEGY Eliminate any choices that do not multiply to give the original expression.

The first step in factoring is to pull out any common factors.

For more help with factoring, see page 428.

Practice on Your Own

Standard 11.0

2 Which of the following shows $25x^2 + 40x + 16$ factored completely? **G**

F $(5x + 4)(5x - 4)$

G $(5x + 4)(5x + 4)$

H $(x + 4)(25x - 4)$

J $5(5x^2 + 8x + 16)$

3 Which is a factor of $x^2 + 7x + 6$? **A**

A $(x + 1)$

B $(x + 2)$

C $(x + 3)$

D $(x + 7)$

4 Which of the following shows $x^3 - 25x$ factored completely? **H**

F $(x + 5)(x^2 - 5)$

G $(x - 5)(x^2 + 5x + 25)$

H $x(x + 5)(x - 5)$

J $(x + 5)(x + 5)$

5 If the area of a rectangle is $x^2 + 12x + 36$ and the width of the rectangle is $(x + 6)$, which is the length of the rectangle? **C**

A x

B $x + 2$

C $x + 6$

D $x + 30$

6 What is the factored form of $6x^2 + 7x - 5$? **F**

F $(3x + 5)(2x - 1)$

G $3(2x + 5)(x - 1)$

H $(3x + 1)(2x - 5)$

J $(6x + 5)(x - 1)$

7 Which is a factor of $x^2 + 11x + 10$? **A**

A $(x + 10)$

B $(x + 5)$

C $(x + 2)$

D $(x - 1)$

Practice by Standard

Standard 12.0: Students simplify fractions with polynomials in the numerator and denominator by factoring both and reducing them to the lowest terms.

DIRECTIONS Choose the best answer.

QUICK Practice

1 What is $\dfrac{2x^2 + 4x}{x^2 + 5x + 6}$ reduced to lowest terms? **D**

A $\dfrac{x + 2}{x + 8}$

B $\dfrac{2}{3}$

C $2x$

D $\dfrac{2x}{x + 3}$

QUICK Review

> **READING HINT** Reduced to lowest terms means that all common factors have been removed.

Factor both the numerator and denominator and then cancel any common factors.

For more help with simplifying rational expressions, see page 583.

---

2 Simplify $\dfrac{9x^2 - 25}{6x^2 + 13x + 5}$ to lowest terms. **F**

F $\dfrac{3x - 5}{2x + 1}$

G $\dfrac{9x^2 - 25}{6x^2 + 13x + 5}$

H $\dfrac{3x + 5}{2x + 1}$

J $\dfrac{3}{2}$

> **READING HINT** Factor the difference of two squares in the numerator.

Factor both the numerator and denominator, and then cancel any common factors.

For more help with simplifying rational expressions, see page 583.

---

3 What is $\dfrac{x^2 + 6x}{x^2 + 12x + 36}$ reduced to lowest terms? **A**

A $\dfrac{x}{x + 6}$

B $x + 6$

C 1

D $\dfrac{x}{x - 6}$

> **READING HINT** Factor the perfect square trinomial in the denominator.

Factor both the numerator and denominator, and then cancel any common factors.

For more help with simplifying rational expressions, see page 583.

Practice by Standard: Standard 12.0 **CA23**

Practice on Your Own

4 Simplify $\dfrac{4x^2 - 9}{10x^2 + 13x - 3}$ to lowest terms. **H**

F $\dfrac{2x + 3}{5x - 1}$

G $\dfrac{4x^2 - 9}{10x^2 + 13x - 3}$

H $\dfrac{2x - 3}{5x - 1}$

J $\dfrac{2}{5}$

7 Simplify $\dfrac{3x^2 + 6x}{4x^2 + 5x - 6}$ to lowest terms. **D**

A $\dfrac{3}{4}$

B $\dfrac{3x^2 + 6x}{4x^2 + 5x - 6}$

C $\dfrac{3x + 6}{4x + 6}$

D $\dfrac{3x}{4x - 3}$

5 What is $\dfrac{x^2 - 5x}{x^2 - 10x + 25}$ reduced to lowest terms? **D**

A $\dfrac{x}{x + 5}$

B $x + 5$

C 1

D $\dfrac{x}{x - 5}$

8 If the area of the rectangle below is $2x^2 - x - 15$, which expression represents the width? **G**

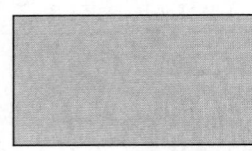

$6x^2 + 15x$

F 3

G $\dfrac{x - 3}{3x}$

H $\dfrac{3x}{x - 3}$

J $\dfrac{2x + 5}{x}$

6 If the area of the rectangle below is $x^2 + 9x + 14$, which expression represents the width? **J**

$x^2 + 7x$

F 2

G $\dfrac{x + 7}{x}$

H $\dfrac{x}{x + 2}$

J $\dfrac{x + 2}{x}$

9 What is $\dfrac{2x^2 - 10x}{4x^2 - 16x}$ reduced to lowest terms? **A**

A $\dfrac{x - 5}{2(x - 4)}$

B $x - 5$

C $\dfrac{x + 5}{x + 4}$

D $\dfrac{1}{2}$

Practice by Standard

Standard 13.0: Students add, subtract, multiply, and divide rational expressions and functions. Students solve both computationally and conceptually challenging problems by using these techniques.

DIRECTIONS Choose the best answer.

QUICK Practice	QUICK Review
1 $\dfrac{3x^2 + 3x}{3x + 9} \cdot \dfrac{x^2 - 9}{x^2 + 3x + 2} = $ **D** **A** $\dfrac{x - 3}{x + 2}$ **B** $\dfrac{x(x - 3)}{x + 1}$ **C** $\dfrac{x(x + 3)}{x + 2}$ **D** $\dfrac{x(x - 3)}{x + 2}$	**STRATEGY** Work the problem, and then look for your answer among the choices. Factor each numerator and denominator completely, and then simplify by removing common factors. For more help with multiplying rational expressions, see page 590.
2 $\dfrac{x}{x + 5} + \dfrac{2x}{x - 1} = $ **J** **F** $\dfrac{3x}{2x + 4}$ **G** $\dfrac{3x}{x + 4}$ **H** $\dfrac{3x^2 + 4}{x + 4}$ **J** $\dfrac{3x^2 + 9x}{x^2 + 4x - 5}$	**READING HINT** To add rational expressions with unlike denominators, first find a common denominator. After determining the common denominator, rewrite each fraction so that it has the common denominator. After rewriting each fraction, add the numerators and simplify. For more help with adding rational expressions, see page 614.
3 $\dfrac{2x}{x - 4} - \dfrac{3}{x - 2} = $ **A** **A** $\dfrac{2x^2 - 7x + 12}{x^2 - 6x + 8}$ **B** $\dfrac{2x^2 - 7x - 12}{x^2 - 6x + 8}$ **C** $\dfrac{2x - 3}{-6}$ **D** $\dfrac{2x - 3}{-2}$	**READING HINT** To subtract rational expressions with unlike denominators, first find a common denominator. After determining the common denominator, rewrite each fraction so that it has the common denominator. After rewriting each fraction, subtract the numerators by distributing the negative through the second numerator and simplify. For more help with subtracting rational expressions, see page 614.

Practice by Standard: Standard 13.0 **CA25**

Practice on Your Own

4 Which fraction equals the quotient

$$\frac{2x+3}{x-4} \div \frac{2x+3}{x+4}?\ \text{H}$$

F 1

G $\dfrac{4x^2 + 12x + 9}{x^2 - 16}$

H $\dfrac{x+4}{x-4}$

J -1

5 $\dfrac{2x^2 + 4x}{2x - 8} \cdot \dfrac{x^2 - 16}{x^2 + 7x + 10} = \text{C}$

A $\dfrac{x-4}{x+5}$

B $\dfrac{x(x-4)}{x+2}$

C $\dfrac{x(x+4)}{x+5}$

D $\dfrac{x(x-4)}{x+5}$

6 Which expression represents the area, in simplified form, of the rectangle below? **H**

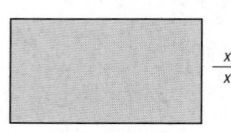

$$\frac{x+5}{x-2}$$

$$\frac{x^2 - 2x}{x + 10}$$

F $\dfrac{x}{x+2}$

G $\dfrac{x+5}{x+10}$

H $\dfrac{x(x+5)}{x+10}$

J $\dfrac{(x^2 - 2x)(x+5)}{(x+10)(x-2)}$

7 $\dfrac{5}{x-3} - \dfrac{1}{x-6} = \text{C}$

A $\dfrac{4x - 33}{(x-3)(x-6)}$

B $\dfrac{4}{3}$

C $\dfrac{4x - 27}{(x-3)(x-6)}$

D $\dfrac{4}{(x-3)(x-6)}$

8 Which expression represents the perimeter, in simplified form, of the rectangle below?

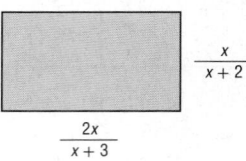

$$\frac{x}{x+2}$$

$$\frac{2x}{x+3}$$

F $\dfrac{3x}{(x+2)(x+3)}$

G $\dfrac{6x^2 + 14x}{(x+2)(x+3)}$

H $\dfrac{3x^2 + 7x}{(x+2)(x+3)}$

J $\dfrac{2x^2}{(x+2)(x+3)}$

9 Which fraction equals the quotient

$$\frac{x+5}{x-1} \div \frac{x-5}{x-1}?\ \text{C}$$

A 1

B $\dfrac{(x+5)(x-5)}{(x-1)(x-1)}$

C $\dfrac{x+5}{x-5}$

D $\dfrac{x-5}{x+5}$

Practice by Standard

Standard 14.0: Students solve a quadratic equation by factoring or completing the square.

DIRECTIONS Choose the best answer.

QUICK Practice

1 What quantity should be added to both sides of this equation to complete the square? **D**

$$x^2 - 6x = 10$$

A −3   C −9

B 3   D 9

2 What are the solutions for the quadratic equation $x^2 + 8x = 9$? **G**

F −9 and −1

G −9 and 1

H −1 and 9

J 1 and 9

3 If x^2 is added to $2x$, the sum is 8. Which of the following could be a value of x? **A**

A −4   C 4

B 0   D 8

4 What are the solutions for the quadratic equation $x^2 + 9x + 20 = 0$?

F −5 and −4   H −4 and 5

G −5 and 4   J 4 and 5

QUICK Review

READING HINT Complete the square means to rewrite the equation so that the left side is a perfect square.

To complete the square, divide the coefficient of x by 2 and square the result.

For more help with completing the square, see page 486.

STRATEGY Replace x with the choices given to determine which pair is correct.

To solve this equation, rewrite so that it is equal to 0. Then factor and use the Zero Product Property.

For more help with solving quadratic equations, see page 430.

READING HINT Translate the sentence into the equation $x^2 + 2x = 8$.

To solve this equation, rewrite so that it is equal to 0. Then factor and use the Zero Product Property.

For more help with factoring, see page 434.

STRATEGY Replace x with the choices given to determine which pair is correct.

To solve this equation, factor and use the Zero Product Property.

For more help with factoring, see page 434.

Practice on Your Own

5 What quantity should be added to both sides of this equation to complete the square? **B**

$$x^2 - 10x = 11$$

A -25

B 25

C -5

D 5

6 What are the solutions for the quadratic equation $2x^2 - 11x = 6$? **J**

F -2 and -6

G -1 and 6

H $\frac{1}{2}$ and 6

J $-\frac{1}{2}$ and 6

7 If x^2 is added to $3x$, the sum is 18. Which of the following could be the value of x? **B**

A -3

B 3

C 6

D 18

8 Solve by completing the square. **J**

$$x^2 + 4x = 10$$

F $-2 \pm \sqrt{12}$

G 2 and -2

H $2 \pm \sqrt{14}$

J $-2 \pm \sqrt{14}$

9 What quantity should be added to both sides of this equation to complete the square? **C**

$$x^2 - x = 5$$

A $-\frac{1}{2}$ C $\frac{1}{4}$

B $-\frac{1}{4}$ D 5

10 What are the solutions for the quadratic equation $x^2 - x - 20 = 0$? **H**

F -5 and -4

G -5 and 4

H -4 and 5

J 4 and 5

11 If x^2 is added to x, the sum is 90. Which of the following could be the value of x? **C**

A 90

B 10

C 9

D -9

12 Solve by completing the square. **F**

$$x^2 + 6x = 2$$

F $-3 \pm \sqrt{11}$

G $3 \pm \sqrt{11}$

H 3 and -3

J $-3 \pm \sqrt{5}$

13 What quantity should be added to both sides of this equation to complete the square? **C**

$$x^2 - 5x = 3$$

A $\frac{5}{2}$ C $\frac{25}{4}$

B $-\frac{5}{2}$ D $-\frac{25}{4}$

14 What are the solutions for the quadratic equation $2x^2 - 9x + 4 = 0$? **H**

F 1 and 4

G $-\frac{1}{2}$ and 4

H $\frac{1}{2}$ and 4

J $-\frac{1}{2}$ and -4

Practice by Standard

Standard 15.0: Students apply algebraic techniques to solve rate problems, work problems, and percent mixture problems.

DIRECTIONS Choose the best answer.

QUICK Practice

1 Justin can mow a lawn in 2 hours. David can mow a lawn in 3 hours. How long will it take them to mow one lawn together? **A**

A $\frac{6}{5}$ hours   **C** 5 hours

B 2 hours   **D** 6 hours

QUICK Review

▶ **READING HINT** Since they are working together, the time should be less than the time it takes either of them alone.

Use the equation $\frac{1}{2}t + \frac{1}{3}t = 1$ to solve this problem.

For more help with work problems, see page 627.

---

2 The Dreyer family drove to the beach at an average speed of 55 mph and later returned home at an average speed of 65 mph. Find the distance from their house to the beach if they drove for a total of 12 hours. **J**

F 6.5 miles   **H** 300 miles

G 715 miles   **J** 357.5 miles

▶ **READING HINT** The formula for rate problems is $d = rt$.

Create a chart like the following to organize your work.

	d	r	t
there	d	55	t
back	d	65	$12 - t$

For more help with rate problems, see page 628.

---

3 Susan mixed 11 pounds of raisins that cost $2.30 per pound with peanuts that cost $4.50 per pound to make a mixture that cost $3.29 per pound. About how many pounds of peanuts did she use? **D**

A 50 pounds

B 20 pounds

C 11 pounds

D 9 pounds

▶ **STRATEGY** Use estimation to identify reasonable answers. If an equal amount of raisins and peanuts are used, the price for the mixture would be the average of the two prices. More raisins would lower the mixture price and more peanuts would raise the mixture price.

Create a chart like the following to organize your work.

	Amount	Cost	Value
raisins	11	2.30	2.30(11)
peanuts	x	4.50	4.50(x)
mixture	$11 + x$	3.29	3.29($11 + x$)

So, the equation to solve is
$2.30(11) + 4.50(x) = 3.29(11 + x)$.

For more help with mixture problems, see page 122.

Practice by Standard: Standard 15.0   **CA29**

Practice on Your Own

4 Joe mixes 10 ounces of a metal that contains 30% gold with 20 ounces of a metal that contains 15% gold. What is the percent of gold in the resulting metal? **H**

F 30% **H** 20%

G 22.5% **J** 15%

5 Tim and Lynne are jogging in opposite directions. They start at the same place and at the same time. Tim jogs at a rate of $5\frac{1}{2}$ miles per hour, and Lynne jogs at a rate of $4\frac{3}{4}$ miles per hour. How far apart will they be in $1\frac{1}{4}$ hours? **C**

A $10\frac{1}{4}$ miles

B 12 miles

C $12\frac{13}{16}$ miles

D 13 miles

6 A jet traveling at 570 miles per hour overtakes a prop-plane that is traveling 150 miles per hour. The prop-plane had a 2.8 hour head start. How far from the starting point does the jet overtake the prop-plane? **J**

F 150 miles

G 300 miles

H 420 miles

J 570 miles

7 How many ounces of pure water must be added to 60 ounces of a solution that is 20% water to make a solution that is 30% water? Round to the nearest hundredth if necessary. **B**

A 2 ounces

B 8.57 ounces

C 12.56 ounces

D 60 ounces

8 A pool can be filled by one pipe in 10 hours and by another pipe in 6 hours. How long would it take to fill the pool with both pipes together? **G**

F $2\frac{1}{2}$ hours

G $3\frac{3}{4}$ hours

H 8 hours

J 16 hours

9 The speed of a boat in still water is 28 miles per hour. The boat traveled 70 miles downstream in the same amount of time that it took to travel 42 miles upstream. What is the rate of the current of the river? **A**

A 7 miles per hour

B 14 miles per hour

C 28 miles per hour

D 112 miles per hour

10 Libby can solve a math problem in 12 minutes. Nate can solve the same problem in 8 minutes. How long would it take Libby and Nate, working together, to solve the problem? **H**

F 2 minutes

G 4 minutes

H 4.8 minutes

J 20 minutes

11 How many liters of a 24% salt solution must be mixed with 24 liters of a 40% salt solution to get a 34% salt solution? **A**

A 14.4 liters

B 14 liters

C 13.4 liters

D 12.8 liters

Practice by Standard

Standard 16.0: Students understand the concepts of a relation and a function, determine whether a given relation defines a function, and give pertinent information about given relations and functions.

DIRECTIONS Choose the best answer.

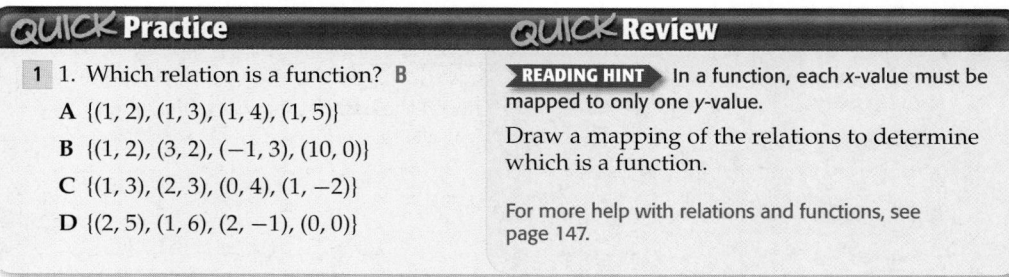

QUICK Practice

1. 1. Which relation is a function? **B**

   A $\{(1, 2), (1, 3), (1, 4), (1, 5)\}$

   B $\{(1, 2), (3, 2), (-1, 3), (10, 0)\}$

   C $\{(1, 3), (2, 3), (0, 4), (1, -2)\}$

   D $\{(2, 5), (1, 6), (2, -1), (0, 0)\}$

QUICK Review

READING HINT In a function, each x-value must be mapped to only one y-value.

Draw a mapping of the relations to determine which is a function.

For more help with relations and functions, see page 147.

Practice on Your Own

Standard 16.0

2 Which relation is a function? **J**

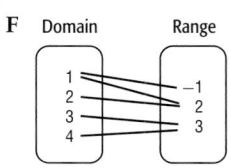

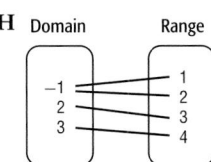

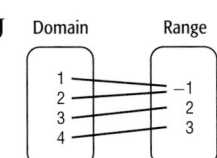

3 Which relation is *not* a function? **B**

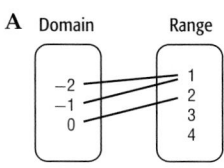

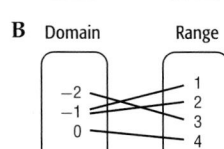

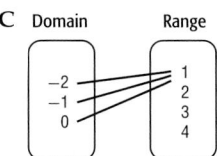

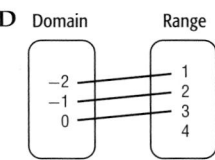

Practice by Standard: Standard 16.0 **CA31**

Practice by Standard

Standard 17.0: Students determine the domain of independent variables and the range of dependent variables defined by a graph, a set of ordered pairs, or a symbolic expression.

DIRECTIONS **Choose the best answer.**

QUICK Practice

1 What is the range of the function shown below? **B**

{(2, 3), (−1, 5), (3, 1), (1, 0)}

A {−1, 1, 2, 3} **C** {0, 5}

B {0, 1, 3, 5} **D** {5}

QUICK Review

READING HINT The range is the set of y-values.

Choose the list that includes all of the y-values.

For more help with domain and range, see page 55.

Practice on Your Own

Standard 17.0

2 What is the domain of the function shown in the graph below? **F**

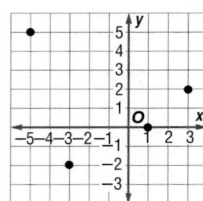

F {−5, −3, 1, 3}

G {−5, 2}

H {−2, 0, 2, 5}

J {−2, 5}

3 For which equation graphed below are all the x-values positive? **C**

A

C

B

D

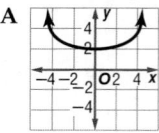

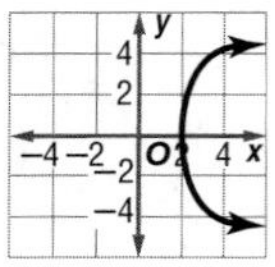

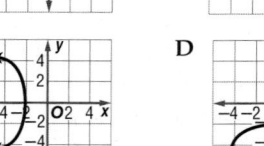

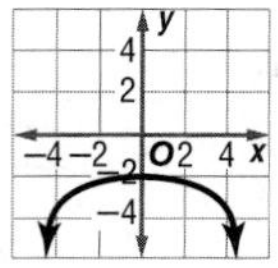

4 What is the domain of the function shown below? **J**

{(−1, 3), (1, 5), (0, 2), (5, 2)}

F {2}

G {2, 3, 5}

H {−1, 5}

J {−1, 0, 1, 5}

5 What is the range of the function shown below? **B**

{(3, 3), (5, 5), (6, 6), (8, 8)}

A {3, 3}

B {3, 5, 6, 8}

C {3, 8}

D {5}

6 What is the range of the function $f(x) = x^2 + 1$ given the domain {−1, 0, 1, 3}? **F**

F {1, 2, 10} **H** {0, 1, 9}

G {0, 1, 2, 4} **J** {0, 1, 2, 10}

CA32 California Standards Review

Practice by Standard

Standard 18.0: Students determine whether a relation defined by a graph, a set of ordered pairs, or a symbolic expression is a function and justify the conclusion.

DIRECTIONS Choose the best answer.

QUICK Practice

1 Is the following graph a function? Explain. **D**

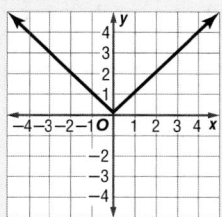

   A No, because it does not pass the vertical line test.

   B No, because it has a V shape.

   C Yes, because it has a V shape.

   D Yes, because it passes the vertical line test.

QUICK Review

READING HINT Use the vertical line test to determine whether the graph is a function.

The vertical line test states that if a vertical line can be drawn so that it crosses the graph in more than one point, then the graph is not a function.

For more help with graphs and functions, see page 149.

Practice on Your Own

Standard 18.0

2 Which graph below shows the graph of a function? **F**

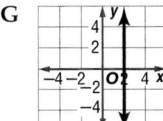

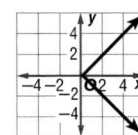

3 Is the following graph a function? Explain. **A**

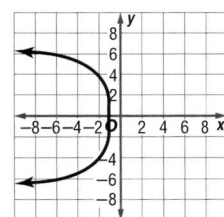

   A No, because it does not pass the vertical line test.

   B No, because it has a U shape.

   C Yes, because it has a U shape.

   D Yes, because it passes the vertical line test.

Practice by Standard

Standard 19.0: Students know the quadratic formula and are familiar with its proof by completing the square.

DIRECTIONS Choose the best answer.

QUICK Practice

1 Margaret is solving $ax^2 + bx = c$ where $a \geq 0$. What should be her first step? **C**

  A To subtract a from each side.

  B To subtract c from each side.

  C To divide everything by a.

  D To divide everything by b.

QUICK Review

> **READING HINT** Eliminate choices that are not part of the completing the square process.

Since the constant term is already on the side of the equation opposite the variable terms, the first step is to make the coefficient of the x^2 term 1.

For more help with completing the square, see page 486.

Practice on Your Own

Standard 19.0

2 The steps to derive the quadratic formula are shown below.

1. $x = \dfrac{-b \pm \sqrt{b^2 - 4ac}}{2a}$

2. $ax^2 + bx = -c$

3. $x + \dfrac{b}{2a} = \pm\sqrt{\dfrac{b^2 - 4ac}{4a^2}}$

4. $x^2 + \dfrac{b}{a}x + \dfrac{b^2}{4a^2} = \dfrac{-c}{a} + \dfrac{b^2}{4a^2}$

5. $x^2 + \dfrac{b}{a}x = -\dfrac{c}{a}$

6. $\left(x^2 + \dfrac{b}{2a}\right)^2 = \dfrac{b^2 - 4ac}{4a^2}$

What is the correct order for these steps? **H**

  F 1, 2, 3, 4, 5, 6

  G 2, 3, 4, 6, 5, 1

  H 2, 5, 4, 6, 3, 1

  J 6, 5, 4, 3, 2, 1

3 Shana is deriving the Quadratic Formula by completing the square. If she were deriving the formula from $x^2 + bx + c = 0$, what would her result look like? **A**

  A $\dfrac{-b \pm \sqrt{b^2 - 4c}}{2}$

  B $\dfrac{-b \pm \sqrt{b^2 - 4ac}}{2a}$

  C $\dfrac{-1 \pm \sqrt{1^2 - 4ac}}{2a}$

  D $\dfrac{-b \pm \sqrt{b^2 - 4a}}{2a}$

4 Jo is solving $ax^2 + bx = c$ where $a \geq 0$. She has already divided everything by a. What should be her next step? **G**

  F To divide the coefficient of x^2 by 2.

  G To divide the coefficient of x by 2.

  H To square the coefficient of x.

  J To subtract a from each side.

Practice by Standard

Standard 20.0: Students use the quadratic formula to find the roots of a
second-degree polynomial and to solve quadratic equations.

DIRECTIONS Choose the best answer.

QUICK Practice

1 What are the roots of
$y = x^2 + 5x + 2$? **C**

  A $\dfrac{-1 \pm \sqrt{17}}{2}$

  B $\dfrac{-5 \pm \sqrt{3}}{2}$

  C $\dfrac{-5 \pm \sqrt{17}}{2}$

  D $\dfrac{5 \pm \sqrt{17}}{2}$

2 Which statement best explains why
there is one solution to the quadratic
equation $x^2 - 4x + 4 = 0$? **G**

  F The value of the discriminant
$(-4)^2 - 4(1)(4)$ is positive.

  G The value of the discriminant
$(-4)^2 - 4(1)(4)$ is 0.

  H The value of the discriminant
$(-4)^2 - 4(1)(4)$ is negative.

  J The value of the discriminant
$(-4)^2 - 4(1)(4)$ is not a perfect
square.

3 Which is one of the solutions to the
equation $2x^2 + 5x - 4 = 0$? **A**

  A $\dfrac{-5 + \sqrt{57}}{4}$

  B $\dfrac{5 + \sqrt{57}}{4}$

  C $\dfrac{-5 + \sqrt{57}}{2}$

  D $\dfrac{-5 + \sqrt{-7}}{4}$

QUICK Review

> **READING HINT** To find the roots of a function,
let $y = 0$ and solve for x.

If the polynomial is not factorable, use the
Quadratic Formula to solve the equation
$0 = x^2 + 5x + 2$.

For more help with the Quadratic Formula, see
page 493.

> **STRATEGY** Determine the value of the discriminant
$(-4)^2 - 4(1)(4)$ to choose the correct answer.

Be sure that when you calculate $(-4)^2$, you get
16 and not -16.

For more help with the Quadratic Formula, see
page 493.

> **STRATEGY** Since the value of $(5)^2 - 4(2)(-4)$ is
positive, this equation will have two possible roots.

Use the Quadratic Formula to solve the
equation.

For more help with the Quadratic Formula, see
page 493.

Practice by Standard: Standard 20.0 **CA35**

Practice on Your Own

4 What is the solution in the set of real numbers of the quadratic equation $x^2 - 3x + 10 = 0$? **J**

F $\dfrac{3 \pm \sqrt{2}}{14}$

G $\dfrac{3 + \sqrt{37}}{14}$

H $\dfrac{-3 + \sqrt{37}}{14}$

J No real solution

5 What are the roots of $y = 3x^2 + 7x + 3$? **B**

A $\dfrac{7 \pm \sqrt{13}}{6}$

B $\dfrac{-7 \pm \sqrt{13}}{6}$

C $\dfrac{-7 \pm \sqrt{2}}{6}$

D $\dfrac{-3 \pm \sqrt{13}}{6}$

6 Which discriminant statement best explains why there are no real solutions to the quadratic equation $5x^2 - 2x + 6 = 0$? **H**

F The value of $(-2)^2 - 4(5)(6)$ is positive.

G The value of $(-2)^2 - 4(5)(6)$ is 0.

H The value of $(-2)^2 - 4(5)(6)$ is negative.

J The value of $(-2)^2 - 4(5)(6)$ is not a perfect square.

7 Which is one of the solutions to the equation $x^2 + 3x - 5 = 0$? **D**

A $\dfrac{-3 - \sqrt{29}}{6}$

B $\dfrac{-3 + \sqrt{11}}{2}$

C $\dfrac{3 - \sqrt{29}}{2}$

D $\dfrac{-3 - \sqrt{29}}{2}$

8 Which discriminant statement best explains why there are two real solutions to the quadratic equation $x^2 - 3x - 5 = 0$? **F**

F The value of $(-3)^2 - 4(1)(-5)$ is positive.

G The value of $(-3)^2 - 4(1)(-5)$ is 0.

H The value of $(-3)^2 - 4(1)(-5)$ is negative.

J The value of $(-3)^2 - 4(1)(-5)$ is a perfect square.

9 Which is one of the solutions to the equation $3x^2 - 4x - 2 = 0$? **A**

A $\dfrac{2 + \sqrt{10}}{3}$

B $\dfrac{4 + \sqrt{10}}{6}$

C $\dfrac{-4 + \sqrt{10}}{6}$

D No real solution

10 What is the solution set in the set of real numbers of the quadratic equation $2x^2 + 4x - 11 = 0$? **H**

F $\dfrac{-2 \pm \sqrt{13}}{2}$

G $\dfrac{-2 + 2\sqrt{26}}{2}$

H $\dfrac{-2 \pm \sqrt{26}}{2}$

J No real solution

11 What are the roots of $y = 2x^2 + 3x - 4$? **C**

A $\dfrac{3 \pm \sqrt{41}}{4}$

B $\dfrac{-3 \pm \sqrt{41}}{2}$

C $\dfrac{-3 \pm \sqrt{41}}{4}$

D $\dfrac{-3 \pm \sqrt{17}}{4}$

Practice by Standard

Standard 21.0: Students graph quadratic functions and know that their roots are the x-intercepts.

DIRECTIONS Choose the best answer.

QUICK Practice

1 The graph of the equation $y = x^2 - 4x - 5$ is shown below.

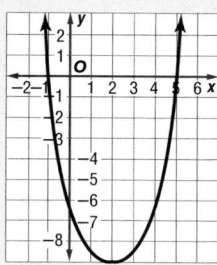

For what values of x is $y = 0$? **C**

A $x = -1$ only

B $x = 5$ only

C $x = -1$ and 5

D $x = -5$ and 1

QUICK Review

> **STRATEGY** Use the graph to determine the x-values when $y = 0$.

Solve the equation $0 = x^2 - 4x - 5$ by factoring to determine the x-values when $y = 0$.

For more help with graphs of quadratic equations, see page 471.

---

2 The graph of the equation $y = x^2 - 2x + 1$ is shown below.

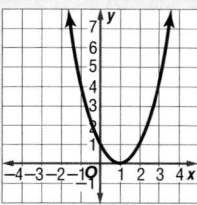

For what values of x is $y = 0$? **F**

F $x = 1$ only   **H** $x = -1$ and 1

G $x = -1$ only   **J** $x = 0$ and 1

> **READING HINT** The values of x when $y = 0$ are the roots or x-intercepts of the equation.

Since the value of $(-2)^2 - 4(1)(1)$ is 0, there will only be one root.

For more help with graphs of quadratic equations, see page 471.

Practice on Your Own

3 Which is the correct graph of $y = x^2 + 5x + 4$? **B**

A
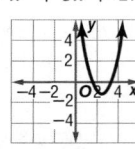

B
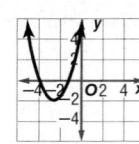

C
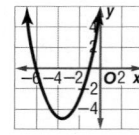

D
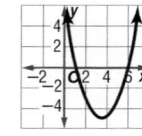

4 The graph of the equation $y = -x^2 + x + 12$ is shown below.

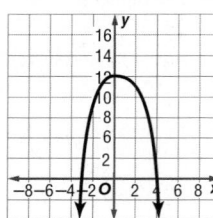

For what values of x is $y = 0$? **H**

F $x = -4$ only

G $x = 3$ only

H $x = -3$ and 4

J $x = -4$ and 3

5 The graph of the equation $y = x^2 + 4x + 5$ is shown below.

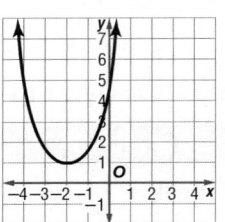

For what values of x is $y = 0$? **D**

A $x = 1$ only

B $x = 5$ only

C $x = 1$ and 5

D No real solution

6 Which is the correct graph of $y = x^2 - 1$? **G**

F
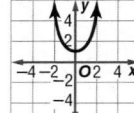

G
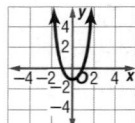

H
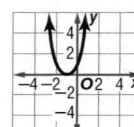

J
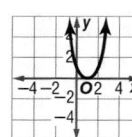

Practice by Standard

Standard 22.0: Students use the quadratic formula or factoring techniques or both to determine whether the graph of a quadratic function will intersect the *x*-axis in zero, one, or two points.

DIRECTIONS Choose the best answer.

QUICK Practice

1 How many times does the graph of $y = x^2 + 4x + 4$ intersect the *x*-axis? **B**

  A zero

  B one

  C two

  D three

QUICK Review

> **READING HINT** The graph will intersect the *x*-axis when $y = 0$.

Find the value of $(4)^2 - 4(1)(4)$ to determine in how many places the graph will intersect the *x*-axis.

For more help with quadratic equations, see page 490.

Practice on Your Own

Standard 22.0

2 How many times does the graph of $y = x^2 + 2x + 5$ intersect the *x*-axis? **F**

  F zero

  G one

  H two

  J three

3 For what values of *b* will the graph of $y = x^2 + bx + 4$ cross the *x*-axis two times? **C**

  A $b = 4$

  B $b = -4$ or 4

  C $b > 4$ or $b < -4$

  D $b > 4$

4 For what values of *b* will the graph of $y = 2x^2 + bx + 2$ cross the *x*-axis one time? **G**

  F $b = 4$

  G $b = -4$ or 4

  H $b > 4$ or $b < -4$

  J $b > 4$

5 How many times does the graph of $y = x^2 + 8x + 7$ intersect the *x*-axis? **C**

  A zero

  B one

  C two

  D three

6 Which quadratic equation only crosses the *x*-axis one time? **H**

  F $y = x^2 + 9$

  G $y = x^2 - 9$

  H $y = x^2 - 6x + 9$

  J $y = x^2 - 5x + 6$

7 For what values of *c* will the graph of $y = x^2 + 6x + c$ cross the *x*-axis two times? **D**

  A $c = 9$

  B $c = -9$ or 9

  C $c > 9$ or $c < -9$

  D $c < 9$

Practice by Standard: Standard 22.0   **CA39**

Practice by Standard

Standard 23.0: Students apply quadratic equations to physical problems, such as the motion of an object under the force of gravity.

DIRECTIONS Choose the best answer.

QUICK Practice

1 The height of a triangle is 2 inches less than 3 times its base. The area of the triangle is 20 square inches. What is the length of the base of the triangle? **C**

  A 20 inches

  B 8 inches

  C 4 inches

  D 2 inches

QUICK Review

▶**READING HINT** Recall that the area of a triangle is given by the formula $A = \frac{1}{2}bh$, where $b =$ base and $h =$ height.

Draw a picture like the one below to help solve the problem.

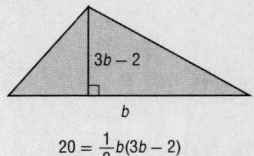

$3b - 2$

b

$$20 = \frac{1}{2}b(3b - 2)$$

For more help with solving quadratic equations, see page 443.

---

2 The height H of an object t seconds after it is thrown upward with an initial velocity v is given by the formula $H = -4.9t^2 + vt + h$, where h is the initial height. Suppose Vicki throws a baseball upward with an initial velocity of 8 meters per second from a height of 10 meters off the ground. At what time will the ball reach the ground? **G**

  F 0.79 second   **H** 4.9 seconds

  G 2.46 seconds   **J** 10 seconds

▶**READING HINT** To determine when the ball will hit the ground, let $H = 0$ and solve the quadratic equation.

Solve the equation $0 = -4.9t^2 + 8t + 10$ by using the Quadratic Formula. Notice that $a = -4.9$.

For more help with solving quadratic equations, see page 493.

---

3 The length of a rectangle is 6 less than twice the width. The area of the rectangle is 80 square centimeters. What is the length of the rectangle? **B**

  A 10 cm   **C** 6 cm

  B 8 cm   **D** 4 cm

▶**READING HINT** The area of a rectangle is given by the formula $A = \ell w$.

Solve the quadratic equation $80 = w(2w - 6)$ to determine the width. Then find the length by substituting the value of w into $2w - 6$.

For more help with solving quadratic equations, see page 443.

Practice on Your Own

4 The height H of an object t seconds after it is thrown upward with an initial velocity v is given by the formula $H = -4.9t^2 + vt + h$, where h is the initial height. Suppose Todd throws a ball upward with an initial velocity of 12 meters per second from a height of 2.5 meters off the ground. At what time will the ball reach the ground? **H**

F　1 second

G　1.34 seconds

H　2.64 seconds

J　4 seconds

5 The height of a triangle is 4 feet less than 4 times its base. The area of the triangle is 24 square feet. What is the height of the triangle? **B**

A　24 ft　　　　**C**　8 ft

B　12 ft　　　　**D**　4 ft

6 The height H of an object t seconds after it is thrown upward with an initial velocity v on the moon is given by the formula $H = -0.8t^2 + vt + h$, where h is the initial height. Suppose an astronaut throws a ball upward with an initial velocity of 10 meters per second from a height of 2.5 meters off the ground. At what time will the ball reach the surface of the moon? **G**

F　13 seconds

G　12.75 seconds

H　0.8 second

J　0.21 second

7 The length of a rectangle is 2 more than twice the width. The area of the rectangle is 24 square meters. What is the length of the rectangle? **B**

A　24 m　　　　**C**　3 m

B　8 m　　　　**D**　2 m

8 What is the length of the rectangle shown below? **G**

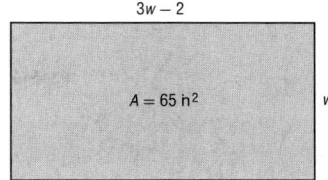

3w − 2

$A = 65\ \text{in}^2$

w

F　65 in.　　　　**H**　5 in.

G　13 in.　　　　**J**　3 in.

9 The height H of an object t seconds after it is thrown upward with an initial velocity v on Mars is given by the formula $H = -1.85t^2 + vt + h$, where h is the initial height. Suppose an astronaut throws a ball upward with an initial velocity of 12 meters per second from a height of 2 meters off the ground. At what time will the ball reach the surface of Mars? **C**

A　0.1 second　　　　**C**　6.65 seconds

B　2 seconds　　　　**D**　12 seconds

10 The height of a triangle is 3 centimeters more than its base. The area of the triangle is 27 square centimeters. What is the length of the base of the triangle? **J**

F　18 cm　　　　**H**　9 cm

G　12 cm　　　　**J**　6 cm

11 The height H of an object t seconds after it is thrown upward with an initial velocity v on Pluto is given by the formula $H = -0.3t^2 + vt + h$, where h is the initial height. Suppose an astronaut throws a ball upward with an initial velocity of 10 meters per second from a height of 2 meters off the ground. At what time will the ball reach the surface of Pluto? **A**

A　33.5 seconds

B　20 seconds

C　2 seconds

D　0.1 second

Practice by Standard

Standard 24.0: Students use and know simple aspects of a logical argument.

DIRECTIONS Choose the best answer.

QUICK Practice

1 What is the hypothesis of the following statement? **A**

If it is raining, then the pool is closed.

A It is raining.

B It is sunny.

C The pool is closed.

D The pool is open.

QUICK Review

READING HINT The hypothesis follows the word *if*.

Eliminate the choices that do not include phrases from the original statement.

For more help with logical reasoning, see page 39.

Practice on Your Own

Standard 24.0

2 What is the conclusion of the following statement? **H**

If $-2x > 6$, then $x < -3$.

F $-2x > 6$

G $-2x = 6$

H $x < -3$

J $x = -3$

3 Which is the correct conditional written in *if-then* form of the following statement? **C**

I will do my homework after dinner.

A If I am doing my homework, then it is after dinner.

B If it is not after dinner, then I am not doing my homework.

C If it is after dinner, then I am doing my homework.

D If it is the weekend, then I am not doing homework.

4 Which is a valid conclusion from the following statement if the two numbers are 4 and 6? **G**

If two numbers are even, then their sum is even.

F The sum of 4 and 6 is odd.

G The sum of 4 and 6 is even.

H The product of 4 and 6 is even.

J No valid conclusion

5 Which numbers disprove the following statement? **A**

If $xy > 0$, then $x > 0$ and $y > 0$.

A $x = -2$ and $y = -3$

B $x = -1$ and $y = 2$

C $x = 1$ and $y = 0$

D $x = 2$ and $y = 3$

Practice by Standard

Standard 25.0: Students use properties of the number system to judge the validity of results, to justify each step of a procedure, and to prove or disprove statements.

DIRECTIONS Choose the best answer.

QUICK Practice

1 Which property can be used to show that the areas of the rectangles are equal? **B**

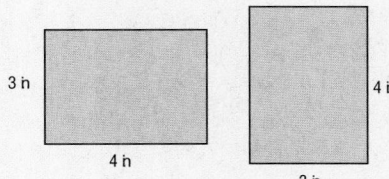

A Associative Property of Multiplication

B Commutative Property of Multiplication

C Distributive Property

D Transitive Property of Equality

QUICK Review

READING HINT Recall that the area of a rectangle is found using the formula $A = \ell w$.

The area of the first rectangle is 3(4) or 12. The area of the second rectangles is 4(3) or 12. So, 3(4) = 4(3). Which property does this represent?

For more help with properties, see page 33.

Practice on Your Own

Standard 25.0

2 The steps to simplify an expression are shown below.

Step 1: $13 + 28 + 17 + 12$

Step 2: $13 + 17 + 28 + 12$

Step 3: $30 + 40$

Step 4: 70

Which property justifies Step 2? **G**

F Associative Property of Addition

G Commutative Property of Addition

H Distributive Property

J Transitive Property of Equality

3 Rachel performs the following simplification.

Step 1: $4(x + 2) + 3x$

Step 2: $4x + 2 + 3x$

Step 3: $4x + 3x + 2$

Step 4: $7x + 2$

Which step is incorrect and why? **B**

A Step 2; did not use Commutative Property correctly

B Step 2; did not use Distributive Property correctly

C Step 3; did not use Commutative Property correctly

D Step 4; did not use Distributive Property correctly

Practice by Standard: Standard 25.0 **CA43**

Student Handbook

Built-In Workbooks

Reference

How to Use the Student Handbook

The Student Handbook is the additional skill and reference material found at the end of the text. This Handbook can help you answer these questions.

What if I Forget What I Learned Last Year?
Use the **Prerequisite Skills** section to refresh your memory about things you have learned in other math classes. Here's a list of the topics covered in your book.

1. Operations with Fractions: Adding and Subtracting
2. Adding and Subtracting Rational Numbers
3. Operations with Fractions: Multiplying and Dividing
4. Multiplying and Dividing Rational Numbers
5. The Percent Proportion
6. Perimeter and Area of Squares and Rectangles
7. Area and Circumference of Circles
8. Volume
9. Probability: Simple Probability and Odds
10. Mean, Median, and Mode
11. Box-and-Whisker Plots
12. Representing Data
13. Absolute Value

What If I Need More Practice?
You, or your teacher, may decide that working through some additional problems would be helpful. The **Extra Practice** section provides these problems for each lesson so you have ample opportunity to practice new skills.

What If I Have Trouble with Word Problems?
The **Mixed Problem Solving** portion of the book provides additional word problems that use the skills presented in each lesson. These problems give you real-world situations where math can be applied.

What If I Forget a Vocabulary Word?
The **English-Spanish Glossary** provides a list of important or difficult words used throughout the textbook. It provides a definition in English and Spanish as well as the page number(s) where the word can be found.

What If I Need to Check a Homework Answer?
The answers to odd-numbered problems are included in **Selected Answers**. Check your answers to make sure you understand how to solve all of the assigned problems.

What If I Need to Find Something Quickly?
The **Index** alphabetically lists the subjects covered throughout the entire textbook and the pages on which each subject can be found.

What if I Forget a Formula?
Inside the back cover of your math book is a list of **Formulas and Symbols** that are used in the book.

Prerequisite Skills

1 Operations with Fractions: Adding and Subtracting

To add or subtract fractions with the same denominator, add or subtract the numerators and write the sum or difference over the denominator.

EXAMPLE 1
Find each sum or difference.

a. $\frac{3}{5} + \frac{1}{5}$

$\frac{3}{5} + \frac{1}{5} = \frac{3+1}{5}$ The denominators are the same. Add the numerators

$= \frac{4}{5}$ Simplify.

b. $\frac{5}{9} - \frac{4}{9}$

$\frac{5}{9} - \frac{4}{9} = \frac{5-4}{9}$ The denominators are the same. Subtract the numerators.

$= \frac{1}{9}$ Simplify.

To write a fraction in simplest form, divide both the numerator and the denominator by their greatest common factor (GCF).

EXAMPLE 2
Write each fraction in simplest form.

a. $\frac{4}{16}$

$\frac{4}{16} = \frac{4 \div 4}{16 \div 4}$ Divide 4 and 16 by their GCF, 4.

$= \frac{1}{4}$ Simplify.

b. $\frac{24}{36}$

$\frac{24}{36} = \frac{24 \div 12}{36 \div 12}$ Divide 24 and 36 by their GCF, 12.

$= \frac{2}{3}$ Simplify.

EXAMPLE 3
Find each sum or difference. Write in simplest form.

a. $\frac{7}{16} - \frac{1}{16}$

$\frac{7}{16} - \frac{1}{16} = \frac{6}{16}$ The denominators are the same. Subtract the numerators.

$= \frac{3}{8}$ Simplify.

b. $\frac{5}{8} + \frac{7}{8}$

$\frac{5}{8} + \frac{7}{8} = \frac{12}{8}$ The denominators are the same. Add the numerators.

$= 1\frac{4}{8}$ or $1\frac{1}{2}$ Rename $\frac{12}{8}$ as a mixed number in simplest form.

To add or subtract fractions with unlike denominators, first find the least common denominator (LCD). Rename each fraction with the LCD, and then add or subtract. Simplify if necessary.

EXAMPLE 4
Find each sum or difference. Write in simplest form.

a. $\frac{2}{9} + \frac{1}{3}$

$\frac{2}{9} + \frac{1}{3} = \frac{2}{9} + \frac{3}{9}$ The LCD for 9 and 3 is 9. Rename $\frac{1}{3}$ as $\frac{3}{9}$.

$= \frac{5}{9}$ Add the numerators.

b. $\frac{1}{2} + \frac{2}{3}$

$\frac{1}{2} + \frac{2}{3} = \frac{3}{6} + \frac{4}{6}$ The LCD for 2 and 3 is 6. Rename $\frac{1}{2}$ as $\frac{3}{6}$ and $\frac{2}{3}$ as $\frac{4}{6}$.

$= \frac{7}{6}$ or $1\frac{1}{6}$ Simplify.

c. $\frac{3}{8} - \frac{1}{3}$

$\frac{3}{8} - \frac{1}{3} = \frac{9}{24} - \frac{8}{24}$ The LCD for 8 and 3 is 24. Rename $\frac{3}{8}$ as $\frac{9}{24}$ and $\frac{1}{3}$ as $\frac{8}{24}$.

$= \frac{1}{24}$ Simplify.

d. $\frac{7}{10} - \frac{2}{15}$

$\frac{7}{10} - \frac{2}{15} = \frac{21}{30} - \frac{4}{30}$ The LCD for 10 and 15 is 30. Rename $\frac{7}{10}$ as $\frac{21}{30}$ and $\frac{2}{15}$ as $\frac{4}{30}$.

$= \frac{17}{30}$ Simplify.

Exercises   Find each sum or difference.

1. $\frac{2}{5} + \frac{1}{5}$ $\frac{3}{5}$
2. $\frac{2}{7} - \frac{1}{7}$ $\frac{1}{7}$
3. $\frac{4}{3} + \frac{4}{3}$ $\frac{8}{3}$ or $2\frac{2}{3}$
4. $\frac{3}{9} + \frac{7}{9}$
5. $\frac{5}{16} - \frac{4}{16}$ $\frac{1}{16}$
6. $\frac{7}{2} - \frac{3}{2}$ $\frac{3}{2}$ or $1\frac{1}{2}$

Simplify.

7. $\frac{6}{9}$ $\frac{2}{3}$
8. $\frac{7}{14}$ $\frac{1}{2}$
9. $\frac{28}{40}$ $\frac{7}{10}$
10. $\frac{16}{100}$ $\frac{4}{25}$
11. $\frac{27}{99}$ $\frac{3}{11}$
12. $\frac{24}{180}$ $\frac{2}{15}$

Find each sum or difference. Write in simplest form.

13. $\frac{2}{9} + \frac{1}{9}$ $\frac{1}{3}$
14. $\frac{2}{15} + \frac{7}{15}$ $\frac{3}{5}$
15. $\frac{2}{3} + \frac{1}{3}$ 1
16. $\frac{7}{8} - \frac{3}{8}$ $\frac{1}{2}$
17. $\frac{4}{9} - \frac{1}{9}$ $\frac{1}{3}$
18. $\frac{5}{4} - \frac{3}{4}$ $\frac{1}{2}$
19. $\frac{1}{4} + \frac{3}{4}$ 1
20. $\frac{1}{2} - \frac{3}{6}$ 0
21. $\frac{4}{3} + \frac{5}{9}$ $1\frac{8}{9}$
22. $1\frac{1}{2} - \frac{3}{2}$ 0
23. $\frac{1}{4} + \frac{1}{5}$ $\frac{9}{20}$
24. $\frac{2}{3} + \frac{1}{4}$ $\frac{11}{12}$
25. $\frac{3}{2} + \frac{1}{2}$ 2
26. $\frac{8}{9} - \frac{2}{3}$ $\frac{2}{9}$
27. $\frac{3}{7} + \frac{5}{14}$ $\frac{11}{14}$
28. $\frac{13}{20} - \frac{2}{5}$ $\frac{1}{4}$
29. $1 - \frac{18}{19}$ $\frac{1}{19}$
30. $\frac{9}{10} - \frac{3}{5}$ $\frac{3}{10}$
31. $\frac{3}{4} - \frac{2}{3}$ $\frac{1}{12}$
32. $\frac{4}{15} + \frac{3}{4}$ $1\frac{1}{60}$
33. $\frac{11}{12} - \frac{4}{15}$ $\frac{13}{20}$
34. $\frac{3}{11} + \frac{1}{8}$ $\frac{35}{88}$
35. $\frac{94}{100} - \frac{11}{25}$ $\frac{1}{2}$
36. $\frac{3}{25} + \frac{5}{6}$ $\frac{143}{150}$

2 Adding and Subtracting Rational Numbers

You can use a number line to add rational numbers.

EXAMPLE

1 Use a number line to find each sum.

a. $-3 + (-4)$

Step 1 Draw an arrow from 0 to -3.

Step 2 Then draw a second arrow 4 units to the left to represent adding -4.

Step 3 The second arrow ends at the sum -7. So, $-3 + (-4) = -7$.

$(-3) + (-4) = -7$

b. $2.5 + (-3.5)$

Step 1 Draw an arrow from 0 to 2.5.

Step 2 Then draw a second arrow 3.5 units to the left.

Step 3 The second arrow ends at the sum -1. So, $2.5 + (-3.5) = -1$.

$2.5 + (-3.5) = -1$

You can use absolute value to add rational numbers.

Same Signs

$+ \quad +$

$3 + 5 = 8$

3 and 5 are positive, so the sum is positive.

$- \quad -$

$-3 + (-5) = -8$

-3 and -5 are negative, so the sum is negative.

Different Signs

$+ \quad -$

$3 + (-5) = -2$

Since -5 has the greater absolute value, the sum is negative.

$- \quad +$

$-3 + 5 = 2$

Since 5 has the greater absolute value, the sum is positive.

EXAMPLE

2 Find each sum.

a. $-11 + (-7)$

$-11 + (-7) = -(|-11| + |-7|)$ Both numbers are negative, so the sum is negative.

$= -(11 + 7)$

$= -18$

b. $\frac{7}{16} + \left(-\frac{3}{8}\right)$

$\frac{7}{16} + \left(-\frac{3}{8}\right) = \frac{7}{16} + \left(-\frac{6}{16}\right)$ The LCD is 16. Replace $-\frac{3}{8}$ with $-\frac{6}{16}$.

$= +\left(\left|\frac{7}{16}\right| - \left|-\frac{6}{16}\right|\right)$ Subtract the absolute values.

$= +\left(\frac{7}{16} - \frac{6}{16}\right)$ Since the number with the greater absolute value is $\frac{7}{16}$, the sum is positive.

$= \frac{1}{16}$

Every positive rational number can be paired with a negative rational number. These pairs are called **opposites**. A number and its opposite are **additive inverses** of each other. Additive inverses can be used when you subtract rational numbers.

EXAMPLE

Find each difference.

a. $18 - 23$

$18 - 23 = 18 + (-23)$ To subtract 23, add its inverse.

$= -(|-23| - |18|)$ Subtract the absolute values.

$= -(23 - 18)$ The absolute value of -23 is greater, so the result is negative.

$= -5$ Simplify.

b. $-32.25 - (-42.5)$

$-32.25 - (-42.5) = -32.25 + 42.5$ To subtract -42.5, add its inverse.

$= |42.5| - |-32.25|$ Subtract the absolute values.

$= 42.5 - 32.25$ The absolute value of 42.5 is greater, so the result is positive.

$= 10.25$ Simplify.

Exercises Find each sum.

1. $-8 + 13$ 5

2. $-11 + 19$ 8

3. $41 + (-63)$ -22

4. $80 + (-102)$ -22

5. $-77 + (-46)$ -123

6. $-92 + (-64)$ -156

7. $-1.6 + (-3.8)$ -5.4

8. $-32.4 + (-4.5)$ -36.9

9. $-38.9 + 24.2$ -14.7

10. $-7.007 + 4.8$ -2.207

11. $43.2 + (-57.9)$ -14.7

12. $38.37 + (-61.1)$ -22.4

13. $\frac{6}{7} + \frac{2}{3}$ $\frac{32}{21}$ or $1\frac{11}{21}$

14. $\frac{3}{18} + \frac{6}{17}$ $\frac{53}{102}$

15. $-\frac{4}{11} + \frac{3}{5}$ $\frac{13}{55}$

16. $-\frac{2}{5} + \frac{17}{20}$ $\frac{9}{20}$

17. $-\frac{4}{15} + \left(-\frac{9}{16}\right)$ $-\frac{199}{240}$

18. $-\frac{16}{40} + \left(-\frac{13}{20}\right)$ $\frac{21}{20}$ or $1\frac{1}{20}$

Find each difference.

19. $-19 - 8$ -27

20. $16 - (-23)$ 39

21. $9 - (-24)$ 33

22. $12 - 34$ -22

23. $22 - 41$ -19

24. $-9 - (-33)$ 24

25. $-58 - (-42)$ -16

26. $79.3 - (-14.1)$ 93.4

27. $1.34 - (-0.458)$ 1.798

28. $-9.16 - 10.17$ -19.33

29. $67.1 - (-38.2)$ 105.3

30. $72.5 - (-81.3)$ 153.8

31. $\frac{1}{6} - \frac{2}{3}$ $-\frac{5}{6}$

32. $\frac{1}{2} - \frac{4}{5}$ $\frac{3}{10}$

33. $-\frac{7}{8} - \left(-\frac{3}{16}\right)$ $-\frac{11}{16}$

34. $-\frac{1}{12} - \left(-\frac{3}{4}\right)$ $\frac{2}{3}$

35. $2\frac{1}{4} - 6\frac{1}{3}$ $-\frac{49}{12}$ or $-4\frac{1}{12}$

36. $5\frac{3}{10} - 1\frac{31}{50}$ $3\frac{17}{25}$

3 Operations with Fractions: Multiplying and Dividing

To multiply fractions, multiply the numerators and multiply the denominators.

EXAMPLE 1 Find each product.

a. $\dfrac{2}{5} \cdot \dfrac{1}{3}$

$\dfrac{2}{5} \cdot \dfrac{1}{3} = \dfrac{2 \cdot 1}{5 \cdot 3}$ Multiply the numerators. Multiply the denominators.

$= \dfrac{2}{15}$ Simplify.

b. $\dfrac{7}{3} \cdot \dfrac{1}{11}$

$\dfrac{7}{3} \cdot \dfrac{1}{11} = \dfrac{7 \cdot 1}{3 \cdot 11}$ Multiply the numerators. Multiply the denominators.

$= \dfrac{7}{33}$ Simplify.

If the fractions have common factors in the numerators and denominators, you can simplify before you multiply by canceling.

EXAMPLE 2 Find each product. Simplify before multiplying.

a. $\dfrac{3}{4} \cdot \dfrac{4}{7}$

$\dfrac{3}{4} \cdot \dfrac{4}{7} = \dfrac{3}{4} \cdot \dfrac{4}{7}$ Divide by the GCF, 4.

$= \dfrac{3}{7}$ Multiply.

b. $\dfrac{4}{9} \cdot \dfrac{45}{49}$

$\dfrac{4}{9} \cdot \dfrac{45}{49} = \dfrac{4}{9} \cdot \dfrac{45}{49}$ Divide by the GCF, 9.

$= \dfrac{20}{49}$ Multiply.

Two numbers whose product is 1 are called **multiplicative inverses** or **reciprocals**.

EXAMPLE 3 Name the reciprocal of each number.

a. $\dfrac{3}{8}$

$\dfrac{3}{8} \cdot \dfrac{8}{3} = 1$ The product is 1.

The reciprocal of $\dfrac{3}{8}$ is $\dfrac{8}{3}$.

b. $\dfrac{1}{6}$

$\dfrac{1}{6} \cdot \dfrac{6}{1} = 1$ The product is 1.

The reciprocal of $\dfrac{1}{6}$ is 6.

c. $2\dfrac{4}{5}$

$2\dfrac{4}{5} = \dfrac{14}{5}$ Write $2\dfrac{4}{5}$ as an improper fraction.

$\dfrac{14}{5} \cdot \dfrac{5}{14} = 1$ The product is 1.

The reciprocal of $2\dfrac{4}{5}$ is $\dfrac{5}{14}$.

To divide one fraction by another fraction, multiply the dividend by the multiplicative inverse of the divisor.

EXAMPLE 4 Find each quotient.

a. $\dfrac{1}{3} \div \dfrac{1}{2}$

$\dfrac{1}{3} \div \dfrac{1}{2} = \dfrac{1}{3} \cdot \dfrac{2}{1}$ Multiply $\dfrac{1}{3}$ by $\dfrac{2}{1}$, the reciprocal of $\dfrac{1}{2}$.

$= \dfrac{2}{3}$ Simplify.

b. $\dfrac{3}{8} \div \dfrac{2}{3}$

$\dfrac{3}{8} \div \dfrac{2}{3} = \dfrac{3}{8} \cdot \dfrac{3}{2}$ Multiply $\dfrac{3}{8}$ by $\dfrac{3}{2}$, the reciprocal of $\dfrac{2}{3}$.

$= \dfrac{9}{16}$ Simplify.

c. $4 \div \dfrac{5}{6}$

$4 \div \dfrac{5}{6} = \dfrac{4}{1} \cdot \dfrac{6}{5}$ Multiply 4 by $\dfrac{6}{5}$, the reciprocal of $\dfrac{5}{6}$.

$= \dfrac{24}{5}$ or $4\dfrac{4}{5}$ Simplify.

d. $\dfrac{3}{4} \div 2\dfrac{1}{2}$

$\dfrac{3}{4} \div 2\dfrac{1}{2} = \dfrac{3}{4} \cdot \dfrac{2}{5}$ Multiply $\dfrac{3}{4}$ by $\dfrac{2}{5}$, the reciprocal of $2\dfrac{1}{2}$.

$= \dfrac{6}{20}$ or $\dfrac{3}{10}$ Simplify.

Exercises   Find each product.

1. $\dfrac{3}{4} \cdot \dfrac{1}{5}$ $\dfrac{3}{20}$
2. $\dfrac{2}{7} \cdot \dfrac{1}{3}$ $\dfrac{2}{21}$
3. $\dfrac{1}{5} \cdot \dfrac{3}{20}$ $\dfrac{3}{100}$
4. $\dfrac{2}{5} \cdot \dfrac{3}{7}$ $\dfrac{6}{35}$
5. $\dfrac{5}{2} \cdot \dfrac{1}{4}$ $\dfrac{5}{8}$
6. $\dfrac{7}{2} \cdot \dfrac{3}{2}$ $\dfrac{21}{4}$ or $5\dfrac{1}{4}$
7. $\dfrac{1}{3} \cdot \dfrac{2}{5}$ $\dfrac{2}{15}$
8. $\dfrac{2}{3} \cdot \dfrac{1}{11}$ $\dfrac{2}{33}$

Find each product. Simplify before multiplying if possible.

9. $\dfrac{2}{9} \cdot \dfrac{1}{2}$ $\dfrac{1}{9}$
10. $\dfrac{15}{2} \cdot \dfrac{7}{15}$ $\dfrac{7}{2}$ or $3\dfrac{1}{2}$
11. $\dfrac{3}{2} \cdot \dfrac{1}{3}$ $\dfrac{1}{2}$
12. $\dfrac{1}{3} \cdot \dfrac{6}{5}$ $\dfrac{2}{5}$
13. $\dfrac{9}{4} \cdot \dfrac{11}{18}$ $\dfrac{11}{8}$
14. $\dfrac{11}{3} \cdot \dfrac{3}{44}$ $\dfrac{1}{4}$
15. $\dfrac{2}{7} \cdot \dfrac{14}{3}$ $\dfrac{4}{3}$ or $1\dfrac{1}{3}$
16. $\dfrac{2}{11} \cdot \dfrac{110}{17}$ $\dfrac{20}{17}$ or $1\dfrac{3}{17}$
17. $\dfrac{1}{3} \cdot \dfrac{12}{19}$ $\dfrac{4}{19}$
18. $\dfrac{1}{3} \cdot \dfrac{15}{2}$ $\dfrac{5}{2}$ or $2\dfrac{1}{2}$
19. $\dfrac{30}{11} \cdot \dfrac{1}{3}$ $\dfrac{10}{11}$
20. $\dfrac{6}{5} \cdot \dfrac{10}{12}$ 1

Name the reciprocal of each number.

21. $\dfrac{6}{7}$ $\dfrac{7}{6}$ or $1\dfrac{1}{6}$
22. $\dfrac{3}{2}$ $\dfrac{2}{3}$
23. 22 $\dfrac{1}{22}$
24. $\dfrac{14}{23}$ $\dfrac{23}{14}$ or $1\dfrac{9}{14}$
25. $2\dfrac{3}{4}$ $\dfrac{4}{11}$
26. $5\dfrac{1}{3}$ $\dfrac{3}{16}$

Find each quotient.

27. $\dfrac{2}{3} \div \dfrac{1}{3}$ 2
28. $\dfrac{16}{9} \div \dfrac{4}{9}$ 4
29. $\dfrac{3}{2} \div \dfrac{1}{2}$ 3
30. $\dfrac{3}{7} \div \dfrac{1}{5}$ $\dfrac{15}{7}$ or $2\dfrac{1}{7}$
31. $\dfrac{9}{10} \div \dfrac{3}{7}$ $\dfrac{21}{10}$ or $2\dfrac{1}{10}$
32. $\dfrac{1}{2} \div \dfrac{3}{5}$ $\dfrac{5}{6}$
33. $2\dfrac{1}{4} \div \dfrac{1}{2}$ $\dfrac{9}{2}$ or $4\dfrac{1}{2}$
34. $1\dfrac{1}{3} \div \dfrac{2}{3}$ 2
35. $\dfrac{11}{12} \div 1\dfrac{2}{3}$ $\dfrac{11}{20}$
36. $\dfrac{3}{8} \div \dfrac{1}{4}$ $\dfrac{3}{2}$ or $1\dfrac{1}{2}$
37. $\dfrac{1}{3} \div 1\dfrac{1}{5}$ $\dfrac{5}{18}$
38. $\dfrac{3}{25} \div \dfrac{2}{15}$ $\dfrac{9}{10}$

4 Multiplying and Dividing Rational Numbers

The product of two numbers having the *same sign* is positive. The product of two numbers having *different signs* is negative.

EXAMPLE 1 Find each product.

a. $4(-5)$

$4(-5) = -20$ different signs → negative product

b. $(-12)(-14)$

$(-12)(-14) = 168$ same signs → positive product

c. $\left(-\dfrac{3}{4}\right)\left(\dfrac{3}{8}\right)$

$\left(-\dfrac{3}{4}\right)\left(\dfrac{3}{8}\right) = -\dfrac{9}{32}$ different signs → negative product

You can evaluate expressions that contain rational numbers.

EXAMPLE 2 Evaluate $n^2\left(-\dfrac{5}{8}\right)$ if $n = -\dfrac{2}{5}$.

$n^2\left(-\dfrac{5}{8}\right) = \left(-\dfrac{2}{5}\right)^2\left(-\dfrac{5}{8}\right)$ Substitution

$= \left(\dfrac{4}{25}\right)\left(-\dfrac{5}{8}\right)$ $\left(-\dfrac{2}{5}\right)^2 = \left(-\dfrac{2}{5}\right)\left(-\dfrac{2}{5}\right)$ or $\dfrac{4}{25}$

$= -\dfrac{20}{200}$ or $-\dfrac{1}{10}$ different signs → negative product

The quotient of two numbers having the *same sign* is positive. The quotient of two numbers having *different signs* is negative.

EXAMPLE 3 Find each quotient.

a. $\dfrac{-51}{-3}$

$\dfrac{-51}{-3} = -51 \div (-3)$

$= 17$ positive quotient

b. $245.66 \div (-14.2)$

$245.66 \div (-14.2) = -17.3$ Use a calculator.

different signs → negative quotient

c. $-\dfrac{2}{5} \div \dfrac{1}{4}$

$-\dfrac{2}{5} \div \dfrac{1}{4} = -\dfrac{2}{5} \cdot \dfrac{4}{1}$ Multiply by $\dfrac{4}{1}$, the reciprocal of $\dfrac{1}{4}$.

$= -\dfrac{8}{5}$ or $-1\dfrac{3}{5}$ different signs → negative quotient

---

You can use the Distributive Property to evaluate rational expressions.

EXAMPLE 4 Evaluate $\dfrac{ab}{c^2}$ if $a = -7.8$, $b = 5.2$, and $c = -3$. Round to the nearest hundredth.

$\dfrac{ab}{c^2} = \dfrac{(-7.8)(5.2)}{(-3)^2}$ Replace a with -7.8, b with 5.2, and c with -3.

$= \dfrac{-40.56}{9}$ Find the numerator and denominator separately.

≈ -4.51 Use a calculator; different signs → negative quotient.

Exercises Find each product.

1. $5(18)$ 90
2. $8(22)$ 176
3. $-12(15)$ -180
4. $-24(8)$ -192
5. $-47(-29)$ -1363
6. $-81(-48)$ 3888
7. $\left(\dfrac{4}{5}\right)\left(\dfrac{3}{8}\right)$ $\dfrac{3}{10}$
8. $\left(\dfrac{5}{12}\right)\left(\dfrac{4}{9}\right)$ $\dfrac{5}{27}$
9. $\left(-\dfrac{3}{5}\right)\left(\dfrac{5}{6}\right)$ $-\dfrac{1}{2}$
10. $\left(-\dfrac{2}{5}\right)\left(\dfrac{6}{7}\right)$ $-\dfrac{12}{35}$
11. $\left(-3\dfrac{1}{5}\right)\left(-7\dfrac{1}{2}\right)$ 16
12. $\left(-\dfrac{4}{5}\right)\left(-2\dfrac{1}{2}\right)$ $4\dfrac{1}{2}$
13. $7.2(0.2)$ 1.44
14. $6.5(0.13)$ 0.845
15. $(-5.8)(2.3)$ -13.34
16. $(-0.075)(6.4)$ -0.48
17. $\dfrac{3}{5}(-5)(-2)$ 6
18. $\dfrac{2}{11}(-11)(-4)$ 8

Evaluate each expression if $a = -2.7$, $b = 3.9$, $c = 4.5$ and $d = -0.2$.

19. $-5c^2$ -101.25
20. $-2b^2$ -30.42
21. $-4ab$ 42.12
22. $-5cd$ 4.5
23. $ad - 8$ -7.46
24. $ab - 3$ -13.53
25. $d^2(b - 2a)$ 0.372
26. $b^2(d - 3c)$ -208.377

Find each quotient.

27. $-64 \div (-8)$ 8
28. $-78 \div (-4)$ 19.5
29. $-78 \div (-1.3)$ 60
30. $108 \div (-0.9)$ -120
31. $42.3 \div (-6)$ -7.05
32. $68.4 \div (-12)$ 5.7
33. $-23.94 \div 10.5$ -2.28
34. $-60.97 \div 13.4$ -4.55
35. $-32.25 \div (-2.5)$ 12.9
36. $-98.44 \div (-4.6)$ 21.4
37. $-\dfrac{1}{3} \div 4$ $-\dfrac{1}{12}$
38. $\dfrac{3}{4} \div 12$ $\dfrac{1}{16}$
39. $-7 \div \dfrac{3}{5}$ $-\dfrac{35}{3}$ or $-11\dfrac{2}{3}$
40. $-5 \div \dfrac{2}{7}$ $-\dfrac{35}{2}$ or $-17\dfrac{1}{2}$
41. $\dfrac{16}{36} \div \dfrac{24}{60}$ $\dfrac{10}{9}$ or $1\dfrac{1}{9}$
42. $\dfrac{24}{56} \div \dfrac{31}{63}$ $\dfrac{31}{27}$
43. $\dfrac{14}{32} \div \left(-\dfrac{12}{15}\right)$ $-\dfrac{175}{192}$
44. $\dfrac{80}{25} \div \left(-\dfrac{2}{3}\right)$ $-\dfrac{24}{5}$ or $-4\dfrac{4}{5}$

Evaluate each expression if $m = -8$, $n = 6.5$, $p = 3.2$, and $q = -5.4$. Round to the nearest hundredth.

45. $\dfrac{mn}{p}$ -16.25
46. $\dfrac{np}{m}$ -2.6
47. $mq \div np$ 2.08
48. $pq \div mn$ 0.33
49. $\dfrac{n+p}{m}$ -1.21
50. $\dfrac{m+p}{q}$ 0.89
51. $\dfrac{m-2n}{-n+q}$ 1.76
52. $\dfrac{p-3q}{-q-m}$ 1.45

5 The Percent Proportion

A **percent** is a ratio that compares a number to 100. To write a percent as a fraction, express the ratio as a fraction with a denominator of 100. Fractions should be stated in simplest form.

EXAMPLE 1

Express each percent as a fraction.

a. 25%

$25\% = \dfrac{25}{100}$ or $\dfrac{1}{4}$ Definition of percent

b. 107%

$107\% = \dfrac{107}{100}$ or $1\dfrac{7}{100}$ Definition of percent

c. 0.5%

$0.5\% = \dfrac{0.5}{100}$ Definition of percent

$= \dfrac{5}{1000}$ or $\dfrac{1}{200}$ Simplify.

In the **percent proportion**, the ratio of a part of something (part) to the whole (base) is equal to the percent written as a fraction.

part → $\dfrac{a}{b} = \dfrac{p}{100}$ ← percent   Example: 10 is 25% of 40.
base →

part   percent   base

EXAMPLE 2

40% of 30 is what number?

$\dfrac{a}{b} = \dfrac{p}{100}$ The percent is 40, and the base is 30.
Let a represent the part.

$\dfrac{a}{30} = \dfrac{40}{100}$ Replace b with 30 and p with 40.

$100a = 30(40)$ Find the cross products.

$100a = 1200$ Simplify.

$\dfrac{100a}{100} = \dfrac{1200}{100}$ Divide each side by 100.

$a = 12$ The part is 12. So, 40% of 30 is 12.

EXAMPLE 3

Kelsey took a survey of some of the students in her lunch period. 42 out of the 70 students Kelsey surveyed said their family had a pet. What percent of the students had pets?

$\dfrac{a}{b} = \dfrac{p}{100}$ The part is 42, and the base is 70.
Let p represent the percent.

$\dfrac{42}{70} = \dfrac{p}{100}$ Replace a with 42 and b with 70.

$4200 = 70p$ Find the cross products.

$\dfrac{4200}{70} = \dfrac{70p}{70}$ Divide each side by 70.

$60 = p$ The percent is 60, so $\dfrac{60}{100}$ or 60% of the students had pets.

EXAMPLE 4

67.5 is 75% of what number?

$\dfrac{a}{b} = \dfrac{p}{100}$ The percent is 75, and the part is 67.5.
Let b represent the base.

$\dfrac{67.5}{b} = \dfrac{75}{100}$ $75\% = \dfrac{75}{100}$, so $p = 75$. Replace a with 67.5 and p with 75.

$6750 = 75b$ Find the cross products.

$\dfrac{6750}{75} = \dfrac{75b}{75}$ Divide each side by 75.

$90 = b$ The base is 90, so 67.5 is 75% of 90.

Exercises Express each percent as a fraction.

1. 5% $\dfrac{5}{100}$ or $\dfrac{1}{20}$
2. 60% $\dfrac{60}{100}$ or $\dfrac{3}{5}$
3. 11% $\dfrac{11}{100}$
4. 120% $\dfrac{120}{100}$ or $\dfrac{6}{5}$
5. 78% $\dfrac{78}{100}$ or $\dfrac{39}{50}$
6. 2.5% $\dfrac{2.5}{100}$ or $\dfrac{1}{40}$
7. 0.9% $\dfrac{9}{1000}$
8. 0.4% $\dfrac{4}{1000}$ or $\dfrac{1}{250}$
9. 1400% 14

Use the percent proportion to find each number.

10. 25 is what percent of 125? 20
11. 16 is what percent of 40? 40
12. 14 is 20% of what number? 70
13. 50% of what number is 80? 160
14. What number is 25% of 18? 4.5
15. Find 10% of 95. 9.5
16. What percent of 48 is 30? 62.5
17. What number is 150% of 32? 48
18. 5% of what number is 3.5? 70
19. 1 is what percent of 400? 0.25
20. Find 0.5% of 250. 1.25
21. 49 is 200% of what number? 24.5
22. 15 is what percent of 12? 125
23. 48 is what percent of 32? 150
24. Madeline usually makes 85% of her shots in basketball. If she shoots 20 shots, how many will she likely make? 17
25. Brian answered 36 items correctly on a 40-item test. What percent did he answer correctly? 90%
26. José told his dad that he won 80% of the solitaire games he played yesterday. If he won 4 games, how many games did he play? 5
27. A glucose solution is prepared by dissolving 6 milliliters of glucose in 120 milliliters of solution. What is the percent of glucose in the solution? 5%

HEALTH For Exercises 28–30, use the following information.
The U.S. Food and Drug Administration requires food manufacturers to label their products with a nutritional label. The sample label shown at the right shows a portion of the information from a package of macaroni and cheese.

28. The label states that a serving contains 3 grams of saturated fat, which is 15% of the daily value recommended for a 2000-Calorie diet. How many grams of saturated fat are recommended for a 2000-Calorie diet? 20 grams
29. The 470 milligrams of sodium (salt) in the macaroni and cheese is 20% of the recommended daily value. What is the recommended daily value of sodium? 2350 mg or 2.375 g
30. For a healthy diet, the National Research Council recommends that no more than 30 percent of total Calories come from fat. What percent of the Calories in a serving of this macaroni and cheese come from fat? 44%

Nutrition Facts	
Serving Size 1 cup (228g)	
Servings per container 2	
Amount per serving	
Calories 250	Calories from Fat 110
	%Daily value*
Total Fat 12g	18%
Saturated Fat 3g	15%
Cholesterol 30mg	10%
Sodium 470mg	20%
Total Carbohydrate 31g	10%
Dietary Fiber 0g	0%
Sugars 5g	
Protein 5g	
Vitamin A 4% • Vitamin C 2%	
Calcium 20% • Iron 4%	

6 Perimeter and Area of Squares and Rectangles

Perimeter is the distance around a geometric figure. Perimeter is measured in linear units.

- To find the perimeter of a rectangle, multiply two times the sum of the length and width, or $2(\ell + w)$.
- To find the perimeter of a square, multiply four times the length of a side, or $4s$.

$$P = 2(\ell + w) \text{ or } 2\ell + 2w \qquad P = 4s$$

Area is the number of square units needed to cover a surface. Area is measured in square units.

- To find the area of a rectangle, multiply the length times the width, or $\ell \cdot w$.
- To find the area of a square, find the square of the length of a side, or s^2.

$$A = \ell w \qquad\qquad A = s^2$$

EXAMPLE 1

Find the perimeter and area of each rectangle.

a. A rectangle has a length of 3 units and a width of 5 units.

$P = 2(\ell + w)$	Perimeter formula
$= 2(3 + 5)$	Replace ℓ with 3 and w with 5.
$= 2(8)$	Add.
$= 16$	Multiply.
$A = \ell \cdot w$	Area formula
$= 3 \cdot 5$	Replace ℓ with 3 and w with 5.
$= 15$	Simplify.

The perimeter is 16 units, and the area is 15 square units.

b. A rectangle has a length of 1 inch and a width of 10 inches.

$P = 2(\ell + w)$	Perimeter formula
$= 2(1 + 10)$	Replace ℓ with 1 and w with 10.
$= 2(11)$	Add.
$= 22$	Multiply.
$A = \ell \cdot w$	Area formula
$= 1 \cdot 10$	Replace ℓ with 1 and w with 10.
$= 10$	Simplify.

The perimeter is 22 inches, and the area is 10 square inches.

EXAMPLE 2

Find the perimeter and area of each square.

a. A square has a side length of 8 feet.

$P = 4s$	Perimeter formula
$= 4(8)$	$s = 8$
$= 32$	Multiply.
$A = s^2$	Area formula
$= 8^2$	$s = 8$
$= 64$	$8^2 = 8 \cdot 8 \text{ or } 64$

The perimeter is 32 feet, and the area is 64 square feet.

b. A square has a side length of 2 meters.

$P = 4s$	Perimeter formula
$= 4(2)$	$s = 2$
$= 8$	Multiply.
$A = s^2$	Area formula
$= 2^2$	$s = 2$
$= 4$	$2^2 = 2 \cdot 2 \text{ or } 4$

The perimeter is 8 meters, and the area is 4 square meters.

Exercises Find the perimeter and area of each figure.

1.

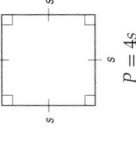

$P = 10$ cm; $A = 6$ cm²

2.

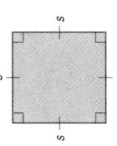

$P = 4$ in.; $A = 1$ in²

3.

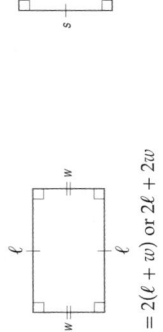

$P = 16$ yd; $A = 7$ yd²

4.

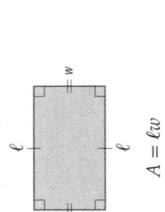

$P = 28$ km; $A = 49$ km²

5. a rectangle with length 6 feet and width 4 feet $P = 20$ ft; $A = 24$ ft²

6. a rectangle with length 12 centimeters and width 9 centimeters $P = 42$ cm; $A = 108$ cm²

7. a square with length 3 meters $P = 12$ m; $A = 9$ m²

8. a square with length 15 inches $P = 60$ in.; $A = 225$ in²

9. a rectangle with width $8\frac{1}{2}$ inches and length 11 inches $P = 39$ in.; $A = 9$ in²

10. a rectangular room with width $12\frac{1}{4}$ feet and length $14\frac{1}{2}$ feet $P = 53\frac{1}{2}$ ft; $A = 177\frac{5}{8}$ ft²

11. a square with length 2.4 centimeters $P = 9.6$ cm; $A = 5.76$ cm²

12. a square garden with length 5.8 meters $P = 23.2$ m; $A = 33.64$ m²

13. **RECREATION** The Granville Parks and Recreation Department uses an empty city lot for a community vegetable garden. Each participant is allotted a space of 18 feet by 90 feet for a garden. What is the perimeter and area of each plot? 216 ft; 1620 ft²

⑦ Area and Circumference of Circles

A **circle** is the set of all points in a plane that are the same distance from a given point.

The given point is called the **center**.

The distance across the circle through its center is its **diameter**.

The distance from the center to any point on the circle is its **radius**.

The distance around the circle is called the **circumference**.

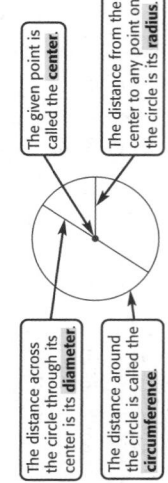

The formula for the circumference of a circle is $C = \pi d$ or $C = 2\pi r$.

EXAMPLE 1

Find the circumference of each circle to the nearest tenth.

a. The radius is 3 feet.

$C = 2\pi r$	Circumference formula
$= 2\pi(3)$	Replace r with 3.
$= 6\pi$	Simplify.

The exact circumference is 6π feet.

6 $\boxed{\pi}$ $\boxed{\text{ENTER}}$ 18.8495592   Use a calculator to evaluate 6π.

The circumference is about 18.8 feet.

b. The diameter is 24 centimeters.

$C = \pi d$	Circumference formula
$= \pi(24)$	Replace d with 24.
$= 24\pi$	Simplify.
$= 75.4$	Use a calculator to evaluate 24π.

The circumference is about 75.4 centimeters.

The formula for the area of a circle is $A = \pi r^2$.

EXAMPLE 2

Find the area of each circle to the nearest tenth.

a. The radius is 4 inches.

$A = \pi r^2$	Area formula
$= \pi(4)^2$	Replace r with 4.
$= 16\pi$	Simplify.
$= 50.3$	Use a calculator to evaluate 16π.

The area is about 50.3 square inches.

b. The diameter is 20 centimeters.

The radius is one half times the diameter, or 10 centimeters.

$A = \pi r^2$	Area formula
$= \pi(10)^2$	Replace r with 10.
$= 100\pi$	Simplify.
$= 314.2$	Use a calculator to evaluate 100π.

The area is about 314.2 square centimeters.

EXAMPLE 3

HISTORY Stonehenge is an ancient monument in Wiltshire, England. Historians are not sure who erected Stonehenge or why. It may have been used as a calendar. The giant stones of Stonehenge are arranged in a circle 30 meters in diameter. Find the circumference and the area of the circle.

$C = \pi d$	Write the formula.
$= \pi(30)$	Replace d with 30.
$= 30\pi$ or about 94.2	Simplify.

Find the radius to evaluate the formula for the area.

$A = \pi r^2$	Write the formula.
$= \pi(15)^2$	Replace r with $\frac{1}{2}(30)$ or 15.
$= 225\pi$ or about 706.9	Simplify.

The circumference of Stonehenge is about 94.2 meters, and the area is about 706.9 square meters.

Exercises

Find the circumference of each circle. Round to the nearest tenth.

1. 3 m   **18.8 m**

2. 10 in.   **31.4 in.**

3. 12 cm   **75.4 cm**

4. The radius is 1.5 kilometers. **9.4 km**

5. The diameter is 1 yard. **3.1 yd**

6. The diameter is $5\frac{1}{4}$ feet. **16.5 ft**

7. The radius is $24\frac{1}{2}$ inches. **153.9 in.**

Find the area of each circle. Round to the nearest tenth.

8. 5 in.   **78.5 ft²**

9. 2 ft   **12.6 ft²**

10. 2 km   **3.1 km²**

11. The diameter is 4 yards. **12.6 yd²**

12. The radius is 1 meter. **3.1 m²**

13. The radius is 1.5 feet. **7.1 ft²**

14. The diameter is 15 centimeters. **176.7 cm²**

15. GEOGRAPHY Earth's circumference is approximately 25,000 miles. If you could dig a tunnel to the center of the Earth, how long would the tunnel be? **about 3979 mi**

16. CYCLING The tire for a 10-speed bicycle has a diameter of 27 inches. Find the distance the bicycle will travel in 10 rotations of the tire. **about 848.2 in.**

17. PUBLIC SAFETY The Belleville City Council is considering installing a new tornado warning system. The sound emitted from the siren would be heard for a 2-mile radius. Find the area of the region that will benefit from the system. **about 13 mi²**

18. CITY PLANNING The circular region inside the streets at DuPont Circle in Washington, D.C., is 250 feet across. How much area do the grass and sidewalk cover? **about 49,087.4 ft²**

8 Volume

Volume is the measure of space occupied by a solid. Volume is measured in cubic units. The prism at the right has a volume of 12 cubic units.

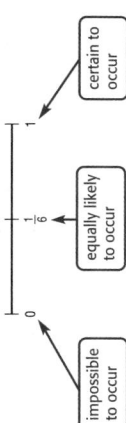

To find the volume of a rectangular prism, use the formula $V = \ell \cdot w \cdot h$. Stated in words, volume equals length times width times height.

EXAMPLE

Find the volume of the rectangular prism.

A rectangular prism has a height of 3 feet, width of 4 feet, and length of 2 feet.

$V = \ell \cdot w \cdot h$ Volume formula
$= 2 \cdot 4 \cdot 3$ Replace ℓ with 2, w with 4, and h with 3.
$= 24$ Simplify.

The volume is 24 cubic feet.

Exercises Find the volume of each rectangular prism given the length, width, and height.

1. $\ell = 2$ in., $w = 5$ in., $h = \frac{1}{2}$ in. **5 in³**
2. $\ell = 12$ cm, $w = 3$ cm, $h = 2$ cm **72 cm³**
3. $\ell = 6$ yd, $w = 2$ yd, $h = 1$ yd **12 yd³**
4. $\ell = 100$ m, $w = 1$ m, $h = 10$ m **1000 m³**

Find the volume of each rectangular prism.

5. 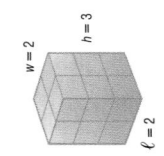 **20 m³**

6. **144 in³**

7. **AQUARIUMS** An aquarium is 8 feet long, 5 feet wide, and 5.5 feet deep. What is the volume of the tank? **220 ft³**

8. **COOKING** What is the volume of a microwave oven that is 18 inches wide by 10 inches long with a depth of $11\frac{1}{2}$ inches? **2070 in³**

9. **GEOMETRY** A cube measures 2 meters on a side. What is its volume? **8 m³**

FIREWOOD For Exercises 10–12, use the following information.
Firewood is usually sold by a measure known as a cord. A full cord may be a stack $8 \times 4 \times 4$ feet or a stack $8 \times 8 \times 2$ feet.

10. What is the volume of a full cord of firewood? **128 ft³**

11. A "short cord" or "face cord" of wood is $8 \times 4 \times$ the length of the logs. What is the volume of a short cord of $2\frac{1}{2}$-foot logs? **80 ft³**

12. If you have an area that is 12 feet long and 2 feet wide in which to store your firewood, how high will the stack be if it is a full cord of wood? **5 ft 4 in.**

9 Probability and Odds

The **probability** of an event is the ratio of the number of favorable outcomes for the event to the total number of possible outcomes.

When there are n outcomes and the probability of each one is $\frac{1}{n}$, we say that the outcomes are **equally likely**. For example, when you roll a die, the 6 possible outcomes are equally likely because each outcome has a probability of $\frac{1}{6}$.

impossible to occur — 0
equally likely to occur — $\frac{1}{6}$
certain to occur — 1

EXAMPLE

1 Find the probability of rolling an even number on a die.

There are six possible outcomes. Three of the outcomes are favorable. That is, three of the six outcomes are even numbers.

Sample space: 1, 2, 3, 4, 5, 6

3 even numbers → $\frac{3}{6}$
6 total possible outcomes → $\frac{3}{6}$

So, $P(\text{even number}) = \frac{3}{6}$ or $\frac{1}{2}$.

EXAMPLE

2 A bowl contains 5 red chips, 7 blue chips, 6 yellow chips, and 10 green chips. One chip is randomly drawn. Find each probability.

a. **blue**

There are 7 blue chips and 28 total chips.

$P(\text{blue chip}) = \frac{7}{28}$ ← number of favorable outcomes
  ← number of possible outcomes

$= \frac{1}{4}$ The probability can be stated as $\frac{1}{4}$, 0.25, or 25%.

b. **red or yellow**

$P(\text{red or yellow}) = \frac{11}{28}$ ← number of favorable outcomes
  ← number of possible outcomes

≈ 0.39 The probability can be stated as $\frac{11}{28}$, 0.39, or 39%.

c. **not green**

$P(\text{not green}) = \frac{18}{28}$ ← number of favorable outcomes
  ← number of possible outcomes

$= \frac{9}{14}$ or about 0.64   The probability can be stated as $\frac{9}{14}$, about 0.64, or about 64%.

⑩ Mean, Median, and Mode

Measures of central tendency are numbers used to represent a set of data.
Three types of measures of central tendency are mean, median, and mode.

The **mean** is the sum of the numbers in a set of data divided by the number of items.

EXAMPLE

1 **Katherine is running a lemonade stand. She made $3.50 on Tuesday, $4.00 on Wednesday, $5.00 on Thursday, and $4.50 on Friday. What was her mean daily profit?**

$$\text{mean} = \frac{\text{sum of daily profits}}{\text{number of days}}$$

$$= \frac{\$3.50 + \$4.00 + \$5.00 + \$4.50}{4}$$

$$= \frac{\$17.00}{4} \text{ or } \$4.25$$

Katherine's mean daily profit was $4.25.

The **median** is the middle number in a set of data when the data are arranged in numerical order. If there are an even number of data, the median is the mean of the two middle numbers.

EXAMPLE

2 **The table shows the number of hits Marcus made for his team. Find the median of the data.**

To find the median, order the numbers from least to greatest. The median is in the middle.

2, 3, 3, 5, 6, 7

$$\frac{3+5}{2} = 4$$

There is an even number of items. Find the mean of the middle two.

The median number of hits is 4.

Team Played	Number of Hits by Marcus
Badgers	3
Hornets	6
Bulldogs	5
Vikings	2
Rangers	3
Panthers	7

The **mode** is the number or numbers that appear most often in a set of data. If no item appears most often, the set has no mode.

EXAMPLE

3 **The table shows the heights in inches of the members of the 2005–2006 University of Dayton Men's Basketball team. What is the mode of the heights?**

2005-2006 Dayton Flyers Men's Basketball Team				
74	78	79	80	78
72	81	83	76	78
76	75	77	79	72

Source: ESPN

The mode is the number that occurs most frequently. 78 occurs three times, 72, 76, and 79 each occur twice, and all the other heights occur once. The mode height is 78.

The **odds** of an event occurring is the ratio that compares the number of ways an event can occur (successes) to the number of ways it cannot occur (failures).

EXAMPLE

Find the odds of rolling a number less than 3.

There are 6 possible outcomes, 2 are successes and 4 are failures.

Sample space: 1, 2, 3, 4, 5, 6

2 numbers less than 3

4 numbers not less than 3

$$\frac{2}{4} \text{ or } \frac{1}{2}$$

So, the odds of rolling a number less than three are $\frac{1}{2}$ or 1:2.

Exercises

One coin is randomly selected from a jar containing 70 nickels, 100 dimes, 80 quarters, and 50 1-dollar coins. Find each probability.

1. P(quarter) $\frac{4}{15}$ or about 27%
2. P(dime) $\frac{1}{3}$ or about 33%
3. P(nickel or dollar) $\frac{2}{5}$ or 40%
4. P(quarter or nickel) $\frac{1}{2}$ or 50%
5. P(value less than $1.00) $\frac{5}{6}$ or about 83%
6. P(value greater than $0.10) $\frac{13}{30}$ or about 43%
7. P(value at least $0.25) $\frac{13}{30}$ or about 43%
8. P(value at most $1.00) 1 or 100%

Two dice are rolled and their sum is recorded. Find each probability.

9. P(sum less than 7) $\frac{5}{12}$ or about 42%
10. P(sum less than 8) $\frac{7}{12}$ or about 58%
11. P(sum is greater than 12) 0 or 0%
12. P(sum is greater than 1) 1 or 100%
13. P(sum is between 5 and 10) $\frac{5}{9}$ or about 56%
14. P(sum is between 2 and 9) $\frac{25}{36}$ or about 69%

One of the polygons is chosen at random. Find each probability.

15. P(triangle) $\frac{1}{2}$ or 50%
16. P(pentagon) $\frac{1}{6}$ or about 17%
17. P(not a triangle) $\frac{1}{2}$ or 50%
18. P(not a quadrilateral) $\frac{2}{3}$ or about 67%
19. P(more than three sides) $\frac{1}{6}$ or about 17%
20. P(more than one right angle) $\frac{1}{2}$ or 50%

Find the odds of each outcome if a computer randomly picks a letter in the name *The United States of America*.

21. the letter a 3:21 or 1:7
22. the letter t 4:20 or 1:5
23. a vowel 11:13
24. a consonant 13:11
25. an uppercase letter 4:20 or 1:5
26. a lowercase vowel 9:15 or 3:5

You can use measures of central tendency to solve problems.

EXAMPLE

4 On her first five history tests, Yoko received the following scores: 82, 96, 92, 83, and 91. What test score must Yoko earn on the sixth test so that her average (mean) for all six tests will be 90%?

$mean = \dfrac{\text{sum of the first five scores + sixth score}}{6}$ Write an equation.

$90 = \dfrac{82 + 96 + 92 + 83 + 91 + x}{6}$ Use x to represent the sixth score.

$90 = \dfrac{444 + x}{6}$ Simplify.

$540 = 444 + x$ Multiply each side by 6.

$96 = x$ Subtract 444 from each side.

To have an average score of 90, Yoko must earn a 96 on the sixth test.

Exercises   Find the mean, median, and mode for each set of data.

1. {1, 2, 3, 5, 5, 6, 13} **5; 5; 5**
2. {3, 5, 8, 1, 4, 11, 3} **5; 4; 3**
3. {52, 53, 53, 53, 55, 55, 57} **54; 53; 53**
4. {8, 7, 5, 19} **9.75; 7.5; no mode**
5. {3, 11, 26, 4, 1} **9; 4; no mode**
6. {201, 201, 200, 199, 199} **200; 200; 201, and 199**
7. {4, 5, 6, 7, 8} **6; 6; no mode**
8. {3, 7, 21, 23, 63, 27, 29, 95, 23} $32\frac{1}{3}$; **23, 23**

9. **SCHOOL** The table shows the cost of some school supplies. Find the mean, median, and mode costs.
mean: $2.50, median: $2.25, mode: $2.00

Cost of School Supplies

Supply	Cost
Pencils	$0.50
Pens	$2.00
Paper	$2.00
Pocket Folder	$1.25
Calculator	$5.25
Notebook	$3.00
Erasers	$2.50
Markers	$3.50

10. **NUTRITION** The table shows the number of servings of fruits and vegetables that Cole eats one week. Find the mean, median, and mode.
mean: 5, median: 5, mode: 3 and 5

Cole's Fruit and Vegetable Servings

Day	Number of Servings
Monday	5
Tuesday	7
Wednesday	5
Thursday	4
Friday	3
Saturday	3
Sunday	8

11. **TELEVISION RATINGS** The ratings for the top television programs during one week are shown in the table at the right. Find the mean, median, and mode of the ratings. Round to the nearest hundredth. **13.45; 13.2; 11.4**

Network Primetime Television Ratings

Program	Rating
1	17.6
2	16.0
3	14.1
4	13.7
5	13.5
6	12.9
7	12.3
8	11.6
9	11.4
10	11.4

Source: Nielsen Media

12. **EDUCATION** Bill's scores on his first four science tests are 86, 90, 84, and 91. What test score must Bill earn on the fifth test so that his average (mean) will be exactly 88? **89**

13. **BOWLING** Sue's average for 9 games of bowling is 108. What is the lowest score she can receive for the tenth game to have an average of 110? **128**

14. **EDUCATION** Olivia has an average score of 92 on five French tests. If she earns a score of 96 on the sixth test, what will her new average score be? **92.7**

---

11 Box-and-Whisker Plots

Data can be organized and displayed by dividing a set of data into four parts using the median and quartiles. This is a **box-and-whisker plot**.

EXAMPLE

1 Draw a box-and-whisker plot for these data.
14.03, 30.11, 16.03, 19.61, 18.15, 16.34, 20.43, 18.46, 22.24, 12.70, 8.25

Step 1 Order the data from least to greatest. Use this list to determine the quartiles.

8.25, 12.70, 14.03, 16.03, 16.34, 18.15, 18.46, 19.61, 20.43, 22.24, 30.11
$\qquad\qquad$ Q1 $\qquad\qquad$ Q2 $\qquad\qquad$ Q3

Determine the interquartile range.
$IQR = 20.43 - 14.03$ or 6.4

Check to see if there are any outliers.
$14.03 - 1.5(6.4) = 4.43$ $20.43 + 1.5(6.4) = 30.03$

Any numbers less than 4.43 or greater than 30.03 are outliers. The only outlier is 30.11.

Step 2 Draw a number line. Assign a scale to the number line and place bullets to represent the three quartile points, any outliers, the least number that is not an outlier, and the greatest number that is not an outlier.

8.25 $\quad$ 14.03 $\quad$ 18.15 20.43 22.24 $\qquad$ 30.11
8 10 12 14 16 18 20 22 24 26 28 30 32

Step 3 Draw a box to designate the data between the upper and lower quartiles. Draw a vertical line through the point representing the median. Draw a line from the lower quartile to the least value that is not an outlier. Draw a line from the upper quartile to the greatest value that is not an outlier.

8 10 12 14 16 18 20 22 24 26 28 30 32

Exercises   For Exercises 1–3, use the box-and-whisker plot below.

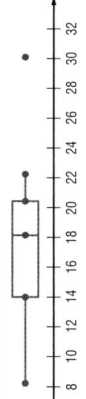

80 90 100 110 120 130

1. What is the median of the data? **95**
2. What is the range of the data? **45**
3. What is the interquartile range of the data? **30**

Draw a box-and-whisker plot for each set of data.
4. 15, 8, 10, 1, 3, 2, 6, 5, 4, 27, 1 **4–6. See Student Handbook Answer Appendix.**
5. 20, 2, 12, 5, 4, 16, 17, 7, 6, 16, 5, 0, 5, 30
6. 4, 1, 1, 1, 10, 15, 4, 5, 27, 5, 14, 10, 6, 2, 2, 5, 8

12 Representing Data

Data can be displayed and organized by different methods. In a **frequency table**, you use tally marks to record and display the frequency of events. A **bar graph** compares different categories of data by showing each as a bar with a length that is related to the frequency.

EXAMPLE

1 The frequency table shows the results of a survey of student's favorite sports. Make a bar graph to display the data.

Sport	Tally	Frequency
Basketball	卌 卌 卌	15
Football	卌 卌 卌 卌 卌	25
Soccer	卌 卌 卌 III	18
Baseball	卌 卌 卌 卌 I	21
Tennis	卌 卌 卌 I	16

Step 1 Draw a horizontal axis and a vertical axis. Label the axes as shown. Add a title.

Step 2 Draw a bar to represent each sport. The vertical scale is the number of students who chose each sport. The horizontal scale identifies the sport chosen.

Favorite Sport

Another way to represent data is by using a *line graph*. A line graph usually shows how data changes over a period of time.

EXAMPLE

2 Sales at the Marshall High School Store are shown in the table below. Make a line graph of the data.

School Store Sales Amounts

September	$670	December	$168	March	$412
October	$229	January	$290	April	$309
November	$300	February	$388	May	$198

Step 1 Draw a horizontal axis and a vertical axis and label them as shown. Include a title.

Step 2 Plot the points to represent the data.

Step 3 Draw a line connecting each pair of consecutive points.

School Store Sales

Another way to organize and display data is by using a **stem-and-leaf display**. In a stem-and-leaf display, the greatest common place value is used for the stems. The numbers in the next greatest place value are used to form the leaves.

EXAMPLE

3 ANIMALS The speeds (mph) of 20 of the fastest land animals are listed below. Use the data to make a stem-and-leaf display.

45	70	43	45	32	42	40	40	35	50
40	35	61	48	35	32	50	36	50	40

Source: *The World Almanac*

The greatest place value is tens. Thus, 32 miles per hour would have a stem of 3 and a leaf of 2.

Stem	Leaf
3	2 2 5 5 5 6
4	0 0 0 0 2 3 5 5 8
5	0 0 0
6	1
7	0

Key: 3|2 = 32

Exercises 1–5. See Student Handbook Answer Appendix.

1. **SURVEYS** Alana surveyed several students to find the number of hours of sleep they typically get each night. The results are shown in the table. Make a bar graph of the data.

Hours of Sleep

Alana	8	Kwam	7.5	Tomas	7.75
Nick	8.25	Kate	7.25	Sharla	8.5

2. **LAWN CARE** Marcus started a lawn care service. The chart shows how much money he made over the 15 weeks of summer break. Make a line graph of the data.

Lawn Care Profits ($)

Week	1	2	3	4	5	6	7	8
Profit	25	40	45	50	75	85	95	95
Week	9	10	11	12	13	14	15	
Profit	125	140	135	150	165	165	175	

Use each set of data to make a stem-and-leaf display.

3. 6.5 6.3 6.9 7.1 7.3 5.9 6.0 7.0 7.2 6.6 7.1 5.8

4. 31 30 28 26 22 34 26 31 47 32 18 33 26 23 18 29

5. The frequency table below shows the ages of people attending a high school play. Make a bar graph to display the data.

Age	Tally	Frequency
under 20	卌 卌 卌 卌 卌 卌 卌 II	47
20–39	卌 卌 卌 卌 卌 卌 卌 III	43
40–59	卌 卌 卌 卌 卌 卌 I	31
60 or over	卌 III	8

Extra Practice

Lesson 1-1
(pages 6–9)

Write an algebraic expression for each verbal expression. 3. $4 + 6z$

1. the sum of b and 21 $b + 21$
2. the product of x and 7 $7x$
3. the sum of 4 and 6 times a number z
4. the sum of 8 and -2 times n $8 + (-2n)$
5. one-half the cube of a number x $\frac{1}{2}x^3$
6. four-fifths the square of m $\frac{4}{5}m^2$

Evaluate each expression.

7. 2^4 **16**
8. 10^2 **100**
9. 7^3 **343**
10. 20^3 **8000**
11. 3^6 **729**
12. 4^5 **1024**

Write a verbal expression for each algebraic expression. 13–18. Sample answers given.

13. $2n$ two times n
14. 10^7 ten to the seventh power
15. m^5 m to the fifth power
16. xy the product of x and y
17. $5n^2 - 6$ five times n squared minus 6
18. $9a^3 + 1$ nine times a cubed plus 1

Lesson 1-2
(pages 10–14)

Evaluate each expression.

1. $3 + 8 \div 2 - 5$ **2**
2. $4 + 7 \cdot 2 + 8$ **26**
3. $5(9 + 3) - 3 \cdot 4$ **48**
4. $9 - 3^2$ **0**
5. $(8 - 1) \cdot 3$ **21**
6. $4(5 - 3)^2$ **16**
7. $3(12 + 3) - 5 \cdot 9$ **0**
8. $5^3 + 6^3 - 5^2$ **316**
9. $16 \div 2 \cdot 5 \cdot 3 \div 6$ **20**
10. $7(5^3 + 3^2)$ **938**
11. $\dfrac{9 \cdot 4 + 2 \cdot 6}{6 \cdot 4}$ **2**
12. $25 - \dfrac{1}{3}(18 + 9)$ **16**

Evaluate each expression if $a = 2$, $b = 5$, $x = 4$, and $n = 10$.

13. $8a + b$ **21**
14. $48 + ab$ **58**
15. $a(6 - 3n)$ **-48**
16. $bx + an$ **40**
17. $x^2 - 4n$ **-24**
18. $3b + 16a - 9n$ **-43**
19. $n^2 + 3(a + 4)$ **118**
20. $(2x)^2 + an - 5b$ **59**
21. $[a + 8(b - 2)]^2 \div 4$ **169**

Lesson 1-3
(pages 15–20)

Find the solution of each equation if the replacement sets are
$x = \{0, 2, 4, 6, 8\}$ and $y = \{1, 3, 5, 7, 9\}$.

1. $x - 4 = 4$ **8**
2. $25 - y = 18$ **7**
3. $3x + 1 = 25$ **8**
4. $5y - 4 = 11$ **3**
5. $14 = \dfrac{96}{x} + 2$ **8**
6. $0 = \dfrac{y}{3} - 3$ **9**

Solve each equation.

7. $x = \dfrac{27 + 9}{2}$ **18**
8. $\dfrac{18 - 7}{13 - 2} = y$ **1**
9. $n = \dfrac{6(5) + 3}{2(4) + 3}$ **3**
10. $\dfrac{5(4) - 6}{2^2 + 3} = z$ **2**
11. $\dfrac{7^2 + 9(2 + 1)}{2(10) - 1} = t$ **4**
12. $a = \dfrac{3^3 + 5^2}{2(3 - 1)}$ **13**

Find the solution set for each inequality if the replacement sets are
$x = \{4, 5, 6, 7, 8\}$ and $y = \{10, 12, 14, 16\}$.

13. $x + 2 > 7$ $\{6, 7, 8\}$
14. $x - 1 < 8$ $\{4, 5, 6, 7, 8\}$
15. $2x \le 15$ $\{4, 5, 6, 7\}$
16. $3y \ge 36$ $\{12, 14, 16\}$
17. $\dfrac{x}{3} < 2$ $\{4, 5\}$
18. $\dfrac{5y}{4} \ge 20$ $\{16\}$

---

13 Absolute Value

On a number line, 4 is four units from zero in the positive direction, and -4 is four units from zero in the negative direction. This number line illustrates the meaning of **absolute value**.

EXAMPLE 1   Absolute Value of Rational Numbers

Find each absolute value.

a. $|-7|$

-7 is seven units from zero in the negative direction.

$|-7| = 7$

b. $\left|\frac{7}{9}\right|$

$\frac{7}{9}$ is seven-ninths unit from zero in the positive direction.

$\left|\frac{7}{9}\right| = \frac{7}{9}$

EXAMPLE 2   Expressions with Absolute Value

Evaluate $15 - |x + 4|$ if $x = 8$.

$15 - |x + 4| = 15 - |8 + 4|$ Replace x with 8.

$= 15 - |12|$ $8 + 4 = 12$

$= 15 - 12$ $|12| = 12$

$= 3$ Simplify.

Exercises   Find each absolute value.

1. $|-2|$ **2**
2. $|18|$ **18**
3. $|2.5|$ **2.5**
4. $\left|-\frac{5}{6}\right|$ $\frac{5}{6}$
5. $|-38|$ **38**
6. $|10|$ **10**
7. $|97|$ **97**
8. $|-61|$ **61**
9. $|-3.9|$ **3.9**
10. $|-6.8|$ **6.8**
11. $\left|-\frac{23}{56}\right|$ $\frac{23}{56}$
12. $\left|\frac{35}{80}\right|$ $\frac{35}{80}$

Evaluate each expression if $a = 6$, $b = \frac{2}{3}$, $c = \frac{5}{4}$, $x = 12$, $y = 3.2$, and $z = -5$.

13. $48 + |x - 5|$ **55**
14. $25 + |17 + x|$ **54**
15. $|17 - a| + 23$ **34**
16. $|43 - 4a| + 51$ **70**
17. $|z| + 13 - 4$ **14**
18. $28 - 13 + |z|$ **20**
19. $6.5 - |8.4 - y|$ **1.3**
20. $7.4 + |y - 2.6|$ **8**
21. $\frac{1}{6} + \left|b - \frac{7}{12}\right|$ $\frac{1}{4}$
22. $\left(b + \frac{1}{2}\right) - \left|-\frac{5}{6}\right|$ $\frac{1}{3}$
23. $|c - 1| + \frac{2}{5}$ $\frac{13}{20}$
24. $|-c| + \left(2 + \frac{1}{2}\right)$ $\frac{15}{4}$ or $3\frac{3}{4}$
25. $-a + |2x - a| + \frac{1}{2}$ $12\frac{1}{2}$
26. $|y - 2z| - 3$ **10.2**
27. $3|3b - 8c| - 3$ **21**
28. $|2x - z| + 6b$ **33**
29. $-3|z| + 2(a + y)$ **3.4**
30. $-4|c - 3| + 2|z - a|$ **15**

Lesson 1-4 (pages 21–25)

Find the value of n in each equation. Then name the property that is used.

1. $4 \cdot 3 = 4 \cdot n$ **3; Reflexive Prop.**
2. $\frac{5}{4} = n + 0$ **$\frac{5}{4}$; Additive Identity**
3. $15 = 15 \cdot n$ **1; Multiplicative Identity**
4. $\frac{2}{3}n = 1$ **$\frac{3}{2}$; Multiplicative Inverse**
5. $2.7 + 1.3 = n + 2.7$ **1.3; Symmetric Prop.**
6. $n\left(6^2 \cdot \frac{1}{36}\right) = 4$
7. $8n = 0$ **0; Multiplicative Prop. of 0**
8. $n = \frac{1}{9} \cdot 9$ **1; Multiplicative Inverse**

6. **4; Multiplicative Identity and Multiplicative Inverse**

Evaluate each expression. Name the property used in each step.

9. $\frac{2}{3}[15 \div (12-2)]$
10. $\frac{7}{4}\left[4 \cdot \left(\frac{1}{8} \cdot 8\right)\right]$
11. $[(18 \div 3) \cdot 0] \cdot 10$

9–11. **See Student Handbook Answer Appendix.**

Lesson 1-5 (pages 26–31)

Rewrite each expression using the Distributive Property. Then evaluate.

1. $5(2+9)$ **55**
2. $8(10+20)$ **240**
3. $6(y+4)$ **$6y+24$**
4. $9(3n+5)$ **$27n+45$**
5. $32\left(x-\frac{1}{8}\right)$ **$32x-4$**
6. $c(7-d)$ **$7c-cd$**

1–6. **See Student Handbook Answer Appendix for expressions.**

Use the Distributive Property to rewrite each expression. Then find the product.

7. $6 \cdot 55$ **330**
8. $15(108)$ **1620**
9. $1689 \cdot 5$ **8445**
10. 7×314 **2198**
11. $36\left(5\frac{1}{4}\right)$ **189**
12. $\left(4\frac{1}{18}\right) \cdot 18$ **73**

7–12. **See Student Handbook Answer Appendix for expressions.**

Simplify each expression. If not possible, write simplified.

13. $13a + 5a$ **18a**
14. $21x - 10x$ **11x**
15. $8(3x+7)$ **$24x+56$**
16. $4m - 4n$ **simplified**
17. $3(5am-4)$ **$15am-12$**
18. $15x^2 + 7x^2$ **$22x^2$**
19. $9y^2 + 13y^2 + 3$ **$22y^2 + 3$**
20. $11a^2 - 11a^2 + 12a^2$ **$12a^2$**
21. $6a + 7a + 12b + 8b$ **$13a+20b$**

Lesson 1-6 (pages 33–37)

Evaluate each expression using properties of numbers.

1. $23 + 8 + 37 + 12$ **80**
2. $19 + 46 + 81 + 54$ **200**
3. $10.25 + 2.5 + 3.75$ **16.5**
4. $22.5 + 17.6 + 44.5$ **84.6**
5. $2\frac{1}{3} + 6 + 3\frac{2}{3} + 4$ **16**
6. $5\frac{6}{7} + 15 + 4\frac{1}{7} + 25$ **50**
7. $6 \cdot 8 \cdot 5 \cdot 3$ **720**
8. $18 \cdot 5 \cdot 2 \cdot 5$ **900**
9. $0.25 \cdot 7 \cdot 8$ **14**
10. $90 \cdot 12 \cdot 0.5$ **540**
11. $5\frac{1}{3} \cdot 4 \cdot 6$ **128**
12. $4\frac{5}{6} \cdot 10 \cdot 12$ **580**

Simplify each expression. 15. $3a + 13b + 2c$ 17. $-4p - 2q$ 21. $24b^3 + 12$

13. $5a + 6b + 7a$ **$12a+6b$**
14. $8x + 4y + 9x$ **$17x+4y$**
15. $3a + 5b + 2c + 8b$
16. $\frac{2}{3}x^2 + 5x + x^2$ **$\frac{5}{3}x^2 + 5x$**
17. $(4p-7q)+(5q-8p)$
18. $8q + 5r - 7q - 6r$ **$q-r$**
19. $4(2x+y)+5x$ **$13x+4y$**
20. $9r^5 + 2r^2 + r^5$ **$10r^5 + 2r^2$**
21. $12b^3 + 12 + 12b^3$
22. $7 + 3(uv-6)+u$ **$-11+3uv+u$**
23. $3(x+2y)+4(3x+y)$ **$15x+10y$**
24. $6.2(a+b)+2.6(a+b)+3a$ **$11.8a+8.8b$**

Lesson 1-7 (pages 39–44)

Identify the hypothesis and conclusion of each statement.

1. If an animal is a dog, then it barks.
2. If a figure is a pentagon, then it has five sides.
3. If $3x - 1 = 8$, then $x = 3$.
4. If 0.5 is the reciprocal of 2, then $0.5 \cdot 2 = 1$.

1–4. **See Student Handbook Answer Appendix.**

Identify the hypotheses and conclusion of each statement. Then write the statement in if-then form. 5–8. **See Student Handbook Answer Appendix.**

5. A square has four congruent sides.
6. $6a + 10 = 34$ when $a = 4$.
7. The video store is open every night.
8. The band will not practice on Thursday.

Find a counterexample for each conditional statement.

9. If the season is spring, then it does not snow.
10. If you live in Portland, then you live in Oregon.
11. If $2y + 4 = 10$, then $y < 3$.
12. If $a^2 > 0$, then $a > 0$.

9–12. **See Student Handbook Answer Appendix.**

Lesson 1-8 (pages 46–52)

Find each square root. If necessary, round to the nearest hundredth.

1. $\sqrt{121}$ **11**
2. $-\sqrt{36}$ **−6**
3. $\sqrt{2.89}$ **1.7**
4. $-\sqrt{125}$ **−11.18**
5. $\sqrt{\frac{81}{100}}$ **$\frac{9}{10}$**
6. $-\sqrt{\frac{36}{196}}$ **$-\frac{3}{7}$**
7. $\pm\sqrt{9.61}$ **±3.1**
8. $\pm\sqrt{\frac{7}{8}}$ **±0.94**

Name the set or sets of numbers to which each real number belongs.

9. $-\sqrt{149}$ **irrationals**
10. $\frac{5}{6}$ **rationals**
11. $\sqrt{\frac{8}{2}}$ **rationals, integers, whole numbers, natural numbers**
12. $\frac{66}{55}$ **rationals**
13. $\sqrt{225}$ **rationals, integers, whole numbers, natural numbers**
14. $-\sqrt{\frac{3}{4}}$ **irrationals**
15. $-\frac{1}{7}$ **rationals**
16. $\sqrt{0.0016}$ **rationals**

Replace each ● with <, >, or = to make each sentence true.

17. $6.\overline{16} ● 6$ **>**
18. $3.88 ● \sqrt{15}$ **>**
19. $-\sqrt{529} ● -20$ **<**
20. $-\sqrt{0.25} ● -0.5$ **>**
21. $\frac{1}{3} ● \frac{\sqrt{3}}{3}$ **<**
22. $\frac{1}{\sqrt{3}} ● \frac{\sqrt{3}}{3}$ **=**
23. $-\sqrt{\frac{1}{4}} ● -\frac{1}{4}$ **<**
24. $-\frac{1}{6} ● -\frac{1}{\sqrt{6}}$ **>**

Lesson 1-9 (pages 53–58)

Describe what is happening in each graph. 1–2. **See Student Handbook Answer Appendix.**

1. The graph shows the average monthly high temperatures for a city over a one-year period.

(graph: Temperature vs. Month)

2. The graph shows the speed of a roller coaster car during a two-minute ride.

(graph: Speed vs. Time)

Lesson 2-1 (pages 70–76)

Translate each sentence into an equation or formula.

1. A number z times 2 minus 6 is the same as m divided by 3. $2z - 6 = m \div 3$
2. The cube of a decreased by the square of b is equal to c. $a^3 - b^2 = c$
3. Twenty-nine decreased by the product of x and y is the same as z. $29 - xy = z$
4. The perimeter P of an isosceles triangle is the sum of twice the length of leg a and the length of the base b. $P = 2a + b$
5. Thirty increased by the quotient of s and t is equal to v. $30 + (s \div t) = v$
6. The area A of a rhombus is half the product of lengths of the diagonals a and b. $A = 0.5ab$

Translate each equation into a verbal sentence.

7. $0.5x + 3 = -10$
8. $\frac{n}{-6} = 2n + 1$
9. $18 - 5h = 13h$
10. $n^2 = 16$
11. $2x^2 + 3 = 21$
12. $\frac{m}{n} + 4 = 12$

7–12. See Student Handbook Answer Appendix for sample answers.

Lesson 2-2 (pages 78–84)

Solve each equation. Check your solution. 17. 64.141   18. −49.773

1. $-2 + g = 7$ 9
2. $9 + s = -5$ −14
3. $-4 + y = -9$ −5
4. $m + 6 = 2$ −4
5. $t + (-4) = 10$ 14
6. $v - 7 = -4$ 3
7. $a - (-6) = -5$ −11
8. $-2 - x = -8$ 6
9. $d + (-44) = -61$ −17
10. $b - (-26) = 41$ 15
11. $p - 47 = 22$ 69
12. $-63 - f = -82$ 19
13. $c + 5.4 = -11.33$ −16.73
14. $-6.11 + b = 14.321$ 20.431
15. $-5 = y - 22.7$ 17.7
16. $-5 - q = 1.19$ −6.19
17. $n + (-4.361) = 59.78$
18. $t - (-46.1) = -3.673$
19. $\frac{7}{10} - a = \frac{1}{2}$ $\frac{1}{5}$
20. $f - \left(-\frac{1}{8}\right) = \frac{3}{10}$ $\frac{7}{40}$
21. $-4\frac{5}{12} = t - \left(-10\frac{1}{36}\right)$ $-14\frac{4}{9}$
22. $x + \frac{3}{8} = 1 - \frac{1}{8}$ $\frac{1}{2}$
23. $1\frac{7}{16} + s = \frac{9}{8}$ $-\frac{5}{16}$
24. $17\frac{8}{9} = d + \left(-2\frac{5}{6}\right)$ $20\frac{13}{18}$

Lesson 2-3 (pages 85–90)

Solve each equation. Check your solution.

1. $7p = 35$ 5
2. $-3x = -24$ 8
3. $2y = -3$ −1.5
4. $62y = -2356$ −38
5. $\frac{a}{-6} = -2$ 12
6. $\frac{c}{-59} = -7$ 413
7. $\frac{f}{14} = -63$ −882
8. $84 = \frac{x}{97}$ 8148
9. $\frac{w}{5} = 3$ 15
10. $\frac{q}{9} = -3$ −27
11. $\frac{2}{5}x = \frac{4}{7}$ $\frac{10}{7}$
12. $\frac{z}{6} = -\frac{5}{12}$ $-\frac{5}{2}$
13. $-\frac{5}{9}r = 7\frac{1}{2}$ $-13\frac{1}{2}$
14. $2\frac{1}{6}j = 5\frac{1}{5}$ $2\frac{2}{5}$
15. $3 = 1\frac{7}{11}q$ $1\frac{5}{6}$
16. $-1\frac{3}{4}p = -\frac{5}{8}$ $\frac{5}{14}$
17. $57k = 0.1824$ 0.0032
18. $0.0022b = 0.1958$ 89
19. $5j = -32.15$ −6.43
20. $\frac{w}{-2} = -2.48$ 4.96
21. $\frac{z}{2.8} = -6.2$ −17.36
22. $\frac{x}{-0.063} = 0.015$ −0.000945
23. $15\frac{3}{8} = -5p$ $-3\frac{3}{40}$
24. $-18\frac{1}{4} = 2.5x$ −7.3

Lesson 2-4 (pages 92–97)

Solve each equation. Check your solution. 10. −5.5   11. −14.35

1. $2x - 5 = 3$ 4
2. $4t + 5 = 37$ 8
3. $7a + 6 = -36$ −6
4. $47 = -8g + 7$ −5
5. $-3c - 9 = -24$ 5
6. $5k - 7 = -52$ −9
7. $5s + 4s = -72$ −8
8. $3x - 7 = 2$ 3
9. $8 + 3x = 5$ −1
10. $-3y + 7.569 = 24.069$
11. $7 - 9.1f = 137.585$
12. $6.5 = 2.4m - 4.9$ 4.75
13. $\frac{n}{5} + 6 = -2$ −40
14. $\frac{d}{4} - 8 = -5$ 12
15. $-\frac{4}{13}y - 7 = 6$ $-42\frac{1}{4}$
16. $\frac{p+3}{10} = 4$ 37
17. $\frac{h-7}{6} = 1$ 13
18. $\frac{5f+1}{8} = -3$ −5
19. $\frac{4n-8}{-2} = 12$ −4
20. $\frac{-3t-4}{2} = 8$ $-6\frac{2}{3}$
21. $4.8a - 3 + 1.2a = 9$ 2

Lesson 2-5 (pages 98–103)

Solve each equation. Check your solution.

1. $5x + 1 = 3x - 3$ −2
2. $6 - 8n = 5n + 19$ −1
3. $-3z + 5 = 2z + 5$ 0
4. $\frac{2}{3}h + 5 = -4 - \frac{1}{3}h$ −9
5. $\frac{1}{2}a - 4 = 3 - \frac{1}{4}a$ $9\frac{1}{3}$
6. $6(y - 5) = 18 - 2y$ 6
7. $-28 + p = 7(p - 10)$ 7
8. $\frac{1}{3}(b - 9) = b + 9$ −18
9. $-4x + 6 = 0.5(x + 30)$ −2
10. $4(2y - 1) = -8(0.5 - y)$ all real numbers
11. $1.9s + 6 = 3.1 - s$ −1
12. $2.85y - 7 = 12.85y - 2$ −0.5
13. $2.9m + 1.7 = 3.5 + 2.3m$ 3
14. $3(x + 1) - 5 = 3x - 2$ all real numbers
15. $\frac{x}{2} - \frac{1}{3} = \frac{x}{3} - \frac{1}{2}$ −1
16. $\frac{6v-9}{3} = v$ 3
17. $\frac{3t+1}{4} = \frac{3}{4}t - 5$ no solution
18. $0.4(x - 12) = 1.2(x - 4)$ 0
19. $3y - \frac{4}{5} = \frac{1}{3}y$ $\frac{3}{10}$
20. $\frac{3}{4}x - 4 = 7 + \frac{1}{2}x$ 44
21. $-0.2(1 - x) = 2(4 + 0.1x)$ no solution
22. $3.2(y + 1) = 2(1.4y - 3)$ −23

Lesson 2-6 (pages 105–110)

Solve each proportion. If necessary, round to the nearest hundredth.

1. $\frac{4}{5} = \frac{x}{20}$ 16
2. $\frac{b}{63} = \frac{3}{7}$ 27
3. $\frac{y}{5} = \frac{3}{4}$ 3.75
4. $\frac{7}{4} = \frac{3}{a}$ $\frac{12}{7}$
5. $\frac{t-5}{4} = \frac{3}{2}$ 11
6. $\frac{x}{9} = \frac{0.24}{3}$ 0.72
7. $\frac{n}{3} = \frac{n+4}{7}$ 3
8. $\frac{12q}{-7} = \frac{30}{14}$ $-\frac{5}{4}$
9. $\frac{1}{9} = \frac{3}{y-5}$ 32
10. $\frac{x}{8.71} = \frac{4}{17.42}$ 2
11. $\frac{a-3}{8} = \frac{3}{4}$ 9
12. $\frac{6p-2}{7} = \frac{5p+7}{8}$ 5
13. $\frac{2}{9} = \frac{k+3}{9}$ $\frac{23}{9}$ or -2.5
14. $\frac{5m-3}{4} = \frac{5m+3}{6}$ 3
15. $\frac{w-5}{4} = \frac{w+3}{3}$ −27
16. $\frac{96.8}{t} = \frac{12.1}{7}$ 56
17. $\frac{r-1}{r+1} = \frac{3}{5}$ 4
18. $\frac{4n+5}{5} = \frac{2n+7}{7}$ 0

Extra Practice

Lesson 2-7

(pages 111–115)

State whether each percent of change is a percent of increase or a percent of decrease. Then find each percent of change. Round to the nearest whole percent.

1. original: $100
new: $67 **decrease, 33%**

2. original: 62 acres
new: 98 acres **increase, 58%**

3. original: 322 people
new: 289 people **decrease, 10%**

4. original: 78 pennies
new: 36 pennies **decrease, 54%**

5. original: $212
new: $230 **increase, 8%**

6. original: 35 mph
new: 65 mph **increase, 86%**

Find the final price of each item.

7. television: $299
discount: 20% **$239.20**

8. book: $15.95
sales tax: 7% **$17.07**

9. software: $36.90
sales tax: 6.25% **$39.21**

10. boots: $49.99
discount: 15%
sales tax: 3.5% **$43.98**

11. jacket: $65
discount: 30%
sales tax: 4% **$47.32**

12. backpack: $28.95
discount: 10%
sales tax: 5% **$27.36**

Lesson 2-8

(pages 117–121)

Solve each equation or formula for x.

1. $x + r = q \ \ q - r$

2. $ax + 4 = 7 \ \ \dfrac{3}{a}$

3. $2bx - b = -5 \ \ \dfrac{-5+b}{2b}$

4. $\dfrac{x-c}{c+a} = a \ \ a^2 + ac + c$

5. $\dfrac{x+y}{c} = d \ \ cd - y$

6. $\dfrac{ax+1}{2} = b \ \ \dfrac{2b-1}{a}$

7. $d(x - 3) = 5 \ \ \dfrac{3d+5}{d}$

8. $nx - a = bx + d \ \ \dfrac{a+d}{n-b}$

9. $3x - r = r(-3 + x) \ \ \dfrac{-2r}{3-r}$

10. $y = \dfrac{5}{9}(x - 32) \ \ \dfrac{9}{5}y + 32$

11. $A = \dfrac{1}{2}h(x + y) \ \ \dfrac{2A}{h} - y$

12. $A = 2\pi r^2 + 2\pi rx \ \ \dfrac{A}{2\pi r} - r$

Lesson 2-9

(pages 122–128)

1. **ADVERTISING** An advertisement for grape drink claims that the drink contains 10% grape juice. How much pure grape juice would have to be added to 5 quarts of the drink to obtain a mixture containing 40% grape juice? **2.5 qt**

2. **GRADES** In Ms. Pham's social studies class, a test is worth four times as much as homework. If a student has an average of 85% on tests and 95% on homework, what is the student's average? **87%**

3. **ENTERTAINMENT** At the Golden Oldies Theater, tickets for adults cost $5.50 and tickets for children cost $3.50. How many of each kind of ticket were purchased if 21 tickets were bought for $83.50? **5 adults, 16 children**

4. **FOOD** Wes is mixing peanuts and chocolate pieces. Peanuts sell for $4.50 a pound and the chocolate sells for $6.50 a pound. How many pounds of chocolate mixes with 5 pounds of peanuts to obtain a mixture that sells for $5.25 a pound? **3 lb**

5. **TRAVEL** Missoula and Bozeman are 210 miles apart. Sheila leaves Missoula for Bozeman and averages 55 miles per hour. At the same time, Casey leaves Bozeman and averages 65 miles per hour as he drives to Missoula. When will they meet? How far will they be from Bozeman? **1.75 h; 113.75 mi**

Lesson 3-1

(pages 143–148)

Express each relation as a table, a graph, and a mapping. Then determine the domain and range. 1–2. See Student Handbook Answer Appendix.

1. {(5, 2), (0, 0), (−9, −1)}

2. {(−4, 2), (2, 0), (−2, 0), (0, 2), (2, 4)}

3–8 See Student Handbook Answer Appendix.
Express the relation shown in each table, mapping, or graph as a set of ordered pairs. Then write the inverse of the relation.

3.

x	y
1	3
2	4
3	5
4	6
5	7

4.

x	y
−4	1
2	3
0	5
2	3
4	1

5.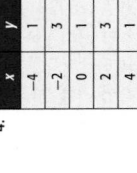

6.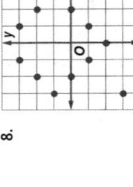

7.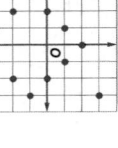

8.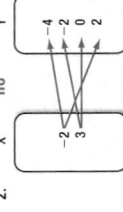

Lesson 3-2

(pages 149–154)

Determine whether each relation is a function. 6. no

1.

x	y
1	3
2	5
1	−7
2	9

no

2. 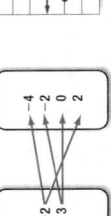 **no**

3.  **yes**

4. $x^2 + y = 11$ **yes**

5. $y = 2$ **yes**

6. {(−2, 4), (1, 3), (5, 2), (1, 4)}

If $f(x) = 2x + 5$ and $g(x) = 3x^2 - 1$, find each value.

7. $f(-4) \ \ -3$

8. $g(2) \ \ 11$

9. $f(3) \ \ -5$

10. $\dfrac{g(a + 1)}{3a^2 + 6a + 2}$

Lesson 3-3

(pages 156–162)

Determine whether each equation is a linear equation. If so, write the equation in standard form.

1. $3x = 2y$

2. $2x - 3 = y^2$

3. $4x = 2y + 8$

4. $5x - 7y = 2x - 7$

5. $2x + 5x = 7y + 2$

6. $\dfrac{1}{x} + \dfrac{5}{y} = -4$

1–6. See Student Handbook Answer Appendix.
Graph each equation. 7–18. See Student Handbook Answer Appendix.

7. $3x + y = 4$

8. $y = 3x + 1$

9. $3x - 2y = 12$

10. $2x - y = 6$

11. $2x - 3y = 8$

12. $y = -2$

13. $y = 5x - 7$

14. $x = 4$

15. $x + \dfrac{1}{3}y = 2$

16. $5x - 2y = 8$

17. $4.5x + 2.5y = 9$

18. $\dfrac{1}{2}x + 3y = 12$

Lesson 3-4 (pages 166–171)

Determine whether each sequence is an arithmetic sequence. If it is, state the common difference. **4. yes; 5 5. yes; 0.25**

1. $-2, -1, 0, 1, \ldots$ **yes; 1**
2. $3, 5, 8, 12, \ldots$ **no**
3. $2, 4, 8, 16, \ldots$ **no**
4. $-21, -16, -11, -6, \ldots$
5. $0, 0.25, 0.5, 0.75, \ldots$
6. $\frac{1}{3}, \frac{1}{9}, \frac{1}{27}, \frac{1}{81}, \ldots$ **no**

Find the next three terms of each arithmetic sequence. **8. $-12, -14, -16$ 9. $0.4, 1.0, 1.6$**

7. $3, 13, 23, 33, \ldots$ **43, 53, 63**
8. $-4, -6, -8, -10, \ldots$
9. $-2, -1.4, -0.8, -0.2, \ldots$
10. $5, 13, 21, 29, \ldots$ **37, 45, 53**
11. $\frac{3}{4}, \frac{7}{8}, 1, \ldots$ $\frac{9}{8}, \frac{5}{4}, \frac{11}{8}$
12. $-\frac{1}{3}, -\frac{1}{6}, \ldots$ $\frac{5}{6}, \ldots$ $-\frac{7}{3}, -\frac{17}{6}, \frac{10}{3}$

Find the nth term of each arithmetic sequence described.

13. $a_1 = 3, d = 6, n = 12$ **69**
14. $a_1 = -2, d = 4, n = 8$ **26**
15. $a_1 = -1, d = -3, n = 10$ **-28**
16. $2\frac{1}{2}, 2\frac{1}{8}, 1\frac{3}{4}, 1\frac{3}{8}, \ldots$ for $n = 10$ **$-\frac{7}{8}$**

Write an equation for the nth term of the arithmetic sequence. Then graph the first five terms in the sequence.

17. $-3, 1, 5, 9, \ldots$
18. $25, 40, 55, 70, \ldots$
19. $-9, -3, 3, 9, \ldots$
20. $-3.5, -2, -0.5, \ldots$
17–20. See Student Handbook Answer Appendix.

Lesson 3-5 (pages 172–176)

Find the next three terms in each sequence.

1. $12, 23, 34, 45, \ldots$
2. $39, 33, 27, 21, \ldots$
3. $6.0, 7.2, 8.4, 9.6, \ldots$
4. $15, 16, 18, 21, 25, 30, \ldots$
5. $w - 2, w - 4, w - 6, \ldots$
6. $13, 10, 11, 8, 9, 6, \ldots$

1–6. See Student Handbook Answer Appendix.
Write an equation in function notation for each relation.

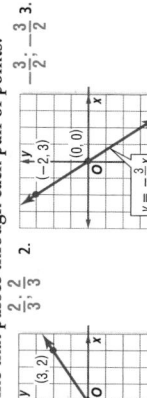

7.
8.
9.
10.

7–10. See Student Handbook Answer Appendix.

Lesson 4-1 (pages 187–195)

Find the slope of the line that passes through each pair of points.

1. **2**
2. **$-\frac{3}{4}$**
3. $(-2, 2), (3, -3)$ **-1**
4. $(-2, -8), (1, 4)$ **4**
5. $(3, 4), (4, 6)$ **2**
6. $(-5, 4), (-1, 11)$ **$\frac{7}{4}$**
7. $(18, -4), (6, -10)$ **$\frac{1}{2}$**
8. $(-4, -6), (-4, -8)$ **undefined**
9. $(0, 0), (-1, 3)$ **-3**
10. $(-8, 1), (2, 1)$ **0**

Find the value of r so the line that passes through each pair of points has the given slope.

11. $(-1, r), (1, -4), m = -5$ **6**
12. $(r, -2), (-7, -1), m = -\frac{1}{4}$ **-3**

Lesson 4-2 (pages 196–202)

Name the constant of variation for each equation. Then determine the slope of the line that passes through each pair of points.

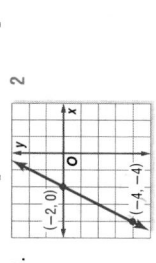
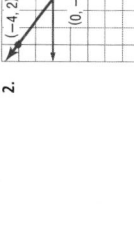

1. $\frac{2}{3}; \frac{2}{3}$
2. $-\frac{3}{2}; -\frac{3}{2}$
3. $-\frac{1}{5}; -\frac{1}{5}$

Graph each equation. 4–6. See Student Handbook Answer Appendix.

4. $y = 5x$
5. $y = -6x$
6. $y = -\frac{4}{3}x$

Suppose y varies directly as x. Write a direct variation equation that relates x and y. Then solve.

7. If $y = 45$ when $x = 9$, find y when $x = 7$. **$y = 5x$; 35**
8. If $y = -7$ when $x = -1$, find x when $y = -84$. **$y = 7x$; -12**

Lesson 4-3 (pages 204–209)

Write an equation, in slope-intercept form, of the line with the given slope and y-intercept. 1–6. See Student Handbook Answer Appendix.

1. m: 5, y-intercept: -15
2. m: -6, y-intercept: 3
3. m: 0.3, y-intercept: -2.6
4. m: $-\frac{4}{3}$, y-intercept: $\frac{5}{3}$
5. m: $-\frac{2}{5}$, y-intercept: 2
6. m: $\frac{7}{4}$, y-intercept: -2

Write an equation in slope-intercept form of the line shown in each graph.

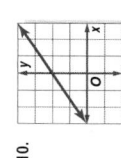
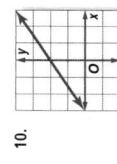
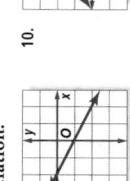

7. $y = -x + 3$
8. $y = -\frac{1}{2}x - 3$
9. $y = \frac{1}{3}x + 2$

Graph each equation. 10–12. See Student Handbook Answer Appendix.

10. $y = 5x - 1$
11. $y = -2x + 3$
12. $3x - y = 6$

Lesson 4-4 (pages 213–218)

Write an equation of the line that passes through each point with the given slope. **4. $y = -\frac{1}{4}x + 2$ 5. $y = \frac{2}{3}x - \frac{17}{3}$**

1. $(0, 0); m = -2$
2. $(-3, 2); m = 4$
3. $(0, 5); m = -1$
4. $(-2, 3); m = -\frac{1}{4}$
5. $(1, -5); m = \frac{2}{3}$
6. $\left(\frac{1}{2}, \frac{1}{4}\right); m = 8$

1. $y = -2x$ 2. $y = 4x + 14$ 3. $y = -x + 5$ 6. $y = 8x - \frac{15}{4}$

Write an equation of the line that passes through each pair of points.

7. $(-1, 7), (8, -2)$ **$y = -x + 6$**
8. $(4, 0), (0, 5)$ **$y = -\frac{5}{4}x + 5$**
9. $(8, -1), (7, -1)$ **$y = -1$**
10. $(-2, 3), (1, 3)$ **$y = 3$**
11. $(0, 0), (-4, 3)$ **$y = -\frac{3}{4}x$**
12. $\left(-\frac{1}{2}, \frac{1}{2}\right), \left(\frac{1}{4}, \frac{3}{4}\right)$ **$y = \frac{1}{3}x + \frac{2}{3}$**

Extra Practice

Lesson 4-5 (pages 220–225)

Write the point-slope form of an equation for a line that passes through each point with the given slope.

1. $(5, -2)$, $m = 3$
2. $(0, 6)$, $m = -2$
3. $(-3, 1)$, $m = 0$
4. $(-2, -4)$, $m = \frac{3}{4}$

$y + 2 = 3(x - 5)$ $y - 6 = -2x$ $y - 1 = 0$ $y + 4 = \frac{3}{4}(x + 2)$

Write each equation in standard form. 5–10. See Student Handbook Answer Appendix.

5. $y + 3 = 2(x - 4)$
6. $y + 3 = -\frac{1}{2}(x + 6)$
7. $y - 4 = -\frac{2}{3}(x - 5)$
8. $y + 2 = \frac{4}{3}(x - 6)$
9. $y - 1 = 1.5(x + 3)$
10. $y + 6 = -3.8(x - 2)$

Write each equation in slope-intercept form. 11–16. See Student Handbook Answer Appendix.

11. $y - 1 = -2(x + 5)$
12. $y + 3 = 4(x - 1)$
13. $y - 6 = -4(x - 2)$
14. $y + 1 = \frac{4}{5}(x + 5)$
15. $y - 2 = -\frac{3}{4}(x - 2)$
16. $y + \frac{1}{4} = \frac{2}{3}\left(x + \frac{1}{2}\right)$

Lesson 4-6 (pages 227–233) 1–2. See Student Handbook Answer Appendix.

Determine whether each graph shows a *positive correlation*, a *negative correlation*, or *no correlation*. If there is a correlation, describe its meaning in the situation.

1.

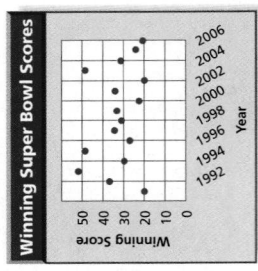

Value and Age of Car

2.

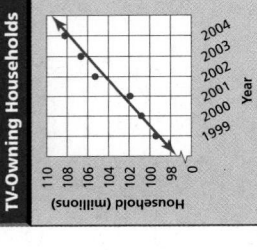

Winning Super Bowl Scores

Use the scatter plot that shows the year and the number of TV-owning households in millions. 3. positive correlation

TV-Owning Households

3. Describe the relationship that exists in the data.

4. Let x represent years since 1999. Use the points (1, 100.8) and (4, 106.7) to write the slope-intercept form of an equation for the line of fit shown in the scatter plot. $y = \frac{59}{30}x + \frac{593}{6}$

5. Predict the number of TV-owning households in 2015. 130.3 million

Lesson 4-7 1–6. See Student Handbook Answer Appendix. (pages 236–251)

Write the slope-intercept form of an equation for the line that passes through the given point and is parallel to the graph of each equation. Then write an equation in slope-intercept form for the line that passes through the given point and is perpendicular to the graph of each equation.

1. $(1, 6)$, $y = 4x - 2$
2. $(4, 6)$, $y = 2x - 7$
3. $(-3, 0)$, $y = \frac{2}{3}x + 1$
4. $(5, -2)$, $y = -3x - 7$
5. $(0, 4)$, $3x + 8y = 4$
6. $(2, 3)$, $x - 5y = 7$

Lesson 5-1 (pages 253–258)

Graph each system of equations. Then determine whether the system has *no solution*, *one solution*, or *infinitely many* solutions. If the system has one solution, name it. 1–12. See Student Handbook Answer Appendix for graphs.

1. $y = 3x$
   $4x + 2y = 30$ (3, 9)
2. $x = -2y$
   $x + y = 1$ (2, −1)
3. $y = x + 4$
   $3x + 2y = 18$ (2, 6)

4. $x + y = 6$
   $x - y = 2$ (4, 2)
5. $x + y = 6$
   $3x + 3y = 3$ no solution
6. $y = -3x$
   $4x + y = 2$ (2, −6)

7. $2x + y = 8$
   $x - y = 4$ (4, 0)
8. $\frac{1}{5}x - y = \frac{12}{5}$
   $3x - 5y = 6$ (−3, −3)
9. $x + 2y = 0$
   $y + 3 = -x$ (−6, 3)

10. $x + 2y = -9$
    $x - y = 6$ (1, −5)
11. $x + \frac{1}{2}y = 3$
    $y = 3x - 4$ (2, 2)
12. $\frac{2}{3}x + \frac{1}{2}y = 2$
    $4x + 3y = 12$ infinitely many

Lesson 5-2 (pages 260–265)

Use substitution to solve each system of equations. If the system does *not* have exactly one solution, state whether it has *no solutions* or *infinitely many* solutions.

1. $y = x$
   $5x = 12y$ (0, 0)
2. $y = 7 - x$
   $2x - y = 8$ (5, 2)
3. $x = 5 - y$
   $3y = 3x + 1$ $\left(\frac{7}{3}, \frac{8}{3}\right)$

4. $3x + y = 6$
   $y + 2 = x$ (2, 0)
5. $x - 3y = 3$
   $2x + 9y = 11$ $\left(4, \frac{1}{3}\right)$
6. $3x = -18 + 2y$
   $x + 3y = 4$ $\left(-\frac{46}{11}, \frac{30}{11}\right)$

7. $x + 2y = 10$
   $-x + y = 2$ (2, 4)
8. $2x = 3 - y$
   $2y = 12 - x$ (−2, 7)
9. $6y - x = -36$
   $y = -3x$ $\left(\frac{36}{19}, \frac{108}{19}\right)$

10. $\frac{3}{4}x + \frac{1}{3}y = 1$
    $x - y = 10$ (4, −6)
11. $x + 6y = 1$
    $3x - 10y = 31$ (7, −1)
12. $3x - 2y = 12$
    $\frac{3}{2}x - y = 3$ no solution

13. $2x + 3y = 5$
    $4x - 9y = 9$ $\left(\frac{12}{5}, \frac{1}{15}\right)$
14. $x = 4 - 8y$
    $3x + 24y = 12$ infinitely many
15. $3x - 2y = -3$
    $25x + 10y = 215$ (5, 9)

Lesson 5-3 (pages 266–270)

Use elimination to solve each system of equations.

1. $x + y = 7$
   $x - y = 9$ (8, −1)
2. $2x - y = 32$
   $2x + y = 60$ (23, 14)
3. $-y + x = 6$ $\left(\frac{11}{2}, -\frac{1}{2}\right)$
   $y + x = 5$

4. $s + 2t = 6$
   $3s - 2t = 2$ (2, 2)
5. $x = y - 7$
   $2x - 5y = -2$ (−11, −4)
6. $3x + 5y = -16$
   $3x - 2y = -2$ (−2, −2)

7. $x - y = 3$
   $x + y = 3$ (3, 0)
8. $x + y = 8$
   $2x - y = 6$ $\left(\frac{14}{3}, \frac{10}{3}\right)$
9. $2s - 3t = -4$
   $s = 7 - 3t$ (1, 2)

10. $-6x + 16y = -8$
    $6x - 42 = 16y$ no solution
11. $3x + 0.2y = 7$
    $3x = 0.4y + 4$ (2, 5)
12. $9x + 2y = 26$
    $1.5x - 2y = 13$ $\left(\frac{26}{7}, -\frac{26}{7}\right)$

13. $x = y$
    $x + y = 7$ (3.5, 3.5)
14. $4x - \frac{1}{3}y = 8$
    $5x + \frac{1}{3}y = 6$ $\left(\frac{14}{9}, -\frac{16}{3}\right)$
15. $2x - y = 3$
    $\frac{2}{3}x - y = -1$ (3, 3)

Lesson 5-4 (pages 272–278)

Use elimination to solve each system of equations.

1. $-3x + 2y = 10$
   $-2x - y = -5$ $(0, 5)$
2. $2x + 5y = 13$
   $4x - 3y = -13$ $(-1, 3)$
3. $5x + 3y = 4$
   $-4x + 5y = -18$ $(2, -2)$

4. $\frac{1}{3}x - y = -1$
   $\frac{1}{5}x - \frac{2}{5}y = -1$ $(-9, -2)$
5. $3x - 5y = 8$
   $4x - 7y = 10$ $(6, 2)$
6. $x - 0.5y = 1$
   $0.4x + y = -2$ $(0, -2)$

7. $x + 8y = 3$
   $4x - 2y = 7$ $\left(\frac{31}{17}, \frac{5}{34}\right)$
8. $4x - y = 4$
   $x + 2y = 3$ $\left(\frac{11}{9}, \frac{8}{9}\right)$
9. $3y - 8x = 9$
   $y - x = 2$ $\left(-\frac{3}{5}, \frac{7}{5}\right)$

10. $x + 4y = 30$
    $2x - y = -6$ $\left(\frac{2}{3}, \frac{22}{3}\right)$
11. $3x - 2y = 0$
    $4x + 4y = 5$ $\left(\frac{1}{2}, \frac{3}{4}\right)$
12. $9x - 3y = 5$
    $x + y = 1$ $\left(\frac{2}{3}, \frac{1}{3}\right)$

13. $2x - 7y = 9$
    $-3x + 4y = 6$ $(-6, -3)$
14. $2x - 6y = -16$
    $5x + 7y = -18$ $(-5, 1)$
15. $6x - 3y = -9$
    $-8x + 2y = 4$ $\left(\frac{1}{2}, 4\right)$

Lesson 5-5 (pages 280–284)

Determine the best method to solve each system of equations. Then solve the system. 1–15. See Student Handbook Answer Appendix.

1. $y = 2x + 1$
   $y = -3x + 1$
2. $y = 5x - 8$
   $y = 3x$
3. $x + 2y = -6$
   $x = y + 3$

4. $2x - 3y = 5$
   $y = -6x$
5. $x = -1$
   $y = 8$
6. $4x + y = 5$
   $-4x - 2y = 9$

7. $-7x + 3y = -4$
   $2x + 3y = 5$
8. $4x - y = 11$
   $x + 2y = 5$
9. $2y - x = -7$
   $x + 3y = 5$

10. $-13x + 8y = -6$
    $3x - 4y = 2$
11. $-x + 7y = 9$
    $-4x + 6y = -8$
12. $2x + 5y = 7$
    $5x - 2y = 13$

13. $12x - 3y = 7$
    $x = 2 + 13y$
14. $6x = 5$
    $9y - 2x = 7$
15. $17x + 8y = -4$
    $-8y - 2x = 9$

Lesson 6-1 (pages 294–299)

Solve each inequality. Check your solution, and then graph it on a number line. 1–16. See Student Handbook Answer Appendix.

1. $c + 9 \leq 3$
2. $d - (-3) < 13$
3. $z - 4 > 20$
4. $h - (-7) > -2$
5. $-11 > d - 4$
6. $2x > x - 3$
7. $2x - 3 \geq x$
8. $16 + w < -20$
9. $14p > 5 + 13p$
10. $-7 < 16 - z$
11. $1.1v - 1 > 2.1v - 3$
12. $\frac{1}{2}t + \frac{1}{4} \geq \frac{7}{4}t - \frac{2}{3}$
13. $9x < 8x - 2$
14. $-2 + 9n \leq 10n$
15. $a - 2.3 \geq -7.8$
16. $5z - 6 > 4z$

Define a variable, write an inequality, and solve each problem. Then check your solution.

17. The sum of a number and negative six is greater than 9.
18. Negative five times a number is less than the sum of negative six times the number and 12. **17–18. See Student Handbook Answer Appendix for sample answers.**

Lesson 6-2 1–16. See Student Handbook Answer Appendix. (pages 301–307)

Solve each inequality. Check your solution.

1. $7b \geq -49$
2. $-5j < -60$
3. $\frac{w}{3} > -12$
4. $\frac{p}{5} < 8$
5. $-8f < 48$
6. $-0.25t \geq -10$
7. $\frac{g}{-8} < 4$
8. $-4.3x < -2.58$
9. $4c \geq -6$
10. $6 \leq 0.8n$
11. $\frac{2}{3}m \geq -22$
12. $-25 > -0.05a$
13. $-15a < -28$
14. $-\frac{7}{9}x < 42$
15. $0.375q \leq 32$
16. $-7y \geq 91$

Define a variable, write an inequality, and solve each problem. Then check your solution. 17–19. Let n = the number.

17. Negative one times a number is greater than -7. $-n > -7; \{n \mid n < 7\}$
18. Three fifths of a number is at least negative 10. $\frac{3}{5}n \geq -10; \{n \mid n \geq -\frac{50}{3}\}$
19. Seventy-five percent of a number is at most 100. $0.75n \leq 100; \{n \mid n \leq 133.\overline{3}\}$

Lesson 6-3 (pages 308–313)

Solve each inequality. Check your solution.

1. $3y - 4 > -37$ $\{y \mid y > -11\}$
2. $7s - 12 < 13$ $\left\{s \mid s < \frac{25}{7}\right\}$
3. $-5q + 9 > 24$ $\{q \mid q < -3\}$
4. $-6v - 3 \geq -33$ $\{v \mid v \leq 5\}$
5. $-2k + 12 < 30$ $\{k \mid k > -9\}$
6. $-2x + 1 < 16 - x$ $\{x \mid x > -15\}$
7. $15t - 4 > 11t - 16$ $\{t \mid t > -3\}$
8. $13 - y \leq 29 + 2y$ $\left\{y \mid y \geq -\frac{16}{3}\right\}$
9. $5q + 7 \leq 3(q + 1)$ $\{q \mid q \leq -2\}$
10. $2(w + 4) \geq 7(w - 1)$ $\{w \mid w \leq 3\}$
11. $-4t - 5 > 2t + 13$ $\{t \mid t < -3\}$
12. $\frac{2t + 5}{3} < -9$ $\{t \mid t < -16\}$
13. $\frac{z}{4} + 7 \geq -5$ $\{z \mid z \geq -48\}$
14. $13r - 11 > 7r + 37$ $\{r \mid r > 8\}$
15. $8c - (c - 5) > c + 17$ $\{c \mid c > 2\}$
16. $-5(k + 4) \geq 3(k - 4)$ $\{k \mid k \leq -1\}$
17. $9m + 7 < 2(4m - 1)$ $\{m \mid m < -9\}$
18. $3(3y + 1) < 13y - 8$ $\left\{y \mid y > \frac{11}{4}\right\}$
19. $5x \leq 10(3x + 4)$ $\left\{x \mid x \geq -\frac{8}{5}\right\}$
20. $3\left(a + \frac{2}{3}\right) \geq a - 1$ $\left\{a \mid a \geq -\frac{3}{2}\right\}$

Lesson 6-4 1–16. See Student Handbook Answer Appendix. (pages 315–320)

Solve each compound inequality. Then graph the solution set.

1. $2 + x < -5$ or $2 + x > 5$
2. $-4 + t > -5$ or $-4 + t < 7$
3. $3 \leq 2g + 7$ and $2g + 7 \leq 15$
4. $2v - 2 \leq 3v$ and $4v - 1 \geq 3v$
5. $3b - 4 \leq 7b + 12$ and $8b - 7 \leq 25$
6. $-9 < 2z + 7 < 10$
7. $5m - 8 \geq 10 - m$ or $5m + 11 < -9$
8. $12c - 4 \leq 5c + 10$ or $-4c - 1 \leq c + 24$
9. $2h - 2 \leq 3h \leq 4h - 1$
10. $3p + 6 < 8 - p$ and $5p + 8 \geq p + 6$
11. $2r + 8 > 16 - 2r$ and $7r + 21 < r - 9$
12. $-4j + 3 < j + 22$ and $j - 3 < 2j - 15$
13. $2(q - 4) \leq 3(q + 2)$ or $q - 8 \leq 4 - q$
14. $\frac{1}{2}w + 5 \geq w + 2 \geq \frac{1}{2}w + 9$
15. $n - (6 - n) > 10$ or $-3n - 1 > 20$
16. $-(2x + 5) \leq x + 5 \leq 2x - 9$

Lesson 6-5 (pages 322–327)

1–9. See Student Handbook Answer Appendix.

Solve each open sentence. Then graph the solution set.

1. $|c - 5| = 4$
2. $|e + 3| = 7$
3. $|4 - g| = 6$
4. $|10 - k| = 8$
5. $|2j + 4| = 12$
6. $|2r - 6| = 10$
7. $|6 - 3w| = 8$
8. $|7 + 2x| = 14$
9. $|4z + 6| = 12$

Lesson 6-6 (pages 329–333)

1–12. See Student Handbook Answer Appendix.

Solve each open sentence. Then graph the solution set.

1. $|y - 9| < 19$
2. $|8 + 6| > 8$
3. $|t - 5| \le 3$
4. $|a + 5| \le 0$
5. $|2m - 5| > 13$
6. $|14 - w| \ge 20$
7. $|3p + 5| \le 23$
8. $|6b - 12| \le 36$
9. $|25 - 3x| < 5$
10. $|4 - 5s| > 46$
11. $|4 - (1 - x)| \ge 10$
12. $\left|\frac{7 - 2b}{2}\right| \le 3$

Lesson 6-7 (pages 334–339)

Determine which ordered pairs are part of the solution set for each inequality.

1. $x + y \ge 0$, $\{(0, 0), (1, -3), (2, 2), (3, -3)\}$ $\{(0, 0), (2, 2), (3, -3)\}$
2. $2x + y \le 8$, $\{(0, 0), (-1, -1), (3, -2), (8, 0)\}$ $\{(0, 0), (-1, -1), (3, -2)\}$

Graph each inequality. 3–8. See Student Handbook Answer Appendix.

3. $y \le -2$
4. $x < 4$
5. $x + y < -2$
6. $y > 4x - 1$
7. $3x + y > 1$
8. $3y - 2x \le 2$

Lesson 6-8 (pages 341–345)

1–9. See Student Handbook Answer Appendix.

Solve each system of inequalities by graphing.

1. $x > 3$
   $y < 6$
2. $y > 2$
   $y > -x + 2$
3. $x \le 2$
   $y + 3 \ge 5$
4. $x + y \le -1$
   $2x + y \le 2$
5. $y \ge 2x + 2$
   $y \ge -x - 1$
6. $y \le x + 3$
   $y \ge x + 2$
7. $y - x \ge 0$
   $y \le 3$
   $x \ge 0$
8. $y > 2x$
   $x > -3$
   $y < 4$
9. $y \le x$
   $x + y < 4$
   $y \ge -3$

Lesson 7-1 (pages 358–364)

Determine whether each expression is a monomial. Write yes or no.
Explain. 1–4. See Student Handbook Answer Appendix for explanations.

1. $n^2 - 3$ no
2. 53 yes
3. $9a^2b^3$ yes
4. $15 - x^2y$ no

Simplify.

5. $a^5(a)(a^7)$ a^{13}
6. $(r^3t^4)(r^4t^4)$ r^7t^8
7. $(x^3y^4)(xy^3)$ x^4y^7
8. $(bc^3)(b^4c^3)$ b^5c^6
9. $(-3mn^2)(5m^3n^2)$ $-15m^4n^4$
10. $[(3^3)^2]^2$ 531,441
11. $(3s^3t^2)(-4s^3t^2)$ $-12s^6t^4$
12. $x^3(x^4y^3)$ x^7y^3
13. $(1.1g^2h^4)^3$ $1.331g^6h^{12}$
14. $-\frac{3}{4}a(a^2b^3c^4)$ $-\frac{3}{4}a^3b^3c^4$
15. $\left(\frac{1}{2}w^3\right)^2(w^4)^2$ $\frac{1}{4}w^{14}$
16. $[(-2^3)^3]^2$ 262,144

Lesson 7-2 (pages 366–373)

Simplify. Assume that no denominator is equal to zero.

1. $\frac{6^{10}}{6^7}$ 6^3 or 216
2. $\frac{t^6c^5}{t^3c^2}$ t^3c^3
3. $\frac{(-a)^4b^8}{a^4b^7}$ b
4. $\frac{(-x)^3y^3}{x^3y^6}$ $\frac{1}{y^3}$
5. $\frac{12ab^5}{4u^4b^3}$ $\frac{3b^2}{a^3}$
6. $\frac{24x^5}{-8x^2}$ $-3x^3$
7. $\frac{-9h^2k^4}{18h^5j^3k^4}$ $-\frac{1}{2h^3j^3}$
8. $\left(\frac{2a^2b^4}{3a^3b^3}\right)^2$ $\frac{4b^6}{9a^2}$
9. $a^5b^0a^{-7}$ $\frac{1}{a^2}$
10. $\frac{(-u^{-3}v^3)}{(u^3v)^{-3}}$ u^6v^9
11. $\left(\frac{a^3}{b^2}\right)^{-3}$ $\frac{b^6}{a^9}$
12. $\left(\frac{2x}{y^{-3}}\right)^{-2}$ $\frac{1}{4x^2y^6}$
13. $\frac{(-r)^5}{r^{-3}s^{-4}}$ $-r^8s^9$
14. $\frac{28a^{-4}b^0}{14a^3b^{-1}}$ $\frac{2b}{a^7}$
15. $\frac{(j^2k^3m)^4}{(jk^4)^{-1}}$ $j^9k^{16}m^4$
16. $\left(\frac{-2x^4y}{4y^2}\right)^{10}$ 1
17. $\left(\frac{-18x^4a^{-3}}{-6x^{-2}a^{-3}}\right)$ $3x^2$
18. $\left(\frac{2a^2b^{-2}}{2^{-1}a^{-3}b^3}\right)^{-1}$ $\frac{b^5}{4a^8}$
19. $\left(\frac{5n^{-1}m^2}{2mn^{-2}}\right)^{10}$ 1
20. $\frac{(3ab^2c)^{-3}}{(2a^2bc^2)^2}$ $\frac{1}{108a^7b^8c^7}$

Lesson 7-3 (pages 376–381)

State whether each expression is a polynomial. If the expression is a polynomial, identify it as a *monomial*, a *binomial*, or a *trinomial*.

1. $5x^2y + 3xy - 7$ yes; trinomial
2. 0 yes; monomial
3. $\frac{5}{k} - k^2y$ no
4. $3a^2x - 5a$ yes; binomial

Find the degree of each polynomial.

5. $a + 5c$ 1
6. $14abcd - 6d^3$ 4
7. $\frac{a^3}{4}$ 3
8. 10 0
9. $-4j^5$ 5
10. $\frac{x^2}{3} - \frac{x}{2} + \frac{1}{5}$ 2
11. -6 0
12. $a^2b^3 - a^3b^2$ 5

Arrange the terms of each polynomial so that the powers of x are in ascending order. 13–18. See Student Handbook Answer Appendix.

13. $2x^2 - 3x + 4x^3 - x^5$
14. $x^3 - x^2 + x - 1$
15. $2a + 3ax^2 - 4ax$
16. $-5bx^3 - 2bx + 4x^2 - b^3$
17. $x^8 + 2x^2 - x^6 + 1$
18. $cdx^2 - c^2d^2x + d^3$

Arrange the terms of each polynomial so that the powers of x are in descending order. 19–24. See Student Handbook Answer Appendix.

19. $5x^2 - 3x^3 + 7 + 2x$
20. $-6x + x^5 + 4x^3 - 20$
21. $5b + b^3x^2 + \frac{2}{3}bx$
22. $21p^2x + 3px^3 + p^4$
23. $3ax^2 - 6a^2x^3 + 7a^3 - 8x$
24. $\frac{1}{3}\cdot\frac{5}{2}x^3 + 4x^4 - \frac{2}{5}\cdot4x^2$

Lesson 7-4 (pages 384–388)

Find each sum or difference. 5–12. See Student Handbook Answer Appendix.

1. $(3a^2 + 5) + (4a^2 - 1)$ $7a^2 + 4$
2. $(5x - 3) + (-2x + 1)$ $3x - 2$
3. $(6z + 2) - (9z + 3)$ $-3z - 1$
4. $(-4n + 7) - (-7n - 8)$ $3n + 15$
5. $(-7f^2 + 4ts - 6s^2) + (-5f^2 - 12ts + 3s^2)$
6. $(6a^2 - 7ab - 4b^2) - (2a^2 + 5ab + 6b^2)$
7. $(4a^2 - 10b^2 + 7c^2) + (-5a^2 + 2c^2 + 2b)$
8. $(z^2 + 6z - 8) - (4z^2 - 7z - 5)$
9. $(4d + 3e - 8f) - (-3d + 10e - 5f + 6)$
10. $(7g + 8h - 9) + (-g - 3h - 6k)$
11. $(9x^2 - 11xy - 3y^2) - (x^2 - 16xy + 12y^2)$
12. $(-3m + 9mn - 5n) + (14m - 5mn - 2n)$
13. $(6 - 7y + 3y^2) + (3 - 5y - 2y^2) + (-12 - 8y + y^2)$ $2y^2 - 20y - 3$
14. $(-7c^2 - 2c - 5) + (9c - 6) + (16c^2 + 3) + (-9c^2 - 7c + 7)$ -1

Lesson 7-5 (pages 390–395)

Find each product. 6. $5y^3 - 15y^2 + 30y$ 7–9. See Student Handbook Answer Appendix.

1. $-3(8x + 5)$ $-24x - 15$
2. $3b(5b + 8)$ $15b^2 + 24b$
3. $1.1a(2a + 7)$ $2.2a^2 + 7.7a$
4. $\frac{1}{2}x(8x - 6)$ $4x^2 - 3x$
5. $7xy(5x^2 - y^2)$ $35x^3y - 7xy^3$
6. $5y(y^2 - 3y + 6)$
7. $-ab(3b^2 + 4ab - 6a^2)$
8. $4m^2(9m^2n + mn - 5n^2)$
9. $4st^2(-4s^2t^3 + 7s^5 - 3st^3)$

Simplify. 10–15. See Student Handbook Answer Appendix.

10. $-3a(2a - 12) + 5a$
11. $6(12b^2 - 2b) + 7(-2 - 3b)$
12. $x(x - 6) + x(x - 2) + 2x$
13. $11(n - 3) + 2(n^2 + 22n)$
14. $-2x(x + 3) + 3(x + 3)$
15. $4m(n - 1) - 5n(n + 1)$

Solve each equation. 23. -1.5

16. $-6(11 - 2x) = 7(-2 - 2x)$ 2
17. $11(n - 3) + 5 = 2n + 44$ 8
18. $a(a - 6) + 2a = 3 + a(a - 2)$ -1.5
19. $q(2q + 3) + 20 = 2q(q - 3)$ $-\frac{20}{9}$
20. $w(w + 12) = w(w + 14) + 12$ -6
21. $x(x - 3) + 4x - 3 = 8x + x(3 + x)$ $\frac{3}{10}$
22. $-3(x + 5) + x(x - 1) = x(x + 2) - 3$ -2
23. $n(n - 5) + n(n + 2) = 2n(n - 1) + 1.5$

Lesson 7-6 (pages 398–403)

Find each product. 1–27. See Student Handbook Answer Appendix.

1. $(d + 2)(d + 5)$
2. $(z + 7)(z - 4)$
3. $(m - 8)(m - 5)$
4. $(a + 2)(a - 19)$
5. $(c + 15)(c - 3)$
6. $(x + y)(x - 2y)$
7. $(2x - 5)(x + 6)$
8. $(7a - 4)(2a - 5)$
9. $(4x + y)(2x - 3y)$
10. $(7v + 3)(v + 4)$
11. $(7s - 8)(3s - 2)$
12. $(4g + 3h)(2g - 5h)$
13. $(4a + 3)(2a - 1)$
14. $(7y - 1)(2y - 3)$
15. $(2x + 3y)(4x + 2y)$
16. $(12x - 4s)(5r + 8s)$
17. $(-a + 1)(-3a - 2)$
18. $(2n - 4)(-3n - 2)$
19. $(x - 2)(x^2 + 2x + 4)$
20. $(3x + 5)(2x^2 - 5x + 11)$
21. $(4s + 5)(3s^2 + 8s - 9)$
22. $(5x - 2)(-5x^2 + 2x + 7)$
23. $(-n + 2)(-2n^2 + n - 1)$
24. $(x^2 - 7x + 4)(2x^2 - 3x - 6)$
25. $(x^2 + x + 1)(x^2 - x - 1)$
26. $(a^2 + 2a + 5)(a^2 - 3a - 7)$
27. $(5x^4 - 2x^2 + 1)(x^2 - 5x + 3)$

Lesson 7-7 4. $100x^2 - 121y^2$ 6. $4b^2 - 16d^2$ 9. $36m^2 + 24mn + 4r^2$ (pages 404–409)

Find each product. 16–21. See Student Handbook Answer Appendix.

1. $(t + 7)^2$ $t^2 + 14t + 49$
2. $(w - 12)(w + 12)$ $w^2 - 144$
3. $(q - 4h)^2$ $q^2 - 8qh + 16h^2$
4. $(10x + 11y)(10x - 11y)$
5. $(4p + 3)^2$ $16p^2 + 24p + 9$
6. $(2b - 4d)(2b + 4d)$
7. $(a + 2b)^2$ $a^2 + 4ab + 4b^2$
8. $(3x + y)^2$ $9x^2 + 6xy + y^2$
9. $(6m + 2n)^2$
10. $(3m - 7d)^2$ $9m^2 - 42md + 49d^2$
11. $(5b - 6)(5b + 6)$ $25b^2 - 36$
12. $(1 + x)^2$ $1 + 2x + x^2$
13. $(5x - 9y)^2$ $25x^2 - 90xy + 81y^2$
14. $(8a - 2b)(8a + 2b)$ $64a^2 - 4b^2$
15. $\left(\frac{1}{4}x + 4\right)^2$ $\frac{1}{16}x^2 + 2x + 16$
16. $\left(\frac{1}{2}x - 10\right)\left(\frac{1}{2}x + 10\right)$
17. $\left(\frac{1}{3}n - m\right)\left(\frac{1}{3}n + m\right)$
18. $(a - 1)(a - 1)(a - 1)$
19. $(x + 2)(x - 2)(2x + 5)$
20. $(4x - 1)(4x + 1)(x - 4)$
21. $(x - 5)(x + 5)(x + 4)(x - 4)$
22. $(a + 1)(a + 1)(a - 1)(a - 1)$ $a^4 - 2a^2 + 1$
23. $(n - 1)(n + 1)(n - 1)$ $n^3 - n^2 - n + 1$
24. $(2c + 3)(2c + 3)(2c - 3)(2c - 3)$ $16c^4 - 72c^2 + 81$
25. $(4d + 5g)(4d + 5g)(4d - 5g)(4d - 5g)$ $256d^4 - 800g^2d^2 + 625g^4$

Lesson 8-1 (pages 420–423)

Factor each monomial completely. 1–6. See Student Handbook Answer Appendix.

1. $240mn$
2. $-64a^3b$
3. $-26xy^2$
4. $-231xy^2z$
5. $44rs^2t^3$
6. $-756m^2n^2$

Find the GCF of each set of monomials. 17. $4pq$

7. $16, 60$ 4
8. $15, 50$ 5
9. $45, 80$ 5
10. $29, 58$ 29
11. $55, 305$ 5
12. $126, 252$ 126
13. $128, 245$ 1
14. $7y^2, 14y^2$ $7y^2$
15. $4xy, -6x$ $2x$
16. $35t^2, 7t$ $7t$
17. $16pq^2, 12p^2q, 4pq$ 18. $5, 15, 10$ 5
19. $12mn, 10mn, 15mn$ mn
20. $14xy, 12y, 20x$ 2
21. $26jk^4, 16jk^3, 8j^2$ $2j$

Lesson 8-2 (pages 426–431)

Factor each polynomial. 1–15. See Student Handbook Answer Appendix.

1. $10a^2 + 40a$
2. $15wx - 35wx^2$
3. $27z^2b + 9b^3$
4. $11x + 44x^2y$
5. $16y^2 + 8y$
6. $14mn^2 + 2mn$
7. $25a^2b^2 + 30ab^3$
8. $2m^3n^2 - 16mn^2 + 8mn$
9. $2ax + 6xc + ba + 3bc$
10. $6mx - 4m + 3rx - 2r$
11. $3ax - 6bx + 8b - 4a$
12. $a^2 - 2ab + a - 2b$
13. $8ac - 2ad + 4bc - bd$
14. $2c^2g + 2fg + 4c^2h + 4fh$
15. $x^2 - xy - xy + y^2$

Solve each equation. Check your solutions. 19. $\{-3, 1\}$ 20. $\left\{-\frac{2}{3}, \frac{7}{4}\right\}$

16. $a(a - 9) = 0$ $\{0, 9\}$
17. $d(d + 11) = 0$ $\{-11, 0\}$
18. $z(z - 2.5) = 0$ $\{0, 2.5\}$
19. $(2y + 6)(y - 1) = 0$
20. $(4n - 7)(3n + 2)$
21. $(a - 1)(a + 1) = 0$ $\{-1, 1\}$
22. $10x^2 - 20x = 0$ $\{0, 2\}$
23. $8b^2 - 12b = 0$ $\{0, 1.5\}$
24. $14d^2 + 49d = 0$ $\{0, -3.5\}$
25. $15a^2 = 60a$ $\{0, 4\}$
26. $33z^2 = -22z$ $\left\{-\frac{2}{3}, 0\right\}$
27. $32x^2 = 16x$ $\left\{0, \frac{1}{2}\right\}$

Lesson 8-3 (pages 434–439)

Factor each trinomial. 1–18. See Student Handbook Answer Appendix.

1. $x^2 - 9x + 14$
2. $a^2 - 9a - 36$
3. $x^2 + 2x - 15$
4. $n^2 - 8n + 15$
5. $b^2 + 22b + 21$
6. $c^2 + 2c - 3$
7. $x^2 - 5x - 24$
8. $n^2 - 8n + 7$
9. $m^2 - 10m - 39$
10. $z^2 + 15z + 36$
11. $s^2 - 13st - 30t^2$
12. $y^2 + 2y - 35$
13. $r^2 + 3r - 40$
14. $x^2 + 5x - 6$
15. $x^2 - 4xy - 5y^2$
16. $r^2 + 16r + 63$
17. $v^2 + 24v - 52$
18. $k^2 - 27kj - 90j^2$

Solve each equation. Check your solutions. 21. $\{-8, -3\}$ 24. $\{-3, 16\}$ 30. $\{-11, -3\}$

19. $a^2 + 3a - 4 = 0$ $\{-4, 1\}$
20. $x^2 - 8x - 20 = 0$ $\{-2, 10\}$
21. $b^2 + 11b + 24 = 0$
22. $y^2 + y - 42 = 0$ $\{-7, 6\}$
23. $k^2 + 2k - 24 = 0$ $\{-6, 4\}$
24. $r^2 - 13r - 48 = 0$
25. $n^2 - 9n = -18$ $\{3, 6\}$
26. $2z + z^2 = 35$ $\{-7, 5\}$
27. $-20x + 19 = -x^2$ $\{1, 19\}$
28. $10 + a^2 = -7a$ $\{-5, -2\}$
29. $z^2 - 57 = 16z$ $\{-3, 19\}$
30. $x^2 = -14x - 33$
31. $22x - x^2 = 96$ $\{6, 16\}$
32. $-144 = q^2 - 26q$ $\{8, 18\}$
33. $x^2 + 84 = 20x$ $\{6, 14\}$

Extra Practice

Lesson 8-4 (pages 441–446)

Factor each trinomial, if possible. If the trinomial cannot be factored using integers, write *prime*. 1–30. See Student Handbook Answer Appendix.

1. $4a^2 + 4a - 63$
2. $3x^2 - 7x - 6$
3. $4r^2 - 25r + 6$
4. $2z^2 - 11z + 15$
5. $3a^2 - 2a - 21$
6. $4y^2 + 11y + 6$
7. $6n^2 + 7n - 3$
8. $5x^2 - 17x + 14$
9. $2n^2 - 11n + 13$
10. $5a^2 - 3a + 15$
11. $18z^2 + 24v + 12$
12. $4k^2 + 2k - 12$
13. $10x^2 - 20xy + 10y^2$
14. $12c^2 - 11cd - 5d^2$
15. $30n^2 - mn - m^2$

Solve each equation. Check your solutions.

16. $8t^2 + 32t + 24 = 0$
17. $6y^2 + 72y + 192 = 0$
18. $5x^2 + 3x - 2 = 0$
19. $9x^2 + 18x - 27 = 0$
20. $4x^2 - 4x - 4 = 4$
21. $12n^2 - 16n - 3 = 0$
22. $12x^2 - x - 35 = 0$
23. $18x^2 + 36x - 14 = 0$
24. $15d^2 + a - 2 = 0$
25. $14b^2 + 7b - 42 = 0$
26. $13r^2 + 21r - 10 = 0$
27. $35y^2 - 60y - 20 = 0$
28. $16x^2 - 4x - 6 = 0$
29. $28d^2 + 5d - 3 = 0$
30. $30x^2 - 9x - 3 = 0$

Lesson 8-5 (pages 447–452)

Factor each polynomial, if possible. If the polynomial cannot be factored, write *prime*. 1–16. See Student Handbook Answer Appendix.

1. $x^2 - 9$
2. $a^2 - 64$
3. $4x^2 - 9y^2$
4. $1 - 9z^2$
5. $16x^2 - 9b^2$
6. $8x^2 - 12y^2$
7. $a^2 - 4b^2$
8. $75x^2 - 48$
9. $x^2 - 36y^2$
10. $3a^2 - 16$
11. $9x^2 - 100y^2$
12. $49 - a^2b^2$
13. $5a^2 - 48$
14. $169 - 16t^2$
15. $8t^2 - 4$
16. $-45m^2 + 5$

Solve each equation by factoring. Check your solutions.

17. $4x^2 = 16$ {±2}
18. $2x^2 = 50$ {±5}
19. $9n^2 - 4 = 0$ $\left\{\pm\frac{2}{3}\right\}$
20. $a^2 - \frac{25}{36} = 0$ $\left\{\pm\frac{5}{6}\right\}$
21. $\frac{16}{9} - b^2 = 0$ $\left\{\pm\frac{4}{3}\right\}$
22. $18 - \frac{1}{2}x^2 = 0$ {±6}
23. $20 - 5g^2 = 0$ {±2}
24. $16 - \frac{1}{4}p^2 = 0$ {±8}
25. $\frac{1}{4}c^2 - \frac{4}{9} = 0$ $\left\{\pm\frac{4}{3}\right\}$
26. $2g^3 - 2g = 0$ (-1, 0, 1)
27. $3r^3 = 48r$ {-4, 0, 4}
28. $100d - 4d^3 = 0$ (-5, 0, 5)

Lesson 8-6 (pages 454–460)

Determine whether each trinomial is a perfect square trinomial. If so, factor it.

1. $x^2 + 12x + 36$ yes; $(x + 6)^2$
2. $n^2 - 13n + 36$ no
3. $a^2 + 4a + 4$ yes; $(a + 2)^2$
4. $x^2 - 10x - 100$ no
5. $2n^2 + 17n + 21$ no
6. $4a^2 - 20a + 25$ yes; $(2a - 5)^2$

Factor each polynomial, if possible. If the polynomial cannot be factored, write *prime*. 7–14. See Student Handbook Answer Appendix.

7. $3x^2 - 75$
8. $4p^2 + 12pr + 9r^2$
9. $6a^2 + 72$
10. $s^2 + 30s + 225$
11. $24x^2 + 24x + 9$
12. $1 - 10z + 25z^2$
13. $28 - 63b^2$
14. $4c^2 + 2c - 7$

Solve each equation. Check your solutions.

15. $x^2 + 22x + 121 = 0$ (-11)
16. $343d^2 = 7$ $\left\{\pm\frac{1}{7}\right\}$
17. $(a - 7)^2 = 5$ $7 \pm \sqrt{5}$
18. $c^2 + 10c + 36 = 11$ (-5)
19. $16z^2 + 81 = 72s$ $\left\{\frac{9}{4}\right\}$
20. $9p^2 - 42p + 20 = -29$ $\left\{\frac{7}{3}\right\}$

Lesson 9-1 (pages 471–477)

Use a table of values to graph each function. 1–3. See Student Handbook Answer Appendix.

1. $y = x^2 + 6x + 8$
2. $y = -x^2 + 3x$
3. $y = -x^2$

Write the equation of the axis of symmetry, and find the coordinates of the vertex of the graph of each function. Identify the vertex as a maximum or minimum. Then graph the function. 4–18. See Student Handbook Answer Appendix.

4. $y = -x^2 + 2x - 3$
5. $y = 3x^2 + 24x + 80$
6. $y = x^2 - 4x - 4$
7. $y = 5x^2 - 20x + 37$
8. $y = 3x^2 + 6x + 3$
9. $y = 2x^2 + 12x$
10. $y = x^2 - 6x + 5$
11. $y = x^2 + 6x + 9$
12. $y = -x^2 + 16x - 15$
13. $y = 4x^2 - 1$
14. $y = -2x^2 - 2x + 4$
15. $y = 6x^2 - 12x - 4$
16. $y = -x^2 - 1$
17. $y = -x^2 + x + 1$
18. $y = -5x^2 - 3x + 2$

Lesson 9-2 $10. \ 0 < r < 1, 3 < r < 4$ $14. \ -1 < b < 0, 5 < b < 6$ (pages 480–485)

Solve each equation by graphing. 1–6. See Student Handbook Answer Appendix for graphs.

1. $a^2 - 25 = 0$ -5, 5
2. $n^2 - 8n = 0$ 0, 8
3. $d^2 + 36 = 0$ ∅
4. $b^2 - 18b + 81 = 0$ 9
5. $x^2 + 3x + 27 = 0$ ∅
6. $-y^2 - 3y + 10 = 0$ -5, 2

Solve each equation by graphing. If integral roots cannot be found, estimate the roots by stating the consecutive integers between which the roots lie. 7–24. See Student Handbook Answer Appendix for graphs.

15. $-3 < x < -2, 0 < x < 1$ 21. $-1 < x < 0, 0 < x < 1$
17. $-3 < n < -2, 2 < n < 3$

7. $x^2 + 2x - 3 = 0$ -3, 1
8. $-x^2 + 6x - 5 = 0$ 1, 5
9. $-a^2 - 2a + 3 = 0$ -3, 1
10. $2r^2 - 8r + 5 = 0$
11. $-3x^2 + 6x - 9 = 0$ ∅
12. $c^2 + c = 0$ -1, 0
13. $3t^2 + 2 = 0$ ∅
14. $-b^2 + 5b + 2 = 0$
15. $3x^2 + 7x = 1$
16. $x^2 + 5x - 24 = 0$ -8, 3
17. $8 - n^2 = 0$
18. $x^2 - 7x = 18$ -2, 9
19. $a^2 + 12a + 36 = 0$ -6
20. $64 - x^2 = 0$ -8, 8
21. $-4x^2 + 2x = -1$
22. $5z^2 + 8z = 1$
23. $p = 27 - p^2$
24. $6w = -15 - 3w^2$ ∅

$-2 < z < -1, 0 < z < 1$ $-6 < p < -5, 4 < p < 5$

Lesson 9-3 (pages 486–491)

Solve each equation by taking the square root of each side. Round to the nearest tenth if necessary. 3. -8.3, -1.7

1. $x^2 - 4x + 4 = 9$ -1, 5
2. $t^2 - 6t + 9 = 16$ -1, 7
3. $b^2 + 10b + 25 = 11$
4. $a^2 - 22a + 121 = 3$ 9.3, 12.7
5. $x^2 + 2x + 1 = 81$ -10, 8
6. $t^2 - 36t + 324 = 85$ 8.8, 27.2

Find the value of c that makes each trinomial a perfect square.

7. $a^2 + 20a + c$ 100
8. $x^2 + 10x + c$ 25
9. $t^2 + 12t + c$ 36
10. $y^2 - 9y + c$ $\frac{81}{4}$
11. $p^2 - 14p + c$ 49
12. $b^2 + 13b + c$ $\frac{169}{4}$

Solve each equation by completing the square. Round to the nearest tenth if necessary.

13. $a^2 - 8a - 84 = 0$ -6, 14
14. $c^2 + 6 = -5c$ -3, -2
15. $p^2 - 8p + 5 = 0$ 0.7, 7.3
16. $2y^2 + 7y - 4 = 0$ -4, $\frac{1}{2}$
17. $t^2 + 3t = 40$ 5, -8
18. $x^2 + 8x - 9 = 0$ -9, 1
19. $y^2 + 5y - 84 = 0$ -12, 7
20. $t^2 + 12t + 32 = 0$ -4, -8
21. $2x - 3x^2 = -8$ 2, -1.3
22. $2y^2 - y - 9 = 0$ -1.9, 2.4
23. $2z^2 - 5z - 4 = 0$ -0.6, 3.1
24. $8t^2 - 12t - 1 = 0$ -0.1, 1.6

Lesson 9-4
(pages 493–499)

Solve each equation by using the Quadratic Formula. Round to the nearest tenth if necessary. 7. $-0.6, -3.4$ 12. $-2.4, -0.3$ 13. $-0.8, -0.5$ 14. $0.7, -0.3$

1. $x^2 - 8x - 4 = 0$ $-0.5, 8.5$ 2. $x^2 + 7x - 8 = 0$ $-8, 1$ 3. $x^2 - 5x + 6 = 0$ $2, 3$
4. $y^2 - 7y - 8 = 0$ $-1, 8$ 5. $m^2 - 2m = 35$ $-5, 7$ 6. $4n^2 - 20n = 0$ $0, 5$
7. $m^2 + 4m + 2 = 0$ 8. $2t^2 - t - 15 = 0$ $-2.5, 3$ 9. $5t^2 = 125$ $-5, 5$
10. $t^2 + 16 = 0$ ∅ 11. $-4x^2 + 8x = -3$ $-0.3, 2.3$ 12. $3k^2 + 2 = -8k$
13. $8t^2 + 10t + 3 = 0$ 14. $3x^2 - \frac{5}{4}x - \frac{1}{2} = 0$ 15. $-5b^2 + 3b - 1 = 0$ ∅
16. $n^2 - 3n + 1 = 0$ $2.6, 0.4$ 17. $2z^2 + 5z - 1 = 0$ $0.2, -2.7$ 18. $3h^2 = 27$ $3, -3$
19. 76; 2 real roots 20. 2.89; 2 real roots 21. -92; no real roots

State the value of the discriminant for each equation. Then determine the number of real roots of the equation.

19. $3f^2 + 2f = 6$ 20. $2x^2 = 0.7x + 0.3$ 21. $3w^2 - 2w + 8 = 0$
22. $4f^2 - 12r + 9 = 0$ 23. $x^2 - 5x = -9$ 24. $25t^2 + 30t = -9$
0; 1 real root -11; no real roots 0; 1 real root

Lesson 9-5
(pages 502–508)

Graph each function. State the y-intercept. Then use the graph to determine the approximate value of the given expression. Use a calculator to confirm the value. 1–3. See Student Handbook Answer Appendix for graphs.

1. $y = 7^x$; $7^{1.5}$ 1; 18.5 2. $\left(\frac{1}{3}\right)^x$; $\left(\frac{1}{3}\right)^{5.6}$ 1; 0.002 3. $y = \left(\frac{3}{5}\right)^x$; $\left(\frac{3}{5}\right)^{-4.2}$ 1; 8.5

4–15. See Student Handbook Answer Appendix for graphs. Graph each function. State the y-intercept.

4. $y = 3^x + 1$ 2 5. $y = 2^x - 5$ -4 6. $y = 2^x + 3$ 8 7. $y = 3^x + 1$ 3
8. $y = \left(\frac{2}{3}\right)^x$ 1 9. $y = 5\left(\frac{2}{5}\right)^x$ 5 10. $y = 5(3^x)$ 5 11. $y = 4(5)^x$ 4
12. $y = 2(5)^x + 1$ 3 13. $y = \left(\frac{1}{2}\right)^{x+1}$ $\frac{1}{2}$ 14. $y = \left(\frac{1}{8}\right)^x$ 1 15. $y = \left(\frac{3}{4}\right)^x - 2$ -1

Determine whether the data in each table display exponential behavior. Explain why or why not. 16–17. See Student Handbook Answer Appendix.

16.
x	-1	0	1	2
y	-5	-1	3	7

17.
x	1	2	3	4
y	25	125	625	3125

Lesson 9-6
2. $V = 21{,}500(1 - 0.08)^5$; \$14,170.25 (pages 510–514)

1. **MONEY** Marco deposited \$8500 in a 4-year certificate of deposit earning 7.25% compounded monthly. Write an equation for the amount of money Marco will have at the end of the four years. Then find the amount. $M = 8500\left(1 + \frac{0.0725}{12}\right)^{12(4)}$; \$11,349.73
2. **TRANSPORTATION** Elise is buying a new car for \$21,500. The rate of depreciation on this type of car is 8% per year. Write an equation for the value of the car in 5 years. Then find the value of the car in 5 years.
3. **POPULATION** In 2000, the town of Belgrade had a population of 3422. For each of the next 8 years, the population increased by 4.9% per year. Find the projected population of Belgrade in 2008. 5017

Lesson 10-1
(pages 528–534)

Simplify.

1. $\sqrt{50}$ $5\sqrt{2}$ 2. $\sqrt{200}$ $10\sqrt{2}$ 3. $\sqrt{162}$ $9\sqrt{2}$ 4. $\sqrt{700}$ $10\sqrt{7}$
5. $\frac{\sqrt{3}}{\sqrt{5}}$ $\frac{\sqrt{15}}{5}$ 6. $\frac{\sqrt{72}}{\sqrt{6}}$ $2\sqrt{3}$ 7. $\sqrt{\frac{8}{7}}$ $\frac{2\sqrt{14}}{7}$ 8. $\sqrt{\frac{7}{32}}$ $\frac{\sqrt{14}}{8}$
9. $\sqrt{\frac{5}{8}} \cdot \sqrt{\frac{2}{6}}$ $\frac{\sqrt{30}}{12}$ 10. $\sqrt{\frac{2}{3}} \cdot \sqrt{\frac{3}{2}}$ 1 11. $\sqrt{\frac{2x}{30}}$ $\frac{\sqrt{15x}}{15}$ 12. $\sqrt{\frac{50}{z^2}}$ $\frac{5\sqrt{2}}{|z|}$
13. $\sqrt{10} + \sqrt{20}$ $10\sqrt{2}$ 14. $\sqrt{7} \cdot \sqrt{3}$ $\sqrt{21}$ 15. $6\sqrt{2} \cdot \sqrt{3}$ $6\sqrt{6}$ 16. $5\sqrt{6} \cdot 2\sqrt{3}$ $30\sqrt{2}$
17. $\sqrt{4x^4y^3}$ $2x^2|y|\sqrt{y}$ 18. $\sqrt{200m^2y^3}$ $10|my|\sqrt{2y}$ 19. $\sqrt{12ts^3}$ $2|s|\sqrt{3st}$ 20. $\sqrt{175a^4b^6}$ $5a^2|b^3|\sqrt{7}$
21. $\sqrt{\frac{54}{g^2}}$ $\frac{3\sqrt{6}}{|g|}$ 22. $\sqrt{\frac{99x^3y^7}{3|xy^3|}}$ $\sqrt{11xy}$ 23. $\sqrt{\frac{32c^5}{9d^2}}$ $\frac{4c^2\sqrt{2c}}{3|d|}$ 24. $\sqrt{\frac{27p^4}{3p^2}}$ $3|p|$
25. $\frac{1}{3+\sqrt{5}}$ $\frac{3-\sqrt{5}}{4}$ 26. $\frac{2}{\sqrt{3}-5}$ $\frac{\sqrt{3}+5}{-11}$ 27. $\frac{\sqrt{3}}{\sqrt{3}-5}$ $\frac{3+5\sqrt{3}}{-22}$ 28. $\frac{\sqrt{6}}{7-2\sqrt{3}}$ $\frac{7\sqrt{6}+6\sqrt{2}}{37}$

Lesson 10-2
(pages 536–540)

Simplify. 1. $7\sqrt{11}$ 4. $9\sqrt{7} - \sqrt{2}$ 5. in simplest form 6. $8\sqrt{2} - 3\sqrt{5}$

1. $3\sqrt{11} + 6\sqrt{11} - 2\sqrt{11}$ 2. $6\sqrt{13} + 7\sqrt{13}$ $13\sqrt{13}$ 3. $2\sqrt{12} + 5\sqrt{3}$ $9\sqrt{3}$
4. $9\sqrt{7} - 4\sqrt{2} + 3\sqrt{2}$ 5. $3\sqrt{5} - 5\sqrt{3}$ 6. $4\sqrt{8} - 3\sqrt{5}$
7. $2\sqrt{27} - 4\sqrt{12} - 2\sqrt{3}$ 8. $8\sqrt{32} + 4\sqrt{50}$ $52\sqrt{2}$ 9. $\sqrt{45} + 6\sqrt{20}$ $15\sqrt{5}$
10. $2\sqrt{63} - 6\sqrt{28} + 8\sqrt{45}$ 11. $14\sqrt{3t} + 8$ $22\sqrt{3t}$ 12. $7\sqrt{6x} - 12\sqrt{6x}$ $-5\sqrt{6x}$
13. $5\sqrt{7} - 3\sqrt{28}$ $-\sqrt{7}$ 14. $7\sqrt{8} - \sqrt{18}$ $11\sqrt{2}$ 15. $7\sqrt{98} + 5\sqrt{32} - 2\sqrt{75}$
16. $4\sqrt{6} + 3\sqrt{2} - 2\sqrt{5}$ 17. $-3\sqrt{20} + 2\sqrt{45} - \sqrt{7}$ 18. $4\sqrt{75} + 6\sqrt{27}$ $38\sqrt{3}$
19. $10\sqrt{\frac{1}{5}} - \sqrt{45} - 12\sqrt{\frac{5}{9}}$ 20. $\sqrt{15} - \sqrt{\frac{3}{5}}$ $\frac{4\sqrt{15}}{5}$ 21. $3\sqrt{\frac{1}{3}} - 9\sqrt{\frac{1}{12}} + \sqrt{243}$
10. $-6\sqrt{7} + 24\sqrt{5}$ 15. $69\sqrt{2} - 10\sqrt{3}$ 16. in simplest form 17. $-\sqrt{7}$ 19. $-5\sqrt{5}$ 21. $\frac{17\sqrt{3}}{2}$

Find each product.

22. $\sqrt{3}(\sqrt{5} + 2)$ $\sqrt{15} + 2\sqrt{3}$ 23. $\sqrt{2}(\sqrt{2} + 3\sqrt{5})$ $2 + 3\sqrt{10}$
24. $(\sqrt{2} + 5)^2$ $27 + 10\sqrt{2}$ 25. $(3 - \sqrt{7})(3 + \sqrt{7})$ 2
26. $(\sqrt{2} + \sqrt{3})(\sqrt{3} + \sqrt{2})$ $2\sqrt{6} + 5$ 27. $(4\sqrt{7} + \sqrt{2})(\sqrt{3} - 3\sqrt{5})$ $4\sqrt{21} - 12\sqrt{35} + \sqrt{6} - 3\sqrt{10}$

Lesson 10-3
(pages 541–546)

Solve each equation. Check your solution. 17. no solution

1. $\sqrt{5x} = 5$ 5 2. $4\sqrt{7} = \sqrt{-m}$ -112 3. $\sqrt{t} - 5 = 0$ 25
4. $\sqrt{3b} + 2 = 0$ no solution 5. $\sqrt{x} - 3 = 6$ 81 6. $5 - \sqrt{3x} = 1$ $\frac{16}{3}$
7. $2 + 3\sqrt{y} = 13$ $\frac{121}{9}$ 8. $\sqrt{3g} = 6$ 12 9. $\sqrt{a} - 2 = 0$ 4
10. $\sqrt{2j} - 4 = 8$ 72 11. $5 + \sqrt{x} = 9$ 16 12. $\sqrt{5y} + 4 = 7$ 9
13. $7 + \sqrt{5c} = 9$ $\frac{4}{5}$ 14. $2\sqrt{5t} = 10$ 5 15. $\sqrt{44} = 2\sqrt{p}$ 11
16. $4\sqrt{x} - 5 = 15$ $\frac{305}{16}$ 17. $4 - \sqrt{x} - 3 = 9$ 18. $\sqrt{10x^2} - 5 = 3x$ $\sqrt{5}$
19. $\sqrt{2a^2 - 144} = a$ 12 20. $\sqrt{3y + 1} = y - 3$ 8 21. $\sqrt{2c^2 - 12} = x$ $2\sqrt{3}$
22. $\sqrt{b^2 + 16} + 2b = 5b$ $\frac{\sqrt{325}}{24}$ 23. $\sqrt{m + 2} + m = 4$ 7 24. $\sqrt{3 - 2c} + 3 = 2c$ 1

Lesson 10-4
(pages 549–554)

If c is the measure of the hypotenuse of a right triangle, find each missing measure. If necessary, round to the nearest hundredth.

1. $b = 20, c = 29, a = ?$ **21**
2. $a = 7, b = 24, c = ?$ **25**
3. $a = 2, b = 6, c = ?$ **6.32**
4. $b = 10, c = \sqrt{200}, a = ?$ **10**
5. $a = 3, c = 3\sqrt{2}, b = ?$ **3**
6. $a = 6, c = 14, b = ?$ **12.65**
7. $a = \sqrt{11}, c = \sqrt{47}, b = ?$ **6**
8. $a = \sqrt{13}, b = 6, c = ?$ **7**
9. $a = \sqrt{6}, b = 3, c = ?$ **3.87**
10. $b = \sqrt{75}, c = 10, a = ?$ **5**
11. $b = 9, c = \sqrt{130}, a = ?$ **7**
12. $a = 9, c = 15, b = ?$ **12**

Determine whether the following side measures form right triangles.

13. 14, 48, 50 **yes**
14. 20, 30, 40 **no**
15. 21, 72, 75 **yes**
16. 5, 12, $\sqrt{119}$ **yes**
17. 15, 39, 36 **yes**
18. 10, 12, $\sqrt{22}$ **no**
19. 2, 3, 4 **no**
20. $\sqrt{7}$, 8, $\sqrt{71}$ **yes**

Lesson 10-5
1–24. See Student Handbook Answer Appendix. (pages 555–559)

Find the distance between each pair of points whose coordinates are given. Express answers in simplest radical form and as decimal approximations rounded to the nearest hundredth if necessary.

1. (4, 2), (−2, 10)
2. (−5, 1), (7, 6)
3. (4, −2), (1, 2)
4. (−2, 4), (4, −2)
5. (3, 1), (−2, −1)
6. (−2, 4), (7, −8)
7. (−5, 0), (−9, 6)
8. (5, −1), (5, 13)
9. (2, −3), (10, 8)
10. (−7, 5), (2, −7)
11. (−6, −2), (−5, 4)
12. (8, −10), (3, 2)
13. (4, −3), (7, −9)
14. (6, 3), (9, 7)
15. (10, 0), (9, 7)
16. (2, −1), (−3, 3)
17. (−5, 4), (3, −2)
18. (0, −9), (0, 7)
19. (−1, 7), (8, 4)
20. (−9, 2), (3, −3)
21. (3√2, 7), (5√2, 9)
22. (6, 3), (10, 0)
23. (3, 6), (5, −5)
24. (−4, 2), (5, 4)

Find the possible values of a if the points with the given coordinates are the indicated distance apart.

25. (0, 0), (a, 3); d = 5 **−4 or 4**
26. (2, −1), (−6, a); d = 10
27. (1, 0), (a, 6); d = √61
28. (−2, a), (5, 10); d = √85
29. (15, a), (0, 4); d = √274
30. (3, 3), (a, 9); d = √136
26. **−7 or 5**
27. **−4 or 6**
28. **4 or 16**
29. **−3 or 11**
30. **−7 or 13**

Lesson 10-6
1–3. See Student Handbook Answer Appendix. (pages 560–565)

Determine whether each pair of triangles is similar. Justify your answer.

1. 75°, 50°, 60°

2. 78°, 78°, 52°

3. 60°, 60°

For each set of measures given, find the measures of the missing sides if $\triangle ABC \sim \triangle DEF$.

4. $a = 5, d = 10, b = 8, c = 7$ $e = 16, f = 14$
5. $a = 2, b = 3, c = 4, d = 3$ $e = 4.5, f = 6$
6. $a = 6, d = 4.5, e = 7, f = 7.5$ $b = 9\tfrac{1}{3}, c = 10$
7. $a = 15, c = 20, b = 18, f = 10$ $d = 7.5, e = 9$
8. $f = 17.5, d = 8.5, e = 11, a = 1.7$ $b = 2.2, c = 3.5$

Lesson 11-1
(pages 577–582)

Graph each variation if y varies inversely as x. 1–6. See Student Handbook Answer Appendix.

1. $y = 10$ when $x = 7.5$
2. $y = -5$ when $x = 3$
3. $y = -6$ when $x = -2$
4. $y = 1$ when $x = -0.5$
5. $y = -2.5$ when $x = 3$
6. $y = -2$ when $x = -1$

Write an inverse variation equation that relates x and y. Assume that y varies inversely as x. Then solve. 7–16. See Student Handbook Answer Appendix.

7. If $y = 54$ when $x = 4$, find x when $y = 27$.
8. If $y = 18$ when $x = 6$, find x when $y = 12$.
9. If $y = 12$ when $x = 24$, find x when $y = 9$.
10. If $y = 8$ when $x = -8$, find y when $x = -16$.
11. If $y = 3$ when $x = -1$, find y when $x = 4$.
12. If $y = 27$ when $x = \frac{1}{3}$, find y when $x = \frac{3}{4}$.
13. If $y = -3$ when $x = -8$, find y when $x = 2$.
14. If $y = -3$ when $x = -3$, find x when $y = 4$.
15. If $y = -7.5$ when $x = 2.5$, find y when $x = -2.5$.
16. If $y = -0.4$ when $x = -3.2$, find x when $y = -0.2$.

Lesson 11-2
(pages 583–588)

State the excluded values for each rational expression.

1. $\frac{x}{x+1}$ −1
2. $\frac{m}{n}$ $n \neq 0$
3. $\frac{c-2}{c^2-4}$ −2, 2
4. $\frac{b^2-5b+6}{b^2-8b+15}$ 3, 5

5–16. See Student Handbook Answer Appendix.
Simplify each expression. State the excluded values of the variables.

5. $\frac{13a}{39a^2}$
6. $\frac{38x^2}{42xy}$
7. $\frac{p+5}{2(p+5)}$
8. $\frac{a+b}{a^2-b^2}$
9. $\frac{y+4}{y^2-16}$
10. $\frac{c^2-4}{c^2+4c+4}$
11. $\frac{a^2-a}{a-1}$
12. $\frac{x^2+4}{x^4-16}$
13. $\frac{r^3-r^2}{r-1}$
14. $\frac{4t^2-8}{4t-4}$
15. $\frac{6y^3-12y^2}{12y^2-18}$
16. $\frac{5x^2+10x+5}{3x^2+6x+3}$

Lesson 11-3
(pages 590–594)

Find each product.

1. $\frac{a^2b}{b^2c} \cdot \frac{c}{d} \cdot \frac{a^2}{bd}$
2. $\frac{6a^2n}{8n^2} \cdot \frac{12n}{9a} \cdot a$
3. $\frac{2a^2d}{3bc} \cdot \frac{9b^2c}{16ad^2} \cdot \frac{3ab}{8d}$
4. $\frac{10m^3}{6x^3} \cdot \frac{12n^2x^4}{25n^2x^2} \cdot \frac{4n^3}{5x}$
5. $\frac{6m^3n}{10a^2} \cdot \frac{4a^2m}{9n^3} \cdot \frac{4m^4}{15n^2}$
6. $\frac{5n-5}{} \cdot \frac{9}{n-1} \cdot \frac{15}{n-1}$
7. $\frac{(a-5)(a+1)}{(a+1)(a+7)} \cdot \frac{(a+7)(a-6)}{(a+8)(a-5)} \cdot \frac{a-6}{a+8}$
8. $\frac{x-1}{(x+2)(x-3)} \cdot \frac{x+2}{(x-3)(x-1)} \cdot (x-3)^2$
9. $\frac{a^2}{a-b} \cdot \frac{3a-3b}{a} \cdot 3a$
10. $\frac{2a+4b}{5} \cdot \frac{25}{6a+8b} \cdot \frac{5a+10b}{3a+4b}$
11. $\frac{3}{x-y} \cdot \frac{x-y^2}{6} \cdot \frac{x-y}{2}$
12. $\frac{x+5}{3x} \cdot \frac{12x^2}{x^2+7x+10} \cdot \frac{4x}{x+2}$
13. $\frac{4a+8}{a^2-25} \cdot \frac{a-5}{5a+10} \cdot \frac{4}{5a+25}$
14. $\frac{r^2}{r-s} \cdot \frac{r^2-s^2}{r^2-s^2} \cdot \frac{r^2s}{s^2}$
15. $\frac{x^2+10x+9}{x^2+11x+18} \cdot \frac{x^2-6x+5}{x^2+3x+2} \cdot \frac{x+1}{x+6}$
16. $\frac{x^2+14x+40}{x^2+5x-50} \cdot \frac{x-1}{x+3}$

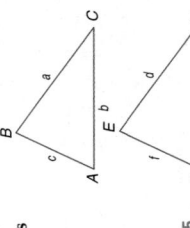
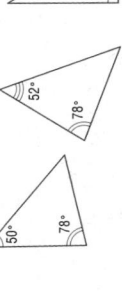
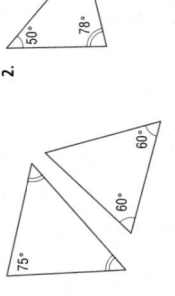

Lesson 11-4
(pages 595–599)

Find each quotient.

1. $\frac{5m^2n}{12a^2} \div \frac{30m^4}{18an}$
2. $\frac{x^4}{12z^2}$
6. $\frac{1}{(5d+1)^2}$
3. $\frac{6a+4b}{36} \div \frac{3a+2b}{45}$ $\frac{5}{2}$

4. $\frac{x^2y}{18z} \div \frac{2yz}{3x^2}$
5. $\frac{p^2}{14pr^3} \div \frac{2r^2p}{7q}$ $\frac{p}{4r^5}$
6. $\frac{5d-f}{5d+f} \div (25d^2-f^2)$

7. $\frac{t^2-2t-15}{t-5} \div \frac{t+3}{t+5}$ $t+5$
8. $\frac{5x+10}{x+2} \div (x+2)$ $\frac{5}{x+2}$
9. $\frac{3d}{2d^2-3d} \div \frac{9}{2d-3}$ $\frac{1}{3}$

10. $\frac{3v^2-27}{15v} \div \frac{v+3}{v^2}$ $\frac{v(v-3)}{5}$
11.
12. $\frac{b^2-9}{4b} \div (b-3)$ $\frac{b+3}{4b}$

13. $\frac{p^2}{y^2-4} \div \frac{p}{2-y}$ $\frac{-p}{y+2}$
14. $\frac{k^2-81}{k^2-36} \div \frac{k-9}{k+6}$ $\frac{k+9}{k-6}$
15. $\frac{2a^3}{a+1} \div \frac{a^2}{a+1}$ $2a$

16. $\frac{x^2-16}{16-x^2} \div \frac{7}{x}$ $\frac{-x}{7}$
17. $\frac{y}{5} \div \frac{y^2-25}{5-y}$ $\frac{-y}{5y+25}$
18. $\frac{3m}{m+1} \div (m-2)$

Lesson 11-5
(pages 601–606)

Find each quotient.

1. $(2x^2-11x-20) \div (2x+3)$
12. $2a^2+3a-4$
2. $(a^2+10a+21) \div (a+3)$ $a+7$

3. $(m^2+4m-5) \div (m+5)$ $m-1$
4. $(x^2-2x-35) \div (x-7)$ $x+5$

5. $(c^2+6c-27) \div (c+9)$ $c-3$
6. $(y^2-6y-25) \div (y+7)$ $y-13+\frac{66}{(y+7)}$

7. $(3t^2-14t-24) \div (3t+4)$ $t-6$
8. $(2r^2-3r-35) \div (2r+7)$ $r-5$

9. $\frac{12n^2+36n+15}{6n+3}$ $2n+5$
10. $\frac{10x^2+29x+21}{5x+7}$ $2x+3$
11. $\frac{4t^3+17t^2-1}{4t+1}$ t^2+4t-1

13. $\frac{27c^2-24c+8}{9c-2}$ $3c-2+\frac{4}{9c-2}$
14. $\frac{4b^3+7b^2-2b+4}{b+2}$ $4b^2-b+\frac{4}{b+2}$

Lesson 11-6
(pages 608–613)

Find each sum.

1. $\frac{4}{z}+\frac{3}{z}+\frac{7}{z}$
2. $\frac{a}{12}+\frac{2a}{12}$ $\frac{a}{4}$
3. $\frac{5}{2t}+\frac{-7}{2t}$ $\frac{-1}{t}$

4. $\frac{y}{2}+\frac{y}{2}+y$
5. $\frac{b}{x}+\frac{2}{x}+\frac{b+2}{x}$
6. $\frac{y}{2}+\frac{y-6}{2}$ $y-3$

7. $\frac{x}{x+1}+\frac{1}{x+1}$ 1
8. $\frac{2n}{2n-5}+\frac{5}{5-2n}$ 1
9. $\frac{x-y}{2-y}+\frac{x+y}{y-2}$ $\frac{2y}{y-2}$

10. $\frac{r^2}{r-s}+\frac{s^2}{r-s}$
11. $\frac{12n}{3n+2}+\frac{8}{3n+2}$ 4
12. $\frac{6x}{x+y}+\frac{6y}{x+y}$ 6

Find each difference.

13. $\frac{5x}{24}-\frac{3x}{24}$ $\frac{x}{12}$
14. $\frac{7p}{3}-\frac{8p}{3}$ $\frac{-p}{3}$
15. $\frac{8k}{5m}-\frac{3k}{5m}$ $\frac{k}{m}$

16. $\frac{8}{m-2}-\frac{6}{m-2}$ $\frac{2}{m-2}$
17. $\frac{y}{b+6}-\frac{b+3}{b+6}$ $\frac{-y}{b+6}$
18. $\frac{a+2}{6}-\frac{a+3}{6}$ $\frac{1}{6}$

19. $\frac{2a}{2a+5}-\frac{5}{2a+5}$ $\frac{2a-5}{2a+5}$
20. $\frac{1}{4z+1}-\frac{(-4z)}{4z+1}$ 1
21. $\frac{3a}{a-2}-\frac{3a}{a-2}$ 0

22. $\frac{n}{n-1}-\frac{1}{1-n}$ $\frac{n+1}{n-1}$
23. $\frac{a}{a-7}-\frac{(-7)}{7-a}$ 1
24. $\frac{2a}{6a-3}-\frac{(-1)}{3-6a}$ $\frac{1}{3}$

Lesson 11-7
(pages 614–619)

Find the LCM for each pair of expressions.

1. $27a^2bc$, $36ab^2c^2$
2. $3m-1$, $6m-2$ $6m-2$
3. x^2+2x+1, x^2-2x-3 $(x+1)^2(x-3)$

Find each sum.

4. $\frac{s}{3}+\frac{2s}{7}+\frac{13s}{21}$
5. $\frac{5}{2a}+\frac{-3}{6a}$ $\frac{2}{a}$
6. $\frac{6}{5x}+\frac{7}{10x^2}+\frac{12x+7}{10x^2}$

7. $\frac{5}{xy}+\frac{6}{yz}+\frac{5z+6x}{xyz}$
8. $\frac{2}{t}+\frac{t+3}{s}+\frac{2s+t^2+3t}{st}$
9. $\frac{a}{a-b}+\frac{b}{2b+3a}+\frac{b}{a}$

10. $\frac{4a}{2a+6}+\frac{3}{a+3}+\frac{2a+3}{a+3}$
11. $\frac{3t+2}{3t-2}+\frac{t^2+2}{t^2-4}+\frac{t+2}{t^2-12}$
12. $\frac{-3}{a-5}+\frac{-6}{a^2-5a}+\frac{-3a-6}{a^2-5a}$

Find each difference.

13. $\frac{2n}{5}-\frac{3m}{4}$ $\frac{8n-15m}{20}$
14. $\frac{a}{a^2-4}-\frac{4}{a+2}$ $\frac{-3a+8}{a^2-4}$
15. $\frac{s}{t^2}-\frac{r}{3t}$ $\frac{3s-rt}{3t^2}$

16. $\frac{t}{t^2-100}-\frac{1}{10-t}$ $\frac{2}{t-10}$
17. $\frac{m}{m-n}-\frac{5}{m}$ $\frac{m^2-5m+5n}{m^2-mn}$
18. $\frac{3z}{7w^2}-\frac{2z}{w}$ $\frac{7w^2}{w}$

19. $\frac{3t^3+2t^2-8t-12}{3t^3+5t^2-8t-12}$
20. $\frac{2a-6}{a^2-3a-10}-\frac{a^2-8a+61}{(a+2)(a-5)(a-6)}$

Lesson 11-8
(pages 620–625)

Write each mixed expression as a rational expression.

1. $4+\frac{2}{x}$ $\frac{4x+2}{x}$
2. $8+\frac{5}{3t}$ $\frac{24t+5}{3t}$
3. $3b+\frac{b+1}{2b}$ $\frac{6b^2+b+1}{2b}$

4. $3z+\frac{z+2}{z}$ $\frac{3z^2+z+2}{z}$
5. $\frac{2}{a-2}+a^2$ $\frac{a^3-2a^2+2}{a-2}$
6. $3r^2+\frac{4}{2r+1}$ $\frac{6r^3+3r^2+4}{2r+1}$

Simplify each expression.

7. $\dfrac{3\frac{1}{2}}{4\frac{3}{4}}$ $\frac{14}{19}$
8. $\dfrac{\frac{x^2}{y}}{\frac{x^5}{x^3}}$ $\frac{y^2(x-3)}{x^2(x+1)}$
9. $\dfrac{\frac{t^4}{u}}{\frac{t^3}{u^2}}$ tu
10. $\dfrac{\frac{x-3}{x+1}}{\frac{x^2}{y^2}}$

11. $\dfrac{\frac{y}{3}+\frac{5}{6}}{2+\frac{y}{6}}$
12. $\dfrac{\frac{1}{x}+\frac{1}{y}}{\frac{1}{y}-\frac{1}{x}}$ $\frac{x+y}{x-y}$
13. $\dfrac{t-2}{t^2-4}$ $\frac{t-2}{t^2+5t+6}$
14. $\dfrac{a+\frac{2}{a+1}}{a-\frac{3}{a-2}}$

Lesson 11-9
(pages 626–632)

Solve each equation. State any extraneous solutions.

1. $\frac{k}{6}+\frac{2k}{3}=-\frac{5}{2}$ -3
2. $\frac{2x}{7}+\frac{27}{10}=\frac{4x}{5}$ 5.25
3. $\frac{18}{b}=\frac{3}{b}+\frac{3}{5}$ 5

4. $\frac{3}{5x}+\frac{7}{2x}=1$ $\frac{41}{10}$
5. $\frac{2a-3}{6}=\frac{2a}{3}+\frac{1}{2}$ -3
6. $\frac{3x+2}{x}+\frac{x+3}{x}=5$ 5

7. $\frac{2b-3}{b}-\frac{b}{2}=\frac{b+3}{14}$ $\frac{9}{4}$
8. $\frac{2y}{y-4}-\frac{3}{5}=3$ 9
9. $\frac{2t}{t+3}+\frac{3}{t}=2$ 3

10. $\frac{5x}{x+1}+\frac{1}{x}=5\frac{1}{4}$
11. $\frac{r-2}{r+2}=\frac{2r}{r+9}=6$ $-6, -3$
12. $\frac{m}{m+1}+\frac{5}{m-1}=1$ $\frac{3}{2}$

13. $\frac{2x}{x-3}-\frac{4x}{3-x}=12$ 6
14. $\frac{14}{b-6}=\frac{1}{2}+\frac{6}{b-8}$ $10, 20$
15. $\frac{a}{4a+15}-3=-2$ -5

16. $\frac{5x}{3x+10}+\frac{2x}{x+5}=2$ $-4, 517$
17. $\frac{2a-3}{a-3}-2=\frac{12}{a+2}$ $\frac{14}{3}$
18. $\frac{z+3}{z-1}+\frac{z+1}{z-3}=2$ 2

Lesson 12-1

(pages 642–648)

Identify each sample, suggest a population from which it was selected, and state whether it is *unbiased* (random) or *biased*. If unbiased, classify the sample as *simple, stratified,* or *systematic*. If biased, classify as *convenience* or *voluntary response.* 1–4. See Student Handbook Answer Appendix.

1. The sheriff has heard that many dogs in the county do not have licenses. He checks the licenses of the first ten dogs he encounters.

2. Every fifth car is selected from the assembly line. The cars are also identified by the day of the week during which they were produced.

3. A table is set up outside of a large department store. All people entering the store are given a survey about their preference of brand for blue jeans. As people leave the store, they can return the survey.

4. A community is considering building a new swimming pool. Every twentieth person on a list of residents is contacted for their opinion.

Lesson 12-2

(pages 650–654)

Draw a tree diagram to show the sample space for each event. Determine the number of possible outcomes.

1. choosing a dinner special at a restaurant offering lettuce salad or coleslaw; chicken, beef, or fish; and ice cream, pudding, or cookies 18

2. tossing a coin four times 16

1–2. See Student Handbook Answer Appendix for diagrams.
Determine the number of possible outcomes.

3. A state's license plates feature two digits, a space, and two letters. Any digit or any letter can be used in the space. 67,600

4. At the Big Mountain Ski Resort, you can choose from three types of boots, four types of skis, and five types of poles. 60

Find the value of each expression.

5. 8! 40,320   6. 1! 1   7. 0! 1   8. 5! 120   9. 2! 2   10. 9! 362,880

Lesson 12-3

(pages 655–662)

Determine whether each situation involves a *permutation* or *combination*. Explain.

1. three topping flavors for a sundae from ten topping choices combination

2. selection and placement of four runners on a relay team from 8 runners permutation

3. five rides to ride at an amusement park with twelve rides combination

4. first, second, and third place winners for a 10K race permutation

5. a three-letter arrangement from eight different letters permutation

6. selection of five digits from ten digits for a combination lock permutation

7. selecting six items from twelve possible items to include in a custom gift basket combination

1–7. See Student Handbook Answer Appendix for explanations.
Evaluate each expression. 14. 10,886,400

8. $_5P_2$ 20   9. $_7P_7$ 5040   10. $_{10}C_2$ 45   11. $_6C_5$ 6

12. $(_7P_3)(_4P_2)$ 2520   13. $(_8C_6)(_7C_3)$ 588   14. $(_3C_2)(_{10}P_{10})$ 15. $(_3P_2)(_{10}C_{10})$ 6

Lesson 12-4

(pages 663–670)

A red die and a blue die are rolled. Find each probability.

1. P(red 1, blue 1) $\frac{1}{36}$
2. P(red even, blue even) $\frac{1}{4}$
3. P(red prime number, blue even) $\frac{1}{4}$
4. P(red 6, blue greater than 4) $\frac{1}{18}$
5. P(red greater than 2, blue greater than 3) $\frac{1}{3}$

At a carnival game, toy ducks are selected from a pond to win prizes. Once a duck is selected, it is not replaced. The pond contains 8 red, 2 yellow, 1 gold, 4 blue, and 40 black ducks. Find each probability.

6. P(red, then gold) $\frac{4}{1485}$
7. P(2 black) $\frac{52}{99}$
8. P(2 yellow) $\frac{1}{1485}$
9. P(black, then gold) $\frac{4}{297}$
10. P(3 black, then red) $\frac{304}{5247}$
11. P(yellow, then blue, then gold) $\frac{4}{78,705}$

Lesson 12-5

(pages 672–676)

1–2. See Student Handbook Answer Appendix.

Consider finding the product of the numbers shown rolling two dice and the number of ways each product can be found.

1. Draw a table to show the sample space of all possible outcomes.

2. Find the probability for $X = 9$, $X = 12$, and $X = 24$.

3. What is the probability that the product of two dice is greater than 15 on two separate rolls? 3. $\frac{121}{1296}$

Use the table that shows a probability distribution for the number of customers that enter a particular store during a business day.

Number of Customers	0–500	501–1000	1001–1500	1501–2000	2000–2500
Probability	0.05	0.25	0.35	0.30	0.05

4. Define a random variable and list its values. See Student Handbook Answer Appendix.

5. Show that this is a valid probability distribution. 0.05 + 0.25 + 0.35 + 0.30 + 0.05 = 1

6. What is the probability that fewer than 1001 customers enter in a day? 0.30

Lesson 12-6

(pages 677–683)

1–2. See students' work.

For Exercises 1–3, toss 4 coins, one at a time, 50 times and record your results.

1. Based on your results, what is the probability that any two coins show tails?

2. Based on your results, what is the probability that the first and fourth coins show heads?

3. What is the theoretical probability that all four coins show heads? $\frac{1}{16}$
4. See Student Handbook Answer Appendix.
For Exercises 4–6, use the table that shows the results of a survey about household occupancy.

4. Find the experimental probability distribution for the number of households of each size.

5. Based on the survey, what is the probability that a person chosen at random lives in a household with five or more people? about 0.11 or 11%

6. Based on the survey, what is the probability that a person chosen at random lives in a household with 1 or 2 people? about 0.34 or 34%

Number in Household	Number of Households
1	172
2	293
3	482
4	256
5 or more	148

Mixed Problem Solving

Chapter 1 The Language and Tools of Algebra

For answers not here, see Student Handbook Answer Appendix. (pp. 4–67)

GEOMETRY For Exercises 1 and 2, use the following information.

The surface area of a cone is given by $SA = \pi r^2 + \pi r \ell$, where r is the radius and ℓ is the slant height. (Lesson 1-1)

1. Write an expression that represents the surface area of the cone. $\pi r^2 + \pi r \ell$

2. Suppose the radius and the slant height of a cone have the same measure r. Write an expression that represents the surface area of this cone. $2\pi r^2$

SALES For Exercises 3 and 4, use the following information.

At the Farmer's Market, merchants can rent a small table for $5.00 and a large table for $8.50. One time, 25 small and 10 large tables were rented. Another time, 35 small and 12 large were rented. (Lesson 1-2)

3. Write an expression to show the total amount of money collected.

4. Evaluate the expression. $487
$25(5) + 10(8.5) + 35(5) + 12(8.5)$

ENTERTAINMENT For Exercises 5–7, use the following information.

The Morrows are planning to go to a water park. The table shows the ticket prices. The family has 2 adults, 2 children, and a grandparent who wants to observe. They want to spend no more than $55. (Lesson 1-3)

Admission Prices ($)		
Ticket	Full Day	Half Day
Adult	16.95	10.95
Child (6–18)	12.95	8.95
Observer	4.95	3.95

6. $64.75; $43.75

5. Write an inequality to show the cost for the family to go to the water park.

6. How much would it cost the Morrows to go for a full day? a half day?

7. Can the family go to the water park for a full day and stay within their budget? no

RETAIL For Exercises 8–10, use the following information.

A department store is having a sale on children's clothing. The table shows the prices. (Lesson 1-4)

Shorts		T-Shirts		Tank Tops	
$7.99		$8.99		$6.99	
$5.99		$4.99		$2.99	

8. Write three different expressions that represent 8 pairs of shorts and 8 tops.

9. Evaluate the three expressions in Exercise 8 to find the costs of the 16 items. What do you notice about all the total costs?

10. If you buy 8 shorts and 8 tops, you receive a discount of 15% on the purchase. Find the greatest and least amount of money you can spend on the 16 items at the sale. $115.46; $61.06

11. **CRAFTS** Mandy makes baby blankets and stuffed rabbits to sell at craft fairs. She sells blankets for $28 and rabbits for $18. Write and evaluate an expression to find her total amount of sales if she sells 25 blankets and 25 rabbits. (Lesson 1-5)
$25(28 + 18) = 1150

12. **BASEBALL** Tickets to a baseball game cost $18.95, $12.95, or $9.95. A hot dog and soda combo costs $5.50. The Madison family is having a reunion. They buy 10 tickets in each price category and plan to buy 30 combos. What is the total cost for the tickets and meals? (Lesson 1-6) $583.50

13. **GEOMETRY** Two perpendicular lines meet to form four right angles. Write two different if-then statements for this definition. (Lesson 1-7)

14. **JOBS** Laurie mows lawns to earn extra money. She knows that she can mow at most 30 lawns in one week. She determines that she profits $15 on each lawn she mows. Identify a reasonable domain and range for this situation and draw a graph. (Lesson 1-9)

Chapter 2 Solving Linear Equations (pp. 68–137)

GEOMETRY For Exercises 1–4, use the following information.

The lateral surface area L of a cylinder is two times π times the product of the radius r and the height h. (Lesson 2-1)

1. Write a formula for the lateral area of a cylinder. $L = 2\pi r h$

2. Find the lateral area of a cylinder with a radius of 4.5 inches and a height of 7 inches. Use 3.14 for π and round the answer to the nearest tenth. 197.8 in²

3. The total surface area T of a cylinder includes the area of the two bases of the cylinder, which are circles. The formula for the area of one circle is πr^2. Write a formula for the total surface area T of a cylinder. $T = 2\pi r h + 2\pi r^2$

4. Find the total surface area of the cylinder in Exercise 2. Round to the nearest tenth. 325.0 in²

RIVERS For Exercises 5 and 6, use the following information.

The Congo River in Africa is 2900 miles long. That is 310 miles longer than the Niger River, which is also in Africa. (Lesson 2-2)

5. Write an equation you could use to find the length of the Niger River. $n + 310 = 2900$

6. What is the length of the Niger River? 2590 mi

ANIMALS For Exercises 7 and 8, use the following information.

The average length of a yellow-banded angelfish is 12 inches. This is 4.8 times as long as an average common goldfish.
Source: Scholastic Records (Lesson 2-3)

7. Write an equation you could use to find the length of the common goldfish. $4.8g = 12$

8. What is the length of an average common goldfish? 2.5 in.

9. **PETS** In 2003, there were 8949 Great Danes registered with the American Kennel Club. The number of registered Labrador Retrievers was 1750 more than sixteen times the number of registered Great Danes. How many registered Labrador Retrievers were there? Source: The World Almanac (Lesson 2-4) 144,934 retrievers

10. **GEOMETRY** One angle of a triangle measures 10° more than the second. The measure of the third angle is twice the sum of the measures of the first two angles. Find the measure of each angle. (Lesson 2-5) 25°, 35°, 120°

11. **POOLS** Tyler needs to add 1.5 pounds of a chemical to the water in his pool for each 5000 gallons of water. The pool holds 12,500 gallons. How much chemical should he add to the water? (Lesson 2-6) 3.75 pounds

SKIING For Exercises 12 and 13, use the following information.

Michael is registering for a ski camp in British Columbia, Canada. The cost of the camp is $1254, but the Canadian government imposes a general sales tax of 7%. (Lesson 2-7)

12. What is the total cost of the camp including tax? $1341.78

13. As a U.S. citizen, Michael can apply for a refund of one-half of the tax. What is the amount of the refund he can receive? $43.89

FINANCE For Exercises 14 and 15, use the following information.

Allison is using a spreadsheet to solve a problem about investing. She is using the formula $I = Prt$, where I is the amount of interest earned, P is the amount of money invested, r is the rate of interest as a decimal, and t is the period of time the money is invested in years. (Lesson 2-8)

14. Allison needs to find the amount of money invested P for given amounts of interest, given rates, and given time. The formula needs to be solved for P to use in the spreadsheet. Solve the formula for P. $P = I \div rt$

15. Allison uses these values in the formula in Exercise 17: $I = \$1848.75$, $r = 7.25\%$, $t = 6$ years. Find P. $4250

16. **CHEMISTRY** Isaac had 40 gallons of a 15% iodine solution. How many gallons of a 40% iodine solution must he add to make a 20% iodine solution? (Lesson 2-9) 10 gal

Chapter 3 Functions and Patterns

For answers not here, see Student Handbook Answer Appendix. (pp. 140–183)

HEALTH For Exercises 1–3, use the following information.

The table shows suggested weights for adults for various heights in inches. (Lesson 3-1)

Height	Weight	Height	Weight
60	102	68	131
62	109	70	139
64	116	72	147
66	124	74	155

Source: The World Almanac

1. Graph the relation.

2. Do the data lie on a straight line? Explain.

3. Estimate a suggested weight for a person who is 78 inches tall. Explain your method.

SPORTS For Exercises 4–6, use the following information.

The table shows the winning times of the Olympic mens' 50-km walk for various years. The times are rounded to the nearest minute. (Lesson 3-2)

Year	Years Since 1980	Time
1980	0	229
1984	4	227
1988	8	218
1992	12	230
1996	16	224
2000	20	222

Source: ESPN

4. Graph the relation using columns 2 and 3.

5. Is the relation a function? Explain.

6. Predict a winning time for the 2008 games.

PLANETS For Exercises 7–9, use the following information.

An astronomical unit (AU) is used to express great distances in space. It is based upon the distance from Earth to the Sun. A formula for converting any distance d in miles to AU is $AU = \dfrac{d}{93,000,000}$. The table shows the average distances from the Sun of four planets in miles. (Lesson 3-3)

Planet	Distance from Sun
Mercury	36,000,000
Mars	141,650,000
Jupiter	483,750,000
Pluto	3,647,720,000

Source: The World Almanac

7. Find the number of AU for each planet rounded to the nearest thousandth.

8. How can you determine which planets are farther from the Sun than Earth?

9. Alpha Centauri is 270,000 AU from the Sun. How far is that in miles?

HOME DECOR For Exercises 10 and 11, use the following information.

Pam is having blinds installed at her home. The cost for installation for any number of blinds can be described by $c = 25 + 6.5x$. (Lesson 3-3)

10. Graph the equation.

11. If Pam has 8 blinds installed, what is the cost? **$77**

JEWELRY For Exercises 12 and 13, use the following information.

A necklace is made with beads placed in a circular pattern. The rows have the following numbers of beads: 1, 6, 11, 16, 21, 26, and 31. (Lesson 3-4)

12. Write a formula for the beads in each row. $a_n = 5n - 4$

13. If a larger necklace is made with 20 rows, find the number of beads in row 20. **96**

14. **GEOMETRY** The table below shows the area of squares with sides of various lengths. (Lesson 3-5)

Side	Area	Side	Area	Side	Area
1	1	1	4	1	4
2	4	2	5	2	5
3	9	3	9	3	6

Write the first 10 numbers that would appear in the area column. Describe the pattern.

Chapter 4 Analyzing Linear Equations

For answers not here, see Student Handbook Answer Appendix. (pp. 184–249)

FARMING For Exercises 1–3, use the following information.

The table shows wheat prices per bushel from 1940 through 2000. (Lesson 4-1)

Year	1940	1950	1960	1970
Price	$0.67	$2.00	$1.74	$1.33
Year	1980	1990	2000	
Price	$3.91	$2.61	$2.62	

1. 1970–1980; 1990–2000
1. For which time period was the rate of change the greatest? the least? 2. $0.133

2. Find the rate of change from 1940 to 1950.

3. Explain the meaning of the slope from 1980 to 1990. **a drop in price**

SOUND For Exercises 4 and 5, use the following information.

The table shows the distance traveled by sound in water. (Lesson 4-2)

Time, x (seconds)	Distance, y (feet)
0	0
1	4820
2	9640
3	14,460
4	19,280

Source: New York Public Library

4. Write an equation that relates distance traveled to time. $y = 4820x$

5. Find the time for 72,300 feet. **15 s**

POPULATION For Exercises 6–8, use the following information.

In 1990, the population of Wyoming was 453,588. Over the next decade, it increased by about 4019 per year. Source: The World Almanac (Lesson 4-3)

6. Assume the rate of change remains the same. Write a linear equation to find the population y of Wyoming at any time. Let x represent the number of years since 1990. $y = 453,588 + 4019x$

7. Graph the equation.

8. Estimate the population in 2015. **554,063**

HEALTH For Exercises 9 and 10, use the following information. 9. $y = 4x - 128$

A person with height of 60 inches should have a weight of 112 pounds and a person with height of 66 inches should have a weight of 136 pounds. Source: The World Almanac (Lesson 4-4)

9. Write a linear equation to estimate the weight of a person of any height.

10. Estimate the weight of a person who is 72 inches tall. **160 lb**

TRAVEL For Exercises 11–13, use the following information.
11. $y - 3,600,000 = 300,000(x - 1990)$

Between 1990 and 2000, the number of people taking cruises increased by about 300,000 each year. In 1990, about 3.6 million people took cruises. Source: USA Today (Lesson 4-5)

11. Write the point-slope form of an equation to find the total number of people taking a cruise y for any year x.

12. Write the equation in slope-intercept form.

13. Estimate the number of people who will take a cruise in 2010. **9,600,000 people**
12. $y = 300,000x - 593,400,000$

ADOPTION For Exercises 14–16, use the following information.

The table shows the number of children from Russia adopted by U.S. citizens. (Lesson 4-6)

Years Since 1996 x	Number of Children y
0	2454
1	3386
2	4491
3	4348
4	4269
5	4279
6	4939
7	5209

Source: The World Almanac

14. Draw a scatter plot and a line of fit.

15. Write the slope-intercept form of the equation for the line of fit.

16. Predict the number of children who will be adopted in 2015. **8690 children**

GEOMETRY For Exercises 17 and 18, use the following information.

A quadrilateral has sides with equations $y = -2x$, $2x + y = 6$, $y = \dfrac{1}{2}x + 6$, and $x - 2y = 9$. (Lesson 4-7)

17. Is the figure a rectangle? **yes**

18. Explain your reasoning.

Chapter 5   Solving Systems of Linear Equations

(pp. 250–291)

WORKING For Exercises 1–3, use the following information.

The table shows the percent of men and women 65 years and older that were working in the U.S. in the given years.   (Lesson 5-1)

U.S. Workers over 65		
Year	Percent of Men	Percent of Women
2000	17.7	9.4
2003	18.6	10.6

Source: *The World Almanac*

1. Let the year 2000 be 0. Assume that the rate of change remains the same for years after 2003. Write an equation to represent the percent of working elderly men y in any year x. $y = 0.31x + 17.7$

2. Write an equation to represent the percent of working elderly women. $y = 0.4x + 9.4$

3. Assume the rate of increase or decrease in working men and women remains the same for years after 2003. Estimate when the percent of working men and women will be the same.
in about 83 years from 2000 or in 2083

SPORTS For Exercises 4–7, use the following information.

The table shows the winning times for the men's and women's Triathlon World Championship for 1995 and 2000.   (Lesson 5-2)

Year	Men's	Women's
2000	1:51:39	1:54:43
2005	1:49:31	1:58:03

Source: International Triathlon Union

4. The times in the table are in hours, minutes, and seconds. Rewrite the times in minutes rounded to the nearest minute. men: 112, 110; women: 115, 118

5. $y = -0.4x + 112$ 6. $y = 0.6x + 115$

5. Let the year 2000 be 0. Assume that the rate of change remains the same for years after 2000. Write an equation to represent the men's winning times y in any year x.

6. Write an equation to represent the women's winning times in any year.

7. If the trend continues, when would you expect the men's and women's winning times to be the same? never

748   Mixed Problem Solving

MONEY For Exercises 8–10, use the following information.

In 2004, the sum of the number of $2 bills and $50 bills in circulation was 1,857,573,945. The number of $50 bills was 494,264,809 more than the number of $2 bills.   (Lesson 5-3)

8. Write a system of equations to represent this situation. See Student Hdbk Answer App.

9. Find the number of each type of bill in circulation. $2: 681,654,568; $50: 1,175,919,377

10. Find the amount of money that was in circulation in $2 and $50 bills.
$47,821,358,494

SPORTS For Exercises 11–14, use the following information.

In the 2004 Summer Olympic Games, the total number of gold and silver medals won by the U.S. was 74. Gold medals are worth 3 points and silver medals are worth 2 points. The total points scored for gold and silver medals was 183.   (Lesson 5-4) Source: ESPN Almanac

11. Write an equation for the sum of the number of gold and silver medals won by the U.S. $g + s = 74$ 12. $3g + 2s = 183$

12. Write an equation for the sum of the points earned by the U.S. for gold and silver medals.

13. How many gold and silver medals did the U.S. win? 35 gold, 39 silver

14. The total points scored by the U.S. was 212. Bronze medals are worth 1 point. How many bronze medals were won? 29

15. **GEOMETRY** Supplementary angles are two angles whose measures have the sum of 180 degrees. Angles X and Y are supplementary, and the measure of angle X is 24 degrees greater than the measure of angle Y. Write and solve a system of equations to find the measures of angles X and Y.   (Lesson 5-5) $m\angle X = 102$; $m\angle Y = 78$

16. **CHEMISTRY** MX Labs needs to make 500 gallons of a 34% acid solution. The only solutions available are a 25% acid solution and a 50% acid solution. Write and solve a system of equations to find the number of gallons of each solution that should be mixed to make the 34% solution.   (Lesson 5-5)
320 gal of 25%; 180 gal of 50%

Chapter 6   Solving Linear Inequalities

For answers not here, see Student Handbook Answer Appendix.

MONEY For Exercises 1 and 2, use the following information. 1. $a + 26 \le 50$; $a \le 24$

Scott's allowance for July is $50. He wants to attend a concert that costs $26.   (Lesson 6-1)

1. Write and solve an inequality that shows how much money he can spend in July after buying a concert ticket.

2. He spends $2.99 for lunch with his friends and $12.49 for a CD. Write and solve an inequality that shows how much money he can spend after all of his purchases.
$a + 26 + 2.99 + 12.49 \le 50$; $a \le 8.52$

ANIMALS For Exercises 3 and 4, use the following information.

The world's heaviest flying bird is the great bustard. A male bustard can be up to 4 feet long and weigh up to 40 pounds.   (Lesson 6-2)

3. Write inequalities to describe the ranges of lengths and weights of male bustards.

4. Male bustards are usually about four times as heavy as females. Write and solve an inequality that describes the range of weights of female bustards.
$0 < 4w \le 40$; $0 < w \le 10$

FOOD For Exercises 5–7, use this information.

Jennie wants to make at least $75 selling caramel-coated apples at the County Fair. She plans to sell each apple for $1.50.   (Lesson 6-3)

5. Let a be the number of apples she makes and sells. Write an inequality to find the number of apples she needs to sell to reach her goal if it costs her $0.30 per apple. $1.5a - 0.3a \ge 75$

6. Solve the inequality. $a \ge 62.5$

7. Interpret the meaning of the solution.

RETAIL For Exercises 8–10, use the following information. 8. $9.95 \le p \le 134.95$

A sporting goods store is offering a $15 coupon on any pair of shoes.   (Lesson 6-4)

8. The most expensive pair of shoes is $149.95 and the least expensive pair of shoes is $24.95. What is the range of prices for customers who have the coupons?

9. You customers have a choice of buying a pair of shoes with a regular price of $109.95 using the coupon or having a 15% discount on the price. Which option is best?
15% discount

10. For what price of shoe is a 15% discount the same as $15 off the regular price? $100

WEATHER For Exercises 11 and 12, use the following information.

The following are average normal monthly temperatures for Honolulu, Hawaii, in degrees Fahrenheit.   (Lessons 6-5 and 6-6)

73, 73, 74, 76, 78, 79, 81, 81, 81, 80, 77, 74

11. What is the mean of the temperatures to the nearest whole degree? 77°

12. Write an inequality to show the normal range of temperatures for Honolulu during the year. $|t - 77| \le 4$

QUILTING For Exercises 13–15, use the following information. 13. $2w + 2\ell \le 318$

Ingrid is making a quilt in the shape of a rectangle. She wants the perimeter of the quilt to be no more than 318 inches.   (Lesson 6-7)

13. Write an inequality for this situation.

14. Graph the inequality and name two different dimensions for the quilt.

15. What are the dimensions and area of the largest possible quilt Ingrid can make?
79.5 in. by 79.5 in.; 6320.25 in²

RADIO For Exercises 16–20, use the following information.

KSKY radio station is giving away tickets to an amusement park. Each child ticket costs $15 and each adult ticket costs $20. The station wants to spend no more than $800 on tickets. They also want the number of child tickets to be greater than twice the number of adult tickets.   (Lesson 6-8) 16. $15c + 20a \le 800$

16. Write an inequality for the total cost of c child tickets and a adult tickets.

17. Write an inequality for the relationship between the number of child and adult tickets. $c > 2a$

18. Write two inequalities that would assure you that the numbers of adult and child tickets would not be negative. $a \ge 0$; $c \ge 0$

19. Graph the four inequalities to show possible numbers of tickets they can buy.

20. Give three possible combinations of child and adult tickets for the station to buy.
Sample answer: (adult, child) = (5, 40),
(10, 30), (12, 32)   Mixed Problem Solving   **749**

Chapter 7 Polynomials

For answers not here, see Student Handbook Answer Appendix.

(pp. 356–417)

GEOMETRY For Exercises 1–3, use the following information.

If the side length of a cube is s, then the volume is presented by s^3 and the surface area is represented by $6s^2$. (Lesson 7-1)

1. Are the expressions for volume and surface area monomials? Explain.

2. If the side of a cube measures 3 feet, find the volume and surface area.

3. Find a side length s such that the volume and surface area have the same measure.

4. The volume of a cylinder can be found by multiplying the radius squared times the height times π, or $V = \pi r^2 h$. Suppose you have two cylinders. Each measure of the second is twice the measure of the first, so $V = \pi (2r)^2 (2h)$. What is the ratio of the volume of the first cylinder to the second cylinder? (Lesson 7-2) **1:8**

POPULATION For Exercises 5–7, use the following information.

The table shows the population density for Nevada for various years. (Lesson 7-3)

Year	Years Since 1930	People/Square Mile
1930	0	0.8
1960	30	2.6
1980	50	7.3
1990	60	10.9
2000	70	18.2

Source: The World Almanac

5. The population density d of Nevada from 1930 to 1990 can be modeled by $d = 0.005y^2 - 0.127y + 1$, where y represents the number of years since 1930. Identify the type of polynomial for $0.005y^2 - 0.127y + 1$. **trinomial**

6. What is the degree of this polynomial? **2**

7. Predict the population density of Nevada for 2010. Explain your method.

RADIO For Exercises 8 and 9, use the following information.

From 1997 to 2000, the number of radio stations presenting primarily news and talk N and the total number of radio stations of all types R in the U.S. could be modeled by the following equations, where x is the number of years since 1997. (Lesson 7-4) Source: The World Almanac

$N = 25.7x + 1098.0 \qquad R = 74.2x + 10,246.3$

8. Find an equation that models the number of radio stations O that are not primarily news and talk for this time period.

9. If this trend continues, how many radio stations that are not news and talk will there be in the year 2015? **about 10,021 stations**

GEOMETRY For Exercises 10–12, use the following information.

The number of diagonals of a polygon can be found by using the formula $d = 0.5n(n - 3)$, where d is the number of diagonals and n is the number of sides of the polygon. (Lesson 7-5)

10. Use the Distributive Property to write the expression as a polynomial. $0.5n^2 - 1.5n$

11. Find the number of diagonals for polygons with 3 through 10 sides.

12. Describe any patterns you see in the numbers you wrote in Exercise 11. **11. 0, 2, 5, 9, 14, 20, 27, 35**

GEOMETRY For Exercises 13 and 14, use the following information. $13.\ 2x^3 + 11x^2 + 15x$

A rectangular prism has dimensions of x, $x + 3$, and $2x + 5$. (Lesson 7-6)

13. Find the volume of the prism in terms of x.

14. Choose two values for x. How do the volumes compare? **See students' work.**

MONEY For Exercises 15–17, use the following information.

Money invested in a certificate of deposit or CD collects interest once per year. Suppose you invest $4000 in a 2-year CD. (Lesson 7-7)

15. If the interest rate is 5% per year, the expression $4000(1 + 0.05)^2$ can be evaluated to find the total amount of money you will have at the end of two years. Explain the numbers in this expression.

16. Find the amount of money at the end of two years. **$4410**

17. Suppose you invest $10,000 in a CD for 4 years at a rate of 6.25%. What is the total amount of money you will have at the end of 4 years? **about $12,744**

Chapter 8 Factoring

For answers not here, see Student Handbook Answer Appendix.

(pp. 418–467)

FLOORING For Exercises 1 and 2, use the following information.

Eric is refinishing his dining room floor. The floor measures 10 feet by 12 feet. Flooring World offers a wood-like flooring in 1-foot by 1-foot squares, 2-foot by 2-foot squares, 3-foot by 3-foot squares, and 2-foot by 3-foot rectangular pieces. (Lesson 8-1)

1. Without cutting the pieces, which of the four types of flooring can Eric use in the dining room? Explain.

2. The price per piece of each type is shown in the table. If Eric wants to spend the least money, which should he choose? What will be the total cost of his choice? **2 by 3; $420**

Size	1×1	2×2	3×3	2×3
Price	$3.75	$15.00	$32.00	$21.00

FIREWORKS For Exercises 3–5, use the following information.

At a Fourth of July celebration, a rocket is launched with an initial velocity of 125 feet per second. The height h of the rocket in feet above sea level is modeled by the formula $h = 125t - 16t^2$, where t is the time in seconds after the rocket is launched. (Lesson 8-2)

3. What is the height of the rocket when it returns to the ground? **0 ft**

4. Let $h = 0$ in the equation $h = 125t - 16t^2$ and solve for t. **[0, 7.8125]**

5. How many seconds will it take for the rocket to return to the ground? **about 7.8 s**

FOOTBALL For Exercises 6–8, use the following information. 7. 120 ft by 300 ft

Some small high schools play six-man football as a team sport. The dimensions of the field are less than the dimensions of a standard football field. Including the end zones, the length of the field, in feet, is 60 feet more than twice the width. (Lesson 8-3)

6. Write an expression for the area. $w(2w + 60)$

7. If the area of the field is 36,000 square feet, what are the dimensions of the field?

8. What are the dimensions of the field in yards? **40 yd by 100 yd**

PHYSICAL SCIENCE For Exercises 9 and 10, use the following information.

Teril throws a ball upward while standing on the top of a 500-foot tall apartment building. Its height h, in feet, after t seconds is given by the equation $h = -16t^2 + 48t + 506$. (Lesson 8-4)

9. What do the values 48 and 506 in the equation represent?

10. The ball falls on a balcony that is 218 feet above the ground. How many seconds was the ball in the air? **6 s**

DECKS For Exercises 11 and 12, use the following information.

Zelda is building a deck in her backyard. The plans for the deck show that it is to be 24 feet by 24 feet. Zelda wants to reduce one dimension by a number of feet and increase the other dimension by the same number of feet. (Lesson 8-5)

11. If the area of the reduced deck is 512 square feet, what are the dimensions of the deck? **16 ft by 32 ft**

12. Suppose Zelda wants to reduce the deck to one-half the area of the deck in the plans. Can she reduce each dimension by the same length and use dimensions that are whole numbers? Explain.

POOLS For Exercises 13–16, use the following information.

Susan wants to buy an above ground swimming pool for her yard. Model A is 42 inches deep and holds 1750 cubic feet of water. The length of the pool is 5 feet more than the width. (Lesson 8-6) **14. 20 ft by 25 ft**

13. What is the area of water that is exposed to the air? **500 ft²**

14. What are the dimensions of the pool?

15. A Model B pool holds twice as much water as Model A. What are some possible dimensions for this pool?

16. Model C has length and width that are both twice as long as Model A, but the height is the same. What is the ratio of the volume of Model A to Model C? **1:4**

Chapter 9 Quadratic and Exponential Functions

For answers not here, see Student Handbook Answer Appendix. (pp. 468–523)

PHYSICAL SCIENCE For Exercises 1–4, use the following information.

A ball is released 6 feet above the ground and thrown vertically into the air. The equation $h = -16t^2 + 112t + 6$ gives the height of the ball if the initial velocity is 112 feet per second. (Lesson 9-1)

1. Write the equation of the axis of symmetry and find the coordinates of the vertex of the graph of the equation. **$x = 3.5$; (3.5, 202)**

2. What is the ball's maximum height? **202 ft**

3. How many seconds after release does the ball reach its maximum height? **3.5 s**

4. How many seconds is the ball in the air? **about 7 s**

RIDES For Exercises 5–7, use this information.

A popular amusement park ride whisks riders to the top of a 250-foot tower and drops them at speeds exceeding 50 miles per hour. A function for the path of a rider is $h = -16t^2 + 250$, where h is the height and t is the time in seconds. (Lesson 9-2) **5. 40 = $-16t^2 + 250$**

5. The ride stops the descent of the rider 40 feet above the ground. Write an equation that models the drop of the rider.

6. Solve the equation by graphing the related function. How many roots are there?

7. About how many seconds does it take to complete the ride? **about 3.6 s**

PROJECTS For Exercises 8–10, use the following information.

Jude is making a poster for his science project. The poster board is 22 inches wide by 27 inches tall. He wants to cover two thirds of the area with text or pictures and leave a top margin 3 times as wide as the side margins and a bottom margin twice as wide as the side margins. (Lesson 9-3) **8. (22 − 2x)(27 − 5x) = 396 9. 15.1, 1.3**

8. Write an equation for this situation.

9. Solve your equation for x by completing the square. Round to the nearest tenth.

10. What should be the widths of the margins? **about 1.3 in. on the sides, 3.9 in. on the top, and 2.6 in. on the bottom**

TELEVISION For Exercises 11 and 12, use the following information.

The number of U.S. households with cable television has been on the rise. The percent of households with cable y can be approximated by the quadratic function $y = -0.11x^2 + 4.95x + 12.69$, where x stands for the number of years after 1977. (Lesson 9-4)

11. Use the Quadratic Formula to solve for x when $y = 30$. What do these values represent?

12. Is a quadratic function a good model for these data? Why or why not?

POPULATION For Exercises 13–15, use the following information.

The population of Asia from 1650 to 2000 can be estimated by the function $P(x) = 335(1.007)^x$, where x is the number of years since 1650 and the population is in millions of people. (Lesson 9-5) **14. 335,000,000 people in 1650**

13. Graph the function and name the y-intercept. **y-intercept: 335**

14. What does the y-intercept represent?

15. Use the function to approximate the number of people in Asia in 2050.

POPULATION For Exercises 16 and 17, use the following information.

The percent of the U.S. population P that is at least 65 years old can be approximated by $P = 3.86(1.013)^t$, where t represents the number of years since 1900. (Lesson 9-6)

16. To the nearest percent, how much of the population will be 65 years of age or older in the year 2010? **about 16%**

17. Predict the year in which people aged 65 years or older will represent 20% of the population if this trend continues. (Hint: Make a table.) **2028**

27 in.
22 in.
3x in.
x in.
2x in.
x in.

Chapter 10 Radical Expressions and Triangles

(pp. 526–573)

SATELLITES For Exercises 1–3, use the following information.

A satellite is launched into orbit 200 kilometers above Earth. The orbital velocity of a satellite is given by the formula

$$v = \sqrt{\frac{Gm_E}{r}},$$ where v is velocity in meters per second, G is a given constant, m_E is the mass of Earth, and r is the radius of the satellite's orbit. (Lesson 10-1)

1. The radius of Earth is 6,380,000 meters. What is the radius of the satellite's orbit in meters? **6,580,000 m**

2. The mass of Earth is 5.97×10^{24} kilogram and the constant G is 6.67×10^{-11} N·m²/kg² where N is in Newtons. Use the formula to find the orbital velocity of the satellite in meters per second. **7779 m/s**

3. The orbital period of the satellite can be found by using the formula $T = \frac{2\pi r}{v}$, where r is the radius of the orbit and v is the orbital velocity of the satellite in meters per second. Find the orbital period of the satellite in hours. **about 1.5 h**

RIDES For Exercises 4–6, use the following information.

The designer of a roller coaster must consider the height of the hill and the velocity of the coaster as it travels over the hill. Certain hills give riders a feeling of weightlessness. The formula $d = \sqrt{\frac{2hv^2}{g}}$ allows designers to find the correct distance from the center of the hill that the coaster should begin its drop for maximum fun. (Lesson 10-2)

4. In the formula above, d is the distance from the center of the hill, v is the height of the hill, v is the velocity of the coaster at the top of the hill in meters per second, and g is a gravity constant of 9.8 meters per second squared. If a hill is 10 meters high and the velocity of the coaster is 10 m/s, find d. **14.29 m**

5. Find d if the height of the hill is 10 meters but the velocity is 20 m/s. How does d compare to the value in Exercise 4? **28.57 m; twice as great**

6. Suppose you find the same formula in another book written as $d = 1.4\sqrt{\frac{hv^2}{g}}$. Will this produce the same value of d? Explain. **Yes; because $\sqrt{2} \approx 1.4$.**

7. **PACKAGING** A cylindrical container of chocolate drink mix has a volume of about 162 in³. The formula for volume of a cylinder is $V = \pi r^2 h$, where r is the radius and h is the height. The radius of the container can be found by using the formula $r = \sqrt{\frac{V}{\pi h}}$. If the height is 8.25 inches, find the radius of the container. (Lesson 10-3) **about 2.5 in.**

TOWN SQUARES For Exercises 8 and 9, use the following information.

Tiananmen Square in Beijing, China, is the largest town square in the world, covering 98 acres. **Source:** *The Guinness Book of World Records* (Lesson 10-4)

8. One square mile is 640 acres. Assuming that Tiananmen Square is a square, how many feet long is a side to the nearest foot? **2066 ft**

9. To the nearest foot, what is the diagonal distance across Tiananmen Square? **2922 ft**

PIZZA DELIVERY For Exercises 10 and 11, use the following information.

The Pizza Place delivers pizza to any location within a radius of 5 miles from the store for free. Tyrone drives 32 blocks north and then 45 blocks east to deliver a pizza. In this city, there are about 6 blocks per half mile. (Lesson 10-5) **10–11. See Student Hdbk Answer App.**

10. Should there be a charge for the delivery? Explain.

11. Describe two delivery situations that would result in about 5 miles.

12. **BRIDGES** Truss bridges use triangles in their support beams. Mark plans to make a model of a truss bridge in the scale 1 inch = 12 feet. If the height of the triangles on the actual bridge is 40 feet, what will the height be on the model? (Lesson 10-6) **$3\frac{1}{3}$ in.**

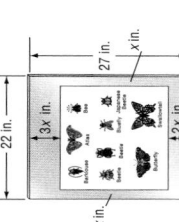

Mixed Problem Solving

Chapter 11 Rational Expressions and Equations

For answers not here, see Student Handbook Answer Appendix. (pp. 574–639)

OPTOMETRY For Exercises 1–3, use the following information.

When a person does not have clear vision, an optometrist can prescribe lenses to correct the condition. The power P of a lens, in a unit called diopters, is equal to 1 divided by the focal length f, in meters, of the lens. The formula is $P = \frac{1}{f}$. (Lesson 11-1)

1. Graph the inverse variation $P = \frac{1}{f}$.

2. Find the powers of lenses with focal lengths $+20$ and -40 centimeters. (*Hint:* Change centimeters to meters.)

3. What do you notice about the powers in Exercise 2?

2. 5 diopters; −2.5 diopters

PHYSICS For Exercises 4 and 5, use the following information.

Some principles in physics, such as gravitational force between two objects, depend upon a relationship known as the inverse square law. This law states that two variables are related by the relationship $y = \frac{1}{x^2}$, where x is distance. (Lesson 11-2)

4. Make a table of values and graph $y = \frac{1}{x^2}$. Describe the shape of the graph.

5. If x represents distance, how does this affect the domain of the graph?

FERRIS WHEELS For Exercises 6–8, use the following information.

George Ferris built the first Ferris wheel for the World's Columbian Exposition in 1892. It had a diameter of 250 feet. (Lesson 11-3)

6. To find the speed traveled by a car located on the circumference of the wheel, you can find the circumference of a circle and divide by the time it takes for one rotation of the wheel. (Recall that $C = \pi d$.) Write a rational expression for the speed of a car rotating in time t, $\frac{\pi d}{t}$.

7. Suppose the first Ferris wheel rotated once every 5 minutes. What was the speed of a car on the circumference in feet per minute? **7. 157 ft/min**

8. Use dimensional analysis to find the speed of a car in miles per hour. **1.8 mi/h**

For answers not here, see Student Handbook Answer Appendix. (pp. 574–639)

MOTOR VEHICLES In 1999, the U.S. produced 13,063,000 motor vehicles. This was 23.2% of the total motor vehicle production for the whole world. How many motor vehicles were produced worldwide in 1999? (Lesson 11-4) **56,306,034 vehicles**

LIGHT The speed of light is approximately 1.86×10^5 miles per second. The table shows the distances, in miles, of the planets from the Sun. Find the amount of time in minutes that it takes for light from the Sun to reach each planet. (Lesson 11-5)

Planet	Miles	Planet	Miles
Mercury	5.79×10^{10}	Jupiter	7.78×10^{11}
Venus	1.08×10^{11}	Saturn	1.43×10^{12}
Earth	1.496×10^{11}	Uranus	2.87×10^{12}
Mars	2.28×10^{11}	Pluto	4.50×10^{12}

11. **GEOGRAPHY** The land areas of all the continents, in thousands of square miles, are shown. What fraction of the land area of the world do North and South America occupy? (Lesson 11-6)

Continent	Area
North America	9400
South America	6900
Europe	3800
Asia	17,400
Africa	11,700
Oceania	3300
Antarctica	5400

Source: *The World Almanac*

12. **GARDENING** Celeste builds decorative gardens in her landscaping business. She uses either 35, 50, or 75 bricks per garden. What is the least number of bricks she should order that would allow her to build a whole number of each type of garden? (Lesson 11-7) **1050**

CRAFTS For Exercises 13 and 14, use the following information.

Ann makes tablecloths to sell at craft fairs. A small one takes one-half yard of fabric, a medium takes five-eighths yard, and a large takes one and one-quarter yard. (Lesson 11-8)

13. How many yards of fabric does she need to make one of each type of tablecloth?

14. One bolt contains 30 yards of fabric. Can she use the entire bolt by making an equal number of each type? Explain.

11. $\frac{163}{579}$

13. $2\frac{3}{8}$ yd

Chapter 12 Statistics and Probability

For answers not here, see Student Handbook Answer Appendix. (pp. 640–691)

CAREERS For Exercises 1 and 2, use the following information.

The graph below shows the results of a survey of students who were asked their preferences for a future career. (Lesson 12-1)

Looking into the Future
Top career choices of students age 14–18

Male
- Engineering 11%
- Business 7%
- Computer software Development 6%
- Computer hardware Development 6%

Female
- Teaching 12%
- Medical doctor 10%
- Law 7%
- Nursing 7%

Source: *USA TODAY*

1. Write a statement to describe what you do know about the sample.

2. What additional information would you like to have about the sample to determine whether the sample is biased?

FLOWERS For Exercises 3–5, use this information.

A flower shop is making special floral arrangements for a holiday. The tables show the options available. (Lesson 12-2)

Vase	Deluxe	Standard	Economy
Cost	$12.00	$8.00	$5.00

Ribbon	Velvet	Satin
Cost	$3.00	$2.00

Flowers	Orchids	Roses	Daisies
Cost	$35.00	$20.00	$12.00

Card	Large	Small
Cost	$2.50	$1.75

3. How many floral arrangements are possible? Each arrangement has one vase, one ribbon, one type of flowers, and one card. **36**

4. What is the cost of the most expensive arrangement? the least expensive?

5. What is the cost of each of the four most expensive arrangements? $52.50; $51.75; $51.50; $50.75

GAMES For Exercises 6–8, use this information.

Melissa is playing a board game in which you make words to score points. There are 12 letters left in the box, and she must choose 4. She cannot see the letters. (Lesson 12-3)

6. Suppose the 12 letters are all different. In how many ways can she choose 4 of the 12?

7. She chooses A, T, R, and E. How many different arrangements of three letters can she make from her letters?

8. How many of the three-letter arrangements are words? List them.

7. 24

495

DRIVING For Exercises 9 and 10, use the following information.

The table shows a probability distribution for various age categories of licensed drivers in the U.S. in 1998. (Lesson 12-5)

X = Age Category	Probability
under 20	0.053
20–34	0.284
35–49	0.323
50–64	0.198
65 and over	0.142

Source: *The World Almanac*

9. Is this a valid probability distribution? Justify your answer.

10. If a driver in the U.S. is randomly selected, what is the probability that the person is under 20 years old? 50 years old or over? 0.053; 0.34

LOTTERIES For Exercises 11–13, use the following information.

In a certain state, lottery numbers are five-digit numbers. Each digit can be 1, 2, 3, 4, 5, or 6. Once a week, a random 5-digit number is chosen as the winning number. (Lesson 12-6)

11. How many five-digit numbers are possible? Explain how you calculated the number of possible outcomes.

12. Perform a simulation for winning the lottery. Describe the objects you used.

13. According to your experiment, if you buy one ticket, what is the experimental probability of winning the lottery?

See students' work. The theoretical probability is about 0.00013.

Page 713, Prerequisite Skills 11

4.

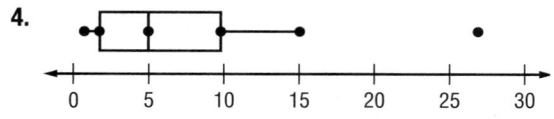

5.

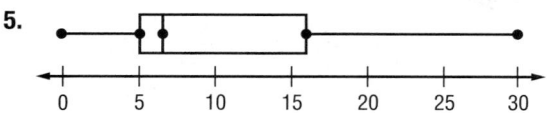

6.

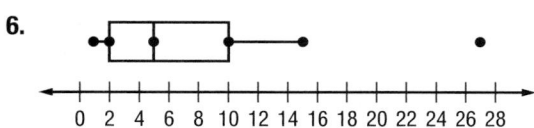

Page 715, Prerequisite Skills 12

1.

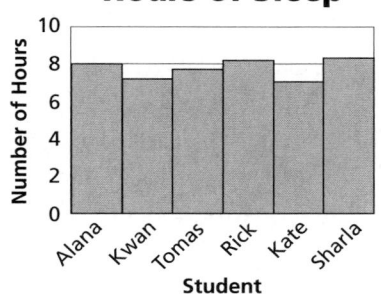

Hours of Sleep

2.

Lawn Care Profits

3.

Stem	Leaf
5	8 9
6	0 3 5 6 9
7	0 1 1 2 3

$\frac{5}{8} = 5.8$

4.

Stem	Leaf
1	8 8
2	2 3 6 6 6 8 9
3	0 1 1 2 3 4
4	7

$\frac{1}{8} = 18$

5.

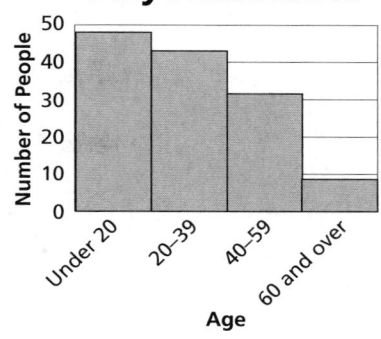

Play Attendance

Page 718, Extra Practice, Lesson 1-4

9. $\frac{2}{3}[15 \div (10)]$, Substitution; $\frac{2}{3}\left(\frac{3}{2}\right)$, Substitution; 1, Multiplicative Inverse

10. $\frac{7}{4}[4 \cdot 1]$, Multiplicative Inverse; $\frac{7}{4}(4)$, Multiplicative Identity; 7, Substitution

11. $[(6) \cdot 0] \cdot 10$, Substitution; $(0) \cdot 10$, Multiplicative Prop. of 0; 0, Multiplicative Prop. of 0

Page 718, Extra Practice, Lesson 1-5

1. $5(2) + 5(9)$; 55

2. $8(10) + 8(20)$; 240

3. $6(y) + 6(4)$; $6y + 24$

4. $9(3n) + 9(5)$; $27n + 45$

5. $32(x) - 32\left(\frac{1}{8}\right)$; $32x - 4$

6. $c(7) - c(d)$; $7c - cd$

7. $6(50 + 5)$; 330

8. $15(100 + 8)$; 1620

9. $(1600 + 89)(5)$; 8445

10. $7(300 + 14)$; 2198

11. $36\left(5 + \frac{1}{4}\right)$; 189

12. $\left(4 + \frac{1}{18}\right)(18)$; 73

Page 719, Extra Practice, Lesson 1-7

1. hypothesis: an animal is a dog; conclusion: it barks

2. hypothesis: a figure is a pentagon; conclusion: it has five sides

3. hypothesis: $3x - 1 = 8$; conclusion: $x = 3$

4. hypothesis: 0.5 is the reciprocal of 2; conclusion: $0.5 \cdot 2 = 1$

5. hypothesis: a figure is a square; conclusion: it has four congruent sides; If a figure is a square, then it has four congruent sides.

6. hypothesis: $a = 4$; conclusion: $6a + 10 = 34$; If $a = 4$, then $6a + 10 = 34$.

7. hypothesis: it is night; conclusion: the video store is open; If it is night, then the video store is open.

8. hypothesis: it is Thursday; conclusion: the band does not have practice; If it is Thursday, then the band does not have practice.

9. It can snow in May in some locations.

10. You may live in Portland, Maine.

11. If $y = 3$, then $2y + 4 = 10$, is true, but $y < 3$ is false.

12. Sample answer: $a = -1$

Page 719, Extra Practice, Lesson 1-9

1. Sample answer: The temperatures increase from January through the summer and then begin to decrease again.

2. Sample answer: The roller coaster goes down a small hill, coasts at about the same speed, increases in speed on the way down the hill, decreases again on the way up the hill, increases down another hill, and then slows down for the end of the ride.

Page 720, Extra Practice, Lesson 2-1

7. Sample answer: The sum of five-tenths times x and three is equal to negative ten.

8. Sample answer: The quotient of n and negative six is the same as the sum of two times n and one.

9. Sample answer: Eighteen decreased by five times h is the same as thirteen times h.

10. Sample answer: The square of n is equal to sixteen.

11. Sample answer: The sum of 3 and twice x squared is equal to twenty-one.

12. Sample answer: The sum of 4 and the quotient of m and n is equal to twelve.

Page 723, Extra Practice, Lesson 3-1

1. $D = \{-9, 0, 5\}$; $R = \{-1, 0, 2\}$

x	y
5	2
0	0
-9	-1

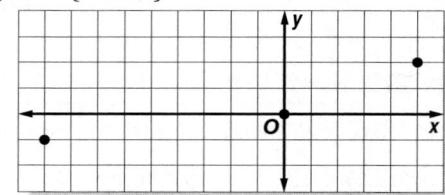

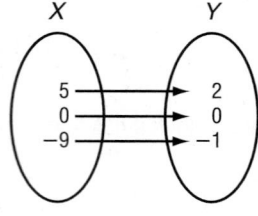

2. $D = \{-4, -2, 0, 2\}$; $R = \{0, 2, 4\}$

x	y
-4	2
-2	0
0	2
2	4

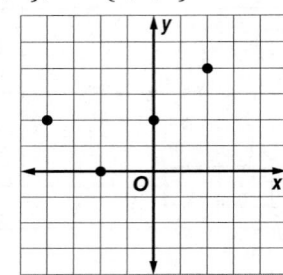

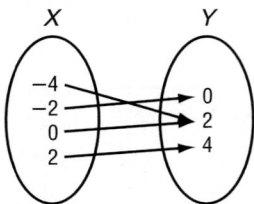

3. $\{(1, 3), (2, 4), (3, 5), (4, 6), (5, 7)\}$; $\{(3, 1), (4, 2), (5, 3), (6, 4), (7, 5)\}$

4. $\{(-4, 1), (-2, 3), (0, 1), (4, 6), (2, 3), (4, 1)\}$; $\{(1, -4), (3, -2), (1, 0), (3, 2), (1, 4)\}$

5. $\{(-1, 5), (-2, 5), (-2, 4), (-2, 1), (-6, 1)\}$; $\{(5, -1), (5, -2), (4, -2), (4, -2), (1, -2), (1, -6)\}$

6. $\{(3, 7), (5, 2), (9, 1), (-3, 2)\}$; $\{(7, 3), (2, 5), (1, 9), (2, -3)\}$

7. $\{(-4, -3), (-2, 2), (-2, -1), (0, 0), (1, 1), (2, 3), (2, -1)\}$; $\{(-3, -4), (2, -2), (-1, -2), (0, 0), (1, 1), (3, 2), (-1, 2)\}$

8. $\{(-3, 1), (-3, -3), (-2, 2), (-2, 0), (-1, 3), (-1, -1), (0, -2), (1, -1), (1, 3), (2, 0), (2, 2), (3, 1), (3, -3)\}$; $\{(1, -3), (-3, -3), (2, -2), (0, -2), (3, -1), (-1, -1), (-2, 0), (-1, 1), (3, 1), (0, 2), (2, 2), (1, 3), (-3, 3)\}$

Page 723, Extra Practice, Lesson 3-3

1. yes; $3x - 2y = 0$

2. no

3. yes; $4x - 2y = 8$

4. yes; $3x - 7y = -7$

5. yes; $7x - 7y = 2$

6. no

7.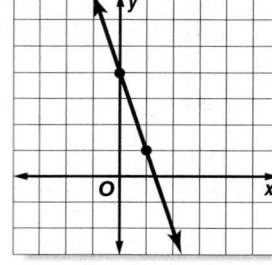

8.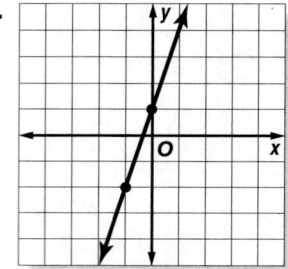

9.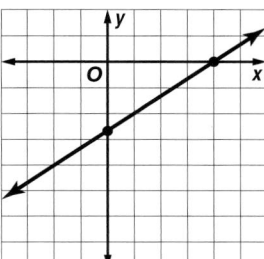

10.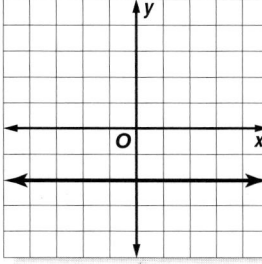

11.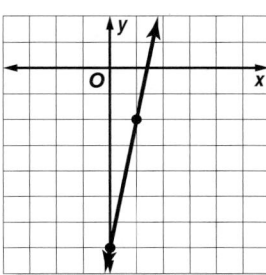

12.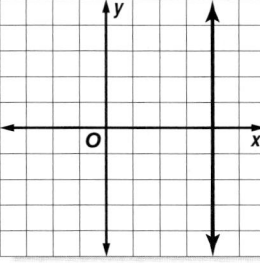

13.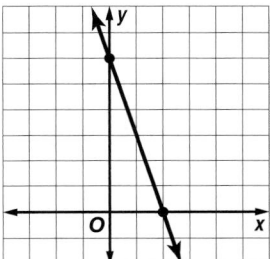

14.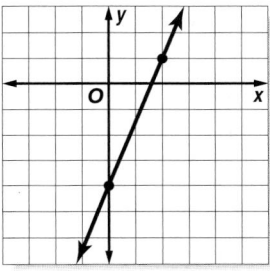

15.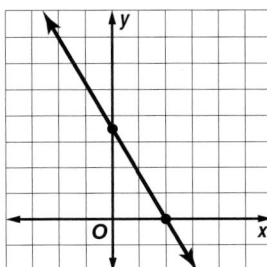

16.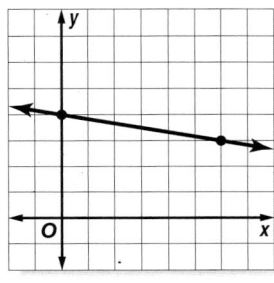

17.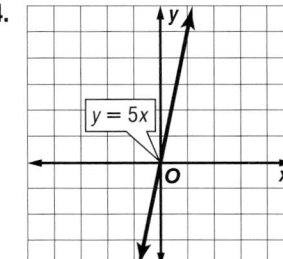

18.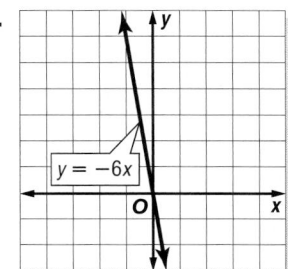

Page 724, Extra Practice, Lesson 3-4

17. $a_n = -7 + 4n$

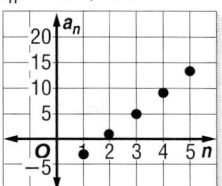

18. $a_n = 10 + 15n$

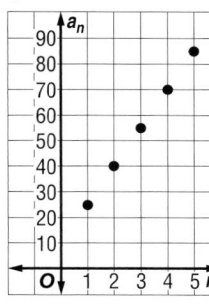

19. $a_n = -15 + 6n$

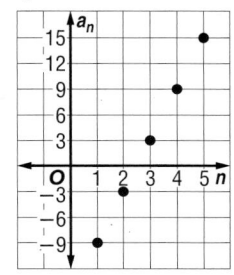

20. $a_n = -5 + 1.5n$

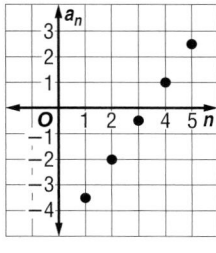

Page 724, Extra Practice, Lesson 3-5

1. $56, 67, 78$

2. $15, 9, 3$

3. $10.8, 12.0, 13.2$

4. $36, 43, 51$

5. $w - 10, w - 12, w - 14$

6. $7, 4, 5$

7. $f(x) = -x$

8. $f(x) = -3$

9. $f(x) = -\frac{1}{2}x - 1$

10. $f(x) = \frac{2}{3}x + 2$

Page 725, Extra Practice, Lesson 4-2

4.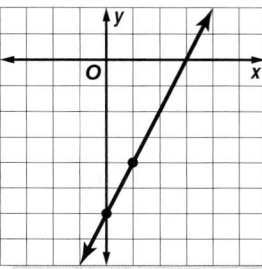

$y = 5x$

5.

$y = -6x$

6.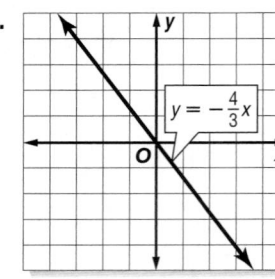

$y = -\frac{4}{3}x$

7. $y = 5x$

8. $y = 7x$

Page 725, Extra Practice, Lesson 4-3

1. $y = 5x - 15$

2. $y = -6x + 3$

3. $y = 0.3x - 2.6$

4. $y = -\frac{4}{3}x + \frac{5}{3}$

5. $y = -\frac{2}{5}x + 2$

6. $y = \frac{7}{4}x - 2$

10.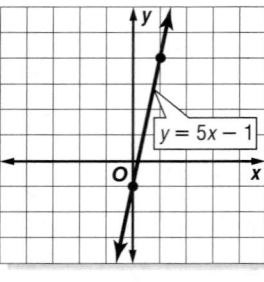

$y = 5x - 1$

11.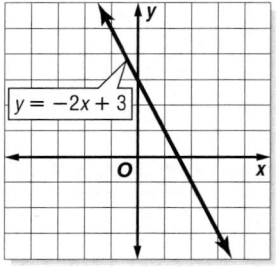

$y = -2x + 3$

12.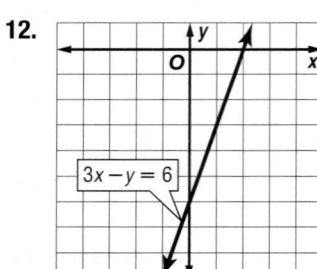

$3x - y = 6$

Page 726, Extra Practice, Lesson 4-5

5. $2x - y = 11$

6. $x + 2y = -12$

7. $2x + 3y = 22$

8. $4x - 3y = 30$

9. $3x - 2y = -11$

10. $19x + 5y = 8$

11. $y = -2x - 9$

12. $y = 4x - 7$

13. $y = -4x + 14$

14. $y = \frac{4}{5}x + 3$

15. $y = -\frac{3}{4}x + \frac{7}{2}$

16. $y = \frac{2}{3}x + \frac{1}{12}$

Page 726, Extra Practice, Lesson 4-6

1. Negative; the value of a car decreases as it ages.

2. no correlation

Page 726, Extra Practice, Lesson 4-7

1. $y = 4x + 2$; $y = -\frac{1}{4}x + \frac{25}{4}$

2. $y = 2x - 2$; $y = -\frac{1}{2}x + 8$

3. $y = \frac{2}{3}x + 2$; $y = -\frac{3}{2}x - \frac{9}{2}$

4. $y = -3x + 13$; $y = \frac{1}{3}x - \frac{11}{3}$

5. $y = -\frac{3}{8}x + 4$; $y = \frac{8}{3}x + 4$

6. $y = \frac{1}{5}x + \frac{13}{5}$; $y = -5x + 13$

Page 727, Extra Practice, Lesson 5-1

1.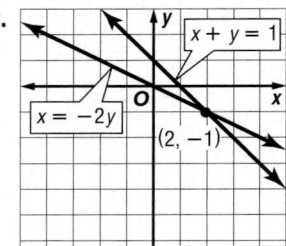

$4x + 2y = 30$; $(3, 9)$; $y = 3x$

2.

$x + y = 1$; $x = -2y$; $(2, -1)$

3.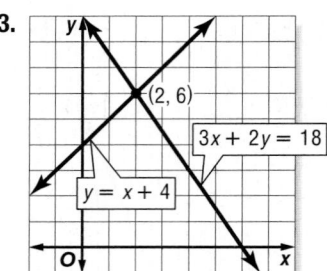

$(2, 6)$; $3x + 2y = 18$; $y = x + 4$

4.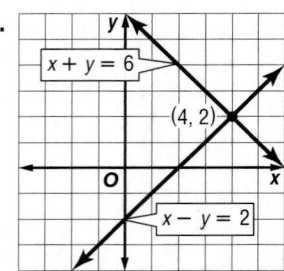

$x + y = 6$; $(4, 2)$; $x - y = 2$

5.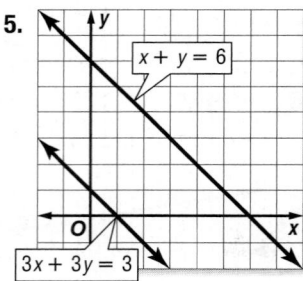

$x + y = 6$; $3x + 3y = 3$

6.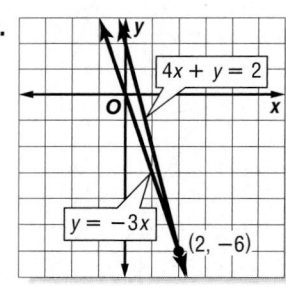

$4x + y = 2$; $y = -3x$; $(2, -6)$

7.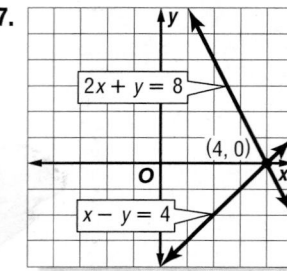

$2x + y = 8$; $(4, 0)$; $x - y = 4$

8.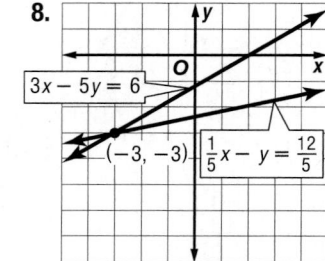

$3x - 5y = 6$; $(-3, -3)$; $\frac{1}{5}x - y = \frac{12}{5}$

9.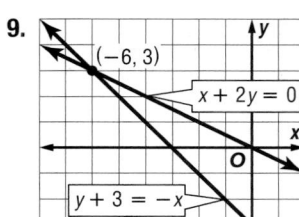

10.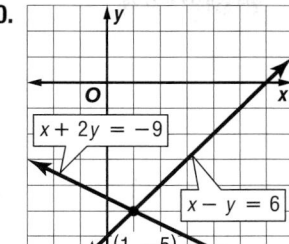

11.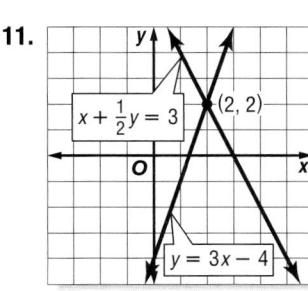

12.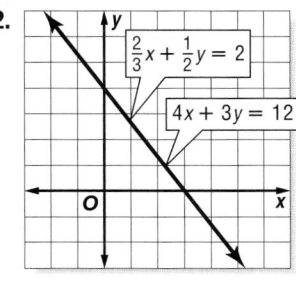

Page 728, Extra Practice, Lesson 5-5

1. graphing; (0, 1)

2. substitution; (4, 12)

3. substitution; (0, −3)

4. substitution; (0.25, 1.5)

5. graphing; (−1, 8)

6. elimination (+); (4.75, −14)

7. elimination (−); (1, 1)

8. elimination (x); (3, 1)

9. elimination (+); $\left(\frac{31}{5}, -\frac{2}{5}\right)$

10. elimination (x); $\left(\frac{2}{7}, -\frac{2}{7}\right)$

11. elimination (x); (5, 2)

12. elimination (x); $\left(\frac{79}{29}, \frac{9}{29}\right)$

13. substitution; $\left(-\frac{1}{9}, \frac{5}{9}\right)$

14. elimination (x); $\left(\frac{5}{6}, \frac{26}{27}\right)$

15. elimination (+); $\left(\frac{1}{3}, -\frac{29}{24}\right)$

Page 728, Extra Practice, Lesson 6-1

1. $\{c \mid c \le -6\}$

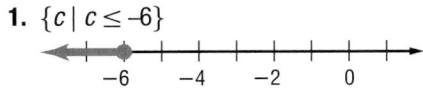

2. $\{d \mid d < 10\}$

3. $\{z \mid z > 24\}$

4. $\{h \mid h > -9\}$

5. $\{d \mid d < -7\}$

6. $\{x \mid x > -3\}$

7. $\{x \mid x \ge 3\}$

8. $\{w \mid w < -36\}$

9. $\{p \mid p > 5\}$

10. $\{z \mid z < 23\}$

11. $\{v \mid v < 2\}$

12. $\left\{t \mid t \le \frac{11}{12}\right\}$

13. $\{x \mid x < -2\}$

14. $\{n \mid n \ge -2\}$

15. $\{a \mid a \ge -5.5\}$

16. $\{z \mid z > 6\}$

17. Sample answer if $n =$ the number: $n + (-6) > 9$; $\{n \mid n > 15\}$

18. Sample answer if $n =$ the number: $-5n < -6n + 12$; $\{n \mid n < 12\}$

Page 729, Extra Practice, Lesson 6-2

1. $\{b \mid b \ge -7\}$

2. $\{j \mid j > 12\}$

3. $\{w \mid w > -36\}$

4. $\{p \mid p < 40\}$

5. $\{f \mid f > -6\}$

6. $\{t \mid t \le 40\}$

7. $\{g \mid g > -32\}$

8. $\{x \mid x > 0.6\}$

9. $\{c \mid c \ge -1.5\}$

10. $\{n \mid n \ge 7.5\}$

11. $\{m \mid m \ge -33\}\{a \mid a > 500\}$

12. $\{a \mid a > 500\}$

13. $\left\{a \mid a > \frac{28}{15}\right\}$

14. $\{x \mid x > -54\}$

15. $\left\{y \mid y \le \frac{256}{3}\right\}$

16. $\{y \mid y \le -13\}$

Page 729, Extra Practice, Lesson 6-4

1. $\{x \mid x < -7 \text{ or } x > 3\}$

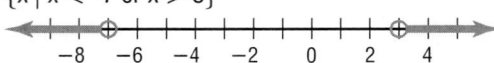

2. $\{t \mid t \text{ is a real number.}\}$

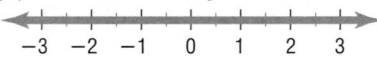

3. $\{g \mid -2 \le g \le 4\}$

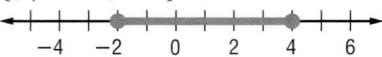

4. $\{v \mid v \ge 1\}$

5. $\{b \mid -4 \le b \le 4\}$

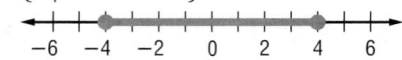

6. $\{z \mid -8 < z < 1.5\}$

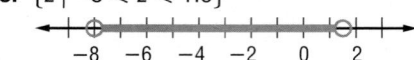

7. $\{m \mid m < -4 \text{ or } m \ge 3\}$

8. $\{c \mid c \text{ is a real number.}\}$

9. $\{h \mid h \ge 1\}$

10. $\left\{p \mid -\dfrac{1}{2} \le p \le \dfrac{1}{2}\right\}$

11. $\varnothing$

12. $\{j \mid j > 12\}$

13. $\{q \mid -14 \le q \le 6\}$

14. $\varnothing$

15. $\{n \mid n < -7 \text{ or } n > 8\}$

16. $\{x \mid x \ge 14\}$

Page 730, Extra Practice, Lesson 6-5

1. $\{1, 9\}$

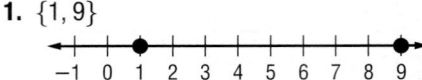

2. $\{-10, 4\}$

3. $\{-2, 10\}$

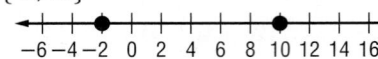

4. $\{2, 18\}$

5. $\{-8, 4\}$

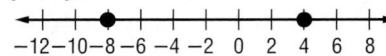

6. $\{-2, 8\}$

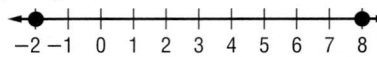

7. $\left\{-\dfrac{2}{3}, 4\dfrac{2}{3}\right\}$

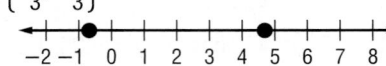

8. $\left\{-10\dfrac{1}{2}, 3\dfrac{1}{2}\right\}$

9. $\left\{-4\dfrac{1}{2}, 1\dfrac{1}{2}\right\}$

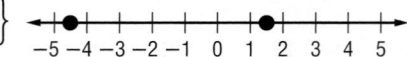

Page 730, Extra Practice, Lesson 6-6

1. $\{y \mid -10 < y < 28\}$

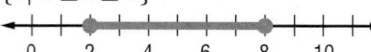

2. $\{g \mid g < -14 \text{ or } g > 2\}$

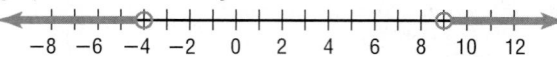

3. $\{t \mid 2 \le t \le 8\}$

4. $\{a \mid a \text{ is a real number.}\}$

5. $\{m \mid m < -4 \text{ or } m > 9\}$

6. $\{w \mid w \le -6 \text{ or } m \ge 34\}$

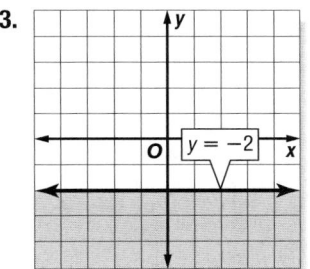

(number line showing -8 to 32)

7. $\left\{p \mid -\dfrac{28}{3} \le p \le 6\right\}$

(number line showing -10 to 6)

8. $\{b \mid -4 \le b \le 8\}$

(number line showing -6 to 8)

9. $\left\{x \mid 6\dfrac{2}{3} < x < 10\right\}$

(number line showing 0 to 12)

10. $\{s \mid s < -8.4 \text{ or } s > 10\}$

(number line showing -8 to 10)

11. $\{x \mid x \le -13 \text{ or } x \ge 7\}$

(number line showing -16 to 8)

12. $\{b \mid 0.5 \le b \le 6.5\}$

(number line showing 0 to 6)

Page 730, Extra Practice, Lesson 6-7

3.
$y = -2$

4.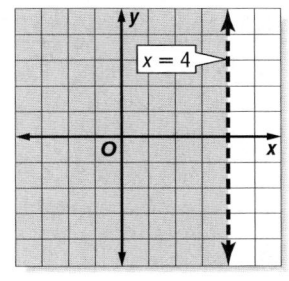
$x = 4$

5.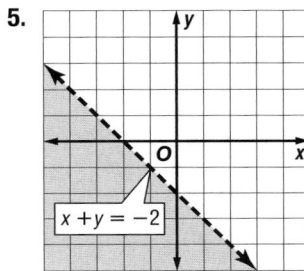
$x + y = -2$

6.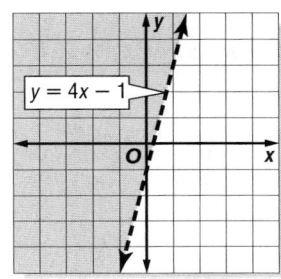
$y = 4x - 1$

7.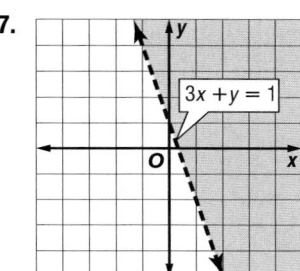
$3x + y = 1$

8.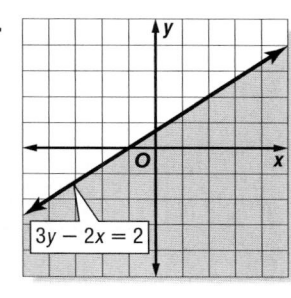
$3y - 2x = 2$

Page 730, Extra Practice, Lesson 6-8

1.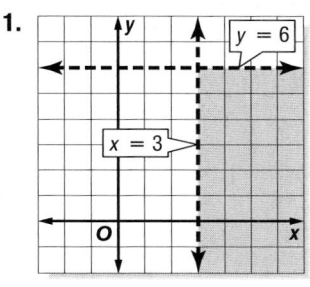
$y = 6$
$x = 3$

2.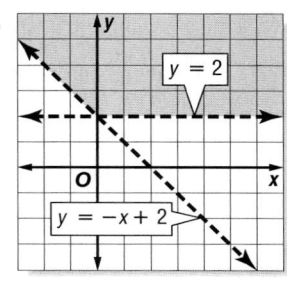
$y = 2$
$y = -x + 2$

3.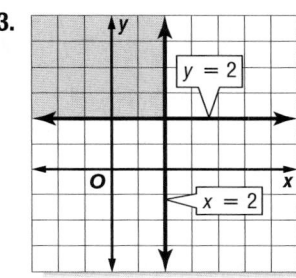
$y = 2$
$x = 2$

4.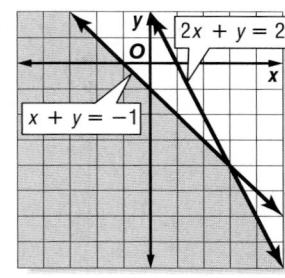
$2x + y = 2$
$x + y = -1$

5.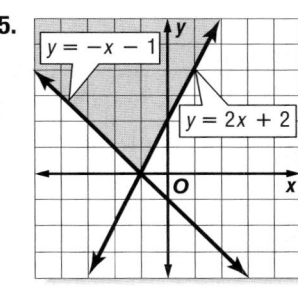
$y = -x - 1$
$y = 2x + 2$

6.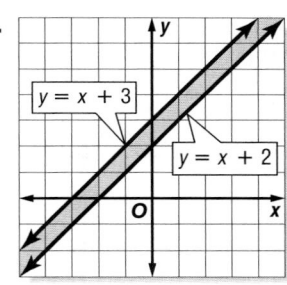
$y = x + 3$
$y = x + 2$

7.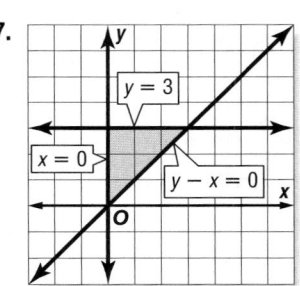
$y = 3$
$x = 0$
$y - x = 0$

8.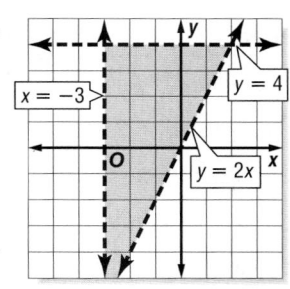
$x = -3$
$y = 4$
$y = 2x$

9.

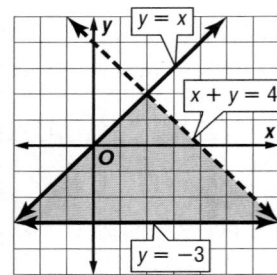

Page 730, Extra Practice, Lesson 7-1

1. It shows subtraction, not multiplication of variables.

2. It is a real number and therefore a monomial.

3. It is a product of a number and two variables.

4. It shows subtraction, not multiplication of variables.

Page 731, Extra Practice, Lesson 7-3

13. $-3x + 2x^2 + 4x^3 - x^5$　　**14.** $-1 + x - x^2 + x^3$

15. $2a - 4ax + 3ax^2$　　**16.** $-b^3 - 2bx + 4x^2 - 5bx^3$

17. $1 + 2x^2 - x^6 + x^8$　　**18.** $d^3 - c^2d^2x + cdx^2$

19. $-3x^3 + 5x^2 + 2x + 7$　　**20.** $x^5 + 4x^3 - 6x - 20$

21. $b^3x^2 + \frac{2}{3}bx + 5b$　　**22.** $3px^3 + 21p^2x + p^4$

23. $-6a^2x^3 + 3ax^2 - 8x + 7a^3$　　**24.** $4x^4 + \frac{1}{3}s^2x^3 - \frac{2}{5}s^4x^2$

Page 731, Extra Practice, Lesson 7-4

5. $-12t^2 - 8ts - 3s^2$　　**6.** $4a^2 - 12ab - 10b^2$

7. $-a^2 - 10b^2 + 9c^2 + 2b$　　**8.** $-3z^2 + 13z - 3$

9. $7d - 7e - 3f - 6$　　**10.** $6g + 5h - 9 - 6k$

11. $8x^2 + 5xy - 15y^2$　　**12.** $11m + 4mn - 7n$

Page 732, Extra Practice, Lesson 7-5

7. $-3ab^3 - 4a^2b^2 + 6a^3b$　　**8.** $36m^4n + 4m^3n - 20m^2n^2$

9. $-16s^3t^5 + 28s^6t^2 - 12s^2t^5$　　**10.** $-6a^2 + 41a$

11. $72b^2 - 33b - 14$　　**12.** $2x^2 - 6x$

13. $2n^2 + 55n - 33$　　**14.** $-2x^2 - 3x + 9$

15. $4mn - 4m - 5n^2 - 5n$

Page 732, Extra Practice, Lesson 7-6

1. $d^2 + 7d + 10$　　**2.** $z^2 + 3z - 28$

3. $m^2 - 13m + 40$　　**4.** $a^2 - 17a - 38$

5. $c^2 + 12c - 45$　　**6.** $x^2 - xy - 2y^2$

7. $2x^2 + 7x - 30$　　**8.** $14a^2 - 43a + 20$

9. $8x^2 - 10xy - 3y^2$　　**10.** $7v^2 + 31v + 12$

11. $21s^2 - 38s + 16$　　**12.** $8g^2 - 14gh - 15h^2$

13. $8a^2 + 2a - 3$　　**14.** $14y^2 - 23y + 3$

15. $8x^2 + 16xy + 6y^2$　　**16.** $60r^2 + 76rs - 32s^2$

17. $3a^2 - a - 2$　　**18.** $-6n^2 + 8n + 8$

19. $x^3 - 8$　　**20.** $6x^3 - 5x^2 + 8x + 55$

21. $12s^3 + 47s^2 + 4s - 45$

22. $-25x^3 + 20x^2 + 31x - 14$　　**23.** $2n^3 - 5n^2 + 3n - 2$

24. $2x^4 - 17x^3 + 23x^2 + 30x - 24$

25. $x^4 - x^2 - 2x - 1$　　**26.** $a^4 - a^3 - 8a^2 - 29a - 35$

27. $5x^6 - 25x^5 + 13x^4 + 10x^3 - 5x^2 - 5x + 3$

Page 732, Extra Practice, Lesson 7-7

16. $\frac{1}{4}x^2 - 100$　　**17.** $\frac{1}{9}n^2 - m^2$

18. $a^3 - 3a^2 + 3a - 1$　　**19.** $2x^3 + 5x^2 - 8x - 20$

20. $16x^3 - 64x^2 - x + 4$　　**21.** $x^4 - 41x^2 + 400$

Page 733, Extra Practice, Lesson 8-1

1. $2 \cdot 2 \cdot 2 \cdot 2 \cdot 3 \cdot 5 \cdot m \cdot n$

2. $-1 \cdot 2 \cdot 2 \cdot 2 \cdot 2 \cdot 2 \cdot 2 \cdot a \cdot a \cdot a \cdot b$

3. $-1 \cdot 2 \cdot 13 \cdot x \cdot y \cdot y$　　**4.** $-1 \cdot 3 \cdot 7 \cdot 11 \cdot x \cdot y \cdot y \cdot z$

5. $2 \cdot 2 \cdot 11 \cdot r \cdot s \cdot s \cdot t \cdot t \cdot t$

6. $-1 \cdot 2 \cdot 2 \cdot 3 \cdot 3 \cdot 3 \cdot 7 \cdot m \cdot m \cdot n \cdot n$

Page 733, Extra Practice, Lesson 8-2

1. $10a(a + 4)$　　**2.** $5wx(3 - 7x)$

3. $9b(3a^2 + b^2)$　　**4.** $11x(1 + 4xy)$

5. $8y(2y + 1)$　　**6.** $2mm(7n + 1)$

7. $5ab^2(5a + 6b)$　　**8.** $2mn(m^2n - 8n + 4)$

9. $(2x + b)(a + 3c)$　　**10.** $(2m + r)(3x - 2)$

11. $(3x - 4)(a - 3b)$　　**12.** $(a + 1)(a - 2b)$

13. $(2a + b)(4c - d)$　　**14.** $2(e^2 + f)(g + 2h)$

15. $(x - y)(x - y)$

Page 733, Extra Practice, Lesson 8-3

1. $(x - 7)(x - 2)$　　**2.** $(a - 12)(a + 3)$

3. $(x + 5)(x - 3)$　　**4.** $(n - 5)(n - 3)$

5. $(b + 21)(b + 1)$　　6. $(c + 3)(c - 1)$

7. $(x - 8)(x + 3)$　　8. $(n - 7)(n - 1)$

9. $(m - 13)(m + 3)$　　10. $(z + 12)(z + 3)$

11. $(s - 15f)(s + 2f)$　　12. $(y + 7)(y - 5)$

13. $(r + 8)(r - 5)$　　14. $(x + 6)(x - 1)$

15. $(x - 5y)(x + y)$　　16. $(r + 9)(r + 7)$

17. $(v + 26)(v - 2)$　　18. $(k - 30j)(k + 3j)$

Page 734, Extra Practice, Lesson 8-4

1. $(2a - 7)(2a + 9)$　　2. $(3x + 2)(x - 3)$

3. $(4r - 1)(r - 6)$　　4. $(2z - 5)(z - 3)$

5. $(3a + 7)(a - 3)$　　6. $(4y + 3)(y + 2)$

7. $(2n + 3)(3n - 1)$　　8. $(5x - 7)(x - 2)$

9. prime　　10. prime

11. $6(3v^2 + 4v + 2)$　　12. $2(2k - 3)(k + 2)$

13. $10(x - y)(x - y)$　　14. $(3c + d)(4c - 5d)$

15. $(5n - m)(6n + m)$　　16. $\{-3, -1\}$

17. $\{-8, -4\}$　　18. $\left\{-1, \dfrac{2}{5}\right\}$

19. $\{-3, 1\}$　　20. $\{-1, 2\}$

21. $\left\{-\dfrac{1}{6}, \dfrac{3}{2}\right\}$　　22. $\left\{-\dfrac{5}{3}, \dfrac{7}{4}\right\}$

23. $\left\{-\dfrac{7}{3}, \dfrac{1}{3}\right\}$　　24. $\left\{-\dfrac{2}{5}, \dfrac{1}{3}\right\}$

25. $\left\{-2, \dfrac{3}{2}\right\}$　　26. $\left\{-2, \dfrac{5}{13}\right\}$

27. $\left\{-\dfrac{2}{7}, 2\right\}$　　28. $\left\{\dfrac{1}{2}, \dfrac{3}{4}\right\}$

29. $\left\{\dfrac{3}{7}, \dfrac{1}{4}\right\}$　　30. $\left\{\dfrac{1}{5}, \dfrac{1}{2}\right\}$

Page 734, Extra Practice, Lesson 8-5

1. $(x - 3)(x + 3)$　　2. $(a - 8)(a + 8)$

3. $(2x - 3y)(2x + 3y)$　　4. $(1 - 3z)(1 + 3z)$

5. $(4a - 3b)(4a + 3b)$　　6. $4(2x^2 - 3y^2)$

7. $(a - 2b)(a + 2b)$　　8. $3(5r - 4)(5r + 4)$

9. $(x - 6y)(x + 6y)$　　10. prime

11. $(3x - 10y)(3x + 10y)$　　12. $(7 - ab)(7 + ab)$

13. prime　　14. $(13 - 4t)(13 + 4t)$

15. $4(2r^2 - 1)$　　16. $-5(3m - 1)(3m + 1)$

Page 734, Extra Practice, Lesson 8-6

7. $3(x - 5)(x + 5)$　　8. $(2p + 3r)^2$

9. $6(a^2 + 12)$　　10. $(s + 15)^2$

11. $3(8x^2 + 8x + 3)$　　12. $(1 - 5z)^2$

13. $7(2 - 3b)(2 + 3b)$　　14. prime

Page 735, Extra Practice, Lesson 9-1

1. 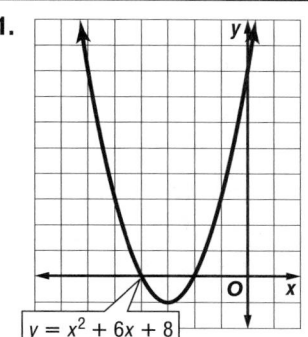　　2.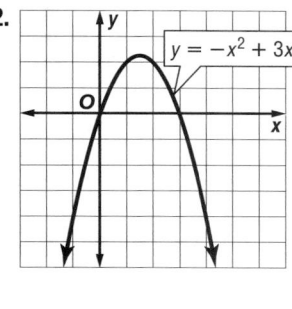

3. $x = 1$; $(1, -2)$; maximum　　4. $x = -4$; $(-4, 32)$; minimum

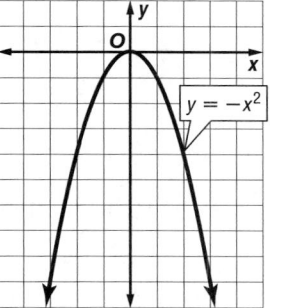　　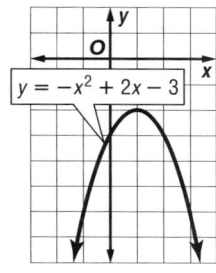

5. $x = 2$; $(2, -8)$; minimum

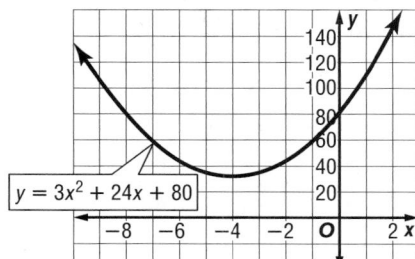

6. $x = 2$; $(2, 17)$; minimum

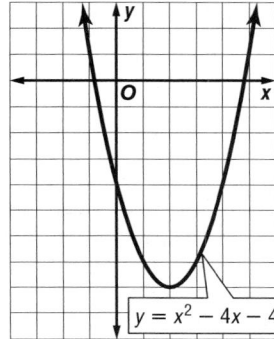

7. $x = -1$; $(-1, 0)$; minimum

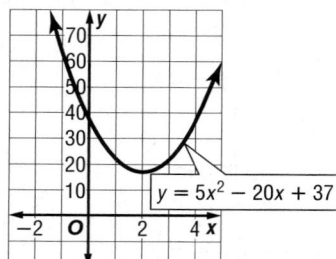

8. $x = -3$; $(-3, -18)$; minimum

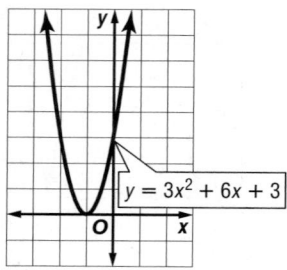

9. $x = -3$; $(-3, -18)$; mimimum

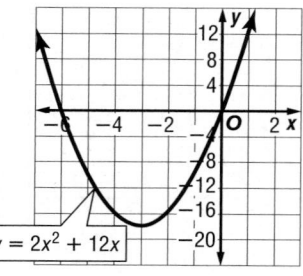

10. $x = 3$; $(3, -4)$; minimum

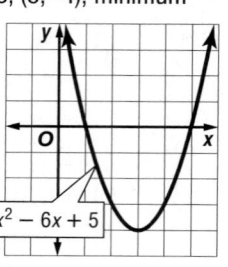

11. $x = -3$; $(-3, 0)$; minimum

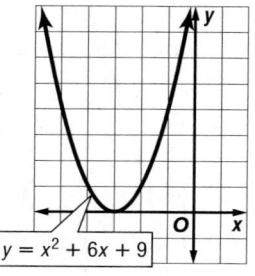

12. $x = 8$; $(8, 49)$; maximum

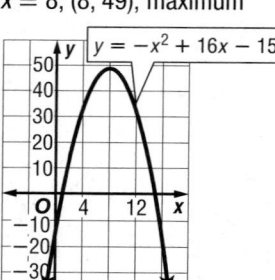

13. $x = 0$; $(0, -1)$; minimum

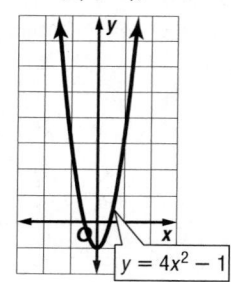

14. $x = -\dfrac{1}{2}$; $\left(-\dfrac{1}{2}, 4\dfrac{1}{2}\right)$;

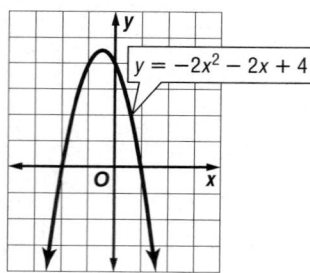

15. $x = 1$; $(1, -10)$; minimum

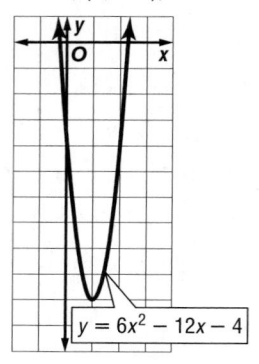

16. $x = 0$; $(0, -1)$; maximum

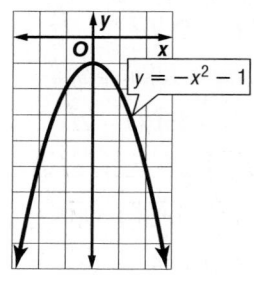

17. $x = \dfrac{1}{2}$; $\left(\dfrac{1}{2}, 1\dfrac{1}{4}\right)$; maximum

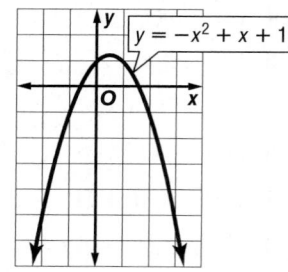

18. $x = -0.3$; $(-0.3, 2.45)$; maximum

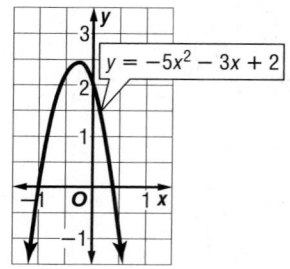

Page 735, Extra Practice, Lesson 9-2

1.

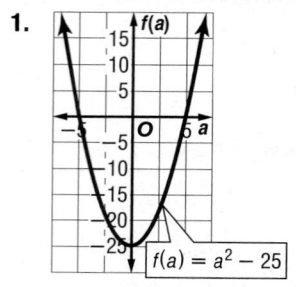

2.

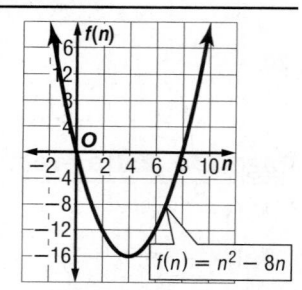

3.

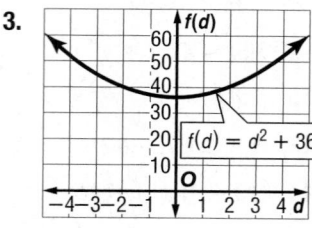

4.

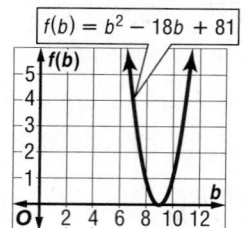

5.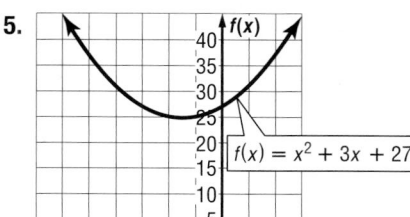

$f(x) = x^2 + 3x + 27$

6.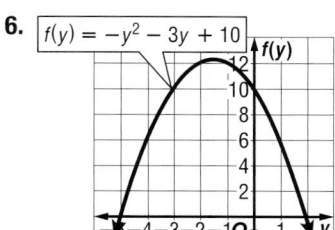

$f(y) = -y^2 - 3y + 10$

7.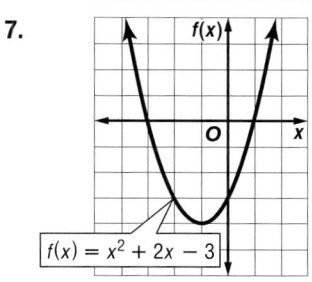

$f(x) = x^2 + 2x - 3$

8.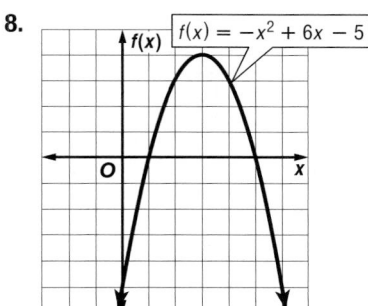

$f(x) = -x^2 + 6x - 5$

9.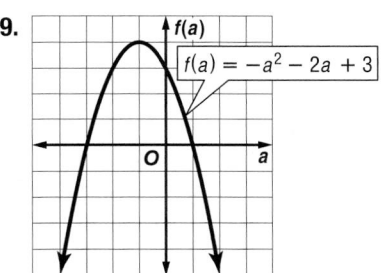

$f(a) = -a^2 - 2a + 3$

10.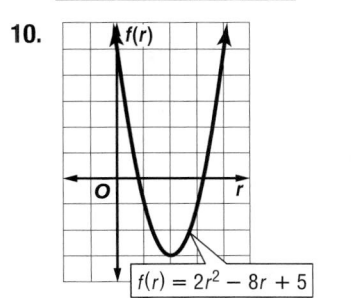

$f(r) = 2r^2 - 8r + 5$

11.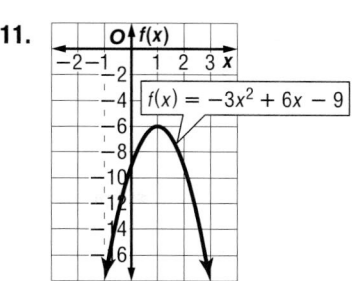

$f(x) = -3x^2 + 6x - 9$

12.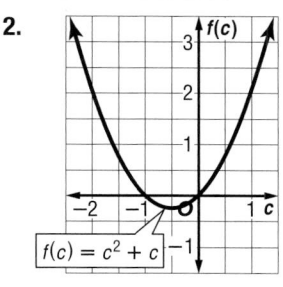

$f(c) = c^2 + c$

13.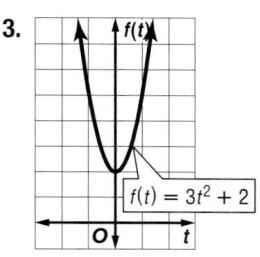

$f(t) = 3t^2 + 2$

14.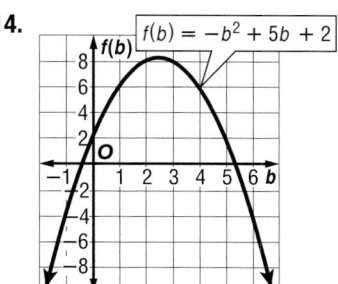

$f(b) = -b^2 + 5b + 2$

15.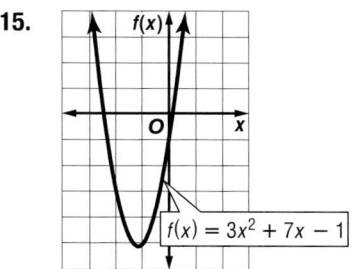

$f(x) = 3x^2 + 7x - 1$

16.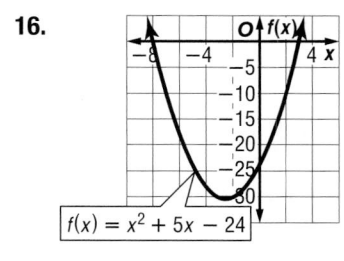

$f(x) = x^2 + 5x - 24$

17.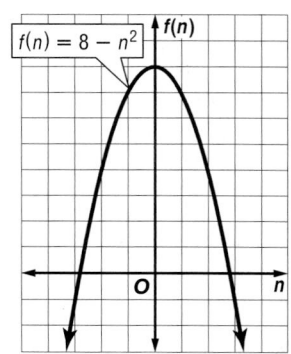

$f(n) = 8 - n^2$

18.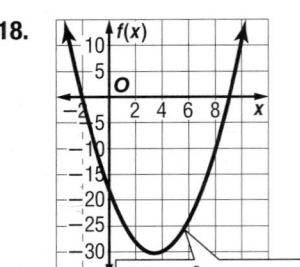

$f(x) = x^2 - 7x - 18$

19.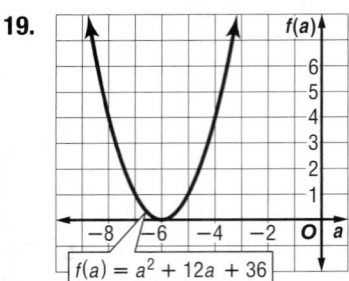

$f(a) = a^2 + 12a + 36$

20.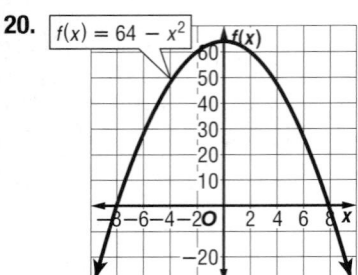

$f(x) = 64 - x^2$

21.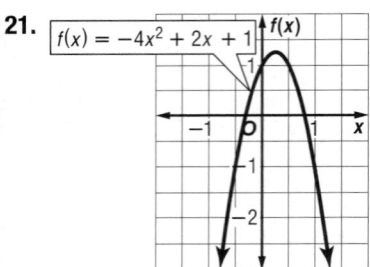

$f(x) = -4x^2 + 2x + 1$

22.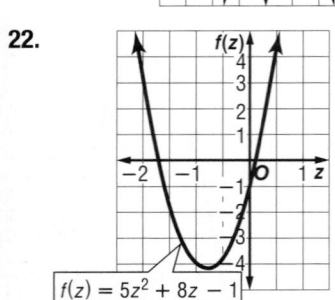

$f(z) = 5z^2 + 8z - 1$

23.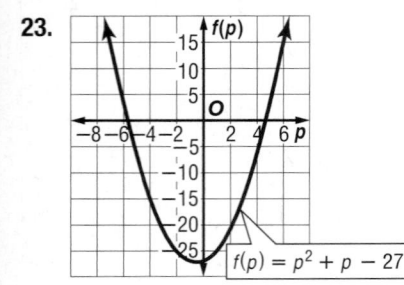

$f(p) = p^2 + p - 27$

24.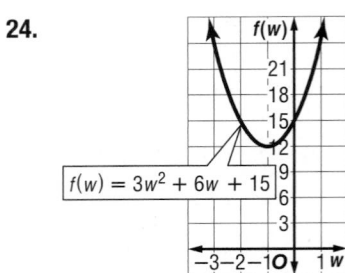

$f(w) = 3w^2 + 6w + 15$

Page 736, Extra Practice, Lesson 9-5

1.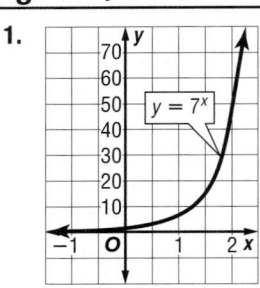

$y = 7^x$

2.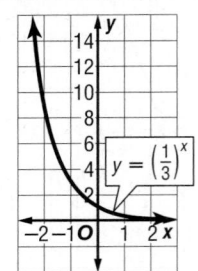

$y = \left(\frac{1}{3}\right)^x$

3.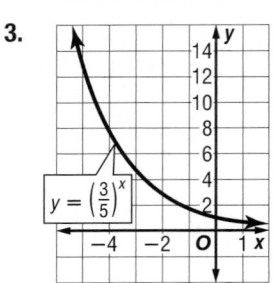

$y = \left(\frac{3}{5}\right)^x$

4.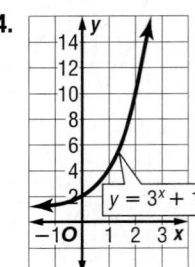

$y = 3^x + 1$

5.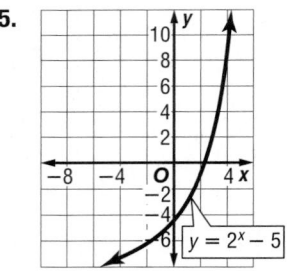

$y = 2^x - 5$

6.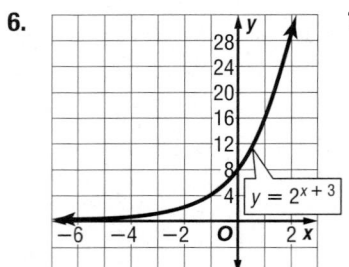

$y = 2^x + 3$

7.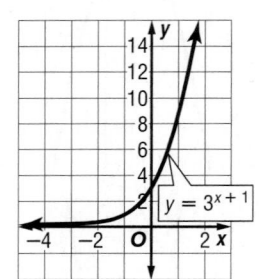

$y = 3^x + 1$

8.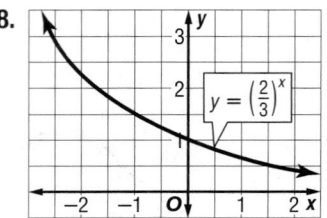

$y = \left(\frac{2}{3}\right)^x$

9.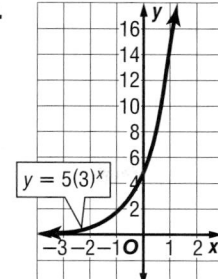
$y = 5\left(\frac{2}{5}\right)^x$

10.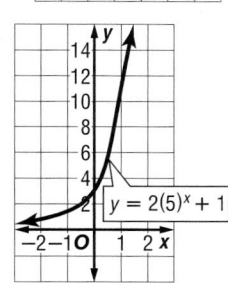
$y = 5(3)^x$

11.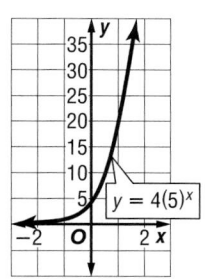
$y = 4(5)^x$

12.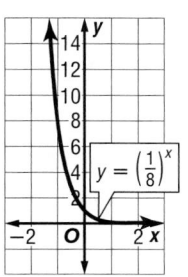
$y = 2(5)^x + 1$

13.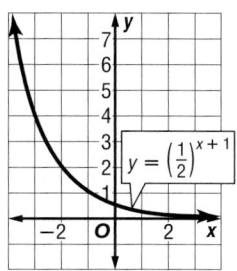
$y = \left(\frac{1}{2}\right)^{x+1}$

14.
$y = \left(\frac{1}{8}\right)^x$

15.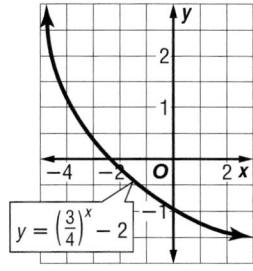
$y = \left(\frac{3}{4}\right)^x - 2$

16. No; the domain values are at regular intervals and the range values have a common difference of 4.

17. Yes; the domain values are at regular intervals and the range values have a common factor of 5.

Page 738, Extra Practice Lesson 10-5

1. 10

2. 13

3. 5

4. $6\sqrt{2}$ or 8.49

5. $\sqrt{29}$ or 5.39

6. 15

7. $2\sqrt{13}$ or 7.21

8. 14

9. $\sqrt{185}$ or 13.60

10. 15

11. $\sqrt{37}$ or 6.08

12. 13

13. $3\sqrt{5}$ or 6.71

14. 5

15. $5\sqrt{2}$ or 7.07

16. $\sqrt{41}$ or 6.40

17. 10

18. 16

19. $3\sqrt{10}$ or 9.49

20. 13

21. $2\sqrt{3}$ or 3.46

22. 5

23. $5\sqrt{5}$ or 11.18

24. $\sqrt{85}$ or 9.22

Page 738, Extra Practice Lesson 10-6

1. No; corresponding angles do not have equal measures.

2. Yes; corresponding angles have equal measures.

3. Yes; corresponding angles have equal measures.

Page 739, Extra Practice Lesson 11-1

1. $y = \frac{75}{x}$
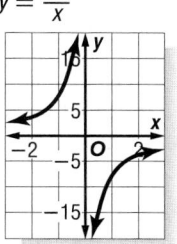

2. $y = \frac{-15}{x}$
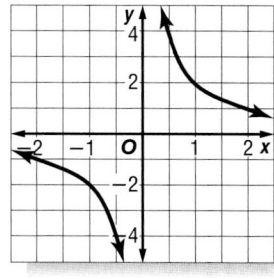

3. $y = \frac{12}{x}$
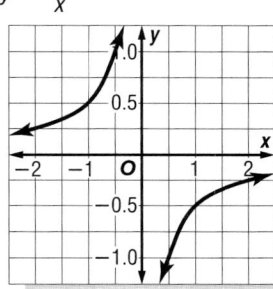

4. $y = \frac{-0.5}{x}$
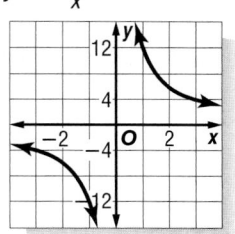

5. $y = \frac{-7.5}{x}$
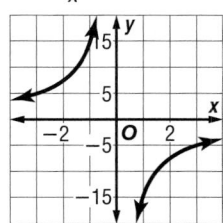

6. $y = \frac{2}{x}$
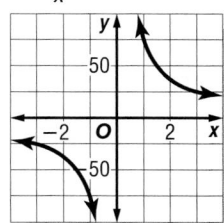

7. $y = \frac{216}{x}$; 8

8. $y = \frac{108}{x}$; 9

9. $y = \frac{288}{x}$; 32

10. $y = \frac{-64}{x}$; 4

11. $y = \frac{-24}{x}$; -6

12. $y = \frac{9}{x}$; 12

13. $y = \frac{24}{x}$; 12

14. $y = \frac{9}{x}$; 2.25

15. $y = \frac{-18.75}{x}$; 7.5

16. $y = \frac{1.28}{x}$; -6.4

Page 739, Extra Practice Lesson 11-2

5. $\frac{1}{3a}$; $a \neq 0$

6. $\frac{19x}{21y}$; $x, y \neq 0$

7. $\frac{1}{2}$; $p \neq -5$

8. $\frac{1}{a-b}$; $a \neq \pm b$

9. $\frac{1}{y-4}$; $y \neq -4, 4$

10. $\frac{c-2}{c+2}$; $c \neq -2$

11. a; $a \neq 1$

12. $\frac{1}{x^2-4}$; $x \neq \pm 2$

13. r^2; $r \neq 1$

14. $\frac{t^2-2}{t-1}$; $t \neq 1$

15. $\frac{y^2(y-2)}{2y^2-3}$; $y \neq \pm\frac{\sqrt{6}}{2}$

16. $\frac{5}{3}$; $x \neq -1$

Page 742, Extra Practice Lesson 12-1

1. 10 dogs from a county; all dogs in the county; biased; convenience

2. a group of automobiles manufactured at a particular plant; all automobiles manufactured at the plant; unbiased; stratified random sample

3. a group of people shopping at a department store; all people shopping at the department store; biased; voluntary response

4. a group of community residents; all residents of the community; unbiased; systematic random sample

Page 742, Extra Practice Lesson 12-2

1.

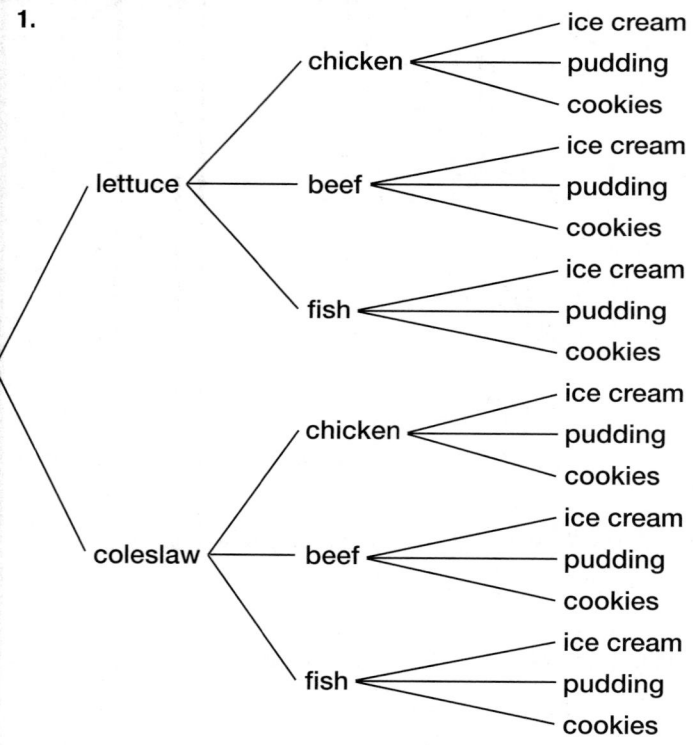

2.

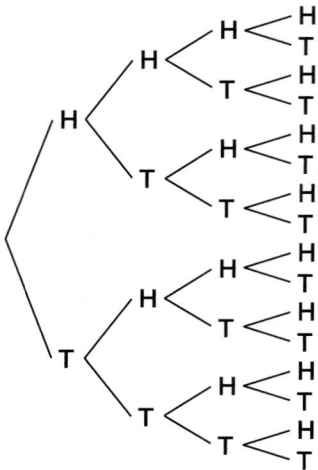

Page 742, Extra Practice Lesson 12-3

1. Order is not important.

2. Order of runners can make a difference.

3. Order is not important.

4. Order of winning is important.

5. Order is important with letters.

6. Order is important with a lock.

7. Order is not important.

Page 743, Extra Practice Lesson 12-5

1.

×	1	2	3	4	5	6
1	1	2	3	4	5	6
2	2	4	6	8	10	12
3	3	6	9	12	15	18
4	4	8	12	16	20	24
5	5	10	15	20	25	30
6	6	12	18	24	30	36

2. $P(X=9) = \frac{1}{36}$; $P(X=12) = \frac{1}{9}$; $P(X=24) = \frac{1}{18}$

4. Let $X =$ number of customers; $x = 500, 1000, 1500, 2000, 2500$

Page 743, Extra Practice Lesson 12-6

4. $P(1) \approx 12.7\%$; $P(2) \approx 21.7\%$; $P(3) \approx 35.7\%$; $P(4) \approx 18.9\%$; $P(5 \text{ or more}) \approx 11.0\%$

Page 744, Mixed Problem Solving, Chapter 1

5. Let a represent adult price, c represent child price, and g represent observer price. Then $2a + 2c + g \leq 55$.

8. Sample answer: $8(7.99) + 4(4.99) + 4(6.99); 8(5.99) + 4(8.99) + 4(2.99); 4(7.99) + 4(5.99) + 4(4.99) + 4(2.99)$

9. Sample answer; $111.84; $95.84; $87.84; All totals end in $0.84.

13. If two lines are perpendicular, then they meet to form four right angles. If two lines meet to form four right angles, then they are perpendicular.

14.

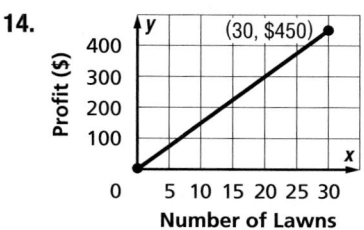

Page 746, Mixed Problem Solving, Chapter 3

1.

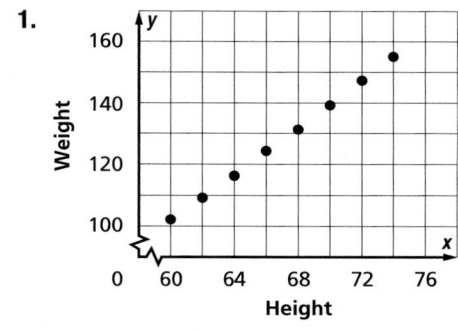

2. No; for each 2 unit increase in height, the increase in weight is not constant.

3. Sample answer: 171 lb; from 72 to 74 in., there is an increase of 8 in., so $8 \cdot 2 = 16$ and added to 155 is 171.

4.

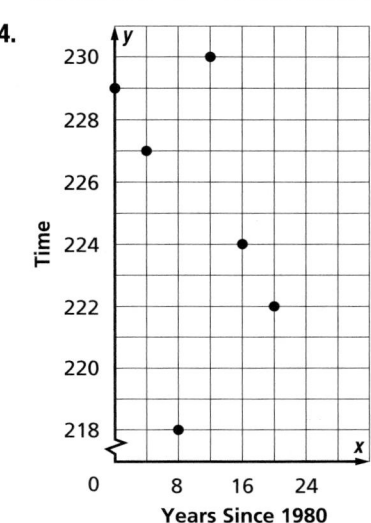

5. Yes; each value of x is paired with only one value of y.

6. Sample answer: 218 min

7. Mercury: 0.387 AU; Mars: 1.523 AU; Jupiter: 5.202 AU; Pluto: 39.223 AU

8. If the number of AU is less than 1, the planet is closer than Earth. If the number of AU is greater than 1, the planet is further from Earth.

9. 25,110,000,000,000 miles

10.

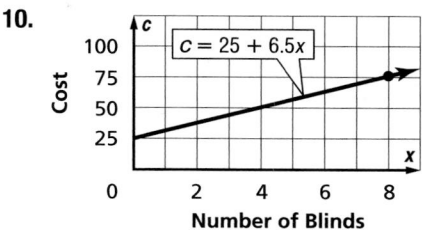

14. 1, 4, 9, 16, 25, 36, 49, 64, 81, 100; The values for area are the squares of consecutive integers.

Page 747, Mixed Problem Solving, Chapter 4

7.

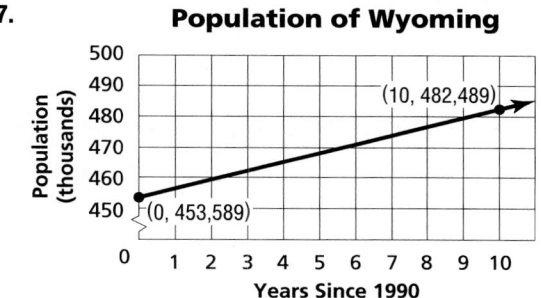

14.

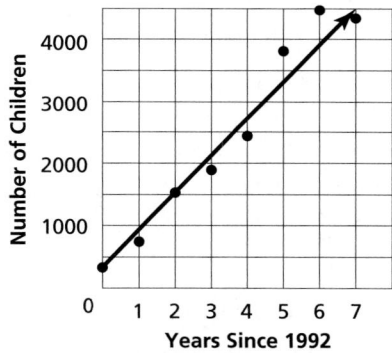

15. Sample answer using (0, 324) and (2, 1530): $y = 603x + 324$

18. Opposite sides have the same slopes, so they are parallel. Consecutive sides have slopes that are opposite reciprocals, so they are perpendicular.

Page 748, Mixed Problem Solving, Chapter 5

8. $x + y = 1{,}857{,}573{,}945$
$y = x + 494{,}264{,}809$

Page 749, Mixed Problem Solving, Chapter 6

3. $0 < \ell \le 4$; $0 < \ell \le 4$

7. inequality; Jennie must make and sell 63 or more apples to make $75 or more.

14.

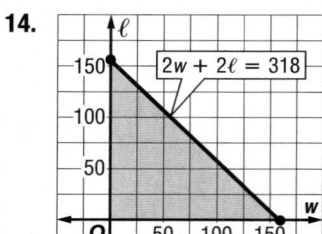

19.

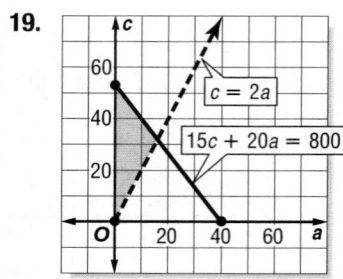

Page 750, Mixed Problem Solving, Chapter 7

1. Yes; each is the product of variables and/or a real number.

2. 27 ft^3; 54 ft^2

3. 6 units

7. 17.3 people/square mile; Since 2010 is 90 years after 1920, substitute 90 into the polynomial and simplify.

8. $0 = 95.6x + 8962.6$

12. You add one more each time to the previous number. For example, $0 + 2 = 2$, $2 + 3 = 5$, $5 + 4 = 9$, and so on.

15. 4000 is the amount of the investment, 1 will add the amount of the investment to the interest, 0.05 is the interest rate as a decimal, and 2 is the number of years of the investment.

Page 751, Mixed Problem Solving, Chapter 8

1. 1 by 1, 2 by 2, and 2 by 3; The 3-foot squares will not cover the 10-foot dimension without cutting.

9. 48 is the initial velocity of the ball and 506 is the height from which the ball is thrown which is 500 feet plus 6 feet, Teril's height.

12. No; the equation is not factorable, so there are no whole number solutions.

15. Sample answer: 20 ft by 50 ft by 42 in.

Page 752, Mixed Problem Solving, Chapter 9

6.

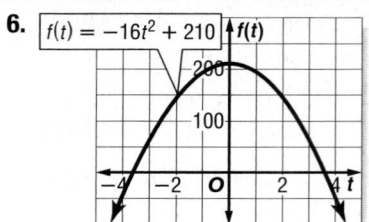

11. 3.8, 41.2; The values mean that 3.8 years and 41.2 years after 1977, 30% of households had cable TV.

12. No; the parabola only reaches a maximum height of about 68, meaning that no more than 68% of homes will ever have cable, which is not realistic.

15. about 5,455,480,760 people

Page 753, Mixed Problem Solving, Chapter 10

10. No; the distance is about 55 blocks or about 4.6 mi.

11. Sample answer: 40 blocks south and 45 blocks west; 38 blocks north and 47 blocks west

Page 754, Mixed Problem Solving, Chapter 11

1.

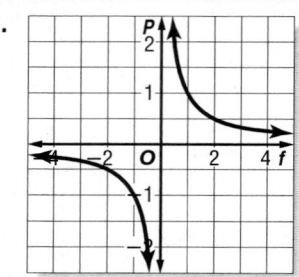

3. Sample answer: One value is negative and the other is positive.

4.

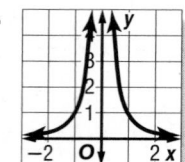

5. The values of x must be positive since x represents distance.

10. Mercury: about 5188 min; Venus: about 9677 min; Earth: 13,405 min; Mars: 20,430 min; Jupiter: about 69,713 min; Saturn: about 128,136 min; Uranus: about 257,168 min; Pluto: aobut 403,226 min

14. No; they need $2\frac{3}{8}$ yd for one of each type. Then $30 \div 2\frac{3}{8}$ yd is not a whole number so they cannot use the entire bolt by making an equal number of each type.

Page 755, Mixed Problem Solving, Chapter 12

1. Sample answer: The sample contained students ages 14–18.

2. Sample answers: How were the students sampled? Was it random or were they volunteers? Were the students given only certain careers as choices? How many students responded?

4. $52.50; $20.75

8. 9; ART, ATE, ARE, TAR, TEA, RAT, EAT, EAR, ERA

9. yes; $0.053 + 0.284 + 0.323 + 0.198 + 0.142 = 1$

11. 7776 numbers; Find $6 \cdot 6 \cdot 6 \cdot 6 \cdot 6$ since there are 6 possibilities for each digit.

12. Sample answer: Roll five dice and record the results each time. Each roll represents one person picking a winning number.

Glossary/Glosario

Math Online A mathematics multilingual glossary is available at www.math.glencoe.com/multilingual_glossary.
The glossary includes the following languages.

Arabic	Haitian Creole	Russian	Vietnamese
Bengali	Hmong	Spanish	
Cantonese	Korean	Tagalog	
English	Portuguese	Urdu	

English

absolute value function (p. 324) A function written as $f(x) = |x|$, in which $f(x) \geq 0$ for all values of x.

additive identity (p. 21) For any number a, $a + 0 = 0 + a = a$.

additive inverse (p. 21) Two integers, x and $-x$, are called additive inverses. The sum of any number and its additive inverse is zero.

algebraic expression (p. 6) An expression consisting of one or more numbers and variables along with one or more arithmetic operations.

arithmetic sequence (p. 165) A numerical pattern that increases or decreases at a constant rate or value. The difference between successive terms of the sequence is constant.

axis of symmetry (p. 472) The vertical line containing the vertex of a parabola.

base (p. 6) In an expression of the form x^n, the base is x.

best-fit line (p. 228) The line that most closely approximates the data in a scatter plot.

biased sample (p. 643) A sample in which one or more parts of the population are favored over others.

binomial (p. 376) The sum of two monomials.

boundary (p. 334) A line or curve that separates the coordinate plane into regions.

R2 Glossary

Cómo usar el glosario en español:
1. Busca el término en inglés que desees encontrar.
2. El término en español, junto con la definición, se encuentran en la columna de la derecha.

Español

función del valor absoluto Una función que se escribe $f(x) = |x|$, donde $f(x) \geq 0$, para todos los valores de x.

identidad de la adición Para cualquier número $a, a + 0 = 0 + a = a$.

inverso aditivo Dos enteros x y $-x$ reciben el nobre de inversos aditivos. La suma de cualquier número y su inverso aditivo es cero.

expresión algebraica Una expresión que consiste en uno o más números y variables, junto con una o más operaciones aritméticas.

sucesión aritmética Un patrón numérico que aumenta o disminuye a una tasa o valor constante. La diferencia entre términos consecutivos de la sucesión es siempre la misma.

eje de simetría La recta vertical que pasa por el vértice de una parábola.

base En una expresión de la forma x^n, la base es x.

recta de ajuste óptimo La recta que mejor aproxima los datos de una gráfica de dispersión.

muestra sesgada Muestra en que se favorece una o más partes de una población en vez de otras partes.

binomio La suma de dos monomios.

frontera Recta o curva que divide el plano de coordenadas en regiones.

C

coefficient (p. 29) The numerical factor of a term.

combination (p. 657) An arrangement or listing in which order is not important.

common difference (p. 165) The difference between the terms in a sequence.

complements (p. 665) One of two parts of a probability making a whole.

completing the square (p. 486) To add a constant term to a binomial of the form $x^2 + bx$ so that the resulting trinomial is a perfect square.

complex fraction (p. 621) A fraction that has one or more fractions in the numerator or denominator.

composite number (p. 420) A whole number, greater than 1, that has more than two factors.

compound event (p. 663) Two or more simple events.

compound inequality (p. 315) Two or more inequalities that are connected by the words *and* or *or*.

compound interest (p. 511) A special application of exponential growth.

conclusion (p. 39) The part of a conditional statement immediately following the word *then*.

conditional statements (p. 39) Statements written in the form *If A, then B.*

conjugates (p. 531) Binomials of the form $a\sqrt{b} + c\sqrt{d}$ and $a\sqrt{b} - c\sqrt{d}$.

consecutive integers (p. 94) Integers in counting order.

consistent (p. 253) A system of equations that has at least one ordered pair that satisfies both equations.

constant (p. 358) A monomial that is a real number.

coeficiente Factor numérico de un término.

combinación Arreglo o lista en que el orden no es importante.

diferencia común Diferencia entre términos consecutivos de una sucesión.

complementos Una de dos partes de una probabilidad que forma un todo.

completar el cuadrado Adición de un término constante a un binomio de la forma $x^2 + bx$, para que el trinomio resultante sea un cuadrado perfecto.

fracción compleja Fracción con una o más fracciones en el numerador o denominador.

número compuesto Número entero mayor que 1 que posee más de dos factores.

evento compuesto Dos o más eventos simples.

desigualdad compuesta Dos o más desigualdades que están unidas por las palabras y u o.

interés compuesto Aplicación especial de crecimiento exponencial.

conclusión Parte de un enunciado condicional que sigue inmediatamente a la palabra *entonces*.

enunciados condicionales Enunciados de la forma *Si A, entonces B.*

conjugados Binomios de la forma $a\sqrt{b} + c\sqrt{d}$ y $a\sqrt{b} - c\sqrt{d}$.

enteros consecutivos Enteros en el orden de contar.

consistente Sistema de ecuaciones para el cual existe al menos un par ordenado que satisface ambas ecuaciones.

constante Monomio que es un número real.

Glossary R3

constant of variation (p. 196) The number k in equations of the form $y = kx$.

continuous function (p. 55) A function that can be graphed with a line or a smooth curve.

convenience sample (p. 643) A sample that includes members of a population that are easily accessed.

converse (p. 551) The statement formed by exchanging the hypothesis and conclusion of a conditional statement.

coordinate (p. 48) The number that corresponds to a point on a number line.

coordinate plane (p. 53) The plane containing the x- and y-axes.

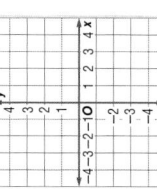

coordinate system (p. 53) The grid formed by the intersection of two number lines, the horizontal axis and the vertical axis.

counterexample (p. 41) A specific case in which a statement is false.

D

deductive reasoning (p. 40) The process of using facts, rules, definitions, or properties to reach a valid conclusion.

defining a variable (p. 71) Choosing a variable to represent one of the unspecified numbers in a problem and using it to write expressions for the other unspecified numbers in the problem.

degree of a monomial (p. 377) The sum of the exponents of all its variables.

degree of a polynomial (p. 377) The greatest degree of any term in the polynomial.

dependent (p. 253) A system of equations that has an infinite number of solutions.

dependent events (p. 664) Two or more events in which the outcome of one event affects the outcome of the other events.

dependent variable (p. 54) The variable in a relation with a value that depends on the value of the independent variable.

difference of squares (pp. 404, 448) Two perfect squares separated by a subtraction sign. $a^2 - b^2 = (a + b)(a - b)$ or $a^2 - b^2 = (a - b)(a + b)$.

dimensional analysis (p. 119) The process of carrying units throughout a computation.

direct variation (p. 196) An equation of the form $y = kx$, where $k \neq 0$.

discrete function (p. 55) A function of points that are not connected.

discrete random variable (p. 672) A variable with a value that is a finite number of possible outcomes.

discriminant (p. 496) In the Quadratic Formula, the expression under the radical sign, $b^2 - 4ac$.

Distance Formula (p. 555) The distance d between any two points with coordinates (x_1, y_1) and (x_2, y_2) is given by the formula $d = \sqrt{(x_2 - x_1)^2 + (y_2 - y_1)^2}$.

domain (p. 55) The set of the first numbers of the ordered pairs in a relation.

E

element (p. 15) 1. Each object or number in a set. (p. 715) 2. Each entry in a matrix.

elimination (p. 266) The use of addition or subtraction to eliminate one variable and solve a system of equations.

empirical study (p. 678) Performing an experiment repeatedly, collecting and combining data, and analyzing the results.

equation (p. 15) A mathematical sentence that contains an equals sign, =.

equivalent equations (p. 79) Equations that have the same solution.

---

constante de variación El número k en ecuaciones de la forma $y = kx$.

función continua Función cuya gráfica puedes ser una recta o una curva suave.

muestra de conveniencia Muestra que incluye miembros de una población que son fácilmente accesibles.

recíproco Enunciado que se obtiene al intercambiar la hipótesis y la conclusión de un enunciado condicional dado.

coordenada Número que corresponde a un punto en una recta numérica.

plano de coordenadas Plano que contiene los ejes x y y.

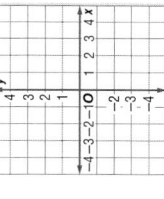

sistema de coordenadas Cuadriculado formado por la intersección de dos rectas numéricas: los ejes x y y.

contraejemplo Ejemplo específico de la falsedad de un enunciado.

D

razonamiento deductivo Proceso de usar hechos, reglas, definiciones o propiedades para sacar conclusiones válidas.

definir una variable Consiste en escoger una variable para representar uno de los números desconocidos en un problema y luego usarla para escribir expresiones para otros números desconocidos en el problema.

grado de un monomio Suma de los exponentes de todas sus variables.

grado de un polinomio El grado mayor de cualquier término del polinomio.

dependiente Sistema de ecuaciones que posee un número infinito de soluciones.

eventos dependientes Dos o más eventos en que el resultado de un evento afecta el resultado de los otros eventos.

variable dependiente La variable de una relación cuyo valor depende del valor de la variable independiente.

diferencia de cuadrados Dos cuadrados perfectos separados por el signo de sustracción. $a^2 - b^2 = (a + b)(a - b)$ or $a^2 - b^2 = (a - b)(a + b)$.

análisis dimensional Proceso de tomar en cuenta las unidades de medida al hacer cálculos.

variación directa Una ecuación de la forma $y = kx$, donde $k \neq 0$.

función discreta Función de puntos desconectados.

variable aleatoria discreta Variable cuyo valor es un número finito de posibles resultados.

discriminante En la fórmula cuadrática, la expresión debajo del signo radical, $b^2 - 4ac$.

Fórmula de la distancia La distancia d entre cualquier par de puntos con coordenadas (x_1, y_1) y (x_2, y_2) viene dada por la fórmula $d = \sqrt{(x_2 - x_1)^2 + (y_2 - y_1)^2}$.

dominio Conjunto de los primeros números de los pares ordenados de una relación.

E

elemento 1. Cada número u objeto de un conjunto. 2. Cada entrada de una matriz.

eliminación El uso de la adición o la sustracción para eliminar una variable y resolver así un sistema de ecuaciones.

estudio empírico Ejecución repetida de un experimento, recopilación y combinación de datos y análisis de resultados.

ecuación Enunciado matemático que contiene el signo de igualdad, =.

ecuaciones equivalentes Ecuaciones que poseen la misma solución.

G

equivalent expressions (p. 29) Expressions that denote the same number.

evaluate (p. 7) To find the value of an expression.

event (p. 650) Any collection of one or more outcomes in the sample space.

excluded values (p. 583) Any values of a variable that result in a denominator of 0 must be excluded from the domain of that variable.

experimental probability (p. 677) What actually occurs when conducting a probability experiment, or the ratio of relative frequency to the total number of events or trials.

exponent (p. 6) In an expression of the form x^n, the exponent is n. It indicates the number of times x is used as a factor.

exponential decay (p. 511) When an initial amount decreases by the same percent over a given period of time.

exponential function (p. 502) A function that can be described by an equation of the form $y = a^x$, where $a > 0$ and $a \neq 1$.

exponential growth (p. 510) When an initial amount increases by the same percent over a given period of time.

extraneous solutions (pp. 542, 629) Results that are not solutions to the original equation.

extremes (p. 106) In the ratio $\frac{a}{b} = \frac{c}{d}$, a and d are the extremes.

F

factored form (p. 421) A monomial expressed as a product of prime numbers and variables in which no variable has an exponent greater than 1.

factorial (p. 652) The expression $n!$, read n factorial, where n is greater than zero, is the product of all positive integers beginning with n and counting backward to 1.

factoring (p. 426) To express a polynomial as the product of monomials and polynomials.

expresiones equivalentes Expresiones que denotan el mismo número.

evaluar Calcular el valor de una expresión.

evento Cualquier colección de uno o más resultados de un espacio muestral.

valores excluidos Cualquier valor de una variable cuyo resultado sea un denominador igual a cero, debe excluirse del dominio de dicha variable.

probabilidad experimental Lo que realmente sucede cuando se realiza un experimento probabilístico o la razón de la frecuencia relativa al número total de eventos o pruebas.

exponente En una expresión de la forma x^n, el exponente es n. Este indica cuántas veces se usa x como factor.

desintegración exponencial La cantidad inicial disminuye según el mismo porcentaje a lo largo de un período de tiempo dado.

función exponencial Función que puede describirse mediante una ecuación de la forma $y = a^x$, donde $a > 0$ y $a \neq 1$.

crecimiento exponencial La cantidad inicial aumenta según el mismo porcentaje a lo largo de un período de tiempo dado.

soluciones extrañas Resultados que no son soluciones de la ecuación original.

extremos En la razón $\frac{a}{b} = \frac{c}{d}$, a y d son los extremos.

forma reducida Monomio escrito como el producto de números primos y variables y en el que ninguna variable tiene un exponente mayor que 1.

factorial La expresión $n!$, que se lee n factorial, donde n que es mayor que cero, es el producto de todos los números naturales, comenzando con n y contando hacia atrás hasta llegar al 1.

factorización La escritura de un polinomio como producto de monomios y polinomios.

factoring by grouping (p. 427) The use of the Distributive Property to factor some polynomials having four or more terms.

factors (p. 6) In an algebraic expression, the quantities being multiplied are called factors.

family of graphs (pp. 197, 478) Graphs and equations of graphs that have at least one characteristic in common.

FOIL method (p. 399) To multiply two binomials, find the sum of the products of the First terms, the Outer terms, the Inner terms, and the Last terms.

formula (p. 72) An equation that states a rule for the relationship between certain quantities.

four-step problem-solving plan (p. 71)
Step 1 Explore the problem.
Step 2 Plan the solution.
Step 3 Solve the problem.
Step 4 Check the solution.

function (pp. 53, 149) A relation in which each element of the domain is paired with exactly one element of the range.

function notation (p. 150) A way to name a function that is defined by an equation. In function notation, the equation $y = 3x - 8$ is written as $f(x) = 3x - 8$.

Fundamental Counting Principle (p. 651) If an event M can occur in m ways and is followed by an event N that can occur in n ways, then the event M followed by the event N can occur in $m \times n$ ways.

G

general equation for exponential decay (p. 511) $y = C(1 - r)^t$, where y is the final amount, C is the initial amount, r is the rate of decay expressed as a decimal, and t is time.

general equation for exponential growth (p. 510) $y = C(1 + r)^t$, where y is the final amount, C is the initial amount, r is the rate of change expressed as a decimal, and t is time.

factorización por agrupamiento Uso de la Propiedad distributiva para factorizar polinomios que poseen cuatro o más términos.

factores En una expresión algebraica, los factores son las cantidades que se multiplican.

familia de gráficas Gráficas y ecuaciones de gráficas que tienen al menos una característica común.

método FOIL Para multiplicar dos binomios, busca la suma de los productos de los primeros (First) términos, los términos exteriores (Outer), los términos interiores (Inner) y los últimos términos (Last).

fórmula Ecuación que establece una relación entre ciertas cantidades.

plan de cuatro pasos para resolver problemas
Paso 1 Explora el problema.
Paso 2 Planifica la solución.
Paso 3 Resuelve el problema.
Paso 4 Examina la solución.

función Una relación en que a cada elemento del dominio le corresponde un único elemento del rango.

notación funcional Una manera de nombrar una función definida por una ecuación. En notación funcional, la ecuación $y = 3x - 8$ se escribe $f(x) = 3x - 8$.

Principio fundamental de contar Si un evento M puede ocurrir de m maneras y lo sigue un evento N que puede ocurrir de n maneras, entonces el evento M seguido del evento N puede ocurrir de $m \times n$ maneras.

ecuación general de desintegración exponencial $y = C(1 - r)^t$, donde y es la cantidad final, C es la cantidad inicial, r es la tasa de desintegración escrita como decimal y t es el tiempo.

ecuación general de crecimiento exponencial $y = C(1 + r)^t$, donde y es la cantidad final, C es la cantidad inicial, r es la tasa de cambio del crecimiento escrita como decimal y t es el tiempo.

graph (pp. 48, 195) To draw, or plot, the points named by certain numbers or ordered pairs on a number line or coordinate plane.

graficar Marcar los puntos que denotan ciertos números en una recta numérica o ciertos pares ordenados en un plano de coordenadas.

greatest common factor (GCF) (p. 421) The product of the prime factors common to two or more integers.

máximo común divisor (MCD) El producto de los factores primos comunes a dos o más enteros.

H

half-plane (p. 334) The region of the graph of an inequality on one side of a boundary.

semiplano Región de la gráfica de una desigualdad en un lado de la frontera.

hypotenuse (p. 549) The side opposite the right angle in a right triangle.

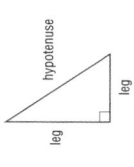

hipotenusa Lado opuesto al ángulo recto en un triángulo rectángulo.

hypothesis (p. 39) The part of a conditional statement immediately following the word *if*.

hipótesis Parte de un enunciado condicional que sigue inmediatamente a la palabra *si*.

I

if-then statements (p. 39) Conditional statements in the form *If A, then B*.

enunciados si-entonces Enunciados condicionales de la forma *Si A, entonces B*.

inclusive (p. 666) Two events that can occur at the same time.

inclusivos Dos eventos que pueden ocurrir simultáneamente.

inconsistent (p. 253) A system of equations with no ordered pair that satisfy both equations.

inconsistente Un sistema de ecuaciones para el cual no existe par ordenado alguno que satisfaga ambas ecuaciones.

independent (p. 253) A system of equations with exactly one solution.

independiente Un sistema de ecuaciones que posee una única solución.

independent events (p. 663) Two or more events in which the outcome of one event does not affect the outcome of the other events.

eventos independientes El resultado de un evento no afecta el resultado del otro evento.

independent variable (p. 55) The variable in a function with a value that is subject to choice.

variable independiente La variable de una función sujeta a elección.

inductive reasoning (p. 172) A conclusion based on a pattern of examples.

razonamiento inductivo Conclusión basada en un patrón de ejemplos.

---

inequality (p. 16) An open sentence that contains the symbol $<$, $\leq$, $>$, or $\geq$.

desigualdad Enunciado abierto que contiene uno o más de los símbolos $<$, $\leq$, $>$, o $\geq$.

integers (p. 46) The set $\{..., -2, -1, 0, 1, 2, ...\}$.

enteros El conjunto $\{..., -2, -1, 0, 1, 2, ...\}$.

intersection (p. 315) The graph of a compound inequality containing *and*; the solution is the set of elements common to both inequalities.

intersección Gráfica de una desigualdad compuesta que contiene la palabra *y*; la solución es el conjunto de soluciones de ambas desigualdades.

inverse (p. 145) The inverse of any relation is obtained by switching the coordinates in each ordered pair.

inversa La inversa de una relación se halla intercambiando las coordenadas de cada par ordenado.

inverse variation (p. 577) An equation of the form $xy = k$, where $k \neq 0$.

variación inversa Ecuación de la forma $xy = k$, donde $k \neq 0$.

irrational numbers (p. 46) Numbers that cannot be expressed as terminating or repeating decimals.

números irracionales Números que no pueden escribirse como decimales terminales o periódicos.

L

least common denominator (LCD) (p. 615) The least common multiple of the denominators of two or more fractions.

mínimo denominador común (mcd) El mínimo común múltiplo de los denominadores de dos o más fracciones.

least common multiple (LCM) (p. 614) The least number that is a common multiple of two or more numbers.

mínimo común múltiplo (mcm) El número menor que es múltiplo común de dos o más números.

legs (p. 549) The sides of a right triangle that form the right angle.

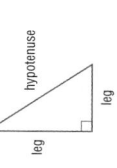

catetos Lados de un triángulo rectángulo que forman el ángulo recto del mismo.

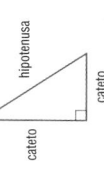

like terms (p. 29) Terms that contain the same variables, with corresponding variables having the same exponent.

términos semejantes Expresiones que tienen las mismas variables, con las variables correspondientes elevadas a los mismos exponentes.

linear equation (p. 155) An equation in the form $Ax + By = C$, with a graph that is a straight line.

ecuación lineal Ecuación de la forma $Ax + By = C$, cuya gráfica es una recta.

linear extrapolation (p. 216) The use of a linear equation to predict values that are outside the range of data.

extrapolación lineal Uso de una ecuación lineal para predecir valores fuera de la amplitud de los datos.

Glossary/Glosario

linear function (p. 155) A function with ordered pairs that satisfy a linear equation.

función lineal Función cuyos pares ordenados satisfacen una ecuación lineal.

linear interpolation (p. 230) The use of a linear equation to predict values that are inside of the data range.

interpolación lineal Uso de una ecuación lineal para predecir valores dentro de la amplitud de los datos.

line of fit (p. 228) A line that describes the trend of the data in a scatter plot.

recta de ajuste Recta que describe la tendencia de los datos en una gráfica de dispersión.

look for a pattern (p. 172) Find patterns in sequences to solve problems.

buscar un patrón Encontrar patrones en sucesiones para resolver problemas.

lower quartile (p. 713) Divides the lower half of the data into two equal parts.

cuartil inferior Éste divide en dos partes iguales la mitad inferior de un conjunto de datos.

M

mapping (p. 143) Illustrates how each element of the domain is paired with an element in the range.

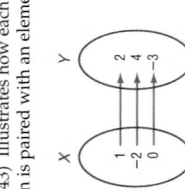

aplicaciones Ilustra la correspondencia entre cada elemento del dominio con un elemento del rango.

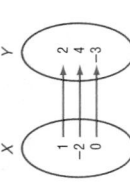

maximum (p. 472) The highest point on the graph of a curve.

máximo El punto más alto en la gráfica de una curva.

means (p. 106) The middle terms of the proportion.

medios Los términos centrales de una proporción.

minimum (p. 472) The lowest point on the graph of a curve.

mínimo El punto más bajo en la gráfica de una curva.

mixed expression (p. 620) An expression that contains the sum of a monomial and a rational expression.

expresión mixta Expresión que contiene la suma de un monomio y una expresión racional.

mixture problems (p. 122) Problems in which two or more parts are combined into a whole.

problemas de mezclas Problemas en que dos o más partes se combinan en un todo.

monomial (p. 358) A number, a variable, or a product of a number and one or more variables.

monomio Número, variable o producto de un número por una o más variables.

multiplicative identity (p. 21) For any number a, $a \cdot 1 = 1 \cdot a = a$.

identidad de la multiplicación Para cualquier número a, $a \cdot 1 = 1 \cdot a = a$.

multiplicative inverses (p. 21) Two numbers with a product of 1.

inversos multiplicativos Dos números cuyo producto es igual a 1.

multi-step equations (p. 92) Equations with more than one operation.

ecuaciones de varios pasos Ecuaciones con más de una operación.

mutually exclusive (p. 665) Events that cannot occur at the same time.

mutuamente exclusivos Eventos que no pueden ocurrir simultáneamente.

N

natural numbers (p. 46) The set {1, 2, 3, …}.

números naturales El conjunto {1, 2, 3, …}.

negative correlation (p. 227) In a scatter plot, as x increases, y decreases.

correlación negativa En una gráfica de dispersión, a medida que x aumenta, y disminuye.

negative number (p. 46) Any value less than zero.

número negativo Cualquier valor menor que cero.

O

open sentence (p. 15) A mathematical statement with one or more variables.

enunciado abierto Un enunciado matemático que contiene una o más variables.

ordered pair (p. 53) A set of numbers or coordinates used to locate any point on a coordinate plane, written in the form (x, y).

par ordenado Un par de números que se usa para ubicar cualquier punto de un plano de coordenadas y que se escribe en la forma (x, y).

order of operations (p. 10)
1. Evaluate expressions inside grouping symbols.
2. Evaluate all powers.
3. Do all multiplications and/or divisions from left to right.
4. Do all additions and/or subtractions from left to right.

orden de las operaciones
1. Evalúa las expresiones dentro de los símbolos de agrupamiento.
2. Evalúa todas las potencias.
3. Multiplica o divide de izquierda a derecha.
4. Suma o resta de izquierda a derecha.

origin (p. 53) The point where the two axes intersect at their zero points.

origen Punto donde se intersecan los dos ejes en sus puntos cero.

P

parabola (p. 471) The graph of a quadratic function.

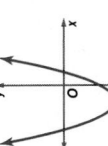

parábola La gráfica de una función cuadrática.

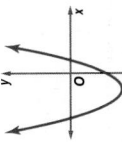

Glossary

parallel lines (p. 236) Lines in the same plane that never intersect and have the same slope.

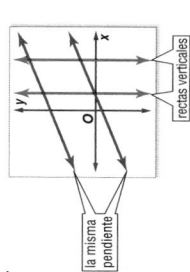

same slope / vertical lines

parent graph (p. 197) The simplest of the graphs in a family of graphs.

percent of change (p. 111) When an increase or decrease is expressed as a percent.

percent of decrease (p. 111) The ratio of an amount of decrease to the previous amount, expressed as a percent.

percent of increase (p. 111) The ratio of an amount of increase to the previous amount, expressed as a percent.

perfect square (p. 46) A number with a square root that is a rational number.

perfect square trinomial (p. 454) A trinomial that is the square of a binomial.
$(a + b)^2 = (a + b)(a + b) = a^2 + 2ab + b^2$ or
$(a - b)^2 = (a - b)(a - b) = a^2 - 2ab - b^2$

permutation (p. 655) An arrangement or listing in which order is important.

piecewise function (p. 324) A function written using two or more expressions.

point-slope form (p. 220) An equation of the form $y - y_1 = m(x - x_1)$, where m is the slope and (x_1, y_1) is a given point on a nonvertical line.

polynomial (p. 376) A monomial or sum of monomials.

population (p. 642) A large group of data usually represented by a sample.

positive correlation (p. 227) In a scatter plot, as x increases, y increases.

positive number (p. 46) Any value that is greater than zero.

power (p. 6) An expression of the form x^n, read x to the nth power.

prime factorization (p. 420) A whole number expressed as a product of factors that are all prime numbers.

prime number (p. 420) A whole number, greater than 1, with only factors that are 1 and itself.

prime polynomial (p. 443) A polynomial that cannot be written as a product of two polynomials with integral coefficients.

principal square root (p. 49) The nonnegative square root of a number.

probability distribution (p. 673) The probability of every possible value of the random variable x.

probability histogram (p. 673) A way to give the probability distribution for a random variable and obtain other data.

product (p. 6) In an algebraic expression, the result of quantities being multiplied is called the product.

product rule (p. 578) If (x_1, y_1) and (x_2, y_2) are solutions to an inverse variation, then $y_1x_1 = y_2x_2$.

proportion (p. 105) An equation of the form $\frac{a}{b} = \frac{c}{d}$ stating that two ratios are equivalent.

Pythagorean Theorem (p. 549) If a and b are the measures of the legs of a right triangle and c is the measure of the hypotenuse, then $c^2 = a^2 + b^2$.

Pythagorean triple (p. 550) Whole numbers that satisfy the Pythagorean Theorem.

Q

quadratic equation (p. 480) An equation of the form $ax^2 + bx + c = 0$, where $a \neq 0$.

Quadratic Formula (p. 493) The solutions of a quadratic equation in the form $ax^2 + bx + c = 0$, where $a \neq 0$, are given by the formula $x = \frac{-b \pm \sqrt{b^2 - 4ac}}{2a}$

quadratic function (p. 471) An equation of the form $y = ax^2 + bx + c$, where $a \neq 0$.

Glosario

rectas paralelas Rectas en el mismo plano que no se intersecan jamás y que tienen pendientes iguales.

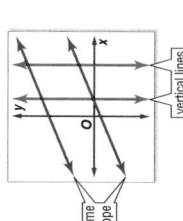

la misma pendiente / rectas verticales

gráfica madre La gráfica más sencilla en una familia de gráficas.

porcentaje de cambio Cuando un aumento o disminución se escribe como un tanto por ciento.

porcentaje de disminución Razón de la cantidad de disminución a la cantidad original, escrita como un tanto por ciento.

porcentaje de aumento Razón de la cantidad de aumento a la cantidad original, escrita como un tanto por ciento.

cuadrado perfecto Número cuya raíz cuadrada es un número racional.

trinomio cuadrado perfecto Un trinomio que es el cuadrado de un binomio.
$(a + b)^2 = (a + b)(a + b) = a^2 + 2ab + b^2$ o
$(a - b)^2 = (a - b)(a - b) = a^2 - 2ab - b^2$

permutación Arreglo o lista en que el orden es importante.

función por partes Función que se escribe usando dos o más expresiones.

forma punto-pendiente Ecuación de la forma $y - y_1 = m(x - x_1)$, donde m es la pendiente y (x_1, y_1) es un punto dado de una recta no vertical.

polinomio Un monomio o la suma de monomios.

población Grupo grande de datos, representado por lo general por una muestra.

correlación positiva En una gráfica de dispersión, a medida que x aumenta, y aumenta.

número positivos Cualquier valor mayor que cero.

potencia Una expresión de la forma x^n, se lee x a la enésima potencia.

factorización prima Número entero escrito como producto de factores primos.

número primo Número entero mayor que 1 cuyos únicos factores son 1 y sí mismo.

polinomio primo Polinomio que no puede escribirse como producto de dos polinomios con coeficientes enteros.

raíz cuadrada principal La raíz cuadrada no negativa de un número.

distribución de probabilidad Probabilidad de cada valor posible de una variable aleatoria x.

histograma probabilístico Una manera de exhibir la distribución de probabilidad de una variable aleatoria y obtener otros datos.

producto En una expresión algebraica, se llama producto al resultado de las cantidades que se multiplican.

regla del producto Si (x_1, y_1) y (x_2, y_2) son soluciones de una variación inversa, entonces $y_1x_1 = y_2x_2$.

proporción Ecuación de la forma $\frac{a}{b} = \frac{c}{d}$ que afirma la equivalencia de dos razones.

Teorema de Pitágoras Si a y b son las longitudes de los catetos de un triángulo rectángulo y si c es la longitud de la hipotenusa, entonces $c^2 = a^2 + b^2$.

Triple pitagórico Números enteros que satisfacen el Teorema de Pitágoras.

Q

ecuación cuadrática Ecuación de la forma $ax^2 + bx + c = 0$, donde $a \neq 0$.

Fórmula cuadrática Las soluciones de una ecuación cuadrática de la forma $ax^2 + bx + c = 0$, donde $a \neq 0$, vienen dadas por la fórmula $x = \frac{-b \pm \sqrt{b^2 - 4ac}}{2a}$

función cuadrática Función de la forma $y = ax^2 + bx + c$, donde $a \neq 0$.

Glossary/Glosario

R

ecuaciones radicales Ecuaciones que contienen radicales con variables en el radicando.

expresión radical Expresión que contiene una raíz cuadrada.

signo radical El símbolo $\sqrt{\ }$, que se usa para indicar la raíz cuadrada no negativa.

radicando La expresión debajo del signo radical.

muestra aleatoria Muestra tomada sin preferencia alguna y que es representativa de toda la población.

variable aleatoria Una variable cuyos valores son los resultados numéricos de un evento aleatorio.

rango Conjunto de los segundos números de los pares ordenados de una relación.

tasa Razón de dos medidas que tienen distintas unidades de medida.

tasa de cambio Cómo cambia una cantidad con el tiempo.

problemas de tasas Ecuaciones racionales que se usan para resolver problemas de tasas de transportación.

razón Comparación de dos números mediante división.

aproximación racional Número racional que está cercano, pero que no es igual, al valor de un número irracional.

ecuaciones racionales Ecuaciones que contienen xpresiones racionales.

expresión racional Fracción algebraica cuyo numerador y denominador son polinomios.

racionalizar el denominador Método que se usa para eliminar radicales del denominador de una fracción.

números racionales Conjunto de los números que pueden escribirse en forma de fracción $\frac{a}{b}$, donde a y b son enteros y $b \neq 0$.

radical equations (p. 541) Equations that contain radicals with variables in the radicand.

radical expression (p. 528) An expression that contains a square root.

radical sign (p. 49) The symbol $\sqrt{\ }$, used to indicate a nonnegative square root.

radicand (p. 528) The expression that is under the radical sign.

random sample (p. 642) A sample that is chosen without any preference, representative of the entire population.

random variable (p. 672) A variable with a value that is the numerical outcome of a random event.

range (p. 55) The set of second numbers of the ordered pairs in a relation.

rate (p. 107) The ratio of two measurements having different units of measure.

rate of change (p. 187) How a quantity is changing over time.

rate problems (p. 628) Rational equations are used to solve problems involving transportal rates.

ratio (p. 105) A comparison of two numbers by division.

rational approximation (p. 50) A rational number that is close to, but not equal to, the value of an irrational number.

rational equations (p. 626) Equations that contain rational expressions.

rational expression (p. 583) An algebraic fraction with a numerator and denominator that are polynomials.

rationalizing the denominator (p. 530) A method used to eliminate radicals from the denominator of a fraction.

rational numbers (p. 46) The set of numbers expressed in the form of a fraction $\frac{a}{b}$, where a and b are integers and $b \neq 0$.

números reales El conjunto de los números racionales junto con el conjunto de los números irracionales.

recíproco Inverso multiplicativo de un número.

relación Conjunto de pares ordenados.

frecuencia relativa Número de veces que aparece un resultado en un experimento probabilístico.

conjunto de sustitución Conjunto de números del cual se pueden escoger sustituciones para una variable.

raíces Las soluciones de una ecuación cuadrática.

real numbers (p. 46) The set of rational numbers and the set of irrational numbers together.

reciprocal (p. 21) The multiplicative inverse of a number.

relation (p. 55) A set of ordered pairs.

relative frequency (p. 677) The number of times an outcome occurred in a probability experiment.

replacement set (p. 15) A set of numbers from which replacements for a variable may be chosen.

roots (p. 428) The solutions of a quadratic equation.

S

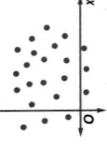

muestra Porción de un grupo más grande que se escoge para representarlo.

espacio muestral Lista de todos los resultados posibles.

escala Razón o tasa que se usa al construir un modelo de algo que es demasiado grande o pequeño como para mostrarlo de tamaño natural.

gráfica de dispersión Dos conjuntos de datos graficados como pares ordenados en un plano de coordenadas.

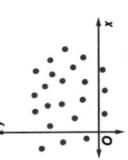

sucesión Conjunto de números en un orden específico.

conjunto Colección de objetos o números, que a menudo se exhiben usando paréntesis de corchete { } y se identifican por lo general mediante una letra mayúscula.

sample (p. 642) Some portion of a larger group selected to represent that group.

sample space (p. 650) The list of all possible outcomes.

scale (p. 108) A ratio or rate used when making a model of something that is too large or too small to be conveniently shown at actual size.

scatter plot (p. 227) Two sets of data plotted as ordered pairs in a coordinate plane.

sequence (p. 165) A set of numbers in a specific order.

set (p. 15) A collection of objects or numbers, often shown using braces { } and usually named by a capital letter.

Glossary/Glosario (English)

set-builder notation (p. 295) A concise way of writing a solution set. For example, $\{t \mid t < 17\}$ represents the set of all numbers t such that t is less than 17.

similar triangles (p. 560) Triangles having the same shape but not necessarily the same size.

simple event (pp. 98, 663) A single event.

simple random sample (p. 642) A sample that is as likely to be chosen as any other from the population.

simplest form (p. 29) An expression is in simplest form when it is replaced by an equivalent expression having no like terms or parentheses.

simulation (p. 678) Using an object to act out an event that would be difficult or impractical to perform.

slope (p. 189) The ratio of the change in the y-coordinates (rise) to the corresponding change in the x-coordinates (run) as you move from one point to another along a line.

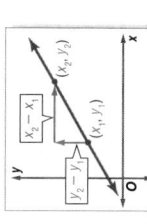

slope-intercept form (p. 204) An equation of the form $y = mx + b$, where m is the slope and b is the y-intercept.

solution (pp. 15, 214) A replacement value for the variable in an open sentence.

solution set (p. 15) The set of elements from the replacement set that make an open sentence true.

solve an equation (p. 79) The process of finding all values of the variable that make the equation a true statement.

solving an open sentence (p. 15) Finding a replacement value for the variable that results in a true sentence or an ordered pair that results in a true statement when substituted into the equation.

Glossary/Glosario (English, R17)

square root (p. 46) One of two equal factors of a number.

standard form (p. 155) The standard form of a linear equation is $Ax + By = C$, where $A \geq 0$, A and B are not both zero, and A, B, and C are integers with a greatest common factor of 1.

stratified random sample (p. 642) A sample in which the population is first divided into similar, nonoverlapping groups; a simple random sample is then selected from each group.

substitution (p. 260) Use algebraic methods to find an exact solution of a system of equations.

symmetry (p. 472) A geometric property of figures that can be folded and each half matches the other exactly.

system of equations (p. 253) A set of equations with the same variables.

system of inequalities (p. 341) A set of two or more inequalities with the same variables.

systematic random sample (p. 642) A sample in which the items in the sample are selected according to a specified time or item interval.

T

term (p. 29) A number, a variable, or a product or quotient of numbers and variables.

terms (p. 165) The numbers in a sequence.

theoretical probability (p. 677) What should happen in a probability experiment.

tree diagram (p. 650) A diagram used to show the total number of possible outcomes.

trinomials (p. 376) The sum of three monomials.

U

uniform motion problems (p. 123) Problems in which an object moves at a certain speed or rate.

Glosario (Español, R16)

notación de construcción de conjuntos Manera concisa de escribir un conjunto solución. Por ejemplo, $\{t \mid t < 17\}$ representa el conjunto de todos los números t que son menores o iguales que 17.

semejantes Que tienen la misma forma, pero no necesariamente el mismo tamaño.

evento simple Un sólo evento.

muestra aleatoria simple Muestra de una población que tiene la misma probabilidad de escogerse que cualquier otra.

forma reducida Una expresión está reducida cuando se puede sustituir por una expresión equivalente que no tiene ni términos semejantes ni paréntesis.

simulación Uso de un objeto para representar un evento que pudiera ser difícil o poco práctico de ejecutar.

pendiente Razón del cambio en la coordenada y (elevación) al cambio correspondiente en la coordenada x (desplazamiento) a medida que uno se mueve de un punto a otro en una recta.

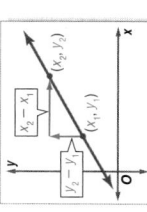

forma pendiente-intersección Ecuación de la forma $y = mx + b$, donde m es la pendiente y b es la intersección y.

solución Valor de sustitución de la variable en un enunciado abierto.

conjunto solución Conjunto de elementos del conjunto de sustitución que hacen verdadero un enunciado abierto.

resolver una ecuación Proceso en que se hallan todos los valores de la variable que hacen verdadera la ecuación.

resolver un enunciado abierto Hallar un valor de sustitución de la variable que resulte en un enunciado verdadero o un par ordenado que resulte en una proposición verdadera cuando se lo sustituye en la ecuación.

Glosario (Español, R17)

raíz cuadrada Uno de dos factores iguales de un número.

forma estándar La forma estándar de una ecuación lineal es $Ax + By = C$, donde $A \geq 0$, ni A ni B son ambos cero, y A, B, y C son enteros cuyo máximo común divisor es 1.

muestra aleatoria estratificada Muestra en que la población se divide en grupos similares que no se sobreponen; luego se selecciona una muestra aleatoria simple, de cada grupo.

sustitución Usa métodos algebraicos para hallar una solución exacta a un sistema de ecuaciones.

simetría Propiedad geométrica de figuras que pueden plegarse de modo que cada mitad corresponde exactamente a la otra.

sistema de ecuaciones Conjunto de ecuaciones con las mismas variables.

sistema de desigualdades Conjunto de dos o más desigualdades con las mismas variables.

muestra aleatoria sistemática Muestra en que los elementos de la muestra se escogen según un intervalo de tiempo o elemento específico.

término Número, variable o producto, o cociente de números y variables.

términos Los números de una sucesión.

probabilidad teórica Lo que debería ocurrir en un experimento probabilístico.

diagrama de árbol Diagrama que se usa para mostrar el número total de resultados posibles.

trinomios Suma de tres monomios.

problemas de movimiento uniforme Problemas en que el cuerpo se mueve a cierta velocidad o tasa.

Glossary/Glosario

union (p. 316) The graph of a compound inequality containing *or*; the solution is a solution of either inequality, not necessarily both.

V

variable (p. 6) Symbols used to represent unspecified numbers or values.

vertex (p. 472) The maximum or minimum point of a parabola.

vertical line test (p. 150) If any vertical line passes through no more than one point of the graph of a relation, then the relation is a function.

voluntary response sample (p. 643) A sample that involves only those who want to participate.

W

weighted average (p. 122) The sum of the product of the number of units and the value per unit divided by the sum of the number of units, represented by M.

whole numbers (p. 46) The set {0, 1, 2, 3, …}.

work problems (p. 627) Rational equations are used to solve problems involving work rates.

X

x-axis (p. 53) The horizontal number line on a coordinate plane.

unión Gráfica de una desigualdad compuesta que contiene la palabra *or*; la solución es el conjunto de soluciones de por lo menos una de las desigualdades, no necesariamente ambas.

variable Símbolos que se usan para representar números o valores no especificados.

vértice Punto máximo o mínimo de una parábola.

prueba de la recta vertical Si cualquier recta vertical pasa por un sólo punto de la gráfica de una relación, entonces la relación es una función.

muestra de respuesta voluntaria Muestra que involucra sólo aquellos que quieren participar.

promedio ponderado Suma del producto del número de unidades por el valor unitario dividida entre la suma del número de unidades y la cual se denota por M.

números enteros El conjunto {0, 1, 2, 3, …}.

problemas de trabajo Las ecuaciones racionales se usan para resolver problemas de tasas de trabajo.

eje x Recta numérica horizontal que forma parte de un plano de coordenadas.

---

x-coordinate (p. 53) The first number in an ordered pair.

Y

y-axis (p. 53) The vertical number line on a coordinate plane.

y-coordinate (p. 53) The second number in an ordered pair.

Z

zeros (p. 480) The roots, or x-intercepts, of a quadratic function.

coordenada x El primer número de un par ordenado.

eje y Recta numérica vertical que forma parte de un plano de coordenadas.

coordenada y El segundo número de un par ordenado.

ceros Las raíces o intersecciones x de una función cuadrática.

Selected Answers

Chapter 1 The Language and Tools of Algebra

Page 5   **Chapter 1**   **Get Ready**

1. 4   3. $\frac{3}{5}$ 5. $\frac{13}{50}$ 7. 17   9. $\frac{1}{6}$ 11. 19.1 cm
13. $135\frac{3}{4}$ ft   15. 6.72   17. 1.8   19. 9   21. $\frac{5}{12}$

Pages 8–9   **Lesson 1-1**

1. $n + 14$ 3. $3n - 24$ 5. $\frac{5}{2}j^2$ 7. $20 - p$
9. 256   11. Sample answer: one half of n cubed
13. $7 + x$ 15. $5n$ 17. $\frac{7}{10}$ 19. $49 + 2x$ 21. $k^2 - 11$
23. πr^2 25. 14 lb   27. 1,000,000   29. 3375
31. Sample answer: one eighth of y 33. Sample
answer: w minus 24   35. Sample answer: r to the
fourth power divided by 9   37. Sample answer:
n cubed times p to the fifth power   39. Sample answer:
12 times z squared divided by 5   41. $s + 12d$
43. Sometimes; the product is negative when a is a
positive number, the product is positive when a is a
negative value. The product is zero when a is
zero.   45. Sample answer: You can use the expression
$4s$ to find the perimeter of a baseball diamond. The
perimeter of a baseball diamond is four times the
length of the sides and the sum of the four sides;
$s + s + s + s$.   47. G   49. 6.76   51. 3.2   53. $\frac{1}{6}$

Pages 12–14   **Lesson 1-2**

1. 23   3. 67   5. 26   7. $\frac{3}{5}$ or $\frac{1}{5}$ 9. $\frac{11}{150}$ 11. 20
13. $n(2n + 3)$; 44 cm^2 15. 14   17. 4   19. 14   21. 142
23. 36   25. 3   27. 1   29. 9   31. 149   33. 50(7.5) +
90(5); $825   35. 4   37. 55   39. $\frac{3}{32}$ 41. $s + 12c + 4b$
43. Chase; Leonora squared the incorrect quantity.
45. Sample answer: using 1, 2, 3; $1 + 2 + 3 = 6$; $1 + 2 \cdot$
$3 = 7$; $1 \cdot 2 + 3 = 5$; $3 - 2 \cdot 1 = 1$; $(2 - 1) \cdot 3 = 3$ 47. B
49. 13p 51. 20 + 2n 53. 23,500 + 14m 55. Sample
answer: q squared minus 12   57. 0.425   59. 15.42
61. $3\frac{11}{35}$

Pages 18–20   **Lesson 1-3**

1. 13   3. 12   5. 18   7. 27   9. 5   11. [10, 15, 20, 25]
13. 39n + 10.95 ≤ 102.50; 2 sweaters   15. 12   17. 17
19. 3   21. 5   23. 4   25. 78   27. 8   29. 5   31. 11
33. 3550 = 75x; about 47 light bulbs   35. {4, 5, 6, 7}
37. {12, 14, 16}   39. 3(41.99) + 26.99c ≤ 300, where c is
the number of children. 6 children could go to the park
with 3 adults.   41. $\frac{1}{3}$ 43. 2.4   45. [3.5, 4]
47. 1000 Calories   49. Sample answer: $x \geq 8$
represents the inequality because it includes the set
of all whole numbers greater than or equal to 8.
51. The solution set includes all numbers less than
or equal to $\frac{1}{3}$.   53. B   55. D   57. 53   59. 1004
61. Sample answer: n to the fifth power minus 8

63. Sample answer: 6 divided by the product of 5 and a
65. $6 + \frac{1}{2}n$ 67. $\frac{1}{4}n^3$ 69. $\frac{4}{21}$ 71. $\frac{2}{7}$ 73. $\frac{11}{15}$

Pages 23–25   **Lesson 1-4**

1. 0; Multiplicative Property of Zero
3. 6; Multiplicative Inverse
5. 6(12 − 48 ÷ 4)
   = 6(12 − 12)   Substitution
   = 6(0)   Substitution
   = 0 Multiplicative Property of Zero
7. 4(20) + 7
   = 80 + 7 Substitution
   = 87 Substitution; 87 yr
9. 5; Multiplicative Identity
11. 0; Additive Identity   13. $\frac{1}{2}$; Multiplicative Inverse
15. 1; Multiplicative Inverse   17. $\frac{1}{2}$; Additive Inverse
19. $7 + (9 - 3^2)$
   = $7 + (9 - 9)$ Substitution
   = $7 + 0$ Substitution
   = 7 Additive Identity
21. $[3 \div (2 \cdot 1)]\frac{2}{3}$
   = $[3 \div 2]\frac{2}{3}$ Multiplicative Identity
   = $\frac{3}{2} \cdot \frac{2}{3}$ Substitution
   = 1 Multiplicative Inverse
23. $6 \cdot \frac{1}{6} + 5(12 \div 4 - 3)$
   = $6 \cdot \frac{1}{6} + 5(3 - 3)$ Substitution
   = $6 \cdot \frac{1}{6} + 5(0)$ Substitution
   = $6 \cdot \frac{1}{6} + 0$ Multiplicative Prop. of Zero
   = $1 + 0$ Multiplicative Inverse
   = 1 Additive Identity
25. $2 \cdot \frac{22}{7} \cdot 14^2 + 2 \cdot \frac{22}{7} \cdot 14 \cdot 7$
   = $2 \cdot \frac{22}{7} \cdot 196 + 2 \cdot \frac{22}{7} \cdot 14 \cdot 7$ Substitution
   = $\frac{44}{7} \cdot 196 + \frac{44}{7} \cdot 14 \cdot 7$ Substitution
   = 1232 + 616 Substitution
   = 1848 Substitution; 1848 in^2
27. 3; Multiplicative Identity
29. $3 + 5(4 - 2^2) - 1$
   = $3 + 5(4 - 4) - 1$ Substitution
   = $3 + 5(0) - 1$ Substitution
   = $3 + 0 - 1$ Multiplicative Property of Zero
   = $3 - 1$ Additive Identity
   = 2 Substitution
31. $[\frac{5}{8}(1 + \frac{1}{5})] \cdot 17$
   = $\frac{5}{8}(\frac{6}{5}) \cdot 17$ Substitution
   = $1 \cdot 17$ Multiplicative Inverse
   = 17 Multiplicative Identity
33. $25(2 - 0.3) + 80(2.5 - 1) + 40(10 - 6)$

35. Sometimes; sample answer: true: $x = 2$, $y = 1$, $z = 4$, $w = 3$; $2 \cdot 4 > 1 \cdot 3$; false: $x = 1$, $y = -1$, $z = -2$, $w = -3$; $1(-2) < (-1)(-3)$ 37. Sample answer: $5 = 3 + 2$ and $3 + 2 = 4 + 1$, so $5 = 4 + 1$; $5 + 7 = 8 + 4$, and $8 + 4 = 12$, so $5 + 7 = 12$.   39. You can use the Identity and Equality properties to see if data is the same. Answers should include the following; Reflexive: $r = r$, or Symmetric: $a = b$, so $b = a$; Southern California, week 1 = a, week 2 = b, week 3 = c, $a = b$ and $b = c$, so $a = c$. 41. J   43. [11, 12, 13]   45. 2(213) − 59; $367   47. 80
49. 28

Pages 29–31

1. $6(12) - 6(3)$; 54   3. $19(10) + 3(10)$; 220   5. $16(100 + 3)$; 1648   7. $8 + 2t$ 9. $14m$ 11. $9x$ 13. $7(13) + 7(12)$;
175   15. $3(15) + 8(15)$; 165   17. $10(13) - 7(13)$; 39
19. $4(110,000 + 17,500)$; 510,000   21. $8(900 + 90)$; 7920
23. $(3 + \frac{1}{6})48$; 152   25. $15 + 3n$ 27. $-3x + 18$
29. $9b - 1$ 31. $17a^2 + a$ 33. $45x - 75$ 35. $\frac{4}{7}1956$
37. $4p + 4q - 4r$ 39. $30m^3 + 5n$ 41. $7y^3 + y^4$
43. Sample answer: The numbers inside the
parentheses are each multiplied by the number outside
the parentheses, then the products are added.
45. Courtney; she correctly used the Distributive
Property.   47. You can use the Distributive Property to
calculate quickly by expressing any number as a sum
or difference of a more convenient number. Answers
should include the following; Both methods result in
the correct answer. In one method you multiply then
add, and in the other you add then multiply.
49. J   51. Multiplicative Identity   53. Reflexive
55. 15   57. 9   59. 168 cm^2

Pages 35–37   **Lesson 1-6**

1. Sample answer:
$14 + 18 + 26$
   = $14 + 26 + 18$ Commutative (+)
   = $(14 + 26) + (18)$ Associative (+)
   = $40 + 18$ Add.
   = 58 Add.
3. Sample answer:
$5 \cdot 3 \cdot 6 \cdot 4$
   = $5 \cdot 6 \cdot 3 \cdot 4$ Commutative (×)
   = $(5 \cdot 6) \cdot (3 \cdot 4)$ Associative (×)
   = 30 · 12 Multiply.
   = 360 Multiply.
5. $10x + 5y$ 7. $14x + 6$ 9. $xy + 10 + 2x$ 11. 60
13. 16   15. 12   17. 440   19. 4.8   21. 60   23. 46.8 in^2
25. $5a + 2b$ 27. $6x^2 + 5x$ 29. $10x + 14$
31. $2(s + t) - s$
   = $2(s) + 2(t) - s$ Distributive
   = $2s + 2t - s$ Multiply.
   = $2t + 2s - s$ Commutative (+)
   = $2t + s(2 - 1)$ Distributive
   = $2t + s(1)$ Subtract.
   = $2t + s$ Multiplicative Identity
33. $6z^2 + (7 + z^2 + 6)$
   = $6z^2 + (z^2 + 7 + 6)$ Commutative (+)
   = $(6z^2 + z^2) + (7 + 6)$ Associative (+)
   = $z^2(6 + 1) + (7 + 6)$ Distributive
   = $z^2(7) + 13$ Add.
   = $7z^2 + 13$ Multiply.

35. $5q$ 37. $20m + 3n + 2mm$ 39. $\frac{3}{4} + \frac{5}{5} + \frac{4}{3}$
41. $291   43. $149.35   45. $n \div 2 = 2 \div n$; This equation
is true for $n = 2$ or $n = -2$ only because division is not
commutative. The other three sentences illustrate the
Commutative Property of Addition or Multiplication
and are therefore true for all values of the variables.
47. You can use the Commutative and Associative
Properties to rearrange and group numbers for easier
calculations. Answers should include: $d = (0.4 + 1.1) +$
$(1.5 + 1.5) + (1.9 + 1.8 + 0.8)$.   49. J   51. simplified
53. $15 + 6p$ 55. $8d + 40 + 2f$ 57. Sample answer:
$50x \leq 180$; 3 loads   59. 60   61. 13

Pages 42–44   **Lesson 1-7**

1. H: it is April; C: it might rain   3. H. $34 - 3x = 16$;
C: $x = 6$ 5. H: a number is divisible by 10; C: it is
divisible by 5; If a number is divisible by 10, then it is
divisible by 5.   7. The number is divisible by 2.   9. No
valid conclusion; the last digit is a 6.   11. A book can
have more than 384 pages.   13. $x = 15$ 15. H: both
parents have red hair; C: their children have red
hair   17. H: $2n - 7 > 25$; C: $n > 16$ 19. H: it is
Monday; C: the trash is picked up; If it is Monday, then
the trash is picked up.   21. H: $x = 8$; C: $x^2 - 3x = 40$; If
$x = 8$, then $x^2 - 3x = 40$.   23. H: a triangle with all
sides congruent; C: it is an equilateral triangle; If all the
sides of a triangle are congruent, then it is an
equilateral triangle.   25. Ian will buy a DVD box
set.   27. The DVD box set cost $70 or more.
29. A person born in North Carolina moved to
California.   31. $2 \cdot 3 = 6$ 33. $4(15) - 8 = 52$
35. Sample answer:

     37. The perimeter is
     doubled.   41. Sample
     answer: If a number is
     divisible by 2 and 3,
then it must be a multiple of 6.   43. No; sample answer:
Let $a = 1$ and $b = 2$; then $1 * 2 = 1 + 2(2)$ or 5 and
$2 * 1 = 2 + 2(1)$ or 4.   45. Sample answer: You can use
deductive reasoning to determine whether a hypothesis
and its conclusion are both true or whether one or both
are false.   47. A   49. A   51. $23mm + 24$ 53. $100d +$
$80d + 8d$; $(100 + 80 + 8)d$ 55. 7: Reflexive   57. $\frac{1}{4}$:
Multiplicative Inverse   59. 0: Multiplicative Property
of Zero   61. 64   63. 132.25

Pages 50–52   **Lesson 1-8**

1. integers, rationals   3. irrationals   5. No; Sample
answer: $3 \div 4 = \frac{3}{4}$
7. Yes; Sample answer: $3.2 \div 1.5 = 2.1\overline{3}$
9.

   -5–4–3–2–1 0 1 2 3 4 5 6 7 8
11.

   –8–7–6–5–4–3–2–1 0 1
13. 1.2   15. 19   17. >   19. <   21. $\sqrt{\frac{1}{30}}, \frac{4}{5}\sqrt{30}, 13$
23. naturals, wholes, integers, rationals   25. rationals
27. irrationals   29. No; Sample answer: $\sqrt{5} - \sqrt{5} = 0$
31. Yes; Sample answer: $3 \times 2 = 6$ 33. No; Sample
answer: $2\sqrt{3} \div \sqrt{3} = 2$ 35. Yes; Sample answer:
$\frac{3}{5} - \frac{1}{5} = \frac{2}{5}$ 37. Yes; Sample answer: $-3 \times -8 = 24$

39. $\leftarrow\!\!\mid\!\!\mid\!\!\mid\!\!\mid\!\!\mid\!\!\mid\!\!\mid\!\!\mid\!\!\rightarrow$ -2 -1 0 1 2 3 4 5 6

41. $\leftarrow\!\!\rightarrow$ -10 -9

43. ±0.8 45. -2.5 47. $\frac{5}{18}$ 49. < 51. < 53. $\frac{5}{9}$
55. $-\sqrt{\frac{5}{8}}$, -0.25, 0.1̄4̄, $\sqrt{0.5}$ 57. 6 59. 12
61. Side lengths: 1 unit, 2 units, 3 units, 4 units, 5 units; Perimeters: 4 units, 8 units, 12 units, 16 units, 20 units
63. $4\sqrt{3}$ 65. True; the average of $\sqrt{2}$ and $\sqrt{3}$ is a decimal number that does not terminate or repeat, so it is irrational. 69. C 71. 3 + 3 = 6 73. 9x + 2y
75. 4 + 80x + 32y 77. $48

Pages 56-58   Lesson 1-9
1. (2, 35); On day 2, the average temperature is about 35°F. 3. independent: day; dependent: temperature
5. Graph B
7.

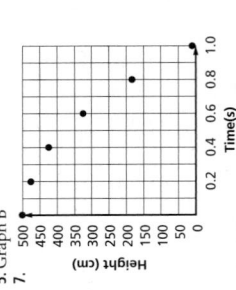

9. The function is discrete because the points are not connected with a line or a curve. 11. (5, 25); The dog walker earns $25 for walking 5 dogs. 13. (02, 3); In the year 2002, sales were about $3 million. 15. independent: year; dependent: sales 17. Their altitude is increasing as they ascend. Then they go down a steep incline. They then make a longer climb up another hill. 19. Graph B
21. $\leftarrow\!\!\mid\!\!\mid\!\!\mid\!\!\mid\!\!\mid\!\!\mid\!\!\mid\!\!\mid\!\!\mid\!\!\mid\!\!\mid\!\!\rightarrow$ -2 -1 0 1 2 3 4 5 6 7 8

35. $ab(a + b) = (ab)a + (ab)b$ Distributive
$= a(ab) + (ab)b$ Commutative (×)
$= (a · a)b + a(b · b)$ Associative (×)
$= a^2b + ab^2$ Substitution
37. 3x - 10

Pages 60-64   Chapter 1   Study Guide and Review
1. true 3. false; set 5. false; real 7. true 9. $5y^2$
11. 2k - 8 13. 32 15. six times the square of a number p 17. 20b 19. 3 21. 34 23. 96 25. 20
27. [7] 29. [5] 31. 13 33. 35 35. p = 15(3) +9(1); p = $54 37. $-\frac{1}{5}$; Multiplicative Inverse
39. $3(4 ÷ 4)^2 - \frac{1}{4}(4) = 3(1)^2 - \frac{1}{4}(4)$ Substitution
$= 3(1) - \frac{1}{4}(4)$ Substitution
$= 3 - \frac{1}{4}(4)$ Multiplicative Inverse
$= 3 - 1$ Multiplicative Inverse
$= 2$ Substitution
41. $\frac{1}{2} · 2 + 2[2 · 3 - 1] = \frac{1}{2} · 2 + 2[6 - 1]$ Substitution
$= \frac{1}{2} · 2 + 2(5)$ Substitution
$= \frac{1}{2} · 2 + 10$ Substitution
$= 1 + 10$ Multiplicative Inverse
$= 11$ Substitution
43. 8(15) - 8(6) = 72 45. 2w + 7v 47. 9(550 + 225 + 110 + 150) = $9,315 49. 6 + 30x 51. H: it is a school day; C: the day begins at 7:30 A.M.; If it is a school day, then the day begins at 7:30 A.M. 53. H: lightning has struck twice; C: it has not done so in the same place; If lightning has struck twice, then it has not done so in the same place. 55. irrationals
57. $\leftarrow\!\!\mid\!\!\mid\!\!\mid\!\!\mid\!\!\mid\!\!\mid\!\!\mid\!\!\mid\!\!\mid\!\!\mid\!\!\mid\!\!\rightarrow$ -2 -1 0 1 2 3 4 5 6 7 8

59. $-\sqrt{34}$, $-\frac{47}{9}$, $\sqrt{27}$, and $5\frac{1}{5}$ 61. (2, 60); This represents a score of 60 on the math test with 2 hours of study. 63. Graph C

Chapter 2 Solving Linear Equations

Page 69   Chapter 2   Get Ready
1. $\frac{1}{2} + 5$ 3. $3a + b^2$ 5. 15 7. 16 9. 63 11. 5
13. $40 15. 300% 17. 51%

Pages 73-76   Lesson 2-1
1. 2t - 8 = 70 3. $\frac{1}{2}p = p - 3$ 5. 1900 + 30w = 2500; 20 weeks 7. C = 2πr 9. Sample answer: 14 plus d equals 6 times d. 11. Sample answer: The original cost of a suit is c. After a $25 discount, the suit costs $150. What is the original cost of the suit? 13. Sample answer: 2r + 3s = 13 15. Sample answer: 200 - 3n = 9 17. Sample answer: $m^2 - n^3 = 16$ 19. 0.46E = P
21. 1912 + y = 1928; 16 yr 23. A = bh

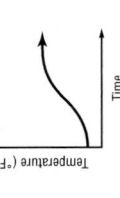

25. P = 2(a + b) 27. Sample answer: d minus 14 equals 5. 29. Sample answer: k squared plus 17 equals 53 minus j. 31. Sample answer: $\frac{3}{4}$ of p plus $\frac{1}{2}$ equals p. 33. Sample answer: Lindsey is 7 inches taller than Yolanda. If 2 times Yolanda's height plus Lindsey's height equals 193 inches, find Yolanda's height. 35. $\frac{1}{2}(9 + n) = n - 3$ 37. $V = \frac{1}{3}\pi r^2h$
39. $V = \frac{4}{3}\pi r^3$ 41. 4a + 15 43. 9 min
45. Sample answer: 4 times the quantity t minus s equals 5 times s plus 12.
47. Sample answer: $S = 3ah + \frac{a^2\sqrt{3}}{2}$; the area of the two triangular bases is $2\left(\frac{1}{2}\right)(a)\left(\frac{a\sqrt{3}}{2}\right)$, which simplifies to $\frac{a^2\sqrt{3}}{2}$. The area of the three rectangular sides is 3ah. So, the total surface area S is the sum $3ah + \frac{a^2\sqrt{3}}{2}$.
49. Sample answer: Equations can be used to describe the relationships of the heights of various parts of a structure. The equation representing the Sears Tower is 1454 + a = 1707. 51. J 53. 90 55. 9.49 57. 8d + 3
59. 8a + 6b 61. 396 63. 3.37 65. 1.65 67. $\frac{5}{6}$

Pages 81-84   Lesson 2-2
1. 25 3. -3 5. -13 7. $\frac{3}{10}$ 9. $\frac{5}{6}$ 11. n + 91 = 37; -54 13. 23 15. -43 17. 22 19. -19 21. 73
23. $-1\frac{1}{9}$ 25. $1\frac{1}{8}$ 27. n - 18 = 31; 49 29. n + (-16) = -21; -5 31. Sample equation: $\ell + 10 = 34$; 24 mi 33. -4.4 35. 7.7 37. 11.03 39. $n - \frac{1}{2} = -\frac{3}{4}$; $-\frac{1}{4}$ 41. $\ell + 8.1 = 24.9$; 16.8 h 43. -19 45. 14.6 + x = 14.7; 0.1 million volumes 47. 28.7 + 14.7 + 14.6 = x; 58.0 million volumes 51a. Sometimes; if ix = 0, x + x = x is true. 51b. Always; any number plus 0 always equals the number. 53. C 55. $A = \pi r^2$
57. < 59. = 61. H: y = 2; C: 4y - 6 = 2; If y = 2, then 4y - 6 = 2. 63. 18.20 65. $\frac{5}{12}$

Pages 88-90   Lesson 2-3
1. -35 3. 15 5. -36 7. 10 m 9. 5 11. 42
13. $\frac{1}{3} = -7n$; $-\frac{1}{21}$ 15. -77 17. $5\frac{1}{3}$ 19. -10
21. $-1\frac{3}{7}$ 23. 18 25. 225 27. about 95 ft
29. -5 31. -7 33. 14 35. $\frac{2}{5}n = -24$; -60
37. $12 = \frac{1}{5}n$; 60 39. $\frac{11}{15}$ 41. 2.1 43. -3.5
45. $2\frac{1}{2}n = 1\frac{1}{5}$; $\frac{12}{15}$ 47. 0.48 s 49. 8x 51. 53 g; 424 g
53. Sample answer: Both properties can be used to solve equations. The Multiplication Property of Equality says you can multiply each side of an equation by the same number. The Division Property of Equality says you can divide each side of an equation by the same number. Dividing each side of an equation by a number is the same as multiplying each side of the equation by the number's reciprocal. 55. Camila; to find an equivalent equation with 1n on one side of the equation, you must divide each side by 8 or multiply each side by $\frac{1}{8}$. Casey incorrectly multiplied each side by 8. 57. D 59. 67
61. -72 63. 40 + 3n 65. 0 67. $\frac{3}{19}$

Pages 95-97   Lesson 2-4
1. -1 3. 56 5. 163 7. 12 - 2n = -34; 23 9. n + (n + 1) + (n + 2) = 42; 13, 14, 15 11. -2 13. 5
15. 7 17. -15 19. 23 21. 34 23. $\frac{2}{3}n - 6 = -10$; -6
25. n + (n + 2) + (n + 4) = 51; 15, 17, 19 27. n + (n + 1) + (n + 2) + (n + 3) = 94; 22, 23, 24, 25
29. 450.5 mi 31. 21,000 ft 33. -42.72 35. -56
37. 1.5 39. 2 45. Never; let n and n + 2 be the even numbers and m, m + 2 be the odd numbers. Write and solve the equation n + (n + 2) = m + (m + 2) gives the solution n = m. Thus, n must equal m, so n is not even or m is not odd. 47. D 49. A 51. -120
53. m + 9 = 56; 47 models 55. 13(100 + 1); 1313
57. $5m + \frac{n}{2}$ 59. 3d 61. 14t 63. -3f

Pages 101-103   Lesson 2-5
1. 4 3. 3 5. 3, 4 7. no solution 9. all numbers
11. 4 13. -3 15. -16 17. 1 19. -1 21. -3
23. 3 25. 120 27. 60 29. 17, 19 31. no solution
33. all numbers 35. 30 years 37. -2 39. 4
41. 2.5 43. about 5.6 yr 45. Sample answer: 3(x + 1) = x - 1 47a. Incorrect; the 2 must be distributed over both g and 5; 6. 47b. correct
49. D 51. 90 53. -2
55. (1, 8), (2, 12), (3, 4), (4, 2);

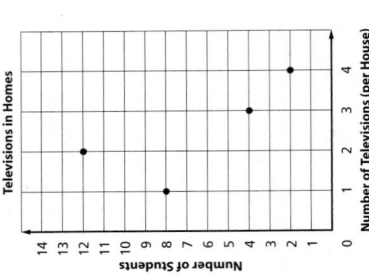

57. $3x^2 + x^2 + 7x$; $4x^2 + 7x$; Distributive Property and Substitution 59. [1, 3, 5] 61. $8\frac{1}{3}$ 63. $\frac{4}{7}$ 65. $\frac{1}{15}$

R24 side (left page)

Pages 108–110   Lesson 2-6

1. yes 3. no 5. 15 7. about 14.6 gal 9. yes 11. no
13. no 15. 20 17. 18 19. $9\frac{1}{3}$ 21. 1.32 23. 0.84
25. 2.28 27. 14 days 29. $4\frac{1}{6}$ ft 31. 19.33 33. 2.56
35. USA: $\frac{907}{2219}$; USSR/UT/Russia: $\frac{525}{1370}$; Germany: $\frac{388}{1230}$;
GB: $\frac{189}{668}$; France: $\frac{199}{631}$; Italy: $\frac{189}{511}$; Sweden: $\frac{140}{476}$ 39. $\frac{9}{19}$
41. C 43. $1\frac{1}{11}$ 45. $3\frac{3}{5}$ 47. −125
49. Sample answer:

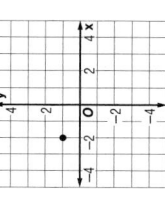

51. 4.3 53. 30% 55. 40%

Pages 113–115   Lesson 2-7

1. dec.; 50% 3. inc.; 14% 5. 347 mi 7. $16.91
9. $13.37 11. dec.; 28% 13. inc.; 193% 15. inc.; 14%
17. dec.; 19% 19. $130,200 21. $37.45 23. $19.66
25. $31.71 27. $4.80 29. $16.25 31. $55.99
33. $52.43 35. 47% 37. China: about 1.52 billion
people; India: about 1.53 billion people; United States:
about 0.39 billion people; India 39. always; $x\%$ of
$y \Rightarrow \frac{x}{100} \cdot y$ or $P = \frac{xy}{100}$; $y\%$ of $x \Rightarrow \frac{y}{100} \cdot x$ or $P = \frac{xy}{100}$
41. Laura; Cory used the new number as the base
instead of the original number. 43. A 45. 9 47. 24
49. −6 51. $75,000 53. 20 55. −3 57. 11

Pages 119–121   Lesson 2-8

1. $x = \frac{b}{9}$ 3. $y = 3c - a$ 5. $h = \frac{2A}{b}$ 7. 24 min
9. $a = \frac{v}{t} - r$ 11. $b = \frac{5}{4} - t$ 13. $m = \frac{5}{3}(b - a)$
15. $y = \frac{3c - 2}{b}$ 17. $t = -\frac{r}{4}$ 19. $a = \frac{2b + c}{5}$
21. $g = \frac{5 + m}{2 + h}$ 23. 6 m 25. 3 errors 27. $t = \frac{-2 - p}{p}$
29. $t - 7 = r + 6$; $t = r + 13$ 31. $\frac{5}{8}x = \frac{1}{2}y + 3$;
$y = \frac{5}{4}x - 6$ 33. 225 lb 35. Sample answer: $A = \frac{5}{2}s^2$;
the area of the square is s^2 and the area of the triangle
is $\frac{1}{2}(3s)(s)$ or $\frac{3}{2}s^2$. So, the total area is $s^2 + \frac{3}{2}s^2$ or $\frac{5}{2}s^2$.
37. Sample answer for a triangle: $A = \frac{1}{2}bh$; $b = \frac{2A}{h}$
39. B 41. 10 g 43. 3.75 45. 12 − 6t 47. −21a − 7b

R24 Selected Answers

Pages 125–128   Lesson 2-9

1.

	Number of Pounds	Price per Pound	Total Price
Votive Wax	8	$0.90	0.90(8)
Low Shrink	p	$1.04	1.04p
Blend	8 + p	$0.98	0.98(8 + p)

3. $10\frac{2}{3}$ lb
5.

	Quarts	Total Amount of Juice
20% Juice	5 − n	0.20(5 − n)
100% Juice	n	1.00n
50% Juice	5	0.50(5)

7. $1\frac{7}{8}$ qt; $3\frac{1}{8}$ qt 9. 10 mph 11. 2 h 13. 87
15.

Number of Ounces	Price per Ounce	Value
Gold	g	$432	432g
Silver	15 − g	$735	735(15 − g)
Alloy	15	$1721	1721(15)

17. 6 oz. 19. 270 rolls of solid wrap, 210 rolls of print
wrap 21. 2.00b + 3.50(b − 36) = 281.00 23. 38 doz
25. 10 gal of cream, 25 gal of 2% milk 27. 22.2 mph
29.

	r	t	d = rt
Eastbound Train	40	h	40h
Westbound Train	30	h	30h

31. $3\frac{1}{2}$ h 33. 90t = 70t + 300 35. No; it takes the
sprinter $\frac{200}{8.2} \approx 24.39$ seconds and his opponent
$\frac{200}{8} = 25$ seconds to run 200 meters. Since the sprinter
lost 1 second at the start, his time would be 25.39,
which is 0.39 second slower than his opponent's
time. 37. Sample answer: grade point average
39. Sample answer: A weighted average is used to
determine a skater's average. The score of the short
program is added to twice the score of the long
program. The sum is divided by 3. $\frac{4.9(1) + 5.2(2)}{1 + 2} = 5.1$
41. H 43. $t = \frac{s - 4}{3}$ 45. increase; 20% 47. Sample
answer: 80 + d = 115; $35

Pages 130–134   Chapter 2   Study Guide and Review

1. true 3. true 5. true 7. true 9. mn = 3(m + 8)

R25 side (right page)

11. Sample answer: The quotient of 56 and g equals
seven minus three times g. 13. Sample answer: Let
s = the millions of sq. km of land surface on Earth;
$\frac{1}{3}s = 50$; s = 150 million km² 15. $-\frac{1}{15}$ 17. −48
19. x + (−71) = 29; 100 21. 203 23. 3 25. $\frac{3}{8}n = 9$; 24
27. 25,000,000x = 45,000,000,000; x = 1800 chopsticks
29. −153 31. 136 33. n + (n + 2) + (n + 4) = 39; 11,
13, and 15 35. 5 37. 160 cans 39. 18 41. dec.; 15%
43. $3.56 45. $k = \frac{4}{7}(s + g)$ or $k = \frac{4(s + g)}{7}$ or $k = \frac{4s + 4g}{7}$
47. $h = \frac{pq - z}{7}$ 49. 27 lb Brand A, 18 lb Brand B
51. $\frac{4}{25}$ mi/min or 0.16 mi/min

Chapter 3 Functions and Patterns

Page 141   Chapter 3   Get Ready

1. 6 3. −21 5. $4.55 7. y = 8 − x 9. $y = -\frac{2}{3}x + 3$
11. y = 3x + 1
13.

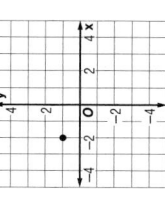

15.

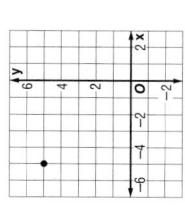

17.

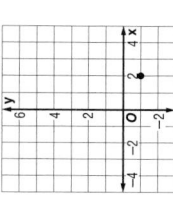

Pages 146–148   Lesson 3-1

1.

x	y
5	−2
8	3
−7	1

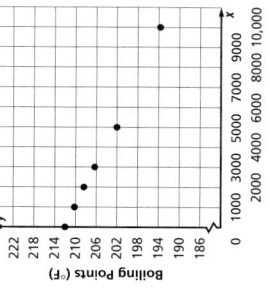

D = {−7, 5, 8}; R = {−2, 1, 3}
3. D = {0, 1000, 2000, 3000, 5000, 10,000}; R = {212.0,
210.2, 208.4, 206.5, 201.9, 193.7}

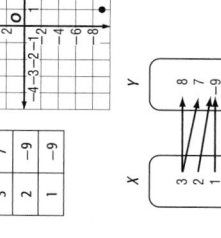

5. {(3, −2), (−6, 7), (4, 3), (−6, 5)}; {(−2, 3), (7, −6),
(3, 4), (5, −6)} 7. {(−1, 2), (2, 4), (3, −3), (4, −1)};
{(2, −1), (4, 2), (−3, 3), (−1, 4)}
9.

x	y
3	8
3	7
2	−9
1	−9

D = {1, 2, 3}; R = {−9, 7, 8}

Selected Answers   **R25**

Left page (R26)

11.

x	y
0	2
-5	1
0	6
-1	9

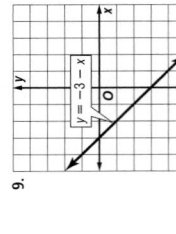

13.

x	y
7	6
3	4
4	5
-2	6
-3	2

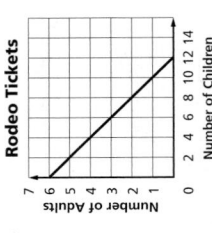

D = {-5, -1, 0}; R = {1, 2, 6, 9}

D = {-3, -2, 3, 4, 7}; R = {2, 4, 5, 6}
15. {1992, 1993, 1994, 1995, 1996, 1997, 1998, 1999, 2000, 2001, 2002} 17. There are fewer students per computer in more recent years. 19. 2007; 2014 21. Sample answer: 13.0; this means that the production of apples is projected to be 13.0 billion pounds in the year 2015.
23. {(0, 0), (4, 7), (8, 10.5), (12, 18), (16, 14.5)}; {(0, 0), (7, 4), (10.5, 8), (18, 12), (14.5, 16)} 25. {(-3, 2), (-3, -8), (6, 5), (7, 4), (11, 4)}; {(2, -3), (-8, -3), (5, 6), (4, 7), (4, 11)} 27. {(-3, -1), (-3, -3), (-3, -5), (0, 3), (2, 3), (4, 3)}; {(-1, -3), (-3, -3), (-5, -3), (3, 0), (3, 2), (3, 4)} 29. {(1, 8), (3, 16), (4, 20), (7, 28)}; D = {1, 3, 4, 7}; R = {8, 16, 20, 28}; {(8, 1), (16, 3), (20, 4), (28, 7)}

31. D = {100, 105, 110, 115, 120, 125, 130}; R = {40, 42, 44, 46, 48, 50, 52}

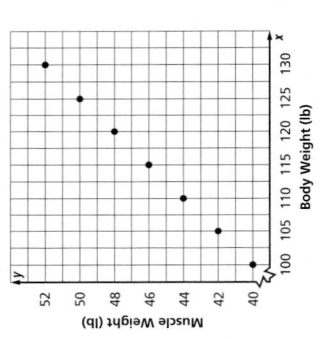

33.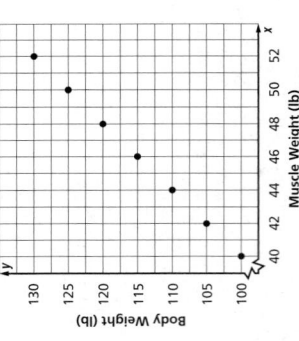

35. Sample answer: The number of movie tickets bought and the total cost of the tickets can be represented using a relation. The total cost depends on the number of tickets bought. {(0, 0), (1, 9), (2, 18), (3, 27)}

Number of Tickets	Total Cost
0	$0.00
1	$9.00
2	$18.00
3	$27.00

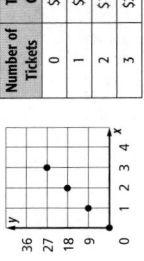

37. D 39. 10 mL 41. $h = \frac{6w - b}{3}$ 43. 48 45. 7

Lesson 3-2
Pages 152-154
1. yes 3. no 5. no 7. 3 9. $4x + 15$ 11. $t^2 - 3$ 13. $f(x) = 0.25v$; $1.25, $3.00; It costs $1.25 to send 5 photos and $3.00 to send 12 photos. 15. no 17. yes 19. yes 21. yes 23. yes 25. yes 27. 16 29. 15 31. 16 33. $4c^2 - 4c$ 35. $3k + 13$ 37. $9r + 21$ 39. $f(h) = 77 - 0.005h$; 76.5, 76, 72

Right page (R27)

9.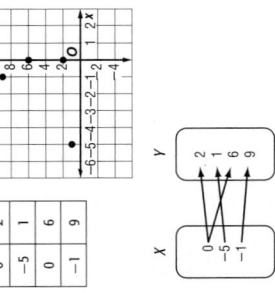

11. Rodeo Tickets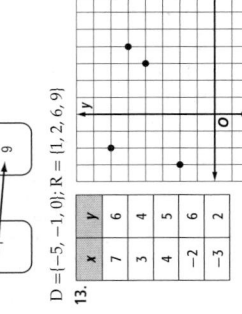

41.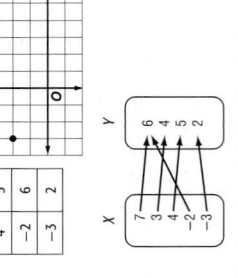

43.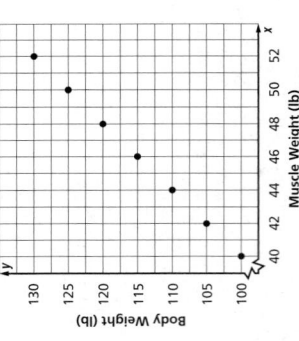

The x-intercept 12 means that 12 children could attend the rodeo if there are 0 adults attending. The y-intercept 6 means that 6 adults and 0 children could attend the rodeo. 13. yes; $2x + y = 6$ 15. yes; $y = -5$ 17. no 19. -2, 2, -2 21. 6, 20; The x-intercept represents the number of seconds that it takes the eagle to land. The y-intercept represents the initial height of the eagle. 23. 8, 4; The x-intercept 8 means that it took Eva 8 minutes to get home. The y-intercept 4 means that Eva was initially 4 miles from home.
25.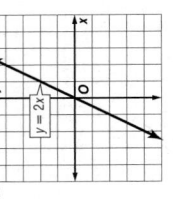
27.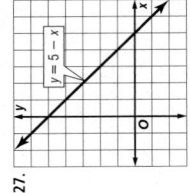

45. no 47. yes 49. No; one member of the domain is paired with two different members of the range. 51. Sometimes; if each domain value is paired with a different range value, then the inverse is also a function. If two or more domain values are paired with the same range value, then the inverse is not a function. 53. Sample answer: Functions can be used in meteorology to determine if there is a relationship between certain weather conditions. This can help to predict future weather patterns. As barometric pressure decreases, temperature increases. As barometric pressure increases, temperature decreases. The relation is not a function since there is more than one temperature for a given barometric pressure. However, there is still a pattern in the data and the two variables are related. 55. F 57. about 324.5 mph 59. 21 61. -4

Lesson 3-3
Pages 158-161
1. no 3. yes; $3x - 2y = 25$ 5. 12; -24; The x-intercept 12 means that after 12 seconds, the scuba diver is at a depth of 0 meters, or at the surface. The y-intercept -24 means that at time 0, the scuba diver is at a depth of -24 meters, or 24 meters below sea level.
7.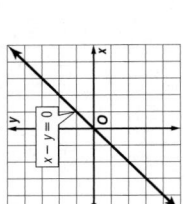

5.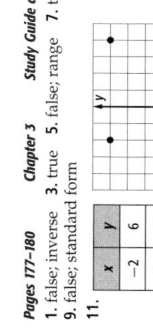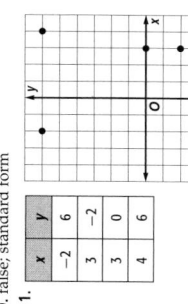

7. 370°C **9.** 10, 13, 11 **11.** 27, 35, 44 **13.** $4x + 1.5x + 1$, $6x + 1$ **15.** $f(x) = \frac{1}{2}x$ **17.** $f(x) = 6 - x$ **19.** 1, 1, 2, 3, 5, 8, 13, 21, 34, 55, 89, 144 **21.** $f(x) = -\frac{3}{2}x + 6$ **23.** $f(a) = -0.9a + 193$ **25.** Once you recognize a pattern, you can find a general rule that can be written as an algebraic expression. **27.** Sample answer: In scientific experiments you try to find a relationship or develop a formula from observing the results of your experiment. For every 11 cubic feet the volume of water increases, the volume of ice increases 12 cubic feet. **29.** J **31.** −1, 5, 11

33. 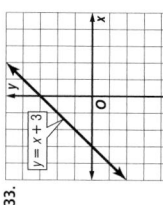 $y = x + 3$
35. 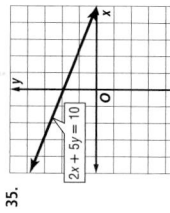 $2x + 5y = 10$

Pages 177–180   **Chapter 3**   **Study Guide and Review**
1. false; inverse **3.** true **5.** false; range **7.** true **9.** false; standard form
11.

x	y
−2	6
3	−2
3	0
4	6

13. no **15.** yes; 0.5 **17.** 42, 48, 54 **19.** 5, 14, 23 **21.** 38 **23.** 1264 **25.** 25 **27.** 25 **29.** 28; yes, by 4 seats
31. $a_n = n + 7$
33. $a_n = 2n - 20$

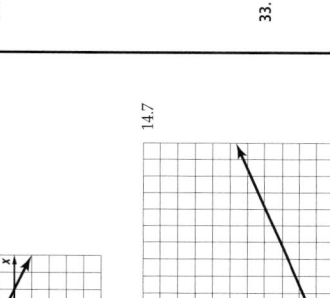 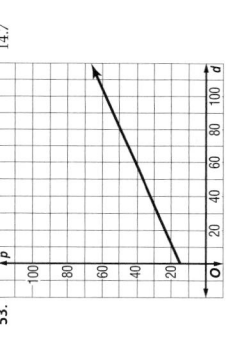

35. $3\frac{7}{12}, 4\frac{1}{3}, 5\frac{1}{12}$ **37.** 9 **39.** −1 **41.** $a_n = 4n + 5$; 145 cm **43.** Sample answer: Yes; the rate of change is greater. **45.** \$92,500 **47.** Yes; $4x + 5 - (2x + 5) = 2x$, $6x + 5 - (4x + 5) = 2x$, $8x + 5 - (6x + 5) = 2x$. The common difference is $2x$. **49.** Sample answer: The formula $a_t = 8.2t - 1.9$ represents the altitude a_t of the probe after t seconds. Replace t with 15 in the equation for a_t to find that the altitude of the probe after 15 seconds is 121.1 feet. **51.** J **53.** no **55.** yes; $2x - y = 3$ **57.** $2r + 3s = 13$ **59, 61.**

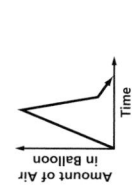 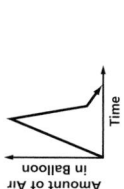

Pages 174–176   **Lesson 3-5**
1. $f(x) = x$
3.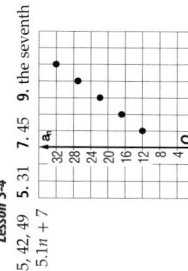

The length and the perimeter are proportional.

29. 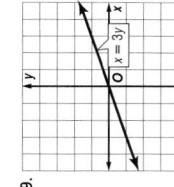 $x = 3y$
31. 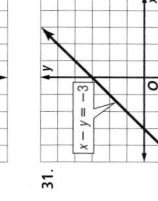 $x - y = -3$
33.

t	d
0	0
2	0.42
4	0.84
6	1.26
8	1.68
10	2.10
12	2.52
14	2.94
16	3.36

35. about 14 s **37.** 7.5, 15; No; the x-intercept 7.5 means that the length would be 7.5 inches if the width were 0. The y-intercept means that the width would be 7.5 inches if the length were 0. A rectangle cannot have only a length or only a width, so these values do not make sense in the context of the problem. **39.** no
41. yes; $6m - 7n = -4$ **43.** no

45. 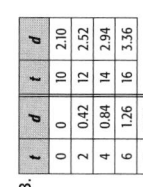 $1.5x + y = 4$
47. 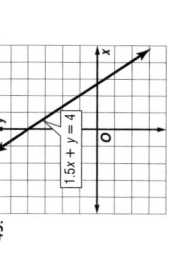 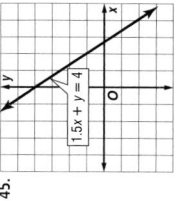 $\frac{4x}{3} = \frac{3y}{4} + 1$

49. 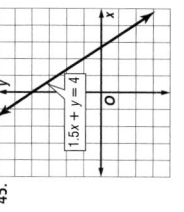 $\frac{1}{2}x + y = 4$
51. $\frac{7}{2}, -2$ **53.** 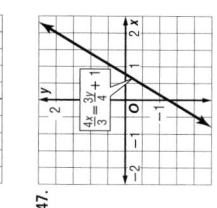 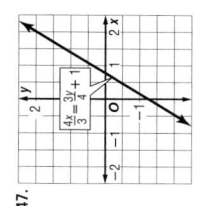 14.7

55. $2 = \frac{1}{2}(-4) + 4$
$2 = -2 + 4$
$2 = 2$

Since substituting the ordered pair in the equation yields a true equation, the point lies on the line.
57. Sample answer: $x = 5$ **59.** Substitute the values for x and y into the equation $2x - y = 8$. If the value of $2x - y$ is less than 8, then the point lies *above* the line. If the value of $2x - y$ is greater than 8, then the point lies *below* the line. If the value of $2x - y$ equals 8, then the point lies *on* the line. Sample answers: (1, 5) lies above the line, (5, 1) lies below the line, (6, 4) lies on the line. **61.** A **63.** D **65.** 4 **67.** $f(x) = 2.25x$; \$9.00, \$15.75; It costs \$9.00 to buy 4 energy bars and \$15.75 to buy 7 energy bars. **69.** −6
71. Sample answer:

Amount of Air in Balloon vs. Time

73. 3 **75.** −15

Pages 168–170   **Lesson 3-4**
1. yes; −8 **3.** 35, 42, 49 **5.** 31 **7.** 45 **9.** the seventh week **11.** $a_n = 5.1n + 7$

R30 (left page)

11. (continued)

$D = \{-2, 3, 4\}$; $R = \{-2, 0, 6\}$
13. $D = \{45, 52, 55, 60, 80\}$; $R = \{72, 137, 118, 195, 300\}$
15. no **17.** 3 **19.** $a^2 - a + 1$ **21.** $-8, 6, -8$
23.

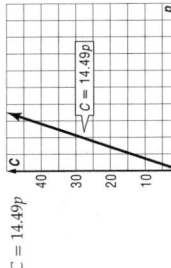

$y = -x + 2$

25.

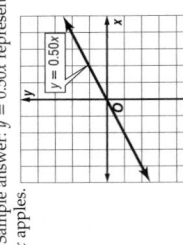

$2x - 3y = 6$

27. Speed of Sound about 11 km

$d = 1.6t$

Distance (km) vs Time (s)

29. 0.6, 0.4, 0.2 **31.** 56 **33.** $a_n = 12 + 8.5n$; $182
35. $f(x) = -x - 1$ **37.** $f(x) = 1.25x$

Chapter 4 Analyzing Linear Equations

Page 185   **Chapter 4**   **Get Ready**
1. $\frac{1}{5}$ **3.** $-\frac{1}{4}$ **5.** $\frac{1}{3}$ **7.** 3   **9.** $-2\frac{3}{5}$ **11.** $-\frac{3}{4}$
13. $0.055   **15.** $(-4, 1)$ **17.** $(-1, -4)$ **19.** $(-1, 3)$

Pages 192–195   **Lesson 4-1**
1. 4   **3.** 2.005; There was an average increase in ticket price of $2.005 per year.   **5.** Sample answer: 1998–2000; Ticket prices show a sharp increase.   **7.** $\frac{4}{5}$
9. $-\frac{3}{2}$ **11.** undefined   **13.** 2   **15.** -6 **17.** $-\frac{1}{3}$
19. 12.75%; There was an average increase of 12.75% per year of teens who had cell phones.   **21.** $-\frac{2}{5}$
23. 0   **25.** $\frac{3}{4}$ **27.** $-\frac{2}{3}$ **29.** $\frac{3}{8}$ **31.** undefined   **33.** $\frac{3}{4}$
35. 6   **37.** undefined   **39.** $\frac{3}{200}$ **41.** Sample answer: $\frac{1}{3}$
43. undefined   **45.** $\frac{1}{3}$ **47.** 7   **49.** 12–14; steepest part of the graph   **51.** '90–'95; '80–'85   **53.** a decline in enrollment
55.

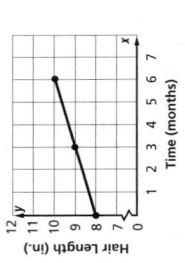

Hair Length (in.) vs Time (months)

57. 12 ft 10 in.   **59.** $(-4, -5)$ is in Quadrant III and $(4, 5)$ is in Quadrant I. The segment connecting them goes from lower left to upper right, which is a positive slope.   **61.** No, they do not. Slope of $\overline{QR}$ is $\frac{4}{3}$ and slope of $\overline{RS}$ is $\frac{1}{3}$. If they lie on the same line, the slopes should be the same.   **63.** Sample answer: Analysis of the slope of a roof might help to determine the materials of which it should be made and its functionality. To find the slope of the roof, find a vertical line that passes through the peak of the roof and a horizontal line that passes through the eave. Find the distances from the intersection of those two lines to the peak and to the eave. Use those measures as the rise and run to calculate the slope. A roof that is steeper than one with a rise of 6 and a run of 12 would be one with a rise greater than 6 and the same run. A roof with a steeper slope appears taller than one with a less steep slope.   **65.** H   **67.** $f(x) = 11 - x$
69. 3, 6, 9   **71.** $-20, -11, -2$ **73.** 9   **75.** $\frac{1}{8}$

Pages 200–202   **Lesson 4-2**
1. $-\frac{1}{3}$; $\frac{1}{3}$
3.

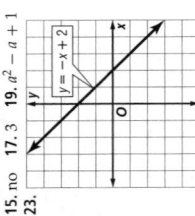

$y = 2x$

R31 (right page)

5.

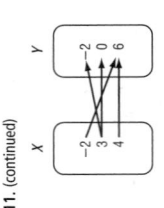

$y = -3x$

7. $y = \frac{9}{2}x$; 10   **9.** $y = 6x$ **11.** $180   **13.** 4; 4
15. -1; -1 **17.** $-\frac{1}{4}$; $-\frac{1}{4}$
19.

$y = -x$

21.

$y = \frac{5}{2}x$

23.

$y = -\frac{2}{3}x$

25.

$y = \frac{9}{2}x$

27. $y = -4x$; -5 **29.** $y = \frac{4}{5}x$; 26.25   **31.** 189 yd
33. 5 yr 4 mo   **35.** $y = -\frac{2}{3}x$; -4.4 **37.** $y = 9x$; $\frac{4}{3}$
39. 2   **41.** 3

43. $P = 4s$

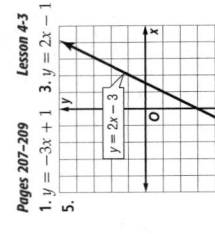

$P = 4s$

45. $C = 14.49p$

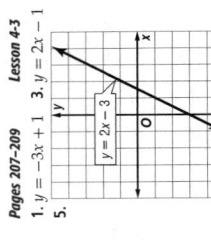

$C = 14.49p$

47. Sample answer: They all pass through $(0, 0)$, but these have negative slopes.   **49.** Sample answer: Find the absolute value of k in each equation. The one with the greatest value of $|k|$ has the steeper slope.
51. Sample answer: $y = 0.50x$ represents the cost of x apples.

$y = 0.50x$

The rate of change, 0.50, is the cost per apple.   **53.** Sample answer: The slope of the equation that relates number of ringtones and total cost is the cost of each ringtone; $y = 1.5x$; The graph of this equation is less steep; the slope is less than the slope of the graph on page 196.   **55.** J   **57.** $f(x) = 4x + 1$ **59.** $209.93
61. $y = 2x + 5$

Pages 207–209   **Lesson 4-3**
1. $y = -3x + 1$ **3.** $y = 2x - 1$
5.

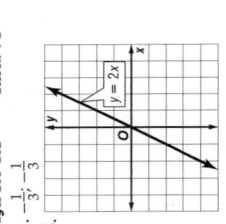

$y = 2x - 3$

7.

9. $T = 50 + 5w$

11. $85 **13.** $y = 3x - 5$ **15.** $y = -\frac{3}{5}x + 12$

17. $y = -x$ **19.** $y = \frac{3}{2}x - 4$ **21.** $y = \frac{3}{2}x$ **23.** $y = 2$

25. (graph, $y = 3x + 1$)

27. (graph, $y = \frac{1}{2}x + 4$)

29. (graph, $3x + y = -2$)

31. (graph, $3y = 2x + 3$)

33. $y = 8t + 5$ **35.** $S = 23.4 + 1.2t$ **37.** $T = 232.31c + 11{,}968$ **39.** $y = -x$ **41.** $y = 7$ **43.** $y = -5$ **45.** They all have a y-intercept of 3. **47.** Sample answer: The y-intercept is the flat fee in an equation that represents a price. If a mechanic charges $25 plus $40 per hour to work on your car, the graph representing this situation would have a y-intercept of $25. **49.** G **51.** $y = \frac{3}{4}x$, $10\frac{2}{3}$ **53.** $-\frac{1}{4}$ **55.** 1932.2 mi **57.** $\frac{4}{5}$

Pages 216–218 Lesson 4-4

1. $y = 2x - 10$ **3.** $y = -x + 2$ **5.** $y = -\frac{2}{3}x + 4$ **7.** A **9.** 995 **11.** $y = -x + 3$ **13.** $y = -5x + 29$ **15.** $y = \frac{1}{2}x + \frac{1}{2}$ **17.** $y = -\frac{5}{3}x - 10$ **19.** $y = 2x - 8$ **21.** $y = 4x - 10$ **23.** $y = 5$ **25.** $y = \frac{1}{5}x + 6$ **27.** about 312 thousand or 312,000 **29.** 24.1 thousand or 24,100 **31.** $y = -\frac{1}{4}x + \frac{11}{16}$ **33.** $y = \frac{5}{3}x + 5$ **35.** $(7, 0)$, $(0, -2)$ **37.** Sample answer: Let y represent the quarts of water in a pitcher and let x represent the time in seconds.

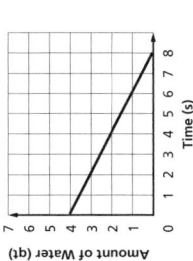

As the time increases by 1 second, the amount of water in the pitcher decreases by $\frac{1}{2}$ quart. An equation is $y = -\frac{1}{2}x + 4$. The slope $-\frac{1}{2}$ represents the rate at which the water is emptying from the pitcher, $\frac{1}{2}$ quart per second. The y-intercept 4 represents the initial amount of water in the pitcher, 4 quarts. **39.** Sample answer: Linear extrapolation is when you use a linear equation to predict values that are outside of the given points on the graph. You can use the slope-intercept form of the equation to find the y-value for any requested x-value. **41.** J

43.

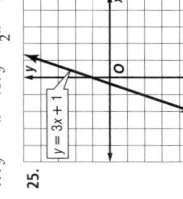

45. $V = 2.5b$ **47.** 45, 3; The x-intercept 3 means that it took Tara 45 minutes to walk home. The y-intercept 45 means that she was initially 3 miles from her home. **49.** $D = \{-2, 0, 5\}$; $R = \{-3, 1, 7\}$ **51.** -7 **53.** -5

23.

25. Sample answer: Using $(0, 4.5)$ and $(16, 12.7)$, $y = 0.5125x + 4.5$. **27.** Sample answer: The amount spent will probably not increase at a constant rate, so the linear equation that is useful in making predictions in the near future would not be useful for making predictions in the distant future. **33.** Linear extrapolation predicts values outside the range of the data set. Linear interpolation predicts values inside the range of the data. **35.** Sample answer: You can visualize a line to determine whether the data has a positive or negative correlation. The graph below shows the ages and heights of people. To predict a person's age given his or her height, write a linear equation for the line of fit. Then substitute the person's height and solve for the corresponding age. You can use the pattern in the scatter plot to make decisions.

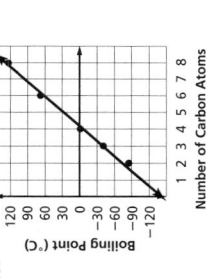

Pages 223–225 Lesson 4-5

1. $y - 3 = -2(x - 1)$ **3.** $y + 2 = 0$ **5.** $y - 50 = 25(x - 0)$ **7.** $3x + 4y = -9$ **9.** $y = 2x - 10$ **11.** $y = x + 13$ **13.** $2x - y = -5$ **15.** $y + 3 = x + 4$ **17.** $y - 6 = 0$ **19.** $y + 3 = -\frac{5}{8}(x - 1)$ **21.** $y - 7 = 0$ **23.** $y - 176 = 8(x - 22)$ or $y - 304 = 8(x - 38)$ **25.** $y - 883.4 = 1.7(x - 1500)$ **27.** $2x + y = -7$ **29.** $x - 2y = 12$ **31.** $2x + 5y = 26$ **33.** $17x - 10y = -3$ **35.** $y = 6x + 11$ **37.** $y = \frac{1}{2}x - 1$ **39.** $y = -\frac{1}{4}x - \frac{7}{2}$ **41.** $y = 9x + 5$ **43.** $y = 5x + 150$ **45.** $y - 35{,}170 = 410(x - 2001)$ **47.** 37,630 **49.** $5x - 2y = -11$ **51.** $y = x - 1$ **53.** $y = -3x - \frac{7}{2}$ **55.** $y + 6 = \frac{3}{2}(x - 1)$; $y = \frac{3}{2}x - \frac{15}{2}$; $3x - 2y = 15$ **57.** Sample answer: The total cost of going to the zoo is $4 for parking plus $9 per person; $y = 9x + 4$, $y - 5 = 9(x + 1)$. **59.** $f(x) = -60x + 720$ **61.** Write the definition of the slope using (x, y) as one point and (x_1, y_1) as the other. Then solve the equation so that the y's are on one side and the slope and x's are on the other. **63.** H **65.** $y = -1$ **67.** $y = 3x + 10$ **69.** 5 **71.** 90 **73.** $y = -\frac{1}{2}x + \frac{3}{2}$ **75.** $y = -5x + 11$ **77.** $y = 9$

Pages 230–233 Lesson 4-6

1. Positive; the longer you study, the better your test score.

3.

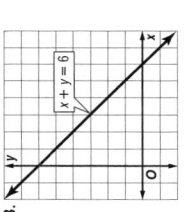

5. Sample answer: Using $(31.2, 31.0)$ and $(26.2, 25.6)$, $y = 1.08x - 2.696$. **7.** No; at this temperature, there would be no insects. **9.** no correlation **11.** Positive; the higher the sugar content, the more Calories. **13.** about 210 **15.** $y = -1200x + 12{,}000$ **17.** No; the equation would give a price of $-\$48{,}000$. In reality, this car would be an antique and would more than likely be valuable. **19.**

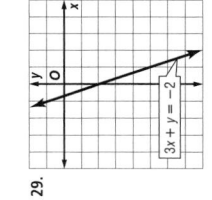

21. Sample answer: 32°C

37. G **39.** $y - 3 = -2(x + 2)$ **41.** $C = 0.22m + 0.99$; $3.63 **43.** $\frac{1}{10}$ **45.** $\frac{3}{2}$ **47.** $-\frac{4}{3}$

Pages 239–241 Lesson 4-7

1. $y = -2x - 1$ **3.** $y = 2x - 5$ **5.** Slope of $\overline{AC} = \frac{-1 - 7}{-2 - 5}$ or $\frac{6}{7}$; slope of $\overline{BD} = \frac{-3 - 4}{3 - (-3)}$ or $-\frac{7}{6}$; the paths are perpendicular. **7.** $y = -\frac{5}{3}x + 8$ **9.** $y = -\frac{1}{6}x + \frac{1}{6}$ **11.** $y = 2x - 5$ **13.** $y = \frac{2}{3}x + 1$ **15.** $y = -\frac{1}{2}x + \frac{3}{2}$ **17.** $y = -\frac{1}{3}x + 6$ **19.** No; the slopes are $-\frac{1}{2}$ and $\frac{3}{2}$ **21.** $y = -\frac{1}{4}x + \frac{5}{4}$ **23.** $y = -2x - 1$ **25.** $y = -\frac{3}{2}x + 13$ **27.** $y = -\frac{1}{2}x + 2$ **29.** parallel **31.** They are perpendicular because the slopes are 3 and $-\frac{1}{3}$. **33.** 0 **35.** Sample answer: If two equations have the same slope, then the lines are parallel. If the product of their slopes equals -1, then the lines are perpendicular. The graph of $y = \frac{3}{2}x$ is parallel to the

23. no solution

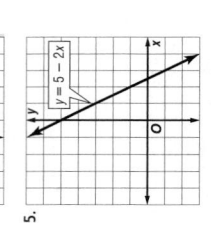

25. one; (−6, 8)

27. infinitely many

29. $40   **31.** 70 m; yes, 70 m is a reasonable height for balloons to fly.

33. infinitely many

35. neither
37. $p = 64.4 + 0.3t$

39.

The solution (1.75, 65) means that 1.75 years after 2000, or in 2002, the population of the West and the Midwest were approximately equal, 65 million.   **41.** Sample answer: $y = 5x + 3$, $y = -x - 3$, $2y = 10x - 6$
43. Graphs can show when the units sold of one item is greater than the units sold of the other item and when the units sold of the items are equal. The units sold of CD singles equaled the units sold of music videos in about 1.5 years, or between 2001 and 2002.

45. H   **47.** $y = -2x + 3$ **49.** $y = 2x$ **51.** $q = \dfrac{7m - n}{10}$

Pages 255–258   *Lesson 5-1*

1. one   **3.** infinitely many

5. one; (0, −4)

7. no solution

9. 13 m by 7 m   **11.** one   **13.** no solution
15. no solution
17.

19. one; (2, −2)

21. one; (2, 0)

---

graph of $y = \dfrac{3}{2}x + 1$ because their slopes both equal $\dfrac{3}{2}$.
The graph of $y = -\dfrac{2}{3}x$ is perpendicular to the graph of $y = \dfrac{3}{2}x + 1$ because the slopes are negative reciprocals of each other.   **37.** G   **39.** $y - 5 = -2(x - 3)$
41. $y + 3 = -\dfrac{1}{2}(x + 1)$ **43.** $c = \dfrac{7b + t}{6}$

49.

Weight (long tons) vs Length (ft)

51. 38.9 long tons   **53.** $y = 3x - 6$ **55.** $y = 5x - 15$
57. Yes, $\overline{AC} \perp \overline{AB}$.

Pages 242–246   *Chapter 4*   *Study Guide and Review*

1. true   **3.** false; standard form   **5.** false; parallel
7. false; 0   **9.** false; direct variation   **11.** 3   **13.** $-\dfrac{1}{2}$
15. 0.08; an average decrease in cost of $0.08 per year
17.

Chapter 5 Solving Systems of Linear Equations

Page 251   *Chapter 5*   *Get Ready*

1.

3.

5.

7.

9. $a = \dfrac{16 - y}{8}$ **11.** $q = \dfrac{7m + n}{2m}$ **13.** $-6y$

19. $y = 0.35 + 0.10x$ **33.** $y = -\dfrac{3}{5}x - \dfrac{3}{5}$
35. $y = -2x + 6$ **37.** $y = -5x + 25$
39. $y - 5 = -\dfrac{2}{3}(x + 3)$ **41.** $y + 3 = \dfrac{1}{2}(x - 5)$
43. $3x - 2y = 20$ **45.** $y = 2x + 3$
47. $y - 165 = 25(x - 8)$

19. $y = 7.5x$; $y = 60$ **21.** $y = -x$; $y = -7$
23. $y = 3x + 2$ **25.** $y = 0x + 4$ or $y = 4$
27.

29.

Pages 263–265   Lesson 5-2

1. $(5, -1)$ 3. no solution 5. $(-2, 3)$ 7. about 135.5 mi
9. $(16, 4)$ 11. $(2, 7)$ 13. infinitely many 15. $(13, 30)$
17. $(-4, 3)$ 19. $(2, 5)$ 21. 320 gal of 25% acid, 180 gal
of 50% acid 23. $(5, 2)$ 25. $\left(2\frac{2}{3}, \frac{1}{3}\right)$ 27. The second
offer is better if she sells less than $80,000. The first
offer is better if she sells more than $80,000. 29. 23 yr
31. Josh; $b = 3$ means that 3 bananas were bought.
Solving the first equation for a gives $a = 4$. This means
that 4 apples were bought.
33. Sample answer: $x + y = 3$
$3x + 2y = 6$

Discount movie tickets for one adult and one child cost
$3. The cost for 3 adults and two children is $6. The
solution $(2, 1)$ means that an adult ticket costs $2 and a
child's ticket costs $1. 35. A 37. C

39.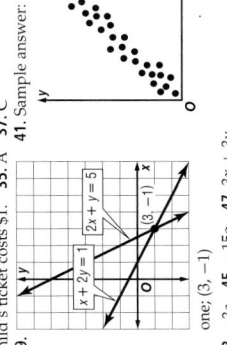

41. Sample answer:
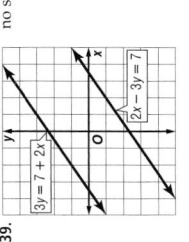

43. $-3a$ 45. $-15g$ 47. $3x + 3y$

Pages 268–270   Lesson 5-3

1. $(-1, 3)$ 3. $(0, -5)$ 5. 6, 18 7. $(-1, -2)$ 9. $(5, 1)$
11. $(-5, 20)$ 13. $(-5, 4)$ 15. $(2, -2)$ 17. $(4.5, 2)$
19. 36, 12 21. 6, 0 23. adult: $16; student: $9
25. $y = 0.0022x + 1.28$ 27. Sample answer: The
solution $(23, 1.33)$ means that 23 years after 2002, or in
2025, the populations of China and India are predicted
to be the same, 1.33 billion. 29. $(-1.4, 5630)$; About
1.4 years before 2004, or in 2002, the number of online
catalogs and the number of print catalogs were both
5630. 31. $A = 6$, $B = 3$; In each equation, replace
x with 2 and y with 1 to get $2A + B = 15$ and $2A -
B = 9$. Next, eliminate the B variables by adding the
equations to get $4A = 24$. Divide each side by 4 to get
$A = 6$. Now substitute 6 for A in either equation to get
$B = 3$. 33. B 35. $(2, 10)$ 37. $(-9, -7)$
39. no solution

41. $\frac{12}{11}x$ or $1\frac{1}{11}x$ 43. $12a - 30b$ 45. $-20t + 10s$

Pages 275–278   Lesson 5-4

1. $(2, -2)$ 3. $(5, -2)$ 5. B 7. $(5, -2)$ 9. $(2, 1)$
11. $(-4, -7)$ 13. $(-1, -2)$ 15. $(0, 1)$ 17. 2, -5
19. $(10, 12)$ 21. $(2, -8)$ 23. 86 25. $(1.5, 2)$;
A batting token costs $1.50 and a game of miniature
golf costs $2.00. 27. $(4, 1)$ 29. If one of the variables
cannot be eliminated by adding or subtracting the
equations, you must multiply one or both of the
equations by numbers so that a variable will be
eliminated when the equations are added or
subtracted. 31. Sample answer: $3x + 2y = 5$,
$5x - 10y = -6$ 33. Sample answer: By having two
equations that represent the time restraints, a manager
can determine the best use of employee time. The
following is a solution to the system of equations on
top of page 272.

$$
\begin{aligned}
20c + 10b &= 800 \rightarrow & 20c + 10b &= 800 \\
10c + 30b &= 900 \rightarrow & -20c - 60b &= -1800 \\
\hline
& & -50b &= -1000 \\
& & \frac{-50b}{-50} &= \frac{-1000}{-50} \\
& & b &= 20
\end{aligned}
$$

$$
\begin{aligned}
20c + 10b &= 800 \\
20c + 10(20) &= 800 \\
20c + 200 &= 800 \\
20c + 200 - 200 &= 800 - 200 \\
20c &= 600 \\
\frac{20c}{20} &= \frac{600}{20} \\
c &= 30
\end{aligned}
$$

In order to make the most of the employee and oven
time, the manager should make assignments to bake
30 batches of cookies and 20 loaves of bread.
35. J 37. $(6, 2)$ 39. $(11, 7)$ 41. $(-4, 4)$ 43. 4; For
every 4-feet increase in height, there is a 1-foot increase
in horizontal distance. 45. $-8, 2, -8$ 47. 2

Pages 283–284   Lesson 5-5

1. elimination (×); $(4, 1)$ 3. substitution; $(-3, -1)$
5. Sample answer: $3s + 5p = 233$ and $s = p + 11$;
Denzel sold 25 pizzas and 36 subs. 7. substitution;
$(2, 6)$ 9. elimination (×) or substitution; $(3, 1)$
11. elimination (−); no solution 13. 880 books; If they
sell this number, then their income and expenses both
equal $35,200. 15. elimination (×); $(-6, 2)$ 17. Let
x = the cost per pound of aluminum cans and let y =
the cost per pound of newspaper; $9x + 9y = 3.77$ and
$26x + 114y = 4.65$. 19. Sample answer: $x + y = 12$
and $3x + 2y = 29$, where x represents the cost of a
student ticket for the football game and y represents
the cost of an adult ticket; substitution could be used
to solve the system; $(5, 7)$ means the cost of a student
ticket is $5 and the cost of an adult ticket is $7.
21. Sample answer: You should always check that the
answer makes sense in the context of the original
problem. If it does not, you may have made an
incorrect calculation. If $(1, -7)$ was the solution, then it
is probably incorrect since distance in this case cannot
be a negative number. The solution should be
recalculated. 23. $(0, -3)$ 25. $(-5, -1)$

---

21. 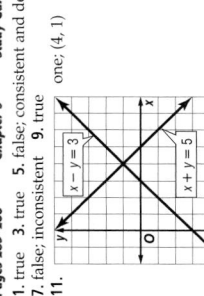 one; $(4, 1)$

23. 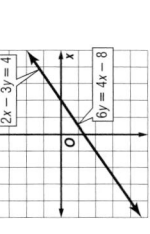 infinitely many

Pages 285–288   Chapter 5   Study Guide and Review

1. true 3. true 5. false; consistent and dependent
7. false; inconsistent 9. true
11. 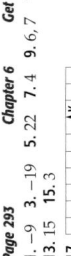 one; $(4, 1)$

13. 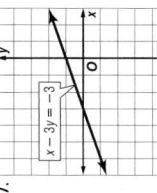 infinitely many

15. 15 mi; 3 h 17. infinitely many 19. $(4, 0)$
21. $(2, 2)$ 23. $(4, 1)$ 25. Denver: 10th; Detroit: 19th
27. $(-9, -7)$ 29. $(0.6, 3)$ 31. substitution; $(1.6, 3.2)$
33. substitution or elimination (−); $(0, 0)$ 35. $900 at
4% and $600 at 6%

Chapter 6 Solving Linear Inequalities

Page 293   Chapter 6   Get Ready

1. -9 3. -19 5. 22 7. 4 9. 6, 7 11. 1.5
13. 15 15. 3
17.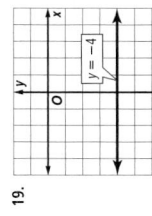

19.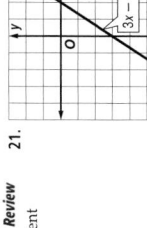

Pages 297–299   Lesson 6-1

1. $\{t \mid t \geq 12\}$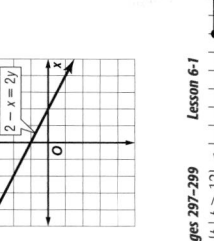

3. $\{a \mid a < -2\}$

5. $\{n \mid n < 11\}$

7. $\{r \mid r > 6\}$

9. Sample answer: Let n = the number; $n - 8 \leq 14$;
$\{n \mid n \leq 22\}$. 11. no more than 2043 lb
13. $\{d \mid d \leq 2\}$

15. $\{s \mid s > 4\}$

17. $\{r \mid r < -5\}$

19. $\{q \mid q \leq 7\}$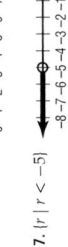

Selected Answers

21. $\{h \mid h < 30\}$
26 27 28 29 30 31 32 33 34

23. $\{c \mid c < -27\}$
-31 -29 -27 -25 -23

25. $\{f \mid f < -3\}$
-8 -7 -6 -5 -4 -3 -2 -1 0

27. $\{w \mid w \geq 1\}$
-4 -3 -2 -1 0 1 2 3 4

29. $\{a \mid a > -9\}$
-13 -11 -9 -7 -5

31. Sample answer: Let n = the number, $n - 5 < 33$; $\{n \mid n < 38\}$. **33.** Sample answer: Let n = the number, $n + (-7) \leq 18$; $\{n \mid n \leq 25\}$. **35.** more than 5 million

37. $\{y \mid y > 5.6\}$
0 1 2 3 4 5 6 7 8

39. $\left\{a \mid a > -\dfrac{1}{8}\right\}$
-4 -3 -2 -1 0 1 2 3 4

41. Sample answer: Let n = the number, $30 \leq n + (-8)$; $\{n \mid n \geq 38\}$. **43.** Sample answer: Let n = the amount of money in the account, $m - 1300 - 947 \geq 1500$; $\{m \mid m \geq 3747\}$; Mr. Hayashi must have at least \$3747 in his account. **45.** $12 < 4 + x$; more than 8 in. **47.** In both graphs, the line is darkened to the left. In the graph of $a < 4$, there is a circle at 4 to indicate that 4 is not included in the graph. In the graph of $a \leq 4$, there is a dot at 4 to indicate that 4 is included in the graph. **49.** Sample answers: $y + 1 < -2$, $y - 1 < -4$, $y + 3 < 0$ **51.** B **53.** A **55.** substitution; (16, 2) **57.** \$1.50; 3.75 **59.** 36 h **61.** 145 **63.** −21

Pages 305–307   Lesson 6-2

1. $\{t \mid t < -108\}$ **3.** $\{r \mid r \geq 8\}$ **5.** Sample answer: Let n = the number, $-4n > 12$; $\{n \mid n < -3\}$. **7.** Sample answer: Let n = the number of DVDs sold, $15n > 5500$; $\{n \mid n \geq 366.6\}$, they sold at least 367 DVDs.
9. $\{x \mid x > -5\}$ **11.** $\{s \mid s \leq 7\}$ **13.** $\{m \mid m < -68\}$
15. $\{r \mid r > 49\}$ **17.** $\{y \mid y \geq -24\}$ **19.** $\{x \mid x \geq 20\}$
21. Sample answer: Let n = the number, $7n > 28$; $\{n \mid n > 4\}$. **23.** Sample answer: Let n = the number,
$24 \leq \frac{1}{3}n$; $\{n \mid n \geq 72\}$. **25.** $\{g \mid g \leq 24\}$ **27.** $\{d \mid d \leq -6\}$
29. $\{y \mid y > -16\}$ **31.** $\{s \mid s > -1\}$ **33.** Sample answer: Let b = the number of bags of mulch, $2.5b \geq 2000$; $\{b \mid b \geq 800\}$, at least 800 bags. **35.** $\{b \mid b \geq 13.5\}$

37. $\{w \mid w > -2.72\}$ **39.** $\left\{c \mid c < -\dfrac{1}{10}\right\}$

41. $\{m \mid m \geq 3\}$
0 1 2 3 4 5 6 7 8

43a. 3.5 **43b.** −14 **43c.** −6 **45.** Sample answer: Let n = the number, $0.40n \leq 45$; $\{n \mid n \leq 112.5\}$. **47.** Sample answer: Let r = the radius of the flower garden, $2\pi r \leq 38$; $\{r \mid r \leq 6.04\}$, up to about 6 ft. **49.** Sample answer: Let v = the number of visits to the zoo, $128 <$

$v(2 \cdot 19.50 + 2 \cdot 11.75)$; $\{v \mid v > 2.05\}$, at least 3 times. **51.** You could solve the inequality by multiplying each side by $-\frac{1}{7}$ or by dividing each side by -7. In either case, you must reverse the direction of the inequality symbol. **53a.** Sample answer: $2 > -3$, but $4 < 9$. **53b.** Sample answer: $-1 < 2$ and $-3 < -2$, but $3 > -4$. **55.** Sample answer: Inequalities can be used to compare the heights of cases of beverages. If x represents the number of cases of water and the cases must be no higher than 3 ft or 36 in., then $8x \leq 36$. To solve this inequality, divide each side by 8 and do not change the direction of the inequality. The solution is $x \leq 4.5$. This means that the stack must be 4 cases high or fewer. **57.** J **59.** $\{g \mid g \leq -7\}$ **61.** 12 months, \$240 **63.** $y = -2$ **65.** 7 **67.** 12

Pages 311–313   Lesson 6-3

1. $\{h \mid h \geq 7\}$ **3.** $\{y \mid y > -10.5\}$ **5.** $4n + 60 \leq 800$; $n \leq 185$; less than 185 lb **7.** $\{v \mid v \geq 0\}$ **9.** $\varnothing$
11. $\{a \mid a < 3\}$ **13.** $\{w \mid w > 56\}$ **15.** $\{f \mid f > -8\}$
17. $\{a \mid a < -4\}$ **19.** $\{k \mid k > 8\}$ **21.** Sample answer:
Let n = the number, $\frac{2}{3}n + 8 > 12$; $\{n \mid n > 6\}$.
23. Sample answer: Let n = the number, $10 \leq 4(2n + 3)$;
$\left\{n \mid n \geq -\dfrac{1}{4}\right\}$. **25.** Sample answer: Let w = the number of weeks, $1.25w > 90 - 75$; $\{w \mid w > 12\}$, it will take more than 12 weeks for the dog to reach a healthy weight. **27.** $\{a \mid a \leq 11\}$ **29.** $\{b \mid b$ is a real number.$\}$
31. $\{a \mid a \geq -9\}$
33. $-5(k + 4) > 3(k - 4)$ Original inequality
$-5k - 20 > 3k - 12$ Distributive Property
$-5k - 20 + 5k > 3k - 12 + 5k$ Add $5k$ to each side.
$\qquad -20 > 8k - 12$ Simplify.
$-20 + 12 > 8k - 12 + 12$ Add 12 to each side.
$\qquad -8 > 8k$ Simplify.
$\qquad \dfrac{-8}{8} > \dfrac{8k}{8}$ Divide each side by 8.
$\qquad -1 > k$ Simplify.
35. at least 94 **37.** Sample answer: $7.5 + 1.25x + 0.15(7.5 + 1.25x) < 13$; 3 or fewer toppings **39.** $x < 0$
41. $-\dfrac{7}{3}$ **43.** 7, 9; 5.7, 3.5; 1.3 **45.** $\{v \mid v \geq 4.5\}$
47. $\{n \mid 7\} > 5n - 13$; $\{n \mid x < 17\}$
49. Sample answers: $2x + 5 < 2x + 3$; $2x + 5 > 2x + 3$
51. $4y + 9 > -3$; it is the only inequality that does not have a solution set of $\{y \mid y > 3\}$. **53.** C
55. up to 416 mi
57. $\{t \mid t < 8\}$
5 6 7 8 9 10 11 12 13

59. $2x - y = 5$ **61.** $y - 6 = 0$ **63.** Sample answer: A steeper segment means greater rate of change.

65.
-6 -5 -4 -3 -2 -1 0 1 2

67.
0 1 2 3 4 5 6 7 8

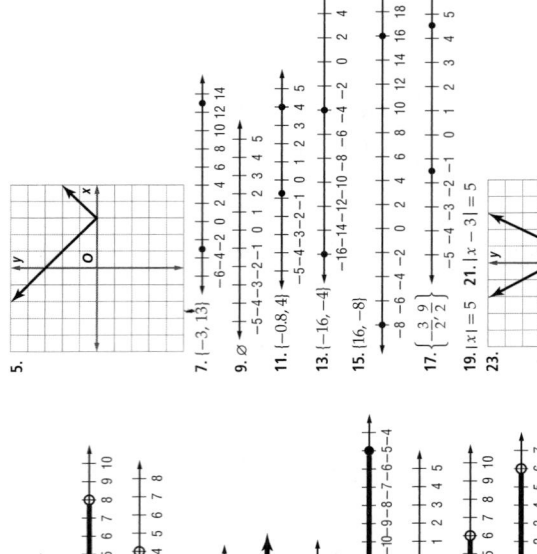

Pages 317–320   Lesson 6-4

1.
-3 -2 -1 0 1 2 3 4 5 6 7

3. $\{w \mid 3 < w < 8\}$
0 1 2 3 4 5 6 7 8 9 10

5. $\{z \mid z < 4\}$
-2 -1 0 1 2 3 4 5 6 7 8

7. 11 psi $\leq x \leq 56$ psi

9.
-10 -9 -8 -7 -6 -5 -4 -3 -2 -1 0

11.
-7 -6 -5 -4 -3 -2 -1 0 1 2 3

13.
-5 -4 -3 -2 -1 0 1 2 3 4 5

15. $\{f \mid -13 \leq f \leq -5\}$
-14 -13 -12 -11 -10 -9 -8 -7 -6 -5 -4

17. $\{h \mid h < -1\}$
-5 -4 -3 -2 -1 0 1 2 3 4 5

19. $\{y \mid 3 < y < 6\}$
0 1 2 3 4 5 6 7 8 9 10

21. $\{q \mid -1 < q < 6\}$
-3 -2 -1 0 1 2 3 4 5 6 7

23. $\{n \mid n \leq 4\}$
0 1 2 3 4 5 6 7 8 9 10

25. $t < 18$ or $t > 22$ **27.** $-7 < x < -3$
29. $x \leq -7$ or $x \geq -6$ **31.** $x = 2$ or $x > 5$
33. $\varnothing$
-5 -4 -3 -2 -1 0 1 2 3 4 5

35. $\{b \mid b < -12$ or $b > -12\}$
-18 -16 -14 -12 -10 -8 -6 -4 -2 0 2

37. between \$51 and \$110 inclusive **39.** Sample answer: Let n = the number, $-8 < 3n + 4 < 10$; $\{n \mid -4 < n < 2\}$. **41.** Sample answer: Let n = the number, $0 < \frac{1}{2}n \leq 1$; $\{n \mid 0 < n \leq 2\}$. **43.** $\{h \mid 15 \leq h \leq 50,000\}$; $\{h \mid 20 \leq h \leq 20,000\}$ **45.** Sample answer: troposphere: $a \leq 10$, stratosphere: $10 < a \leq 30$, mesosphere: $30 < a \leq 50$, thermosphere: $50 < a \leq 400$, exosphere: $a > 400$ **47.** Sample answer: $x < -2$ and $x > 3$ **49a.** $x \geq 5$ and $x \leq 8$ **49b.** $x > 6$ or $x < 1$ **51.** A **53.** D **55.** $\{d \mid d \geq 5\}$ **57.** $\{t \mid t < 169\}$ **59.** 2.25 **61.** 5 **63.** 2 **65.** −1 **67.** −2

Pages 325–327   Lesson 6-5

1. $[-13, 7]$
-14 -12 -10 -8 -6 -4 -2 0 2 4 6 8

3. $\varnothing$
-5 -4 -3 -2 -1 0 1 2 3 4 5

5.
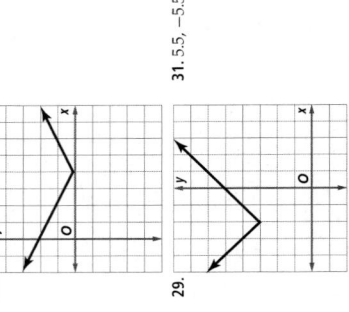

7. $[-3, 13]$

9. $\varnothing$
-6 -4 -2 0 2 4 6 8 10 12 14

11. $(-0.8, 4)$
-5 -4 -3 -2 -1 0 1 2 3 4 5

13. $(-16, -4)$
-16 -14 -12 -10 -8 -6 -4 -2 0 2 4

15. $[16, -8]$
-8 -6 -4 -2 0 2 4 6 8 10 12 14 16 18

17. $\left\{-\dfrac{3}{2}, \dfrac{9}{2}\right\}$
-5 -4 -3 -2 -1 0 1 2 3 4 5

19. $|x| = 5$ **21.** $|x - 3| = 5$

23.

25.

27.

29.

31. 5.5, −5.5

Lesson 6-6

1. $\{c|-4 < c < 8\}$

-10-8-6-4-2 0 2 4 6 8 10

3. $\varnothing$
-5-4-3-2-1 0 1 2 3 4 5

5. $\{g|g \le -6 \text{ or } g \ge 1\}$
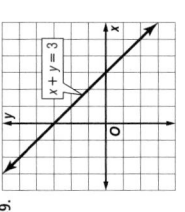
-8-7-6-5-4-3-2-1 0 1 2

7. $\{d|1.499 \le d \le 1.501\}$

9. $\{t|-10 < t < -6\}$
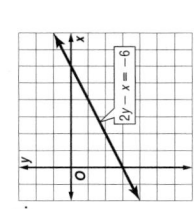
-10-9-8-7-6-5-4-3-2-1 0

11. $\{v|v < -4 \text{ or } v > -2\}$
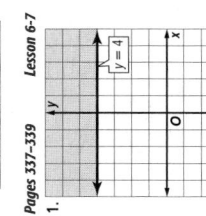
-8-7-6-5-4-3-2-1 0 1 2

13. $\{a|a \text{ is a real number.}\}$
-5-4-3-2-1 0 1 2 3 4 5

15. $\{n|-5 < n < 4\}$
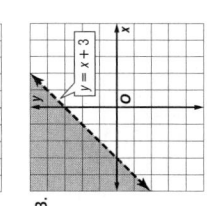
-5-4-3-2-1 0 1 2 3 4 5

17. $\{p|2000 < p < 3000\}$ **19.** $|x| \le 3$ **21.** $|x - 11| > 2$

23. $\left\{-8\frac{4}{5}, 8\right\}$
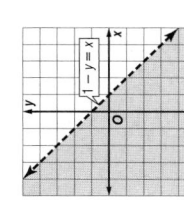
-10-8-6-4-2 0 2 4 6 8 10

25. $\{s|s \text{ is a real number.}\}$
-5-4-3-2-1 0 1 2 3 4 5

27. $|p - 7.5| \le 0.3$ **29.** $|s - 98| \le 6$ **31.** $|p \mid 28 \le p \le 32|$ **33.** $|g - 52| \le 5$ **35.** The solution of $|x - 2| > 6$ includes all values that are less than -4 or greater than 8. The solution of $|x - 2| < 6$ includes all values that are greater than -4 and less than 8. **37.** $|x - 2| < 0.3$ **39.** C **41.** B **43.** $\varnothing$
-5-4-3-2-1 0 1 2 3 4 5

45. $0 \le x \le 25$; $25.01 \le x \le 50$ **47.** $y = \frac{1}{2}x + \frac{3}{4}$

49. 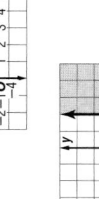 $x + y = 3$

51. 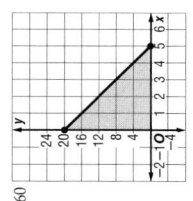 $2y - x = -6$

33. D: all real numbers; $\{y|y \ge 4\}$ **35.** D: all real numbers; R: $\{y|y \ge 1\}$ **37.** 45–51%

39.
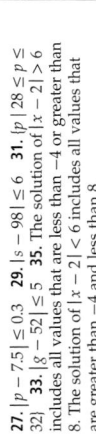
Time (s) — Height (ft)

41. Sample answer: Let x = the time in minutes to run one mile. Then the time to run one mile is 10 ± 4. **43.** Sometimes; when c is a negative value, x is a positive value. **45.** Sometimes; when $c < 0$ and $0 < x < -2$, then the expression is less than 0. **47.** Leslie; you need to consider the case when the value inside the absolute value symbols is positive and the case when the value inside the absolute value symbols is negative. So $x + 3 = 2$ or $x + 3 = -2$.

49. C **51.** D **53.** $\{m|m > 5\}$ **55.** $\{w|w \le 15\}$ **57.** $\frac{3}{2}$, 2

59. $\{(6, 0), (-3, 5), (2, -2), (-3, 3)\}$; $\{-3, 2, 6\}$; $\{-2, 0, 3, 5\}$; $\{(0, 6), (5, -3), (-2, 2), (3, -3)\}$ **61.** $\{(3, 4), (3, 2), (2, 9), (5, 4), (5, 8), (-7, 2)\}$; $\{-7, 2, 3, 5\}$; $\{2, 4, 8, 9\}$; $\{(4, 3), (2, 3), (9, 2), (4, 5), (8, 5), (2, -7)\}$ **63.** $x = \dfrac{3z + 2y}{c}$ **65.** $m \ge 2$ **67.** $z \le 6$ **69.** $r \le 7$

Lesson 6-7

1. 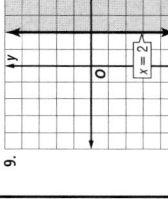 $y = 4$

3. 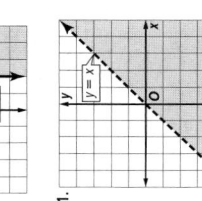 $y = x + 3$

5. 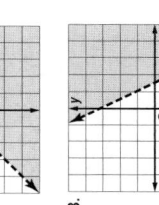 $1 - y = x$

7. $12x + 3y \le 60$

9. 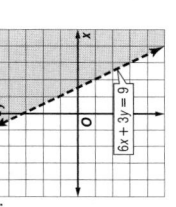 $x = 2$

11. 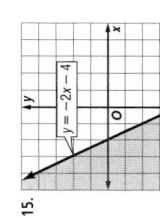 $y = x$

13. 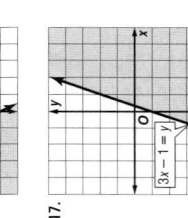 $6x + 3y = 9$

15. 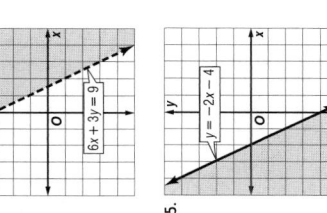 $y = -2x - 4$

17. 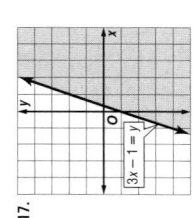 $3x - 1 = y$

19. The solution set is limited to pairs of positive numbers. **21.** No, the weight will be greater than 4000 pounds. **23.** $\{(-1, 3), (-4, 5)\}$ **25.** $\{(-13, 10), (4, 4), (-6, -2)\}$ **27.** c **29.** d **31.** $\{(-3, 2)\}$

33. 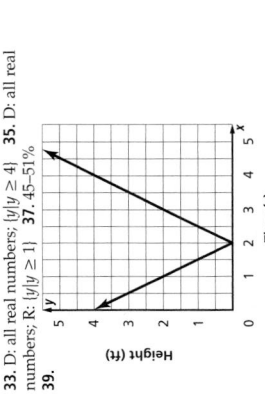 $3(x + 2y) = -18$

35. $8x + 4y \le 96$ **37.** The graph of $y = x + 2$ is a line. The graph of $y < x + 2$ does not include the boundary $y = x + 2$, and it includes all ordered pairs in the half-plane that contains the origin. **39.** If the test point results in a true statement, shade the half-plane that contains the point. If the test point results in a false statement, shade the other half-plane. **41.** The amount of money spent in each category must be less than or equal to the budgeted amount. How much you spend on individual items can vary. The domain and range must be positive integers. Sample answers: Hannah could buy 5 cafeteria lunches and 3 restaurant lunches, 2 cafeteria lunches and 5 restaurant lunches, or 8 cafeteria lunches and 1 restaurant lunch. **43.** F **45.** $\{d \mid 266 \le d \le 294\}$ **47.** $\{-2, 3\}$
-5-4-3-2-1 0 1 2 3 4 5

49. $y = -x + 4$ **51.** 31, 37 **53.** 48, 96 **55.** increase; 42% **57.**
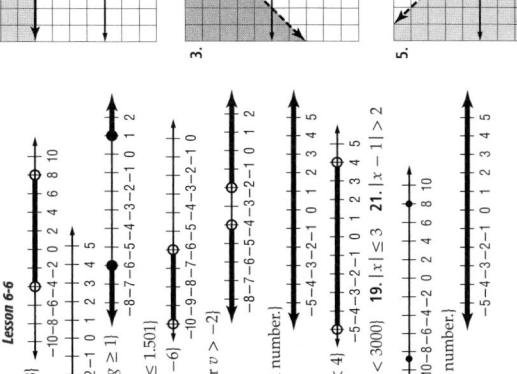 $y = 3x + 1$

59.  $5x + 2y = 6$

35. Jocelyn; the graph of $x + 2y \geq -2$ is the region representing $x + 2y = -2$ and the half-plane above it. **37.** A

39.

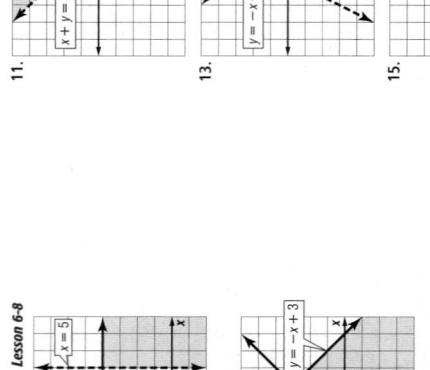

41.

43. $(2, -1)$ **45.** $(-2, 3)$ **47.** yes **49.** no

Chapter 6 Study Guide and Review

Pages 346–350

1. true **3.** false; greater than or equal to **5.** false; intersection **7.** false; or **9.** true

11. $\{x \mid x < 25\}$

13. $\{w \mid w \geq 4\}$

15. Sample answer: Let n = the number, $16 < n + 31$; $\{n \mid n > -15\}$. **17.** $\{v \mid v > 4\}$ **19.** $\{m \mid m > -11\}$ **21.** Sample answer: Let n = the number, $0.8n \geq 24$; $\{n \mid n \geq 30\}$. **23.** $\{y \mid y < 4\}$ **25.** $\{x \mid x \leq -2\}$ **27.** Sample answer: Let n = the number, $\frac{2}{3}n - 27 \geq 9$; $\{n \mid n \geq 54\}$.

29.

31. $\{w \mid w \text{ is a real number.}\}$

33. $33 \leq m \leq 37$

35. $\{4, -1\}$

37. $|c - 13.6| = 0.408$; 14.008 gal, 13.192 gal **39.** $\varnothing$

41. $\{x \mid x \leq -1 \text{ or } x \geq 6\}$

43. $\{w \mid -19 \leq w \leq 3\}$

45.

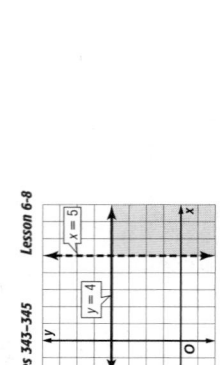

23.

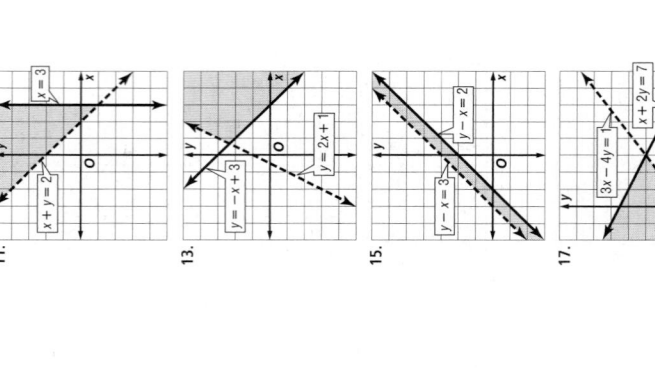

25.

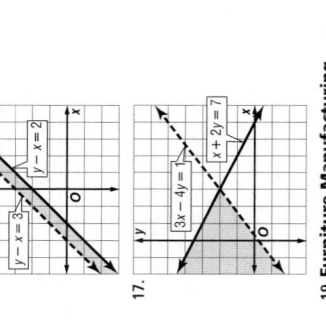

27. $y \leq \frac{2}{3}x + 2$, $y > -x - 3$ **29.** Any point in the shaded region is a possible solution. For example, since $(7, 8)$ is a point in the region, Mr. Hobson could plant corn for 7 days and soybeans for 8 days. In this case, he would use 15 days to plant 250(7) or 1750 acres of corn and 200(8) or 1600 acres of soybeans.

31.

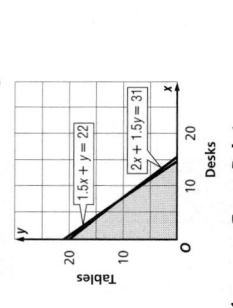

33. Sample answer: $\varnothing$

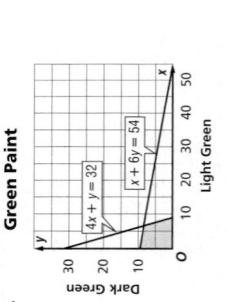

11.

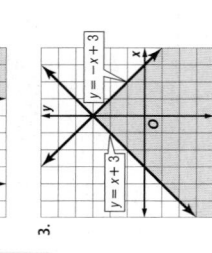

13.

15.

17.

19. Furniture Manufacturing

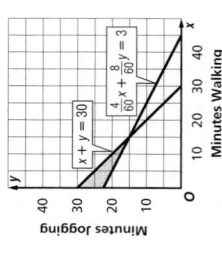

21. Green Paint

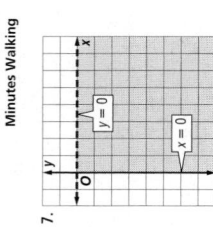

Lesson 6-8

Pages 343–345

1.

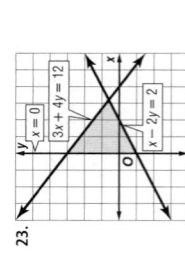

3.

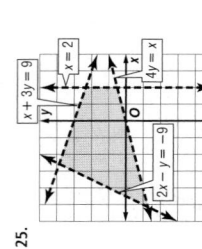

5. Natasha's Daily Exercise

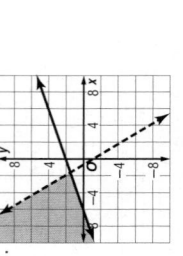

7.

9.

47.

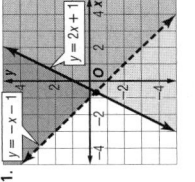

49. $95n + 0.08m \le 500$; Yes; Brenda can afford to hire this moving company.

51.

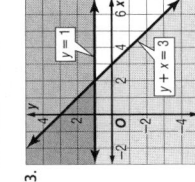

53.

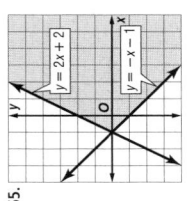

Chapter 7 Polynomials

Page 357   Chapter 7   Get Ready

1. 2^5 **3.** 5^2 **5.** a^6 **7.** $\left(\frac{1}{2}\right)^5$ **9.** 9 **11.** 36 **13.** $\frac{16}{81}$ **15.** The probability of correctly guessing the outcome of a flipped penny six times in a row is $\frac{1}{64}$. **17.** 36π m² or about 113.04 **19.** 125 cm³

Pages 361–364   Lesson 7-1

1. No; $5 - 7d$ shows subtraction, not multiplication. **3.** Yes; a single variable is a monomial. **5.** $36a^8b^4$ **7.** 3^8 or 6,561 **9.** $-8l^6b^3$ **11.** $6a^5b^6$ **13.** $800x^8y^{12}z^4$ **15.** Yes; $4x^3$ is the product of a number and three variables. **17.** No; $4n + 5m$ shows addition, not multiplication of variables. **19.** Yes; $\frac{1}{5}abc^{14}$ is the product of a number, $\frac{1}{5}$, and several variables. **21.** p^7q^5 **23.** $24r^8k^{13}$ **25.** $343b^9c^{18}$ **27.** 4^{12} or 16,777,216 **29.** a^4b^2 units² **31.** $-432c^2d^8$ **33.** $144a^8g^{14}$ **35.** $40b^{12}$ **37.** 10^5 E **39.** $30a^5b^7c^6$ **41.** $0.25x^6$ **43.** $\frac{-27}{64}c^3$ or $-0.421875c^3$ **45.** $-9x^3y^9$ **47.** $64k^9$ units³ **49.** $16\pi n^5$ units³ **51.** $(10^6)4$ or 10^{24} **53.** The collision impact quadruples, since $2(2s)^2$ is $4(2s^2)$. **55.** $\frac{1}{4,194,304}$

57. False; let $a = 2$. Then $(-a)^2 = (-2)^2 = 4$ and $-a^2 = -2^2 = -4$. **59.** False; let $a = 3$, $b = 4$, and $n = 2$. Then $(a + b)^n = (3 + 4)^2$ or 49 and $a^n + b^n = 3^2 + 4^2$ or 25. **61a.** no; $(5m)^2 = 25m^2$ **61b.** Yes; the power of a product is the product of the powers. **61c.** no; $(-3a)^2 \ne 9a^2$ **61d.** no; $2(c^3)^3 = 2c^{21}$ **63.** B

65.

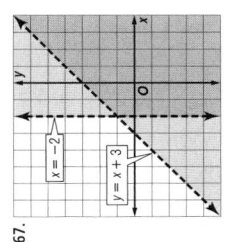

67.

69. $\{(-4, 2), (-3, 0), (1, 4)\}$
71. $|a| - 2 < a < 3)$
73. $\{m \mid m > 1\}$

75. $(-3, -4)$ **77.** $f(x) = -2x$ **79.** $\{(-5, 2), (-2, 3), (0.5), (4, 9)\}$; $\{(-3, 2), (3, -2), (5, 0), (9, 4)\}$ **81.** $\{(-3, 2), (0, 4), (2, -1), (-1, -3)\}$; $\{(2, -3), (4, 0), (-1, 2), (-3, -1)\}$ **83.** $\frac{1}{3}$ **85.** 2 **87.** $\frac{17}{18}$ **89.** $\frac{11}{8}$

Pages 370–373   Lesson 7-2

1. 7^6 or 117,649 **3.** $\frac{g^4}{2p^5}$ **5.** $\frac{4a^4b^2}{c^6}$ **7.** $\frac{1}{y^4}$ **9.** 1 **11.** $\frac{g^8}{d^2c^5}$ **13.** D **15.** 3^6 or 729 **17.** y^2z^7 **19.** $\frac{81m^{28}}{256z^{20}y^{12}}$ **21.** 1 **23.** $\frac{1}{125}$ **25.** $\frac{8}{27}$ **27.** $4a^4c^4$ **29.** $3x^4y$ units **31.** $-\frac{1}{5a^5}$ **33.** $\frac{6k^{17}}{h^3}$ **35.** $\frac{19}{3z^{12}}$ **37.** $\frac{p}{q}$ **39.** $\frac{b^2}{5n^2z^3}$ **41.** 2^{-n} **43.** jet plane **45.** $\frac{1}{10^5}$ cm; $\frac{1}{10^4}$ cm; $\frac{1}{100,000}$ $\frac{1}{10,000}$ cm **47.** 100 **49.** $\frac{a^3b^5}{ab^2} = a^3a^{-1}b^5b^{-2} = a^{3-1}b^{5-2} = a^2b^3$ **51.** 5^{6c-2} **53.** Since each number is obtained by dividing the previous number by 3, $3^1 = 3$ and $3^0 = 1$. **55.** You can compare pH levels by finding the ratio of one pH to another written in terms of the concentration c of hydrogen ions, $c = \left(\frac{1}{10}\right)^{pH}$. Sample answer: To

compare a pH of 8 with a pH of 9 requires simplifying the quotient of powers, $\frac{\left(\frac{1}{10}\right)^8}{\left(\frac{1}{10}\right)^9} = 10$. Thus, a pH of 8 is

ten times more acidic than a pH of 9. **57.** J **59.** $12x^8y^4$ **61.** $9c^2d^{10}$ **63.** $-108a^2b^9$ **65.** Sample answer: 3 oz of mozzarella, 4 oz of Swiss; 4 oz of mozzarella, 3 oz of Swiss; 5 oz of mozzarella, 3 oz of Swiss **67.** 37

Pages 378–381   Lesson 7-3

1. yes; binomial **3.** yes; trinomial **5.** 0 **7.** 5 **9.** $2a + 4x^2 - 7t^2x^3 - 2ax^5$ **11.** $-3 + 3x^2y + 3xy^2 + y^3$ **13.** no **15.** yes; trinomial **17.** no **19.** $ab - 4x^2$ **21.** $\pi r^2 - r^2$ **23.** 1 **25.** 0 **27.** 4 **29.** 9 **31.** 6 **33.** 9 **35.** $7 + 9x^3 - 3x^5$ **37.** $4a + x^3 + 5a^2x^6$ **39.** $5y^4 + 2x^2 + 10x^3y^2 - 3x^4y$ **41.** $-5 - 8a^5x - a^4x^2 + 2ax^4$ **43.** $6x^2 + 2x - 1$ **45.** $x^2 - 2cb + b^2$ **47.** $4nx^3 + 9x^2 - 2a^2x + 3$ **49.** $4x^3y - x^2y^3 + 3xy^4 + y^4$ **51.** $t > 15$; For $t > 15$, the number of quadruplet births declines dramatically. **53.** about 92.15 in³ **55.** Sample answer: -8 **57.** True; for the degree of a binomial to be zero, the highest degree of both terms would need to be zero. Then the terms would be like terms. With these like terms combined, the expression is not a binomial, but a monomial. Therefore, the degree of a binomial can never be zero. **59.** A polynomial model of a set of data can be used to predict future trends in data. Answers should include the following:

t	H	Actual Data Values
0	70	70
1	78.75	79
2	89.5	90
3	97.75	97
4	105	103
5	118.75	115

The polynomial function models the data almost exactly for the first three values of t, and then closely for the next three values.
Someone might point to this model as evidence that the time people spend playing video games is on the rise. This model may assist video game manufacturers in predicting production needs. **61.** F **63.** $\frac{c^5}{n^3}$ **65.** $-y^9m^{15}$ **67.** no **69.** no **71.** 102 mi **73.** ± 1.8 **75.** $8n$ **77.** $a - 2b$

Pages 386–388   Lesson 7-4

1. $2p^2 + 6p$ **3.** $10cd - 3d + 4c - 6$ **5.** $11a^2 + 6a + 1$ **7.** $3a^2 - 9x - 9a + 8a^2x$ **9.** $T = 2,829n + 224,395$ **11.** $4hr^2 + 5$ **13.** $2a^2 - 6a + 8$ **15.** $5x + 2y + 3$ **17.** $10d^2 + 8$ **19.** $-8y^3 - 3y^2 - y + 17$ **21.** $-2x^2 + 8x + 8$ **23.** $4x + 2y$ **25.** $-4a + 6b - 5c$ **27.** $2y^2 - y + 5$ **29.** $D = 1.8n^2 - 42n + 860$ **31.** $60 - 2x$; $40 - 2x$; $80 - 2x$ **33.** 19 in. **35.** Sample answer: $6x^2 + 4x + 7$ and $4x^2 + 3x + 4$ **37.** $x + 1$ **39.** 4 **41.** A **43.** 5 **45.** 3 **47.** $\frac{7z^3b^3}{c}$ **49.** $1728n^{20}$

Pages 392–395   Lesson 7-5

1. $-15y^2 - 6y$ **3.** $8a^4x - 6ax^2 + 12x^3$ **5.** $5.12^2 - 11t$ **7.** $20n^4 + 30n^3 - 14nt^2 - 13n$ **9.** $10,000 - x$ **11.** $\$10,440$ **13.** 20 **15.** 1 **17.** $2a^4 - 9a^3$ **19.** $-10y^3 - 35y^2$ **21.** $-3n^2p + 6mp^2$ **23.** $30x^3 + 18x^4 - 66x^5$ **25.** $-3cd^3 - 2c^3d^3 + 4c^2d^2$ **27.** $-9x^3 + 2x^2$ **29.** $10n^4 + 5n^3 - n^2 + 44n$ **31.** $-2y^3 - 17y^2 + 24y - 6$ **33.** savings account: $\$1500$; certificate of deposit: $\$4500$ **35.** $1.50t + 1.25mt$ **37.** $-\frac{1}{3}$ **39.** 8 **41.** 1 **43.** $3x -$

$2x - 2 = x - 2$ **45.** $4a^5b - \frac{8}{9}a^3bp + 6a^2b^3$ **47.** $8p^4y^2 - 4p^3y^4 + 36p^5q^2 + 12p^2y^3$ **49.** $19x^3 - x^2 + 2x$ **51.** 7 **53.** $15p^2 + 8p + 6$ **55.** $\$2.20$ **57.** $\$126$ **59.** $x + 2$ **61.** Sample answer: $4x$ and $x^2 + 2x + 3$; $4x^3 + 8x^2 + 12x$ **63.** $2x + 1$ or $2x - 1$ **65.** The product of a monomial and a polynomial can be modeled using an area model. The area of the figure shown at the beginning of the lesson is the product of its length $2x$ and width $(x + 3)$. This product is $2x(x + 3)$, which when the Distributive Property is applied becomes $2x(x) + 2x(3)$ or $2x^2 + 6x$. This is the same result obtained when the areas of the algebra tiles are added together. **67.** J **69.** $-4y^2 + 5y + 3$ **71.** $7p^3 - 3p^2 - 2p - 7$ **73.** yes; binomial **75.** yes; monomial **77.** $9n + 4 \ge 7 - 13n$; $\{n \mid n \ge \frac{3}{22}\}$ **79.** $y = -2x - 3$ **81.** 7 **83.** no solution **85.** a^2 **87.** $-24y^4$ **89.** $-10n^3 + 40n^2 - 20n$

Pages 401–403   Lesson 7-6

1. $y^2 + 7y + 12$ **3.** $a^2 - 3a - 40$ **5.** $27p^2 - 21p + 2$ **7.** $6x^2 + 7x - 3$ or $3x^2 + \frac{7}{2}x - \frac{3}{2}$ **9.** $8x^4 + 24x^3 - 12x - 2$ **11.** $15m^4 + 13m^3 - 6m^2 + 11m - 63$ **13.** $n^2 + 13n + 42$ **15.** $a^2 - 8a + 15$ **17.** $p^2 - 8p - 20$ **19.** $3k^2 + 34k - 24$ **21.** $36g^2 + 51g + 18$ **23.** $18a^2 - 63a + 40$ **25.** $25m^2 - 60m + 36$ **27.** $49t^2 - 25$ **29.** $22a^2 + 21ab - 18b^2$ **31.** $6x^2 - \frac{17}{2}x + 3$ units² **33.** $9\pi x^2 + 24\pi x + 16\pi$ units² **35.** $a^3 - 11a^2 + 29a - 15$ **37.** $21k^3 + 34k^2 - 19k - 36$ **39.** $y^4 + y^3 - 38g^2 + 41y - 5$ **41.** $5l^2 - 34l + 56$ **43.** $63y^3 - 57y^2 - 36y$ units³ **45.** $x - 2, x + 4$ **47.** bigger; 10 sq ft **49.** The three monomials that make up the trinomial are similar to the three digits that make up the 3-digit number. The single monomial is similar to a 1-digit number. With each procedure you perform 3 multiplications. The difference is that polynomial multiplication involves variables and the resulting product is often the sum of two or more monomials while numerical multiplication results in a single number. **51.** Sometimes; the product of $x + 1$ and $x^2 + 2x + 3$ is $x^3 + 3x^2 + 5x + 3$, which has 4 terms; the product of $y + 1$ and $x^2 + 2x + 3$ is $x^2y + 2xy + 3y + x^2 + 2x + 3$, which has 6 terms. **53.** Multiplying binomials and two-digit numbers involve the use of the Distributive Property twice. Each procedure involves four multiplications and the addition of like terms.   *(continued)*

$24 \times 36 = (4 + 20)(6 + 30)$
$= (4 + 20)6 + (4 + 20)30$
$= (24 + 120) + (120 + 600)$
$= 144 + 720$
$= 864$

The like terms in vertical two-digit multiplication are digits with the same place value. **55.** J **57.** $20a^3 + 2t^2 - 10a + 27$ **59.** -13 **61.** $2a + 1$ **63.** $y = \frac{ax - 2cz}{b}$ **65.** 23 **67.** 3.25 **69.** $49x^2$ **71.** $16y^4$ **73.** 9_g^8

Pages 407–409   Lesson 7-7
1. $a^2 + 12a + 36$ **3.** $9x^2 + 54xy + 81y^2$ **5.** $x^4 - 12x^2y + 36y^2$ **7.** $0.5Bb + 0.5b^2$ **9.** $64x^2 - 25$ **11.** $16y^4 - 9z^2$ **13.** $y^2 + 8y + 16$ **15.** $a^2 - 10a + 25$ **17.** $49 - 56y + 16y^2$ **19.** 25% **21.** $c^2 - 4$ **23.** $81x^2 + 54x + 9$ **25.** $144p^5 - 9$ **27.** $m^2 + 14mn + 49n^2$ **29.** $9n^2 - 60np + 100p^2$ **31.** $16a^2 - 169$ **33.** $9a^4 - 6a^2b^2 + b^4$ **35.** $25x^8 - y^2$ **37.** $\frac{16}{25}x^2 + 16x + 100$ **39.** $p^4 - 25p^2 + 144$ **41.** $a^2 + 2a + 1$ **43.** 1 **45.** $(1189.66 - 3.14s^2 + 56.52s)$ ft^2

47.

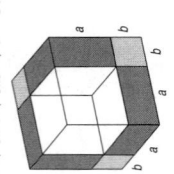

49.

51a. $a^3 + 3a^2b + 3ab^2 + b^3$ **51b.** $x^3 + 6x^2 + 12x + 8$ **51c.**

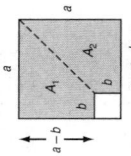

53. D **55.** $x^2 + 9x + 14$ **57.** $20p^2 - 29y + 6$ **59.** $3x^3 - 11x^2 + 14x - 8$ **61.** 4 **63.** 0 **65.** (0, 25) **67.** (5, -2) **69.** $y = -2.5x + 2$ **71.** 71 **73.** b

Pages 410–414   Chapter 7   Study Guide and Review
1. negative exponent **3.** polynomial **5.** trinomial **7.** polynomial **9.** Product of Powers **11.** y^7 **13.** $20a^5x^5$ **15.** $576x^5y^2$ **17.** $-\frac{1}{2}m^4n^8$ **19.** $16\pi x^6y^2$ **21.** $\frac{27b^3 \cdot 5}{64d^3}$ **23.** $\frac{27b}{14}$ **25.** $\frac{bx^3}{3aq^2}$ **27.** $\frac{1}{64a^6}$ **29.** $\frac{4n}{m^2}$ **31.** 2 **33.** 5 **35.** $3x^4 + x^2 - x - 5$ **37.** $2\pi x^2 + 12x + 5$ **39.** $4x^2 - 5xy + 6y^2$ **41.** $21m^4 - 10m - 1$ **43.** $-7p^2 - 2p + 25$ **45.** $4b^2 + 9b$ **47.** $61y^3 - 16y^2 + 167y - 18$ **49.** 2 **51.** $\$16.05x + \$27.52y + \$13.41z$ **53.** $4a^2 + 13a - 12$ **55.** $18x^2 - 0.125$ **57.** $12p^3 - 13p^2 + 11p - 6$ **59.** $x^2 - 36$ **61.** $64x^2 - 80x + 25$ **63.** $36a^2 - 60ab + 25b^2$ **65.** $0.25RR + 0.5Rr + 0.25rr$; 0.25

Chapter 8 Factoring

Page 419   Get Ready
1. $12 - 3x$ **3.** $-7n^2 + 21n - 7$ **5.** $4(4e + 10p + 20t)$ **7.** $3n^2 + 11n - 20$ **9.** $-2x - 4xy + 96t^2$ **11.** $y^2 + 18y + 81$ **13.** $9m^2 + 30mn + 25n^2$

Pages 422–424   Lesson 8-1
1. $2 \cdot 2 \cdot p \cdot p$ **3.** $-1 \cdot 2 \cdot 2 \cdot 5 \cdot 5 \cdot x \cdot x \cdot x \cdot y \cdot z \cdot z$ **5.** 5 **7.** 18y **9.** 4r **11.** $2 \cdot 3 \cdot 11 \cdot d \cdot d \cdot d \cdot d$ **13.** $-1 \cdot 7 \cdot 7 \cdot a \cdot a \cdot b \cdot b$ **15.** $2 \cdot 2 \cdot 2 \cdot 2 \cdot 5 \cdot p \cdot q \cdot q$ **17.** The minimum value is 40 mm; the factors of 96 whose sum when doubled is the least are 12 and 8. The maximum value is 194 mm; the factors of 96 whose sum when doubled is the greatest are 1 and 96. **19.** 9 **21.** 1 (relatively prime) **23.** 6d **25.** 5s **27.** 2mn **29.** base 1 cm, height 40 cm; base 2 cm, height 20 cm; base 4 cm, height 10 cm; base 5 cm, height 8 cm; base 8 cm, height 5 cm; base 10 cm, height 4 cm; base 20 cm, height 2 cm; base 40 cm, height 1 cm **31.** false; 2 **33.** Sample answer: $5x^2$ and $10x^3$; $5x^2 = 5 \cdot x \cdot x$ and $10x^3 = 2 \cdot 5 \cdot x \cdot x \cdot x$. The GCF is $5 \cdot x \cdot x$

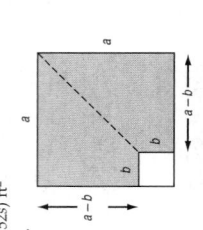

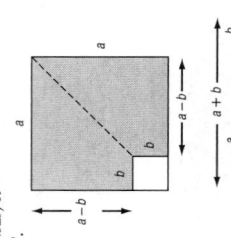

Area of rectangle = $(a - b)(a + b)$
or
$A_1 = \frac{1}{2}(a - b)(a + b)$
$A_2 = \frac{1}{2}(a - b)(a + b)$
Total area of shaded region
$= \left[\frac{1}{2}(a - b)(a + b)\right] + \left[\frac{1}{2}(a - b)(a + b)\right]$
$= (a - b)(a + b)$

Area of a trapezoid $= \frac{1}{2}$(height)(base 1 + base 2)

or $5x^2$. **35.** D **37.** $4x^2 - 4x + 1$ **39.** $49p^4 + 56p^2 + 16$ **41.** $20t^2 + 52hk + 5k^2$ **43.** Sample answer: Let n = the number of video minutes, $10n + 50 \le 500$; $n \le 45$; up to 45 min. **45.** 0 **47.** $10x + 40$ **49.** $6g^2 - 8g$ **51.** $7(b + c)$

Pages 429–431   Lesson 8-2
1. $9x(x + 4)$ **3.** $(5y + 4)(y - 3)$ **5.** $0, -5$ **7.** $0, \frac{5}{3}$ **9.** $5(x + 6y)$ **11.** $2h(7g - 9)$ **13.** $x(15xy^2 + 25y + 1)$ **15.** $(x + 3)(x + 2)$ **17.** $(6x - 1)(3x - 5)$ **19.** $(2x - 3)(4a - 3)$ **21.** 0, 24 **23.** $-4, 5$ **25.** $\frac{3}{2}, \frac{8}{3}$ **27.** $-4, 0$ **29.** 3 s; yes **31.** $4xy^2 - (3x + 10yz)$ **33.** $(9x^2 + 30xy + 25y^2)$ in^2 **35.** $\frac{1}{3}n(n - 3)$; 35 diagonals **37.** 63 games **39.** $3r^2(4 - \pi)$ **41.** Sample answer: $(x + 3)(x + 2) = 0$; set each factor equal to zero and solve each equation; $x + 3 = 0, x = -3$; $x + 2 = 0, x = -2$. The roots are -3 and -2. **43.** $(a^4 - b^4)(a^4 + b^4)$; Sample answer: Group terms with common factors, $(a^{x+y} + a^x b^y)$ and $(-a^y b^x - b^{x+y})$. Factor the GCF from each grouping to get $a^x(a^y + b^y) - b^x(a^y + b^y)$. Then use the Distributive Property to get $(a^x - b^x)(a^y + b^y)$. **45.** B **47.** a **49.** $3xy$ **51.** $4p^2 - 25p^2$ **53.** 37 shares **55.** $x^2 - 9x + 20$ **57.** $18a^2 - 6a - 4$ **59.** $8y^2 - 14y - 15$

Pages 437–439   Lesson 8-3
1. $(x + 3)(x + 8)$ **3.** $(w - 3)(w + 16)$ **5.** $(y - 4)(y + 5)$ **7.** $-1, -6$ **9.** 1, 9 **11.** -13 and -12 or 12 and 13 **13.** $(c + 5)(c + 7)$ **15.** $(d - 5)(d - 2)$ **17.** $(n - 6)(n + 9)$ **19.** $(n - 6)(n + 9)$ **21.** $(z + 2)(z - 20)$ **23.** $(x - 6)(x + 15)$ **25.** $-6, 2$ **27.** 3, 16 **29.** $-15, -1$ **31.** $-25, 2$ **33.** $36 = \frac{n^2 - n}{2}$, 9 justices **35.** 120 m by 68 m **37.** $4x + 26$ **39.** $-35, 15$ **41.** In this trinomial, $b = 6$ and $c = 9$. This means that $m + n$ is positive and mn is positive. Only two positive numbers have both a positive sum and product. Therefore, negative factors of 9 need not be considered. **43.** Aleta; to use the Zero Product Property, one side of the equation must equal zero. **45.** $-15, -9, 9, 15$ **47.** 4, 6 **49.** C **51.** $-3, \frac{5}{3}$ **53.** $-\frac{5}{9}, 0$ **55.** $3pq^3$ **57.** at least 5 days **59.** $(a + 4)(3a + 2)$ **61.** $(2p + 7)(p - 3)$ **63.** $(2g - 3)(2g - 1)$

Pages 444–446   Lesson 8-4
1. $(3a + 2)(a + 2)$ **3.** $2(p + 3)(p + 4)$ **5.** $3(2x - 1)(x + 3)$ **7.** $-3, -\frac{2}{3}$ **9.** $-\frac{5}{2}, \frac{4}{3}$ **11.** $(2x + 5)(x + 1)$ **13.** $(5d - 4)(d + 2)$ **15.** $(3g - 2)(3g - 2)$ **17.** $(x - 4)(2x + 5)$ **19.** prime **21.** $2(3r + 2)(r - 3)$ **23.** $-\frac{5}{2}$ **25.** $-\frac{5}{4}, \frac{5}{7}$ **27.** $-\frac{5}{7}, 1$ **29.** $\frac{3}{7}, \frac{5}{5}$ **31.** 3 s **33.** $(12x + 20y)$ in.; The area of the square equals $(3x + 5y)(3x + 5y)$ or the length of one side is $(3x + 5y)$ in. The perimeter is $4(3x + 5y)$ or $(12x + 20y)$ in. **35.** $-\frac{3}{2}, \frac{5}{3}$ **37.** $\frac{7}{2}, \frac{7}{5}$ **39.** 5 in. by 7 in. **41.** $\pm 25, \pm 14, \pm 11, \pm 10$ **43.** Sample answer: Find two numbers, m and n, that are the factors of ac and that

add to b. **45.** G **47.** prime **49.** $-\frac{7}{5}, 4$ **51.** 0, 12 **53.** $1(5.5) + 8.09(5.5) = (1 + 8.09)(5.5)$ or $9.09(5.5)$ **55.** 6 **57.** 11 **59.** 15

Pages 450–452   Lesson 8-5
1. $(n + 9)(n - 9)$ **3.** $2x^3(x + 7)(x - 7)$ **5.** prime **7.** $\frac{5}{2}, \frac{5}{2}$ **9.** $-\frac{9}{7}, 0, \frac{11}{7}$ **11.** $(x + 7)(x - 7)$ **13.** prime **15.** $3(5 + 2p)(5 - 2p)$ **17.** $(12a + 7b)(12a - 7b)$ **19.** $(n + 2)(n - 2)(n + 5)$ **21.** $(z^2 + 4)(z - 2)(z + 2)$ **23.** $-\frac{6}{5}, \frac{6}{5}$ **25.** $-\frac{3}{2}, \frac{3}{2}$ **27.** $-\frac{2}{7}, \frac{2}{7}$ **29.** $-18, 18$ **31.** 2 in. **33.** $P = \frac{1}{2}d(v_1 + v_2)(v_1 - v_2)$ **35.** Sample answer: $x^2 - 25 = (x + 5)(x - 5)$ **37.** Manuel; $4x^2 + y^2$ is not the difference of squares. **39.** Sample answer: A maximum height would be 1 foot. To find the hang time of a student athlete who attains a maximum height of 1 foot, solve the equation $4f^2 - 1 = 0$. You can factor the left side using the difference of squares pattern since $4f^2$ is the square of $2t$ and 1 is the square of 1. Thus, the equation becomes $(2t + 1)(2t - 1) = 0$. Using the Zero Product Property, each factor can be set equal to zero, resulting in two solutions, $t = -\frac{1}{2}$ and $t = \frac{1}{2}$. Since time cannot be negative, the hang time is $\frac{1}{2}$ second.
41. J **43.** $(2x - 1)(3x - 4)$ **45.** $-16, -2$ **47.** $-2, 4$ **49.** $x^2 + 2x + 1$ **51.** $9x^2 - 24x + 16$

Pages 458–460   Lesson 8-6
1. yes; $(y + 4)^2$ **3.** $2(x^2 + 9)$ **5.** $(2x - 7)(4x + 5)$ **7.** -3 **9.** $-1, 7$ **11.** about 3.35 s **13.** no **15.** $3(5u - 12b)^2$ **17.** $4(a - 3b)(a + 3b)$ **19.** $2(5g + 2)^2$ **21.** $2(5n + 1)(2n + 3)$ **23.** $2(3y - 4)^2$ **25.** 5 **27.** $-\frac{2}{3}$ **29.** $-\frac{2}{5}$ **31.** $-3 \pm \sqrt{2}$ **33.** $6 \pm \sqrt{11}$ **35.** 144 ft **37.** yes; 2 s **39.** prime **41.** $2mn(m^2 - 4n)(2m + 3)$ **43.** $8x^2 - 22x + 14$ in^2 if $x > \frac{7}{4}$; $8x^2 - 34x + 35$ in^2 if $x < \frac{7}{4}$ **45.** Sample answer: $x^3 + 5x^2 - 4x - 20$; group terms with common factors and factor out the GCF from each grouping to get $(x^2 - 4)(x + 5)$. Then factor the perfect square trinomial to get $(x - 2)(x + 2)(x + 5)$. **47.** 4, -4
49. 100 **51.** C **53.** $\frac{4}{3}$ **55.** $-3, \frac{1}{4}$ **57.** $|r| > -55)$ **59.** $|t| |t > 19|$ **61.** $y = 65x + 50$

Pages 461–464   Chapter 8   Study Guide and Review
1. false; composite **3.** false; sample answer: 64 **5.** false; $2^4 \cdot 3$ **7.** true **9.** true **11.** $2^2 \cdot 7 \cdot n \cdot n$ **13.** $2 \cdot 3 \cdot 5^2 \cdot s \cdot t$ **15.** 5 **17.** $4ab$ **19.** $5n$ **21.** 12-in. square **23.** $(a - 4c)(a + b)$ **25.** $2a(13b + 9c + 16a)$ **27.** $(8m - 3n)(3a + 5b)$ **29.** $0, -\frac{7}{4}$ **31.** 0.75 s **33.** $(x - 12)(x + 3)$ **35.** $(x - 3)(r - 6)$ **37.** $-6, 11$ **39.** prime **41.** $(4b + 3)(3b + 2)$ **43.** $4, -\frac{2}{5}$ **45.** 2 s **47.** $2y(y - 8)(y + 8)$ **49.** $\left(\frac{1}{2}n - \frac{3}{4}\right)\left(\frac{1}{2}n + \frac{3}{4}\right)$ **51.** $-\frac{5}{3}, \frac{5}{3}$ **53.** $-\frac{5}{7}, \frac{5}{7}$ **55.** $(a + 9)^2$ **57.** $(2 - 7r)^2$ **59.** 0, 2 **61.** $\frac{6}{7}$ **63.** 1 in.

Chapter 9 Quadratic and Exponential Functions

Page 469   **Chapter 9**   **Get Ready**

1.

x	y
−6	−1
−4	1
−2	3
0	5
2	7

3.

x	y
−4	−1
−2	0
0	1
2	2
4	3

5.

x	y
0	−4
3	−2
6	0

7. $T = 200 + 35m$

Money Saved over Time

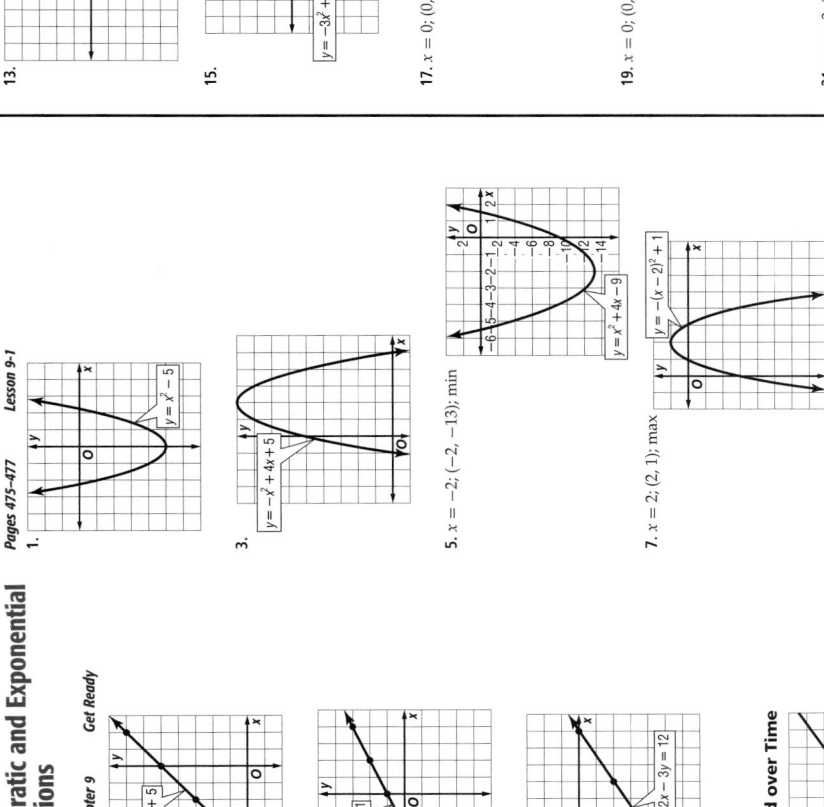

9. yes; $(a − 7)^2$ 11. no   13. no   15. yes ; $(4s − 3)^2$
17. −16, −23, −30   19. 56, 64, 72

Pages 475–477   **Lesson 9-1**

1. $y = x^2 − 5$

3. $y = −x^2 + 4x + 5$

5. $x = −2$; $(−2, −13)$; min $y = x^2 + 4x − 9$

7. $x = 2$; $(2, 1)$; max $y = −(x − 2)^2 + 1$

9. B   11. $y = −x^2 + 7$

13. $y = x^2 − 4x + 3$

15. $y = −3x^2 + 6x + 1$

17. $x = 0$; $(0, 0)$; max $y = −2x^2$

19. $x = 0$; $(0, 5)$; max $y = −x^2 + 5$

21. $x = −3$; $(−3, 24)$; max $y = −x^2 − 6x + 15$

23. $x = 2$; $(2, 1)$; min $y = 9 − 8x + 2x^2$

25. $x = \frac{5}{8}$ 27. No; The height needs to be 20 ft to win a prize.   29. 10 m; 100 m²
31. $x = 5$; $(5, −2)$; min $y + 2 = x^2 − 10x + 25$

33. $x = −1$; $(−1, −1)$; min $y + 1 = \frac{2}{3}(x + 1)^2$

35. $x = −1$ 37. 630 ft   39. 74 ft
41. $t = 0$ and 5.625 s; The height of the ball is zero before it is kicked and again when the ball lands on the ground.

43. $y = x^2$

45. $\{y \mid y \geq −9\}$
47. domain: $x \leq −3$ and $x \geq 3$; range: $y \geq 0$

49. Sample answer: $y = 4x^2 + 3x + 5$; write the equation for the axis of symmetry of a parabola, $x = −\frac{b}{2a}$. From the equation, $b = 3$ and $2a = 8$, so $a = 4$. Substitute these values for a and b into the equation $y = ax^2 + bx + c$.   **51.** B   **53.** prime   **55.** $(2m − 1)^2$
57. prime   59. $13x + 20y$ 61. $6p^2 − p − 18$
63. 8   65. −3.5

Pages 483–485   **Lesson 9-2**

1. 1, 6

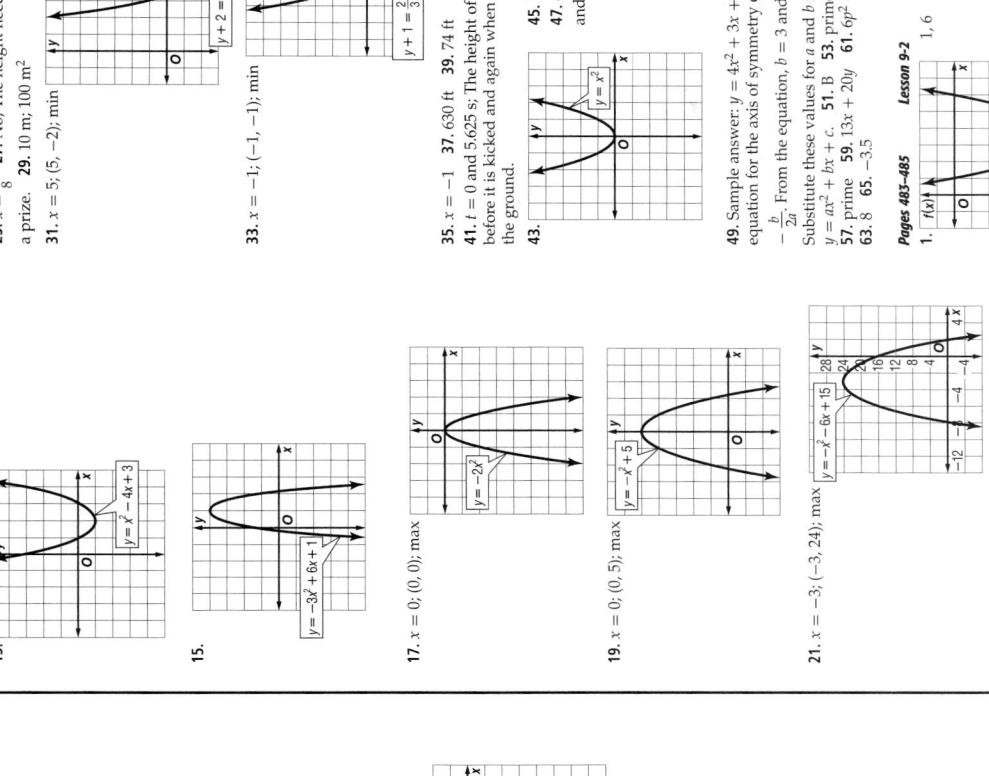

$f(x) = x^2 − 7x + 6$

he added 4 rectangles with length x units long and width $\frac{8}{4}$ or 2 units long. This area represents 35.

To make this a square, four 4×4 squares must be added. To solve $x^2 + 8x = 35$ by completing the square, use the following steps.

$x^2 + 8x = 35$

$x^2 + 8x + 16 = 35 + 16$ Since $(\frac{8}{2})^2 = 16$, add 16 to each side.

$(x + 4)^2 = 51$ Factor $x^2 + 8x + 16$.

$x + 4 = \pm\sqrt{51}$ Take the square root of each side.

$x + 4 - 4 = \pm\sqrt{51} - 4$ Subtract 4 from each side.

$x = -4 \pm \sqrt{51}$ Simplify.

$x = -4 - \sqrt{51}$ or $x = -4 + \sqrt{51}$ Simplify.

$x \approx 3.14$

$x \approx -11.14$

The solutions are −11.14 and 3.14.

49. J   **51.** −4, 4

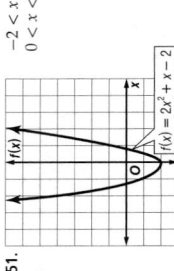

$f(x) = x^2 - 16$

53. $A = (280 - 2x)x$ or $A = 280 - 2x^2$ **55.** ab^2
57. $-3 < x < 1$ **59.** (3, 6)   **61.** (7, 2)   **63.** 5   **65.** 9.4

Pages 497–499   **Lesson 9-4**
1. −6, −1   **3.** −8.6, −1.4   **5.** about 18.8 cm by 18.8 cm
7. 0; 1 real root   **9.** −10, −2   **11.** −0.8, 1   **13.** ∅   **15.** 5
17. −0.4, 3.9   **19.** −0.5, 0.6   **21.** 5 cm by 16 cm
23. 25; 2 real roots   **25.** 0; 1 real root
27. $\frac{61}{12}$; no real roots   **29.** ∅   **31.** −0.3, 0.9   **33.** about
0.6 and 1.6   **35.** 2   **37.** 0   **39.** about 2.5 s   **41.** Juanita;
you must first write the equation in the form $ax^2 + bx + c = 0$ to determine the values of a, b, and c.
Therefore, the value of c is −2, not 2.   **43.** The function
can be factored to $f(x) = (x - 4)^2$, so there is one real
root at (4, 0). Using the discriminant to determine the
number of roots involves more computation and
potential for error.   **45.** C   **47.** 1, 7   **49.** −0.4, 12.4
51. $-2 < x < -1$, $0 < x < 1$

$f(x) = 2x^2 + x - 2$

53. 12 cm   **55.** $y^3(15x + y)$ **57.** $\{m \mid m > 5\}$
59. $\{k \mid k \le -4\}$ **61.** $y = -7$ **63.** 16   **65.** 250

33. about 9 s   **35.** 6 ft   **37.** about 180 ft²
39. $(500 - 2x)(400 - 2x) = 100,000$ or $4x^2 - 1800x + 100,000 = 0$; about 65 ft
41. Sample answer:

The only solution to the equation with the graph shown is 4.
43. Always; the shaded region of the graph includes y-values greater than 2.
45. D
47. $x = -3$; (−3, 0); min

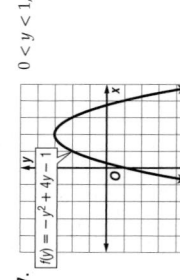

$y = x^2 + 6x + 9$

49. $x = 6$; (6, −13); min

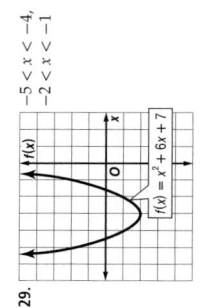

$y = 0.5x^2 - 6x + 5$

51. {5}   **53.** $\frac{m^3}{3}$ **55.** $\frac{m^5 y^4}{3}$ **57.** yes; $(a + 7)^2$ **59.** no

Pages 489–491   **Lesson 9-3**
1. −2, 8   **3.** 36   **5.** −1, 7   **7.** −15, 1   **9.** −2.4, 0.1
11. 12 in.   **13.** −6, 4   **15.** −12.2, −3.8   **17.** 25   **19.** $\frac{121}{4}$
21. −5, 2   **23.** −27, 7   **25.** −3, 7   **27.** 1, 7   **29.** 2.3
31. −0.1, 1.4   **33.** about 2017   **35.** 2.5   **37.** $\frac{1}{2}$, 3
39. −24, 24   **41.** $3 \pm \sqrt{9 - c}$
43. Sample answer: $x^2 + 4x + 4$

x	1	1
x	1	1
x^2	x	x

45. There are no real solutions since completing the square results in $(x + 2)^2 = -8$ and the square of a number cannot be negative.   **47.** Sample answer: Al-Khwarizmi used squares to geometrically represent quadratic equations. He represented x^2 by a square whose sides were each x units long. To this square,

---

17. The graph is wider than the graph of $y = x^2$ and opens downward rather than upward. Also, the vertex is 3 units left and 4 units up from the vertex of the graph of $y = x^2$.

(−3, 4), (0, 0), (−6, 0)

19. 2; −4, −8   **21.** 0; no real roots   **23.** $-3 < n < -2$, $2 < n < 3$

$f(n) = -n^2 + 7$

25. −4, 1

$f(s) = 3s^2 + 9s - 12$

27. $0 < y < 1, 3 < y < 4$

$f(y) = -y^2 + 4y - 1$

29. $-5 < x < -4$, $-2 < x < -1$

$f(x) = x^2 + 6x + 7$

31. 4, 5

3. ∅

$f(c) = c^2 + 3$

5. 1; −7

7. −4, 4

$f(x) = x^2 - 16$

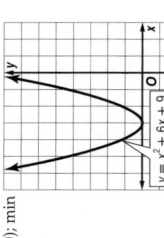

9. −2, 6   **11.** ∅

$f(n) = 5n^2 + 2n + 6$

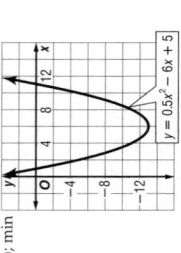

13. 2

$f(b) = -b^2 + 4b - 4$

15. −3, 0

$f(a) = -2r^2 - 6r$

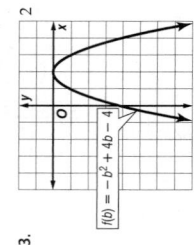

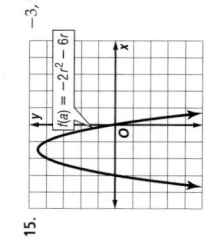

Lesson 9-5

1. 1; 3.7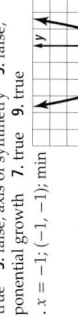

3. 1; 5.8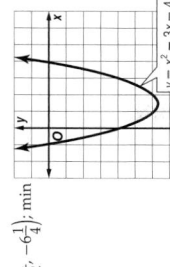

5. −36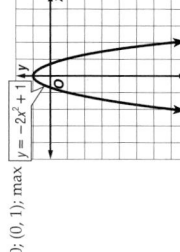

7. Yes; the domain values are at regular intervals and the range values have a common factor 6.

9. 1; 5.9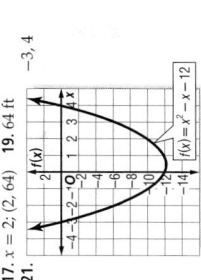

11. 1; 20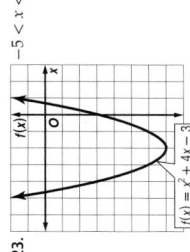

13. 1; 1.7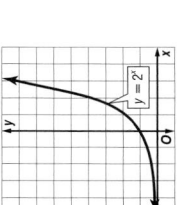

15. 5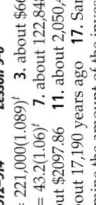

17. −6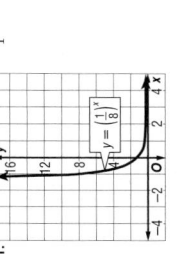

19. about 312   21. about \$37.27 million; about \$41.74 million; about \$46.75 million   23. No; the domain values are at regular intervals and the range values have a common difference 3.   25. Yes; the domain values are at regular intervals and the range values have a common factor 0.75.

27. 1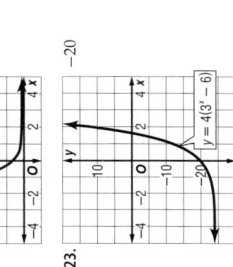

29. −12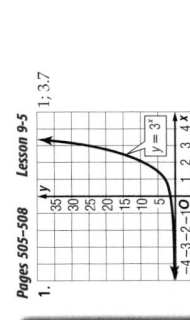

31. quadratic   33. quadratic   35. linear
37. 27 schools

Study Guide and Review

Chapter 9

1. true   3. false; axis of symmetry   5. false; exponential growth   7. true   9. true
11. $x = -1$; $(-1, -1)$; min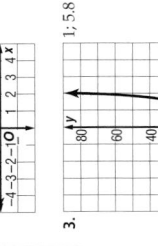

13. $x = 1\frac{1}{2}$; $\left(1\frac{1}{2}, -6\frac{1}{4}\right)$; min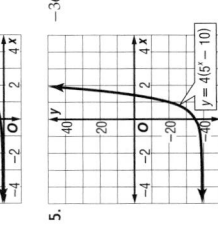

15. $x = 0$; $(0, 1)$; max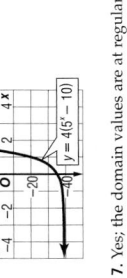

17. $x = 2$; $(2, 64)$ 19. 64 ft
21. 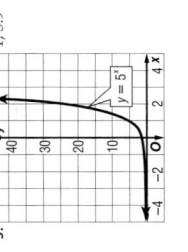 −3, 4

23. 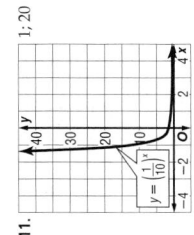 $-5 < x < -4$, $0 < x < 1$

39.

Week	Distance (miles)
1	22
2	24.2
3	26.62
4	29.282

41. Never; the graph will never intersect the x-axis.
43. Hannah; the graph of $y = \left(\frac{1}{3}\right)^x$ decreases as x increases.   45. a translation 2 units up
47. Sample answer: If the number of items on each level of a piece of art is a given number times the number of items on the previous level, an exponential function can be used to describe the situation. For the carving of the pliers, $y = 2^x$. For this situation, x is an integer between 0 and 8, inclusive. The values of y are 1, 2, 4, 8, 16, 32, 64, 128, and 256.

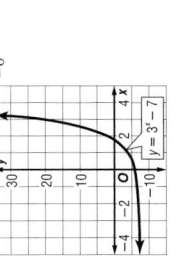

49. H   51. −1.8, 0.3   53. 2, 5   55. −5.4, −0.6   57. prime
59. $\{x \mid x > -5\}$ 61. $\{y \mid y < -5\}$ 63. 11.25   65. 144

Lesson 9-6

1. $I = 221{,}000(1.089)^t$ 3. about \$661.44
5. $W = 43.2(1.06)^t$ 7. about 122,848,204 people
9. about \$2097.86   11. about 2,050,422   13. about 128 g
15. about 17,190 years ago   17. Sample answer: Determine the amount of the investment if \$500 is invested at an interest rate of 7% compounded quarterly for 6 years.   19. D
21. 1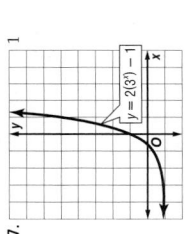

23. −20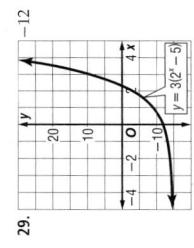

25. −0.6, 2.6   27. Yes; slope $= \frac{60}{250} = 0.24 < 0.33$.

Selected Answers

Chapter 10 (continued)

25.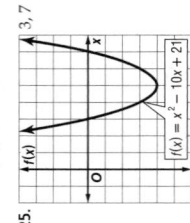

27. −3 and 8 29. −4, 6 31. 2.3, 13.7 33. 6 cm
35. −9, −1 37. −3, −6, −0.4 39. −0.7, 0.5
41. 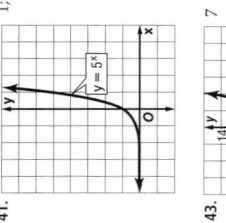 1; 3.1
43.
45. about 568 47. $7705.48 49. $1006.86
51. about $570 billion

Chapter 10 Radical Expressions and Triangles

Page 527 *Chapter 10* *Get Ready*
1. 5 3. 7.48 5. 16c 7. 25m + 6n 9. (−6, −4)
11. 8 cm 13. no 15. 11.375 feet

Pages 531–534 *Lesson 10-1*
1. $2\sqrt5$ 3. $8\sqrt2$ 5. $3\sqrt6$ 7. 28 ft² 9. $2x^2|y^3|\sqrt{15x}$
11. $\frac{2\sqrt6}{3}$ 13. $\frac{\sqrt{210}}{7}$ 15. $\frac{8(3+\sqrt2)}{7}$ 17. $3\sqrt2$
19. $4\sqrt5$ 21. $\sqrt{30}$ 23. $84\sqrt5$ 25. $2J^2\sqrt{10}$
27. $7x^3|y^3|\sqrt{3y}$ 29. $\frac{2l}{3}$ 31. $\frac{\sqrt{2l}}{4}$ 33. $\frac{c^2\sqrt{5cd}}{2l^3}$
35. $\frac{54+9\sqrt2}{3}$ 37. $2\sqrt7 - 2\sqrt2$ 39. $\frac{16+12\sqrt3}{-11}$
41. $3\sqrt{2l}$ 43. $6\sqrt{55} \approx 44$ mph, $4\sqrt{165} \approx 51$ mph
45. $s = \sqrt{Ai}$; $6\sqrt2$ in. 47. $6\sqrt5$ m/s 49. 2.4 km/s; The Moon has a much lower escape velocity than Earth.
51. $x^2 + \frac{b}{a}x + \frac{b^2}{4a^2}$ 53. 5; $\frac{1}{\sqrt{4(x-4)}} = \frac{1}{2}$
55. No; to solve the equation, take the square root of each side, remembering that $a^2 = b^2$ implies $a = \pm b$.

Thus, $3x - 2 = 2x + 6$ yields $x = 8$; but $3x - 2 = -(2x + 6)$ yields $x = -\frac{4}{5}$. 57. A lot of formulas and calculations that are used in space exploration contain radical expressions. To determine the escape velocity of a planet, you would need to know its mass and the radius. It would be very important to know the escape velocity of a planet before you landed on it so you would know if you had enough fuel and velocity to launch from it to get back into space. 59. J 61. 16, −32, 64 63. 144, 864, 5184 65. 0.08, 0.016, 0.0032
67. 84.9°C 69. $(5x − 4)(7x − 3)$ 71. $x^2 − x − 6$
73. $2J^2 − 11t − 6$ 75. $15x^2 + 4xy − 3y^2$

Pages 538–540 *Lesson 10-2*
1. $11\sqrt3$ 3. $-\sqrt5$ 5. $9\sqrt5 + 5\sqrt6$ 7. $4 + 4\sqrt6$
9. $P = 16 + 12\sqrt6$ ft; $A = 70 + 24\sqrt6$ ft² 11. $11\sqrt5$
13. $-7\sqrt{15}$ 15. $18\sqrt x$ 17. $13\sqrt3 + \sqrt2$ 19. $5\sqrt2 + 2\sqrt3$ 21. $-\sqrt7$ 23. $3\sqrt2 + 10\sqrt3$ 25. $4 + 2\sqrt{10}$
16 29. $19\sqrt5$ 31. $20\sqrt7 + 2\sqrt5$ in.; $52. - 16\sqrt{35}$ in²
33. $15\sqrt6$ cm² 35. $\frac{4\sqrt{10}}{5}$ 37. $\frac{53\sqrt7}{7}$ 39. Approximately 853 feet; solve $\sqrt{\frac{3(1250)}{2}} - \sqrt{\frac{3h}{2}} = 7.53$; may guess and test, graphical, or analytical methods. 41. No, each pipe would need to carry 500 gallons per minute, so the pipes would need at least a 6-inch radius.
43. The velocity doubled because $\sqrt4 = 2$.
45. Sample answer: Let $x = 2$ and $y = 3$. $(\sqrt2 + \sqrt3)^2 = 2 + 2\sqrt6 + 3$ or $5 + 2\sqrt6$ 47. Sample answer: $a = 1$, $b = 1$; $(\sqrt{1+1})^2 = (\sqrt1)^2 + (\sqrt1)^2 = 1 + 1$ or 2
49. D 51. $2\sqrt{10}$ 53. $-14|x||y|\sqrt y$ 55. $\frac{5|c|\sqrt{2d}}{2}$
57. 4096 59. −0.4194304 61. $\{\pm\frac{6}{11}\}$ 63. $\{-4, -3, 4\}$
65. $x^2 - 4x + 4$ 67. $x^2 + 12x + 36$ 69. $4x^2 - 12x + 9$

Pages 543–546 *Lesson 10-3*
1. 25 3. 7 5. 2 7. 3 9. 6 11. −12 13. −16
15. −63 17. 9 19. 29 21. 34 23. 2 25. 2, 3
27. 3 29. 10,569 lb 31. 57 33. no solution 35. $\frac{3}{25}$
37. 6 39. 2 41. 11 43. $r = \sqrt{\frac{A}{\pi}}$ 45. $4\sqrt3$ m
47. 9.8 m/s 49. approximately 296 m/s 51. 0.36 ft
53. $\frac{24l^2}{\pi^2}$ 55. 16°C 57. 8 59. −2 61. 1.70 63. The solution may not satisfy the original equation.
65. Alex; the square of $-\sqrt x - 5$ is $x - 5$. 67. You can determine the time it takes an object to fall from a given height using a radical equation. It would take a skydiver approximately 42 seconds to fall 10,000 feet. Using the equation, it would take 25 seconds. The time is different in the two calculations because air resistance slows the skydiver. 69. H 71. $20\sqrt3$ 73. $8\sqrt3$
75. $3(\sqrt{10} - \sqrt3)$ 77. $6z^2 + 44z + 70$ 79. $95° \le F \le 104°$ 81. $2x + y = 15$ 83. 3.9% decrease 85. 25
87. 10 89. $4\sqrt{13}$

Pages 551–554 *Lesson 10-4*
1. 26 3. 8 5. 18.44 7. A 9. yes; $10^2 + 24^2 = 26^2$
11. 30 13. 5 15. $\sqrt{45} \approx 6.71$ 17. $\sqrt{27} \approx 5.20$
19. $\sqrt{124} \approx 11.14$ 21. $\sqrt{40x} \approx 6.32x$ 23. 11.40

25. 13.08 27. 20 29. 111.1 units² 31. no; $6^2 + 12^2 \ne 18^2$ 33. yes; $45^2 + 60^2 = 75^2$ 35. yes; $4^2 + 7^2 = (\sqrt{65})^2$ 37. 14.56 39. 212.6 ft 43. 18 ft 45. $4\sqrt3$ in. or about 6.93 in. 47. 900 49. The area of the largest semicircle is $\frac{\pi c^2}{4} = \frac{\pi}{4}(a^2 + b^2)$. Using the Pythagorean Theorem, $c^2 = a^2 + b^2$, we can show that the sum of the two small areas is equal to the area of the largest semicircle. 51. B 53. 144 55. 12 57. $-3\sqrt z$ 59. 425 mph 61. $f(x) = x - 2$ 63. 10

Pages 557–559 *Lesson 10-5*
1. 10 3. $3\sqrt2$ or 4.24 5. yes; $AB = \sqrt{68}$, $BC = \sqrt{85}$, $AC = \sqrt{85}$ 7. 20.6 yd 9. 2 or −14 11. 13 13. 17
15. $2\sqrt{13}$ or 7.21 17. $\sqrt{185}$ or 13.60 19. 0.53 mi
21. Duluth, (44, 116); St. Cloud, (−46, 39); Eau Claire, (71, −8); Rochester, (27, −58) 23. all cities except Duluth 25. 17 or −13 27. −2 or −12 29. 2 or 38 31. $\sqrt{157} \ne \sqrt{101}$; The trapezoid is not isosceles.
33. 9 35. $\frac{17}{4}$ or 4.25 37. $\frac{\sqrt{74}}{7}$ or 1.23 39. $2\sqrt3$ or 3.46 41. The values that are subtracted are squared before being added and the square of a negative number is always positive. The sum of two positive numbers is positive, so the distance will never be negative. 43. Compare the slopes of the two potential legs to determine whether the slopes are negative reciprocals of each other. You can also compute the lengths of the three sides and determine whether the square of the longest side length is equal to the sum of the squares of the other two side lengths. Neither test holds true in this case because the triangle is not a right triangle. 45. B 47. 25 49. 3 51. 4
53. $\{m|m \ge 9\}$
55. $\{x|x \le -3\}$
−8 −7 −6 −5 −4 −3 −2 −1 0
57. 5 hours 59. −8 61. 5

Pages 563–565 *Lesson 10-6*
1. No; the angle measures are not equal. 3. $a = 21$, $b = 27$ 5. $b = \frac{25}{7}$, $c = \frac{30}{7}$ 7. 65 ft 9. No; the angle measures are not equal. 11. Yes; the angle measures are equal. 13. Yes, the angle measures are equal.
15. $o = 20$, $p = 10$ 17. $n = \frac{112}{13}$, $p = \frac{84}{13}$ 19. $n = 7$, $o = 10$ 21. $l = 16.2$, $n = 6.3$ 23. 1.25 in 25. 8
27. Viho's eyes are 6 feet off the ground, Viho and the building each create right angles with the ground, and the two angles with the ground at P have equal measure. 29. The angles will always be the same because the sides are proportional with a scale factor of three which means the triangles are similar and the angles are congruent. 31. Yes; all circles are similar because they have the same shape. 33. 4:1; The area of the first is πr^2 and the area of the other is $\pi(2r)^2 = 4\pi r^2$. 35. D 37. 5 39. 7 41. no 43. (3, −2) 45. (6, 12)

Pages 567–570 *Chapter 10* *Study Guide and Review*
1. false, $-3 - \sqrt7$ 3. true 5. true 7. true 9. $\frac{2\sqrt{15}}{|y|}$
11. $57 - 24\sqrt3$ 13. $\frac{3\sqrt{35} - 5\sqrt{21}}{-15}$ 15. about 2 h

17. $2\sqrt6 - 4\sqrt3$ 19. $\frac{9\sqrt2}{2}$ 21. $\sqrt6 - 1$ 23. about 250.95 ft/s 25. 32 27. 3 29. 5 31. 34 33. $2\sqrt{34} \approx 11.66$ 35. 24 37. no 39. yes 41. yes 43. $\sqrt{58}$ or 7.62 45. $\sqrt{74}$ or 8.60 47. 18 or −8 49. $d = \frac{45}{8}$, $e = \frac{27}{4}$ 51. $b = \frac{44}{3}$, $d = 6$ 53. 4 in.

Chapter 11 Rational Expressions and Equations

Page 575 *Chapter 11* *Get Ready*
1. $\frac{63}{16}$ 3. 5 5. 4.62 7. 10.8 9. 6 11. 16
13. $3m(2n + 5)$ 15. $(x - 5)(x + 9)$ 17. $3(x - 3)(x - 1)$

Pages 580–582 *Lesson 11-1*
1.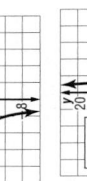

3. $xy = 21.87$, 4.05 5. $xy = 72$; 9 7. approximately 311 cycles per second
9.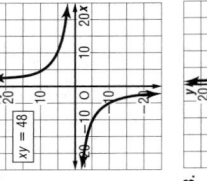

11.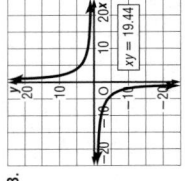

13.
15. 7.2 h 17. $xy = 12.4$; −20 19. $xy = 0.8$; 0.25
21. $xy = -14$; −2 23. $xy = 12$; $\frac{12}{5}$ 25. $xy = -\frac{14}{3}$; $-\frac{2}{3}$

R56 (left page)

27. $xy = 26.84; 8.3875$ **29.** $PV = k$ or $P_1V_1 = P_2V_2$ **31.** 27.5 m^3 **33.** 24 kg **35.** neither **37.** Sample answer: Though it has been replaced by Einstein's theory of relativity, Newton's law of Gravitational Force is an example of an indirect variation which models real world situations. The gravitational force exerted on two objects is inversely proportional to the square of the distances between the two objects. The force exerted on the two objects, times the square of the distance between the two objects, is equal to the gravitational constant times the masses of the two objects. **39.** It is half. **41.** When the gear ratio is lower, the pedaling revolutions increase to keep a constant speed. Lower gears at a constant rate will cause a decrease in speed, while higher gears at a constant rate will cause an increase in speed. **43.** J **45.** $a = 6, f = 14$ **47.** $a = 8$ or 18 **49.** A and C sharp **51.**

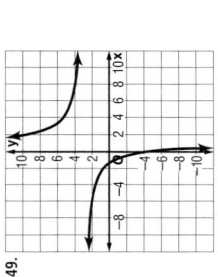

53. -9 **55.** 3 **57.** 30 **59.** $6xy^2$

Pages 586–588 **Lesson 11-2**

1. -3 **3.** $-5, 4$ **5.** $x - 7; -7$ **7.** $\frac{3}{x-4}; 4, 3$ **9.** $\frac{x+3}{2}; \frac{7}{4}$, 4 **11.** $\frac{4}{9+2g}$ **13.** -5 **15.** $-5, 5$ **17.** $-5, -7$ **19.** 178.13 lb **21.** The difference is 12 minutes. **23.** $\frac{a^2}{3b}; 0, 0$ **25.** $\frac{3x}{8z}; 0, 0, 0$ **27.** $\frac{mn}{12x-4m}$; $m \neq 3n, 0, 0$ **29.** $z + 8; -2$ **31.** $\frac{2}{y+5}; -5, 2$ **33.** $\frac{a+3}{a+9}$; $\frac{(b+4)(b-2)}{(b-4)(b-16)}; -4, 16$ **37.** $\frac{n-2}{n(n-6)}; 0, 6$ **39.** $\frac{3}{4}; -2, -1$ **41.** $\frac{450+4n}{n}$ **43.** $\frac{450+4(n+2)}{n}$ **45.** Sample answer: $\frac{1}{(x+4)(x+7)}$; since the excluded values are -4 and -7, the denominator of the rational expression must contain the factors $(x+4)$ and $(x+7)$. **47.** Sample answer: The first graph has a hole at $x = 4$ because it is an excluded value of the equation. **49.** B **51.** $xy = 60; -5$ **53.** $xy = -54; -18$ **55.** $o = 6, p = 4$ **57.** 1 **59.** -3 **61.** 372.32 **63.** 450 **65.** 95,040 **67.** 0.22

Pages 592–594 **Lesson 11-3**

1. $8y$ **3.** $\frac{4m}{3(m+5)}$ **5.** $\frac{n+2}{n-4}$ **7.** 16.36 mph **9.** $2x$ **11.** $\frac{4wy}{5x^2}$ **13.** $\frac{x+4}{x+8}$ **15.** $\frac{(z+6)(z-5)}{(z-6)(z+3)}$ **17.** $\frac{(x+5)^2}{9}$

19. $\frac{x}{(x+4)^2}$ **21.** $\frac{b+1}{(b+3)(b-3)}$ **23.** \$336 if carpet is sold in square feet; it is not reasonable to assume that carpet is sold only in square feet. If the carpet is sold in square yards the price will be \$360. **27.** 16.67 m/s **29.** 20 yd³ **31.** 5 tracks · 2 miles/1 track · 5280 feet/1 mile · 1 car/75 feet **33.** 1.1 h **35.** c and e; sample answer: the expressions each have a GCF which can be use to simplify the expressions. **37.** Sample answer: When the negative sign in front of the first expression is distributed, the numerator is $-x - 6$; Distributive Property. **39.** B **41.** $-6, 6$ **43.** -3 **45.** $xy = 19.44$; 5.4 **47.** $xy = 28.16; 8.8$ **49.** $|r| \geq 2.1)$ **51.** -7^3 or -343 **53.** $\frac{4b^4c^5}{a^3}$ **55.** $(x+5)(x-3)$ **57.** $(x-6)^2$ **59.** $(2x+1)(x-3)$

Pages 597–599 **Lesson 11-4**

1. $6n$ **3.** 18 **5.** $\frac{1}{2(k+2)}$ **7.** 23.61 m/s **9.** about 57 pieces **11.** n^4p **13.** $\frac{a^3cg}{b}$ **15.** $\frac{a-4}{a-3}$ **17.** $\frac{(n+2)^2}{4}$ **19.** $\frac{b+4}{2(b+3)}$ **21.** $\frac{(x-3)(x+4)}{(x-6)(x+3)}$ **23.** $\frac{1}{(m+7)(m+1)}$ **25.** 350,000 **27.** 0.00173 **29.** about 105.4 cups **31.** $n = 45$ yd³ **33.** 3.5 ft(10 ft + 17 ft) **35.** 1 yd³ · 4ft · $\frac{1 \text{ yd}^3}{27 \text{ ft}^3}$; 7 loads **37.** $\frac{\left(x - \frac{1}{2}\right)\left(x - \frac{3}{4}\right)(x)}{x^3} \div$

33. 63.5 mph **35.** $(10 \cdot 85 \text{ pounds}) \div$ **37.** Sometimes; sample answer: 0 has no reciprocal and it is a real number. **39.** Sample answer: Divide the number of cans recycled by $\frac{5}{8}$ to find the total number of cans produced. Answers should include $x = 63,900,000 \div \frac{5}{8} \cdot \frac{1 \text{ pound}}{33 \text{ cans}}$ **41.** F **43.** $\frac{x-2}{x+2}$ **45.** $\frac{1}{c-6}$ **47.** $\frac{1}{a+1}$ **49.** $y = 1.67x - 1300$ **51.** $\frac{m^3}{5}$ **53.** $\frac{3y}{7x}$

Pages 604–606 **Lesson 11-5**

1. $5q$ **3.** $2x^2 + x - \frac{5}{2x}$ **5.** $n + 4$ **7.** $b + 2 - \frac{3}{2b} - 1$ **9.** $2m^2 + 3m + 7$ **11.** \$360,000 **13.** $4k - \frac{3}{k}$ **15.** $\frac{a}{7} +$ $1 - \frac{4}{a}$ **17.** $3a^2 + 4b^2$ **19.** $x + 8$ **21.** $s + 2$ **23.** $a + 7 - \frac{1}{a-3}$ **25.** $3x^2 + 2x - 3 - \frac{1}{x+2}$ **27.** $3g^2 + 2g +$ $3 - \frac{2}{3g-2}$ **29.** $t^2 + 4t - 1$ **31.** $7^2 \div 8$ **33.** $x^2 \div$ $(x+1) = x - 1 + \frac{1}{x+1}$ **35.** $x + 3$ **37.** $t + 20; t + 35$ **39.** 0.7; 0.84; 0.946; 0.97 **41.** $9d + 3$ **43.** $3x^2 - 12 +$ $\frac{16}{x} + 5$ **45.** $-x^4 - 4x^2 + 2x$ **47.** $2w + 4$

R57 (right page)

49. $\frac{9x+6}{(x+1)(x+2)^2}$ **51.** Sample answer: To find the LCD, determine the least common multiple of all of the factors of the denominators. **53.** Sample answer: Multiply both the numerator and denominator by factors necessary to form the LCD. **55.** Sample answer: You can use rational expressions and their least common denominators to determine when elections will coincide. Use each factor of the denominators the greatest number of times it appears. **57.** J **59.** $\frac{4x+5}{2x+3}$ **61.** $b + 10$ **63.** $2m - 3 + \frac{2}{2m+7}$ **65.** $(24, 6)$ **67.** $\frac{5}{6}$ **69.** $\frac{x+3}{x}$ **71.** $\frac{3x}{(x+2)(x-1)}$

Pages 623–625 **Lesson 11-8**

1. $\frac{3x+4}{x}$ **3.** $\frac{6a^2-a-1}{3a}$ **5.** $\frac{14}{19}$ **9.** $\frac{a-b}{x+y}$ **9.** $\frac{4a+5}{a}$ **11.** $\frac{6wz+2z}{w}$ **13.** $\frac{6a^2-a-1}{2a}$ **19.** $\frac{p^2+p-15}{p-4}$ **21.** $66\frac{2}{3}$ lb/in² **17.** $\frac{3s^3-3s^2-1}{s-1}$ **25.** n **27.** $\frac{s^3(s-t)}{t^2(s+t)}$ **29.** $\frac{1}{a-1}$ **31.** 1 **23.** $\frac{145}{84}$ **33.** $\frac{(n+5)(n-2)}{(n+12)(n-9)}$ **35.** 49.21 cycles/min **37.** $\frac{32b^2}{35}$ **39.** a and c **41.** Sample answer: Most measurements used in baking are fractions or mixed numbers, which are examples of rational expressions. Divide the expression in the numerator of a complex fraction by the expression in the denominator. **43.** J **45.** $\frac{3a^2+3ab-b^2}{(a-b)(2b+3a)}$ **47.** $\frac{4}{x^2}$ **49.** $\frac{d}{t+1}$ **51.** 3.2×10^0 **53.** -48 **55.** 16 **57.** -14.4

Pages 630–632 **Lesson 11-9**

1.2 **3.** $-1, \frac{1}{5}$ **5.** 3, 5 **7.** 10 **9.** 8 **11.** 3 **13.** -3 **15.** 0 **17.** $\frac{1}{2}$ **19.** -4; extraneous 1 **21.** extraneous -2 and 0; no solution **23.** $-3, 4$ **25.** $0, -3, 2$ **27.** 5 h and 15 min **29.** 900 min or 15 h **31.** about 22 min **33.** 9 **35a.** line **35b.** $f(x) = \frac{(x+5)(x-6)}{x+5} = x + 5$ **35c.** -5 **37a.** parabola **37b.** $f(x) = x^2 + 6x + 12$ **37c.** no real roots **39.** $d = t(r - w), d = t(r + w); t = \frac{d}{r-w}, t = \frac{d}{r+w}$ **41.** Sample answer: $\frac{x}{4} = 0$ **43.** Sample answer: Rational equations are used in solving rate problems, so they can be used to determine traveling times, speeds, and distances related to subways. Since both trains leave at the same time, their traveling time is the same. The sum of the distances of both trains is equal to the total distance between the two stations. So, add the two expressions to represent the distance each train travels and solve for time. **45.** J **47.** $\frac{a-5}{a+7}$ **49.** $\frac{6+m}{2(2m-3)}$ **51.** $\frac{4a^2+7a+2}{(6a+1)(a-3)(a+3)}$

Chapter 11 **Study Guide and Review**

1. false; rational **3.** true **5.** false; $x^2 - 144$ **7.** true **9.** $xy = 1176$; 21 **11.** 6.25 ft or 6 feet 3 inches **13.** n **15.** $\frac{x+3}{x(x-6)}$ **17.** $\frac{x}{x+2}$ **19.** $\frac{3axy}{10}$ **21.** $\frac{3}{a^2-3a}$ **23.** $2p$

51. As x approaches 1 from the left y approaches negative infinity, and as x approaches y from the right y approaches positive infinity. **53.** 185.9° F **55.** Sample answer: $x^3 + 2x^2 + 8; x^3 + 2x^2 + 0x + 8$ **57.** 3, 4 **59.** 63 **61.** D **63.** $x + 5$ **65.** $b + 7$ **67.** 2300 cards **69.** $4x^2 + 13xy + 2y^2$ **71.** $2g^3 - 4g^2 - 2h$

Pages 611–613 **Lesson 11-6**

1. $\frac{a}{b}$ **3.** $\frac{3-n}{n-1}$ **5.** $\frac{8x-6}{5}$ **7.** $\frac{3}{n-3}$ **9.** $\frac{x^2+y^2}{x-y}$ **11.** $\frac{1}{2x}$ **13.** 3.3 **15.** $\frac{n-3}{n+3}$ **17.** $\frac{22x+7}{2x+5}$ **19.** square **21.** $\frac{2}{5}$ **23.** -2 **25.** $\frac{60}{y-3}$ **27.** $\frac{6}{y-3}$ **29.** $\frac{4-7m}{7m-2}$ **31.** $\frac{1}{3}$ **33.** $\frac{7}{x+7}$ **35.** $\frac{1}{5}$ **37.** 8.3 lb **39.** Russell; sample answer: Ginger factored incorrectly in the next-to-last step of her work. **41.** Sample answer: Since any rational number can be expressed as a fraction, values on graphics can be written as rational expressions for clarification. The numbers in the graphic are percents which can be written as rational expressions with a denominator of 100. To add rational expressions with inverse denominators, factor -1 out of either denominator so that it is like the other. **43.** F **45.** $8x^2 - 9$ **47.** $\frac{x+3}{x}$ **49.** 90 **51.** 720

Pages 617–619 **Lesson 11-7**

1. $35d^2$ **3.** $(n+4)(n-1)^2$ **5.** $\frac{12x+7}{10x^2}$ **7.** $\frac{y^2+12y+25}{(y-5)(y+5)}$ **9.** $\frac{a^2+16}{a^2-16}$ **11.** $\frac{y^2-7y-6}{y^2+7y+12}$ **13.** a^2b^3 **15.** $(x-4)(x+2)$ **17.** $(x+7)(x-2)^2$ **19.** $\frac{3+5x}{x^2}$ **21.** $\frac{7+10a}{6a^2}$ **23.** $\frac{7x+8}{(x+5)(x-4)}$ **25.** $\frac{8a^2-9a}{(a+5)(a-2)}$ **27.** $\frac{3a+20}{(a-5)(a+5)}$ **29.** $\frac{2x+1}{(x+1)^2}$ **31.** $\frac{14x-3}{6x^2}$ **33.** $\frac{-2x}{x-1}$ **35.** $\frac{2+3x}{(x-5)}$ **37.** $\frac{-n^2-5n-3}{(n-5)(n+5)}$ **39.** $\frac{k^2-2k-2}{(2x+1)(k+2)}$ **41.** 12 miles; \$30 **43.** $\frac{4-25x}{15x^2}$ **45.** $\frac{22x-7xy}{6y^2}$ **47.** $\frac{a^3-a^2b+a^2+ab}{(a+b)(a-b)^2}$

25. $\frac{3}{(x+4)(x-2)}$ 27. 22,581,504 slices per day
29. $x^2 + 2x - 2$ 31. $x^2 + 4x + 1$ 33. $\frac{2m+3}{5}$
35. $a+b$ 37. 2 39. $\frac{4c^2 + 9c}{6cd^2}$ 41. $\frac{14a-3}{6a^2}$
43. $\frac{5x-8}{x-2}$ 45. $\frac{x^2+8x-65}{x^2+8x+12}$ 47. -5
49. -1; extraneous 0 51. 1 hr and 40 minutes

Chapter 12 Statistics and Probability

Page 641 Chapter 12 Get Ready

1. $\frac{3}{7}$ 3. $\frac{4}{7}$ 5. $\frac{3}{5}$ 7. $\frac{7}{95}$ 9. $\frac{1}{52}$ 11. 87.5% 13. 85.6%
15. 29.3%

Pages 645–648 Lesson 12-1

1. a group of readers of a newspaper; all readers of the newspaper; biased; voluntary response 3. 25 nails; all nails on the store shelves; unbiased; stratified 5. 3 sophomores; all sophomores in the school; unbiased; simple 7. people who are home between 9 A.M. and 4 P.M.; all people in the neighborhood; biased; convenience 9. 10 scooters; all scooters manufactured on a particular production line during one day; biased; convenience 11. an 8-oz jar of corn; all corn in the storage silo; biased; convenience 13. a group of people who watch the television station; all people who watch the television station; biased; voluntary response 15. a handful of Bing cherries; all Bing cherries in the produce department; biased; convenience 17. a group of employees; all employees of the company; unbiased; stratified 19. We know that the results are from a national survey conducted by Yankelovich Partners for Microsoft Corporation. 21. Sample answer: Get a copy of the school's list of students and call every 10th person on the list. 25. Sample answer: Randomly pick 5 rows from each field of tomatoes and then pick a tomato every 50 ft along each row. 27. All three are unbiased samples. However, the methods for selecting each type of sample are different. In a simple random sample, a sample is as likely to be chosen as any other from the population. In a stratified random sample, the population is first divided into similar, nonoverlapping groups. Then a simple random sample is selected from each group. In a systematic random sample, the items are selected according to a specified time or item interval. 29. Sample answer: Ask the members of the school's football team to name their favorite sport. 31. Usually it is impossible for a company to test every item coming off its production lines. Therefore, testing a sample of these items is helpful in determining quality control. Sample Answers: A biased way to pick the CDs to be checked is to take the first 5 CDs coming off the production line in the morning. An unbiased way to pick the CDs to be checked is to take every 25th CD off the production line. 33. H 35. 8 37. $\frac{6}{x}$ 39. $\frac{(t-2)^2}{t+3}$ 41. $-4, 10$
43. $-0.3, 4.8$ 45. $c^2 - 10c + 21$ 47. 6 49. 720
51. 5814

Pages 653–654 Lesson 12-2

1.
Spin 1 Spin 2 Spin 3 Outcomes

Outcomes: RRR, RRB, RRY, RRG, RBR, RBB, RBY, RBG, RYR, RYB, RYY, RYG, RGR, RGB, RGY, RGG, BRR, BRB, BRY, BRG, BBR, BBB, BBY, BBG, BYR, BYB, BYY, BYG, BGR, BGB, BGY, BGG, YRR, YRB, YRY, YRG, YBR, YBB, YBY, YBG, YYR, YYB, YYY, YYG, YGR, YGB, YGY, YGG, GRR, GRB, GRY, GRG, GBR, GBB, GBY, GBG, GYR, GYB, GYY, GYG, GGR, GGB, GGY, GGG

3. 64 5. 720

7. 12;

			Outcomes
CD-ROM		Printer	CD-M1-P
	Monitor 1	Scanner	CD-M1-S
	Monitor 2	Printer	CD-M2-P
		Scanner	CD-M2-S
CD recorder	Monitor 1	Printer	CDR-M1-P
		Scanner	CDR-M1-S
	Monitor 2	Printer	CDR-M2-P
		Scanner	CDR-M2-S
DVD	Monitor 1	Printer	DVD-M1-P
		Scanner	DVD-M1-S
	Monitor 2	Printer	DVD-M2-P
		Scanner	DVD-M2-S

9. 180 11. 24 13. 39,916,800 15. 100 17. Columbus in three games : C-C-C; Columbus in four games: C-C-D-C, C-D-C-C, D-C-C-C; Columbus in 5 games: C-C-D-D-C, C-D-C-D-C, C-D-D-C-C, D-C-C-D-C, D-C-D-C-C, D-D-C-C-C; Dallas in three games: D-D-D; Dallas in four games: C-D-D-D, D-C-D-D, D-D-C-D, D-D-D-C; Dallas in five games: C-C-D-D-D, C-D-C-D-D, C-D-D-C-D, C-D-D-D-C, D-C-C-D-D, D-C-D-C-D, D-C-D-D-C, D-D-C-C-D, D-D-C-D-C, D-D-D-C-C 19. 10 21. Sample answer: choosing 2 books in order from 7 books on a shelf 23. Sample answer: You can make a chart showing all possible outcomes to help determine a football team's record. You can use a tree diagram or calculations to show 16 possible outcomes.
25. G 27. all calendars printed in a day 29. $-3, 1$
31. 1, 5.5 33. $\frac{2n+3}{n+3}$ 35. $\frac{7}{34}$ 37. $\frac{13}{34}$ 39. $\frac{19}{34}$

Pages 658–662 Lesson 12-3

1. Combination; order is not important. 3. 6720
5. Permutation; order is important. 7. $\frac{1}{12}$ 9. $\frac{49}{646}$
11. 60 13. Permutation; order is important.
15. Permutation; order is important.
17. Combination; order is not important.
19. Combination; order is not important. 21. 4
23. 35 25. 125,970 27. 524,160 29. 16,598,400
31. 6720 33. 495 35. $\frac{1}{12}$ 37. 362,880 39. 7776
41. 61,425 43. 36 45. $\frac{1}{12}$ or about 8% 47. 24
49. 792 51. $\frac{1}{7} \approx 14\%$ 53. determining class rank in a senior class of 100 students 55. 5040 57. Sample answer: Combinations can be used to determine how many different ways a committee can be formed by various members. Without seniority, order of selection is not important. Order is important when seniority is involved, so you need to find the number of permutations. 59. H 61. unbiased; systematic
63. $\frac{x+7}{x+5}$ 65. $2\sqrt{53}$; 14.56 67. $2\frac{1}{2}$, 2.5 69. $\frac{5}{2}$, -3
71. $\frac{3}{13}$ 73. $\frac{3}{5}$ 75. $\frac{5}{6}$

Pages 667–670 Lesson 12-4

1. independent 3. $\frac{1}{3}$ 5. $\frac{80}{3087}$ 7. $\frac{4}{133}$ 9. 1 11. $\frac{7}{8}$
13. $\frac{3}{10}$ 15. $\frac{1}{10}$ 17. $\frac{1}{4}$ 19. $\frac{7}{16}$ 21. 98% or 0.98
23. no; $P(A$ and $B) \neq P(A) \cdot P(B)$ 25. $\frac{2}{51}$ 27. $\frac{7}{408}$
29. ≈ 0.03 31. $\frac{1}{4}$ 33. $\frac{23}{42}$ 35. $\frac{5}{6}$ 37. $\frac{5}{3}$ 39. $\frac{5}{8}$ 41. $\frac{1}{4}$

43. Sample answer: In a dependent event, an object is selected and not replaced. In an independent event, an object is selected and replaced. 45. Sample answer: The probability of rolling a number less than or equal to six on a number cube and tossing heads or tails on a coin. 47. 101 49. $\frac{39}{40}$ 51. C 53. 10 55. 604,800
57. $(m+5)(m+3)$ 59. $8\sqrt{2}$ 61. $2|a|\sqrt{30ab}$ 63. $3 + 3\sqrt{2}$ 65. 0.133 67. 0.096 69. 0.289 71. 0.015

Pages 674–676 Lesson 12-5

1.

	1	2	3	4	5	6
1	2	3	4	5	6	7
2	3	4	5	6	7	8
3	4	5	6	7	8	9
4	5	6	7	8	9	10
5	6	7	8	9	10	11
6	7	8	9	10	11	12

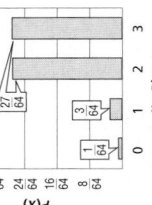

$P(X)$
$X = \text{Blue}$
0   1   2   3

3. $\frac{343}{1728}$ 5. 0.95 7. RRR, RRB, RBR, RBB, BRR, BRB, BBR, BBB 9.
$\frac{32}{64}$
$\frac{24}{64}$
$\frac{16}{64}$
$\frac{8}{64}$

$\frac{27}{64}$
$\frac{3}{64}$

11. Let X = number of CDs; X = 100, 200, 300, 400, 500. 13. 0.90 15. 0.646 17. Sample answer: Add the values for the bars representing bachelor's and advanced degrees. 19. 3 21a. $P(X=1) = \frac{1}{2}$, $P(X=2) = \frac{1}{4}$, $P(X=3) = \frac{1}{8}$, $P(X=4) = \frac{1}{16}$ 21b. $\frac{1}{16}$
23. C 25. $\frac{2}{13}$ 27. $\frac{25}{52}$ 29. 792 31. $1065.82 33. Sample answer: Monthly; the interest earned is higher than quarterly. 35. 38% 37. 48% 39. 33%

Pages 680–683 Lesson 12-6

1. $\frac{3}{10}$ or 30% 3. Sample answer: a spinner with 3 red sections of 10 equal sections, a spin on a red section simulates a hit 7. Yes; 70% of the marbles in the bag represent water and 30% represent land. 9. 0.25 or 25% 11. P(Preschool) = 0.060; P(Kindergarten) = 0.058; P(Elementary) = 0.480; P(High School) = 0.256; P(College) = 0.146 13. 123 15. Sample answer: a spinner divided into 3 sections, where $\frac{1}{2}$ represents cola, $\frac{1}{3}$ represents diet cola, and $\frac{1}{6}$ represents root beer 17. Sample answer: toss a coin and roll a number cube 100 times each 23. Sample answer: 4 coins

Selected Answers

33. Sample answer: a survey of 100 people voting in a two-person election where 50% of the people favor each candidate; 100 coin tosses **35.** Sample answer: Probability can be used to determine the likelihood that a medication or treatment will be successful. Experimental probability is determining probability based on trials or studies. To have the experimental more closely resemble the theoretical probability, the researches should perform more tials. **37.** J **39.** 0.145 **41.** $\frac{125}{1331}$ **43.** $\frac{80}{1749}$ **45.** yes

Chapter 12   Study Guide and Review

Pages 684–688
1. permutation **3.** independent **5.** are not **7.** 1 **9.** 8 test tubes with results of chemical reactions; the results of all chemical reactions performed; biased; convenience **11.** 720 **13.** 20 **15.** 56 **17.** 140 **19.** 12 **21.** 5040 **23.** $\frac{1595}{32,412}$ **25.** $\frac{4}{13}$ **27.** $0.04 + 0.12 + 0.37 +$ $0.30 + 0.17 = 1$ **29.**

Extracurricular Activities

X = Number of Activities

31. Sample answer: There are 6 possible outcomes. So, you could use a die.

Photo Credits

Cover: Fraser Hall/Getty Images; **iv (tl)** David Dennison; **iv (tr)** David Dennison; **iv (bl)** Aaron Haupt; **iv (bl)** David Dennison; **iv (bc)** David Dennison; **v (tl)** David Dennison; **v (tc)** David Dennison; **v (tr)** David Dennison; **v (bl)** David Dennison; **v (bc)** File Photo; **v (br)** File Photo; **viii–ix** Beneluz Press/Index Stock Imagery/PictureQuest; **x–xi** John Warden/Index Stock Imagery; **xii–xiii** Gibson Stock Photography; **xiv–xv** Bill Brooks/Masterfile; **xvi–xvii** Peter Gridley/Getty Images; **xviii–xix** Lester Lefkowitz/CORBIS; **2–3** Beneluz Press/Index Stock Imagery/PictureQuest; **4** Roy Ooms/Masterfile; **12** BP/Taxi/Getty Images; **24** Troy Wayrynen/NewSport/CORBIS; **27** Mt. San Jacinto College, CA; **34** Gary Conner/Index Stock Imagery; **36** CORBIS; **38** Brand X/SuperStock; **40** Gail Mooney/Masterfile; **43** Diaphor Agency/Index Stock Imagery; **49** Aflo Foto Agency/Alamy Images; **58** E. John Thawley III/Alamy Images; **68** Paul Jasienski/Getty Images; **70** CORBIS; **71** Francisco Cruz/SuperStock; **74** The Everett Collection; **75** CORBIS; **81** Joseph Sohm/ChromoSohm/CORBIS; **82** H. Gousse/AP/Wide World Photos; **86** Bettmann/CORBIS; **88** Buddy Mays/CORBIS; **89** (t)Louis DeLuca/MLB Photos via Getty Images, (bl br)Mark Burnett; **92** Fritz Prenzel/Animals Animals; **96** Jess Stock/Getty Images; **102** Reuters/CORBIS; **108** Randy Wells/Getty Images; **112** HOF/NFL Photos; **114** Michael A. Dwyer/Stock Boston; **116** Alex Wilson/Getty Images; **118** Erika Nelson/World's Largest Things, Lucas, KS; **124** Keith Wood/Getty Images; **138–139** David Gray/Reuters/CORBIS; **138 139** Stephanie Sinclair/CORBIS; **140** Michael S. Yamashita/CORBIS; **144 147** CORBIS; **153** The Lawrence Journal-World, Nick Krug/AP/Wide World Photos; **160** Chris Harvey/Getty Images; **165** SuperStock; **169** Nikos Desyllas/SuperStock; **173** Reuters/CORBIS; **175** Gavriel Jecan/Getty Images; **184** NASA; **186** (t)The McGraw-Hill Companies, (b)PHOTOSPORT; **187** Joanna McCarthy/Getty Images; **188** Steve Vidler/SuperStock; **189** Eric Sanford/Index Stock Imagery; **190** Michael Boys/CORBIS; **193** (l)Streeter Lecka/Getty Images, (c)CORBIS, (r)Laura Hinshaw/Index Stock Imagery; **199** John Warden/Index Stock Imagery; **201** age fotostock/SuperStock; **206** Carl Schneider/Getty Images; **208** Doug Young-Wolff/PhotoEdit; **210** Stockbyte/Getty Images; **215** Matt Brown/Icon SMI/CORBIS; **224** Schenectady Museum/Hall of Electrical History Foundation/CORBIS; **226** Bruce Burkhardt/CORBIS; **228** Aaron Haupt; **229** Gail Mooney/Masterfile; **232** NASA; **250** CORBIS; **255** Lori Adamski Peek/Getty Images; **263** Kieran Doherty/Reuters/Hulton Archive/Getty Images; **264** LWA-Stephen Welstead/CORBIS; **266** Alaska Stock LLC/Alamy Images; **269** Gibson Stock Photography; **274** Bruce Forster/Stone/Getty Images; **280** © Robert Holmes/CORBIS; **282** B2M Productions/Getty Images; **292** Courtesy Santa Cruz Beach Boardwalk;

296 Ilya Pitalev/ITAR-TASS/CORBIS; **297** Bruce Coleman, Inc./PictureQuest; **302** Galen Rowell/CORBIS; **306** Ticor Collection/San Diego Historical Society; **308** John Downer/Getty Images; **312** Min Roman/Masterfile; **315** Gustavo Vanderput; **316** Bruce Forster/Getty Images; **318** CORBIS; **319** Square Peg Productions/Getty Images; **329** LWA-Sharie Kennedy/CORBIS; **332** SuperStock; **336** Jose Luis Pelaez, Inc./CORBIS; **342** Andre Jenny/Alamy Images; **343** Bob Daemmrich; **354–355** Bill Brooks/Masterfile; **356** Ross Kinnaird/Allsport/Getty Images; **362** Duomo/CORBIS; **372** Jose Luis Pelaez, Inc./CORBIS; **374** Bob Daemmrich/PhotoEdit; **380** Paul Barton/CORBIS; **384** CORBIS; **385** Jim Cummins/Getty Images; **387** Robert D. Macklin; **391** Eric Kamp/PhotoTake NYC; **393** Bobbi Lane/Getty Images; **393** Kunio Owaki/CORBIS; **394** Tony Freeman/PhotoEdit; **402** D. Logan/H. Armstrong Roberts; **405** Mark Joseph/Getty Images; **408** Yves Herman/Reuters/CORBIS; **418** Tom Brakefield/Getty Images; **420** Bill Frymire/Masterfile; **426** Lisa Blumenfeld/Getty Images; **430** Douglas Faulkner/Photo Researchers; **438** Steve Vidler/SuperStock; **447** Tim Shaffer/Reuters/CORBIS; **459** Esa Hiltula/Alamy Images; **468** Mark Gibson/Index Stock Imagery; **476** Robert Glusic/Getty Images; **483** Paul J. Sutton/Duomo/CORBIS; **488** Peter Gridley/Getty Images; **490** Stephen Simpson/Getty Images; **495** NASA/Science Source/Photo Researchers; **498** Zoom Agence/Allsport/Getty Images; **502** Don Gibson; **504** Gary Buss/Getty Images; **507** AFP/CORBIS; **511** Bob Krist/CORBIS; **524–525** David Wall/Alamy Images; **526** Dong Lin/California Academy of Sciences; **528** Joseph Drivas/Getty Images; **532** Bob Daemmrich/Stock Boston; **537** Science Photo Library/Photo Researchers; **539** Alan Schein Photography/CORBIS; **541** Zefa Visual Media/IndexStock/PictureQuest; **544** NASA Dryden Flight Research Photo Collection; **549** AP Photo/Tina Fineberg; **553** Paul L. Ruben; **556** Michael Zito/SportsChrome; **562** Andy Caulfield/Getty Images; **566** Phillip Spears/Getty Images; **574** David Gonzales/Icon SMI/CORBIS; **581** "Snake and the Cross," 1936. Alexander Calder. Private Collection/Art Resource, NY; **587** Ariel Skelley/CORBIS; **590** Sally Moskol/Index Stock Imagery; **591** Hulton Archive/Getty Images; **592** Bruce Fier/Getty Images; **596** NASA/Roger Ressmeyer/CORBIS; **598** Jay Dickman/CORBIS; **601** Larry Hamill; **605** K. Hackenberg/zefa/CORBIS; **612** Ken Samuelsen/Getty Images; **614** Joseph Sohm/Visions of America/CORBIS; **620** Buccina Studios/Getty Images; **631** Roger Ressmeyer/CORBIS; **640** Visions of America, LLC/Alamy Images; **643** Curtis R. Lantinga/Masterfile; **646** Michael S. Yamashita/CORBIS; **652** Lester Lefkowitz/CORBIS; **660** Inga Spence/Index Stock Imagery; **668** Tony Freeman/PhotoEdit; **673** Getty Images; **678** (c)CORBIS, (b)Geoff Butler; **682** O'Brien Productions/CORBIS; **684** Eclipse Studios.

Index

G

S

Scope and Sequence

Number Sense

Concept	Kindergarten	Grade 1	Grade 2	Grade 3	Grade 4	Grade 5	Grade 6	Grade 7	Algebra Readiness	Algebra 1
Understand, Represent, and Relate Numbers: Whole Numbers										
One-to-one correspondence	◑	●	●							
Ordinal numbers	●	●	●	●	●					
Count, read, write, name, rename, represent — Numbers to 30	◑	●	●	●	●	●	●	●		
Numbers to 100	●	◑	◑	●	●	●	●	●		
Numbers to 1,000		●	◑	●	●	●	●	●		
Numbers to 10,000				◑	●	●	●	●		
Numbers to 1 million				●	●	●	●	●		
Numbers to 1 billion and above						◑	●	●		
Count on, count back	◑	◑	●	●						
Skip count	◑	◑	●	●	●					
Equivalent Forms (word, expanded, standard)	●	◑	●	●	●	●	●	●	●	●
Place value	●	◑	●	●	●	●	●	●	●	●
Powers and exponents					●	◑	●	●	●	●
Scientific notation						●	●	◑		
Round whole numbers			◑	●	●	●			●	
Compare and order whole numbers	●	◑	●	●	●	●	●	●	●	●
Represent on a number line	●	◑	●	●	●	●	●	●	●	
Even and odd numbers, doubles	●	●	●	●	●					
Divisibility				●	●	●	●	●		
Factors				●	◑	●	●	●	●	●
Prime and composite numbers				●	●	●	●		●	●

● Introduce   ● Develop   ● Reinforce   ● Maintain and Apply   ● Prerequisite Skills

Concept	Kindergarten	Grade 1	Grade 2	Grade 3	Grade 4	Grade 5	Grade 6	Grade 7	Algebra Readiness	Algebra 1
Prime factorization				○	◐	●	●	●	●	
Greatest common factor (GCF)				○	◐	●	●	●	●	
Least common multiple (LCM)					◐	●	●	●	●	
Perfect squares, cubes, roots						◐	●	●		

Understand, Represent, and Relate Numbers: Fractions

Concept	Kindergarten	Grade 1	Grade 2	Grade 3	Grade 4	Grade 5	Grade 6	Grade 7	Algebra Readiness	Algebra 1
Model fractional parts of a whole, of a set	○	○	●	●	●	●	●	●	●	
Read and write fractions		○	●	●	●	●	●	●	●	●
Represent fractions on a number line				○	◐	●	●	●	●	●
Compare and order fractions		○	◐	●	●	●	●	●	●	●
Equivalent fractions				○	◐	●	●	●	●	●
Simplify fractions				○	◐	●	●	●	●	●
Least common denominator (LCD)					◐	●	●	●	●	●
Reciprocal, multiplicative inverse						●	●	●	●	●
Mixed numbers and improper fractions				○	◐	●	●	●	●	●
Round mixed numbers						●	●	●		●
Relate fractions and decimals				○	◐	●	●	◐	●	◐

Underrstand, Represent, and Relate Numbers: Decimals

Concept	Kindergarten	Grade 1	Grade 2	Grade 3	Grade 4	Grade 5	Grade 6	Grade 7	Algebra Readiness	Algebra 1
Model decimals			○	○	◐	●	●	●	●	●
Read and write decimals			○	◐	●	◐	●	●	●	●
Represent decimals on a number line				○	◐	●	●	●	◐	●
Compare and order decimals				○	○	●	●	●	◐	
Round decimals				○	◐	●	●	●	●	●
Terminating and repeating decimals						◐	◐	◐	●	●
Nonrepeating decimals/ irrational numbers						○	○	○		◐

Scope and Sequence

Understand, Represent, and Relate Numbers: Ratio, Rate, and Proportion

Concept	Kindergarten	Grade 1	Grade 2	Grade 3	Grade 4	Grade 5	Grade 6	Grade 7	Algebra Readiness	Algebra 1
Concept of a ratio						◐	●	◐	●	●
Model ratios						○	◐	●	●	
Read and write ratios						◐	●	●	●	●
Equivalent ratios						●	●	◐	●	
Relate ratios to fractions						○	●	●	◐	●
Rates						○	◐	●	●	●
Ratio and probability						○	◐	●		●
Unit rate						◐	◐	◐	●	
Dimensional analysis						○	○	◐	●	◐
Solve proportions						◐	●	●	◐	●
Proportional reasoning						◐	●	●	◐	●
Scale drawings						◐	◐	●		●
Scale factor							◐	◐	○	●
Similar figures							●	●	●	●
Indirect measurement							◐		◐	

Understand, Represent, and Relate Numbers: Percent

Concept	Kindergarten	Grade 1	Grade 2	Grade 3	Grade 4	Grade 5	Grade 6	Grade 7	Algebra Readiness	Algebra 1
Concept of percent, model					○	◐	●	●	●	●
Relate fractions and decimals to percents					○	◐	●	●	◐	●
Percent of a number						◐	●	◐	●	●
Percent one number is of another							◐	●	●	●
Percent of change						○	◐	●	●	●
Percent proportion (P/B = R/100)							◐	●	●	◐
Percent equation (RB = P)							◐	●	●	

Concept

Understand, Represent, and Relate Numbers: Integers

Concept	Kindergarten	Grade 1	Grade 2	Grade 3	Grade 4	Grade 5	Grade 6	Grade 7	Algebra Readiness	Algebra 1
Concept of integers, negative numbers					○	◐	●	●	●	●
Read and write integers					○	◐	●	●	●	●
Represent on a number line					○	◐	●	●	●	
Compare and order integers						◐	●	●	●	●
Absolute value						○	◐	●	●	

Understand, Represent, and Relate Numbers: Rational Numbers

Concept	Kindergarten	Grade 1	Grade 2	Grade 3	Grade 4	Grade 5	Grade 6	Grade 7	Algebra Readiness	Algebra 1
Identify and simplify rational numbers					◐	○	◐	●		●
Represent on a number line					◐	○	●	●		
Relate rational numbers to decimals					○	◐	◐	●		
Compare and order rational numbers					◐	○	◐	●		

Understand, Represent, and Relate Numbers: Real Numbers

Concept	Kindergarten	Grade 1	Grade 2	Grade 3	Grade 4	Grade 5	Grade 6	Grade 7	Algebra Readiness	Algebra 1
Identify irrational numbers							○	◐	○	●
Represent irrational, real numbers on a number line								◐		●
Identify and classify real numbers								◐		●
Estimate square roots							◐	◐	○	●

Understand Operations

Concept	Kindergarten	Grade 1	Grade 2	Grade 3	Grade 4	Grade 5	Grade 6	Grade 7	Algebra Readiness	Algebra 1
Meaning of addition	○	◐	●	◐	●	●	●	●	●	
Meaning of subtraction	○	◐	●	◐	●	●	●	●	●	
Meaning of multiplication: repeated addition, equal groups, arrays			◐	◐	◐	●	●	●	●	
Meaning of division: repeated subtraction, equal shares			○	◐	●	●	●	●	●	

Scope and Sequence

Concept	Kindergarten	Grade 1	Grade 2	Grade 3	Grade 4	Grade 5	Grade 6	Grade 7	Algebra Readiness	Algebra 1
Inverse operations		○	◐	◐	●	●	●	●	●	
Check subtraction by adding		○	◐	●	●					
Check division by multiplying				○	●					

Operations: Whole Numbers										
Add whole numbers — Basic facts	○	●	●	●	●	●	●	●	●	
Fact families		◐	◐	●	●	●	●	●	●	
Algorithm		○	●	●	●	●	●	●	●	
Three or more addends		◐	●	●	●				●	
Subtract whole numbers — Basic facts	○	◐	●	●	●	●	●	●	●	
Fact families		○	●	●	●	●	●	●	●	
Algorithm		○	●	●	●	●	●	●	●	
Multiply whole numbers — Basic facts			○	◐	●	●	●	●	●	
Fact families			○	◐	●	●	●	●	●	
Algorithm				◐	●	●	●	●	●	
Divide whole numbers — Basic facts			○	◐	●	●	●	●	●	
Fact families				○	●	●	●	●	●	
Algorithm				◐	●	●	●	●	●	

Operations: Fractions										
Add and subtract fractions and mixed numbers — Like denominators				◐	●	●	◐	●	◐	●
Unlike denominators					○	●	●	◐	●	●
Multiply and divide fractions, mixed numbers						◐	●	●	◐	●

Concept

Concept	Kindergarten	Grade 1	Grade 2	Grade 3	Grade 4	Grade 5	Grade 6	Grade 7	Algebra Readiness	Algebra 1
Operations: Decimals										
Add and subtract decimals — Money amounts			◐	●	◐	●	●	●	●	●
Non-money amounts					◐	●	◐	●	●	●
Multiply decimals					○	●	●	●	●	●
Divide decimals						◐	●	●	◐	●
Operations: Integers, Rational, and Real Numbers										
Add and subtract integers						◐	●	●	●	●
Multiply and divide integers						◐	●	●	●	●
Add, subtract, multiply, and divide rational numbers						◐	◐	◐	●	●
Rules of exponents						○	◐	●	●	●
Operations: Mental Arithmetic and Estimation Strategies										
Add/subtract multiples of powers of 10		○	○	●	●	●	●	●		
Multiply multiples of powers of 10				○	●	●	●	●		
Divide multiples of powers of 10				○	●	◐	●	●		
Use compensation			○		○					
Break numbers apart				○	○					
Use Distributive Properties					○	●	●	●		●
Multiply/divide by powers of 10							●	●		
Estimation	◐	◐	●	●	●	●	●	◐	●	
Estimate very large and very small numbers						◐	●	●		
Use rounding			○	◐	●	◐	●		●	●
Front-end estimation				◐	○	●				
Use compatible numbers				○	○	◐	◐		●	
Use clustering					◐	●				

Scope and Sequence

Algebra and Functions

Properties

Concept	Kindergarten	Grade 1	Grade 2	Grade 3	Grade 4	Grade 5	Grade 6	Grade 7	Algebra Readiness	Algebra 1
Order of Operations				○	●	●	●	●	●	●
Associative and Commutative Properties	○	○	◑	●	●	●	●	●	●	●
Distributive Property				○	○	◑	●	●	●	●
Identity Properties			○	◑	●	●	●	●	●	●
Zero Property of Multiplication				○	◑	●	●	●	●	●
Addition and Subtraction Properties of Equality					○	◑	◑	●	●	●
Multiplication and Division Properties of Equality						◑	◑	●	●	●
Additive Inverse Property							◑	●	●	●
Multiplicative Inverse Property						○	◑	●	●	●
Closure Property									○	◑

Use Algebraic Representations

Concept	Kindergarten	Grade 1	Grade 2	Grade 3	Grade 4	Grade 5	Grade 6	Grade 7	Algebra Readiness	Algebra 1
Write and solve number sentences using symbols, +, −, =	○	◑	●	●	●				●	
Use formulas					○				●	
Variables, expressions, equations		○	○	○	◑	●	●	◑	●	●
Order of operations					◑	●	●	●	●	●
Evaluate algebraic expressions					○	●	●	●	●	●
Write algebraic expressions and equations				○	◑	●	●	●	●	●
Equivalent expressions; simplify expressions						○	◑	◑	●	●
Monomials								◑	●	●
Operations with monomials								◑	●	●

Concept

Key: ● = full, ◐ = half, ○ = introductory (light)

Concept	Kindergarten	Grade 1	Grade 2	Grade 3	Grade 4	Grade 5	Grade 6	Grade 7	Algebra Readiness	Algebra 1
Polynomials										◐
Operations with polynomials										◐
Factor polynomials										◐
Radical expressions										◐
Rational expressions										◐
Pythagorean Theorem						◐	◐	●	●	●
Distance formula							◐	●	●	

Solve Equations and Inequalities

Concept	Kindergarten	Grade 1	Grade 2	Grade 3	Grade 4	Grade 5	Grade 6	Grade 7	Algebra Readiness	Algebra 1
Addition/subtraction equations				○	○	●	●	●	●	●
Multiplication/division equations				○	○	●	●	●	●	●
Multi-step equations						○	◐	●	●	●
Equations with variables on both sides								◐	●	●
Use formulas to solve problems					○	●	●	●	●	●
Write inequalities with variables	○	○	●	●	●	○	○	◐		●
Solve inequalities									◐	●
Graph inequalities on number line									◐	●
Addition/subtraction inequalities									◐	◐
Multiplication/division inequalities									◐	◐
Multi-step inequalities									◐	◐
Compound inequalities										◐

Graph Linear and Nonlinear Equations and Inequalities

Concept	Kindergarten	Grade 1	Grade 2	Grade 3	Grade 4	Grade 5	Grade 6	Grade 7	Algebra Readiness	Algebra 1
Relationships between equations and their graphs					○	●	●	●	●	●
Linear equations						○	◐	●	●	●
Slope							◐	◐	●	●
Intercepts							◐	○		●

Scope and Sequence

Concept	Kindergarten	Grade 1	Grade 2	Grade 3	Grade 4	Grade 5	Grade 6	Grade 7	Algebra Readiness	Algebra 1
Slope-intercept form							◐	●		●
Point-slope form										◐
Systems of linear equations and inequalities, graph and solve							◐			◐

Functions and Relations										
Function tables		◐	◐	◐	●	●	●	●	●	●
Function rules and equations		○	◐	●	●	●	●	●	●	●
Definition of function				○	○	○	●	●	●	●
Definition of relation										●
Domain and range of functions							○	○		◐
Identify linear and nonlinear functions						○	○	◐	●	●
Graph ordered pairs					◐	●	●	●	●	●
Graph functions				○	●	●	●	●	●	●
Graph relations							◐	●	●	●
Model real-world data				○	◐	◐	●	●	●	●
Proportional functions, direct variation								◐	●	●
Quadratic and cubic functions								◐		◐
Families of non-linear functions								○		◐
Exponential functions										◐
Rational functions										◐
Arithmetic sequences and series						○	◐			●

Analyze Change										
Describe qualitative change (e.g., grow taller)		●	●	●	◐	●				
Describe quantitative change (e.g., grow 2 inches in one year)			○	○	◐	●				

Concept

Concept	Kindergarten	Grade 1	Grade 2	Grade 3	Grade 4	Grade 5	Grade 6	Grade 7	Algebra Readiness	Algebra 1
Identify/describe constant and varying rates of change						◐	●	●	●	●
Change in one variable relates to change in another			○	○	○	◐	◐	●	●	●
Use graphs to analyze change			○	○	◐			◐	●	●
Slope as rate of change							◐		●	●
Direct and inverse variation							◐		●	●
Approximate and interpret rates of change from graphical or numerical data						○	◐		●	●

Geometry and Measurement

Measurable Attributes and Units of Measure: Length, Weight, and Capacity

Concept	Kindergarten	Grade 1	Grade 2	Grade 3	Grade 4	Grade 5	Grade 6	Grade 7	Algebra Readiness	Algebra 1
Nonstandard units	○	◐	●	●	●	●				●
Customary units		○	◐	●	●	●	●	●	●	●
Metric units			○	●	●	●	●	●	●	
Convert units within a system		○	○	◐	●	●	●	◐		●
Convert units between systems			○	○	○	◐	◐	●		

Measurable Attributes and Units of Measure: Temperature

Concept	Kindergarten	Grade 1	Grade 2	Grade 3	Grade 4	Grade 5	Grade 6	Grade 7	Algebra Readiness	Algebra 1
Temperature (Celsius, Fahrenheit)		○	○	●	●	◐	●	●		●

Measurable Attributes and Units of Measure: Time

Concept	Kindergarten	Grade 1	Grade 2	Grade 3	Grade 4	Grade 5	Grade 6	Grade 7	Algebra Readiness	Algebra 1
A.M., P.M.	○	◐	●	●	●					
Calendar	○	◐	●	●	●					
Tell time, concept	○	◐	●	◐	●					
Estimate time	○	●	●	●	○					
Units of time	○	○	◐	●	●					
Convert time			○	◐	●					

Scope and Sequence

Concept	Kindergarten	Grade 1	Grade 2	Grade 3	Grade 4	Grade 5	Grade 6	Grade 7	Algebra Readiness	Algebra 1
Elapsed time		○	◐	●	●					
Sequence of events	○	◐	●	●	●					

Measurable Attributes and Units of Measure: Money

	Kindergarten	Grade 1	Grade 2	Grade 3	Grade 4	Grade 5	Grade 6	Grade 7	Algebra Readiness	Algebra 1
Recognize and count coins	○	◐	●	●	●					
Recognize and count bills	○	○	●	●	●					
Compare money amounts		◐	●	●	●					
Find values of coins and bills	○	◐	◐	●	●					
Make change			◐	●	●					

Measurement Formulas and Techniques

	Kindergarten	Grade 1	Grade 2	Grade 3	Grade 4	Grade 5	Grade 6	Grade 7	Algebra Readiness	Algebra 1
Use formulas					○	◐	●	●	●	●
Perimeter of rectangle			○	○	●	●	●	●	●	●
Circumference of circle					○	◐	●	●	●	●
Estimate area				◐	◐	●	●			
Area of rectangle			○	○	◐	●	●	●	●	●
Area of square			○	○	◐	●	●	●	●	●
Area of parallelogram						◐	●	●	●	●
Area of triangle					○	◐	●	●	●	●
Area of trapezoid						○	●	●	●	●
Area of circle							◐	●	●	●
Area of complex figures							◐	●	●	
Surface area of cube						◐	●	●	●	●
Surface area of rectangular prism						◐	●	●	●	●
Surface area of cylinder							●	●	◐	●
Surface area of cone, pyramid									◐	●
Estimate volume				◐	◐	●	●			

Concept	Kindergarten	Grade 1	Grade 2	Grade 3	Grade 4	Grade 5	Grade 6	Grade 7	Algebra Readiness	Algebra 1
Volume of rectangular prism			○	○	○	◐	●	●	◐	●
Volume of cube				○		◐	●	●	◐	●
Volume of cylinder						◐	●	●	◐	●
Volume of cone, pyramid								◐		●
Precision and significant digits						○	○	◐		
Angle measurement in degrees					○	●	●	●	●	
Measurements as rates								◐	●	
Indirect measurement			○	○	○	○	◐		◐	

Attributes and Properties of Plane and Solid Shapes and Relationships

Concept	Kindergarten	Grade 1	Grade 2	Grade 3	Grade 4	Grade 5	Grade 6	Grade 7	Algebra Readiness	Algebra 1
Identify attributes of plane shapes	◐	◐	●	●	●	●	●	●	●	●
Identify attributes of solid shapes	○	◐	●	●	●	●	●	●	●	●
Classify and describe properties of plane shapes	○	◐	●	●	●	●	●	●	●	●
Classify and describe properties of solid shapes	○	◐	●	●	●	●	●	●	●	●
Relate plane and solid figures	○	●	●	●	●	●	●	●	●	●
Classify and measure angles				◐	◐	●	●	●	●	●
Angle relationships					○	◐	◐	●	●	●
Identify and define polygons	○	◐	◐	●	●	●	●	◐	●	●
Classify quadrilaterals	○	◐	●	●	●	●	●	●	●	
Classify triangles				○	◐	●	●	●		
Sum of angles in a triangle						◐	●	●	◐	
Sum of angles of polygons						◐	◐	●	◐	
Parts of plane and solid shapes							◐	●	◐	
Parts of circles					○	○	●	●	●	
Congruent figures			○	○	◐		◐	●	●	
Similar figures				○	◐		◐	●	●	●
Corresponding parts							◐	●	●	○

Scope and Sequence

Concept	Kindergarten	Grade 1	Grade 2	Grade 3	Grade 4	Grade 5	Grade 6	Grade 7	Algebra Readiness	Algebra 1
Scale drawings							●	●		●
Right triangles and parts					○	◐	●	●		●
Pythagorean Theorem						◐	●	●		◐

Coordinate Geometry

Concept	Kindergarten	Grade 1	Grade 2	Grade 3	Grade 4	Grade 5	Grade 6	Grade 7	Algebra Readiness	Algebra 1
Position and direction	○	●	●	●						
Graph ordered pairs			○	○	◐	◐	●	●	●	●
Horizontal, vertical distance on a grid					○	○	●	●	●	
Distance formula							◐	●		●
Graph linear equations					○	○	○	●	●	●
Slope							◐	●		●
Slope-intercept form of line							◐			●
Point-slope form of line										◐
Slope of parallel, perpendicular lines									○	◐

Transformations and Symmetry

Concept	Kindergarten	Grade 1	Grade 2	Grade 3	Grade 4	Grade 5	Grade 6	Grade 7	Algebra Readiness	Algebra 1
Translations (slide)	○	○	◐	●	●		◐	●		
Reflections (flip)	○	○	◐	○	●	●	◐	●		
Rotations (turn)	○	○	◐	○	●			◐		
Dilations										
Transformations with coordinates							◐	◐		
Symmetry (line and rotation)	○	◐	●	◐	●		◐	●		
Tessellations			○	○	◐		◐			

Spatial Reasoning and Geometric Modeling

Concept	Kindergarten	Grade 1	Grade 2	Grade 3	Grade 4	Grade 5	Grade 6	Grade 7	Algebra Readiness	Algebra 1
Draw angles, lines, polygons						◐	●	◐		

Concept	Kindergarten	Grade 1	Grade 2	Grade 3	Grade 4	Grade 5	Grade 6	Grade 7	Algebra Readiness	Algebra 1
Constructions					◐	●	●			
Draw 3-dimensional objects					●	●	●			
Nets			○	○	◐	●	◐			
Apply geometry to the real world	◐	●	●	●	●	●	●	●	●	

Statistics, Data Analysis, and Probability

Use Patterns

	Kindergarten	Grade 1	Grade 2	Grade 3	Grade 4	Grade 5	Grade 6	Grade 7	Algebra Readiness	Algebra 1
Sort and classify by attribute	◐	●	●	●						
Number patterns	○	◐	◐	●	●	●	●		●	
Extend patterns	◐	●	●	●	●	●	●		●	
Create patterns	○	◐	●	●	●	●				
Describe patterns	○	◐	●	●	●	●			●	
Use addition/subtraction patterns	○	○	●	●	●	●				
Use multiplication patterns				◐	●	●				
Use division patterns				○	◐	●	●			

Collect, Organize, and Display Data

	Kindergarten	Grade 1	Grade 2	Grade 3	Grade 4	Grade 5	Grade 6	Grade 7	Algebra Readiness	Algebra 1
Collect data	○		○	◐	●	●				
Organize data with a table	○	◐	◐	●	●	●	●	●		●
Organize data with a graph	○	◐	◐	●	●	●	●	●		●
Frequency tables; tally charts		○	◐	●	●	●	●	●		●
Surveys		○	◐	◐	●	●	●	●		
Samples					○	◐	◐	●		●
Use sampling to predict								◐		

Represent Data

	Kindergarten	Grade 1	Grade 2	Grade 3	Grade 4	Grade 5	Grade 6	Grade 7	Algebra Readiness	Algebra 1
Picture graphs	◐	●	●	●	○					

Scope and Sequence

Concept	Kindergarten	Grade 1	Grade 2	Grade 3	Grade 4	Grade 5	Grade 6	Grade 7	Algebra Readiness	Algebra 1
Bar graphs; double bar graphs	◐	●	●	●	●	●	●			●
Line plots	○	◐	◐	●	●	●	●			●
Circle graphs			○	○	●	●	●			●
Line graphs		○	◐	◐	●	●	●			●
Stem-and-leaf plots				○	●	◐	●			●
Box-and-whisker plots					◐	○	◐			●
Histograms					◐	◐	◐			●
Scatter plots				○	○		●	●		●
Venn diagrams	○	○	○	●	●	○	●			
Choose an appropriate display		○		○	●	●	●	●		

Make Inferences and Predictions	Kindergarten	Grade 1	Grade 2	Grade 3	Grade 4	Grade 5	Grade 6	Grade 7	Algebra Readiness	Algebra 1
Use data	○	◐	●	●	●	●				
Mode	○	○	◐	●	●	●	●	●		●
Median			○	○	◐	●	●	●		●
Mean				○	●	◐	●	●		●
Range		○	◐	●	●	●	●	●		●
Quartiles							◐			●
Misleading graphs and statistics						◐				
Make predictions from graphs					○	◐	◐	◐		●
Make predictions from a sample			○		○	◐	◐	◐	●	●

Probability	Kindergarten	Grade 1	Grade 2	Grade 3	Grade 4	Grade 5	Grade 6	Grade 7	Algebra Readiness	Algebra 1
Certain, probable, impossible	○	○	○	◐	●	●			●	●
Compare likelihoods	○	○	○	●	●					●
Predict outcomes		○	○	●	●	●				

Concept

Concept	Kindergarten	Grade 1	Grade 2	Grade 3	Grade 4	Grade 5	Grade 6	Grade 7	Algebra Readiness	Algebra 1
Outcomes and sample space				○	◐	◐	●	●		●
Probability of a simple event				○	◐	◐	●	●	●	◐
Complementary events						◐	◐	◐		●
Compound events: Independent, Dependent						○	◐	●		●
Mutually exclusive or inclusive events, disjoint							○			●
Odds										●
Experimental probability						◐	◐	●		●
Theoretical probability				○	○	◐	◐	●		●
Probability and ratio						◐	●	◐		●
Simulations						○	○			◐
Tree diagrams					○	◐	●	◐		◐
Fundamental Counting Principle						○	◐	●		◐
Combinations			○	○	○	○	◐			●
Permutations						○	◐			●

Mathematical Reasoning

Strategies and Skills for Problem Solving

	Kindergarten	Grade 1	Grade 2	Grade 3	Grade 4	Grade 5	Grade 6	Grade 7	Algebra Readiness	Algebra 1
Use tools and strategies to model problems	○	◐	●	●	●	●	●	●	●	●
Make connections between problems or ideas		○	◐			●	●	●	●	●
Look for a pattern	○	●	●	●	●	●	●	●	◐	●
Solve a simpler problem					○	●	●	●	◐	●
Act it out/ use objects/ use simulation	○	●	●	●	●	●	●	●	●	●
Guess and check	○	●	●	◐	●	●	●	●	◐	●
Draw a picture or diagram	○	●	●	●	●	●	●	●	◐	●
Make a table	○	◐	●	●	●	●	●	●	◐	●

Scope and Sequence

Concept	Kindergarten	Grade 1	Grade 2	Grade 3	Grade 4	Grade 5	Grade 6	Grade 7	Algebra Readiness	Algebra 1
Work backward			○	◐	●	●	●	●	●	●
Make a list			○	○	●	●	●	●	●	●
Make a model			◐	●	●	●	●	●	●	●
Make a graph	○	○	○	◐	●	●	●	●	●	●
Write an equation			○	○	○	●	●	●	●	●
Use logical reasoning	○	○	◐	●	◐	●	●	●		●
Choose a strategy		○		◐	●	●		●	●	●
Use a four-step plan			○	○	●	●	●	●	●	●
Choose an operation	○	○	●	●	●	●	●	●	●	●
Conduct a poll or survey			○	◐	◐	●				●
Use formulas					○	●	●	●	●	●
Check for reasonableness		○	○	◐	●	●	●	●	●	●
Decide whether to estimate or compute an exact answer				○	●	●	●	●	●	●
Identify missing or irrelevant information			○	◐	●	●	●	●		●
Solve multi-step problems			○	○	●	●	◐		●	●
Eliminate possibilities				○	○	○	●	●		●
Interpret a remainder					○	●	●			●
Choose a representation					○	●	●	●		●

Mathematical Reasoning and Justification										
Use mathematical reasoning to solve problems	○	○	◐	●	●	●	●	●	●	●
Explain, justify, and defend reasoning	○	◐	◐	◐	●	●	●	●	●	●
Check validity of calculated results	○	◐				◐	●	●	●	●
Create problems		○	●	●	●	●	●	●	●	●
Make generalizations	○	○	○	●	●	●	●	●		●

Concept	Kindergarten	Grade 1	Grade 2	Grade 3	Grade 4	Grade 5	Grade 6	Grade 7	Algebra Readiness	Algebra 1
Write informal mathematical arguments		○	○	◐	●	●	●	●		◐
Inductive reasoning	○	○	○	○	○	○	○	◐		◐
Deductive reasoning	○	○	○	○	○	○	○	◐		◐
Make and test conjectures				○	○	◐	◐	◐	●	◐
Use Venn diagrams	○	○	○	○	○	○	●	◐		●
Develop a proof										◐

How Can I Help My Students Read and Understand the Textbook?

Mathematics teachers do not have to be reading teachers to help students read and understand their textbooks. Often poor readers lack interest in the topic, have trouble concentrating, cannot understand a word or sentence, or are confused as to how the information fits together.

> "The research evidence on adolescents and their learning indicates that students must learn how to take notes, use graphic organizers, focus on vocabulary, and develop their thinking through writing. In other words, students must read, write, speak, listen, and view content in order to learn."
>
> **Douglas Fisher, Ph.D.**
> *San Diego State University*
> *Reading Consultant*

Activate Prior Knowledge

Activating prior knowledge provides opportunities for students to discover and articulate what they already know about key concepts and ideas. It stimulates student interest and prepares students to incorporate new information into a larger picture. In addition, it helps the teacher to determine a starting place for instruction.

✔ Write the topic on the board and have students brainstorm what they know about it. Record their responses on the board.

✔ Ask general or specific questions about the topic and see how students respond to them.

✔ Use the Anticipation Guide from the *Chapter Resource Masters*. It provides a series of statements about the concepts in the chapter. Students read each statement and tell whether they agree or disagree, based on their prior understandings and experiences.

✔ Use a K-W-L-H or K-W-L chart to activate prior knowledge and set reading purposes. Students identify what they already **know** (or think they know) and what they **want** to find out about the topic. After reading, students complete the chart.

K	W	L	H
What I **Know**	What I **Want** to Find Out	What I **Learned**	**How** I Can Learn More

Set Reading Purposes

Reading is a purposeful activity. We read to find answers to specific questions, to satisfy curiosity, and to be entertained.

✔ Have students preview the lesson. Tell students to read the title, bolded words, and key concept boxes. Draw students' attention to diagrams, tables, and other visuals and their captions. Discuss how these will help comprehension.

✔ Prompt students to predict what they might learn in the lesson, based on their preview. Invite them to list additional questions they hope to answer studying the lesson. Have them identify possible problems, such as unfamiliar words or ideas.

✔ Discuss the need to "shift gears" to a lower reading speed when reading. Support students as they plan how best to read a lesson—slowly, to watch for new vocabulary and ideas, or quickly, to review previously learned ideas. They can also discuss new information with a buddy as they read.

Vocabulary Development

Vocabulary knowledge and reading comprehension are closely related.

✔ Before students read, preteach vocabulary that is crucial for understanding key topics and concepts.

✔ Relate new vocabulary to known words and ideas.

✔ If a student encounters an unfamiliar word while reading, have him or her try to pronounce it aloud. Sometimes saying the word will trigger one's memory of its meaning.

✔ Encourage students to use the context of surrounding words, sentences, and diagrams to determine a word's meaning.

✔ If context clues and structural analysis fail to help a student understand an important word as they read, have students find the definition in a glossary or dictionary. If the word is not critical for understanding, have students note the word and read on. Later, have students reread the word in context. If the meaning is still unclear, have students consult the dictionary.

Taking Notes

Taking notes challenges readers to determine what is most important and to organize information in a way that makes sense. Note-taking can also help students stay focused as they read. Reviewing notes can build students' retention of important information.

✔ Have students take notes after they have read each paragraph or example rather than the entire lesson. This helps them focus on important ideas and details and prevents them from losing track of the flow of information.

✔ Remind students to look for graphic elements that highlight important items. These include colored text, boxed text, and large or bold fonts.

✔ Have students take notes using note cards. Notes should be recorded in the students' own words and labeled with the page number where the entire text appears. They can also use their Foldables™ for that chapter or their Noteables™ Interactive Study Notebook.

✔ To use notes to review a lesson, have students read through the notes, highlighting the most important information. As they review, encourage students to annotate their notes, making

connections between related ideas and clarifying difficult concepts.

Summarizing

Summarizing demands that students identify the most important ideas and details to create a streamlined version of the text.

✔ After reading the section, have students recall as much of the information as possible. If the main idea and its supporting details are presented in a certain order, make sure

students can recall that organization.

✔ As they summarize, students should try to answer the following questions:
 • How do the examples and key words fit into the main idea?
 • How does the lesson relate to the concepts studied earlier?

Project CRISS STUDY SKILL

Project CRISS [**CR**eating **I**ndependence through **S**tudent-owned **S**trategies] is a research-based staff development program created to help students better organize, understand and retain course information. In short, students receiving the CRISS method of instruction will "LEARN HOW TO LEARN."

CRISS strategies are designed to develop thoughtful and independent readers and learners.

To enhance student learning, CRISS employs several concepts drawn from cognitive psychology.

 • Students must be able to integrate new information with prior knowledge.

 • Students need to be actively involved in their own learning by discussing, writing, and organizing information.

 • Students must self-monitor to identify which strategies are the most effective for their own learning.

These behaviors need to be taught by content teachers to maximize student learning.

For more information on Project CRISS℠, visit www.projectcriss.com.

Cooperative Group Strategies

How Can I Use Cooperative Learning to Teach Mathematics?

Today's social and economic climate requires flexibility. Workers must be able to function independently, work well with groups, and engage in fair-minded competition. For this reason, most educators recommend a healthy balance of instructional strategies to foster cooperative, competitive, and individualistic styles of problem solving and learning. Cooperative learning requires students to work together—each with a specific task—to pursue a common goal. Because part of each student's evaluation is determined by the overall quality of the group's work, students help one another accomplish the group goal.

How Do I Form Cooperative Groups?

✔ **Composition** Most experts recommend that cooperative groups be heterogeneous, reflecting a range of student abilities, backgrounds, and learning styles. However, this does not necessarily mean that students should be assigned to groups on a random basis.

✔ **Group Size** The size of cooperative groups can change, depending upon the task. Some cooperative tasks are best accomplished in pairs. For most projects, groups of three to five students are ideal.

✔ **Abilities** Consider the tasks and projects the groups will undertake as you make group assignments. You may want to make sure each group has a strong manager, a strong writer, a strong artist, a good listener, and so forth.

✔ **Balance** Some teachers use a "family-of-five" approach to grouping. A strong leader heads each group. Two pairs of students with opposing styles or strengths complete the "family." Paired students might exhibit traits such as outgoing and shy, creative and conventional, spontaneous and methodical, and so on. Each group continues to work together throughout the semester or year, with the goal that students develop greater flexibility in their own problem-solving abilities and greater respect for the contributions of others.

✔ **Roles** In most instances, you will want to assign a specific role for each student to play in a group, such as designer, moderator, recorder, researcher, presenter, graphic artist, actor, and so forth. Roles should be interdependent, requiring students to rely upon one another in order to successfully carry out their individual responsibilities. As students gain experience in working in cooperative groups, turn over more of the responsibility for establishing individual roles and responsibilities to the group.

How Do I Help Groups Run Smoothly?

✔ **Seating Arrangements** Explain how and where groups should sit. Pairs can sit with desks or chairs face-to-face. Larger groups do well with desks or chairs gathered in a circle or with students seated around a table.

✔ **Warm-Ups** Provide an introductory activity for new groups. Even when students know one another, they can benefit by making formal introductions and sharing their thoughts on a sentence starter, such as "If I could go anywhere in the world, I would go to . . ." or "If I could have lived at any period in history, I would choose. . ."

✔ **Rules** Set clear expectations and rules for groups. Typical rules include addressing group members by name, making eye contact, listening politely, expressing disagreement with respect, welcoming others' questions, valuing others' contributions, providing positive feedback, and assisting others when asked.

How Do I Use Cooperative Groups in My Classroom?

✔ **Share and Tell** Have students form groups of four. Assign each group member a number between one and four. Ask a factual recall question. Have group members discuss the question and come up with an answer. Call out a number between one and four. The student with that number who is first to raise his or her hand answers the question. The group earns a point for a correct answer.

✔ **Circle Partners** Have the class separate into two equal groups and form two circles, with one circle inside the other. Each student faces a partner in the opposing circle. Ask a question and have partners discuss the answer. If partners do not know the answer they can ask another pair for help. Then, call on students in the inside circle, the outside circle, or all students to say the answer aloud together.

✔ **In the Know** Provide students with a set of end-of-chapter questions or other questions covering content you want students to master. Tell students to circulate around the room to find someone who can answer a question on the worksheet. After listening to the answer, the student paraphrases it, writes the answer on the worksheet, and asks the "expert" to read and sign off on the answer if it is correct. Students move on to find a student to answer the next question. The process continues until students have completed their worksheets.

✔ **Open-Ended Projects** The best long-term projects for cooperative groups are those that are open-ended and multidimensional. That is, the task or question should have many possible answers and should lend itself to many different presentation possibilities.

Multiple intelligences Appropriate projects should challenge students and allow students of various abilities and backgrounds to contribute significantly to solving the problem and executing the project. One way to assess the validity of a potential project is to see whether it requires the use of many different strengths or "intelligences."

Assigning roles Because of the complexity of long-term projects, it is essential that students have clearly assigned roles and responsibilities. Once cooperative groups are established and successful in your classroom, be sure to vary the assignments given to each student from project to project.

✔ **Deadlines** Define interim and final deadlines to encourage students to pace their efforts appropriately.

How Do I Assess Group and Individual Efforts?

✔ **Expectations** As with any assignment, set clear guidelines and high expectations for projects. Show models of excellent past projects, if possible, and define what criteria projects must meet to earn the highest grade.

✔ **Group and Individual Grades** Before students begin, define what percentage of the grade will be based on group work and how much will be based on individual effort. Many teachers give two equally weighted grades: a group grade—the same for each team member—and an individual grade.

✔ **Self-Assessment** Provide a checklist or rating scale for each group member. Have students evaluate their own contribution to the group, as well as the contributions of other group members. In addition to assessing the quality of the finished product, have students evaluate the processes they used within the group, such as showing respect for others' ideas. Provide space on the evaluation sheet for students to explain why they rated themselves and group members as they did.

Troubleshooting

Advice from Carey Boswell, M.Ed.
Humble Independent School District
Humble, Texas

Modern research overwhelmingly suggests that student learning is enhanced when cooperative groups are used in the classroom. Like many other teachers, I was uncertain of how much learning was taking place when I set up cooperative groups. I struggled with noise and control issues and off-task behavior by some students. I found a solution, though.

A cooperative group activity occurs whenever a student works with another student. Cooperative groups do not have to be large groups. Smaller groups ensure that all students are engaged and contribute to the group effort. Smaller groups also guarantee that members perform multiple tasks so that real learning occurs. I often combine two or more small groups into a larger group for short comparative tasks. After making this small adjustment, I am able to assign cooperative group tasks to students at least once a week and student performance, comprehension, and learning has increased in my classroom.

Differentiated Instruction

How Can I Help ALL My Students Learn Mathematics?

"To differentiate instruction, teachers must acknowledge students differences in background knowledge, current English language skills, learning styles and preferences, interests, needs, and react accordingly. Some of the general guidelines for differentiating instruction include:
- Link assessment with instruction.
- Clarify key concepts and generalizations.
- Emphasize critical and creative thinking.
- Include teacher- and student-selected tasks."

Nancy Frey, Ph.D.
San Diego State University
Differentiated Instruction Consultant

Today's classroom contains students from a variety of backgrounds and with a variety of learning styles, strengths, and challenges. With careful planning, you can address the needs of all students in the social studies classroom. The following tips for instruction can assist your efforts to help all students reach their maximum potential.

✔ Survey students to discover their individual differences. Use interest inventories of their unique talents so you can encourage contributions in the classroom.
✔ Model respect of others. Adolescents crave social acceptance. Your behavior will set the tone for how students treat one another.
✔ Expand opportunities for success. Provide a variety of instructional activities that reinforce skills and concepts.
✔ Establish measurable objectives and decide how you can best help students meet them.
✔ Celebrate successes and praise "work in progress."
✔ Keep it simple. Avoid overwhelming students with too many goals at one time.
✔ Assign cooperative group projects that challenge all students to contribute to solving a problem or creating a product.

Students with Learning Disabilities

✔ Provide support and structure. Clearly specify rules, assignments, and responsibilities.
✔ Practice skills frequently. Use games and drills to help maintain student interest.
✔ Incorporate many modalities into the learning process. Provide opportunities to say, hear, write, read, and act out important concepts and information.
✔ Link new skills and concepts to those already mastered.
✔ Allow students to record answers on audiotape.
✔ Allow extra time to complete tests and assignments.
✔ Let students demonstrate proficiency with alternative presentations, including oral reports, role plays, art projects, and with music.

✔ Provide outlines, notes, or tape recordings of lecture material.
✔ Pair students with peer helpers, and provide class time for pair interaction.

English Language Learners

✔ Remember, students' ability to speak English does not reflect their academic abilities.
✔ Try to incorporate the students' cultural experience into your instruction. The help of a bilingual aide may be effective.
✔ Avoid cultural stereotypes.
✔ Pre-teach important vocabulary and concepts.
✔ Encourage students to preview text before they begin reading, noting headings, graphic organizers, photographs, and maps.

"English Language Learners need teachers who understand the current and historic mathematical functions of their students' originating countries and cultures, make mathematics meaningful by tying instruction to local languages and cultures, and are curious and fascinated themselves about mathematics."

Mary A. Avalos, Ph.D.
University of Miami
English Language Learner Consultant

Gifted Students

"Instruction for mathematically gifted children should help the student:
- Understand and appreciate mathematics and its place in the world.
- Learn to think deeply and with insight.
- Take intellectual risks.
- Have confidence in their ability to solve difficult problems independently.
- Understand and value their gift."

Ed Zaccaro
Bellevue, Iowa
Gifted and Talented
Consultant

Students with Physical Challenges

✔ Openly discuss with the student any uncertainties you have about when to offer aid.
✔ Ask parents or therapists and students what special devices or procedures are needed, and whether any special safety precautions need to be taken.
✔ Welcome students with physical challenges into all activities, including field trips, special events, and projects.

Visual Impairments

✔ Facilitate independence. Modify assignments as needed.
✔ Teach classmates how and when to serve as guides.
✔ Limit unnecessary noise in the classroom, if it distracts the student with visual impairments.
✔ Provide tactile models whenever possible.
✔ Foster a spirit of inclusion.
✔ Team the student with a sighted peer for written work.

Students with Hearing Impairments

✔ Seat students where they can see your lip movements easily and where they can avoid visual distractions.
✔ Avoid standing with your back to the window or light source.
✔ Use an overhead projector to maintain eye contact while writing.
✔ Seat students where they can see speakers.
✔ Write all assignments on the board, or hand out written instructions.
✔ If the student has a manual interpreter, allow both student and interpreter to select the most favorable seating arrangements.
✔ Teach students to look directly at each other when they speak.

Good Teaching Practices

✔ Differentiated Instruction is simply the implementation of good teaching practices from which all students can benefit.

"Effective instruction for English language learners, called sheltered instruction, builds upon practices common in math teaching such as providing a visual representation of math problems, modeling how to solve problems and encouraging repetition and practice for mastery of skills. These students also require additional support to make instruction understandable for them since they are learning new concepts and material in a new language."

Jana Echevarria
California Statue University,
Long Beach
English Language Learner
Consultant

Research Bibliography

Selected Research Bibliography— California Algebra

The following resources represent a sample of the research used as the foundation of this Glencoe *California Algebra* program.

General

Bransford, J. D., Brown, A.L., Cocking, R.R., et al. (2000). *How People Learn: Brain, Mind, Experience, and School.* Washington, DC: National Academy Press, p. 24.

California State Board of Education. Mathematics Framework for California Public Schools. Sacramento, CA: California State Board of Education, 1999.

Driscoll, M. "Thinking About Algebraic Thinking: A Framework for Belief, Reflection, Discussion, and Student Work Analysis. Adapted from *The Leadership for Urban Mathematics Reform Project (LUMR) for Linked Learning in Mathematics.* Newton, MA. (August, 1997)

Edwards, Edgar L., Jr., ed. (1990). *Algebra for Everyone.* Reston, VA: NCTM.

Grouws, Douglas A. ed. (1992). *Handbook of Research on Mathematics Teaching.* New York: Maxwell Macmillan.

Kloosterman, P. and Gainey, P.H. (1993). "Students' Thinking: Middle Grades Mathematics," in *Research Ideas for the Classroom: Middle Grades Mathematics.* Reston, Virginia: National Council of Teachers of Mathematics, p. 10.

National Research Council. *Adding It Up: Helping Children Learn Mathematics.* J. Kilpatrick, J. Swafford, and B. Findell, eds. (2001). Washington: National Academy Press.

Selby, Alan M. "Mathematics from Primary School to College." *Mathematics Curriculum Notes,* Volume 1B, August 1997.

Van De Walle, John. *Elementary and Middle School Mathematics: Teaching Developmentally.* White Plains, NY: Addison Wesley Longman, Inc., 1997.

Vygotsky, L. 1962. *Thought and Language.* Cambridge, MA: MIT Press.

Assessment

Adams, T., & Hsu, J-W. (1998). Classroom assessment: Teachers' conceptions and practices in mathematics. *School Science and Mathematics, 98,* 174–180.

Black, Paul, and Dylan William. "Inside the Black Box: Raising Standards through Classroom Assessment." Phi Delta Kappan (October 1998): 139–48.

Nicholls, J. G. "Achievement Motivations: Conceptions of Ability, Subjective Experience, Task Choice, and Performance." Psychological Review Volume 91: 328-46.

Differentiated Instruction

Alexander, P.A. (1984). Training analogical reasoning skills in the gifted. *Roeper Review,* 6(4), 191–193.

Banks, J. A. (2001). *Cultural Diversity and Education: Foundations, Curriculum and Teaching.* Boston: Allyn and Bacon. (4th edition of *Multiethnic education: Theory and practice.*)

Banks, James, and Cherry Banks. (1993). *Multicultural Education: Issues and Perspectives,* Second Edition. Boston: Allyn and Bacon.

Baroody, Arthur J. "An Investigative Approach to the Mathematics Instruction of Children Classified as Learning Disabled." In Cognitive Approaches to Learning Disabilities, edited by D. Kim Reid, Wayne P. Hresko, and H. Lee Swanson, pp 547–615. Austin, TX: Pro-Ed, 1996.

Brimijoin, K. Marquisee, E. & Tomlinson, C. (2003, February). Using data to differentiate instruction. *Educational Leadership, 60*(5), 70–72.

Chambers, D. "The Right Algebra for All." *Educational Leadership* 51 (March, 1994): 85.

Fisher, D., & Kennedy, C.H. (2001). "Differentiated instruction for diverse middle school students" *Inclusive Middle Schools.* Baltimore, MD: Paul H. Brookes.

Stevenson, H.W., and J.W. Stigler. *The Learning Gap.* Simon & Schuster, New York, NY, 1992.

Tomlinson, C. (2005). Quality curriculum and instruction for highly able students. *Theory into Practice, 44*(2), 160–166.

Tomlinson, C. (2004). The mobius effect: Addressing learner variance in schools. *Journal of Learning Disabilities, 37*(6), 516–524.

Tomlinson, C.A., Brighton, C., Hertberg, H., Callahan, C.M., Moon, T.R., Brimijoin, K., Conover, L.A., and Reynolds, T. (2003). "Differentiating instruction in response to student readiness, interest, and learning profile in academically diverse classroom: A review of literature." *Journal for the Education of the Gifted,* 27, 119–145.

English-Language Learners

Abedi, J. (2004, Janury/February). The no child left behind act and English language learners: Assessment and accountability issues. *Educational Researcher.* 33 (1), 4–14.

Mohan, B. (2001). The second language as a medium of learning. In B. Mohan, C. Leung, and C. Davison (eds.), *English as a second language in the mainstream* (pp. 107–126). Harlow, UK: Longman.

Research Bibliography

Snow, M.A., M. Met, and F. Genesee (1989). A conceptual framework for the integration of language and content in second/foreign language instruction. *TESOL Quarterly*, 23(2), 201–217.

Swain, M. (1996). Integrating language and content in immersion classrooms: Research perspectives. *The Canadian Modern Language Review,* 52(4), 529–548.

Foldables™/Graphic Organizers

Alvermann, D.E., & Boothby, P. R. (1986). Children's transfer of graphic organizer instruction. *Reading Psychology,* 7(2), 87-100

Darch, C.B., Carnine, D.W., & Kameenui, E.J. (1986). The role of graphic organizers and social structure in content area instruction. *Journal of Reading Behavior,* 18(4) 275-295.

Gerlic, I., & Jausovec, N. (1999). Multimedia: Differences in cognitive processes observed with EEG. *Educational Technology Research and Development,* 47(3), 5–14.

Horton, S.V., Lovitt, T.C., & Bergerud, D. (1990). The effectiveness of graphic organizers for three classifications of secondary students in content area classes. *Journal of Learning Disabilities*, 23(1), 12–22.

Mayer, R.E. (1979) Can advance organizers influence meaningful learning? *Review of Educational Research,* 49, 371-383; (1989) Models of understanding. *Review of Educational Research*, 59(1), 43–64.

Robinson, D.H., & Kiewra, D.A. (1996). Visual argument: Graphic organizers are superior to outlines in improving learning from text. *Journal of Educational Psychology*, 87(3), 455–467.

Instructional Strategies

Behr, M.J, and T.R. Post. "Teaching Rational Number and Decimal Concepts." In *Teaching Mathematics in Grades K–8: Research Based Methods.* (1992). Boston: Allyn and Bacon.

Carpenter, T.P., E. Fennema, M.L. Franke, L. Levi, and S.E. Empson. (1999). *Children's Mathematics: Cognitively Guided Instruction*. Westport, CT: Heinemann.

Carpenter, T. P., & Lehrer, R. (1999). Teaching and learning mathematics with understanding. In E. Fennema & T. A. Romberg (Eds.). (1999). *Mathematics classrooms that promote understanding* (pp. 19–32). Mahwah, NJ, Lawrence Erlbaum.

Cohen, E. & Benton, J. (1988). Making groupwork work. *American Educator*, 12(3) 10–17, 45–46.

Crawford, M. and M. Witte. (1999). "Strategies for Mathematics: Teaching in Context." *Educational Leadership*, Vol. 57, ASCD, November 1999.

Hiebert, J., Carpenter, T.P., Fennema, E., Fuson, K.C., Murray, H., Olivier, A., Human, P., and Wearner, D. (1997) *Making Sense: Teaching and Learning Mathematics with Understanding*. Portsmouth, New Hampshire, Heinemann.

Jones, B., Palincsar, A., Ogle, D., & Carr, E. (1987). *Strategic Teaching and Learning: Cognitive Instruction in the Content Areas*. Alexandria, Virginia: Association for Supervision and Curriculum Development.

Kintsch, W. (1979). On modeling comprehension. *Educational psychologist*, 1, 3–14.

Mason, L. (1994). Cognitive and metacognitive aspects in conceptual change by analogy. *Instructional Science* 22(3), 157-187. (1995). Analogy, meta-conceptual awareness and conceptual change: A classroom study. *Educational Studies*, 20(2), 267–291.

Means, B., C. Chelener, and M. Knapp. (1991). *Teaching Advanced Skills to At-Risk Students*. TK: Dale Seymour Publications.

Medin, D., Goldstone, R.L., and Markman, A.B. (1995) Comparison and choice: Relationship between similarity processes and decision processes. *Psychonomic Bulletin & Review*, 2(1) 1–19.

Newby, T.J., Ertmer, P.A., & Stepich, D.A. (1995). Instructional analogies and the learning of concepts. *Educational Technology Research and Development*, 43(1), 5–18.

Palincsar, A.S., and Brown, A.L. (1984). Reciprocal teaching of comprehension fostering and comprehension monitoring activities. *Cognition and Instruction*, 1(2), 117–175.

Ripoll, T. (1999). Why this made me think of that. *Thinking and Reasoning*. 4(1), 15–43.

Rosenshine, B., & Meister, C.C. (1994). Reciprocal teaching: A review of the research. *Review of Educational Research*, 64(4), 479–530.

Rosenshine, B., Meister, C., Chapman, S. (1996). Teaching students to generate questions. A review of the intervention studies. *Review of Educational Research*, 66(2), 181–221.

Ross, B.H. (1987). This is like that: The use of earlier problems and the separation of similarity effects. *Journal of Experimental Psychology*, 13(4), 629–639.

Wood, T. and Turner-Vorbeck, T. (2001). "Extending the Conception of Mathematics Teaching," in T. Wood, B.S. Nelson, and J.Warfield (Eds.), *Beyond Classical Pedagogy*: *Teaching Elementary School Mathematics*. Mahwah, New Jersey: Lawrence Eribaum Associates, pp. 185–208.

Mathematical Content

Anghileri, J., & D.C. Johnson. (1992). Arithmetic operations on whole numbers: Multiplication and division. In *Teaching Mathematics in Grades K–8* (pp. 157–200) Boston: Allyn and Bacon, 1992.

Brodie, J.P. (1995). Constructing *Ideas About Large Numbers*. TK: Creative Publications.

California State Board of Education, 1999. Carey, D.A. "Number Sentences: Linking Addition and Subtraction Word Problems and Symbols," *Journal for Research in Mathematics Education*. Volume 22, 1991.

Cathcart,W., George, Pothier,Y., Ashlock, R.B. (1998). *Error Patterns in Computation*. Seventh Edition. Columbus, Ohio: Merrill.

Clements, D. (2003). *Learning and Teaching Measurement*. Ralston, VA: NCTM.

Franco, B., et al. (1998). *Understanding Geometry*. TK: Great Source Education Group.

Gersten, R., Gall, M., Grace, D., Erickson, D., & Steiber, S. (1987). *Instructional correlates of achievement gains in algebra for low-performing high school students*. Paper presented at the annual meeting of the American Educational Research Association, Washington, DC.

Herbert, K., & Brown, R. "Patterns as Tools for Algebraic Reasoning." *Teaching Children Mathematics 3* (February 1997): 340–344.

Hoffer, A.R., and S.A.K. Hoffer. "Ratios and Proportional Thinking." *In Teaching Mathematics in Grades K–8: Research Based Methods*. (1992). Boston: Allyn and Bacon.

Kaput, J., and Sims-Knight, J.E. (1983). Errors in Translations to Algebraic Equations: Roots and Implications. *Focus on Learning Problems in Mathematics*, 5(3), pp. 63–78.

Lamon, S. (1999). *Teaching Fractions and Ratios for Understanding*. Mahwah, NJ: Lawrence Erlbaum Associates.

Piccirilli, R. (1996). *Mental Math: Computation Activities for Anytime*. TK: Scholastic Books.

Rathmell, Edward C. "Using Thinking Strategies to Teach the Basic Facts." In *Developing Computational Skills*, edited by Marilyn N. Suydam. Reston, Virginia: NCTM, 1978.

Trafton, P., and D. Thiesen. (1999). *Learning Through Problems: Number Sense and Computational Strategies/A Resource for Teachers*. TK: Heinemann.

Vance, J. "Number Operations from an Algebraic Perspective." *Teaching Children Mathematics* 4 (January 1998): 282–285.

Problem Solving

Chen, Z. (1996). Children's analogical problem solving: The effects of superficial, structural, and procedural similarities. *Journal of Experimental Child psychology*, 62(3), 410–431.

Chen, Z. (1999). Schema induction in children's analogical problem solving. *Journal of Educational Psychology*, 91(4), 703–715.

Duncker, K. (1945). On problem-solving (L.S. Less, Trans.). *Psychological Monographs*, 58, 270.

English, L.D. (1997). Children's reasoning in classifying and solving computational word Problems. In L.D. English (ed.), *Mathematical reasoning: Analogies, metaphors and images* (pp. 191–220). Mahwah, NJ: Lawrence Erlbaum.

Gick, M.L., and Holyoak, K.J. (1980). Analogical problem solving. *Cognitive Psychology*, 12, 306–355.

Charles, R.I. and Lester, Jr., F.K. (1984). "An Evaluation of a Process Oriented Mathematical Problem-Solving Instructional Program in Grades 5 and 7." *Journal for Research in Mathematics Education*, 15(1), pp. 15–34.

Hiebert, J. (2003). "Signposts for Teaching Mathematics Through Problem Solving," in F.K. Lester, Jr. and R.I. Charles (Eds.) *Teaching Mathematics Through Problem Solving*. Reston, Virginia: National Council of Teachers of Mathematics, pp. 53–61.

Polya, G. (1957). *How to Solve It: A New Aspect of Mathematical Method*. Second Edition. Princeton, New Jersey: Princeton University Press.

Stanic, G.M.A. and Kilpatrick, J. (1989). "Historical Perspectives on Problem Solving in the mathematics Curriculum," in R.I. Charles and E.A. Silver (Ed.), *The Teaching and Assessing of Mathematical Problem Solving*. Reston: National Council of Teacher of Mathematics, pp. 1–22.

Steen, L.A. and Forman, S.L. (1995). "Mathematics for Work and Life," In Iris M. Carl (Ed.) *Prospects for School Mathematics; Seventy-Five years of Progress*. Reston: National Council of Teachers of Mathematics, p. 221.

Suydam, M.N. (1980). "Untangling Clues from research on Problem Solving," In S. Krulik and R.E. Reys (Eds.), *Problem Solving in School Mathematics: 1980 Yearbook*. Reston, Virginia: National Council of Teachers of Mathematics, P. 43.

Reading & Writing

Armbruster, B. B. (1996). Considerate texts. In D. Lapp, J. Flood, & N. Farnan (Eds.). *Content area reading and learning: Instructional strategies.* Needham Heights, MA: Allyn & Bacon, 47–57.

Armbruster, B.,B., Anderson, T.H., & Ostertag, J. (1987). Does text structure/summarization instruction facilitate learning from expository text? *Reading Research Quarterly*, 22(3), 331–346.

Baumann, J.F., and E. J. Kameenui. 1991. "Research on Vocabulary Instruction: Ode to Voltaire." In J. Flood, J. M. Jensen, D. Lapp, and J. R. Squire, eds., *Handbook on Teaching the English Language Arts*. New York: Macmillan.

Blachowicz, C.L.Z. 1986. "Making Connections: Alternatives to the Vocabulary Notebook." *Journal of Reading* 29 (2): 643–649.

Burton, Leone and Candia Morgan. "Mathematicians Writing," *Journal for Research in Mathematics Education*, Volume 31, Number 4, 2000.

Carr, E., and D. Ogle. 1987. "K-W-L Plus: A Strategy for Comprehension and Summarization." *Journal of Reading* 30: 626–631.

Davey, B. 1986. "Using Textbook Activity Guides to Help Students Learn from Textbooks." *Journal of Reading* 29: 489–494.

Eanet, M., and A. Manzo. 1976. "R.E.A.P.--A Strategy for Improving Reading/Writing Study Skills." *Journal for Reading* 19: 647–652.

Fielding, L. G., and P. D. Pearson. 1994. "Synthesis of Research: Reading Comprehension: What Works." *Educational Leadership* 51 (5): 62–67.

Golembo, Vadim. "Writing a PEMDAS Story," *Mathematics Teaching in the Middle School*, Volume 5, Number 9, 2000.

Hoffman, J. 1992. "Critical Reading/Thinking Across the Curriculum: Using I-Charts to Support Learning." *Language Arts* 69: 121–127.

Manzo, A. 1969. "The ReQuest Procedure." *Journal of Reading* 13: 23–26.

Martin, C. E., M.A. Martin, and D. G. O'Brien. 1984. "Spawning Ideas for Writing in the Content Area." *Reading World* 11: 11–15.

Marzano, R.J.. Building Background Knowledge for Academic Achievement: Research on What Works in Schools (2004)

McKeown, M., I. Beck, G. Sinatra, and J. Loxterman. 1992. "The Contribution of Prior knowledge and Coherent Text to Comprehension." *Reading Research Quarterly* 27: 79–93.

Nagy, W. 1997. "On the Role of Context in First- and Second-language Vocabulary Learning." In N. Schmitt and M. McCarthy, eds., *Vocabulary*: *Description, Acquisition, and Pedagogy*, pp. 64-83. Cambridge, UK: Cambridge University Press.

Nagy, W., and P. Herman. 1987. "Breadth and Depth of Vocabulary Knowledge: Implication for Acquisition and Instruction." In M. McKeown and M. Curties, eds., *The Nature of Vocabulary Acquisition*. Hillsdale, NJ: Erlbaum.

Palinscar, A.S., and A. Brown. 1986. "Interactive Teaching to Promote Independent Learning from Text." *Reading Teacher* 39 (8): 771–777.

Raphael, T., and P. D. Pearson. 1982. The *Effect of Metacognitive Awareness Training on Children's question Answering Behavior*. Technical report No. 238. Urbana, IL: Center for the Study of Reading.

Raphael, T. 1984 "Teaching Learners About Sources of Information for Answering Comprehension Questions." *Journal of Reading* 27: 303–311.

Siegel, M., Borasi, R., Fonzi, J.M., Sandridge, L.G., and Smith, C. (1996), "Using reading to construct mathematical meaning," in P.C. Elliot (ed.) *Communication in Mathematics, K–12 and Beyond: 1996 Yearbook*. Reston, VA: National Council of Teachers of Mathematics, P. 74.

Whitin, D.J. and Whitin, P.E. "The 'Write'Way to Mathematical Understanding." In the Teaching and Learning of Algorithms in School Mathematics, edited by Lorna J. Morrow, pp. 161–169. Reston, VA: National Council of Teachers of Mathematics, Inc. 1998.

Symbols and Properties

Symbols

$\pm$	plus or minus	$\overline{AB}$	line segment AB
$\times$ or $\cdot$	times	AB	measure of $\overline{AB}$
$\neq$	is not equal to	$f(x)$	f of x, the value of f at x
$>$	is greater than	$-a$	opposite or additive inverse of a
$<$	is less than	(a, b)	ordered pair a, b
$\geq$	is greater than or equal to	O	origin
$\leq$	is less than or equal to	π	pi
$\approx$	is approximately equal to	$P(A)$	probability of A
$\lvert a \rvert$	absolute value of a	$a:b$	ratio of a to b
$\angle$	angle	$0.7\overline{5}$	repeating decimal $0.75555\ldots$
$^{\circ}$	degree	$\sqrt{a}$	square root of a
$!$	factorial	$\triangle$	triangle

Algebraic Properties

Additive Identity	For any number a, $a + 0 = 0 + a = a$.
Multiplicative Identity	For any number a, $a \cdot 1 = 1 \cdot a = a$.
Substitution (=)	If $a = b$, then a may be replaced by b.
Reflexive (=)	$a = a$
Symmetric (=)	If $a = b$, then $b = a$.
Transitive (=)	If $a = b$ and $b = c$, then $a = c$.
Commutative (+)	For any numbers a and b, $a + b = b + a$.
Commutative ($\times$)	For any numbers a and b, $a \cdot b = b \cdot a$.
Associative (+)	For any numbers a, b, and c, $(a + b) + c = a + (b + c)$.
Associative ($\times$)	For any numbers a, b, and c, $(a \cdot b) \cdot c = a \cdot (b \cdot c)$.
Distributive	For any numbers a, b, and c, $$a(b + c) = ab + ac \text{ and } a(b - c) = ab - ac.$$
Additive Inverse	For any number a, there is exactly one number $-a$ such that $a + (-a) = 0$.
Multiplicative Inverse	For any number $\frac{a}{b}$, where $a, b \neq 0$, there is exactly one number $\frac{b}{a}$ such that $\frac{a}{b} \cdot \frac{b}{a} = 1$.
Multiplicative (0)	For any number a, $a \cdot 0 = 0 \cdot a = 0$.
Addition (=)	For any numbers a, b, and c, if $a = b$, then $a + c = b + c$.
Subtraction (=)	For any numbers a, b, and c, if $a = b$, then $a - c = b - c$.
Division and Multiplication (=)	For any numbers a, b, and c, with $c \neq 0$, if $a = b$, then $ac = bc$ and $\frac{a}{c} = \frac{b}{c}$.
Addition ($>$)*	For any numbers a, b, and c, if $a > b$, then $a + c > b + c$.
Subtraction ($>$)*	For any numbers a, b, and c, if $a > b$, then $a - c > b - c$.
Division and Multiplication ($>$)*	For any numbers a, b, and c, 1. if $a > b$ and $c > 0$, then $ac > bc$ and $\frac{a}{c} > \frac{b}{c}$. 2. if $a > b$ and $c < 0$, then $ac < bc$ and $\frac{a}{c} < \frac{b}{c}$.
Zero Product	For any real numbers a and b, if $ab = 0$, then $a = 0$, $b = 0$, or both a and b equal zero.

* These properties are also true for $<$, $\geq$, and $\leq$.

Formulas and Measures

Formulas

Slope		$m = \dfrac{y_2 - y_1}{x_2 - x_1}$
Distance on a coordinate plane		$d = \sqrt{(x_2 - x_1)^2 + (y_2 - y_1)^2}$
Midpoint on a coordinate plane		$M = \left(\dfrac{x_1 + x_2}{2}, \dfrac{y_1 + y_2}{2}\right)$
Pythagorean Theorem		$a^2 + b^2 = c^2$
Quadratic Formula		$x = \dfrac{-b \pm \sqrt{b^2 - 4ac}}{2a}$
Perimeter of a rectangle		$P = 2\ell + 2w$ or $P = 2(\ell + w)$
Circumference of a circle		$C = 2\pi r$ or $C = \pi d$
Area	rectangle	$A = \ell w$
	parallelogram	$A = bh$
	triangle	$A = \dfrac{1}{2}bh$
	trapezoid	$A = \dfrac{1}{2}h(b_1 + b_2)$
	circle	$A = \pi r^2$
Surface Area	cube	$S = 6s^2$
	prism	$S = Ph + 2B$
	cylinder	$S = 2\pi rh + 2\pi r^2$
	regular pyramid	$S = \dfrac{1}{2}P\ell + B$
	cone	$S = \pi r\ell + \pi r^2$
Volume	cube	$V = s^3$
	prism	$V = Bh$
	cylinder	$V = \pi r^2 h$
	regular pyramid	$V = \dfrac{1}{3}Bh$
	cone	$V = \dfrac{1}{3}\pi r^2 h$

Measures

Measure	Metric	Customary
Length	kilometer (km) = 1000 meters (m) 1 meter = 100 centimeters (cm) 1 centimeter = 10 millimeters (mm)	1 mile (mi) = 1760 yards (yd) 1 mile = 5280 feet (ft) 1 yard = 3 feet 1 foot = 12 inches (in.) 1 yard = 36 inches
Volume and Capacity	1 liter (L) = 1000 milliliters (mL) 1 kiloliter (kL) = 1000 liters	1 gallon (gal) = 4 quarts (qt) 1 gallon = 128 fluid ounces (fl oz) 1 quart = 2 pints (pt) 1 pint = 2 cups (c) 1 cup = 8 fluid ounces
Weight and Mass	1 kilogram (kg) = 1000 grams (g) 1 gram = 1000 milligrams (mg) 1 metric ton (t) = 1000 kilograms	1 ton (T) = 2000 pounds (lb) 1 pound = 16 ounces (oz)